RHS PL
FINDER
2008-2009

DEVISED BY CHRIS PHILIP
AND REALISED BY TONY LORD

CONSULTANT EDITOR
TONY LORD

RHS EDITORS
JAMES ARMITAGE JANET CUBEY
DAWN EDWARDS NEIL LANCASTER

COMPILER
JUDITH MERRICK

A Dorling Kindersley Book

LONDON, NEW YORK, MUNICH, MELBOURNE, DELHI

Published by
Dorling Kindersley Ltd
80 Strand, London WC2R 0RL
A Penguin company

First edition April 1987
Twenty-second edition April 2008

British Library Cataloguing Publication Data.
A Catalogue record for this book is available from the British Library.

ISBN 978-1-4053-3190-6

Compiled by
The Royal Horticultural Society
80 Vincent Square,
London SW1P 2PE
Registered charity no: 222879/SCO38262

www.rhs.org.uk

Illustrations by Sarah Young
Maps by Alan Cooper

Produced for Dorling Kindersley Ltd by
COOLING BROWN

Printed and bound in England by Clays Ltd, St Ives Plc

The Compiler and the Editors of the *RHS Plant Finder* have taken every care, in the time available, to check all the information supplied to them by the nurseries concerned. Nevertheless, in a work of this kind, containing as it does hundreds of thousands of separate computer encodings, errors and omissions will, inevitably, occur. Neither the RHS, the Publisher nor the Editors can accept responsibility for any consequences that may arise from such errors.

If you find mistakes we hope that you will let us know so that the matter can be corrected in the next edition.

Back cover photographs from top to bottom: *Rudbeckia fulgida* var. *deamii*, *Cotinus coggygria* 'Royal Purple', Carex *siderosticha* 'Variegata', *Hemerocallis* 'Missenden', *Hydrangea serrata* 'Bluebird'
Front cover and spine: *Tulipa* 'Orange Emperor' by Polina Plotnikova/flowerphotos.com

Contents

INTRODUCTION

The *RHS Plant Finder* exists to put enthusiastic gardeners in touch with suppliers of plants. The book is divided into two related sections – **PLANTS** and **NURSERIES. PLANTS** includes an A–Z Plant Directory of more than 70,000 plant names, against which are listed a series of nursery codes. These codes point the reader to the full nursery details contained in the **NURSERIES** section towards the back of the book.

The *RHS Plant Finder* is comprehensively updated every year and provides the plant lover with the richest source of suppliers known to us, whether you are looking for plants locally, shopping from your armchair or touring the country in search of the rare and unusual.

As you will see from the entries in the **NURSERY DETAILS BY CODE** many nurseries do not now publish a printed catalogue but produce an online version only. This is a growing trend, fuelled by the cost of printing a full catalogue.

It is important to remember when ordering that many of the nurseries listed in the book are small, family-run, businesses that propagate their own material. They cannot therefore guarantee to hold large stocks of the plants they list. Many will, however, propagate to order.

NEW IN THIS EDITION

The question posed by horticultural advisers Leigh Hunt and Fiona Dennis in this edition's topical essay is: "why should gardeners consider growing drought-tolerant plants?" In answering this, they give practical advice on how to deal with drought conditions in the garden and recommend plants that will thrive in dry conditions.

In this edition, revisions have been made to many genera. These include *Oxalis*, *Schisandra*, *Furcraea* and palm genera. Additionally, *Styphnolobium* has now been recognised as distinct from *Sophora*; *Harrimanella* distinct from *Cassiope* and conversely, *Abromeitiella* is now included within *Deuterocohnia*.

Many of these changes are the result of decisions taken by the RHS Advisory Panel on Nomenclature and Taxonomy. These decisions are never taken lightly. If there is an issue you wish the Panel to discuss, then please do consider contacting them.

AVAILABLE FROM THE COMPILER

APPLICATION FOR ENTRY

Nurseries appearing in the *RHS Plant Finder* for the first time this year are printed in bold type in the *Nursery Index by Name* starting on p.928.

If you wish your nursery to be considered for inclusion in the next edition of the *RHS Plant Finder* (2009-2010), please write for details to the Compiler at the address below.

PLANTS LAST LISTED IN EARLIER EDITIONS

Plants cease to be listed for a variety of reasons. For more information turn to *How to Use the Plant Directory* on p.18. A listing of the 35,000 or so plants listed in earlier editions, but for which we currently have no known supplier, is available online at www.rhs.org.uk/RHSPlantFinder/documents/PF_Lastlisted_2008.pdf.

LISTS OF NURSERIES FOR PLANTS WITH MORE THAN 30 SUPPLIERS

To prevent the book from becoming too big, we do not print the nursery codes where more than 30 nurseries offer the same plant. The plant is then listed as being "Widely available". This is detailed more fully in *How to Use the Plant Directory* on p.18.

If any readers have difficulty in finding such a plant, we will be pleased to send a full list of all the nurseries that we have on file as stockists. All such enquiries must include the full name of the plant being sought, as shown in the *RHS Plant Finder*, together with an A5 size SAE. For more than one plant, please send an A4 1st class SAE.

The above may be obtained from:
The Compiler, *RHS Plant Finder,* RHS Garden Wisley, Woking, Surrey GU23 6QB
Email: plantfinder@rhs.org.uk

This information is also available online.

THE RHS PLANT FINDER ONLINE

The *RHS Plant Finder* is available on the Internet. Visit the Royal Horticultural Society's website **www.rhs.org.uk** and search the *RHS Plant Finder* database online.

ACKNOWLEDGMENTS

Judith Merrick, supported by Wendy Marsh and with the help of June Skinner and Patty Boardman, compiled this edition. Richard Sanford managed the editing of the plant names on the database and provided assistance to Rupert Wilson in administering the Horticultural Database, using the BG-BASE ™ Collection Management Software, from which the book is produced.

We should like to acknowledge the help of Graham Hawkes, Simon Maughan, RHS Publications, John David, RHS Head of Botany, Christopher Whitehouse, Keeper of the Herbarium, Kerry Walter of BG-BASE (UK) Ltd., Max Phillips of Strange Software Ltd. and Alan Cooper, who produces the nursery maps.

We are greatly indebted to Peter Cooling of Cooling Brown Ltd., for enabling us to turn our mass of raw data into a published format.

RHS botanists, James Armitage, Dawn Edwards and Neil Lancaster, have undertaken the task of editing the plant names this *RHS Plant Finder* season.

We are once again indebted to our colleagues on the RHS Advisory Panel on Nomenclature and Taxonomy, along with the RHS International Cultivar Registrars all of whom have provided much valuable guidance and information. Scores of nurseries have sent helpful information about plants which has proved immensely useful in verifying some of the most obscure names, as well as suggesting corrections to existing entries. Some of these suggested corrections remain to be checked and entered in our next edition and we are grateful for your patience while information is checked and processed, though those that contravene the Codes of Nomenclature may have to be rejected. We are grateful, too, to all our regular correspondents.

Cistus	R. Page ('02)
Clematis	V. Matthews ('00-'06) & D. Donald ('07), International Cultivar Registrar, RHS
Dahlia	R. Hedge, RHS Wisley ('00 & '02)
Dianthus	Dr A.C. Leslie, International Cultivar Registrar, RHS ('00 & '02)
Erica	Dr E.C. Nelson, International Cultivar Registrar
Geranium	D.X. Victor, International Cultivar Registrar ('03)
Ilex	S. Andrews ('06)
Iris	J. Hewitt ('02, '05 & '07)
Lavandula	S. Andrew ('02, '03 & '05)
Lilium	Dr A.C. Leslie ('00 & '02) & K. Donald ('07), International Cultivar Registrar, RHS
Meconopsis	Dr E. Stevens ('02-'03, '05 & '07)
Narcissus	S. Kington, International Cultivar Registrar, RHS ('00 & '02)
Rhododendron	Dr A.C. Leslie, International Cultivar Registrar, RHS ('00 & '02)
Sorbus	Dr H. McAllister ('01)
Thymus	M. Easter ('03-'07)

To all these, as well as to the many readers and nurseries who have also made comments and suggestions, we are once again extremely grateful.

Tony Lord, Consultant Editor and Janet Cubey, RHS Principal Botanist, February 2008

Conservation and the Environment

As the ***RHS Plant Finder*** demonstrates, gardens in Britain have been greatly enriched by the diversity of plants introduced to cultivation from abroad. Whilst the vast majority of those introduced have enhanced our gardens, a few have proved to be highly invasive and to threaten native habitats. Once such plants are established it is very difficult, costly and potentially damaging to native ecosystems to eradicate or control the invasive "alien" species. Gardeners can help by choosing not to buy or distribute non-native invasive plants and by taking steps to prevent them escaping into the wild and by disposing of them in a responsible way.

The top eight invasive non-native species are no longer listed in the *RHS Plant Finder*. Any cultivars or varieties of them that are listed are believed to be less invasive than the species themselves. These seven plants are:

- *Azolla filiculoides* – fairy fern
- *Crassula helmsii* – New Zealand pygmy weed
- *Fallopia japonica* – Japanese knotweed
- *Heracleum mantegazzianum* – giant hogweed
- *Hydrocotyle ranunculoides* – floating pennywort
- *Impatiens glandulifera* – Himalayan balsam
- *Ludwigia grandiflora* – water primrose
- *Myriophyllum aquaticum* – parrot's feather

Bringing plants back from abroad

Travelling can be a great source of inspiration for gardeners and often provides an introduction to new and interesting plants. Anyone thinking of bringing plants back into Britain from overseas must realise, however, that this is a complex matter. Various regulations are in force which apply to amateur gardeners as well as to commercial nurseries. The penalties for breaking these can be serious.

Some of the most important regulatory bodies are listed below.

Plant Health regulations are in place to control the spread of pests and diseases. Plants are divided into the categories of prohibited, controlled and unrestricted, but there are also limits that vary according to the part of the world you are travelling from. For full details contact the Plant Health division of DEFRA, or visit www.defra.gov.uk/planth/ph.htm DEFRA has produced a leaflet that summarises the Horticultural Code of Practice. This is available online at www.defra.gov.uk or by phoning the helpline on 08459 335577.

The Convention on International Trade in Endangered Species (CITES) affects the transport of animal and plant material across international boundaries. Its aim is to prevent exploitative trade and thereby to prevent harm and the ultimate extinction of wild populations. Export and import licences are required for any plants listed on the CITES Appendices. A broad range of plants is covered in these Appendices, including *Cactaceae* and *Orchidaceae* and, although species are mentioned in the convention title, the restrictions cover all cultivars and hybrids too. Details of the plants listed in the Appendices can be found on the CITES website, www.ukcites.gov.uk/intro/cites_species.htm, or in the leaflets detailed below.

The Convention on Biological Diversity (CBD or the "Rio Convention") recognises the property rights of individual countries in relation to their own biodiversity. It exists to enable access to that biodiversity, but equally to ensure the sharing of any benefit derived from it. Export permits are required for plant material taken from the country of origin, with prior informed consent being gained for any uses that the material will be used for in the future. Further information on the Convention can be found on the CBD website, www.cbd.int.

If you would like to read more about these subjects, *Conservation and Environment Guidelines* leaflets are available on request from the RHS. Please write to the Compiler at the address given on page 4 enclosing an A4 SAE, or find them online at www.rhs.org.uk/publications. Leaflets are also available on a wider range of subjects, with topics including:

- *Peat and the gardener*
- *Potentially harmful garden plants*
- *The use of limestone in horticulture*
- *Trees and timber products*
- *Wild and endangered plants in cultivation*
- *Wildlife in gardens*

DROUGHT-TOLERANT PLANTS

Why should gardeners consider growing drought-tolerant plants? With climate change predicted to bring hotter and drier summers, plants that once thrived in British gardens are likely to require additional watering. This problem will be exacerbated as rainfall is predicted to decrease during the summer months, further depleting water supplies and increasing the need to water thirsty plants.

The overriding factor for climate change is that the weather will be more erratic and extreme with exceptionally hot spells, flash floods or storms, but it is easier to say that the seasons will be less typical. Take the last two years as an example of weather that fits the climate change predictions. 2006 was the hottest on record and many gardeners in southern England faced hosepipe bans while, in contrast, the summer of 2007 was the wettest on record with large amounts of rain falling in short periods.

This does not mean that gardeners can ignore the predictions for hotter, drier summers, hoping that a deluge is around the corner. Overall, it is best to plan for the future, both by choosing the right plants to cope with the predicted conditions and using good gardening practice.

The cost of ignoring the problem

Have you ever bought a plant from the nursery only to watch it deteriorate in your garden? Do you wonder why, despite your best efforts, it fails? A common reason is that the wrong plant was selected for the position you had to offer, or you needed to plant it somewhere else. For example, what will grow on a moist, shady site usually will not thrive in a hot, dry garden with free-draining soil. As a result, choosing a site that suits the plant not only helps the plant to flourish but it also means less watering, less work and less expense for the gardener.

The benefits of change

Watering your garden throughout the summer is tedious work and can detract from the overall pleasure of gardening. There are also economic benefits to be gained with a drought-tolerant garden, such as reducing your metered water bills and preventing money being wasted on unsuitable plants.

Above all, though, there are great environmental benefits to reducing water use or using rainwater collected on site. Tap water requires energy to be pumped to our gardens and so is linked to producing the climate change gas carbon dioxide and if excessive amounts of water are abstracted from the environment, it can harm wildlife in rivers and wetlands.

Choosing drought-tolerant plants

Selecting plants to cope with dry conditions need not be daunting. Just look out for those with the following drought-tolerant adaptations. These allow plants to cope with low rainfall by reducing the loss of water from their leaves, storing water for use when there is no rain or simply by minimising their water requirements.

Small leaves shed heat and have few pores from which to lose water. Good examples are *Rosmarinus officinalis* (rosemary) and *Thymus* (thyme).

Long, narrow leaves are very good at shedding heat without losing water. Plants with these include grasses (eg. *Helictotrichon sempervirens*) and phormiums.

Grey leaves usually signify drought resistance. They can typically be seen on *Artemisia*, *Lavandula* (lavender), and *Verbascum*.

Hairy leaves shade themselves with their own hairs. *Verbascum bombyciferum* and *Stachys byzantina* (lamb's ears) are just two easy-to-grow examples.

Leathery foliage loses less water than soft leaves. Look out for plants such as *Salvia officinalis* (sage) and *Cistus* 'Silver Pink'.

Waxy leaves have a shiny surface created by the waxy cuticle in which they are enveloped. This reduces evaporation, particularly in windy conditions: examples include pine trees, *Pittosporum*, *Acacia* and *Eucalyptus*.

Fleshy, succulent leaves store moisture for dry spells. *Sedum spectabile* (ice plant) is a hardy example, while *Aeonium* can be grown outdoors in summer.

Aromatic leaves contain volatile scented compounds that are thought to cool foliage as they evaporate, reducing water loss. Try *Cistus* and *Lavandula*.

Spikes act as 'cooling fins', ensuring plants like *Acanthus spinosus* (bear's breeches) and *Eryngium* × *oliverianum* (sea holly) lose heat but not too much water.

Slow growth By restricting growth of both stems and leaves, plants can conserve limited supplies of water (e.g. many cacti and succulents, including *Sempervivum arachnoideum*).

Underground storage organs enable plants to save water for long periods of drought (e.g. daffodils, *Dahlia, Eremerus*).

The thirsty garden

Why do some plants need more water than others? The thirsty garden will have plants that are from regions of the world where there is a high and fairly consistent rainfall all year around: e.g. the Himalayas (rhododendrons), northern China (hydrangeas), eastern USA (acers and kalmias), whilst plants from drier parts of the world have low water requirements: e.g. cacti (Mexico), proteas (Australia), rosemary (the Mediterranean), *Ceanothus* (California).

The same rule applies to herbaceous plants. *Helenium, Hosta, Aster lateriflorus, Paeonia delavayi, Helleborus niger* are all plants that naturally grow in moist, humus-rich soils that receive and retain plenty of water. Likewise they will require plenty of water in your garden.

Plants that can tolerate harsh conditions in their native home may well be more suitable candidates for the dry garden. Plants that grow in windswept mountains where the soil is shallow and temperatures low are well adapted to managing periods of drought, for example *Arctostaphylos uva-ursi* (bearberry), and even our native heathers which can survive dry, sandy heathland. Plants that grow in rocky outcrops develop very long roots to explore the cracks and crevices for modest reservoirs of water; e.g. *Eryngium planum, Rosmarinus officinalis, Helianthemum apenninum* (the rock rose) and *Saponaria caespitosa* (soapwort) are examples that can be found growing wild in the mountains of southern Spain.

Establishing plants in the dry garden
It may not be practical to replant your entire garden to meet the challenges of our increasingly hot, dry summers. In which case, you can approach the matter from an ecological perspective.

First of all, identify the areas in your garden that have distinct localised climate, dry areas, by walls, under trees, on a south-facing border and those sites that have a damper, shadier aspect, perhaps north-facing or in a small hollow or lower down in the garden where water tends to drain. Draw a rough map of these areas and refine this map as the year progresses. Then look at the plants that you have and assess their moisture requirements. Are there plants that always wilt first and may benefit from moving to a shadier or moister place in the garden? Likewise there may be plants that would grow better in a more sunny position and could tolerate dry conditions. In the autumn move the shade/moisture lovers to the appropriate sites in the garden as shown on your map. In the spring move the sun-loving, drought-tolerant plants.

The next step is to identify the plants that have outgrown their allotted space, failed to develop an attractive habit of growth or are dominating a favourable aspect and remove them altogether. Finally, select drought-tolerant plants according to the requirements of the spaces that are left.

Tips for establishing a drought-tolerant garden:
- Buy young plants rather than mature, e.g. whips not semi-mature trees as they will establish quicker and better
- Plants often grow better when direct sown rather than transplanted, e.g. *Eryngium* (sea holly) and carrots
- When planting, add plenty of organic matter to help the soil hold water like a sponge so more is available to the plants
- After planting, ensure that the roots are well watered and then place 8cm of mulch over the root area

Aftercare
Seedlings and young plants should be kept moist while they establish. It is important that the young plant roots are encouraged to search through a large volume of soil to find water. This encourages a good root system to develop that can help to sustain the plant in times of water stress. Similarly, water vegetables when newly transplanted but also when the part of the plant you will eat is developing.

Good watering aims to apply enough water to replenish soil levels without overdoing it. Apply it at a steady rate at the base of stems and beneath the canopy of foliage as wetting the leaves is a waste. This should leave the surrounding soil dry, ensuring that all the water goes to where it is needed – the roots. Keeping much of the soil surface dry will also help to limit weed problems.

There is little point in applying excess water as it will quickly drain below where the roots can reach. So, always check the weather forecast and only water or top up if not enough rain falls. Watering in the evening gives it time to sink in while evaporation rates are low. Unfortunately summer evenings are times of peak water demand. It is often better to water early in the morning as water pressure is high and demand low.

Alternatives to lawns
Aromatic chamomile and wild thyme lawns are suitable for open, well-drained and sunny sites that are not heavily used. They remain neat and attractive throughout the year and form a low-growing cover sufficiently dense to deter weeds.

Chamomile (*Chamaemelum nobile*) has small, white daisy-like flowers and is good for infrequently used areas in the garden. It requires a well-drained, not dry soil and will tolerate periods of drought. It prefers a sunny site but will cope with lightly dappled shade. The best form for ground cover is *C. nobile* 'Treneague', a non-flowering clone 10cm in height. Propagate chamomile by division or cuttings. Plants of the flowering form are raised from seed.

Low-growing thymes have masses of tiny lavender, pink or white flowers in summer and they thrive on stony, well-drained soils. There are many suitable plants including *Thymus serpyllum* var. *albus* and *T. serpyllum* 'Pink Chintz'. Thymes can be raised from seed, but cultivars will need to be purchased or propagated from small-rooted runners.

For both chamomile and thymes, the spacing can be from 10cm (100 plants per square metre) to 20cm apart (25 plants per square metre), according to size of plant. Close spacing gives more rapid cover but increases the cost.

How do plants react to water stress?
Brown tips or margins often indicate drought in spring or summer. Young growth is particularly susceptible. It may also indicate a failure to establish. This is particularly common where dry weather follows spring planting before new roots have grown out into the soil. Brown, desiccated lower leaves are common on climbers due to dryness at roots. Regular watering is particularly important for new plantings but in prolonged dry spells even established plants may require additional watering

Too much rain can lead to water stress of another kind. Flooding and waterlogging can quickly cause the roots to rot, especially with drought-tolerant plants as they are not well adapted to coping with these conditions. The symptoms include blackening of leaves, usually starting along the veins. This particularly happens after wet winters on heavy soils and is frequently seen on *Aucuba*. The roots, when examined, are a bluish black and fall apart when teased out. On larger roots the outer sheath may pull away easily leaving the inner core. There is often a sour smell to both the soil and roots.

Where waterlogging is a permanent problem, consider installing a drainage system. Alternatively, where the soils are known to be consistently wet, consider using plants that thrive in damp conditions or plant in raised beds.

Fiona Dennis, Horticultural Adviser
Leigh Hunt, RHS Horticultural Adviser

Extended Glossary

This glossary combines some of the helpful introductory sections from older editions in an alphabetical listing. A fuller, more discursive account of plant names, *Guide to Plant Names,* and a detailed guide to the typography of plant names, *Recommended Style for Printing Plant Names*, are both available as RHS Advisory Leaflets. To request a copy of either please send an A4 SAE to The Compiler at the contact address given on page 4.

Advisory Panel on Nomenclature and Taxonomy

This Panel advises the RHS on individual problems of nomenclature regarding plants in cultivation and, in particular, use of names in the *RHS Horticultural Database*, reflected in the annual publication of the *RHS Plant Finder*.

The aim is always to make the plant names in the *RHS Plant Finder* as consistent, reliable and stable as possible and acceptable to gardeners and botanists alike, not only in the British Isles but around the world. Recent proposals to change or correct names are examined with the aim of creating a balance between the stability of well-known names and botanical and taxonomic correctness. In some cases the Panel feels that the conflicting views on the names of some groups of plants will not easily be resolved. The Panel's policy is then to wait and review the situation once a more obvious consensus is reached, rather than rush to rename plants only to have to change them again when opinions have shifted.

The Panel is chaired by Dr Alan Leslie (RHS) with Dr Janet Cubey (RHS) (Vice-Chair) and includes: Dr Crinan Alexander (RBGE), Susyn Andrews, Chris Brickell, Dr James Compton, Dr John David (RHS), Mike Grant (RHS Publications), Dr Stephen Jury (University of Reading), Sabina Knees, Dr Tony Lord, Julian Shaw (RHS) & Adrian Whiteley, with Dr Christopher Whitehouse (RHS) as Secretary.

Authorities

In order that plant names can be used with precision throughout the scientific world, the name of the person who coined the name of a plant species (its author, or authority) is added to the plant name. Usually this information is irrelevant to gardeners, except in cases where the same name has been given to two different plants or a name is commonly misapplied. Although only one usage is correct, both may be encountered in books, so indicating the author is the only way to be certain about which plant is being referred to. This can happen equally with cultivars. Authors' names, where it is appropriate to cite them, appear in a smaller typeface after the species or cultivar name to which they refer and are abbreviated following Brummitt and Powell's *Authors of Plant Names*.

🏆 Award Of Garden Merit

The Award of Garden Merit (AGM) is intended to be of practical value to the ordinary gardener and is therefore awarded only after a period of assessment by the Society's Standing and Joint Committees. An AGM plant:

- must be available
- must be of outstanding excellence for garden decoration or use
- must be of good constitution
- must not require highly specialist growing conditions or care
- must not be particularly susceptible to any pest or disease
- must not be subject to an unreasonable degree of reversion

The AGM symbol is cited in conjunction with the **hardiness** rating. A full list of AGM plants may be found on the RHS website at www.rhs.org.uk/plants/award_plants.asp.

Botanical Names

The aim of the botanical naming system is to provide each different plant with a single, unique, universal name. The basic unit of plant classification is the species. Species that share a number of significant characteristics are grouped together to form a genus (plural **genera**). The name of a species is made up of two elements; the name of the genus followed by the specific epithet, for example, *Narcissus romieuxii*.

Variation within a species can be recognised by division into subspecies (usually abbreviated to subsp.), varietas (or variety abbreviated to var.) and forma (or form abbreviated to f.). Whilst it is unusual for a plant to have all of these, it is possible, as in this example, *Narcissus romieuxii* subsp. *albidus* var. *zaianicus* f. *lutescens.*

The botanical elements are always given in italics, with only the genus taking an initial capital letter. The rank indications are never in italics. In instances where the rank is not known it is necessary to form an invalid construction by quoting a second epithet without a rank. This is an unsatisfactory situation, but requires considerable research to resolve.

In some genera, such as *Hosta*, we list the cultivar names alphabetically with the species or **hybrid** to which they are attributed afterwards in parentheses. For example, *Hosta* 'Reversed' (*sieboldiana*). In other situations where the aim is not to create a list alphabetically by cultivar name we would recommend styling this as *Hosta sieboldiana* 'Reversed'.

Classification of Genera

Genera that include a large number of species or with many cultivars are often subdivided into informal horticultural classifications or more formal Cultivar Groups, each based on a particular characteristic or combination of characteristics. Colour of flower or fruit and shape of flower are common examples and, with fruit, whether a cultivar is grown for culinary or dessert purposes. How such groups are named differs from genus to genus.

To help users of the *RHS Plant Finder* find the plants they want, the classifications used within cultivated genera are listed using codes and plants are marked with the appropriate code in brackets after its name in the Plant Directory. To find the explanation of each code, simply look it up under the genus concerned in the **Classification of Genera** starting on p.29. The codes relating to edible fruits are also listed here, but these apply across several genera.

Collectors' References

Abbreviations (usually with numbers) following a plant name refer to the collector(s) of the plant. These abbreviations are expanded, with a collector's name or expedition title, in the section **Collectors' References** starting on p.20.

A collector's reference may indicate a new, as yet unnamed range of variation within a species. The inclusion of collectors' references in the *RHS Plant Finder* supports the book's role in sourcing unusual plants.

The Convention on Biological Diversity calls for conservation of biodiversity, its sustainable use and the fair and equitable sharing of any derived benefits. Since its adoption in 1993, collectors are required to have prior informed consent from the country of origin for the acquisition and commercialisation of collected material.

Common Names

In a work such as this, it is necessary to refer to plants by their botanical names for the sake of universal comprehension and clarity. However, at the same time we recognise that with fruit and vegetables most people are more familiar with their common names than their botanical ones. Cross-references are therefore given from common to botanical names for fruit, vegetables and the commoner culinary herbs throughout the Plant Directory.

Cultivar

Literally meaning cultivated variety, cultivar names are given to denote variation within species and that generated by hybridisation, in cultivation. To make them easily distinguishable from botanical names, they are not printed in italics and are enclosed in single quotation marks. Cultivar names coined since 1959 should follow the rules of the International Code of Nomenclature for Cultivated Plants (**ICNCP**).

Descriptive Terms

Terms that appear after the main part of the plant name are shown in a smaller font to distinguish them. These descriptive elements give extra information about the plant and may include the **collector's reference**, **authority**, or what colour it is. For example, *Fritillaria thessala* SBEL 443, *Penstemon* 'Sour Grapes' M. Fish, *Lobelia tupa* dark orange.

Families

Genera are grouped into larger groups of related plants called families. Most family names, with the exception of eight familiar names, end with the same group of letters, *-aceae*. While it is still acceptable to use these eight exceptions, the modern trend adopted in the *RHS Plant Finder* is to use alternative names with *–aceae* endings. The families concerned are *Compositae* (*Asteraceae*), *Cruciferae* (*Brassicaceae*), *Gramineae* (*Poaceae*), *Guttiferae* (*Clusiaceae*), *Labiatae* (*Lamiaceae*), *Leguminosae* (split here into *Caesalpiniaceae*, *Mimosaceae* and *Papilionaceae*), *Palmae* (*Arecaceae*) and *Umbelliferae* (*Apiceae*). Also the traditionally large family *Liliaceae* is split into a number of smaller, more natural, families that as yet may be unfamiliar to readers.

Apart from these exceptions we follow Brumitt's *Vascular Plant Families and Genera* for our family names.

Genus (plural – genera)

Genera used in the *RHS Plant Finder* are almost always those given in Brummitt's *Vascular Plant Families and Genera*. For spellings and genders of generic names, Greuter's *Names in Current Use for Extant Plant Genera* has also been consulted. See **Botanical Names**.

Grex

Within orchids, hybrids of the same parentage, regardless of how alike they are, are given a grex name. Individuals can be selected, given cultivar names and propagated vegetatively. For example, *Pleione* Versailles gx 'Bucklebury', where Versailles is the grex name and 'Bucklebury' is a selected **cultivar**.

Group

This is a collective name for a group of cultivars within a genus with similar characteristics. The word Group is always included and, where cited with a cultivar name, it is enclosed in brackets, for example, *Actaea simplex* (Atropurpurea Group) 'Brunette', where 'Brunette' is a distinct cultivar in a group of purple-leaved cultivars.

Another example of a Group is *Rhododendron polycladum* Scintillans Group. In this case *Rhododendron scintillans* was a species that is now botanically 'sunk' within *R. polycladum*, but it is still recognised horticulturally as a Group.

Group names are also used for swarms of hybrids with the same parentage, for example, *Rhododendron* Polar Bear Group. These were formerly treated as **grex** names, a term now used only for orchids. A single clone from the Group may be given the same cultivar name, for example, *Rhododendron* 'Polar Bear'.

Hardiness

Hardiness ratings are shown for **Award of Garden Merit** plants. The categories used are as follows:

H1 = plants requiring heated glass in the British Isles
H2 = plants requiring unheated glass in the British Isles
H3 = plants hardy outside in some regions of the British Isles or in particular situations, or which, while usually grown outside in summer, need frost-free protection in winter (eg. dahlias)
H4 = plants hardy throughout the British Isles
H1-2, H2-3, H3-4 = plants intermediate between the two ratings given
H1+3 = requiring heated glass; may be grown outside in summer

Hybrids

Some species, when grown together, in the wild or in cultivation, are found to interbreed and form hybrids. In some instances a hybrid name is coined, for example hybrids between *Primula hirsuta* and *P. minima* are given the name *Primula* × *forsteri*, the multiplication sign indicating hybrid origin. Hybrid formulae that quote the parentage of the hybrid are used where a unique name has not been coined, for example *Rhododendron calophytum* × *R. praevernum*. In hybrid formulae you will find parents in alphabetical order, with the male (m) and female (f) parent indicated where known. Hybrids between different genera are also possible, for example × *Mahoberberis* is the name given to hybrids between *Mahonia* and *Berberis*.

There are also a few special-case hybrids called graft hybrids, where the tissues of two plants are physically rather than genetically mixed. These are indicated by an addition rather than a multiplication sign, so *Laburnum* + *Cytisus* becomes +*Laburnocytisus*.

ICNCP

The ICNCP is the International Code of Nomenclature for Cultivated Plants. First published in 1959, the most recent edition was published in 2004.

Cultivar names that do not conform to this Code, and for which there is no valid alternative, are flagged I (for invalid). This code states that the minimum requirement is for a cultivar name to be given in conjunction with the name of the genus. However, in the ***RHS Plant Finder*** we choose to give as full a name as possible to give the gardener and botanist more information about the plant.

Notes on Nomenclature and Identification

The **Notes on Nomenclature and Identification**, starting on p.23, give further information for names that are complex or may be confusing. See also **Advisory Panel on Nomenclature and Taxonomy**.

Plant Breeders' Rights

Plants covered by an *active* grant of Plant Breeders' Rights (PBR) are indicated throughout the Plant Directory. Grants indicated are those awarded by both UK and EU Plant Variety Rights offices. Because grants can both come into force and lapse at any time, this book can only aim to represent the situation at one point in time, but it is hoped that this will act as a useful guide to growers and gardeners. UK grants represent the position as of the end of December 2006 and EU grants as of the end of October 2006. We do not give any indication where PBR grants may be pending.

To obtain PBR protection, a new plant must be registered and pass tests for distinctness, uniformity and stability under an approved name. This approved name, under the rules of the **ICNCP**, established by a legal process, has to be regarded as the cultivar name. Increasingly however, these approved names are a code or "nonsense" name and are therefore often unpronounceable and meaningless, so the plants are given other names designed to attract sales when they are released. These secondary names are often referred to as selling names but are officially termed **trade designations**.

For further information on UK PBR contact:

Plant Variety Rights Office, White House Lane, Huntingdon Road, Cambridge CB3 0LF
Tel: (01223) 342396
Fax: (01223) 342386.
Website: www.defra.gov.uk/planth/pvs/default.htm

For details of plants covered by EU Community Rights contact:

Community Plant Variety Office (CPVO),
3 Boulevard Maréchal Foch, BP 10121
FR-49101 Angers, Cedex 02, France
Tel: 00 33 (02) 41 25 64 00
Fax: 00 33 (02) 41 25 64 10
Website: www.cpvo.europa.eu

The *RHS Plant Finder* takes no responsibility for ensuring that nurseries selling plants with PBR are licensed to do so.

Reverse Synonyms

It is likely that users of this book will come across names in certain genera that they did not expect to find. This may be because species have been transferred from another genus (or **genera**). In the list of **Reverse Synonyms** on p.34, the name on the left-hand side is that of an accepted genus to which species have been transferred from the genus on the right. Sometimes all species will have been transferred, but in many cases only a few will be affected. Consulting **Reverse Synonyms** enables users to find the genera from which species have been transferred. Where the right-hand genus is found in the Plant Directory, the movement of species becomes clear through the cross-references in the nursery code column.

Selling Names

See **Trade Designations**

Series

With seed-raised plants and some popular vegetatively-propagated plants, especially bedding plants and pot plants such as *Petunia* or *Impatiens*, Series have become increasingly popular. A Series contains a number of similar cultivars, but differs from a **Group** in that it is a marketing device, with cultivars added to create a range of flower colours in plants of similar habit. Individual colour elements within a series may be represented by slightly different cultivars over the years.

The word Series is always included and, where cited with a cultivar name it is enclosed in brackets, for example *Aquilegia* 'Robin' (Songbird Series). The Series name usually follows the rest of the plant name, but sometimes in this book we list it before the cultivar name in order to group members of a series together when they occur next to one another on the page.

Species

See under **Botanical Names**

Subspecies

See under **Botanical Names**

Synonyms

Although the ideal is for each species or cultivar to have only one name, anyone dealing with plants soon comes across a situation where one plant has received two or more names, or two plants have received the same name. In each case, only one name and application, for reasons of precision and stability, can be regarded as correct. Additional names are known as synonyms. Further information on synonyms and why plants change names is available in *Guide to Plant Names*. See the introduction to this glossary for details of how to request a copy.

See also **Reverse Synonyms**.

Trade Designations

A **trade designation** is the name used to market a plant when the cultivar name is considered unsuitable for selling purposes. It is styled in a different typeface and without single quotation marks.

In the case of **Plant Breeders' Rights** it is a legal requirement for the cultivar name to appear with the trade designation on a label at the point of sale. Most plants are sold under only one trade designation, but some, especially roses, are sold under a number of names, particularly when cultivars are introduced from other countries.

Usually, the correct cultivar name is the only way to ensure that the same plant is not bought unwittingly under two or more different trade designations. The *RHS Plant Finder* follows the recommendations of the **ICNCP** when dealing with trade designations and PBR. These are always to quote the cultivar name and trade designation together and to style the trade designation in a different typeface, without single quotation marks.

Translations

When a cultivar name is translated from the language of first publication, the translation is regarded as a **trade designation** and styled accordingly. We endeavour to recognise the original cultivar name in every case and to give an English translation where it is in general use.

Variegated Plants

Following a suggestion from the Variegated Plant Group of the Hardy Plant Society, a (v) is cited after those plants which are "variegated". The dividing line between variegation and less distinct colour marking is necessarily arbitrary and plants with light veins, pale, silver or dark zones, or leaves flushed in paler colours, are not shown as being variegated unless there is an absolutely sharp distinction between paler and darker zones.

For further details of the Variegated Plant Group, please write to:

Jerry Webb, Esq.,
17 Heron Way, Minster Heights,
Ilminster TA19 0BX

Variety

See under **Botanical Names** and **Cultivar**

'The question of nomenclature is always a vexed one. The only thing certain is, that it is impossible to please everyone.'

W.J. Bean – Preface to first edition of *Trees & Shrubs Hardy in the British Isles*

SYMBOLS AND ABBREVIATIONS

SYMBOLS APPEARING TO THE LEFT OF THE NAME

*	Name not validated. Not listed in the appropriate International Registration Authority checklist nor in works cited in the Bibliography. For fuller discussion see p.10
I	Invalid name. See *International Code of Botanical Nomenclature 2000* and *International Code of Nomenclature for Cultivated Plants 2004*. For fuller discussion see p.10
N	Refer to Notes on Nomenclature and Identification on p.23
§	Plant listed elsewhere in the Plant Directory under a synonym
×	Hybrid genus
+	Graft hybrid genus

SYMBOLS APPEARING TO THE RIGHT OF THE NAME

✿	National Council for the Conservation of Plants and Gardens (NCCPG) National Plant Collection® exists for all or part of this genus. Provisional Collections appear in brackets. Full details of the NCCPG Plant Collections are found in the *National Plant Collections® Directory 2008* available from: www.nccpg.com or NCCPG, Home Farm, Loseley Park, Guildford, Surrery GU3 1HS
♀H4	The Royal Horticultural Society's Award of Garden Merit, see p.10
(d)	double-flowered
(F)	Fruit
(f)	female
(m)	male
(v)	variegated plant, see p.14
PBR	Plant Breeders Rights see p.12
new	New plant entry in this edition

For abbreviations relating to individual genera see **Classification of Genera** p.29
For **Collectors' References** see p.20
For symbols used in the **Nurseries** section see p.817

SYMBOLS AND ABBREVIATIONS USED AS PART OF THE NAME

×	hybrid species
aff.	affinis (akin to)
agg.	aggregate, a single name used to cover a group of very similar plants, regarded by some as separate species
ambig.	ambiguous, a name used by two authors for different plants and where it is unclear which is being offered
cf.	compare to
cl.	clone
f.	forma (botanical form)
gx	grex
sensu lato	in the broadest sense
sp.	species
subsp.	subspecies
subvar.	subvarietas (botanical subvariety)
var.	varietas (botanical variety)

IT IS NOT WITHIN THE REMIT OF THIS BOOK TO CHECK that nurseries are applying the right names to the right plants or to ensure nurseries selling plants with Plant Breeders' Rights are licensed to do so.

Please, never use an old edition

RHS Plant Trials Bulletins

In December 2007 the twentieth Trials Bulletin, entitled Herbaceous Sedums, was published. These publications give the results and findings of RHS Trials. The detailed descriptions and images of the plants that have been given the Award of Garden Merit are included, as well as updates on nomenclature, cultivation details and a table comparing the different characteristics of the entries in the trial.

Begonia Rex Cultorum Group
Canna
Daisies (yellow perennial)
Delphinium
Fuchsia, hardy
Geranium, hardy (Stage 1)
Geranium, hardy (Stage 2)
Geranium, hardy (Stage 3)
Hyacinthaceae (little blue bulbs)
Iris, bearded
Lavandula, hardy
Miscanthus
Peppers, sweet
Potatoes, salad
Potentilla, shrubby
Rhododendron yakushimanum hybrids
Runner Beans
Saxifraga, silver
Sedum, herbaceous
Spiraea japonica

If you would like a copy of any of these, please contact:
The Trials Office, RHS Garden Wisley, Woking, Surrey GU23 6QB. Please enclose an A4 SAE and a cheque for £2.00 per copy (as a donation towards costs) made out to the Royal Horticultural Society.

In addition to the above there are three bulletins that are only available on the RHS Website: *Caryopteris*, *Perovskia* and *Pittosporum*.
To view and download any of these RHS Plant Trials Bulletins online, please visit:
www.rhs.org.uk/plants/trials_bulletins.asp

Plants

Whatever plant you are looking for, maybe an old favourite or a more unusual cultivar, search here for a list of the suppliers that are closest to you.

How to Use the Plant Directory

Nursery Codes

Look up the plant you require in the alphabetical Plant Directory. Against each plant you will find one or more four-letter codes, for example WCru, each code represents one nursery offering that plant. The first letter of each code indicates the main area of the country in which the nursery is situated. For this geographical key, refer to the **Nursery Codes and Symbols** on p.816.

Turn to the **Nursery Details by Code** starting on p.820 where, in alphabetical order of codes, you will find details of each nursery which offers the plant in question. If you wish to visit any nursery, you may find its location on one of the maps (following p.937). Please note, however, that not all nurseries, especially mail order only nurseries, choose to be shown on the maps. For a fuller explanation of how to use the nursery listings please turn to p.817. **Always check that the nursery you select has the plant in stock before you set out.**

Plants with more than 30 Suppliers

In some cases, against the plant name you will see the term 'Widely available' instead of a nursery code. If we were to include every plant listed by all nurseries, the *RHS Plant Finder* would become unmanageably bulky. We therefore ask nurseries to restrict their entries to those plants that are not already well represented. As a result, if more than 30 nurseries offer any plant the Directory gives no nursery codes and the plant is listed instead as having 'Widely available'.

You should have little difficulty in locating these in local nurseries or garden centres. However, if you are unable to find such plants, we will be pleased to send a full list of all the nurseries that we have on file as stockists. To obtain a list, please see the Introduction on p.4.

Finding Fruit, Vegetables and Herbs

You will need to search for these by their botanical names. Common names are cross-referenced to their botanical names in the Plant Directory.

If you have Difficulty Finding your Plant

If you cannot immediately find the plant you seek, look through the various species of the genus. You may be using an incomplete name. The problem is most likely to arise in very large genera such as *Phlox* where there are a number of possible species, each with a large number of cultivars. A search through the whole genus may well bring success. Please note that, for space reasons, the following are not listed in the Plant Directory: annuals, orchids, except hardy terrestrial orchids; cacti, except hardy cacti.

Cross-references

It may be that the plant name you seek is a synonym. Our intention is to list nursery codes only against the correct botanical name. Where you find a synonym you will be cross-referred to the correct name. Occasionally you may find that the correct botanical name to which you have been referred is not listed. This is because it was last listed in an earlier edition as explained below.

Plants Last Listed in Earlier Editions

It may be that the plant you are seeking has no known suppliers and is thus not listed.

The loss of a plant name from the Directory may arise for a number of reasons – the supplier may have gone out of business, or may not have responded to our latest questionnaire and has therefore been removed from the book. Such plants may well be still available but we have no current knowledge of their whereabouts. Alternatively, some plants may have been misnamed by nurseries in previous editions, but are now appearing under their correct name.

To obtain a listing of plants last listed in earlier editions please see the Introduction on p.4.

Please, never use an old edition

USING THE PLANT DIRECTORY

The main purpose of the Plant Directory is to help the reader correctly identify the plant they seek and find its stockist. Each nursery has a unique identification code which appears to the right of the plant name. Turn to **Nursery Details by Code** (p.820) for the address, opening times and other details of the nursery. The first letter of each nursery code denotes its geographical region. Turn to the map on p.816 to find your region code and then identify the nurseries in your area.

Another purpose of the Directory is to provide more information about the plant through the symbols and other information. For example, if it has an alternative names, is new to this edition or has received the RHS Award of Garden Merit.

Euonymus (*Celastraceae*)

	Name	Nursery codes
	B&L 12543	EPla EWes
	B&SWJ 4457	WPGP
	CC 4522	CPLG
	alatus ♀H4	Widely available
	- B&SWJ 8794	WCru
	- var. ***apterus***	EPfP
	- Chicago Fire	see *E. alatus* 'Timber Creek'
	- 'Ciliodentatus'	see *E. alatus* 'Compactus'
§	- 'Compactus' ♀H4	Widely available
§	- 'Fire Ball'	EPfP
	- Little Moses = 'Odom'	MBlu
*	- 'Macrophyllus'	EPfP
	- 'Rudy Haag'	CPMA EPfP
	- 'Select'	see *E. alatus* 'Fire Ball'
	- 'Silver Cloud' **new**	EPfP
§	- 'Timber Creek'	CPMA EPfP MBlu MBri NLar
	americanus	EPfP GIBF MBlu NLar
	- 'Evergreen' **new**	EPfP
	- narrow-leaved	EPfP NLar
	atropurpureus	EPfP
	'Benkomoki' **new**	MGos
	bungeanus	CMCN EPfP EPla NLar
	- 'Dart's Pride'	CPMA EPfP NLar
	- 'Fireflame'	EPfP NLar
*	- var. ***mongolicus***	EPfP
	- 'Pendulus'	EPfP MBlu SIFN
	- var. ***semipersistens***	CPMA EPla
	carnosus	EPfP NLar
	'Copper Wire'	EMil SPoG
	cornutus var. ***quinquecornutus***	CPMA EPfP LPan MBlu NBhm NLar SIFN SPoG WPGP WPat
	'Den Haag'	EPfP MBri
	echinatus	EPfP EPla
	- BL&M 306	SLon
	europaeus	Widely available
	- f. ***albus***	CPMA CTho EPfP LTwo NLar
	- 'Atropurpureus'	CMCN CTho EPfP MBlu MBri NLar SIFN
	- 'Atrorubens'	CPMA
	- 'Aucubifolius' (v)	EPfP
*	- 'Aureus'	CNat
	- 'Brilliant' **new**	EPfP
*	- f. ***bulgaricus***	EPfP
	- 'Chrysophyllus'	EPfP MBlu NLar
	- 'Howard'	EPfP
	- var. ***intermedius***	ENot EPfP MAsh MBlu NLar
	- 'Miss Pinkie'	CEnd CMCN
	- 'Pumilis' **new**	EPfP
	- 'Red Cascade' ♀H4	Widely available
	- 'Scarlet Wonder'	CPMA EPfP MBri NLar
	- 'Thornhayes'	CTho EPfP
I	- 'Variegatus' **new**	EPfP
	farreri	see *E. nanus*
	fimbriatus	EPfP
	fortunei Blondy = 'Interbolwi'PBR (v)	Widely available

ABBREVIATIONS
To save space a dash indicates that the previous heading is repeated. If written out in full the name would be Euonymus alatus *'Fire Ball'.*

NEW
Plant new to this edition.

DESCRIPTIVE TERM
See p.11.

SYMBOLS TO THE LEFT OF THE NAME
Provides information about the name of the plant. See p.15 for the key.

SYMBOLS TO THE RIGHT OF THE NAME
Tells you more about the plant itself, e.g. (v) *indicates that the plant is variegated,* (F) *= fruit. See p.15 for the key.*

SELLING NAMES
See p.13.

♀H4
This plant has received the RHS Award of Garden Merit. See p.10.

CROSS-REFERENCES
Directs you to the correct name of the plant and the nursery codes. See p.18.

NURSERY CODE
A unique code identifying each nursery. Turn to p.820 for details of the nurseries.

Widely available
Indicates that more than 30 Plant Finder nurseries supply the plant, and it may be available locally. See p.18.

PBR
Plant Breeders' Rights. See p.12.

Supplementary Keys to the Directory

Collectors' References

Abbreviations following a plant name, refer to the collector(s) of the plant. These abbreviations are expanded below, with a collector's name or expedition title. For a fuller explanation, see p.11.

A&JW A. & J. Watson
A&L Ala, A.; Lancaster, Roy
AB&S Archibald, James; Blanchard, John W; Salmon, M.
AC Clark, Alan J.
AC&H Apold, J.; Cox, Peter; Hutchison, Peter
AC&W Albury; Cheese, M.; Watson, J.M.
ACE AGS Expedition to China (1994)
ACL Leslie, Alan C.
AER Robinson, Allan
AGS/ES AGS Expedition to Sikkim (1983)
AGSJ AGS Expedition to Japan (1988)
AH Hoog, A.
AIM Avent, Tony Mexico 1994
Airth Airth, Murray
Akagi Akagi Botanical Garden
AL&JS Sharman, Joseph L.; Leslie, Alan C.
ARG Argent, G.C.G.
ARJA Ruksans, J. & Siesums, A.
B Blanchard, John
B&F MA Brown, Robert & Fisher, Rif & Middle Atlas 2007
B L. Beer, Len
B&L Brickell, Christopher D.; Leslie, Alan C.
B&M & BM Brickell, Christopher D.; Mathew, Brian
B&S Bird P. & Salmon M.
B&SWJ Wynn-Jones, Bleddyn; Wynn-Jones, Susan
B&V Burras, K. & Vosa, C.G.
BB Bartholomew, B.
BC Chudziak, W.
BC&W Beckett; Cheese, M.; Watson, J.M.
Beavis Beavis, Derek S.
Berry Berry, P.
Berry & Brako Berry, P. & Brako, Lois
BKBlount Blount, B.K.
BL&M University of Bangor Expedition to NE Nepal
BM Mathew, Brian F.
BM&W Binns, David L.; Mason, M.; Wright, A.
BOA Boardman, P.
Breedlove Breedlove, D.
BR Rushbrooke, Ben
BS Smith, Basil
BSBE Bowles Scholarship Botanical Expedition (1963)
BSSS Crûg Expedition, Jordan (1991)
Bu Bubert, S.
Burtt Burtt, Brian L.
C Cole, Desmond T.
C&C Cox, P.A. & Cox, K.N.E.
C&Cu Cox, K.N.E. & Cubey, J.
C&H Cox, Peter; Hutchison, Peter
C&K Chamberlain & Knott
C&R Christian & Roderick
C&S Clark, Alan; Sinclair, Ian W.J.
C&V K.N.E. Cox & S. Vergera
C&W Cheese, M.; Watson, J.M.
CC Chadwell, Christopher
CC&H Chamberlain, David F.; Cox, Peter; Hutchison, P.
CC&McK Chadwell, Christopher; McKelvie, A.
CC&MR Chadwell, Christopher; Ramsay
CCH&H Chamberlain, D.F.; Cox, P.; Hutchison, P.; Hootman, S.
CCH&H Chamberlain, Cox, Hootman & Hutchison
CD&R Compton, J.; D'Arcy, J.; Rix, E.M.
CDB Brickell, Christopher D.
CDC Coode, Mark J.E.; Dockrill, Alexander
CDC&C Compton, D'Arcy, Christopher & Coke
CDPR Compton, D'Arcy, Pope & Rix
CE&H Christian, P.J.; Elliott; Hoog
CEE Chengdu Edinburgh Expedition China 1991
CGW Grey-Wilson, Christopher
CH Christian, P. & Hoog, A.
CH&M Cox, P.; Hutchison, P.; Maxwell-MacDonald, D.
CHP&W Kashmir Botanical Expedition
CL Lovell, Chris
CLD Chungtien, Lijiang & Dali Exped. China (1990)

CM&W Cheese M., Mitchel J. & Watson, J.
CN&W Clark; Neilson; Wilson
CNDS Nelson, C. & Sayers D.
Cooper Cooper, R.E.
Cox Cox, Peter A.
CPC Cobblewood Plant Collection
CPN Compton, James
CS Stapleton, Christopher
CSE Cyclamen Society Expedition (1990)
CT Teune, Carla
Dahl Dahl, Sally
DBG Denver Botanic Garden, Colorado
DC Cheshire, David
DF Fox, D.
DG Green, D.
DHTU Hinkley, D., Turkey 2000
DJH Hinkley, Dan
DJHC Hinkley China
DJHV Hinkley, Dan, Vietnam
DM Millais, David
Doleshy Doleshy, F.L.
DS&T Drake, Sharman J.; Thompson
DWD Rose, D.
DZ Zummell, D.
ECN Nelson, E. Charles
EDHCH Hammond, Eric D.
EGM Millais, T.
EKB Balls, Edward K.
EM East Malling Research Station
EMAK Edinburgh Makalu Expedition (1991)
EMR Rix, E.Martyn
EN Needham, Edward F.
ENF Fuller, E. Nigel
ETE Edinburgh Taiwan Expedition (1993)
ETOT Kirkham, T.S.; Flanagan, Mark
F Forrest, G.
F&M Fernandez & Mendoza, Mexico
F&W Watson, J.; Flores, A.
Farrer Farrer, Reginald
FK Kinmonth, Fergus W.
FMB Bailey, F.M.
G Gardner, Martin F.
G&K Gardner, Martin F.; Knees, Sabina G.
G&P Gardner, Martin F.; Page, Christopher N.
GDJ Dumont, Gerard
GG Gusman, G.
GS Sherriff, George
Green Green, D.
Guitt Guittoneau, G.G.
Guiz Guizhou Expedition (1985)
GWJ Goddard, Sally; Wynne-Jones, Bleddyn & Susan
G-W&P Grey-Wilson, Christopher; Phillips
H Huggins, Paul
H&B Hilliard, Olive M.; Burtt, Brian L.
H&D Howick, C.; Darby
H&M Howick, Charles; McNamara, William A.
H&W Hedge, Ian C.; Wendelbo, Per W.
Harry Smith Smith, K.A.Harry
Hartside Hartside Nursery
HCM Heronswood Expedition to Chile (1998)
HECC Hutchison, Evans, Cox, P., Cox, K.
HH&K Hannay, S&S & Kingsbury, N
HLMS Springate, L.S.
HM&S Halliwell, B., Mason, D. & Smallcombe
HOA Hoog, Anton
Hummel Hummel, D.
HW&E Wendelbo, Per; Hedge, I.; Ekberg, L.
HWEL Hirst, J.Michael; Webster, D.
HWJ Crûg Heronswood Joint Expedition
HWJCM Crûg Heronswood Expedition
HWJK Crûg Heronswood Expedition, East Nepal (2002)
HZ Zetterlund, Henrik
ICE Instituto de Investigaciónes Ecológicas Chiloé & RBGE
IDS International Dendrological Society
ISI Int. Succulent Introductions
J&JA Archibald, James; Archibald, Jennifer
J. Jurasek Jurasek, J.
JCA Archibald, James
JE Jack Elliott
JJ Jackson, J.
JJ&JH Halda, J.; Halda, J.
JJH Halda, Joseph J.
JLS Sharman, J.L.
JM-MK Mahr, J.; Kammerlander, M.
JMT Mann Taylor, J.
JN Nielson, Jens
JR Russell, J.
JRM Marr, John
JW Watson, J.M.
K Kirkpatrick, George
K&LG Gillanders, Kenneth; Gillanders, L.
K&Mc Kirkpatrick, George; McBeath, Ronald J.D.
K&P Josef Kopec, Milan Prasil
K&T Kurashige, Y.; Tsukie, S.
KC Cox, Kenneth
KEKE Kew/Edinburgh Kanchenjunga Expedition (1989)
KGB Kunming/Gothenburg Botanical Expedition (1993)
KM Marsh, K.
KR Rushforth, K.D.
KRW Wooster, K.R. (distributed after his death by Kath Dryden)
KW Kingdon-Ward, F.
L Lancaster, C. Roy
L&S Ludlow, Francis; Sherriff, George
LA Long Ashton Research Station clonal selection scheme
LB Bird P., Salmon, M.
LEG Lesotho Edinburgh/Gothenburg Expedition (1997)

Lismore	Lismore Nursery, Breeder's Number
LM&S	Leslie, Mattern & Sharman
LP	Palmer, W.J.L.
LS&E	Ludlow, Frank; Sherriff, George; Elliott, E. E.
LS&H	Ludlow, Frank; Sherriff, George; Hicks, J. H.
LS&T	Ludlow, Frank; Sherriff, George; Taylor, George
M&PS	Mike & Polly Stone
M&T	Mathew; Tomlinson
Mac&W	McPhail & Watson
McB	McBeath, R.J.D.
McLaren	McLaren, H.D.
MDM	Myers, Michael D.
MECC	Scottish Rock Garden Club, Nepal (1997)
MESE	Alpine Garden Society Expedition, Greece 1999
MF	Foster, Maurice
MH	Heasman, Matthew T.
MK	Kammerlander, Michael
MP	Pavelka, Mojmir
MPF	Frankis, M.P.
MS	Salmon, M.
MS&CL	Salmon, M.; Lovell, C.
MSF	Fillan, M.S.
NICE	North India Expedition 1997
NJM	Macer, N.J.
NNS	Ratko, Ron
NS	Turland, Nick
NVFDE	Northern Vietnam First Darwin Expedition
Og	Ogisu, Mikinori
OS	Sonderhousen, O.
P. Bon	Bonavia, P.
P&C	Paterson, David S.; Clarke, Sidney
P&W	Polastri; Watson, J. M.
PB	Bird, Peter
PC&H	Pattison, G.; Catt, P.; Hickson, M.
PD	Davis, Peter H.
PF	Furse, Paul
PJC	Christian, Paul J.
PJC&AH	P.J. Christian & A. Hogg
PNMK	Nicholls, P.; Kammerlander, M.
Polunin	Polunin, Oleg
Pras	Prasil, M.
PS&W	Polunin, Oleg; Sykes, William; Williams, John
PW	Wharton, Peter
R	Rock, J.F.C.
RB	Brown, R.
RBS	Brown, Ray, Sakharin Island
RCB AM	Brown, Robert, Expedition to Armenia
RCB/Arg	Brown, Robert, Argentina, (2002)
RCB E	Brown, Robert, Expedition to Spain (Andalucia)
RCB/Eq	Brown, Robert, Ecuador, (1988)
RCB RA	Brown, Robert
RCB RL	Brown, Robert, Expedition to Lebanon
RCB/TQ	Brown, Robert, Turkey (2001)
RH	Hancock, R.
RKMP	Ruksans, J., Krumins, A., Kitts, M., Paivel, A.
RM	Ruksans, J. & Kitts, M.
RMRP	Rocky Mountain Rare Plants, Denver, Colorado
RS	Suckow, Reinhart
RSC	Richard Somer Cocks
RV	Richard Valder
RWJ	Crûg Farm-Rickards Ferns Expedition to Taiwan (2003)
S&B	Blanchard, J.W.; Salmon, M.
S&F	Salmon, M. & Fillan, M.
S&L	Sinclair, Ian W.J.; Long, David G.
S&SH	Sheilah and Spencer Hannay
Sandham	Sandham, John
SB&L	Salmon, Bird and Lovell
SBEC	Sino-British Expedition to Cangshan
SBEL	Sino-British Lijiang Expedition
SBQE	Sino-British Expedition to Quinghai
Sch	Schilling, Anthony D.
SD	Sashal Dayal
SDR	Rankin, Stella; Rankin, David
SEH	Hootman, Steve
SEP	Swedish Expedition to Pakistan
SF	Forde, P.
SG	Salmon, M. & Guy, P.
SH	Hannay, Spencer
Sich	Simmons, Erskine, Howick & Mcnamara
SL	Sinclair, I. & Long, D.
SLIZE	Swedish-Latvian-Iranian Zagros Expedition to Iran (May 1988)
SOJA	Kew / Quarryhill Expedition to Southern Japan
SS&W	Stainton, J.D.Adam; Sykes, William; Williams, John
SSNY	Sino-Scottish Expedition to NW Yunnan (1992)
T	Taylor, Nigel P.
T&K	Taylor, Nigel P.; Knees, Sabina
TH	Hudson, T.
TS&BC	Smythe, T and Cherry, B
TSS	Spring Smyth, T.L.M.
TW	Tony Weston
USDAPI	US Department of Agriculture Plant Index Number
USDAPQ	US Dept. of Agriculture Plant Quarantine Number
USNA	United States National Arboretum
VHH	Vernon H. Heywood
W	Wilson, Ernest H.
WM	McLewin, William
Woods	Woods, Patrick J.B.
Wr	Wraight, David & Anke
WWJ	Wharton, Peter; Wynn-Jones, Bleddyn & Susan
Yu	Yu, Tse-tsun

Notes on Nomenclature and Identification

These notes refer to plants in the Plant Directory that are marked with a 'N' to the left of the name. 'Bean Supplement' refers to W.J. Bean *Trees & Shrubs Hardy in the British Isles* (Supplement to the 8th edition) edited by D L Clarke 1988.

Acer davidii **'Ernest Wilson' and** ***A. davidii*** **'George Forrest'**
These cultivars should be grafted in order to retain the characteristics of the original clones. However, many plants offered under these names are seed-raised.

Acer palmatum **'Sango-kaku' / 'Senkaki'**
Two or more clones are offered under these names. *A. palmatum* 'Eddisbury' is similar with brighter coral stems.

Achillea ptarmica **The Pearl Group /** ***A. ptarmica*** **(The Pearl Group) 'Boule de Neige' /** ***A. ptarmica*** **(The Pearl Group) 'The Pearl'**
In the recent trial of achilleas at Wisley, only one of the several stocks submitted as 'The Pearl' matched the original appearance of this plant according to Graham Stuart Thomas, this being from Wisley's own stock. At rather less than 60cm (2ft), this needed little support, being the shortest of the plants bearing this name, with slightly grey, not glossy dark green, leaves and a non-invasive habit. This has been designated as the type for this cultivar and only this clone should bear the cultivar name 'The Pearl'. The Pearl Group covers all other double-flowered clones of this species, including seed-raised plants which are markedly inferior, sometimes scarcely double, often invasive and usually needing careful staking. It has been claimed that 'The Pearl' was a re-naming of Lemoine's 'Boule de Neige' but not all authorities agree: all plants submitted to the Wisley trial as 'Boule de Neige' were different from each other, not the same clone as Wisley's 'The Pearl' and referrable to The Pearl Group.

Anemone nemorosa **'Alba Plena'**
This name is used for several double white forms including *A. nemorosa* 'Flore Pleno' and *A. nemorosa* 'Vestal'.

Artemisia ludoviciana **subsp.** ***ludoviciana*** **var.** ***latiloba*** **/** ***A. ludoviciana*** **'Valerie Finnis'**
Leaves of the former are glabrous at maturity, those of the latter are not.

Artemisia stelleriana **'Boughton Silver'**
This was thought to be the first validly published name for this plant, 'Silver Brocade' having been published earlier but invalidly in an undated publication. However, an earlier valid publication for the cultivar name 'Mori' has subsequently been found for the same plant. A proposal to conserve 'Boughton Silver' has been tabled because of its more widespread use.

Aster amellus Violet Queen
It is probable that more than one cultivar is sold under this name.

Aster dumosus
Many of the asters listed under *A. novi-belgii* contain varying amounts of *A. dumosus* blood in their parentage. It is not possible to allocate these to one species or the other and they are therefore listed under *A. novi-belgii*.

Aster × frikartii **'Mönch'**
The true plant is very rare in British gardens. Most plants are another form of *A. × frikartii*, usually 'Wunder von Stäfa'.

Aster novi-belgii
See note under *A. dumosus*. *A. laevis* is also involved in the parentage of most cultivars.

Berberis buxifolia **'Nana' misapplied / 'Pygmaea'**
See explanation in Bean Supplement.

Betula utilis **var.** ***jacquemontii***
Plants are often the clones *B. utilis* var. *jacquemontii* 'Inverleith' or *B. utilis* var. *jacquemontii* 'Doorenbos'

Brachyscome
Originally published as *Brachyscome* by Cassini who later revised his spelling to *Brachycome*. The original spelling has been internationally adopted.

Calamagrostis × acutiflora **'Karl Foerster'**
C. × acutiflora 'Stricta' differs in being 15cm taller, 10–15 days earlier flowering with a less fluffy inflorescence.

Calceolaria integrifolia sensu lato
Christine Ehrhart (*Systematic Botany*. (2005. 30(2):383–411) has demonstrated that this is a complex involving nine distinct species (*C. andina*, *C. angustifolia*, *C. auriculata*, *C. georgiana*, *C. integrifolia sensu stricto*, *C. rubiginosa*, *C. talcana*, *C. verbascifolia* and *C. viscosissima*). However, it is not yet clear to which species plants in cultivation belong or whether they are hybrids.

Caltha polypetala
This name is often applied to a large-flowered variant of *C. palustris*. The true species has more (7–10) petals.

Camassia leichtlinii **'Alba'**
The true cultivar has blueish-white, not cream flowers.

Camassia leichtlinii **'Plena'**
This has starry, transparent green-white flowers; creamy-white 'Semiplena' is sometimes offered under this name.

***Campanula lactiflora* 'Alba'**
This refers to the pure white-flowered clone, not to blueish- or greyish-white flowered plants, nor to seed-raised plants.

***Carex morrowii* 'Variegata'**
C. oshimensis 'Evergold' is sometimes sold under this name.

Carya illinoinensis
The correct spelling of this name is discussed in *Baileya*, **10**(1) (1962).

Cassinia retorta
Now included within *C. leptophylla*. A valid infraspecific epithet has yet to be published.

***Ceanothus* 'Italian Skies'**
Many plants under this name are not true to name.

***Chamaecyparis lawsoniana* 'Columnaris Glauca'**
Plants under this name might be *C. lawsoniana* 'Columnaris' or a new invalidly named cultivar.

***Chrysanthemum* 'Anastasia Variegated'**
Despite its name, this seems to be derived from 'Mei-kyo', not 'Anastasia'.

Clematis chrysocoma
The true *C. chrysocoma* is a non-climbing erect plant with dense yellow down on the young growth, still uncommon in cultivation.

Clematis montana
This name should be used for the typical white-flowered variety only. Pink-flowered variants are referable to *C. montana* var. *rubens*.

***Clematis* 'Victoria'**
Raised by Cripps (1867). There is also a Latvian cultivar of this name with petals with a central white bar in the collection of Janis Ruplēns which is probably, though not certainly, of his own raising.

***Colchicum* 'Autumn Queen'**
Entries here might refer to the slightly different *C.* 'Prinses Astrid'.

***Cornus* 'Norman Hadden'**
See note in Bean Supplement, p.184.

Cotoneaster dammeri
Plants sold under this name are usually *C. dammeri* 'Major'.

***Cotoneaster frigidus* 'Cornubia'**
According to Hylmø this cultivar, like all other variants of this species, is fully deciduous. Several evergreen cotoneasters are also grown under this name; most are clones of *C.* × *watereri* or *C. salicifolius*.

Crataegus coccinea
C. intricata, *C. pedicellata* and *C. biltmoreana* are occasionally supplied under this name.

***Crocus cartwrightianus* 'Albus'**
The plant offered is the true cultivar and not *C. hadriaticus*.

***Dianthus* fringed pink**
D. 'Old Fringed Pink' and *D.* 'Old Fringed White' are also sometimes sold under this name.

***Dianthus* 'Musgrave's Pink' (p)**
This is the registered name of this white-flowered cultivar.

***Epilobium glabellum* misapplied**
Plants under this name are not *E. glabellum* but are close to *E. wilsonii* Petrie or perhaps a hybrid of it.

Erodium glandulosum
Plants under this name are often hybrids.

Erodium guttatum
Doubtfully in commerce; plants under this name are usually *E. heteradenum, E. cheilanthifolium* or hybrids.

***Fagus sylvatica* Atropurpurea Group / Cupreа Group**
It is desirable to provide a name, Cuprea Group, for less richly coloured forms, used in historic landscapes before the purple clones appeared.

***Fagus sylvatica* 'Pendula'**
This name refers to the Knap Hill clone, the most common weeping form in English gardens. Other clones occur, particularly in Cornwall and Ireland.

Fuchsia loxensis
For a comparison of the true species with the hybrids 'Speciosa' and 'Loxensis' commonly grown under this name, see Boullemier's Check List (2nd ed.) p.268.

***Geum* 'Borisii'**
This name refers to cultivars of *G. coccineum* Sibthorp & Smith, especially *G.* 'Werner Arends' and not to *G.* × *borisii* Kelleper.

Halimium halimifolium
Plants under this name are sometimes *H.* × *pauanum* or *H.* × *santae.*

***Hebe* 'Carl Teschner'**
See note in Bean Supplement, p.264.

***Hedera helix* 'Caenwoodiana' / 'Pedata'**
Some authorities consider these to be distinct cultivars while others think them different morphological forms of the same unstable clone.

***Hedera helix* 'Oro di Bogliasco'**
Priority between this name and 'Jubiläum Goldherz' and 'Goldheart' has yet to be finally resolved.

***Helleborus* × *hybridus* / *H. orientalis* misapplied**
The name *H.* × *hybridus* for acaulescent hellebore hybrids does not seem to follow the *International Code of Botanical Nomenclature* Article H.3.2 requiring one of the parent species to be designated and does not seem to have been typified, contrary to Article 7 of the Code. However, the illustration accompanying the original description in Vilmorin's *Blumengärtnerei* 3(1): 27 (1894) shows that one parent of the cross must have been *H. guttatus*, now treated as part of *H. orientalis*. Taking this illustration as the type for this hybrid species makes it possible to

retain *H.* × *hybridus* formally as a hybrid binomial (rather than *H. hybridus* as in a previous edition), as the Code's requirement to distinguish one parent is now met.

Hemerocallis fulva **'Kwanso', 'Kwanso Variegata', 'Flore Pleno' and 'Green Kwanso'**
For a discussion of these plants see *The Plantsman*, 7(2).

Heuchera villosa **'Palace Purple'**
This cultivar name refers only to plants with deep purple-red foliage. Seed-raised plants of inferior colouring should not be offered under this name.

Hosta montana
This name refers only to plants long grown in Europe, which differ from *H. elata.*

Hydrangea macrophylla **Teller Series**
This is used both as a descriptive common name for Lacecap hydrangeas (German *teller* = plate, referring to the more or less flat inflorescence) and for the series of hybrids raised by Wädenswil in Switzerland bearing German names of birds. It is not generally possible to link a hydrangea described by the series name plus a colour description (e.g. Teller Blau, Teller Rosa, Teller Rot) to a single cultivar.

Hypericum fragile
The true *H. fragile* is probably not available from British nurseries.

Hypericum **'Gemo'**
Either a selection of *H. prolificum* or *H. prolificum* × *H. densiflorum.*

Ilex × ***altaclerensis***
The argument for this spelling is given by Susyn Andrews, *The Plantsman*, 5(2) and is not superseded by the more recent comments in the Supplement to Bean's Trees and Shrubs.

Iris
Apart from those noted below, cultivar names marked 'N' are not registered. The majority of those marked 'I' have been previously used for a different cultivar.

Iris histrioides **'Major'**
Two clones are offered under this name, the true one pale blue with darker spotting on the falls, the incorrect one violet-blue with almost horizontal falls.

Juniperus × ***media***
This name is illegitimate if applied to hybrids of *J. chinensis* × *J. sabina*, having been previously used for a different hybrid (P.A. Schmidt, *IDS Yearbook 1993*, 47–48). Because of its importance to gardeners, a proposal to conserve its present use was tabled but subsequently rejected.

Lavandula spica
This name is classed as a name to be rejected (*nomen rejiciendum*) by the *International Code of Botanical Nomenclature.*

Lavatera olbia **and** ***L. thuringiaca***
Although *L. olbia* is usually shrubby and *L. thuringiaca* usually herbaceous, both species are very variable. Cultivars formerly ascribed to one species or the other have been shown to be hybrids and are referable to the recently-named hybrid species *L.* × *clementii.*

Lobelia **'Russian Princess'**
This name, originally for a pink-flowered, green-leaved cultivar, is now generally applied to a purple-flowered, dark-leaved cultivar that seems to lack a valid name.

Lonicera periclymenum **'Serotina'**
See note in Bean Supplement, p.315.

Lonicera sempervirens **f.** ***sulphurea***
Plants in the British Isles usually a yellow-flowered form of *L. periclymenum.*

Malus domestica **'Dummellor's Seedling'**
The phonetic spelling 'Dumelow's Seedling' contravenes the ICBN ruling on orthography, i.e. that, except for intentional latinisations, commemorative names should be based on the original spelling of the person's name (Article 60.11). The spelling adopted here is that used on the gravestone of the raiser in Leicestershire.

Meconopsis **Fertile Blue Group**
This Group comprises seed-raised and intrinsically perennial tall blue poppies of as yet indeterminate origin. The only cultivars so far established are 'Lingholm' (synonyms 'Blue Ice' and 'Correnie') and 'Kingsbarns'.

Meconopsis napaulensis **misapplied**
In his revision of the evergreen monocarpic species, Dr C. Grey-Wilson has established that *M. napaulensis* DC., a dwarfish yellow-flowered species not usually more than 1.1m tall and endemic to C Nepal, is not currently in cultivation. The well-known plants of gardens which pass for *M. napaulensis* are hybrids, for the present to be known as *M. napaulensis* misapplied. The parents of the hybrids are *M. staintonii* (from W Nepal) and *M. paniculata* (a yellow-flowered species with a purple stigma) or *M. staintonii* and *M. regia* or a complex mixture of all three species. *M. staintonii*, newly described by C. Grey-Wilson (*Bot. Mag.* (2006) 23(2):176–209), is a tall (to 2.5m), robust species with red or pink flowers and a dark green stigma, near in appearance to *M. napaulensis* of gardens, but less so to true *M. napaulensis*. As *M. staintonii*, like its near relatives, readily hybridises in cultivation, it is rarely seen in an unadulterated form.

Melissa officinalis **'Variegata'**
The true cultivar of this name has leaves striped with white.

***Nemesia caerulea* 'Joan Wilder'**
The lavender-blue clone 'Joan Wilder', described and illustrated in *The Hardy Plant,* 14(1), 11–14, does not come true from seed; it may only be propagated from cuttings.

***Osmanthus heterophyllus* 'Gulftide'**
Probably correctly *O.* × *fortunei* 'Gulftide'.

***Pelargonium* 'Lass o' Gowrie'**
The American plant of this name has pointed, not rounded leaf lobes.

Pelargonium quercifolium
Plants under this name are mainly hybrids. The true species has pointed, not rounded leaf lobes.

***Penstemon* 'Taoensis'**
This name for a small-flowered cultivar or hybrid of *P. isophyllus* originally appeared as 'Taoense' but must be corrected to agree in gender with *Penstemon* (masculine). Presumably an invalid name (published in Latin form since 1958), it is not synonymous with *P. crandallii* subsp. *glabrescens* var. *taosensis*.

Pernettya
Botanists now consider that *Pernettya* (fruit a berry) is not separable from *Gaultheria* (fruit a capsule) because in some species the fruit is intermediate between a berry and a capsule. For a fuller explanation see D. Middleton, *The Plantsman,* 12(3).

Pinus ayacahuite
P. ayacahuite var. *veitchii* (syn. *P. veitchii)* is occasionally sold under this name.

***Pinus nigra* 'Cebennensis Nana'**
A doubtful name, possibly a synonym for *P. nigra* 'Nana'.

Polemonium archibaldiae
Usually sterile with lavender-blue flowers. A self-fertile white-flowered plant is sometimes sold under this name.

***Prunus laurocerasus* 'Castlewellan'**
We are grateful to Dr Charles Nelson for informing us that the name 'Marbled White' is not valid because although it has priority of publication it does not have the approval of the originator who asked for it to be called 'Castlewellan'.

Prunus serrulata* var. *pubescens
See note in Bean Supplement, p.398.

***Prunus* × *subhirtella* 'Rosea'**
Might be *P. pendula* var. *ascendens* 'Rosea', *P. pendula* 'Pendula Rosea', or *P.* × *subhirtella* 'Autumnalis Rosea'.

Rheum* × *cultorum
The name *R.* × *cultorum* was published without adequate description and must be abandoned in favour of the validly published *R.* × *hybridum*.

***Rhododendron* (azaleas)**
All names marked 'N', except for the following, refer to more than one cultivar.

***Rhododendron* 'Hinomayo'**
This name is based on a faulty transliteration (should be 'Hinamoyo') but the spelling 'Hinomayo' is retained in the interests of stability.

Rhus hirta and R. typhina
Linnaeus published both *R. typhina* and *R. hirta* as names for the same species. Though *R. hirta* has priority, it has been proposed that the name *R. typhina* should be conserved.

Rosa gentiliana
Plants under this name are usually the cultivar 'Polyantha Grandiflora' but might otherwise be *R. multiflora* 'Wilsonii', *R. multiflora* var. *cathayensis, R. henryi* or another hybrid.

***Rosa* 'Gros Chou de Hollande' (Bb)**
It is doubtful if this name is correctly applied.

***Rosa* 'Jacques Cartier' misapplied**
For a discussion on the correct identity of this rose see *Heritage Rose Foundation News,* Oct. 1989 & Jan. 1990.

***Rosa* 'Kazanlik'**
For a discussion on the correct identity of this rose see *Heritage Roses,* Nov. 1991.

***Rosa* Sweetheart**
This is not the same as the Sweetheart Rose, a common name for *R.* 'Cécile Brünner'.

Rosa wichurana
This is the correct spelling according to the ICBN 1994 Article 60.11 (which enforces Recommendation 60C.1c) and not *wichuraiana* for this rose commemorating Max Wichura.

***Rubus fruticosus* L. agg.**
Though some cultivated blackberries do belong to *Rubus fruticosus* L. *sensu stricto,* others are more correctly ascribed to other species of *Rubus* section *Glandulosus* (including *R. armeniacus, R. laciniatus* or *R. ulmifolius)* or are hybrids of species within this section. Because it is almost impossible to ascribe every cultivar to a single species or hybrid, they are listed under *R. fruticosus* L. agg. (i.e. aggregate) for convenience.

Salvia microphylla* var. *neurepia
The type of this variety is referable to the typical variety, *S. microphylla* var. *microphylla*.

***Salvia officinalis* 'Aurea'**
S. officinalis var. *aurea* is a rare variant of the common sage with leaves entirely of gold. It is represented in cultivation by the cultivar 'Kew Gold'. The plant usually offered as *S. officinalis* 'Aurea' is the gold variegated sage *S. officinalis* 'Icterina'.

***Sambucus nigra* 'Aurea'**
Plants under this name are usually not *S. nigra*.

***Skimmia japonica* 'Foremanii'**
The true cultivar, which belongs to *S. japonica* Rogersii Group, is believed to be lost to cultivation. Plants offered under this name are usually *S. japonica* 'Veitchii'.

***Spiraea japonica* 'Shirobana'**
Shirobana-shimotsuke is the common name for *S. japonica* var. *albiflora*. Shirobana means white-flowered and does not apply to the two-coloured form.

Staphylea holocarpa* var. *rosea
This botanical variety has woolly leaves. The cultivar 'Rosea', with which it is often confused, does not.

***Stewartia ovata* var. *grandiflora*.**
Most, possibly all, plants available from British nurseries under this name are not true to name but are derived from the improved Nymans form.

***Thymus* Coccineus Group**
Thymes under this name have dark crimson (RHS 78A) flowers whereas those of 'Alan Bloom' are purplish-pink (RHS 78C).

***Thymus serpyllum* cultivars**
Most cultivars are probably correctly cultivars of *T. polytrichus* or hybrids though they will remain listed under *T. serpyllum* pending further research.

***Thymus* 'Silver Posie'**
The cultivar name 'Silver Posie' is applied to several different plants, not all of them *T. vulgaris*.

***Tricyrtis* Hototogisu**
This is the common name applied generally to all Japanese *Tricyrtis* and specifically to *T. hirta*.

Tricyrtis macropoda
This name has been used for at least five different species.

Uncinia rubra
This name is also misapplied to *U. egmontiana* and *U. uncinata*.

***Viburnum opulus* 'Fructu Luteo'**
See note below.

***Viburnum opulus* 'Xanthocarpum'**
Some entries under this name might be the less compact *V. opulus* 'Fructu Luteo'.

Viburnum plicatum
Entries may include the 'snowball' form, *V. plicatum* f. *plicatum* (syn. *V. plicatum* 'Sterile'), as well as the 'lacecap' form, *V. plicatum* f. *tomentosum*.

Viola labradorica
See Note in *The Garden*, **110**(2): 96.

***Wisteria floribunda* 'Violacea Plena' and *W. floribunda* 'Yae-kokuryū'**
We are grateful to Yoko Otsuki, who has established through Engei Kyokai (the Horticultural Society of Japan) that there are two different double selections of *Wisteria floribunda*. 'Violacea Plena' has double lavender/lilac flowers, while 'Yae-kokuryū' has more ragged and tightly double flowers with purple/indigo centres. Each is distinctive but it is probable that both are confused in the British nursery trade. 'Yae-fuji' might be an earlier name for 'Violacea Plena' or a Group name covering a range of doubles but, as *fuji* is the Japanese common name for the species, it would not be a valid name under the ICNCP.

CLASSIFICATION OF GENERA

Genera including a large number of species, or with many cultivars, are often subdivided into informal horticultural classifications, or formal cultivar groups in the case of *Clematis* and *Tulipa*. The breeding of new cultivars is sometimes limited to hybrids between closely-related species, thus for *Saxifraga* and *Primula*, the cultivars are allocated to the sections given in the infrageneric treatments cited. Please turn to p.11 for a fuller explanation.

ACTINIDIA

(s-p) Self-pollinating

BEGONIA

(C) Cane-like
(R) Rex Cultorum
(S) Semperflorens Cultorum
(T) × *tuberhybrida* (Tuberous)

CHRYSANTHEMUM

(By the National Chrysanthemum Society)
(1) Indoor Large (Exhibition)
(2) Indoor Medium (Exhibition)
(3a) Indoor Incurved: Large-flowered
(3b) Indoor Incurved: Medium-flowered
(3c) Indoor Incurved: Small-flowered
(4a) Indoor Reflexed: Large-flowered
(4b) Indoor Reflexed: Medium-flowered
(4c) Indoor Reflexed: Small-flowered
(5a) Indoor Intermediate: Large-flowered
(5b) Indoor Intermediate: Medium-flowered
(5c) Indoor Intermediate: Small-flowered
(6a) Indoor Anemone: Large-flowered
(6b) Indoor Anemone: Medium-flowered
(6c) Indoor Anemone: Small-flowered
(7a) Indoor Single: Large-flowered
(7b) Indoor Single: Medium-flowered
(7c) Indoor Single: Small-flowered
(8a) Indoor True Pompon
(8b) Indoor Semi-pompon
(9a) Indoor Spray: Anemone
(9b) Indoor Spray: Pompon
(9c) Indoor Spray: Reflexed
(9d) Indoor Spray: Single
(9e) Indoor Spray: Intermediate
(9f) Indoor Spray: Spider, Quill, Spoon or Any Other Type
(10a) Indoor, Spider
(10b) Indoor, Quill
(10c) Indoor, Spoon
(11) Any Other Indoor Type
(12a) Indoor, Charm
(12b) Indoor, Cascade
(13a) October-flowering Incurved: Large-flowered
(13b) October-flowering Incurved: Medium-flowered
(13c) October-flowering Incurved: Small-flowered
(14a) October-flowering Reflexed: Large-flowered
(14b) October-flowering Reflexed: Medium-flowered
(14c) October-flowering Reflexed: Small-flowered
(15a) October-flowering Intermediate: Large-flowered
(15b) October-flowering Intermediate: Medium-flowered
(15c) October-flowered Intermediate: Small-flowered
(16) October-flowering Large
(17a) October-flowering Single: Large-flowered
(17b) October-flowering Single: Medium-flowered
(17c) October-flowering Single: Small-flowered
(18a) October-flowering Pompon: True Pompon
(18b) October-flowering Pompon: Semi-pompon
(19a) October-flowering Spray: Anemone
(19b) October-flowering Spray: Pompon
(19c) October-flowering Spray: Reflexed
(19d) October-flowering Spray: Single
(19e) October-flowering Spray: Intermediate
(19f) October-flowering Spray: Spider, Quill, Spoon or Any Other Type
(20) Any Other October-flowering Type
(21a) Korean: Anemone
(21b) Korean: Pompon
(21c) Korean: Reflexed
(21d) Korean: Single
(21e) Korean: Intermediate
(21f) Korean: Spider, Quill, Spoon, or any other type
(22a) Charm: Anemone
(22b) Charm: Pompon
(22c) Charm: Reflexed
(22d) Charm: Single
(22e) Charm: Intermediate
(22f) Charm: Spider, Quill, Spoon or Any Other Type
(23a) Early-flowering Outdoor Incurved: Large-flowered

(23b)	Early-flowering Outdoor Incurved: Medium-flowered
(23c)	Early-flowering Outdoor Incurved: Small-flowered
(24a)	Early-flowering Outdoor Reflexed: Large-flowered
(24b)	Early-flowering Outdoor Reflexed: Medium-flowered
(24c)	Early-flowering Outdoor Reflexed: Small-flowered
(25a)	Early-flowering Outdoor Intermediate: Large-flowered
(25b)	Early-flowering Outdoor Intermediate: Medium-flowered
(25c)	Early-flowering Outdoor Intermediate: Small-flowered
(26a)	Early-flowering Outdoor Anemone: Large-flowered
(26b)	Early-flowering Outdoor Anemone: Medium-flowered
(27a)	Early-flowering Outdoor Single: Large-flowered
(27b)	Early-flowering Outdoor Single: Medium-flowered
(28a)	Early-flowering Outdoor Pompon: True Pompon
(28b)	Early-flowering Outdoor Pompon: Semi-pompon
(29a)	Early-flowering Outdoor Spray: Anemone
(29b)	Early-flowering Outdoor Spray: Pompon
(29c)	Early-flowering Outdoor Spray: Reflexed
(29d)	Early-flowering Outdoor Spray: Single
(29e)	Early-flowering Outdoor Spray: Intermediate
(29f)	Early-flowering Outdoor Spray: Spider, Quill, Spoon or Any Other Type
(30)	Any Other Early-flowering Outdoor Type

Clematis

(Cultivar Groups as per Matthews, V. (2002) *The International Clematis Register & Checklist 2002*, RHS, London.)

(A)	Atragene Group
(Ar)	Armandii Group
(C)	Cirrhosa Group
(EL)	Early Large-flowered Group
(F)	Flammula Group
(Fo)	Forsteri Group
(H)	Heracleifolia Group
(I)	Integrifolia Group
(LL)	Late Large-flowered Group
(M)	Montana Group
(T)	Texensis Group
(Ta)	Tangutica Group
(V)	Viorna Group
(Vb)	Vitalba Group
(Vt)	Viticella Group

Dahlia

(By the National Dahlia Society with corresponding numerical classification according to the RHS's International Register)

(Sin)	1 Single
(Anem)	2 Anemone-flowered
(Col)	3 Collerette
(WL)	4 Waterlily (unassigned)
(LWL)	4B Waterlily, Large
(MWL)	4C Waterlily, Medium
(SWL)	4D Waterlily, Small
(MinWL)	4E Waterlily, Miniature
(D)	5 Decorative (unassigned)
(GD)	5A Decorative, Giant
(LD)	5B Decorative, Large
(MD)	5C Decorative, Medium
(SD)	5D Decorative, Small
(MinD)	5E Decorative, Miniature
(SBa)	6A Small Ball
(MinBa)	6B Miniature Ball
(Pom)	7 Pompon
(C)	8 Cactus (unassigned)
(GC)	8A Cactus, Giant
(LC)	8B Cactus, Large
(MC)	8C Cactus, Medium
(SC)	8D Cactus, Small
(MinC)	8E Cactus, Miniature
(S-c)	9 Semi-cactus (unassigned)
(GS-c)	9A Semi-cactus, Giant
(LS-c)	9B Semi-cactus, Large
(MS-c)	9C Semi-cactus, Medium
(SS-c)	9D Semi-cactus, Small
(MinS-c)	9E Semi-cactus, Miniature
(Misc)	10 Miscellaneous
(Fim)	11 Fimbriated
(SinO)	12 Single Orchid (Star)
(DblO)	13 Double Orchid
(B)	Botanical
(DwB)	Dwarf Bedding
(Lil)	Lilliput (in combination)

Dianthus

(By the RHS)

(b)	Carnation, border
(M)	Carnation, Malmaison
(pf)	Carnation, perpetual-flowering
(p)	Pink
(p,a)	Pink, annual

FRUIT

(B) Black (*Vitis*), Blackcurrant (*Ribes*)
(Ball) Ballerina (*Malus*)
(C) Culinary (*Malus, Prunus, Pyrus, Ribes*)
(Cider) Cider (*Malus*)
(D) Dessert (*Malus, Prunus, Pyrus, Ribes*)
(F) Fruit
(G) Glasshouse (*Vitis*)
(O) Outdoor (*Vitis*)
(P) Pinkcurrant (*Ribes*)
(Perry) Perry (*Pyrus*)
(R) Red (*Vitis*), Redcurrant (*Ribes*)
(S) Seedless (*Citrus, Vitis*)
(W) White (*Vitis*), Whitecurrant (*Ribes*)

FUCHSIA

(E) Encliandra
(T) Variants and hybrids of F. triphylla

GLADIOLUS

(B) Butterfly
(E) Exotic
(G) Giant
(L) Large
(M) Medium
(Min) Miniature
(N) Nanus
(P) Primulinus
(S) Small
(Tub) Tubergenii

HYDRANGEA MACROPHYLLA

(H) Hortensia
(L) Lacecap

IRIS

(By the American Iris Society)
(AB) Arilbred
(BB) Border Bearded
(Cal-Sib) Series *Californicae* × Series *Sibiricae*
(CH) Californian Hybrid
(DB) Dwarf Bearded (not assigned)
(Dut) Dutch
(IB) Intermediate Bearded
(J) Juno (subgenus) *Scorpiris*
(La) Louisiana Hybrid
(MDB) Miniature Dwarf Bearded
(MTB) Miniature Tall Bearded
(SDB) Standard Dwarf Bearded
(Sino-Sib) Series *Sibiricae*, chromosome number 2n=40
(SpH) Species Hybrid
(Spuria) Spuria
(TB) Tall Bearded

LILIUM

(Classification according to *The International Lily Register* (ed. 3, 1982) with amendments from Supp. 17 (1999), RHS)
(I) Early-flowering Asiatic Hybrids derived from *L. amabile, L. bulbiferum, L. cernuum, L. concolor, L. davidii, L. × hollandicum, L. lancifolium, L. leichtlinii, L. × maculatum* and *L. pumilum*
(II) Hybrids of Martagon type, one parent having been a form of *L. hansonii* or *L. martagon*
(III) Hybrids from *L. candidum, L. chalcedonicum* and other related European species (excluding *L. martagon*)
(IV) Hybrids of American species
(V) Hybrids derived from *L. formosanum* and *L. longiflorum*
(VI) Hybrid Trumpet Lilies and Aurelian hybrids from Asiatic species, including *L. henryi* but excluding those from *L. auratum, L. japonicum, L. rubellum* and *L. speciosum*.
(VII) Hybrids of Far Eastern species as *L auratum, L. japonicum, L. rubellum* and *L. speciosum* (Oriental Hybrids)
(VIII) All hybrids not in another division
(IX) All species and their varieties and forms
a/ upward-facing flowers
b/ outward-facing flowers
c/ downward-facing flowers
/a trumpet-shaped flowers
/b bowl-shaped flowers
/d recurved flowers

MALUS *SEE* FRUIT

NARCISSUS

(By the RHS, revised 1998)
(1) Trumpet
(2) Large-cupped
(3) Small-cupped
(4) Double
(5) Triandrus
(6) Cyclamineus
(7) Jonquilla and Apodanthus
(8) Tazetta
(9) Poeticus
(10) Bulbocodium
(11a) Split-corona: Collar
(11b) Split-corona: Papillon

(12) Miscellaneous
(13) Species

NYMPHAEA

(H) Hardy
(D) Day-blooming
(N) Night-blooming
(T) Tropical

PAPAVER

(SPS) Super Poppy Series

PAEONIA

(S) Shrubby

PELARGONIUM

(A) Angel
(C) Coloured Foliage (in combination)
(Ca) Cactus (in combination)
(d) Double (in combination)
(Dec) Decorative
(Dw) Dwarf
(DwI) Dwarf Ivy-leaved
(Fr) Frutetorum
(I) Ivy-leaved
(Min) Miniature
(MinI) Miniature Ivy-leaved
(R) Regal
(Sc) Scented-leaved
(St) Stellar (in combination)
(T) Tulip (in combination)
(U) Unique
(Z) Zonal

PRIMULA

(Classification by Section as per Richards. J. (2002) *Primula* (2nd edition). Batsford, London)

(Ag) *Auganthus*
(Al) *Aleuritia*
(Am) *Amethystinae*
(Ar) *Armerina*
(Au) *Auricula*
- (A) Alpine Auricula
- (B) Border Auricula
- (S) Show Auricula
- (St) Striped Auricula

(Bu) *Bullatae*
(Ca) *Capitatae*
(Cf) *Cordifoliae*
(Ch) *Chartaceae*
(Co) *Cortusoides*
(Cr) *Carolinella*
(Cu) *Cuneifoliae*
(Cy) *Crystallophlomis*
(Da) *Davidii*
(De) *Denticulatae*
(Dr) *Dryadifoliae*
(F) *Fedtschenkoanae*
(G) *Glabrae*
(Ma) *Malvaceae*
(Mi) *Minutissimae*
(Mo) *Monocarpicae*
(Mu) *Muscarioides*
(Ob) *Obconicolisteri*
(Or) *Oreophlomis*
(Pa) *Parryi*
(Pe) *Petiolares*
(Pf) *Proliferae*
(Pi) *Pinnatae*
(Pr) *Primula*
- (Poly) Polyanthus
- (Prim) Primrose

(Pu) *Pulchellae*
(Py) *Pycnoloba*
(R) *Reinii*
(Si) *Sikkimenses*
(So) *Soldanelloides*
(Sp) *Sphondylia*
(Sr) *Sredinskya*
(Su) *Suffrutescentes*
(Y) *Yunnannenses*

PRUNUS *SEE* FRUIT

PYRUS *SEE* FRUIT

RHODODENDRON

(A) Azalea (deciduous, species or unclassified hybrid)
(Ad) Azaleodendron
(EA) Evergreen azalea
(G) Ghent azalea (deciduous)
(K) Knap Hill or Exbury azalea (deciduous)
(M) Mollis azalea (deciduous)
(O) Occidentalis azalea (deciduous)
(R) Rustica azalea (deciduous)
(V) Vireya rhododendron
(Vs) Viscosa azalea (deciduous)

RIBES *SEE* FRUIT

ROSA

(A) Alba
(Bb) Bourbon
(Bs) Boursault

(Ce) Centifolia
(Ch) China
(Cl) Climbing (in combination)
(D) Damask
(DPo) Damask Portland
(F) Floribunda or Cluster-flowered
(G) Gallica
(Ga) Garnette
(GC) Ground Cover
(HM) Hybrid Musk
(HP) Hybrid Perpetual
(HT) Hybrid Tea or Large-flowered
(Min) Miniature
(Mo) Moss (in combination)
(N) Noisette
(Patio) Patio, Miniature Floribunda or Dwarf Cluster-flowered
(Poly) Polyantha
(Ra) Rambler
(RH) Rubiginosa hybrid (Hybrid Sweet Briar)
(Ru) Rugosa
(S) Shrub
(SpH) Spinosissima Hybrid
(T) Tea

Saxifraga

(Classification by Section from Gornall, R.J. (1987). *Botanical Journal of the Linnean Society,* 95(4): 273-292)
(1) *Ciliatae*
(2) *Cymbalaria*
(3) *Merkianae*
(4) *Micranthes*
(5) *Irregulares*
(6) *Heterisia*
(7) *Porphyrion*
(8) *Ligulatae*
(9) *Xanthizoon*
(10) *Trachyphyllum*
(11) *Gymnopera*
(12) *Cotylea*
(13) *Odontophyllae*
(14) *Mesogyne*
(15) *Saxifraga*

Tulipa

(Classification by Cultivar Group from *Classified List and International Register of Tulip Names* by Koninklijke Algemeene Vereening voor Bloembollenculture 1996)
(1) Single Early Group
(2) Double Early Group
(3) Triumph Group
(4) Darwin Hybrid Group
(5) Single Late Group (including Darwin Group and Cottage Group)
(6) Lily-flowered Group
(7) Fringed Group
(8) Viridiflora Group
(9) Rembrandt Group
(10) Parrot Group
(11) Double Late Group
(12) Kaufmanniana Group
(13) Fosteriana Group
(14) Greigii Group
(15) Miscellaneous

Verbena

(G) Species and hybrids considered by some botanists to belong to the separate genus *Glandularia.*

Viola

(C) Cornuta Hybrid
(dVt) Double Violet
(ExVa) Exhibition Viola
(FP) Fancy Pansy
(PVt) Parma Violet
(SP) Show Pansy
(T) Tricolor
(Va) Viola
(Vt) Violet
(Vtta) Violetta

Vitis *see* Fruit

Reverse Synonyms

The following list of reverse synonyms is intended to help users find from which genus an unfamiliar plant name has been cross-referred. For a fuller explanation see p.13.

Abelmoschus – Hibiscus
Abutilon – Corynabutilon
Acacia – Racosperma
Acca – Feijoa
× *Achicodonia – Eucodonia*
Achillea – Anthemis
Achillea – Tanacetum
Acinos – Calamintha
Acinos – Clinopodium
Acinos – Micromeria
Acmella – Spilanthes
Actaea – Cimicifuga
Actaea – Souliea
Aethionema – Eunomia
Agapetes – Pentapterygium
Agarista – Leucothoe
Agastache – Cedronella
Agathosma – Barosma
Agave – Manfreda
Ageratina – Eupatorium
Agrostis – Eragrostis
Aichryson – Aeonium
Ajania – Chrysanthemum
Ajania – Dendranthema
Ajania – Eupatorium
Albizia – Acacia
Alcea – Althaea
Allardia – Waldheimia
Allocasuarina – Casuarina
Aloysia – Lippia
Althaea – Malva
Alyogyne – Anisodontea
Alyogyne – Hibiscus
Alyssum – Ptilotrichum
Amana – Tulipa
× *Amarygia – Amaryllis*
Amaryllis – Brunsvigia
Amomyrtus – Myrtus
Amsonia – Rhazya
Anacamptis – Orchis
Anaphalis – Gnaphalium
Anchusa – Lycopsis
Androsace – Douglasia
Androstoma – Cyathodes
Anemanthele – Oryzopsis
Anemanthele – Stipa
Anemone – Eriocapitella

Anisodontea – Malvastrum
Anisodus – Scopolia
Anomatheca – Freesia
Anomatheca – Lapeirousia
Anredera – Boussingaultia
Antirrhinum – Asarina
Aphanes – Alchemilla
Apium – Apium × *Petroselinum*
Arctanthemum – Chrysanthemum
Arctostaphylos – Arbutus
Arctotis – Venidium
Arctotis – × *Venidioarctotis*
Arenga – Didymosperma
Argyranthemum – Anthemis
Argyranthemum – Chrysanthemum
Armoracia – Cochlearia
Arnoglossum – Cacalia
Arundinaria – Pseudosasa
Asarina – Antirrhinum
Asarum – Hexastylis
Asparagus – Myrsiphyllum
Asparagus – Smilax
Asperula – Galium
Asphodeline – Asphodelus
Asplenium – Camptosorus
Asplenium – Ceterach
Asplenium – Phyllitis
Asplenium – Scolopendrium
Aster – Crinitaria
Aster – Doellingeria
Aster – Erigeron
Aster – Microglossa
Aster – Symphyotrichum
Astilboides – Rodgersia
Asyneuma – Campanula
Athanasia – Hymenolepis
Atropanthe – Scopolia
Aurinia – Alyssum
Austrocedrus – Libocedrus
Austromyrtus – Myrtus
Azorella – Bolax
Azorina – Campanula

Bambusa – Arundinaria
Bashania – Arundinaria
Bassia – Kochia
Beaucarnea – Nolina
Bellevalia – Muscari
Bellis – Erigeron
Bignonia – Campsis
Blechnum – Lomaria
Blepharocalyx – Temu
Bolax – Azorella
Bolboschoenus – Scirpus

Bonia – Indocalamus
Borago – Anchusa
Bothriochloa – Andropogon
Bouteloua – Chondrosum
Boykinia – Telesonix
Brachyglottis – Senecio
Brimeura – Hyacinthus
Brodiaea – Triteleia
Brugmansia – Datura
Brunnera – Anchusa
Buglossoides – Lithospermum
Bulbine – Bulbinopsis

Cacalia – Adenostyles
Calamagrostis – Stipa
Calamintha – Clinopodium
Calamintha – Thymus
Calibrachoa – Petunia
Callisia – Phyodina
Callisia – Tradescantia
Calocedrus – Libocedrus
Calomeria – Humea
Caloscordum – Nothoscordum
Calylophus – Oenothera
Calytrix – Lhotzkya
Camellia – Thea
Campanula – Campanula × *Symphyandra*
Campanula – Symphyandra
Cardamine – Dentaria
Carmichaelia – Chordospartium
Carmichaelia – Corallospartium
Carpobrotus – Lampranthus
Cedronella – Agastache
Centaurium – Erythraea
Centella – Hydrocotyle
Centranthus – Kentranthus
Centranthus – Valeriana
Cephalaria – Scabiosa
Ceratostigma – Plumbago
Chaenomeles – Cydonia
Chaenorhinum – Linaria
Chamaecytisus – Cytisus
Chamaedaphne – Cassandra
Chamaemelum – Anthemis
Chamerion – Chamaenerion
Chamerion – Epilobium
Chasmanthium – Uniola
Cheilanthes – Notholaena
Chiastophyllum – Cotyledon
Chimonobambusa – Arundinaria
Chimonobambusa – Qiongzhuea
Chionohebe - Parahebe

Chionohebe – Pygmea
× *Chionoscilla – Scilla*
Chlorophytum – Diuranthera
Chromolaena – Eupatorium
Chrysanthemum – Dendranthema
Chrysopsis – Heterotheca
Cicerbita – Lactuca
Cissus – Ampelopsis
Cissus – Parthenocissus
× *Citrofortunella – Citrus*
Clarkia – Eucharidium
Clarkia – Godetia
Clavinodum – Arundinaria
Claytonia – Calandrinia
Claytonia – Montia
Clematis – Atragene
Clematis – Clematopsis
Cleyera – Eurya
Clinopodium – Calamintha
Clytostoma – Bignonia
Clytostoma – Pandorea
Cnicus – Carduus
Conoclinium – Eupatorium
Codonopsis – Campanumoea
Consolida – Delphinium
Cordyline – Dracaena
Cornus – Chamaepericlymenum
Cornus – Dendrobenthamia
Coronilla – Securigera
Cortaderia – Gynerium
Corydalis - Capnoides
Corydalis – Fumaria
Corydalis – Pseudofumaria
Cosmos – Bidens
Cotinus – Rhus
Cotula – Leptinella
Crassula – Rochea
Crassula – Sedum
Crassula – Tillaea
Cremanthodium – Ligularia
Crinodendron – Tricuspidaria
Crocosmia – Antholyza
Crocosmia – Curtonus
Crocosmia – Montbretia
Cruciata – Galium
Ctenanthe – Calathea
Ctenanthe – Stromanthe
× *Cupressocyparis – Chamaecyparis*
× *Cupressocyparis -*
× *Cuprocyparis*
Cupressus – Chamaecyparis
Cyclosorus – Pneumatopteris
Cymbalaria – Linaria
Cymophyllus – Carex
Cyperus – Mariscus
Cypripedium – Criogenes
Cyrtanthus – Anoiganthus
Cyrtanthus – Vallota
Cyrtomium – Phanerophlebia
Cyrtomium – Polystichum
Cytisus – Argyrocytisus
Cytisus – Genista
Cytisus – Lembotropis
Cytisus – Spartocytisus

Daboecia – Menziesia
Dacrycarpus – Podocarpus
Dactylorhiza – Orchis
Dalea – Petalostemon
Danae – Ruscus
Darmera – Peltiphyllum
Datura – Brugmansia
Davallia – Humata
Delairea – Senecio
Delosperma – Lampranthus
Delosperma – Mesembryanthemum
Desmodium – Lespedeza
Deuterocohnia – Abromeitiella
Dicentra – Corydalis
Dichelostemma – Brodiaea
Dicliptera – Barleria
Dicliptera – Justicia
Diervilla – Weigela
Dietes – Moraea
Diplazium – Athyrium
Dipogon – Dolichos
Disporopsis – Polygonatum
Dracaena – Pleomele
Dracunculus – Arum
Dregea – Wattakaka
Drepanostachyum – Bambusa
Drepanostachyum –
Chimonobambusa
Drepanostachyum –
Gelidocalamus
Drepanostachyum –
Thamnocalamus
Drimys – Tasmannia
Duchesnea – Fragaria
Dypsis – Chrysalidocarpus
Dypsis – Neodypsis

Echeveria – Cotyledon
Echinacea – Rudbeckia
Echinospartum – Genista
Edraianthus – Wahlenbergia
Egeria – Elodea
Elatostema – Pellionia
Eleutherococcus – Acanthopanax
Elliottia – Botryostege
Elliottia – Cladothamnus
Elymus – Agropyron
Elymus – Leymus
Ensete – Musa
Epipremnum – Philodendron
Epipremnum – Scindapsus
Episcia – Alsobia
Eranthis – Aconitum
Eremophila – Myoporum
Erepsia - Semnanthe
Erigeron – Haplopappus
Erysimum – Cheiranthus
Eucalyptus – Corymbia
Eupatorium – Ageratina
Eupatorium – Ayapana
Eupatorium – Bartlettina
Euphorbia – Poinsettia
Euryops – Senecio
Eustachys – Chloris
Eustoma – Lisianthus

Fallopia – Bilderdykia
Fallopia – Polygonum
Fallopia – Reynoutria
Farfugium – Ligularia
Fargesia – Arundinaria
Fargesia – Borinda
Fargesia – Semiarundinaria
Fargesia – Sinarundinaria
Fargesia – Thamnocalamus
Fatsia – Aralia
Felicia – Agathaea
Felicia – Aster
Fibigia – Farsetia
Filipendula – Spiraea
Foeniculum – Ferula
Fortunella – Citrus

Galium – Asperula
Gaultheria – Chiogenes
Gaultheria – Pernettya
Gaultheria – × *Gaulnettya*
Gelasine – Sisyrinchium
Genista – Chamaespartium
Genista – Cytisus
Genista – Echinospartum
Genista – Teline
Gethyum – Ancrumia
Geum – Sieversia
Gladiolus – Acidanthera
Gladiolus – Anomalesia
Gladiolus – Homoglossum
Gladiolus – Petamenes
Glebionis – Chrysanthemum
Glebionis – Xanthophthalmum
Glechoma – Nepeta
Gloxinia – Seemannia
Gomphocarpus – Asclepias
Gomphocarpus – Asclepias
Goniolimon – Limonium
Graptopetalum – Sedum
Graptopetalum – Tacitus
Greenovia – Sempervivum
Gymnadenia – Nigritella

Gymnospermium – Leontice
Habranthus – Zephyranthes
Hacquetia – Dondia
× *Halimiocistus – Cistus*
× *Halimiocistus – Halimium*
Halimione – Atriplex
Halimium – Cistus
Halimium – Helianthemum
Halimium – × *Halimiocistus*
Halocarpus – Dacrydium
Hanabusaya – Symphyandra
Harrimanella – Cassiope
Hedychium – Brachychilum
Helianthella – Helianthus
Helianthemum – Cistus
Helianthus – Coreopsis
Helianthus – Heliopsis
Helichrysum – Gnaphalium
Helicodiceros – Dracunculus
Helictotrichon – Avena
Helictotrichon – Avenula
Hepatica – Anemone
Herbertia – Alophia
Hermodactylus – Iris
Heterocentron – Schizocentron
Heteromeles – Photinia
Heterotheca – Chrysopsis
× *Heucherella – Heuchera*
× *Heucherella – Tiarella*
Hibbertia – Candollea
Hieracium – Andryala
Himalayacalamus – Arundinaria
Himalayacalamus – Chimonobambusa
Himalayacalamus – Drepanostachyum
Himalayacalamus – Drepanostachyum
Himalayacalamus – Thamnocalamus
Hippocrepis – Coronilla
Hippolytia – Achillea
Hippolytia – Tanacetum
Hoheria – Plagianthus
Homalocladium – Muehlenbeckia
Howea – Kentia
Hyacinthoides – Endymion
Hyacinthoides – Scilla
Hylomecon – Chelidonium
Hymenocallis – Elisena
Hymenocallis – Ismene
Hymenoxys – Dugaldia
Hymenoxys – Helenium
Hyophorbe – Mascarena
Hypoxis – Rhodohypoxis

Incarvillea – Amphicome
Indocalamus – Sasa
Iochroma – Acnistus
Iochroma – Cestrum
Iochroma – Dunalia
Ipheion – Tristagma
Ipheion – Triteleia
Ipomoea – Calonyction
Ipomoea – Mina
Ipomoea – Pharbitis
Ipomopsis – Gilia
Ischyrolepis – Restio
Isolepis – Scirpus
Isotoma – Laurentia
Isotoma – Solenopsis

Jamesbrittenia – Sutera
Jeffersonia – Plagiorhegma
Jovibarba – Sempervivum
Juncus – Scirpus
Jurinea – Jurinella
Justicia – Beloperone
Justicia - Duvernoia
Justicia – Jacobinia
Justicia – Libonia

Kalanchoe – Bryophyllum
Kalanchoe – Kitchingia
Kalimeris – Aster
Kalimeris – Asteromoea
Kalimeris – Boltonia
Kalopanax – Acanthopax
Kalopanax – Eleutherococcus
Keckiella - Penstemon
Keckiella – Penstemon
Kitagawia – Peucedanum
Knautia – Scabiosa
Kniphofia – Tritoma
Kohleria – Isoloma
Krascheninnikovia – Ceratoides
Kunzea – Leptospermum

Lablab – Dolichos
Lagarosiphon – Elodea
Lagarostrobos – Dacrydium
Lamium – Galeobdolon
Lamium – Lamiastrum
Lampranthus – Mesembryanthemum
Lavatera – Malva
Ledebouria – Scilla
× *Ledodendron – Rhododendron*
Ledum – Rhododendron
Leontodon – Microseris
Lepechinia – Sphacele
Lepidothamnus – Dacrydium
Leptecophylla – Cyathodes
Leptinella – Cotula
Leptodactylon – Gilia
Leucanthemella – Chrysanthemum
Leucanthemella – Leucanthemum
Leucanthemopsis – Chrysanthemum
Leucanthemum – Chrysanthemum
Leucocoryne – Beauverdia
Leucophyta – Calocephalus
Leucopogon – Cyathodes
Leucopogon – Styphelia
× *Leucoraoulia – Raoulia*
× *Leucoraoulia – Raoulia* × *Leucogenes*
Leymus – Elymus
Ligularia – Senecio
Ligustrum – Parasyringa
Lilium – Nomocharis
Limonium – Statice
Linanthus – Linanthastrum
Lindelofia – Adelocaryum
Ligularia – Cacalia
Lindera – Parabenzoin
Lindernia – Ilysanthes
Liriope – Ophiopogon
Lithodora – Lithospermum
Lobelia – Monopsis
Lophomyrtus – Myrtus
Lophospermum – Asarina
Lophospermum – Maurandya
Lotus – Dorycnium
Lotus – Tetragonolobus
Ludwigia – Jussiaea
Luma – Myrtus
× *Lycene – Lychnis*
Lychnis – Agrostemma
Lychnis – Silene
Lychnis – Viscaria
Lycianthes – Solanum
Lytocaryum – Cocos
Lytocaryum – Microcoelum

Macfadyena – Bignonia
Macfadyena – Doxantha
Machaeranthera – Xylorhiza
Machaerina – Baumea
Mackaya – Asystasia
Macleaya – Bocconia
Maclura - Cudrania
Macropiper – Piper
Magnolia – Parakmeria
Mahonia – Berberis
Maianthemum – Smilacina
Mandevilla – Dipladenia
Mandragora – Atropa
Marrubium – Ballota
Matricaria – Tripleurospermum
Maurandella – Asarina
Maurandya – Asarina
Melanoselinum – Thapsia
Melicytus – Hymenanthera
Melinis – Rhynchelytrum
Mentha – Preslia

Merremia – Ipomoea
Mimulus – Diplacus
Minuartia – Arenaria
Moltkia – Lithodora
Moltkia – Lithospermum
Morina – Acanthocalyx
Morina – Acanthocalyx
Mukdenia – Aceriphyllum
Muscari – Hyacinthus
Muscari – Leopoldia
Muscari – Muscarimia
Muscari – Pseudomuscari
Myrteola – Myrtus

Naiocrene – Claytonia
Naiocrene – Montia
Nectaroscordum – Allium
Nematanthus – Hypocyrta
Nemesia – Diascia × Linaria
Neolitsea – Litsea
Neopaxia – Claytonia
Neopaxia – Montia
Neoregelia – Nidularium
Nepeta – Dracocephalum
× *Niduregelia – Guzmania*
Nipponanthemum – Chrysanthemum
Nipponanthemum – Leucanthemum
Nolina – Beaucarnea
Notospartium – Carmichaelia
Nymphoides – Villarsia

Ochagavia – Fascicularia
Oemleria – Osmaronia
Oenothera – Chamissonia
Olsynium – Sisyrinchium
Onixotis – Dipidax
Onoclea – Matteuccia
Ophiopogon – Convallaria
Orchis – Anacamptis
Orchis – Dactylorhiza
Oreopteris – Thelypteris
Orostachys – Sedum
Oscularia – Lampranthus
Osmanthus – Phillyrea
Osmanthus – × *Osmarea*
Othonna – Hertia
Othonna – Othonnopsis
Ozothamhus – Helichrysum

Pachyphragma – Cardamine
Pachyphragma – Thlaspi
Pachystegia - Olearia
Packera – Senecio
Paederota – Veronica
Pallenis – Asteriscus
Papaver – Meconopsis
Parahebe – Derwentia
Parahebe – Hebe
Parahebe – Veronica
Parasenecio – Cacalia
Paraserianthes – Albizia
Paris – Daiswa
Parthenocissus – Ampelopsis
Parthenocissus – Vitis
Passiflora – Tetrapathaea
Paxistima – Pachystema
Pecteilis – Habenaria
Pelargonium – Geranium
Peltoboykinia – Boykinia
Penstemon – Chelone
Penstemon – Nothochelone
Penstemon – Pennellianthus
Pentaglottis – Anchusa
Pericallis – Senecio
Persea – Machilus
Persicaria – Aconogonon
Persicaria – Antenoron
Persicaria – Bistorta
Persicaria – Polygonum
Persicaria – Tovara
Petrocoptis – Lychnis
Petrophytum – Spiraea
Petrorhagia – Tunica
Petroselinum – Carum
Phegopteris – Thelypteris
Phoenicaulis – Parrya
Photinia – Stransvaesia
Photinia – × *Stravinia*
Phuopsis – Crucianella
Phyla – Lippia
Phymatosorus – Microsorum
Phymosia – Sphaeralcea
Physoplexis – Phyteuma
Physostegia – Dracocephalum
Pieris – Arcterica
Pilosella – Hieracium
Platycladus – Thuja
Plecostachys – Helichrysum
Plectranthus – Coleus
Plectranthus – Solenostemon
Pleioblastus – Arundinaria
Pleioblastus – Sasa
Podophyllum – Dysosma
Podranea – Tecoma
Polygonum – Persicaria
Polypodium – Phlebodium
Polyscias – Nothopanax
Poncirus – Aegle
Potentilla – Comarum
Pratia – Lobelia
Prenanthes – Nabalus
Pritzelago – Hutchinsia
Prumnopitys – Podocarpus
Prunus – Amygdalus
Pseudocydonia – Chaenomeles
Pseudogynoxys – Senecio
Pseudopanax – Metapanax
Pseudopanax – Neopanax
Pseudosasa – Arundinaria
Pseudotsuga – Tsuga
Pseudowintera – Drimys
Pterocephalus – Scabiosa
Pteryxia - Cymopterus
Ptilostemon – Cirsium
Pulicaria – Inula
Pulsatilla – Anemone
Purshia – Cowania
Puschkinia – Scilla
Pyrrocoma – Aster
Pyrrocoma – Haplopappus

Reineckea – Liriope
Retama – Genista
Retama – Lygos
Rhamnus – Frangula
Rhapis – Chamaerops
Rhodanthe – Helipterum
Rhodanthemum – Argyranthemum
Rhodanthemum – Chrysanthemopsis
Rhodanthemum – Chrysanthemum
Rhodanthemum – Leucanthemopsis
Rhodanthemum – Leucanthemum
Rhodanthemum – Pyrethropsis
Rhodiola – Clementsia
Rhodiola – Rosularia
Rhodiola – Sedum
Rhododendron – Azalea
Rhododendron – Azaleodendron
Rhododendron – Rhodora
Rhododendron – Therorhodion
Rhododendron – Tsusiophyllum
Rhodophiala – Hippeastrum
× *Rhodoxis – Hypoxis* × *Rhodohypoxis*
× *Rhodoxis – Rhodohypoxis*
Rhus – Toxicodendron
Rhyncospora – Dichromena
Rosularia – Cotyledon
Rosularia – Sempervivella
Rothmannia – Gardenia
Ruellia – Dipteracanthus

Saccharum – Erianthus
Sagina – Minuartia
Sanguisorba – Dendriopoterium
Sanguisorba – Poterium
Sasa – Arundinaria
Sasaella – Arundinaria
Sasaella – Pleioblastus
Sasaella – Sasa
Sauromatum – Arum
Scadoxus – Haemanthus

Schefflera – Brassaia
Schefflera – Dizygotheca
Schefflera – Heptapleurum
Schizachyrium – Andropogon
Schizostachyum – Arundinaria
Schizostachyum – Thamnocalamus
Schizostylis – Hesperantha
Schoenoplectus – Scirpus
Scilla – Oncostema
Scirpoides – Scirpus
Sedum – Cotyledon
Sedum – Hylotelephium
Sedum – Sedastrum
Semiaquilegia – Aquilegia
Semiaquilegia – Paraquilegia
Semiarundinaria – Arundinaria
Semiarundinaria – Oligostachyum
Senecio – Cineraria
Senecio – Kleinia
Senecio – Ligularia
Senna – Cassia
Seriphidium – Artemisia
Shortia – Schizocodon
Sibbaldiopsis – Potentilla
Silene – Lychnis
Silene – Melandrium
Silene – Saponaria
Sinacalia – Ligularia
Sinacalia – Senecio
Sinningia – Gesneria
Sinningia – Rechsteineria
Sinobambusa – Pleioblastus
Sinobambusa – Pseudosasa
Siphocranion – Chamaesphacos
Sisymbrium – Hesperis
Sisyrinchium – Phaiophleps
Smallanthus – Polymnia
Solanum – Lycianthes
Soleirolia – Helxine
Solenostemon – Coleus
× *Solidaster – Aster*
× *Solidaster – Solidago*
Sophora – Styphnolobium
Sorbaria – Spiraea
Sparaxis – Synnotia
Sphaeralcea – Iliamna
Sphaeromeria – Tanacetum

Spirodela – Lemna
Stachys – Betonica
Stemmacantha – Centaurea
Stemmacantha – Leuzea
Stenomesson – Urceolina
Stewartia – Stuartia
Stipa – Achnatherum
Stipa – Agrostis
Stipa – Calamagrostis
Stipa – Lasiagrostis
Stipa – Nassella
Strobilanthes – Parachampionella
Strobilanthes – Pteracanthus
Styphnolobium – Sophora
Succisa – Scabiosa
Sutera – Bacopa
Syagrus – Arecastrum
Syagrus – Cocos
Syncarpha - Helipterum
Syzygium – Caryophyllus

Talbotia – Vellozia
Tanacetum – Achillea
Tanacetum – Balsamita
Tanacetum – Chrysanthemum
Tanacetum – Matricaria
Tanacetum – Pyrethrum
Tanacetum – Spathipappus
Tecoma – Tecomaria
Telekia – Buphthalmum
Tetradium – Euodia
Tetraneuris - Actinella
Tetraneuris – Actinella
Tetraneuris – Hymenoxys
Tetrapanax – Fatsia
Thamnocalamus – Arundinaria
Thlaspi – Hutchinsia
Thlaspi – Noccaea
Thlaspi – Vania
Thuja – Thujopsis
Thymus – Origanum
Tiarella – × *Heucherella*
Tonestus – Haplopappus
Toona – Cedrela
Trachelium – Diosphaera
Trachycarpus – Chamaerops
Tradescantia – Rhoeo

Tradescantia – Setcreasea
Tradescantia – Zebrina
Trichopetalum – Anthericum
Tripetaleia – Elliottia
Tripogandra – Tradescantia
Tristaniopsis – Tristania
Triteleia – Brodiaea
Tritonia – Crocosmia
Tritonia – Montbretia
Trochiscanthes – Angelica
Tropaeolum – Nasturtium hort.
Tupistra – Campylandra
Tutcheria – Pyrenaria
Tweedia – Oxypetalum

Ugni – Myrtus
Utricularia – Polypompholyx
Uvularia – Oakesiella

Vaccaria – Melandrium
Vaccinium – Oxycoccus
Verbascum – Celsia
Verbascum – × *Celsioverbascum*
Verbena – Glandularia
Verbena – Lippia
Veronicastrum – Veronica
Vigna – Phaseolus
Viola – Erpetion
Vitaliana – Androsace
Vitaliana – Douglasia

Wedelia – Zexmenia
Weigela – Diervilla
Weigela – Macrodiervilla

Xanthorhiza – Zanthorhiza
Xerochrysum – Bracteantha
Xerochrysum – Helichrysum

Yushania – Arundinaria
Yushania – Sinarundinaria
Yushania – Thamnocalamus

Zantedeschia – Calla
Zauschneria – Epilobium
Zephyranthes – × *Cooperanthes*
Zephyranthes – Cooperia

THE PLANT DIRECTORY

A

Abelia ✿ (*Caprifoliaceae*)

Auderose = 'Minaud' **new**	MAsh
chinensis misapplied	see *A.* × *grandiflora*
§ ***chinensis*** R.Br.	CPLG EBee ECre EPfP GKir MAsh MMuc NBlu SDnm SEND SPer SRms WFar WGrn WHCG WPat
'Edward Goucher'	CAlb CDoC CDul CMac CWSG CWib EBee ECrN ELan EPfP LBMP LSRN MGos MRav MSwo NBir NHol SEND SPer SPlb SRGP SWvt WDin WFar WPat WSHC
engleriana	CPLG CWan EBee EPfP LRHS NLar SLon WFar
floribunda ΨH3	CBcs CDul CMac CPLG CSBt CSam CWib EBee ECre ELan EPfP LRHS NLar SDnm SPer SPoG SSpi WAbe WFar WGob WPat WSHC
§ × ***grandiflora*** ΨH4	Widely available
- 'Aurea'	see *A.* × *grandiflora* 'Gold Spot'
- 'Compacta'	LRHS WFar
- Confetti = 'Conti'PBR (v)	Widely available
- dwarf	CDoC
§ - 'Francis Mason' (v)	Widely available
§ - 'Gold Spot' (v)	CWSG EBee EMil EPfP LRHS MGos MWat MWhi NMun WGob WRHF
- 'Gold Strike'	see *A.* × *grandiflora* 'Gold Spot'
- Golden Panache = 'Minpan' **new**	MAsh
- 'Goldsport'	see *A.* × *grandiflora* 'Gold Spot'
- 'Hopleys'PBR (v)	CBcs CDoC CMac CSBt CWib EBee EBtc EPfP LHop LRHS MAsh MGos NHol SEND SLim SLon SWvt WFar WGob WGrn WHar
- 'Kaleidoscope' (v)	CAbP CDoC CWit EBee EMil EShb LRHS LSRN MAsh MGos NCGa SBch SLim SPoG SWvt WGrn
- 'Mardi Gras' (v)	LRHS
- 'Panache' (v)	CAlb LLHF MAsh MGos MRav WPat
- 'Prostrate White'	MAsh NLar SBch
- 'Semperflorens'	EMil LRHS SBch
- 'Sherwoodii'	CWSG EBee EMil EPfP LRHS MAsh SLim WPat
- 'Sunrise'PBR (v)	CDoC EBee ELan EPfP EQua ERas MGos NLar SBod SLim
- 'Tanya'	EBee
- 'Variegata'	see *A.* × *grandiflora* 'Francis Mason'
mosanensis	EBee LRHS MBlu MBri NLar SSpi
rupestris misapplied	see *A.* × *grandiflora*
rupestris Lindl.	see *A. chinensis* R.Br.
schumannii ΨH4	Widely available
- 'Saxon Gold'PBR	EBee LRHS
spathulata	WFar
triflora	CAbP CBot CPLG CWib EBee ECre EPfP LAst LHop MMuc NLar SLon WFar WGob WSHC

Abeliophyllum (*Oleaceae*)

distichum	CAbP CBcs CBot CDoC CDul CWib EBee ECrN ELan EPfP GKir IDee LAst LBMP LRHS LSou MAsh MBlu MBri MGos SBch SPer SSpi SSta SWvt WBVN WCFE WDin WFar WSHC
- Roseum Group	CBcs CDoC CPLG CPMA EBee ELan ELon EPfP GBuc LAst LHop LRHS MAsh MGos MRav NSti SLon SPer SPoG WFar

Abies (*Pinaceae*)

alba	CDul IFFs MBar NWea WMou
- 'Bystricka' **new**	MAsh
- 'Compacta'	CKen
- 'King's Dwarf'	CKen
- 'Microphylla'	CKen
- 'Münsterland'	CKen NLar
- 'Nana' misapplied	see *Picea glauca* 'Nana'
- 'Nana' ambig.	CKen
amabilis	GLin WEve
- 'Spreading Star'	GKir
× ***arnoldiana***	MGos NLar
balsamea	CDul GKir NWea WMou
- Hudsonia Group ΨH4	CDoC CKen CMac ECho EHul EMil GKir IMGH LRHS MBar NDlv NHol NLar NMen SLim SPoG WEve
- 'Jamie'	CKen MAsh NLar
- 'Le Feber'	CKen
- 'Nana'	CKen ECho EHul EOrn EPla MAsh NLar NPCo WDin WFar
- var. ***phanerolepis*** 'Bear Swamp'	CKen NHol NLar
- 'Piccolo'	CDoC CKen ECho EHul IMGH LRHS NLar SLim SPoG WEve WFar WGor
- 'Prostrata'	ECho EHul WEve
- 'Renswoude'	CKen
- 'Tyler Blue'	CKen
- 'Verkade's Prostrate'	CKen
* ***borisii-regis*** 'Pendula'	CKen
brachyphylla dwarf	see *A. homolepis* 'Prostrata'
bracteata	GKir
cephalonica	CDul CMCN
- 'Greg's Broom'	CKen ECho
§ - 'Meyer's Dwarf'	CDoC EBrs ECho EHul GKir LRHS MBar NLar NPCo SCoo SLim SPoG WEve
- 'Nana'	see *A. cephalonica* 'Meyer's Dwarf'
chensiensis subsp. ***salouensis*** **new**	GKir
concolor ΨH4	CBcs CDul CTho EHul EMac EWTr GKir IFFs LMaj MBar MMuc NWea SPer WDin WEve
- 'Archer's Dwarf'	CKen ECho LRHS MGos NLar SLim
- 'Argentea' Niemetz, 1903	CKen
- 'Aurea'	MGos NLar WEve
- 'Birthday Broom'	CKen
- 'Blue Sapphire'	CKen

	- 'Blue Spreader'	CKen ECho MGos
§	- 'Compacta' ♀H4	CDoC CKen EBrs ECho EOrn GKir LRHS MAsh MBar MGos NHol NLar SCoo SLim SPoG WEve WFar
	- 'Fagerhult'	CKen NLar
	- 'Gable's Weeping'	CKen
	- 'Glauca'	see *A. concolor* Violacea Group
	- 'Glauca Compacta'	see *A. concolor* 'Compacta'
	- 'Hillier Broom'	see *A. concolor* 'Hillier's Dwarf'
§	- 'Hillier's Dwarf'	CKen
	- 'Husky Pup'	CKen
	- (Lowiana Group) 'Creamy'	CKen
	- 'Masonic Broom'	CKen
	- 'Mike Stearn'	CKen NLar
	- 'Mora'	CKen
	- 'Ostrov nad Ohri'	CKen
	- 'Piggelmee'	CKen ECho MAsh NLar
	- 'Pygmy'	CKen
	- 'Scooter'	CKen
	- 'Sherwood's Blue'	ECho
*	- 'Swift's Silver'	LRHS WBVN WEve
§	- Violacea Group	CKen ECho MAsh MBar MBri MGos SCoo SLim WEve WFar
	- 'Wattez Prostrate'	LRHS NLar SCoo SLim SPoG WFar
	- 'Wattezii'	CKen ECho GKir
	- 'Wintergold'	CKen EBrs ECho GKir MGos NLar NPCo WEve
	delavayi	GKir MGos NWea
	- SDR 3269	GKev
	- var. ***delavayi*** Fabri Group	see *A. fabri*
I	- 'Nana'	CKen
	- 'Nana Headfort'	see *A. fargesii* 'Headfort'
§	***fabri***	CDul GKir
	fargesii	NLar
	- var. ***faxoniana***	GKir
§	- 'Headfort'	NLar
	firma	GKir
	forrestii	CKen GKir
	- var. ***ferreana*** SF 95168	ISea
	- - SF 95226	ISea
	- var. ***georgei***	GKir
	fraseri	IFFs MBar MMuc NWea SCoo WEve WMou
	- 'Blue Bonnet'	CKen
	- 'Piglet's' witches' broom **new**	MAsh NLar
	- 'Raul's Dwarf'	CKen ECho
	grandis	CBcs CDul EMac IFFs MBar NWea SCoo WDin WMou
	- 'Compacta'	CKen
	- 'Van Dedem's Dwarf'	CKen MAsh NLar WEve
	holophylla	GKir NLar NWea
	homolepis	CDul GKir NLar
§	- 'Prostrata'	CKen
	kawakamii	CKen
	koreana	Widely available
	- 'Alpin Star'	CKen MAsh
	- 'Aurea'	see *A. koreana* 'Flava'
	- 'Blaue Zwo'	CKen MAsh NLar
	- 'Blauer Eskimo'	CDoC CKen MAsh NLar SLim
	- 'Blauer Pfiff'	CKen ECho NLar
	- 'Blinsham Gold'	CKen
	- 'Blue Emperor'	CKen NLar
	- 'Blue Magic'	CKen MAsh NLar
	- 'Blue 'n' Silver'	ECho NLar WEve
	- 'Bonsai Blue'	NLar
	- 'Cis'	CDoC CKen NHol NLar SCoo SLim
	- 'Compact Dwarf'	ECho MAsh MBar MGos NLar WEve
	- 'Crystal Globe'	CKen NLar
	- 'Cumivetta' **new**	MBri
	- 'Dark Hill'	NLar
	- 'Doni Tajuso'	CKen
	- 'Eisregen' **new**	CKen
	- 'Festival' **new**	NLar
§	- 'Flava'	CKen IMGH MBar MGos NPCo SCoo WEve
	- 'Frosty'	SLim SPoG
	- 'Gait'	CKen ECho MAsh NLar
	- 'Golden Dream'	CKen
	- 'Golden Glow'	NLar WFar
	- 'Green Carpet'	CKen GKir NLar SLim
	- 'Grübele' witches' broom	CKen
	- 'Inverleith'	CKen
	- 'Kleiner Prinz' **new**	NLar
	- 'Kohout'	CKen
	- 'Kristallkugel' **new**	MAsh
	- 'Lippetal'	CKen
	- 'Luminetta'	CKen MGos NLar SLim
	- 'Nadelkissen'	CKen NHol
	- 'Nisbet'	ECho IMGH NPCo SCoo SLim WEve WGor
	- 'Oberon'	CKen MAsh NHol NLar SLim
	- 'Piccolo'	CKen
	- 'Pinocchio'	CDoC CKen MGos NLar
	- 'Prostrata'	see *A. koreana* 'Prostrate Beauty'
§	- 'Prostrate Beauty'	ECho NPCo WEve WFar WGor
	- 'Scherenbach' **new**	NLar
	- 'Schweden König' **new**	NLar
	- 'Sherwood Compact' **new**	CKen
	- 'Silberkugel'	CKen CMen ECho NLar SLim
	- 'Silberlocke' ♀H4	CDoC CDul CKen EBrs ECho EMil EPla LRHS MBar MBlu MBri MGos NBea NEgg NLar SCoo SLim SPer SPoG SSpi WEve WFar
	- 'Silbermavers'	CKen
	- 'Silberperl'	CKen CMen MAsh NLar
	- 'Silberschmelze'	ECho MGos NLar
	- 'Silver Show'	CKen NWea
	- 'Taiga'	NLar
	- 'Threave'	CKen
	- 'Tundra'	MAsh NLar
	- 'Vengels' **new**	NLar
	- 'Verdener Dom' **new**	NLar
	- 'Winter Goldtip'	ECho WEve
	lasiocarpa	CDul NWea
	- 'Alpine Beauty'	CKen MAsh NLar
	- var. ***arizonica*** 'Argentea'	WEve
	- - 'Compacta' Hornibr. ♀H4	CDoC CKen CMac EBrs ECho EHul ELan EPla GKir LRHS MAsh MBar MBri MGos SCoo SLim SPoG WFar WGor
	- - 'Kenwith Blue'	CKen ECho MGos NLar SLim WFar
	- 'Compacta' Beissn.	NHol WEve WFar
	- 'Day Creek'	CKen
	- 'Duflon'	CKen
	- 'Glauca'	see *A. lasiocarpa* var. *arizonica* 'Argentea'
	- 'Green Globe'	CKen ECho LRHS MBar NLar WEve
	- 'Hobby Time' **new**	NLar
	- 'Joe's Alpine'	CKen
*	- 'King's Blue'	CKen
	- 'Logan Pass'	CKen NLar
	- 'Mulligan's Dwarf'	CKen ECho
	- 'Prickly Pete'	CKen NLar
	- 'Toenisvorst'	CKen
	magnifica	GKir
I	- 'Nana'	CKen
	- witches' broom	CKen
	marocana	see *A. pinsapo* var. *marocana*
	nebrodensis **new**	GKir
	nephrolepis	GKir
	nobilis	see *A. procera*

	nordmanniana ♀H4	CAlb CDul CMac CTri EHul EMac EPfP EWTr GKir IFFs LBuc LMaj MBar MGos MMuc NEgg NWea SPer SPoG WDin WEve WMou
	- 'Arne's Dwarf'	CKen
	- 'Barabits' Compact'	ECho MBar MBri MGos NLar
	- 'Barabits' Gold'	ECho
	- 'Barabits' Spreader'	CKen ECho
	- subsp. ***equi-trojani***	NWea
	- - 'Archer'	CKen NPCo
	- 'Golden Spreader' ♀H4	CDoC CKen EBrs ECho EOrn EPla GKir LRHS MAsh MBar MBri MGos NLar NPCo SCoo SLim SPoG WEve WFar
	- 'Hasselt'	CKen
	- 'Jakobsen'	CKen
	- 'Silberspitze'	CKen
	numidica 'Glauca'	CKen
	- 'Lawrenceville'	ECho NPCo WFar
	pindrow	ECho GKir NWea
	pinsapo	CDul GKir IFFs MBar SEND
	- 'Atlas' **new**	MAsh
	- 'Aurea'	CKen EBrs ECho GKir MGos NLar SLim WEve WFar
I	- 'Aurea Nana'	CKen
	- 'Fastigiata'	MGos MPkF
	- 'Glauca' ♀H4	CDoC CDul CKen CTho ECho EHul ELan GKir LMaj LRHS MBar MBlu NLar SCoo SLim SPoG WDin WEve WMou
	- 'Hamondii'	CKen
I	- 'Horstmann'	CKen ECho GKir NLar NPCo SLim WEve
	- 'Kelleriis'	MAsh
§	- var. ***marocana***	GKir
	- 'Pendula'	ECho MGos MPkF NLar WEve
	- 'Quicksilver'	CKen
§	***procera*** ♀H4	CAlb CBcs CDul EHul EMac GKir IFFs MBar NWea WBVN WDin WEve WMou
	- 'Bizarro'	ECho NLar
	- 'Blaue Hexe'	CKen ECho NLar SLim SPoG WFar
	- Glauca Group	CDoC CMac CTho MAsh MBar MBlu MBri MGos WEve WFar
	- - 'Glauca Prostrata'	ECho EPla GKir MBar MGos SCoo WEve WFar
	- 'La Graciosa'	NLar
	- 'Noble's Dwarf'	ECho GKir
	- 'Obrighofen'	NLar
	- 'Prostrata' **new**	MAsh
	- 'Seattle Mount'	NLar
	- 'Sherwoodii'	CKen ECho
	recurvata	NLar
	- var. ***ernesti***	GKir
	Rosemoor hybrid	CKen
	sibirica	NWea
	squamata	GKir
	veitchii	CDul GKir NWea
	- 'Heddergott'	CKen ECho MAsh MGos NLar
	- 'Heine'	CKen
I	- 'Pendula'	CKen
	- 'Rumburg'	CKen MAsh NLar

Abromeitiella see *Deuterocohnia*

Abrotanella (*Asteraceae*)

	sp.	ECho
	forsterioides **new**	ECho

Abutilon ✿ (*Malvaceae*)

	'Amiti'	ELar
	'Apricot Belle'	SMDP
	'Ashford Red'	CBcs CCCN CWGN ELan LRHS MAsh SAga SBch SMDP WKif
	Bella Series **new**	LRHS
*	'Benary's Giant'	CPLG
	'Boule de Neige'	CBot SMrm
	'Canary Bird' ♀H2	CBcs CBot CCCN CHEx ELon ERea SAga SMDP SUsu
	'Cannington Carol' (v) ♀H2	CCCN ELan ERea LSRN SMDP SRGP
	'Cannington Peter' (v) ♀H2	CCCN ERea LSRN SMDP
	'Cannington Sally' (v)	ERea SRGP
	'Cannington Sonia' (v)	SMDP
	'Cynthia Pike' (v)	LRHS
	'Flamenco'	NEgg
	'Frances Elizabeth'	SMDP
	'Heather Bennington'	SMDP
	'Henry Makepeace'	ELar SMDP
	'Hinton Seedling'	CCCN CRHN
	× ***hybridum***	CHEx
	apricot-flowered	
	- red-flowered	CHEx
	indicum	CCCN
	'Isles of Scilly'	CCCN
	'Jacqueline Morris'	ELon LRHS MAsh SMrm SPoG
	'John Thompson'	CCCN CWGN LSRN
	'Kentish Belle' ♀H2-3	CBcs CCCN CDoC CHEx CMHG CMac CRHN ECGP ELan ELon EPfP ERas LRHS LSRN NEgg NPal SBch SCoo SEND SPer SPlb WFar
I	'Kentish Belle Variegatum' (v)	ELan
	'Kreutzberger' **new**	ELar
	'Lemon Queen'	ELar
	'Linda Vista Peach' ♀H2	ELar SMDP
	'Louis Marignac'	ELar
	'Marion' ♀H2	CRHN ELar LRHS LSRN SMDP SMrm SPoG
	'Master Michael'	CMac SMDP
	megapotamicum ♀H3	CBcs CBot CCCN CHEx CMHG CRHN CSBt CTri EBee ELan EPfP EShb GQui LOck LRHS MAsh MGos MRav SPer SPoG SRms WClo WHar WSHC
	- 'Variegatum' (v)	CBcs CCCN CSBt CStu ELan ELar EPfP GQui LRHS MAsh MGos NEgg SBch SBod SLon SPer SPoG SWvt WFar
	- 'Wisley Red'	CRHN SMDP
	× ***milleri*** hort. ♀H2	CMac CRHN WWlt
	- 'Variegatum' (v)	CCCN CHEx CMac LRHS NEgg SEND
	- 'Ventnor Gold'	SBch
	'Nabob' ♀H2	CCCN CDoC CRHN ERea EShb LRHS SBch SMDP SMrm SPoG
	'Old Rose Belle' **new**	SMDP
	'Orange Glow' (v) ♀H2	ERea
	'Orange Vein'	EShb SMDP WPrP
	'Patrick Synge'	CCCN CMHG CWit EBtc EShb SBch SPhx SUsu
	pictum 'Thompsonii' (v)	CHEx EShb IDee SBch SMDP WDyG
	'Pink Lady'	EShb SMDP
	'Red Bells'	ELar
	'Red Queen' **new**	ELar
	'Rotterdam'	ERea
	'Russels Dwarf'	CCCN
	'Satin Pink Belle' **new**	SMDP
	'Savitzii' (v) ♀H2	MCot SBch SMDP
	'Silver Belle'	SMDP
	'Simcox White'	CCCN
	'Snow Boy' **new**	ELar
	'Snowfall'	SMDP

'Souvenir de Bonn' (v) ♀H2	ELar ERea EShb LSou SAga SBch SMDP
× ***suntense***	CBcs CCCN CMHG CPLG CSBt EBee EPfP ERas LHyd LRHS LSou NPer SChF SEND
- 'Jermyns' ♀H3	CAbP EPfP GCra LRHS LSRN MBri SCoo SPoG SSpi SWvt WFar
- Ralph Gould seedling	ECGP
- 'Violetta'	CEnd WKif
variegated, salmon-flowered (v)	LAst
'Victory'	CWGN
vitifolium	CBcs CBot CCCN CDTJ CWib EPfP EQua EWTr GGar ISea NBid NEgg NLar SPad SPer SPoG WBor WKif
- var. ***album***	CBcs CDul EPfP EQua GCal LHyd SEND SSpi WFar WSHC WSpi
- 'Buckland'	CGHE
- 'Ice Blue'	CBot
- 'Tennant's White' ♀H3	CAbP CBot CCCN EPfP ERas GGal LRHS MBri NBur
- 'Veronica Tennant' ♀H3	CPLG SAga WKif
'Wakehurst'	WCom
'Westfield Bronze'	CRHN SMDP

Acacia (*Mimosaceae*)

acinacea	SPlb
adunca	SPlb
armata	see *A. paradoxa*
baileyana ♀H2	CBcs CCCN CDul CGHE CMac CSBt CTrG CTsd ELan EPfP IFFs ISea LRHS LSRN MAsh MGos MRav SBch SBig SCoo SEND SLim SPad SPer SPlb SPoG SWvt WFar WPat
- var. ***aurea***	SPlb
- 'Purpurea' ♀H2	Widely available
'Bon Accueil' **new**	LRHS
boormanii	ISea
brachybotrya	CDTJ
caven **new**	EBee
'Clair de Lune' **new**	LRHS
cultriformis	CCCN CTrC CTsd CWit ESwi SBch
dealbata ♀H2	Widely available
- 'Gaulois Astier'	EBee ELon LRHS LSRN MBri MGos MREP SBch SWvt WBrE WCot WPGP
- 'Pendula' **new**	LRHS
- subsp. ***subalpina***	WPGP
drummondii subsp. ***elegans***	SSpi
erioloba	CPLG
Exeter hybrid	CSBt
fimbriata	CRHN
floribunda 'Lisette'	EPfP
julibrissin	see *Albizia julibrissin*
juniperina	see *A. ulicifolia*
karroo	CArn CCCN CDTJ CPLG
kybeanensis	EBee WPGP
longifolia	CBcs CCCN CDTJ CMac CTsd EBee EPfP LRHS SEND SRms
- subsp. ***sophorae***	CCCN
macradenia	SPlb
mearnsii	CCCN SEND
melanoxylon	CBcs CDTJ CDul CTrC CTsd EBee GGar SLim
mucronata	CTrC EShb
§ ***paradoxa*** ♀H2	CCCN ECou ELon ESwi LRHS WPat
pataczekii	EBee EPfP EWes LRHS
pendula	IDee
podalyriifolia	EBee IDee SPlb
pravissima ♀H2-3	Widely available
retinodes ♀H2	CBcs CCCN CDoC CRHN CTrC CTsd CWit EAmu EBee EPfP ESwi IFFs LRHS LSRN MREP SEND SLim SWvt WCFE
- blue-leaved **new**	ESwi
riceana	CCCN CTrG CTsd
rubida	IDee MGos MREP SPlb
sentis	see *A. victoriae*
spectabilis	CCCN SPlb
suaveolens	SPlb
§ ***ulicifolia***	CPLG CSBt CTrG
verticillata	CBcs CCCN CDTJ CHll CTrG CTsd CWit EBee GGar WCot
- riverine	CPLG CTrC EPfP LRHS SPoG
§ ***victoriae***	ECre

Acaena (*Rosaceae*)

adscendens misapplied	see *A. magellanica* subsp. *magellanica*, *A. saccaticupula* 'Blue Haze'
adscendens Vahl	see *A. magellanica* subsp. *laevigata*
adscendens ambig. 'Glauca'	EHoe NBir
§ ***affinis***	ECha SDix
anserinifolia misapplied	see *A. novae-zelandiae*
§ ***anserinifolia*** (Forst. & Forst. f.) Druce	MRav NHol
buchananii	CSpe CTri EBee ECho EDAr EHoe GAbr GGar SRms STre WCom WFar WPer
caerulea hort.	see *A. caesiiglauca*
§ ***caesiiglauca***	CTri GAbr GGar GQue MLHP NBid SGar WCom WPer
- 'Frikart' **new**	EBee
fissistipula	WMoo
glaucophylla	see *A. magellanica* subsp. *magellanica*
inermis	MMuc SPlb WCom
- 'Purpurea'	EBee ECha EDAr EGoo EHoe EShb GAbr GBin GGar GKev GQue LRHS NLar SIng SPlb WHoo WMoo
magellanica	EBee GCal MSCN
§ - subsp. ***laevigata***	GGar
§ - subsp. ***magellanica***	EBee EDAr
microphylla ♀H4	CSam CTri EAlp EBee ECGP ECho GAbr GGar LBee LRHS NLar NMen SIng SPlb SRms WCon WFar WMoo
- Copper Carpet	see *A. microphylla* 'Kupferteppich'
- 'Glauca'	see *A. caesiiglauca*
- 'Grüner Zwerg'	EBee
§ - 'Kupferteppich'	EBee ECho EDAr EHoe ETod GAbr GCal GGar GKir GQue LHop LRHS MBri MMuc MRav NBir NChi NLar NVic SBch WCom WMoo WPat WPer WWEG
- 'Pulchella'	EBee
myriophylla	EBee ECho EDAr
§ ***novae-zelandiae***	CTri EBee GGar SDix WCom WMoo WPer
ovalifolia	EBee ECho
'Pewter'	see *A. saccaticupula* 'Blue Haze'
profundeincisa	see *A. anserinifolia* (Forst. & Forst. f.) Druce
'Purple Carpet'	see *A. microphylla* 'Kupferteppich'
'Purple Haze'	CSpe
saccaticupula	WFar
§ - 'Blue Haze'	CMoH EBee ECha ECho EDAr EHoe EShb GGar GKir LHop LRHS MRav NVic SIng SPer SPlb SRms WFar WHoo WMoo

	sanguisorbae	see *A. anserinifolia* (Forst. & Forst. f.) Druce
	viridior	see *A. anserinifolia* (Forst. & Forst. f.) Druce

Acalypha (*Euphorbiaceae*)

	hispida ΨH1	ERea LRHS MBri
	pendula	see *A. reptans*
§	***reptans***	EShb
	wilkesiana **new**	EShb

Acanthocalyx see *Morina*

Acantholimon (*Plumbaginaceae*)

	androsaceum	see *A. ulicinum*
	glumaceum	GKev
§	***ulicinum***	EPot GKev

Acanthopanax see *Eleutherococcus*

	ricinifolius	see *Kalopanax septemlobus*

Acanthus ✿ (*Acanthaceae*)

	balcanicus misapplied	see *A. hungaricus*
	'Candelabra'	WHil
	dioscoridis	EBee GCal MAvo
	- var. ***perringii***	CDes ECha GBin LHop MAvo MNrw NChi WCot WFar WPGP WSHC
	- smooth-leaved	WHil
	eminens	WHil
	hirsutus	LPio NBre SBig SPav WCot
	- f. ***roseus***	WFar
	- subsp. ***syriacus***	EHrv GCal LRHS NBre NLar WCot WFar
	'Hollande du Nort'	EBee
§	***hungaricus***	CArn CHar CHid EBee EBla EBrs ECtt ELan EShb EWTr GBBs GCal GKir LBMP LRHS MCot NCGa NLar SDix SPav SPer SWat WCot WFar WHil WMnd WWEG
	- MESE 561	EPPr
	longifolius Host	see *A. hungaricus*
	mollis	Widely available
	- from Turkey **new**	GCal
	- 'Fielding Gold'	see *A. mollis* 'Hollard's Gold'
	- free-flowering	GCal MAvo
§	- 'Hollard's Gold'	Widely available
	- 'Jefalba'	see *A. mollis* (Latifolius Group) 'Rue Ledan'
	- Latifolius Group	EBee EPfP MCot MRav NHol SRms WHil WHoo WTin
§	- - 'Rue Ledan'	EBee EPPr EShb GBin IPot LHop LPio MAvo MDKP NBPC NGdn NLar SPhx SUsu WCot WFar WHil WTin
	- - 'Sjaak'	EBee
	- 'Long Spike' **new**	GCal
	- 'Tasmanian Angel' (v) **new**	CBow NBhm SGol WCot
	'Morning Candle'	EBee
	pubescens	WHil
	sennii	CMdw LPio SMad SPhx WHil WSHC
	spinosus misapplied	see *A. spinosus* Spinosissimus Group
	spinosus L. ΨH4	Widely available
	- Ferguson's form	WCot WHil
	- 'Lady Moore' (v)	IBlr IPot MCCP NLar SBch WCot
	- 'Royal Haughty'	EWes GBin GCal WFar
	- Spinosissimus Group	CBct CFir CMHG ECha EHrv ELan ELon GCal LEdu LPio MCCP MRav SAga SBch SPhx SWat WCot WFar WHil WMnd WTin
	'Summer Beauty'	EBee EWes GCal GKir LHop LPio LRHS MAvo MBri NBre NLar WCon WCot WFar WHil

Acca (*Myrtaceae*)

	sp.	SWvt WBrE
	sellowiana (F)	CBcs CDul CMHG CMac CPLG CSBt CSam CTrG CWit EBee ELan EPfP ERom GQui LAst LHop LRHS MGos MREP SBch SLim SPer SPlb SPoG SVic WFar WSHC
	- 'Apollo' (F)	EBee ERea
	- 'Coolidge' (F)	CAgr ERea
	- 'Mammoth' (F)	CAgr CBcs CCCN ERea
	- 'Marian' (F)	EBee
	- 'Triumph' (F)	CAgr CBcs CCCN ERea
	- 'Unique' (F)	CAgr ERea
	- 'Variegata' (F/v)	CCCN CHid EBee ELan LAst SPoG

Acer ✿ (*Aceraceae*)

	albopurpurascens	WPGP
	amoenum B&SWJ 10916 **new**	WCru
	argutum	IMGH
	barbinerve	CMCN EPfP
	buergerianum	CDul CLnd CMCN CMen CPMA IArd LMaj LRHS MMuc MPkF NEgg NLar SCoo
	- var. ***formosanum*** B&SWJ 7032 **new**	WCru
	- 'Himcode' **new**	NLar
	- 'Mino-yatsubusa'	MPkF
	- 'Miyasama-yatsubusa'	MPkF
	- 'Naruto'	CMCN MPkF
	calcaratum	CDul CMCN
	campbellii B&SWJ 7685	WCru
	- SF 06041	ISea
*	- var. ***fansipanense*** B&SWJ 8270	WCru
	- - HWJ 569	WCru
§	- subsp. ***flabellatum*** B&SWJ 8057	WCru
	- - var. ***yunnanense***	CBcs EBee ECrN IFFs IMGH MSnd WHCr
	campestre ΨH4	Widely available
	- 'Carnival' (v)	CDul CEnd CMCN CPMA CWib EBee ECrN EMil EPla LRHS MAsh MBlu MBri MPkF NLar NPCo SMad SPer SPoG SPur SWvt WMou WPGP
	- 'Elsrijk'	CCVT CLnd LMaj LRHS SCoo
	- 'Evelyn'	see *A. campestre* 'Queen Elizabeth'
	- 'Pendulum'	CEnd ECrN
	- 'Postelense'	CMCN CPMA MBlu MGos MPkF
	- 'Pulverulentum' (v)	CEnd CMCN CPMA MGos NPCo SMad SSta
§	- 'Queen Elizabeth'	LMaj MGos
	- 'Red Shine'	GKir MGos
	- 'Royal Ruby'	CPMA CWSG MGos WFar
*	- 'Ruby Glow'	CEnd ECrN
	- 'Schwerinii'	CDul
I	- 'Silver Celebration' (v)	CPMA
	- 'William Caldwell'	CEnd CTho ECrN
	capillipes ΨH4	CAlb CBcs CCVT CDul CLnd CMCN CSBt CTho CWib EBee ECrN EMui GKir IFFs LAst LMaj LRHS MAsh MBar MGos NBea NWea SBir SPer SPoG WDin WFar WHCr WPGP WPat
	- B&SWJ 10845	WCru
	- 'Candy Stripe'	see *A.* × *conspicuum* 'Candy Stripe'
	- 'Gimborn'	WPGP
	- 'Honey Dew'	NLar

	Name	Suppliers
	cappadocicum	CCVT CDul CEnd CMCN ECrN GKir IFFs LMaj MMuc MSnd NWea SBir WDin
	- 'Aureum' ♀H4	CBcs CDoC CDul CEnd CLnd CMCN CTho EBee ECrN ELan EPfP GKir IArd LRHS MAsh MBlu MBri MGos MRav NBea NLar SLim SMad SPer SPoG SSpi SWvt WDin WFar
§	- subsp. ***divergens***	CMCN MPkF
§	- subsp. ***lobelii***	CLnd WPGP
	- var. ***mono***	see *A. pictum*
	- 'Rubrum' ♀H4	CBcs CDul CLnd CMCN EBee ECrN EPfP GAuc GKir LAst LBuc LMaj LRHS MBlu MBri MGos MRav SLim SPer WDin WFar WHer
	- var. ***sinicum***	EPfP GBin WFar WPGP
	- var. ***tricaudatum***	CPLG WPGP
	carpinifolium	CBcs CMCN IArd MBlu MPkF NLar SBir
	- B&SWJ 10955	WCru
	- B&SWJ 11124	WCru
	catalpifolium	see *A. longipes* subsp. *catalpifolium*
§	***caudatifolium***	CMCN WPGP
	- B&SWJ 6734	WCru
	- RWJ 9843	WCru
§	***caudatum*** GWJ 9279	WCru
	- HWJK 2338	WCru
	- subsp. ***ukurunduense***	CMCN GAuc MPkF
	- - B&SWJ 8658	WCru
	circinatum	CBcs CDoC CDul CLnd CMCN CPMA ECrN EPfP IFFs MBlu MBri MMuc MPkF MSnd NBea NLar NWea SCoo SPlb SSta WDin WFar
	- B&SWJ 9565	WCru
	- 'Little Gem'	CPMA
	- 'Little Joe'	CPMA
	- 'Monroe'	CPMA
	- 'Pacific Fire'	CPMA
	- 'Sunglow'	CPMA NLar
	circinatum* × *palmatum	GKir SBig
	cissifolium	CBcs CMCN EPfP EPla IArd LRHS MBri NLar
	- B&SWJ 10801	WCru
§	× ***conspicuum*** 'Candy Stripe'	CBcs CLnd CPMA GKir NLar SLim SSpi SSta
	- 'Elephant's Ear'	CPMA EPfP NLar
I	- 'Phoenix'	CBcs CEnd CMCN CPMA EPfP LRHS MAsh MBlu MBri NLar SSpi WDin WPGP WPat
	- 'Red Flamingo'	LRHS MBri MGos
	- 'Silver Ghost'	MPkF
§	- 'Silver Vein'	CDoC CEnd CMCN CPMA EBee EPfP MWea NLar SPur SSpi SSta WPGP
	crataegifolium B&SWJ 11036	WCru
	- B&SWJ 11355	WCru
	- 'Meuri-keade-no-fuiri' (v)	MPkF
	- 'Meuri-no-ōfu' (v)	MPkF
	- 'Veitchii' (v)	CMCN CPMA EPfP MBri MPkF SBig SSpi
	creticum L., non F. Schmidt.	see *A. sempervirens*
	dasycarpum	see *A. saccharinum*
	davidii	CAbP CBcs CCVT CDoC CDul CLnd CMCN CSam CTrG ECrN GAuc GKir IFFs LMaj MBar MBlu MGos MRav NBea NHol SLim SPer WDin WFar WPat
	- B&SWJ 8183	WCru
§	- 'Canton'	CPMA MPkF
	- 'Cantonspark'	see *A. davidii* 'Canton'
	- 'Chinese Temple'	SBir
N	- 'Ernest Wilson'	CBcs CMCN CSBt MBlu NLar
N	- 'George Forrest' ♀H4	CBcs CCVT CDoC CDul CMCN CMac CSBt CTho EBee ECrN ELan EPfP IFFs LAst LRHS MAsh MBlu MMuc NBea NWea SBod SEND SLim SPer SPoG WDin WFar WPat
	- 'Hagelunie'	MPkF SBir
	- 'Karmen'	CBcs CGHE CPMA MPkF SBir WPGP
	- 'Madeline Spitta'	CMCN CPMA GKir MBlu MBri MPkF
	- 'Purple Bark'	NLar SBir
	- 'Rosalie'	CBcs CPMA EPfP MBlu MBri SBir
	- 'Serpentine' ♀H4	CBcs CDoC CMCN CPMA EBee EPfP IDee MBlu MBri NEgg NLar SBir SSpi SSta WFar WPGP
	- 'Silver Vein'	see *A.* × *conspicuum* 'Silver Vein'
	divergens	see *A. cappadocicum* subsp. *divergens*
	elegantulum	CDoC CPMA EBee GBin LLHF WPGP
	erianthum	CLnd MSnd WHCr
	erythranthum B&SWJ 11733 new	WCru
	- DJHV 06147	WCru
	fabri	CBcs CDul
	flabellatum	see *A. campbellii* subsp. *flabellatum*
	forrestii	CMCN EPfP NBea NHol
	- BWJ 7515	WCru
	- 'Alice'	CBcs CEnd CPMA EBee
	- 'Sirene'	CPMA
	- 'Sparkling'	CPMA
	× ***freemanii***	CMCN
	- 'Armstrong'	WFar
	- Autumn Blaze = 'Jeffersred'	CBcs CCVT CDoC CDul CMCN EBee EPfP LMaj LRHS MBlu MGos MMuc SCoo SMad WDin WFar WPat
	- Autumn Fantasy = 'Dtr 102'	LRHS SCoo
	- Celebration = 'Celzam'	MGos WFar
	- 'Indian Summer'	see *A.* × *freemanii* 'Morgan'
§	- 'Morgan'	CEnd CPMA LRHS SBir
	fulvescens	see *A. longipes*
	ginnala	see *A. tataricum* subsp. *ginnala*
	globosum	see *A. platanoides* 'Globosum'
	grandidentatum	see *A. saccharum* subsp. *grandidentatum*
	griseum ♀H4	Widely available
	grosseri	CDul CMCN CTri
	- var. ***hersii*** ♀H4	CBcs CCVT CDoC CDul CLnd CMac CWib EBee ECrN EPfP GKir LRHS MAsh MRav NBea NLar NWea SPer SWvt WDin WFar WHCr WPGP
	- 'Leiden'	EPfP
	heldreichii	CMCN EGFP EPfP
	henryi	CDul CLnd CMCN EPfP LMaj MBri NEgg NLar
	heptaphlebium B&SWJ 11713 new	WCru
	- DJHV 06063	WCru
	hyrcanum	CMCN
	japonicum	CMCN MBar MMuc SSta WHCr
	- B&SWJ 5950	WCru
§	- 'Aconitifolium' ♀H4	Widely available
	- 'Ao-jutan'	CPMA
	- 'Attaryi'	MPkF
	- 'Aureum'	see *A. shirasawanum* 'Aureum'
	- 'Ezo-no-momiji'	see *A. shirasawanum* 'Ezo-no-momiji'
	- 'Filicifolium'	see *A. japonicum* 'Aconitifolium'

	Name	Suppliers
	- 'Green Cascade'	CEnd CMCN CMac CMen CPMA ECho LRHS MPkF NLar NPCo SBig WPGP WPat
	- 'Kalmthout'	NLar
	- 'King's Copse'	LRHS
	- 'Laciniatum'	see *A. japonicum* 'Aconitifolium'
	- f. ***microphyllum***	see *A. shirasawanum* 'Microphyllum'
	- 'Ogurayama'	see *A. shirasawanum* 'Ogurayama'
	- 'Ō-isami'	EPfP MPkF SBig
	- 'Ō-taki'	CPMA
	- 'Vitifolium' Υ^{H4}	CDoC CEnd CMCN CMac CPMA CSBt ECho ELan EPfP LRHS MBlu MBri MGos MPkF NBea NEgg NLar NPCo NPal SBig SPer SPoG SSpi SSta WCFE WDin WPGP WPat
	kawakamii	see *A. caudatifolium*
	laevigatum	CMCN
§	- var. ***reticulatum*** B&SWJ 11698 **new**	WCru
	laxiflorum	EBee EPla
	- HWJK 2240	WCru
	lobelii Tenore	see *A. cappadocicum* subsp. *lobelii*
	lobelii Bunge	see *A. turkestanicum*
§	***longipes***	CMCN
	- Sich 731	WPGP
§	- subsp. ***catalpifolium***	CMCN
	macrophyllum	CDul CMCN CTho EPfP LHyd MBlu
	mandschuricum	CDul EPfP MBri MPkF WDin
§	***maximowiczianum***	CBcs CDul CMCN CTho ELan MPkF WFar
	maximowiczii	ECrN MPkF NWea WHCr
	micranthum	CDoC CDul CGHE CMCN EBee EPfP LLHF MPkF NLar SHGN SSpi WPGP
	miyabei	MPkF
	mono	see *A. pictum*
*	- f. ***ambiguum*** B&SWJ 8806 **new**	WCru
	monspessulanum	CDul CLnd CMCN SEND
	morifolium	MPkF
	- B&SWJ 10959	WCru
	- B&SWJ 11473	WCru
	morrisonense	see *A. caudatifolium*
	negundo	CDul CMCN CWib ECrN IFFs LMaj NWea
	- 'Auratum'	CMCN LRHS MBar WDin
	- 'Aureomarginatum' (v)	ECrN LAst LMaj
	- 'Aureovariegatum' (v)	CBcs MBar
§	- 'Elegans' (v)	CDul CEnd CMCN ECrN EPfP LRHS SCoo SPer WFar
	- 'Elegantissimum'	see *A. negundo* 'Elegans'
	- 'Flamingo' (v)	Widely available
	- 'Kelly's Gold'	CBcs CWSG LRHS MAsh MBri MGos NLar NMun NWea SBch SCoo SLim SPoG WDin WFar WHar
	- subsp. ***mexicanum*** F&M 48	WPGP
	- 'Variegatum' (v)	CBcs ECrN LAst LRHS SPer WDin WFar
	- var. ***violaceum***	CEnd CMCN
	- 'Winter Lightning'	CPMA
	nikoense	see *A. maximowiczianum*
	oblongum	CDul CMCN WPGP
	- HWJK 2422	WCru
	- var. ***concolor*** HWJ 869	WCru
§	***obtusifolium***	WCot
	oliverianum	EBee EPfP WPGP
	- subsp. ***formosanum*** B&SWJ 6773	WCru
	- - B&SWJ 6797	WCru
	- - RWJ 9912	WCru
	opalus	CMCN SEND
	orientale	see *A. sempervirens*
	orizabense	EBee
	Pacific Sunset = 'Warrenred'	EBee
	palmatum	Widely available
	- 'Akane'	CMen MPkF
§	- 'Aka-shigitatsu-sawa'	CBcs CMCN CMac CMen CPMA ECho LRHS MGos MPkF NLar SPer WFar WHar
	- 'Akebono'	CPMA
	- 'Akegarasu'	CMen LRHS NLar
	- 'Akita-yatsubusa' **new**	MPkF
	- 'Alpenweiss'	CPMA
	- 'Alpine Sunrise'	MPkF
	- 'Alpine Surprise'	CPMA
	- 'Amagi-shigure'	CPMA
	- 'Aoba-jo'	CMen CPMA ECho MPkF NLar NPCo
	- 'Ao-kanzashi' (v)	MPkF
	- 'Ao-shichigosan' **new**	LRHS
	- 'Aoshime-no-uchi'	see *A. palmatum* 'Shinobuga-oka'
	- 'Aoyagi'	CEnd CMCN CMen CPMA ECho EPfP LRHS MGos NHol NLar NPCo WFoF WPat
§	- 'Arakawa'	CEnd CMCN CMac CMen ECho MPkF NPCo
	- 'Arakawa-ukon'	CPMA
	- 'Aratama'	CBty CPMA LRHS MGos NLar SCoo WPat
	- 'Ariake-nomura'	CMen MPkF
	- 'Asahi-zuru' (v)	CBcs CDoC CMCN CMen CPMA EBee ECho LRHS MBri MGos MPkF NHol NLar NPCo SPer WDin WFar WFoF WHar WPat
	- 'Ashurst Wood'	SBig
	- 'Atrolineare'	CMen MPkF NBea NLar WPat
	- 'Atropurpureum'	Widely available
	- 'Atropurpureum Novum'	MPkF
	- 'Attraction'	CMCN CMen NPCo
	- 'Aureum'	CMCN CMac CMen CWib ECho EPfP LAst LMil LRHS MBlu MGos MPkF NHol NLar NPCo SBod SSpi WCFE WFar
	- Autumn Glory Group	CEnd CMac CPMA ECho
	- 'Autumn Red'	ECho NPCo
*	- 'Autumn Showers'	CEnd CPMA
	- 'Azuma-murasaki'	CMen CPMA MPkF NLar
	- 'Beni-chidori'	CMen ECho
	- 'Beni-gasa'	CPMA
	- 'Beni-hime'	MBri MPkF NLar
	- 'Beni-hoshi'	MPkF WPat
	- 'Beni-kagami'	CEnd CMCN CPMA EPfP MPkF NBea NLar
	- 'Beni-kawa'	CMen CPMA MPkF NPCo SBig SSpi WPat
	- 'Beni-komachi'	CBcs CBty CEnd CMCN CMac CMen CPMA ECho EGxp EPfP LRHS MBri MGos MPkF NLar WHar WPat
	- 'Beni-maiko'	CEnd CMCN CMen CPMA CWib EPfP GKir LBuc LRHS LSou MBri MGos MPkF MWea NLar NPCo SBig SCoo SWvt WBVN WDin WHar WPGP WPat
	- 'Beni-musume'	MPkF NLar
	- 'Beni-otake'	CBcs CBty CLnd CMen CPMA ECho EPfP LRHS MBri MGos MPkF NLar NPCo SBig SPer WPat
	- 'Beni-otome' **new**	MPkF
	- 'Beni-schichihenge' (v)	CBcs CBty CEnd CMCN CMen CPMA CWCL CWGN ECho EPfP

	Name	Suppliers
		LRHS MAsh MBri MGos MPkF NHol NPCo SBig SCoo WPGP WPat
	- 'Beni-shi-en'	CPMA MPkF NLar
	- 'Beni-shigitatsu-sawa'	see *A. palmatum* 'Aka-shigitatsu-sawa'
	- 'Beni-tsukasa' (v)	CEnd CMen CPMA ECho LMil LRHS MPkF NPCo SSpi WPGP
	- 'Beni-ubi-gohon'	CPMA LRHS MPkF NLar
	- 'Berry Broom'	MPkF
	- 'Berry Dwarf'	MPkF
	- 'Bloodgood' ♀H4	Widely available
	- 'Bonfire' misapplied	see *A. palmatum* 'Seigai'
	- 'Bonfire' ambig.	CPMA
	- 'Bonnie Bergman'	CPMA
	- 'Boskoop Glory'	ECho
	- 'Brandt's Dwarf'	MPkF WPat
	- 'Burgundy Lace' ♀H4	CBcs CBty CDoC CEnd CMCN CMen CPMA CWib EMac GKir LMil LRHS LSRN MAsh MBri MGos MPkF NHol NPCo SBig SCoo SPer SPoG WDin WFar WHar WPGP WPat
	- 'Butterfly' (v)	CBcs CDoC CEnd CMCN CMac CMen CPMA CWCL CWGN CWSG CWib LAst LMaj LMil LRHS LSRN MBar MGos NBlu NHol NLar NPCo SBch SCoo SLim SMad SPoG WDin WFar
	- 'Calico'	CPMA
	- 'Caperci Dwarf' **new**	MPkF
	- 'Carlis Corner'	CPMA MPkF
	- 'Carminium'	see *A. palmatum* 'Corallinum'
	- 'Chikuma-no'	MPkF
	- 'Chirimen-nishiki' (v)	MPkF
	- 'Chitose-yama' ♀H4	CBty CEnd CMCN CMac CMen CPMA CWCL CWib ECho EPfP LMil LRHS MBar MBri MGos MPkF MRav NHol NLar NPCo SCoo SLim SSpi SSta WFar WPat
§	- 'Chiyo-hime'	ECho ELan MGos NLar NPCo
	- 'Coonara Pygmy'	CBty CMCN CMen CPMA ECho IDee LRHS MGos MPkF NLar NPCo SBod SCoo WFar WPat
	- 'Coral Pink'	CMen CPMA MPkF
§	- 'Corallinum'	CDul CEnd CMCN CMen CPMA LRHS MPkF NLar NPCo NPal WDin WPat
	- var. ***coreanum***	CMCN
	- - B&SWJ 8606	WCru
	- - 'Korean Gem'	CPMA MPkF NPCo
	- 'Crimson Prince'	CBcs EMac LRHS MPkF SBod SCoo
	- 'Crippsii'	CBcs CBty CMac CMen ECho LRHS MGos MPkF SCoo WFar WPat
	- 'Curtis Strapleaf' **new**	MPkF
	- 'Demi-sec'	ECho
	- 'Deshōjō'	CBty CMCN CMen CWib EGxp LRHS MBar MBlu MGos MPkF NHol NLar SCoo
	- 'Diana'	CMen MPkF NLar
	- 'Diane Verkade'	MPkF
	- var. ***dissectum*** ♀H4	CDoC CDul CEnd CTri CWCL CWSG CWib EBee EPfP GBin LBuc LHyd LRHS LSRN MBar MBri MGos NBlu NHol NWea SBch SLim SPoG SReu WBVN WCFE WDin WFar WHCr WPat
	- - 'Ao-shidare'	CPMA LRHS
	- - 'Ariadne' (v)	CBty CEnd CPMA CWib LRHS MBri MGos MPkF NLar SBig SCoo SPoG WPat
	- - 'Autumn Fire'	CPMA
	- - 'Baby Lace'	CPMA MPkF NLar
	- - 'Balcombe Green'	SBig
	- - 'Baldsmith'	CPMA LRHS MGos WPat

	Name	Suppliers
	- - 'Barrie Bergman'	CPMA
	- - 'Beni-fushigi'	MPkF NLar WPat
	- - 'Beni-shidare Tricolor' (v)	CMen MPkF NLar
	- - 'Beni-shidare Variegated' (v)	CMCN CPMA ECho
	- - 'Berrima Bridge'	CPMA
	- - 'Bewley's Red'	CPMA
	- - 'Brocade'	MPkF WPat
	- - 'Bronzewing'	CPMA
	- - 'Chantilly Lace'	CPMA
	- - 'Crimson Queen' ♀H4	Widely available
	- - Dissectum Atropurpureum Group	CBcs CCVT CMac CPMA CTri CWCL ELan EPfP LHyd LRHS MGan MGos NBea NHol NLar NWea SBig SCoo SLim SReu SSpi SSta STre WDin WFar WHCr
	- - 'Dissectum Flavescens'	CEnd CMac CMen CPMA ECho MBlu MPkF NPCo
§	- - 'Dissectum Nigrum'	CMac CMen CPMA CTri CWSG ECho MAsh MPkF NBea NHol NLar NPCo SSpi WPat
	- - 'Dissectum Palmatifidum'	CDoC CLnd CMen EQua LRHS MPkF NPCo SCoo SPer WFar
	- - 'Dissectum Rubrifolium'	MGos
§	- - 'Dissectum Variegatum' (v)	CBcs CPMA EPfP MPkF NPCo
	- - Dissectum Viride Group	CBcs CMCN CMac CMen CPMA CSBt CWSG ECho ELan EMui EPfP GKir LMil LRHS MAsh MBlu MGos MSwo NBea NEgg NPCo NWea SBch SBod SLim SPer SSta WFar
	- - 'Ellen'	CPMA WPat
	- - 'Emerald Lace'	CPMA LRHS MPkF NLar WCFE
	- - 'Felice'	CPMA MPkF WPat
	- - 'Filigree' (v)	CMCN CMen CPMA CWCL ECho EPfP LRHS MGos MPkF NLar NPCo SBig SSpi WDin WPGP WPat
	- - 'Garnet' ♀H4	Widely available
	- - 'Goshiki-shidare' (v)	CEnd CMen CPMA MPkF
	- - 'Green Globe'	LRHS NLar
	- - 'Green Hornet'	CPMA
	- - 'Green Lace'	CMen MPkF
	- - 'Green Mist'	CPMA WPat
	- - 'Hanzel'	WPat
	- - 'Inaba-shidare' ♀H4	CBcs CBty CDoC CEnd CMCN CMen CPMA CSBt CSam CWCL CWib EPfP IMGH LRHS MBar MGos MRav NHol NLar NPCo SBch SBod SPer SSta WDin WPGP WPat
	- - 'Jeddeloh Orange' **new**	MPkF
I	- - 'Kawaii'	CPMA
	- - 'Kiri-nishiki'	CMen CPMA MPkF NLar NPCo
*	- - 'Lionheart'	CDoC CMen CPMA ECho EMac LRHS MGos MPkF NLar SBod SCoo SPer WFar WHar
	- - 'Nomura-nishiki' (v)	CMen
	- - 'Octopus'	CPMA
	- - 'Orangeola'	CBcs CBty CMen CPMA CSBt LRHS MAsh MBri MGos MPkF NHol NLar NPCo SBig SCoo SPoG WPat
	- - 'Ornatum'	CDoC CDul CMCN CMen CWCL CWib ECho ELon EPfP IMGH MBar MGos MPkF MRav NBea NEgg NPCo SBch SCoo WCFE WDin WFar WHCr WHar
	- - 'Otto's Dissectum'	CPMA
	- - 'Pendulum Julian'	CMCN LRHS MPkF NLar SBod
	- - 'Pink Ballerina' (v)	CPMA
	- - 'Pink Filigree'	CMen MPkF
	- - 'Raraflora'	CPMA
	- - 'Red Autumn Lace'	CPMA WPat

	- - 'Red Dragon'	CDoC CMen CPMA CWGN ECho EQua LRHS MPkF NLar NPCo SBig SBod WHar WPat
	- - 'Red Feather'	CPMA
	- - 'Red Filigree Lace'	CEnd CMCN CMen CPMA CWGN ECho EPfP MGos MPkF NHol NPCo SBig
	- - 'Red Select'	CBty LRHS MPkF
	- - 'Seiryū' ♀H4	Widely available
§	- - 'Shōjō-shidare'	CDul CEnd CMen CPMA LRHS MPkF NLar
	- - 'Spring Delight'	CPMA MPkF NLar
	- - 'Suisei' (v) **new**	MPkF
	- - 'Sunset'	CPMA EMui MPkF WPat
	- - 'Tamukeyama'	CBcs CBty CLnd CMCN CMen CPMA CWCL EBee ECho ELan EMac LRHS MBri MGos MPkF NLar NPCo SBod SCoo SLau SPoG WFar WPat
	- - 'Toyama-nishiki' (v)	CMCN CMen CWGN ECho LRHS NPCo WPat
	- - 'Waterfall'	CMCN CPMA
	- - 'Watnong'	CPMA
	- - 'Zaaling'	CMen ECho NPCo
	- 'Doctor Tilt'	MPkF
	- 'Dormansland'	LMil SBig SCoo
	- 'Dragon's Fire'	EMui
	- 'Earthfire' **new**	MPkF WPat
	- 'Eddisbury'	CEnd CMen CPMA MPkF NBea NLar SSta WPGP WPat
	- 'Edna Bergman'	CPMA
	- 'Effegi'	see *A. palmatum* 'Fireglow'
	- 'Eimini'	MPkF WPat
	- 'Elegans'	CMen EPfP MPkF NPCo WDin
	- 'Elizabeth' **new**	MPkF
	- Emperor 1	see *A. palmatum* 'Wolff'
	- 'Enkan'	CBty CEnd CPMA CWGN LRHS MBri MGos MPkF NLar WPat
	- 'Eono-momiji'	CMen
	- 'Ever Red'	see *A. palmatum* var. *dissectum* 'Dissectum Nigrum'
	- 'Fall's Fire'	CPMA
	- 'Fascination'	CPMA
	- 'Fior d'Arancio'	CPMA MPkF NBea NLar NPCo
§	- 'Fireglow'	CBcs CBty CDoC CEnd CLnd CMCN CMen CPMA CSBt CWCL CWib ECho LMaj LRHS MBlu MBri MGos MPkF NBea NEgg NLar NPCo SCoo WFar WHar WPGP WPat
	- 'First Ghost'	CPMA
	- 'Fjellheim'	CPMA MPkF
	- 'Frederici Guglielmi'	see *A. palmatum* var. *dissectum* 'Dissectum Variegatum'
	- 'Garyū'	MPkF
	- 'Geisha'	CPMA MGos MPkF
	- 'Germaine's Gyration'	CPMA
	- 'Gibbsii'	ECho NPCo
I	- 'Globosum' **new**	MPkF
	- 'Glowing Embers'	MPkF WPat
	- 'Golden Pond'	CPMA
	- 'Goshiki-kotohime' (v)	CBty CMCN CPMA LRHS MPkF
	- 'Green Trompenburg'	CMen CPMA MGos MPkF NEgg NLar NPCo
	- 'Groundcover'	MPkF
§	- 'Hagoromo'	CDoC CMen ECho MPkF NPCo SCoo WFar
	- 'Hanami-nishiki'	CMen MPkF NEgg WPat
	- 'Haru-iro' **new**	CPMA
	- 'Harusame' (v)	MPkF
	- 'Hazeroino' (v)	CMen MPkF
	- 'Heartbeat'	CPMA
	- 'Helena'	see *A. shirasawanum* 'Helena'
	- ***heptalobum***	CMCN
§	- 'Heptalobum Elegans'	CMCN LRHS MBlu SSpi
	- 'Heptalobum Elegans Purpureum'	see *A. palmatum* 'Hessei'
	- 'Herbstfeuer'	CPMA MPkF
§	- 'Hessei'	CEnd CMCN CWCL LRHS MBlu MPkF NBea NLar
	- 'Higasayama' (v)	CBcs CEnd CMCN CMen CPMA ECho GKir LRHS MGos MPkF NHol NLar NPCo SCoo WHar WPGP WPat
	- 'Hino-tori-nishiki'	CMen
	- 'Hōgyoku'	CMCN CMen CPMA LRHS MPkF WPat
	- 'Hoshi-kuzu'	MPkF
	- 'Hupp's Dwarf'	MPkF
	- 'Ibo-nishiki'	CMen MPkF
	- 'Ichigyōji'	CEnd CMen CPMA ECho LRHS NPCo SBig SChF WPGP WPat
	- 'Iijima-sunago' **new**	MPkF
	- 'Inazuma'	CBcs CDoC CMCN CMen CPMA EPfP LRHS MGos MPkF NLar SBod SCoo SLau WFar WPat
	- 'Irish Lace'	CPMA MPkF
	- 'Iso-chidori' **new**	MPkF
	- 'Issai-nishiki'	ECho MPkF NPCo
*	- 'Issai-nishiki-kawazu'	MPkF
	- 'Jane'	MPkF
	- 'Japanese Sunrise'	CPMA MPkF WPat
	- 'Jerre Schwartz'	MGos MPkF NLar WPat
	- 'Jirō-shidare'	CPMA EPfP MPkF NLar SBig
	- 'JJ' **new**	CPMA
	- 'Julia D.'	CPMA NLar
	- 'Kaba'	CMen MPkF
	- 'Kagero' (v)	MPkF WFar
§	- 'Kagiri-nishiki' (v)	CBcs CDul CMCN CMen CPMA CWSG ECho LRHS MPkF NEgg NHol NLar WFar
	- 'Kamagata'	CBty CEnd CMCN CMen CPMA ECho EPfP IDee LMil LRHS MGos MPkF NHol NLar NPCo SCoo SPer WPGP WPat
	- 'Kandy Kitchen'	CPMA LRHS MGos MPkF
	- 'Karaori-nishiki' (v)	CMen ECho MPkF NLar
	- 'Karasugawa' (v)	CMen CPMA MGos MPkF NLar NPCo
	- 'Kasagiyama'	CEnd CMCN CMen CPMA MGos MPkF NBea NLar WPGP
	- 'Kasen-nishiki'	CMen ECho MPkF
	- 'Kashima'	CEnd CMCN CMen CPMA ECho MPkF NPCo WFar
	- 'Kashima-yatsubusa'	LRHS MPkF
	- 'Katja'	CMen
	- 'Katsura' ♀H4	Widely available
	- 'Ki-hachijō'	CMCN CMen CPMA EPfP MPkF NLar WPat
	- 'Kingsville Variegated' (v)	MPkF
	- 'Kinran'	CMen MPkF NPCo WPat
	- 'Kinshi'	CBty CEnd CMCN CMen CPMA ECho EPfP LRHS MPkF NBea NHol NPCo SPoG SSta WPat
	- 'Kiyohime'	CDoC CMCN CMen ECho MPkF NBea WFar WPat
	- 'Kogane-sakae'	CPMA MPkF
	- 'Kokobunji-nishiki' (v)	MPkF
	- 'Komache-hime'	CMen CPMA ECho WPat
*	- 'Komaru'	NLar
	- 'Komon-nishiki' (v)	CMen CPMA ECho MPkF
	- 'Koriba'	CPMA MPkF NLar
	- 'Koshibori-nishiki'	MPkF
§	- 'Koshimino'	CPMA
	- 'Kotohime'	CAbP CMCN CMen CPMA LRHS MBri MGos MPkF NLar SBig SCoo SPoG

	Name	Suppliers
	- 'Koto-ito-komachi'	CMen CPMA ECho LRHS MPkF NLar NPCo WPat
	- 'Koto-maru'	MPkF
	- 'Koto-no-ito'	CMCN CWGN LRHS MGos MPkF NLar WHar WPat
	- 'Koya-san'	CMen MPkF
	- 'Krazy Krinkle'	CPMA
	- 'Kurabu-yama'	CMen MPkF
	- 'Kurui-jishi'	MGos MPkF WPat
	- 'Kyōryū' **new**	MPkF
	- 'Kyra'	CMen MPkF
	- 'Linearilobum'	ECho EPfP LHyd LMil MBlu MGos MPkF NBea NLar NPCo SCoo WFar WHar WPat
	- 'Linearilobum Atropurpureum'	NBea
	- 'Little Princess'	see *A. palmatum* 'Chiyo-hime'
	- 'Lozita'	WPat
	- 'Lutescens'	MPkF NPCo
	- 'Lydia'	MPkF
	- 'Maiko'	CMen MPkF
	- 'Mama'	CMen NPCo
	- 'Mapi-no-machihime'	CEnd CMCN CMen CPMA ELan LRHS MAsh MBri MGos MPkF NHol WPGP WPat
	- 'Marakumo'	MPkF
	- 'Mardi Gras'	CPMA
	- 'Margaret'	MPkF
	- 'Margaret Bee'	MPkF
	- 'Marjan'	MPkF NLar
	- 'Masamurasaki'	CMen WPat
	- 'Masukagami' (v)	CEnd CPMA MPkF NLar
	- 'Matsuga-e' (v)	CMen MPkF NPCo
	- 'Matsukaze'	CMCN CMen CPMA
	- var. ***matsumurae*** B&SWJ 11100 **new**	WCru
	- 'Matsuyoi' **new**	CPMA
	- 'Meihō-nishiki'	CPMA
	- 'Melanie'	CPMA SBig
	- 'Midori-no-teiboku'	MPkF
	- 'Mikawa-yatsubusa'	CMCN CMac CMen CPMA ECho EPfP LRHS MGos MPkF NBhm NLar NPCo WPat
	- 'Mimaye'	CPMA
	- 'Mini Mondo'	MPkF
	- 'Mirte'	CMen CPMA MPkF SBig WFar WPat
	- 'Mizuho-beni'	CPMA NPCo
	- 'Mizu-kuguri'	MPkF NLar
	- 'Momoiro-koya-san'	CPMA MPkF WPat
	- 'Mon Papa'	CPMA NLar
	- 'Monzukushi'	CPMA MPkF
	- 'Moonfire'	CMCN CPMA EPfP LRHS MGos MPkF WPat
	- 'Mr Sun'	CPMA
*	- 'Muncaster'	LMil SBig
	- 'Murasaki-hime'	MPkF
	- 'Murasaki-kiyohime'	CBty CEnd CMCN CMen CPMA ECho GBin LRHS MPkF NPCo WPat
	- 'Mure-hibari'	CPMA MPkF
	- 'Murogawa'	CMen CPMA NPCo
	- 'Nanase-gawa'	MPkF
	- 'Nicholsonii'	CMCN CMen CTri EPfP MPkF NLar NPCo WFar WPat
	- 'Nigrum' ♀H4	CMCN NLar WPat
	- 'Nishiki-gasane' (v)	MPkF
§	- 'Nishiki-gawa'	CEnd CMCN CMen CPMA ECho MPkF NPCo WPGP
	- 'Nishiki-momiji'	CMen
	- 'Nomura'	CMen CPMA
	- 'Nomurishidare' misapplied	see *A. palmatum* var. *dissectum* 'Shojo-shidare'
	- 'Nomurishidare' Wada	SSpi
	- 'Nuresagi'	CEnd CPMA MPkF WPat
	- 'Ōgi-nagashi' (v)	MPkF
	- 'Ōgi-no-sen' **new**	MPkF
	- 'Ōgon-sarasa'	CPMA MPkF
	- 'Ojishi'	CMen MPkF
	- 'Ō-kagami'	CBcs CBty CDoC CEnd CMen CPMA CSBt ECho ELon GKir LMil LRHS MGos MPkF NLar NPCo SCoo WPGP
	- 'Okukuji-nishiki'	CPMA
	- 'Okushimo'	CEnd CMCN CMen CPMA LRHS MPkF NHol NLar NPCo WPGP
	- 'Omato'	CPMA MPkF SBig WFar
	- 'Omurayama'	CBcs CBty CDoC CEnd CMCN CMen CPMA ECho EPfP LMil LRHS MGos MPkF NBhm NBlu NLar NPCo SCoo SPer SSta WFar
	- 'Orange Dream'	Widely available
	- 'Oregon Sunset'	MGos MPkF WPat
	- 'Oridono-nishiki' (v)	CBcs CDoC CDul CEnd CMCN CMac CMen CPMA CWCL ECho ELan EPfP LMil LRHS MBar MBlu MGos MPkF NEgg NLar NPCo SBch SCoo SPer SPoG SSta WFar WHar
	- 'Ōsakazuki' ♀H4	Widely available
	- 'Ōshio-beni'	CMen CPMA NPCo
	- 'Ōshū-shidare'	CMen CPMA ECho EPfP MPkF WFar
	- 'Oto-hime'	CMen CPMA ECho MPkF NPCo
	- 'Otome-zakura'	CMen CPMA ECho LRHS MPkF WPat
	- 'Peaches and Cream' (v)	CBcs CMen CPMA MPkF NLar NPCo WPat
	- 'Peve Chameleon'	MPkF
	- 'Peve Dave'	MPkF NLar
	- 'Peve Multicolor'	CPMA MGos MPkF NLar
	- 'Peve Ollie' **new**	NLar
	- 'Phoenix'	MBri MPkF
	- 'Pine Bark Maple'	see *A. palmatum* 'Nishiki-gawa'
	- 'Pixie'	CBty CMen CPMA MGos MPkF NLar WPat
	- 'Pung-kil'	MPkF
	- 'Purple Ghost'	NLar
	- 'Red Baron'	CPMA
	- 'Red Cloud'	MPkF NLar
	- 'Red Crusader' **new**	NLar
	- 'Red Elf' **new**	MPkF
	- 'Red Embers'	CWib
	- 'Red Emperor'	CWGN NLar SPer WPat
	- 'Red Flame' **new**	NLar
	- 'Red Flash'	MPkF
	- 'Red Jonas'	MPkF NLar
	- 'Red Pygmy' ♀H4	CBcs CDoC CEnd CMCN CMac CMen CPMA CWCL CWGN CWib ECho EMac LMil LRHS MBar MBlu MBri MGos NBea NHol NPCo SCoo SPer SPoG SSpi SSta WFar WPat
	- 'Red Spider'	CPMA
	- 'Red Wood'	CDoC CPMA GBin MPkF SBod SCoo SLau WPat
	- 'Reticulatum'	see *A. palmatum* 'Shigitatsu-sawa'
	- 'Ribesifolium'	see *A. palmatum* 'Shishigashira'
*	- 'Rigassii'	LMaj
	- 'Rising Sun'	CPMA
	- 'Rokugatsu-en-nishiki'	WPat
	- 'Roseomarginatum'	see *A. palmatum* 'Kagiri-nishiki'
	- 'Rough Bark Maple'	see *A. palmatum* 'Arakawa'
	- 'Royle'	CPMA
	- 'Rubrum'	CMen
I	- 'Rubrum Kaiser'	CPMA
	- 'Ruby Ridge'	CPMA
	- 'Ruby Star'	CPMA MPkF NLar

	Cultivar	Suppliers
	- 'Rufescens'	MPkF
	- 'Ryokū-ryū'	CMen MPkF
	- 'Ryuzu'	CPMA MPkF WPat
	- 'Sagara-nishiki' (v)	CEnd CMen CPMA ECho MPkF NPCo
	- 'Sai-ho' **new**	MPkF
	- 'Saint Jean'	MPkF
	- 'Samidare'	CPMA EPfP MPkF NLar
	- 'Sandra'	CMen MPkF
N	- 'Sango-kaku' ♀H4	Widely available
	- 'Saoshika'	CMen CPMA MPkF
	- 'Sa-otome'	CMen MPkF
	- 'Satsuki-beni'	CMen ECho NPCo
	- 'Sazanami'	CDoC CEnd CMen CPMA CWCL MPkF NBea NLar WPGP WPat
	- 'Scolopendriifolium'	CBcs CBty CDoC GBin LMil LRHS MPkF SCoo SLau WFar WPat
§	- 'Seigai'	CPMA MPkF
	- 'Seigen'	CEnd CMCN CMen CPMA ECho MPkF NPCo WPGP
I	- 'Seigen Aureum'	CPMA
	- 'Seiun-kaku'	CMen CPMA ECho MBri MPkF WPat
	- 'Sekimori'	CPMA SBig
	- 'Sekka-yatsubusa'	CMCN CMen ECho MPkF
N	- 'Senkaki'	see *A. palmatum* 'Sango-kaku'
	- 'Septemlobum Elegans'	see *A. palmatum* 'Heptalobum Elegans'
	- 'Septemlobum Purpureum'	see *A. palmatum* 'Hessei'
	- 'Sessilifolium' dwarf	see *A. palmatum* 'Hagoromo'
	- 'Sessilifolium' tall	see *A. palmatum* 'Koshimino'
	- 'Shaina'	CBcs CDoC CEnd CMen CPMA CSBt CWCL CWGN CWib LRHS MBri MGos MPkF NBhm NLar NPCo NPal SBod SCoo WFar WHar WPat
	- 'Sharp's Pygmy'	CBty CMen CPMA ECho GBin LRHS MPkF NPCo WPat
	- 'Sherwood Flame'	CDoC CMCN CMen CPMA CWib ECho LRHS MAsh MGos MPkF NLar NPCo SCoo WFar WPat
	- 'Shichigosan'	CMen LRHS
	- 'Shidava Gold'	CPMA MPkF
	- 'Shi-en'	MPkF
	- 'Shigarami'	CPMA MPkF
§	- 'Shigitatsu-sawa' (v)	CBcs CBty CEnd CMCN CMac CMen CPMA ECho LRHS MGos MPkF NBea NLar NPCo SBig
	- 'Shigure-bato'	CPMA MPkF
	- 'Shigurezome'	MPkF
	- 'Shikageori-nishiki'	CMen CPMA MPkF
	- 'Shime-no-uchi'	CPMA LMil MPkF SBig
	- 'Shindeshōjō'	Widely available
§	- 'Shinobuga-oka'	CMCN CMen CPMA LRHS MPkF SCoo SLau
	- 'Shinonome'	CPMA MPkF
	- 'Shirazz' (v)	LRHS MGos MPkF
§	- 'Shishigashira'	CDoC CMCN CMac CMen CPMA EBee ECho EPfP LMil LRHS MBar MBlu MBri MDun MGos MPkF NBea NLar NPCo SCoo SPoG WDin WFar WPat
	- 'Shishio'	CBcs CBty CMCN CMen LAst LHyd LRHS MPkF NPCo SBig SSpi WPat
	- 'Shishio Improved'	CEnd CMCN CMac CPMA CTho CWSG EPfP MGos MPkF NBhm NHol NLar NPCo SBig SWvt WHar
	- 'Shishio-hime'	MPkF
	- 'Shishi-yatsubusa' **new**	CPMA MPkF
	- 'Shōjō'	CMCN CPMA WFar
	- 'Shōjō-no-mai'	CPMA
	- 'Shōjō-nomura'	CAbP CEnd CMen MGos MPkF NBea NLar WPGP WPat
	- 'Sister Ghost'	CPMA
	- 'Skeeter's Broom'	CBcs CBty CMen CPMA ECho LBuc LRHS MBri MGos MPkF NPCo SBig SCoo WPat
*	- 'Sode-nishiki'	CPMA MPkF NLar
	- 'Stella Rossa'	CEnd CPMA MPkF NBea NLar WPat
	- 'Suminagashi'	CBcs CBty CDoC CMen CWCL LMil LRHS MGos MPkF NLar NPCo SBod SChF SCoo SLau WPat
I	- 'Summer Gold'	MBri SWvt
*	- 'Sunago'	NLar
	- 'Susan'	MPkF
	- 'Taiyō-nishiki'	CPMA MPkF
	- 'Takao'	CMen
	- 'Takinogawa'	LRHS
	- 'Tama-hime'	CMen CPMA MPkF NPCo
	- 'Tana'	CMCN CMen CPMA EPfP MPkF WFar WPat
	- 'Tarō-yama'	CPMA WPat
	- 'Tatsuta'	CMen MPkF WHar
	- 'Taylor'[PBR] (v)	CEnd EGxp LRHS LSou MBri MGos MPkF NLar SCoo
	- 'Tennyo-no-hoshi'	CMen MPkF NLar NPCo
	- 'Tiger Rose'	CPMA NLar
	- 'Tiny Tim'	CPMA
	- 'Trompenburg' ♀H4	Widely available
	- 'Tsuchigumo'	CMen CPMA MPkF NLar
	- 'Tsukubane'	WPat
	- 'Tsukuma-no' **new**	MPkF
	- 'Tsukushigata'	MPkF WPat
	- 'Tsuma-beni'	CMCN CMen EPfP LRHS MPkF NPCo
	- 'Tsuma-gaki'	CDoC CMen CPMA ECho EGxp EPfP MBri MGos MPkF NLar NPCo WPat
	- 'Tsuri-nishiki'	CMen CPMA MPkF NLar
	- 'Ueno-homare'	LRHS MPkF SCoo WPat
	- 'Ueno-yama'	CBcs CPMA GBin MGos MPkF WPat
	- 'Ukigumo' (v)	CBcs CEnd CLnd CMCN CMac CMen CPMA CSBt CWSG CWib ELan LMil LRHS MBlu MBri MGos MPkF NHol NPCo SBch SBig SBod SCoo SPer SPoG SSta WDin WFar WPat
	- 'Ukon'	CMen CPMA ECho GBin LMil MPkF NPCo SBod SCoo
	- 'Umegae'	CPMA
	- 'Uncle Ghost'	CPMA
	- 'Usu-midori'	CPMA
	- 'Utsu-semi'	CPMA MPkF
	- 'Van der Akker'	CPMA
	- 'Versicolor' (v)	CEnd CMCN CPMA LRHS
	- 'Vic Pink'	CPMA
	- 'Victoria' **new**	MPkF
	- 'Villa Taranto'	CBty CDoC CEnd CMCN CMen CPMA ECho EPfP LMil LRHS MBri MGos MPkF NBea NHol NLar NPCo SCoo SSpi SSta WHar WPGP WPat
	- 'Volubile'	CMCN CMen EPfP MPkF NPCo
	- 'Wabito'	CMCN CMen CPMA LRHS MPkF
	- 'Waka-midori'	CMen
	- 'Waka-momiji' (v)	CPMA
	- 'Wakehurst Pink' (v)	CMCN MPkF WPat
	- 'Wendy'	CMen CPMA MPkF NLar WPat
	- 'Wetumpka Red'	CPMA
	- 'Whitney Red'	CMen
	- 'Wildgoose' **new**	MPkF
	- 'Will D'	CPMA

- 'Wilson's Pink Dwarf' CBty CEnd CMen CPMA CWib ECho LRHS MBri MGos MPkF NLar NPCo SCoo SPoG
- 'Winter Flame' CPMA LRHS MPkF NHol NLar WHar WPat
§ - 'Wolff' MPkF WPat
- 'Wolff's Broom' MPkF
- 'Wou-nishiki' CMCN CMen ECho MPkF NPCo
- 'Yana-gawa' CMen
- 'Yasemin' CMen CPMA MPkF NLar NPCo SBig
- 'Yatsubusa' MPkF
- 'Yezo-nishiki' CMen LRHS MPkF WFar
- 'Yūba e' MPkF WFar WPat
- 'Yūgure' MPkF NLar WFar
papilio see *A. caudatum*
pectinatum GWJ 9360 WCru
pensylvanicum ♀H4 CBcs CCVT CDul CMCN CTho EBee ECrN ELan EPfP IFFs LMaj LRHS MBri MGos MMuc MRav NBlu NHol NWea SLim SPer SSpi WDin WFar WHCr
- 'Erythrocladum' CEnd CMCN CPMA EPfP LRHS MAsh MBri NBea NEgg NHol NLar SBig SLim SPur SSta WFar WPGP
pentaphyllum CDul SBig SBir SMad SPur SSpi
* ***phlebanthum*** B&SWJ 9751 WCru
§ ***pictum*** CMCN LRHS
- subsp. ***okamotoanum*** CMCN WPGP
- - B&SWJ 8516 WCru
- 'Shufu-nishiki' CMCN
- 'Usugomo' WPat
platanoides ♀H4 CBcs CCVT CDoC CDul CLnd CMCN CSBt CTri CWib EBee ECrN EMac EPfP IFFs LBuc MGos MMuc MSwo NWea SBch SPer STre WDin WFar WHar WMou
- 'Charles Joly' LMaj
- 'Cleveland' CBcs
- 'Columnare' CCVT CDul CLnd CMCN CWib SCoo
- 'Crimson King' ♀H4 Widely available
- 'Crimson Sentry' CDoC CDul CEnd CLnd CMCN CWib EBee ECrN ELan EPfP IArd LAst MAsh MBri MGos MRav SBch SCoo SLim SPoG WDin WFar WHar
- 'Deborah' CBcs CTho LMaj SCoo
- 'Drummondii' (v) Widely available
- 'Emerald Queen' CCVT CLnd CWib ECrN LMaj WDin
- 'Faassen's Black' CPMA
§ - 'Globosum' CLnd CMCN EBee ECrN LBuc LMaj NLar SWvt
- 'Goldsworth Purple' CDul CLnd NEgg
- 'Laciniatum' CEnd CMCN ECrN
- 'Lorbergii' see *A. platanoides* 'Palmatifidum'
- 'Marit' WPat
§ - 'Palmatifidum' CLnd
- Princeton Gold = 'Prigo'PBR CDoC CDul EBee ELan EMil LRHS MAsh MGos SBch SCoo SLim SPoG WHar
- 'Reitenbachii' CDul LMaj
- 'Royal Red' CBcs CDul CWib EBee ECrN EWTr LMaj MRav NLar SCoo
- 'Schwedleri' ♀H4 CDul CMCN EPfP MGos WDin
- 'Walderseei' CLnd
pseudoplatanus CBcs CCVT CDul CLnd CMCN CSBt CTri ECrN EMac IFFs LBuc MBar MGos NWea SBch SPer WDin WFar WHar WMou
§ - 'Atropurpureum' CDoC CDul CLnd ECrN EWTr NWea WDin WHar
- 'Brilliantissimum' ♀H4 Widely available
- 'Erectum' WFar
- 'Gadsby' CDul EBee LRHS
- 'Leopoldii' misapplied see *A. pseudoplatanus* f. *variegatum*
- 'Prinz Handjéry' CBcs CDul CEnd CLnd CMCN CTri CWib EBee LRHS MAsh MBar MGos NHol NLar NWea SPer SPoG SSpi WHar
- f. ***purpureum*** SEND
- 'Spaethii' misapplied see *A. pseudoplatanus* 'Atropurpureum'
- 'Sunshine' LRHS MGos
§ - f. ***variegatum*** (v) LRHS NEgg
- - 'Esk Sunset' (v) CBcs ECho LRHS MGos MPkF NLar
- - 'Leopoldii' ambig. (v) CBcs CDul CLnd CMCN EBee ECrN ELan LAst SCoo SEND SPer SWvt WDin WFar
- - 'Leopoldii' Vervaene (v) SCrf
- - 'Simon-Louis Frères' (v) CCVT CDul CEnd CLnd CMCN CWSG CWib EBee ECrN EMui LAst LRHS MAsh MBar MGos NEgg NLar SBch SBod SCrf SPer SPoG SWvt WCFE WFar WFoF WHar
- 'Worley' CBcs CCVT CDul CLnd CMCN CTri EBee ECrN LRHS MAsh MBar MRav NWea SBch SEND SLim SPer WDin WHar
pseudosieboldianum CMCN CPMA IDee MBlu MPkF
- B&SWJ 8746 WCru
- B&SWJ 8769 WCru
- var. ***microsieboldianum*** B&SWJ 8766 WCru
pycnanthum EPfP
reticulatum see *A. laevigatum* var. *reticulatum*
rubescens CPMA WPGP
- B&SWJ 6735 WCru
- RWJ 9840 WCru
- variegated seedlings (v) CPMA WPGP
rubrum Widely available
- 'Autumn Spire' CPMA
- 'Bowhall' SBir
- 'Brandywine' CPMA GKir LRHS MAsh MBlu MBri SPoG SSpi
- 'Candy Ice' (v) CPMA
- 'Columnare' CMCN EPfP
- 'Embers' CPMA
- 'Fairview Flame' SPer
- Fireball = 'Firzam' CPMA
- 'Firedance' CPMA
- 'New World' GKir NLar
- 'Northwind' **new** CPMA
- 'Northwood' CPMA
- 'October Glory' ♀H4 Widely available
- 'Red King' CPMA
- 'Red Rocket' SPoG SSpi
- Red Sunset = 'Franksred' CDoC CDul CEnd CMCN CPMA CTho EBee EPfP GKir LMaj LRHS MBlu NLar SBir SCoo SLim SMad SSta WPGP
- 'Scanlon' CBcs CDoC CDul CEnd CMCN CPMA CTho EBee ECho EPfP LAst LMaj MBlu SPer
- 'Schlesingeri' CEnd CMCN CMac CPMA EPfP
- 'Somerset' CPMA LRHS
- Summer Red = 'Hosr' CPMA GKir LRHS
- 'Sun Valley' CPMA GKir LRHS MAsh
- 'Tilford' CPMA SBir SSta
§ ***rufinerve*** ♀H4 CAlb CBcs CCVT CDoC CDul CLnd CMCN CTho CTri EBee ECrN EPfP EPla IFFs LMaj LRHS MAsh MBri MMuc NBea NEgg NLar NWea SCoo SPer WBVN WDin WPGP
- B&SWJ 11571 WCru
- 'Albolimbatum' see *A. rufinerve* 'Hatsuyuki'

	- 'Erythrocladum'	CBcs CPMA
§	- 'Hatsuyuki' (v)	CEnd CMCN CPMA SBig WPGP
	- 'Winter Gold'	CPMA EPfP LRHS NLar SPur SSpi
§	***saccharinum***	CBcs CCVT CDoC CDul CLnd CMCN CTri CWib EBee ECrN ELan EMac EPfP IFFs LRHS MGos MMuc MSnd NWea SCoo SPer WDin WFar WHar
	- 'Born's Gracious'	CPMA EMil IFFs
	- 'Fastigiatum'	see *A. saccharinum* f. *pyramidale*
	- f. ***laciniatum***	EBee LAst MBlu MGos MMuc SPer WDin
	- 'Laciniatum Wieri'	CDul CMCN EBee ECrN LAst WDin
	- f. ***lutescens***	CDul CMCN
§	- f. ***pyramidale***	CDoC CLnd EBee ECrN IFFs LMaj SPer WDin
	saccharum	CAgr CBcs CDoC CDul CLnd CMCN CTho ECrN EPfP MBlu NWea SPer
	- 'Adirondak'	CPMA
	- 'Arrowhead'	CPMA
	- 'Brocade'	CPMA MPkF
	- 'Caddo'	CPMA
	- 'Fiddlers Creek'	CPMA
§	- subsp. ***grandidentatum***	MBlu NLar
	- 'Green Mountain'	CPMA
	- 'Majesty'	CPMA
	- subsp. ***nigrum***	CMCN
	- - 'Greencolumn'	CPMA
	- 'Sugar Cone'	CPMA
§	***sempervirens***	CGHE CPMA EBee LEdu MBlu WPGP
	'Sensu'	CPMA
	serrulatum B&SWJ 6760	WCru
	- RWJ 9912	WCru
	shirasawanum	CMCN
§	- 'Aureum' ♀H4	Widely available
	- 'Autumn Moon'	CBcs CBty CEnd CMCN CMen CPMA CWGN EPfP LRHS MBri MPkF NLar NPCo SCoo WPat
§	- 'Ezo-no-momiji'	CMen CPMA MPkF NLar NPCo
	- 'Gloria'	CBty MPkF
§	- 'Helena'	MPkF
	- 'Johin'	CPMA
	- 'Jordan' PBR	CEnd CWGN MBri MGos NLar
	- 'Lovett'	CPMA
§	- 'Microphyllum'	ECho MPkF
§	- 'Ogurayama'	CPMA ECho NPCo
	- 'Palmatifolium'	CPMA
	- 'Susanne'	CPMA MPkF
	- var. ***tenuifolium*** B&SWJ 11073	WCru
	sieboldianum	CDul CMCN CMen CTri ECho IFFs SSpi WHCr WHar WPat
	- B&SWJ 10962	WCru
	- B&SWJ 11049	WCru
	- 'Sode-no-uchi'	CMen MPkF NPCo
	aff. ***sikkimense*** HWJK 2040 **new**	WCru
	'Silver Cardinal' (v)	CBcs CEnd CMCN CPMA EBee EPfP LRHS MBlu MGos MPkF NBhm NLar WHar
	'Silver Vein'	see *A.* × *conspicuum* 'Silver Vein'
	spicatum	EPfP NLar
§	***stachyophyllum***	GAuc GQui
	- BWJ 8101	WCru
§	***sterculiaceum***	CMCN EBee WPGP
	- subsp. ***franchetii***	NLar
	- subsp. ***sterculiaceum*** GWJ 9317	WCru
	syriacum	see *A. obtusifolium*
	takesimense B&SWJ 8500	WCru
	tataricum	CMCN
	- subsp. ***aidzuense*** B&SWJ 10958	WCru
§	- subsp. ***ginnala***	CBcs CDul CLnd CMCN CTri CWSG ECrN EMac EPfP IFFs LMaj MBlu MGos NBea NPal NWea SPer WDin
	- - 'Flame'	CPMA CWSG EBee ELan EPfP LRHS MGos MMuc MSnd NLar NWea SPoG
	- - 'Red Wing'	CPMA
	tegmentosum	CBcs CMCN CPMA EPfP MBlu
	- B&SWJ 8421	WCru
	- subsp. ***glaucorufinerve***	see *A. rufinerve*
	tetramerum	see *A. stachyophyllum*
	tonkinense DJHV 06173	WCru
	trautvetteri	CMCN EPfP
	triflorum ♀H4	CCVT CDul CMCN CPMA CTho EPfP LMaj LRHS MBlu NBea NLar SSpi WDin WFar
	truncatum	CMCN ISea MPkF
	- 'Akikaze-nishiki' (v)	CPMA MPkF
	tschonoskii	GQui
	- subsp. ***koreanum***	MPkF
§	***turkestanicum***	CMCN WFar
	velutinum	CMCN
	- var. ***vanvolxemii***	WPGP
	villosum	see *A. sterculiaceum*
	'White Tigress'	CDoC CPMA CTho LRHS NLar WPGP
	wilsonii	CSam
	× ***zoeschense***	CMCN
	- 'Annae'	NHol

Aceriphyllum see *Mukdenia*

× *Achicodonia* (*Gesneriaceae*)

'Dark Velvet'	WDib

Achillea (*Asteraceae*)

	ageratifolia ♀H4	EBla ECho ECtt EDAr EOHP LBee LRHS MTho NBre SMad SRms WClo WFar
	- subsp. ***serbica***	ECho
§	***ageratum***	CArn CHby CPrp ECho ELau GBar GPoy MHer MNHC NGHP NPri SIde SRms WGwG WHer WJek WPer
	'Alabaster'	CSli EBee GBuc SAga SPhx
	aleppica subsp. ***zederbaueri*** **new**	GKev
	Anthea = 'Anblo' PBR	CKno CWCL EBee EBla EBrs ECtt GBBs LBMP LPio LRHS LSRN MCot MRav NChi NCob NLar SRGP SRkn SRms WFar
§	'Apfelblüte' (Galaxy Series)	CSli CWCL EBee EBla ECha ECtt ELan EWTr GMac LRHS LSRN MMuc MRav NGdn NHol SEND SPer WCAu WFar WMnd WPer WWEG
	Appleblossom	see *A.* 'Apfelblüte'
	'Apricot Beauty'	CSli EBee ECtt GBBs GMaP GQue LSRN NPro SSvw WCon
	argentea misapplied	see *A. clavennae*, *A. umbellata*
	argentea Lamarck	see *Tanacetum argenteum*
	argentea ambig.	NMen
	aurea	see *A. chrysocoma*
	'Bahama'	EPPr GBin GQue MAvo NBre NBro
	'Belle Epoque' ♀H4	CSli
	'Breckland Bouquet'	ECtt EWes
	'Breckland Ruby'	ECtt EWes
	'Brilliant'	LRHS
	'Carmina Burana'	CMea

	Name	Suppliers
	'Caroline'	LRHS
	cartilaginea	see *A. salicifolia*
	'Christine's Pink' ♀H4	CSli EPPr EShb MSpe SUsu
§	***chrysocoma***	ECho EDAr MWat WMoo
	- 'Grandiflora'	EBee ECha ELan ELon LPla NGdn
§	***clavennae***	CMea ECho EDAr LPio MBel MWat SAga SMrm SRms WAbe WFar WPat
	clypeolata Sibth. & Sm.	EBee EPPr EShb LPio LRHS NBre NLar SPlb SRms
	coarctata	NBir WPer
	Colorado Group	CWCL EAro GAbr LRHS NChi SPav WFar WHrl
	'Coronation Gold' ♀H4	CDoC CPrp CWCL EBee EBla ECtt ELan EPfP LAst LRHS MBri MNFA MRav MWat SAga SWvt WCAu WCot WEas WFar WWEG
	'Cranberry Fool'	EBee
	'Credo' ♀H4	CSli EBee EBla EBrs ECha ECtt EPPr EPfP GBuc LPio LRHS MBel MCot MNFA MRav MSpe NGdn NHol SMad SMrm SPer WCot WMnd WPtf WWEG
	crithmifolia	GKir
	decolorans	see *A. ageratum*
	erba-rotta	WPer
	- subsp. ***moschata***	ECho NBro
§	'Fanal'	Widely available
	'Faust'	CHar CSli EBla ELon SMrm STes SUsu WCon WPGP WPrP
	'Feuerland'	CSam CSli EBee EBla ECha ECtt ELon EPPr EPfP LRHS MBel MRav NBir NGdn NSti SMad SMrm SPer SWat WCAu WCot WFar WPer WWEG
	filipendulina	GKir SWal WHrl
	- 'Cloth of Gold' ♀H4	Widely available
	- 'Gold Plate' ♀H4	Widely available
	- 'Parker's Variety' ♀H4	EBee GQue NBre WFar WMoo
	Flowers of Sulphur	see *A.* 'Schwefelblüte'
	(Forncett Series) 'Forncett Beauty'	CSli WPtf
	- 'Forncett Bride'	CSli NBre WHil
	- 'Forncett Candy'	CSli WWEG
	- 'Forncett Citrus'	CSli MAvo NBre WPGP
	- 'Forncett Fletton'	CFir CSli CWCL EBee ECtt EPPr EPfP EShb IPot LHop LRHS MNFA MNrw MRav MSpe NCob NGdn NHol SAga WCAu WFar WPtf WWEG WWlt
	- 'Forncett Ivory'	CSli EPPr NBre
	fraasii	MDKP
	'Gloria Jean'	CSli SHar
	'Gold and Grey'	CSli WWEG
	'Goldstar'	EBee LRHS NBPC WFar
	grandifolia misapplied	see *Tanacetum macrophyllum* (Waldst. & Kit.) Sch.Bip.
§	***grandifolia*** Friv.	CElw COIW CPrp CSam GBuc LPla LRHS MRav NBro SMad SSvw WAul WBor WFar WHer WMnd WMoo WOld
	'Great Expectations'	see *A.* 'Hoffnung'
	'Grey and Gold'	SMrm
	'Hartington White'	GBuc
	'Heidi' ♀H4	CCVN CSli WWEG
	'Heinrich Vogeler' **new**	EBee
	'Helios' ♀H4	EBee
	'Hella Glashoff' ♀H4	CMea CSli CWCL CWan EBee EBrs ECho ECtt EGoo EPPr GBin LRHS MWea SAga WCot WFar WHoo
§	'Hoffnung'	CPrp CSli CWCL EBee EBla ECtt LRHS MRav MSpe NPro SPer WMnd WPer WWEG
	× ***huteri***	CStu EAlp EAro EBla ECho ECtt EDAr EPfP LBee LRHS MMuc MRav SPoG WCom WFar
	'Inca Gold'	CWCL EBee EBla ECha ECtt EHrv EPPr EShb GBuc GQue LRHS MRav NCob NGdn NHol NPro NSti SAga SPav WCFE WWEG
	'Jacqueline'	EBee EWll MAvo
	'Judity'	LRHS
	'King Alfred'	LAst MMuc
	× ***kolbiana***	MWat NMen SRms WPat
§	- 'Weston'	ECho NBre
§	'Lachsschönheit' (Galaxy Series) ♀H4	Widely available
	'Lemon Dream' **new**	MBri
	× ***lewisii***	NMen
	- 'King Edward' ♀H4	CSam EAlp ECha ECho EDAr EPfP GMaP LPio NBir SAga SIng SPoG WClo WCom WFar
	ligustica	WCot
	'Lucky Break' ♀H4	EBla SDix SUsu
	macrophylla	MBNS NBre
	'Marie Ann'	CPar CWCL EBee ECtt EKen EWll GQue LPio LSRN MBNS MBel NBPC NBhm NLar NSti SPhx SRGP
	'Marmalade'	CSli SMrm WMnd WPGP WWEG
	'Martina' ♀H4	CDoC CKno CMMP CPrp CSli EBee ECtt EPPr EPfP GAbr GBuc IPot LAst LBMP LHop LRHS MBNS MBri MCot MRav NCGa NGdn NHol NOrc NPro SRGP WWEG
	'McVities'	CSli CWCL ECtt EPPr LEdu MBel NPro SDnm SPav STes WCAu WMnd WPtf WTin WWEG
	millefolium	CArn COld CWan EBWF ELau GBar GPoy MNHC NLan NMir NSco SECG SPlb WHer WJek WSFF
	- 'Bloodstone'	CSli EBee ECtt EWes GBar MRav
	- 'Bright Cerise'	WFar
	- 'Carla Hussey'	WFar
	- 'Cassis'	CCVN CSpe EAro GQue LDai LRHS MNHC NGBl SDnm SPav SWal WFar WOut
§	- 'Cerise Queen'	Widely available
	- 'Cherry King'	MCot
	- 'Christel'	CCVN CSli EBee EWes GBin SUsu
	- 'Christine'	GBin
	- 'Dark Lilac Beauty' **new**	EWTr
	- dark red-flowered	CSli
	- Galaxy Series, red-flowered **new**	WSpi
	- 'Harlekin'	EBee
	- 'Kelwayi' ♀H4	CSli
	- Kirschkönigin	see *A. millefolium* 'Cerise Queen'
	- 'Lansdorferglut' ♀H4	CKno CSli EBrs EPPr LRHS NPro SPhx
	- 'Lavender Beauty'	see *A. millefolium* 'Lilac Beauty'
§	- 'Lilac Beauty'	CHar COIW CSli EBee EBrs ECha EHrv ELon EPPr EWTr GMaP IPot LRHS LSRN MRav NBir NEgg NGHP NHol NPri NSti SBch SPav WFar WHoo WPer WWEG
*	- 'Lilac Queen'	CSli MArl
	- 'Lollypop'	LDai
	- 'Oertels Rose'	WFar
	- 'Old Brocade'	CSli EShb NGby WPGP WWEG
	- pastel shades	GKir IFoB WMoo
	- 'Prospero'	WCot WWEG
	- 'Raspberry Ripple'	GBin
	- 'Red Beauty'	CSli CWCL EBee MBNS MBri MWea SMad SRms SWat WCFE WWEG
	- 'Red Velvet'	Widely available

	- 'Rose Madder'	CPrp CWCL EBee EBla ECtt EHoe EPPr GMaP LRHS MBel MBri MCot MLHP MSCN NCGa NCob NGHP NGdn NHol NOrc NSti SPav SWvt WCot WGwG WKif WPrP
	- 'Rosie'	GBar
	- 'Rougham Beauty'	CSli
	- 'Rougham Cream'	CSli
	- 'Rougham White'	CSli
	- 'Ruby Port'	WFar
	- 'Salmon Pink'	WFar
	- 'Salmon Queen'	NGHP NHol
	- 'Sammetriese'	CSli CWan EBee GBuc LRHS MNrw NCGa SMad WCot WFar WWEG
	- 'Schneetaler'	EBee GBin
	- 'Serenade'	EBee EBla WFar
	- 'Sue's Pink' **new**	CSam
	- 'Summertime'	LAst SBod SPav
	- 'Tickled Pink'	WPer
	- 'White Queen'	EBee WPer
	'Mondpagode' ♀H4	CHar CPrp CSli EBee ECGP EPPr LRHS LSRN MAvo MBNS MNFA MRav NGdn SPhx WFar WKif
	'Moonshine' ♀H3	Widely available
	'Moonwalker'	CAbP EBee NBre NGBl SIde SPav WCot WFar WPer
	nana	GEdr
	nobilis	MMuc
	- subsp. ***neilreichii***	CSli CSpe EBee EBla ECGP EGoo EHoe EHrv IKil LRHS NSti WHal WPrP WPtf WTin WWEG
	'Nostalgia'	EBee
	odorata	EBee
	'Paprika' (Galaxy Series)	Widely available
	'Peardrop'	NBre
	'Petra'	EBee WCAu
	pindicola subsp. ***integrifolia***	EWes
	'Pink Lady'	EBee EBla GBBs WCon
	pink-flowered from Santa Cruz Island	CKno CWCL
	'Pretty Belinda'	EBee ECtt EPfP IPot MBNS MBri NBPC NCGa NPri WWlt
	'Pretty Flamingo'	WOut
	ptarmica	CArn CBre EBWF ELau EMFW GBar MHer NMir NPri SECG SIde
*	- 'Ballerina'	MBNS MWhi NBre NLar WOut
	- Innocence	see *A. ptarmica* 'Unschuld'
	- 'Major'	NBre
	- 'Nana Compacta'	CSli CSpe EBee EBla ECha IGor MBel NBir NCGa SPlb SPoG SUsu WCFE WFar WHil WWEG
	- 'Perry's White'	CBcs CBre EBee ECha LRHS MNFA MNrw NGHP NGdn NHol SRGP WCot
	- 'Stephanie Cohen'	see *A. sibirica* 'Stephanie Cohen'
N	- The Pearl Group seed-raised (d)	CTri ELan LAst NVic SPlb SPoG SWat WFar WMoo WPer WTin
N	- - 'Boule de Neige' (clonal) (d)	EPfP GKir MBri MRav NBre NCob NPer NSti SPer SPet WFar
N	- - 'The Pearl' (clonal) (d) ♀H4	Widely available
§	- 'Unschuld'	NBir
	- 'Weihenstephan'	EBee
	'Rougham Bright Star'	CSli
	'Rougham Salmon'	CSli
	'Ruby Wine'	CSli
§	***salicifolia***	CSli SPav WFar
	- 'Silver Spray'	EBee GQue NBre NLar SDnm SPav WPtf
	'Sally'	EPPr
	Salmon Beauty	see *A.* 'Lachsschönheit'
	'Sandstone'	see *A.* 'Wesersandstein'
§	'Schwefelblüte'	MRav NBir SBch SMrm
	'Schwellenburg'	CDes CHar CSli EBee NBre WPGP
	sibirica	SRGP
	- subsp. ***camschatica***	WPtf
	- - 'Love Parade'	CSli EAEE EBee EPfP IFro IPot ITim LBMP LRHS MBNS MMuc MNFA MRav NBPC NGdn SAga SGSe SPer SRGP SSvw WFar WMoo WWEG
§	- 'Stephanie Cohen'	CPrp EBee ECtt GBin MBel NBhm NGdn WFar WWEG
	'Stephanie'	ECtt EPPr EWes LSRN NBre
	Summer Pastels Group	GKir IFro LLWG LRHS MNHC NBir NHol NOrc SBch SPav SPoG SRms SWal WClo WFar WHil
	'Summerwine' ♀H4	Widely available
	'Sunbeam'	CSli SHar
I	'Taygetea'	CSam CSli EBee EBla ELan EPfP EShb LRHS MBNS SDix SPer SPet WCAu WFar WKif WPer WSHC WWEG
	'Terracotta'	Widely available
	'The Beacon'	see *A.* 'Fanal'
	'Tissington Old Rose'	MAvo SUsu
	tomentosa ♀H4	CTri ECha ECho ECtt EPfP
§	- 'Aurea'	EBla ECho MSCN NBlu NBre NBro
	- 'Maynard's Gold'	see *A. tomentosa* 'Aurea'
	'Tri-colour' **new**	NGdn
§	***umbellata***	EBee WBrk
	- 'Weston'	see *A.* × *kolbiana* 'Weston'
	'Velour' **new**	WCAu
	'W.B. Childs'	CSli CSpe ECha ELan GBuc MCot MNrw SHar
	'Walther Funcke'	Widely available
§	'Wesersandstein'	CFir CHar CSli CWCL EBee ECtt EPPr EShb GMaP LRHS MAvo MBel NBir NPro SAga STes WCot WFar WPer WWEG
	'Wilczekii'	NBre NChi SRms
	'Yellowstone'	EBee EWes LAst LDai

× *Achimenantha* (*Gesneriaceae*)

'Aries'	WDib
'Inferno' ♀H1	EABi WDib
'Tyche'	EABi

Achimenes (*Gesneriaceae*)

'Ambroise Verschaffelt' ♀H1	EABi LAma WDib
'Blue David'	EABi
'Blue Sparkles'	EBrs
'Boy David'	EABi
'Cattleya'	LAma
'Charity'	WDib
'Clouded Yellow'	EABi
'Coral Cameo Mix'	EABi
'Cornell Favourite' **new**	EABi
'Crummock Water'	WDib
'Derwentwater'	EABi
'Donna'	EABi
'Dot'	EABi
'English Waltz'	EABi
erecta	WDib
'Extravaganza'	WDib
'Glory'	WDib
grandiflora 'Robert Dressler'	EABi
'Harry Williams'	LAma WDib
'Hilda Michelssen' ♀H1	WDib
'India'	EShb
'Jennifer Goode'	EABi
'Jubilee Gem'	EABi
'Just Divine'	EABi
'Kim Blue'	WDib

'Little Beauty' WDib
longiflora EABi
'Luneberg' EABi
'Maxima' LAma
'Mozelle' EABi
'Orange Delight' WDib
(Palette Series) 'Palette Mix Lilac' EABi
- 'Palette Mix Red Dwarf' EABi
- 'Palette Mix Salmon' EABi
- 'Palette Mix White' EABi
- 'Palette Red Mix' EABi
'Patens Major' WDib
'Peach Blossom' EBrs LAma
'Pearly Queen' EABi
'Pink Beauty' EABi
'Pink Rose' (d) **new** EABi
'Platinum' EABi
I 'Purple Hybrid' EABi
'Purple King' SWal
'Rainbow' **new** WDib
'Red Giant' EABi
'Rose Dream' EABi
'Stan's Delight' (d) ♀H1 EABi WDib
'Summer Sunset' EABi
'Tarantella' EABi WDib
'Teresa' EABi
(Tetra Series) 'Tetra Verschaffelt' EABi
- 'Tetra Wine Red Charm' EABi
'Trailing Yellow' EABi
'Vivid' EABi
'Weinrot Elfe' WDib
'Wetterflow's Triumph' EABi WDib
'Yellow Beauty' WDib

Achlys (*Berberidaceae*)

japonica GEdr WCru
triphylla GGar WCru

Achnatherum see *Stipa*

Achyranthes (*Amaranthaceae*)

bidentata CArn

Acidanthera see *Gladiolus*

Acinos (*Lamiaceae*)

§ ***alpinus*** CArn CPBP EAlp EAro EDAr EPot GJos GPWP LLHF LRHS SBch WJek
§ ***arvensis*** MHer
§ ***corsicus*** NMen NWCA WHoo WKif

Aciphylla (*Apiaceae*)

aurea EBee GBin GCal NLar NWCA SMad SPlb
dieffenbachii CWit GKev ITim
ferox **new** GBin
glaucescens ECou GAbr GBin NLar SMad
kirkii GBin
monroi LLHF
pinnatifida GGar
scott-thomsonii GBin
squarrosa CTrC
subflabellata ECou

Acis ✿ (*Amaryllidaceae*)

§ ***autumnalis*** ♀H4 Widely available
- 'Cobb's Variety' EBee ECho WCot
- var. ***oporantha*** CSsd CStu CWCL ERos SMrm
- - from Morocco ECho
- var. ***pulchella*** EBrs ECho ERos GKev
§ ***longifolia*** ECho ERos
nicaeensis ♀H2-3 CPBP CStu EBrs EBur ECho EPot ERos ITim LRHS MAsh MTho SCnR WAbe WCom WCot
§ ***rosea*** CStu EBur ECho ERos NMen NWCA SCnR WAbe
§ ***tingitana*** CBro EBrs ECho WCot
- SB&L 203 WCot
§ ***trichophylla*** EBrs ECho LLHF SCnR WCot
- f. ***purpurascens*** EBrs ECho WCot
* - var. ***rosea*** ECho
§ ***valentina*** CBro CPBP EBrs ECho EPot SCnR SRot WCot

Acmella (*Asteraceae*)

§ ***oleracea*** CArn EOHP SCoo

Acmena (*Myrtaceae*)

smithii EShb

Acnistus (*Solanaceae*)

australis see *Iochroma australe*

Acoelorrhaphe (*Arecaceae*)

wrightii EAmu

Aconitum (*Ranunculaceae*)

ACE 1449 GBuc
B&SWJ 2954 from Nepal WCru
CNDS 036 from Burma WCru
GWJ 9393 from northern India WCru
GWJ 9417 from northern India WCru
SDR 4842 EBee
SDR 4912 EBee GKev
SDR 4948 EBee GKev
SDR 5171 GKev
alboviolaceum GCal
- var. ***alboviolaceum*** f. ***albiflorum*** B&SWJ 4105 WCru
- - B&SWJ 8444 WCru
altissimum see *A. lycoctonum* subsp. *vulparia*
anglicum see *A. napellus* subsp. *napellus* Anglicum Group
§ ***anthora*** EBee EPfP SMrm
arcuatum see *A. fischeri* var. *arcuatum*
austroyunnanense EBee
- BWJ 7902 WCru
autumnale misapplied see *A. carmichaelii* Wilsonii Group
autumnale Rchb. see *A. fischeri* Rchb.
× ***bicolor*** see *A.* × *cammarum* 'Bicolor'
'Blue Opal' CDes EBee ECtt EWes WPGP
'Blue Sceptre' EBee GBin LDai MBri NLar NMoo
brachypodum **new** GKev
'Bressingham Spire' ♀H4 EBee ECtt EHrv ELan ELon EPfP EShb GAbr GCra GKir GMaP LAst LRHS MAvo MBri MCot MRav MWat NBPC NCGa NOrc NPer SMrm SPer SRms WCAu WMoo WWEG
§ × ***cammarum*** 'Bicolor' ♀H4 Widely available
- 'Eleanora' CFir EBee ECtt EPPr EWTr EWes GBuc GCra LHop LSou MBri MDun NBPC NGHP NGdn NLar NMoo NSti SPer WCot WMoo WWEG
- 'Grandiflorum Album' CAby LPla
- 'Pink Sensation' CAby EBee ECtt GBin LLHF MBNS NBPC NBre NGHP NLar NSti SPoG WSpi WWEG

§ ***carmichaelii*** CArn CBot CMea CSam EBee GKir IFoB IFro LAst LRHS LSou MBri MMuc NBro NChi NEgg NOrc SPoG SRms WCot WFar WHoo WHrl WTin
- Arendsii Group CAby ECtt LAst LRHS SRot
- - 'Arendsii' ♀H4 Widely available
- 'Blue Bishop' LSou
- 'Redleaf'PBR see *A. carmichaelii* 'Royal Flush'
- 'River Arrow' **new** WCot
- 'River Lugg' **new** WCot
- 'River Lune' **new** WCot
- 'River Nene' **new** WCot
- 'River Ouse' **new** WCot
- 'River Tees' **new** WCot
- 'River Trent' **new** WCot
§ - 'Royal Flush'PBR CMil CWGN EBee MBNS NCob NGdn NLar WCot
- var. ***truppelianum*** HWJ 732 WCru
§ - Wilsonii Group CPrp EBee GGar GKir GMaP LRHS MBel MCot MRav MWat NEgg SPhx WFar WPGP WPer
- - 'Barker's Variety' CFir CKno EBee ECtt ELon EPfP GBuc GCal GMac LPio NHol NLar NSti SMrm WCot
- - 'Kelmscott' ♀H4 EBee ECtt EWes MCot MRav SAga SDix SMrm SSvw WFar WRHF WSpi
- - 'Spätlese' CAbP CWGN EBee ECtt ELon EPfP GCal LHop MCot MNFA NBir NGdn SAga SMrm SPer STes SUsu WCot WWEG
chiisanense B&SWJ 4446 WCru
chrysotrichum SDR 2926 **new** EBee
cilicicum see *Eranthis hyemalis* Cilicica Group
'Cloudy' CPrp MSCN NBPC NGdn SPer
compactum see *A. napellus* subsp. *vulgare*
confertiflorum see *A. anthora*
elwesii EBee LRHS NBre
episcopale WCru WFar
aff. ***episcopale*** WSHC
- CLD 1426 GBuc WFar
excelsum see *A. lycoctonum* subsp. *lycoctonum*
ferox EBee ELon EWes GAuc GBin MBel
- HWJK 2217 WCru
fischeri misapplied see *A. carmichaelii*
§ ***fischeri*** Rchb. CSpe CWib NCGa NMoo SAga
- B&SWJ 8809 WCru
§ - var. ***arcuatum*** B&SWJ 774 WCru
formosanum LEdu
- B&SWJ 3057 WCru
forrestii **new** EBee GKev
fukutomei MRav NBre
- B&SWJ 337 WCru
gammiei GWJ 9418 WCru
gmelinii see *A. lycoctonum* subsp. *lycoctonum*
grossedentatum EBee GBin
§ ***hemsleyanum*** CBgR CBot CPLG CPrp CRHN CWGN EBee ECtt EPfP GCra GKev MDun NBid NGHP NHol SGSe WBrE WCru WFar
hyemale see *Eranthis hyemalis*
'Ivorine' CBgR CBot CElw CRow CTri EBee ECha ECtt ELan EPPr EPfP GBBs GBuc GCra GGar GMaP LAst LBMP LRHS LSRN MAvo MCot NSti SPer WCAu WFar WPnP WSpi WTin WWEG
jaluense B&SWJ 8741 WCru
japonicum EBee GCal LRHS WCon WFar
- var. ***hakonense*** EBee
- var. ***montanum*** B&SWJ 5507 **new** WCru
§ - subsp. ***napiforme*** EBee EWes SAga WPGP
- - B&SWJ 943 ELon SMeo WCru
§ - subsp. ***subcuneatum*** B&SWJ 6228 WCru
kusnezoffii EBee
laciniatum GWJ 9254 WCru
lamarckii see *A. lycoctonum* subsp. *neapolitanum*
lasianthum see *A. lycoctonum* subsp. *vulparia*
longecassidatum B&SWJ 4277 WCru
- B&SWJ 8486 WCru
- B&SWJ 8488 WCru
lycoctonum GKir NLar SRms
- 'Darkeyes' CAbP CFir EBee LOck LRHS LSou NCob NGdn WCot
§ - subsp. ***lycoctonum*** GAuc SRms
§ - subsp. ***neapolitanum*** EBee ECtt ELan EPfP EWTr GCal GKir GMaP MBel MMuc NBPC NGHP NGdn NLar SPoG WFar WSpi WWEG
- 'Russian Yellow' EWld GCal
§ - subsp. ***vulparia*** CArn CPrp CSam EBee GAuc GKev GMac GPoy LPio LRHS MNFA MRav NEgg WAul WPer
mairei see *A. vilmorinianum*
nagarum BWJ 7644 WCru
napellus CArn CMHG CPrp CSpe EBee ECtt GAbr GBar GGar GKir GPoy LAst LEdu LRHS MCot NEgg NGHP SPet SRms SWat WBor WFar WHoo WMoo WShi WWEG
- 'Bergfürst' CAby CMea EBrs LRHS MBri SPhx
- 'Blue Valley' CSpe EBee ECtt EPfP EWes LRHS MSCN NCGa NPro WFar
- subsp. ***napellus*** LEdu
§ - - Anglicum Group CRow CSev CWan MCot NLar SMac WCot WPen WSpi
- 'Rubellum' EBee ELan EPfP LAst NBir NBro NEgg NPri SMrm SPur WCAu WMnd WSpi
- 'Schneewittchen' EBee EWes SSvw
- 'Sphere's Variety' NOrc
§ - subsp. ***vulgare*** WFar
- - 'Albidum' CPrp EBee EHrv ELan ELon EPfP GAbr GMaP LEdu LRHS MCot NBid NGHP NHol NLar NPri SPer SPet WAul WBrE WFar
- - 'Carneum' GCra LRHS MBel WFar WHer WKif
napiforme see *A. japonicum* subsp. *napiforme*
neapolitanum see *A. lycoctonum* subsp. *neapolitanum*
'Newry Blue' CMea CSam EBee ELan GBuc MWhi NBir NHol NLar SGar SRms WFar WPer WWEG
orientale misapplied see *A. lycoctonum* subsp. *vulparia*
orientale ambig. NPro
paniculatum see *A. variegatum* subsp. *paniculatum*
piepunense GKev
'Pink Sensation'PBR CFir ECtt EKen EPfP EWTr GQue IPot LLWG NLar
proliferum B&SWJ 4107 WCru
pseudohuiliense CPLG
pseudolaeve B&SWJ 8663 WCru
- var. ***erectum*** B&SWJ 8466 WCru

	pyramidale	see *A. napellus* subsp. *vulgare*
	pyrenaicum	see *A. lycoctonum* subsp. *neapolitanum*
	ranunculifolius	see *A. lycoctonum* subsp. *neapolitanum*
	sachalinense new	LLHF
	seoulense B&SWJ 694	WCru
	- B&SWJ 864	WCru
	septentrionale	see *A. lycoctonum* subsp. *lycoctonum*
	'Spark's Variety' ♀H4	Widely available
	spicatum	GKir
	- GWJ 9418	WCru
	'Stainless Steel'	Widely available
	subcuneatum	see *A. japonicum* subsp. *subcuneatum*
	tanguticum new	GKev
	× ***tubergenii***	see *Eranthis hyemalis* Tubergenii Group
	uchiyamae	EPPr NLar
	- B&SWJ 1005	WCru
	- B&SWJ 1216	ELon WCru
	variegatum	EBee
§	- subsp. ***paniculatum***	EBee MBri NBre WCot
	- - 'Roseum'	EBee WFar
§	***vilmorinianum*** BWJ 8055	WCru
	volubile misapplied	see *A. hemsleyanum*
	volubile Pall.	CFir EBee GCal
	vulparia	see *A. lycoctonum* subsp. *vulparia*
	yamazakii	WCru
	yezoense	GCal

Aconogonon see *Persicaria*

Acorus ✿ (*Acoraceae*)

	calamus	CArn CBen CRow CWat EHon ELau EMFW GKir GPoy LPBA MCCP MSKA NPer SWat WHer
	- subsp. ***angustatus*** new	GPoy
	- 'Argenteostriatus' (v)	CBen CRow CWat EBee ECha ECtt EHon EMFW LPBA NOrc SWat WMAq
*	***christophii***	EBee ELon EPPr EWes SApp WMoo
	gramineus	ELau LPBA MSKA NPer SWat WHer WMoo WTin
	- 'Golden Delight'	CKno SGSe
	- 'Golden Edge' (v)	EBee NHol WMoo WRHF
	- 'Hakuro-nishiki' (v)	EBee ECtt EHoe EHul EOrn EPPr EShb GBuc GKev GKir IFFs LPBA LRHS MBar MCCP MGos MMoz NBid NHol SBch SGSe SRms SWvt WMoo
	- 'Kinchinjunga' (v)	IFro
	- 'Licorice'	EAlp EBee EPPr GCal MBNS MDKP NHol WCHb WGrn WMoo WPnP
	- 'Masamune' (v)	EBee EPla EWes GBin GCal IFro MSCN NHol SApp WMoo WPat WTin
	- 'Minimus Aureus'	CBre GCal LBMP
	- 'Oborozuki' misapplied	see *A. gramineus* 'Ogon'
	- 'Oborozuki' (v)	CKno EBee EHoe EPla SMrm
§	- 'Ogon' (v)	Widely available
	- 'Omogo'	EBee
	- var. ***pusillus***	EBee EPla NBro WWEG
	- 'Variegatus' (v)	Widely available
	- 'Yodo-no-yuki' (v)	EBee EPla IFro
	'Intermedius'	NPer

Acradenia (*Rutaceae*)

	frankliniae	CBcs CCCN CMHG CMac CPne CTrC CTrG CTsd EBee EWTr GGar GKir IDee SEND WFar WPGP WSHC

Actaea (*Ranunculaceae*)

	alba misapplied	see *A. pachypoda*, *A. rubra* f. *neglecta*
	arizonica	CLAP EBee EBrs GCal WCru
	asiatica	CLAP EBee WPGP
	- B&SWJ 616	WCru
	- B&SWJ 6351 from Japan	WCru
	- B&SWJ 8694 from Korea	WCru
	- BWJ 8174 from China	WCru
	biternata	CLAP
	- B&SWJ 5591	WCru
	- B&SWJ 11190	WCru
§	***cimicifuga***	CDes CLAP EBee GCal GPoy
	- B&SWJ 2657	WCru
§	***cordifolia***	EBee GBin GMaP LPBA LRHS MBel NBPC SMrm WBor
	- 'Blickfang'	CLAP
	dahurica	EBee GKir LRHS NLar SWat
	- B&SWJ 8426	WCru
	- B&SWJ 8573	WCru
	- B&SWJ 8653	GEdr
	- tall	GCal
	erythrocarpa	see *A. rubra*
	europaea	EBee GCal SPhx
	frigida B&SWJ 2966	WCru
	heracleifolia B&SWJ 8843	WCru
§	***japonica***	CLAP CRow GCal LRHS WCot WFar
	- B&SWJ 11136	WCru
	- B&SWJ 5828	WCru
	- var. ***acutiloba*** B&SWJ 6257	WCru
	- compact	GBin
	- - B&SWJ 8758A	WCru
I	- 'Minima' new	LRHS
	mairei	LRHS
	- ACE 2374	WCot
	- BWJ 7635	WCru
	- BWJ 7939	WCru
§	***matsumurae***	CPLG
	- 'Elstead Variety' ♀H4	CPLG CRow GCal MBri MRav NBre
	- 'Frau Herms'	CLAP LRHS
	- 'White Pearl'	CRow EBee EBrs ECha EHrv ELan EPfP GAbr GGar GMaP LHop LRHS MBel MBri MRav NBPC NCGa NGdn NSti SMad SPer SPoG WCAu WFar WMnd WMoo WPGP WWEG
§	***pachypoda*** ♀H4	CBro COld EBee ECGP ECha EPfP EWTr GBBs GBuc GCal GGar GKev GKir GPoy IGor MCot NBid NLar SMad WBVN WCru
	- f. ***rubrocarpa***	GCal
§	***podocarpa***	SPlb SRms WCru
	racemosa ♀H4	CArn CMac COld CRow CSam EBee ELan EPfP EWTr GCal GPoy LFur LRHS MBel MHer MRav NBid NGdn NSti SPer WCAu WFar WMnd
§	***rubra*** ♀H4	CBro CHid CMHG EBee ECha ELan EWTr GBBs GBuc GCal GGar GKir MCot MMHG MRav NBid SMad WCru WFar WPGP
	- B&SWJ 9555	WCru
	- ***alba***	see *A. pachypoda*, *A. rubra* f. *neglecta*
§	- f. ***neglecta***	CDes EBee GAbr GBuc GCal GGar NLar WCru
	simplex	CBot CSam EBee ECha GCra GKir LRHS NEgg NPri SWat
	- B&SWJ 8664	WCru
§	- Atropurpurea Group	Widely available
	- - 'Bernard Mitchell'	CFir
	- - 'Black Negligee'	CSpe EBee ECtt NBhm NLar WCot

- - 'Brunette' ♀H4	Widely available
- - 'Hillside Black Beauty'	CCVN CLAP EBee ECtt GMaP IPot LHop MBel MNrw NBir NCob WBor WCAu
- - 'James Compton'	Widely available
- - 'Mountain Wave'	CLAP EBee ECtt EWll IPot WFar
- 'Pink Spike'	Widely available
§ - 'Prichard's Giant'	CLAP EBee EBrs ECha GBin GBuc GKir LRHS MBri MRav MSpe WFar
- ramosa	see *A. simplex* 'Prichard's Giant'
- 'Scimitar'	SMeo
- 'Silver Axe'	GCal LRHS NBre
- variegated (v)	CDes WCot
spicata	COld EBee EWTr GBin GBuc GCra GEdr GKir GPoy NLar WCot WCru
- from England	GCal WCru
taiwanensis	CLAP
- B&SWJ 343	CLAP
- B&SWJ 3413	WCru
- RWJ 9996	WCru
yesoensis	GCal
- B&SWJ 6355	WCru
yunnanensis	EBee GCal
- ACE 1880	GBuc

Actinella see *Tetraneuris*

Actinidia (*Actinidiaceae*)

BWJ 8161 from China	WCru
arguta (f/F)	CAgr EMui NLar WPGP
- (m)	EMui
- B&SWJ 569	WCru
- 74-32 (m) **new**	CAgr
- 'Ananasnaya' (f/F) **new**	CAgr
- var. ***cordifolia*** (f/F) **new**	CAgr
- 'Geneva 2' (f/F) **new**	CAgr
- 'Issai' (s-p/F)	CAgr CBcs CCCN CDul EMui EPfP ERea LBuc LSRN MGos NLar
- 'Ken's Red' (F) **new**	CAgr
- 'Kiwai Vert' (f/F)	CAgr
- LL#1 (m)	CAgr
- LL#2 (f/F)	CAgr
- LL#3 (m)	CAgr
- 'Meader' (m) **new**	CAgr
- 'Shoko' (F)	WCru
- 'Unchae' (F)	WCru
- 'Weiki'	MGos
chinensis misapplied	see *A. deliciosa*
§ ***deliciosa***	ERom MGos SBch WFar WSHC
- 'Atlas' (m)	CAgr ERea MREP NLar WBVN
* - 'Boskoop'	ELan LBMP MGos MWat
- 'Hayward' (f/F)	CAgr CBcs CCCN CDoC CHEx EBee EMui EPfP ERea LHop LRHS LSRN MCoo MREP NLar NPal SDea SPer SWvt WBVN WFar
- hermaphrodite (F) **new**	SBch
- 'Jenny' (s-p/F)	CAgr CSut CTri EMui ERea IMon LAst LBuc LRHS MAsh MBri MCoo MGos SBch SDea SLim SPoG SVic WBVN
- 'Solo'	CCCN CDoC ECrN EPfP LBuc LRHS LSRN MBri MCoo MREP NLar NPri SBch SEND SPer SPoG WPGP
- 'Tomuri' (m)	CBcs CCCN CDoC CHEx EBee EMui EPfP ERea LRHS LSRN NLar NPal SPer SWvt
hypoleuca B&SWJ 5942	WCru
kolomikta ♀H4	Widely available
- (m)	CAgr MBlu NScw
- B&SWJ 4243	WCru
- 'MSU' (F) **new**	CAgr
- 'Red Beauty' (F) **new**	CAgr
- 'Tomoko' (F)	WCru
- 'Yazuaki' (m)	WCru
latifolia B&SWJ 3563	WCru
petelotii HWJ 628	WCru
pilosula	CBcs CCCN CPLG CSPN CWGN EBee EPfP EWTr GCal GGal GKir LEdu LHop LRHS LSRN MAsh MBri MGos SCoo SPoG WCru WPGP WSHC
polygama (F)	EWld GCal IDee
- B&SWJ 5444	WCru
- B&SWJ 8525 from Korea	WCru
- B&SWJ 8923 from Japan	WCru
purpurea (f/F)	CAgr
rufa B&SWJ 3525	WCru
aff. ***strigosa*** HWJK 2367	WCru
tetramera B&SWJ 3564	WCru

Adansonia (*Bombacaceae*)

gregorii	SPlb

Adelocaryum see *Lindelofia*

Adenium (*Apocynaceae*)

obesum 'Petra Pink'	LRHS
- 'Scooby' PBR	LRHS

Adenocarpus (*Papilionaceae*)

complicatus	SEND
decorticans	SPlb

Adenophora (*Campanulaceae*)

BWJ 7696 from China	WCru
'Afterglow'	see *Campanula rapunculoides* 'Afterglow'
asiatica	see *Hanabusaya asiatica*
aurita	CFir EWTr WCot
bulleyana	CFir EBee ELan GBuc GCra GJos IKil LRHS NBid SDnm SGSe SPav SPlb WCot WFar WPer
capillaris subsp. ***leptosepala*** BWJ 7986	WCru
coelestis	NBid NBre
- ACE 2455	GBuc
- B&SWJ 7998	WCru
confusa	LDai LHop MDKP NBre SAga SPav WFar WHer WSHC
* ***cymerae***	LDai
divaricata	WFoF
forrestii	NBre WFar
grandiflora B&SWJ 8555	WCru
jasionifolia BWJ 7946	WCru
khasiana	LLHF MDKP NLar WPrP
koreana	NBre SPav
lamarkii B&SWJ 8738	WCru
latifolia misapplied	see *A. pereskiifolia*
latifolia Fischer	WFar
latifolia ambig. white-flowered	MMuc
liliifolia	CMoH ECtt ELan GCal GGar GJos LBMP NPer SMad SPav WFar WHal
morrisonensis RWJ 10008	WCru
§ ***nikoensis***	GAuc NBid
§ - var. ***stenophylla***	NBre
nipponica	see *A. nikoensis* var. *stenophylla*
§ ***pereskiifolia***	CBrd EBee EWes GKev NBre SGSe SHar SPlb WCot WPer
polyantha	CHar EHrv GBuc NLar SBod SRms WFar
polymorpha	see *A. nikoensis*
potaninii	CFir EBee EHrv ELan GBuc SEND SPav WCHb WFar WHal WWEG
- pale-flowered	EHrv WHal

	remotiflora B&SWJ 11016	WCru
	- B&SWJ 8562	WCru
	stricta subsp. ***sessilifolia***	GBuc NBre
	takedae var. ***howozana***	LHop MLHP
	taquetii	EBee GKev
	- B&SWJ 1303	WCru
	tashiroi	CMHG CPrp ECtt EPfP GBuc NLar WCHb
	triphylla	NBir SGSe SPav
	- B&SWJ 10916	WCru
	- var. ***hakusanensis***	LLHF NBre
	- var. ***japonica***	LDai
	- - B&SWJ 8835	WCru
	uehatae	GEdr
	- B&SWJ 126	WCru

Adenostyles see *Cacalia*

Adiantum ✿ (*Adiantaceae*)

§	***aleuticum*** ♀H4	CBcs CLAP EBee ELan EWld NBid NBro NLar WAbe WFib WPGP WRic
	- 'Imbricatum'	CBcs CBty CElw CLAP EBee ELon LRHS MAsh MGos NLar NMyG SBch SDix SPer SRms WCot WFar WFib WRic
§	- 'Japonicum'	CDes CLAP CMil EBee EFtx ELan NBir SRms WAbe WFar WHal WPGP
	- 'Laciniatum'	SRms
	- 'Miss Sharples'	CDTJ CLAP CMil EBee ELan LRHS MAsh MGos NLar SRms WFar WRic WWEG
§	- 'Subpumilum' ♀H4	CLAP EBee MRav NBid SRms WAbe WFib WRic
	bonatianum	CPLG
	capillus-veneris	CHEx SChr SGSe WCot WFib WRic
	- 'Mairisii'	see *A.* × ***mairisii***
	chilense **new**	EBee EFtx
	cuneatum	see *A. raddianum*
	fulvum	WRic
	hispidulum	CBty CCCN CMil EBee EShb LRHS SRms WRic
	- 'Bronze Venus'	CCCN EBee LRHS
§	× ***mairisii*** ♀H3	EFtx
	pedatum misapplied	see *A. aleuticum*
	pedatum ambig.	CBty EBee GKir
	pedatum L. ♀H4	CBcs CHEx CLAP ECha EFer ELan EPfP GEdr GMaP LAst LBMP LPBA LRHS MAsh MBri MMoz NMoo NVic SApp SPer SSpi SWat WFar WPGP
	- Asiatic form	see *A. aleuticum* 'Japonicum'
	- 'Japonicum'	see *A. aleuticum* 'Japonicum'
	- 'Roseum'	see *A. aleuticum* 'Japonicum'
	- var. ***subpumilum***	see *A. aleuticum* 'Subpumilum'
	pubescens	MBri WRic
§	***raddianum*** ♀H2	EFtx
	- 'Brilliantelse' ♀H2	LRHS
	- 'Fragrans'	see *A. raddianum* 'Fragrantissimum'
§	- 'Fragrantissimum'	EShb LRHS MBri
	- 'Fritz Lüthi' ♀H2	LRHS MBri
	- 'Micropinnulum'	EFtx WRic
	- 'Monocolor'	MBri
	venustum ♀H4	CGHE CHEx CLAP EBee EFer EFtx EPot MCot MWat SChr SDix SRms SSpi SWat WAbe WCom WCot WEas WFar WFib WHal WIvy WPGP WRic

Adina (*Rubiaceae*)

rubella	NLar

Adlumia (*Papaveraceae*)

fungosa	CSpe EBee GKev LBMP

Adonis (*Ranunculaceae*)

	aestivalis	MCot
	amurensis misapplied	see *A.* 'Fukujukai', *A. multiflora*
	amurensis ambig.	CMea EBee EPot LAma LLHF MBri SCnR WCot WCru WFar
	- 'Pleniflora'	see *A. multiflora* 'Sandanzaki'
	brevistyla	GBuc GKir
	'Chichibu-beni' **new**	WWst
§	'Fukujukai'	EBee ECha GEdr WFar WWst
§	***multiflora*** 'Sandanzaki' (d)	EBee EPot EWes MBri MMHG WCot
	vernalis	GKir GPoy LBMP NLar SMrm

Adoxa (*Adoxaceae*)

moschatellina	CRWN EBWF NMen WAbe WHer WSFF WShi

Adromischus (*Crassulaceae*)

cooperi	STre WCot WEas

Aechmea (*Bromeliaceae*)

sp.	XBlo
'Blue Rain'PBR **new**	LRHS
caudata var. ***variegata***	CHEx
chantinii ♀H1	LRHS
fasciata ♀H1	LRHS MBri WCor XBlo
- 'Primera'PBR **new**	LRHS
'Maya'PBR	LRHS
'Mohican' **new**	LRHS
ramosa	LRHS XBlo
'Romero'	LRHS
victoriana	XBlo

Aegle (*Rutaceae*)

sepiaria	see *Poncirus trifoliata*

Aegopodium (*Apiaceae*)

podagraria	CHid WCHb
'Dangerous' (v)	
- gold-margined (v)	EPPr
- 'Variegatum' (v)	CDoC COlW CRow EBee ECha ECrN EHoe EHrv EPPr EPla GMaP LBMP LHop LRHS MBri MRav MSCN NBid NPri NSti NVic SMac SPer SPoG WCFE WCot WHil WMoo WWEG

Aeonium (*Crassulaceae*)

	arboreum ♀H1	CAbb CDTJ CHEx CTsd ERea EShb LPio LRHS NPal SBch SMrm WCor
	- 'Albovariegatum' (v)	LPio MSCN
	- 'Atropurpureum' ♀H1	CAbb CHEx CHVG EAmu EPfP ERea EShb IDee MAsh MBri MRav NEgg NPer SBch SEND SPer SPoG SWal WCor
	- green-leaved	SEND
I	- 'Magnificum'	EBee EPfP EShb SAPC SArc
	- 'Variegatum' (v)	CBow EShb NPer
	balsamiferum	CAbb CCCN CDTJ CHEx CSpe EBee EPfP IDee SAPC SArc SBch SChr WCom
	'Black Cap'	CCCN LRHS
	'Blush'	MRav
	'Blushing Beauty'	CAbb LRHS SBst
	canariense	CBrP CCCN CDTJ CHEx LPio LRHS
	castello-paivae	EShb
	ciliatum **new**	WCor
	'Cristata Sunburst'	WCot
	cuneatum	SChr SEND SPet WCor
	decorum	SEND
*	- 'Variegatum' (v)	CBow LPio WCot
	'Dinner Plate'	CHEx CTsd
	'Dinner Plate' × ***haworthii***	CHEx

	× ***domesticum***	see *Aichryson* × *aizoides* var. *domesticum*
	gomerense	STre
	goochiae	CBow
	haworthii ♀H1	CArn CBrP CHEx LPio LRHS MSCN SBHP SEND WCor
	- 'Variegatum' (v)	EShb LPio SChr
	holochrysum Webb & Berth.	CAbb
	lindleyi	SChr
	nobile	CBrP
	percarneum	EShb
	simsii variegated (v)	EShb
	tabuliforme ♀H1	CCCN CDTJ CSpe ERea LRHS
	urbicum	CHEx
	'Zwartkop' ♀H1	Widely available

Aeschynanthus (*Gesneriaceae*)

	'Big Apple'	WDib
	Black Pagoda Group	WDib
	'Carina'	LRHS
	'Caroline'	LRHS
	'Fire Wheel'	WDib
	hildebrandii	WDib
	'Holiday Bells'	WDib
	'Hot Flash'	WDib
	longicalyx	WDib
§	***longicaulis*** ♀H1	WDib
	marmoratus	see *A. longicaulis*
	'Mona'	MBri
	'Mona Lisa'	LRHS
	radicans ♀H1	MBri WDib
	'Rasta'PBR **new**	LRHS
	'Scooby Doo'	WDib
	speciosus ♀H1	EShb WDib
	'Twister'PBR	LRHS

Aesculus ✿ (*Hippocastanaceae*)

	arguta	see *A. glabra* var. *arguta*
	× ***arnoldiana***	CDul CMCN
	- 'Autumn Splendor'	EPfP
§	× ***bushii***	CDul CMCN MGos NLar
	californica	CDul CMCN CMac EBee EPfP ERod LRHS WPGP
	× ***carnea***	CDul CTri ELan IFFs MBar
	- 'Aureomarginata' (v)	ERod LLHF SMad WHar WPat
	- 'Briotii' ♀H4	Widely available
	- 'Marginata' (v)	MBlu
	- 'Plantierensis'	CDul ECrN MBlu
*	- 'Variegata' (v)	CBcs CDul CMCN MGos
	chinensis	CMCN MBri
	'Dallimorei' (graft-chimaera)	WPat
	flava ♀H4	CCVT CMCN CTho EBee ECrN EPfP EWTr GKir LMaj MBri MMuc MWat NWea SLim SPer SSpi WFar WPGP
	- f. ***vestita***	CDoC CDul MBlu
	georgiana	see *A. sylvatica*
	glabra	CDul CMCN CTho EGFP GKir LRHS
§	- var. ***arguta***	CMCN GKir
	- 'Autumn Blaze'	EPfP MBlu MBri SMad
	- 'October Red'	EPfP MBlu MBri WPGP
	glaucescens	see *A.* × *neglecta*
	hippocastanum ♀H4	Widely available
	- 'Aureomarginata' (v)	CMac
§	- 'Baumannii' (d) ♀H4	CDoC CDul CLnd EBee ECrN ELan EPfP ERod GKir IFFs LMaj MGos MSwo NWea SPer WDin WFar
	- 'Digitata'	CDul CMCN WPat
	- 'Flore Pleno'	see *A. hippocastanum* 'Baumannii'
	- 'Hampton Court Gold'	CBcs CDoC CDul CMCN CMac
	- f. ***laciniata***	CDul CMCN ERod IArd MAsh MBlu NLar SMad WPat
	- 'Monstrosa'	MBri SMad
	- 'Wisselink'	CDul CMCN ECrN MBlu SMad
	indica	CDul CHEx CLnd CMCN CTho EBee ECrN ELan EPfP GKir IArd IFFs ISea LMaj SEND SMHT SPer SSpi WDin WPGP
	- 'Sydney Pearce' ♀H4	CDul CEnd CMCN EPfP ERod EWTr GKir MBlu MBri MGos NLar SSpi WDin WPGP
	× ***marylandica***	CDul
	× ***mississippiensis***	see *A.* × *bushii*
	× ***mutabilis*** 'Harbisonii'	NLar
	- 'Induta'	CDul CLnd CMCN EBee EPfP IArd LRHS MBri NLar NSti SDix SSpi WFar
§	- 'Penduliflora'	CDul CEnd LRHS MBlu
§	× ***neglecta***	CLnd CMCN
	- 'Autumn Fire'	LRHS MBlu MBri SPoG
	- 'Erythroblastos' ♀H4	CBcs CDul CEnd CMCN EBee EPfP ERod GKir LRHS MAsh MBlu MBri MRav NLar SBir SCoo SLim SMad SPoG SSpi SSta WDin WPGP WPat
	parviflora ♀H4	CBcs CDul CLnd CMCN CTri EBee ECrN ELan EPfP IDee IFFs LMaj LRHS MBar MBlu MBri MGos MRav NBea NEgg SLPl SLim SMad SPer SSpi SWvt WDin WFar WPGP
§	***pavia*** ♀H4	CBcs CDul CLnd CMCN CTho EPfP MBri SSpi WDin
	- 'Atrosanguinea'	CEnd CLnd CMCN EBee EPfP ERod MBlu MBri NPal
I	- 'Biltmore Buckeye' **new**	MPkF
	- var. ***discolor*** 'Koehnei'	CDul CMCN LRHS MBlu MBri NLar SPoG
	- 'Penduliflora'	see *A.* × *mutabilis* 'Penduliflora'
	- 'Purple Spring'	MBlu
	- 'Rosea Nana'	CMCN WPat
	splendens	see *A. pavia*
§	***sylvatica***	CMCN LRHS
	turbinata	CDul CMCN GKir ISea SSpi
	- var. ***pubescens***	WPGP
	wilsonii	CDul CPLG CTho WPGP

Aethionema (*Brassicaceae*)

	armenum	EDAr
	capitatum **new**	EDAr
§	***grandiflorum*** ♀H4	EPot NBro SRms WFar WPer
	- Pulchellum Group ♀H4	CSpe
	iberideum	MDKP MWat SRms
*	***kotschyi*** hort.	ECho WAbe
	membranaceum	ECho EDAr WFar
	oppositifolium	LFur MWat WHoo
	pulchellum	see *A. grandiflorum*
	schistosum	LLHF
	spicatum	WFar
	'Warley Rose' ♀H4	ECho ELan EPot GKir GMaP LHop LRHS MWat NLAp NMen SBch SIng SRms WFar
	'Warley Ruber'	CMea CPBP NBir NMen WAbe WFar

Aextoxicon (*Aextoxicaceae*)

	punctatum	EBee

Afrocarpus (*Podocarpaceae*)

	falcatus	CTrC ECou

Agapanthus ✿ (*Alliaceae*)

	from Johannesburg	ECha
	'Aberdeen'	CPne XPde
	'Adonis'	CPrp IBal IBlr

	Name	Suppliers
	'African Moon'	CPen CPne CPrp
§	***africanus*** ♀H1	CElw CWib EBee ECho EHrv ELan EPfP GAbr ISea LEdu MNHC NBlu SAPC SArc SBod SPav SPer SRot SSwd SVic SWat WBor WBrE WFar WPer WWEG
*	- 'Albus' ♀H1	CBcs CDoC CKno EBee EBrs ECho EPfP IFoB LAst LRHS LSRN NBlu SBod SEND SMeo SMrm SPav SPer WFar WGwG WPer WWEG
	'Albatross'	CPne ECha GCra
	'Albus' ambig.	CPLG ECrN GMaP LRHS MGos MHer MWat SAga SHom
I	'Albus Nanus'	ECho
	'Amsterdam'	CPen NHoy XPde
	'Angela'	CBgR CPen CPne NHoy XPde
	'Anthea'	XPde
	'Aphrodite'	IBlr
	'Apple Court'	XPde
	'Aquamarine'	CAvo CFFs NHoy SBch
	'Arctic Star'	CPLG CPne XPde
	Ardernei hybrid	CDes CPne CPrp EBee ECha ECtt EWes GCal GQue IBal IBlr LFur LPio LSou MAvo NEgg SAga SMrm SRos SUsu WCFE WClo WCot WGwG WPGP XPde
§	'Argenteus Vittatus' (v) ♀H1	CDes CPen CPne CPrp ELan EPfP LRHS NHoy WPGP
	'Atlas'	IBlr
	'Aureovittatus' (v)	IBal NHoy
	'Baby Blue'	see *A.* 'Blue Baby'
	'Back in Black'	CPne CSpe CWCL CWGN EBee ELan EPfP EWTr EWes GAbr IBal IPot LPio LRHS MBNS NBPC NCob NHoy NOrc SMrm SPer
	'Ballyrogan'	IBlr
	'Balmoral'	CPne
	'Bangor Blue'	CPrp IBal IBlr
	'Barnsley' **new**	NHoy
	'Basutoland'	EBla LRHS
	'Beatrice'	CPne XPde
	'Beeches Dwarf'	CPne ELan NHoy
	'Beloved' **new**	NHoy
	'Ben Hope'	GBuc IBal IBlr NHoy SDnm SPav WCot XPde
	'Beth Chatto'	see *A. campanulatus* 'Albovittatus'
	'Bethlehem Star'	CBgR CPne SRos
	'Bianco'	XPde
	'Bicton Bell'	CPne IBal IBlr
	'Big Blue'	EBee EPfP LRHS LSRN LSou SEND SRkn
	'Black Buddhist'	CPrp EBee ECtt EWTr EWll GBuc MSCN NBhm NGdn NHoy
	'Black Magic' **new**	CPne
	'Black Pantha' PBR	Widely available
§	'Blue Baby' Rom.	CCCN CPen CPrp ELan ELon EPfP IBal IBlr LRHS NHoy WCom WFar XPde
	'Blue Bird'	XPde
	'Blue Boy'	XPde
	'Blue Brush'	CPrp CSBt EBee IBal LRHS LSou NHoy SCoo SEND
	'Blue Cascade'	IBlr
	'Blue Companion'	CPne CPrp IBal IBlr NHoy WMnd
	'Blue Crane' **new**	EBla
	'Blue Diamond' ambig.	EBee EHrv NHoy SRos
	'Blue Dot'	CPrp EBee LBMP LRHS
	'Blue Dragon' **new**	NHoy
	'Blue Formality'	CPne IBal IBlr
	'Blue Fortune'	WWEG
	'Blue Giant'	CBcs CBro CCVN CPen CPrp EBee EPfP IBal IBlr LRHS MBri MNFA NHoy SAga SWat WCFE WFar WPGP WSpi WWEG
	'Blue Globe'	CHid CMMP EBee GMaP LAst MSCN STes WWEG
	'Blue Gown'	CPne CSam IBal
	'Blue Haze'	SRos XPde
	'Blue Heaven' PBR	CPne EBee NHoy WCot
	'Blue Ice'	CAvo CPne
	'Blue Imp'	CBro EBee GBin GBuc IBlr NHol SApp
	'Blue Lakes'	XPde
	'Blue Méoni'	XPde
	'Blue Moon'	CBro CPen CSev EBee ECha IBal IBlr LLWG LRHS LSou MCot NHoy SAga SMrm SPer WCot
	'Blue Nile'	CPne XPde
	'Blue Prince'	CPen CPrp EBee LBuc LRHS NHoy
	'Blue Ribbon'	XPde
	'Blue Skies' ambig.	NCGa NHoy XPde
I	'Blue Skies' Dunlop	IBlr
	'Blue Spear'	CPen
	'Blue Triumphator'	EBee EBrs EPfP EWTr EWll GMaP IBlr LRHS MHer NHoy NScw SMeo WWEG XPde
	'Blue Umbrella'	EBee LRHS NHoy
	'Blue Velvet'	CPne XPde
	Bluestorm = 'Atiblu' PBR	CPrp LBuc NHoy
	'Bluety' PBR	CPen NHoy
	'Bressingham Blue'	CBro CPne CPrp CTri EBrs ECho ECtt EWes GCal GKir IBal IBlr IFoB LRHS MAvo MRav NHoy NVic SWat XPde
	'Bressingham Bounty'	EBrs LRHS XPde
	'Bressingham White'	CPne EBee ECGP ECtt EHrv LEdu LRHS MBri MRav NCGa NHoy SWat XPde
	'Bristol'	XPde
	'Buckingham Palace'	CBro CDes CPrp EBee ECho EWes GAbr IBal IBlr NHoy WCot WPGP XPde
	'Cally Blue'	GAbr GCal NHoy
	'Cally Longstem' **new**	GCal
	'Cally Pale Blue' **new**	GCal
	'Cambridge'	CPne XPde
	campanulatus	CPLG CPrp CWCL EAEE EBee EBla ECho ELan EPfP IBal IBlr IGor ITim LPio LRHS MCot MRav NCob NEgg NHoy SWat WAbe WCot WFar WPGP
	- var. ***albidus***	CDes CWCL EBee ECha ECho ELan EPfP EShb GKev IBlr LHop LPio LRHS MCot NBid NGdn NHol NHoy NSti NVic SPer WFar WHoo WPGP XPde
§	- 'Albovittatus'	CPrp CSam EBee ECho EWTr IBal LPio MCot NHoy
	- 'Beth Chatto' (v)	CPrp EBla IBal
	- bright blue-flowered	CWCL GCal
	- 'Buckland'	IBlr
	- 'Cobalt Blue'	CPrp EBee LRHS NGdn NHoy
	- dark blue-flowered	XPde
	- 'Oxford Blue'	CPen CPrp EBrs ECGP GBuc IBal IBlr LRHS NHoy SRos WPGP XPde
	- subsp. ***patens*** ♀H3	CPrp EBee EBla EPfP GBuc IBal LPio SWat WPGP
	- - deep blue-flowered	CFir CPrp IBlr LRHS NHoy XPde
	- 'Profusion'	CBro EBrs ECha IBal IBlr LRHS NHoy SRos WFar XPde
	- variegated (v)	EBla ECha NPer
	- 'Wedgwood Blue'	CPrp EBee EBrs IBal IBlr LRHS NHoy SRos XPde

	Plant	Suppliers
	- 'Wendy'	CPne CPrp IBal IBlr LRHS NHoy XPde
	- 'White Hope'	IBal IBlr SRos
	'Carefree'	CPrp IBal
	'Castle of Mey'	CBro CPne CPrp EBee GAbr GBuc IBal IBlr LPio LPla LRHS MTho NHoy SPav SRos WPGP XPde
	'Catharina'	CPne XPde
§	***caulescens*** ♀H1	EBee EBrs GBuc IBal IBlr IGor WPGP XPde
	- subsp. ***angustifolius***	CPne IBlr SPer WCot WPGP
	- subsp. ***caulescens***	CPne IBlr SWat
	- 'Nigel Marshall' **new**	GCal
	'Cedric Morris'	IBlr LPio NHoy SRos XPde
	'Chandra'	IBlr
	'Charlotte'PBR	EBee IBal LRHS NHoy XPde
	'Cherry Holley'	CPne SRos XPde
	'Clarence House'	CBro CPne XPde
	coddii	CPLG EWes IBlr WCot WHil XPde
	'Columba'	CPen CPne CPrp EBee IBal LAma LDai NBid NHoy XPde
	comptonii	see *A. praecox* subsp. *minimus*
	'Congratulations' **new**	NHoy
	'Cool Blue'	CPne XPde
	'Corina'	EBee
	'Cornish Sky'	CPne
	'Crystal Drop'	CBgR CPne SWat
	'Dainty Lady'	NHoy
	Danube	see *A.* 'Donau'
	'Dark Star'	WFar
	'Dartmoor'	CPne
	'Davos'	IPot
	'Dawn Star'	XPde
	'Debbie'	XPde
	'Delft'	CPrp IBal IBlr
	Dell Garden hybrids **new**	LRHS
	'Density'	IBlr
	'Devon Dawn'	CPne
	'Diana'	XPde
	'Dnjepr'	XPde
	'Dokter Brouwer'	CCVN CPen CPne EBee IBal IKil LRHS LSRN MCot MDKP NBid NHoy WGwG XPde
§	'Donau'	CBro CDoC CPen EBee EBrs EShb IBal LAst LSou NBid NBir NHoy NOrc SWat WFar XPde
	'Dorothy Kate'	CPne
	'Double Diamond'	CPen CPne NHoy
	'Dream' **new**	NHoy
	'Dublin'	CPne
	'Duivenbrugge Blue'	CPne XPde
	'Duivenbrugge White'	XPde
	dyeri	see *A. inapertus* subsp. *intermedius*
	'Ed Carman' (v)	WCot
	'Elisabeth'	CPne XPde
	'Enigma'	CAbb CPar CPen CPne CWGN EBee EKen EShb IBal LRHS LSRN LSou NHoy SBch SRkn SWat
	'Essence of Summer'	WCot
	'Ethel's Joy'	CPen
	'Eve'	IBlr XPde
	'Evening Star'	CPne ECha LRHS XPde
	'Exmoor'	CPne
	'Farncombe'	NCot
	'Fast Track'	WCot
	'Findlay's Blue'	GBuc WHil WPGP
	'Finnline' (v)	CPne CPrp
	'Flanders Giant'	XPde
	'Flore Pleno' (d)	CDes CDoC CPne CPrp CWGN EBee ECha EHrv ELan IBal IBlr LRHS LSou NBPC NCob NEgg NGdn NHoy NLar SMrm SPoG WCot WFar WKif WPGP WPrP XPde

	Plant	Suppliers
	'Forget-me-not' **new**	NHoy
	'Gayle's Lilac'	CBcs CBro CElw CPne CPrp CSam CWGN EBee ECtt ELan IBal LPio LRHS LSRN LSou MBel MRav NBPC NCGa NCob NHoy NSti SApp SBch SDnm SPav SPoG WCot WWEG
	'Gem'	CPne
	'Getty White'	GBin
I	'Giganteus Albus'	CPne XPde
	'Glacier Stream'	CBro CCVN CPen EBee ECtt EHrv IKil NHoy WSpi
	'Glen Avon'	CAbb CBro CFir CPne CPrp EBee EMil IBal LRHS LSRN NBPC NHoy NLar SApp SCoo SEND WSpi XPde
	'Golden Rule' (v)	CBow CDes CPrp EBee EHoe GBuc IBal IBlr WPGP XPde
	'Grey Ruler'	WCot
	'Happy Birthday' **new**	NHoy
	'Harvest Blue'	CPne XPde
§	Headbourne hybrids	Widely available
	- dark blue-flowered **new**	LRHS
	- dwarf	LRHS
	'Heavenly Blue'	CPne
	'Helen'	IBlr
	'Holbeach'	CPen CPne XPde
	'Holbrook'	CSam XPde
	'Holly Ann' **new**	NHoy
	'Hoyland' **new**	NHoy
	'Hyacinth' **new**	NHoy
	'Hydon Mist'	XPde
	'Ice Blue Star'	SRos XPde
	'Ice Lolly'	CBro CPen EBee EWTr IKil XPde
	inapertus	CAvo CBro CPLG CPrp CSpe EWes GGal IGor LPio MHer SMrm SWat WCot WPGP XPde
	- dwarf	IBlr
	- subsp. ***hollandii***	CPne CSpe EBee GCal IBal IBlr MAvo NHoy SWat WCot XPde
	- - 'Zealot'	IBlr
	- subsp. ***inapertus***	IBlr SWat WCot
I	- - 'Albus'	IBlr
	- - 'Cyan'	IBlr
	- - 'White'	CPne
§	- subsp. ***intermedius***	CBgR CBro CPne CPrp IBal IBlr NHoy SWat WCot
	- - white-flowered **new**	CPen
	- 'Midnight Cascade'	CPne NHoy SUsu SWat
	- 'Nigrescens' **new**	WCot
	- subsp. ***parviflorus***	IBlr
	- subsp. ***pendulus***	CDes CFir CPne EBrs GCal IBlr IPot WPGP
	- - 'Graskop'	CBgR CPne EBee IBlr LSou SGSe
	- - 'Violet Dusk'	IBlr
	- 'Sapphire Cascade' **new**	SWat
	'Innocence'	IBlr
I	'Intermedius' van Tubergen	EBee NBid
	'Intermedius' Leichtlin	IBal XPde
	'Isis'	CAvo CBro CFir CPrp CSam CTri EBee EBla EBrs ECha GBuc IBal IBlr LRHS NHoy SRos XPde
	'Jack Elliott'	SMeo
	'Jack's Blue'	Widely available
	'Jersey Giant'	IBal NHoy XPde
	'Jodie'	CPne XPde
	'Johanna'	CPne EBee XPde
	'Jolanda'	CPne
	'K. Wiley'	SUsu
	'Kew White'	SDix

	Name	Suppliers
	'Kingston Blue'	CPrp EBee ECha EHrv IBal IBlr LSou NBid NHoy SRGP WFar WPrP WSHC WWEG XPde
	'Kirsty'	CPne
	'Kobold'	CPne NHoy WFar
	'Lady Edith'	IBlr
§	'Lady Grey'	IBlr
	'Lady Moore'	IBlr IGor XPde
	'Lady Wimborne'	CPne
	'Latent Blue'	IBlr
	'Lavender Haze'	CPen CPne EBee EPfP IBal LRHS LSou MBri NHoy
	'Leicester'	XPde
	'Liam's Lilac' **new**	CPen CPne
	'Lilac Bells'	CPne
	'Lilac Flash' **new**	CPne
	'Lilac Time'	CPen CPne IBlr XPde
	'Lilliput'	Widely available
	'Limoges'	XPde
	'Little Beauty' **new**	NHoy
	'Little Diamond'	LRHS
	'Loch Hope' ♀H3	CBro CDoC CPne CPrp CSam EBrs GAbr GGar IBal IGor LAst LRHS LSou MRav NCob NHoy SApp SPav SRos WCot WHoo WSpi XPde
	'Lowland Nursery'	XPde
	'Luly'	CPne CPrp IBal LRHS NHoy SWat XPde
	'Lydenburg'	CPen IBal IBlr
	'Lyn Valley'	CPne
	'Mabel Grey'	see *A.* 'Lady Grey'
	'Magnifico'	CPrp IBal IBlr
	'Malaga'	XPde
	'Malvern Hills'	XPde
	'Margaret' **new**	NHoy
	'Marianne'	CPne XPde
	'Mariètte'	CPen CPne EBee XPde
	'Marjorie'	CPne SApp XPde
	'Martine'	CPne EBee
	'May Snow' (v) **new**	WCot
	'Meibont' (v)	CPne WCot XPde
	'Mercury'	CPne IBlr
	'Metalica' **new**	NHoy
	'Middleburg'	CPne
	Midknight Blue = 'Monmid'	EBee MWte NHoy
	'Midnight'	EWes SAga WSHC
	'Midnight Blue' ambig.	ECha ELan GBuc IBal IGor LRHS SPav WFar
	'Midnight Blue' P. Wood	CPrp GCal IBlr
§	'Midnight Star'	Widely available
	'Miniature Blue'	SWat
	mixed seedlings	CPen EPfP IBal MGos NOrc SEND SRos WHil XPde
	mixed whites	WCFE
	'Montreal'	XPde
	'Mood Indigo'	CPne
I	'Mooreanus' misapplied	EBee EPfP IBlr NBid WPGP XPde
	'Morning Star'	CPne SRos
	'Mount Stewart'	IBal IBlr
	'My Love' **new**	NHoy
	'Navy Blue'	see *A.* 'Midnight Star'
	'New Love'	EBee
	'New Orleans'	XPde
	'Newa'	XPde
	'Nikki'	CPne
	'Norman Hadden'	IBlr
	nutans	see *A. caulescens*
	- 'Polar White'	NHoy
	'Nyx'	IBlr
	'NZ Blue'	XPde
	'NZ White'	XPde
	'Oslo'	CPne NHoy XPde
	'Oxbridge'	IBlr
	Palmer's hybrids	see *A.* Headbourne hybrids
	'Paris'	CPen XPde
	'Patent Blue'	CPrp IBlr
	'Patriot'	LRHS
	'Penelope Palmer'	CPrp IBal IBlr
	'Penny Slade'	SAga SRos XPde
	'Peter Pan' ambig.	Widely available
	'Phantom'	CDes CPne CPrp GCal IBal IBlr XPde
	'Pinchbeck'	CPne XPde
	'Pinky'	XPde
	'Pinocchio'	CPen CWib ECho NHol NHoy XPde
	'Plas Merdyn Blue'	CPrp IBal IBlr
	'Plas Merdyn White'	CFir CPrp IBal IBlr NHoy XPde
	'Podge Mill'	CPne IBlr XPde
	'Polar Ice'	CFir CPen EBee ECtt ELon GBin IBal IBlr LRHS SPad WFar XPde
	'Porcelain'	IBal IBlr
	praecox	CPrp EBee EBrs EShb GAbr IBal IBlr LRHS NHoy
	- 'Albiflorus'	CBro CDes CPne CPou EBee EWTr IBal LAst LBMP LRHS NEgg NHoy SEND XPde
	- 'Floribundus'	SWat
	- 'Maximus Albus'	CPou IBal IBlr WBrE
§	- subsp. ***minimus***	CElw CPne CPou EWTr IBlr LPio NHoy SWat WHil XPde
	- - 'Adelaide'	EBee SWat
	- - blue-flowered	SWat
	- - white-flowered	CPne SWat
	- 'Neptune'	IBlr
§	- subsp. ***orientalis***	CCCN CPne CSut EHrv GGar IBlr SBch SWat
	- - 'Weaver'	CPne
	- subsp. ***praecox***	IBlr IGor
	- - azure-flowered	SWat
	- - 'Variegatus'	see *A.* 'Argenteus Vittatus'
	- 'Saturn'	IBlr
	- Slieve Donard form	IBlr
	- 'Storms River'	SWat
	- 'Uranus'	IBlr
	- 'Venus'	IBlr
	- 'Vittatus' (v)	NHoy WCot WFar
	'Premier'	CPrp EBee EBrs IBal IBlr LRHS NHoy SRos WPGP
	'Princess Margaret'	CPne XPde
	'Proteus'	XPde
§	'Purple Cloud'	Widely available
	'Purple Star'	EBee LRHS
	'Queen Anne'	LRHS NHoy
	'Queen Elizabeth The Queen Mother'	CPrp XPde
	'Raveningham Hall'	XPde
	'Regal Beauty'	CPar CPne CPrp CSBt CSpe CWGN EBee EShb IBal IPot LRHS LSRN LSou MBri NBid NHoy SBch SRkn
	'Remembrance' **new**	NHoy
	'Rhone'	IBlr XPde
	rich blue-flowered	XPde
	'Rosemary'	CPne XPde
	'Rosewarne'	CCCN CKno CPne CPrp EBee IBal IBlr LRHS NCGa NHoy SBch XPde
	'Rotterdam'	CPen CPne NHoy XPde
	'Royal Blue'	CBro CHar GBin GBuc GMaP NHol NHoy SBch WSpi
	'Royal Lodge'	XPde
	'Royal Purple'	XPde
	'Sally Anne'	CPne
	'San Gabriel' (v)	CPne XPde
	'Sandringham'	CDes CPrp EBee EWes IBlr WPGP XPde

'Sapphire' CPrp IBal IBlr XPde
'Sarah'PBR LSou NCGa
'Sea Coral' CCCN CFir CPne CPrp EBee GAbr GGar IBal LRHS MAvo MBNS NHoy NSti SHom
'Sea Foam' CPen CPne CPrp EBee IBal NLar SBch WSpi XPde
'Sea Mist' CCCN CPne EBee IBal WSpi
'Sea Spray' CCCN CPne EBee IBal LRHS LSRN NHoy XPde
'Selma Bock' new CPne
'Septemberhemel' CPen XPde
'Sevilla' XPde
'Silver Baby' CAbb CPen CPne CPrp CWGN ELon LRHS MAvo MNrw NHoy SRos
'Silver Jubilee' XPde
'Silver Mist' CBgR CPne IBlr SWat XPde
Silver Moon = 'Notfred'PBR (v) CBow EBee EHrv ELan EPfP GQue IBal LRHS LSou MBNS MGos NCob NHoy XPde
'Silver Sceptre' IBlr
'Sky' CAbb CPar CSBt CWGN EBee IBal IBlr LBuc LRHS LSRN LSou NBid SHar SWat
'Sky Rocket' CPrp IBal IBlr
'Sky Star' IBal XPde
'Slieve Donard' IBlr WFar
'Sneeuwwitje' XPde
'Snow Cloud' CAbb CBro CPne EBee ELon IBal LRHS NEgg NHoy SEND SLon WSpi XPde
'Snow Pixie' CBro CPne CSpe CWGN EBee LSRN LSou NHoy WSpi
'Snow Princess' CPen EBee IBal LRHS
'Snowball' CAby CDoC CPne CPrp EBee ECho EWTr GAbr GKev IBal LHop LRHS LSou NBPC NHoy SBch SGSe WClo WSpi WWEG XPde
'Snowdrops' CBro CPne CPrp EBee EHrv GAbr GBuc IBal LSRN MBel MNrw NCob SApp SBod SDnm SGSe SMrm SPav WCFE WFar
'Snowstorm'PBR IPot LBuc
'Southern Star' CPne
'Spokes' IBlr
'Starburst' IBlr
'Stéphanie' CPne XPde
'Stéphanie Charm' CPen XPde
'Storm Cloud' Reads see A. 'Purple Cloud'
'Storm Cloud' (d) CBro CFir
'Streamline' Widely available
'Summer Clouds' CPne EBee ELan IBal MBNS NHoy
'Summer Skies' CPne IBal NHoy SRos
'Summer Snow' CPne
'Sunfield' CKno CPen CPrp EBee GAbr GBin GBuc IBal LAma LRHS LSRN MCot NCGa NHoy NLar NPer SPad XPde
'Super Star' CPne XPde
I 'Supreme' IBal IBlr
'Suzan' XPde
'Sylvia'PBR NHoy
'Sylvine' CPen XPde
'Tall Boy' IBal IBlr
'Tarka' CPne
'Taw Valley' CPne
'Thumbelina' CBro CPne CSpe EBee IBal LSou NHoy
'Timaru' Widely available
'Tinkerbell' (v) Widely available
'Tiny Tim' EBee XPde
'Titan' IBlr
'Tom Thumb' new LSou
'Torbay' CBgR CPrp EAEE EBee ECtt EShb IBlr LHop LLWG LRHS MBNS MWte NCGa NEgg SRos SUsu XPde
'Tornado' NBhm NHoy
'Tranquil' new NHoy
Tresco hybrid CHEx
'Tresco Select' NHoy
'Triangle' new CPne
'Trudy' XPde
'Twilight' IBlr
umbellatus L'Hérit. see *A. africanus*
umbellatus Redouté see *A. praecox* subsp. *orientalis*
'Underway' EWes GCal IBlr SMrm XPde
'Vague Bleue' XPde
'Velvet Night' CPen
'Virginia' XPde
'White Dragon' new NHoy
'White Dwarf' see A. white dwarf hybrids
§ white dwarf hybrids CBro CPen EBee ECha ECtt EPfP EShb GBuc LRHS WFar
'White Heaven'PBR CKno CPne EBee NHoy SWat WCot
'White Ice' CBcs CPne SApp WSpi
'White Ice' LRHS
'White Orb' EBee IBal NHoy SPoG
'White Star' XPde
'White Starlet' NHoy XPde
'White Superior' CMMP CSpe GMaP LAst SPet XPde
'White Triumphator' WCot
'White Umbrella' LRHS NHoy
white-flowered CHEx GGar NCob
'Whitestorm' NHoy
'Whitney'PBR IBlr
'Wholesome' IBal
'Windlebrooke' CPne EBee ECha XPde
'Windsor Castle' CPen CPrp IBal IBlr XPde
'Windsor Grey' Widely available
'Winsome' IBlr
'Winter Sky' XPde
'Wolga' EBee EWll SAga
'Wolkberg' Kirstenbosch CPne IBlr
'Yellow Tips' XPde
'Yolande' LAma
'Yves Klein' CPrp IBlr
'Zachary' CPen CPne
'Zebra' new NHoy
'Zella Thomas' CPne EBee LHyd XPde
'Zomba' new CPne

Agapetes (*Ericaceae*)

'Ludgvan Cross' ♀H1-2 CCCN EMil SSpi
serpens ♀H1 CCCN CHEx CWib EShb SLon
- 'Scarlet Elf' CCCN
smithiana var. ***major*** GGGa

Agarista (*Ericaceae*)

§ ***populifolia*** WFar

Agastache (*Lamiaceae*)

(Acapulco Series) LRHS
Acapulco Orange = 'Kiegador'PBR ♀H3-4 new
- Acapulco Purple = 'Kiegapur'PBR LRHS
anethiodora see *A. foeniculum* (Pursh) Kuntze
anisata see *A. foeniculum* (Pursh) Kuntze
aurantiaca EAro GCal NLar SPhx WFar WWEG
- 'Apricot Sprite' EAro EBee LDai LRHS MHav MHer MNFA NEgg SBch SDnm SPav SPoG SRkn WCHb WFar
- 'Navajo Sunset' new GJos
'Black Adder' Widely available
'Blue Delight' SBch

'Blue Fortune' 🏆H3-4	CBcs EBee ECha EPfP LPio LRHS MBel MBri MCot MSCN NBro NMoo SMrm SPoG WFar WHlf
§ ***cana***	LDai WFar
- 'Cinnabar Rose'	NBir WFar
- 'Purple Pygmy'	CSpe EBee EPfP EWll LRHS LSou SVil
'Firebird'	CBot EAEE EBee EBla ECtt EHrv ELan LHop LRHS MBri MNrw NBir NCGa SPer SUsu SWat SWvt WAul WCAu WCot WFar WWEG
foeniculum misapplied	see *A. rugosa*
§ ***foeniculum*** (Pursh) Kuntze	CArn CChe CMea CPrp EBee ECha ELan GMaP GPoy MHer MNHC NGHP SGar SPav SPhx SRms WCAu WFar WPer WWEG
- 'Alabaster'	CBcs EAro EBee SPhx WCHb
- 'Alba'	NBre NGHP SBch SHDw SPav WFar
- Apache Fuchsia = 'Puragaat52'	LHop NPri
* 'Fragrant Delight'	SRms
'Giant' **new**	SUsu
'Glowing Embers'	ECtt EPfP
'Hazy Days'	LSou
§ ***mexicana***	EAro LDai LPio SDnm SPav
- 'Champagne'	WCHb
- 'Marchants Pink'	SMrm
- 'Red Fortune' PBR	EBee EBla ECtt LHop LLWG LRHS MBri MWea NCGa NEgg SMrm
- 'Rosea'	see *A. cana*
- 'Sangria' **new**	EWTr
nepetoides	EPPr SDnm SPav WCHb
'Painted Lady'	CSpe ECtt LPio MNrw MWea SAga SBch SMrm SUsu
pallidiflora var. ***neomexicana*** 'Lavender Haze'	EBee EPfP GAbr LRHS
palmeri	LHop
'Pink Beauty' **new**	NCGa
'Pink Panther'	LHop
'Pink Pearl'	LRHS
'Pink Pop'	EBee LRHS SPoG
pringlei	EAro WMoo
'Purple Candle'	EWes
§ ***rugosa***	CArn GKir GPoy LHop MCot MNHC NEgg SDnm SMeo SPav SPhx SWat WJek WMoo WPer
- B&SWJ 4187 from Korea	WCru
- f. ***albiflora***	NBre NEgg SDnm WCAu
- - 'Liquorice White'	EBee EPfP GQue LRHS NBre NLar SPav SPer WHrl
- 'Golden Jubilee'	CSam CSpe EAEE EAro EBee EBla EBrs ECha ECtt EGoo ELan EPfP LBMP LDai LHop LPio LRHS MBri MCCP MHer MNHC NHol NLar NOrc SPhx WFar WMoo WWEG
- 'Honey Bee Blue'	LRHS NHol
- 'Korean Zest'	EBee EGoo WCru
- 'Liquorice Blue'	EAEE EAro EBla LBMP LRHS MCot NChi NEgg NGBl NGdn NLar NOrc SDnm SGar SPav SPer SPhx WFar WMoo WPer
- pink-flowered	CEnt
rupestris	CSpe EAro LHop NLar SBch SPhx WKif
- 'Apache Sunset'	CBow MBri SDnm SGar SPav SPlb WHal WWEG
scrophulariifolia	WCHb
'Serpentine'	EBee EWTr SPhx SSvw
'Spicy'	ECha
'Tangerine Dreams' 🏆H3	CDoC EAro EBee EBla ECtt LHop LRHS MWea NCob NEgg NGdn SCoo SPoG
'Tutti-frutti'	CWGN EBee ECtt EHrv LDai LHop SDnm SPav SUsu
urticifolia	CSpe NBre WClo
- 'Alba'	CSpe EAro NBre WPer
- 'Liquorice'	EBee WFar

Agathaea see *Felicia*

Agathis (*Araucariaceae*)

australis	CDoC
montana **new**	SBst

Agathosma (*Rutaceae*)

ovata	CCCN
- 'Igoda'	EShb

Agave ✿ (*Agavaceae*)

acicularis	MAga
aktites	MAga
albescens	MAga
albomarginata	CDTJ MAga
amaniensis	MAga
americana 🏆H1	Widely available
- var. ***expansa***	MAga
- 'Marginata' (v) 🏆H3-4	CBrP CDTJ CHll IBlr MAga MREP SDnm SSwd STre
- 'Mediopicta' misapplied	see *A. americana* 'Mediopicta Alba'
- 'Mediopicta' (v) 🏆H1	CDTJ CHEx SAPC SArc SBig WEas
§ - 'Mediopicta Alba' (v) 🏆H1	CBrP CDTJ EAmu ESwi MAga SChr WCot
- 'Mediopicta Aurea' (v)	MAga
- var. ***oaxacensis***	MAga
- subsp. ***protamericana***	MAga WPGP
- subsp. ***protamericana*** × ***scabra*** F&M 310	WPGP
- - NJM 05.057	WPGP
- 'Striata' (v)	EShb MAga MCot WCot
- 'Variegata' (v) 🏆H1	Widely available
angustiarum	MAga
angustifolia	see *A. vivipara* var. *vivipara*
- var. ***marginata*** hort.	NExo SBig WCot
applanata **new**	WPGP
asperrima	CDTJ MREP
§ - subsp. ***maderensis***	MAga
- subsp. ***potosiensis***	MAga
§ - subsp. ***zarcensis***	MAga
attenuata	CAbb CBrP CHEx EAmu ETod EWll MAga SAPC SArc SBig WCot WPGP
attenuata × ***shawii***	MAga
aurea	MAga
avellanidens	MAga
beauleriana	EAmu MAga SBig
'Blue Glow' **new**	NExo
boldinghiana	MAga WCot
bovicornuta	MAga NExo WCot
bracteosa	CCCN MAga MREP SChr
brittoniana	MAga
cantala	MAga
capensis	MAga
celsii	see *A. mitis* var. *mitis*
cerulata subsp. ***nelsonii***	MAga
chiapensis	MAga
chrysantha	CCCN CTrC EAmu EBee ETod MAga SChr WGrn WPGP
- 'Black Canyon'	WCot
chrysoglossa	MAga WPGP
colimana	see *A. ortgiesiana*
colorata	CCCN CDTJ NExo WCot
- dwarf	MAga
congesta	MAga
cundinmarcensis from Columbia **new**	MAga

cupreata	ETod MAga
dasylirioides	MAga
datylio	MAga
decipiens	MAga
- dwarf	MAga
delamateri	MAga
de-meesteriana	EAmu
variegated (v) new	
deserti	CBrP LRHS WCot
- NNS 03-7	EBee
- var. ***simplex***	MAga
variegated (v)	
desmetiana	EAmu ETod MAga
- var. ***marginata***	MAga
difformis	ETod MAga
- NJM 05.034	WPGP
durangensis	MAga
eggersiana	MAga
ellemeetiana	MAga
elongata	see *A. vivipara* var. *vivipara*
ensifera	MAga
- var. ***marginata***	MAga
- variegated new	MAga
evadens	MAga
felgeri	CDTJ MAga
ferdinandi-regis	see *A. victoriae-reginae*
ferox	see *A. salmiana* var. *ferox*
filifera ♀H1	CBcs CCCN CDTJ CHEx EAmu ETod MAga SBst SChr SEND SPlb
- 'Compacta'	MAga
- subsp. ***microceps*** ISI 1184	MAga
flexispina	ETod MAga
fortiflora	MAga
fourcroydes	MAga MREP
funkiana	MAga
- blue-leaved	MAga
garciae-mendozae	CDTJ
- NJM 05.073	WPGP
geminiflora	CCCN CDTJ EAmu EShb MAga WCot
gentryi	CDTJ EBee MAga
- F&M 213A	WPGP
ghiesbreghtii	MAga MREP
gigantea	see *Furcraea foetida*
gigantensis	MAga NExo
× ***glomeruliflora***	MAga
goldmaniana	see *A. shawii* subsp. *goldmaniana*
× ***gracilipes***	MAga WPGP
guadalajarana	CDTJ MAga NExo WPGP
- dwarf	MAga
guiengola	MAga NExo
gypsophila	MAga
havardiana	CTrC EAmu MAga WCot WPGP
- dwarf	MAga
hiemiflora	MAga
hookeri	MAga
horrida	ETod MAga SBig
- 'Perotensis'	EShb
hurteri	CDTJ MAga
impressa new	WCot
inaequidens	MAga
isthmensis new	NExo
'Joe Hoak' (v) new	NExo
karwinskii	MAga
kerchovei	MAga
lechuguilla	CDTJ EBee MAga SChr WPGP
lophantha	see *A. univittata*
- var. ***caerulescens***	see *A. univittata*
lurida Aiton	see *A. vera-cruz*
macroacantha	CDTJ MAga
maculosa new	WCot
mapisaga	MAga
- NJM 05.036	WPGP
- var. ***lisa***	MAga
marmorata new	MAga
maximilliana	MAga
- 'Katharinae'	MAga
missionum from The Virgin Islands	MAga
mitis var. ***albidior***	MAga WPGP
§ - var. ***mitis***	CHEx EShb MAga SAPC SArc SChr WCot
- var. ***mitis*** × ***variegata*** new	
montana	CDTJ CGHE EAmu EBee MAga NExo
- F&M 221	WPGP
moranii	MAga
multifilifera	MAga
nayaritensis new	MAga
neglecta	MAga
neomexicana	CCCN EAmu ETod IDee MAga WPGP
- S&B 948	WCot
× ***nigra*** hort.	EAmu
nizandensis	CHEx MAga
§ ***obscura***	CDTJ ETod MAga
ocahui	ETod MAga
- var. ***longifolia***	MAga
ornithobroma	MAga
oroensis	MAga
§ ***ortgiesiana***	ETod MAga
ovatifolia	MAga NExo SPlb
pachycentra	MAga
palmeri	CCCN CTrC MAga WPGP
panamana	see *A. vivipara* var. *vivipara*
parrasana	EAmu MAga WCot WPGP
- dwarf	MAga
parryi	CBcs CDTJ CDoC CSpe EAmu ETod EWll GKev MAga SBst SChr WGrn WPGP
- var. ***couesii*** new	WPGP
- 'Cream Spike' (v) new	WCot
- var. ***huachucensis***	CDTJ CTsd
- 'Ohi Kissho ten Nishiki' (v) new	NExo
- var. ***parryi***	CBrP CDTJ MAga MREP WPGP
- var. ***truncata***	NExo
parvidentata	MAga
- blue-leaved	MAga
parviflora ♀H1	MAga SChr
- subsp. ***flexiflora***	MAga
- - dwarf	MAga
× ***peacockii***	MAga
pedunculifera	MAga NExo
pelona	MAga
pendula	MAga
petiolata	MAga
polianthiflora	MAga
polyacantha	MAga
- F&M 120	WPGP
- var. ***xalapensis***	see *A. obscura*
potatorum ♀H1	NExo SChr
- 'Funkalicious' dwarf new	NExo
- var. ***potatorum***	MAga
- var. ***verschaffeltii***	MREP
- - dwarf	MAga
promontorii	MAga
pumila	MAga NExo
pygmaea	see *A. seemanniana*
rhodacantha	MAga
salmiana	CDTJ EAmu MAga SBig
- F&M 290	WPGP
- var. ***angustifolia***	MAga
- subsp. ***crassispina***	MAga

§	- var. ***ferox***	CBrP CDTJ CTrC EAmu EWll MAga MREP NExo SAPC SArc SBig SChr
	- - 'Marginata' (v)	MAga
	- subsp. ***salmiana*** variegated (v)	MAga
	scabra	CCCN EBee MAga
	- subsp. ***maderensis***	see *A. asperrima* subsp. *maderensis*
	- subsp. ***zarcensis***	see *A. asperrima* subsp. *zarcensis*
	scaposa	MAga
	schidigera	CBrP MAga WCot
	schottii	CDTJ MAga
	- var. ***treleasei***	MAga
§	***seemanniana***	MAga
	shawii	MAga
§	- subsp. ***goldmaniana***	MAga
	shrevei new	ETod
	- subsp. ***matapensis***	MAga
	sileri new	WCot
	sisalana	ETod MAga
I	- f. ***armata***	MAga
	- 'Mediopicta' new	MAga
	sobria	MAga
	- subsp. ***frailensis***	MAga
	- subsp. ***sobria***	MAga
§	***spicata***	MAga
	stictata new	WCot
	striata	CTrC EAmu ETod
	- subsp. ***falcata***	MAga WCot
*	- ***rubra***	CDTJ
	stricta ♀H1	CCCN CDTJ MAga MREP
	- dwarf	CBrP MAga
	- 'Nana'	CDTJ
	- 'Nana' blue-leaved	MAga
	stringens	MAga
	subsimplex	MAga
	tecta	MAga
	tenuifolia	MAga
	tequilana blue-leaved	MAga
	- green-leaved	MAga
	- variegated (v)	MAga WCot
	thomasiae	MAga
	titanota	ETod MAga NExo
	toumeyana	MAga SChr WCot
	- var. ***bella***	CDTJ MAga
	triangularis	ETod MAga
	underwoodii	MAga
§	***univittata***	CDTJ MAga WCot
	- 'Quadricolor' (v) new	NExo
	univittata × ***lechuguilla***	MAga
	univittata × ***scabra***	MAga
	utahensis ♀H1	MAga SEND
	- var. ***discreta***	MAga
	- dwarf	MAga
	- var. ***eborispina***	MAga
	- var. ***nevadensis***	MAga
§	***vera-cruz***	MAga
§	***victoriae-reginae*** ♀H1	CBrP CCCN CDTJ EShb EWll MAga SChr SWal WCot
	- dwarf	MAga
	- f. ***ornata***	MAga
	- variegated (v)	SChr
	victoria-reginae × ***lechuguilla***	MAga
	vilmoriniana	MAga
	vivipara	MAga
	- var. ***letonae***	MAga
	- 'Marginata'	MAga
	- var. ***nivea***	MAga
	- var. ***sargentii***	MAga
§	- var. ***vivipara***	MAga SBig WCot
	vizcainoensis	MAga
	warelliana	MAga
	weberi	EAmu MAga
	wendtii	MAga
	wercklei	MAga
	× ***winteriana***	MAga
	wocomahi	MAga
	xylonacantha	ETod MAga SChr
	yuccifolia	see *A. spicata*
	zebra	MAga

Ageratina (*Asteraceae*)

§	***altissima***	CHid EBee ELan EPfP GBar LRHS MAvo MCot NLar SPav SSvw WCHb WFar WSpi WTin
	- 'Braunlaub'	CPrp EBee ECtt EHrv GKir LPla NBir NBre NGdn SWat WHrl WMnd WPtf
	- 'Chocolate' ♀H4	Widely available
§	***aromatica***	EBee MRav NBre NBro SWat WCHb WPer WSFF
§	***glechonophylla***	EBee MAvo
§	***ligustrina*** ♀H3	Widely available
§	***occidentalis*** NNS 94-53	WCot

Ageratum (*Asteraceae*)

	'Basso Rose' (Artist Basso Series) new	LRHS
	corymbosum	CHll CSpe SUsu

Aglaomorpha (*Polypodiaceae*)

	coronans	WRic

Aglaonema (*Araceae*)

	'Christina'	LRHS
	'Cleopatra' PBR	LRHS
	crispum 'Marie'	MBri
	'Greenlight' PBR	LRHS
	'Maria Christina'	LRHS
	'Pattaya Beauty' PBR new	LRHS
	'Silver Queen' ♀H1	MBri

Agonis (*Myrtaceae*)

	flexuosa	CCCN CTrC

Agrimonia (*Rosaceae*)

	eupatoria	CArn COld CRWN EBWF EBee GPoy MHer MNHC NMir SECG SHlg SIde SWat WHer
*	- var. ***alba***	NBre NLar
	grandiflora	EBee NBre
	odorata misapplied	see *A. procera*
	odorata (L.) Mill.	see *A. repens*
	pilosa	CArn EBee
§	***procera***	EBWF
§	***repens***	GBar WCHb WMoo

Agropyron (*Poaceae*)

	glaucum	see *Elymus hispidus*
	magellanicum	see *Elymus magellanicus*
	pubiflorum	see *Elymus magellanicus*

Agrostemma (*Caryophyllaceae*)

	coronaria	see *Lychnis coronaria*
	githago	CArn SBch SECG
	- 'Ocean Pearl'	CSpe

Agrostis (*Poaceae*)

	calamagrostis	see *Stipa calamagrostis*
§	***canina*** 'Silver Needles' (v)	CBre EWes GKir NBir WFar WWEG
	karsensis	see *A. stolonifera*
	'Lago Lago'	EBee
§	***montevidensis*** new	NWsh

nebulosa CKno
- 'Fibre Optics' CSpe

§ ***stolonifera*** EBWF
- 'Julia Ann' (v) **new** WCot

Aichryson (*Crassulaceae*)

§ × ***aizoides*** var. ***domesticum*** STre WCor
- - 'Variegatum' (v) 🏆H1 EBak WCot

tortuosum CFee

Ailanthus (*Simaroubaceae*)

§ ***altissima*** CBcs CCVT CDul CHEx CLnd CMac CPLG CTho EBee ECrN EPfP EWTr IFFs LAst MBlu NMun NWea SAPC SArc SCoo SDnm SEND SPer SPlb SWvt WBVN WDin
- var. ***tanakae*** B&SWJ 6777 WCru
- - RWJ 9906 WCru

glandulosa see *A. altissima*

Ainsliaea (*Asteraceae*)

acerifolia B&SWJ 4795 WCru
- B&SWJ 6059 WCru

apiculata B&SWJ 11397 **new** WCru

cordifolia EBee

aff. ***elegans*** WWJ 11720 **new** WCru

petelotii B&SWJ 11732 **new** WCru

tonkinensis B&SWJ 11819 **new** WCru

Ajania (*Asteraceae*)

§ ***pacifica*** LRHS WHer
- 'Silver Edge' EBee

Ajuga (*Lamiaceae*)

ciliata var. ***villosior*** CFir GBin WHil

genevensis WOut
- 'Tottenham' EBee WOut

incisa EBee GCal SPhx
- 'Bikun' (v) CLAP CMoH EBee EPPr EShb LOck LRHS SRGP
- 'Blue Enigma' CLAP EWes NCGa NHol SMac WWEG
- 'Blue Ensign' LDai

'Little Court Pink' see *A. reptans* 'Purple Torch'

metallica hort. see *A. pyramidalis*

'Pink Spires' NCot

§ ***pyramidalis*** CFee EBee GKir WHer
- 'Metallica Crispa' CBct CBow EBee ECho ECtt EPfP EWes LAst LRHS MBNS NBPC NHol NLar SPoG SRms SSvw SWvt WFar

reptans CArn CRWN CTri CWan EBWF EBee ECtt GKev GKir GPoy LPBA LRHS MCot MHer MNHC NMir NSco SGar WFar
- f. ***albiflora*** 'Alba' CArn CWan EBee ECtt EPfP GGar MNrw MRav MSCN NBro SBch SRms WAlt WCAu WCHb WFar WMoo
- - 'Sanne' EBee
- - 'Silver Shadow' NChi
- 'Arctic Fox' (v) CCVN EBee ECho EHrv GBuc LBMP LHop LRHS MAvo MNrw MRav NRya SAga SWvt WCot WFar WHer WWEG
- 'Argentea' see *A. reptans* 'Variegata'
- § 'Atropurpurea' CCVT CHrt CWan EBee ECha ECho ELan EMFW EPfP GAbr GGar LPBA LRHS MAvo MCot MGos MLHP MSCN NHol NVic SIng SPlb SRms SWvt WBrk WFar WWEG
- Black Scallop ='Binblasca' CBgR CSpe EAEE EBee ECGP ECtt EKen EPPr EShb ETod GAbr GKir LBMP LRHS MAvo MBri MCot MGos MMHG MWhi NHol NSti SBch SPer SPhx SPoG SRot WClo WFar WHal
- 'Braunherz' CTri EBee ECho ECtt EHoe ELan EPfP EShb GBuc GGar GKir GMaP IFoB LHop LRHS MBNS MBri MHer MNHC MWat NMir NPri SBch SPer SPoG SWvt WFar WHoo WMoo WTin
- 'Burgundy Glow' (v) Widely available
- § 'Catlin's Giant' 🏆H4 Widely available
- 'Chocolate Chip' see *A. reptans* 'Valfredda'
- 'Delight' (v) ECho
- 'Ebony' LRHS LSRN
- 'Ermine' (v) SAga
- 'Evening Glow' GGar WMoo
- 'Flisteridge' CNat WAlt
- 'Golden Beauty' CBow EBee ECho ECtt LAst SGar WWEG
- 'Grey Lady' GBuc WWEG
- 'Harlequin' (v) SWvt WBrE
- 'John Pierpoint' LRHS SHar
- 'Jumbo' see *A. reptans* 'Jungle Beauty'
- § 'Jungle Beauty' CSev EAEE EBee EPfP GBar LRHS MRav NCob WFar
- 'Lush Blue' WAlt
- 'Macrophylla' see *A. reptans* 'Catlin's Giant'
- § 'Multicolor' (v) CBcs EBee ECho ELan GKir LRHS MAvo MBar MCot MRav NHol SPer SPlb SPoG SRms SWvt WFar WMoo
- 'Palisander' EAEE EBee LRHS NEgg NLar
- 'Party Colours' **new** EBee
- 'Pink Elf' CMHG ECho MRav NBro SWat WBrk WFar
- 'Pink Splendour' NBre NChi
- 'Pink Surprise' EBee ECtt EHoe GBar GBuc MHer MLHP NRya WFar WGwG WMoo WWEG
- 'Purple Brocade' EHoe
- § 'Purple Torch' EBee GKir LRHS WOut
- 'Purpurea' see *A. reptans* 'Atropurpurea'
- 'Rainbow' see *A. reptans* 'Multicolor'
- 'Rosea' EAEE EBee WAlt WFar WMoo
- 'Rowden Amethyst' CRow
- 'Rowden Appleblossom' CRow
- 'Rowden Royal Purple' CRow
- 'Silver Carpet' EBee
- 'Silver Queen' ECtt
- 'Sugar Plum' **new** EBee
- 'Toffee Chip' (v) **new** CBow SGol
- 'Tricolor' see *A. reptans* 'Multicolor'
- § 'Valfredda' CEnt EAlp EBee ECho ECtt EPfP EShb GBar GGar LAst LBMP LRHS MAvo NEgg NLar NPro SHar WCot WFar WGwG WMoo WOut WPtf
- 'Vanilla Chip' (v) EBee
- § 'Variegata' (v) EBee ECho ECtt EPfP EShb MNHC NPri SBod SPer SPoG SRms SWat WFar
- 'Wild Purple' WAlt

Akebia (*Lardizabalaceae*)

longeracemosa CBcs LEdu NLar WCot
- B&SWJ 3606 WCru

× ***pentaphylla*** EBee ELan EPfP LRHS MAsh NLar SPer
- B&SWJ 2829 WCru

	quinata	Widely available
	- B&SWJ 4425	WCru
	- 'Alba'	CBcs CSPN CWGN NLar WPat
	- 'Amethyst Glow'	EPfP LRHS MAsh MBri SPer SPoG
	- cream-flowered	EBee EPfP LRHS MAsh MRav MWea SBch SPer SPoG SSta SWvt WCru WPGP
	- variegated (v)	CBcs CBow LLHF SMad WCot WCru WPat
	- 'White Chocolate'	NLar WCru WSHC
	trifoliata	CBcs EBee EPfP EWld GKir LRHS SLim SLon
	- B&SWJ 2829	WCru
	- B&SWJ 5063	WCru

Alangium (*Alangiaceae*)

	chinense	CBcs EPla WBVN
	platanifolium	CAbP CBcs CPLG MBlu MBri NLar WPGP
	- var. ***macrophyllum***	EPfP WPGP
	- var. ***platanifolium***	NLar

Albizia (*Mimosaceae*)

	distachya	see *Paraserianthes lophantha*
§	***julibrissin***	CArn CDTJ CTrC CWib EAmu EPfP IDee LAst LMaj LRHS NEgg NMun SMad WDin
	- Ombrella = 'Boubri'[PBR]	EBee ELan EMil LRHS MBri MREP SBch SCoo SPoG
	- f. ***rosea*** ♀H2-3	Widely available
	- 'Rouge d'Été'	EBee
I	- 'Rouge Selection'	LRHS SPoG
	- 'Summer Chocolate' new	CAbP CBcs LRHS SMad SPer
	lophantha	see *Paraserianthes lophantha*

Albuca (*Hyacinthaceae*)

	JCA 15856	NWCA
	from Lesotho	GCal
	angolensis	CPou WHil
	aurea	WHil WPrP
*	***batliana***	ECho
	batteniana	CFir EBrs ECho
	canadensis	MAvo
	clanwilliamigloria	WHil WPrP
	cooperi	ECho
	'Dirk Wallace'	CPLG
	fastigiata	WHil
	flaccida	WHil
	fragrans	CDes
	humilis	CDes CPLG CPrp CStu EBee ECho LLHF NMen NRya WAbe WHil WPat WPrP
	juncifolia	EBee
	maxima	CPou EBee ECho WCot
	nelsonii	CAvo CPne EBee EBrs ECho ERea LRHS WPGP
	rupestris	WCot WHil
	setosa	EBee
	shawii	CAvo CBgR CBro CDes CFFs CPne CPou CPrp CStu EAEE EBee EBla EBrs ECho ERos LAst LRHS NSla NWCA SAga SGar SPad SPet SPoG WAbe WCot WHil WPGP WPrP
	trichophylla	ECho MHer
	wakefieldii	EBee

× *Alcalthaea* (*Malvaceae*)

	suffrutescens 'Parkallee' (d)	CBgR CDes EBee ECtt GMac LDai LHop LOck LPla LRHS LSou MAvo MBNS MCCP MCot MNrw NGdn NSti SPhx SUsu WClo WCot WHoo
	- 'Parkfrieden' (d)	CSpe EBee ECtt MAvo SPhx WCot
	- 'Parkrondell' (d)	CBgR EBee ECha ECtt GMac LHop LPla LRHS MAsh MAvo MBNS MSCN NPri WCot
	- white-flowered new	IFro

Alcea (*Malvaceae*)

	'Apple Blossom' (d)	NCGa
	'Arabian Nights'	SPav
	'Blackcurrant Whirl'	SPav
	ficifolia	MAvo MCCP NChi SDnm SPav SWal WCon WFar WMoo
	'Happy Lights'	CWib
	pallida	GMac
	'Peaches 'n' Dreams'	CWib EBee NCGa NGBl WRHF
§	***rosea***	GKir LRHS SECG SVic WFar
	- 'Black Beauty'	NBur
	- Chater's Double Group (d)	CWib ECtt EPfP MBri MWat NBlu SPoG SRms WRHF
	- - chamois-flowered (d)	EPfP GKir
	- - chestnut brown-flowered (d)	EPfP
	- - pink-flowered (d)	EPfP NPri SPer WWEG
	- - purple-flowered (d)	EGxp EPfP EWTr LRHS SPer SPoG WWEG
	- - red-flowered (d)	EPfP NPri SPoG
	- - salmon pink-flowered (d)	EPfP WWEG
	- - scarlet-flowered (d)	EPfP SPoG WWEG
	- - violet-flowered (d)	EPfP SPer
	- - white-flowered (d)	EPfP MWat NPri SPer SPoG WWEG
	- - yellow-flowered (d)	EPfP IMon NPri SPer SPoG WWEG
	- 'Crème de Cassis'	EPfP MWat NBPC NCGa NGBl SPav SPoG
	- double apricot-flowered (d)	NBur
	- double pink-flowered (d)	MHer
	- double red-flowered (d)	MHer
	- double rose-flowered (d)	EBee SPer
	- double scarlet-flowered (d)	SPer
	- double white-flowered (d)	MHer WHil
	- double yellow-flowered (d)	EBee MHer
	- 'Lemon Light'	LHop NBur
	- 'Nigra'	CMea CSpe EBee ECtt EHrv ELan EPfP IMon LBMP LHop LRHS LSRN MCot MHer MWat NGBl NGdn NPri SPer WCAu WFar WWEG
	- single-flowered	MWat SPoG
	- Summer Carnival Group	CWib LAst SRms
§	***rugosa***	CMea LHop MCot SPav SWal WPGP

Alchemilla ✿ (*Rosaceae*)

	abyssinica	EBee WHrl WWEG
	alpina misapplied	see *A. conjuncta*, *A. plicatula*
	alpina ambig.	EOHP MCot
	alpina L.	CEnt CFee EBee EBla ECho ECrN EHoe EPfP GKir LEdu LHop LRHS MRav MWat SBch SPet SRms SWat WFar WKif WMoo WPer
	aroanica	EBee EBla
§	***conjuncta***	Widely available
	elisabethae	WCHb
	ellenbeckii	CDes CFee CMoH EBee ECho EDAr EPfP GBar GGar LAst MTho NChi WCHb WFar WPGP WWEG
	epipsila	EBee EShb NBPC NLar SPhx WPer WPtf
	erythropoda ♀H4	Widely available
	faeroensis	WMoo WPer WPtf
	- var. ***pumila***	EBla GEdr NMen
	filicaulis	EBWF
	- 'Minima'	CNat
§	***fulgens***	LEdu

	glaucescens	EBla
	hoppeana misapplied	see *A. plicatula*
	hoppeana (Reichenb.) Dalla Torre	EBee
	iniquiformis	EBee WPGP
	lapeyrousei	EBee NChi
	mollis ♀H4	Widely available
*	- 'Robusta'	MMuc NBur SEND SPlb SWat WFar WMoo WPnP
*	- 'Senior'	LHop
	- 'Thriller'	EBee IBal LRHS NBur WSpi
	monticola	WPer
	'Mr Poland's Variety'	see *A. venosa*
	pedata	NChi
	pentaphylla	EBee
§	***plicatula***	WPer
	pumila	NBre
	saxatilis	IFoB WPer
*	***sericophylla***	EBee
	splendens misapplied	see *A. fulgens*
	straminea	EBee MRav NBre
§	***venosa***	CMoH
	vetteri	EBee GMac WHrl
	vulgaris misapplied	see *A. xanthochlora*
§	***xanthochlora***	CArn CWan EBee GBar GPoy NBre NLar NSco SHlg SRms WCon WFar WHer WPer

Aldrovanda (*Droseraceae*)

	vesiculosa	EFEx

alecost see *Tanacetum balsamita*

Alectorurus (*Liliaceae*)

	yedoensis var. ***platypetalus***	EBee

Alectryon (*Sapindaceae*)

	excelsus	CBcs ECou

Alisma (*Alismataceae*)

	plantago-aquatica	CBen CRow EBWF EHon EMFW LPBA MSKA NPer NSco SWat WMAq WPnP
	- var. ***parviflorum***	CBen LPBA MSKA SPlb SWat WMAq

Alkanna (*Boraginaceae*)

	tinctoria HH&K 345	CMdw

Allamanda (*Apocynaceae*)

	cathartica	ERea MBri
	- 'Birthe'	MBri
	neriifolia	see *A. schottii*
§	***schottii*** ♀H1	CCCN

Alliaria (*Brassicaceae*)

	petiolata	CArn EBWF GPoy NLan SECG WHer WSFF

Allium ✿ (*Alliaceae*)

§	***acuminatum***	CPom EBee ECho GBin NBir NMen WWst
I	- 'Album'	ECho
	aflatunense misapplied	see *A. hollandicum*
	aflatunense ambig.	ECho IBal LRHS LSRN WCot WFar WWEG
	aflatunense B. Fedtsch.	ECho LHop SApp
I	- 'Alba'	EBee EBrs ECho
	akaka	NWCA
	'Akbulak'	EBee ECho ERCP LAma
	albopilosum	see *A. cristophii*
	altaicum	ECho
	altissimum 'Goliath'	CGrW EBee EBrs ECho LRHS WCot
	amabile	see *A. mairei* var. *amabile*
	'Ambassador'	CBro CMea EBee ERCP LAma LRHS MNrw SPhx
	ampeloprasum	CPrp EBWF EBee EBrs ECha ECho LAma NGHP WHer WShi
	- var. ***babingtonii***	CAgr CArn CPrp ECho GPWP GPoy ILis LEdu WHer WShi
§	- 'Elephant'	CArn ECho
	amphibolum	EBee EBrs ECho EHrv EPot
	amplectens	EBee EBrs ECho LAma
§	***angulosum***	CAvo CMea EBee EBrs ECho LAma SMrm WCot
	angustitepalum	see *A. jesdianum* subsp. *angustitepalum*
	atropurpureum	EBee EBrs ECha EHrv ELan EPfP ERCP GAbr LAma LEdu LRHS MBel MWat NGHP SPer SPhx
	atropurpureum × ***schubertii***	LRHS
	atroviolaceum	EBee ECho
	azureum	see *A. caeruleum*
	backhousianum	MPoH
	balansae	ECho
	barszczewskii	ECho
	'Beau Regard' ♀H4	CWCL EBee EBrs ECho ERCP LAma
	beesianum misapplied	see *A. cyaneum*
	beesianum W.W. Smith	CDes GEdr NBir NRya SMeo
	- from Sichuan, China	ECho
	- 'Album'	EBrs ECho
	blandum	see *A. carolinianum*
	bolanderi	EBee ECho
	brevicaule	ECho
	brevistylum	EBee
	bucharicum	ECho ERos
	bulgaricum	see *Nectaroscordum siculum* subsp. *bulgaricum*
§	***caeruleum*** ♀H4	Widely available
	- ***azureum***	see *A. caeruleum*
	caesium ♀H4	EBrs ECho IPot
	- RS 188/84	WWst
	- tall **new**	WWst
	- 'Tashkent'	ECho
	caespitosum	ECho
	callimischon	CBro
	- subsp. ***callimischon***	EBrs ECho MPoH SPhx WWst
	- subsp. ***haemostictum***	CBgR CDes EBrs ECho NMen
	canadense	CArn EBee ECho GPWP SHar
	cardiostemon	MPoH
§	***carinatum***	ECho
§	- subsp. ***pulchellum*** ♀H4	CArn CAvo CBgR CBro CHar CMea EBee EBrs ECha ECho EPot LAma LHop LLWP LRHS MHer MNFA MNrw MTho MWat NMen SMad SMrm SPhx WBor WCom WPer
	- - f. ***album*** ♀H4	CArn CAvo CBgR CBro CSWP EBee EBrs ECha ECho ELon EPot ERCP LEdu LLWP LRHS MNrw NMen SBch SMeo SMrm SPhx WBor WCom WCot
	- - 'Tubergen'	ECho
§	***carolinianum***	EBee ECho
	cassium subsp. ***hirtellum***	LRHS
	cepa Aggregatum Group	ELau GPoy
	- 'Kew White'	WCot
	- 'Perutile'	CArn CHby GPoy ILis LEdu MHer SBch SHDw
	- Proliferum Group	CArn CBod CHby CPrp CSev CWan ECho EOHP GBar GPoy ILis LEdu MHer MNHC NGHP SBch SIde WCHb WGwG WHer WJek
	- var. ***viviparum***	EBrs ECho LAma

	- 'White Lisbon' ♀H4 new	LRHS
	cernuum	Widely available
§	- 'Hidcote' ♀H4	CSam ECho WBVN WKif
	- 'Major'	see *A. cernuum* 'Hidcote'
	- var. ***neomexicanum*** new	ECho
	- var. ***obtusum***	ECho
	- pink-flowered	EBrs NBir
	cirrhosum	see *A. carinatum* subsp. *pulchellum*
	commutatum	ECho
	cowanii	see *A. neapolitanum* Cowanii Group
	crenulatum	EBrs ECho
§	***cristophii*** ♀H4	Widely available
	cupanii	EBee EBrs ECho
	- subsp. ***hirtovaginatum***	ECho
	cupuliferum	ECho WWst
	cuthbertii new	WWst
§	***cyaneum*** ♀H4	CPBP CPom EBee ECho ERos GEdr LBee LRHS MPoH NMen NRya WCot
*	- ***album*** new	ECho
	- 'Cobalt Blue' new	ECho
	cyathophorum	ECho LFur NWCA
§	- var. ***farreri***	CArn CAvo CBgR CBre CBro EBee EBrs ECho EPot ERos GAuc GEdr GKir LBee LEdu LLWP LRHS MLHP MRav NChi NRya SBch WBVN WCot WPrP
	darwasicum	ECho
	- RM 8274	MPoH
	decipiens	ECho
	delicatulum	EBee
	dichlamydeum	CPom ECho ERos WWst
§	***drummondii***	CPom EBee ECho ERos LRHS
	'Early Emperor'	EBee ERCP LRHS
	elatum	see *A. macleanii*
	'Emir'	EBee ECho
	ericetorum	EBee ECho ERos WCot WWst
	falcifolium	EBee EBrs ECho EPot LAma NMen NMin
	farreri	see *A. cyathophorum* var. *farreri*
	fasciculatum	LAma
	fimbriatum	ECho
	- var. ***abramsii***	ECho
	- var. ***purdyi***	ECho
	'Firmament'	CAvo CBro CFFs EBee EBrs ECGP ECha ECho ERCP IHer IPot LAma LRHS SPhx WCot
	fistulosum	CArn CHby CHrt CWan EBee EBrs ECho ELau GBar GPoy ILis LAma LEdu MHer MMuc MNHC NGHP NHol NPri SIde WCHb WGwG WPer
	- 'Red Welsh'	CPrp ILis WJek
	- red-flowered	NGHP
	flavum ♀H4	CArn CBro ECha ECho EDAr EPot ERCP IFoB LAma MRav SBch SMad SMrm WGor WGwG WWEG
§	- 'Blue Leaf'	ECho ERos NBir SMrm
	- subsp. ***flavum***	EBee EBrs ECho MMHG MNrw
	- - var. ***minus***	EBee ECho IFro MTho NWCA WAbe
	- 'Glaucum'	see *A. flavum* 'Blue Leaf'
	- var. ***nanum***	EBrs EPot GKir
	- subsp. ***tauricum***	CSpe EBee EBrs ECho SPhx
	'Forelock' new	ERCP
	forrestii	EBee ECho GBin MDKP WCot
	geyeri	EBee ECho WCot
	giganteum ♀H4	Widely available
	'Gladiator' ♀H4	CFir CWCL EBee EBrs ECho ECtt ERCP LAma LRHS LSRN MBel MNrw MRav NOrc SPad WWEG
	'Globemaster' ♀H4	Widely available
	globosum	ECho
	'Globus'	EBee EBrs ECho IBal LAma
	goodingii	CPom EBee EBrs ECho GMaP
	'Guna'	LRHS
	guttatum	EBee ECho
	subsp. ***dalmaticum***	
	- - AH 9114	MPoH
	- - Hoa 9114	WWst
	- subsp. ***sardoum***	EBee ECho
	- - CH 859	MPoH WWst
	gypsaceum ARJA 9836	MPoH
	haematochiton	ECho WCot
	- NNS 95-23	EBee WWst
	'Hair'	see *A. vineale* 'Hair'
	heldreichii	EBee EBrs ECho MPoH WWst
*	***hirtifolium*** var. ***album***	EBee EBrs ECho LAma LRHS
	'His Excellency'	CFir EBee EBrs ERCP IBal LAma LRHS
§	***hollandicum*** ♀H4	CAvo CBro CFFs CKno CWCL EBee EBrs ECha ECho ECtt EHrv EPfP GKir LAma MBel MNrw MWat NEgg NOrc SPer SPlb WFar WPer
	- 'Purple Sensation' ♀H4	Widely available
	- 'Purple Surprise' ♀H4	GKir
	hookeri ACE 2430	EBee EPot WCot
	- var. ***muliense***	GEdr
	howellii var. ***clokeyi*** new	WWst
	huber-morathii new	WWst
	humile	EBee ECho GEdr
	hyalinum	EBrs
	- pink-flowered	EBee WCon WCot WPrP
	hymenorrhizum	ECho
§	***insubricum*** ♀H4	EBrs ECho LEdu NBir NHol WAbe
	jajlae	see *A. rotundum* subsp. *jajlae*
	jesdianum	CBro ECho LRHS
§	- subsp. ***angustitepalum***	EBee EBrs
	- 'Michael Hoog'	see *A. rosenorum* 'Michael H. Hoog'
	- 'Purple King'	CPom EBee EBrs ECho LAma LRHS MNrw
	- white-flowered	EBrs
	kansuense	see *A. sikkimense*
	karataviense ♀H3	Widely available
	- subsp. ***henrikii*** new	WWst
	- 'Ivory Queen'	CAvo CBro CFFs CMea EBee EBrs ECha ECho ECtt EPfP ERCP GKev IBal LAma LRHS LSRN NHol SBch SPad SPlb WAul WFar WHil WWEG
	- 'Kara Tau'	ECho LRHS
	kazemunii	MPoH WWst
	kharputense	EBee
	komarovianum	see *A. thunbergii*
	lacunosum var. ***lacunosum***	ECho
	ledebourianum	EBee EBrs ECho LAma MPoH
	lenkoranicum	CAvo EBee EBrs ECho MPoH WCot WWst
	libani	WPer
§	***lineare***	ECho
	longicuspis	ECho
	loratum	WWst
	'Lucy Ball'	EBee EBrs ECho EPot ERCP LAma LRHS MBel NBir NLar
§	***macleanii***	CArn EBee EBrs ECho LAma LRHS
	macranthum	CPom EBee EBrs ECho EPot GEdr LRHS WCot
	- S&L 5369	MPoH WWst
	macrochaetum	ECho
	macropetalum	ECho
	mairei	EBee EBrs ECho EPot ERos LHop LLWP LRHS NMen NRya WTin

Name	Suppliers
§ - var. ***amabile***	ECho ERos GEdr LRHS NChi NRya NSla WThu
- - pink-flowered	ECho
- - red-flowered **new**	ECho
maximowiczii	EBee EBrs ECho
'Mercurius'	CMea EBee ERCP LRHS SPhx WCot
meteoricum	MPoH
moly	CArn CBro CWCL EBee EBrs ECho GKir IFoB LAma LRHS MBri MRav NBPC NGHP NRya SBch SMrm SRms SWal WCHb WCot WTin
- 'Jeannine' ♀H4	CBro CMea EBee EBrs ECho EPot LAma LRHS MMHG SPhx
'Mont Blanc'	CMea EBee EBrs ECho ELan ERCP GBin IPot LAma LRHS MNrw
multibulbosum	see *A. nigrum*
murrayanum misapplied	see *A. unifolium*
murrayanum Reg.	see *A. acuminatum*
myrianthum	EBee ECho
narcissiflorum misapplied	see *A. insubricum*
§ ***narcissiflorum*** Villars	ECho NWCA
neapolitanum	CArn EBee ECho EPot GBuc LAma LRHS MBri MCot SEND SMrm SPer SRms WGwG
§ - Cowanii Group	CBro EBee EBrs ECho EHrv LHop LRHS MWat WCot
- 'Grandiflorum'	CSam EBee EBrs ECho LRHS MBel SPhx WRHF
nevii	WWst
nevskianum	EBee EBrs ECho LAma LRHS
§ ***nigrum***	CArn CAvo CBro CFFs EBee EBrs ECho EHrv EPot ERCP LAma LRHS MBel MCot NBir SPhx WCot
nutans	CBod CPrp EBee EBrs ECho LAma LEdu MHer NGHP SHDw WHal WHil WJek
nuttallii	see *A. drummondii*
§ ***obliquum***	CArn EBee EBrs ECha ECho ERCP LRHS WCot WPrP WTin WWst
odorum L.	see *A. ramosum* L.
oleraceum	EBee ECho WHer
olympicum	ECho WWst
§ ***oreophilum***	CArn CBro CMea CSam EBee EBrs ECha ECho ECtt EHrv EPfP LAma LRHS MWat NRya NWCA SMrm SPer SRms STes WCot WHoo WTin WWEG
- 'Agalik'	ECho
- 'Agalik Giant'	ECho LRHS
- 'Zwanenburg' ♀H4	ECho EPot WCot
oreoprasum	ECho
ostrowskianum	see *A. oreophilum*
ovalifolium var. ***leuconeurum***	WCot
pallasii	ECho MPoH WWst
pallens	CBre ECho NBir
§ ***paniculatum***	CAvo EBrs ECho GKir SCnR WWst
- Hoa 0129	EBee
paradoxum	ECho LEdu NBir
- var. ***normale***	CBgR CBro CDes EBee EBrs ECho EPot ERCP MMHG NBir NMen WCot
pedemontanum	see *A. narcissiflorum* Villars
pendulinum	ECho WWst
peninsulare	CPBP
'Pinball Wizard'	CBro EBee ECho ERCP LAma LRHS MNrw
platycaule	WCot
platyspathum	ECho
plummerae	EBee EBrs ECho MPoH
plurifoliatum	ECho LAma
polyastrum	CPom
polyphyllum	see *A. carolinianum*
polyrrhizum	ECho
prattii	EBee
przewalskianum	ECho MPoH
pskemense	EBee ECho WCot
- RKMP 8207	MPoH
pulchellum	see *A. carinatum* subsp. *pulchellum*
'Purple Giant'	CBro ECho ERCP
pyrenaicum misapplied	see *A. angulosum*
pyrenaicum Costa & Vayreda	ELan
ramosum Jacquin	see *A. obliquum*
§ ***ramosum*** L.	EBee EBrs ECho LAma LEdu NCob NGHP WPer
'Renaissance'	ECho ERCP
'Rien Poortvliet'	CArn EBee ECho LAma
robustum	EBrs ECho
rosenbachianum misapplied	see *A. stipitatum*
rosenbachianum Regel	CArn CBro EBee EPot
- 'Akbulak'	EBrs ECho LRHS
- 'Album'	EBee EBrs ECha ECho EPot ERCP LAma LRHS MBel SPhx WCot
- 'Michael Hoog'	see *A. rosenorum* 'Michael H. Hoog'
- 'Purple King'	ECho
- 'Shing'	EBee EBrs IBal LAma LRHS
§ ***rosenorum*** 'Michael H. Hoog'	EBee EBrs ECho EPot LAma LRHS
roseum	CArn CMea CPBP CStu EBee EBrs ECho ECtt EPfP ERos LAma LLWP MDKP
- ***album***	ECho
§ - var. ***bulbiferum***	ECho
- 'Grandiflorum'	see *A. roseum* var. *bulbiferum*
rotundum	ECho LRHS MPoH
§ - subsp. ***jajlae***	EBee ECho LLWP MPoH
- subsp. ***rotundum***	ECho
'Round and Purple'	CPom EBee EBrs ERCP IPot LAma LRHS
rubellum	ERos
sanbornii var. ***sanbornii***	ECho
sarawschanicum	ECho WWst
- 'Bright Boy'	EBee ECho WWst
- 'Chinoro'	EBrs ECho
sativum	CArn ECho MHer MNHC NPri SIde SPoG SVic
- 'Albigensian Wight'	NGHP
- 'Arno' ♀H4	CPrp
- 'Chengdou'	ECho
- 'Cristo' ♀H4	CPrp
- 'Elephant'	see *A. ampeloprasum* 'Elephant'
- golden	GPoy
- 'Iberian Wight'	NGHP
- 'Lautrec'	NGHP
- 'Mediterranean Wight'	NGHP
- var. ***ophioscorodon***	EBee ECho GPoy ILis LAma
- - 'Early Wight' ♀H4	NGHP
- - 'Purple Wight'	NGHP
- 'Purple Heritage Moldovan'	NGHP
- 'Solent White' ♀H4	NGHP
- 'Sprint'	CPrp
- 'Thermidrôme'	ECho
saxatile	EBee EBrs ECho ERos
schmitzii	ECho
schoenoprasum	Widely available
- f. ***albiflorum***	CArn CPrp CSWP EBrs ECha ECho GMaP GPWP LEdu MHer NBir NCGa NHol SIde WCHb WHer
- 'Black Isle Blush'	GPoy LPla MHer
- 'Corsican White'	LEdu

- fine-leaved ELau
- 'Forescate' CBod CPrp EBee EBla EBrs ECha ECho EWes GBar LAma LAst LHop LRHS MRav NBir NGdn SBch SIde SPet SSvw WCHb
- medium-leaved ELau
- 'Netherbyres Dwarf' CArn ECho
- 'Pink Perfection' GPoy MHer
- 'Polyphant' CBre WCHb
- var. ***sibiricum*** ECho GBar GGar SDix WShi
- 'Silver Chimes' CDes CWan EBee MRav SBch SHDw
- thick-leaved ELau NPri
- 'Wallington White' GBar

schubertii Widely available
scorodoprasum EBWF EBee ECho SIde WCHb
- subsp. ***jajlae*** see *A. rotundum* subsp. *jajlae*
- subsp. ***scorodoprasum*** EBrs ECho LAma LEdu

semenowii ECho
senescens CArn CBro CTri EBee ECGP ERos LAma LRHS MRav NChi NWsh SApp SBch SEND SIng SRms SSvw WTin
- subsp. ***glaucum*** CArn CBgR CMea CPBP CPom CPrp CSpe CSsd EAEE EBee EBla EBrs ECha ECho EPla GEdr LEdu LPio LRHS MNFA NGdn NRya SAga SIng SMeo SPet WCot WPer WTin

§ - subsp. ***montanum*** CBro EBla ECha ECho EGoo EPot ERCP GAuc LAma LEdu LPio NBre NMen SDix SIng WAbe WClo WMoo
- subsp. ***senescens*** CAvo EBee EBrs ECho LEdu LPio MBel WPrP

serra new WCot
sessiliflorum ECho
setifolium ECho
sewerzowii ECho WWst
- ARJA 9883 MPoH

sibthorpianum see *A. paniculatum*
siculum see *Nectaroscordum siculum*
sieheanum EBee
§ ***sikkimense*** CFir CSsd CWCL EBee EBla ECho ERos GBee LBee LRHS MDKP NSla SPet SSvw WCon WCot WPer WPrP
- SBQE B EDAr

'Silver Spring' CAvo CMea CPom EBee ECho ERCP IPot LRHS SMeo SPhx
sinkiangense EBee
siskiyouense ECho
- NNS 02-43 WWst

sphaerocephalon Widely available
splendens EBrs ECho ERos
stellatum EBee LRHS WGwG WWst
stellerianum WPer
- var. ***kurilense*** CPBP ECho WThu

§ ***stipitatum*** EBee EBrs ECho ERCP LAma LRHS SPhx WCot
- 'Album' CArn CBro EBee EBrs ECho EPot LRHS
- 'Glory of Pamir' ECho LRHS
- 'Mars' CFir EBee EBrs ECho EPfP ERCP LAma LRHS MBel MCot NLar
- 'Mount Everest' CAvo CBro CFFs CFir EBee EBrs ECho EPot ERCP GMaP LAma LRHS MWat NBPC NPri SMrm SPer SPhx WClo WShi
- 'Violet Beauty' CMdw CWCL EBee ECho LAma LFur LRHS SPhx WCot
- 'White Giant' EBee EBrs ECho ERCP LRHS SPhx

stracheyi WCot
'Stratos' new ERCP
strictum Schrad. see *A. lineare*
strictum Ledeb. see *A. szovitsii*
suaveolens ECho
subhirsutum ECho
subvillosum ERos WCot
'Summer Beauty' see *A. senescens* subsp. *montanum*
'Summer Drummer' new ERCP
'Sweet Discovery' EBee EBrs ECho LAma LRHS
§ ***szovitsii*** ECho
tanguticum LRHS
tauricola new WWst
textile ERos
§ ***thunbergii*** ♀H4 CAvo CBgR EBee EBrs ECho NBir NDlv NRya SCnR WWEG
- 'Album' new SIng
- 'Nanum' CSsd
- 'Ozawa' EBee LBee LFur LRHS NMen SIng WAbe WCot

tibeticum see *A. sikkimense*
togashii ECho
* ***tournefortii*** EBee ECho
triquetrum EBee EBrs ECho ELan ELau EPfP EPot GGar GPWP IBlr ILis LAma LEdu NBir NSti SEND SIng SPhx WCot WHer WMoo
tuberosum Widely available
- B&SWJ 8881 WCru
- purple/mauve-flowered CHby ECho ELau

tubiflorum ECho
turkestanicum ECho
umbilicatum new WWst
§ ***unifolium*** ♀H4 CArn CAvo CBgR CBro CFFs CPom CSam EBee EBrs ECho EPfP EPot ERCP GKev LAma LHop MBel MNrw MRav NBir SGar SPhx WAbe WCot WFar WPer
ursinum CArn CBgR CHby CWan EBWF EBee EBrs ECho EOHP GGar GPWP GPoy LAma MWat NGHP NMir SECG SVic WAul WCHb WFar WJek WShi
'Valerie Finnis' CPBP
victorialis EBee EBrs ECho WCot
- 'Cantabria' EBee WWst

vineale CArn EBWF NMir WHer
§ - 'Hair' EBee EBrs ECho EPfP ERCP ITim LAma LRHS MCot NBir SGar SMad WCon WHil
violaceum see *A. carinatum*
virgunculae CPBP CStu WAbe
wallichii EBee EBrs ECho GAuc GMaP MBNS NBir NChi WCot WTin
- ACE 2458 WCot
- purple-flowered GEdr

'World Cup' LRHS
woronowii new WWst
zaprjagajevii ECho WCot
zebdanense EBee EBrs ECho ERos LAma LRHS

Allocasuarina (*Casuarinaceae*)

monilifera ECou

almond see *Prunus dulcis*

Alnus ✿ (*Betulaceae*)

cordata ♀H4 CBcs CCVT CDoC CDul CLnd CMCN CMac CSBt CSto CTho CTri EBee ECrN ELan EMac EPfP EWTr GKir IFFs LBuc LMaj MGos NEgg NWea SPer SPlb SSta WDin WFar WMou
cremastogyne EGFP NLar
crispa see *A. viridis* subsp. *crispa*
fauriei from Niigata, Japan CSto

firma	CDul CMCN CSto IDee
glutinosa	CBcs CCVT CDoC CDul CLnd CMac CRWN CSBt CTri ECrN EMac EPfP EWTr GKir IFFs LBuc LMaj MGos NBlu NWea SPer WDin WMou
- from Corsica	CSto
- 'Aurea'	CDul CEnd CLnd CTho CWib ECrN GKir MBlu MGos SPer
- var. ***barbata***	CSto
- 'Imperialis' ♀H4	CCVT CDoC CDul CEnd CPMA CTho EBee ECrN ELan EPfP EWTr GKir LBuc LHop LRHS MAsh MBlu MBri MDun MMuc NBro NPal NWea SBch SPer SPoG WDin
- 'Laciniata'	CDoC CDul CMac CTho ECrN GKir MBlu MDun MGos NBlu WFar
hirsuta	CMCN CSto
incana	CDoC CDul CLnd CMCN CWib EBee ECrN EMac GKir LBuc MBar MGos MMuc MSnd NWea SPer WDin WMou
- 'Aurea'	CBcs CDul CEnd CLnd CMac CTho EBee ECrN ELan EMil EPfP ERas GAuc GKir IArd LMaj LRHS MBlu MBri MGos NBea NBro NEgg NPal SBch SPer SPoG WDin WFar WPat
- 'Laciniata'	CTho MGos NLar SCoo WDin WFar
- 'Pendula'	CTho LRHS
japonica	CSto NLar
maximowiczii	CSto NLar
nitida	CMCN CSto IDee
oregana	see *A. rubra*
pendula	CSto
- B&SWJ 10895	WCru
rhombifolia	CMCN
§ ***rubra***	CCVT CDoC CDul CLnd CMCN ECrN ELan EMac GKir NWea WDin WMou
- f. ***pinnatisecta***	CMCN CTho MBlu
§ ***rugosa***	CMCN
serrulata	see *A. rugosa*
sieboldiana	CSto
× ***spaethii***	CDoC GKir LRHS MBlu MMuc
subcordata	CSto
viridis	CAgr CSto ECrN NWea
§ - subsp. ***crispa***	CSto GKir
- subsp. ***sinuata***	CAgr CSto GAuc GKir

Alocasia ✿ (*Araceae*)

× ***amazonica*** ♀H1	ERea MBri XBlo
- 'Polly'	LRHS
- 'Polly Bambino'	LRHS
'Calidora'	CDTJ
cucullata	XBlo
gageana	CDTJ
macrorrhiza	CDTJ EAmu SBig SBst
odora	CDTJ EAmu XBlo
plumbea	XBlo
'Portodora'	EAmu LRHS WCot
robusta	CDTJ
wentii	CDTJ EAmu LRHS WCot

Aloe × *Gasteria* see × *Gasteraloe*

Aloe (*Aloaceae*)

aculeata	CAbb EShb WCot
africana	CAbb
alooides	CAbb
arborescens	CAbb CBrP CDTJ CHEx EShb EWll IDee LRHS MAga SBst SChr SEND
aristata ♀H1	CAbb CHEx ERea ETod MAga MBri SAPC SArc SBch SChr SEND SWvt WCor WGwG WPGP
barbadensis	see *A. vera*
barberae	CAbb CCCN EShb
'Bedford's Beau' **new**	MAga
bellatula	MAga
'Black Frost' **new**	MAga
bowiea **new**	MAga
branddraaiensis	WCot
'Brazen' **new**	MAga
brevifolia ♀H1	CAbb CBrP EAmu EShb MAga SAPC SArc SBst
broomii	CAbb CCCN EPfP MAga SChr
camperi	MAga
- 'Maculata'	SChr SEND
castanea	CAbb
chabaudii **new**	MAga
ciliaris	ERea EShb SChr
comptonii	CAbb EShb MAga
cooperi	CAbb CCCN CDTJ EShb
* ***delaetii*** **new**	MAga
deltoideodonta	MAga
ISI 898 **new**	
descoingsii ♀H1	MAga
ISI 948 **new**	
descoingsii × ***bakeri*** × ***parvula***	MAga
descoingsii × ***haworthioides*** **new**	MAga
descoingsii × ***rauhii*** **new**	MAga
dewetii	CAbb
dichotoma	CAbb EShb
distans	SEND
'Doran Black' **new**	MAga
dyeri **new**	MAga
ecklonis	CAbb CCCN CTrC SPlb
ferox	CAbb CBod CBrP CCCN CDTJ CTrC EShb GPoy LRHS MAga SBch SBig SChr SEND SWal
'Firebird' **new**	MAga
'Flurry' **new**	MAga
fosteri	CAbb CBrP CDTJ
gariepensis	MAga
globuligemma	CAbb
- ISI 1248	MAga
'Gold Rush' **new**	MAga
'Grande' **new**	MAga
greatheadii	CTrC
- var. ***davyana***	CAbb
harlana ISI 334	MAga
haworthioides ♀H1 **new**	MAga
hereroensis ISI 89-34 **new**	MAga
'Hey Babe' **new**	MAga
humilis	CBrP CTrC MAga SChr SEND
imalotensis	MAga
immaculata	WCot
jucunda ISI 533 **new**	MAga
juvenna	MAga
karasbergensis	MAga
kedongensis **new**	SEND
krapohliana	CAbb
littoralis	CAbb
'Lizard Lips' **new**	MAga
maculata	CDTJ CTrC SEND
- ISI 537	MAga
marlothii	CAbb CCCN EShb
- ISI 92-37	MAga
melanacantha ♀H1 **new**	STre
microstigma	CAbb CCCN
- ISI 1249	MAga

'Midnight' new	MAga
'Midnight Child' new	MAga
'Midnight Exchange' new	MAga
'Midnight Feast' new	MAga
millotii new	MAga
mitriformis	CBrP EPfP MAga SChr SEND
mutabilis	CHEx CTrC SChr SEND
parvula ISI 23 new	MAga
peglerae	CAbb MAga
'Pepe' new	MAga
petricola	CAbb
'Pink Lace' new	MAga
plicatilis	CAbb CCCN CDTJ EShb MAga
polyphylla	EAmu WPGP
pratensis	CCCN CDTJ SChr
'Quicksilver' new	MAga
ramosissima	EShb
rauhii ♀H1 new	MAga
rauhii × ***sinkatana*** ISI 97-54 new	MAga
rauhii × ***somaliensis*** new	MAga
reitzii	CAbb CTrC
sinkatana new	MAga
'Snowflake' new	MAga
somaliensis ♀H1 ISI 133 new	MAga
speciosa	CAbb EShb
spicata	CAbb
× ***spinosissima***	SChr STre
striata	CAbb CCCN EShb SChr
- ISI 627	MAga
striatula	CAbb CBrP CDTJ CGHE CHEx CTrC EAmu EBee EShb IBlr LPJP LRHS SAPC SArc SBHP SBig SChr SEND SMad WCot WPGP
- var. ***caesia***	IBlr
succotrina	CAbb
suprafoliata new	MAga
swynnertonii new	MAga
'Teigelberg Triumph' new	MAga
thraskii	CAbb
vaombe ISI 95-21 new	MAga
variegata (v) ♀H1	CSpe EShb STre SWal SWvt
§ ***vera*** ♀H1	CArn CCCN CDoC CHby COld CSpe EOHP ERea EShb GPWP GPoy ILis LRHS MNHC NPer NPri NScw SBch SEND SIde SVic SWal WCot
'White Diamond' new	MAga
wickensii	CAbb

Alonsoa (*Scrophulariaceae*)

'Bright Spark'	CSpe
incisifolia	CCCN
meridionalis	CCCN
- 'Rebel'	LSou SBch
* - 'Salmon Beauty'	LAst
'Pink Beauty'	CSpe NBur
unilabiata	CSpe
warscewiczii	CCCN CHll ELan
- 'Peachy-keen'	CSpe

Alopecurus (*Poaceae*)

alpinus	see *A. borealis*
§ ***borealis***	MMoz
- subsp. ***glaucus***	CSpe EAlp EBee EHoe ELan EPPr GBin NSti SIng SPer WWEG
geniculatus	CRWN
lanatus	NBea
pratensis	EBWF NOrc
- 'Aureovariegatus' (v)	CWan EBee EHoe EPPr EPla GKir GMaP LBMP LRHS MBar MMoz NBPC NBid NHol SApp SLim SPer WFar WMoo
- 'Aureus'	ECha GBin LRHS MRav NBro NSti SPlb WWEG
- 'No Overtaking' (v)	EPPr

Alophia (*Iridaceae*)

drummondii	ERos
lahue	see *Herbertia lahue*

Aloysia (*Verbenaceae*)

citriodora	see *A. triphylla*
gratissima	EOHP
§ ***triphylla*** ♀H2	Widely available

Alpinia (*Zingiberaceae*)

B&SWJ 3775	WPGP
formosana	LEdu
- f. ***variegata*** new	LRHS
galanga	CArn
japonica	CPLG LEdu
- B&SWJ 8889	WCru
officinarum	CArn
zerumbet 'Variegata' (v)	EShb XBlo

Alsobia see *Episcia*

Alstroemeria (*Alstroemeriaceae*)

'Adonis'	LRHS WViv
'Aimi'	CFir LRHS MBri SPer SWal SWvt WFar
'Alexis'	LRHS WViv
Amanda = 'Stabuwit' new	EMui
'Angelina'	LRHS SWvt
'Apollo' ♀H4	CBcs CFir CTsd LRHS MBNS MBri MNrw NBre SPer SWvt
'Athena' new	WViv
aurantiaca	see *A. aurea*
§ ***aurea***	GGar MRav NBPC NLar SRms
- 'Apricot'	GCal
- 'Dover Orange'	IGor SCoo SEND
- 'Lutea'	EBrs EWll NBre SPlb
- 'Orange King'	CTsd EBee EBrs EGxp ELan EPfP EWll NLar SMrm WCot
'Avanti'	LRHS WViv
'Blushing Bride'	CFir ELon LRHS MBNS MBri SWvt
'Bolero'	WViv
'Bonanza'	SLon SPer
brasiliensis	CBgR CTsd EBee EShb GCal LHop MNrw NChi WCot WSHC WViv
Butterfly hybrids	SWal
'Cahors' new	LRHS
'Candy Floss'	EBee EPfP
'Cerres' new	LRHS
'Champagne Bucket' new	LRHS
'Charm'	WFar WViv
'Christina' PBR	LRHS MBNS SLon SWvt WViv
'Coronet' ♀H4	MBNS WViv
'Dandy Candy'	CAbP CWGN EBrs ECtt ELon ITim MDun MNrw NBPC NLar SPoG WClo WCot
'Devotion'	LRHS MGos
Diana, Princess of Wales = 'Stablaco'	EMui
diluta subsp. ***chrysantha*** F&W 8700	WCot
Doctor Salter's hybrids	ECGP LLHF SRms
'Douceur d'Automne' new	LRHS
'Dutch Pink'	SEND
'Dwarf Lemon'	SEND
'Dwarf Pink'	SEND

'Elvira'	LRHS SPer WViv
'Eternal Love'	EMui
'Evening Song'	CFir EKen LRHS MBNS SLon SPer SWvt WViv
'Flaming Star'	CBcs LRHS MBri WCot WViv
'Freedom'	CAbP CBgR COIW CWGN EBee ECtt ELon GBin LAst MBNS NBPC NEgg NGdn SMad SMrm SPoG SUsu WClo WCot WSpi
'Friendship' ♀H4	CBcs CTsd LRHS NBre SWvt WViv
'Gloria'	MBNS SWvt WViv
'Glory of the Andes' (v)	CWGN NGdn NLar
'Golden Delight'	LRHS MBri SPer WViv
'Golden Queen'	WFar
H.R.H. Princess Alexandra = 'Zelblanca' ♀H2	EMui
§ H.R.H. Princess Alice = 'Staverpi' ♀H2	EMui GKir
haemantha	EBrs MDKP
I 'Hatch Hybrid'	GCal
'Hawera'	GCal SMrm
hookeri	CStu EBee ECho GCal GGar GKev NLar SCnR
- subsp. ***cummingiana***	LLHF WCot
Inca Adore = 'Koadore'PBR	LHop MAvo
Inca Classic **new**	WViv
Inca Desert = 'Konesert' **new**	WViv
Inca Devotion = 'Konevotio'	WViv
Inca Exotica = 'Koexotica'PBR	LRHS MGos WViv
Inca Glow = 'Koglow'PBR	LRHS MGos WViv
Inca Ice = 'Koice'	LHop LRHS MAvo MGos WViv
Inca Moonlight = 'Komolight'	WViv
Inca Obsession = 'Koobsion'	LRHS WViv
Inca Pride = 'Kopride' **new**	WViv
Inca Pulse = 'Konpulse'	WViv
Inca Serin = 'Koserin'PBR	CBgR WViv
Inca Tropic = 'Kotrop'	LRHS MAvo MGos WViv
Intichana Red = 'Tesrobiri' **new**	EGxp
Jubilee = 'Stalilas'	EMui
kingii	see *A. versicolor*
'Laguna' **new**	WViv
ligtu hybrids	CAvo CBcs CFFs CSBt EBrs ECha ELan EPfP IFoB LAst LHop MDun MNrw MWat NPer NVic SRms SRot SWvt WBrE WFar WHoo
- var. ***ligtu***	SPhx WCot
'Lilac Wonder'	NBhm
'Little Eleanor'	GBin WCot WFar WViv
'Little Miss Charlotte'	WFar WViv
'Little Miss Davina' **new**	NPri WViv
'Little Miss Isabel'	LRHS WViv
'Little Miss Matilda'	WViv
'Little Miss Rosanna'	WViv
'Little Miss Roselind'	see *A.* 'Roselind'
'Little Miss Veronica'	MBNS WViv
'Lucinda'	CBcs MBri SWvt
magnifica	WCot
- subsp. ***magnifica***	WCot
Manon	see *A.* Princess Marie-Louise
'Marina'	MBNS
'Marissa'	GMaP
'Mars'	GKir SWal
Meyer hybrids	EWTr MTho
Monika = 'Stalmon'	EMui
'Moulin Rouge'	LRHS MBNS MBri SLon WViv
'Natalie'	NPri WViv
'Neptune'	LRHS
'Orange Gem' ♀H4	MBNS WFar
'Orange Glory' ♀H4	GKir GMaP IArd LRHS MBNS SWvt WFar WViv WWlt
'Orange Supreme'	WViv
'Oriana'	LRHS MBri SWvt WViv
pallida	CPBP WCot
- JCA 2.028.500	WCot
patagonica 'Maxi'	CPBP
pelegrina	EBrs ECho MTho
- 'Alba'	ELan
- 'Rosea'	ELan
'Perfect Blue'	LRHS WViv
'Perfect Love'	EMui MNrw
philippii	WCot
'Phoenix' (v)	CFir LRHS SLon SWvt
'Pink Perfection'	NLar
'Polka'	MBNS
presliana RB 94103	WCot
- subsp. ***australis***	SMrm
Princess Aiko = 'Zapriko'PBR	EMui LRHS
Princess Alice	see *A.* H.R.H. Princess Alice
Princess Angela = 'Staprilan'PBR	CBcs EMui LRHS MBNS NLar SCoo
Princess Anouska = 'Zaprinous'PBR	EMui LRHS MNrw SLon
Princess Astrid = 'Stabopink'	EMui
Princess Beatrix = 'Stadoran'	EMui GKir
Princess Camilla = 'Stapricamil'PBR	CBcs EMui LRHS SLon SPer SPoG
Princess Carmina = 'Stasilva'	EMui
§ Princess Caroline = 'Stakaros'	EMui
§ Princess Charlotte = 'Staprizsa'PBR	EMui GKir LRHS
Princess Daniela = 'Stapridani'PBR	EMui SCoo SPoG
Princess Domanique **new**	EMui
Princess Elizabeth	see *A.* Queen Elizabeth The Queen Mother = 'Stamoli'
Princess Ella = 'Staprirange'	EMui LRHS NLar
Princess Emily = 'Staprimil'	EMui
Princess Fabiana = 'Zaprifabi'PBR	LRHS SPoG
* Princess Freckles	EMui
Princess Frederika = 'Stabronza'	EMui GKir
Princess Grace = 'Starodo'	EMui GKir
Princess Ileana = 'Stalvir'	EMui
Princess Isabella = 'Zapribel'PBR	EMui LRHS
Princess Ivana = 'Staprivane'PBR	EMui LRHS NLar SPoG
Princess Juliana = 'Staterpa'	EMui SPoG
Princess Julieta = 'Zaprijul'PBR	EMui LRHS SPoG
Princess Letizia **new**	MNrw
Princess Leyla = 'Stapriley'PBR	CBcs EMui LRHS MBNS MNrw SLon SPer SPoG
'Princess Margaret'	EMui GKir NLar
'Princess Margarita'	EMui
§ Princess Marie-Louise = 'Zelanon'	EMui

Princess Marilene = 'Staprilene'PBR — EMui LRHS MBNS
Princess Mary = 'Zaprimary'PBR **new** — EMui MNrw
Princess Mira = 'Stapripur' — EMui
Princess Monica = 'Staprimon'PBR — EMui GKir MBNS SPoG
Princess Morana = 'Staprirana' — EMui
Princess Oxana = 'Staprioxa'PBR — EMui MNrw NLar SCoo
Princess Pamela = 'Stapripame' — EMui
Princess Paola = 'Stapripal'PBR — EMui MBNS MNrw SCoo
Princess Ragna — see *A.* Princess Stephanie
Princess Samora **new** — EMui
Princess Sara = 'Staprisara'PBR — LRHS MNrw SPoG
Princess Sarah = 'Stalicamp' — EMui MBNS
Princess Sissi = 'Staprisis'PBR — EMui MNrw SPoG
§ Princess Sophia = 'Stajello' — EMui SPoG
§ Princess Stephanie = 'Stapirag' — EMui GKir NLar
Princess Susana = 'Staprisusa'PBR — EMui NLar SCoo SPoG
Princess Theresa = 'Zapriteres'PBR **new** — EMui
Princess VictoriaPBR — see *A.* 'Victoria'
Princess Violet — EMui
Princess Zavina = 'Staprivina'PBR — CBcs CFir EMui MBNS MNrw NLar SPer
Princess Zsa ZsaPBR — see *A.* Princess Charlotte
§ ***psittacina*** — Widely available
- 'Mona Lisa' — EShb EWll LLHF NLar WCot WViv
- 'Royal Star' (v) — CBro CWCL EBee EBla ELan ELon EPPr EPfP EPla GCal MAvo MDun MRav NLar SHar SPoG WCom WCot WFar WHil WHoo WPrP WSHC WWEG
pulchella Sims — see *A. psittacina*
pulchra — LLHF
'Purple Rain' — LRHS MBri MNrw SLon SWvt WViv
pygmaea — MTho
§ Queen Elizabeth The Queen Mother = 'Stamoli' — EMui GKir
'Red Beauty' (v) — see *A.* 'Spitfire'
'Red Beauty' — GKir GMaP LRHS MBNS MBri NBir SPer SPlb SWvt WCot
'Red Elf' — MBNS NBre SUsu SWvt WFar
'Regina'PBR — see *A.* 'Victoria'
'Rhubarb and Custard' — EBee EPfP
§ 'Roselind' — CFir LRHS MBNS NPri SWvt WViv
'Rosy Wonder' — NMoo
'Saturne' **new** — LRHS
'Selina' — GBin MBNS NBre SWal WFar WViv
'Serenade' — CBcs LRHS
'Short Purple' — WCot
'Sirius' — LRHS
'Solent Wings' — WFar
'Sonata' — WViv
'Sophie'PBR — LRHS MBNS NPri SLon SWvt WHlf WViv
'Sovereign' — MDKP
§ 'Spitfire' (v) — GKir LRHS MBri SLon SWvt WCom WViv
'Spring Delight' (v) — WCot
'Staroko' — see *A.* Princess Caroline
'Strawberry Lace' — EBee EPfP
'Sunrise' — WWlt
'Sunstar' — GMaP
'Sweet Laura'PBR — ECtt GGar LAst LLHF LLWG LSRN NBPC NEgg NLar WClo
'Tanya' — WViv
'Tara'PBR — MBNS NPri SWvt WViv
'Tessa' — LRHS MBNS NBre SLon WViv
'Turkish Delight' — EBee EPfP
'Uranus' — LRHS
'Ventura' — WViv
§ ***versicolor*** — WCot
§ 'Victoria'PBR — EMui GKir
'White Queen' — WViv
'Yellow Friendship' ♀H4 — MBNS NLar SPlb SWvt WFar
Yellow King — see *A.* Princess Sophia

Alternanthera (*Amaranthaceae*)

dentata 'Purple Knight' — EShb LRHS

Althaea (*Malvaceae*)

armeniaca — EBee LBMP NLar WCot
cannabina — CAby CFir CSpe ELan GCal GQui MHer MWea SGSe SUsu WBor WHal WHoo WOld WSHC
officinalis — CArn CPrp CSev CWan EBWF ELan GBar GMac GPoy ILis MHer MNHC SECG SIde WGwG WPer WSpi
- ***alba*** — LSou NLar WCom WHer
§ - 'Romney Marsh' — EBee EWll GCal MRav NCot SBHP WFar WKif WSHC
rosea — see *Alcea rosea*
rugosostellulata — see *Alcea rugosa*

Altingia (*Hamamelidaceae*)

gracilipes — WPGP
poilanei B&SWJ 11756 **new** — WCru

× *Alworthia* (*Aloaceae*)

'Black Gem' — CBct EBee EShb EWll LSou

Alyogyne (*Malvaceae*)

'Attraction' **new** — ECou
hakeifolia — CSpe ECou
- 'Elle Maree' — ECou
- 'Melissa Anne' — ECou
§ ***huegelii*** — CBcs ECou ELon ERas EShb LRHS SRkn WDyG
- 'Lavender Lass' — ECou
- 'Santa Cruz' — CCCN CHll CMdw CSpe ECou ERea LHop MAsh SEND SUsu WPGP

Alyssoides (*Brassicaceae*)

utriculata — WPer

Alyssum (*Brassicaceae*)

montanum — ECha ECho NBlu SPlb SRms WMoo
§ - 'Berggold' — ECho EPfP LRHS
- 'Luna' — EAlp
- Mountain Gold — see *A. montanum* 'Berggold'
oxycarpum — CMea WAbe
saxatile — see *Aurinia saxatilis*
scardicum — LLHF
serpyllifolium — NWCA
§ ***spinosum*** 'Roseum' ♀H4 — CMea CSpe CTri ECha ELan EPot GMaP LBee LRHS MLHP MWat NMen NWCA SBch WAbe WFar WPer
* - 'Roseum Variegatum' — EPot
- 'Strawberries and Cream' — WAbe WFar
tortuosum — SEND WMoo
wulfenianum — EDAr IFoB LLHF NLar SEND STre

Amaranthus (*Amaranthaceae*)

	hypochondriacus 'Pygmy Torch' Υ^{H3}	CSpe

× *Amarcrinum* (*Amaryllidaceae*)

	'Dorothy Hannibal'	WCot
	memoria-corsii	CPrp ECho
	- 'Howardii'	CDes CFir EBee EBrs ECho EShb LEdu LPio LRHS WCot

× *Amarine* (*Amaryllidaceae*)

	tubergenii	CAvo
	- 'Zwanenburg'	CAby EBee WCot

× *Amarygia* (*Amaryllidaceae*)

§	***parkeri*** 'Alba'	CBro EBee EBrs ECho LPio WCot
	- 'Rosea'	EBrs

Amaryllis (*Amaryllidaceae*)

§	***belladonna*** Υ^{H2-3}	CAby CBcs CBro CHEx CPne CPrp EBee EBrs ECho EPfP ERCP EShb LAma LEdu LRHS MBri NBPC NCGa SChr SDnm SEND SMrm SPav WCot WHil
	- 'Bloemfontein'	CAvo
	- 'Johannesburg'	CAvo WCot
	- 'Kimberley'	CPne
	- 'Major'	CAvo
	- 'Parkeri Alba'	see × *Amarygia parkeri* 'Alba'
	- 'Purpurea'	EBrs LRHS WCot
	- white-flowered	EBee ECho WCot
	- 'Windhoek'	CAvo

Amberboa (*Asteraceae*)

§	***moschata***	WCot

Ambrosina (*Araceae*)

	bassii	EBrs
	- from Tunisia	ECho WCot

Amelanchier ✿ (*Rosaceae*)

	alnifolia	EPla LRHS
	- 'Forestburg'	MBri
	- 'Obelisk'[PBR]	CDoC CDul EBee LBuc LHop LLHF LRHS MAsh MBri MGos NCGa NLar SCoo SPoG SSta
§	- var. ***pumila***	CPMA LHop LRHS WTin
	- 'Smokey'	CDul NLar
§	***arborea***	SRms
	bartramiana	CTho LRHS SSta
	- 'Eskimo'	NLar
	canadensis K. Koch	see *A. lamarckii*
	canadensis Sieb. & Zucc.	see *A. arborea*
	canadensis ambig.	GAuc GKir IFFs NPri
	canadensis (L.) Medik.	Widely available
	- Rainbow Pillar = 'Glenn Form' **new**	MBlu
	denticulata F&M 176	WPGP
	× ***grandiflora*** 'Autumn Brilliance'	CEnd CPMA LRHS NHol NLar
	- 'Ballerina' Υ^{H4}	Widely available
	- 'Princess Diana'	EBee LRHS MAsh MBlu NLar
	- 'Robin Hill'	CBcs CMac CWSG EBee ECrN ELon EMil GKir LAst LBuc LRHS MBlu MGos MRav NEgg NLar SCoo SLim WFar WPat
	- 'Rubescens'	CDul CEnd CPMA EBee EPfP GKir LRHS
	humilis	GAuc
	'La Paloma'	CWSG EBee GKir LRHS MBri SCoo
	laevis	CBcs CDul CTri EPfP MGos NLar SPer STre WGor
	- 'Cumulus'	NLar
	- 'Prince Charles'	MBri NLar
	- 'R.J. Hilton'	EBee GKir MBri SCoo
	- 'Snow Cloud'	CDoC
	- 'Snowflakes'	CDoC CEnd CPMA CWSG EBee GKir LRHS MAsh MDun MGos NHol NLar SLim SPoG SPur
§	***lamarckii*** Υ^{H4}	Widely available
	ovalis Medik.	SPlb
	- 'Edelweiss'	CEnd CPMA LRHS MGos NEgg NLar SCoo
	- 'Helvetia'	WEas
	pumila	see *A. alnifolia* var. *pumila*
	rotundifolia ambig. **new**	MCoo
	spicata	ECrN IFFs MCoo

Amianthium (*Melanthiaceae*)

	muscitoxicum	LRHS

Amicia (*Papilionaceae*)

	zygomeris	CBot CHEx CHll CMdw CPom CSpe EBee ELon EWes EWld GBuc GCal MCot SAga SDix SMad SMrm SPoG WBor WCot WSHC

Ammi (*Apiaceae*)

	majus	CArn CSpe MCot SDix
	visnaga	CArn CBre CSpe WHal

Ammocharis (*Amaryllidaceae*)

	coranica	ECho WCot

Ammophila (*Poaceae*)

	arenaria	CBod CRWN EBWF GFor GQui

Amomyrtus (*Myrtaceae*)

§	***luma***	CAgr CDoC CDul CHEx CTrG CTri ELan GQui IDee IFFs SAPC SArc WCot

Amorpha (*Papilionaceae*)

	candicans **new**	SEND
	canescens	CBcs EBee GKir LRHS MBri SPlb WBVN WSHC
	fruticosa	CBcs EShb EWTr LEdu MBlu MBri NLar SPlb
	herbacea	NLar
	ouachitensis	NLar
	paniculata	NLar

Amorphophallus ✿ (*Araceae*)

	albispathus **new**	WCot
	albus	CDTJ LEdu WCot
	bulbifer	CDTJ EAmu EBee EBrs LAma LRHS SBig WPGP
	dunnii	CDTJ
	kerrii	CPLG WCot
	kiusianus B&SWJ 4845	WCru
	konjac	CDTJ CDes CFir CGHE CHEx CPLG EAmu EBee LEdu LRHS SHaC WCot WPGP WPat
	nepalensis	CDTJ EBee EBrs
	paeoniifolius	SBig
	rivieri	EBee EBrs GCal
	stipitatus	CAby WCot
	yunnanensis	EBee

Ampelocalamus (*Poaceae*)

	scandens	CGHE EPla WPGP

Ampelocissus (Vitaceae)

sikkimensis HWJK 2066	WCru

Ampelodesmos (Poaceae)

mauritanica	CHar CHrt CKno COIW CSam EBee ECha EHoe EPPr EShb EWes GFor LOck LRHS MWhi NLar SEND SMad SPlb WCot WPGP WRHF WWEG

Ampelopsis (Vitaceae)

aconitifolia	ELon MGos NLar
- 'Chinese Lace'	EBee LHop LRHS MRav NLar WPGP
brevipedunculata	ELan LHop MMHG SCoo SGar SLim SPer WDin WFar
- var. ***maximowiczii*** 'Elegans' (v)	CBcs CHEx CMac CWib EBee ELan EPfP EShb LAst LHop LRHS MBar MGos MRav MSwo NBlu NBro SAga SPer SPoG STes SWvt WCot WDin WPat WSHC
delavayana	EBee
henryana	see *Parthenocissus henryana*
megalophylla	CBot CHEx EBee ELan EPfP EShb GCal IDee MBri NCGa NLar SPer WBVN WCru WFar
sempervirens hort. ex Veitch	see *Cissus striata*
tricuspidata 'Veitchii'	see *Parthenocissus tricuspidata* 'Veitchii'

Amphicome see *Incarvillea*

Amsonia (Apocynaceae)

ciliata	CFir CHid EBee ELan SMad WPer
elliptica	EBee
hubrichtii	CAby CEnt CMdw EBee EBrs ECha ELon EPPr GBuc LBMP LHop SMad SMrm WCot WHoo WPer WPnP
illustris	CAbP CEnt EBee EBrs GCal GKir GMac LRHS SHar SUsu WHoo WHrl WPer WRHF WTin
§ ***orientalis***	CHar CHll CMea CTri EBee ECha EHrv GBBs GBuc GCal LEdu LHop MBri MLHP MRav SAga SGar SMrm SPhx SPoG SUsu WAul WBor WCAu WFar WOld WPnP WPtf WTin
tabernaemontana	Widely available
- var. ***salicifolia***	CAby CEnt EBee GKir LRHS NBPC WAbb WCAu WTin

Amygdalus see *Prunus*

Anacamptis (Orchidaceae)

× ***callithea***	NLAp
champagneuxii	NLAp
§ ***laxiflora***	NLAp
longicornu × ***morio***	NLAp
§ ***morio***	GAuc NLAp
- ***alba*** × ***sancta***	NLAp
morio × ***papilionacea***	NLAp
palustris	NLAp
pyramidalis	EFEx NLAp WHer
sancta	NLAp

Anacyclus (Asteraceae)

pyrethrum	GPoy
- var. ***depressus***	CTri EBee ECho ELan EPfP EPot GKir GMaP LRHS NBlu NVic NWCA SIng SPlb WCFE WFar WHoo WPer WRHF
- - 'Garden Gnome'	CTri ECho MSCN SRms WFar
- - 'Silberkissen'	EDAr SBch

Anagallis (Primulaceae)

arvensis	MHer
- var. ***caerulea***	SHlg
monellii Blue Compact = 'Wesanacomp'	LSou SVil
- subsp. ***linifolia*** 'Blue Light'	CSpe
- 'Skylover'	CCCN LAst NPri
- 'Sunrise'	CPBP LAst SUsu
tenella 'Studland'	CEnt EPot GAbr NWCA SIng WAbe

Anagyris (Papilionaceae)

foetida	WCot

Ananas (Bromeliaceae)

comosus (F)	CCCN LRHS
- var. ***variegatus*** (v)	LRHS MBri
'Elyne'	LRHS

Anaphalioides (Asteraceae)

§ ***bellidioides***	CTri ECha ECou GGar

Anaphalis (Asteraceae)

alpicola	EBee EPot NMen
margaritacea	CBcs CSBt EBee ECha ECtt GMaP LRHS MMuc NBid SRms WFar WMoo WPtf
§ - 'Neuschnee'	CTri CWan EBee EPfP NBPC NBre NGdn NPri WFar WPer WWEG
- New Snow	see *A. margaritacea* 'Neuschnee'
- var. ***yedoensis*** ♀H4	CTri MCot MLHP NBre SDix SGar SPer WBrE WCAu
§ ***nepalensis*** var. ***monocephala***	ELan MCot NBre NSti WCAu
nubigena	see *A. nepalensis* var. *monocephala*
transnokoensis	EBee EWes
§ ***trinervis***	CPLG
triplinervis ♀H4	CHrt EBee ECrN EHoe ELan EPPr EPfP GGar GKir GMaP IFoB LRHS MBel MCot MRav NBid NBir NVic SMrm SPer SPoG SRms WBor WCot WFar WHoo WMoo WWEG
- 'Silberregen'	EBee
§ - 'Sommerschnee' ♀H4	EBee ECha ECtt EPfP GKir LBMP LRHS MBri MCot MRav NEgg SPer WMnd WPer
- Summer Snow	see *A. triplinervis* 'Sommerschnee'

Anchusa (Boraginaceae)

angustissima	see *A. leptophylla* subsp. *incana*
§ ***azurea***	CArn EBee EGxp WPer
- 'Dropmore'	CTri EBee ELan EPfP GJos LAst LRHS MAvo MLHP MNHC NBPC NEgg NOrc SMrm SPad SPav SRms SSth WPer WWEG
- 'Feltham Pride'	CSBt EBee GJos GKir LRHS MBri SPav SRms SWvt WFar WHoo WPGP WPer
- 'Little John'	EBee SRms
- 'Loddon Royalist' ♀H4	Widely available
- 'Opal'	EBee ECtt EPfP GCal LRHS MMHG WCAu
- 'Royal Blue'	CElw GKir
caespitosa misapplied	see *A. leptophylla* subsp. *incana*
capensis 'Blue Angel'	MNHC SWvt WFar
cespitosa Lam.	ECho ELan EWes LLHF SIng WAbe
italica	see *A. azurea*
laxiflora	see *Borago pygmaea*
§ ***leptophylla*** subsp. ***incana***	SBch
- - F&W 9550	MDKP
myosotidiflora	see *Brunnera macrophylla*

officinalis CArn SPav
sempervirens see *Pentaglottis sempervirens*

Ancylostemon (*Gesneriaceae*)

convexus B&SWJ 6624 WCru

Andrachne (*Euphorbiaceae*)

colchica EBee WCot

Androcymbium (*Colchicaceae*)

gramineum ECho
- from Morocco ECho

Andrographis (*Acanthaceae*)

paniculata CArn

Andromeda (*Ericaceae*)

glaucophylla MBar
polifolia ECho GAuc GKev NWCA WDin WFar
- 'Alba' ECho GKev LRHS MAsh MBar NBlu NLAp NRya SPer SPlb SPoG SWvt WFar
- 'Blue Ice' ELan EPfP GKir LRHS MAsh MBri MNHC NLar NMen SLim SPer SPoG SSpi WAbe WFar WPat
- 'Compacta' ♀H4 CDoC CMac EBee ECho EPfP GEdr GGar GKir LRHS LSRN MBar MBri MMuc NHol NMen SBch SPer SPoG SRms SWvt WGwG WSHC
- 'Compacta Alba' ♀H4 ECho
- 'Grandiflora' ECho GEdr LRHS
- 'Kirigamine' GKir LRHS MAsh NHol
- 'Macrophylla' ♀H4 ECho GEdr WAbe WPat
- 'Nana' CSBt ELan EPfP LRHS MAsh NMen
- 'Nikko' CMac NHol
- 'Shibutsu' NMen

Andropogon (*Poaceae*)

gerardii CKno CRWN EBee EHoe EHul EPPr GFor LEdu MWhi NWsh SApp SGSe WDyG WWEG
ischaemum see *Bothriochloa ischaemum*
scoparius see *Schizachyrium scoparium*

Androsace (*Primulaceae*)

CC 3845 GKev
CD&R 2477 from China WCru
alpina WAbe
barbulata CPBP
bulleyana GKev WAbe WWEG
carnea CPBP ECho GKev LRHS
- ***alba*** LRHS NWCA
- subsp. ***brigantiaca*** GKev ITim NLAp NSla WAbe WHoo
- subsp. ***laggeri*** ♀H4 ECho GKev LLHF NLAp NSla WAbe WFar
carnea* × *pyrenaica ECho EPot NMen SIng
chamaejasme ECho
ciliata CPBP EPot WAbe
cylindrica ITim LRHS NLAp NMen WFar
cylindrica* × *hirtella ECho EPot ITim LRHS WAbe
delavayi NLAp WAbe
- ACE 1786 WAbe
geraniifolia EBee ECha SRms
globifera CPBP EPot WAbe
gracilis PB 99/20 EPot
hedraeantha EPot ITim NRya NSla WAbe
himalaica CPBP EPot NMen WAbe
hirtella ITim WAbe
idahoensis WAbe
jacquemontii see *A. villosa* var. *jacquemontii*
kosopoljanskii WAbe
lactea WAbe
laevigata NMen WAbe
- var. ***ciliolata*** NWCA
- 'Gothenburg' WAbe
- 'Saddle Mount' WAbe
lanuginosa ♀H4 CMea CPBP CSpe ECho EPot MWat NMen NPri NWCA SRms SRot WAbe WFar
lehmannii GKev
limprichtii see *A. sarmentosa* var. *watkinsii*
mariae WAbe
- SDR 4768 GKev
× ***marpensis*** EPot NMen WAbe
mathildae EPot
microphylla see *A. mucronifolia* G.Watt
'Millstream' CPBP
§ ***mollis*** CPBP
montana WAbe
mucronifolia misapplied see *A. sempervivoides*
§ ***mucronifolia*** G.Watt WAbe
mucronifolia* × *sempervivoides EPot
muscoidea WAbe
- SEP 132 CPBP
- 'Breviscapa' EPot
- Schacht's form WAbe
nivalis 'Chumstick Form' LLHF
ochotensis WAbe
primuloides see *A. studiosorum*
pubescens ITim LLHF LRHS NMen
pyrenaica ECho ITim LRHS NLAp NMen SIng
rigida WAbe
robusta subsp. ***purpurea*** WAbe
rotundifolia GEdr GKev
sarmentosa misapplied see *A. studiosorum*
sarmentosa ambig. EAlp GJos MWat
sarmentosa Wall. SRms WHoo
- CC 5797 GKev
- from Namche, Nepal EPot EWld WAbe
- Galmont's form see *A. studiosorum* 'Salmon's Variety'
- 'Sherriffii' EPot GEdr SRms WHoo
§ - var. ***watkinsii*** EPot GKev NMen
- var. ***yunnanensis*** misapplied see *A. studiosorum*
- var. ***yunnanensis*** Knuth see *A. mollis*
selago WAbe
§ ***sempervivoides*** ♀H4 ECho EDAr EPot GEdr GJos GKev GMaP LHop LRHS NDlv NHol NLAp NMen NWCA SPlb SRms WPat
- CC 4631 GKev
- CC 5299 GKev
- 'Greystone' NMen
- 'Susan Joan' (v) CPBP EPot GEdr GKev WAbe
septentrionalis new GKev
- 'Stardust' ECho
spinulifera SDR 2950 GKev
- SDR 4808 GKev
strigillosa GKev WAbe
§ ***studiosorum*** ♀H4 ECho EPot GAbr GEdr GKev WPat
- 'Chumbyi' GEdr LLHF NLAp NWCA SRms WPat
- 'Doksa' CPBP EPot GEdr NLAp NMen WAbe WPat
§ - 'Salmon's Variety' CMea CTri ECho WAbe
tapete WAbe
vandellii ITim
§ ***villosa*** var. ***jacquemontii*** CPBP EDAr GEdr NWCA
- - lilac-flowered EPot
- - pink-flowered EPot NLAp WAbe
vitaliana see *Vitaliana primuliflora*

	watkinsii	see *A. sarmentosa* var. *watkinsii*
	yargongensis	WAbe
	zambalensis	WAbe

Andryala (*Asteraceae*)

	agardhii	WPat
	lanata	see *Hieracium lanatum*

Anemanthele (*Poaceae*)

§	***lessoniana*** ♀H4	Widely available
	- 'Gold Hue'	EBee

Anemarrhena (*Anthericaceae*)

	asphodeloides	CArn WCot

Anemone ✿ (*Ranunculaceae*)

	Chen Yi T49	WCot
	SDR 4623	GKev
	aconitifolia Michx.	see *A. narcissiflora*
	afghanica	LRHS
	altaica	ECho GKev NLar SRms
	amurensis	CPLG EBla ECho
	apennina ♀H4	CAvo CLAP EBla ECho WShi WTin
	- var. ***albiflora***	CDes CLAP EBee EBrs ECho EPPr EPot ERCP ERos LRHS MAvo SMeo SPhx WPnP
	- double-flowered (d)	CDes EBla ECho EPPr WCru
	- 'Petrovac'	CLAP EBee EBrs EPot ERCP LLHF WCot
	baissunensis new	WWst
	baldensis	EBee ECho EDAr ITim LRHS NBur SRms
	barbulata	CPLG ECho EWes GAuc GBuc GEdr GMac NLar SHar SMad WBor WSHC
	blanda ♀H4	EBrs ECho GKir IHer LAma LBMP LHop LRHS MBri MLHP MNHC NBlu NChi SEND SWal WBor WFar WShi
I	- 'Alba' new	LRHS
	- 'Blue Star'	ECho
	- blue-flowered	Widely available
	- 'Charmer'	EBrs ECho EPot NMen
	- 'Ingramii'	EPot MCot WCot
	- pink-flowered new	LRHS
	- var. ***rosea*** ♀H4	EBrs ECho ELan EPfP LAma LRHS MBel SMrm SPer SPoG WFar
	- - 'Pink Charmer'	ECho
	- - 'Pink Star'	EBrs ECho ERCP LAma LRHS MCot NBir
	- - 'Radar' ♀H4	CAvo CFFs CMea EBrs ECho EPot ERCP LAma MNrw NBir WAbe
	- 'Violet Star'	EBrs ECho EPot ERCP LRHS
	- 'White Charmer'	ECho
	- 'White Splendour' ♀H4	CAvo CBro CFFs CMea CTri EBrs ECho ELan EPfP EPot ERCP GAbr GKev LAma LBMP LRHS MCot MNFA NBir NChi NMen SMeo SPer SPhx SPoG SRms WCot WFar WSHC
	- white-flowered new	LRHS
	blue-flowered from China	CDes
	canadensis	CHar CLAP CWCL EBee ECho ELon EPPr GBuc ITim MNrw NBur WBVN WCot
	caroliniana	EBee ECho GBuc GKev GKir LRHS
	caucasica	ECho SCnR WWst
	chapaensis HWJ 631	WCru
	coronaria 'Bicolor'	EBrs NBur
	- De Caen Group	EBrs EPfP LAma LHop LRHS SPoG SWal WFar
§	- - 'Die Braut'	CMea EBrs LRHS NBir NBur WFar
	- - 'His Excellency'	see *A. coronaria* (De Caen Group) 'Hollandia'
§	- - 'Hollandia'	EBrs
	- - 'Mister Fokker'	EBrs ERCP LAma WFar
	- - The Bride	see *A. coronaria* (De Caen Group) 'Die Braut'
	- - 'The Governor'	EBrs NBur WFar WHil
	- Jerusalem hybrids	WFar
	- Saint Bridgid Group (d)	EBrs EPfP LAma SWal WFar WRHF
	- - 'Lord Lieutenant' (d)	CMea EBrs EPfP ERCP LRHS NBir NBur WFar
	- - 'Mount Everest' (d)	EBrs ERCP LRHS NBir NBur
	- - 'Saint Bridgid' (d)	EBrs LRHS
	- - 'The Admiral' (d)	EBrs EPfP LRHS NBir NBur WFar
	- Saint Piran Group	CBgR
	- 'Sylphide' (Mona Lisa Series)	EBrs ERCP NBir WFar
	crinita	GBuc GMac WBVN
	cylindrica	CSam EBee MDKP NBre NLar
	deltoidea NNS 04-38	EBee
	demissa	GAbr GBuc GKev WCot
	- SDR 3307	EBee
	- SDR 4306	GKev
	dichotoma	SSvw
	drummondii	GAbr GKev NBur NChi WBVN
	eranthoides	EBee EBrs ECho WWst
	fanninii	GCal
	fasciculata	see *A. narcissiflora*
	flaccida	CBro CDes CLAP EBee EHrv EPPr GBuc GEdr GMac LRHS MAvo SPhx WCot WCru WFar WHal WSHC
	× ***fulgens***	ECha ECho
	- 'Annulata Grandiflora'	ECGP
	- 'Multipetala'	EBrs ECho
	geum	GKev
	subsp. ***ovalifolia*** new	
	globosa	see *A. multifida* Poir.
	gortschakowii new	WWst
	'Guernica'	EBee ECho EWes
	'Hatakeyama Double' (d)	CMdw GCal LPla
	'Hatakeyama Single'	CDes CMdw LPla
	hepatica	see *Hepatica nobilis*
§	***hortensis***	EBee ECho LRHS NBre SPhx
	- ***alba***	CLAP
	- subsp. ***heldreichii***	ECho
§	***hupehensis***	CBot CPLG EBee GBBs GMaP IGor NOrc WFar WPer
	- BWJ 8190	WCru
	- f. ***alba***	CLAP CSpe EBla IFro WPGP
§	- 'Bowles's Pink' ♀H4	CElw CPLG EBee ECho EPPr IGor MAvo MWat SPet WCru WPGP WTin
	- 'Crispa'	see *A.* × *hybrida* 'Lady Gilmour' Wolley-Dod
	- 'Eugenie'	EBee GBuc MBNS MWea NBir NGdn NHol
	- 'Hadspen Abundance' ♀H4	Widely available
	- 'Hadspen Red'	WFar
§	- var. ***japonica***	CPou NBPC NCob
	- - B&SWJ 4886	WCru
	- - 'Bodnant Burgundy'	CDes EBee ECtt WPGP
§	- - 'Bressingham Glow'	CMHG CMac CPLG CSam EAEE EBee ECtt ELan EPfP EPot LHop LRHS MBri MNrw MRav NBir NCGa NGdn NHol NOrc NVic SPer SPet WAbb WBrk WCAu WFar
§	- - 'Pamina' ♀H4	Widely available
	- - Prince Henry	see *A. hupehensis* var. *japonica* 'Prinz Heinrich'
§	- - 'Prinz Heinrich' ♀H4	Widely available
§	- - 'Rotkäppchen'	EBee EBla EBrs ECtt GAbr GBin LRHS LSou MAvo NBur NGdn NHol SMrm WCot WSHC

	- - 'Splendens'	CMHG COIW EBee EBrs GBBs GBuc LAst LHop MCot MRav NEgg NGdn SPoG SPur SWvt WAbb WFar WHal WKif WWEG
	- 'Ouvertüre'	EBee MAvo WPGP
	- 'Praecox'	CKno CMea CSam EAEE EBee EBla EHrv EPfP GBBs GBuc LRHS MAvo MBNS NBPC NBir NGdn NHol NPri NSti SBch SBod SPoG SWvt WAbb WFar WHal WMnd WWEG
	- 'September Charm'	see *A.* × *hybrida* 'September Charm'
	- 'Superba'	EPfP WKif
§	× ***hybrida***	ECho LRHS MWat NChi NCob NEgg SGar WFar WMoo
	- 'Alba Dura'	see *A. tomentosa* 'Albadura'
	- 'Alba' misapplied (UK)	see *A.* × *hybrida* 'Honorine Jobert'
	- 'Albert Schweitzer'	see *A.* × *hybrida* 'Elegans'
	- 'Andrea Atkinson'	Widely available
	- 'Bowles's Pink'	see *A. hupehensis* 'Bowles's Pink'
	- 'Bressingham Glow'	see *A. hupehensis* var. *japonica* 'Bressingham Glow'
	- 'Coupe d'Argent'	EBee IKil NBre WCAu
§	- 'Elegans' ♀H4	CSam CWCL EBee ECtt GMaP LHop MRav NBPC NBir NGdn SMrm SWat SWvt WCAu WFar WHil WSpi
§	- 'Géante des Blanches'	CHar EBee IGor LPla LRHS WCAu WHoo
§	- 'Honorine Jobert' ♀H4	Widely available
§	- 'Königin Charlotte' ♀H4	Widely available
	- 'Kriemhilde'	EBee GBin
§	- 'Lady Gilmour' Wolley-Dod	CSam CSpe EBee ECtt EHrv EPfP GAbr GCra GKir GMac LEdu LRHS MAvo MBri MRav NBPC NBir NEgg NGdn SAga SRGP WCot WCru WFar WWEG
	- 'Lady Gilmour' misapplied	see *A.* × *hybrida* 'Montrose'
	- 'Lady Gilmour' ambig.	GMaP MCot NBPC
	- 'Little Princess' new	CHid EBee
	- 'Loreley'	CMea CPrp EBee GBuc MWat NLar SBch WWEG
	- 'Luise Uhink'	CPou IGor LRHS NBir
	- 'Margarete' Kayser & Seibert	CPLG CPar EBee EBrs ECtt ELan EPPr EPfP IBlr LAst LHop MBri MWat NGdn SBch SMrm WCot WCru
	- 'Max Vogel'	see *A.* × *hybrida* 'Elegans'
	- 'Monterosa'	see *A.* × *hybrida* 'Montrose'
§	- 'Montrose'	CPou CSpe EBee EHrv EWes GAbr GCal GKir GMaP LSou NBir SRms SWat
	- 'Pamina'	see *A. hupehensis* var. *japonica* 'Pamina'
	- Prince Henry	see *A. hupehensis* var. *japonica* 'Prinz Heinrich'
	- 'Profusion'	CTri LBuc WHal
	- Queen Charlotte	see *A.* × *hybrida* 'Königin Charlotte'
	- 'Richard Ahrens'	EBee ECtt EShb GBuc GCal GKir GMaP IBlr LAst LHop LRHS MAvo MLHP NBPC NCGa NEgg NGdn NHol NOrc SAga SBch SMeo SWat WCru WFar WMnd WWEG
§	- 'Robustissima'	CSpe EBee ECtt EPfP GBBs GBuc GMaP GMac LLWP LRHS LSRN MCot MGos MRav NBir NCob NGdn NPri NSti SPer SWat SWvt WAbb WFar WMnd WMoo WWEG
	- 'Rosenschale'	EBee GMac LRHS WCAu WCru
	- 'Rotkäppchen'	see *A. hupehensis* var. *japonica* 'Rotkäppchen'
§	- 'September Charm' ♀H4	Widely available
	- 'Serenade'	CChe CMHG CPar CSam EBee ECtt EPfP GBBs LSRN MBel MRav NBir NCGa SMrm SPad SPoG SRkn SSvw WCAu WCot WFar WHoo WMoo WWEG
	- Tourbillon	see *A.* × *hybrida* 'Whirlwind'
§	- 'Whirlwind'	Widely available
	- 'White Queen'	see *A.* × *hybrida* 'Géante des Blanches'
	- Wirbelwind	see *A.* × *hybrida* 'Whirlwind'
	japonica	see *A. hupehensis*, *A.* × *hybrida*
	keiskeana	EBee GEdr WCru WWst
§	× ***lesseri***	CBro CFir CSpe EBee ECha ECho ECtt EDAr EHrv ELan GKev LHop MHer NChi SPhx SRms WFar WHoo
	leveillei	Widely available
	- BWJ 7919	WCru
§	× ***lipsiensis***	CAvo CBro CDes CFwr CPBP EBee EBla EBrs ECho EPfP EPot ERos EShb GBBs GEdr GMaP IFro MAvo MTho NMen NRya NWCA SMeo WCot WCru WFar WHal WPGP WSHC
	- 'Pallida' ♀H4	CPMA EBee EBla ECho ELon ERos GBuc GEdr GKev IGor LLWP LRHS MAvo NWCA SMrm WCot
	lyallii	GBuc WBrE
N	***magellanica*** hort. ex Wehrh.	see *A. multifida* Poir.
	matsudae B&SWJ 1452	WCru
	- 'Taiwan's Tiny Treasure'	WCru
	multifida misapplied, red-flowered	see *A.* × *lesseri*
§	***multifida*** Poir.	CBgR CPrp CStu EBee ECha ECho EPfP GGar IFoB LHop LRHS MAvo MNrw NBir NSti NSum SPoG SRms WFar WHoo WPtf WTin
	- RCB/Arg RA-F-5	WCot
	- Annabella Series new	GKev
	- 'Major'	CFir CHar CMea CSpe EPfP MCot NCob NGdn NPro NWCA SMrm SPhx WBVN WFar
	- pink-flowered	GBuc
	- f. ***polysepala***	NEgg
*	- 'Rubra'	CBgR CPrp EAEE EBee EDAr EHrv EPfP EWll GAbr GBuc GGar LBMP LRHS MAvo MBNS MNFA MNrw NBPC NBir NDlv NEgg NWCA SMrm SPoG STes
	- yellow-flowered	GBBs GGar NSum
§	***narcissiflora***	EBee ECho EHrv GBuc GKev IGor NBir NBre NChi WCom WFar WSHC
	nemorosa ♀H4	Widely available
N	- 'Alba Plena' (d)	CBro CPMA CSWP CSam CStu EBee EBla EBrs ECha ECho EPPr ERos GBuc GEdr GGar GMac LRHS MTho NMen SIng WAbb WCru WFar WPnP WSHC
	- 'Allenii' ♀H4	CBro EBee EBla EBrs ECha ECho ELon EPot ERos GBuc GEdr GMaP ITim LRHS MAvo MRav NMen NRya SIng SMac WCom WCot WCru WFar WPGP WShi
	- 'Amy Doncaster'	CLAP ECho
	- 'Atrocaerulea'	CLAP GBuc IBlr NLar WCru WFar
	- 'Atrorosea'	EBee
	- 'Bill Baker's Pink'	CDes CLAP MAvo
	- 'Blue Beauty'	CLAP CPMA EBee ELon ERos GBuc GMaP IBlr MAvo NMen SBch WCru
	- 'Blue Bonnet'	CElw CPMA ECho GBuc IGor ITim MAvo MNrw SMrm

- 'Blue Eyes' (d)	CAby CDes CElw CLAP CStu EBee EBla GBuc GEdr GMaP IBlr IGor ITim MAvo NBir NMen NSla WCot WCru WFar WPGP
- 'Blue Queen'	GAbr GBuc
- 'Bowles's Purple'	CPMA CPom EBee EBrs ECho EPot GBBs GBuc GMaP IBlr LRHS MNrw NBid NLAp NMyG NRya SPoG WCot WCru WFar WIvy WPGP WPnP WPtf WTin
- 'Bracteata'	ECho EHrv ERos GEdr NMen NSla
- 'Bracteata Pleniflora' (d)	CBow CLAP CPMA CStu EBee EBla EBrs ECho GBuc GMaP IBlr IGor LHop MAvo MNrw NBir NMen WCot WCru WFar WHal
- 'Buckland'	CDes CFwr CLAP EBee EHrv EPfP EPot IBlr SMad WCru WFar
- 'Cedric's Pink'	CLAP CPMA EBee EBla ECho EPPr ERos IBlr IGor LLHF MNrw WCru WFar
- 'Celestial'	EBee EBla ECho EPPr GBuc
- 'Dee Day'	CLAP EBee EHrv GBuc MAvo MNrw SCnR SMrm WCru WFar
- 'Evelyn Meadows' ♀H4	CLAP
- 'Flore Pleno' (d)	CAby CDes EBla ECho GAbr GKir NBir NMen WPGP
- 'Frühlingsfee'	CPMA EBee ECho NLar
- 'Gerda Ramusen'	CLAP EBla ECho GBuc LLHF
- 'Green Fingers'	CLAP CPMA EBla ECho EHrv EPPr GBuc GEdr GMaP IGor MAvo MNrw NGby SCnR WCot WCru WIvy
- 'Hannah Gubbay'	CLAP GBuc IBlr IGor MAvo MNrw
- 'Hilda'	EBee EBrs ECho EPot ERos GBuc GEdr IPot MAvo MNrw NDlv NLAp NMen NRya NSla
- 'Ice and Fire'	MAvo
- 'Jack Brownless'	CLAP ITim WCot
- 'Kentish Pink'	GBBs GBuc GMaP
- 'Knightshayes Vestal' (d)	CLAP EBee ECho MRav NHol WCot WIvy
- 'Lady Doneraile'	CDes CLAP EPot GBuc NBir NLar SSvw WCru WFar
- 'Latvian Pink'	EBee ECho EPot
- 'Leeds' Variety'	CLAP GMaP IGor ITim MAvo MNrw MTho NMen NSla WCot
- 'Lionel Bacon' **new**	WWst
- 'Lismore Blue'	EBee ECho EPPr EPot
- 'Lismore Pink'	EHrv GBuc GEdr
- 'Lucia'	EPot
- 'Lychette'	CAvo CHid CPMA ECho EHrv EPot GAbr GBuc IBlr ITim LPio MAvo NSla NWCA SHar WCot WCru WFar
- 'Marie Rose' **new**	EPot
- 'Martin'	CStu
- 'Mart's Blue'	GBuc
- 'Merlin'	WCot
- 'Miss Eunice'	CLAP
- 'Monstrosa'	EBee EBla EBrs ECho GBuc LRHS WCot
- 'New Pink'	CLAP CPom IBlr
- 'Parlez Vous'	EBee EHrv EPPr GEdr LPio MAvo MNrw NMen SCnR SSvw WCru WFar
- 'Pat's Pink'	WShi
- 'Pentre Pink'	EPot IBlr MAvo MNrw MSSP MTho WBVN WCru WFar WIvy
- 'Picos Pink'	EHrv GBuc SCnR WWst
- 'Pink Carpet'	GBuc GEdr
- pink-flowered	CLAP ECho WCru
- 'Polar Star'	CLAP
- 'Robinsoniana' ♀H4	Widely available
- 'Rosea'	CLAP EBee EBrs ECho GEdr SMrm WCru
- 'Royal Blue'	CDes CLAP CPMA EBee EBrs ECho EHrv EPPr EPot ERCP GAbr GBuc GEdr GMaP LAma MAvo NHol NLAp NMen WCot WCru WFar WPnP WTin
- 'Rubra'	EBee EPot
- 'Salt and Pepper'	MAvo
- 'Slack Top Pink'	NSla
- 'Stammheim' (d) **new**	CLAP
- 'Super Allenii'	EBee GBuc
- 'Tinney's Blush'	CLAP
- 'Tomas'	CLAP EBee ECho ELon EPot GBin GBuc GEdr NWCA SPoG SUsu
- 'Vestal' (d) ♀H4	Widely available
- 'Virescens' ♀H4	CAby CAvo CLAP CWCL EBee ECho EHrv EPPr ERos GAbr GBuc GEdr GKir GMaP MAvo NSla NWCA SPoG SUsu WCom WIvy WPGP WShi
- 'Viridiflora'	CFwr CLAP ECho EPfP GAbr GBuc LHop MNrw MTho NBir NSti SMrm SSvw WCon WCot WCru WFar WSHC
- 'Westwell Pink'	CAby CLAP CPMA CSpe EPPr LLHF MAvo MSSP WCot WPGP
- white-flowered **new**	LRHS
- 'Wilks' Giant'	CLAP MAvo WCru WFar
- 'Wilks' White'	CLAP EBee EBla ELon EPPr GEdr NSla WCru WFar
- 'Wisley Pink' **new**	EPot
- 'Wyatt's Pink'	CLAP CPMA ELon GBuc MAvo NCGa NSla WCru WFar WPnP WTin
- 'Yerda Ramusem'	EBee ECho EPPr MAvo
nemorosa* × *ranunculoides	see *A.* × *lipsiensis*
nikoensis **new**	ECho WWst
obtusiloba	CLAP GBuc GEdr GKir MTho SRms WAbe
- CLD 1549	GEdr
- ***alba***	GMac WAbe
I - 'Sulphurea'	CDes GEdr NMen
- yellow-flowered	GBuc WAbe
palmata	CLAP EDAr EWTr GKir LDai MDKP MWea NBre SGSe SMad WCru WFar
parviflora	EBee ECho GBuc GKev
patens	see *Pulsatilla patens*
pavonina	CAby CPMA CSpe ECha ERos GMac LRHS MAsh MBri MSSP MTho NBir SPoG SUsu WAbe WCom WCru
- 'Grecian Sunset'	MAsh WPGP
- pink-flowered	SUsu
petiolulosa **new**	WWst
petiolulosa* × *gortschakowii **new**	WWst
polyanthes	GKev WCot
prattii	CLAP CPLG EPPr GEdr WHal
pseudoaltaica	EBee GEdr WCot WCru WWst
- pale blue-flowered	CLAP
- 'Yuki-no-sei' (d)	GEdr
pulsatilla	see *Pulsatilla vulgaris*
quinquefolia	CLAP WAbe WCot
raddeana	EBrs ECho WWst
ranunculoides ♀H4	Widely available
- 'Frank Waley'	WCot
* - ***laciniata***	CLAP GBuc NMen WCot
- 'Pleniflora' (d)	CFwr CLAP EBla EBrs ECha ECho EHrv GBBs GMaP NLar NMen WCom WCot WFar WIvy
- subsp. ***ranunculoides***	EBrs ECho WHil
- 'Semi Plena'	EBrs ECho

- subsp. ***wockeana***	CDes EBee ECho MAvo
reflexa	EBee GKev
riparia	see *A. virginiana* var. *alba*
rivularis	Widely available
- BWJ 7611	WCru
- GWJ 9391	WCru
- 'Glacier'	LAst NEgg WPer
rupicola	EBee GMac NBir
× ***seemannii***	see *A.* × *lipsiensis*
stellata	see *A. hortensis*
stolonifera	CAby CElw EBee ECho ITim MAvo
double-flowered (d)	WCot
sulphurea	see *Pulsatilla alpina* subsp. *apiifolia*
sylvestris	Widely available
- 'Elise Fellmann' (d)	EBee EPfP GBuc IGor MAvo WCot WHal
- 'Flore Pleno' (d)	CDes SHar WCot
- 'Macrantha'	CDes CLAP EBee EPfP GAbr NGdn NMyG SMrm WBrE WPGP WPrP
tetrasepala	WCot WPGP
§ ***tomentosa***	EBee ECha GGar IGor LBMP LRHS MWhi NBre SDix SRms SWat WBVN WFar
§ - 'Albadura'	EBee LRHS NBre
- 'Robustissima'	see *A.* × *hybrida* 'Robustissima'
trifolia	EPPr ERos GBuc NBid SCnR SRms WCot WPGP WPat
- pink-flowered	CLAP WFar
trullifolia	EBee EPfP GAbr GBin GBuc GCra GEdr GGar GKev GKir GMaP GMac LRHS MMHG MRav NSla WAbe
- var. ***coelestina***	GBuc NBir
- var. ***linearis***	GMac
tschernjaewii new	WWst
vernalis	see *Pulsatilla vernalis*
virginiana	CSpe GAbr ILad LDai MDKP NBid NBur WBVN WFar WOut WWEG
§ - var. ***alba***	EKen WBVN WPrP WPtf
vitifolia misapplied	see *A. tomentosa*
vitifolia DC. B&SWJ 8202 from Vietnam	WCru
- GWJ 9434	WCru
- HWJK 2044	WCru

Anemonella (*Ranunculaceae*)

thalictroides	CBct CElw CFir CLAP EBee ECho EFEx EHrv ELon EPot EWTr GEdr GGar ITim LAma LPio MAvo NHol NMen NRya NWCA SMrm WAbe WCon WCru WFar WPrP WSHC
- 'Alba Plena' (d)	ECho GBuc
- 'Amelia'	CLAP EPPr GEdr SCnR WAbe
- 'Babe'	WWst
- 'Betty Blake' (d)	ECho GEdr WCot
- 'Big'	WWst
- 'Cameo'	CLAP EBee EFEx EPPr GEdr MAvo SCnR WCot WCru WFar WWst
- 'Charlotte'	WWst
- 'Diamante' new	WWst
- 'Double Green' (d)	CLAP EBee EFEx IMou WWst
- 'Full Double White' (d)	EFEx GEdr
- 'Green Hurricane' (d)	EBee EFEx GEdr ITim WWst
- 'Jade Feather'	CElw
- f. ***rosea***	CAby CElw CLAP GBuc WAbe WCru WFar
- - 'Oscar Schoaf' (d)	CLAP EBee GBuc GEdr ITim WAbe WWst
- - semi-double pink-flowered (d)	CElw CLAP EHrv GKir MAvo NLar WWst
- semi-double white-flowered (d)	CElw CLAP EBee EHrv EPPr GBuc NMen WAbe WCot
- 'Tairin'	EBee GEdr WWst
- white-flowered	WSpi

Anemonopsis (*Ranunculaceae*)

macrophylla	CElw CLAP CMoH CPBP EBee ECha ECho EPot GBuc GCal GEdr GKir IGor LBMP MNrw MTho NLar SMrm SPhx WAbe WCru WFar WSHC
- 'White Swan'	ECho WCru

Anemopsis (*Saururaceae*)

californica	CDes EBee IFoB LLWG MSKA NLar WCot WPGP

Anethum (*Apiaceae*)

graveolens	CArn GKir GPoy MHer MNHC SBch SIde SWal
- 'Dukat'	CSev ELau NGHP

angelica see *Angelica archangelica*

Angelica (*Apiaceae*)

acutiloba	CSpe MMHG NGHP NLar WFar
- var. ***iwatensis*** B&SWJ 11197	WCru
anomala B&SWJ 10886	WCru
archangelica	Widely available
- subsp. ***archangelica***	GAuc
- 'Corinne Tremaine' (v)	CBow MDKP NExo NGHP WCHb
atropurpurea	CArn EBee ECtt EPfP EShb EWll GKev LRHS MHer MNHC MNrw MRav NBur NCGa NChi NGHP NLar SMrm SWat WCHb WFar WJek WMnd WWEG
dahurica B&SWJ 8603	WCru
decursiva	CArn WCot
- B&SWJ 5746	WCru
'Ebony'	CMea GKev ILad MDKP NExo SMrm
edulis B&SWJ 10968	WCru
florentii	CDes WPGP
gigas	Widely available
- B&SWJ 4170	WCru
hispanica	see *A. pachycarpa*
japonica B&SWJ 11480	WCru
- B&SWJ 8816a	WCru
montana	see *A. sylvestris*
morii RWJ 9802	WCru
§ ***pachycarpa***	Widely available
pubescens	SPhx
- B&SWJ 5593	WCru
- var. ***matsumurae*** B&SWJ 6387	WCru
sachalinensis	CSpe EBee
sinensis	CArn GAuc GPoy WCHb
'Summer Delight'	see *Ligusticum scoticum*
§ ***sylvestris***	CArn CRWN EBWF GBar NSco WCHb
- 'Boraston Pink Lace'	WCHb
* - 'Purpurea'	CKno CSpe EWes MCot SDnm WPGP
- 'Vicar's Mead'	CWan EBee IPot LEdu LHop LPla LSRN MBel MDKP NBPC NCGa NChi NGHP NLar NSti SPhx SRkn WBrk WCHb WPtf WSHC
taiwaniana	CArn CWan EBee ELan LRHS MBel MDKP NGHP NLar SGar WPer
ursina	GAuc
- B&SWJ 10829	WCru

Angelonia (*Scrophulariaceae*)

(Angelface Series) Angelface Blue = 'Anzwei'PBR — CSpe
- Angelface Blue Bicolour = 'Anstern' — LAst NPri
- Angelface Wedgewood Blue 'Anwedg' new — LAst
angustifolia (AngelMist Series) AngelMist Lavender Pink = 'Balanglapi — 'LAst
- - AngelMist Light Pink = 'Balangpili' — NPri

Anigozanthos (*Haemodoraceae*)

flavidus — CHEx CTrC ECre EOHP MBri SPlb
- 'Ember' — SPoG
- 'Illusion' — CCCN
- 'Opal' — CCCN
- 'Pearl' — CCCN SPoG
- 'Splendour' — CCCN
- yellow — WBrE
'Galileo' — LRHS
manglesii ♀H1 — CTrC SPlb

Anisacanthus (*Acanthaceae*)

quadrifidus var. ***wrightii*** — WCot

anise see *Pimpinella anisum*

Anisodontea (*Malvaceae*)

§ ***capensis*** — CCCN EBee ELan ERea EShb GBee GKir LAst MCot NBir SBch SBod SChF SLim SMrm SRkn SRms SWvt WDyG
- 'Tara's Pink' — CSpe EWes IFoB LRHS MAsh SAga SMrm
elegans — LHop
'Elegant Lady' — GFai SUsu
huegelii — see *Alyogyne huegelii*
× ***hypomadara*** misapplied — see *A. capensis*
§ × ***hypomadara*** (Sprague) D.M. Bates — SRms
julii — SPlb
malvastroides — WWlt
'Orchard Pink' new — SUsu
scabrosa — CChe

Anisodus (*Solanaceae*)

§ ***luridus*** — EWld GCal

Anisotome (*Apiaceae*)

latifolia — WCot
lyallii — GBin ITim

Annona (*Annonaceae*)

cherimola (F) — CCCN MREP XBlo

Anoiganthus see *Cyrtanthus*

Anomalesia see *Gladiolus*

Anomatheca (*Iridaceae*)

cruenta — see *A. laxa*
grandiflora — CHll CPLG ECho ERos
§ ***laxa*** ♀H2-3 — Widely available
- var. ***alba*** ♀H2-3 — CPLG CPom CRHN CSev CSpe CStu EBee ECho EDif EHrv ELan ERos ITim LEdu MCot MTho MWea NMen SBch WAbe WBrk WCFE WCom
- blue-flowered — CRHN ECho ERos WAbe
- 'Joan Evans' — CRHN CStu EBee ECho ELan ERos EShb LLHF NDlv NMen NWCA SHom SRms WAbe WBrk WHrl
- red-spotted — CPLG ECho EDif ITim SGar
- ***viridiflora*** — ECho
viridis — CDes CPLG CPou ECho ERos LRHS WBrk WPGP

Anopterus (*Escalloniaceae*)

glandulosus — IBlr WPGP WSHC

Anredera (*Basellaceae*)

§ ***cordifolia*** — CRHN EBrs ECho EShb LEdu LRHS

Antennaria (*Asteraceae*)

aprica — see *A. parvifolia*
dioica — CArn CEnt CTri EDAr GAbr GJos GKir GPoy LBMP SPlb SRms WFar
- 'Alba' — EHoe
- 'Alex Duguid' — GEdr GMaP LBee LRHS NLAp WCom
- 'Aprica' — see *A. parvifolia*
- 'Minima' — ECho EPot MWat NBro NMen SIng WAbe
- 'Nyewoods Variety' — EPot NLAp
- red-flowered — ECho
- var. ***rosea*** — see *A. rosea*
- 'Rotes Wonder' new — EPot
* - 'Rubra' — CTri ECha ECho EDAr GBin GEdr LBMP LRHS MHer NMen NWCA
'Joy' — WAbe
macrophylla hort. — see *A. microphylla*
§ ***microphylla*** — ECho MBar SRms WEas
§ ***parvifolia*** — CTri ECho MBar NPri SRms WPer
- var. ***rosea*** — see *A. microphylla*
plantaginifolia — EBee
'Red Wonder' — CMea NLar
§ ***rosea*** ♀H4 — ECho GKir LRHS MSCN NHol NLAp NMen NVic SPlb SRms WFar

Antenoron see *Persicaria*

Anthemis ✿ (*Asteraceae*)

from Turkey — ECtt EWes LLWP SUsu
arvensis — SECG
§ 'Beauty of Grallagh' — EBee GBuc GCal IGor MDKP SDix WSpi
'Cally Cream' — GCal SMrm
'Cally White' — GCal NBid
carpatica — IMon MAvo NBro
- 'Karpatenschnee' — EBee ELon LBMP LRHS NBre
'Catforth White' new — NCob
§ ***cretica*** subsp. ***cretica*** — CMac NWCA
- subsp. ***leucanthemoides*** new — GKev
'Daisy Bee' — EBee LRHS
frutescens hort. & Siebert & Voss. — see *Argyranthemum frutescens*
'Grallagh Gold' misapplied, orange-yellow — see *A.* 'Beauty of Grallagh'
'Grallagh Gold' — CMoH EBla ECha ECtt EWes LDai NPer WFar WSpi
§ ***marschalliana*** — CMea CPBP EAlp EBee ECha ECho ECtt EDAr EPot LBee LRHS SMrm SPlb SUsu WAbe WCot
montana — see *A. cretica* subsp. *cretica*
nobilis — see *Chamaemelum nobile*
punctata — WCor
- subsp. ***cupaniana*** ♀H3-4 — Widely available
- - 'Nana' — NPer SHar
rudolphiana — see *A. marschalliana*

sancti-johannis	CWib EAEE EAro EBee EBla EPfP IGor LDai LRHS LSou MBri NPer SBch SMad SPoG SRms WMoo WPer
'Sauce Béarnaise'	GCra WMnd
Susanna Mitchell = 'Blomit'	CHar EBee EBla ECtt ELon EPfP EShb EWll GKir GMac LRHS LSRN MAvo MLHP MNrw MWte NBir NCob SMrm SRGP SUsu SWvt WCom WMnd WSHC WSpi WTin WWEG
'Tetworth'	EBee EBla ECha ECtt EHrv ELan EPfP GBuc LSRN MAvo MBNS MRav NCGa NOrc SMad SUsu WFar WPer WWEG
tinctoria	CArn CHby CMac EAro EBee GPoy LRHS MHer NPer SECG SPet SWvt WAbe WJek WSFF
- 'Alba'	EBee GGar GKir NBre WClo WFar WPer WWEG
- 'Charme'PBR	CPrp SBch SUsu
- 'Compacta'	EWes GCal NBre NCob NGdn
- dwarf	EBee EBla MAvo WAbe WFar
- 'E.C. Buxton'	Widely available
- 'Eva'	LRHS NBre NCob NLar WEas WWEG
I - 'Golden Rays'	MDKP NPro SBch SDix
- 'Kelwayi'	CEnt CPrp CSBt CTri EBee EPfP EShb GKir LRHS NBPC NBro NCob NPer SBch SPer SPoG SRms WFar WMoo
- 'Kelwayi Alba' new	WWEG
- 'Lemon Maid'	CFir EPfP GBin LRHS NBre NBur NCob SMrm
- 'Powis White'	MSCN
- 'Sauce Hollandaise'	Widely available
- subsp. ***tinctoria***	SMrm
- 'Wargrave Variety'	Widely available
'Tinpenny Sparkle'	EBee LSou MAvo NBPC NSti WCot WTin
triumfettii	NPer
tuberculata	SAga
'White Water'	WAbe WFar

Anthericum (*Anthericaceae*)

algeriense	see *A. liliago*
baeticum	EBee ERos
§ ***liliago***	CBro EBee ECho ELan ERas ERos EWTr GCal GKev GMaP GMac IFoB LHop LRHS MAvo MBel MCot MRav NCGa WHrl WPer WWEG
- 'Major' ♀H4	ECha ECho EHrv GBuc IGor MLHP NBre SPhx SUsu WPGP
ramosum	CSpe EBee ECha ECho ELan EPot ERos EWes GCal GMac MBel MBrN NBid NBir NCGa NWCA SMrm SPhx SUsu WPGP WPer
- ***plumosum***	see *Trichopetalum plumosum*
undulatum	ERos

Antholyza (*Iridaceae*)

coccinea	see *Crocosmia paniculata*
× ***crocosmioides***	see *Crocosmia* × *crocosmioides*
paniculata	see *Crocosmia paniculata*

Anthoxanthum (*Poaceae*)

odoratum	CArn CRWN EBWF GBar GPoy

Anthriscus (*Apiaceae*)

cerefolium	CArn CSev EPfP GPoy ILis MDun MHer MNHC SBch WJek
sylvestris	CArn EBWF NMir NSco SECG
- 'Broadleas Blush'	WAlt
- 'Kabir'	CNat
- 'Moonlit Night'	EHoe
- 'Ravenswing'	Widely available

Anthurium (*Araceae*)

amazonicum	MBri
andraeanum ♀H1	MBri
- 'Glowing Pink'	XBlo
- 'Red Heart'	XBlo
- 'Tivolo'	XBlo
'Aztec'	XBlo
Baleno = 'Anthauf4'PBR	LRHS XBlo
'Caribo'	LRHS XBlo
clarinervium	LRHS
crenatum	XBlo
'Crimson'	XBlo
'Fantasy Love'	LRHS
'Magenta'	XBlo
'Maxima Eleganica'	LRHS
'Mikra'	XBlo
'Octavia'	XBlo
'Olivia'	LRHS
'Orange Love'PBR	LRHS
'Pico Bello'	XBlo
'Pink Champion'	LRHS XBlo
'Polaris White'	LRHS
'Porcelaine White'	XBlo
Red Champion = 'Anthbnena'PBR	LRHS XBlo
'Red Love'PBR	LRHS
'Rima'	LRHS
'Robino Red'	LRHS
scherzerianum ♀H1	MBri
'Sharada'	LRHS
'Sugar Love'PBR	LRHS
'Sunny Love'	LRHS
'Tender Love'PBR	LRHS
'Texan Rose'	LRHS
'Tricolor'	LRHS
'Vitara'	LRHS XBlo
'Vivaro Red'	LRHS
'White Butterfly'	LRHS
White Champion = 'Anthefaqyr'PBR	LRHS XBlo

Anthyllis (*Papilionaceae*)

barba-jovis	CSpe LRHS
hermanniae 'Compacta'	see *A. hermanniae* 'Minor'
§ - 'Minor'	NLar NMen
lachnophora new	GKev
- SDR 5518	EBee
montana	LRHS
subsp. ***atropurpurea***	
- 'Rubra' ♀H4	ECho EPot EWes LHop LLHF NMen
vulneraria	CFee EBWF ECho EDAr NMir NRya NSco SECG WSFF
- var. ***coccinea***	CSpe CSsd EBee GAbr GGar GKev MCCP MSCN MTho NLar NSla NWCA SGSe WCFE WCom WFar WHal WHil
- dark red-flowered	WCom

Antirrhinum (*Scrophulariaceae*)

asarina	see *Asarina procumbens*
barrelieri	SEND
braun-blanquetii	EBee SEND WCot
'Carambola Yellow' (Fruit Salad Series) new	LSou
glutinosum	see *A. hispanicum* subsp. *hispanicum*
§ ***hispanicum***	CPBP
- 'Avalanche'	ECtt

§ - subsp. ***hispanicum*** SRot
- - 'Roseum' CMea CPom CSpe SBHP
(Luminaire Series) LAst
Luminaire Deep Purple = 'Balumdepur'PBR
- Luminaire Yellow = 'Balumyell'PBR LAst NPri
majus 'Black Prince' CSpe ECtt EShb LHop LSou
- 'Night and Day' CSpe
molle CPom CSpe ECtt MCot NBir NPer NWCA SChF SRot SUsu WAbe
- pink-flowered WAbe
pulverulentum SAga WAbe WSHC
sempervirens SAga WAbe
siculum EBee WMoo

añu see *Tropaeolum tuberosum*

Aphelandra (*Acanthaceae*)

squarrosa MBri
- 'Citrina' XBlo
- 'Dania' (v) LRHS

Aphyllanthes (*Aphyllanthaceae*)

monspeliensis CFee EBee ECho

Apios (*Papilionaceae*)

§ ***americana*** CAgr CMdw CPom EBee EBrs ECho GBin LEdu LFur NBir NLar NSti WBVN WCot WCru WSHC
tuberosa see *A. americana*

Apium (*Apiaceae*)

graveolens CArn CBgR CBod CPrp EBWF ELau GPoy MHer MNHC SBch SIde WJek
- (Secalinum Group) 'Par-cel' MHer NGHP
nodiflorum EBWF

Apium × *Petroselinum* (*Apiaceae*)

hybrid, misapplied see *A. graveolens* Secalinum Group

Apocynum (*Apocynaceae*)

cannabinum CArn COld GPoy

Apodolirion (*Amaryllidaceae*)

macowanii **new** ECho

Aponogeton (*Aponogetonaceae*)

distachyos CRow CWat EHon EMFW EPfP LPBA MSKA NPer SCoo SVic SWat WFar WMAq WPnP

apple see *Malus domestica*

apricot see *Prunus armeniaca*

Aptenia (*Aizoaceae*)

cordifolia ♀H1-2 CCCN CSev NPer SChr SDnm SEND SPet WCor
- 'Variegata' (v) CCCN MRav

Aquilegia ✿ (*Ranunculaceae*)

akitensis misapplied see *A. flabellata* var. *pumila*
'Alaska' (State Series) ♀H3-4 SMrm
* ***alba variegata*** (v) ECho WEas
alpina CBot CMea CPrp EBee ECho ECtt EPfP GGar LRHS MHer MNHC MRav SBch SPer SRms WCAu WFar WMoo WPer
amaliae see *A. ottonis* subsp. *amaliae*
amurensis CLAP
'Apple Blossom' MCot WTou
§ ***atrata*** CLAP CPou EBee ECho MDKP MDun MWea NBre SMrm WBVN WHil WPer
- SDR 5446 GKev
atrovinosa MWea
aurea misapplied see *A. vulgaris* golden-leaved
barnebyi CMea EBee NLAp
bernardii CWCL
bertolonii ♀H4 CMea ECho GKev LHop LRHS NDlv NMen NRya SRms WHoo
- ***alba*** NWCA
Biedermeier Group EBee ECho GKir LRHS NOrc SBch SPoG WFar WPer WTou
'Blackberry Ice' **new** WRHF
'Blue Jay' (Songbird Series) GKir LRHS MHer NPri SMrm SPer STes SWvt
'Blue Star' (Star Series) CSam EAEE EBee ELan EPfP LRHS NEgg WPer
'Bluebird' (Songbird Series) ♀H2 NPer
buergeriana GEdr MDKP STes WPer WTou
- 'Calimero' CSsd LBMP MDKP NLar NPri WFar WHil
- var. ***oxysepala*** see *A. oxysepala*
'Bunting' (Songbird Series) ♀H2 NLar NPri SCoo WFar
canadensis ♀H4 CLAP CMHG CSpe EBee ELan GKev GQue LBMP MNFA NBir NBro NWCA SBch SGar SRms WPer WTou
- 'Corbett' GBuc GEdr MDKP WHil
- 'Little Lanterns' CSam CTsd EBee ECtt EPPr GGar GKev LBMP LHop MDKP NCGa NLar NSum SGSe SPad SVil WCot WFar
- 'Nana' GBuc GEdr GKev WThu
- 'Pink Lanterns' **new** NPri SMrm
'Cardinal' (Songbird Series) GKir LRHS MBri MHer NLar NPri SPer WFar
chaplinei CBot EBee NBir SBch
chrysantha CSam GBuc GKev MNFA NBre SGSe SRms WBrE WEas WKif WPer WTou
- 'Denver Gold' WRHF
- 'Yellow Queen' CHrt CPLG CPrp CWCL EBee EGoo ENor EPPr EPfP GMaP LBMP LFur LHop LRHS MAvo MDKP MWat NBre NLar NMoo SMrm SPad SPur SSvw STes WCFE WHil WTou
clematiflora see *A. vulgaris* var. *stellata*
Clementine Series EPfP LRHS SPoG
coerulea ♀H4 GKev MDKP SRms
- var. ***coerulea*** GKev SMrm
- 'Himmelblau' EGoo NBre
- 'Mrs Nicholls' WSpi
- var. ***ochroleuca*** WCot
'Crimson Star' EBee EPfP GKir LRHS MBNS MDKP SPer SPoG SPur WMoo WTou WWEG
'Debutante' EBee LLWP MDKP MWea WGwG
desertorum MDKP
discolor LLHF LRHS WTou
'Double Rubies' (d) GCra LSRN SHar WMoo
'Dove' (Songbird Series) ♀H2 EWll LRHS MBri MHer NLar NPri SHar SMrm SPer WFar
I 'Dragonfly' CBcs CTsd CWib EPfP LRHS MAvo MNHC NBre SBch SPer SPet SPoG WFar WTou WWEG
ecalcarata see *Semiaquilegia ecalcarata*
einseleana EBee LLHF
elegantula GKev MWea

Plant	Suppliers
Fairytale Series **new**	LRHS
flabellata ♀H4	GCra GGar GKir WAbe WKif WPer
- from Rebun-tō, Japan	CStu
- f. ***alba***	CTri ECho ELan NWCA WEas
* - - 'White Angel'	WPer
- 'Amethyst' (Jewel Series)	GKir
- 'Blackcurrant Ice' **new**	EWll
- 'Blue Angel'	WPer
- 'Blue Jewel' (Jewel Series)	ECho
- Cameo Series	EWll LRHS WFar WGor
- - 'Cameo Blue and White'	CWib ECho NCGa WFar
- - 'Cameo Blue'	ECho
- - 'Cameo Blush'	WFar
- - 'Cameo Pink and White'	ECho MHer NCGa WFar
- - 'Cameo Rose'	NBir
- 'Georgia' (State Series) ♀H3-4	SMrm
- Jewel Series	ECho LRHS WPer
- 'Ministar'	EAlp ECho EPfP GKir MHer NBlu NVic WBrE WFar WPer
- 'Nana Alba'	see *A. flabellata* var. *pumila* f. *alba*
§ - var. ***pumila*** ♀H4	CFir CSam ECha ECho EPfP GKir LHop LRHS MDKP NLAp NPri SIng WFar WPer
§ - - f. ***alba*** ♀H4	CBot ECha ECho GKev LHop LRHS NChi NLAp SIng SMrm SRms
- - 'Atlantis' **new**	SVil WHlf
- - 'Flore Pleno'	ECho
- 'Vermont' (State Series)	SMrm
flavescens	WCot WPer
'Florida' (State Series) ♀H2	SMrm
formosa	CBot CMea EBee ECho LBMP MDKP NChi NPri NWCA WCot WGwG WKif WPer WTou
- var. ***truncata***	EBee GBuc GCal
formosa × ***pubescens*** NNS 05-76 **new**	WCot
§ ***fragrans***	CHrt CLAP COIW CPrp CTsd EBee EPfP GEdr GKev LBMP LRHS MTho NWCA SGar STes SWal WGwG WHoo
- CC 5233	GKev
- white-flowered	ELan
glandulosa	LLHF NDlv NLar WEas
glauca	see *A. fragrans*
'Golden Guiness'	WPnP WTou
'Goldfinch' (Songbird Series)	LRHS MHer NBir NPri SCoo SMrm SPer
grata	MDKP
'Heavenly Blue'	NGdn SMrm WHil
'Hensol Harebell' ♀H4	EBee GBuc SRms WPtf WSpi WTou
'Ice Blue'	WCot
'Irish Elegance'	EGoo
japonica	see *A. flabellata* var. *pumila*
jonesii	LRHS WAbe
jonesii × ***saximontana***	GKev NLAp WAbe
'Koralle'	COIW CSam MDKP NBre WFar WHil
'Kristall'	EBee EShb LSRN MDKP NBre STes WHil
laramiensis	CPBP
'Leprechaun Gold' (v) **new**	NGdn SMrm
longissima ♀H4	CHar CMea GBuc ILad LFur MBel MDKP MHer MWea SGSe SHar STes WEas WGwG WHoo WPen
'Louisiana' (State Series) ♀H2	SMrm
'Magpie'	see *A. vulgaris* 'William Guiness'
'Maxi'	LRHS MDKP NBre WHil
McKana Group	CTri EAEE ELan EPfP GJos GMaP LAst LBMP LHop LRHS MBel MLHP MNHC NEgg NGdn NVic SBch SPer SPlb SPoG SRms SWal WBor WCAu WMnd WMoo WTou WWEG WWlt
'Milk and Honey'	CBre EBee LFur LRHS
moorcroftiana	EBee
Mrs Scott-Elliot hybrids	CSBt EPfP SGar SPer SPet WFar
Music Series ♀H4	SRms
'Nightingale' (Songbird Series)	LRHS NPri
nigricans	see *A. atrata*
nivalis	LLHF
olympica	EWes WPer
'Oranges and Lemons'	LSou SGSe
Origami Series	WFar
ottonis	LHop
§ - subsp. ***amaliae***	GEdr
§ ***oxysepala***	CPLG EBee GCal WCot WCru WPrP
- B&SWJ 4775	WCru
parviflora	EBee
pleated burgundy-flowered **new**	LRHS
'Purple Emperor' PBR	LRHS
'Red Hobbit'	CBct CSpe EAEE EBee EPfP GKev GKir LHop LRHS LSou MDKP MHer NBre NEgg SUsu WBrE WFar WHoo
'Red Star' (Star Series)	CPrp EAEE EBee EPfP NEgg SHar WFar WHil WPer WTou
'Robin' (Songbird Series)	EWll MHer NPri SCoo SMrm WFar
rockii	CFir CHrt CLAP CSam EBee EWes GCal GKev GKir LFur LHop MDKP NCGa SSvw WHil
- B&SWJ 7965	WCru
'Roman Bronze'	see *Aquilegia* × *Semiaquilegia* 'Roman Bronze'
'Rose Queen'	CSam EBee MAvo MDKP NBre SSvw WHil WHoo
saximontana	GEdr GKev NLAp NLar NWCA WCot WPer
§ 'Schneekönigin'	CWCL GMaP WPer WWEG
scopulorum	GKev LLHF WAbe WCot
shockleyi	GBuc NWCA
sibirica	LLHF WPer WTou
'Silver Queen'	EBee ELan MDKP
skinneri	CPLG CSpe EShb IFro WMnd WMoo WSpi
- 'Tequila Sunrise'	CWib EBee ECtt EWll LSRN LSou NHol NPri NWsh WPer
Snow Queen	see *A.* 'Schneekönigin'
Songbird Series	LRHS NPri WFar
(Spring Magic Series) 'Spring Magic Blue and White'	LBuc LRHS NNor
- 'Spring Magic Pink and White' **new**	LRHS
stellata	see *A. vulgaris* var. *stellata*
'Stoulton Blue'	EBee WSpi
'Sunburst Ruby'	EBee MDKP WMoo WTou
'Sweet Lemon Drops'	LSou
viridiflora	CBot CLAP CPom EBee ELan EPPr EPfP GBuc GCal LBMP MAvo MCot SGar SMad WCot WEas WFar WHil WMnd WPGP WPer
- 'Chocolate Soldier'	CSpe ENor LEdu LSou MWea
vulgaris	CArn CMHG CRWN EPfP GPoy LLWP LRHS MHer NBro NMir NSco SBod SGar SPlb WCAu WMoo WPer WShi WTin WWEG
- SDR 5436	GKev
- 'Adelaide Addison'	ECGP ECha GBuc SUsu WEas WFar WHoo WKif
- var. ***alba***	CMea EBee LBMP LLWP LRHS MNFA SMrm SUsu WCAu WTou
- 'Altrosa'	NBre

* - 'Anemoniflora'	WSpi
- 'Aureovariegata'	see *A. vulgaris* Vervaeneana Group
- 'Burnished Rose'	ECtt WHil WTou
- ***clematiflora***	see *A. vulgaris* var. *stellata*
- (Clementine Series) 'Clementine Dark Purple' (d) **new**	EPfP
- - 'Clementine Red' (d) **new**	EPfP
- - 'Clementine Salmon Rose' (d) **new**	EPfP
- - 'Clementine White' (d) **new**	EPfP
- 'Crystal Star'	LRHS
- var. ***flore-pleno*** (d)	LLWP WPer
- - black-flowered (d)	LRHS WCot WTou
- - 'Blue Bonnet' (d)	WHil WTou
- - blue-flowered (d)	WTou
- - Dorothy Series (d)	GBuc LHop
- - - 'Dorothy Rose' (d)	LSRN SPad
- - 'Double Pleat' (d)	GGar
- - 'Double Pleat' blue/white-flowered (d)	CPrp WHil WPer
- - 'Double Pleat' pink/white-flowered (d)	CPrp NGdn WPer
* - - 'Frilly Dilly Rose' (d)	WTou
- - 'Jane Hollow' (d)	CPou
- - pale blue-flowered (d)	LLWP WCot
- - 'Pink Bonnet' (d)	WFar
- - pink-flowered (d)	GGar WTou
- - purple-flowered (d)	LLWP WTou
- - red-flowered (d)	WTou
- - 'Strawberry Ice Cream' (d)	NBro NBur
- - (Tower Series) 'Tower Light Blue' (d)	CSpr EGoo
- - - 'Tower White' (d)	EGoo
* - - 'White Bonnet' (d)	LRHS SRos
- - white-flowered (d)	LLWP WTou
- 'Foggy Bottom Blues'	GKir LRHS
§ - golden-leaved	ECho WOut WTou
- Grandmother's Garden Group	WTou WWEG
- 'Granny's Gold'	LRHS
- 'Heidi'	CBot NBre
- 'Mellow Yellow'	CTsd ELon GBuc GCra ILad LFur MDKP SDix SGSe WMoo WPer WWEG
- Munstead White	see *A. vulgaris* 'Nivea'
- subsp. ***nevadensis***	EBee
§ - 'Nivea' ♀H4	CBot COlW CPou CSpe EBee ECGP ECha LAst NChi SPoG
- 'Pink Spurless'	see *A. vulgaris* var. *stellata* pink-flowered
- (Pom Pom Series) 'Pom Pom Crimson'	NBro NBur WCot
- - 'Pom Pom Violet'	WSpi
- scented	WTou
§ - var. ***stellata***	CHrt ELan GBuc GKev LEdu NBro NWsh WMoo WPer WTou
- - Barlow Series (d)	WFar WTou WWEG
- - - 'Black Barlow' (d)	Widely available
- - - 'Blue Barlow' (d)	CElw CSpe EBee ECtt EPfP GMaP IBal LFur LRHS LSRN NBre SMrm SPad SPer SPhx WMnd WPer WWEG
- - 'Blue Fountain'	WTou
- - blue-flowered **new**	LRHS
- - 'Christa Barlow' (Barlow Series) (d)	EBee LRHS NBre NCGa NGdn SMrm SPer
- - double-flowered (d)	WTou
- - 'Firewheel'	WMoo WTou
- - 'Gisela Powell'	EBee WTou
- - 'Greenapples' (d)	CBre EBee MNFA NGdn NPri SMrm SPad WCot WTou WWEG
* - - 'Iceberg'	WSpi
- - 'Nora Barlow' (Barlow Series) (d) ♀H4	Widely available
§ - - pink-flowered	LLWP WTou
- - purple-flowered	LLWP MGos WTou
- - red-flowered	ELan LLWP MGos WTou
- - 'Rose Barlow' (Barlow Series) (d)	EPfP IBal LRHS LSRN SPad SPhx WMnd WTou
- - 'Royal Purple' (d)	NBro WBVN
- - 'Ruby Port' (d)	CAby CBcs CHrt COlW CWCL EAEE EBee EGoo EPfP EShb GCal GGar GMaP IBal LRHS LSRN MNrw NBPC NPri SMrm SPer SSvw STes SUsu WCAu WFar WPrP
- - 'Ruby Port' crimped (d)	WPnP
- - 'Sunlight White' (d)	WPer
- - 'White Barlow' (Barlow Series) (d)	LRHS SPer WTou
- - white-flowered	CSpe GCra LHop LRHS NBro WFar
- variegated foliage	see *A. vulgaris* Vervaeneana Group
§ - Vervaeneana Group (v)	CMHG CSam CWCL ECtt EPfP EWll LRHS MCot MNrw NBir NBre NPer SBch SGSe SMrm SPer SPlb SPoG SRms SWat WFar WHoo WMoo WTou
- - 'Graeme Iddon' (v)	GBuc
- - 'Woodside Blue' (v)	ECtt EGoo GKir LRHS NHol WTou WWEG
- - 'Woodside Pink' (v)	MGos
- - 'Woodside White' (v)	NBir WBrk WWEG
§ - 'William Guiness'	Widely available
- 'William Guiness Doubles' (d)	WMoo WTou
'White Star' (Star Series)	CPrp EBee ELan EPfP LAst MRav NEgg WHil WPer WWEG
white-flowered	WTou
Winky Series	ECtt
- 'Winky Blue-White'	LRHS MHer NBre NLar NPri SMrm WCFE WFar WHil
- 'Winky Double White-White' (d)	NPri WHil
- 'Winky Pink'	NLar
- 'Winky Purple-White'	NBre NPri WFar WHil
- 'Winky Red-White'	NBre NPri SWvt WCot WFar WHil
- 'Winky Rose-Rose'	LRHS NBre SMrm
yabeana	EBee EGoo GGar GKev ILad MWhi WCot WMoo

Aquilegia × *Semiaquilegia* (*Ranunculaceae*)

hybrid, blue-flowered	WCru
§ 'Roman Bronze'	ILad MHer WMoo WTou

Arabis (*Brassicaceae*)

from Ethiopia **new**	GCal
aculeolata	GAuc
albida	see *A. alpina* subsp. *caucasica*
alpina	NBlu SPlb
§ - subsp. ***caucasica***	ECho WFar
- - 'Corfe Castle'	ECho ECtt
- - 'Douler Angevine' (v)	ECtt NBlu NPri SPoG
- - 'Flore Pleno' (d) ♀H4	CElw CSpe CTri CWCL ECha ECho ECtt ELan EWld GAbr GMaP MTho SBch SRms WBrk WCom WEas WFar WHoo
- - 'Pink Pearl'	ECho NBlu
- - 'Pinkie'	ECho SBch
- - 'Pixie Cream'	EWTr LBMP

- - 'Rosea'	GJos LRHS NBir NBlu NPri SRms WFar WMoo
§ - - 'Schneehaube' ♀H4	CTri CWib ECho ECtt EPfP GKir GMaP LRHS MBar NBlu NPri SPoG SRms WMoo
- - Snowcap	see *A. alpina* subsp. *caucasica* 'Schneehaube'
- - 'Snowdrop'	WFar
- - 'Variegata' (v)	ECho ECtt ELan GMaP LAst LBee LHop LRHS MHer NPri SAga SPoG SRms WEas WFar
- 'Revolution'	WCot
androsacea	SRms WCom WFar
× ***arendsii*** 'Compinkie'	GJos LBMP SGar SPlb SRms
- 'Rosabella' (v)	LRHS
blepharophylla	EPfP WFar
§ - 'Frühlingszauber' ♀H4	CTri CWib EPfP GJos GKir LRHS NBir SPoG SRms WFar
- 'Rose Delight' new	LRHS
- 'Rote Sensation'	NPri WRHF
- Spring Charm	see *A. blepharophylla* 'Frühlingszauber'
bryoides	LRHS NMen
caucasica	see *A. alpina* subsp. *caucasica*
cypria	LSou
double white-flowered (d)	CFee
'Doulier Anguine'	WFar
ferdinandi-coburgi	ECho MWat
- 'Aureovariegata' (v)	CMea CTri ECho ECtt EDAr SPet SWvt
- 'Old Gold'	ECho EDAr EHoe EPfP GKir LBee LRHS MBar MHer NBlu NHol NPri SPoG SRms SWvt WCFE WFar WHoo WRHF
- 'Variegata'	see *A. procurrens* 'Variegata'
glabra	EBWF WPer
§ ***procurrens*** 'Variegata' (v) ♀H4	CMoH CTri ECha ECho ECtt EHoe ELan EPfP EWes GEdr GKev LBee LEdu LRHS MBar MBrN MHer NHol NPri SHGN SPlb SPoG SRms WFar
§ ***scabra***	CNat
Snow Cap	see *A. alpina* subsp. *caucasica* 'Schneehaube'
stricta	see *A. scabra*
'Tu Tu'	LRHS NLar SIng

Arachniodes (*Dryopteridaceae*)

aristata	MAsh
simplicior	CBty CCCN EBee LRHS WCot WRic
standishii	WRic

Araiostegia (*Davalliaceae*)

faberiana new	CPLG
hymenophylloides	WCot
perdurans new	WCot

Aralia ✿ (*Araliaceae*)

CD&R 2289 from China	WCru
apioides EDHCH 9720	WCru
armata B&SWJ 6719	WCru
- RWJ 10060	WCru
cachemirica	CDTJ CDes CLAP EWes GAbr GCal NBid NLar SDix SMad SPlb WHal WPGP
californica	CAby COld EBee GCal GPoy LEdu NLar SDix WCru
chapaensis B&SWJ 11812	WCru
- HWJ 723	WCru
chinensis misapplied	see *A. elata*, *A. stipulata*
chinensis L.	WBVN
- BWJ 8102	WCru
continentalis	CLAP EBee EPPr EShb GKev LEdu NLar
- B&SWJ 4152	WCru
- B&SWJ 8524	WCru
cordata	EBee EWes GAbr GCal GKev LEdu NLar
- B&SWJ 5511	WCru
decaisneana RWJ 9910	WCru
§ ***elata*** ♀H4	Widely available
- B&SWJ 5480	WCru
- 'Albomarginata'	see *A. elata* 'Variegata'
- 'Aureo-marginata' (v)	CMac
- 'Aureovariegata' (v)	CBcs CDoC ELan EWes MBlu NLar NMoo NPal SCoo WDin
- 'Golden Umbrella' (v)	LSRN NLar WDin
- 'Silver Umbrella'	CDoC MGos NLar
§ - 'Variegata' (v) ♀H4	CBcs CBot CDoC CDul ELan EPfP MBlu MGos NLar NMoo NPal SCoo SPoG WCot WDin
foliolosa B&SWJ 8360	WCru
kansuensis BWJ 7650	WCru
leschenaultii B&SWJ 11789	WCru
montana RWJ 10101	WCru
nudicaulis	GPoy
papyrifera	see *Tetrapanax papyrifer*
racemosa	CArn EBee GPoy MNrw NLar SRms WFar
- B&SWJ 9570	WCru
sieboldii	see *Fatsia japonica*
spinifolia B&SWJ 11745 new	WCru
spinosa L.	GKev MBlu NLar SPlb
§ ***stipulata***	NLar WPGP
subcordata HWJK 2385	WCru
verticillata B&SWJ 11797 new	WCru

Araucaria (*Araucariaceae*)

angustifolia	CDoC WPGP
§ ***araucana***	Widely available
bidwillii	CTrC
columnaris	LRHS
cunninghamii	ECou
excelsa misapplied	see *A. heterophylla*
§ ***heterophylla*** ♀H1	CCCN CDoC CTsd ECho EShb LRHS MBri SAPC SArc SEND
imbricata	see *A. araucana*

Araujia (*Asclepiadaceae*)

sericifera	CMac CPne CRHN CTrG EBee EShb GQui SDnm SGar SPav WFoF WSHC WSpi

Arbutus ✿ (*Ericaceae*)

andrachne	EPfP
× ***andrachnoides*** ♀H4	CAbP CBcs CPMA CTri EBee ELan EPfP GGal LRHS LSRN MAsh MRav SAPC SArc SDnm SPer SPoG SReu SSpi SSta WHCG WPGP WPat WSpi
glandulosa	see *Arctostaphylos glandulosa*
'Marina'	CAbP CDoC CEnd CPMA CSam CTrC EBee ELan EPfP LHop LRHS MAsh MBlu SEND SMad SPer SPoG SRGP SReu SSpi SSta SWvt WFar WPGP WPat
menziesii ♀H3	CBcs CDoC CEnd CMCN CTho EBee ECrN EPfP LRHS LSRN MGos MMuc MSnd NLar SMad SPer WDin WFar WPGP
unedo ♀H4	Widely available

- 'Atlantic'	CAlb CCCN EBee ECrN LRHS LSRN MAsh MGos SBch SBig SPoG SWvt WPat
- 'Compacta'	CAlb CBcs CCCN CDoC EMil GKir IMon LRHS MAsh MGos SLon SWvt WCFE WDin
- 'Elfin King'	ELan EPfP LRHS MAsh SDnm SPoG SSta SWvt
- 'Quercifolia'	CPMA EBee ELan MAsh MMHG NLar SDnm WFar WPat
- Roselily = 'Minlily' **new**	SBig
- f. ***rubra*** ♀H4	Widely available
xalapensis F&M 206	WPGP

Archontophoenix (*Arecaceae*)

alexandrae	EAmu LPal
cunninghamiana ♀H1	CBrP EAmu LPal XBlo

Arctanthemum (*Asteraceae*)

§ ***arcticum***	CKno ECha NBre WPer
- 'Roseum'	EBee GBin
- 'Schwefelglanz'	NCGa

Arcterica see *Pieris*

Arctium (*Asteraceae*)

lappa	CArn GBar GPoy MHer NMir SIde SVic
- 'Takinogawa Long'	MNHC
minus	CArn EBWF NSco
- 'Plus'	WAlt

Arctomecon (*Papaveraceae*)

californica **new**	MPoH
merriamii **new**	MPoH

Arctostaphylos (*Ericaceae*)

§ ***glandulosa***	SAPC SArc
× ***media*** 'Wood's Red'	MBar
myrtifolia	MBar
uva-ursi	GPoy MBar NLar NMen SLon SPlb SSta WDin
- 'Massachusetts'	GKir LRHS NLar
- 'Snowcap'	MAsh NHol
- 'Vancouver Jade'	CDoC EBee GKir LRHS LSRN MAsh MBar MBri SBch SCoo SLon SPer SPoG SReu SRms SSta SWvt

Arctotis (*Asteraceae*)

Hannah = 'Archnah'PBR	CHVG CSpe LAst MBNS SVil
Hayley = 'Archley'PBR	CCCN LAst MBNS SVil
× ***hybrida*** hort. 'Apricot'	CCCN CHEx LAst SAga SMrm
- 'China Rose'	SMrm
- cream-flowered	CHEx SAga
- 'Flame' ♀H1+3	CAby CCCN LAst MBNS SAga SCoo SMrm WHlf
- 'Red Devil'	CCCN CSpe LAst LSou MBNS SAga SCoo SMrm SUsu
- 'Wine'	CCCN CHEx LAst LSou MBNS SCoo SMrm SRkn SVil
'Prostrate Raspberry'	CSpe SAga

Ardisia (*Myrsinaceae*)

crenata	LRHS MBri
japonica B&SWJ 1841	WCru
- B&SWJ 3809	WCru
- var. ***angusta***	WCot
- 'Miyo-nishiki' (v)	WCot
pusilla	CBcs

Areca (*Arecaceae*)

catechu	MBri
triandra	XBlo

Arecastrum see *Syagrus*

Arenaria (*Caryophyllaceae*)

balearica	CWCL ECho EWes GKir LBee LRHS SIng SPlb SRms
bertolonii	LRHS
capillaris	CTri
ledebouriana	EDAr EPot MWat NLar
magellanica	see *Colobanthus quitensis*
montana ♀H4	Widely available
- 'Avalanche'	SHGN
- 'Blizzard' **new**	EPfP
pinifolia	see *Minuartia circassica*
pseudacantholimon	WAbe
purpurascens	ECho EDAr EPot EWes LLHF NMen NWCA SRms SRot WFar
- 'Elliott's Variety'	NMen WPat
roseiflora	GKev
serpyllifolia	EDAr
tetraquetra	NLAp
- subsp. ***amabilis***	EPot LRHS NMen NSla SIng
tmolea	NMen
verna	see *Minuartia verna*

Arenga (*Arecaceae*)

engleri	EAmu LPal
micrantha **new**	WCot

Argania (*Sapotaceae*)

spinosa **new**	WPGP

Argemone (*Papaveraceae*)

grandiflora	CSpe SBch SPav
mexicana	ELan SPav
pleiacantha	SPav

Argyranthemum ✿ (*Asteraceae*)

'Anastasia'	MAJR
'Apricot Surprise'	see *A.* 'Peach Cheeks'
'Beth'	GBee MAJR
'Blanche' (Courtyard Series)	MAJR
Blazer Rose = 'Supaglow'PBR (Daisy Crazy Series)	MAJR
§ 'Blizzard' (d)	MAJR
Blushing Rose = 'Supaellie' (Daisy Crazy Series)	MAJR
'Bofinger'	MAJR
'Bon Bon'	MAJR MBNS
'Bridesmaid'	CCCN MAJR
Bright Carmine = 'Supalight'PBR (Daisy Crazy Series)	LSou MAJR
broussonetii	MAJR
Butterfly = 'Ulyssis' ♀H1+3	MAJR WGor
'Camilla Ponticelli'	MAJR
canariense hort.	see *A. frutescens* subsp. *canariae*
'Champagne'	MAJR
Cherry Love (Daisy Crazy Series)	CCCN EPfP MAJR
'Christy Bell'	GBee MAJR
'Citronelle'	SVil
* ***compactum***	MAJR
'Comtesse de Chambord'	MAJR SPet
'Cornish Gold' ♀H1+3	CBcs CCCN LSou MAJR SBch
coronopifolium	MAJR
'Donington Hero' ♀H1+3	MAJR MHom
double white-flowered (d)	MAJR
'Edelweiss' (d)	MAJR MHom
'Ella'	MAJR
'Flamingo'	see *Rhodanthemum gayanum*

§ ***foeniculaceum*** misapplied CTri ELan GKir WKif
- pink-flowered see *A.* 'Petite Pink'
§ ***foeniculaceum*** (Willd.) Webb & Sch.Bip. MAJR MCot
- 'Royal Haze' ♀H1+3 CCCN CHll MAJR NPer
'Frosty' MAJR MBNS
§ ***frutescens*** CHEx LRHS MAJR
§ - subsp. ***canariae*** ♀H1+3 CCCN MAJR
- Cherry Harmony (Daisy Crazy Series) **new** MAJR
- subsp. ***succulentum*** MAJR
- - 'Margaret Lynch' MAJR
'Fuji Sundance' MAJR
'George' MAJR
'Gill's Pink' CCCN MAJR MHom WPnn
'Golden Treasure' GBee MAJR
gracile CHll
- 'Chelsea Girl' ♀H1+3 CCCN CHEx COlW MAJR MCot MHom WKif
'Gretel' GBee MAJR
'Guernsey Pink' GBee MAJR MHom
Gypsy Rose = 'M9/18d' CCCN MAJR
'Harvest Snow' LAst MBNS
'Henriette' MAJR
'Icknield Jubilee' MAJR
'Icknield Lemon Ice' MAJR
'Icknield Pink' MAJR
'Icknield Surprise' MAJR
'Icknield Sylvia' MAJR
'Icknield Yellow' MAJR
'Jamaica Primrose' ♀H1+3 CBot CHEx CSpe CTri ECtt MAJR SAga SDix
'Jamaica Snowstorm' see *A.* 'Snow Storm'
'Julieanne' CBcs LAst MAJR MBNS SMrm
'Lemon Delight' LAst MAJR
'Lemon Meringue' (d) CCCN
'Lemon Soufflé' GBee MAJR
lemsii MAJR
'Levada Cream' ♀H1+3 MAJR MHom
'Libby Brett' MAJR
'Lilliput' MAJR
(Madeira Series) Machio Double Pink = 'Ohar01245' MAJR
- Madelana = 'Ohmadmade'PBR SVil
- Monte = 'Ohar01241'PBR MAJR
- Santana = 'Ohmadsant' MAJR SVil
- São Martinho = 'Ohmadsaom' MAJR SVil
- Madeira São Vicente = 'Ohmadsavi'PBR MAJR
§ ***maderense*** ♀H1+3 CHll GBee GCal MAJR
- pale-flowered MAJR
'Mary Cheek' (d) ♀H1+3 CCCN MAJR SPet SRGP
'Mary Wootton' (d) ECtt MAJR MHom
mawii see *Rhodanthemum gayanum*
'Mike's Pink' MAJR
'Millennium Star' MAJR
'Mini-snowflake' see *A.* 'Blizzard'
Molimba Duplo Pearl = 'Argydupea' MAJR
§ 'Mrs F. Sander' (d) GBee MAJR MCot
ochroleucum see *A. maderense*
'Pacific Gold' CBcs MAJR SVil
§ 'Peach Cheeks' (d) CCCN
§ 'Petite Pink' ♀H1+3 CCCN ECtt GBee LAst MAJR MHom
Ping-Pong = 'Innping'PBR (d) CCCN MAJR MBNS SVil
'Pink Australian' (d) CCCN GBee MAJR MHom
'Pink Delight' see *A.* 'Petite Pink'
'Pink Pixie' MAJR
Pink Wonder = 'Supalily' (Daisy Crazy Series) MAJR
pinnatifidium subsp. ***succulentum*** MAJR
Polly = 'Innpolly' MAJR SBch SMrm SVil
'Pomponette Pink' CBcs SVil
'Porto Moritz' MAJR
'Powder Puff' (d) ECtt MAJR
'Primrose Petite'PBR (Courtyard Series) MAJR SVil
prostrate double pink-flowered (d) MAJR
'Rising Sun' MAJR
'Saimi' MAJR
'São Catarina' MAJR
'Silver Leaf' MAJR
'Silver Queen' see *A. foeniculaceum* misapplied
§ 'Snow Storm' ♀H1+3 LAst MAJR MHom WClo WPnn
'Snowball' MAJR
'Snowflake' misapplied see *A.* 'Mrs F. Sander'
'Sole Mio' **new** CWCL MAJR
'Starlight' MAJR
Strawberry Pink = 'Suparosa'PBR (Daisy Crazy Series) EPfP LRHS
'Sugar and Ice'PBR CCCN MAJR
'Sugar Baby'PBR CCCN MAJR
Sugar Cheer = 'Cobeer' MAJR
'Sugar Lace' MAJR
Sultan's Dream = 'Supadream'PBR (Daisy Crazy Series) EPfP
Sultan's Lemon = 'Supalem'PBR (Daisy Crazy Series) EPfP MAJR
Sultan's Pride = 'Cosupri' (Daisy Crazy Series) MAJR
'Summer Angel' (d) MAJR
'Summer Cloud' MCot
'Summer Eyes' GBee MAJR
'Summer Melody'PBR (d) CBcs CCCN CSpe MAJR MBNS
'Summer Pink'PBR CCCN LAst LSou MAJR SMrm SVil
'Summer Stars' (Daisy Crazy Series) (d) MAJR
Summersong Lemon = 'Supa601' (Daisy Crazy Series) LSou MAJR
Summersong White = 'Supa594' (Daisy Crazy Series) LSou MAJR
'Summertime' MAJR
Summit Pink = 'Cobsing'PBR (Daisy Crazy Series) EPfP MAJR
'Sweety' MAJR
'Tony Holmes' MAJR
'Tweeny' MAJR
'Tweety' GBee MAJR
'Vancouver' (d) ♀H1+3 CBot CCCN CHll CWCL ECtt EShb LAst MAJR SBHP SPet
Vanilla Ripple = 'Supabright' (Daisy Crazy Series) MAJR
* 'Vera' CCCN MAJR
'Wellwood Park' CCCN
'Weymouth Pink' MAJR
'Weymouth Surprise' MAJR
White Blush = 'Supamorni' (Daisy Crazy Series) MAJR
White Crystal = 'Supagem' (Daisy Crazy Series) MAJR

'White Spider'	CCCN ELan GBee MAJR MHom
'White Star' (d)	MAJR
'Whiteknights' ♀H1+3	GBee MAJR
'Yellow Australian' (d)	CCCN MAJR

Argyrocytisus see *Cytisus*

Argyroderma (*Aizoaceae*)

testiculare	LRHS

Arisaema ✿ (*Araceae*)

ACE 2408	GBuc
C&H 7026	NMen
CC 4904	CPLG
CC 5511	CPLG
Chen Yi 14	WCot
Chen Yi 38	WCot
Chen Yi 41	WCot
SDR 3276	GKev
album	EBee
amurense	CElw CLAP CStu EBee ECho GAuc GBuc GCal GGar LAma LFur MMoz WCot WFar WPnP
§ - subsp. ***robustum***	ECho LFur LRHS NMen WCot WWst
* ***angustatum*** var. ***amurense***	LAma
asperatum	EBee LAma MLul WCot
auriculatum	EBee
biauriculatum	see *A. wattii*
brachyspathum	see *A. heterophyllum*
brevipes	CPLG
candidissimum ♀H4	Widely available
- pink-flowered	MLul NWCA
- white-flowered	GEdr LAma MLul WCot
ciliatum	CBro CDes CPom CSpe CStu EBee EBla GBuc GEdr LAma LFur MLul MMoz MNrw NLar SRot WCot WSHC
- var. ***liubaense***	CFwr CGHE CLAP CPLG CWCL EBee EPfP EWld GEdr MMoz WIvy WPGP
- - CT 369	CSpr SCnR SDys WCot
concinnum	CFir EAmu EBee EBrs EPot EWld GAuc GBin GEdr LAma MLul NHol WCot WPnP
consanguineum	Widely available
- B&SWJ 071	WCru
- CC 3635	WCot
- GG 92112	WCot
- PJ 277	WCot
- SDR 3214	GKev
- dark-flowered	WCot
- 'J. Balis'	WCot
- subsp. ***kelung-insulare*** B&SWJ 256	WCru
- marble-leaf red	WCot
- 'Qinling'	WCot
- variegated (v) **new**	WCot
cf. ***consanguineum*** ACE 2031 **new**	WCot
costatum	CCCN CHEx CLAP CPom EAmu EBee EBrs ECho EPfP EPot ETod GBuc GEdr GGar LAma LRHS MLul MMoz NHol NMen WCot WPGP
- CC 2924	WCot
dahaiense	LAma MLul
dilatatum	EBee LAma MLul
dracontium	CLAP EBee EBrs ECho LAma NLar NMen
du-bois-reymondiae	EBee LAma
ehimense	WWst
elephas	EBee ECho LAma MLul WCot WWst
engleri	MLul
erubescens	CPom CStu EPot ERos MLul NLar WBVN
aff. ***erubescens***	WCot
- marbled-leaved	GEdr
exappendiculatum	CDes EBee MMoz WPGP
fargesii	CLAP CPLG EBee EBrs ECho GEdr LAma MLul MMoz SChF WCot WWst
flavum	CBro CDes CGHE CLAP CStu EBee EBrs ECho EPfP EPot GBuc GCal GKev ITim LAma LFur MLul MMoz MTho NHol NMen SGSe WBVN WPGP WPrP
* - ***minus***	NWCA
- tall	CLAP ECho
- subsp. ***tibeticum***	EBee
formosanum B&SWJ 280	WCru
- B&SWJ 390	CPou
- var. ***bicolorifolium*** B&SWJ 3528	WCru
- f. ***stenophyllum*** B&SWJ 1477	WCru
§ ***franchetianum***	CPLG EBee GEdr LAma MLul WCot
fraternum	WWst
galeatum	EBee ECho EPot LAma MLul NHol
grapsospadix B&SWJ 7000	WCru
§ ***griffithii***	EBee EBrs ECho GAuc GEdr GGar LAma LRHS MLul NHol WCot WPnP
- 'Numbuq'	GCra
- var. ***pradhanii***	EBee GAuc MLul WWst
handelii	CPom
helleborifolium	see *A. tortuosum*
§ ***heterophyllum***	EBee GEdr LFur WWst
inkiangense	LAma
intermedium	EBee EBrs ECho GEdr LAma MLul MNrw NHol NMen
iyoanum	EBee WCru
- subsp. ***nakaianum***	GEdr WWst
jacquemontii	CBro CLAP EBla EBrs ECho EWld GBuc GCra GEdr GKir LRHS NLar NMen WCot WPGP
- MECC 29	EBee
aff. ***jacquemontii*** MECC 29	NMen
-MECC 76	NMen
japonicum Blume	see *A. serratum* var. *mayebarae*
japonicum Komarov	see *A. serratum*
jinshajiangense	CPLG LAma MLul
kishidae	EBee GEdr
kiushianum	EBee EFEx GEdr LAma MMoz WCot WWst
leschenaultii	LAma WWst
lichiangense	GEdr LAma LFur
lingyunense	WCot
§ ***lobatum***	CPLG EBee LAma LFur MLul WCot
maximowiczii	EBee GEdr WWst
meleagris	EBee LAma
negishii	WCru WWst
§ ***nepenthoides***	CBro EAmu EBee EBrs ECho EHrv EPot ETod GBin GEdr ITim LAma LRHS MLul MNrw NHol WPnP
ochraceum	see *A. nepenthoides*
omeiense	EBee NLar WCot
onoticum	see *A. lobatum*
petelotii B&SWJ 9706	WCru
polyphyllum B&SWJ 3904	WCru
propinquum	CLAP CPom EBee EBrs ECho GBin GBuc LAma LRHS MLul NMen WCot
purpureogaleatum	see *A. franchetianum*

rhizomatum	LAma
rhombiforme	EBee LAma MLul WCot WWst
ringens misapplied	see *A. amurense* subsp. *robustum*
ringens ambig.	LFur
ringens (Thunberg) Schott	CDes EBee EFEx EPot GEdr LAma MLul WWst
- f. ***praecox*** B&SWJ 1515	WCru
- f. ***sieboldii***	EBrs
- - B&SWJ 551	WCru
robustum	see *A. amurense* subsp. *robustum*
saxatile	EBee LAma MLul WCot WWst
sazensoo	EBee GEdr LAma LRHS WWst
§ ***serratum***	EBee EBrs ECho LAma MMoz MNrw WPGP
§ - var. ***mayebarae***	EBee WWst
sikokianum	CBro EBee EBrs ECho EFEx EHrv EPPr EPot GEdr LAma LRHS MLul SPoG WCru
- var. ***serratum***	CFir
- variegated (v)	EBee GEdr WWst
speciosum	CHEx CPLG EAmu EBee EBrs ECho EPot ETod GBuc GEdr GGar IHer LAma LRHS MLul NHol NMen SPlb WCot WFar WPnP
- CC 3100	WCot
* - var. ***magnificum***	EBee EHrv ETod EWld GBin GEdr MLul NHol
- var. ***mirabile***	EBee GEdr
* - var. ***sikkimense***	LAma
taiwanense	CFwr CLAP CPom WCot
- B&SWJ 269	WCru
- B&SWJ 356	CPou
- var. ***brevipedunculatum*** B&SWJ 1859	WCru
- f. ***cinereum*** B&SWJ 19121	WCru
- silver-leaved	WCot
tashiroi	EBee GEdr WWst
ternatipartitum	EBee GEdr WWst
thunbergii	CPom CStu EFEx EPPr LRHS SPoG WCot
- subsp. ***autumnale*** B&SWJ 1425	WCru
- subsp. ***urashima***	CLAP EBee EBrs EFEx GEdr LAma LFur LRHS MLul WCot WWst
§ ***tortuosum***	Widely available
- CC 1452	CPou
- CC 1760	WCot
- CC 4596	WCot
- from high altitude	GBuc NMen
tosaense	EBee WWst
triphyllum	CElw CLAP CPLG EBee EBrs ECho EPot GBuc GGar GKev ITim LAma MTho NHol NWCA SMad WCot WFar WPGP WPnP
- subsp. ***stewardsonii***	EBee EBrs GGar NMen WWst
- subsp. ***triphyllum*** var. ***atrorubens***	CLAP
§ ***utile***	EAmu EBee EBrs ECho EPot GAuc GEdr LAma MLul WPnP
- CC 3101	WCot
verrucosum	see *A. griffithii*
- var. ***utile***	see *A. utile*
§ ***wattii***	LAma MLul
yamatense	EBee WWst
- subsp. ***sugimotoi***	LAma
- - B&SWJ 5092	WCru
yunnanense	CLAP EBee LAma

Arisarum (*Araceae*)

proboscideum	Widely available
vulgare	ECho WCot
- from Crete	ECho
* - f. ***maculatum***	ECho
- subsp. ***simorrhinum***	EBee EBrs ECho WCot
- subsp. ***vulgare***	EBee ECho WCot WHal

Aristea (*Iridaceae*)

sp.	CStu GGal
ecklonii	CBod CHEx CPLG CPou CPrp CTrC CTsd EShb IGor MCot SChr SGar SHom WCot WDyG WOut
ensifolia	CMdw ELan MWea SAga WSHC
grandis	CFir WCot
inaequalis	CDes
§ ***major***	CHll CTrC
- pink-flowered	CDes CTrC WPGP
thyrsiflora	see *A. major*

Aristolochia (*Aristolochiaceae*)

baetica	CArn CPLG WPGP
californica	LEdu
chilensis	CCCN
clematitis	CArn EBee EBrs ECho GPoy LEdu
contorta	EBee
cucurbitifolia B&SWJ 7043	WCru
delavayi	CHEx
durior	see *A. macrophylla*
gigantea	CCCN CHll CSpe
grandiflora	CCCN CHll
griffithii B&SWJ 2118	WCru
heterophylla	see *A. kaempferi* f. *heterophylla*
kaempferi	CCCN WSHC
- B&SWJ 293	WCru
§ - f. ***heterophylla*** B&SWJ 3109	WCru
× ***kewensis***	CCCN
longa	WThu
§ ***macrophylla***	CBcs CBot CCCN CHEx CMac EBee EPfP GKir LRHS MBri MRav NEgg NPal SLim WDin WSpi
manshuriensis B&SWJ 962	WCru
moupinensis BWJ 8181	WCru
onoei B&SWJ 4960	WCru
pearcei	CCCN
sempervirens	WDin WSHC
sipho	see *A. macrophylla*
tomentosa	IDee

Aristotelia (*Elaeocarpaceae*)

§ ***chilensis***	LEdu NMun
- 'Variegata' (v)	CCCN CWib EBee GQui SPlb WCom
fruticosa (f)	ECou
- (m)	ECou
- black-fruited (f)	ECou
- white-fruited (f)	ECou
macqui	see *A. chilensis*
peduncularis	CPLG
serrata	ECou
- (f)	ECou
- (m)	ECou

Armeria (*Plumbaginaceae*)

§ ***alliacea***	CSpe ECha
- SDR 5498	GKev
- f. ***leucantha***	SRms WMoo
alpina	GAuc MWat
arenaria	EBWF
Bees' hybrids	WMoo
'Bees' Ruby'	WPer
'Bloodgood'	ECho
'Brutus'	MAvo SUsu

	caespitosa	see *A. juniperifolia*
	- 'Bevan's Variety'	see *A. juniperifolia* 'Bevan's Variety'
	euscadiensis	CSpe
	Joystick Series	CHrt ECho GJos NVic SPoG
	- 'Joystick Lilac Shades'	EBee EGoo EPfP EShb LBMP NLar SPoG
	- 'Joystick Pink'	SPoG SWal
	- 'Joystick Red'	EBee EPPr EShb GKir SPoG WHil
	- 'Joystick White'	EGoo EShb GKir NLar SPoG
§	***juniperifolia*** ♀H4	CMea ECho EDAr ELan EPfP GMaP LBee LRHS MAsh MHer MWat NHol NMen NVic NWCA SIng SPoG SRms
	- 'Alba'	CMea ECho ELan EPfP EPot GBin LRHS MAsh MHer MMuc NBlu NMen NPri NWCA SIng SPoG SRms WAbe WFar WHoo WThu
	- 'Beechwood'	LRHS
§	- 'Bevan's Variety' ♀H4	EAlp ECha ECho ECtt ELan EPfP EPot GGar GKir GMaP LEdu LRHS MLHP MMuc MWat NLAp NMen NPri NRya SPoG SRms SRot WAbe WFar WHoo WPat
	- 'Brookside'	EPot
	- dark-flowered	WAbe
	- rose-flowered	ITim
	juniperifolia × ***maritima***	SIng
§	***maritima***	CArn EBWF ECho EPfP GJos GKir LAst LRHS MBar MNHC NEgg SPet WCFE WFar WGwG WMoo
	- 'Alba'	Widely available
	- 'Bloodstone'	CTri ECho ELan LRHS MWat
	- 'Corsica'	CMea CTri ECha NBir WFar
	- Düsseldorf Pride	see *A. maritima* 'Düsseldorfer Stolz'
§	- 'Düsseldorfer Stolz'	CElw CPBP EAlp ECha ECho ECtt EDAr ELan EPfP EPot GGar GKir GMaP LHop LRHS MCot MLHP NLAp NMen NPri SPoG
	- 'Laucheana'	WHoo WMoo
*	- 'Pink Lusitanica'	ECho
	- 'Rossi'	NHol
I	- 'Rubrifolia'	CFir CMea COlW CSpe EAlp EBee ECho ECtt EDAr EHoe EPPr EShb GEdr GGar GMaP LAst LEdu LRHS MAvo MHer NLAp NLar NRya SPoG SRot WAbe WBor WFar WHoo WPat
	- 'Ruby Glow'	CTri
	- 'Splendens'	CBcs CHrt CTri ECho EDAr EPfP GGar GMaP LAst LBMP LRHS MGos NBlu NMir NNor NRya NVic SBch SPoG SWal WFar WMoo WPer
	- 'Splendens Alba'	EDAr
	- 'Vindictive' ♀H4	CMea CTri EPfP
	morisii	SBch
	'Nifty Thrifty' (v)	CBod CMea CTri EAlp EBee ECho ECtt EHoe EWes LRHS MAsh MHer NLAp NRya SCoo SIde SPoG SRot WCom WFar WPat WWFP
	'Ornament'	ECtt SBch
	plantaginea	see *A. alliacea*
	pseudarmeria	CHrt EBee ECho ELan EPfP GCal MWhi NBlu
	- 'Drumstick Red'	ECho WPer
	- 'Drumstick White'	WPer
	- hybrids	CTri ELan GGar
	pungens SDR 5622	EBee GKev
	'Vesuvius'	SIng
	vulgaris	see *A. maritima*
	welwitschii	IFoB SRms
	'Westacre Beauty'	EWes

Armoracia (*Brassicaceae*)

§	***rusticana***	CArn CBod COld CPrp CSev CTri ELau EPfP GAbr GPoy ILis MBri MHer MMuc MNHC NPer NPri SBch SIde SVic WHer WJek WSpi
	- 'Variegata' (v)	CHid CPrp ELau GCal IFoB LHop MAvo NSti SMad WCHb WHer WMoo

Arnica (*Asteraceae*)

	angustifolia subsp. ***alpina***	SRms
	- subsp. ***iljinii***	NBir
	chamissonis Less.	CHby EBee GBar MNHC NBre NLar WHil WJek WPer
	chamissonis Schmidt	see *A. sachalinensis*
	longifolia	NBre
	montana	CArn EBee GBar GKev GPWP GPoy MHer MNHC NMun SRms SWat WPer
§	***sachalinensis***	NBre
	- RBS 0206	EPPr
	unalaschkensis	EBee

Aronia (*Rosaceae*)

	arbutifolia	CBcs CDul CTri EPfP EWTr LSRN MBlu MGan NBlu SLon SPlb WDin WEas
	- 'Erecta'	CBgR CDul EBee ELan EPfP GBin LHop LRHS MBNS MBlu MBri NLar SBch SLPl SPoG SRms SSpi
	melanocarpa	CBgR CDul CMCN CMHG CSpe CTsd CWib EBee ELan EPfP GKir LEdu LRHS MAsh MBar SPer SSpi WDin WFar WHCG
	- 'Autumn Magic'	CBcs CDoC CPMA EBee EPfP GBin LAst LHop LRHS MAsh NMyG SCoo SLPl SLon
	- var. ***grandifolia***	CPMA
	- 'Hugin'	CAgr CPMA NLar
*	- 'Red Viking'	EBee
	× ***prunifolia***	CDoC CDul CMHG GAbr GKir LEdu WHCG
	- 'Aron' (F)	CPMA
	- 'Brilliant'	CDoC CTri EBee EMil IFFs LRHS MAsh NEgg NLar SCoo SPer SPur
	- 'Karhumäki' (F) **new**	LRHS
	- 'Nero' (F)	CAgr NLar
	- 'Serina' (F)	CPMA NLar
	- 'Viking' (F)	CAgr CMCN CPMA EBee ECrN EMil EPfP GKir LBuc LHop LRHS MAsh MBlu NBro NLar SLim WDin

Aronia × *Sorbus* (*Rosaceae*)

§	'Burka'	WPat

Arracacia (*Apiaceae*)

B&SWJ 9023 from Guatemala WCru

Arrhenatherum (*Poaceae*)

	elatius var. ***bulbosum***	SBod WFar
	- - 'Variegatum' (v)	CSpe EBee EHoe ELan GBin GMaP LEdu LRHS MMoz MWhi NBid NHol NOak NOrc WFar WMoo WPtf WWEG

Artemisia ✿ (*Asteraceae*)

	RBS 0207	CPLG EPPr
	from Taiwan	WHer
§	***abrotanum*** ♀H4	Widely available

	Name	Suppliers
	absinthium	CArn CEls CSev CWan GPWP GPoy MBar MBel MHer MNHC NSti SIde SVic SWat WPer
	- 'Corinne Tremaine' (v)	WHer
	- 'Lambrook Giant'	CEls
	- 'Lambrook Mist' ♀H3-4	CEls CPrp CSev EBee EBla ECtt ELan EPfP GBar GCal GKir GMaP GMac LRHS MRav SBch SWat WMnd WWEG
	- 'Lambrook Silver' ♀H4	CArn CEls CPLG CSam EBee ECha EHrv EPfP GBar GKir GMaP LHop LRHS LSRN MHer MRav NBro SLim SPer SPoG SWat SWvt WDin WFar WMnd WPer
	- 'Silver Ghost'	CEls
	afra	CArn CEls EBee IFro
§	***alba***	CEls EOHP GBar GPoy MHer NBur SIde SMad WPer
§	- 'Canescens' ♀H4	CArn CEls CSam CTri EBee ECha ECtt EHrv EPfP GBar GMaP LAst LBMP LRHS MCot MHer MRav SDix SMrm SPer WAul WCFE WCot WFar WHCG WMnd WPer WWEG
	annua	CEls GPoy SIde
	anomala	CArn CEls
	arborescens ♀H3	CArn CEls CMHG ECrN ERas NEgg SDix SPer WDin WHer WKif
	- 'Brass Band'	see *A.* 'Powis Castle'
	- 'Faith Raven'	CEls EBee EPfP GBin GBuc MBNS WFar
	- 'Little Mice'	CEls EBee SSvw WGwG WWEG
	- 'Porquerolles'	CEls EAro
	arctica	CEls
	argyi	CEls
§	***armeniaca***	CEls ECho
	assoana	see *A. caucasica*
	atrata	CEls
	barrelieri	CEls
	brachyloba	WCHb
	caerulescens	see *Seriphidium caerulescens*
	californica	CEls
	- KM C-12-02	EBee
	- 'Canyon Gray'	CEls
	campestris subsp. ***borealis***	CEls
	- subsp. ***campestris***	CEls
	- subsp. ***maritima***	CEls
	- - from Wales	CEls
	camphorata	see *A. alba*
	cana	see *Seriphidium canum*
	canariensis	see *A. thuscula*
	canescens misapplied	see *A. alba* 'Canescens'
	canescens Willd.	see *A. armeniaca*
	capillaris	CArn CEls
§	***caucasica*** ♀H3-4	CEls ECho EWes MBrN MHer SChF SPhx SRms SRot WCHb WEas WPer
	- ***caucasica***	CEls WFar
	chamaemelifolia	CEls EBee GPWP IGor MHer NBre WJek
	cretacea	see *Seriphidium nutans*
	discolor Dougl. ex Besser	see *A. michauxiana*
	douglasiana	CEls
	- 'Valerie Finnis'	see *A. ludoviciana* 'Valerie Finnis'
	dracunculus	ECha GAbr MBar MCot MNHC MRav NVic SBch SPlb SWal WBrk WFar WPer
	- French	CArn CBod CEls CHby CHrt CSev CWan ELau GBar GPoy LEdu MHer NGHP NPri SBch SIde WGwG
	- Russian	CArn CEls GBar SVic
	ferganensis	see *Seriphidium ferganense*
	filifolia	CEls

	Name	Suppliers
	fragrans Willd.	see *Seriphidium fragrans*
	frigida ♀H3-4	CEls WCot WHCG
	genipi	CEls
	glacialis	CEls
	gmelinii	CEls GBar
	gnaphalodes	see *A. ludoviciana*
	gorgonum	CEls EBee EWes
	herba-alba	CEls EAro
	'Huntington'	CEls WFar
	kawakamii B&SWJ 088	CEls WCru
	kitadakensis	CEls
	- 'Guizhou'	see *A. lactiflora* Guizhou Group
	laciniata	CEls
	lactiflora ♀H4	CArn CEls EBee ECha ECtt ELan GAbr GBar GBee GMaP MRav NGdn NOrc SDix SPer SRms WFar WMoo WTin
	- 'Elfenbein'	EBee GBin GCal LHop LPla
§	- Guizhou Group	Widely available
	- - 'Dark Delight'	EBee ECtt EWes SPoG
	- 'Jim Russell'	CBow CDes CElw EBee ECtt EWes NBre
	- ***purpurea***	see *A. lactiflora* Guizhou Group
	- 'Stonyford'	MSCN
	- 'Weisses Wunder'	EBee
	lagocephala	CEls LSou
	lanata Willd. non Lam.	see *A. caucasica*
	laxa	see *A. umbelliformis*
§	***ludoviciana***	CEls ELan GBar IFoB MRav NOrc NPer SBch SRms WCFE
	- var. ***latifolia***	see *A. ludoviciana* subsp. *ludoviciana* var. *latiloba*
	- subsp. ***ludoviciana*** var. ***incompta***	CEls LAst
N	- - var. ***latiloba***	CEls EBee EHoe GBar GBuc LHop NBro SBch SWvt WCot WHoo WPer
	- subsp. ***mexicana*** var. ***albula***	CEls SMrm WFar
	- 'Silver Queen' ♀H4	Widely available
N	- 'Valerie Finnis' ♀H4	Widely available
	manshurica	LSou
	maritima	see *Seriphidium maritimum*
§	***michauxiana***	CEls EBee NBur NSti WHer
	molinieri	CEls
	mutellina	see *A. umbelliformis*
	niitakayamensis	CEls GBar
	nitida	CEls
	nutans	see *Seriphidium nutans*
	palmeri hort.	see *A. ludoviciana*
	pamirica	CEls
	aff. ***parviflora*** CLD 1531	CEls
	pedemontana	see *A. caucasica*
	pontica	CArn CEls CWan EBee ECha ECrN EHoe ELan GBar GMaP GPWP GPoy MBNS MHer MRav NBro NSti SDix SSvw WFar WHil WHoo WPer WWEG
§	'Powis Castle' ♀H3	Widely available
	princeps	CArn CEls GPWP SIde WTou
	procera Willd.	see *A. abrotanum*
	purshiana	see *A. ludoviciana*
	pycnocephala	CEls
	- 'David's Choice'	CEls
	ramosa	CEls
	'Rosenschleier'	CAby EBee EPPr EWes LPla NBre WFar WPGP WTin WWEG
	sachalinensis	CEls
	schmidtiana ♀H4	CEls ECha MWat NOrc SRms
	- 'Nana' ♀H4	Widely available
	'Sea Foam'	EBee EPPr
	selengensis	CEls
	splendens misapplied	see *A. alba* 'Canescens'
	splendens Willd.	CEls ELan SPhx

	- var. ***brachyphylla***	MAsh
	stelleriana	CArn CEls CTri EBee ECha GBee IFoB LHop MAvo MCot MHer NBro NPri SPhx SRms WCAu
	- RBS 0207	CEls NLar
N	- 'Boughton Silver'	CEls CHrt EBee ECtt EGoo EHoe ELan EPfP GBBs GGar GMaP GMac LDai LRHS MAsh MCot MRav MWat NSti SMrm SPer SRms SWvt WCom WFar WMnd WWEG
N	- 'Mori'	see *A. stelleriana* 'Boughton Silver'
	- 'Nana'	CEls SWvt
	- 'Prostrata'	see *A. stelleriana* 'Boughton Silver'
	- 'Silver Brocade'	see *A. stelleriana* 'Boughton Silver'
	taurica	CEls
§	***thuscula***	CEls
	tridentata	see *Seriphidium tridentatum*
§	***umbelliformis***	CEls
	vallesiaca	see *Seriphidium vallesiacum*
	verlotiorum	CEls GBar
	vulgaris L.	CArn CEls EBWF ELau GBar GPoy MHer MNHC WHer
	- 'Cragg-Barber Eye' (v)	CEls EBee NBid SAga WCHb WCom
	- Oriental Limelight = 'Janlim' (v)	CEls COlW EBee ECtt EHoe EPfP EWTr GAbr ILad LBMP LEdu LHop LRHS MCCP MWhi NBir NEgg NPri SBch SWal SWvt WFar WHer WJek
	- 'Variegata' (v)	CEls CEnt EBee EPfP NBir WAlt WCHb WFar WHer WMoo WPer
	- 'Woolaston' (v)	WAlt
	× ***wurzellii***	CEls

Arthropodium (*Anthericaceae*)

	candidum	CBot CStu EBrs ECGP ECha ECho ECou LRHS MSCN NWCA WPer WPtf
	- 'Cappucino'	CBcs LHop
	- ***maculatum***	ECho GEdr LEdu SGSe SPlb WWEG
	- ***purpureum***	CWit EAlp EBee ECho EWll GGar IKil NWCA WPGP
	cirratum	CHEx CSpe ECho ECou EPot IDee IKil LEdu SBch
	- 'Matapouri Bay'	CAbP CAbb CBcs CDes CHEx EBee ECre WPGP
	milleflorum	NWCA
	minus	CPLG

Arthrostylidium (*Poaceae*)

	naibuense	CDTJ CGHE EBee WPGP

artichoke, globe see *Cynara cardunculus* Scolymus Group

artichoke, Jerusalem see *Helianthus tuberosus*

Arum (*Araceae*)

	alpinum	see *A. cylindraceum*
	besserianum	ECho
	byzantinum new	ECho
	'Chameleon'	CDes EBee EPPr LFur MAvo MNrw MTho NBir NLar SMad SPer WCot WCru WFar WHil WHoo WPGP WPrP WTin WWEG
§	***concinnatum***	CStu EBee EBrs ECho SChr WPrP
	- black-spotted	EBee ECho
	- purple	ECho
	- variegated (v)	WCot
	concinnatum × ***cyrenaicum***	EBrs ECho GKev
	- from Crete new	WWst
	cornutum	see *Sauromatum venosum*
	creticum	CArn CBgR CBro CFir CSpe EBee ECha ECho EPot GBuc GCal LEdu LRHS MNrw MRav MTho SCnR SRot SUsu WBor WCom WFar WHil
	- MS 696	MNrw
	- FCC form	EBrs ECho WPGP
	- 'Karpathos' FCC form new	WCot
	- 'Marmaris White'	SCnR WCot
	- white-spotted	MNrw MTho
	- yellow-spotted	NBir WFar WIvy
	creticum × ***italicum***	MAvo MDKP WFar
§	***cylindraceum***	EBrs ECho NLar
	- CE&H 741	WWst
	cyrenaicum	CStu EBee ECho EWld LEdu MNrw MTho WCot WPGP WWst
	- from Crete	ECho WCot
	dioscoridis	CEnt CPom EBrs ECho EWes MTho NLar WCot
	- JCA 195.197	WCot
	- var. ***cyprium***	EBee EBrs ECho WPrP WWst
§	- var. ***dioscoridis***	ERos LFur WCot
	- - JCA	WWst
	- - JCA 195200	WPrP
	- var. ***liepoldtii***	see *A. dioscoridis* var. *dioscoridis*
	- var. ***philistaeum***	WWst
	- var. ***smithii***	see *A. dioscoridis* var. *dioscoridis*
	dracunculus	see *Dracunculus vulgaris*
	elongatum	EBrs WCot
	- RS 274/87	EBee
	euxinum new	ECho
	hygrophilum	EBrs WWst
	idaeum	EBrs
	italicum	CArn CEnt CLAP ECho GKir LAma LBMP MTho NBPC NLar SBod SEND SWat WCor WCot WFar WPnP WSHC WShi
	- subsp. ***albispathum***	CDes CHid CPom CStu EBee ECho EDAr WCot WFar WPGP
	- black-spotted	ECho SCnR WFar
	- giant	ECho WHil
	- 'Green Marble'	CBct WFar WWEG
	- subsp. ***italicum***	CBct EBee EBrs ECho EPla EShb EWTr LFur NWCA WBrk
	- - 'Bill Baker'	WFar
	- - 'Cyclops'	CHid WCot
§	- - 'Marmoratum' ♀H4	Widely available
	- - 'Sparkler'	EBee MAvo WCot
	- - 'Spotted Jack'	EBee LFur MAvo MNrw WCot WCru WWEG
	- - 'Tiny'	CFir GCal SCnR WFar
§	- - 'White Winter'	CElw EBee ECGP GBuc MAvo NCGa WCot
	- 'Nancy Lindsay'	MAvo
	- subsp. ***neglectum***	SChr WFar
	- - 'Castle Brissac'	MAvo
	- - 'Miss Janay Hall' (v)	EBee EWes LFur LLHF WCot
	- 'Pictum'	see *A. italicum* subsp. *italicum* 'Marmoratum'
	- 'Splish Splash'	CAvo CBow
	- 'Tresahor Beauty'	MAvo
	jacquemontii	ECho
	korolkowii	WCot
	maculatum	CArn CRWN EBee EBrs ECho EPot GPoy LAma MCot MHer MRav NLar WHer WPrP WShi
	- 'Painted Lady' (v)	MAvo WCot
	- 'Pleddel'	MAvo MRav
	nickelii	see *A. concinnatum*
§	***nigrum***	CPom EBrs ECho EWes LLHF WGwG
	- CE&H 524	EBee
	orientale	EPot WCot
	- subsp. ***amoenum***	MNrw

palaestinum	WWst
petteri misapplied	see *A. nigrum*
pictum	CBgR CDes CLAP CMac CPLG CStu EBee EBrs ECho EPot ERos EWes GEdr LEdu LLHF WCot WWst
- from Majorca	WCot
- 'Taff's Form'	see *A. italicum* subsp. *italicum* 'White Winter'
purpureospathum	CPom CStu EBee EBrs ECho WCot WPGP
rupicola var. ***rupicola***	ECho
- var. ***virescens***	ECho SBig WCot WWst
sintenisii	EBee WCot

Aruncus ✿ (*Rosaceae*)

AGSJ 214	NHol
aethusifolius ♀H4	Widely available
- 'Little Gem'	ECho WCru
asiaticus B&SWJ 8624	WCru
dioicus	Widely available
§ - (m) ♀H4	CDoC CRow ECha ELan EPla MBNS MRav NBro NHol NSti SBch SGar SMad SMrm SPer SRms SWat WMoo WPer
- CC 5185	ITim
- var. ***acuminatus***	EBee
- Child of Two Worlds	see *A. dioicus* 'Zweiweltenkind'
- 'Glasnevin'	CRow CSev ECtt LRHS MRav WFar
- var. ***kamtschaticus***	EWes MCCP MGos NBre NHol NLar WPGP WPnP
- - AGSJ 238	NHol
- - RBS 0208	NGdn WBVN
- 'Kneiffii'	Widely available
§ - 'Zweiweltenkind'	CEnt EBee EHrv LRHS MAvo NBre NLar SMad
'Horatio'	EBee GBin IPot LRHS SMeo SPhx WCot
'Johannifest'	CDes EBee GBin WPGP
'Misty Lace' **new**	EBee IPot NGdn SMrm
'Noble Spirit'	CEnt EBee NGdn NLar SGSe SWat
plumosus	see *A. dioicus*
sinensis	NBre WFar
sylvestris	see *A. dioicus*
'Woldemar Meier'	GBin

Arundinaria (*Poaceae*)

amabilis	see *Pseudosasa amabilis* (McClure) Keng f.
anceps	see *Yushania anceps*
auricoma	see *Pleioblastus viridistriatus*
chino	see *Pleioblastus chino*
disticha	see *Pleioblastus pygmaeus* 'Distichus'
falconeri	see *Himalayacalamus falconeri*
fargesii	see *Bashania fargesii*
fastuosa	see *Semiarundinaria fastuosa*
fortunei	see *Pleioblastus variegatus*
funghomii	see *Schizostachyum funghomii*
§ ***gigantea***	CDTJ MWht WJun
- subsp. ***tecta***	CBcs MGos
hindsii	see *Pleioblastus hindsii*
hookeriana misapplied	see *Himalayacalamus falconeri* 'Damarapa'
hookeriana Munro	see *Himalayacalamus hookerianus*
humilis	see *Pleioblastus humilis*
japonica	see *Pseudosasa japonica*
jaunsarensis	see *Yushania anceps*
maling	see *Yushania maling*
marmorea	see *Chimonobambusa marmorea*
murielae	see *Fargesia murielae*
nitida	see *Fargesia nitida*
oedogonata	see *Clavinodum oedogonatum*
palmata	see *Sasa palmata*
pumila	see *Pleioblastus argenteostriatus* f. *pumilus*
pygmaea	see *Pleioblastus pygmaeus*
quadrangularis	see *Chimonobambusa quadrangularis*
simonii	see *Pleioblastus simonii*
spathiflora	see *Thamnocalamus spathiflorus*
tessellata	see *Thamnocalamus tessellatus*
vagans	see *Sasaella ramosa*
variegata	see *Pleioblastus variegatus*
veitchii	see *Sasa veitchii*
viridistriata	see *Pleioblastus viridistriatus*
'Wang Tsai'	see *Bambusa multiplex* 'Floribunda'

Arundo (*Poaceae*)

donax	Widely available
- 'Golden Chain' (v)	CEnt CKno EBee ELan EPPr EShb EWes LHop SBch SEND SMad SPoG
- 'Macrophylla'	CGHE CKno CRow EBee EPPr ETod LEdu LPJP SApp WPGP
- 'Variegata'	see *A. donax* var. *versicolor*
§ - var. ***versicolor*** (v)	Widely available
I - - 'Aureovariegata'	CDTJ IPot MDKP
formosana	CKno CMCo EBee EPPr
- 'Golden Showers'	EAlp LRHS SBch
pliniana	CRow WPGP

Asarina (*Scrophulariaceae*)

antirrhiniflora	see *Maurandella antirrhiniflora*
barclayana	see *Maurandya barclayana*
erubescens	see *Lophospermum erubescens*
hispanica	see *Antirrhinum hispanicum*
lophantha	see *Lophospermum scandens*
lophospermum	see *Lophospermum scandens*
§ ***procumbens***	CEnt CMea CTri ECho EPfP LBMP MNFA MTho NRya SGar SIng SRms WAbe WFar WGwG WKif

Asarum ✿ (*Aristolochiaceae*)

Chen Yi 5	WCot
albomaculatum	ECho
- B&SWJ 1726	WCru
arifolium	EHrv EPPr GBBs NLar
asaroides	EBee WWst
asperum	EBee
blumei **new**	EBee
campaniflorum	EBee ECho EHrv LAma MLul WCot WCru WWst
canadense	CArn CBct EBee ECho EHrv EPPr EPfP ERos GBBs GPoy NLar WCru
caudatum	CDes CHEx CLAP CRow EBee EBrs ECho GBuc GEdr LEdu NBro NHol NLar NSti NWCA SMac SRms WCot WCru WFar WPGP WSpi
- white-flowered	CLAP EBee EHrv EPPr WCru
caudigerum	WCot
- B&SWJ 1517	WCru
caulescens	EBee ECho EHrv EPPr LAma LEdu WCru WWst
- B&SWJ 5886	WCru
costatum	CLAP
delavayi	ECho EHrv LAma WCot WCru
dimidiatum	EBee
dissitum **new**	EBee
epigynum B&SWJ 3443	WCru
- 'Kikko'	GEdr
- 'Silver Web'	WCru
europaeum ♀H4	Widely available

fauriei WCru
forbesii EBee ECho EHrv NLar WWst
hartwegii CAby CLAP EBee EBrs EHrv GBuc GGar NLar WCot WCru WPGP WPtf
- NNS 00-78 WCot
hatsushimae EBee GEdr
hexalobum EBee
hirsutisepalum EBee
hypogynum B&SWJ 3628 WCru
infrapurpureum B&SWJ 1994 WCru
kumageanum EBee WCot
lemmonii WCru
leptophyllum B&SWJ 1983 WCru
longirhizomatosum WCru
macranthum WCot
- B&SWJ 1691 WCru
maculatum B&SWJ 1114 WCru
magnificum CLAP EBee EHrv LAma MLul WCru WWst
maximum CFir CLAP EBee EBrs ECho EHrv LAma MLul NMen WCot WCru
- 'Silver Panda' CBct CDes CSev CWGN CWit EBee ECtt EHrv GEdr LFur LOck LRHS LSou WCot WRHF
megacalyx EBee GEdr
minamitanianum EBee
naniflorum 'Eco Decor' CLAP EBee EBla EHrv GEdr LAst LOck LRHS LSou MBNS MCot WClo WCot
nipponicum EBee GEdr WCot
- var. ***kooyanum*** EBee
pulchellum CAby EHrv WCot WCru WWst
rigescens EHrv EPot
sakawanum EBee
satsumense EBee GEdr
savatieri EBee
shuttleworthii NLar
sieboldii EBee GEdr WCru WFar
simile GEdr
splendens Widely available
stellatum EBee
subglobosum EBee
taipingshanianum B&SWJ 1688 WCot WCru
- 'Elfin Yellow' **new** WCru
taitonense WWst
takaoi EBee
tamaense EBee
unzen GEdr
viridiflorum GEdr

Asclepias (*Asclepiadaceae*)

'Cinderella' EBee NBPC SSvw
curassavica CCCN CSev EShb EWld LRHS MNrw NBre SPav SRkn
incarnata CEnt CMoH CPom ELan EPau IFoB LRHS MBel MRav NBre NChi SMrm SPav SPlb WPer
- 'Alba' ELan MMuc
- 'Cinderella' **new** LSou NGdn
- 'Ice Ballet' CPrp EBee ELan IFoB LHop LSou NBPC NBre NGdn SAga SGSe SPoG WPer
- 'Soulmate' EBee ELan EPfP MBel MMHG MMuc MSCN NBPC NBre NGdn SGSe
- 'White Superior' EBee
physocarpa see *Gomphocarpus physocarpus*
purpurascens CArn EBee
speciosa NBre NLar
sullivantii NBre SPav
syriaca CArn CPom EBee LRHS MBel NBre SGSe SPav
tuberosa CArn CBcs CEnt CPom CWib EBee EBrs EShb GKir GPoy GQue LHop LRHS LSou MHer MNrw NEgg SGSe SMad SPet SPoG
- Gay Butterflies Group NBre NGdn
- 'Hello Yellow' SGSe
verticillata NBre

Asimina (*Annonaceae*)

triloba (F) CBcs CDTJ MBlu MBri NLar SPlb
- 'Davis' (F) CAgr
- 'Sunflowers' CCCN

Asparagus (*Asparagaceae*)

B&SWJ 8309 from northern Vietnam **new** WCru
SDR 4303 GKev
asparagoides ♀H1 EShb
cochinchinensis WPGP
crassicladus EShb
densiflorus 'Mazeppa' EShb
- 'Myersii' ♀H1 ERea EShb SEND
- Sprengeri Group ♀H1 LRHS MBri
- - 'Variegatus' EShb
denudatus EShb
falcatus EShb LRHS SEND
filicinus var. ***giraldii*** WCot
officinalis SEND WFar
* - 'Amarus' EMui
- 'Ariane' **new** EMui
- 'Backlim' ♀H4 ECrN EMil EMui ERea
- 'Butler' SDea
- 'Cito' (m) EMil LRHS NPri SDea
- 'Connover's Colossal' ♀H4 CSBt CWan ECrN ERea LRHS LSRN MNHC SEND
- 'Dariana' EMil ERea SDea
- 'Eros' EMui
- 'Franklim' SEND WFar
- 'Gijnlim' ♀H4 ECrN EMil EMui ERea LRHS SDea WFar WHil
- 'Grolim' PBR EMil
- 'Guelph Millennium' EMui
- 'Jersey Giant' (m) EMui
- 'Jersey Knight' EMui SVic
- 'Mary Washington' SVic
- 'Pacific 2000' **new** EMui
- 'Pacific Purple' EMui
- var. ***prostratus*** from Britain **new** GCal
- 'Purple Jumbo' ECrN
plumosus see *A. setaceus*
pseudoscaber 'Spitzenschleier' EBee EShb MAvo SDix SMad
racemosus EShb
retrofractus EShb WPGP
scandens EShb
schoberioides LEdu
§ ***setaceus*** ♀H1 EShb LRHS MBri
- 'Pyramidalis' ♀H1 MBri
suaveolens EShb
verticillatus SGSe
virgatus EShb WPGP

Asperula (*Rubiaceae*)

§ ***arcadiensis*** ♀H3 ECho WAbe WThu
aristata subsp. ***scabra*** CSpe EBee ECha ELan LRHS
- subsp. ***thessala*** see *A. sintenisii*
boissieri ECho
daphneola ECho EWes WAbe

	gussonei	CMea ECho EPot LRHS MWat NLAp NMen WAbe
	lilaciflora	ECho
	- var. ***caespitosa***	see *A. lilaciflora* subsp. *lilaciflora*
§	- subsp. ***lilaciflora***	ECho NMen
	nitida	CPBP ECho
	- subsp. ***puberula***	see *A. sintenisii*
	odorata	see *Galium odoratum*
	orientalis	WPGP
	scutellaris	EBee
§	***sintenisii*** ♀H2-3	CMea ECho LRHS NMen WAbe WHoo WPat WThu
	suberosa misapplied	see *A. arcadiensis*
	suberosa Sibth. & Sm.	ECho
	taurina	EBee
	- subsp. ***caucasica***	CMoH NLar WBor WCHb
	tinctoria	CArn GBar GPoy MHer SRms WCHb

Asphodeline (*Asphodelaceae*)

§	***brevicaulis***	GAuc WCot
	Cally Hybrids	EDAr
	liburnica	CAvo CBro CMoH CSam EBee ECha ELan ERos GAbr MRav SEND WCAu WCot WFar WHoo WPer
§	***lutea***	Widely available
§	- 'Gelbkerze'	EPfP GKir LRHS NBre
	- Yellow Candle	see *A. lutea* 'Gelbkerze'
	taurica	CBro EBee ECho EPPr GAuc LBMP MBNS NBre WCot WPer

Asphodelus (*Asphodelaceae*)

	acaulis	ECho SCnR WAbe WCot
§	***aestivus***	GAbr GCal MBel NBur SPhx SSvw WPer
	- Cally Spear strain	GCal NCGa
	albus	CArn CAvo CBot CSpe EBrs ECha EPPr EPyc GAuc GBuc IFoB LBMP LRHS MCot NBid NCGa SPer SPlb SRms WAul WPer
	asiaticus KM T-28-03	EBee
	brevicaulis	see *Asphodeline brevicaulis*
	cerasiferus	see *A. ramosus*
	fistulosus	LEdu NBir SAga WPrP
	lusitanicus	see *A. ramosus*
	luteus	see *Asphodeline lutea*
	microcarpus	see *A. aestivus*
§	***ramosus***	CAby CPar EBee ECho GAuc GCal MCot MNrw MTho NCGa WCot WPer

Aspidistra (*Convallariaceae*)

from China	WCot
attenuata	IBlr
- B&SWJ 377	WCru
caespitosa 'Jade Ribbons'	IBlr WCot
'China Star'	IBlr WCot
'China Sun'	IBlr WCot
daibuensis	IBlr
- B&SWJ 312b	WCru
elatior ♀H1	CBct CHEx CTsd EBak EBee EShb IBlr LRHS MBri NLar NPal NScw SAPC SArc SEND SMad STre WCot
- 'Akebono' (v)	WCot
- 'Asahi' (v)	IBlr WCot WFut
- 'Goldfeather' **new**	IBlr
- 'Hoshi-zora' (v)	IBlr WCot
- 'Lennon's Song' (v) **new**	WFut
- 'Milky Way' (v)	CBct CBow CHid CWit EBee EShb EWld IBlr MTho SEND SMad WCot WFut WHil
- 'Morning Frost'	IBlr
- 'Okame' (v)	IBlr WCot WFut
- 'Variegata' (v) ♀H1	CBct CHEx EShb IBlr IFoB IFro MTho NBir WCom WCot
- 'Variegata Exotica'	XBlo
leshanensis (v)	IBlr
linearifolia 'Leopard'	IBlr WCot
longiloba	WCot
lurida	CBct EBee IBlr
- 'Amanogawa' (v)	EBee
- 'Fuji-no-mine' (v)	IBlr
- 'Ginga' (v)	EBee
- 'Ginga Giant' (v) **new**	WFut
- 'Irish Mist' (v)	IBlr
minutiflora	WCot
omeiensis	WCot
punctata	IBlr
- 'Come Here Spot' (v) **new**	WFut
saxicola 'Uan Fat Lady'	WCru
'Singapore Sling' (v) **new**	WFut
sutepensis B&SWJ 5216 **new**	WCru
typica	IBlr
urceolata	IBlr
zongbayi	WCot

Asplenium ✿ (*Aspleniaceae*)

	adiantum-nigrum	GKir SRms WAbe
	antiquum **new**	LRHS
	australasicum **new**	EShb
	bulbiferum misapplied	see *A.* × *lucrosum*
	bulbiferum ambig. × ***oblongifolium***	WRic
	bulbiferum Forst.f.	EBee ESwi
	- 'Suze'	EBee
§	***ceterach***	CLAP EFer SRms WAbe WHer WRic
	daucifolium	EOHP
	× ***ebenoides***	WRic
	flaccidum	WRic
§	× ***lucrosum*** ♀H1-2	CBty CDTJ EFtx
	lyallii	WRic
	'Maori Princess'	WFib
	nidus ♀H1	LRHS MBri XBlo
	oblongifolium	WRic
	obovatum subsp. ***lanceolatum***	WRic
	polyodon	WRic
	ruprechtii	WRic
	ruta-muraria	EFer SRms
§	***scolopendrium*** ♀H4	Widely available
	- 'Angustatum'	Widely available
	- 'Capitatum'	MDun
*	- 'Circinatum'	WPGP
	- 'Conglomeratum'	SRms
	- Crispum Group	CBgR CLAP EFer ELan MRav NBid NHol SApp SRms SRot WAbe WFib WPGP WPtf
	- - 'Crispum Bolton's Nobile' ♀H4	WCot WFib WPGP
	- - 'Golden Queen'	CLAP
	- Crispum Cristatum Group	CLAP NVic
	- Crispum Fimbriatum Group	CLAP GQui
	- Cristatum Group	Widely available
	- Fimbriatum Group	CLAP WRic
	- 'Furcatum'	CBty CDTJ CLAP EBee GEdr MAsh NHol NLar WRic
	- 'Kaye's Lacerated' ♀H4	CLAP EBee EFer WFib WRic
	- Laceratum Group	CLAP SRms
	- Marginatum Group	EFer SWat WPGP
	- - 'Irregulare'	SRms
	- 'Muricatum'	CLAP ELan GBin MRav NBid NHol SRms WFib WTin

	Name	Suppliers
	- 'Ramocristatum'	CLAP
	- Ramomarginatum Group	CLAP ELan SRms WFar WRic
	- 'Sagittatocristatum'	SRms WPGP
	- 'Sagittatoprojectum Sclater'	WFib
*	- 'Sagittatum'	SRms
	- 'Stagshorn'	SRms
	- Undulatum Group	CBgR CBty CDTJ CLAP EAEE EBee ECha EFtx EPfP LRHS MAsh MMoz NBir NEgg NHol NLar NMyG SBch SMac SRms SWat WIvy WPnP WRic
	- Undulatum Cristatum Group	CLAP
	septentrionale	SRms
	trichomanes 🏆H4	Widely available
	- Cristatum Group	SRms WFar
	- Incisum Group	CLAP EBee NOrc SRms
	- 'Ramocristatum'	WAbe
	viride	SRms

Astelia (Asteliaceae)

	Name	Suppliers
	alpina	IBlr
	banksii	CBcs CDoC CHEx CHll CTrC ECou GBin GCal GGar IBal LRHS LSRN MGos SBch SPoG WDyG WPGP
§	***chathamica*** 🏆H3	Widely available
	chathamica* × *fragrans	ECou
	- 'Silver Spear'	see *A. chathamica*
	cunninghamii	see *A. solandri*
	fragrans	CSpe ECou GGar IBlr LEdu WCot WDyG
	graminea	GCal IBlr
	grandis	IBlr LEdu
	nervosa	CTrC CTsd ECou EPPr GKir IBlr LEdu LSRN SAPC SArc WPat
	- 'Alpine Ruby'PBR **new**	IBlr
	- 'Bronze Giant'	IBlr
	- 'Silver Sabre' **new**	IBlr
	- 'Westland'	CAbb CBcs CBod CDoC CKno CPen CTrC CWit EBee GCal GKir IBlr LEdu LRHS LSRN MBri MDun MGos MRav SBch SEND SMrm SPlb SPoG WCot WGrn
	nivicola 'Golden Gem' **new**	IBlr
	- 'Red Gem'	GCal LEdu
	petriei	IBlr
	'Red Devil' **new**	WCot WHer
	'Silver Mound' **new**	EPfP
§	***solandri***	ECou IBlr
	trinervia	IBlr

Aster ✿ (Asteraceae)

	Name	Suppliers
	acris	see *A. sedifolius*
	alpinus 🏆H4	CTri EAlp ECho EPfP GJos GKir LFur LRHS MWat NBlu SRms WFar WPer
	- var. ***albus***	EBee EPfP GKev NBre NBro SPoG SRGP WPer
	- Dark Beauty	see *A. alpinus* 'Dunkle Schöne'
	- var. ***dolomiticus***	GKev
§	- 'Dunkle Schöne'	EBee ECho LDai LRHS NBre NVic SPoG SRGP SRms WPer WRHF
	- 'Goliath'	EBee ECho EPfP NBre NBro SPlb WFar
	- 'Happy End'	CMMP EAlp ECho LDai NBre NBro NLar SPoG SRGP SRms WFar
	- 'Märchenland' (d)	NBre
	- 'Pinkie'	CSam EBee EDAr EPfP NBre NLar SMad WOut
	- 'Trimix'	ECho GAbr NBir SRms WFar
	- violet-flowered	WPer
	- 'White Beauty'	SRms
*	- 'Wolfii'	SRms
	amelloides	see *Felicia amelloides*
	amellus	CArn LRHS LSou SPer WMoo
	- 'Blue King'	EBee NWsh SMrm SWvt
	- 'Breslau'	EBee
	- 'Brilliant'	CPrp EBee EBla ECtt EPPr GBuc LAst LSou MAvo MBNS MNFA MRav MWat SMrs SPer SRGP WIvy WOld
	- 'Butzemann'	EBee GBin
	- 'Forncett Flourish'	WOld
	- 'Framfieldii' 🏆H4	WOld
	- 'Gründer'	WOld
	- 'Jacqueline Genebrier' 🏆H4	CHar WIvy
	- 'King George' 🏆H4	Widely available
	- 'Kobold'	EBrs LRHS
	- 'Lac de Genève'	EBee LRHS NLar WCot WOld
	- 'Lady Hindlip'	CSam ECtt WFar
	- 'Louise'	LRHS MBrN SUsu
	- 'Moerheim Gem'	LRHS WIvy
	- 'Nocturne'	WCot WIvy WOld
	- Pink Zenith	see *A. amellus* 'Rosa Erfüllung'
§	- 'Rosa Erfüllung'	CPrp EBee EBla ECtt EPfP EShb GBuc GMaP GMac LAst LHop LRHS MCot MRav SAga SPet SRGP SWvt WCot WMnd WOld WPer
	- 'Rotfeuer'	ECGP GQue NGby WCot WRHF
	- 'Rudolph Goethe'	EBee ECtt EMil EPfP LAst LRHS MRav SRGP WFar WMoo WOld WWEG
	- 'September Glow'	MHom
	- 'Silbersee'	CSam LRHS
	- 'Sonia'	EBee LRHS MRav NGby NLar
	- 'Sonora'	CPrp ECGP LHop LPla NBre SAga SRGP WCom WKif WOld
	- 'Sternkugel'	GMac WOld
	- 'Vanity'	GBuc LRHS WOld
§	- 'Veilchenkönigin' 🏆H4	Widely available
N	- Violet Queen	see *A. amellus* 'Veilchenkönigin'
	- 'Weltfriede'	WOld
	'Anita Pfeiffer' **new**	LRHS
	'Anja's Choice'	EBee LHop NBre NWsh WCot WOld
	asper	see *A. bakerianus*
	asperulus	EBrs EPPr LPla LRHS SMeo SPhx SUsu
§	***bakerianus***	WFar
	***batangensis* new**	EBee GKev
	capensis 'Variegatus'	see *Felicia amelloides* variegated
§	***carolinianus***	EShb WFar
	'Cassandra'	WOld
	'Cheavers' **new**	LRHS
	'Climax' misapplied	see *A. laevis* 'Arcturus', *A. laevis* 'Calliope'
	'Climax' ambig.	CAby CElw EBee GBuc GCal MMuc MRav NBid NSti SAga SMrm
	'Climax' Vicary Gibbs	WOld
	coelestis	see *Felicia amelloides*
	coloradoensis	LLHF NSla
	'Connecticut Snow Flurry'	see *A. ericoides* f. *prostratus* 'Snow Flurry'
	'Coombe Fishacre' 🏆H4	CAby CHrt COlW CPrp CSam EBee GBuc GCal LPla MCot MNFA MRav NBre SAga SBch SMrm SPoG SSvw SUsu WCAu WCot WFar WHoo WOld WTin
	cordifolius	WFar
	- 'Blutenregen'	EBee
	- 'Chieftain' 🏆H4	CAby IGor MNFA MNrw SAga SPhx WIvy WOld
	- 'Elegans'	CAby IGor MWea WCot WIvy WMnd WMoo WOld
	- 'Ideal'	EBee NLar WOld

	- 'Silver Queen'	WOld
	- 'Silver Spray'	CPrp EBee ECtt GMaP GMac GQue MHom MWat NBre SRGP WOld WPer
	- 'Sweet Lavender' ♀H4	WOld
	corymbosus	see *A. divaricatus*
	'Cotswold Gem'	WCot WOld
	'Dark Pink Star'	WOld
	delavayi	EBee SUsu
	diffusus	see *A. lateriflorus*
	diplostephioides	EBee EDAr EPPr EPfP EShb GCal GQue IKil LBMP LRHS MBNS MMHG MMuc NBPC NBre NHol NLar NSti SGSe SPlb WAul WPer WPtf
§	***divaricatus***	Widely available
§	- 'Eastern Star'	NCGa WBVN WCot WFar WOld
	- Raiche form	see *A. divaricatus* 'Eastern Star'
	- 'Tradescant' **new**	IMou
N	***dumosus***	CPLG WFar WPer
	- 'Biteliness'	NBre NLar
	- Sapphire = 'Kiesapphire'PBR	CBow CPrp LHop LRHS MBNS NEgg NPri SPoG
	ericoides	CKno EShb MCot NBre NOrc NWCA WWEG
	- 'Blue Star' ♀H4	CPrp CSam EBee EBrs GBuc IGor LRHS NBPC NBid NLar SHGN SPer SPoG WMnd WOld
	- 'Brimstone' ♀H4	IGor MRav NBre WOld
	- 'Cinderella'	COIW CPrp GBee GBuc GMac LRHS NSti WOld WWEG
	- 'Cirylle'	NBre
	- 'Constance'	WOld
	- 'Erlkönig'	EBee GCal GQue LAst LRHS MRav NGdn NLar SWat WCot WMnd WOld WPer
	- 'Esther'	CPrp EBee ECha ELan SMrm WOld
	- 'Golden Spray' ♀H4	EBee EPfP GMaP GQue NLar WFar WMnd WOld
	- 'Herbstmyrte'	CSam
	- 'Hon. Edith Gibbs'	WOld
	- 'Monte Cassino'	see *A. pilosus* var. *pringlei* 'Monte Cassino'
	- 'Pink Cloud' ♀H4	CHVG COIW CPrp EBee EBrs ECtt EPfP GBuc GCal GMac LAst LRHS MNFA MRav NCGa NCob NOrc SPer SPoG SRGP STes SWat WCAu WFar WIvy WMnd WOld WPer WTin WWEG
	- f. ***prostratus***	EBee EPot SGar SHGN WFar
§	- - 'Snow Flurry' ♀H4	CMea CSam EBee ECha ECtt GMac IGor IMou MAvo MNFA MNrw SMrm WCom WCot WEas WMnd WOld WOut
	- 'Rosy Veil'	CKno GMac IGor MHom NBir NGdn
	- 'Schneegitter'	EBee MBel WFar WOld
	- 'Schneetanne'	NBre
	- 'Sulphurea'	MWat
	- 'Vimmer's Delight'	WCot
	- 'White Heather'	CPrp IGor MNFA NLar WIvy WMnd WOld WPer WRHF
	- 'Yvette Richardson'	MHom WOld WWEG
	falcatus	EBee WCot
	- var. ***commutatus***	WCot
	'Fanny's Fall'	see *A. oblongifolius* 'Fanny's'
	foliaceus	WHil
	- from Montana	EPPr
	- var. ***parryi*** **new**	EBee
	× ***frikartii***	CPrp EBee ELan EPfP EShb LOck LRHS MRav SAga SMrm SRms SWvt WEas WOld WSHC
	- 'Eiger'	WOld
	- 'Flora's Delight'	GCal LRHS WOld WWEG
	- 'Jungfrau'	CWGN EBee EPPr GMaP GMac LPio LRHS MRav NLar WOld WSHC WWEG
N	- 'Mönch' ♀H4	Widely available
	- Wonder of Stafa	see *A.* × *frikartii* 'Wunder von Stäfa'
§	- 'Wunder von Stäfa' ♀H4	CEnd CKno CPLG EBee ECtt ELan ELon EPfP GBuc GKir GMaP LHop LPio LRHS LSRN MAvo MBNS MCot MRav NBir NLar NVic SMrm WCot WMnd WOld WPGP WWEG
	glaucodes	EBee
	greatae	EBee
	hayatae B&SWJ 8790	WCru
	'Herfstweelde'	CPrp EBee GBuc MAvo SUsu WFar WOld
§	× ***herveyi***	CMoH CSam EBee EBla EBrs ECtt ELan EPfP GCal LBMP LLWP LRHS MBel MMuc NSti NWsh SAga SDix SPhx SPoG SRGP WCot WFar WIvy WMnd WOld
	himalaicus	EShb SRms
	'Hittlemaar'	WHil
	'Hon. Vicary Gibbs' (*ericoides* hybrid)	MNFA WCot WOld WOut
	hybridus luteus	see × *Solidaster luteus*
	'Ivy House'	ECtt
	'Kylie' ♀H4	CAby CHVG CPrp ECtt GBuc GMac IGor LRHS LSRN MHom NCGa SRGP WBor WFar WHil WOld WTin
	laevis	NBre NLar WPer WTin
	- 'Anneke Van der Jeugd'	EBee
§	- 'Arcturus'	CBgR CFir LRHS MBel MHom NBir NBre NCGa NSti SSvw WCot WFar WWlt
	- 'Blauhügel'	LPla
	- 'Blue Bird'	LRHS
§	- 'Calliope'	Widely available
	- var. ***geyeri***	MNrw
	- 'Nightshade'	WOld
	lanceolatus Willd.	NCGa WCot
	- 'Edwin Beckett'	CBre MHom WOld
§	***lateriflorus***	EBee WOld WPer
	- 'Bleke Bet'	WCot WOld
	- 'Buck's Fizz'	CHrt EBee ELan NLar SBch WOld
	- 'Chloe'	NCGa SPhx
	- 'Datschi'	WFar
	- var. ***horizontalis*** ♀H4	Widely available
	- 'Jan'	WOld
	- 'Lady in Black'	Widely available
	- 'Lovely'	EBee EBrs LRHS NBre NNor SRGP
	- 'Prince'	Widely available
	laterifolius 'Snow Flurry'	see *A. ericoides* f. *prostratus* 'Snow Flurry'
§	***linosyris***	EBee EWes GBin NBre NLar SMrm WHer WOld
	- 'Goldilocks'	see *A. linosyris*
	'Little Carlow' (*cordifolius* hybrid) ♀H4	Widely available
	'Little Dorrit' (*cordifolius* hybrid)	NWsh WOld
	maackii	SMrm
	macrophyllus	CPou ELan LRHS NLar WOld
	- 'Albus'	EBee EPPr GBin WFar WIvy WOld
	- 'Twilight'	see *A.* × *herveyi*
	mongolicus	see *Kalimeris mongolica*
	'Mrs Dean'	ECtt
	natalensis	see *Felicia rosulata*
	'Natasha'	LSRN
	'Noreen'	MAvo
	novae-angliae	CArn NBPC NBre WOld
	- 'Alex Deamon'	WOld

	Name	Suppliers
	– 'Andenken an Alma Pötschke'	Widely available
	– 'Andenken an Paul Gerber'	EBee ECtt MAvo MHom MNrw NGby WBrk WCAu WOld
	– 'Annabelle de Chazal'	ECtt WOld
	– Autumn Snow	see *A. novae-angliae* 'Herbstschnee'
	– 'Barr's Blue'	CAby EBee GCra LRHS MAvo MBNS MMuc MWat NLar NWsh SPer SRms WBrk WCAu WMoo WOld
	– 'Barr's Pink'	CBre EBee ECtt EPfP LRHS MCot MHer MHom MLHP MRav MWat NLar SEND WBrk WCAu WFar WHrl WOld WPer WSFF
*	– 'Barr's Purple'	ECtt WCFE WOld
	– 'Barr's Violet'	CAby CWan ECtt EPPr MAvo MHom SRms WBrk WCot WHal WHoo WHrl WMoo WOld WPer WTin WWEG
	– 'Bishop Colenso'	NBre
	– 'Christopher Harbutt'	NPro SRGP WOld
	– 'Colwall Constellation'	WOld
	– 'Colwall Galaxy'	MAvo WOld
	– 'Colwall Orbit'	WOld
	– 'Crimson Beauty'	EPPr MAvo MHom MWat WBrk WCom WOld
	– 'Evensong'	ECtt WOld
	– 'Festival'	CAbx
	– 'Harrington's Pink' 𝕐H4	Widely available
	– 'Helen Picton'	CSam ECtt MAvo MBrN MHom MWat WCom WOld
§	– 'Herbstschnee'	Widely available
	– 'Indian Summer'	GJos
	– 'James Ritchie'	LLHF WHoo WOld
	– 'John Davies'	MAvo WOld
	– 'Lachsglut'	CAby MAvo SMrm WCot
	– 'Lou Williams'	ECtt MAvo MWat WOld
I	– 'Lucida'	WBrk WHal WOld
	– 'Lucinda' **new**	MBel
	– 'Lye End Beauty'	CAby CKno CWan ECtt EPyc LLWP LRHS MAvo MHom MNFA MRav MWat MWte SMrs WBrk WCot WHoo WMoo WOld WTin
	– 'Marina Wolkonsky'	CAby CBgR EBee ECtt EWes LHop WBrk WCot WOld
	– 'Millennium Star'	WOld
	– 'Miss K.E. Mash'	MHom SRGP WBrk WOld WWEG
	– 'Mrs S.T. Wright'	CAby CPrp CTri ECtt EWes MBrN MHom MWea SMrs SRGP WFar WOld
	– 'Mrs S.W. Stern'	WOld
	– 'Pink Parfait'	CSam EBrs ECtt GMac LRHS NBre NGdn SRms WCot WOld
	– 'Pink Victor'	CTri EPPr MMuc SEND SRms WMoo
	– 'Primrose Upward'	CAby NWsh WBrk WCom WCot WOld
	– 'Purple Cloud'	CAby GMac LHop MHer MHom MWat NBre NGdn WBrk WCom WHal WOld WWEG
I	– 'Purple Dome'	Widely available
	– 'Quinton Menzies'	CAbx CSam WCom WOld
	– 'Red Cloud'	NBre WOld
	– 'Rosa Sieger' 𝕐H4	CAbx CAby CBre CElw CPrp EBee ECtt MAvo MHom NGdn SMrs SPhx SUsu WBor WBrk WOld
	– 'Rose Williams'	MAvo WOld
	– 'Roter Stern'	ECtt LRHS
	– 'Rubinschatz'	EBee LRHS MAvo MHom NBre SRms WOld
	– 'Rudelsburg'	WBrk
	– 'Sayer's Croft'	CAbx CWan EBee LRHS MHom MWat NBre WBrk WCot WHil WHoo WOld WTin
	– September Ruby	see *A. novae-angliae* 'Septemberrubin'
§	– 'Septemberrubin'	CAby CBgR CMea CSsd EBee ECtt ELon EWTr GMac IFoB LHop LRHS MHom MNFA MRav NWsh SPhx SRGP SUsu WFar WMoo WOld WPrP
	– 'Treasure'	CBre ECtt LRHS NBre SMrm SMrs WMoo WOld
	– 'Violet Haze'	CAbx CMea
	– 'Violetta'	CAbx CAby EBrs ECtt LRHS LSou MAvo MHom MNFA MWea NMRc SMrs SPhx WBrk WFar WHoo WOld WTin
	– 'W. Bowman'	WOld
	– 'Wow'	NBre SMrm
N	***novi-belgii***	NBlu NSco WHer
	– 'Ada Ballard'	EBee LDai LRHS LSRN NBre NEgg NGdn SBch SMrs SPer SPet SPoG SRGP WOld
	– 'Albanian'	WOld
	– 'Alderman Vokes'	WOld
	– 'Alex Norman'	WOld
	– 'Algar's Pride'	CHrt ECtt WOld WWEG
	– 'Alice Haslam'	CAby EBee ECtt LRHS MCCP NEgg NOrc NPri SBch SPoG SRGP SRms WOld WPer WWEG
	– 'Alpenglow'	WOld
	– 'Anita Ballard'	WOld
	– 'Anita Webb'	NBir WOld
	– 'Anneke'	EBee LRHS MBri SRGP SRkn WOld
	– 'Apollo'	ECrN NEgg NLar NPri WFar WOld
	– 'Apple Blossom'	WOld
	– 'Arctic'	WOld
	– 'Audrey'	CEnt EBee ECtt GMaP LRHS LSRN MBNS NEgg NGdn NOrc SRGP STes WFar WOld
	– 'Autumn Beauty'	WOld
	– 'Autumn Days'	WOld
	– 'Autumn Glory'	WOld
	– 'Autumn Rose'	SMrs WOld
	– 'Baby Climax'	WOld
	– 'Bahamas' (Island Series)	EWll LRHS LSou SGar
	– 'Barbados' (Island Series)	LRHS LSou MBri
	– 'Beauty of Colwall'	WOld
	– 'Beechwood Challenger'	WOld
	– 'Beechwood Charm'	WOld
	– 'Beechwood Rival'	CTri EBee
	– 'Beechwood Supreme'	WOld
	– 'Bewunderung'	WOld
	– 'Blandie'	CTri EBee EPfP MBNS SRGP WOld
	– 'Blauglut'	WOld
	– 'Blue Baby'	WPer
	– 'Blue Bouquet'	CTri SRms WOld
	– 'Blue Boy'	MAvo WBrk WOld
	– 'Blue Danube'	WCom WOld
	– 'Blue Eyes'	CAby CElw SMrs SUsu WOld
	– 'Blue Gown'	CMdw GCal SMrs WOld WOut
	– 'Blue Lagoon'	CMea ELan LRHS MBri SMrs SRGP WBrk WOld
	– 'Blue Patrol'	WOld
	– 'Blue Radiance'	WOld
	– 'Blue Spire' **new**	WOld
	– 'Blue Whirl'	WOld
	– 'Bonanza'	WOld
	– 'Boningale Blue'	WOld
	– 'Boningale White'	WOld
	– 'Bridesmaid'	WOld
	– 'Bridgette'	NBPC

- 'Bright Eyes'	SRGP
- 'Brightest and Best'	WOld
- 'Cameo'	WOld
- 'Cantab'	WOld
- 'Cantonese Queen' (v)	EPPr
- 'Carlingcott'	WOld
- 'Carnival'	CMMP EBee ECtt LDai MBNS MMHG MWea NEgg NOrc SMrs SPer SRGP WOld
- 'Cecily'	WOld WWEG
- 'Charles Wilson'	WOld
- 'Chatterbox'	CPrp EPfP MRav MSpe MWat NEgg NLar SRms WOld
- 'Chelwood'	WOld
- 'Chequers'	CMMP EBee MBNS MWea NEgg SMrs SRGP WOld
- 'Christina'	see *A. novi-belgii* 'Kristina'
- 'Christine Soanes'	WOld
- 'Cliff Lewis'	WOld
- 'Climax Albus'	see *A.* 'White Climax'
- 'Cloudy Blue'	WOld
- 'Colwall Century' **new**	WOld
- 'Coombe Gladys'	WOld
- 'Coombe Joy'	WOld
- 'Coombe Margaret'	WOld
- 'Coombe Queen'	WOld
- 'Coombe Radiance'	WOld
- 'Coombe Ronald'	MWat WOld
- 'Coombe Rosemary'	EBrs ECtt LRHS NLar WBor WOld
- 'Coombe Violet'	MWat WOld
- 'Countess of Dudley'	WOld WPer
- 'Court Herald'	WOld
- 'Crimson Brocade'	CAby EBee MMuc MRav NLar SBch SPoG SRGP WOld
- 'Dandy'	EBee ELan LRHS NBir NEgg NGdn SPoG SRGP WFar WOld
- 'Daniela'	SRms WBrk WOld
- 'Daphne Anne'	WOld
- 'Dauerblau'	WOld
- 'Davey's True Blue'	CTri SMrs WOld
- 'David Murray'	WOld
- 'Dazzler'	WOld
- 'Destiny'	WOld
- 'Diana'	NWsh WOld
- 'Diana Watts'	WOld
- 'Dietgard'	WOld
- 'Dolly'	NBir SRms WOld WWEG
- 'Dora Chiswell'	WOld
- 'Dusky Maid'	WBor WOld
- 'Elizabeth'	CAby CElw WOld
- 'Elizabeth Bright'	WOld
- 'Elizabeth Hutton'	WOld
- 'Elsie Dale'	WOld
- 'Elta'	WOld
- 'Erica'	CElw MWat WOld
- 'Ernest Ballard'	WOld
- 'Eva'	SRms WOld
- 'Eventide'	CElw CTri EBee LSRN WOld WRHF
- 'Fair Lady'	LRHS MWat WOld
- 'Faith'	WOld
- 'Farncombe Lilac'	EBrs
- 'Farrington'	WOld
- 'Fellowship' ♀H4	CAby CBgR CDes CFir CMoH COIW EBee ECtt MAvo MBri MMuc MWat NCGa SAga SHar SRGP SRms WBrk WCot WOld WWEG
- 'Flamingo'	WOld
- 'Fontaine'	WOld
- 'Freda Ballard'	ECtt EWll GMaP LSRN MBNS MWat NGdn SMrs SRGP WCAu WOld WWEG
- 'Freya'	LSRN WOld WSHC
- 'Fuldatal'	SMrs WOld
- 'Gayborder Blue'	WOld
- 'Gayborder Royal'	CFir WOld
- 'Glory of Colwall'	WOld
- 'Goliath'	WOld
- 'Grey Lady'	WOld
- 'Guardsman'	WOld
- 'Gulliver'	WOld WWEG
- 'Gurney Slade'	WOld
- 'Harrison's Blue'	SAga SMrs WBrk WOld WPer
- 'Heinz Richard'	CMMP COIW EBee ECha LBMP MHer NBir NBre NCGa NGdn SBch SMrs SPet SRGP SRms WOld WWEG
- 'Helen'	WOld
- 'Helen Ballard'	CMoH SRms WBrk WOld
- 'Herbstgruss vom Bresserhof'	LRHS NBre WOld
- 'Herbstpurzel'	WOld
- 'Hilda Ballard'	WOld
- 'Ilse Brensell'	WOld WWEG
- 'Irene'	WOld
- 'Isabel Allen'	WOld
- 'Janet Watts'	WOld
- 'Jean'	MWat SBch SRms WOld
- 'Jean Gyte'	WOld
- 'Jeanette'	SRms WOld
- 'Jenny'	COIW CSBt EBee ECtt EPfP GKev GMaP LBMP LHop LRHS LSRN MBri MRav MWat NBir NEgg NGdn SBch SPer SPoG SRGP SRms STes WBrk WEas WFar WMnd WOld WWEG
- 'Jollity'	WOld
- 'Julia'	WOld
- 'Karminkuppel'	NBre WOld
- 'Kassel'	SRms WOld
- 'King of the Belgians'	WOld
- 'King's College'	WOld
§ - 'Kristina'	CBgR COIW CWan EBee ECha LRHS MBri MRav SPet SPoG WCot WOld WWEG
- 'Lady Evelyn Drummond'	WOld
- 'Lady Frances'	SRms WOld
- 'Lady in Blue'	Widely available
- 'Lady Paget'	WOld
- 'Lassie'	CElw LLWP MWat WOld
- 'Lavender Dream'	WOld
- 'Lawrence Chiswell'	WOld
- 'Lilac Time'	WOld
- 'Lisa Dawn'	CSpr ECtt WOld
- 'Little Boy Blue'	NBre SRms WOld WWEG
- 'Little Man in Blue'	WOld WWEG
- 'Little Pink Beauty'	CEnt COIW EBee ECtt ELan EPfP LAst LHop LRHS MBNS NBid NEgg NGdn NVic SPer SRGP SRms STes WFar WOld WWEG
- 'Little Pink Lady'	SRms WOld
- 'Little Pink Pyramid'	SRms WWEG
- 'Little Red Boy'	WOld
- 'Little Treasure'	WOld
- 'Lucy'	WOld
- 'Madge Cato'	MAvo WOld
- 'Mammoth'	WOld
- 'Margaret Rose'	WOld
- 'Margery Bennett'	WOld
- 'Marie Ballard'	COIW CSBt EBee EPfP GKir GMaP LRHS MBri MHer MRav MWat MWhi NBre NCGa NGdn NOrc NPer SBch SMrm SPer SPoG SRGP SRms SWat WBrk WCAu WOld WPer WWEG
- 'Marie's Pretty Please'	WOld
- 'Marjorie'	SBch SPoG WOld
- 'Marjory Ballard'	WOld

- 'Martonie' WOld WPer
- 'Mary Ann Neil' SMrs WOld
- 'Mary Deane' WOld WPer
- 'Mauve Magic' SRms WOld WWEG
- 'Melbourne Belle' WOld
- 'Melbourne Magnet' WOld
- 'Michael Watts' WOld
- 'Midget' WOld
- 'Mistress Quickly' MCot SMrs WOld WWEG
- 'Mount Everest' CAby LHop NCGa SPhx WOld WPer WWEG
- 'Mrs J. Sangster' WOld
- 'Mrs Leo Hunter' WOld
- 'Nesthäkchen' WOld
- 'Niobe' WOld
- 'Nobilis' WOld
- 'Norman's Jubilee' EBee EPfP NBir NEgg WOld WWEG
- 'Nursteed Charm' WOld
- 'Oktoberschneekuppel' EBee WOld
- 'Orlando' WOld
- 'Pamela' WOld
- 'Patricia Ballard' CBcs CElw CPrp CSBt EBrs GCra GMaP LRHS MBri MWat MWhi NLar NPer SBch SMrs SPer SPoG SRGP WCAu WFar WOld WPer WWEG
- 'Peace' WOld
- 'Percy Thrower' ECtt SMrs WOld
- 'Peter Chiswell' SRms WOld
- 'Peter Harrison' GMaP GMac NBir WMnd WOld WPer
- 'Peter Pan' EBee LRHS WOld
- 'Picture' NBre WOld
- 'Pink Gown' WOld
- 'Pink Lace' MBNS WOld WPer
- 'Pink Pyramid' WOld
- 'Plenty' MBri WOld
- 'Porzellan' CAby CElw CMMP COlW EBee ECGP ECtt EGoo MAvo MBNS NGdn SMrs SRGP WCot
- 'Priory Blush' CAby SPhx WOld
- 'Professor Anton Kippenberg' CEnt CWan EBee EPfP GKir GMaP LLWP LRHS MBri MHer MRav NBre SRGP WMnd WOld
- 'Prosperity' NBre WOld
* - 'Prunella' CBgR WOld
- 'Purple Dome' ECha LEdu LSRN MCCP MHer MWat NMoo SHar SPoG SRkn WOld WOut
- 'Queen Mary' WOld
- 'Queen of Colwall' WOld
- 'Ralph Picton' WOld
- 'Raspberry Ripple' WOld
- 'Rector' see *A. novi-belgii* 'The Rector'
- 'Red Robin' MWat
- 'Red Sunset' SRms WOld
- 'Rembrandt' ECtt EWll LDai NEgg NGdn SMrs SRGP
- 'Remembrance' CAby SRms WBrk WOld
- 'Reverend Vincent Dale' WOld
- 'Richness' MAvo SAga WOld
- 'Robin Adair' WOld
- 'Roland Smith' WOld
- 'Rose Bonnet' CSBt SPlb
- 'Rose Bouquet' WOld
- 'Roseanne' WOld
- 'Rosebud' Ballard ECtt WOld
- 'Rosebud' ambig. WWEG
- 'Rosenwichtel' MBri MMuc NLar WBrk WOld WWEG
- 'Royal Ruby' EBee EBrs ECtt LRHS WOld WWEG
- 'Royal Velvet' WOld
- 'Rozika' WOld
- 'Rufus' WOld
- 'Sailor Boy' EBee NCGa WOld
- 'Saint Egwyn' WOld
- 'Sam Banham' WOld
- 'Samoa' (Island Series) EPfP EWll LRHS LSou
- 'Sandford White Swan' GBuc MHom WBrk WEas WPer WWEG
- 'Sapphire' SVil WOld
- 'Sarah Ballard' MBri SRGP WOld
§ - 'Schneekissen' CPrp EBee ECtt EGoo EPfP GMaP MBNS MHer MMuc NPri SBch SPer SRGP SWvt WFar WOld WWEG
- 'Schöne von Dietlikon' CKno MAvo WOld
- 'Schoolgirl' WOld WWEG
- 'Sheena' SRGP WOld
- 'Silberblaukissen' GBin WOld
- Snow Cushion see *A. novi-belgii* 'Schneekissen'
- 'Snowdrift' WOld
- 'Snowsprite' CBcs CSBt ELan EPfP LRHS MWat NEgg NLar NOrc NPro SMrs SRGP SRms SWat WBrk WOld
- 'Sonata' GMaP WOld
- 'Sophia' WOld WWEG
- 'Starlight' EBee NMoo WFar WOld WRHF
- 'Steinebrück' WOld
- 'Sterling Silver' WOld
- 'Sunset' WOld
- 'Susan' WOld
- 'Sweet Briar' CElw WOld
- 'Tapestry' WOld
- 'Terry's Pride' WOld WWEG
- 'The Archbishop' ECtt WOld
- 'The Bishop' WOld
- 'The Cardinal' WOld
- 'The Choristers' WOld
- 'The Dean' WOld
§ - 'The Rector' WOld
- 'The Sexton' WOld
- 'Thundercloud' CAby WBrk WOld
- 'Timsbury' SRms WBrk WOld WWEG
- 'Tony' WOld
- 'Tovarich' WOld
- 'Trudi Ann' NBir WOld
- 'Twinkle' WOld
- 'Victor' WOld
- 'Vignem' NSti
- 'Violet Lady' WOld
- 'Waterperry' MWat WOld
- 'Weisses Wunder' WOld
- 'White Ladies' CAby CBcs ECtt GCra GMaP LLWP MMuc MWat NLar NOrc SBch SPer SPoG SRGP
- 'White Swan' CAby ECtt EPPr SPhx WOld
- 'White Wings' WOld
- 'Winston S. Churchill' CAby CMMP CMoH COlW CTri EBee ELan EPfP GMaP LRHS MWat SBch SPer SPlb SPoG SRGP WBrk WOld WSpi

oblongifolius GCal WOld WPer
§ - 'Fanny's' CAby CPrp EBee EBla ECtt GQue LRHS MNFA SMrm SPet SPoG SRGP WCot WFar WOld

'Ochtendgloren' (*pringlei* hybrid) ♀H4 CDes CPrp CSam EBee ECtt EPPr EWes GBuc MAvo MNrw NCGa SMrm WCAu WCot WFar WHal WOld WOut

Octoberlight see *A.* 'Oktoberlicht'
§ 'Oktoberlicht' SMrm WOld
oolentangiensis EBee LRHS
'Orchidee' EBee ECtt EWes
pappei see *Felicia amoena*
'Pearl Star' WOld

petiolatus see *Felicia petiolata*
'Photograph' ♀H4 EBrs GMac LRHS MAvo MHom SMrm WFar WIvy WMnd WOld
§ ***pilosus*** var. ***demotus*** ♀H4 ECha EWes MRav WFar WOld WTin
§ - var. ***pringlei*** 'Monte Cassino' ♀H4 GBBs LHop LRHS MBNS MRav MWat NBPC SMrm SPav SPer SPhx SRGP WFar WMoo WOld WWEG
- - 'October Glory' CMdw WFar
- - 'Phoebe' WOld
- - 'Pink Cushion' CMHG WCot
'Pink Star' CAby CMea CMoH ECtt GMac MNFA MRav MWat NSti SBch SPhx WBrk WFar WHoo WOld WTin
'Pixie Dark Eye' (*ericoides* hybrid) CDes WCot
'Pixie Red Eye' (*ericoides* hybrid) WCot
'Plowden's Pink' WOld
'Prairie Lavender' WOld
'Prairie Pink' WOld
'Prairie Violet' WOld
'Primrose Path' WCot
§ ***ptarmicoides*** CSam EBee EBla LBMP NBre WOld WPer
- 'Mago' EBee
puniceus NBre
pyrenaeus 'Lutetia' CPrp CSam EBee ECha GAbr GBuc GCal GMaP LRHS MAvo MHom MMuc MNFA MWat NCGa NLar SPoG SRGP WCAu WCot WFar WHil WOld WWEG
radula EBee EWes IMou MAvo MNrw NBre NLar NSti WOld WSHC
'Ringdove' (*ericoides* hybrid) ♀H4 CKno CPrp EBee EBla ECGP ECtt GMac LRHS MCot MHom MNFA MNrw NSti SRGP STes WCot WIvy WOld
'Rosa Star' WOld
rotundifolius 'Variegatus' see *Felicia amelloides* variegated
rugulosus 'Asrugo' EBee
× ***salignus*** WOld
- Scottish form WOld
§ ***scaber*** EBee NWsh WCot WPGP
scandens see *A. carolinianus*
schreberi EBee EPPr MAvo NBre NCGa NWsh WCot WOld
§ ***sedifolius*** EBee ECtt ELan GQue LEdu LPio LRHS MDKP MWat MWea NBid SDix SEND SPoG WCot WFar WHil WMnd WOld WPer
- RCB AM -5 WCot
- 'Nanus' CPLG CSam ELan GCal MBel MNFA MRav MWea NBir NLar SPer WAbe WCot WFar WHil WMnd WOld WOut WSpi WTin
§ ***sibiricus*** EShb NBre NLar
'Snow Flurry' see *A. ericoides* f. *prostratus* 'Snow Flurry'
'Snow Star' WOld
souliei EBee EBrs
- B&SWJ 7655 WCru
spectabilis IMou LRHS WOld
stracheyi EDAr
subcaeruleus see *A. tongolensis*
'Sunhelene' CBgR EBee WCot
'Sunqueen' EBee WCot
tataricus 'Jindai' EBee WFar
thomsonii WFar WOld
- 'Nanus' CAby CMdw CMil CMoH ERas GMaP LRHS MCot MWea SAga SPhx SPoG WCot WOld WSHC WSpi

Tonga = 'Dasfour' CWGN EWTr LRHS LSou SWvt
§ ***tongolensis*** GKev SBHP SRms WWFP
- 'Berggarten' CHar EBee LDai LRHS MBri NMoo WAbe
- 'Dunkleviolette' GBuc NBro SRms
- 'Lavender Star' GBuc
- 'Napsbury' EBee MBri SPoG WPGP
- 'Wartburgstern' CPrp EBee EPfP LRHS NGdn STes WPer WWEG
tradescantii misapplied see *A. pilosus* var. *demotus*
tradescantii L. EBee ELan MBNS MMuc MRav NBre NHol NSti SMad WBrk WCot WOld WTin
'Treffpunkt' **new** IMou
trinervius subsp. ***ageratoides*** CPou WOld
- - 'Asran' CWan EBee ECtt EWes LSou SSvw WOld
- - 'Harry Smith' EBee
- - 'Stardust' EBee
- var. ***harae*** SSvw WOld
tripolium EBWF WHer
'Triumph' EBee WCot
turbinellus misapplied ♀H4 CAby CKno EBee EPfP GBuc GCal IKil SPhx SRkn SSvw SUsu WBrk WCot WHoo WOld WPtf WTin
turbinellus Lindl. CSam EPfP ERas LRHS MWat NCGa
- hybrid SMrm WFar
umbellatus CBre EBee GBin GQue NBre NCGa NLar NSti SRms WCot WOld WPrP WTin
'Vasterival' EBee NCGa WBrk
vimineus Lam. see *A. lateriflorus*
- 'Ptarmicoides' see *A. ptarmicoides*
§ 'White Climax' CAby EBee MHom WBrk WCot
'Wood's Pink' EBee WCAu WSpi
'Yvonne' CBre

Asteranthera (*Gesneriaceae*)

ovata CGHE EBee GGGa GGar LRHS LSou MAsh SLon SPoG WAbe WPGP

Asteriscus (*Asteraceae*)

'Gold Coin' see *Pallenis maritima*
maritimus see *Pallenis maritima*

Asteromoea (*Asteraceae*)

mongolica see *Kalimeris mongolica*
pinnatifida see *Kalimeris pinnatifida*

Asteropyrum (*Ranunculaceae*)

cavaleriei EBee GEdr WCot WCru

Asterotrichion (*Malvaceae*)

discolor ECou GGar

Astilbe ✿ (*Saxifragaceae*)

CC 5201 CPLG
'Alive and Kicking' MBri
'Amerika' (× *arendsii*) CMHG CSBt ECtt
'Amethyst' (× *arendsii*) CMHG EMFW EPfP LRHS MRav NBir NBlu NBre SApp SMac SPer SPoG SRGP WCAu WFar WHoo WMoo WWEG
'Angel Wings' NPro
'Anita Pfeifer' (× *arendsii*) CMHG EBrs ELon GBin GKir LPBA WFar WPnP
'Aphrodite' (*simplicifolia* hybrid) CBcs CWCL GCal GKir MDKP MLHP NBre NGdn NHol NPro SMac WBrE WGor WWEG
× ***arendsii*** IFoB NBre WMoo WPer

	Name	Suppliers
	astilboides	CMHG NHol SWvt
	'Atrorosea' (*simplicifolia* hybrid)	NCot SRms
	'Avalanche'	GAbr GBin GKir NHol WMnd WWEG
	'Beauty of Ernst' (× *arendsii*) **new**	LPBA LRHS
	'Beauty of Lisse' (× *arendsii*) **new**	LRHS
	Bella Group (× *arendsii*)	NBre SPet WMnd
	'Bergkristall' (× *arendsii*)	CMHG
	'Betsy Cuperus' (*thunbergii* hybrid)	CMHG EBee GBin LRHS MRav NBre SApp SRGP WCAu
	biternata	EBee
	'Bonn' (*japonica* hybrid)	CWCL CWat LRHS NBlu SCoo SRms
§	'Brautschleier' (× *arendsii*) ♀H4	CBgR CMHG CMMP CMac CTri EBrs ECrN ECtt EPfP GCra LSRN MDun NGdn NLar NPri SRGP WPnP WPtf
	'Bremen' (*japonica* hybrid)	CMHG CMMP EBrs GBin LPBA LRHS NHol
	'Bressingham Beauty' (× *arendsii*)	CMHG CSam CWCL EBrs ECtt ELan EMFW EPfP EPla GKir GMaP LLWG LPBA LRHS MCot MDun MRav MWhi NGdn NHol NPro SPer SPoG SWvt WBor WClo WFar WMoo WWEG
	Bridal Veil (× *arendsii*)	see *A.* 'Brautschleier'
§	'Bronce Elegans' (*simplicifolia* hybrid) ♀H4	CMHG EBee ECha EPfP GBin GBuc GKir GMaP LRHS MRav NHol NOrc NPro WFar WMoo WWEG
	'Bronzelaub' (× *arendsii*)	GBin GKir
*	***bumalda*** 'Bronze Pygmy'	EBee NHol STes
	'Bumalda' (× *arendsii*)	CFir CSBt CWCL GMaP LLWG NChi NDlv NGdn NMyG NOrc NPro SBch SPlb WFar WMoo
	'Burgunderrot' (× *arendsii*)	CWCL GAbr MAsh MBri MNrw NCGa SMrm WBor
	'Carnea' (*simplicifolia* hybrid)	CMHG
	'Catherine Deneuve'	see *A.* 'Federsee'
	'Cattleya Dunkel' (× *arendsii*)	CMHG WFar
	'Cattleya' (× *arendsii*)	CMHG CSam EBrs NBPC NLar NMoo WFar WMoo
	'Ceres' (× *arendsii*)	CMHG NHol
	'Cherry Ripe'	see *A.* 'Feuer'
	chinensis	CMHG ECho LRHS NBre SBod WFar WSHC
	- B&SWJ 8178	WCru
	- from Russia	GCal
	- 'Brokat'	GBin
	- 'Christian'	GBin
	- var. ***davidii***	CMHG
	- - B&SWJ 8583	WCru
	- - B&SWJ 8645	WCru
	- 'Diamonds and Pearls'	MAvo MBri MWea
	- 'Finale'	CHar COlW EWTr NHol NPro SPer WFar
	- 'Frankentroll'	CMHG
	- 'Intermezzo'	GCal GMaP
	- 'Love and Pride' **new**	MBri
	- 'Milk and Honey'PBR	LRHS MBNS
§	- var. ***pumila*** ♀H4	Widely available
	- - 'Serenade'	CMac MBri NGdn WFar
	- 'Purple Glory'	CMHG GKir MDun
	- 'Spätsommer'	CMHG
	- var. ***taquetii***	CMac EBee NBre NSti SRms
	- - Purple Lance	see *A. chinensis* var. *taquetii* 'Purpurlanze'
§	- - 'Purpurlanze'	Widely available

	Name	Suppliers
§	- - 'Superba' ♀H4	CMHG CMac CRow CTri ECha EPfP GGar LRHS MCCP MCot MLHP NBro NGdn NHol SDix SPer SRms STes WFar WMoo WPGP
	- 'Troll'	GBin
	- 'Veronika Klose'	CMHG EBee GBin GKir NLar NPro WCAu WWEG
	- 'Vision in Pink'PBR	CWCL LRHS LSou MBNS NBhm SBch
	- 'Vision in Red'PBR	CBgR CWCL CWat EKen GBin GGar LRHS LSou MBNS MBri MNrw NBhm NLar NMyG SBch WBor WFar
	- 'Visions'	CMHG CMac CWCL EBee EBrs GBin GQue LRHS LSou MBNS MBri NBro NGdn NMyG NPro SBch STes WFar
	Cologne	see *A.* 'Köln'
	Color Flash	see *A.* 'Beauty of Ernst'
	Color Flash	see *A.* 'Beauty of Lisse'
	'Crimson Feather'	see *A.* 'Gloria Purpurea'
	× ***crispa***	ECho WFar
	- 'Gnom'	EMFW
	- 'Lilliput'	ECtt GBin GGar GKir NDlv NLar NPro NRya WWEG
§	- 'Perkeo' ♀H4	CBcs ECho ECtt ELan EPfP GGar GKir GMaP NBir NLar NMen NPri NPro NSla SRms WAul WBVN WFar WMoo WWEG
	- 'Peter Pan'	see *A.* × *crispa* 'Perkeo'
	- 'Snow Queen'	NBir NMen NPro WFar
	'Darwin's Dream'	NLar NPri WFar
	'Darwin's Favourite' (× *arendsii*)	CWCL
	'Deutschland' (*japonica* hybrid)	CBcs CMHG CSam CWCL EBrs ECtt EPfP GKir GMaP LRHS LSRN MBNS MGos MRav NBir NHol NVic SAga SPer SPoG SRms STes SWat WAbe WAul WFar WHoo WMoo WWEG
§	'Diamant' (× *arendsii*)	CMHG EBrs EShb LRHS MMuc NGdn NHol WFar
	Diamond (× *arendsii*)	see *A.* 'Diamant'
	'Drayton Glory' (× *arendsii*)	see *A.* × *rosea* 'Peach Blossom'
	'Drum and Bass'PBR **new**	LSou
	'Dunkelachs' (simplicifolia hybrid)	CBgR LRHS MSCN NBPC NMyG WAbe WFar
	'Dusseldorf' (*japonica* hybrid)	CMHG CSam CWCL EBrs GKir NHol
	'Eden's Odysseus'	EBee GBin NHol
	'Elegans' (*simplicifolia* hybrid)	CMHG GKir WFar
	Elizabeth Bloom = 'Eliblo'PBR (× *arendsii*)	EBee EBrs EPla GKir LLWG LRHS MRav NEgg NHol WFar
	'Elizabeth' (*japonica* hybrid)	CMHG EBee
	'Ellie' (× *arendsii*)	CMHG CWCL GBin LRHS LSRN LSou MBNS MBri NBPC NBhm NGdn NHol SAga SMrm WBor WPtf
	'Else Schluck' (× *arendsii*)	ECha
	'Erica' (× *arendsii*)	CMHG CTri EWll GKir LRHS MRav NPro WCAu WFar WMnd WMoo WWEG
	'Etna' (*japonica* hybrid)	CBcs CMHG CSam EBee IFFs LRHS MMuc NEgg NGdn NHol NLar NPro SRms WPnP
	'Europa' (*japonica* hybrid)	CMHG CMac ECtt EMFW GBin GKir LHop LRHS MRav SBch SPoG WFar WMoo
	'Fanal' (× *arendsii*) ♀H4	Widely available
	'Fata Morgana' (× *arendsii* hybrid)	CMHG
§	'Federsee' (× *arendsii*)	CBcs CMHG EBrs ECha ECtt ELan EMil EPyc GKir LRHS MBNS NBPC

NBre NBro NGdn NPro SMrm SPer WFar
§ 'Feuer' (× *arendsii*) — CMHG CMMP CMac CPrp ECtt ELan EPfP GBuc GKir LBMP LRHS NEgg NGdn NHol NOrc NPro NVic SPer WBor WMoo
Fire — see *A.* 'Feuer'
'Flamingo'[PBR] (× *arendsii*) — GAbr GBin MAvo MBNS SMrm
'Gertrud Brix' (× *arendsii*) — CBcs CWat GKir NBir NGdn NPro
§ ***glaberrima*** — NBid NHol NMen
§ - var. ***saxatilis*** ♀[H4] — CRow EBee EPfP GBin GGar IFro NSla WAbe WHal WThu
- ***saxosa*** — see *A. glaberrima* var. *saxatilis*
'Gladstone' (× *arendsii*) — see *A.* 'W.E. Gladstone'
§ 'Gloria Purpurea' (× *arendsii*) — CMHG GKir NHol NMoo NMyG SRGP WMoo
'Gloria' (× *arendsii*) — CMHG CMac CTri EBrs LPBA LRHS MRav WFar
Glow (× *arendsii*) — see *A.* 'Glut'
§ 'Glut' (× *arendsii*) — CMHG CWCL EBrs ECtt EPPr GBin GKir GQue LLWG LRHS MAvo NGdn NHol NMyG SRms WFar
'Granat' (× *arendsii*) — CMHG CMMP CMac EMFW GBuc NBir NBre NEgg NHol NPro WFar WMoo
* Grande Group (× *arendsii*) — NBre
grandis — CMHG GBee WHer
'Grete Püngel' (× *arendsii*) — ECha GBin GKir MBel WFar
'Harmony' (× *arendsii*) — CMHG
'Heart and Soul'[PBR] — EPfP MBri MWea
'Hennie Graafland' (*simplicifolia* hybrid) — CBcs CChe CMHG CWCL EBrs GAbr GBin GKir GQue LRHS MBel NCGa NLar
'Holden Clough' (*japonica* hybrid) — NHol
Hyacinth (× *arendsii*) — see *A.* 'Hyazinth'
§ 'Hyazinth' (× *arendsii*) — CMHG CPLG CPrp EBrs EMFW GMaP LBMP LLWG LRHS LSou NGdn NHol WFar
'Inshriach Pink' (*simplicifolia* hybrid) — CBcs CCVN CMHG CPrp EHoe ELan EMFW GBin GKir LRHS MBri NBir NHol SAga SBch SHGN WFar WHal
'Irrlicht' (× *arendsii*) — CMHG EBrs ELan EMFW EPfP EPla EShb GBuc GGar GKir LHop LPBA LRHS MCot MGos NHol SMac SPer SWat WAul WPnP WWEG
japonica — CPLG
* - 'Pumila' — NBir NGdn
- var. ***terrestris*** — see *A. glaberrima*
'Jo Ophorst' (*davidii* hybrid) — CMHG ECtt GBin GBuc LRHS MRav NEgg NGdn NHol NLar SPer WFar
'Jump and Jive'[PBR] — LSou MAsh
'Koblenz' (*japonica* hybrid) — CMHG CWCL MDKP NMyG
§ 'Köln' (*japonica* hybrid) — CMHG CWat GBin LPBA LRHS NMyG WFar
koreana — GGar WCot WPGP
- B&SWJ 8611 — WCru
- B&SWJ 8680 — WCru
'Kriemhilde' — CMHG MSCN
'Kvële' (× *arendsii*) — CMHG GKir WFar WMoo
§ 'Lachskönigin' (× *arendsii*) — CMHG GKir
'Lilli Goos' (× *arendsii*) — CMHG GBin
'Lollipop' — GBin MBNS MBri NBhm NPro
longicarpa B&SWJ 6711 — WCru
macroflora — GCal
'Maggie Daley' — CMMP EBee MBri NBro NPro WMoo
'Mainz' (*japonica* hybrid) — CMHG ELan LPBA
'Mars' (× *arendsii*) — CMHG
microphylla — CMHG NHol
- B&SWJ 11085 — WCru
- pink-flowered — CMHG NHol
'Moerheim Glory' (× *arendsii*) — CMMP GBin MSCN NBre NGdn
'Moerheimii' (*thunbergii* hybrid) — CMHG GKir
'Mont Blanc' (× *arendsii*) — CMHG
'Montgomery' (*japonica* hybrid) — CMHG CWCL EBrs EShb EWTr GAbr GBin GKir LHop LRHS LSRN MAvo MBNS MBri MCot MMuc MRav NBro NCGa NEgg NGdn NHol SAga SBch SMrm SPad WBVN WFar
'Nikki' **new** — NCGa
'Obergärtner Jürgens' (× *arendsii*) — CMMP GBin
Ostrich Plume — see *A.* 'Straussenfeder'
'Paul Gaärder' (× *arendsii*) — CMHG
'Peaches and Cream' — EBee GKir MMHG NBro NLar
'Peter Barrow' (*glaberrima* hybrid) — GBin SRms
'Pink Fanal' **new** — LRHS
'Pink Lightening'[PBR] (*simplicifolia* hybrid) — CBow CWCL EBee EShb MAvo MBNS MBri NBPC NBhm NLar NOrc SMrm WBor
Pink Pearl (× *arendsii*) — see *A.* 'Rosa Perle'
'Poschka' — CFir NPro
I 'Poschka Alba' — CFir NMyG NPro
'Professor van der Wielen' (*thunbergii* hybrid) — CMHG EBee GGar GKir MDun MWte NHol SDix SPer SRms WCAu WFar WSpi WWEG
pumila — see *A. chinensis* var. *pumila*
* 'Queen' — LPBA
'Radius' — CBgR CMMP EBee GBin LPBA NGdn WPnP
Red Light (× *arendsii*) — see *A.* 'Rotlicht'
'Red Sentinel' (*japonica* hybrid) — CBcs CMMP CWCL CWat EBrs EMFW EPfP GBin GMaP MBri MSCN NBro NGdn NHol NPro SBch SMrm SPoG WBor WCAu WFar WHrl
'Rheinland' (*japonica* hybrid) ♀[H4] — CBcs CMHG CMMP CWCL EPfP LPBA MAvo NPri SRot STes WCAu WFar WHoo WPnP
rivularis — CMHG EBee GBin WCot
- CC 4744 — GKev
- CC 5201 — GKev
- GWJ 9366 — WCru
- var. ***myriantha*** — NBre
- - BWJ 8076a — WCru
'Rock and Roll'[PBR] — LPBA NBPC
§ 'Rosa Perle' (× *arendsii*) — CMHG CSam NHol
'Rose of Cimarron' — NPro
§ × ***rosea*** 'Peach Blossom' — CBcs CBgR CMHG CMMP CMoH EBrs ELon GBuc GKir IFFs LPBA LRHS NBir NCGa NHol NPro SPoG WFar WHoo WMoo
- 'Queen Alexandra' — WFar
'Rosea' (*simplicifolia* hybrid) — EBrs LRHS NHol WFar
Rosemary Bloom — see *A.* 'Sheila Haxton'
'Rot Straussenfeder' (× *arendsii*) — GBin
§ 'Rotlicht' (× *arendsii*) — CMHG EBrs GKir LRHS NHol NMyG NPro SBch WFar WGor
Salmon Queen (× *arendsii*) — see *A.* 'Lachskönigin'
'Salmonea' (*simplicifolia* hybrid) — CMHG
'Saxosa' — see *A. glaberrima* var. *saxatilis*
'Sheila Haxton' — EBee EBrs NHol LRHS
Showstar Group (× *arendsii*) — LRHS MMuc MSnd NBre
simplicifolia ♀[H4] — CRow WFar
- 'Alba' — CMHG NPro
- Bronze Elegance — see *A.* 'Bronce Elegans'

- 'Darwin's Snow Sprite'	CMac GBin GQue MBri NHol NLar NMyG NPri WFar
- 'Jacqueline'	EBee LSou NHol NLar WFar
* - 'Nana Alba'	NPro
- 'Praecox Alba'	EBee GBin NEgg SMac WWEG
- 'White Sensation'PBR **new**	NBPC
'Snowdrift' (× *arendsii*)	CHid CMHG CWat EBrs EPla EWTr GKir GMaP LBMP LLWG LRHS MBNS MDKP MMuc NBir NEgg NOrc NPro SPer SWat WFar WWEG
'Solferino' (× *arendsii*)	CMHG
'Spartan' (× *arendsii*)	see *A.* 'Rotlicht'
'Spinell' (× *arendsii*)	CWCL LRHS MDun NBre NMRc NOrc WFar WPnP WWEG
'Sprite' (*simplicifolia* hybrid) 🏆H4	Widely available
'Stand and Deliver'PBR	MBri
§ 'Straussenfeder' (*thunbergii* hybrid) 🏆H4	CMHG CTri EBrs ECtt EPfP EPla GKir GMaP LBMP LHop LRHS NBid NBir NBro NHol NOrc SMac SPer SPoG WAul WCAu WClo WFar WMoo WPnP WPtf WWEG
'Sugar Plum' (*simplicifolia* hybrid)	EBee NGdn
'Superba'	see *A. chinensis* var. *taquetii* 'Superba'
thunbergii	CEnt CPLG
- var. ***hachijoensis***	EBee
- - B&SWJ 5622	WCru
- var. ***sikokumontanum*** B&SWJ 11164 **new**	WCru
- var. ***terrestris*** B&SWJ 6125	WCru
'Venus' (× *arendsii*)	CSam ECha ECtt EMFW GGar GMaP LPBA MBNS MCot NHol NOrc NVic SPer SWat WFar WMoo
'Vesuvius' (*japonica* hybrid)	CBcs EWTr MDKP NBro
§ 'W.E. Gladstone' (*japonica* hybrid)	CWat NBlu NHol NPro WAbe WGor
'Walküre' (× *arendsii*)	CMHG
'Walter Bitner'	GBin LLWG LRHS MBNS NHol SRGP
'Washington' (*japonica* hybrid)	EBee IFFs LAst MDKP NBre NGdn
§ 'Weisse Gloria' (× *arendsii*)	CMHG CMac CPrp EBrs ECha GBuc GKir LLWG LPBA LRHS NBPC NBro NEgg NHol NMyG NOrc SBch SCoo SMrm SPad SRGP WBor WClo WMoo WTin
'Weisse Perle' (× *arendsii*)	GKir
White Gloria (× *arendsii*)	see *A.* 'Weisse Gloria'
'White Queen' (× *arendsii*)	NHol
'White Wings'PBR (*simplicifolia* hybrid)	LFur NLar
'William Reeves' (× *arendsii*)	CMHG NHol
'Willie Buchanan' (*simplicifolia* hybrid)	CBcs CHid CMHG CPrp EHoe GAbr GGar GKir GMaP LBMP LRHS MBar MBel NEgg NGdn NHol NMen SApp SIng SPer SRms WAbe WFar WMoo WWEG
'Zuster Theresa' (× *arendsii*)	CBgR CMHG EBee EBrs GKir LPBA MBNS MSCN NBPC NBro SMrm WFar

Astilboides (*Saxifragaceae*)

§ ***tabularis***	Widely available

Astragalus (*Papilionaceae*)

SDR 4557 **new**	GKev
adsurgens	GKev
canadensis	GKir SPhx
candelarius	SPhx
chlorostachys **new**	LFur
glycyphyllos	CArn LLHF
membranaceus	CArn
parryi **new**	LFur

Astrantia ✿ (*Apiaceae*)

bavarica	EBee GCal MDKP WFar
'Berendien Stam'	EBee LRHS MAvo
'Bloody Mary'	CBct EBee GBin IBal LSRN MAvo NBPC NGdn NLar SPer
'Buckland'	Widely available
carniolica	EPyc NEgg
- ***major***	see *A. major*
- 'Rubra'	CBcs EBee GMaP MMuc NBre WHal WSHC
- 'Variegata'	see *A. major* 'Sunningdale Variegated'
'Dark Shiny Eyes'	CBct CLAP EBee ECtt MAvo MBNS NBhm NCGa NGdn NLar NSti
'Hadspen Blood'	Widely available
Harptree hybrid	CHar
'Helen'	NLar
helleborifolia misapplied	see *A. maxima*
'Madeleine'	EBee NBhm
§ ***major***	Widely available
- 'Abbey Road'PBR	CBct CLAP EBee EBla LAst LHop LRHS LSou MAvo MBNS MGos NBPC NEgg NLar NPro SMrm SPoG STes WAul
* - ***alba***	CBcs CMHG COIW CWCL EBee EBla ECha EHrv GMac IBal LRHS MCot MNFA MRav NBir NGdn NPer SMad SMrm WMnd WMoo
- 'Ann Cann'	CBct
- subsp. ***biebersteinii***	EBla LRHS NBir NBre
- 'Bo-Ann'	CWCL EBla IBal LPio MAvo MBri NCob NLar WAul WFar
- 'Celtic Star'	EBla GBuc LHop NCob NGdn
- 'Claret'	Widely available
- 'Côte d'Azur'	CBct
- 'Cottage Herbery'	WCHb
- dwarf	WFar
- 'Gill Richardson'	Widely available
- 'Gracilis'	EBee
- 'Greenfingers'	EWes
- 'Gwaun Valley'	WFar
- 'Hillview Red'	CElw
- subsp. ***involucrata***	EBla EHrv LRHS MBel SWat WFar
- - 'Barrister'	CSam GBuc LRHS NLar WFar WPGP
- - 'Canneman'	EBee EBla EWes LPla SMeo SUsu WCot WFar
- - 'Margery Fish'	see *A. major* subsp. *involucrata* 'Shaggy'
- - 'Moira Reid'	CBct CKno CLAP CMil CSam EBee EBla ECGP ECtt ELan GCal GMaP IPot LRHS LSRN MAvo MCot MRav NBro NCGa NCob NSti SMrm SMrs SUsu WFar
- - 'Orlando'	CLAP
§ - - 'Shaggy' 🏆H4	Widely available
- 'Jade Lady'	WFar
- 'Jitse'	EBee NCot
- 'Lars'	Widely available
- 'Little Snowstar'	EHrv IBal MBNS
- 'Lola'	EBee NCGa
- 'Madeleine van Bennekom' **new**	EBee
- 'Magnum Blush'	EBee LRHS NBhm SPoG
- 'Paper Moon'	WFar
- 'Pink Pride'	CBct EBee LSou NCGa
- 'Pink Sensation' **new**	EBee

- 'Primadonna' CBct EBee EBla EHrv GMaP MNFA NHol NLar NWsh SPlb WFar WPer WSpi WWEG
- 'Princesse Sturdza' new EBee
- 'Rosa Lee' CWCL EBee IBal NCGa NCob NLar WAul
- var. ***rosea*** CBre CWCL EBee EBla EDAr EHrv EPfP IBal LHop LRHS LSRN MCot MRav MWhi NDlv NGdn SAga SMrm SPer WCAu WFar WMoo
- - George's form CBct CKno CMac CSam EBee EBla ECtt IPot LAst LHop LRHS LSRN MBNS NCGa NCob NEgg NHol SMrs SUsu
- 'Rosensinfonie' EBee EBla GMaP NBro NGdn NPro WFar WMnd
§ - 'Rubra' Widely available
- 'Ruby Cloud' CHid EBee EBla EDAr EHrv IBal LLWG MCot MNrw NBro NGdn NLar NSti SGSe SRot WFar WFoF WMnd WPnP WSpi WWEG
- 'Ruby Glow' new LRHS
- 'Ruby Star' new EBee
- 'Ruby Wedding' Widely available
- 'Silver Glow' EBee ECtt IBal NBPC NGdn NLar NMyG SPer SRot WFar
- 'Star of Summer' CBct EBee EKen MAvo MWea NSti
- 'Starburst' WFar
- 'Sue Barnes' (v) GCal
§ - 'Sunningdale Variegated' (v) ♀H4 Widely available
- 'Titoki Point' WCot
- 'Venice' EBee NBhm
- 'White Giant' new EBee
§ ***maxima*** ♀H4 Widely available
- 'Mark Fenwick' NBir
* - ***rosea*** EBla ECtt MCot MDKP MWhi NBir NGdn WWEG
minor EBee WCru WFar
'Moulin Rouge'PBR Widely available
'Queen's Children' EBee NBhm
'Rainbow' NLar
'Roma'PBR Widely available
rubra see *A. major* 'Rubra'
'Snow Star'PBR CWCL CWib EBee EHrv EWTr GBin IPot MBri WHlf
'Star of Beauty'PBR CBct NLar
'Stonehouse Perpetual' new ECha
'Warren Hills' CLAP EBee EBla

Astrodaucus (*Apiaceae*)

orientalis SPhx

Asyneuma (*Campanulaceae*)

canescens CEnt LSou NBre SGar
§ ***prenanthoides*** SMrm
pulvinatum CPBP EPot SIng WAbe

Asystasia (*Acanthaceae*)

bella see *Mackaya bella*
§ ***gangetica*** CSev EShb
violacea see *A. gangetica*

Athamanta (*Apiaceae*)

turbith subsp. ***haynaldii*** EBee

Athanasia (*Asteraceae*)

§ ***parviflora*** SPlb

Atherosperma (*Monimiaceae*)

moschatum CBcs CHll WSHC

Athrotaxis (*Cupressaceae*)

cupressoides CDoC CDul CKen GKir MBar WThu
laxifolia CDoC CKen EMil GKir MBar MGos WThu
selaginoides CDoC CTrG

Athyrium ✿ (*Woodsiaceae*)

'Branford Beauty' CBty CCCN CDes CLAP EBee EFtx LRHS MAsh NLar WPGP WRic
'Branford Rambler' CLAP EBee WRic
filix-femina ♀H4 Widely available
- subsp. ***angustum*** new CBty
- - f. ***rubellum*** 'Lady in Red' CCCN CDes CElw CLAP EBee EFtx EMil LBMP LLHF LRHS LSRN MAsh MBri MGos NBid NLar SPad WMoo WRic WWEG
- 'Corymbiferum' GQui SRms
- 'Crispum Grandiceps Kaye' SRms
- Cristatum Group CLAP EBee EFer EFtx ELan LSRN MMoz SWat WFib
§ - Cruciatum Group CLAP EBee ELan MMoz NHol SPer SRms WFib WMoo WRic
- 'Dre's Dagger' new EFtx MAsh WFar
- 'Encourage' new WFar
- 'Fieldii' CLAP SRms
- 'Frizelliae' ♀H4 Widely available
- 'Frizelliae Capitatum' CLAP WFib WPGP
- 'Frizelliae Cristatum' EFtx SRms
- 'Grandiceps' CLAP EBee SRms
- 'Minutissimum' CDes CGHE CLAP EBee ECha ELan MMoz WPGP
* - 'Nudicaule' SRms
- Plumosum Group CLAP GQui WAbe WFib
* - 'Plumosum Aureum' NBhm
- 'Plumosum Axminster' CBty CLAP CMil EFer MAsh NWsh WFar
- 'Plumosum Cristatum' CLAP
- 'Plumosum Divaricatum' SRms
- 'Plumosum Druery' CLAP
- Red Stem see *A. filix-femina* 'Rotstiel'
§ - 'Rotstiel' CDTJ CFwr CLAP EBee LRHS MMoz MMuc SBch WFar WMoo WPnP WRic
- 'Vernoniae' ♀H4 CBty CDTJ CLAP CWCL EBee ELan LPBA NHol NLar NWsh SGSe WRic
- 'Vernoniae Cristatum' CLAP NHol WFib
- 'Victoriae' CBty CCCN CDTJ CDes CFwr CPrp CWCL EKen GEdr GMaP LPBA LRHS MAsh MMuc NBPC NBid NGdn NHol NLar SGSe STes WPat WWEG
- Victoriae Group see *A. filix-femina* Cruciatum Group
- 'Victoriae' seedling new WPtf
'Ghost' CBty CCCN CDes CLAP EBee EFtx LRHS MAsh MGos NLar WPat WRic WWEG
goeringianum 'Pictum' see *A. niponicum* var. *pictum*
grammitoides var. ***oldhamii*** EBee
niponicum LRHS WHal
- f. ***metallicum*** see *A. niponicum* var. *pictum*
§ - var. ***pictum*** ♀H3 Widely available
- - 'Apple Court' CBty CCCN EBee EFtx LRHS MAsh NLar WRic
- - 'Burgundy Glow' CBow
- - 'Burgundy Lace'PBR CBcs CBty CLAP EFtx LHop MAsh NPri SMrm WPat WPtf
* - - 'Cristatoflabellatum' CLAP ELan LRHS
- - 'Pewter Lace'PBR CBty EFtx MAsh

- - 'Red Beauty' CBcs CBty CDTJ CFwr CLAP EBee ECha EFer EPfP EWTr GAbr GBin GCal LRHS LSRN MAsh MAvo NBlu NHol NLar SBch WClo WCot WPat WPnP
- - 'Silver Falls' CBcs CBty CCVN CHid CLAP CMil EAmu EBee EShb MAvo NCob NMyG WCot WHal WPGP WWEG
- - 'Soul Mate' CLAP
- - 'Ursula's Red' CBcs CBty CCVN CElw CLAP CTrC EFtx EPot EShb GBin IBal LHop LRHS LSRN LSou MAsh MAvo NBid NBir NEgg NMoo NPri SMrm SPad SPer WClo WCot WFar WPGP
- - 'Wildwood Twist' CBty CLAP EFtx MAsh
otophorum 🏆H4 NBid NHol SRms WIvy WPGP WRic
- var. ***okanum*** Widely available
vidalii CBow CDTJ CFwr CLAP EBee MMoz NEgg NLar NMyG SMac WFib WRic

Atractylodes (*Asteraceae*)

japonica EFEx
macrocephala CArn EFEx

Atragene see *Clematis*

Atriplex (*Chenopodiaceae*)

canescens NLar WDin
cinerea ECou
halimus CArn CBcs CBot EBee ECha EHoe ELau EPPr MBel MBlu MBri MRav NLar SLon SPer SPlb WCom WCot WDin WKif
hortensis var. ***rubra*** CArn CEnt CSpe ELan LSou MHer MNHC MWte NGHP SIde WCHb WCot WEas WJek WTou

Atropa (*Solanaceae*)

bella-donna CArn GBar GPoy SEND WTin
mandragora see *Mandragora officinarum*

Aubrieta ✿ (*Brassicaceae*)

'Alba' see *A.* 'Fiona'
albomarginata see *A.* 'Argenteovariegata'
'Alix Brett' CMea ECho LRHS SPoG
'Ann Kendall' ECtt
§ 'Argenteovariegata' (v) 🏆H4 ECho ELan GKir LRHS MAvo WAbe WFar
'Astolat' (v) ECho LRHS SRms WAbe
§ 'Aureovariegata' (v) 🏆H4 CMea ECho ELan GKir LRHS MHer NPer WAbe WFar
Blaue Schönheit see *A.* 'Blue Beauty'
'Blaumeise' GKir LRHS WSpi
§ 'Blue Beauty' ECtt EPfP MAsh WClo WSpi
'Blue Chip' ECtt
'Blue Emperor' NCGa WSpi
'Blue Gown' GKir
'Blue Whale' **new** SRot
§ 'Bob Saunders' (d) CMea ECho LLHF LRHS
'Bressingham Pink' (d) 🏆H4 CMea ECtt ELan EPfP SPoG WFar
'Bressingham Red' ECho ECtt EPfP GKir MAvo NCGa SIng SPoG
'Bubble Purple' **new** EPfP
canescens subsp. ***cilicica*** EPot
Cascade Series GJos GKir SPoG
- 'Blue Cascade' EPfP GKir MBNS MWat NNor SPlb SPoG WGor WRHF
- 'Lilac Cascade' SPoG
- 'Purple Cascade' CTri CWCL CWib EPfP LRHS LSRN MBNS MWat SPlb SPoG SRms WFar WGor
- 'Red Cascade' 🏆H4 CTri CWib ECtt EPfP LSRN MBNS NNor SPlb SPoG SWal
deltoidea SVic WClo
- 'Nana Variegata' (v) CMea CPBP EPot WGor
- Variegata Group (v) ECtt LRHS NSla WFar WRHF
- - 'Shaw's Red' GKir
'Doctor Mules' 🏆H4 ECtt GKir LRHS SRms
'Doctor Mules Variegata' (v) CTri EAlp ECho ECtt EPfP LAst MAsh MHer NBlu SPoG SWvt WFar WHoo
Double Stock-flowered Group pink LAst NCGa
'Downers Variegata' (v) **new** LRHS
'Eila' (d) STre
'Elsa Lancaster' EPot NMen NSla WAbe WPat
§ 'Fiona' SIng
§ 'Frühlingszauber' SRms
glabrescens EPot WAbe
'Gloriosa' SIng
'Golden King' see *A.* 'Aureovariegata'
gracilis EPot WAbe
- 'Kitte Rose' EAlp
* 'Graeca' LRHS NPri
'Greencourt Purple' 🏆H4 CMea ECho ELan MHer MWat SIng
'Gurgedyke' SRms
'Hamburger Stadtpark' CWCL EAlp ECho ECtt EPfP NBlu
'Harknoll Red' ECtt
'Hartswood' SIng
'Hemswell Purity' PBR see *A.* 'Snow Maiden'
'Hendersonii' SRms
'J.S. Baker' SRms
'Jeeves' LRHS
'Joy' (d) ECtt LLHF NSla SIng
'Kitte' ECho EPfP LRHS NBlu NLar NPri SPoG
'Leichtlinii' LRHS
'Lemon and Lime' ECho LRHS
macedonica EPot WAbe
'Magician' WCFE
'Mrs Rodewald' 🏆H4 SRms
'Novalis Blue' SRms
'Oakington Lavender' GKir
pinardii EPot
'Pink Beauty' ECtt
'Purple Charm' SRms
'Purple Emperor' SIng
'Red Carpet' ECho ECtt ELan EPot MHer SIng SPoG SRms
'Red Carpet Variegated' (v) CMea
'Red Dyke' SIng
'Riverslea' SIng
'Rosanna Miles' SIng
'Rose Queen' CMea CPBP SAga
Royal Series 🏆H4 COIW
- 'Royal Blue' EPfP LRHS NEgg WFar WMoo
- 'Royal Lavender' LRHS WFar
- 'Royal Lilac' WFar
- 'Royal Red' EPfP LRHS NPri SBch SRms WClo WFar WGor WMoo
- 'Royal Rose' LRHS WFar
- 'Royal Violet' CTri EPfP LRHS NHol SBch WFar WMoo WPer
'Schofield's Double' see *A.* 'Bob Saunders'
'Silberrand' ECha NSla
§ 'Snow Maiden' PBR ECtt NPri WFar
'Somerfield Silver' MBar NPri
'Somerford Lime' (v) ECtt LRHS MBar NPri
Spring Charm see *A.* 'Frühlingszauber'
'Swan Red' (v) ECtt EPot LAst LIMB MAsh MHer NEgg NPro NSla SPoG WAbe WClo WFar WHoo

thessala	CPBP
'Triumphante'	ECtt LLHF LRHS
'Wanda'	SIng
'Whitewell Gem'	EAlp ECho LRHS MAvo NHol SRms WMoo

Aucuba ✿ (*Aucubaceae*)

japonica	CAlb
- (f)	CDul WDin
- (m)	SReu
- var. ***borealis***	EMil
- 'Crassifolia' (m)	CMac EPla EQua SAPC SArc
- 'Crotonifolia' (f/v) ♀H4	Widely available
- 'Crotonifolia' (m/v)	CMac LBMP MAsh SRms
- 'Dentata'	CHEx
- 'Gold Splash' (v)	GKir
- 'Golden King' (m/v) ♀H4	CAlb CDoC CMac CWib EBee ELan EPfP GKir LRHS LSRN MAsh MGos MWat NLar SLim SPer WBrE
- 'Golden Spangles' (f/v)	CAlb CBcs CDoC EBee ERas LRHS NLar NMun SWvt
- 'Goldstrike' (v)	EBee LRHS LSRN MAsh NEgg SMad
- 'Hillieri' (f)	EQua
- f. ***longifolia*** ♀H4	CMac NHol NLar SAPC SArc SDix WCru
- - 'Lance Leaf' (m)	EPla EQua
- - 'Salicifolia' (f)	CHEx EBee EPla LAst MRav NLar WCru WDin WFar WPGP
- 'Maculata' hort.	see *A. japonica* 'Variegata'
- 'Marmorata'	EPla LRHS
- 'Mr Goldstrike' (m/v)	SBch SLim
- 'Nana Rotundifolia' (f)	EPla
- Pepper Pot = 'Shilpot' (m/v)	CHEx EPfP LRHS MAsh SLon SPoG SSta
- 'Picturata' (m/v)	CBow CDul CHEx CMac CSBt EBee ELan GKir LRHS MAsh MGan MGos MRav NHol SLim SPer SPoG WFar
- 'Rozannie' (f/m) ♀H4	CBcs CDoC CDul CEnd CSBt EBee ECrN ELan EPfP EPla EWTr GKir LAst LRHS LSRN MAsh MBlu MGos MRav NLar NPri SBch SLim SPer SPoG SReu SWvt WClo WDin WFar
- 'Speckles'	NLar
- 'Sulphurea Marginata' (f/v)	CBcs CBow CMac CTri EBee ECrN EMil NPro SPer SPoG
§ - 'Variegata' (f/v)	Widely available
- Windsor form (f)	EQua MBri
omeiensis	WPGP
- BWJ 8048	WCru

Aurinia (*Brassicaceae*)

§ ***saxatilis*** ♀H4	ECho EPfP LAst MBar SPlb WFar
- 'Argentea'	ECho
- 'Citrina' ♀H4	ECha ECho ECtt MWat SRms
- 'Compacta'	CTri ECho ECtt GJos LRHS
- 'Dudley Nevill'	ECho LRHS
- 'Dudley Nevill Variegated' (v)	ECha ECho ECtt EWes GMaP LIMB MHer NBir SIng WFar
- 'Flore Pleno' (d)	ECho
- Gold Ball	see *A. saxatilis* 'Goldkugel'
- 'Gold Dust'	ECho ECtt SRms
- 'Golden Queen'	ECtt MHer
§ - 'Goldkugel'	ECho GKir IFoB NBlu SPoG SRms WFar WRHF
- 'Silver Queen'	WEas
- 'Variegata' (v)	NPri SPoG

Austrocedrus (*Cupressaceae*)

§ ***chilensis***	CKen CTho IDee LRHS SBig
- 'Thornhayes Ghost'	CTho LRHS

Austromyrtus (*Myrtaceae*)

§ ***dulcis***	ECou

Avena (*Poaceae*)

candida	see *Helictotrichon sempervirens*
sativa 'French Black'	CSpe

Avenula see *Helictotrichon*

avocado see *Persea americana*

Azalea see *Rhododendron*

Azara ✿ (*Flacourtiaceae*)

sp.	NEgg
dentata	CBcs CHll CMac EBee GGal GKir LAst SPoG WDin WFar
- 'Variegata'	see *A. integrifolia* 'Variegata'
* ***integerrima***	GQui
integrifolia	CCCN
- 'Uarie'	CCCN
§ - 'Variegata' (v)	CWib LRHS NEgg SDnm
lanceolata	CDul CMCN CPLG CTri EBee ECrN GGal IDee LEdu NSti SLon SPer WFar
microphylla ♀H3	CBcs CChe CDul CLnd CMCN CPLG CTri EBee EPfP GGal GKir LAst LBMP LRHS MAsh NSti SAPC SArc SDnm SPer WFar WPGP WSHC WSpi
- 'Gold Edge' (v)	WFar
- 'Variegata' (v)	CBcs CDoC CMac CPLG CPMA CWib EBee EBtc EHoe EPfP GQui LAst LBMP LRHS MAsh MRav MSCN NHol NLar NSti SDnm SLon SPoG SSpi SSta WFar WPat WSHC
* ***paraguayensis***	CDoC GGar SDnm WFar
petiolaris	EPfP
serrata ♀H3	Widely available
- 'Patagonica'	GKir
uruguayensis	CCCN CPLG EBee EBtc GBin

Azorella (*Apiaceae*)

filamentosa	ECou
glebaria misapplied	see *A. trifurcata*
glebaria A. Gray	see *Bolax gummifer*
gummifer	see *Bolax gummifer*
lycopodioides	GEdr WAbe
* ***speciosa***	EPot
§ ***trifurcata***	CPar CSpe CTri ECho ECtt EPot GAbr GEdr GKir MMuc NLAp NWCA SIng SPlb WPer
- 'Nana'	ECho GGar MWat WPat WThu

Azorina (*Campanulaceae*)

§ ***vidalii***	CBot CSpe EShb IDee SGar
- 'Rosea'	WCot

B

Babiana (*Iridaceae*)

ambigua	CStu
angustifolia	CGrW CPLG GGar
'Blue Gem'	EBrs ECho
disticha	see *B. plicata*
framesii	CStu
- var. ***kamiesbergensis***	CPLG

nana	CGrW CPBP CStu
odorata	CGrW
§ ***plicata***	CGrW
pygmaea	WCot
ringens	CGrW CPLG
rubrocyanea	CGrW
sinuata	CGrW
stricta ♀H1-2	CCCN CPLG CStu EBrs ECho LFur SBch
- var. ***erectifolia***	WPrP
- 'Purple Star'	CPLG EBrs ECho EPot
- 'Tubergen's Blue'	EBrs ECho
- white-flowered **new**	CGrW
truncata	CStu
tubulosa	CGrW
vanzyliae	CStu
villosa	ECho WCot
'Zwanenburg's Glory'	EBrs ECho

Baccharis (*Asteraceae*)

genistelloides	SMad
glomeruliflora	MBri
halimifolia	CBcs CTrC GQui IFFs LRHS SEND SLon
patagonica	GGar LRHS MMuc SAPC SArc WPat
salicifolia	WCot
'Sea Foam'	SMad

Bacopa (*Scrophulariaceae*)

'Snowflake'	see *Sutera cordata* 'Snowflake'

Baeckea (*Myrtaceae*)

densifolia	ECou
gunniana	CPLG
linifolia	SPlb
virgata	CBcs CTrC ECou SPlb

Baillonia (*Verbenaceae*)

juncea	WSHC

Balbisia (*Geraniaceae*)

peduncularis	CCCN

Baldellia (*Alismataceae*)

ranunculoides	CRow EMFW WMAq
- f. ***repens***	LLWG

Ballota ✿ (*Lamiaceae*)

acetabulosa ♀H3-4	EBee ECha EGoo EWes SBch WCot
'All Hallow's Green'	see *Marrubium bourgaei* var. *bourgaei* 'All Hallow's Green'
nigra	CArn EBWF GPoy MHer MNHC NMir SECG WMoo
§ - 'Archer's Variegated' (v)	CBow LDai MAvo
- 'Variegata'	see *B. nigra* 'Archer's Variegated'
pseudodictamnus ♀H3-4	Widely available
- from Crete	ECha
rupestris 'Frogswell Carolyn' (v)	IFro

Balsamita see *Tanacetum*

Balsamorhiza (*Asteraceae*)

deltoidea	GEdr
incana **new**	LFur
sagittata	ECho

Bambusa (*Poaceae*)

glaucescens	see *B. multiplex*
gracilis	see *Drepanostachyum falcatum*
§ ***multiplex***	XBlo
- 'Alphonso-Karrii'	CGHE EPla LEdu SBig
- 'Elegans'	see *B. multiplex* 'Floribunda'
- 'Fernleaf'	see *B. multiplex* 'Floribunda'
§ - 'Floribunda'	CHEx EShb XBlo
- 'Golden Goddess'	XBlo
- 'Silverstripe'	see *B. multiplex* 'Variegata'
§ - 'Variegata' (v)	XBlo
- 'Wang Tsai'	see *B. multiplex* 'Floribunda'
pubescens	see *Dendrocalamus strictus*
textilis	WJun
ventricosa	SBig XBlo
vulgaris	XBlo
- 'Vittata'	XBlo

banana see *Musa*

Banksia (*Proteaceae*)

canei	SPlb
ericifolia	LRHS WBor
- var. ***ericifolia***	CBcs CCCN CTrC SSta
- var. ***macrantha***	SPlb
grandis	CBcs CCCN LRHS
integrifolia	CBcs CCCN CTrC LRHS SSta
marginata	CTrC CTsd ECou SPlb SSpi
media	SPlb
oblongifolia	SPlb
paludosa	CTrC SPlb
robur	CBcs CCCN LRHS SPlb
serrata	SPlb
speciosa	SPlb
spinulosa	CTrC LRHS WBor
- var. ***collina***	CTrC SPlb
- var. ***spinulosa***	CBcs CCCN
violacea	SPlb

Baptisia (*Papilionaceae*)

§ ***alba***	EBee NLar WCot
- var. ***alba*** 'Wayne's World'	IPot
§ - var. ***macrophylla***	CMdw EBee EWes LPla LRHS NBir NLar SDix WCot
australis ♀H4	Widely available
- 'Caspian Blue'	CWCL EWll LEdu MWat WFar WHil WSHC
- 'Exaltata'	ELan GBuc LHop
- var. ***minor***	CAby EBee NLar WPGP
- 'Nelson's Navy'	EBee EWll IPot LRHS MMHG WAul
× ***bicolor*** 'Starlite' (Prairieblues Series) **new**	EBee
bracteata var. ***leucophaea***	LRHS LSou WCot WFar
'Carolina Moonlight'	EBee IPot
lactea	see *B. alba* var. *macrophylla*
leucantha	see *B. alba* var. *macrophylla*
pendula	see *B. alba*
'Purple Smoke'	EBee EWll MMuc NBre SPhx SUsu
'Solar Flare' (Prairieblues Series) **new**	EBee
sphaerocarpa **new**	EBee
- 'Screamin' Yellow' **new**	EBee
tinctoria	CArn
× ***variicolor*** 'Twilite' (Prairieblues Series) **new**	EBee

Barbarea (*Brassicaceae*)

praecox	see *B. verna*
rupicola 'Sunnyola' **new**	EDAr
§ ***verna***	GPoy MHer NGHP SVic
vulgaris 'Variegata' (v)	CArn CMoH EBee LDai MAvo NBro NCob SPav WCHb WCom WCot WMoo
- 'Variegated Winter Cream' (v)	CSpr WFar

Barleria (*Acanthaceae*)

lupulina new	EShb WHil
micans	CCCN
obtusa	WHil
- 'Amethyst Lights' (v)	EShb
suberecta	see *Dicliptera sericea*

Barosma see *Agathosma*

Bartlettina (*Asteraceae*)

§ ***sordida***	CCCN EBee SPoG

Basella (*Basellaceae*)

rubra	SVic

Bashania (*Poaceae*)

faberi Og 94053	EPla
§ ***fargesii***	CDoC ENBC EPla ERod MRav MWht SEND WJun
I ***qingchengshanensis***	CGHE EBee EPla WJun WPGP

basil see *Ocimum basilicum*

Basutica (*Thymelaeaceae*)

aff. ***aberrans***	WAbe

Bauera (*Cunoniaceae*)

rubioides aff. var. ***alba***	ECou
- pink-flowered	ECou

Bauhinia (*Caesalpiniaceae*)

SDR 4941 new	GKev
galpinii	EShb SPlb
* ***lutea*** new	CCCN
natalensis	EShb SPlb
purpurea L. new	CCCN
tomentosa	CCCN EShb
'White Lady' new	CCCN

Baumea see *Machaerina*

bay see *Laurus nobilis*

Beaucarnea (*Dracaenaceae*)

recurvata ♀H1	CTrC EShb LPal MBri WFar

Beaufortia (*Myrtaceae*)

squarrosa	SPlb

Beaumontia (*Apocynaceae*)

grandiflora	EShb

Beauverdia see *Leucocoryne*

Bedfordia (*Asteraceae*)

linearis	GGar

Beesia (*Ranunculaceae*)

calthifolia	CFir CLAP CPLG EBee EHrv EWld GBBs IMou LLHF WCot WCru WPGP
deltophylla	WCot

Begonia ✿ (*Begoniaceae*)

B&SWJ 6881 from Taiwan	WCru
B&SWJ 10279 from Mexico	WCru
B&SWJ 10442 from Guatemala	WCru
B&SWJ 10479 from Costa Rica	WCru
BWJ 7840 from China	WCru
Chen Yi 5	WCot
Chen Yi 7	WCot
DJHC 580	WCot
from China	NShi
from Ruwenzori, Uganda	NShi
from Sikkim, India	WCot
from Vietnam	ERhR NShi
'Abel Carrière' (R)	ERhR NShi WDib
acetosa	NShi
acida	ERhR NShi
aconitifolia (C)	ERhR EShb NShi
acutifolia Jacq.	ERhR NShi
'Aladdin'	ERhR NShi
'Alamo III'	ERhR NShi
albopicta (C)	EBak ERhR NShi
- 'Rosea' (C)	EShb NShi WDib
'Albuquerque Midnight Sky' (R)	NShi
alice-clarkiae	ERhR NShi
'Alleryi'	ERhR NShi
alnifolia	ERhR
'Alto Scharff' ♀H1	ERhR NShi
'Alzasco' (C)	ERhR NShi
'Amigo Pink' (C)	ERhR NShi
ampla	NShi
'Andre' (R) new	NShi
'Anita Roseanna' (C)	ERhR NShi
'Ann Anderson' (C)	ERhR NShi
'Anna Christine' (C)	ERhR NShi
§ ***annulata***	ERhR NShi
'Aquarius'	ERhR NShi
'Arabian Sunset' (C)	ERhR NShi
arborescens var. ***arborescens***	ERhR
'Arctic Breeze'PBR (R)	LRHS
'Argentea' (R)	EBak MBri NShi
'Argenteo Guttata'	ERhR EShb NShi
'Aries'	ERhR NShi
'Art Monday' (C)	NShi
'Arthur Mallet' (Mallet Series) (C)	ERhR NShi
'Aruba'	ERhR
'Atlanta Jazz' (R)	NShi
'Autumn Glow' (T)	ERhR NShi
'Avalanche' (T)	ERhR NShi
'Axel Lange' (R)	NShi
'Aya' (C)	NShi WDib
'Baby Grand' (R) new	NShi
'Baby Perfection'	NShi WDib
'Bahamas'	ERhR NShi
'Bantam Delight'	ERhR NShi
'Barbara Ann' (C)	ERhR
'Barbara Hamilton' (C)	ERhR
'Barbara Parker' (C)	ERhR
'Barclay Griffiths'	ERhR NShi
'Baronessa' new	NShi
'Beatrice Haddrell'	ERhR NShi WDib
* ***benichoma***	WDib
'Benitochiba' (R)	CSpe ERhR LOck NShi NSti WCot WFut
'Bess'	ERhR NShi
'Bessie Buxton'	ERhR NShi
'Bethlehem Star'	ERhR NShi WDib
§ 'Bettina Rothschild' (R)	ERhR NShi WDib
'Beverly Jean'	ERhR NShi
'Big Mac'	ERhR NShi
'Bill's Beauty'	ERhR NShi
'Bishop's Irish Eyes' (C)	NShi
'Black Jack' (C)	ERhR NShi
'Black Knight' (R)	NShi
'Black Raspberry'	ERhR NShi
'Black Velvet'	NShi
'Blackberry Swirl' (R) new	WDib

	'Blanc de Neige'	ERhR NShi
	'Blue Vein'	ERhR NShi
	'Blue Wave'	NShi
	'Bokit'	ERhR NShi WDib
	'Bokit' × ***imperialis***	NShi WDib
	boliviensis (T)	CDes CDoC GCal NShi WCot WCru
	'Bonfire'	IMon LBuc LRHS
	'Boomer' (C)	ERhR NShi
	'Botato'	NShi
	bowerae	ERhR NShi
§	- var. ***nigramarga***	ERhR NShi
	'Boy Friend'	ERhR NShi
	bracteosa	ERhR
	bradei	ERhR
	brevirimosa	ERhR NShi
	- subsp. ***exotica***	ERhR
	'Bronze King' (R)	NShi
	'Brown Lace'	NShi
	'Brown Twist'	NShi WDib
	'Bunchii'	ERhR NShi
	'Burgundy Velvet'	ERhR NShi WDib
	'Burle Marx' 🏆H1	ERhR EShb NShi SDix WDib
	'Bush Baby'	NShi
	'Butter Cup'	NShi
	'Calico Kew'	ERhR
	'Calla Queen' (S)	ERhR NShi
	'Can-can' (R)	see *B.* 'Herzog von Sagan'
	'Can-can' (T)	NShi
	'Candy Floss'	NShi WCru
	'Captain Nemo' (R)	ERhR NShi
	cardiocarpa	ERhR NShi
	'Carol Mac'	ERhR NShi
	'Carolina Moon' (R) 🏆H1	ERhR NShi
	carolineifolia	NShi WDib
	carrieae	ERhR NShi
	× ***carrierei***	see *B.* Semperflorens Cultorum Group
	'Casey Corwin' (R) **new**	WDib
	'Cathedral'	ERhR NShi WDib
	'Champagne'	SPer
	'Chantilly Lace'	ERhR NShi
*	***chapaensis***	NShi
	- HWJ 642	WCru
	'Charles Chevalier'	ERhR NShi
	'Charles Jaros'	ERhR NShi
	'Charm' (S)	ERhR NShi WDib
	(Cheimantha Group) 'Gloire de Lorraine' (T)	NShi
	'Cherry Jubilee' (C)	NShi
	'Cherry Sundae' (S)	ERhR
	'Chesson'	ERhR NShi
	'China Curl' (R) 🏆H1	ERhR LRHS NShi
	'China Doll'	NShi
	chitoensis B&SWJ 1954	WCru
	chloroneura	ERhR WDib
	'Chocolate Box'	ERhR
	'Chocolate Chip'	ERhR NShi
	'Christine'	NShi
	'Christmas Candy'	ERhR WDib
	'Christy White'	NShi
	'Chuck Jaros'	NShi
	'Chumash'	ERhR NShi
	'Cistine'	ERhR NShi
	'Clara' (R)	MBri NShi
	'Cleopatra' 🏆H1	ERhR NShi WDib
	'Clifton'	ERhR NShi
	coccinea (C)	ERhR NShi WDib
	'Coconut Ice'	EShb
	'Comte de Lesseps' (C)	NShi WDib
	conchifolia f. ***rubrimacula***	ERhR NShi
	'Concord'	ERhR NShi
	'Connee Boswell'	ERhR NShi WDib
	convolvulacea	ERhR NShi
	cooperi	ERhR NShi
	'Cora Anne'	ERhR
	'Cora Miller' (R)	ERhR NShi
§	***corallina*** (C)	EBak NShi
	- 'Lucerna Amazon' (C)	ERhR NShi
	'Corbeille de Feu'	ERhR NShi
	'Cosie' (C)	NShi
	'Cowardly Lion' (R)	ERhR NShi
	'Cracklin' Rosie' (C)	ERhR NShi
	crassicaulis	ERhR NShi
	'Crestabruchii'	ERhR NShi
	'Crystal Brook'	ERhR NShi
§	***cubensis***	ERhR NShi
	cucullata (S)	ERhR NShi
	'Curly Fireflush' (R)	ERhR NShi WDib
	'Curly Merry Christmas' (R)	NShi
	'Dales' Delight' (C)	ERhR NShi
	'Dancin' Fred'	ERhR NShi
	'Dancing Girl'	ERhR NShi
	'Dannebo'	MBri
	'Dark Mambo' **new**	NShi
	'D'Artagnon'	ERhR NShi
	'David Blais' (R) 🏆H1	NShi WDib
	'Dawnal Meyer' (C)	ERhR NShi WDib
I	'de Elegans'	ERhR NShi WDib
	'Decker's Select'	ERhR NShi
	'Deco Diamond Dust'	ERhR
	decora	ERhR NShi
	deliciosa	ERhR NShi
	'Delray Silver'	NShi
	(Devil Series) 'Devil Red' (S) **new**	LAst
	- 'Devil Rose' (S) **new**	LAst
	- 'Devil White' (S) **new**	LAst
	'Dewdrop' (R) 🏆H1	ERhR NShi WDib
	diadema	ERhR NShi
	'Di-anna' (C)	ERhR NShi
	dichotoma	ERhR NShi
	dichroa (C)	ERhR NShi
	'Dielytra'	ERhR NShi
	'Di-erna' (C)	ERhR NShi
	dietrichiana	ERhR NShi
	'Digswelliana'	ERhR NShi
	dipetala	ERhR
	discolor	see *B. grandis* subsp. *evansiana*
	domingensis misapplied	see *B. obliqua* L.
	domingensis ambig.	ERhR
	domingensis A. DC. **new**	NShi
	'Don Miller' (C)	ERhR NShi WDib
	'Doublet Pink'	ERhR SVil
	'Doublet Red'	ERhR SVil
	'Doublet White'	ERhR SVil
	'Doublonia Rose' **new**	SVil
	'Douglas Nisbet' (C)	ERhR
§	***dregei*** (T) 🏆H1	ERhR GCal NShi
	- 'Bonsai' (T)	NShi STre
	- var. ***dregei*** (T)	ERhR EShb
	- 'Glasgow' (T)	ERhR NShi
	- var. ***macbethii*** (T)	NShi
	'Druryi'	ERhR NShi
	'Dwarf Houghtonii'	ERhR NShi
	'Earl of Pearl'	ERhR NShi
	'Ebony' (C)	ERhR NShi
	echinosepala	ERhR NShi
	echinosepala × ***sanguinea***	NShi
	edmundoi (C)	ERhR
	egregia	ERhR
	'Elaine'	ERhR NShi
	'Elaine Ayres' (C)	ERhR NShi

§	'Elaine Wilkerson'	ERhR NShi
	'Elaine's Baby'	see *B.* 'Elaine Wilkerson'
	'Elda'	ERhR NShi
	'Elda Haring' (R)	ERhR NShi
	'Elizabeth Hayden'	ERhR NShi
	'Elsie M. Frey'	ERhR NShi
	'Emerald Beauty' (R) ♀H1	ERhR NShi
	'Emerald Giant' (R)	ERhR NShi WDib
	'Emerald Isle'	NShi
	'Emerald Princess'	NShi
	'Emma Watson'	ERhR NShi
	'Enchantment'	ERhR NShi
	'Enech'	ERhR NShi
	'English Knight'	ERhR NShi
	'English Lace'	ERhR NShi
	epipsila	ERhR NShi
	'Erythrophylla'	EShb NShi
	'Erythrophylla Bunchii'	ERhR NShi
§	'Erythrophylla Helix'	ERhR NShi
	'Escargot' (R) ♀	LRHS NShi WDib
	'Essie Hunt'	ERhR
	'Esther Albertine' (C) ♀H1	ERhR NShi
	'Etna' (R) **new**	NShi
	'Evening Star'	ERhR NShi
	'Fairy'	ERhR NShi
	feastii 'Helix'	see *B.* 'Erythrophylla Helix'
	fernando-costae	ERhR NShi
§	'Feuerkönigin' (S)	ERhR NShi
	'Fever' (R)	NShi
	'Fiji Islands' **new**	WJun
	'Filigree' (R)	ERhR NShi
	fimbriata Liebm.	EBrs
	Fimbriata Group (T) **new**	LRHS
	'Fire Flush'	see *B.* 'Bettina Rothschild'
	'Fireworks' (R) ♀	ERhR LRHS NShi WDib
	'Five and Dime'	ERhR NShi
	'Flamboyant' (T)	ERhR LSou MBri NShi SVil WGor
	Flaming Queen	see *B.* 'Feuerkönigin'
	'Flamingo' (C)	ERhR NShi
	'Flamingo Queen' (C)	ERhR NShi
	'Flo 'Belle Moseley' (C)	ERhR NShi WDib
	'Florence Carrell'	ERhR NShi
	'Florence Rita' (C)	ERhR NShi
	'Flying High'	ERhR NShi
	foliosa	ERhR NShi WDib
	- var. ***amplifolia***	see *B. holtonis* var. *holtonis*
§	- var. ***miniata*** ♀H1	CDoC CTsd EBak ERhR EShb LPio MArl NShi SDix WCot WDib
	- - pink-flowered	CCCN CDTJ GGar LAst NShi
	- - red-flowered	CCCN CDTJ
	- - 'Rosea'	CDoC NShi
	formosana	NShi
	- B&SWJ 7041	WCru
	'Frances Lyons' (C)	ERhR NShi
	'Frau Hoffman' (R)	NShi
	'Freckles' (R)	ERhR NShi
	'Fred Bedson'	ERhR NShi
	'Fred Martin'	NShi
	friburgensis	ERhR
	'Friendship'	ERhR NShi
	'Frosty' (T)	NShi WDib
	'Frosty Fairyland'	ERhR
	'Frosty Knight'	ERhR NShi
	'Fuchsifoliosa'	ERhR NShi
	fuchsioides	see *B. foliosa* var. *miniata*
	fusca	ERhR NShi
	'Fuscomaculata'	ERhR NShi
	'Gaystar'	NShi
	gehrtii	ERhR NShi
	geranioides (T)	ERhR
	glabra	ERhR
	glandulosa misapplied	see *B. multinervia*

	glandulosa ambig.	ERhR
	glaucophylla	see *B. radicans* Vell.
	'Glen Daniels'	NShi
	'Gloire de Sceaux'	ERhR NShi
	goegoensis	ERhR NShi
	'Good 'n' Plenty'	ERhR NShi
	gracilis (T)	NShi
	'Granada'	ERhR NShi
	grandis (T)	NShi
§	- subsp. ***evansiana*** ♀H3-4	CAvo CHEx CSam CSpe CStu EBee ERhR EShb ETod EWld GCal LEdu LPio LPla MTho NMRc NShi SBch SDix SGSe SMad SPlb WCot WCru WFar WMoo
	- - var. ***alba*** hort.	CAby ERhR EShb ESwi GCal LOck LPla MTho SGSe SIng SMad SSpi WCot WPGP
	- subsp. ***evansiana*** 'Claret Jug'	EBee EShb LPio NShi WCot WPGP
	- subsp. ***evansiana*** hybrid	NShi
	- - 'Pink Parasol'	EBee NShi WCru
	- - 'Simsii'	NShi WFar
	- 'Sapporo'	EBee EPPr GCal LPio NShi WCru
§	- subsp. ***sinensis***	NShi
	- - BWJ 8011	WCru
I	- - 'Red Undies'	WCru
	aff. ***grandis*** subsp. ***sinensis***	NShi
	- - BWJ 8133	WCru
*	'Great Beverly'	ERhR NShi
	'Green Acres'	ERhR
	'Green Gold' (R)	NShi WDib
	'Green Lace'	ERhR NShi
	'Grey Feather'	ERhR NShi
	griffithii	see *B. annulata*
	'Gustav Lind' (S)	ERhR NShi
	'Guy Savard' (C)	NShi WDib
	'Gypsy Maiden' (T)	NShi
	haageana hort. ex W. Watson	see *B. scharffii*
	handelii	ERhR NShi
*	'Happy Heart'	ERhR NShi
	'Harbison Canyon'	NShi
*	'Harry's Beard'	ERhR NShi
	'Hastor'	ERhR NShi
	hatacoa	ERhR NShi
	- silver-leaved	ERhR EShb NShi
	- spotted-leaved	ERhR NShi
	'Hazel's Front Porch' (C)	ERhR NShi
	'Helen Lewis' ♀H1	ERhR NShi
	'Helen Teupel' (R)	ERhR NShi WDib
	'Helene Jaros'	ERhR NShi
	hemsleyana	NShi
	'Her Majesty' (R)	ERhR NShi
§	***heracleifolia***	ERhR NShi
	- var. ***longipila***	see *B. heracleifolia*
	- var. ***nigricans***	see *B. heracleifolia*
	- 'Wisley'	NShi
§	'Herzog von Sagan' (R)	ERhR NShi
	(Hiemalis Group) 'Elatior'	LRHS
	'Hilo Holiday' (R) ♀	NShi
	hispida var. ***cucullifera***	ERhR NShi
	'Holmes Chapel'	ERhR NShi
§	***holtonis*** var. ***holtonis***	ERhR NShi
	homonyma	see *B. dregei*
	'Honeysuckle' (C)	ERhR NShi
	'Hot Tamale'	ERhR NShi
	'Hottentot'	NShi
	'Houston Fiesta' (R)	NShi
	hydrocotylifolia	ERhR NShi
	hypolipara	see *B. sericoneura*

Name	Suppliers
(Illumination Series) 'Illumination Apricot'	SCoo
- 'Illumination Rose'	SCoo
- 'Illumination Salmon Pink' ♀H2-3	SCoo
- 'Illumination White'	SCoo
imperialis	ERhR NShi
'Inca Fire'PBR (R)	LRHS
incarnata	ERhR NShi
- 'Metallica'	see *B. metallica*
'Indian Summer'PBR (R)	LRHS
'Ingramii'	ERhR NShi
'Interlaken' (C)	ERhR NShi
'Ironstone' (R) ♀H1	NShi
'Ivy Ever'	ERhR NShi
'Jade'	NShi
'Jelly Roll Morton'	ERhR
'Joe Hayden'	ERhR NShi
'John Tonkin' (C)	ERhR NShi
johnstonii	ERhR NShi
'Jolly Silver' **new**	NShi
'Joy Porter' (C)	NShi
'Jubilee Mine'	ERhR
juliana	ERhR NShi
'Jumbo Jeans'	ERhR NShi
'Jumbo Jet' (C)	ERhR NShi
'Kagaribi' (C)	ERhR NShi
kellermanii	ERhR NShi
'Ken Lau Ren' (C)	NShi
keniensis	GCal
'Kentwood' (C)	ERhR NShi
kenworthyae	ERhR NShi
kingiana	NShi WDib
'Kit Jeans'	ERhR NShi
'Kit Jeans Mounger'	ERhR NShi
'Knutsford'	NShi
'Kyoto'	NShi
'La Paloma' (C)	NShi WDib
'Lacewing'	ERhR NShi
'Lady Clare'	ERhR NShi
* 'Lady France'	ERhR MBri
'Langeana'	NShi
'Laurie's Love' (C)	ERhR
'Lawrence H. Fewkes'	ERhR NShi
'Lazy River' (R)	NShi
leathermaniae (C)	ERhR NShi
'Legia'	ERhR
'Lenore Olivier' (C)	ERhR NShi
'Leopard'	ERhR MBri NShi
'Lexington'	ERhR
'Libor' (C)	ERhR
'Lillian' (R)	NShi
'Lime Swirl'	ERhR NShi
'Limeade' **new**	WDib
limmingheana	see *B. radicans* Vell.
'Linda Dawn' (C)	ERhR NShi
'Linda Harley'	ERhR
'Linda Myatt'	ERhR NShi
lindeniana	ERhR NShi
listada ♀H1	ERhR MBri NShi WDib
'Lithuania'	ERhR
'Little Brother Montgomery' ♀H1	ERhR EShb GGar NShi SDix WDib
'Little Darling'	ERhR NShi
'Little Iodine'	NShi
'Lois Burks' (C)	ERhR NShi WDib
'Loma Alta'	ERhR NShi
'Looking Glass' (C)	ERhR NShi WDib
'Lospe-tu'	ERhR NShi
'Lubbergei' (C)	ERhR NShi
'Lucerna' (C)	EBak ERhR
'Lucky Colours' (R) **new**	NShi
'Lucy Closson' (R)	NShi
'Lulu Bower' (C)	ERhR NShi
luxurians ♀H1	CHll CSpe ERhR NShi WCot
- 'Ziesenhenne'	ERhR NShi
lyman-smithii	ERhR NShi
'Mabel Corwin'	ERhR NShi
'Mac MacIntyre'	NShi
macdougallii var. ***purpurea***	see *B. thiemei* 'Purpurea'
macduffieana	see *B. corallina*
'Mac's Gold'	ERhR NShi
maculata (C) ♀H1	ERhR NShi
- 'Wightii' (C)	CSpe ERhR NShi WDib
'Mad Hatter'	ERhR NShi
'Madame Butterfly' (C)	ERhR NShi
'Magic Carpet'	ERhR NShi
'Magic Lace'	ERhR NShi
'Magma' (R) **new**	NShi
'Manacris'	ERhR NShi
'Mandarin Orange' (C)	NShi
manicata	ERhR NShi WDib
'Maori Haze'PBR (R)	LRHS
'Maphil'	MBri NShi
'Mardi Gras' (R)	NShi
'Margaritae'	ERhR NShi
* 'Marginata Crispa White'	SPer
'Marmaduke' ♀H1	CTsd NShi WDib
'Martha Floro' (C)	ERhR
'Martin Johnson' (R) ♀H1	ERhR NShi WDib
'Martin's Mystery'	ERhR NShi
masoniana ♀H1	CTsd ERea ERhR NShi WDib WSFF
- light-leaved	NShi
- var. ***maculata*** **new**	NShi
'Maui Mist' (R)	NShi
'Maurice Amey'	ERhR NShi
'Maverick'	ERhR NShi
mazae	ERhR NShi
'Medora' (C)	ERhR NShi
'Melissa' (T)	NShi
'Merry Christmas' (R) ♀H1	ERhR NShi WDib
metachroa	ERhR NShi
§ ***metallica*** ♀H1	ERhR EShb NShi
'Meteor' (R)	NShi
meyeri-johannis	CFir
'Miami Storm' (R)	NShi
'Michaele'	ERhR
'Midnight Magic' (R) ♀H1	NShi
'Midnight Sun'	ERhR NShi
'Midnight Twister'	ERhR NShi
'Mikado' (R) ♀H1	ERhR NShi
Million Kisses	see *B.* 'Passion'
minor	ERhR
'Mirage' ♀H1	ERhR NShi
'Miss Priss' (C)	NShi
mollicaulis	ERhR
'Moon Maid'	ERhR
'Mr Kartuz' (T)	NShi
'Mrs Hashimoto' (C)	ERhR NShi
'Mrs Hatcher' (R)	ERhR NShi
'Mrs Schinkle' (C)	NShi
§ ***multinervia***	ERhR
'Munchkin' ♀H1	ERhR NShi WDib
'My Best Friend'	NShi
* 'Mystic'	ERhR NShi
'Mystique'	ERhR NShi
'Namur' (R) ♀H1	NShi WDib
'Nancy Cummings'	ERhR
natalensis	see *B. dregei*
'Nelly Bly'	ERhR
nelumbiifolia	ERhR NShi
nigramarga	see *B. bowerae* var. *nigramarga*
nigritarum	ERhR NShi

	nitida alba	see *B. obliqua* L.
	'Nokomis' (C)	ERhR NShi
	'Norah Bedson'	ERhR NShi
	'Northern Lights' (S)	ERhR NShi
§	***obliqua*** L.	ERhR NShi
	obscura	ERhR NShi
	'Obsession' (C)	ERhR
	odorata	see *B. obliqua* L.
	'Odorata Alba'	ERhR NShi
	'Odorata Rosea'	NShi
	olbia	ERhR
	'Old Gold' (T)	ERhR
	'Oliver Twist'	ERhR
	'Orange Dainty'	ERhR
	'Orange Pinafore (C)'	ERhR
	'Orange Rubra' (C) ♀H1	ERhR NShi
	'Orient' (R)	ERhR NShi
	'Orococo'	NShi
	'Orpha C. Fox' (C)	ERhR NShi
	'Orrell' (C)	ERhR NShi
	'Othello'	ERhR NShi
	'Otto Forster'	NShi
	'Pachea' (R)	NShi
	paleata	ERhR NShi
	palmata	CDes EBee EBla EShb GCal NShi SIng WCot WPGP
	- B&SWJ 2692 from Sikkim	WCru
	- from China	EBla NShi
	- var. ***palmata***	NShi
	'Palomar Prince'	ERhR NShi
	'Panasoffkee'	ERhR NShi
	'Pantaloon'	NShi
	'Panther'	ERhR NShi
	'Papillon' (T)	ERhR NShi
	paranaënsis	ERhR NShi
	parilis	ERhR NShi
	partita	see *B. dregei*
	'Passing Storm'	ERhR NShi
§	'Passion'	LAst LSou SVil
	'Patricia Ogdon'	ERhR NShi
	'Paul Bee'	ERhR NShi
	'Paul Harley'	ERhR NShi
	'Paul Henry'	NShi
	paulensis	ERhR NShi
	pavonina	NShi
	'Peace' (R)	NShi
	'Peach Parfait' (C)	ERhR NShi
	pearcei (T)	ERhR NShi
	'Pearl Ripple'	ERhR NShi
	'Pearls' (C)	ERhR NShi
	pedatifida DJHC 98473	WCru
	'Peggy Stevens' (C)	ERhR
	peltata	ERhR NShi
	Pendula Group (T) **new**	LRHS
*	'Penelope Jane'	ERhR
	'Persian Brocade'	ERhR NShi
	'Petite Marie' (C)	ERhR
	'Phil Corwin' (R)	NShi
	'Piccolo'	ERhR NShi
	'Pickobeth' (C)	ERhR NShi
	'Picotee' (T)	CSut
	'Pinafore' (C) ♀H1	ERhR NShi
	'Pink Basket'	NShi
	'Pink Champagne' (R) ♀H1	NShi WDib
	'Pink Frosted' (R)	NShi
	'Pink Lady' (R)	NShi WCru
	'Pink Nacre'	ERhR NShi
	'Pink Parade' (C)	ERhR NShi
	'Pink Parfan'	NShi
	'Pink Shasta' (C)	NShi
	'Pink Slate' (C)	NShi
	'Pink Spot Lucerne' (C)	ERhR NShi

	'Pink Taffeta'	ERhR NShi
	'Pinkpop' **new**	NShi
	plagioneura	see *B. cubensis*
	'Plum Rose'	ERhR NShi
	plumieri	ERhR
	polyantha	ERhR NShi
	polygonoides	ERhR
	popenoei	ERhR
	'Posy Wahl' (C)	NShi
	'Potpourri'	ERhR
	'Président Carnot' (C)	ERhR NShi
	'Pretty Rose'	ERhR
	'Preussen'	ERhR NShi
	'Princess of Hanover' (R) ♀H1	ERhR LRHS NShi WDib
	'Princessa Rio de Plata'	ERhR NShi
	prismatocarpa	ERhR NShi
	procumbens	see *B. radicans* Vell.
	'Purple Snow' (R)	LRHS NShi
	pustulata 'Argentea'	ERhR NShi
	putii	NShi
	- B&SWJ 7245	WCru
	'Queen Mother' (R)	ERhR NShi
	'Queen Olympus'	ERhR GGar NShi WDib
	'Quinebaug'	ERhR NShi
§	***radicans*** Vell. ♀H1	ERhR MBri NShi
	rajah	NShi
	'Raquel Wood'	ERhR NShi
	'Raspberry Swirl' (R) ♀H1	ERhR NShi WDib
	ravenii (T)	GCal NShi WCot
	'Raymond George Nelson' ♀H1	ERhR NShi
	'Razzmatazz' (R)	NShi WDib
	'Red Berry' (R)	ERhR NShi
	'Red Bull' **new**	NShi
	'Red Dragon' (R)	WDib
	'Red Flame' (R) **new**	NShi
	'Red Kiss' (R) **new**	NShi
	'Red Planet'	ERhR NShi WDib
	'Red Reign'	ERhR NShi
	'Red Robin' (R)	NShi WDib
	'Red Spider'	ERhR NShi
	'Red Undies' (*grandis*)	see *B. grandis subsp. sinensis* 'Red Undies'
	'Red Undies' (C)	NShi
	'Red Wing' (R)	NShi
	'Regal Minuet' (R)	LRHS NShi WDib
	'Reine des Neiges' (R)	NShi
	reniformis	ERhR NShi
	rex (R)	MBri NShi
	'Richard Galle' **new**	LAst
	'Richmondensis' (S)	ERhR EShb NShi
	'Ricinifolia'	ERhR GCal NShi
	'Ricky Minter' ♀H1	ERhR NShi
	'Rip van Winkle'	ERhR NShi
	'Robert Blais' (R)	NShi
	'Robin' (R)	ERhR NShi
	'Robin's Red' (C)	ERhR NShi
	'Rocheart' (R) ♀H1	NShi WDib
	'Roi de Roses' (R) ♀H1	ERhR NShi
	roxburghii	ERhR NShi
	'Royal Lustre'	ERhR NShi
	'Rubacon'	ERhR NShi
	rubro-setulosa	ERhR
	'Sabre Dance' (R)	ERhR NShi
	'Sachsen'	ERhR NShi
	'Saint Albans Grey'	NShi
	'Salamander' (R)	NShi
	'Sal's Comet' (R) ♀	NShi WDib
	'Sal's Moondust'	NShi WDib
	'San Diego Sunset' (R)	NShi
	sanguinea	ERhR NShi

'Savannah Pink Parfait' (R) NShi
'Scarlett O'Hara' (R) ERhR
scharffiana NShi
§ ***scharffii*** EBak ERhR NShi SDix
'Scherzo' ERhR NShi WDib
'Scottish Star' NShi
'Sea Captain' NShi
'Sea Serpent' ♀H1 NShi
'Secpuoc' ERhR
semperflorens hort. see *B.* Semperflorens Cultorum Group
§ Semperflorens Cultorum Group (S) MBri NShi
§ ***sericoneura*** ERhR NShi
'Serlis' ERhR NShi
serratipetala EBak ERhR EShb MBri NShi WDib
'Shamus' ERhR NShi
'Shaun Henthorn' (R) NShi
* ***sheperdii*** NShi WDib
'Shiloh' (R) ERhR NShi
* 'Shinihart' ERhR NShi
'Shoppy' NShi
'Sierra Mist' (C) ERhR NShi
sikkimensis GCal
'Silbreen' NShi
silletensis subsp. ***mengyangensis*** EBee GCal
'Silver Cloud' (R) ♀H1 ERhR NShi WDib
'Silver Dawn' (R) ERhR NShi
'Silver Dollar' NShi
'Silver Dots' NShi
'Silver Giant' (R) ERhR NShi
'Silver Jewell' NShi WDib
'Silver King' (R) ♀H1 NShi
'Silver Lace' NShi WDib
'Silver Mist' (C) ERhR NShi
'Silver Points' ERhR NShi
'Silver Queen' (R) ♀H1 NShi
'Silver Sweet' (R) ERhR NShi
'Silver Wings' ERhR NShi
'Sinbad' (C) ERhR NShi
sinensis see *B. grandis* subsp. *sinensis*
* 'Sir Charles' ERhR
'Sir John Falstaff' ERhR NShi
sizemoreae NShi WDib
Skeezar Group ERhR NShi
- 'Brown Lake' ERhR NShi
'Snow Storm' NShi
* 'Snowcap' (C) ♀H1 ERhR EShb NShi WDib
socotrana (T) ERhR
solananthera A. DC. ♀H1 ERhR EShb GGar NShi WDib
soli-mutata NShi WDib
sonderiana (T) GCal WBor
'Sophie's Jenny' NShi
'Speckled Roundabout' (T) NShi
'Speculata' (R) ERhR NShi
'Spellbound' ERhR NShi WDib
'Spindrift' ERhR NShi
'Spitfire'PBR **new** NShi
'Splotches' ERhR NShi
'Stained Glass' NShi WDib
'Stichael Maeae' ERhR
stipulacea ambig. ERhR NShi
subvillosa ERhR
'Sugar Plum' ERhR NShi
'Summer Maid' NShi
'Sun God' NShi
'Sun Set' NShi
(Super Olympia Series) LAst
'Super Olympia Red' (S) **new**
- 'Super Olympia Rose' (S) **new** LAst
- 'Super Olympia White' (S) **new** LAst
Superba Group (C) NShi
- 'Irene Nuss' (C) ♀H1 ERhR NShi
- 'Lana' (C) ERhR NShi
- 'Pink Jade' (C) NShi
- 'Sophie Cecile' (C) ♀H1 ERhR NShi
'Superba Azella' (C) NShi
sutherlandii (T) ♀H1 CAvo CCCN CFFs EABi EBak EOHP ERhR ERos EWld GGar LOck LPio NBir NPer NShi SBch SDix WCot WDib WEas WFar WHer
- 'Papaya' (T) CSpe LRHS
'Swan Song' ERhR
'Sweet Magic' ERhR NShi
'Swirly Top' (C) ERhR NShi
'Sylvan Triumph' (C) ERhR NShi
taiwaniana NShi
taliensis EDHCH 042 WCru
'Tapestry' ERhR NShi
'Tar Baby' (T) ERhR NShi
* ***taya*** WDib
'Tea Rose' ERhR NShi
'Tequesta' NShi
teuscheri ERhR NShi
'Texastar' ERhR NShi WDib
'The Wiz' ERhR NShi
thelmae ERhR NShi
thiemei WDib
§ - 'Purpurea' **new** NShi
'Think Pink' NShi
'Thrush' (R) NShi
'Thumotec' ERhR
'Thunderclap' ERhR NShi
'Thurstonii' ♀H1 ERhR EShb NShi
'Tickled Pink' LRHS
'Tiger Paws' ♀H1 CTsd ERhR MBri NShi
'Tim Anderson' (R) NShi
'Tingley Mallet' (Mallet Series) (C) ERhR NShi
'Tiny Bright' (R) ERhR NShi
'Tiny Gem' ERhR NShi
'Tom Ment' (C) ERhR NShi
'Tom Ment II' (C) ERhR NShi
'Tomoshiba' ERhR NShi
'Tondelayo' ERhR NShi
'Tornado' (R) NShi
'Tribute' ERhR NShi
'Trinidad' ERhR NShi
* ***tripartita*** (T) ERhR NShi WDib
'Trout' (C) NShi
'Tucson Bonfire' (R) NShi
'Twilight' ERhR NShi
'Two Face' ERhR NShi WDib
ulmifolia ERhR NShi
undulata (C) ERhR NShi
'Universe' ERhR NShi
'Valentine' (R) NShi
'Venetian Red' (R) ERhR NShi
venosa ERhR NShi
'Venus' ERhR NShi
'Vera Wyatt' NShi
'Verschaffeltii' ERhR NShi
versicolor ERhR
'Vesuvius' (R) NShi WDib
'Viaudii' ERhR NShi
'Viau-Scharff' ERhR
'Vista' (R) NShi
'Wally's World' NShi
'Wanda' NShi

'Weltonensis' ERhR NShi
'Weltoniensis Alba' (T) ERhR
'Westland Beauty' NShi
'White Cascade' ERhR
'White Ice' (C) new NShi
'Wild Swan' NShi WCru
williamsii Rusby & Nash see *B. wollnyi*
'Witchcraft' (R) ERhR NShi
'Withlacoochee' ERhR NShi WDib
§ ***wollnyi*** ERhR NShi
'Wood Nymph' (R) ERhR NShi
'Zuensis' ERhR

Beilschmiedia (*Lauraceae*)

berteroana new EBee IDee

Belamcanda (*Iridaceae*)

chinensis CArn CBro CHll CMea CPen EBee ELan EPfP EShb GKev GPoy MAvo MHer SDnm SIng SMrm SPav SPlb SRms WBrE WGwG WKif WPer
- B&SWJ 8692B WCru
- 'Freckle Face' EBee EKen LSou MSpe NBPC SGSe SPad SPoG
- 'Hello Yellow' EShb GBuc MAvo

Bellevalia (*Hyacinthaceae*)

atroviolacea EBrs ECho
brevipedicellata EBrs ECho
ciliata ECho ERos
'Cream Pearl' new ERCP
desertorum JCA 0.227.690 new WCot
dubia EBee ECho WCot WWst
forniculata ERos WWst
hackelii EBrs ECho ERos
hyacinthoides CStu ECho WCot
kurdistanica ERos
longipes ECho
* ***maura*** EBrs ECho
nivalis EBrs
§ ***paradoxa*** CBgR CHid CMea EBee EBrs ECho EHrv ERCP ERos LLHF LRHS
- white-flowered EBrs ECho
pycnantha misapplied see *B. paradoxa*
romana CPom EBee EBrs ECho ERCP ERos MTho SPhx WCot WHil
sarmatica ECho ERos
sessiliflora ECho
tabriziana ECho ERos WCot WWst
trifoliata new ECho
webbiana ECho ERos

Bellis (*Asteraceae*)

§ ***caerulescens*** GAbr NBro SIng
perennis CArn EBWF EDAr GKir NSco
- 'Alice' WCot
- 'Blue Moon' WCHb
- 'Changeling' WAlt
- 'Dresden China' ECho EWes GAbr MTho WCom
- 'Galaxy White' (Galaxy Series) EPfP
- Hen and Chickens see *B. perennis* 'Prolifera' single-flowered
- 'Hula' CNat
- 'Parkinson's Great White' GAbr
§ - 'Prolifera' single-flowered WAlt WCom WHer
- 'Red Buttons' NBlu
- 'Robert' GAbr
- 'Rusher Rose' EPfP
- 'Single Blue' see *B. caerulescens*
- 'The Pearl' WCot
- 'Upper Seagry' WAlt
rotundifolia 'Caerulescens' see *B. caerulescens*
sylvestris CArn

Bellium (*Asteraceae*)

* ***crassifolium canescens*** WPer
minutum MTho

Beloperone see *Justicia*

guttata see *Justicia brandegeeana*

Bensoniella (*Saxifragaceae*)

oregona CPLG

Benthamiella (*Solanaceae*)

nordenskjoldii new WAbe
patagonica WAbe
- F&W 9345 WAbe

Berberidopsis (*Flacourtiaceae*)

sp. GGal
beckleri WPGP
corallina Widely available

Berberis ✿ (*Berberidaceae*)

CC 4730 CPLG
SDR 4219 GKev
SF 06008 ISea
aetnensis GAuc
aggregata EMac GKir NBir SPer SRms
amurensis var. ***latifolia*** B&SWJ 4353 WCru
angulosa GCal
aquifolium see *Mahonia aquifolium*
- 'Fascicularis' see *Mahonia* × *wagneri* 'Pinnacle'
aristata Parker see *B. glaucocarpa*
asiatica CPLG GPoy
bealei see *Mahonia japonica* Bealei Group
'Blenheim' WFar
'Boughton Red' MBri
brevipaniculata Schneider GAuc
brevipedunculata Bean see *B. prattii*
× ***bristolensis*** SRms
N ***buxifolia*** 'Nana' misapplied see *B. microphylla* 'Pygmaea'
calliantha WFar
candidula C.K. Schneid. EBee EPfP GKir LRHS MBar MGan MMuc MSwo NHol NLar SLon SPer WDin
- 'Jytte' see *B.* 'Jytte'
× ***carminea*** 'Barbarossa' WDin
- 'Buccaneer' EPfP
- 'Pirate King' CSBt LRHS SPoG SWvt WFar WPat
chrysosphaera WFar
coxii GBin GGar
darwinii ♀H4 Widely available
I - 'Compacta' CMac EBee GKir LBuc LHop LRHS MAsh NBlu NEgg NLar SBch SPoG
dictyophylla ♀H4 CPMA EPfP ERas GKir LHop LRHS MGos NLar SEND SPer SPoG SSpi WDin WPat WSHC WSpi
dulcis 'Nana' see *B. microphylla* 'Pygmaea'
empetrifolia WSpi
× ***frikartii*** 'Amstelveen' ♀H4 CDoC EBee ECrN ELan EPfP GKir LAst LRHS MBNS MRav NHol NLar NPri WDin WFar
- 'Telstar' EBee ECrN LAst LBuc MGos MRav NLar NPro SLim WMoo
gagnepainii misapplied see *B. gagnepainii* var. *lanceifolia*
gagnepainii C.K. Schneid. CMac EBee EMac GKir NHol SLPl

§	- var. ***lanceifolia***	CTri EBee ECrN EPla GKir MBar MGos MMuc NHol NWea SLim WDin WFar
	- - 'Fernspray'	EPfP EPla MRav SBod SRms
	- 'Purpurea'	see *B.* × *interposita* 'Wallich's Purple'
	'Georgei' ♀H4	CMHG CWib EPfP GQui LRHS MAsh MBri SPoG
§	***glaucocarpa***	EPfP EPla NHol
	'Goldilocks'	CAbP CDul CPMA EPfP GKir LAst LSRN MBlu SEND SPoG SSpi
	goudotii B&SWJ 10769	WCru
	× ***hybridogagnepainii*** 'Chenaultii'	ELan NHol
	- 'Robin Hood'	WPat
	hypokerina	CMac GCal
	insignis	IDee WFar
	- subsp. ***insignis*** var. ***insignis***	WFar
	- - B&SWJ 2432	WCru
§	× ***interposita*** 'Wallich's Purple'	CCVT EBee ECrN EPfP MBar MDun MRav MSwo SPer WDin WMoo
	jamesiana	WPat
	julianae ♀H4	CBcs CDul CMac CTri EBee ECrN ELan EMac EPfP EWTr GKir LAst MBar MGan MGos MRav MSwo NHol NScw NWea SCoo SLPl SPer SRms SWvt WDin WFar WHar WSHC
§	'Jytte'	EBee EMil WDin
	kawakamii	SLPl
	koreana	EPfP NLar WFar
	- 'Rubin'	CAgr
	linearifolia	CMac
	- 'Orange King'	CBcs CDoC CMac CTri EBee ELan EPfP GKir LRHS MAsh MBlu MGos NEgg NLar NPri SCoo SPer SPoG WDin WFar WHar WPat
	'Little Favourite'	see *B. thunbergii* f. *atropurpurea* 'Atropurpurea Nana'
	× ***lologensis***	MGos WDin
	- 'Apricot Queen' ♀H4	CBcs CMac EBee EPfP GKir LRHS MAsh MGos MHav MRav NLar NPri SCoo SPer SPoG WDin WPat
	- 'Mystery Fire'	EBee GKir MAsh MBri MGos NHol NLar SPoG SWvt WDin WFar WHar WMoo
	- 'Stapehill'	CMac CSam ELan EPfP GKir LRHS MAsh NHol SPoG
	× ***media*** Park Jewel	see *B.* × *media* 'Parkjuweel'
§	- 'Parkjuweel'	CBcs CMac EBee ECrN IArd MRav NLar SCoo WDin WFar WMoo
	- 'Red Jewel' ♀H4	CDoC CMac EBee ECrN EPfP LRHS MGos MRav NLar SCoo SEND SPer SPoG WCFE WDin WFar WMoo
	microphylla	EPfP GKir LEdu WCFE
§	- 'Pygmaea'	CAbP CBcs CSBt EBee EPfP EWTr GKir LAst LRHS MAsh MBar MGos MRav NHol NLar NPri SPer SPoG WDin WFar
	mitifolia	NLar
	montana	WCFE WPGP WPat
	morrisonicola	GAuc
	× ***ottawensis*** 'Auricoma'	EBee SWvt
	- f. ***purpurea***	CMac CWib LRHS MGos SBod WDin WFar WHar
§	- - 'Superba' ♀H4	Widely available
§	- 'Silver Miles' (v)	EHoe EQua MRav NLar WFar WPat
§	***panlanensis***	MBar SLon
	poiretii	CPLG NLar
	polyantha misapplied	see *B. prattii*
§	***prattii***	GAuc

	- var. ***laxipendula***	SMad
	pruinosa	CDul
	'Red Tears'	CPMA CSam MBri MGos MRav NLar SPer WMoo
	× ***rubrostilla*** 'Cherry Ripe'	CMac
	sanguinea misapplied	see *B. panlanensis*
	sargentiana	SLPl
	sieboldii	LLHF MAsh MRav WCFE WPat WSpi
	soulieana	EPfP LRHS MGan
	× ***stenophylla*** Lindl. ♀H4	CBcs CCVT CDoC CDul CSBt CTri EBee ECrN EPfP GKir LBuc LRHS MBar MBri MRav NWea SEND SPer SPoG WCFE WDin WFar WHar WMoo
	- 'Claret Cascade'	LRHS MBri MGos MMuc MRav NHol NLar SEND SPer WFar
	- 'Coccinea'	EPla
	- 'Corallina Compacta' ♀H4	CMac CMea ECho ELan EPfP EPot GKir LHop LRHS MAsh NRya SIng SPer SPoG SRms WAbe WPat
	- 'Crawley Gem'	GBin MBar MGos NHol NLar WFar
	- 'Etna'	ELan LRHS MAsh SPoG
	- 'Irwinii'	CMac EBee ERas LAst LRHS MBar MGos SPer WFar
	- 'Nana'	LRHS SRms
	- 'Pink Pearl' (v)	CMHG MGos
	temolaica ♀H4	CGHE CPMA CSam EBtc EPfP ERas GKir MDun MGos MRav MSnd NEgg NLar NSti NWea SDnm SMad SPer SSpi SSta WAbe WDin WPGP WPat WSpi
	thunbergii ♀H4	CBcs CDoC CDul CMac CSBt EMac EPfP GBin GKir LBuc MRav NLar NWea SCoo SPer SPlb SPoG SWvt WDin WFar
	- f. ***atropurpurea***	CBcs CCVT CDul CMac CSBt CTri EBee EMac EPfP ISea LAst LBuc LRHS MAsh MBar MGan MGos MSwo NEgg NLar NWea SCoo SPer SPoG WBVN WDin WFar WMoo
	- - 'Admiration' PBR	CAbP CBcs CDoC CEnd ELan EPfP LBuc LLHF LRHS LSRN LSqu MAsh MBri MGos MMHG NCGa NEgg NPri NPro SBch SCoo SLon SPer SPoG SWvt WClo WPat
§	- - 'Atropurpurea Nana' ♀H4	Widely available
	- - 'Bagatelle' ♀H4	CDoC EBee ELan EPfP EPot GKir IArd LAst LBMP LHop LRHS LSRN MAsh MBar MBri MGos MLHP MRav NEgg NHol NPri SLim SPer SPoG SWvt WCFE WClo WDin WFar WPat
	- - 'Carmen'	MGos
	- - 'Dart's Purple'	WFar
	- - 'Dart's Red Lady'	CPLG CPMA CSBt CWib EBee ECrN EHoe ELan EPfP LRHS LSRN MAsh MBri MRav NLar NPro SCoo SLim SPer SPoG SWvt WDin WFar WPat
	- - 'Golden Ring' ♀H4	CBcs CDoC CDul EBee EHoe EPfP EWTr GKir LHop LRHS LSRN MAsh MBNS MBar MDun MGos MRav NEgg NHol SLim SPer SPoG SWvt WClo WDin WFar WHar WMoo WPat
	- - 'Harlequin' (v)	CBcs CDoC EBee ELan EPfP GKir LRHS LSRN MAsh MBri MGos MRav NEgg SBch SLim SPer SPoG SWvt WClo WDin WFar WHar WPat
	- - 'Helmond Pillar'	Widely available
	- - 'Red Chief' ♀H4	CBcs CMHG EBee ECrN EHoe ELan EPfP GKir LRHS LSRN MAsh MGos

	MMuc MRav MSwo NEgg NPri SBch SLim SLon SPer SPoG SWvt WDin WFar WHar WMoo WPat
- - 'Red King'	MRav WDin
- - 'Red Pillar'	CDoC CMac EBee EHoe ELan EPfP LAst LRHS MAsh MBar MGos MWat NEgg NHol NLar SWvt WDin WFar WPat
- - 'Red Rocket'	LBuc LRHS MBri MCCP MGos NLar
- - 'Rose Glow' (v) ♀H4	Widely available
- - 'Rosy Rocket' (v) new	LBuc LRHS MGos SPoG
- 'Atropurpurea Superba'	see *B.* × *ottawensis* f. *purpurea* 'Superba'
- 'Aurea'	Widely available
- Bonanza Gold = 'Bogozam'PBR	CBcs CDoC EBee ELan EPfP GKir LBMP LRHS MAsh MRav NCGa NLar SLim SPer SPoG WDin WFar WPat
- 'Boum'	EMil MAsh
- 'Carpetbagger'	WHar
- 'Coronita'	MBri
- 'Crimson Pygmy'	see *B. thunbergii* f. *atropurpurea* 'Atropurpurea Nana'
- 'Diabolic' new	LRHS WClo
- 'Erecta'	CMac EPfP MBar MGos MRav SPer WCFE WDin
- 'Gold Ring' new	ELan MMuc
- 'Golden Carpet'	SBch
- 'Golden Rocket'	LBuc LLHF LRHS MAsh MGos SPer SPoG
- 'Golden Torch'	CSBt EBee ELan EMil EPfP LRHS LSRN MBri MRav NEgg SBch SWvt WPat
- 'Green Carpet'	CMac EBee GKir LHop LRHS MBar MBlu NLar SPoG WFar
- 'Green Mantle'	see *B. thunbergii* 'Kelleriis'
- 'Green Marble'	see *B. thunbergii* 'Kelleriis'
- 'Green Ornament'	NHol
- 'Green Ring'	EQua
§ - 'Kelleriis' (v)	CDoC LHop LRHS MBar MGos MMuc MRav NHol NLar NPro SLon WClo WDin WFar
- 'Kobold'	EBee EPfP LHop LRHS MAsh MBar MGos NEgg NHol NLar SLim SPer SPoG WFar
- 'Maria'PBR	LLHF LRHS LSou MGos NCGa NEgg NHol SPoG WBrE WHar
- 'Moia' new	EKen
- 'Painter's Palette' (v) new	LRHS MGos
- 'Pink Queen' (v)	CDul EBee ELan EPfP EWTr LHop LRHS MAsh SPur WDin WFar WHar WPat
- 'Pow-wow'	CBcs EBee LRHS MGos NEgg NLar SCoo SLim SPoG SWvt WDin WPat
- 'Silver Beauty' (v)	CBcs CMHG ELan MGos MSwo WDin
- 'Silver Mile'	see *B.* × *ottawensis* 'Silver Miles'
- 'Starburst'PBR (v)	CBcs CDoC CDul CSBt EPfP LRHS LSRN MAsh MBri MGos NEgg NPri SBch SCoo SLon SPoG SWvt
- 'Tiny Gold'	CEnd LBuc LRHS LSRN LSqu MAsh MGos NPro SLim SLon SPoG SWvt
* - 'Tricolor' (v)	CMac MRav WFar WPat
valdiviana	CBcs CDul CGHE CPLG CPMA EBee EPfP EPla SMad SSpi WPGP WPat
verruculosa ♀H4	CBcs CChe EBee EPfP GKir LAst LHop LRHS MBar MGan MGos NHol NLar NWea SCoo SEND SPer SRms SWvt WCFE WDin WFar
- 'Hard's Rob'	NLar
aff. ***verticillata*** B&SWJ 10672	WCru
virescens B&SWJ 2646D	WCru
vulgaris	CArn CNat EMac EPfP GPoy MCoo
- 'Wiltshire Wonder' (v)	CNat
wilsoniae	CBcs CDul CMac CTri EBee ELan EMac EPfP GKir LHop MBar MMuc NHol NWea SCoo SPer WCFE WClo WDin WFar
- L 650	CGHE WPGP
- blue-leaved	MAsh WFar WPat
- var. ***guhtzunica***	EPla EWes

Berchemia (*Rhamnaceae*)

racemosa	CMen NLar WSHC

bergamot see *Citrus bergamia*

Bergenia ✿ (*Saxifragaceae*)

'Abendglocken'	ECGP ECha ECtt EPfP GKir LRHS MNFA NGdn NSti WCom WCot WEas WFar
§ 'Abendglut'	Widely available
'Admiral'	CBct CMoH ECha MLHP WCot
* ***agavifolia***	CBct
'Andrea' new	WCot
'Apple Court White'	CBct
'Autumn Magic'	CBct COIW EBee GAbr GQue LAst LHop LRHS LSou NEgg NPri SPoG WFar WSpi
'Baby Doll'	Widely available
'Bach'	WCot
§ 'Ballawley' clonal ♀H4	CMoH EBrs ECha GCal IBlr IGor LRHS MLHP MRav NEgg WCot WFar WMnd WWEG
'Ballawley Guardsman'	CBct EBee EHrv
§ Ballawley hybrids	EBee SDix WSpi
'Ballawley Red'	GBin NEgg
'Ballawley' seed-raised	see *B.* Ballawley hybrids
'Bartók'	WCot
beesiana	see *B. purpurascens*
'Beethoven'	CBct CDes CMoH EBee ECha GCra IGor MRav NBir NBre SUsu WCot WPGP
Bell Tower	see *B.* 'Glockenturm'
'Biedermeir'	ECha
'Bizet'	CBct
'Borodin'	CBct
'Brahms'	CBct GBuc WCot
'Bressingham Beauty'	GKir
'Bressingham Bountiful'	CBct
'Bressingham Ruby'PBR	CBcs CBct CLAP EBee EBrs ECha ECtt EPPr GKir LAst LBMP LRHS LSRN MGos MRav NBir NCGa NEgg WCot WPGP WSpi
'Bressingham Salmon'	CBct CHar CMoH EBee ELan ELon GMaP LRHS LSRN MBri MRav WCot WMnd
'Bressingham White' ♀H4	Widely available
'Britten'	WCot
ciliata	CDes CHEx CLAP EBla EBrs EShb GCal IFro LEdu LRHS MCot MLHP MRav NBir NHol NLar SDix SUsu WCom WKif WPGP WSHC WTin
- f. ***ciliata***	CBct WCot
- f. ***ligulata***	see *B. pacumbis*
- 'Patricia Furness'	CLAP
- 'Wilton'	CBct CLAP WCot
ciliata × ***crassifolia***	see *B.* × *schmidtii*
'Claire Maxine'	GCal

cordifolia	Widely available
- 'Flore Pleno'	CBct
- 'Jelle'	GBin
- 'Purpurea' ♀H4	CBcs CDoC EAEE EBee ECha ELan EMFW EPfP GKir LBuc LRHS MLHP MNFA MRav NBir NEgg SMrm SPer SRms WFar WPnP
- 'Rosa Schwester'	EBee ECha
- 'Rosa Zeiten'	GBin
- 'Tubby Andrews' (v)	CBct CBow EBla ECtt LEdu LLHF LRHS MAvo MBel MBrN MBri MCCP MDKP NEgg NLar NPro SBch WCom WWEG
- 'Vinterglöd'	EBee ELan ELon GMaP IBal IFoB LRHS NBre NGdn SWvt WFar WHil WPnP
crassifolia	EBee GKev NBre SRms WWEG
- 'Autumn Red'	CBct CMoH ECha
- 'Orbicularis'	see *B.* × *schmidtii*
* ***cyanea***	CLAP WCot
'David'	ECha EWes
'Delbees'	see *B.* 'Ballawley' clonal
'Doppelgänger'	EBee SUsu
'Eden's Dark Margin'	CBct EBee LDai NPro
'Eden's Magic Carpet'	CFir
'Eden's Magic Giant'	CBct EBee EWll GBin MBNS
emeiensis	CDes CLAP CPom IMou SMrs WCot WPGP
- hybrid	CBct
'Eric Smith'	CBct EBee ECha GBin GCal IGor MBri WCot WMnd
'Eroica'	CBct COlW CSpe EBee ECha ECtt ELan EPfP GBin LAst LHop LRHS MBri MMuc MRav NBre NSti SPoG WCAu WMnd WPtf WSpi
'Evening Glow'	see *B.* 'Abendglut'
'Frau Holle'	EBee MBri
§ 'Glockenturm'	CBct NEgg
'Harzkristall' **new**	GQue
'Hellen Dillon'	see *B. purpurascens* 'Irish Crimson'
'Herbstblute'	EBee
'Jo Watanabe'	CBct MRav
'Lambrook'	see *B.* 'Margery Fish'
§ 'Margery Fish'	CBct ECha SPer
milesii	see *B. stracheyi*
§ 'Morgenröte' ♀H4	CBcs CBct EBee EBrs ECha ELon EPfP GEdr GKir GMaP LAst LRHS LSRN MGos MRav NHol NSti SBch SPer SRms SWvt WCAu WCFE WCot WWEG
'Morning Light'	EBee ECtt NPro
Morning Red	see *B.* 'Morgenröte'
'Mrs Crawford'	CBct ECha
'Oeschberg'	CBct GBin GCal WCAu
'Opal'	CBct
'Overture'	CBct CSpe EBee ECtt EHrv ELan ELon GEdr LAst LDai LHop LRHS LSRN MAvo MBri MNFA NCGa NCob NGby NGdn SUsu WCAu WCot WFar WWEG WWFP
§ ***pacumbis***	CDes CHEx CLAP EBtc GBin GEdr NBid NBre NSti WCot WSpi
- CC 1793	SBch
- CC 3616	CBct WCot
'Perfect'	CBct EBee WMnd
'Pink Dragonfly'	CWGN EBee GBin LHop LRHS NBhm SPoG WCot
'Pink Ice' **new**	CBct
'Pinneberg'	GBin
'Pugsley's Pink'	CBct GCra
'Purple Queen'	LRHS
§ ***purpurascens*** ♀H4	CMoH EBee EPfP GBuc GKev GMaP IFoB IGor LRHS MBrN SBch SDix SPer WCot WTin WWEG
- SDR 3978	GKev
- SDR 4548	GKev
§ - 'Irish Crimson'	CBct CGHE WCot
- var. ***delavayi*** ♀H4	EBrs LRHS MBri NBre SRms
- - CLD 1366	WPer
aff. ***purpurascens*** ACE 2175	WCot
'Red Beauty'	CMoH IMon LRHS MGos MSnd SBch WPnP
'Reitheim'	CBct EBee
'Rosi Klose'	Widely available
'Rosi Ruffles'	EBee MBNS
'Rotblum'	CBct EBee ECGP ECtt EHoe ELon EPfP GMaP IMon LAst NBir NCob NGdn NOrc NVic WClo WFar WPer
§ × ***schmidtii*** ♀H4	CBct CMac IGor LRHS MRav NBir NBre WCot
'Schneekissen'	CBct CMac CPrp EBee ECGP LRHS MRav WCAu
§ 'Schneekoenigin'	CBct ECha GBin MRav
§ 'Silberlicht' ♀H4	Widely available
Silverlight	see *B.* 'Silberlicht'
'Simply Sweet'	WCot
Snow Queen	see *B.* 'Schneekoenigin'
'Solar Flare' (v) **new**	CBow WCot
§ ***stracheyi***	CBct CMoH CPLG EBee ECha EGoo GCal IGor MLHP MRav NBid NLar SApp SDix WCot WEas
- CC 4609	GKev
- CC 5225	GKev
- Alba Group	CBct CDes CMoH EBee ECha GCal SUsu WPGP
'Sunningdale'	CBcs CBct CMac EBee ECha ECrN ELan EMFW EPfP GCra GKir GMaP LHop LRHS MBel MRav NBir NGdn SWvt WCAu WClo WMnd
tianquanensis	CDes
'Walter Kienli'	EBee GBin
Winter Fairy Tales	see *B.* 'Wintermärchen'
§ 'Wintermärchen'	CBct CChe EBee ECha ECtt ELan ELon EPfP GCra LAst LRHS MGos MMuc MRav NCGa NHol NPro NSti SBch SPoG WCAu WCot WMnd WWEG

Bergeranthus (*Aizoaceae*)

sp.	WThu
multiceps	SChr
scapiger	WCot

Berkheya (*Asteraceae*)

draco	EWld
multijuga	ELon GMac MMuc SBHP WHil WSHC
purpurea	Widely available
- 'Silver Spike'	EPfP LBMP LLWG LRHS LSRN MBri WCon
- 'Zulu Warrior'	CEnt EDif EKen IPot LSou NGBl SBHP SRkn
radula	EBee

Berlandiera (*Asteraceae*)

lyrata	EBee

Berneuxia (*Diapensiaceae*)

thibetica	IBlr

Berula (*Apiaceae*)

erecta	EMFW NPer

Berzelia (*Bruniaceae*)

	galpinii	SPlb
	lanuginosa	CTrC GGar

Beschorneria (*Agavaceae*)

	albiflora	EBee WPGP
	rigida new	WPGP
	septentrionalis	CAbP CDTJ CFir CGHE CSpe CTrC EAmu EBee ECGP ESwi LOck LRHS LSou MBNS MSCN SBch SPad WClo WCot WGrn WPGP WPat
	tubiflora	CDTJ CHEx EBee
	wrightii	EBee WPGP
	yuccoides ♀^{H3}	CAbb CBcs CHEx CTrC CWit EAmu EBee EShb ESwi IBlr IDee ISea LEdu NVic SAPC SArc SDnm SEND SLim
	- subsp. ***dekosteriana*** F&M 102	WPGP
	- 'Quicksilver'	CBcs CCCN CDoC CEnd CKno CTrC EBee EPfP LRHS MBri MGos SBch SDix SDnm SSpi WBrE WCot WGrn WPGP

Bessera (*Alliaceae*)

	elegans	CAvo CFFs CFir EBee EBrs ECho EPot LAma LRHS WCot

Beta (*Chenopodiaceae*)

	trigyna	WCom WCot
	vulgaris	WHer
	- 'Bull's Blood'	CArn CSpe WJek
	- subsp. ***cicla***	CArn MMuc
	var. ***flavescens*** 'Bright Lights' ♀^{H3}	
	- - - 'Rhubarb Chard' ♀^{H3}	MMuc WJek
	- subsp. ***maritima***	CAgr EBWF

Betonica see *Stachys*

Betula ✿ (*Betulaceae*)

	alba L.	see *B. pendula*, *B. pubescens*
	albosinensis misapplied	see *B. utilis*
	albosinensis Burkill ♀^{H4}	CDul CLnd CMCN CTri EBee EPfP EWTr ISea NLar NWea WDin WFar
	- W 4106	CSto
	- from Gansu, China	CSto
	- 'Bowling Green'	CPMA WPGP
	- 'China Ruby'	CDul CLnd CPMA GKir LRHS MBri SMad SSpi
	- 'Chinese Garden'	CPMA MBlu
	- 'Clarenville' new	WPGP
	- clone F	see *B. albosinensis* 'Ness'
	- 'Fascination'	LMaj
	- 'K.Ashburner'	CPMA CTho
	- 'Kansu'	CEnd CLnd CPMA EBee GKir LRHS SBig SCoo SMad SSpi WHCr
§	- 'Ness'	CPMA CTho
	- 'Pink Champagne'	CSto
	- 'Rhinegold'	MBlu
	- 'Sable'	SLim SPer
	- var. ***septentrionalis*** ♀^{H4}	Widely available
	- - 'Purdom'	CPMA GKir SBig SMad
§	***alleghaniensis***	CCVT CDul CMCN CSto EBee ECrN EPfP GKir IDee IFFs MMuc NLar NWea WDin
	alnoides B&SWJ 11751	WCru
	apoiensis 'Mount Apoi'	CPMA GKir LRHS SBig
§	× ***caerulea***	NLar WSpi
	caerulea-grandis	see *B.* × *caerulea*
	calcicola new	MAsh
	chichibuensis	CSto EPla SBir WHer
	'Conyngham'	CPMA CTho MBlu SLau
	cordifolia	see *B. papyrifera* var. *cordifolia*
	costata misapplied	see *B. ermanii* 'Grayswood Hill'
	costata ambig.	CMCN ECrN MMuc
	costata Trautv.	CLnd CTho EBee ELan GKir MSwo WDin
*	- 'Fincham Cream'	CPMA EBee GKir LRHS SBig WHCr
I	× ***cruithnei***	GAuc
	cylindrostachya	EBee
	dahurica Pall.	CDul CMCN CSto GAuc IArd
	- B&SWJ 8462	WCru
	- 'Maurice Foster'	CPMA CTho SBir
	- 'Stone Farm'	CPMA
	delavayi	EBee GKir
	ermanii	Widely available
	- B&SWJ 8801 from South Korea	WCru
	- from Hokkaido, Japan	CSto
	- 'Blush'	CLnd CPMA GKir LRHS MBlu SBig SCoo WHCr
	- var. ***ermanii***	EBee LSRN
	- - MSF 825	EBee
	- - MSF 865	WPGP
§	- 'Grayswood Hill' ♀^{H4}	CDul CEnd CLnd CMHG CPMA CSBt CTho CTri EBee GKir GQui LRHS MAsh MBlu MBri MGos NWea SCoo SLim SMad SPer SSpi WHCr WPGP
	- 'Hakkoda Orange'	CPMA CTho EBee GKir MBri SCoo
	- 'Holland'	LMaj
	- 'Moonbeam'	EBee GKir SMad
	- 'Mount Zao'	CSto
*	- 'Pendula'	CPMA EBee MBlu SBig SBir SCoo SMad
	- 'Polar Bear'	CPMA CWSG EBee GKir LRHS MBlu MBri SCoo SMad WHCr WHar
*	- ***ussuriensis***	GKir
	- 'Zao Purple' new	CDul
	'Fetisowii'	CDul CEnd CMCN CPMA CTho EBee ECrN GKir LRHS MBlu SBig SCoo SSta
	fruticosa	see *B. humilis*
	globispica	CPMA
	'Hergest'	EBee EPfP GKir LRHS MAsh MBri MGos NPal SCoo SLau SLim SMad SPoG WHCr WPGP
§	***humilis***	GKir GQui WDin
	insignis	CSto
	'Inverleith'	see *B. utilis* var. *jacquemontii* 'Inverleith'
	jacquemontii	see *B. utilis* var. *jacquemontii*
	kamtschatica	see *B. humilis*
	lenta	CDul CMCN CSto EPfP IArd IDee IFFs MBlu MMuc NLar NWea WDin
	luminifera	CPMA EBee EBtc GKir IDee NLar SBir
	lutea	see *B. alleghaniensis*
§	***mandshurica***	CSto GQui NEgg WHCr
§	- var. ***japonica***	ECrN GKir MSnd NLar NWea
	- - 'Whitespire Senior'	CDul
	maximowicziana	CDoC CDul CLnd CMCN CTho CWib EPfP LHop LRHS NLar WDin
	medwedewii	CDul CMCN CSto EBee EPfP GQui NHol SCoo
	- 'Gold Bark'	CMCN MBlu
	michauxii	GKev NLar
	nana	CDul GAuc GKir MBar MGos MRav NHol NWea SRms SSta STre WDin
	- 'Glengarry'	EPot GEdr NLar
	nigra	CBcs CCVT CDoC CDul CEnd CLnd CMCN CSBt CTho CTri EBee

		ECrN LMaj MAsh MBri NWea SSta WDin WFar WMou
	- Dura-Heat = 'BNMTF' **new**	MGos
	- Heritage = 'Cully' ♀H4	CDul CLnd CPMA EBee LHop LRHS MGos SBig SBir SCoo SLim SPoG SSta WDin WFar WHCr WMoo
	- 'Little King'	CPMA MGos SPoG
	- 'Summer Cascade'	LRHS MBri
	- Tecumseh Compact = 'Studetec' **new**	MBlu
	- Wakehurst form	EPfP GKir SPer
	papyrifera	Widely available
	- var. ***commutata***	WDin
§	- var. ***cordifolia***	CSto
	- 'Saint George'	CPMA CTho LRHS
	- 'Vancouver'	CPMA CTho
§	***pendula*** ♀H4	Widely available
	- 'Bangor'	CLnd CPMA
	- 'Bibor' **new**	LRHS
*	- 'Boeugh's Variety'	GBin
	- f. ***crispa***	see *B. pendula* 'Laciniata'
	- 'Dalecarlica' misapplied	see *B. pendula* 'Laciniata'
	- 'Dalecarlica' ambig.	CBcs CCVT CSBt ECrN LRHS MDun MRav SCrf SLim WFar
	- 'Dark Prince'	CPMA
	- 'Fastigiata'	CDoC CDul CEnd CLnd CSBt CTho EBee ECrN ELan GKir LMaj LRHS MGos NEgg NWea SCoo SLim SPer WDin WFar WMoo
*	- 'Golden Beauty'	CDoC CMac EBee ECrN ELon GKir IFFs LRHS MAsh MGos NLar NPal SBch SCoo SLim SPer SPoG SSpi WDin WFar
	- 'Golden Cloud'	CMac LAst
§	- 'Laciniata' ♀H4	Widely available
	- 'Long Trunk'	CDul EBee ECrN EMil LRHS LSRN MAsh MBlu SLim
	- 'Purpurea'	CCVT CDul CLnd CMCN CMac CSBt CWib EBee ECrN ELan ELon EPfP EWTr LAst LRHS LSRN MGos MSwo NBea SBch SCoo SPer WDin WFar
	- 'Silver Grace'	EBee ECrN LSRN SSpi
	- 'Swiss Glory'	CLnd LMaj
	- 'Tristis' ♀H4	Widely available
	- 'Youngii'	Widely available
	platyphylla misapplied	see *B. mandshurica*
	platyphylla Sukaczev	CMCN NWea
	- Dakota Pinnacle = 'Fargo'	EBee LRHS SPoG
	populifolia	CSto
§	***pubescens***	CCVT CDul CLnd CSto CTri ECrN IFFs NBlu NWea SLPl WDin WFar WMou
I	***refugia***	GAuc
	'Royal Frost'	CDul CPMA EBee GKir IArd LRHS NLar SLim SPoG WHar
	saposhnikovii	GKir
	schmidtii	EWTr
	szechuanica	GQui NEgg NPCo WDin WPGP
	- 'Liuba White'	CPMA CTho
	- 'Moonlight'	SLau
	'Trost's Dwarf'	CBcs WDin WFoF
§	***utilis***	CDul CMCN CMHG CSBt CSto ECrN EMil ERas LMaj MAsh MBar NWea SSta WDin WFar WPGP
	- BL&M 100 from central Nepal **new**	CSto
	- H&M 1480 from Sichuan, China	CSto
	- RSC 1 from Langtang, Nepal	CSto
	- S&L from Nepal **new**	CDul
	- SICH 667 from Sichuan, China	CSto
	- Yu 10163 from Yunnan, China	CSto
	- from Eastern Nepal	CSto
	- from Uttar Pradesh, India	GAuc
	- 'Buckland'	ECrN
	- 'Darkness'	SLon
	- 'Fascination'	CCVT CDul CEnd CPMA EBee EPfP GKir IArd LRHS MBri MGos NWea SBir SCoo SLim SSpi WHCr
*	- 'Fastigiata'	CLnd CPMA SBig
	- 'Forrest's Blush'	CDul CEnd CLnd CPMA EBee LRHS LSRN MBri SBig SBir
	- 'Himalayan Pink'	WSpi
N	- var. ***jacquemontii***	Widely available
	- - Polunin	WPGP
	- - SF 00004	ISea
	- - 'Doorenbos' ♀H4	Widely available
	- - 'Grayswood Ghost' ♀H4	CDul CEnd CMCN CMHG CPMA CTho ECrN EPfP GKir LRHS MBlu MDun NWea SBig SBir SLau SLim SMad SPer SSpi
§	- - 'Inverleith'	CDul CEnd CLnd CPMA EBee GKir LRHS MAsh MBri SBig SBir SCoo SLim WFar WPGP
	- - 'Jermyns' ♀H4	CDul CEnd CLnd CMac CPMA CTho CTri EBee EPfP GKir LMaj LRHS MBlu MBri SCoo SLau SMad SPer SSpi WHCr
	- - 'McBeath'	SLau
	- - 'Silver Shadow' ♀H4	CDul CEnd CPMA CTho EBee EPfP GKir LRHS LSRN MBlu NWea SBig SBir SCoo SLau SLim SMad SPer SSpi SSta WSpi
	- - 'Trinity College'	CPMA EBee GKir MBri SBig SBir SSpi WHCr
	- 'Knightshayes'	CTho
	- 'Moonbeam'	CDul CLnd CPMA GKir LRHS MAsh MBri SBig SBir SCoo SPur WHar
	- var. ***occidentalis*** 'Kyelang'	CPMA CTho LRHS
	- 'Polar Bear'	GKir
	- var. ***prattii***	CEnd MBlu
	- 'Ramdana River'	CLnd
	- 'Wakehurst Place Chocolate'	CDul CLnd CPMA CSBt CWSG GKir LRHS MBlu MBri SBig SCoo SLim SMad SSpi WHCr
	cf. ***utilis*** GWJ 9259	WCru
	- HWJK 2345	WCru
	verrucosa	see *B. pendula*

Biarum (*Araceae*)

S&L 604	WCot
SB&L 597	WCot
arundanum	WCot
bovei	EBrs ECho WCot
carratracense	WCot
davisii	EBee EBrs ECho EPot WCot
- subsp. ***marmarisense***	ECho WCot WWst
dispar	WCot
- SB&L 294	WCot
- SB&L 564	WCot
ditschianum	WCot
galianii PB 435	WCot
ochridense	EBrs WCot
tenuifolium	EBee EBrs ECho ERos WCot
- LB 295	WCot
- PB 357	WCot
- SL 174	WCot
- subsp. ***abbreviatum***	WWst
- - MS 974	WCot

- - from Greece	ECho
- subsp. ***idomenaeum*** MS 738	WCot
- subsp. ***zelebori***	WCot
- - LB 300	WCot
- - PB 224	WCot
- - PB 334	WCot

Bidens (*Asteraceae*)

B&SWJ 10276 from Mexico	WCru
atrosanguinea	see *Cosmos atrosanguineus*
§ ***aurea***	CEnt EBee EBla ECtt EPPr EWes GCal GGar LAst LEdu MDKP MNrw NCGa NPer SAga SGar SPet SPhx STes WBor WFar WOld
- 'Blacksmith's Flame'	EBla
- 'Cream Streaked Yellow' **new**	GCal WPrP
- cream-flowered	MNrw
- B&SWJ 9049 from Guatemala	WCru
- 'Golden Drop'	EBee EWes
- 'Hannay's Lemon Drop'	CEnt CKno CPen CSev EBee EBla ECtt ELon EPPr EPfP GCal LHop MDKP MNrw NCGa SAga SPoG SSvw STes SUsu WHrl WPGP
- 'Julia's Gold' **new**	STes
- 'Rising Sun'	EBee EWes
- white-flowered **new**	GCal
ferulifolia ♀H1+3	ECtt MBel NPer
- Peter's Gold Carpet = 'Peters Goldteppich' PBR	SVil
- Peter's Gold Rush = 'Topteppich' PBR	LSou NPri
- Peter's Surprise = 'Petersurpr' **new**	SVil
- Solaire = 'Bidtis 1'	WGor
'Golden Star'	LAst LSou
heterophylla misapplied	CAby CEnt CKno ECtt MCot MRav MWat SMrm WFar WHal WHrl WMoo WPrP WWlt
- CD&R 1515	LPla
heterophylla Ortega	see *B. aurea*
humilis	see *B. triplinervia* var. *macrantha*
integrifolia	SMad
pilosa	EBee
triplinervia B&SWJ 10413	WCru
- B&SWJ 10696	WCru
§ - var. ***macrantha***	EBee ELon LHop

Bignonia (*Bignoniaceae*)

capreolata	CCCN EBee WCot WSHC
§ - 'Atrosanguinea'	LRHS
- 'Dragon Lady'	WCot
lindleyana	see *Clytostoma calystegioides*
tweedieana	see *Macfadyena unguis-cati*
unguis-cati	see *Macfadyena unguis-cati*

Bilderdykia see *Fallopia*

Billardiera (*Pittosporaceae*)

longiflora ♀H3	CBcs CMac CSBt CTri CWib EBee ECou ELan EMil EPfP GGar GQui IArd LHop LPio LRHS LSRN MAsh MGos MRav NHol SLim SPer SPoG SSpi SWvt WBrE WPGP WPat WSHC
- 'Cherry Berry'	CBcs CWan EBee ELan GAbr IArd IDee LPio LRHS LSRN MAsh MCCP NLar SLim SPer SPoG SRms SWvt WSHC
- ***fructu-albo***	CBcs EBee ELan EWes GGar GKev IDee SLim SPer SPoG SWvt
- red-berried	GGar
- white-berried	LRHS SLon

Billbergia (*Bromeliaceae*)

nutans	CBen CHEx CHll CPen EBak EOHP EShb ESwi IBlr IDee IMou LEdu LRHS MBri MRav NPal SChr SEND SRms WCor WGwG WSFF
- var. ***schimperiana***	EShb
* - 'Variegata' (v)	CFir CHll CSpe EShb NPal SChr WCom WCot
pyramidalis ♀H1	XBlo
I - 'Variegata' (v)	IBlr
× ***windii*** ♀H1	CFir CHEx EBak SRms

Bismarckia (*Arecaceae*)

nobilis	EAmu LPal NScw SBig WCot

Bistorta see *Persicaria*

Bituminaria (*Papilionaceae*)

bituminosa	WSHC

blackberry see *Rubus fruticosus*

blackcurrant see *Ribes nigrum*

Blechnum (*Blechnaceae*)

alpinum	see *B. penna-marina* subsp. *alpinum*
auriculatum	WRic
brasiliense ♀H1	WRic
chambersii	WRic
§ ***chilense*** ♀H3	CBty CDTJ CDes CGHE CHEx CLAP EBee EFtx EPfP GCal GCra GGar IBlr MMoz NVic SAPC SArc SBig SDix SGSe WCru WMoo WPGP WRic
colensoi	WRic
discolor	CBcs CLAP CTrC GBin IDee LPal WRic
fluviatile	CBcs CDTJ CLAP CTrC GBin IDee MMoz SGSe WRic
fraseri	WRic
gibbum	EFtx EShb MBri
- 'Silver Lady'	CTrC WRic
magellanicum misapplied	see *B. chilense*
magellanicum (Desv.) Mett.	EBee EFtx SBig WPGP WRic
minus	CBty MGos WRic
§ ***niponicum***	EBee
novae-zelandiae	CBcs CDTJ CTrC GBin WRic
nudum	CBty CDTJ EAmu EFtx EPfP EQua MAsh NMoo WRic
penna-marina ♀H4	CCCN CElw CLAP CPLG EFer EFtx EPot GAbr GCal GGar GMaP LEdu MAvo MBri NBir NRya NVic NWCA SIng SRms WAbe WFib WMoo WRic
§ - subsp. ***alpinum***	CLAP EBee ECha GGar GKev SGSe WAbe WMoo
- 'Cristatum'	CLAP GAbr GGar SRms WPGP
punctulatum	WRic
spicant ♀H4	Widely available
tabulare misapplied	see *B. chilense*
tabulare (Thunb.) Kuhn ♀H1	CBcs CDTJ EFtx EPfP GGal NMun WPGP WRic
vulcanicum	CLAP WRic

Blepharocalyx (*Myrtaceae*)

cruckshanksii	CPLG
- 'Heaven Scent'	CCCN EBee GGar LAst LRHS MCCP NLar WBor

Bletilla ✿ (*Orchidaceae*)

hyacinthina	see *B. striata*
ochracea	CPLG EBee NLAp WCot WWst
Penway Bouquet gx new	NLAp
Penway Classic gx new	NLAp
Penway Coral gx new	NLAp
Penway Fancy gx new	NLAp
Penway Fantasy gx new	NLAp
Penway Harlequin gx new	NLAp
Penway Majestic gx new	NLAp
Penway Paris gx	NLAp
Penway Pixie gx new	NLAp
Penway Prelude gx new	NLAp
Penway Pride gx new	NLAp
Penway Rainbow gx	NLAp
Penway Rose gx	NLAp
Penway Sunset gx	NLAp WCot
sinensis	CPLG EBrs
§ ***striata***	CBct CBgR CDes CPLG CPom CStu CTri EBee EBrs ECho IHer LAma LEdu LRHS MREP NCGa NHol NLAp NMen NWCA SMeo SPer WFar WPGP
- ***alba***	see *B. striata* f. *gebina*
- 'Albostriata'	CBct CDes EBee EBrs ECho ELan LAma NCGa NLAp WCot
§ - f. ***gebina***	CAby CDes CMdw CMea CStu CTri EBee EBrs ECho EPot LAma LEdu LRHS NLar WCot WFar WPGP
- - variegated (v)	LEdu NMen WCot WHal
- var. ***japonica***	EPot
- variegated (v)	CBow
- yellow-flowered	EBrs
szetschuanica	EBee WWst

Bloomeria (*Alliaceae*)

crocea	ECho
- var. ***aurea***	EBee EBrs ECho ERos LRHS
- var. ***montana***	ECho

blueberry see *Vaccinium corymbosum*

Bocconia (*Papaveraceae*)

cordata	see *Macleaya cordata* (Willd.) R. Br.
microcarpa	see *Macleaya microcarpa*

Boehmeria (*Urticaceae*)

platanifolia new	IMou
sylvatica	NLar
tricuspis new	IMou

Boenninghausenia (*Rutaceae*)

albiflora	CSpe
- B&SWJ 1479	WCru
- B&SWJ 3112 pink-flowered	WCru
- BWJ 8141 from China	WCru
japonica B&SWJ 4876	WCru

Bolax (*Apiaceae*)

glebaria	see *B. gummifer*
§ ***gummifer***	ECho EPot WAbe

Bolboschoenus (*Cyperaceae*)

§ ***maritimus***	CRWN EBWF GFor LPBA WFar
* ***romanus***	EBee

Boltonia (*Asteraceae*)

asteroides	CFee CSam CSpe ECtt EHrv GCra LEdu LRHS MMuc NGdn SMrm STes SWat WBVN WCAu WCom WDyG WRHF
- var. ***latisquama***	EBee GMaP GQue LSou MAvo MRav MWat NLar SHar SSvw WBor WFar WHal
- - 'Nana'	LEdu MRav NBre SGSe WFar WPer
- - 'Snowbank'	EBee EBla ELan GCal LHop NWsh
- 'Pink Beauty'	EBla LEdu LHop LRHS
- var. ***recognita***	LRHS
decurrens	EBee NBre
incisa	see *Kalimeris incisa*
* ***richardsonii***	EBee

Bomarea (*Alstroemeriaceae*)

F&M 130	WPGP
aff. ***acuminata*** B&SWJ 10617	WCru
acutifolia B&SWJ 9094	WCru WPrP
- B&SWJ 10388	WCru
boliviensis	EBee WCru
- RCB/Arg P-18	WCot
caldasii ♀H1	CBcs CCCN CHEx CRHN EBee ERea EShb IKil SMad WBor WFoF WPGP WSHC
costaricensis	ERea
- B&SWJ 10467	WCru
§ ***edulis***	CBgR CDes CGHE CRHN CWGN EBee LFur WOut WPGP
- B&SWJ 9017	WCru
- F&M 104	WPGP
aff. ***frondea*** B&SWJ 10681	WCru
hirtella	see *B. edulis*
multiflora	CFir EBee GCal
salsilla	CCCN CRHN EBee WCot WCru WPGP WSHC

Bongardia (*Berberidaceae*)

chrysogonum	CAvo EBrs ECho LRHS WCot WHal

Bonia (*Poaceae*)

§ ***solida***	CHEx ERod LPal MMoz MMuc MWht NPal SEND WJun

borage see *Borago officinalis*

Borago (*Boraginaceae*)

alba	MNHC WCHb
laxiflora	see *B. pygmaea*
officinalis	CArn CSev CWan ELau EPfP GKir GPoy MHer MNHC NBir NGHP NVic SBch SVic WHer
- 'Alba'	CBre CSev ELau ILis NGHP SBch SDnm SIde WCHb WHer WJek
- 'Bill Archer' (v)	CBow CNat
§ ***pygmaea***	CArn CHid CPLG CSev CSpe ELan EOHP GBar LHop MHer MTho NGHP NMRc NSti STes SWat WCHb WGwG WHer WMoo WPrP

Borinda (*Poaceae*)

albocerea	EPla ERod MWht WJun
- Yunnan 1	EPla WJun WPGP
- Yunnan 2	CDTJ CEnt EPla MMoz WJun WPGP
- Yunnan 3a	CDTJ CEnt EPla WJun WPGP
- Yunnan 3b new	WJun
- Yunnan 4	CDTJ CEnt EPla WPGP
boliana	EPla SBig WJun
edulis	EPla WJun
frigida	CDTJ CEnt EPla WJun WPGP
grossa	EPla
lushuiensis	EPla WJun
macclureana	EPla
- KR 5050	WJun

- KR 5177	MWht WJun WPGP
- KR 6243	WJun
muliensis **new**	WJun
papyrifera	CEnt EPla WJun WPGP
- CS 1046	WJun
- KR 3968	WJun
- KR 7613	MWht WJun
scabrida	CDTJ CEnt CGHE EPla ETod MMoz MWht WJun WPGP
- 'Asian Wonder'	ENBC NLar

Boronia (*Rutaceae*)

denticulata	ECou
heterophylla	CBcs CCCN CTsd ECou
- 'Ice Charlotte' **new**	CBcs
- white-flowered	ECou
megastigma	ECou
- 'Brown Meg'	CBcs
pinnata	ECou
serrulata	ECou

Bothriochloa (*Poaceae*)

§ ***bladhii***	CKno EPPr MAvo
caucasica	see *B. bladhii*
§ ***ischaemum***	MAvo

Botryostege see *Tripetaleia*

Bougainvillea (*Nyctaginaceae*)

'Ailsa Lambe'	see *B.* (Spectoperuviana Group) 'Mary Palmer'
'Alexandra'	LRHS MBri
'Aussie Gold'	see *B.* 'Carson's Gold'
'Begum Sikander'	ERea
'Brilliant' misapplied	see *B.* × ***buttiana*** 'Raspberry Ice'
× ***buttiana*** 'Ametyst'	MBri
- 'Asia'	ERea
- 'Killie Campbell' ♀H1	ERea
- 'Lady Mary Baring'	ERea
§ - 'Mahara' (d)	ERea
§ - 'Mrs Butt' ♀H1	ERea
§ - 'Poultonii'	ERea
§ - 'Poulton's Special' ♀H1	ERea
§ - 'Raspberry Ice' (v)	ERea EShb
- 'Ratana Red' (v)	ERea
- 'Tiggy'	ERea
§ Camarillo Fiesta = 'Monle' (*spectabilis* hybrid)	ERea
§ 'Carson's Gold' (d)	ERea
§ 'Chiang Mai Beauty'	ERea
'Crimson Lake' misapplied	see *B.* × ***buttiana*** 'Mrs Butt'
'Donya'	ERea
'Double Yellow'	see *B.* 'Carson's Gold'
'Flamingo Pink'	see *B.* 'Chiang Mai Beauty'
'Floribunda'	ERea
glabra ♀H1	CMen ERea LRHS MBri
§ - 'Harrissii' (v)	ERea
§ - 'Sanderiana'	ERea
'Glowing Flame' (v)	ERea
'Golden Tango'	ERea
'Harrissii'	see *B. glabra* 'Harrissii'
'Hawaiian Scarlet'	see *B.* 'San Diego Red'
'James Walker'	ERea
'Jennifer Fernie'	ERea
'Juanita Hatten'	ERea
'Klong Fire'	see *B.* × ***buttiana*** 'Mahara'
'Lord Willingdon' misapplied	see *B.* 'Torch Glow'
§ 'Louis Wathen'	ERea
'Mahara Double Red'	see *B.* × ***buttiana*** 'Mahara'
'Manila Magic Red'	see *B.* × ***buttiana*** 'Mahara'
'Mini-Thai'	see *B.* 'Torch Glow'
'Mrs Butt'	see *B.* × ***buttiana*** 'Mrs Butt'
'Orange Glow'	see *B.* Camarillo Fiesta
'Orange King'	see *B.* 'Louis Wathen'
'Orange Stripe' (v)	ERea
'Pixie'	see *B.* 'Torch Glow'
'Poultonii'	see *B.* × ***buttiana*** 'Poultonii'
'Poultonii Special'	see *B.* × ***buttiana*** 'Poulton's Special'
'Princess Mahara'	see *B.* × ***buttiana*** 'Mahara'
'Purple Robe'	ERea
'Ratana Orange' (v)	ERea
'Red Fantasy' (v)	ERea
'Reggae Gold' (v)	ERea
'Rubyana'	ERea
§ 'San Diego Red' ♀H1	ERea
'Sanderiana'	see *B. glabra* 'Sanderiana'
Scarlett O'Hara	see *B.* 'San Diego Red'
'Smartipants'	see *B.* 'Torch Glow'
'Snow Cap'	see *B.* (Spectoperuviana Group) 'Mary Palmer'
§ (Spectoperuviana Group) 'Mary Palmer'	ERea
- 'Mrs H.C. Buck'	ERea
Surprise	see *B.* (Spectoperuviana Group) 'Mary Palmer'
§ 'Torch Glow'	EAmu
'Tropical Rainbow'	see *B.* × ***buttiana*** 'Raspberry Ice'
'Variegata'	see *B. glabra* 'Harrissii'

Boussingaultia (*Basellaceae*)

baselloides Hook.	see *Anredera cordifolia*

Bouteloua (*Poaceae*)

curtipendula	CRWN EBee GFor SGSe
§ ***gracilis***	EBee EBrs EHoe GFor LRHS MWhi NWsh SGSe SMrm SUsu SWal WPGP WPer WWEG

Bouvardia (*Rubiaceae*)

× ***domestica***	EShb
longiflora	ERea
ternifolia	WCot

Bowiea (*Hyacinthaceae*)

volubilis	EBee EBrs EShb

Bowkeria (*Scrophulariaceae*)

cymosa	SPlb
gerrardiana	CHII
verticillata	WBor

Boykinia (*Saxifragaceae*)

aconitifolia	CAbP EBee EBla GBuc GGar MRav NLar NRya SMad WCru WMoo WSHC
elata	see *B. occidentalis*
heucheriformis	see *B. jamesii*
§ ***jamesii***	GEdr GKev NWCA
lycoctonifolia	EBee
major	EBee GAuc
§ ***occidentalis***	EBee EPot GGar GKev MMHG WCru WMoo WPtf
rotundifolia	EBee EWld GBuc GKev NBir WCru WMoo
tellimoides	see *Peltoboykinia tellimoides*

boysenberry see *Rubus* 'Boysenberry'

Brachychilum see *Hedychium*

Brachychiton (*Sterculiaceae*)

acerifolius	CHEx EShb

discolor	EShb
§ ***rupestris***	EShb

Brachyelytrum (*Poaceae*)

japonicum	GFor ILad MAvo NLar

Brachyglottis ✿ (*Asteraceae*)

§ ***bidwillii***	IDee MDun
- 'Basil Fox'	WAbe
§ ***buchananii***	GKir WSHC
- 'Silver Shadow'	GGar
§ ***compacta***	ECou ELan EPfP LRHS MAsh SPer SPoG WEas
compacta × ***monroi***	ECou LRHS
'County Park'	ECou
'Drysdale'	EBee ELan EPfP GGar LRHS MAsh MBri NPri SBch SLon SRGP SWvt
§ (Dunedin Group) 'Moira Reid' (v)	CPLG GGar
§ - 'Sunshine' ♀H4	Widely available
'Frosty'	ECou
greyi misapplied	see *B.* (Dunedin Group) 'Sunshine'
§ ***greyi*** (Hook. f.) B. Nord.	CMac CTrG EPfP MBar MWhi
greyi × ***repanda***	CDoC GGar SAPC SArc
huntii × ***stewartii***	GGar
laxifolia misapplied	see *B.* (Dunedin Group) 'Sunshine'
'Leith's Gold'	CTrC
§ ***monroi*** ♀H4	CMac CSBt CWib ECou EGoo EHoe ELan EPfP GGar LRHS MRav SLon SPoG WDin WEas
- 'Clarence'	ECou
repanda	CBcs CTrG
- 'Purpurea'	EBee
§ ***rotundifolia***	CBcs CCCN CDoC GGal GGar NLar WEas
'Silver Waves'	ECou
§ ***spedenii***	GGar
I 'Sunshine Improved'	CBcs EHoe NBir SWvt
'Sunshine Variegated'	see *B.* (Dunedin Group) 'Moira Reid'
Walberton's Silver Dormouse = 'Walbrach'PBR	LBuc LRHS MAsh SPoG

Brachypodium (*Poaceae*)

pinnatum	EHoe
sylvaticum	EBWF EHul GCal GFor SEND

Brachyscome (*Asteraceae*)

formosa	ECou
melanocarpa	WCom
'Metallic Blue'	NPri
'Mini Yellow'	NPri
multifida	MBri NPri
nivalis var. ***alpina***	see *B. tadgellii*
'Pink Mist'	SPet
rigidula	ECou
'Strawberry Mousse'	LAst SPet
§ ***tadgellii***	ECou

Brachystachyum (*Poaceae*)

densiflorum	EBee EPla NLar

Bracteantha see *Xerochrysum*

Brahea (*Arecaceae*)

armata	CAbb CBrP CDTJ CPHo EAmu EPfP EShb ETod IDee LPal LRHS MGos MREP SAPC SArc SBst SChr SPer STrG WCot
edulis	CBrP EAmu LPal
'Super Silver' **new**	NExo WCot

Brainea (*Blechnaceae*)

insignis	WRic

Brassaia see *Schefflera*

Brassica (*Brassicaceae*)

japonica	see *B. juncea* var. *crispifolia*
§ ***juncea*** var. ***crispifolia***	CArn MNHC
nigra	CArn
oleracea	EBWF WHer
* ***rapa*** var. ***japonica***	CArn WJek
* - var. ***purpurea***	WJek

Bravoa (*Agavaceae*)

geminiflora	see *Polianthes geminiflora*

Brillantaisia (*Acanthaceae*)

kirungae	CCCN EShb

Brimeura (*Hyacinthaceae*)

§ ***amethystina*** ♀H4	CAvo CBgR CPLG CPom EBrs ECho ERos GBin GKev NWCA SPhx WCot
- 'Alba'	CAvo CBgR EBrs ECho ERos GKev LRHS SMrm SPhx WCot
§ ***fastigiata***	ERos

Briza (*Poaceae*)

maxima	CEnt CHrt CKno CTri EGoo EHoe EPla LEdu LHop NGdn NSti SBch SIng WHal WHer WTou
media	Widely available
- 'Golden Bee' **new**	CKno
- 'Limouzi'	CElw CFir CKno EBee EBrs EGoo EHoe EHrv ELon EPPr GCal GKir LEdu LRHS MAvo MBri NSti SDys SMad SMrm WPrP
- 'Russells'PBR	CElw CKno EAlp EBee EHoe EPPr GBin LEdu LHop LRHS NBPC NCGa SBch SPer SPhx WHil
subaristata	EBee EPPr LRHS MWhi NLar WHrl
triloba	EWes GBin MMHG NWsh SBod WGwG

Brodiaea (*Alliaceae*)

§ ***californica***	EBee EBrs ECho ERos NMen WCot
- NNS 00-108	WCot
capitata	see *Dichelostemma capitatum*
coronaria	CPBP GAuc WCot
'Corrina'	see *Triteleia* 'Corrina'
elegans	EBee ECho ERos GAuc WCot
ida-maia	see *Dichelostemma ida-maia*
jolonensis	ERos
laxa	see *Triteleia laxa*
pallida	WCot
peduncularis	see *Triteleia peduncularis*

Bromus (*Poaceae*)

erectus	EBWF
inermis 'Skinner's Gold' (v)	EBee EHoe EHul EPPr EWes LRHS NLar NSti SMrm SPoG WCot
sterilis 'Chinese Brushstrokes' **new**	CSpe

Broussonetia (*Moraceae*)

kazinoki	CArn CBcs IDee IFFs NLar WDin WPGP
papyrifera	CAbP CAgr CBcs CDul CMCN EBee EGFP ELan IDee LMaj MBri SPer WDin WPGP
- 'Laciniata'	MBri NLar

Browallia (*Solanaceae*)

from Sikkim	CSpe

Bruckenthalia see *Erica*

Brugmansia ✿ (*Solanaceae*)

§ ***arborea***	CArn CDTJ SEND SRms
§ - 'Knightii' (d) ♀^{H1}	CDTJ ELan EPfP ERea
aurea	CCCN CHEx
× ***candida***	CCCN CHEx
§ - 'Grand Marnier' ♀^{H1}	CBot CDTJ CHEx CHll ELan EPfP ERea
- 'Plena'	see *B. arborea* 'Knightii'
- ***plena*** 'Mon Amoure M' (d)	ERea
§ - 'Variegata' (v)	CCCN CDTJ CSam ERea
§ ***chlorantha***	CBcs
× ***cubensis*** 'Charles Grimaldi'	CSam
'Flowerdream' (d)	ERea
'Herzenbrucke'	ERea
'Igea Pink'	CSam
§ × ***insignis***	CHll
- 'Pink'	CTrG SEND
§ - pink-flowered	CHEx EPfP
'Mobishu'	EShb
rosei	see *B. sanguinea* subsp. *sanguinea* var. *flava*
§ ***sanguinea***	CBcs CCCN CHEx CHll EGxp EShb IDee SEND
- red-flowered	CHEx
- 'Rosea'	see *B.* × *insignis* pink-flowered
§ - subsp. ***sanguinea*** var. ***flava***	CHEx
§ ***suaveolens*** ♀^{H1}	CHEx CHll EGxp ELan SPlb
- 'Flore Pleno' (d) **new**	EGxp
- pink-flowered	EShb
- ***rosea***	see *B.* × *insignis* pink-flowered
- 'Variegata' (v)	EShb
- yellow-flowered	EShb
suaveolens* × *versicolor	see *B.* × *insignis*
'Variegata Sunset'	see *B.* × *candida* 'Variegata'
versicolor misapplied	see *B. arborea*
§ ***versicolor*** Lagerh.	CCCN
- 'Ecuador Pink'	EPfP
* 'Yellow Trumpet'	EPfP

Brunfelsia (*Solanaceae*)

americana	CCCN ERea EShb
calycina	see *B. pauciflora*
eximia	see *B. pauciflora* 'Eximia'
lactea	CCCN ERea EShb
nitida	ERea
§ ***pauciflora*** ♀^{H1}	ELan ERea MBri
§ - 'Eximia' **new**	ERea
- 'Floribunda'	ERea
- 'Macrantha'	ERea

Brunia (*Bruniaceae*)

albiflora	SPlb

Brunnera ✿ (*Boraginaceae*)

§ ***macrophylla*** ♀^{H4}	Widely available
- 'Agnes Amez'	CLAP SUsu
- 'Alba'	see *B. macrophylla* 'Betty Bowring'
§ - 'Betty Bowring'	Widely available
- 'Blaukuppel'	CLAP EAEE EBee EBla EWes GBin LRHS NBir NCob WFar
- 'Blue Louise'	CLAP
- 'Dawson's White' (v)	Widely available
- 'Gordano Gold' (v)	CBow EHoe EPPr WCot
- 'Hadspen Cream' (v) ♀^{H4}	Widely available
- 'Jack Frost'^{PBR} ♀^{H4}	Widely available
- 'Langford Hewitt' (v)	MNrw
- 'Langtrees'	Widely available
- 'Looking Glass'^{PBR}	Widely available
- 'Marley's White'	CAbP CLAP CMea EBee EHrv GAbr LLHF MCot NCob NEgg SUsu WCot WPnP WPtf
- 'Mr Morse' (v) **new**	EBee ECtt EPfP GBuc GEdr LLHF MAsh MAvo MCot NBPC NEgg NLar NSti SMrm SPoG WCot WFut WHoo
- 'Silver Wings'	CElw EBee ECtt EPfP EWll GEdr LRHS NBir NLar
- 'Spring Yellow' **new**	EBee MAsh NLar NSti
'Mrs Morse' **new**	NGdn
sibirica	CDes CLAP EBee EPPr EWes

Brunsvigia (*Amaryllidaceae*)

bosmaniae	ECho
marginata **new**	ECho
pulchra	ECho WCot
radulosa	ECho
rosea 'Minor'	see *Amaryllis belladonna*
striata **new**	ECho

Bryonia (*Cucurbitaceae*)

dioica	CArn GPoy NMir

Bryophyllum see *Kalanchoe*

Buchloe (*Poaceae*)

dactyloides	CRWN EBee

Buddleja ✿ (*Buddlejaceae*)

HCM 98.017 from Chile	WPGP
agathosma	CBot EBee SLon WKif WLav WPGP WSHC
albiflora	SLon WLav
alternifolia ♀^{H4}	Widely available
- 'Argentea'	CBcs CBot CDoC CMac EBee ELan EPfP GKir LRHS MBNS MRav NLar NSti SPer SPoG SRGP SSpi WCot WHCG WLav WPat WSHC
asiatica ♀^{H2}	CBot EShb SLon WCot WLav
- B&SWJ 7214	WCru
- B&SWJ 11278	WCru
auriculata	CBcs CBgR CBot CMCN CPLG CWib EBee ELan EPfP ERas EShb LAst LRHS MRav NSti SDix SLon SPoG WBor WCru WHCG WLav WPGP
* 'Blue Trerice'	CPLG
caryopteridifolia	EBee SLon
colvilei	CBcs CDoC CDul ELan EPfP ERas GCal GGal GKir IDee LAst MBri SDnm WBor WSpi
- B&SWJ 2121	WCru
- GWJ 9399	WCru
- 'Kewensis'	CBot CPLG CRHN CSam EBee EWes GCal GCra GGal GKir LAst NLar NSti SLon WCom WCru WLav WPGP WSHC WSpi
cordata	SLon
- F&M 220	WPGP
coriacea	SLon
§ ***crispa***	CBcs CBgR CBot CDul CPLG CSpe EBee ECha ELan EPfP ERas LRHS MCot SDnm SLon SPer SRkn SSpi WAbe WClo WCom WEas WFar WHCG WKif WPGP WSHC WSpi
- var. ***farreri*** **new**	CBgR

- Moon Dance = 'Hulmoon'	EBee
crotonoides subsp. ***amplexicaulis***	SLon
curviflora f. ***venenifera***	SLon
- - B&SWJ 6036	WCru
davidii	CArn NWea SGar STre WDin
- B&SWJ 8083	WCru
- Adonis Blue = 'Adokeep'PBR	EBee MGos SPoG
- 'African Queen'	CAni SLon SRGP
- var. ***alba***	CWib
§ - 'Autumn Beauty'	CAni SLon WSFF
- 'Bath Beauty'	CAni
- 'Beijing'	see *B. davidii* 'Autumn Beauty'
- 'Bishop's Velvet'	CAni
- 'Black Knight' ♀H4	Widely available
- 'Blue Horizon'	CAni CSam SEND SLon SRGP WCot WLav WMoo WRHF
- 'Border Beauty'	CAni SLon
- 'Boskoop Beauty'	CAni
- 'Brown's Beauty'	CAni
- Camberwell Beauty = 'Camkeep' (English Butterfly Series)	MGos NHol SLon SPoG
- 'Car Wash'	CAni
- 'Castle School'	CAni CSam
§ - 'Charming'	CDul WMoo WSHC WWlt
- 'Clive Farrell'	see *B. davidii* 'Autumn Beauty'
- 'Croyde'	CSam
- 'Dartmoor' ♀H4	CAni CDul CMHG CMac CPLG CRow CTri ECtt ELan EPfP GCal GKir LRHS MAsh MCot MGos MRav NPer SDix SIde SPer SPlb SPoG SSta WCom WFar WHCG WSHC WSpi WTin
- 'Dart's Ornamental White'	MRav SLon
- 'Dart's Papillon Blue'	CAni SLon
- 'Dart's Purple Rain'	CAni
- 'Dubonnet'	CAni SLon WLav
- 'Dudley's Compact Lavender'	CAni
- 'Ecolonia'	CAni
- 'Empire Blue' ♀H4	Widely available
- 'Fascinating'	CAni GCal MGan MRav NBir SLon WLav
- 'Flaming Violet'	CAni SLon WLav
- 'Florence'	EBee LLHF LRHS LSRN LSou NEgg NHol NLar SPoG WFar WHar WMoo
- 'Fortune'	CAni
- 'Glasnevin Hybrid'	CAni NSti SDix SLon WLav
- 'Gonglepod'	CAni SLon
- 'Greenway's River Dart'	CAni
- 'Harlequin' (v)	Widely available
- 'Ile de France'	CAni CBcs CWib EBee MGos NBlu NWea SLon SRms WLav
- 'Jane Taylor'	CAni
- 'Les Kneale'	CAni
- 'Lyme Bay'	CAni
- Marbled White = 'Markeep'	NHol SLon SPoG
- Masquerade = 'Notbud'PBR (v)	MBri MGos MRav SPoG WGor
§ - 'Nanho Blue' ♀H4	Widely available
- 'Nanho Petite Indigo'	see *B. davidii* 'Nanho Blue'
- 'Nanho Petite Plum'	see *B. davidii* 'Nanho Purple'
- 'Nanho Petite Purple'	see *B. davidii* 'Nanho Purple'
§ - 'Nanho Purple' ♀H4	CAlb CAni CDoC CMHG CTri CWib EBee ELan EPfP LRHS LSRN MAsh MBar MGos MRav NLar SLim SLon SPer SPlb SPoG SRGP WHar
- Nanho White = 'Monite'	CBgR ELan EPfP GKir LRHS MBar SLon SPer SPoG SRms WFar
- var. ***nanhoensis***	CAni CDul CHrt EBee SEND SIde WHCG WLav
- - blue-flowered	NHol SLon SPer
- 'Orchid Beauty'	CAni SLon WLav
- 'Orpheus'	CAni WLav
- 'Peace'	CChe CDoC CMac CTri EBee EPfP LSRN MBri MRav SLon SPoG WLav
- Peacock = 'Peakeep'PBR (English Butterfly Series)	MGos SPoG
- 'Persephone' **new**	WLav
- 'Petite Indigo'	see *B. davidii* 'Nanho Blue'
- 'Pink Beauty'	CEnt GKir IFFs LAst LSRN SRGP WHCG
- 'Pink Charming'	see *B. davidii* 'Charming'
- 'Pink Pearl'	CAni SEND SLon WLav
- 'Pink Spreader'	CAni SLon
- 'Pixie Blue'	CAni LAst LBMP LBuc LRHS MAsh NBlu NLar NMyG NPri SRGP
- 'Pixie Red'	CAni LBMP LBuc LRHS MAsh NEgg NLar NMyG NPri SEND
- 'Pixie White'	LBuc LRHS MAsh NLar NPri SEND SRGP WLav
- Purple Emperor = 'Pyrkeep' (English Butterfly Series)	NBir SLon SPoG
- 'Purple Friend'	CAni WLav
- 'Purple Prince'	CAni
- 'Red Admiral'	CAni LLHF LRHS MAsh SPoG
- Rêve de Papillon = 'Minpap'	EBee EMil MAsh
- 'Royal Purple'	CAni SLim
- 'Royal Red' ♀H4	Widely available
- 'Santana' (v)	CAni CDul EBee EHoe ELon EWes LRHS LSou MGos MRav MWea NCGa NEgg NHol NLar SAga SBch SPoG WCot WHar WMoo WPat WRHF WSpi
- 'Shapcott Blue'	CAni
- 'Shire Blue' **new**	WLav
- 'Southcombe Splendour'	CAni
- 'Summer Beauty'	CAni CWib EBee LRHS MGos MRav SLon WLav
- 'Summer House Blue'	SLon
- 'Twotones' **new**	WLav
- 'Variegata' (v)	CAni LRHS MAsh SLon WLav WSFF
- 'White Ball'	EBee EPfP NLar SLon
- 'White Bouquet'	CAni CCVT CDul CEnt CSBt EBee EPfP GKir IFFs LAst LRHS MAsh MHer MNHC MSwo MWat NPri NWea SEND SPer SRGP SReu SWal WLav
- 'White Cloud'	CAni CHrt ECrN GQui MGos SRms WGwG
- 'White Harlequin' (v)	WCFE
- 'White Profusion' ♀H4	CAni CBcs CDul CSam EBee ECtt ELan EPfP GKir IMon LRHS MBar MDun MGan MGos MRav NBir NBlu NEgg NWea SBch SLim SPad SWvt WCFE WDin WFar WHCG WHar WMoo
- 'White Wings'	SLon WLav
- 'Widecombe'	CAni
§ ***delavayi***	CPLG EBee GKir SEND WCru
fallowiana misapplied	see *B.* 'West Hill'
fallowiana Balf. f.	ELan LRHS WCom WLav
- ACE 2481	LRHS
- BWJ 7803	WCru
- var. ***alba*** ♀H3	CBgR CBot CDoC CMac EBee ECrN ELan EPfP LRHS MAsh MRav NChi NLar NSti SLon SPer SPoG WAbe WFar WPGP WSHC

	forrestii	CBot CRHN WCru
	globosa ♀H4	Widely available
	- RCB/Arg C-11	WCot
	- 'Cally Orange'	GCal GGar
	- 'Lemon Ball'	MBlu NPer SLon WLav
	glomerata	EBee EShb SLon WCom WPGP
	'Gulliver' new	NHol
	heliophila	see *B. delavayi*
	indica	SLon WBor
	japonica B&SWJ 8912	WCru
	'Leela Kapila'	LBuc MGos
	× ***lewisiana*** 'Margaret Pike'	CBot SLon
	limitanea	SLon
	lindleyana	Widely available
	aff. ***lindleyana*** B&SWJ 11478 new	WCru
	'Lochinch' ♀H3-4	Widely available
	loricata	CBgR CBot CFee CHid CPLG CWib EBee GQui IDee LRHS SGar SLon SMrm SPlb WCFE WCot WLav WPGP
	macrostachya	GBin GLin WPGP
	- HWJ 602	WCru
§	***madagascariensis*** ♀H1	CRHN SGar SLon WCot WHar
*	'Malvern Blue' (English Butterfly Series)	CAni
	megalocephala B&SWJ 9106	WCru
§	'Morning Mist'PBR	CDoC CPLG CWGN EBee EGxp ELan EMil EPfP GBin LBuc LLHF LSRN LSou MGos NBir NEgg NHol NLar SBch SLon SPoG WClo WHar WPGP
	myriantha	CPLG SLon
*	- f. ***fragrans***	EBee WCot
	nappii	SLon
	nicodemia	see *B. madagascariensis*
	nivea	CBot CPLG SLon WCom WLav
	- B&SWJ 2679	WCru
	- pink-flowered	SLon
	officinalis ♀H2	CBot CPLG SLon
	paniculata	SLon
	parvifolia	SLon
	- MPF 148	WLav
	× ***pikei*** 'Hever'	GCal
	'Pink Delight' ♀H4	Widely available
	'Pink Perfection'	CAni WFar
	'Pride of Longstock'	SLon
	'Purple Splendour'	GGal
	saligna	SLon
	'Salmon Spheres'	SAga SLon
	salviifolia	CBcs CBgR CBot CPLG CRHN CSWP CSam CTrG CTsd EBee ELan GGal GGar GQui IDee LAst LRHS MBlu NSti SDnm SWal WAbe WCom WGwG WHer WLav
	- white-flowered	CRHN IFro
	Silver AnniversaryPBR	see *B.* 'Morning Mist'
	stenostachya	CPLG SLon
	sterniana	see *B. crispa*
	tibetica	see *B. crispa*
	tubiflora	CBot SLon WLav
	venenifera B&SWJ 895	WCru
§	'West Hill'	SLon SRGP WLav
	× ***weyeriana***	CBgR CDul CRHN CSam EBee ECtt EPfP GQui IFoB MGos MNrw MSwo NBir SBch SGar SPlb SWvt WBor WBrE WDin WFar WHCG WLav WMoo
	- 'Golden Glow' (v)	CBow CTri ECrN EPfP LRHS LSRN SLon WLav WSFF
	- 'Honeycomb'	EShb GKir MAsh
	- 'Lady de Ramsey'	SEND WPer
	- 'Moonlight'	CBcs CPLG ELan GKir IFro SBch SLon WCot WLav WSpi
	- 'Sungold' ♀H4	Widely available
	'Winter Sun'	SLon
	yunnanensis	GCal GGar SLon WCFE
	- B&SWJ 8146	WCru

Buglossoides (*Boraginaceae*)

§	***purpurocaerulea***	CEnt CHll CMHG CPom CSpe CWGN EBee ECha ELan LHop MLHP MWhi NBid NBir WAul WCot WSHC

Bukiniczia (*Plumbaginaceae*)

	cabulica	CSpe GKev WAbe

Bulbine (*Asphodelaceae*)

	SH 74	CMdw
	annua misapplied	see *B. semibarbata*
	bulbosa misapplied	see *B. semibarbata*
	caulescens	see *B. frutescens*
§	***frutescens***	CHll GKev MBNS WBrk WJek WPrP
	- 'Hallmark'	CCCN
	latifolia	CCCN EShb
§	***semibarbata***	CCCN

Bulbinella (*Asphodelaceae*)

	angustifolia	ECho WCot
	cauda-felis	WCot
	eburnifolia	WCot
	elata	WCot
	floribunda	IBlr
	gibbsii var. ***balanifera***	ECho
	hookeri	CPom EBee ECho ECou EWld GBee GEdr GGar GKev GKir ITim LRHS NChi NLAp NWCA SRms WHal
	latifolia	ECho
	nutans	CDes ECho

Bulbinopsis see *Bulbine*

Bulbocodium (*Colchicaceae*)

	vernum	EBrs ECho EPot ERos GKir LAma LLHF MBri NHol NMin SPhx
	- white-flowered	ECho

bullace see *Prunus insititia*

Bunias (*Brassicaceae*)

	orientalis	CAgr

Bunium (*Apiaceae*)

	bulbocastanum	CAgr IMou LEdu SBch SHDw

Buphthalmum (*Asteraceae*)

	salicifolium	CSam EBee ELan EPfP GKir MMuc MNFA NBlu NBro NGdn SEND SHGN SPer SRms SWat WCAu WFar WPer WWEG
	- 'Alpengold'	ECha GMaP NBre NLar
	- 'Dora'	ECtt WCot
§	- 'Golden Wonder'	GKir
	- 'Sunwheel'	EWll GKir LRHS NBre SRms
	speciosum	see *Telekia speciosa*

Bupleurum (*Apiaceae*)

	angulosum	CSpe LRHS NBir WFar
	- copper-leaved	see *B. longifolium*
	candollei GWJ 9405	WCru
	falcatum	CArn ECha EPPr LRHS NLar SPur WCot WFar

fruticosum	CBcs CBot CSpe ECGP ECtt EPfP LHop MAsh SDix SDnm SPer SPoG SSpi SSta WCot WDin WEas WPGP WPat WSpi
gibraltaricum	EBee
§ ***longifolium***	CElw CFee CPom CSpe EBee ECha EWes GBBs GBin GBuc GKir LRHS MBel MDKP MNrw NCGa NChi NLar WHoo
- subsp. ***aureum***	MAvo NChi NGby SPhx WFar
- bronze-leaved	LSou MAvo
- subsp. ***shikotanense***	EBee
- short bronze	WCru
longiradiatum B&SWJ 729	WCru
ranunculoides	NLar
spinosum	SMad
tenue	CArn

Bursaria (*Pittosporaceae*)

spinosa	CCCN EBee ECou EShb NLar

Butia (*Arecaceae*)

capitata	CAbb CBcs CBrP CCCN CDTJ CHEx CPHo CTrC EAmu EPla ESwi ETod IDee LMaj LPJP LPal MGos MREP NPal SAPC SArc SBst SChr
§ - var. ***odorata***	EAmu LPal
eriospatha	CDTJ EAmu LPal
odorata	see *B. capitata* var. *odorata*
yatay	CDTJ EAmu LPal SBig

Butomus (*Butomaceae*)

umbellatus ♀H4	CBen CRow CWat ECha EHon EMFW EPfP LPBA MCCP MRav MSKA NPer NSco SWat WMAq WPnP WTin
- 'Rosenrot'	CRow LLWG
- 'Schneeweisschen'	CRow LLWG NLar

butternut see *Juglans cinerea*

× *Butyagrus* (*Arecaceae*)

nabonnandii	EAmu

Buxus ✿ (*Buxaceae*)

aurea 'Marginata'	see *B. sempervirens* 'Marginata'
balearica ♀H4	EPla EQua IDee SEND SLan SLon WPGP
bodinieri	EPla EQua SLan
- 'David's Gold'	WPen
colchica	SLan
'Glencoe'	SLan
'Green Gem'	NGHP NHol SLan
'Green Mound'	SLan
'Green Mountain'	SLan
'Green Velvet'	EPfP NHol SLan
harlandii hort.	EPla SLan SRiv
- 'Richard'	SLan STre
henryi	MBri
japonica 'Nana'	see *B. microphylla*
macowanii	SLan STre WSpi
§ ***microphylla***	CSWP MHer NHol SIng SLan STre WSpi
- 'Asiatic Winter'	see *B. microphylla* var. *japonica* 'Winter Gem'
§ - 'Compacta'	CMen LLHF MHer NMen SLan SRiv WCot WPat
- 'Curly Locks'	EPla MHer SLan
- 'Faulkner'	CCVT EBee ELan EPfP EQua LBuc LHop LRHS MBNS MGos NHol SLan SPoG SRiv WDin WSpi
- 'Golden Triumph'PBR	EPfP MWat SLan
- 'Grace Hendrick Phillips'	SLan
- 'Green Pillow'	EPfP MHer SLan SRiv WSpi
- 'Helen Whiting'	SLan
- 'Henry Hohman'	SLan
- 'Herrenhausen'	LRHS SLan
- var. ***insularis***	see *B. sinica* var. *insularis*
- var. ***japonica*** 'Belvédère'	SLan
- - 'Gold Dust'	SLan
- - 'Green Beauty'	SLan
- - 'Green Jade'	SLan
- - 'Jim Stauffer'	SLan
- - 'Morris Dwarf'	SLan
- - 'Morris Midget'	IArd NHol SLan
- - 'National'	SLan WPGP
- - 'Sunnyside'	SLan
- - 'Trompenburg'	SLan
- - 'Variegata' (v)	CStu
§ - - 'Winter Gem'	MHer MRav NHol NLar SLPl SLan
- - f. ***yakushima***	SLan
- 'John Baldwin'	SLan SRiv
- 'Kagushima'	SLan
- var. ***koreana***	see *B. sinica* var. *insularis*
- 'Quiet End'	SLan
'Newport Blue'	see *B. sempervirens* 'Newport Blue'
riparia	EPla SLan
rugulosa	SLan
sempervirens ♀H4	Widely available
- 'Abilene'	SLan
- 'Agram'	SLan
- 'Anderson'	SLan
§ - 'Angustifolia'	EPla MGos MHer MRav NHol SLan SMad
- 'Arabeske' new	SLan
- 'Arborescens'	EQua
- 'Argentea'	see *B. sempervirens* 'Argenteo-variegata'
§ - 'Argenteo-variegata' (v)	EPfP IFoB NEgg NGHP SLan WFar
- 'Aristocrat'	SLan
- 'Aurea'	see *B. sempervirens* 'Aureovariegata'
- 'Aurea Maculata'	see *B. sempervirens* 'Aureovariegata'
- 'Aurea Marginata'	see *B. sempervirens* 'Marginata'
- 'Aurea Pendula' (v)	CPMA EPla SLan SLon WDin
§ - 'Aureovariegata' (v)	EPfP GBar ISea LRHS MAsh MBar MCot MGan MGos MHer MNHC MRav NHol NSti SLan SPer SRiv WDin WFar WMoo
- 'Belleville'	SLan
- 'Bentley Blue'	NHol NWea
- 'Berlin'	SLan
- 'Blauer Heinz'	ELan MHer MRav NHol SLan SRiv WSpi
- 'Blue Belle'	SLan
§ - 'Blue Cone'	CHar NHol
- 'Blue Spire'	see *B. sempervirens* 'Blue Cone'
- 'Bowles's Blue'	EQua SLan
I - 'Brilliantissima'	NHol
- 'Bullata'	SLan
- 'Claverton'	SLan
- clipped ball	CWib EPfP LSRN MGos NBlu NGHP NLar SLan SLim SRiv WFar
- clipped bird new	SRiv
- clipped cone	LSRN SRiv
- clipped pyramid	CWib EPfP LSRN MGos NBlu NGHP NLar SLan SLim SRiv
- clipped spiral	LSRN NBlu SLan SLim SRiv
- 'Crossley'	SLan
- 'Dark Sky' new	SLan
- 'Dee Runk'	SLan
- 'Denmark'	SLan
- 'Egremont'	SLan

- 'Elegans' IFoB LRHS
§ - 'Elegantissima' (v) ♀H4 Widely available
- 'Emir' SLan
- 'Fiesta' SLan
- 'Fleur de Lys' SLan
- 'Giant' **new** SLan
- 'Glauca' SLan
- 'Gold Tip' see *B. sempervirens* 'Notata'
- 'Golden Frimley' (v) LHop
§ - 'Graham Blandy' MHer NHol SLan SRiv WSpi
- 'Grand Rapids' SLan
- 'Green Balloon' LBuc SLan
- 'Greenpeace' see *B. sempervirens* 'Graham Blandy'
- 'Haller' SLan
- 'Handsworthiensis' CLnd EBee NHol SEND SLan SPer WMoo
- 'Handsworthiensis' blue SLan
- 'Handsworthii' CTri NWea SRms
- 'Hardwickensis' **new** SLan
- 'Henry Shaw' SLan
- 'Hermann von Schrenk' SLan
- 'Herman's Low' **new** SLan
- 'Holland' SLan
- subsp. ***hyrcana*** SLan
- 'Ickworth Giant' SLan
- 'Inglis' SLan
- 'Ingrid' SLan
- 'Inverewe' SLan
- 'Ipek' SLan
- 'Jack' **new** SLan
- 'Japonica Aurea' see *B. sempervirens* 'Latifolia Maculata'
- 'Kensington Gardens' SLan WSpi
- 'King Midas' SLan
- 'Kingsville' see *B. microphylla* 'Compacta'
- 'Kingsville Dwarf' see *B. microphylla* 'Compacta'
- 'Krakow' NLar SLan
- 'Lace' NSti SLan
§ - 'Langley Beauty' SLan
- 'Langley Pendula' see *B. sempervirens* 'Langley Beauty'
- 'Latifolia Macrophylla' SLan SLon
§ - 'Latifolia Maculata' (v) ♀H4 CAbP CDoC CWib EBee EPfP EPla MNHC NGHP NHol NPer SEND SLan SPoG SRiv STre WJek WSpi
* - 'Latifolia Pendula' NHol SLan
- 'Lemmens' **new** SLan
- 'Linda' SLan
- 'Longifolia' see *B. sempervirens* 'Angustifolia'
§ - 'Marginata' (v) EPla GBar IFoB LHop LRHS SLan SLon WBrE WHar WSpi
- 'Mary Gamble' SLan
- 'Memorial' MHer NHol SLan SRiv WSpi
- 'Molesworth' SLan
- 'Myosotidifolia' CMHG NPro SLan SRiv WPGP WSpi
- 'Myrtifolia' CBot EPla MHer NHol SLan SLon WSpi
- 'Natchez' SLan
§ - 'Newport Blue' SLan
- 'Northern' SLan
§ - 'Notata' (v) CSWP IFoB MAsh SBch WDin WRHF WSpi
- 'Obelisk' SLan
- 'Ornament' SLan
- 'Parasol' MHer SLan
- 'Pendula' GKir SLan SLon
- 'Pinnacle' SLan
I - 'Planifolia' SLan
- 'Prostrata' NHol NWea SLan WSpi
- 'Pylewell' WSpi
- 'Pyramidalis' SEND SLan WFar
- 'Raket' SLan
- 'Rosalia' **new** SLan
- 'Rosmarinifolia' MHer MRav SLan
- 'Rotundifolia' ELan IFFs MGos SEND SIde SLan WDin WSpi
- 'Roy Lancaster' SLan
- 'Saint Genevieve' SLan
- 'Salicifolia Elata' SLan
- 'Sentinelle' SLan
- 'Silver Beauty' (v) MAsh MGos NEgg
- 'Silver Variegated' see *B. sempervirens* 'Elegantissima'
- 'Suffruticosa' ♀H4 Widely available
I - 'Suffruticosa Blue' NHol
- 'Suffruticosa Variegata' (v) EBee EOHP SRms SWvt
- 'Sultan' SLan
- 'Sunningdale Silver' EQua
- 'Twisty' SLan WFar
- 'Undulifolia' SLan
- 'Vardar Valley' NHol NPro SLan SLon SRiv WSpi
* - 'Variegata' (v) ELan SLan SLon
- 'Varifolia' SLan
- 'Waterfall' MHer SLan
- 'Welleri' SLan
- 'William Borek' SLan
- 'Wisley Blue' SLan WSpi
sinica SLan
§ - var. ***insularis*** MAsh NHol SLan
- - 'Chegu' SLan
- - 'Filigree' NHol SLan WSpi
- - 'Justin Brouwers' MHer SLan SRiv WSpi
- - 'Pincushion' SLan
- - 'Tall Boy' SLan
- - 'Tide Hill' MHer SLan SRiv WFar WSpi
- - 'Winter Beauty' SLan
- - 'Wintergreen' SLan
- var. ***intermedia*** SLan
wallichiana CGHE EPla SLan WPGP

C

Cacalia (*Asteraceae*)

delphiniifolia EBee GEdr IMou LFur
- B&SWJ 5789 WCru
- B&SWJ 11189 WCru
suaveolens EBee

Caesalpinia (*Caesalpiniaceae*)

gilliesii CBcs CDTJ EBee LSRN NLar SPlb
- RCB/Arg N-1 WCot
mexicana WPGP
pulcherrima CCCN SPlb

Cakile (*Brassicaceae*)

maritima **new** CArn

Caladium (*Araceae*)

§ ***bicolor*** (v) EBrs
× ***hortulanum*** see *C. bicolor*

Calamagrostis (*Poaceae*)

from Korea **new** IPot
× ***acutiflora*** 'Avalanche' CKno EHoe EPPr
N - 'Karl Foerster' Widely available
- 'Overdam' (v) Widely available
- 'Stricta' EPPr GKir NWsh
- 'Waldenbuch' GBin
argentea see *Stipa calamagrostis*
arundinacea CElw COlW CPLG CSpe ECha ECou EPla LEdu MNrw NBid NHol

		NVic SDix SGar SPlb WFar WMoo WPGP WPer WPrP
	'Avalanche'	CKno GBin
§	***brachytricha*** ♀H4	Widely available
	emodensis	CEnt CKno CMil CPen CWCL EAlp EBee ECha EHoe EPla LEdu LRHS MMoz NOak NWsh SMad WGrn WMoo WPGP
	epigejos	GFor NBre NHol WHrl WPrP
	nutkaensis **new**	EPPr
	splendens misapplied	see *Stipa calamagrostis*
	varia	CKno EHoe EPPr SMrm WHrl

Calamintha (*Lamiaceae*)

	alpina	see *Acinos alpinus*
§	***ascendens***	CArn EBee MBel SPhx WMoo
	clinopodium	see *Clinopodium vulgare*
	cretica	WPer
*	'Fritz Kuhn'	WWEG
§	***grandiflora***	CArn CSam CSev EBee ECha ELan GGar GJos GPoy LEdu MHer MNHC MRav MWat MWhi NBir NPer SMad SMrm SPer SPlb SSvw SWat WCAu WFar WMoo WTin
	- 'Elfin Purple'	EBee EPfP SBch SPoG
	- 'Variegata' (v)	CPrp EAro EBee ECtt ELan EShb GGar LAst LSou NPri STes WCHb WFar
§	***menthifolia***	NBre NLar
	mimuloides	WCot
	'Supernova' **new**	
§	***nepeta***	CArn CWan EBWF EBee ECha GMaP LAst LBMP LRHS MNHC NBir NBro NPri NWCA SMrm SPhx SPlb SPoG SWal SWat WCAu WFar WMoo WPer WWEG
	- subsp. ***glandulosa***	CEnt EAro EBee WMoo
	- - ACL 1050/90	WHoo
	- - 'White Cloud'	CSpe EBee EHrv ELan GBar GBuc LLWP MBri MRav NBir WCAu WMoo
	- 'Gottfried Kuehn'	EBee MRav
§	- subsp. ***nepeta***	CPrp ELan ELon EPfP GBar GKir LHop MHer MLHP MRav MWat NSti SPer SUsu WCHb WClo WEas WFar WHal WTin
	- - 'Blue Cloud'	CSam CSpe EAro EBee ECha EHrv EPfP MBri NBir SAga SPhx SWat WCAu WCHb WFar WHil WMoo
	- 'Weisse Riese'	SPhx
	nepetoides	see *C. nepeta* subsp. *nepeta*
	officinalis misapplied	see *C. ascendens*
	sylvatica	see *C. menthifolia*
I	- 'Menthe'	EBee
	vulgaris	see *Clinopodium vulgare*

calamondin see × *Citrofortunella microcarpa*

Calandrinia (*Portulacaceae*)

	caespitosa	GKev
	grandiflora	LLHF
	sibirica	see *Claytonia sibirica*
	umbellata	EDAr LBMP LRHS NWCA WPer
	- 'Ruby Tuesday'	NPri

Calanthe (*Orchidaceae*)

	alismifolia	EFEx WWst
	arisanenesis	EFEx
	aristulifera	EFEx GEdr WWst
	bicolor	see *C. striata*
	caudatilabella	EFEx
	discolor	EBee EBrs EFEx GEdr LAma NLAp WCot WWst
	- subsp. ***amamiana***	EFEx
	- var. ***flava***	see *C. striata*
	- subsp. ***tokunoshimensis***	EFEx
	fargesii	WCot WWst
	graciliflora	EFEx
	Hizen gx	GEdr WWst
	Kozu gx	GEdr LEdu WWst
	- red-flowered	GEdr WWst
	mannii	EFEx
	nipponica	CBct EFEx GEdr LAma WWst
	reflexa	EBee EBrs EFEx GEdr LAma NLAp WCot WWst
	sieboldii	see *C. striata*
§	***striata***	CBct EBee EBrs EFEx GEdr LAma WCot WWst
	- Kawakamii Group	GEdr
	sylvatica lilac-flowered **new**	WWst
	- pink-flowered **new**	WWst
	Takane gx	GEdr WWst
	tricarinata	CBct EBrs EFEx GEdr LAma NLAp WWst
	triplicata **new**	WWst

Calathea (*Marantaceae*)

	argyrophylla 'Exotica'	XBlo
	burle-marxii	LRHS
	crocata ♀H1	LRHS
	louisae 'Maui Queen'	XBlo
§	***majestica*** ♀H1	XBlo
	makoyana ♀H1	XBlo
	oppenheimiana	see *Ctenanthe oppenheimiana*
	ornata	see *C. majestica*
	picturata 'Argentea' ♀H1	XBlo
	roseopicta ♀H1	LRHS XBlo
	rufibarba	XBlo
*	***stromata***	XBlo
	zebrina ♀H1	XBlo
	'Zoizia'	XBlo

Calceolaria (*Scrophulariaceae*)

	acutifolia	see *C. polyrhiza* Cav.
	arachnoidea	ERas WCom
	× ***banksii***	WCom
	bicolor	EBee
§	***biflora***	ECho EPfP GGar GKev NLar
	- 'Goldcap'	ECho SMrm
	- 'Goldcrest Amber'	ECho SPlb WPer
	'Briga Elite'	LSou
	'Camden Hero'	GCal MAJR
	chelidonioides	GGar MTho
	falklandica	ECho GKev GKir NLAp SPav SRms
	fothergillii	GKev NLAp
	'Goldcrest'	ECho GKev LRHS SRms
	'Hall's Spotted'	NWCA
N	***integrifolia*** ♀H3	CAbb CDTJ CPLG CSpe EBee ECtt ELan GKir MSCN SEND SGar SIng SPer SPoG SRms WAbe WCom WWlt
	- bronze	MSCN
	- 'Gaines' Yellow'	GCal
	'John Innes'	ECho
	'Kentish Hero'	CSpe GCal MAJR WAbe WCom
	lagunae-blancae	NLAp
	aff. ***pavonii***	CRHN
	perfoliata B&SWJ 10638	WCru
	plantaginea	see *C. biflora*
§	***polyrhiza*** Cav.	ECho NRya
	rugosa	see *C. integrifolia*
	'Stamford Park'	WCom

Sunset Series	EPfP
tenella	NWCA WAbe
uniflora var. ***darwinii***	ECho GKev NLAp WAbe
'Walter Shrimpton'	ECho EPot EWes NWCA SIng WAbe WCom

Caldcluvia (*Cunoniaceae*)

paniculata	ISea

Calendula (*Asteraceae*)

arvensis	CCCN
meuselii	CFee
officinalis	CArn ELau GPoy MHer MNHC SBch SIde SPav WJek
- Fiesta Gitana Group ♀H4	CPrp WJek
- 'Touch of Red' (Touch of Red Series)	CSpe

Calibanus (*Dracaenaceae*)

hookeri	EShb

Calibrachoa (*Solanaceae*)

(Cabaret Series) Cabaret Apricot = 'Balcabapt'	SVil
- Cabaret Cherry Rose = 'Balcabcher'	SVil
- Cabaret Hot Pink = 'Balcabhopi' **new**	NPri
- Cabaret Peach = 'Balcabpea' **new**	NPri
- Cabaret Purple = 'Balcabpurp'	NPri SVil
- Cabaret Scarlet = 'Balcabscar'	NPri
- Cabaret White Improved = 'Balcabwitim'	NPri SVil
- Cabaret Yellow = 'Balcabyel'	NPri SVil
§ Million Bells Series	LRHS
- Million Bells Cherry = 'Sunbelchipi'PBR	LSou WGor
- Million Bells Crackling Fire = 'Sunbelfire'	LSou
- Million Bells Golden Terracotta = 'Sunbelsoil'	NPri
- Million Bells Lemon = 'Sunbelkic'	WGor
- Million Bells Orange Glow = 'Sunbelore'	LSou
- Million Bells Trailing Blue = 'Sunbelkubu'PBR	WGor
- Million Bells Trailing Fuchsia = 'Sunbelrkup' ♀H3	WGor
- Million Bells Trailing Ice = 'Sunbelkuriho'PBR	LSou NPri
- Million Bells Trailing Lavender Vein = 'Sunbelbura'PBR	WGor
- Million Bells Trailing Pink = 'Sunbelkupi'PBR ♀H3	LSou
(Noa Series) Noa Orange Eye	LSou NPri WGor
- Noa Ultra Purple	LSou
- Noa Yellow **new**	WGor
(Superbells Series) Superbells Amarena **new**	LAst
- Superbells Candy White = 'Uscali48'PBR	LSou
- Superbells Indigo = 'Uscali51'PBR	LAst LSou
- Superbells Magenta = 'Uscali17'PBR	LAst LSou NPri
- Superbells Orange **new**	LAst
- Superbells Pink = 'Uscali11'PBR ♀H3	LAst
- Superbells Royal Blue = 'Uscali4'PBR	LAst NPri
- Superbells Strawberry Pink = 'Uscali47'PBR	LAst
- Superbells White = 'Uscali6' **new**	LAst
- Superbells Yellow **new**	LAst

Calla (*Araceae*)

aethiopica	see *Zantedeschia aethiopica*
palustris	CRow CWat EHon EMFW EPfP LPBA MCCP MSKA NPer SWat WFar WMAq WPnP

Calliandra (*Mimosaceae*)

brevipes	see *C. selloi*
'Dixie Pink'	CCCN
portoricensis	CCCN
§ ***selloi***	GKev
surinamensis	CCCN
tweediei	CCCN

Callianthemum (*Ranunculaceae*)

coriandrifolium	GEdr GKev
kernerianum	WAbe

Callicarpa (*Verbenaceae*)

americana	CPLG NLar
- var. ***lactea***	CMCN
bodinieri	GKir NBir WFar
- var. ***giraldii***	GBin MGan MRav NLar WDin
- - 'Profusion' ♀H4	Widely available
cathayana	CBcs CMCN NLar
dichotoma	CPLG CTrG EBee ELan NLar WFar
- 'Issai'	EMil MBri MGos NLar SBch SPur
- 'Shirobana'	NLar
japonica	CPLG NLar
- B&SWJ 8587	WCru
- 'Koshima-no-homate'	MBri NLar
- 'Leucocarpa'	CBcs CMac CPLG EBee ELan EPfP MBNS MRav NLar SPer SPur WFar
- var. ***luxurians*** B&SWJ 8521	WCru
kwangtungensis	CBcs CMCN MBri NLar
mollis	CPLG NLar
shikokiana	NLar
× ***shirasawana***	NLar
yunnanensis	NLar

Callirhoe (*Malvaceae*)

involucrata	CSpr EBee GGar MWea NBur NWCA SMad WHrl

Callisia (*Commelinaceae*)

repens	MBri

Callistemon ✿ (*Myrtaceae*)

acuminatus	CCCN
'Awanga Dam'	ECou
citrinus	CHII CTri EBee ECou EPfP ERom EShb GGar MCot MSCN NHol SPlb WBrE WDin WHar
- 'Albus'	see *C. citrinus* 'White Anzac'
- 'Firebrand'	CDoC LRHS
- 'Splendens' ♀H3	Widely available
§ - 'White Anzac'	CMac ELan EPfP SPoG SSta
comboynensis	CCCN GBin

glaucus	see *C. speciosus*
laevis hort.	see *C. rugulosus*
linearifolius	LSRN
linearis ♀H3	CBcs CMac CTrC CTri ECou ECrN ELan EPfP EPla LRHS LSRN MDun MHer SCoo SLim SLon SPlb SRms SSpi SWvt WSHC
macropunctatus	SPlb
'Mauve Mist'	CCCN CDoC ELan ELon EPfP GBin LRHS MAsh
pachyphyllus	ECou
pallidus	CCCN CHEx CMHG CMac CWib ECou ELan EPfP GGar LRHS MAsh MRav SEND SPer SPlb SPoG SSta
paludosus	see *C. sieberi* DC.
'Perth Pink'	CBcs CCCN CDoC ELan EPfP LRHS SLim SPoG
phoeniceus	ECou
pinifolius	CTsd SPlb
§ ***pityoides***	CPLG ECou
- from Brown's Swamp, Australia	ECou
'Red Clusters'	CDoC CMac CTrG CTsd ELan IArd ISea LRHS MAsh MDun NEgg NLar NPri SBch SBod SChF SPoG SWvt
rigidus	CBcs CDoC CEnt CHEx CMHG CTri CWib ELan EPfP GGar IArd IFFs ISea LRHS MBlu MGos MMuc MRav NLar SBch SBod SWvt WDin
§ ***rugulosus***	CCCN EQua IDee IFFs NCob SWvt
salignus ♀H3	CBcs CCCN CDoC CDul CEnt CHEx CTrC CTri EPfP GLin ISea LRHS MHer MRav NEgg SEND SLim SPer WBVN WDin
- Flaming Fire = 'Flaipp'	EMil NLar
sieberi misapplied	see *C. pityoides*
§ ***sieberi*** DC.	CDoC CMHG CTrC ECou ELan EPfP GGar LRHS MMuc NBir NLar NPal SLim SPlb SPoG WFar
§ ***speciosus***	CDul CTrC NLar SEND SPlb SPoG
subulatus	CDoC CHEx CTrC ECou GGal MCCP NLar SAPC SArc SPlb WMoo
- 'Crimson Tail'	CWCL GBin MMuc NHol NLar SBch SEND
- 'Packer's Selection'	ECou
viminalis	CBcs CCCN SGar SPlb
- 'Captain Cook'	CAlb CMac ECou IDee LRHS LSRN MDun NLar SRms SWvt
- 'Endeavor'	CCCN
- 'Little John'	CAlb CBcs CSBt CTrC CWSG ECou LRHS LSRN MDun NLar SBch SPad SWvt
'Violaceus'	IFFs
viridiflorus	CTrC ECou GGal GGar GQui LRHS MCCP SEND SPlb SWal WGwG
- 'County Park Dwarf'	ECou
- 'Sunshine'	ECou
'White Anzac'	see *C. citrinus* 'White Anzac'

Callitriche (*Callitrichaceae*)

autumnalis	see *C. hermaphroditica*
§ ***hermaphroditica***	EPfP WMAq
§ ***palustris***	EHon EMFW
stagnalis	NSco
verna	see *C. palustris*

Callitris (*Cupressaceae*)

rhomboidea	CDoC CTrC GGar

Calluna ✿ (*Ericaceae*)

vulgaris	EBWF
- 'Aberdeen'	SHeS
- 'Adrie'	SHeS
- 'Alba Argentea'	SHeS
- 'Alba Aurea'	MBar SHeS
- 'Alba Carlton'	SHeS
- 'Alba Dumosa'	SHeS
- 'Alba Elata'	MBar SHeS
- 'Alba Elegans'	SHeS
- 'Alba Elongata'	see *C. vulgaris* 'Mair's Variety'
- 'Alba Erecta'	SHeS
- 'Alba Jae'	MBar SHeS
- 'Alba Minor'	SHeS
- 'Alba Multiflora'	SHeS
- 'Alba Pilosa'	SHeS
§ - 'Alba Plena' (d)	MBar SHeS
- 'Alba Praecox'	SHeS
- 'Alba Pumila'	MBar SHeS
§ - 'Alba Rigida'	MBar SHeS SRms
- 'Alec Martin' (d)	SHeS
- 'Alex Warwick'	SHeS
- 'Alexandra' PBR ♀H4	LRHS NHol SHeS SPoG SRms
- 'Alice Knight'	SHeS
- 'Alicia' PBR (Garden Girls Series) ♀H4	CBcs LRHS NHol SHeS SPoG
- 'Alieke'	SHeS
- 'Alina'	SHeS
- 'Alison Yates'	MBar SHeS
- 'Allegretto'	SHeS
- 'Allegro' ♀H4	EPfP MBar MMuc SHeS SPer SRms
- 'Alportii'	GKir MBar SHeS
- 'Alportii Praecox'	MBar SHeS
- 'Alys Sutcliffe'	SHeS
- 'Amanda Wain'	SHeS
- 'Amethyst' PBR (Garden Girls Series)	LRHS MBar NHol SHeS SPoG
- 'Amilto'	CBcs SHeS SRms
- 'Andrew Proudley'	MBar SHeS
- 'Anette' PBR (Garden Girls Series) ♀H4	LRHS MBar SHeS
- 'Angela Wain'	SHeS
- 'Anna'	SHeS
- 'Annabel' (d)	SHeS
- 'Anne Dobbin'	SHeS
- 'Annegret'	see *C. vulgaris* 'Marlies'
- 'Anneke'	SHeS
- 'Annemarie' (d) ♀H4	CSBt EPfP MBar NHol SCoo SHeS SPer SPlb SRms
- 'Anne's Zwerg'	SHeS SRms
- 'Anthony Davis' ♀H4	MBar NHol SHeS
- 'Anthony Wain'	SHeS
- 'Anton'	SHeS
- 'Antrujo Gold'	SHeS
- 'Aphrodite' PBR (Garden Girls Series)	CBcs SHeS
- 'Apollo'	SHeS
- 'Applecross' (d)	SHeS
- 'Arabella' PBR	SHeS SRms
- 'Argentea'	MBar SHeS
- 'Ariadne'	SHeS
- 'Arina'	SHeS
- 'Arran Gold'	MBar SHeS
- 'Ashgarth Amber'	SHeS
- 'Ashgarth Amethyst'	SHeS
- 'Ashgarth Shell Pink'	SHeS
- 'Asterix'	SHeS
- 'Atalanta'	SHeS
- 'Athene' PBR **new**	LRHS
- 'Atholl Gold'	SHeS
- 'August Beauty'	SHeS
- 'Aurea'	SHeS
- 'Aurora'	SHeS
- 'Autumn Glow'	SHeS
- 'Babette'	SHeS

	– 'Baby Ben'	SHeS
	– 'Baby Wicklow'	SHeS
	– 'Barbara'	SHeS
	– 'Barbara Fleur'	SHeS
	– 'Barja'	SHeS
	– 'Barnett Anley'	SHeS
	– 'Battle of Arnhem'	MBar SHeS
	– 'Bayport'	SHeS
	– 'Beechwood Crimson'	SHeS
	– 'Bella Rosa'	SHeS
	– 'Ben Nevis'	SHeS
	– 'Bennachie Bronze'	SHeS
	– 'Bennachie Prostrate'	SHeS
	– 'Beoley Crimson'	MBar SHeS
	– 'Beoley Crimson Variegated' (v)	SHeS
	– 'Beoley Gold' ♀H4	CSBt CTri EPfP GKir MBar MGos NHol SHeS SRms
	– 'Beoley Silver'	MBar SHeS
	– 'Bernadette'	SHeS
	– 'Betty Baum'	SHeS
	– 'Bispingen'	SHeS
	– 'Blazeaway'	CTri EPfP GKir MBar NHol SHeS SPer SRms
	– 'Blueness'	SHeS
	– 'Bognie'	SHeS
	– 'Bonfire Brilliance'	CSBt MBar NHol SHeS
	– 'Bonita'PBR (Garden Girls Series)	SHeS
	– 'Bonne's Darkness'	SHeS
	– 'Bonsaï'	SHeS
	– 'Boreray'	SHeS
	– 'Boskoop'	MBar NHol SHeS
	– 'Bradford'	SHeS
	– 'Braemar'	SHeS
	– 'Braeriach'	SHeS
	– 'Branchy Anne'	SHeS
	– 'Bray Head'	MBar SHeS
	– 'Brita Elisabeth' (d)	SHeS
	– 'Bronze Beauty'	SHeS
	– 'Bud Lyle'	SHeS
	– 'Bunsall'	SHeS
	– 'Buxton Snowdrift'	SHeS
	– 'C.W. Nix'	CSBt MBar SHeS
	– 'Caerketton White'	SHeS
	– 'Caleb Threlkeld'	SHeS
	– 'Calf of Man'	SHeS
	– 'Californian Midge'	MBar NHol SHeS
	– 'Camla Variety'	SHeS
	– 'Carl Röders' (d)	SHeS
	– 'Carmen'	SHeS
	– 'Carngold'	SHeS
	– 'Carole Chapman'	MBar SHeS
	– 'Carolyn'	SHeS
	– 'Cassa'	SHeS
	– 'Catherine'	SHeS
	– 'Catherine Anne'	SHeS
	– 'Celtic Gold'	SHeS
	– 'Charles Chapman'	SHeS
§	– 'Chernobyl' (d)	NHol SHeS
	– 'Chindit'	SHeS
I	– 'Christin'	SHeS
	– 'Christina'	SHeS
	– 'Cilcennin Common'	SHeS
	– 'Clare Carpet'	SHeS
	– 'Coby'	SHeS
	– 'Coccinea'	MBar SHeS
	– 'Colette'	SHeS
	– 'Con Brio'	MMuc SHeS SRms
	– 'Copper Glow'	SHeS
	– 'Coral Island'	MBar SHeS
	– 'Corbett's Red'	SHeS
	– 'Corrie's White'	SHeS
	– 'Cottswood Gold'	NHol SHeS SRms
	– 'County Wicklow' (d) ♀H4	CBcs CTri EPfP GGar GKir MBar MMuc NBlu NHol SHeS SRms
	– 'Craig Rossie'	SHeS
	– 'Crail Orange'	SHeS
	– 'Cramond' (d)	MBar SHeS
	– 'Cream Steving'	SHeS
	– 'Crimson Glory'	MBar SHeS
	– 'Crimson Sunset'	SHeS
	– 'Crinkly Tuft'	SHeS
	– 'Crowborough Beacon'	SHeS
	– 'Cuprea'	EPfP MBar NHol SHeS
	– 'Dainty Bess'	MBar MSwo SHeS
	– 'Dapiali'	SHeS
	– 'Dark Alicia'PBR	SHeS
	– 'Dark Beauty'PBR (d) ♀H4	CBcs EPfP LRHS MBar NDlv NHol SHeS
	– 'Dark Star' (d) ♀H4	CBcs EPfP MBar MGos MMuc NHol SCoo SHeS SRms
	– 'Darkness' ♀H4	CTri EPfP MBar NHol SCoo SHeS SRms
	– 'Darleyensis'	MBar SHeS
	– 'Dart's Amethyst'	SHeS
	– 'Dart's Beauty'	SHeS
	– 'Dart's Brilliant'	SHeS
	– 'Dart's Flamboyant'	SHeS
	– 'Dart's Gold'	MBar NHol SHeS
	– 'Dart's Hedgehog'	SHeS
	– 'Dart's Parakeet'	SHeS
	– 'Dart's Parrot'	SHeS
	– 'Dart's Silver Rocket'	SHeS
	– 'Dart's Squirrel'	SHeS
	– 'David Eason'	SHeS
	– 'David Hagenaars'	SHeS
	– 'David Hutton'	MBar SHeS
	– 'David Platt' (d)	SHeS
	– 'Denkewitz'	SHeS
	– 'Denny Pratt'	SHeS
	– 'Desiree'	SHeS
	– 'Devon' (d)	SHeS
	– 'Diana'	SHeS
	– 'Dickson's Blazes'	SHeS
	– 'Dirry'	NHol SHeS
	– 'Doctor Murray's White'	see *C. vulgaris* 'Mullardoch'
	– 'Doris Rushworth'	SHeS
	– 'Drum-ra'	MBar SHeS SRms
	– 'Dunnet Lime'	SHeS SPlb
	– 'Dunnydeer'	SHeS
	– 'Dunwood'	MBar SHeS
§	– 'Durford Wood'	SHeS
	– 'Dwingeloo Delight'	SHeS
	– 'E.F. Brown'	SHeS
	– 'E. Hoare'	MBar SHeS
	– 'Easter-bonfire'	NHol SHeS
	– 'Eckart Miessner'	SHeS
	– 'Edith Godbolt'	SHeS
	– 'Elaine'	SHeS
	– 'Elegant Pearl'	MBar SHeS
	– 'Elegantissima'	MMuc SHeS
	– 'Eleonore' (d)	SHeS
	– 'Elkstone White'	MBar SHeS
	– 'Ellen'	SHeS
	– 'Ellie Barbour'	SHeS
	– 'Elly'	SHeS
	– 'Else Frye' (d)	SHeS
	– 'Elsie Purnell' (d) ♀H4	EPfP MBar MGos NHol SHeS SPlb SRms
	– 'Emerald Jock'	SHeS
	– 'Emma Louise Tuke'	SHeS
	– 'Eric Easton'	SHeS
	– 'Eskdale Gold'	SHeS

	Cultivar	Suppliers
	- 'Eurosa'	SHeS
	- 'Fairy'	SHeS
	- 'Falling Star'	SHeS
	- 'Feuerwerk'	SHeS
§	- 'Finale'	MBar SHeS
	- 'Findling'	SHeS
	- 'Fire King'	MBar SHeS
	- 'Fire Star'	SHeS
	- 'Firebreak'	MBar NHol SHeS
	- 'Firefly' ♀H4	CBcs CSBt EPfP MBar MMuc NHol SHeS SRms
	- 'Flamingo'	CSBt MBar MMuc MSwo NHol SHeS SPer SRms
	- 'Flatling'	SHeS
	- 'Flore Pleno' (d)	MBar SHeS
	- 'Floriferous'	SHeS
	- 'Florrie Spicer'	SHeS
	- 'Fokko' (d)	SHeS
	- 'Fort Bragg'	SHeS
	- 'Fortyniner Gold'	SHeS
	- 'Foxhollow Wanderer'	MBar SHeS
	- 'Foxii'	SHeS
	- 'Foxii Floribunda'	MBar SHeS
	- 'Foxii Lett's Form'	see *C. vulgaris* 'Mousehole', 'Velvet Dome'
	- 'Foxii Nana'	MBar NHol SHeS SRms
	- 'Foya'	SHeS
	- 'Fraser's Old Gold'	SHeS
	- 'Fred J. Chapple'	MBar NBlu SHeS
	- 'Fréjus'	SHeS
	- 'French Grey'	SHeS
	- 'Fritz Kircher' PBR	SHeS
	- 'Gaia'	SHeS
	- Garden Girls Series	LRHS MMuc
	- 'Gerda'	SHeS
	- 'Ginkel's Glorie'	SHeS
	- 'Glasa'	SHeS
	- 'Glen Mashie'	SHeS
	- 'Glencoe' (d)	MBar SHeS
	- 'Glendoick Silver'	SHeS
	- 'Glenfiddich'	CSBt MBar NHol SHeS
	- 'Glenlivet'	MBar SHeS
	- 'Glenmorangie'	MBar SHeS
	- 'Gloucester Boy'	SHeS
	- 'Gnome'	SHeS
	- 'Gold Charm'	SHeS
	- 'Gold Finch'	SHeS
	- 'Gold Flame'	MBar SHeS
	- Gold Hamilton	see *C. vulgaris* 'Chernobyl'
	- 'Gold Haze' ♀H4	CTri GKir MBar NHol SCoo SHeS SPer SRms
	- 'Gold Knight'	EPfP MBar SHeS
	- 'Gold Kup'	MBar SHeS
	- 'Gold Mist'	NBlu SHeS
	- 'Gold Spronk'	SHeS
	- 'Goldcarmen'	SHeS
	- 'Golden Blazeaway'	SHeS
	- 'Golden Carpet'	CSBt MBar MGos NDlv NHol SHeS SPer SRms
	- 'Golden Dew'	SHeS
	- 'Golden Dream' (d)	SHeS
	- 'Golden Feather'	MBar SHeS
	- 'Golden Fleece'	SHeS SRms
	- 'Golden Max'	SHeS
	- 'Golden Rivulet'	MBar MSwo SHeS
	- 'Golden Turret'	NHol SHeS
	- 'Golden Wonder' (d)	SHeS
	- 'Goldsworth Crimson'	CSBt SHeS
	- 'Goldsworth Crimson Variegated' (v)	MBar SHeS
	- 'Goscote Wine'	SHeS
	- 'Grasmeriensis'	MBar SHeS

	Cultivar	Suppliers
	- 'Great Comp'	MBar
	- 'Green Cardinal'	SHeS
	- 'Grey Carpet'	MBar SHeS SRms
	- 'Grijsje'	SHeS
	- 'Grizabella'	SHeS
	- 'Grizzly'	SHeS
	- 'Grönsinka'	SHeS
	- 'Guinea Gold'	MBar SHeS
§	- 'H.E. Beale' (d)	CTri EPfP MBar MGos NHol SHeS
	- 'Hamlet Green'	MBar SHeS
	- 'Hammondii'	SHeS
	- 'Hammondii Aureifolia'	MBar SHeS SPlb
	- 'Hammondii Rubrifolia'	MBar SHeS SRms
	- 'Harlekin'	SHeS
	- 'Harry Gibbon' (d)	SHeS
	- 'Harten's Findling'	SHeS
	- 'Hatje's Herbstfeuer' (d)	SHeS
	- 'Hayesensis'	SHeS
	- 'Heidberg'	SHeS
	- 'Heidepracht'	SHeS
	- 'Heidesinfonie'	SHeS
	- 'Heideteppich'	SHeS
	- 'Heidezwerg'	SHeS
	- 'Heike' (d)	SHeS
	- 'Herbert Mitchell'	SHeS
	- 'Hester'	SHeS
	- 'Hetty'	SHeS
	- 'Hibernica'	MBar SHeS
	- 'Hiemalis'	MBar SHeS
	- 'Hiemalis Southcote'	see *C. vulgaris* 'Durford Wood'
	- Highland Cream	see *C. vulgaris* 'Punch's Dessert'
	- 'Highland Rose'	SHeS SPlb SRms
	- 'Highland Spring'	SHeS
	- 'Hilda Turberfield'	SHeS
	- 'Hillbrook Limelight'	SHeS
	- 'Hillbrook Orange'	MBar SHeS
	- 'Hillbrook Sparkler'	SHeS
	- 'Hinton White'	SHeS
	- 'Hirsuta Albiflora'	SHeS
	- 'Hirsuta Typica'	SHeS
	- 'Hollandia'	SHeS
	- 'Holstein'	SHeS
	- 'Hookstone'	MBar SHeS
	- 'Hoyerhagen'	SHeS
§	- 'Hugh Nicholson'	SHeS
	- 'Humpty Dumpty'	MBar NHol SHeS
	- 'Hypnoides'	SHeS
	- 'Ide's Double' (d)	SHeS
	- 'Inchcolm'	SHeS
	- 'Inchkeith'	SHeS
	- 'Ineke'	MBar SHeS
	- 'Inge'	SHeS
	- 'Ingrid Bouter' (d)	SHeS
	- 'Inshriach Bronze'	MBar SHeS
	- 'Iris van Leyen'	MBar SHeS
	- 'Islay Mist'	SHeS
	- 'Isle of Hirta'	MBar SHeS
	- 'Isobel Frye'	MBar SHeS
	- 'Isobel Hughes' (d)	MBar SHeS
	- 'J.H. Hamilton' (d) ♀H4	CTri GKir MBar NHol SHeS SRms
	- 'Jan'	SHeS
	- 'Jan Dekker'	MBar NHol SHeS
	- 'Janice Chapman'	MBar SHeS
	- 'Japanese White'	SHeS
	- 'Jenny'	SHeS
	- 'Jill'	SHeS
	- 'Jimmy Dyce' (d)	SHeS
	- 'Joan Sparkes' (d)	MBar SHeS
	- 'Jochen'	SHeS
	- 'Johan Slegers'	SHeS
	- John Denver	see *C. vulgaris* 'Marleen Select'
	- 'John F. Letts'	MBar NHol SHeS SRms

- 'Johnson's Variety' MBar SHeS
- 'Jos' Lemon' SHeS
- 'Jos' Whitie' SHeS
- 'Josefine' SHeS
- 'Joseph's Coat' SHeS
- 'Joy Vanstone' ♀H4 EPfP GKir MBar MGos NHol SHeS SRms
- 'Julia' SHeS
- 'Julie Ann Platt' SHeS
- 'Juno' SHeS
- 'Kaiser' SHeS
- 'Karin Blum' SHeS
- 'Kermit' SHeS
- 'Kerstin' ♀H4 MBar MMuc MSwo NHol SHeS SPlb SRms
- 'Kerstin Jacke' NHol
- 'Kinlochruel' (d) ♀H4 CBcs CSBt CTri EPfP GGar GKir MBar MGos NBlu NHol SHeS SPlb SRms
- 'Kir Royal' SHeS
- 'Kirby White' MBar NDlv NHol SHeS SPlb
- 'Kirsty Anderson' SHeS
- 'Kit Hill' MBar SHeS
- 'Knaphill' SHeS
- 'Kontrast' SHeS
- 'Kuphaldtii' MBar SHeS
- 'Kuppendorf' SHeS
- 'Kynance' MBar SHeS
- 'Lady Maithe' SHeS
- 'Lambstails' MBar SHeS
- 'L'Ancresse' SHeS
- 'Larissa'PBR SHeS
- 'Lemon Gem' SHeS
- 'Lemon Queen' SHeS
- 'Leprechaun' NHol
- 'Leslie Slinger' MBar NHol SHeS
- 'Lewis Lilac' SHeS
- 'Liebestraum' SHeS
- 'Lilac Elegance' SHeS
- 'Lime Glade' SHeS
- 'Lime Gold' SHeS
- 'Little John' LSRN SHeS
- 'Llanbedrog Pride' (d) MBar SHeS
- 'Loch Turret' MBar SHeS
- 'Loch-na-Seil' MBar SHeS
- 'Long White' MBar SHeS
- 'Loni' SHeS
- 'Lüneberg Heath' SHeS
- 'Lyle's Late White' SHeS
- 'Lyle's Surprise' MBar SHeS
- 'Lyndon Proudley' SHeS
- 'Macdonald of Glencoe' SHeS

§ - 'Mair's Variety' ♀H4 MBar SHeS
- 'Mallard' SHeS
- 'Manitoba' SHeS
- 'Manuel' SHeS
- 'Marianne' SHeS
- 'Marie' SHeS
- 'Marion Blum' MBar SHeS
- 'Marleen' LRHS MBar NHol SHeS

§ - 'Marleen Select' SHeS

§ - 'Marlies' SHeS
- 'Martha Hermann' SHeS
- 'Martine Langenberg' SHeS
- 'Masquerade' MBar SHeS
- 'Matita' SHeS
- 'Mauvelyn' SHeS
- 'Mazurka' SHeS
- 'Melanie' (Garden Girls Series) LRHS MBar MSwo NHol SHeS
- 'Mick Jamieson' (d) SHeS
- 'Mies' SHeS
- 'Minima' MBar SHeS
- 'Minima Smith's Variety' MBar SHeS
- 'Miniöxabäck' SHeS
- 'Minty' SHeS
- 'Mirato' SHeS
- 'Mirelle' SHeS
- 'Miss Muffet' NHol SHeS
- 'Molecule' MBar SHeS
- 'Monika' (d) SHeS
- 'Moon Glow' SHeS
- 'Mountain Snow' SHeS

§ - 'Mousehole' MBar NHol SHeS
- 'Mrs Alf' SHeS
- 'Mrs E. Wilson' (d) SHeS
- 'Mrs Pat' MBar NHol SHeS
- 'Mrs Pinxteren' SHeS
- 'Mrs Ronald Gray' MBar SHeS
- 'Mullach Mor' SHeS

§ - 'Mullardoch' MBar SHeS
- 'Mullion' ♀H4 MBar SHeS
- 'Multicolor' MBar NHol SHeS SRms
- 'Murielle Dobson' MBar SHeS

§ - 'My Dream' (d) ♀H4 CSBt EPfP MBar NHol SCoo SHeS
- 'Nana' SHeS
- 'Nana Compacta' MBar SHeS
- 'Natasja' SHeS
- 'Naturpark' MBar SHeS
- 'Nele' (d) SHeS
- 'Nico' SHeS
- 'Nofretete' SHeS
- Nordlicht see *C. vulgaris* 'Skone'
- 'October White' SHeS
- 'Odette' SHeS
- 'Oiseval' SHeS
- 'Old Rose' SHeS
- 'Olive Turner' SHeS
- 'Olympic Gold' SHeS
- 'Orange and Gold' SHeS
- 'Orange Carpet' SHeS
- 'Orange Max' NHol SHeS
- 'Orange Queen' CSBt MBar SHeS
- 'Öxabäck' MBar SHeS
- 'Oxshott Common' GQui MBar SHeS
- 'Pallida' SHeS
- 'Parsons' Gold' SHeS
- 'Parsons' Grey Selected' SHeS
- 'Pastell' (d) SHeS
- 'Pat's Gold' SHeS
- 'Peace' SHeS
- 'Pearl Drop' MBar SHeS
- 'Peggy' SHeS
- 'Penhale' SHeS
- 'Penny Bun' SHeS
- 'Pennyacre Gold' SHeS
- 'Pennyacre Lemon' SHeS
- 'Pepper and Salt' see *C. vulgaris* 'Hugh Nicholson'
- 'Perestrojka' SHeS
- 'Peter Sparkes' (d) ♀H4 CBcs CSBt EPfP MBar MGos NHol SHeS SRms
- 'Petra' SHeS
- 'Pewter Plate' MBar SHeS
- 'Pink Alicia'PBR (Garden Girls Series) LRHS SHeS
- 'Pink Beale' see *C. vulgaris* 'H.E. Beale'
- 'Pink Dream' (d) SHeS
- 'Pink Gown' SHeS
- 'Pink Spreader' SHeS
- 'Pink Tips' SHeS
- 'Plantarium' SHeS
- 'Platt's Surprise' (d) SHeS
- 'Polly' SHeS
- 'Poolster' SHeS

	Cultivar	Suppliers
	- 'Porth Wen White'	SHeS
	- 'Prizewinner'	SHeS
*	- 'Procumbens'	SHeS
	- 'Prostrata Flagelliformis'	SHeS
	- 'Prostrate Orange'	MBar SHeS
§	- 'Punch's Dessert'	SHeS
	- 'Purple Passion'	EPfP
	- 'Pygmaea'	MBar SHeS
	- 'Pyramidalis'	SHeS
	- 'Pyrenaica'	MBar SHeS
	- 'R.A. McEwan'	SHeS
	- 'Radnor' (d) ♀H4	CSBt MBar SHeS
	- 'Radnor Gold' (d)	MBar SHeS
	- 'Raket'	SHeS
	- 'Ralph Purnell'	MBar SHeS
	- 'Ralph Purnell Select'	SHeS
	- 'Ralph's Pearl'	SHeS
	- 'Ralph's Red'	SHeS
	- 'Randall's Crimson'	SHeS
	- 'Rannoch'	SHeS
	- 'Rebecca's Red'	SHeS SRms
	- 'Red Carpet'	MBar SHeS
	- 'Red Favorit' (d)	CBcs SHeS SRms
	- 'Red Fred'	NHol SHeS
	- 'Red Haze'	EPfP MBar NHol SHeS
	- 'Red Max'	SHeS
	- 'Red Pimpernel'	EPfP MBar NHol SHeS
	- 'Red Rug'	SHeS
	- 'Red Star' (d)	MBar NHol SHeS
	- 'Red Wings'	SHeS
	- 'Redbud'	SHeS
	- 'Redgauntlet'	SHeS
	- 'Reini'	SHeS
	- 'Rica'	SHeS
	- 'Richard Cooper'	MBar SHeS
	- 'Rieanne'	SHeS
	- 'Rigida Prostrata'	see *C. vulgaris* 'Alba Rigida'
	- 'Rivington'	SHeS
	- 'Robber Knight'	SHeS
	- 'Robert Chapman' ♀H4	CSBt CTri GKir MBar NHol SHeS SRms
	- 'Rock Spray'	SHeS
	- 'Röding'	SHeS
	- 'Rokoko'	SHeS
	- 'Roland Haagen' ♀H4	MBar SHeS
	- 'Roma'	MBar SHeS
	- 'Romina'	LRHS MSwo NHol SHeS
	- 'Ronas Hill'	SHeS
	- 'Roodkapje'	SHeS
	- 'Rosalind' ambig.	EPfP MBar
	- 'Rosalind, Crastock Heath'	SHeS
	- 'Rosalind, Underwood's'	EPfP NHol SHeS
	- 'Ross Hutton'	SHeS
	- 'Roswitha'	SHeS
	- 'Roter Oktober'	SHeS
	- 'Rotfuchs'	SHeS
	- 'Ruby Slinger'	MBar NHol SHeS
	- 'Rusty Triumph'	SHeS
	- 'Ruth Sparkes' (d)	MBar NHol SHeS
	- 'Sabrina' (d)	SHeS
	- 'Saima'	SHeS
	- 'Saint Nick'	MBar SHeS
	- 'Salland'	SHeS
	- 'Sally Anne Proudley'	MBar SHeS
	- 'Salmon Leap'	MBar NHol SHeS
	- 'Sam Hewitt'	SHeS
	- 'Sampford Sunset'	SHeS
	- 'Sandhammaren'	SHeS
	- 'Sandwood Bay'	SHeS
	- 'Sandy'PBR (Garden Girls Series)	LRHS NHol SHeS SPoG
	- 'Sarah Platt' (d)	SHeS
	- 'Saskia'	SHeS
	- 'Schneewolke'	SHeS
	- 'Scholje's Jimmy'	SHeS
	- 'Scholje's Rubin' (d)	SHeS
	- 'Scholje's Super Star' (d)	SHeS
	- 'Schurig's Sensation' (d)	MBar SHeS
	- 'Schurig's Wonder' (d)	SHeS
	- 'Scotch Mist'	SHeS
	- 'Sedloňov'	SHeS
	- 'Sellingsloh'	SHeS
	- 'September Pink'	SHeS
	- 'Serlei'	MBar SHeS
	- 'Serlei Aurea' ♀H4	CSBt EPfP MBar NHol SHeS SRms
	- 'Serlei Grandiflora'	MBar SHeS
	- 'Serlei Purpurea'	SHeS
	- 'Serlei Rubra'	SHeS
	- 'Sesam'	SHeS
	- 'Sesse'	SHeS
	- 'Shirley'	MBar SHeS
	- 'Silberspargel'	SHeS
	- 'Silver Cloud'	MBar SHeS
	- 'Silver Fox'	SHeS
	- 'Silver King'	MBar SHeS
	- 'Silver Knight'	CSBt EPfP GGar MBar MGos NHol SHeS SPer SPlb SRms
	- 'Silver Pearl'	SHeS
	- 'Silver Queen' ♀H4	MBar NHol SHeS SRms
	- 'Silver Rose' ♀H4	MBar SHeS
	- 'Silver Sandra'	SHeS
	- 'Silver Spire'	MBar SHeS
	- 'Silver Stream'	MBar SHeS
	- 'Silvie'	SHeS
	- 'Simone'	SHeS
	- 'Sir Anthony Hopkins'	SHeS
	- 'Sir John Charrington' ♀H4	CSBt EPfP MBar MGos NHol SHeS
	- 'Sirsson'	MBar SHeS
	- 'Sister Anne' ♀H4	CSBt EPfP MMuc NBlu NHol SHeS SRms
	- 'Skipper'	MBar NHol SHeS
§	- 'Skone' (v)	SHeS
	- 'Snowball'	see *C. vulgaris* 'My Dream'
	- 'Snowflake'	SHeS
	- 'Soay'	MBar SHeS
	- 'Sonja' (d)	SHeS
	- 'Sonning' (d)	SHeS
	- 'Sonny Boy'	SHeS
	- 'Sophia' (d)	SHeS
	- 'Sparkling Stars'	NHol SHeS
	- 'Sphinx'	SHeS
	- 'Spicata'	SHeS
	- 'Spicata Aurea'	MBar SHeS
	- 'Spicata Nana'	SHeS
	- 'Spider'	SHeS
	- 'Spitfire'	MBar NHol SHeS
	- 'Spook'	SHeS
	- 'Spring Cream' ♀H4	GGar GKir MBar MMuc NHol SHeS SPoG
	- 'Spring Glow'	MBar SHeS
	- 'Spring Torch'	CSBt GGar GKir MBar NHol SCoo SHeS SPer SPoG SRms
	- 'Springbank'	MBar SHeS
	- 'Stag's Horn'	SHeS
I	- 'Startler'	SHeS
	- 'Stefanie'	LRHS NHol SHeS SRms
	- 'Stranger'	SHeS
	- 'Strawberry Delight' (d)	EPfP SHeS
	- 'Summer Elegance'	SHeS
	- 'Summer Gold'	SRms
	- 'Summer Orange'	MBar NHol SHeS
	- 'Summer White' (d)	SHeS

- 'Sunningdale'	see *C. vulgaris* 'Finale'
- 'Sunrise'	CSBt EPfP MBar MGos SHeS
- 'Sunset' ΨH4	CSBt MBar SHeS SRms
- 'Sunset Glow'	SHeS
- 'Talisker'	SHeS
- 'Tenella'	SHeS
- 'Tenuis'	MBar SHeS
- 'Terrick's Orange'	SHeS
- 'The Pygmy'	SHeS
- 'Theresa' (Garden Girls Series)	SHeS
- 'Tib' (d) ΨH4	CSBt MBar NBlu NHol SHeS SRms
- 'Tijdens Copper'	SHeS
- 'Tino'	SHeS
- 'Tom Thumb'	MBar SHeS
- 'Tomentosa Alba'	SHeS
- 'Torogay'	SHeS
- 'Torulosa'	SHeS
- 'Tremans'	SHeS
- 'Tricolorifolia'	EPfP NHol SHeS SPer
- 'Underwoodii'	MBar SHeS
- 'Unity'	SHeS
- 'Valorian'	SHeS
- 'Van Beek'	SHeS
§ - 'Velvet Dome'	MBar SHeS
- 'Velvet Fascination' ΨH4	EPfP MBar MGos NHol SHeS
- 'Violet Bamford'	SHeS
- 'Visser's Fancy'	SHeS
- 'Walter Ingwersen'	SHeS
- 'Waquoit Brightness'	SHeS
- 'Westerlee Gold'	SHeS
- 'Westerlee Green'	SHeS
- 'Westphalia'	SHeS
- 'White Bouquet'	see *C. vulgaris* 'Alba Plena'
- 'White Carpet'	MBar SHeS
- 'White Coral' (d)	EPfP MGos SHeS
- 'White Gold'	SHeS
- 'White Gown'	SHeS
- 'White Lawn' ΨH4	MBar MMuc MSwo NDlv NHol SHeS SRms
- 'White Mite'	MBar SHeS
- 'White Pearl' (d)	SHeS
- 'White Princess'	see *C. vulgaris* 'White Queen'
§ - 'White Queen'	MBar SHeS
- 'White Star' (d)	SHeS
- 'Whiteness'	MBar SHeS
- 'Wickwar Flame' ΨH4	CBcs CSBt EPfP MBar MGos MMuc NHol SHeS SPer SPlb SRms
- 'Wilma'	SHeS
- 'Wingates Gem'	SHeS
- 'Wingates Gold'	SHeS
- 'Winter Chocolate'	CSBt EPfP MBar MSwo NDlv NHol SHeS SPer
- 'Winter Fire'	SHeS
- 'Winter Red'	SHeS
- 'Wollmer's Weisse' (d)	SHeS
- 'Wood Close'	SHeS
- 'Yellow Basket'	SHeS
- 'Yellow Beauty'PBR	SHeS
- 'Yellow Globe'	SHeS
- 'Yellow One'	SHeS
- 'Yvette's Gold'	SHeS
- 'Yvette's Silver'	SHeS
- 'Yvonne Clare'	SHeS

Calocedrus (*Cupressaceae*)

§ ***decurrens*** ΨH4	CBcs CDoC CDul CLnd CMac CTho CTri EHul EPfP EWTr GKir IFFs LRHS MBar MBlu MGos MMuc NPCo NWea SBch SLim SPer SPoG WEve WFar WMou
- 'Aureovariegata' (v)	CBcs CWib EHul LRHS MBar MBlu MBri NLar SCoo SLim SPoG WEve WFar
- 'Berrima Gold'	CDoC CKen EPfP GKir LRHS MGos NLar SLim SPoG WEve
- 'Columnaris'	LMaj
§ - 'Depressa'	CKen
- 'Intricata'	CKen NLar SLim
- 'Maupin Glow' (v)	NLar SLim
- 'Nana'	see *C. decurrens* 'Depressa'
- 'Pillar'	CKen MBri NLar
formosana	WFar

Calocephalus (*Asteraceae*)

'Silver Sand'	LSou SVil

Calochortus (*Liliaceae*)

'Cupido'PBR	EBrs ECho GKev LAma
gunnisonii	LFur
invenustus	ECho
luteus Douglas ex Lindl.	EPot
- 'Golden Orb'PBR	CGrW EBrs ECho LAma LFur
splendens	LAma
- 'Violet Queen'	CGrW ECho LAma
superbus	EBrs ECho EPot
'Symphony'	EBrs ECho EPot LAma
uniflorus	EPot
venustus	CGrW EBrs ECho EPot LAma

Calomeria (*Asteraceae*)

§ ***amaranthoides***	WJek

Calonyction see *Ipomoea*

Calopsis (*Restionaceae*)

paniculata	CCCN CDTJ CHEx CTrC CTsd IArd MAvo WPGP

Caloscordum (*Alliaceae*)

§ ***neriniflorum***	CPom EBur WAbe WCot

Calothamnus (*Myrtaceae*)

quadrifidus	ECou
validus	SPlb

Caltha ✿ (*Ranunculaceae*)

appendiculata new	EPot
'Auenwald'	CLAP CRow
'Honeydew'	CLAP CRow EBee LRHS WPGP
howellii	see *C. leptosepala* subsp. *howellii*
introloba	SWat
laeta	see *C. palustris* var. *palustris*
leptosepala	CLAP CRow EBee EPot LLHF NLar
§ - subsp. ***howellii***	EBee GKev
natans	CRow
palustris ΨH4	Widely available
- var. ***alba***	Widely available
- var. ***barthei***	CFir GEdr
- - f. ***atrorubra***	GEdr
- var. ***enkoso*** new	EBee
- 'Flore Pleno' (d) ΨH4	Widely available
- 'Marilyn'	CLAP
- 'Multiplex' (d)	EBee GBuc SRot
§ - var. ***palustris***	CBen CBre CRow ECha EHon ELan EMFW GGar LPBA SWat WFar
- - 'Plena' (d)	CRow CWat EPfP GGar LRHS MCot MSKA NBPC WFar
- var. ***radicans***	CRow
- - 'Flore Pleno' (d)	CRow
- 'Semiplena' (d)	EBee
- 'Stagnalis'	CRow MSKA
- Trotter's form	GBuc
- 'Tyermannii'	CRow

	Name	Suppliers
N	***polypetala*** misapplied	see *C. palustris* var. *palustris*
N	***polypetala*** Hochst. ex Lorent	CLAP CWat EBee EWll GBuc GCal GKir MSCN MSKA NPer SDix SMad SWat WBor WMAq
	- from Turkey	GBuc SGSe
	sagittata	CRow WSHC

Calycanthus (*Calycanthaceae*)

	Name	Suppliers
	fertilis	see *C. floridus* var. *glaucus*
	floridus	CAgr CArn CBcs CDul CMCN CPMA CTho CTri CWib EBee ELan EPfP EWTr IDee LAst LEdu LRHS MAsh MBNS MBlu MBri MMuc NBea SDnm SPer SPlb SPoG WCFE WDin
	- 'Athens'	CBcs CPMA
§	- var. ***glaucus***	EPfP MGos NBlu NLar WSHC
	- - 'Purpureus'	CBcs CPMA MBlu MBri NLar
	- var. ***laevigatus***	see *C. floridus* var. *glaucus*
	- 'Michael Lindsay'	CPMA MBri
	occidentalis	CAgr CArn CBcs CDul CMCN CWib MBlu MMuc SGar SSpi WBVN WCFE

Calylophus (*Onagraceae*)

	Name	Suppliers
	lavandulifolius	CPBP

Calystegia (*Convolvulaceae*)

	Name	Suppliers
§	***hederacea*** 'Flore Pleno' (d)	EBee ELan NSti SMad
	japonica 'Flore Pleno'	see *C. hederacea* 'Flore Pleno'
	silvatica 'Incarnata'	EBee
	soldanella NNS 99-85	WCot

Calytrix (*Myrtaceae*)

	Name	Suppliers
	tetragona	SPlb

Camassia ✿ (*Hyacinthaceae*)

	Name	Suppliers
	biflora	EBee
	cusickii	Widely available
	- white-flowered	IFoB
	- 'Zwanenburg'	EBee EBrs ERCP LRHS WCot
	esculenta Lindl.	see *C. quamash*
	howellii	EBee
	leichtlinii misapplied	see *C. leichtlinii* subsp. *suksdorfii*
	leichtlinii (Baker) S. Watson	ECho ISea
N	- 'Alba' hort.	see *C. leichtlinii* subsp. *leichtlinii*
*	- 'Alba Plena'	NBPC NBir
	- Blue Danube	see *C. leichtlinii* subsp. *suksdorfii* 'Blauwe Donau'
	- 'Blue Wave' **new**	EBee NHol
	- 'Harlequin' (v) **new**	EBee
§	- subsp. ***leichtlinii*** ΨH4	Widely available
	- 'Magdalen'	CAvo
N	- 'Plena' (d)	ECha
	- 'Sacajawea' **new**	ERCP
	- 'Semiplena' (d)	CAvo CBro CFFs CMea CMil EBee EBrs ERCP GGar LRHS NSti SPhx WAul WCot WHoo
§	- subsp. ***suksdorfii***	CSam ECho GBuc GCra LRHS
§	- - 'Blauwe Donau'	EBee EBrs
	- - Caerulea Group	Widely available
	- - 'Electra'	EBee ECha SUsu
§	***quamash***	Widely available
	- 'Blue Melody' (v)	CBow CBro CMea EBee EBrs EPot ERCP GBuc GMaP GMac LRHS MCCP NMRc NMen SPhx
	- var. ***breviflora***	EBee EBrs
	- 'Orion'	CBro CMea EBee EBrs GBuc GKev GMac LRHS NSti SMeo SPhx WAul WCot

Camellia ✿ (*Theaceae*)

	Name	Suppliers
	'Adorable' (*pitardii* hybrid)	LRHS LSRN
	'Annette Carol'	CDoC
	'Ariel's Song'	CDoC
	'Auburn White'	see *C. japonica* 'Mrs Bertha A. Harms'
	'Baby Bear'	CDoC
	'Barbara Clark' (*reticulata* × *saluenensis*)	CDoC CTrG LRHS LSRN MAsh MGos SCog SCoo
	'Bertha Harms Blush'	see *C. japonica* 'Mrs Bertha A. Harms'
	'Bett's Supreme'	CDoC
	'Black Lace' (*reticulata* × *williamsii*) ΨH4	CTrh CTri EPfP GGGa GLld LBuc LRHS LSRN MAsh MBri NPri SCam SCog SCoo WBVN WGob
	'Blissful Dawn'	CTrh
	'Bonnie Marie'	CBcs CDoC MGos SCog
	brevistyla	CBcs
	'Canterbury'	CDoC
*	'Chatsworth Belle'	CTrh SCam
	'China Lady' (*granthamiana* × *reticulata*)	MBri
	'Christmas Daffodil' (*japonica* hybrid)	LRHS
	'Cinnamon Cindy'	CDoC LRHS SCam SCog
	'Cinnamon Sensation' **new**	SCog
	'Congratulations'	CSBt LSRN
	'Contessa Lavinia Maggi'	see *C. japonica* 'Lavinia Maggi'
*	'Cornish Clay'	ISea
	'Cornish Snow' (*cuspidata* × *saluenensis*) ΨH4	CBcs CDoC CSBt CSam CTri EPfP GGal LHyd MGos SCam SCog SSpi WFar
	'Cornish Spring' (*cuspidata* × *japonica*) ΨH4	CCCN CDoC CSBt CTrh EPfP LHyd LRHS SCam SCog SPer
	cuspidata	LHyd
	'Czar'	see *C. japonica* 'The Czar'
	'Dainty Dale'	CDoC LRHS SCam SSta
	'Debut' (*japonica* × *reticulata*)	LRHS
	'Delia Williams'	see *C.* × *williamsii* 'Citation'
	'Diamond Head' (*japonica* × *reticulata*)	LHyd
	'Diana's Charm'	CDoC LSRN
	'Doctor Clifford Parks' (*japonica* × *reticulata*) ΨH2	CDoC GLld LHyd LRHS SCam SCog
	'Donckelaeri'	see *C. japonica* 'Masayoshi'
	'El Dorado' (*pitardii* × *japonica*)	CDoC CTrG
	'Elizabeth Bolitho'	SCam
	'Extravaganza' (*japonica* hybrid)	CBcs CTrh IArd MBri SCam SCog
	'Fairy Blush'	CDoC LRHS
	'Fairy Wand'	CDoC LRHS
	'Faustina Lechi'	see *C. japonica* 'Faustina'
	'Felice Harris' (*reticulata* × *sasanqua*)	CDoC MBri SCam SCog
	'Fire 'n' Ice'	CDoC SCam SCog
	'Fox's Fancy'	CDoC
	'Fragrant Joy' **new**	LRHS
	'Fragrant Pink' (*japonica* subsp. *rusticana* × *lutchuensis*)	CTrh SCam
	'Francie L' (*reticulata* × *saluenensis*) ΨH3-4	CDoC CDul EPfP LHyd LRHS SCam SCog SSta
	'Freedom Bell' ΨH4	CDoC CMHG CTrG CTrh GGGa GGal ISea LHyd LRHS MAsh MMuc NPri SCam SCog SCoo SPoG
	'Gay Baby'	CDoC
	'Golden Anniversary'	see *C. japonica* 'Dahlohnega'
	grijsii	CPLG CTrh LHyd SCam
	handelii	CBcs CPLG

	'Happy Anniversary'	CSBt LSRN
§	***hiemalis*** 'Bonanza'	CTrh SCam
	- 'Chansonette'	CDoC SCam SCog
	- 'Christmas Candles'	CSam
§	- 'Dazzler'	CBcs CSBt SCam SCog
	- 'Interlude' **new**	LRHS
	- 'Kanjirō'	CDoC LHyd SCam SCog
	- 'Showa Supreme'	SCam
	- 'Shōwa-no-sakae'	LRHS SCog
§	- 'Sparkling Burgundy' ♀H3	CBcs CDoC ELon EPfP GLld LHyd LRHS MGos SCam SCog
	'Hierathlyn' **new**	GGal
	'High Fragrance'	LRHS
	'Hooker'	CDoC
	'Ice Follies'	SCam SCog
	'Imbricata Rubra'	see *C. japonica* 'Imbricata'
	'Innovation' (*reticulata* × (× *williamsii*))	MAsh SCam SCoo
	'Inspiration' (*reticulata* × *saluenensis*) ♀H4	CDoC CMHG CMac CSBt CTrG CTrh CWSG EPfP GGGa GGar LHyd LRHS LSRN MBri MGos SBod SCam SCog SSpi SVic WGob
	japonica 'Aaron's Ruby'	CBcs CDoC ELon LRHS SCam SCog
	- HTB 4	SCam
	- HTB 10	SCam
	- LOR 280	SCam
	- 'Ace of Hearts'	MBri
	- 'Ada Pieper'	CTrh
	- 'Adelina Patti' ♀H4	CBcs CDoC CMHG CSBt CTrh LHyd LRHS MAsh SCog SCoo
	- 'Adolphe Audusson' ♀H4	Widely available
	- 'Adolphe Audusson Special'	LSRN
§	- 'Akashigata' ♀H4	CDoC CMac CTrG EPfP ISea LRHS LSRN MAsh SCog SCoo SPer SPoG SSta
	- 'Alba Plena' ♀H4	CTrh CWSG LHyd MGos SCog SPer WFar
	- 'Alba Simplex'	CDoC CMac ELan EPfP LRHS MGos SCam SCog SPer SSta
	- 'Alexander Hunter' ♀H4	CDoC LHyd LRHS SCam SCog
	- 'Alison Leigh Woodroof'	CDoC
§	- 'Althaeiflora'	CBcs CDoC ELon MGos SCam SCog
	- 'Ama-no-gawa'	LHyd
	- 'Amazing Graces'	CDoC
	- 'Anemoniflora'	CDoC CTrG ELan LRHS SCam SCog WFar
	- 'Angel'	CBcs LSRN SCam SCog WBor
	- 'Angello'	LSou
	- 'Annette Gehry'	CBcs
	- 'Annie Wylam' ♀H4	CTrh LHyd SCog
	- 'Apollo' Paul, 1911	CSam CTrG EPfP MGos MSwo SCam SCog
	- 'Apollo' ambig.	CBcs CDoC CTsd LRHS MAsh MGos
§	- 'Apple Blossom' ♀H4	CBcs ELan
*	- 'Augustine Supreme'	CMac
	- 'Australis' ♀H4	MAsh SCam
	- 'Ave Maria' ♀H4	CDoC CTrh MAsh
	- 'Baby Pearl'	LSRN
	- 'Baby Sis'	LRHS
	- 'Ballet Dancer' ♀H4	CDoC LSRN MGos SCam SCog SVic
	- 'Bambino'	CDoC
	- 'Barbara Woodroof'	CBcs
	- 'Baron Gomer'	see *C. japonica* 'Comte de Gomer'
	- 'Baronne Leguay'	SCam
	- 'Beau Harp'	LRHS SCam
	- 'Bella Lambertii'	NMun
	- 'Bella Romana'	SCam
	- 'Benten' (v)	CTrG SMad
	- 'Berenice Perfection'	CDoC CMHG WFar
	- 'Betty Foy Sanders'	CTrh
	- 'Betty Robinson'	CDoC LRHS
	- 'Betty Sheffield'	CTrG MAsh MGos SCog SCoo WFar
	- 'Betty Sheffield Pink'	CTrG LRHS SCam
	- 'Betty Sheffield Supreme'	CBcs
	- 'Black Tie'	CDoC ISea LRHS MGos SCog SPoG SPur SVic WGob
	- 'Blackburnia'	see *C. japonica* 'Althaeiflora'
	- 'Blaze of Glory'	NLar SCog
§	- 'Blood of China'	CBcs CDoC CSBt CWSG ISea LBuc LRHS LSRN LSou MGos MMuc SCam SCog SCoo SPer WFar WMoo
	- 'Bob Hope' ♀H4	CBcs CDoC CTrh GLld LHyd MAsh MGos SCam
	- 'Bob's Tinsie' ♀H4	CDoC CMHG CSBt CTrh EPfP GBin ISea LSRN MAsh NLar SCog
§	- 'Bokuhan' ♀H4	CDoC EPfP SCog
	- 'Bright Buoy'	CDoC
	- 'Brushfield's Yellow' ♀H4	CBcs CDoC CMHG CSBt ELan EPfP GLld IArd ISea LHyd LMil LRHS LSRN LSou MAsh MBlu MBri MDun MGos NEgg SBch SCam SCog SCoo SPer SSta SVic WFar WGob
	- 'Bush Hill Beauty'	see *C. japonica* 'Lady de Saumarez'
§	- 'C.M. Hovey' ♀H4	CMHG CMac MAsh
	- 'C.M. Wilson'	CDoC CMac SCog
	- 'Campbellii'	LHyd
	- 'Campsii Alba'	CDoC
	- 'Can Can'	CBcs CDoC CTrG SCam SCog
	- 'Candy Stripe'	CDoC
	- 'Canon Boscawen'	CTrG
	- 'Cara Mia'	CDoC SCam
	- 'Carolina Beauty'	LRHS MAsh
	- 'Carter's Sunburst' ♀H4	CBcs CDoC CTrh ELan EPfP LRHS MAsh SCog WGob
	- 'Chandleri'	CBcs
	- 'Chandleri Elegans'	see *C. japonica* 'Elegans'
	- 'Charlotte de Rothschild'	CTrh CTri EPfP GLld SCam
	- 'Cheryll Lynn'	CDoC CTrh
	- 'Christmas Beauty'	SCam
	- 'Cinderella'	CDoC SCog
	- 'Clarise Carleton'	GGGa LHyd MBri
	- 'Colonel Firey'	see *C. japonica* 'C.M. Hovey'
	- 'Commander Mulroy' ♀H4	CDoC CTrh MBri SCam
§	- 'Comte de Gomer'	CDoC ELan ELon EPfP LRHS NPri SCog
	- 'Conspicua'	CBcs
	- 'Contessa Samailoff'	CDoC
§	- 'Coquettii' ♀H4	CBcs CDul LRHS MAsh
	- 'Coral Beauty'	WFar
	- 'Coral Pink Lotus'	CDoC
	- 'Coral Queen'	CDoC SCam
	- 'Cornish Excellence' **new**	SCam
	- 'Curly Lady' **new**	NPri
§	- 'Dahlohnega'	CSBt CTrh LSRN
	- 'Daikagura'	CBcs
	- 'Dainty'	CBcs
	- 'Daitairin'	see *C. japonica* 'Dewatairin'
	- 'Dark of the Moon'	CDoC
	- 'Dear Jenny'	CBcs CTrG
	- 'Debutante'	CBcs CDoC CMac ELon LHyd LRHS MAsh SCam SCog
	- 'Deep Secret' ♀H4	SCog
	- 'Desire' ♀H4	CBcs CDoC CMHG CSBt CTrh EPfP GLld LRHS LSRN MAsh MDun NMun SBch SCam SCog SCoo SPoG WGob
	- 'Devonia'	EPfP LHyd SCog
§	- 'Dewatairin' (Higo)	CBcs CDoC MGos SCam SCog
	- 'Dixie Knight'	CBcs CDoC MGos SCam SCog
	- 'Dobreei'	CMac
	- 'Doctor Burnside'	CBcs CDoC CTrh LRHS NBlu SCam SCog

- 'Doctor King' GLld
- 'Doctor Tinsley' ♀H4 CDoC GLld LRHS MAsh NPri SCoo
- 'Dolly Dyer' CDoC
- 'Dona Herzilia de Freitas Magalhaes' CDoC SCam
- 'Dona Jane Andresson' SCam
- 'Donckelaeri' see *C. japonica* 'Masayoshi'
- 'Donnan's Dream' CTrh
- 'Drama Girl' ♀H2 CBcs CDoC EPfP SBod SCam SCog SVic
- 'Dream Time' CBcs
- 'Duc de Bretagne' SCog
- 'Duchesse Decazes' CBcs MBri
- 'Edelweiss' CDoC MGos SCam SCog
- 'Effendee' see *C. sasanqua* 'Rosea Plena'
- 'Eleanor Hagood' CBcs
§ - 'Elegans' ♀H4 CBcs CDoC CTrG EPfP LBuc LRHS MAsh NEgg SBod SCam SCog SCoo SPer SPoG SSta WFar
- 'Elegans Champagne' NPri
- 'Elegans Splendor' CDoC
- 'Elisabeth' CDoC WFar
- 'Elizabeth Dowd' CBcs SCog
- 'Elizabeth Hawkins' CTrh GLld LHyd LRHS MAsh MMuc NCGa SCam
- 'Emily Wilson' CDoC
- 'Emmett Barnes' LHyd SCam
- 'Emmett Pfingstl' SCam
- 'Emperor of Russia' CBcs
- 'Eric Baker' **new** SCam
- 'Erin Farmer' CBcs
- 'Eugène Lizé' SCam
- 'Evelyn' SCam
- 'Eximia' LRHS SCam SCog
- 'Faith' CBcs
- 'Fashionata' CDoC SCam
§ - 'Faustina' MAsh
- 'Feast Perfection' CDoC
- 'Finlandia Variegated' CDoC SCam SCog SVic
- 'Fire Dance' CDoC
- 'Fire Falls' ♀H4 CMHG
- 'Firebird' CBcs
- 'Flame' CBcs
- 'Flamingo' LHyd
- 'Flashlight' CDoC EPfP LRHS SCam
§ - 'Fleur Dipater' LRHS LSou SCam
- 'Flowerwood' SCog WFar
- 'Forest Green' CDoC ELan MAsh
- 'Fortune Teller' CBcs
- 'Frans van Damme' CBcs
- 'Fred Sander' CBcs CDoC ELon GLld MGos NMun SCam SCog SCoo
- 'Frizzle White' SApp
- 'Frosty Morn' CBcs CDoC ELan
- 'Furo-an' CBcs MAsh
- 'Geisha Girl' SCam SCog
§ - 'Gigantea' SCam
§ - 'Gigantea Red' LRHS
- 'Giuditta Rosani' CDoC
- 'Giuseppina Pieri' LHyd
- 'Gladys Wannamaker' SCog
- 'Glen 40' see *C. japonica* 'Coquettii'
- 'Gloire de Nantes' ♀H4 LRHS NMun SCam SCog
- 'Gold Tone' CDoC MGos SCam
* - 'Golden Wedding' (v) LRHS MAsh
- 'Grace Bunton' CBcs CDoC MGos SCam SCog
- 'Granada' SCog
- 'Grand Prix' ♀H4 CDoC CTrh GLld LRHS LSRN MGos SBod SCam SCog SVic
- 'Grand Slam' ♀H2 CBcs CDoC CDul CTrh EPfP MAsh SCam SCog
- 'Grandiflora Alba' CBcs
- 'Guest of Honor' CBcs CDoC GLld LSou
- 'Guilio Nuccio' ♀H4 CBcs CDoC CTrG CTri EPfP IArd LBuc LRHS LSRN MGos NEgg NPri SBch SCam SCog SPer SVic
- 'Gus Menard' SCam
- 'Gwenneth Morey' CBcs CDoC ELan EPfP SCam
- 'H.A. Downing' CDoC SCam
§ - 'Hagoromo' ♀H4 CBcs CDoC CTrh ELan EPfP LRHS SBch SCam SCog SPer WFar
- 'Hakugan' EMil
§ - 'Hakurakuten' ♀H4 CDoC CMHG GLld IArd ISea LRHS SCog
- 'Hanafûki' CDoC MAsh MGos SCam SCog
- 'Happy Birthday' LSRN
- 'Hatsuzakura' see *C. japonica* 'Dewatairin'
- 'Hawaii' CBcs CDoC CMac CTrh LHyd MGos SCam SCog
- 'Her Majesty Queen Elizabeth II' CDoC
- Herme see *C. japonica* 'Hikarugenji'
- 'High Hat' CBcs SCog
- 'High, Wide 'n' Handsome' CDoC
- 'Higo-momijigari' GLld
§ - 'Hikarugenji' CDoC MGos SCog
- 'Hinomaru' CMac
- 'Holly Bright' CTrh GLld SCam
- 'Honeyglow' **new** CDoC
- 'Ichisetsu' SCog
§ - 'Imbricata' LBuc LRHS MAsh SCog
- 'Italiana Vera' LRHS MAsh
- 'J.J. Whitfield' CMac
- 'Jack Jones Scented' CMHG
- 'Janet Waterhouse' CBcs SCam SCoo WFar
- 'Jean Clere' CDoC CTrG GLld MGos MWea SCog SCoo
- 'Jennifer Turnbull' CDoC
- 'Jessie Katz' **new** CDoC
- 'Jingle Bells' CBcs
- 'Jitsugetsusei' CDoC
- 'Joseph Pfingstl' ♀H4 CDoC CTri EPfP GLld LRHS MAsh MMuc NPri SCam SCog WBVN
- 'Joshua E. Youtz' LHyd SCog
- 'Jovey Carlyon' LRHS MAsh
- 'Joy Sander' see *C. japonica* 'Apple Blossom'
- 'Julia France' SCog
- 'June McCaskill' CDoC
- 'Juno' CBcs LRHS SCam
- 'Jupiter' Paul, 1904 ♀H4 CBcs CDoC CMac CTri EPfP ISea LHyd LRHS LSRN MGos SCog SCoo
§ - 'K. Sawada' SCam
- 'Katie' MDun
- 'Kellingtoniana' see *C. japonica* 'Gigantea'
- 'Kenny' CBcs LRHS
- 'Kentucky' LRHS
- 'Kick-off' CBcs CTrh SCog SCoo
- 'Kimberley' CDoC EPfP GLld SCog WBVN
- 'King Size' CDoC MGos SCam
- 'King's Ransom' CDoC CMac LRHS MAsh
- 'Kingyoba-shiro-wabisuke' CDoC SCam
- 'Kitty Berry' CTrh
- 'Kokinran' CDoC
§ - 'Konronkoku' ♀H4 CBcs CDoC LRHS MAsh SCog
- 'Kouron-jura' see *C. japonica* 'Konronkoku'
- 'Kramer's Beauty' LRHS SCoo
- 'Kramer's Supreme' CBcs CCCN CDoC CTrG CWSG LBuc LRHS LSRN MAsh MGos NLar SBod SCam SCog SCoo SPoG WBrE WFar
- 'La Graciola' see *C. japonica* 'Odoratissima'
- 'Lady Campbell' CTri GAbr GGar LSou MAsh NLar NMun SPad
- 'Lady Clare' see *C. japonica* 'Akashigata'

§ - 'Lady de Saumarez' CBcs CDoC CMac
- 'Lady Erma' CBcs
- 'Lady Loch' CTrh LRHS MAsh MBri MGos SCam
- 'Lady Mackinnon' MAsh
- 'Lady McCulloch' LRHS SCam
- 'Lady Saint Clair' CDoC
- 'Lady Vansittart' CDoC CTrG ELan EPfP GLld LHyd LRHS LSRN MAsh MGos SBch SCog SCoo SPer SPoG WGob
§ - 'Lady Vansittart Pink' CMac SBch SCam
- 'Lady Vansittart Red' see *C. japonica* 'Lady Vansittart Pink'
- 'Lady Vansittart Shell' see *C. japonica* 'Yours Truly'
- 'Lady Vere de Vere' (d) CDoC
- 'Latifolia' GLld LRHS SCam
- 'Laurie Bray' SCog WFar
§ - 'Lavinia Maggi' ♀H4 CBcs CDoC CTrG CTrh CTri ELan EPfP GLld LBuc LHyd LRHS LSRN MAsh MGos SCam SCog SCoo SPer SPoG SReu SRms SSta WBVN WGob
- 'L'Avvenire' SCog
§ - 'Le Lys' SCam
- 'Lemon Drop' CTrh GLld
- 'Leonora Novick' CDoC SCog
- 'Lillian Rickets' **new** CDoC
- 'Lily Pons' ♀H4 CDoC CTrh GLld LHyd
- 'Little Bit' CBcs CDoC CMHG CTrh ELon MGos SCam SCog SPer
- 'Little Slam' CDoC
- 'Lovelight' ♀H4 CTrh
- 'Ludgvan Red' LRHS SCam
- 'Lulu Belle' SCog
- 'Ma Belle' CMHG
- 'Mabel Blackwell' SCam
- 'Madame de Strekaloff' CMac CSBt SCam
- 'Madame Hahn' CDoC
- 'Madame Lebois' CBcs CDoC SCam
- 'Madame Martin Cachet' SCog SCoo
- 'Madge Miller' MAsh
- 'Magic Moments' SCog
- 'Magnoliiflora' see *C. japonica* 'Hagoromo'
- 'Magnoliiflora Alba' see *C. japonica* 'Miyakodori'
- 'Maiden's Blush' CMac
- 'Man Size' CDoC
- 'Margaret Davis' CCCN CDoC CSBt CTrG ELan ELon EPfP GLld LBuc LHyd LRHS LSRN MAsh MDun MGos MWea NEgg NPri SBch SCam SCoo SPoG SVic WGob
- 'Margaret Davis Picotee' ♀H4 CBcs CMHG CTrh SCog SPer SSta
- 'Margaret Rose' SCam
- 'Margaret Short' CDoC
- 'Margherita Coleoni' CBcs LHyd
- 'Marguérite Gouillon' CBcs CDoC ISea LHyd LRHS MAsh
- 'Marian Mitchell' SCam
- 'Mariana' CDoC SCog
- 'Marie Bracey' CBcs SCam
- 'Marinka' CBcs
- 'Marjorie Magnificent' LRHS MAsh
- 'Mark Alan' CDoC LSRN
- 'Maroon and Gold' CDoC LSRN SCog
- 'Marquis of Exeter' **new** NMun
- 'Mars' ♀H4 CBcs MGos SCam SCog WFar
- 'Mary Alice Cox' CDoC
- 'Mary Costa' CBcs CDoC CTrh WFar
- 'Mary J. Wheeler' LSRN
§ - 'Masayoshi' ♀H4 CBcs CSBt CTrG GLld LHyd MAsh SCam SCog
- 'Mathotiana Alba' ♀H4 CDoC CMac CSBt CTri ELan EPfP LSRN MAsh MGos SCam SCog SPer
§ - 'Mathotiana Rosea' ♀H4 CMac SCam
- 'Mathotiana Supreme' CDoC SCam SCog
- 'Matterhorn' CTrh MAsh
- 'Mattie Cole' CDoC LHyd SCam
- 'Maui' CDoC
- 'Mercury' ♀H4 CMac CTrG CWSG GGGa SCog
- 'Mercury Variegated' CMHG
- 'Mermaid' CDoC
- 'Midnight' CBcs CDoC CMHG LBuc LRHS MAsh WFar
- 'Midnight Magic' CTrh CTri
- 'Midnight Serenade' CDoC
- 'Midsummer's Day' CBcs
§ - 'Mikenjaku' CBcs CTrG EPfP LBuc LRHS MAsh NMun NPri SCog SCoo WGob
- 'Minnie Maddern Fiske' SCam
- 'Miriam Stevenson' SCam
- 'Miss Charleston' CBcs LHyd SCog
- 'Miss Lyla' NLar
- 'Miss Universe' CTrh
- 'Mississippi Beauty' CTrh
§ - 'Miyakodori' EPfP
- 'Monsieur Faucillon' CBcs
- 'Monstruosa Rubra' see *C. japonica* 'Gigantea Red'
- 'Monte Carlo' CDoC SBod SCam SCog SVic
- 'Moonlight' **new** CDoC
- 'Moonlight Bay' CTrh SCog
- 'Moshe Dayan' CDoC GLld LBuc LRHS LSou MAsh NPri SCog WGob
- 'Moshio' CDoC
§ - 'Mrs Bertha A. Harms' CDoC MGos SCam SCog SVic
- 'Mrs D.W. Davis' CBcs CDoC EPfP SCam
- 'Mrs Lyman Clarke' CDoC
- 'Mrs Swan' NPri
- 'Mrs William Thompson' SCam
- 'Nagasaki' see *C. japonica* 'Mikenjaku'
- 'Nigra' see *C. japonica* 'Konronkoku'
- 'Nina Avery' CDoC
- 'Nobilissima' CBcs CDoC CMac CTrG CTrh CTri EPfP GAbr GKev ISea LHyd LRHS MAsh MBlu MMuc NLar NPri SCam SCog SCoo SPer SPoG WFar
- 'Nuccio's Amigo' **new** MAsh
- 'Nuccio's Cameo' CDoC CTrh LRHS MAsh SCoo
- 'Nuccio's Gem' ♀H4 CDoC CMHG ELan EPfP LHyd LRHS MGos SCam SCog SSta
- 'Nuccio's Jewel' ♀H4 CBcs CDoC CSBt CTrh CWSG LBuc LHyd LRHS LSRN MAsh SCam SCog SPer WBVN WMoo
- 'Nuccio's Pearl' CBcs CDoC LRHS LSRN LSou NEgg NPri SCam SCog WBVN WGob
- 'Nuccio's Pink Lace' CBcs CDoC CTri
§ - 'Odoratissima' CTrG
- 'Olga Anderson' CDoC MGos
- 'Onetia Holland' CBcs CDoC LSRN MGos SBch SCam SCog SCoo
- 'Optima' CBcs CDoC LRHS SCam SCog SCoo
- 'Optima Rosea' CTrG SPoG
- 'Paeoniiflora Alba' **new** SCam
- 'Patricia Ann' LSRN
- 'Paulette Goddard' SCam
- 'Paul's Apollo' see *C. japonica* 'Apollo' Paul, 1911
- 'Peachblossom' see *C. japonica* 'Fleur Dipater'
- 'Pearl Harbor' SCam
- 'Pensacola Red' CDoC LRHS SCam
- 'Pink Champagne' SBod
- 'Pink Clouds' CBcs
- 'Pope Pius IX' see *C. japonica* 'Prince Eugène Napoléon'
- 'Preston Rose' CBcs CDoC MAsh NMun
- 'Primavera' CTrh LHyd SCog
§ - 'Prince Eugène Napoléon' GLld SCam
- 'Prince Murat' CDoC

	Name	Suppliers
	- 'Princess Baciocchi' Armstrong	CBcs NLar SCam
	- 'Princess du Mahe'	CMac
	- 'R.L. Wheeler' ♀H4	CBcs CDoC CSBt CTri LHyd LRHS LSRN MAsh MWea NPri SBch SCog SCoo
	- 'Red Dandy'	CDoC MGos SCam SCog
	- 'Red Elephant'	SCam
	- 'Red Red Rose'	CDoC
	- 'Reg Ragland'	CDoC CMHG MGos SCam SCog
	- 'Robert Strauss'	SCam
	- 'Roger Hall'	CBcs CDoC CTrh ISea LRHS LSRN MAsh SCog SCoo SPoG WGob
	- 'Roman Soldier'	CBcs
	- 'Rosularis'	SCam SCog
	- 'Royal Velvet'	CDoC
	- 'Rubescens Major' ♀H4	CBcs LHyd
	- 'Ruddigore'	CTrh SCam
§	- subsp. ***rusticana***	CBcs CDoC SCam SCog SCoo WFar
	- - 'Reigyoku' (v)	CBcs CDoC
	- 'Sabiniana'	LRHS
	- 'Saint André'	CMac LRHS MAsh
	- 'Sally Harrell'	SCam
	- 'San Dimas' ♀H4	CDoC CTrh GLld SCam SCog SVic
	- 'Saturnia'	CDoC ELon GLld LBuc LRHS MAsh WBor
	- 'Sawada's Dream'	CDoC SCog
	- 'Scented Red'	CDoC SCam SCog
	- 'Scentsation' ♀H4	CDoC CMHG CTri SCog
	- 'Sea Foam'	ELon LHyd LRHS SCam SSta
	- 'Sea Gull'	CTrh
	- 'Senator Duncan U. Fletcher'	CDoC
	- 'Shikibu'	CTrh
	- 'Shiragiku'	CBcs CDoC SCog SPer
	- 'Shiro Chan'	CDoC MGos SCog
	- 'Shirobotan'	CDoC CTrG GQui LRHS MGos SBod SCog SPur SVic
	- 'Silver Anniversary'	Widely available
	- 'Silver Moon'	see *C. japonica* 'K. Sawada'
	- 'Silver Ruffles'	CDoC
	- 'Snow Chan'	CMHG
	- 'Something Beautiful'	CDoC
	- 'Souvenir de Bahuaud-Litou' ♀H4	SCam SCog
	- 'Spencer's Pink'	CBcs CDoC
	- 'Splendens Carlyon'	LRHS MAsh SCoo
	- 'Spring Fever'	SCam
	- 'Spring Fling'	CTrh
	- 'Spring Formal'	CTrh
	- 'Spring Frill'	SCam SCog
	- 'Strawberry Blonde'	MAsh SCog
	- 'Strawberry Parfait'	CDoC LRHS NPri SCog
	- 'Strawberry Swirl'	SCog
	- 'Sugar Babe'	CDoC CSBt LRHS MAsh SCam SCog WGob
	- 'Sunset Glory'	CMHG SCam
	- 'Sweetheart'	SCog
	- 'Sylva' ♀H4	GGGa GGal SSpi
	- 'Sylvia'	CMac
	- 'Takanini'	CDoC CTrh
	- 'Tammia'	EPfP SCam
	- 'Tarō'an'	GGal
	- 'Teresa Ragland'	CDoC SCam
	- 'Teringa'	CDoC
§	- 'The Czar'	CBcs SCog
	- 'The Mikado'	CDoC SCog
	- 'Tickled Pink'	CDoC
	- 'Tiffany'	CBcs CDoC LHyd LRHS MAsh MGos SCam SCog SCoo SVic
	- 'Tiki'	MBri WFar

	Name	Suppliers
	- 'Tinker Bell'	CDoC MAsh MBri SCog
	- 'Tom Thumb' ♀H4	CDoC CTrh LRHS SCam SRms SSta WGob
	- 'Tomorrow'	CDoC LRHS NEgg SCog
	- 'Tomorrow Park Hill'	CBcs SCog
§	- 'Tomorrow Variegated'	MGos
	- 'Tomorrow's Dawn'	SCam
	- 'Touchdown'	SCam
	- 'Trewithen White'	CDoC CSam
§	- 'Tricolor' ♀H4	CBcs CDoC CMHG CMac CSBt CTrh EPfP GLld LHyd LRHS MAsh MGos SBch SCam SCog SCoo SPer WBrE WFar
	- 'Tricolor Red'	see *C. japonica* 'Lady de Saumarez'
	- 'Trinkett'	CDoC
	- variegated (v)	SCog
	- 'Victor de Bisschop'	see *C. japonica* 'Le Lys'
	- 'Victor Emmanuel'	see *C. japonica* 'Blood of China'
	- 'Ville de Nantes'	MGos
	- 'Ville de Nantes Red'	SCog
	- 'Virginia Carlyon'	CDoC GLld
	- 'Virginia Robinson'	SCam
	- 'Virgin's Blush'	SCam
	- 'Vittorio Emanuele II'	CDoC CTrh GLld LBuc LRHS MAsh MGos
	- 'Vosper's Rose'	CDoC
	- 'Warrior'	SCog
	- 'White Giant'	CBcs
	- 'White Nun'	CBcs SCog
	- 'White Swan'	CSBt GLld LRHS SCoo
	- 'Wilamina' ♀H4	CDoC CMHG GLld LRHS
	- 'Wildfire'	LRHS SCam
	- 'William Bartlett'	CTrh
	- 'William Honey'	CTrh
	- 'Wisley White'	see *C. japonica* 'Hakurakuten'
§	- 'Yours Truly'	CBcs CDoC CMac CTrh GLld LHyd LRHS LSRN MAsh MDun SCog
	'John Tooby'	CDoC
	'Jury's Yellow'	see *C. × williamsii* 'Jury's Yellow'
	'Lasca Beauty' (*reticulata × japonica*)	LHyd
	'Lavender Queen'	see *C. sasanqua* 'Lavender Queen'
	'Leonard Messel' (*reticulata × williamsii*) ♀H4	CBcs CDoC CDul CMHG CMac CTrG CTrh EPfP GGGa GGal LHyd LRHS MAsh MDun MGos SCam SCog SCoo SPer SPoG SReu SVic
	'Liz Henslowe'	CDoC
	'Madame Victor de Bisschop'	see *C. japonica* 'Le Lys'
§	***maliflora*** (d)	CBcs
	'Milo Rowell'	CDoC
	'Mimosa Jury'	CDoC
	'Monticello'	CDoC
	'Mystique'	see *C. reticulata* 'Mystique'
	'Nicky Crisp' (*japonica × pitardii*)	CDoC GLld LHyd
	'Night Rider'	CDoC
	'Nijinski' (*reticulata* hybrid)	CDoC
	'Nonie Haydon' (pitardii hybrid)	CDoC
	oleifera	CPLG CSam SCam SCog WFar
	'Phyl Doak' (*reticulata × saluenensis*)	CDoC
	'Pink Spangles'	see *C. japonica* 'Mathotiana Rosea'
	pitardii	SCog
	- 'Snippet'	CDoC
	'Polar Ice' (*oleifera* hybrid)	CDoC SCog
	'Polyanna'	CDoC SCog
	'Quintessence' (*japonica × lutchuensis*)	CDoC GLld LRHS SCog
	reticulata 'Arch of Triumph'	CTrG
	- 'Captain Rawes'	SCam

	- 'K.O. Hester' **new**	SCam
	- 'Les Jury'	LHyd LMil
	- 'Mary Williams'	GKev LMil MAsh NLar SCoo
	- 'Miss Tulare'	CDoC LHyd
§	- 'Mystique'	CDoC
	- 'Satsuma-kurenai' **new**	CTrh
	rosiflora 'Roseaflora Cascade'	CDoC
	'Royalty' (*japonica* × *reticulata*) ♀H3	CTrG GLld
	rusticana	see *C. japonica* subsp. *rusticana*
	saluenensis 'Bartley Pink' **new**	LHyd
	'Salutation' (*reticulata* × *saluenensis*)	SCam
	sasanqua Thunb.	CDul CSam
I	- 'Apple Blossom'	MAsh
	- 'Baronesa de Soutelinho'	SCam SCog
	- 'Bettie Patricia'	SCog
	- 'Bonanza'	see *C. hiemalis* 'Bonanza'
	- Borde Hill form	SCam
	- 'Cleopatra'	EPfP MAsh
	- 'Cotton Candy'	CDoC
	- 'Crimson King' ♀H3	CDoC SCam
	- 'Dazzler'	see *C. hiemalis* 'Dazzler'
	- 'Early Pearly'	CDoC LRHS
	- 'Evangelica' **new**	LRHS
I	- 'Exquisite'	CDoC
	- 'Flamingo'	see *C. sasanqua* 'Fukuzutsumi'
	- 'Flore Pleno'	see *C. maliflora*
	- 'Fragrans'	SCog
	- 'Fuji-no-mine'	CTrh SCog
§	- 'Fukuzutsumi'	CSBt CTrG LRHS SCam
	- 'Gay Sue'	CDoC CTrh SCam
	- 'Hiryū'	LRHS SCam SCog
	- 'Hugh Evans' ♀H3	CAbP CBcs CDoC CTrh CTri ELon LRHS SCam SCog SPoG SRkn SSta
	- 'Jean May' ♀H3	CDoC EPfP LHyd LRHS SCam SCog SCoo SPer SSta WCot WGob
	- 'Kenkyō'	MGos SCam SCog SSta
§	- 'Lavender Queen'	SCam
	- 'Lucinda'	LHyd SCog
	- 'Maiden's Blush'	LRHS SCam SCog WFar WSpi
	- 'Mignonne'	SCam
	- 'Narumigata'	CAbP CBcs CDoC CMac CTrG CTrh EPfP LHyd LRHS MBlu SCam SCog SCoo SPoG SSta WGob
	- 'Navajo'	CTrh
	- 'New Dawn'	SCam SCog
	- 'Nyewoods'	CMac
	- 'Papaver'	SCam SCog
	- 'Paradise Belinda' PBR	CDoC
	- 'Paradise Blush'	CBcs CDoC SCog
	- 'Paradise Glow'	CBcs CDoC SCam SCog
	- 'Paradise Hilda'	CBcs CDoC SCog
	- 'Paradise Joan'	CDoC
	- 'Paradise Little Liane' PBR	CBcs CDoC SCam SCog
	- 'Paradise Pearl'	CBcs CDoC SCog
	- 'Paradise Petite' PBR	SCog
	- 'Paradise Sayaka'	CDoC
	- 'Paradise Venessa' PBR	CBcs CDoC EPfP SCog
	- 'Peach Blossom'	CBcs LHyd
	- 'Plantation Pink'	CSBt CTrG CTrh EPfP GKev LHyd LRHS SCam SCog SPer SPoG
	- 'Rainbow'	CAbP CDoC CTrG CTrh EPfP GGal GLld LRHS NMun SCam SCog SCoo SRkn SSta WFar WGob
	- 'Rosea'	SCam
§	- 'Rosea Plena'	CBcs CMac SCam
	- 'Sasanqua Rubra'	CMac SCam
	- 'Sasanqua Variegata' (v)	SCam SCog SSta
	- 'Setsugekka'	CDoC SCam SCog
	- 'Shishigashira' Nihon Engei Kai Zasshi, 1894	LHyd
	- 'Silver Dollar' **new**	CDoC
	- 'Snowflake'	SCam SCog SSta
	- 'Sparkling Burgundy'	see *C. hiemalis* 'Sparkling Burgundy'
	- 'Tanya'	CDoC
	- 'Versicolor' **new**	LRHS
	- 'Winter's Joy'	SCam
	- 'Winter's Snowman'	CDoC SCam SCog
	'Satan's Robe' (*reticulata* hybrid)	CDoC MGos SCam SCog WFar
	'Scented Sun'	CTrh
	'Scentuous' (*japonica* × *lutchuensis*)	CDoC CTrh SCam
	'Show Girl' (*reticulata* × *sasanqua*)	LHyd SCam SCog
	'Shōwa-wabisuke' (wabisuke)	CTrh
§	***sinensis***	CCCN CTrG GPoy LRHS SCam
	'Sir Victor Davis'	CDoC
	'Snow Flurry' (*oleifera* hybrid)	SCam SCog
	'Spring Festival' (*cuspidata* hybrid) ♀H4	CDoC CMHG CTrh LHyd LRHS NLar SCog SCoo SPoG WMoo
	'Spring Mist' (*japonica* × *lutchuensis*)	CDoC CMHG CTrh LHyd
	'Sugar Dream'	CDoC CTrh
	'Superscent' **new**	CTrh
	'Swan Lake'	CTrG MAsh SCam SCog
	'Sweet Emily Kate' (*japonica* × *lutchuensis*)	CDoC
	'Tarōkaja' (wabisuke)	SCam
	thea	see *C. sinensis*
	'Tinsie'	see *C. japonica* 'Bokuhan'
	'Tiny Princess' (*fraterna* × *japonica*)	CMac
	'Tom Knudsen' (*japonica* × *reticulata*) ♀H3	CDoC CTrh
	'Tomorrow Supreme'	see *C. japonica* 'Tomorrow Variegated'
	transnokoensis	CMac CPLG
	'Tricolor Sieboldii'	see *C. japonica* 'Tricolor'
	'Tristrem Carlyon' (*reticulata* hybrid) ♀H4	CBcs CDoC CTrG CTri LSou SCam WGob
	tsaii	CDoC
	'Valley Knudsen' (*reticulata* × *saluenensis*)	SCog
	× ***vernalis***	CBcs
	- 'Ginryû' **new**	SCam
	- 'Hiryū'	SCog
	- 'Star Above Star'	CMHG
	- 'Yuletide'	CDoC CTrh LHyd LRHS SCam
	'Volcano'	CDoC
	× ***williamsii*** 'Angel Wings'	LRHS
	- 'Anticipation' ♀H4	Widely available
	- 'Ballet Queen'	CBcs CDoC CSBt LRHS MGos SVic WFar
	- 'Ballet Queen Variegated'	CDoC MGos SCog
	- 'Bartley Number Five'	CMac
	- 'Beatrice Michael'	CMac
	- 'Bow Bells'	CDoC CDul GKir LHyd LRHS SCam SSta
	- 'Bowen Bryant' ♀H4	CTsd GGGa GLld LRHS SCog
	- 'Bridal Gown'	GGGa LHyd
	- 'Brigadoon' ♀H4	CBcs CDoC CMHG CTrG EPfP GGGa GGal GKir GLld LHyd MAsh MBri MDun MGos NPri SCam SCog
	- 'Burncoose'	CBcs
	- 'Burncoose Apple Blossom'	CBcs CDoC
	- 'Buttons 'n' Bows'	CDoC SCog
	- 'C.F. Coates'	CDoC SCog SSta

Plant	Suppliers
- 'Caerhays'	CBcs
- 'Carnation'	LRHS MAsh
- 'Carolyn Williams'	SCam
- 'Celebration'	CBcs CSBt LSRN
- 'Charlean'	CDoC SCam
- 'Charles Colbert'	CDoC
- 'China Clay' ♀H4	CDoC CTrG EPfP LHyd SCog
§ - 'Citation'	CBcs CMac LHyd SCog
- 'Clarrie Fawcett' ♀H4	CDoC
- 'Contribution'	CTrh
- 'Crinkles'	CDoC CDul LRHS SCam SSta
- 'Daintiness' ♀H4	CDoC LHyd SCog
- 'Dark Nite'	CMHG
- 'Debbie' ♀H4	Widely available
- 'Debbie's Carnation'	CDoC CMHG
- 'Donation' ♀H4	Widely available
- 'Dream Boat'	CDoC LHyd
- 'E.G. Waterhouse'	CBcs CDoC CMHG CTrG CTrh CTri EPfP LAst LHyd LRHS MAsh MGos MMuc SCam SCog SCoo SPoG SSta SVic WGob
- 'E.T.R. Carlyon' ♀H4	CBcs CDoC CTrh CTri CTsd EPfP GGar GLld LBuc LHyd LRHS MAsh NLar SCam SCog SCoo SPoG
- 'Elegant Beauty' ♀H4	CDoC CSBt CTrG CWSG GLld MDun SBod SCam SCog SPer SVic
- 'Elizabeth Anderson' ♀H4	CTrh SCam
- 'Elsie Jury' ♀H3	CBcs CDoC CMac CTrG CTri CWSG GLld GQui ISea LHyd MGos SCam SCog SPer SVic
- 'Exaltation'	CDoC SCog
- 'Fiona Colville' **new**	CDoC
- 'Francis Hanger'	CDoC CTrh LHyd MDun SCam SCog
- 'Galaxie' ♀H4	CBcs CDoC SCog
- 'Garden Glory'	LHyd
- 'George Blandford' ♀H4	CBcs CMac GGal
- 'Glenn's Orbit' ♀H4	CBcs CDoC SCam SCog
- 'Golden Spangles' (v)	CBcs CDoC CMac CTrG CTrh CTsd ELan EPfP ISea LHyd LRHS MAsh MDun MGos MMuc NLar SBch SBod SCam SCog SPer SSta WGob
- 'Grand Jury'	LRHS
- 'Gwavas'	CBcs CCCN CDoC GLld LHyd LRHS MAsh SCam SCog SCoo
- 'Hilo'	CDoC SCam
- 'Hiraethlyn'	LHyd
- 'Holland Orchid'	SCog
- 'J.C. Williams' ♀H4	CBcs CMac CSam CTri CWSG EPfP ISea MMuc SCog
- 'Jamie'	CDoC
- 'Jean Claris'	CDoC SCog
- 'Jenefer Carlyon'	CDoC SCog
- 'Jill Totty'	CTrh SCog
- 'Joan Trehane' ♀H4	CTsd LRHS MAsh SCam
- 'Julia Hamiter' ♀H4	CBcs CDoC
§ - 'Jury's Yellow' ♀H4	Widely available
- 'Lady's Maid'	CBcs
- 'Laura Boscawen'	CDoC CTrG LHyd SCam
- 'Les Jury' ♀H4	CDoC CGHE CMHG CSBt CTrh GLld LRHS LSRN MWea NEgg SBch SCog SPer SPoG
- 'Little Lavender'	CDoC
- 'Margaret Waterhouse'	CBcs CDoC SCam SCog
- 'Marjorie Waldegrave' **new**	LRHS MAsh
- 'Mary Christian' ♀H4	CBcs GGal LHyd LRHS SCam SSta
- 'Mary Jobson'	CBcs
- 'Mary Larcom'	CBcs
- 'Mary Phoebe Taylor' ♀H4	CBcs CDoC CTrG CWSG GGal GLld NLar SCam SCog SCoo SPoG
- 'Mildred Veitch'	CSBt
- 'Mirage'	CDoC SCam
- 'Moira Reid'	CDoC
- 'Monica Dance'	CBcs CDoC LRHS SCam
- 'Muskoka' ♀H4	CMHG
- 'November Pink'	CBcs
- 'Palaxie' **new**	SCam
- 'Phillippa Forward'	CBcs CMac
- 'Red Dahlia'	CBcs
- 'Rendezvous'	CDoC SCam SCog SVic
- 'Rose Bouquet'	CDoC
- 'Rose Parade'	LHyd LRHS
- 'Rose Quartz'	LRHS
- 'Rosemary Williams'	CBcs
- 'Ruby Bells'	CMHG
- 'Ruby Wedding' (d)	CBcs CDoC CSBt CTrh EPfP GLld GQui LHyd LMil LRHS LSRN MAsh MWea NEgg NLar NPri SBch SCog SCoo SPoG
- 'Saint Ewe' ♀H4	CBcs CDoC CSBt CTrG CTrh CTri EPfP GGal GKev GLld LBuc LHyd LRHS MAsh MBri MGos MMuc NPri SCam SCog SCoo SPer SPoG
- 'Saint Michael'	CBcs CDoC
- 'Sayonara'	SCog
- 'Senorita' ♀H4	CDoC CTrh ELon LHyd SBod SCam SCog SVic
- 'Shocking Pink'	GLld
- 'Simon Bolitho'	LHyd SCog
- 'Sun Song'	SCog
- 'Taylor's Perfection'	LRHS
- 'The Duchess of Cornwall'	CDoC SCam
- 'Tiptoe'	CDoC MBri
- 'Tregrehan'	GLld
- 'Waltz Time'	CDoC LRHS SCam
- 'Water Lily' ♀H4	CBcs CDoC CTrh CTri ELon EPfP MGos SCam SPur SVic
- 'Wilber Foss' ♀H4	CBcs CDoC CMHG GLld LHyd MGos MMuc SCam SCog
- 'William Carlyon'	CWSG
- 'Wynne Rayner'	CDoC LRHS SCam
- 'Yesterday'	LRHS MMuc
'Winter's Charm' (*oleifera* × *sasanqua*)	SCog
'Winter's Dream' (*biemalis* × *oleifera*)	SCog
'Winter's Interlude' (*oleifera* × *sinensis*)	CDoC SCam SCog
'Winter's Joy'	SCog
'Winter's Toughie' (*sasanqua* hybrid)	CDoC SCam SCog
'Winton' (*cuspidata* × *saluenensis*)	CBcs CDoC SCam WFar
'Wirlinga Belle'	SCog
'Yoimachi' (*fraterna* × *sasanqua*)	CDoC CTrh LRHS

Campanula ✿ (Campanulaceae)

Plant	Suppliers
§ RCB AM 13	WCot
abietina	see *C. patula* subsp. *abietina*
§ ***alliariifolia***	Widely available
- DHTU 0126	WCru
- 'Ivory Bells'	see *C. alliariifolia*
allionii	see *C. alpestris*
§ ***alpestris***	ECho
alpina	MDKP NBur
- subsp. ***orbelica***	see *C. orbelica*
americana	LFur SPav
ardonensis	GKev
argyrotricha	NBur
armena	ELan SWal
arvatica	ECho EPot GMaP LRHS MDKP NMen

	Name	Suppliers
	- 'Alba'	ECho GMaP
	arvatica* × *cochleariifolia	MSCN
	aucheri	see *C. saxifraga* subsp. *aucheri*
	'Azure Beauty'	CSpe EBee ECtt ELan NCGa WCot
§	'Balchiniana' (v)	CBow
	barbata	CFir EBee EDAr GMaP NBur NWCA WAbe WMoo WPer
	- var. ***alba***	NBur
	bayerniana new	EBee GKev
	bellidifolia	NBir NBre
	- subsp. ***saxifraga***	EBur EDAr ITim NBur NMen
	besenginica	EPot GKev
§	***betulifolia*** ♀H4	CSam NBur WFar
	biebersteiniana	GKev
	'Birch Hybrid' ♀H4	EBee ECho ECtt EDAr ELan EPfP GKir LBee LRHS MMuc SIng WFar
	bononiensis	LLHF NBre SRms STes
	'Bumblebee'	WAbe
	'Burghaltii' ♀H4	CHar CPom EBee EHrv ELan GCal GMac LFur SBch SMrm WCot WFar WMnd WPer
	calaminthifolia	EBur
	'Cantata'	CPBP WAbe
§	***carnica***	ECho
	carpatica ♀H4	ECho EPfP GKir MBar MLHP NBre NBro NGdn SPlb SRms SWat
	- f. ***alba***	GKev LRHS NBre NGdn SPlb SWat
	- - 'Bressingham White'	LRHS
	- - 'Snowdrift'	GKir
§	- - 'Weisse Clips'	EAEE EBee ECho ECtt ELan EPfP GGar GKev GKir GMaP LAst LHop LRHS MDun NBlu NCGa NEgg NGdn NPri SBch SMrm SPer SPoG SRms STes SWvt WFar WPer
§	- 'Blaue Clips'	CBcs EBee ECho ECtt ELan EPfP GGar GKev GKir GMaP IFoB LAst LHop LRHS MDun NCGa NEgg NGdn NPri SBch SMrm SPer SPoG SRms STes SWvt WFar WPer WRHF
	- Blue Clips	see *C. carpatica* 'Blaue Clips'
	- 'Blue Moonlight'	EBur LHop LRHS
	- 'Chewton Joy'	CTri GKir LRHS
	- 'Ditton Blue'	GMaP
	- 'Karpatenkrone'	EBee
	- 'Kathy'	CMoH GBuc
	- 'Maureen Haddon'	LRHS
	- 'Silberschale'	NBre
	- 'Suzie'	IPot
	- var. ***turbinata***	ECho SRms WAbe
	- - 'Foerster'	GBuc IPot LRHS MTho WHoo
	- - 'Georg Arends'	ECtt
	- - 'Isabel'	LRHS
	- - 'Jewel'	LHop LRHS
	- White Clips	see *C. carpatica* f. *alba* 'Weisse Clips'
§	***cashmeriana***	EBur NBur
	- 'Blue Cloud'	CWib
	cenisia	WFar
	cephallenica	see *C. garganica* subsp. *cephallenica*
§	***chamissonis***	ECho GEdr LLHF NBur WPat
	- 'Alba'	GEdr
	- 'Major'	EDAr EWes LBee LRHS NBur
	- 'Oyobeni'	NBur NLAp
§	- 'Superba' ♀H4	EBur ECho ELan MTho NBur NMen WAbe
	choruhensis	NBur
§	***cochlearifolia*** ♀H4	CEnt CSpe CTri EBee ECho EDAr EPfP GJos GKir GMaP LRHS MDun MMuc MTho SBch STre WFar WHoo WPer
	- var. ***alba***	CSpe CTri EDAr GMaP MHer MMuc NBlu NRya NWCA SBch SRms WAbe WHoo WPer
	- - 'Bavaria White'	ECho WFar
	- - double white-flowered (d)	WPat
	- - 'White Baby' (Baby Series)	ECho ECtt EPfP EPot GAbr GGar GJos GKir LRHS NHol SPet SPoG
	- 'Annie Hall'	ECho
	- 'Bavaria Blue'	ECho NHol NWCA SMrm SPet
	- 'Blue Baby' (Baby Series)	ECho EPfP GGar GJos GKir MHer NPro SPoG SRms
	- 'Blue Tit'	GBuc
	- 'Blue Wonder'	LRHS
	- 'Cambridge Blue'	LRHS WFar
	- 'Elizabeth Oliver' (d)	CTri ECho ECtt EDAr EPot GBuc GCal GGar GKev GKir GMaP LHop LRHS MAvo MHer MTho NLAp NWCA SPlb SPoG SRms WAbe WCom WFar WHoo WPat
	- 'Miss Willmott'	MTho NBir
	- 'Oakington Blue'	GKir LLHF WAbe WCom
	- var. ***pallida*** 'Miranda'	LRHS
	- - 'Silver Chimes'	ECho
	- 'R.B. Loder' (d)	LRHS
	- 'Tubby'	ECho GKev LLHF MHer MTho SRms
	- 'Warleyensis'	see *C.* × *haylodgensis* W. Brockbank 'Warley White'
	collina	CTri LLHF NBre NBur WCFE WPer
	coriacea	GKev
	'Covadonga'	CMea EBee ECho LHop LLHF LRHS
	cretica	ELan NBre
	'Crystal'	ECtt MAvo MNrw SUsu
	dasyantha	see *C. chamissonis*
	dolomitica	EBee GKev LLHF NMen
	'E.K. Toogood'	CElw CPBP EAlp ECho ECtt MWat NBro NVic NWCA SMac SRms
	elatines	EBee
	ephesia	GKev
	- SDR 1111	GKev
	eriocarpa	see *C. latifolia* 'Eriocarpa'
	'Faichem Lilac'	GCra LLHF MLHP NChi NLar NPro STes
	fenestrellata	EPot MTho NMen NWCA SRms WAbe WFar
	finitima	see *C. betulifolia*
	foliosa	NBur WPer
	formanekiana ♀H2-3	EBur NBur
	fragilis	EBur ECho
	- 'Hirsuta'	ECho
	garganica ♀H4	ECho EPfP GAbr GGar GKev GMaP LAst LRHS MDKP MRav NBlu NEgg SBch SIng SWvt WFar WMoo WPer
	- 'Aurea'	see *C. garganica* 'Dickson's Gold'
	- 'Blue Diamond'	ECho LHop WFar
§	- subsp. ***cephallenica***	CElw NBro
§	- 'Dickson's Gold'	Widely available
	- 'Hirsuta'	ECho
	- 'Major'	EBee ECho GKir LAst SPoG WFar
	- 'Mrs Resholt'	EWll GKir LAst NBlu SWvt WFar
	- 'W.H. Paine' ♀H4	ECho ECtt MDKP MNFA NMen NSla WAbe WFar WHoo
	'Gaven'	IPot
	glomerata	CBot CElw CEnt CPLG CRWN EBWF GCra GJos LSRN MSCN NBro NLan NMir SPet SRms WBrk WEas WFar
	- var. ***acaulis***	CStu EBee EPfP GAbr GGar GKir LRHS NLar NWCA SBch SPoG WFar WPer
	- var. ***alba***	Widely available

	Plant	Suppliers
§	- - 'Alba Nana'	LAst
§	- - 'Schneekrone'	ECha EPfP GKir NBre WFar
	- 'Caroline'	Widely available
	- Crown of Snow	see *C. glomerata* var. *alba* 'Schneekrone'
	- var. ***dahurica***	NBre NLar SMrm SPet WPer
	- 'Emerald'	EBee ECtt LLHF NCGa WCot WHlf
	- 'Joan Elliott'	EBee ECha ECtt GBuc LEdu LSRN MNFA MRav MWat SPoG WAul WCAu
	- 'Nana Alba'	see *C. glomerata* var. *alba* 'Alba Nana'
	- 'Purple Pixie'	LRHS MGos
	- 'Superba' ♀^{H4}	Widely available
	grossekii	EHrv LLHF NBre WHrl
	'Hannah'	LHop LRHS
	Hannay's form	CHar
	× ***haylodgensis*** misapplied	see *C.* × *haylodgensis* 'Plena'
§	× ***haylodgensis***	CPBP ECtt EDAr EPot WAbe WCot
	W. Brockbank 'Marion Fisher' (d)	WHoo
§	- 'Plena' (d)	EBee ECho EDAr ELan EPot LBee LHop LRHS NBro NMen NPri SRms WAbe WCom WCot WFar WHoo WKif
§	- 'Warley White' (d)	EBur ECho ELan
	- 'Yvonne'	EDAr EPot GMaP LRHS SMrm SPoG WFar
	'Hemswell Starlight'	WAbe
	hercegovina 'Nana'	LLHF WAbe
	'Hilltop Snow'	CPBP NMen WAbe WCom
	hofmannii	EBee EBur ELan GGar MBNS NLar WFar
§	***incurva***	CSpe EBee EBur EWTr GAbr GJos GKev
	isophylla ♀^{H2}	ECho EPot
	- 'Alba' ♀^{H2}	ECho
	- 'Flore Pleno' (d)	EBur
	- 'Mayi' misapplied	see *C.* 'Balchiniana'
	- 'Variegata'	see *C.* 'Balchiniana'
	'Joe Elliott' ♀$^{H2-3}$	ECho WAbe
	kemulariae	LLHF NBur SRms WCom WPer
	- alba	ITim
	'Kent Belle' ♀^{H4}	Widely available
	khasiana	EBee GKev
	'Kifu' (v)	CBow EBee LRHS
	lactiflora	CElw CSev EBee ECha EPfP GAbr GCra GKev GKir GMaP IFoB LRHS MCot MLHP MSCN MWhi NEgg NVic SPer WBrE WFar WHoo WMoo WPer WTin WWEG
	- alba	see *C. lactiflora* white-flowered
N	- 'Alba' ♀^{H4}	EBee EBla EPfP GAbr GKir GMaP MAvo MDKP MLHP SMrm STes WFar WMnd
	- 'Avalanche'	EBrs LRHS
	- 'Blue Cross'	CMoH EBrs GKir LEdu LRHS NBre NLar WSpi
	- 'Blue Lady'	NBre WFar
	- 'Dixter Presence'	IPot SUsu
	- dwarf pink-flowered	EBee MBNS NBre NCGa SHGN
	- 'Favourite'	CFir CSpe EBee MNrw NBPC NCGa NGdn NLar STes WFar
	- 'Loddon Anna' ♀^{H4}	Widely available
	- 'Moorland Rose'	WMoo
	- new hybrids **new**	GJos
	- 'Pouffe'	CPrp EAEE EBee EBla ECtt ELan ELon EPfP GGar GKir GMaP LRHS MBri MDKP MRav NBro NGdn SMrm SPer SPet SWat SWvt WFar
	- 'Prichard's Variety' ♀^{H4}	Widely available
	- 'Senior'	EBee
	- 'Superba' ♀^{H4}	EBee ECtt MCot WClo
	- 'Violet'	SWat WPer
	- 'White Pouffe'	CPrp EAEE EBee ECtt ELan ELon EPfP GKir GMaP LRHS MBri MDKP NBPC NLar SPer SPoG STes SWat WFar
§	- white-flowered	CBot ECha GKir MBNS NBir NBur SPer SWat WFar WPer
	lasiocarpa	CPBP GKev
	latifolia	EBWF ECha GAbr GJos LRHS MCot NBid NMir NOrc NVic SPer SRms WFar WMoo
	- var. ***alba***	EBee ELan EPfP GAbr GCra GJos LRHS MWea NGdn SPav SPer SPoG SRms WFar WHal WPer WSpi WWEG
	- - 'White Ladies'	NBur
*	- 'Amethyst'	CPrp SDnm SPav
	- blue- flowered	WSpi
	- 'Brantwood'	GAbr GKir LRHS MRav MWhi NChi SDnm SPav SRms SWat WCot WMnd WSpi
	- 'Buckland'	SPav
§	- 'Eriocarpa'	NBur
	- 'Gloaming'	ECtt MCot NBur
	- var. ***macrantha***	EBee ELan EPfP GMaP LHop LRHS MBri MCot MWat NGdn NHol NSti SPav SPoG SWat SWvt WCAu WMoo WPer WWEG
	- - 'Alba'	CMMP EBee ECha ECtt EShb GMaP LHop LRHS MCot MRav SBch WCAu WMoo WPer WWEG
	- 'Misty Dawn'	WCot WFar
	- 'Roger Wood'	GCal
§	***latiloba***	CElw CMHG GKir MWhi SBch SGar WBrk WCot WFar
§	- 'Alba' ♀^{H4}	CElw EBee ELan EPPr EPfP GCal GCra MCot MDKP NEgg NGdn SBch SGar WBrk WRHF
	- 'Hidcote Amethyst' ♀^{H4}	Widely available
	- 'Highcliffe Variety' ♀^{H4}	CSpe EBee ECtt ELan EPfP GBuc GCra MDKP MNFA MRav SGSe SMrm SPoG WCAu WCot WKif WMnd WWEG
*	- 'Highdown'	WFar
	- 'Percy Piper' ♀^{H4}	CSam ELan GBuc GKir MRav NBre NBro NLar WFar WSpi
	- 'Splash'	CElw EBee MAvo WHil
	linifolia	see *C. carnica*
	longestyla 'Isabella Blue'	EBee
	'Lynchmere'	WAbe WCom
	makaschvilii	CEnt CSpe EBee ECtt EWTr GKev GMac IGor MHer MWhi NBur NLar SAga SBod SGSe SMrm STes WCHb WCot WHrl WPer WSHC
	'Marion Fisher'	see *C.* × *haylodgensis* W. Brockbank 'Marion Fisher'
	medium	LAst
	'Milkshake'	EBee
	mirabilis 'Mist Maiden'	LRHS WFar
	moesiaca	GKev
	'Monic'	EPfP
	muralis	see *C. portenschlagiana*
	nitida	see *C. persicifolia* var. *planiflora*
	'Norman Grove'	ECtt EPot
	ochroleuca	CMea CPom CSpe GCal MCot NBur SGSe SHGN STes SWat WCFE WCot WHrl WMoo
	- 'White Beauty'	CWib
	- 'White Bells'	MWhi
	odontosepala from Iran	EBee EPPr NBre

	'Oliver's Choice'	WHrl
	olympica misapplied	see *C. rotundifolia* 'Olympica'
§	***orbelica***	GKev
	oreadum	GKev
	ossetica	CSpe EBee ECtt ELan MLHP
	pallida subsp. ***tibetica***	see *C. cashmeriana*
	parviflora Lam.	see *C. sibirica*
	patula	EGoo GJos NLar
§	- subsp. ***abietina***	NBre NLar
	'Paul Furse'	ECtt MAvo MBel MDKP NBre NCGa NLar NPro NSti WCAu WTin WWEG
	pelviformis	MNrw
	pendula	CSpe EPfP EWes GBuc GKev LRHS MBNS NBlu NLar
	persicifolia	Widely available
	- var. ***alba***	Widely available
§	- 'Alba Coronata' (d)	GAbr GKir LRHS NBir WCAu WEas WFar
	- 'Alba Plena'	see *C. persicifolia* 'Alba Coronata'
	- Ashfield double ice blue (d)	NBre
	- 'Beau Belle'	EBee EPfP LSou NBPC NLar NMoo
§	- 'Bennett's Blue' (d)	EBee EBla EHrv ELan EPfP GBuc IPot LHop LRHS MAvo MRav NHol NSti SPer SRms SWat WFar
	- 'Blue Bloomers' (d)	CElw CHar CLAP CMil EBee ECtt EWes GGar IKil LLWP LRHS MAvo MNFA MRav NHol SGSe SMrm WBrk WCot WHal
	- blue cup-in-cup (d)	EBla ELon MDKP WFar
	- blue-flowered	GKir IFoB LAst MRav SGSe SPlb WFar
	- 'Boule de Neige' (d)	CMMP CMoH EBla ECtt WCFE WEas WSpi WWEG
	- 'Caerulea Coronata'	see *C. persicifolia* 'Coronata'
§	- 'Chettle Charm' PBR ♀H4	Widely available
	- 'Cornish Mist'	CBgR EBee ECtt EHrv ELan EPfP WSpi
§	- 'Coronata' (d)	ECtt GCra
	- 'Cristine'	MDKP
	- cup and saucer blue (d)	GCra
§	- cup and saucer white (d)	EBla ELan WClo WFar WPer
	- double blue-flowered (d)	NBir NBro WEas
	- double white-flowered (d)	ELan WMoo
	- 'Eastgrove Blue'	NCob
	- 'Fleur de Neige' (d) ♀H4	ECtt MBel NBre NCob WCot WHoo WWEG
	- 'Frances' (d)	CLAP WCom
	- 'Frank Lawley' (d)	LRHS
	- 'Gawen'	EBee ECtt GMaP GMac LRHS MAvo NBre SAga SMrm WCot
	- 'George Chiswell' PBR	see *C. persicifolia* 'Chettle Charm'
	- 'Grandiflora'	NBre SMrm
	- 'Grandiflora Alba'	GBuc NBre NHol SMrm
	- 'Grandiflora Caerulea'	NLar
§	- 'Hampstead White' (d)	ECtt EHrv GBuc GCal LHop NBro WEas WHil WMnd WSpi WWEG
	- 'Hetty'	see *C. persicifolia* 'Hampstead White'
	- 'Kelly's Gold'	EBee EBla EPPr LAst LRHS MCCP NBhm NBir NLar NPri NPro SPav WCot WHil WWEG
	- 'La Belle'	EBee ECtt EPyc NLar STes
	- 'La Bello' PBR	EBee ECtt
	- 'La Bonne Amie'	CDes EBee ECtt NLar
	- 'Moerheimii' (d)	EAEE EPfP EShb NBir STes
	- 'Monita White'	CMoH
	- 'Perry's Boy Blue'	NPer
§	- var. ***planiflora***	CPBP WCom
	- - f. ***alba***	EPot MWat
	- 'Powder Puff' (d)	EBee GBin GMac LFur LSou NCob NEgg SMrm WBor WCot WRHF
	- 'Pride of Exmouth' (d)	CHar CMMP EBee ECtt EHrv ELan EShb GBuc IMon MCCP MHer WCFE WClo WMnd WSpi WWEG
	- subsp. ***sessiliflora***	see *C. latiloba*
	- - 'Alba'	see *C. latiloba* 'Alba'
	- 'Snow White' (d)	EPPr
	- 'Snowdrift'	ELan SRms
	- Takion Series	CSpe
	- - 'Takion Blue'	MSCN WHil
	- - 'Takion White'	WHil
	- 'Telham Beauty' misapplied	CSBt CWCL EBee ECtt ELan EPfP EShb GAbr GKir LRHS MRav SMrm SPer SRms SWvt WFar WMnd WPer
	- 'Telham Beauty' ambig.	EAEE GGar LAst MCot MSCN NEgg NGBl SBch SWvt WSpi WWEG
	- 'Telham Beauty' D. Thurston	SPoG
	- 'Tinpenny Blue'	WTin
	- 'White Cup and Saucer'	see *C. persicifolia* cup and saucer white
	- 'White Queen' (d)	NBur WMnd
	- 'Wortham Belle'	CWCL ECtt MAvo MBNS NEgg NHol WCAu WCot WFar
	- 'Wortham Belle' misapplied	see *C. persicifolia* 'Bennett's Blue'
	- 'Wortham Belle' ambig.	CWGN EShb WSpi
	- 'Yellow Binstead'	EBee
	petrophila	WAbe
	pilosa	see *C. chamissonis*
	- 'Superba'	see *C. chamissonis* 'Superba'
	'Pink Octopus'	CSev CWGN ECtt LLHF LOck MBNS MCot NBPC NBhm NCGa NGdn SMrm SUsu WCot WFut WSpi
	planiflora	see *C. persicifolia* var. *planiflora*
	'Polly Henderson'	CPBP
§	***portenschlagiana*** ♀H4	Widely available
	- 'Catharina'	ECtt
	- 'Lieselotte'	CElw GBuc GMaP LIMB
	- 'Major'	LAst WCom WFar WMoo
	- 'Resholdt's Variety'	CMea CSam EAEE EBee ECho EDAr EPfP GMaP LAst LBee LHop LRHS MRav NPri SMrm WMoo WPer
	poscharskyana	Widely available
	- 'Blauranke'	EBee EWes LRHS
	- 'Blue Gown'	GMaP GMac IPot MNFA
	- 'Blue Waterfall'	EBrs LRHS MBNS SPoG WFar
	- 'E.H. Frost'	CBre CElw EBee ECho ECtt EDAr EPPr EPfP EWTr GMaP LAst LHop MBri MCot MWat NBro NRya SAga SRGP SRms SWvt WBrk WFar WMoo WPer
	- 'Lilacina'	EPPr
	- 'Lisduggan Variety'	CElw EBee EBur ECtt EDAr ELon EPPr EWes GKir GMaP GMac LHop LIMB MBri MHer MNFA NBro SBch WBrk WCom WCot WFar WMoo WPer
	- 'Stella' ♀H4	EBee ECha ECho ECtt EPfP LSRN MAvo MRav NBro SDix SPer SRGP SWvt WCom WFar WMoo WRHF
	- variegated (v)	EHoe
	- white-flowered	CTri ECho ELan LAst MDKP WFar
	prenanthoides	see *Asyneuma prenanthoides*
	primulifolia	CSsd EBee EBrs ELan GKir LRHS MNrw SBod SHGN SRms SWat WCHb WMoo WPer
	- 'Blue Oasis'	CMHG LSRN
	× ***pseudoraineri***	EBur EWes LRHS NMen WCom
	pulla	CPBP CSpe CWCL EBee EBur ECho ECtt EDAr GGar GMaP IFro LAst LRHS MTho SIng SPoG SRot WAbe WFar

	- ***alba***	EBee EBur ECho ECtt EDAr EPot LRHS WAbe
	× ***pulloides*** hort.	LRHS
	- 'G.F.Wilson' ♀H4	EBee EBur ECho ECtt EPot SRkn WFar
	punctata	CBot CMHG CSpe EBee EHrv GJos GKev LEdu LRHS MCot NBPC NBro NSti SBch SMrm SWat WCAu WFar WGwG WMoo WPer
	- f. ***albiflora***	CMMP GKev MBel MNrw SHar WFar WMnd
	- - 'Alba'	CCVN
	- - 'Nana Alba'	NBur SBch
	- 'Alina's Double' (d)	GMac MDKP MNrw WWEG
	- var. ***hondoensis***	GKev IGor MLHP MNrw
	- - 'Bossy Boots'	SMrm
	- hose-in-hose (d)	EBla MMHG MSpe NLar WFar WGwG
	- 'Hot Lips'	CChe CFir CMMP EBee EBla ECtt ELan EPPr EPfP EShb LRHS LSRN MBri NBPC NPro NSti SBch SPet SPoG SRGP WClo WPrP WWEG
*	- var. ***howozana***	GKev
	- var. ***microdonta*** B&SWJ 5553	WCru
	- 'Milky Way' **new**	EPPr
	- 'Millennium'	MAvo WFar
	- 'Milly'	EPPr LLHF WPGP
	- 'Mottled' (v)	NBre
*	- 'Nana'	CCVN
	- 'Pallida'	WBrE
	- 'Pantaloons' (d)	CSpe EBee EBla ECtt LHop LRHS LSRN MBNS MBri MDKP MSpe NCob NLar SBch SHar SMrm WBor
	- 'Pink Chimes'[PBR]	CPou EBee EPPr LSou MBNS MBri NBhm NCGa NPro SRot
	- 'Plum Wine' **new**	MSpe
	- 'Reifrock'	SMrm
	- 'Rosea'	SRms WFar
	- f. ***rubriflora***	CCVN ECtt ELan EPfP EPla GBBs GCra GJos LBMP LHop LRHS MCot MDun MNrw MWat MWhi NEgg NHol NOrc SBch SGar SIng SMad SMrm SPer SWal WFar WMnd WPer WWEG
	- - 'Beetroot'	EBee EBla ECtt EPPr GBBs GKir IKil ITim LSou MBNS MHer NBur NLar WHrl WPGP
	- - 'Bowl of Cherries'[PBR]	EBee EBla ECtt EPPr EShb GKir LLHF LRHS LSRN LSou MBri MMHG NLar NMoo NSti SHar SPav SRkn SRot
	- - 'Cherry Bells'	CFir EAEE EBla ECtt EPfP LBMP LRHS LSRN MAvo MBri MCCP MNrw NCob NLar SPav SPoG
	- - 'Vienna Festival'	CSBt EBee ECtt GMac LEdu LSou NBhm NLar NSti WCot
	- - 'Wine 'n' Rubies'	ECtt EHrv GMac LSRN LSou MAvo MDKP MNrw MSCN SBch SHar SPav WCot
	- 'Twilight Bells'	NBre
	- 'Wedding Bells'	Widely available
I	- 'White Bells'	EPPr MBNS MDKP SMrm
	- white hose-in-hose (d)	MNFA MNrw NCob WBrk
	'Purple Sensation'[PBR]	EBee ECtt EPfP GMac MBNS MNrw NCGa WCot
	pusilla	see *C. cochlearifolia*
	pyramidalis	CBot CMea CMoH CSpe EBee ELan EPfP GJos MCCP MMuc NOrc SBch SDnm SPav SPlb WPer WWEG
	- 'Alba'	CSpe CWib EBee ELan EPfP GJos MMuc NBre NLar SBch SDnm SPav SPlb WBrE WPer WWEG
	- lavender blue-flowered	CWib LAst
	raddeana	MAvo MDKP WBrk
	raineri ♀H4	CPBP EPot GKev NMen NSla WAbe
*	- ***alba***	CPBP EPot WAbe
	- 'Nettleton Gold'	EPot
§	***rapunculoides***	EBee EGoo GJos GKev NBre SWat WFar WMoo
§	- 'Afterglow'	EBee MAvo WCot WDyG
	- 'Alba'	MAvo
	rapunculus	ILis
	recurva	see *C. incurva*
	reiseri	NBur
	rhomboidalis L.	EBee
	rhomboidalis Gorter	see *C. rapunculoides*
	rigidipila	NBur
	rotundifolia	CArn CRWN EBWF ECho EPfP GJos GKir LAst LBMP LRHS MCot MHer MNHC NBid NBre NGBl NLan NMir SGSe SIde SPlb SWat WAbe WBrk WPer
	- var. ***alba***	WAbe WPer
§	- 'Olympica'	EBee EBur IGor MBNS MMuc NLar NPri WFar WHoo
	- 'Superba'	ECho
	- 'White Gem'	GJos LBMP NBre SSvw
	'Royal Wave'	ECtt NBhm
	rupestris	EBur LLHF
	rupicola	WAbe
	'Samantha'	CBow CSpe EBee EBla ECtt GMac LHop LRHS LSRN MWea NPri SHar SPoG SRGP SRot
	'Saragamine'	EBee
	'Sarastro'	Widely available
	sarmatica	EBee ECGP EPfP EWTr GAbr GKev LFur MNFA MWhi NBid NSti SMrm SRms WCHb WKif WPer
	- 'Hemelstraling'	EBee WCot
	sartorii	EBur
§	***saxifraga*** subsp. ***aucheri***	EBee EBur EPot GKev ITim NLAp WFar
	scheuchzeri	EPot
	seraglio	GKir
§	***sibirica***	NBre NBur
	siegizmundii	EBee NBur
	speciosa	EBee EPot MWhi NBre
	'Stansfieldii'	CPBP EBur LRHS NMen WPat
	'Summer Pearl'	ECtt EWll GKev SBch SMrm
	'Swannables'	CPou EBee ECtt LLHF MNFA MRav NCGa NChi WOut
	takesimana	Widely available
	- B&SWJ 8499	WCru
I	- 'Alba'	EBla GKir LBMP MDKP NBre SHar WMoo
	- 'Beautiful Trust'	CLAP CSpe EBee EBla ECtt GMac LFur LHop LRHS NBPC NBhm NLar NSti SGSe SHar SRkn SUsu WCru WPGP
	- 'Elizabeth'	Widely available
	- 'Elizabeth II' (d)	CDes ECtt EPPr MAvo MDKP MTho WCot
	thyrsoides	MCot NBre NBur SDnm SMrm SPav WAbe
	- subsp. ***carniolica***	SGar
	'Timsbury Perfection'	CPBP
	'Tiny Bells' **new**	LLHF
	tommasiniana ♀H4	LRHS NBur WAbe
	trachelium	CEnt CMHG EBWF EBee ELon EPfP GAbr GKir MNrw MRav NBPC NLan SAga SGar SPad STes SWat

	WFar WHer WMoo WPer WWEG
- var. ***alba***	CEnt CLAP GKir MNrw MWhi NLar STes SWat WBrE WCot WFar WMoo WPer
- - 'Alba Flore Pleno' (d)	CHar CLAP STes WFar
- 'Bernice' (d)	CDes CHar EBee ECtt ELan EPfP EShb GBuc GMaP LAst LRHS MAvo MBri MCot NBPC NBid NBre NCGa SAga SMrm SPer WCot WFar WMnd WTin WWEG
- lilac-blue-flowered	SWat
- 'Snowball'	EBee EShb LAst LSRN LSou
troegerae	NWCA
'Tymonsii'	CPBP EBur ECho LLHF NBir NMen WAbe WFar
'Van-Houttei'	CDes CElw CHar EBee EWes GMac NLar SAga SBch WCot WFar WPer
versicolor	CPBP NBre
vidalii	see *Azorina vidalii*
waldsteiniana	CPBP WAbe
wanneri	EBur EPfP LRHS NLar
'Warley Gem'	GKir
'Warley White'	see *C.* × *haylodgensis* W. Brockbank 'Warley White'
'Warleyensis'	see *C.* × *haylodgensis* W. Brockbank 'Warley White'
× ***wockei*** 'Puck'	EBur ECho ECtt EPot LHop LLHF LRHS WAbe
zangezura	CHrt EBee EBur GKev IKil NGdn SBch SGar STes

Campanula × *Symphyandra* see *Campanula*

Campanumoea see *Codonopsis*

Campsis (*Bignoniaceae*)

atrosanguinea	see *Bignonia capreolata* 'Atrosanguinea'
grandiflora	CArn CBcs CSPN CWGN EBee ELan EPfP LRHS LSRN MAsh SPer SWvt WCFE
radicans	CArn CBcs CDul CMac CRHN CSBt CWib EBee ECrN ELan EPfP IFFs LRHS LSRN MCot MPet MSwo SBch SLon SPer SPlb WBVN WBrE WDin
- 'Atrosanguinea'	EPfP
- 'Flamenco'	CDoC CMac EBee ELan LAst LRHS LSRN MAsh NLar SBch SBod SCoo SLim SPoG SWvt WFar WGwG
§ - f. ***flava*** ♀H4	CBcs CDoC CHEx CMac CTri EBee ELan ELon EPfP LHop LRHS MAsh MBlu MCCP MGos NLar NPal NScw NSti SBch SLim SPer SPoG SWvt
- 'Indian Summer'	CWGN EBee EPfP LRHS LSRN LSou MBlu MBri MGos NLar SBch SCoo SLim SPoG
- 'Stromboli' **new**	EPfP MAsh
- 'Yellow Trumpet'	see *C. radicans* f. *flava*
× ***tagliabuana*** Dancing Flame = 'Huidan' PBR	CWit EBee MAsh MGos NLar
- 'Madame Galen' ♀H4	Widely available

Camptosema (*Papilionaceae*)

praeandinum	WPGP

Camptosorus see *Asplenium*

Camptotheca (*Cornaceae*)

acuminata	WPGP

Campylandra see *Tupistra*

Campylotropis (*Papilionaceae*)

macrocarpa	NLar

Canarina (*Campanulaceae*)

canariensis ♀H1	CCCN ECho ERea WCot WPGP

Candollea see *Hibbertia*

Canna ✿ (*Cannaceae*)

'A. Eisenbarth'	WCCa
'Abraham Lincoln'	WCCa
'Adam's Orange'	CDTJ CHEx XBlo
'Admiral Aurellan'	WCCa
'Admiral Courbet'	WCCa
'Alberich'	CSam SBch WCCa WHil
'Albino'	WCCa
'Alfred Young'	WCCa
'Alice McGuigan'	WCCa
'Allemania'	WCCa
'Alt Württemberg'	WCCa
altensteinii	CDTJ SHaC SPlb XBlo
'Ambassador'	EBrs LAma
'Ambassadour'	SBch
'American Flag'	WCCa
'Anetta Dalebö'	WCCa
'Annaeei' ♀H3	EAmu WCCa
'Anthéor'	WCCa
'Apricot Dream'	WCCa
'Apricot Ice'	LRHS
'Argentina'	SBch SHaC
'Arne Dalebö' (v)	WCCa
'Arthur William Paul' (v)	WCCa
'Assaut'	SBch SHaC
'Atlantis'	XBlo
'Auguste Ferrier' (v)	WCCa
'Australia'	CDTJ LRHS LSou SHaC XBlo
'Austria'	WCCa
'Autumn Dragon'	WCCa
'Avon'	WCCa
'Baronne de Pouilly'	WCCa
'Bavaria'	WCCa
'Berenice Emsley'	WCCa
'Bevere'	WCCa
'Black Knight'	CFir EBee EBrs ECGP LAma LSRN SBch SGar SMrm SPad WWlt XBlo
'Bonfire'	CDTJ CHEx
brasiliensis	CFee CHll CRHN LRHS SBch XBlo
'Brillant'	LAma LRHS SBch SBst WDyG
'Brown Sugar' **new**	LRHS
'Burbank'	WCCa
'Burgundia'	WCCa
'Burgundy Blush' (v)	WCCa
'Caballero'	SBch
'Caliméro'	SBch
'Canary'	XBlo
'Carnaval'	SBch
'Carolina Gold'	WCCa
'Centenaire de Rozain-Boucharlat'	SBch
'Centurion'	LAma
'Cerise Davenport'	CFir
'Chameleon'	WCCa
'Champigny'	SBch WCCa
'Champion'	LRHS SBch SHaC WCCa
'Chatei Grandis'	WCCa
Chaumes = 'Turcacha'	WCCa
'Cherry Red' Schmid	LRHS
'China Lady'	WCCa
'Chinese Coral' Schmid	CHEx LAma
I 'Citrina'	XBlo
'City of Gloucester' (v)	WCCa

	Name	Suppliers
§	'City of Portland'	LAma SBch WCCa WWEG
§	'Cleopatra'	CCCN CFir EAmu EBrs EPfP LAma LRHS SBch WGwG WHil XBlo
	coccinea	SHaC
§	'Colibri'	LAma SBch
	'Conestoga'	SBch
	'Confetti'	see *C.* 'Colibri'
	'Constitution'	WCCa
	'Coq d'Or' **new**	LRHS
	'Corail'	SBch SHaC
	'Corrida'	SBch
	'Corsica' (Island Series)	EBee SBch WCCa
	'Creamy White'	CHEx WHil XBlo
	'Crimson Beauty'	EBrs LAma WHil
	'Délibáb'	CSam LAma SBch WDyG
	'Di Bartolo'	WCCa XBlo
	'Doctor Nansen'	WCCa
	'Dondo'	SBch
	'Doreen Morris'	WCCa
	'Duchesse de Montenard'	WCCa
	'Durban' ambig.	CChe CWGN EBee ECtt IHer LAma LAst LRHS LSRN MAvo SAga SMrm WClo WCom WGwG
	'Durban' Hiley, orange-flowered	see *C.* 'Phasion'
	edulis	CDTJ CHEx ETod SBch
	- purple-leaved	ETod
§	× ***ehemanii*** ♀H3	CDTJ CRHN CSev SBch SChr SDix SHaC WCom WPGP
	'Eileen Gallo' (v)	WCCa
	'Ella Dalebö'	WCCa
	'Ellen Layden'	WCCa
	'Emblème'	SBch SHaC
	'En Avant'	CDTJ CHEx LAma SBch SHaC SPlb
	'Endeavour'	CHEx LPJP MSKA SHaC
	'Epi d'Or'	WCCa
	'Erebus' ♀H3	MSKA SBch SDix SHaC
	'Espresso Festival'	NGdn WCCa
	'Étoile du Feu'	XBlo
	'Eureka'	SBch
	'Evening Star'	LAma
	'Extase'	SBch
	'Falstaff'	WCCa
	'Fatamorgana'	LAma SBch WHil
	'Felix Ragout'	LAma WCCa
	'Ferrandii'	WCCa
	'Fire Red'	WCCa
	Firebird	see *C.* 'Oiseau de Feu'
	flaccida	SHaC
	'Flame'	XBlo
	'Flammèche'	WCCa
§	'Florence Vaughan'	SBch
	'Freya'	WCCa
	'Fröken'	WCCa
	'Gaiety'	WCCa
	'General Eisenhower' ♀H3	ETod
	× ***generalis***	SHaC
	glauca	SDix SHaC WCCa WHil
	'Gnom'	SBch WCCa
*	'Gold Ader'	LAma
	'Gold Dream'	LAma
	'Golden Girl'	SBch WHil
	'Golden Lucifer'	EBrs ELan LAma LRHS
	'Goldilocks'	WCCa
	'Gran Canaria'	SBch
	'Grand Duc'	SHaC
	'Grande'	CFir MAJR SBch SHaC
	'Hallow'	WCCa
	'Heinrich Seidel'	CHEx
	'Hellas'	WCCa
	Henlade	CDTJ
	'Henri Cohn'	WCCa

	Name	Suppliers
	'Hercule'	CHEx SBch
	'Hilary Owen'	WCCa
	'Hiley'	ETod
	'Hungaria'	WCCa
	hybrids	ELan
	'Ibis'	EAmu EPfP LRHS SHaC
	indica	CDTJ CSpe EShb ETod LRHS SAPC SArc SBch SHaC SPlb WCCa WHil
	- gold and orange-flowered	WCCa
	- 'Kreta' (Island Series)	LRHS SBch
	- orange-flowered	WCCa
	- 'Purpurea'	CDTJ CHEx EAmu LEdu LRHS MCot SBch SChr SDix SHaC SPlb WDyG WPGP
	- 'Red King Rupert'	CCCN
	- 'Russian Red' ♀H3	SBch SHaC
	- 'Singapore Orange'	WCCa
	'Ingeborg' ♀H3	LAma WCCa
	'Intrigue'	SHaC WCCa
	iridiflora misapplied	see *C.* × ***ehemanii***
	iridiflora Ruiz & Pav.	CDTJ CHEx CSpe LRHS SAPC SArc
	'Iridiflora Rubra' (v)	WCCa
	'Italia'	WCCa WHil
	'J.B. van der Schoot'	WCCa
	jacobiniflora	WCCa
	'Jean Krupp'	WCCa
	'Jessie Dalebö'	WCCa
	'Jivago'	SHaC
	'John Tulett'	WCCa
	'Joseph Bischau'	WCCa
	'Kalimpong'	CDTJ
	'Kansas City' (v)	WCCa
	'Karla Dalebö'	WCCa
I	'King Humbert' (blood-red)	CBcs CDTJ CHEx EBrs EPfP LAma LAst LRHS WCCa XBlo
	King Humbert (orange-red)	see *C.* 'Roi Humbert'
	'King Midas'	see *C.* 'Richard Wallace'
	'Kings' Gold'	WCCa
	'Königin Charlotte'	SBch SHaC SPad
	'Kyneburg'	WCCa
	'La Bohème' (Grand Opera Series)	LAma
	'La France'	WCCa
	'La Quintinie'	SBch
	'Laura Dalebö'	WCCa
	'Lenape' ♀H3	SBch WCCa
	'Lesotho Lil'	CHll
	'Liberté'	see *C.* 'Wyoming'
	'Lincroft'	WCCa
	'Llanthony'	WCCa
	'Louis Cayeux' ♀H3	SDix
	'Louis Cottin'	CBcs CCCN CDTJ CHEx EBrs EPfP LAma LRHS SBch SPad WCCa WHil
	'Lucifer'	CCCN CHEx EBrs LAma LRHS NEgg NPer SEND SPlb WBrE
	'Ludlow'	WCCa
	lutea	CHEx XBlo
	'Madame Angèle Martin'	SBch WCCa XBlo
	'Madame Chabanne'	WCCa
	'Madame Legris'	WCCa
	'Madame Paul Casaneuve'	SBch
	'Madeira' (Island Series)	SBch
	'Malawiensis Variegata'	see *C.* 'Striata'
	'Malvern'	WCCa
	'Mandy Robinson'	WCCa
	'Marabout'	LRHS SBst SHaC WCCa
	'Margaret Strange'	SBch SHaC WCCa
	'Marilyn'	WCCa
	'Mark McGuigan'	WCCa
	'Marvel'	LAma
	'Mary Leyden'	WCCa
	'Maudie Malcolm'	EPfP WCCa

'May Vince' WCCa
'Michelle M.' WCCa
'Milk Festival' LRHS WCCa
'Miss B. Brunner' WCCa
'Molly Guy' WCCa
'Monet' WHil
'Montaigne' SHaC
'Mrs Kate Gray' WCCa
'Mrs Oklahoma' CSut LAma SBch
'Musifolia' ♀H3 CDTJ CHEx EAmu ETod EWes LPJP SBch SDix SEND SHaC WDyG XBlo
I 'Musifolia Rubra' WCCa
'Mystique' ♀H3 EWes SDix SHaC WCCa
'Nero' WCCa
'Oberon' WCCa
'Ointment Pink' XBlo
§ 'Oiseau de Feu' LAma WCCa WHil
'Oiseau d'Or' WHil
'Old Red' WCCa
'Ombersley' WCCa
'Orange Perfection' CSam LAma LAst
'Orange Punch' SBch WCot
'Orchid' see *C.* 'City of Portland'
'Osric' CSpe WCCa
'Pacific Beauty' CSpe EAmu ECtt LRHS LSou NGdn SBch WCot
'Panache' CDTJ CHEx SHaC WCot WDyG
paniculata SHaC WHil
'Paprika' WCCa
'Parténope' WCCa
'Peach Pink' **new** XBlo
'Peach Surprise' WCCa
'Pearlescent Pink' XBlo
'Percy Lancaster' WCCa
'Perkeo' LAma LRHS SBch
§ 'Pfitzer's Salmon Pink' CHEx
§ 'Phasion' (v) ♀H3 CHEx CHll CSpe EBrs ELan EPfP EWes LRHS LSRN MSCN NGdn NPer NScw NVic SBch SBst SDix SHaC SPoG WCCa WCot XBlo
'Picadore' SBch SHaC
'Picasso' ♀H3 CBcs CCCN CDTJ CHEx CPLG CSut EBrs EPfP LAma LRHS SBch SEND XBlo
'Pink Champagne' XBlo
'Pink Futurity' (Futurity Series) SBch
'Pink Perfection' SHaC
'Pink Sunburst' (v) CDTJ LRHS NGdn SBch SHaC SPlb
'Plaster Pink' XBlo
'Porcelain Petals' WCCa
'Powick' WCCa
'Preference' WCCa
'President' EBrs EPfP LAma LRHS SBch SHaC WBrE WCCa XBlo
'President Carnot' WCCa
'Pretoria' see *C.* 'Striata'
'Primrose' WCCa
'Prince Charmant' SBch
'Princess Di' CMdw
'Pringle Bay' (v) SBch
'Professor Lorentz' see *C.* 'Wyoming'
'Puppet' WCCa
'Purpurea Floribunda' WCCa
'Ra' ♀H3 MSKA SHaC
'Red Bird' WCCa
'Red Futurity' (Futurity Series) SBch
'Red Tyrol' WCCa
'Red Wine' LRHS WCCa
§ 'Richard Wallace' CPLG CSam EBrs LAma SBch SPlb WHil WWEG XBlo
'Rigoletto' WCCa
§ 'Roi Humbert' CSam LAst SBch SHaC
'Roi Soleil' ♀H3 LAma
'Roitelet' CHEx
'Roma' WCCa
'Rose Futurity' (Futurity Series) SBch WCCa
'Rosemawr' WCCa
'Rosemond Coles' CHEx CSam EBrs LAma SBch SHaC XBlo
'Russian Lance' WCCa
'Russian Red' SBch WCCa
'Safrano' WCCa
'Salmon Pink' see *C.* 'Pfitzer's Salmon Pink'
'Scorch' WCCa
'Sémaphore' LRHS SBch XBlo
'Shenandoah' ♀H3 SBch WCCa
'Singapore Girl' SBch
'Sky Hawk' WCCa
'Snow-white' XBlo
'Sophia Young' WCCa
'Soudan' CDTJ
'Souvenir de Madame Nardy' WCCa
'Sparks' WCCa
speciosa CDTJ SHaC XBlo
'Spritzii' WCCa
'Star of India' WCCa
'Statue of Liberty' WCCa
'Strasbourg' CSam LAma NPer
'Strawberry Pink' XBlo
'Striata' misapplied see *C.* 'Stuttgart'
§ 'Striata' (v) ♀H3 CCCN CDTJ CHEx CSev CSpe CWGN EBee EBrs ECtt EPfP LPJP LRHS LSRN MAvo MREP NGdn NMoo NScw SAga SBch SEND SHaC SMad SPad WCCa WCom WCot WDyG WWEG XBlo
'Striped Beauty' (v) CCCN CDTJ EBrs LRHS SBch
§ 'Stuttgart' (v) CDTJ CSpe EAmu EPfP EWes LRHS NMoo SBch SHaC SMrm WCCa WCom WCot
'Summer Gold' XBlo
'Summer Joy' SHaC
'Sunbeams' WCCa
'Sundance' NPri
'Sunset' CWGN NGdn WCot WGwG
'Talisman' LAma XBlo
'Taney' MSKA
'Teme' WCCa
'Temploux' WCCa
'Theresa Blakey' WCCa
'Thorvald Dalebö' WCCa
'Tirol' EBrs WCCa
'Tricarinata' CHEx
'Triomphe' SBch SHaC
(Tropical Series) 'Tropical Red' SBch SGar SHaC
- 'Tropical Rose' SBch SHaC SRms WCCa
- 'Tropical Salmon' SHaC
- 'Tropical Sunrise' WCCa
- 'Tropical White' SBch SHaC WHil
- 'Tropical Yellow' SBch SGar SHaC WCCa
Tropicanna see *C.* 'Phasion'
'Ulrich Brunner' WCCa
'Uncle Sam' WCCa
'Uvurderlig' WCCa
'Valentine' WCot
'Vanilla Pink' XBlo
* 'Variegata' (v) LAma
'Verdi' ♀H3 CSpe LAma LRHS SBch SHaC
'Viva' LRHS WCCa

warscewiczii	CDTJ CPLG CSpe SBch SBst SHaC WHil
'Weymouth'	CDTJ
'Whithelm Pride' ♀H3	SHaC
'Wine 'n' Roses'	SHaC
'Woodbridge Pink'	XBlo
'Wye'	WCCa
§ 'Wyoming' ♀H3	CBcs CCCN CDTJ CHEx CSam EBrs ECGP ETod LAma LRHS MCCP NVic SBch SBst SEND SHaC XBlo
'Yara'	EBrs
'Yellow Humbert' misapplied	see *C.* 'Cleopatra', *C.* 'Florence Vaughan', *C.* 'Richard Wallace'
'Yellow Humbert'	LAma WCCa WHil

Cantua (*Polemoniaceae*)

buxifolia ♀H2-3	CAbb CBcs CCCN CFee CPLG EBee ECre ERas EShb LRHS SSpi WPGP
- 'Dancing Oaks' **new**	WCot

Cape gooseberry see *Physalis peruviana*

Capnoides see *Corydalis*

Capparis (*Capparaceae*)

spinosa	CCCN

Capsicum (*Solanaceae*)

annuum	CCCN CSim LRHS MBri
- var. ***annuum*** 'Black Hungarian' **new**	NExo
- - (Grossum Group) 'Corno di Toro Rosso' ♀H2 **new**	ELau
- - (Longham Group) 'Bolivian Rainbow' **new**	ELau
- - - cayenne	CCCN
- - 'Prairie Fire' ♀H2	CCCN
- - 'Sweet Chocolate' **new**	NExo
- 'Apache' ♀H2	CCCN SEND
- 'Tricolor Variegatum' ♀H2 **new**	NExo
baccatum	CSim
- 'Lemon Drop' **new**	NExo
- var. ***pendulum*** 'Friar's Hat' **new**	NExo
chinense	CSim
- 'Chocolate Habanero' **new**	NExo
frutescens	CSim
pubescens	CSim

Caragana (*Papilionaceae*)

CC 3945	CPLG
arborescens	CAgr CArn CMCN EBee EPfP GKir MBar NWea SEND SPer SPlb WDin
- 'Lorbergii'	CEnd GKir MBlu SCoo SPer WFoF
- 'Pendula'	CLnd CMac CWib ELan EPfP GKir LAst LRHS MAsh MBar NEgg NHol SCoo SLim SPer WDin
- 'Walker'	CDul CEnd CMac CWib ELan EPfP GKir LRHS MAsh MBar MBlu MBri MGos NHol NWea SCoo SLim SMad SPer SPoG WSpi
aurantiaca	MBar
jubata	NLar
pygmaea	NLar

carambola see *Averrhoa carambola*

caraway see *Carum carvi*

Cardamine ✿ (*Brassicaceae*)

asarifolia misapplied	see *Pachyphragma macrophyllum*
asarifolia L.	CLAP
bulbifera	CLAP EBee ELon EPPr GBin GBuc GEdr LEdu NRya WCom WCru WSHC
californica	EBee EPPr NRya WCru WMoo
concatenata	CLAP WCru
digitata	MTho
diphylla	CLAP EBee LEdu MBel WCot WCru WFar
- 'American Sweetheart'	WCot
- 'Eco Cut Leaf'	CDes EBee EPPr WCru WPGP
- 'Eco Moonlight'	WCru
enneaphylla	CLAP GBuc GMaP LEdu
glanduligera	CDes EBee ELon EPPr GBuc GEdr LEdu MNrw SMrm WCru WPGP
§ ***heptaphylla***	CAby CLAP EBee ECha ELon EWTr GBuc GKir WCru
- 'Big White'	GCal
- Guincho form	CLAP EPPr GBin WCot WPGP
- white-flowered	CLAP GBBs GMaP
§ ***kitaibelii***	CLAP ECha GBin GBuc LEdu NPol SIng WCru
latifolia Vahl	see *C. raphanifolia*
macrophylla	CAby CLAP EBee EWld LEdu NLar SWat WCot
- 'Bright and Bronzy'	GEdr WCru
maxima	LEdu WCru
microphylla	CLAP EBee
pentaphylla ♀H4	CBro CSpe EBee EBrs ECho ELan ELon EPPr ERos EWTr GBBs GBuc GEdr GGar GKev GKir IFro LPla MCot MDun MNFA NBir SUsu WBor WCot
- bright pink-flowered	CLAP NPol WCot
pratensis	CArn CRWN CWat EBWF EBee EHon EMFW MCot MHer MSKA NLan NMir NPri SECG SIde SWat WFar WHer WMoo WPtf WSFF WShi
- var. ***angustifolia***	WCru
- 'Diane's Petticoat' **new**	WHoo
- 'Edith' (d)	CLAP GBin GBuc MNrw
- 'Flore Pleno' (d)	CBre CFee CHVG CSpe CWan EBee ECha ELan IFro MHer MNrw MTho NBid NBir NBro NLar NPri SBch SUsu SWat WAlt WFar WSFF WSHC
- white-flowered	WAlt
- 'William' (d)	EPPr GBuc WMoo
quinquefolia	CDes CElw CLAP CMea CPom EBee ECha EHrv ELon GBuc LEdu MCot NMyG SDys SMrm WBrk WCot WCru WPGP
§ ***raphanifolia***	CBre CDes CLAP CRow EBee ECha EPPr GAbr GBuc GCal GGar IFro LEdu LLWG NBid NBro NChi NSti SWat WBor WMoo WPGP WTin
trifolia	CSpe ECha EHrv ELon EPPr EWTr GBuc GCal GEdr GGar GKir GMaP IFro MBar MRav NBir NBro NHol NRya NVic SWat WCot WCru WFar WMoo
waldsteinii	CAby CDes CLAP CSpe EBee ECho EHrv GBuc GEdr LEdu NCGa SBch SCnR WCru WHoo WIvy WSHC
yezoensis B&SWJ 4659	WCru

cardamon see *Elettaria cardamomum*

Cardiandra (*Hydrangeaceae*)

alternifolia	CLAP

- B&SWJ 5719 WCru
- B&SWJ 5845 WCru
- B&SWJ 6354 WCru
- 'Pink Geisha' WCru
amamiohshimensis WCru
formosana CGHE CLAP WPGP
- B&SWJ 2005 WCru
- 'Crûg's Abundant' WCru
- 'Hsitou' WCru
- 'Hsitou Splendour' WCru

Cardiocrinum (*Liliaceae*)

cathayanum CBct CSpe EBee GAuc GEdr WCot WPGP
cordatum EBee ECho GAuc WBVN
- B&SWJ 4841 WCru
- var. ***glehnii*** CCCN EBee EBrs ECho GAuc GBuc GEdr GGar
- - B&SWJ 4758 WCru
- red-veined EBrs GBuc GEdr
giganteum Widely available
- B&SWJ 2419 WCru
- HWJK 2158 from Nepal WCru
- var. ***yunnanense*** CBcs CMil CPom EBee EBrs ECho EPfP GAbr GAuc GBuc GEdr GGGa GGar GKir GLin GMaP ITim LRHS NBid WCot WCru WPGP

cardoon see *Cynara cardunculus*

Carduus (*Asteraceae*)

benedictus see *Cnicus benedictus*

Carex (*Cyperaceae*)

from Uganda MMoz SApp
acuta GFor GKir MSKA
- 'Variegata' (v) CBen CRow EHoe EHon ELon EMFW EPla EShb GMaP LPBA MMoz MMuc NBro NHol NOak SApp SBch WAbb WCot WFar WHal WMoo WPnP WWEG
acutiformis CRWN EBWF GFor NSco
alba EPPr GFor WCot
albida EBrs EHul LRHS
albula MMoz MWhi
'Amazon Mist' GFor LRHS NPri
appalachica new EPPr
appressa SApp
arenaria EBWF GBin GFor
atrata EBee EHoe EPla WHrl
aurea EPPr GFor IFoB NHol
baccans CPLG GCal GFor NOak SGSe
bebbii EPPr
berggrenii EBee ECou EHoe ELan GKir LEdu LPBA NCob NWCA SPlb SWat WMoo WPer WTin WWEG
binervis CRWN EBWF
boottiana EWes
brizoides new IMou
brunnea EWes SBch SHDw
- 'Jenneke' CKno EBee EPPr EPfP EPla LRHS MBar MBri SBch SGSe SHDw SLim SMrm SPoG SWvt WCot
- 'Variegata' (v) CEnt EHoe MMoz SApp SBch SHDw WWEG WWFP
buchananii ♀H4 Widely available
- 'Viridis' ELan EPPr GBin WHer
bushii NCob
buxbaumii new SRms
caryophyllea 'The Beatles' EBee EGoo EHoe EPPr LBMP MMoz NBir NHol
chathamica CAby EBee MMoz
'China Blue' EPPr MMoz SApp SGSe
comans EPPr EPfP EShb GKir GQui NBro NHol NPol NWsh
- 'Bronze Perfection' SWal WFar
- bronze-leaved Widely available
- 'Bronzita' new LRHS
- 'Dancing Flame' CPrp CWCL EBee MBri NWsh
- 'Feebers Dwarf' new WWEG
- 'Frosted Curls' Widely available
- green-leaved GFor
- 'Kupferflamme' EBee
- red-leaved LAst MGos SRms
- 'Small Red' see *C. comans* 'Taranaki'
§ - 'Taranaki' EBee EPfP GKir MBNS MMoz SCoo SWal
conica MWat
- 'Hime-kan-suge' see *C. conica* 'Snowline'
- 'Kiku-sakura' (v) EPPr NHol
§ - 'Snowline' (v) Widely available
crinita EPPr
cristatella EBee EPPr
'Curly Whirly' new SPad
curta CRWN EBWF
* ***cyperus*** GKir
dallii EBee ECou EKen EWes GBin MMoz MMuc NLar SGSe WHrl
davisii EPPr
demissa CRWN EBWF EHoe
depauperata CRWN EBWF EHoe
digitata CRWN EBWF
dioica CRWN EBWF
dipsacea Widely available
- 'Dark Horse' CKno GCal LLHF WClo WPtf
divulsa subsp. ***divulsa*** CRWN EBWF
§ ***dolichostachya*** 'Kaga-nishiki' (v) CPen CSBt EBee EPPr LAst LEdu LHop LRHS MMoz MWhi SLim WPnP WPrP
duthiei EBee GCal
- KEKE 494 WPGP
echinata CRWN EBWF
§ ***elata*** GKir
§ - 'Aurea' (v) ♀H4 Widely available
- 'Bowles's Golden' see *C. elata* 'Aurea'
- 'Knightshayes' ♀H4 CKno EBee EWes GBin MMoz SGSe WCot
'Evergold' see *C. oshimensis* 'Evergold'
firma 'Variegata' (v) MWat NMen NWCA WAbe WThu
flacca CRWN EBWF EHoe EPPr GBin GFor GKir WGwG
- 'Bias' (v) EPPr EPla MMoz
§ - subsp. ***flacca*** EBee EWes MMoz NSti WPGP
flagellifera Widely available
- 'Auburn Cascade' EBee EPfP MAvo NBPC NHol NPro SApp SBch SPad
- 'Coca-Cola' CPen LRHS NOak SGSe
- 'Rapunzel' EBee EPPr MMoz WPGP
flava CKno EHoe EPPr GFor
fortunei see *C. morrowii* Boott
fraseri see *Cymophyllus fraserianus*
fraserianus see *Cymophyllus fraserianus*
glauca Scopoli see *C. flacca* subsp. *flacca*
glauca Bosc. ex Boott CKno CWCL EPPr EPla SBch WPGP
'Gold Fountains' see *C. dolichostachya* 'Kaga-nishiki'
granularis EPPr
I 'Grayassina' CKno EPPr
grayi CDes CHrt CKno EBee EBrs EHoe GBuc GFor LEdu LRHS MBlu MSCN MSKA MTho NCGa NLar NOak SGSe WCot WPer WPtf
§ ***hachijoensis*** LAst WFar
'Happy Wanderer' SLPl
hirta CRWN EBWF NSco

hispida	MCCP WMoo
hostiana	CRWN EBWF
'Ice Dance' (v)	CKno CMea CWGN EAlp EBee EPPr EPla GGar GQue LRHS MMoz NHol NLar NOak NOrc SBch STes SWvt WPGP WPrP WPtf WRHF WWEG
kaloides	CSsd EAlp EBee EHoe
'Kan-suge'	see *C. morrowii* Boott
limosa	EBWF
lucida	NNor
lupulina	NOak
lurida	CKno EPfP GFor MAvo MBNS NLar
- 'Silver'	MBNS
macloviana	EPPr
macrocephala	GFor
'Majken'	EBee GFor
maorica	EPPr
maritima	CRWN EBWF
Milk Chocolate = 'Milchoc'[PBR] (v)	CKno CPen CWGN EAlp EBee EPfP LRHS NMun SApp SMrm
montana	EBrs LRHS
morrowii misapplied	see *C. hachijoensis*, *C. oshimensis*
§ ***morrowii*** Boott	CWCL EPPr
- 'Fisher's Form' (v)	CKno CTri EBee EPPr EPla LAst LEdu LHop LRHS MMoz MMuc MRav NGdn NHol NMir NWsh SApp SBch SGSe SMac SWvt WFar WPGP WPer WWEG
- 'Gilt' (v)	EAEE EBee EHoe EPPr EPla LBMP LRHS MBNS NHol
- 'Gold Band' **new**	LRHS
- 'Nana Variegata' (v)	CTri NBir WPGP
- var. ***temnolepis*** **new**	IMou
- - 'Silk Tassel' (v)	EPPr NHol SGSe
N - 'Variegata' (v)	EHoe EHrv EHul ELan EPPr EPfP EPla GCal GKev GMaP LAst LPBA LRHS MBar MMoz MRav NBir NBlu NHol NSti SLPl SMac SRms WCot WEas WFar WPnP
muehlenbergii	EPPr
muricata subsp. ***muricata***	EPPr
muskingumensis	Widely available
- 'Ice Fountains' (v)	EPPr WWEG
- 'Little Midge'	CKno EBee EBrs EPPr EShb GBin GCal GKir LRHS WCot
- 'Oehme' (v)	CKno CWCL EBee EBrs EPPr EPla EPyc EShb GBin GCal LEdu LRHS MSCN NBid NHol WCot WPtf WTin
- 'Silberstreif' (v)	CKno EBee EPPr GBin GGar MMuc NLar SApp
nigra	CRWN EBWF EHon EPPr NLar WPnP
§ - 'On-line' (v)	EHrv EPPr MBNS MMoz NHol NWsh SApp WWEG
- 'Variegata'	see *C. nigra* 'On-line'
No 1, Nanking (Greg's broad leaf)	MMoz
No 4, Nanking (Greg's thin leaf)	EPPr SApp
normalis	EPPr
obnupta	CKno EPPr WWEG
ornithopoda 'Aurea'	see *C. ornithopoda* 'Variegata'
- 'Kumi-sugi' **new**	EBee
§ - 'Variegata' (v)	EBee ECtt EHul GFor MBrN MMoz NBro NGdn NHol NOak NWsh SBch WMoo WWEG
§ ***oshimensis***	EHoe EPPr
§ - 'Evergold' (v) ♀H4	Widely available
- 'Supergold'	EBee
- 'Variegata' (v)	NBir
otrubae	CRWN EBWF
ovalis	CRWN EBWF
pallescens 'Breckland Frost' (v)	EPPr MAvo
panicea	CKno CRWN CSBt CWCL EBWF EBee EHoe EPPr EPla LRHS MMoz MSKA SApp SGSe WGrn WMoo
paniculata	CRWN GFor NSco
pendula	Widely available
- 'Cool Jazz' (v)	EPPr MAvo WAlt
- 'Moonraker'	CBot CWCL EBee EHoe EPPr EPla MAvo MBNS MSKA NOak SApp WCot WSpi WWEG
petriei	CWCL ECha ETod EWes GBuc LLWP LRHS MAvo MBNS MMoz NVic SWal WCot WFar WPer WTin
phyllocephala	EPPr EShb
- 'Sparkler' (v)	CBod CKno CPrp CWCL EBee ECtt EHoe EPPr EPla EShb GGar LAst LEdu LHop LRHS MCCP NCGa NCob NSti SBch SMad SPoG SRms SWvt WClo WCot WFar WGrn WPGP WWEG
plantaginea	EBee EBrs EHoe EPPr EPla GBin LEdu SApp WCot WMoo WPGP WWEG
praegracilis	CKno EPPr
Pritchard's form (v) **new**	IFro
projecta	EPPr
pseudocyperus	CRWN EBWF EHoe EHon GBin GFor GKir LPBA MMoz MMuc MSKA NNor NPer NWsh SRms SWat WMoo WPer WPnP
pulicaris	CRWN
remota	CRWN EBWF EHoe
riparia	CRWN EBWF EMFW LPBA MMoz MMuc MSKA NHol NPer NSco SWal SWat WFar WShi
- 'Bowles's Golden'	see *C. elata* 'Aurea'
rostrata	CRWN EBWF
sabynensis	see *C. umbrosa* subsp. *sabynensis*
secta	CKno ECou EPPr GFor GGar GMaP MNrw SGSe SHDw WDyG WMoo WPer
- from Dunedin, New Zealand	EPPr
siderosticha	EPla SLPl WPGP WPer
- 'Banana Boat'	see *C. siderosticha* 'Golden Falls'
- 'Echigo-nishiki' (v)	EPPr
§ - 'Golden Falls' (v)	EBee EShb LRHS MNrw NOrc SMad
- 'Golden Fountains'	WCot
- 'Kisokaido' (v)	EPPr LRHS MWhi WCot
- 'Old Barn'	EBee EPPr
- 'Shima-nishiki' (v)	CHrt CPen CPrp EBee ECtt EPPr EPfP EShb LAst LBMP LEdu LRHS MBNS NOak NPro SAga SMad WFar WWEG
- 'Variegata' (v)	Widely available
'Silver Sceptre' (v)	EBee EBrs ECtt EHoe EPPr EPla EShb GBuc GFor LBMP LEdu LRHS MBNS MCCP MMoz NHol NPro NSti NWsh SBch SLim SPlb SPoG SWal SWvt WBrk WCot WFar WMoo WWEG
'Silver Sparkler'	NBir
solandri	CSam LEdu MAvo NLar NWsh SApp SBch SGSe SHDw WMoo
spissa	CKno MNrw
sprengelii	EPPr
stricta Gooden.	see *C. elata*
- 'Bowles's Golden'	see *C. elata* 'Aurea'
sylvatica	CRWN EBWF GFor

tenuiculmis	CKno CWCL EAlp EBee EBrs EPPr EShb LBMP LHop MAvo NBPC NHol NOak NSti NWsh SBch SPad SRms SWal WTin WWEG
- 'Cappucino'	CKno LHop
testacea	Widely available
- 'Old Gold'	ELan EWes LRHS MAvo NOak SMad SPlb WFar WGrn WMoo
- 'Prairie Fire' **new**	LRHS
texensis	EPPr
'Treasure Island' (v) **new**	MAsh
trifida	CHEx CHrt CKno EHoe EKen GFor GGar MMoz MNrw NWsh SMad WFar WMoo WPnP
- 'Chatham Blue'	CHid EPPr GBin MAvo NBir SEND
umbrosa	EBee EPPr EShb
subsp. ***sabynensis*** 'Thinny Thin' (v)	
uncifolia	ECou
viridula	EBWF
- subsp. ***viridula***	CRWN EBWF
vulpina	EPPr
vulpinoidea	EPPr

Carica (*Caricaceae*)

papaya 'Babaco' **new**	CCCN

Carissa (*Apocynaceae*)

grandiflora	see *C. macrocarpa*
§ ***macrocarpa*** (F)	CCCN EShb

Carlina (*Asteraceae*)

acanthifolia	ECho
- subsp. ***cyanara*** JJA 274.101	NWCA
acaulis	CArn ECho ELan EPfP GEdr GKir GPWP MNHC NPri NWCA SDnm SPav SPlb SRms WFar WPer
- subsp. ***acaulis***	GPoy
- bronze-leaved	EWll LDai MCCP NBPC
- var. ***caulescens***	see *C. acaulis* subsp. *simplex*
§ - subsp. ***simplex***	ECha GGar GKir GMaP LRHS NPri WFar WPer
- - bronze-leaved	CBow EBee SMad SPhx
vulgaris	EBWF WPer
- 'Silver Star'	GEdr

Carmichaelia (*Papilionaceae*)

'Abundance'	ECou
'Angie'	ECou
angustata 'Buller'	ECou
appressa	ECou GGar
- 'Ellesmere'	ECou
arborea	ECou
- 'Grand'	ECou
astonii	ECou
- 'Ben More'	ECou
- 'Chalk Ridge'	ECou
australis	EBee ECou WSHC
- 'Bright Eyes'	ECou
- 'Cunningham'	ECou
- Flagelliformis Group	ECou
- 'Mahurangi'	ECou
- Ovata Group	ECou
- 'Solander'	ECou
carmichaeliae	ECou
- 'Hodder'	ECou
- 'Seymour'	ECou
'Charm'	ECou
'Clifford Bay'	ECou
'Coral Spears'	ECou
corrugata	ECou
crassicaule 'Jack Sprat'	ECou
crassicaulis	ECou
- subsp. ***racemosa***	ECou
'Culverden'	ECou
curta	ECou
enysii	CCCN
'Essex'	ECou
fieldii 'Westhaven'	ECou
flagelliformis 'Roro'	ECou
glabrescens	ECou
- 'Woodside'	ECou
glabrescens × ***torulosa***	ECou
'Havering'	ECou
'Hay and Honey'	ECou
§ × ***hutchinsii***	ECou
- 'Butterfly'	ECou
- 'County Park'	ECou GGar
- 'Delight'	ECou
- 'Pink Beauty'	ECou
- 'Wingletye'	ECou
'Joy'	ECou
juncea Nigrans Group	ECou
kirkii	ECou
'Lilac Haze'	ECou
monroi	ECou
- 'Rangitata'	ECou
- 'Tekapo'	ECou
muritai	ECou
- 'Huia Gilpen'	ECou
- 'Ron Feron'	ECou
- 'Wayne Nichols'	ECou
nana	ECou
- 'Desert Road'	ECou
- 'Pringle'	ECou
- 'Waitaki'	ECou
nigrans 'Wanaka'	ECou
odorata	CPLG ECou
- Angustata Group	ECou
- 'Green Dwarf'	ECou
- 'Lakeside'	ECou
- 'Riverside'	ECou
ovata 'Calf Creek'	ECou
'Parson's Tiny'	ECou
petriei	ECou SMad
- 'Aviemore'	ECou
- 'Lindis'	ECou
- 'Pukaki'	ECou
- Virgata Group	ECou
'Porter's Pass'	ECou
'Spangle'	ECou
stevensonii	ECou EPfP NLar WBVN WSHC
- 'Duncan'	ECou
- hybrid	ECou
- 'Kiwi'	ECou
- 'Miller'	ECou
'Tangle'	ECou
torulosa	ECou
- 'Blue Butterfly'	ECou
- 'Malvern Hills'	ECou
uniflora	ECou
- 'Bealey'	ECou
'Weka'	ECou
williamsii	ECou
'Yellow Eyes'	ECou

× *Carmispartium* see *Carmichaelia*

astens	see *Carmichaelia* × *hutchinsii*

Carpenteria (*Hydrangeaceae*)

californica ♀H3	CBot CPMA CSBt CTri EBee ELan EPfP GKir IMGH LAst LHop LRHS MBri MGos MWat NCGa NPal NPri

	SEND SPer SPoG SReu SSpi SSta WCot WDin WHCG WPat WSpi
- 'Bodnant'	CDul ELan LRHS MBri MGos MWea WPGP WSpi
- 'Elizabeth'	CAbP CBcs CPMA CWGN EBee ELan EPfP GKir LRHS LSRN MAsh SPer SPoG SSpi SSta WCot WDin WPGP WPat
- 'Ladhams' Variety'	CBcs CPMA EBee EPfP EWTr LRHS MGos MRav NLar SRkn WCFE WKif WSpi

Carpinus ✿ (*Corylaceae*)

sp.	CMen
betulus ♀H4	Widely available
- 'Columnaris'	CDul CLnd CTho GKir
* - 'Columnaris Nana'	CMCN
§ - 'Fastigiata' ♀H4	Widely available
- 'Frans Fontaine'	CCVT CDoC CDul CEnd CMCN CTho EBee EPfP GKir IArd LAst LMaj LRHS MAsh MBlu MBri MGos SCoo SLim SPer
- 'Globus'	MBlu
I - 'Monumentalis'	LMaj
- 'Pendula'	CDul CEnd CLnd CTho EBee GKir MBlu SPoG WDin
- 'Purpurea'	CBcs CEnd LMaj MBlu MGos NLar
- 'Pyramidalis'	see *C. betulus* 'Fastigiata'
- 'Quercifolia'	CDul EBee
caroliniana	CLnd CMCN SBir
- 'Sentinel Dries' **new**	MBlu
cordata	MBlu SBir WDin
fangiana	CEnd CGHE CTho EBee GKir LRHS WPGP
fargesiana **new**	EGFP
fargesii	see *C. viminea*
henryana	CMen SBir
japonica ♀H4	CDul CEnd CMCN CMen CTho EBee EGFP EPfP GKir LLHF LRHS MBlu SBir SCoo WDin
- B&SWJ 10803	WCru
- B&SWJ 11072	WCru
laxiflora	CMen MPkF WFar WPGP
- B&SWJ 10809	WCru
- B&SWJ 11035	WCru
- var. ***longispica*** B&SWJ 8772	WCru
- var. ***macrostachya***	see *C. viminea*
macrocarpa **new**	EGFP
orientalis	CMCN SBir
polyneura	SBir
pubescens	GKir WPGP
rankanensis RWJ 9839	WCru
× ***schuschaensis***	EBtc GKir SBir
shensiensis	CDul
tschonoskii B&SWJ 10800	WCru
turczaninowii ♀H4	CBcs CDul CMHG CMen GKir IDee NLar NPal SBir WDin WPGP
§ ***viminea***	CEnd CMCN MAsh MBri SBir WPat

Carpobrotus (*Aizoaceae*)

§ ***edulis***	CCCN CDTJ CDoC CHrt EShb SAPC SArc SChr SEND WCor WHer
- var. ***edulis***	CHEx
- var. ***rubescens***	CCCN CHEx
muirii	CCCN EShb
rossii	GGar
sauerae	CCCN

Carpodetus (*Escalloniaceae*)

serratus	CBcs CTrC

Carrierea (*Flacourtiaceae*)

calycina	WPGP

carrot see *Daucus carota*

Carthamus (*Asteraceae*)

tinctorius	CArn MNHC SPav

Carum (*Apiaceae*)

carvi	CArn CHrt CWan GPoy MHer MNHC NPri SIde SVic WJek WPer
petroselinum	see *Petroselinum crispum*

Carya ✿ (*Juglandaceae*)

aquatica	CMCN CTho
cordiformis	CTho EPfP MBlu
glabra	WPGP
N ***illinoinensis*** (F)	CAgr CBcs CMCN MBri
- 'Carlson No 3' seedling (F)	CAgr
- 'Colby' seedling (F)	CAgr
- 'Cornfield' (F)	CAgr
- 'Lucas' (F)	CAgr
laciniosa (F)	CBcs CTho EPfP LRHS WPGP
- 'Henry' (F)	CAgr
- 'Keystone' seedling (F)	CAgr
* ***languinossus*** **new**	WSpi
ovata (F)	CAgr CMCN CTho EPfP LRHS MBlu MBri WDin
- 'Grainger' seedling (F)	CAgr
- 'Neilson' seedling (F)	CAgr
- 'Weschcke' (F) **new**	EGFP
- 'Weschcke' seedling (F)	CAgr
- 'Yoder no 1' seedling (F)	CAgr
pallida	EGFP
texana	EGFP
tomentosa	EGFP EPfP

Caryophyllus see *Syzygium*

Caryopteris ✿ (*Verbenaceae*)

× ***clandonensis***	CMac EBee ECtt MGan MLHP MWat NBir WAbe WCFE WDin WFar WHCG
- 'Arthur Simmonds' ♀H4	CSam CTri EBee ECha EPfP GKir LHop LSRN SPer WGor
- 'Dark Knight'	EBee EPfP LBuc LRHS MBri MWat SBch SPoG SPur WClo
- 'Ferndown'	CDoC CWib EBee ELon EPfP GKir LHop NLar SEND SPer SReu SRms
- 'First Choice' ♀H3-4	CAbP CMac CSpe EBee ELan EPfP EShb LAst LHop LRHS LSRN LSqu MAsh MGos NLar SLim SPer SPoG SRkn SWvt WSpi
- Grand Bleu = 'Inoveris'PBR	CMac CSBt EBee ELan EMil EQua EShb LRHS LSRN MAsh MGos MSwo NLar SMad SPoG WCot WSpi
- 'Heavenly Baby' ♀H3-4	LRHS MAsh SPoG
- 'Heavenly Blue'	Widely available
- Hint of Gold = 'Lisaura' ♀H3-4 **new**	LRHS MAsh
- 'Kew Blue'	Widely available
- 'Longwood Blue'	CMdw ELan EPfP LRHS
- 'Moody Blue' (v)	EPfP
- 'Pershore'	EBee
- 'Summer Gold'	GKir LRHS MAsh MRav
- 'Summer Sorbet'PBR (v) ♀H3-4	CBcs CBow CDoC EBee EBrs EHoe ELan ELon EPfP EWes LBuc LHop LRHS MAsh MGos MNHC NEgg NHol NLar NPro SBch SCoo SLim SPoG WCFE WGrn WHar WPat WSpi

	- 'Worcester Gold' ♀H3-4	Widely available
	divaricata	EBee MBri
	- 'Electrum'	ECtt LSou MDKP
	- 'Jade Shades'	EBee ECtt LSou
	- 'Pink Butterfly'	EBee
	- 'Pink Illumination' (v)	EBee
	- 'Snow Fairy' (v) **new**	EBee
	- variegated (v)	CBow
§	***incana***	EBee EPfP GKir SPer WPat WSHC
	- 'Autumn Pink'PBR	EBee ECrN ELan EPfP LRHS LSRN SPoG
	- 'Blue Cascade'	EBee EBtc ELan GBuc GQue MRav NLar WGrn WPat
§	- 'Jason'PBR	EPfP NEgg SPoG WPat
	- Sunshine BluePBR	see *C. incana* 'Jason'
	mastacanthus	see *C. incana*

Caryota (*Arecaceae*)

mitis ♀H1	EAmu LPal
- 'Himalaya'	EAmu LPal
obtusa	EAmu
urens	LPal

Cassandra see *Chamaedaphne*

Cassia (*Caesalpiniaceae*)

corymbosa Lam.	see *Senna corymbosa*
marilandica	see *Senna marilandica*

Cassinia (*Asteraceae*)

	aculeata	GGar
	leptophylla	CBcs GGar SPer
	- 'Avalanche Creek'	ECou
	- subsp. ***fulvida***	CBcs ECou GGar
	- subsp. ***vauvilliersii***	GGar MCot SEND SPer
	- - BR 55	GGar
	- - var. ***albida***	SPer
N	***retorta***	ECou
	'Ward Silver'	CBot CSpe ECou EHoe EWes IDee

Cassinia × *Helichrysum* (*Asteraceae*)

hybrid	WKif

Cassiope ✿ (*Ericaceae*)

	'Askival Snowbird'	ITim
	'Askival Snow-wreath'	see *C.* Snow-wreath Group
	'Askival Stormbird'	MAsh
	'Badenoch'	ECho GEdr GKev NDlv NLar
	'Bearsden'	MBar NDlv
	'Edinburgh' ♀H4	ECho GEdr MBar NDlv NHol NLar
	lycopodioides	ECho GKev LLHF NDlv SRms
	'Beatrice Lilley'	
	- 'Jim Lever'	WAbe
	- 'Rokujō'	ITim
	mertensiana	ECho MBar NDlv SRms
	- var. ***gracilis***	NLar WThu
	'Muirhead' ♀H4	ECho MBar NDlv SRms WThu
	'Randle Cooke' ♀H4	ECho GEdr GGar MBar NDlv SRms WThu
	selaginoides	GKev
	- LS&E 13284	ITim WAbe
§	Snow-wreath Group	ITim
	tetragona	ITim MBar SRms
	- var. ***saximontana***	ITim

Castanea ✿ (*Fagaceae*)

	'Bouche de Betizac' (F)	CAgr
	crenata	CAgr
	dentata	EGFP
	'Ferosacre' (F) **new**	MCoo
	henryi	CBcs CMCN EGFP
	'Layeroka' (F)	CAgr
	'Maraval' (F)	CAgr CTho LRHS MBlu MBri MCoo
	'Maridonne' (F)	CAgr
	'Marigoule' (F)	CAgr EMil LRHS MCoo
	'Marlhac' (F)	CAgr EMil MCoo
	'Marsol' (F)	CAgr MCoo
	mollissima	EGFP
	'Précoce Migoule' (F)	CAgr ECrN
	pumila	CAgr
	'Rousse de Nay' (F)	CAgr
	sativa ♀H4	Widely available
§	- 'Albomarginata' (v) ♀H4	CDoC CDul CEnd CTho EBee EPfP LHop LMaj LRHS MBlu MBri MDun MGos NBea SPoG WDin WFar WPat
	- 'Anny's Red'	MBlu
	- 'Anny's Summer Red'	LRHS SCoo
	- 'Argenteovariegata'	see *C. sativa* 'Albomarginata'
	- 'Aspleniifolia'	CDul
	- 'Aureomarginata'	see *C. sativa* 'Variegata'
	- 'Belle Epine' (F)	CAgr
	- 'Bournette' (F)	CAgr
*	- 'Doré de Lyon'	CAgr
	- 'Herria' (F)	CAgr
	- 'Laguépie' (F)	CAgr
	- 'Marron Comballe' (F)	CAgr
	- 'Marron de Goujounac' (F)	CAgr
	- 'Marron de Lyon' (F)	CAgr CDul CEnd CTho EMil EMui EPfP MBlu MBri MCoo SVic
	- 'Marron de Redon' (F)	CAgr
	- 'Numbo' (F)	CAgr
	- 'Pyramidalis'	WDin
§	- 'Variegata' (v)	CLnd CMCN ELan EMil LMaj MAsh MGos
	- 'Verdale' (F)	CAgr
	seguinii	CAgr
	'Vignols' (F)	CAgr

Castanopsis (*Fagaceae*)

eyrei **new**	CMCN

Castanospermum (*Papilionaceae*)

australe	CArn

Castilleja (*Scrophulariaceae*)

applegatei	GKev
subsp. ***pinetorum*** **new**	
elegans	WAbe
hispida	WAbe
miniata	WAbe

Casuarina (*Casuarinaceae*)

cunninghamiana	CBcs ECou
equisetifolia	MREP

Catalpa (*Bignoniaceae*)

	bignonioides ♀H4	Widely available
	- 'Aurea' ♀H4	Widely available
*	- 'Aurea Nana'	CEnd MBri
	- 'Nana'	EBee LMaj LRHS MBri WDin WPat
	- 'Purpurea'	see *C.* × *erubescens* 'Purpurea'
	- 'Variegata' (v)	EBee EPfP EWTr LRHS MGos NWea SPer SSta WPat
	bungei	EGFP MBlu MGos SAPC SArc SHGN
	- 'Purpurea'	ELan LAst
§	× ***erubescens*** 'Purpurea' ♀H4	CBcs CBot CDoC CDul CEnd CMac CTho EAmu EBee EPfP EWTr LRHS MAsh MBlu MBri MGos MRav SBch SMad SPer SPoG SSta WDin WFar WPGP WPat
	fargesii f. ***duclouxii***	CBcs CDul CEnd EPfP MBlu MBri NLar WPGP WPat
	ovata	CMCN EGFP

- 'Slender Silhouette'	MBri NLar
speciosa	CDul EWTr SEND SPer WBVN
- 'Frederik'	MBri
- 'Pulverulenta' (v)	CDoC CDul CEnd CMCN EMil LRHS MGos NLar SBig SPer

Catananche (*Asteraceae*)

caerulea	Widely available
- 'Alba'	CMea EAEE EBee EBla ECha EPfP GBBs GKir IFoB LRHS NBir NPri SBch SGar SMrm SPer SPoG WCAu WMoo WPer
- 'Amor Blue' **new**	LRHS
- 'Bicolor'	CMMP MHer MNrw STes WHoo WMoo
- 'Major' ♀H4	LDai LRHS SRms

Catha (*Celastraceae*)

edulis	CArn GPoy WJek

Catharanthus (*Apocynaceae*)

roseus ♀H1	EOHP GPoy MBri
- Ocellatus Group	MBri

Cathaya (*Pinaceae*)

argyrophylla	WPGP

Caulophyllum (*Berberidaceae*)

thalictroides	CArn EBee GBBs GBuc GEdr GKir IMou LEdu NLar WCru WFar WMoo WPnP WSHC
- subsp. ***robustum***	WCru

Cautleya ✿ (*Zingiberaceae*)

cathcartii	LEdu WHil
- 'Tenzing's Gold'	CLAP WCru
§ ***gracilis***	CDTJ CPrp EBee ETod GCal IBlr LEdu SBig WHal WHil
- B&SWJ 7186	WCru WDyG
- 'Edinburgh Lemon' **new**	IBlr
lutea	see *C. gracilis*
spicata	CBct CCCN CDTJ CDoC CHEx CTsd EBee EBrs ECho EPPr GGar IBlr NPal SBHP SBig WHil
- SDR 3809	GKev
- SDR 3844	GKev
- 'Arun Flame' **new**	WCru
- 'Crûg Canary'	LEdu WCru
* - var. ***lutea***	CBct CHEx CPne ETod
- 'Robusta'	CAvo CGHE CHEx CPne CPrp EAmu EBee EShb GCal GCra IBlr LEdu MNrw NPal SGSe SMad WBor WCru WPGP WSHC

Cayratia (*Vitaceae*)

§ ***thomsonii*** BWJ 8123	WCru

Ceanothus ✿ (*Rhamnaceae*)

'A.T. Johnson'	ECrN SLim SPer SRms
americanus	CArn
arboreus	SAPC SArc
- 'Owlswood Blue'	LRHS
- 'Trewithen Blue' ♀H3	Widely available
'Autumnal Blue' ♀H3	Widely available
'Blue Carpet'	CMac CWSG
'Blue Cushion'	CBcs CDoC CPMA CWSG EBee LHop LRHS MAsh MGos MRav NHol NLar NPri SEND SLon SWvt WBVN WBrE WFar
'Blue Diamond'[PBR] **new**	MAsh
'Blue Dreams'	WFar
'Blue Jeans'	EBee ELan IArd LRHS WPat
'Blue Mound' ♀H3	Widely available
'Blue Sapphire'[PBR]	CAlb CBcs CDoC CMac CWGN CWSG EBee ELan EPfP LAst LHop LRHS LSRN MAsh MGos MRav NCGa NEgg NLar NPri SPer SPoG SWvt WClo
'Burkwoodii' ♀H3	CAlb CBcs CDoC CDul CSBt CTri CWSG EPfP GKir LAst LRHS LSRN MDun MGan MGos MRav NEgg NHol SBch SPer SPoG SWvt WClo WFar WGwG
'Cascade' ♀H3	CBcs CTri CWSG EBee GKir LRHS LSRN MGos MWat NSti SLim SLon SPer SPlb SPoG
'Centennial'	LBuc LRHS MRav
'Comtesse de Paris'	see *C. × delileanus* 'Comtesse de Paris'
'Concha' ♀H3	Widely available
§ ***cuneatus*** var. ***rigidus***	SRms WSHC
- - 'Snowball'	ELan EPfP
'Cynthia Postan'	CWSG EBee EPfP ERas IArd ISea LRHS MBlu MWat NHol NLar SCoo WAbe
'Dark Star' ♀H3	CAlb CBcs CChe CDoC CMHG CSPN CTri CWSG EBee ELon EPfP LAst LBMP LRHS LSRN MGos NHol NSti SBch SCoo SEND SPoG SSta SWvt
'Delight'	CBcs EBee ELan EPfP MGos WDin WFar
§ × ***delileanus*** 'Comtesse de Paris'	EBee
- 'Gloire de Versailles' ♀H4	CBcs CBot CDoC CDul CWSG CWib EBee ECrN ELan EPfP GKir ISea LAst LHop LRHS MCot MGos MNHC MRav MSwo MWhi NPri SPer SPoG SWvt WDin WFar WSHC
- 'Henri Desfossé'	ELan EPfP ERas LRHS LSRN MRav NLar SPer SPoG WDin
- 'Indigo'	EBee EPfP WKif
- 'Topaze' ♀H4	CWSG EBee ELan EMil EPfP ERas LRHS NLar SLon WDin WHar
dentatus misapplied	see *C. × lobbianus*
dentatus Torr. & A.Gray	LRHS SPlb
- var. ***floribundus***	CSBt ELan SDix
'Diamond Heights'	see *C. griseus* var. *horizontalis* 'Diamond Heights'
'Edinburgh' ♀H3	EPfP WFar
El Dorado = 'Perado' (v)	LRHS MGos
'Eleanor Taylor'	EBee
gloriosus	EBee EWes
- 'Anchor Bay'	EBee ELan EPfP LRHS SPoG
- 'Emily Brown'	CAlb CBcs CDoC CSPN CTrC EBee ELan LAst LRHS LSRN LSou MRav NLar SBch
- 'Hearts Desire'	LRHS
§ ***griseus*** var. ***horizontalis*** 'Diamond Heights' (v)	CMac EPfP LSRN MAsh MBri SPer WFar
- - 'Silver Surprise'[PBR] (v)	CBcs CSPN EBee ELan EPfP LBuc LRHS LSRN MGos NEgg NLar SLim SPoG
- - 'Yankee Point'	CBcs CChe CDoC CMac CSBt CWib EBee ECrN EPfP GKir ISea LRHS LSRN MGos MRav MSwo NBlu NHol SBch SCoo SLim SPlb SPoG SWvt WDin
impressus	CMHG CSBt CTri EBee EPfP MBlu SEND SPer SWvt WCFE WFar
- 'Victoria'	EBee ERas LSRN LSou MAsh MGos MHav NLar SBch SRGP
N 'Italian Skies' ♀H3	CBcs CDoC CSBt CWSG CWib EBee ECrN ELan EPfP GKir LAst

	LRHS LSRN MDun MGos MSwo NEgg SCoo SLim SLon SPer SPlb SPoG SWvt WDin WFar
'Julia Phelps'	CMHG LRHS WEas
§ × ***lobbianus***	CTri EBee WDin
'Madagascar' **new**	LRHS
Marie Bleue = 'Minmari'	LRHS MAsh
Marie-Rose = 'Minmarose' **new**	LRHS MAsh
maritimus 'Frosty Dawn'	LRHS
× ***pallidus*** 'Georges Simon' **new**	EPfP
- 'Marie Simon'	CBot CWib EBee ELan EMil EPfP LAst LBMP LHop LRHS LSRN MAsh MGos SPer SPoG SRms SWvt WCFE WDin WHar WKif
- 'Perle Rose'	CBcs EBee EPfP LAst LLHF LRHS MGos SPer SPoG WKif WSHC
§ 'Pershore Zanzibar' PBR (v)	CBcs CChe CSBt CSPN CWSG EBee EHoe ELan EPfP IMon LAst LBuc LRHS LSRN MGos MRav MSwo MWat NEgg SCoo SPer SPoG SWvt WBrE
'Pin Cushion'	CDoC CWSG CWib EBee EPfP LRHS MAsh NHol SPoG
'Point Millerton'	see *C. thyrsiflorus* 'Millerton Point'
'Popcorn'	LRHS MGos
prostratus	MAsh SMad
'Puget Blue' ♀H4	Widely available
purpureus	LRHS
'Ray Hartman'	EBee NLar
× ***regius***	GKir
repens	see *C. thyrsiflorus* var. *repens*
rigidus	see *C. cuneatus* var. *rigidus*
'Sierra Blue'	EBee
'Snow Flurries'	see *C. thyrsiflorus* 'Snow Flurry'
'Southmead' ♀H3	CDoC CTri EBee ELan EMil EPfP ERas GBuc LRHS MGos MSwo MWat NBlu NHol WDin WHCG WMoo
thyrsiflorus	CMac CTri CWSG CWib NHol SPer SRms SWvt WDin WHar
§ - 'Millerton Point'	CWSG EBee EPfP LAst LRHS MGos NBlu NLar SBch SCoo SLim SPoG WGwG
§ - var. ***repens*** ♀H3	Widely available
- 'Skylark' ♀H3	CAlb CDoC CMac CSam CWSG EBee ELan EPau EPfP GGar LHop LRHS LSRN MAsh MBri MGos MLHP NPri SDix SGar SLim SSpi WDin WFar WPat
§ - 'Snow Flurry'	CBcs CWib EGxp EPfP MSwo NBlu WAbe WFar
'Tilden Park'	EBee LRHS
× ***veitchianus***	CSBt EBee ELan LRHS MBar NHol SCoo SEND SPer WGwG
'White Cascade'	EBee
'Zanzibar' PBR	see *C.* 'Pershore Zanzibar'

Cedrela (*Meliaceae*)

sinensis	see *Toona sinensis*

Cedronella (*Lamiaceae*)

§ ***canariensis***	CArn CBod CHby CHrt CPrp CSev EShb GBar GGar GPoy ILis MHer MNHC NGHP SIde SWat WCHb WHer
mexicana	see *Agastache mexicana*
triphylla	see *C. canariensis*

Cedrus (*Pinaceae*)

atlantica	CDul CLnd CMac CMen CPMA CSBt ECrN EHul IFFs MBar NWea SEND WBVN WEve WMou
- 'Aurea'	CDul MBar MGos NLar NPCo NWea SSta WDin WHar
* - subsp. ***douglasii*** **new**	CMac
- 'Fastigiata'	EHul MBar MGos NLar SCoo SLim SPoG WEve
- Glauca Group ♀H4	Widely available
- - 'Glauca Fastigiata'	CKen CMen ECho GKir NLar WEve
- - 'Glauca Pendula'	CDoC CDul CMen ECho ECrN EHul EOrn EPfP GKir IMGH LMaj LRHS MBar MBlu MBri MGos NEgg NPCo NWea SCoo SLim SPoG SSta WDin WEve WFar
- - 'Silberspitz'	CKen
- 'Pendula'	ECho MAsh WBVN
- 'Saphir Nymph'	ECho MAsh NLar SLim
brevifolia	CAlb ECho GKir MBar MGos NLar SBch WEve
- 'Epstein'	ECho MBar MGos NLar
- 'Hillier Compact'	CKen MGos NLar
- 'Kenwith'	CKen ECho MAsh NLar
deodara ♀H4	Widely available
- 'Albospica' (v)	IFFs SWvt
- 'Argentea'	MBar MGos
- 'Aurea' ♀H4	CDoC CDul CKen CSBt CTho ECho EHul EOrn EPfP GBin GKir IMGH LMaj LRHS MBar MBri MGos NEgg NLar NWea SLim WDin WEve WFar
I - 'Aurea Pendula'	ECho
- 'Blue Dwarf'	CKen ECho NLar WEve
* - 'Blue Mountain Broom'	CKen
- 'Blue Snake'	CKen NLar
- 'Blue Surprise' **new**	SLim
- 'Bush's Electra'	CPMA NLar
- 'Cream Puff'	CSli ECho MBar MGos
- 'Dawn Mist' (v)	ECho
- 'Devinely Blue'	CKen SLim SPoG
- 'Feelin' Blue'	CDoC CDul CKen CSli ECho EHul EPla GKir IMGH LBee LRHS MAsh MBar MBri MGos NEgg NHol NLar NPCo SCoo SLim SWvt WBor WEve WFar
- 'Gold Cascade'	SLim
- 'Gold Cone'	ECho MGos
- 'Gold Gowa'	MGos
- 'Gold Mound'	CKen ECho MAsh WEve
- 'Golden Horizon'	CDoC CKen CMac CMen CSBt ECho ECrN EHul EOrn EPla IMGH LBee LRHS MAsh MBar MBri MGos NEgg NPCo SCoo SLim SPoG WDin WEve WFar
- 'Karl Fuchs'	EWTr GKir MAsh MBri NLar SCoo WGor
- 'Kashmir'	CSli
- 'Kelly Gold'	WEve
- 'Lime Glow'	SLim
- 'Miles High' **new**	CPMA
- 'Mountain Beauty'	CKen
- 'Nana'	CKen
- 'Nivea'	CKen
- 'Pendula'	CDoC CKen ECho EHul LMaj MBar MGos SLim WEve WGor
- 'Pygmy'	CKen
- 'Raywood's Prostrate'	CKen
- 'Robusta'	WEve
- 'Roman Candle'	CSli ECho EOrn NPCo WEve WFar
- 'Scott'	CKen
- 'Silver Mist'	CKen MGos
- 'Silver Spring'	EMil MGos NLar
libani ♀H4	Widely available
- 'Blue Angel' **new**	SLim

- 'Comte de Dijon'	ECho EHul LRHS NLar
- 'Fontaine'	NLar
- 'Gold Tip'	NLar
- 'Home Park'	CKen NLar
- 'May' new	NLar
- Nana Group	CKen ECho NPCo
- 'Pampisford'	ECho NLar
- 'Sargentii'	CKen ECho EHul EOrn IMGH MBar MGos NLar NPCo WEve
- 'Taurus'	MBar NLar
libanii 'Green Prince'	NLar
- 'Hedgehog'	NLar

Celastrus (*Celastraceae*)

flagellaris B&SWJ 8572	WCru
orbiculatus	CBcs CDoC CMac ELan LHop LRHS MRav NCGa NSti SLon WBor
- 'Diana' (f)	CMac NBea
- 'Hercules' (m)	CMac NBea NLar
- Hermaphrodite Group ♀H4	EBee SDix SEND SPer
scandens	CMac EBee SPlb WDin
stephanotiifolius B&SWJ 4727	WCru

Celmisia (*Asteraceae*)

allanii	IBlr WAbe
angustifolia	IBlr
argentea	ECho WAbe
armstrongii	ECho
Ballyrogan hybrids	IBlr
bellidioides	ECho EPot EWes MDKP WAbe
bonplandii	IBlr
brevifolia	IBlr
coriacea misapplied	see *C. semicordata*
coriacea Raoul	see *C. mackaui*
coriacea (G. Forst.) Hook. f.	MDun
costiniana	IBlr
'David Shackleton'	IBlr
densiflora	GKev IBlr
- silver-leaved	IBlr
densiflora × ***walkeri*** new	GKev
discolor	IBlr
glandulosa	IBlr
gracilenta	GKev NSla
- CC 563	NWCA
graminifolia	ECho
haastii	IBlr
'Harry Bryce'	IBlr
hectorii	IBlr WAbe
hectorii × ***ramulosa***	WAbe
hookeri	IBlr ITim
Inshriach hybrids	GKir IBlr
insignis	IBlr
latifolia	IBlr
- large-leaved	IBlr
longifolia large-leaved	IBlr
- small-leaved	IBlr
§ ***mackaui***	GGar IBlr
monroi	IBlr
prorepens	IBlr
pugioniformis	IBlr
ramulosa	EPot NLAp SIng
- var. ***tuberculata***	IBlr NSla
§ ***semicordata***	GAbr GBuc GCra IBlr IDee NSla WAbe
- subsp. ***aurigans***	IBlr
- subsp. ***stricta***	IBlr
sericophylla	GKev
sessiliflora	GKev
spectabilis	ECho GGar GKir MDun
- 'Eggleston Silver'	GKev NEgg
- subsp. ***magnifica***	GKev
tomentella	IBlr
verbascifolia	IBlr
§ ***walkeri***	IBlr ITim
webbiana	see *C. walkeri*

Celosia (*Amaranthaceae*)

argentea var. ***cristata***	MBri
- - Plumosa Group	MBri

Celsia see *Verbascum*

× *Celsioverbascum* see *Verbascum*

Celtica see *Stipa*

Celtis (*Ulmaceae*)

africana	EGFP
australis	CBcs EBtc MGos MMuc
biondii	EGFP
bungeana	IDee NLar
caucasica	GAuc NLar
julianae	IArd NLar
koraiensis	EGFP
occidentalis	CDul ELan IArd WBVN
sinensis	CMen NLar

Cenolophium (*Apiaceae*)

denudatum	CDes CHrt EBee ECha EPPr NChi WPGP

Centaurea ✿ (*Asteraceae*)

HH&K 271	NBid
RCB AM -1	WCot
RCB AM -6	WCot
RCB EA-1	WCot
from Turkey	MSpe WPGP
achtarovii	NWCA
alba	LDai
alpestris	CSam NBre NLar WPer
argentea	CBot
athoa new	GKev
§ ***atropurpurea***	CDes EBee EWes GMac GQue LDai MRav NBPC NLar SMeo SMrm SPhx SUsu WClo WHal WHil WHrl WPer WPGP
bagadensis	EBee GAuc
bella	CBgR CBot CPrp CSam CSev EBee ECtt GCal GKir LHop LLWG LPla LRHS MAvo MLHP MNFA MRav MSpe NBro NChi NMRc SGSe SMeo SPet SPhx SPoG SWat WMnd WWFP
benoistii misapplied	see *C. atropurpurea*
cana hort.	see *C. triumfettii* subsp. *cana*
candidissima misapplied	see *C. cineraria*
'Caramia'	CDes EBee SMeo
carniolica SDR 5443 new	GKev
cheiranthifolia	ECha EPPr MSpe NBir WFar WPGP
- var. ***purpurascens***	MAvo
§ ***cineraria***	EBee ECre LDai SRms WEas
- subsp. ***cineraria*** ♀H3	WCot
clementei	CSpe
cyanus	CArn MHer MNHC NPri WJek
- 'Black Ball'	CSpe
cynaroides	see *Stemmacantha centaureoides*
dealbata	CBot CMac COIW CPrp CWib EBee EPfP GJos GKir IFoB LBMP NBPC NBlu NBro NMir NOrc NPri SBch SECG SMrm STes WBor WCot WFar WMoo WPer WWEG
- 'Steenbergii'	CMac EBee EBla ELan GCal GGar GKir MNFA NBid NBir NGdn NPer

		NSti SGSe SPer SPoG WAbb WCAu WCot WFar WHoo WMnd
	- 'Steenbergii' variegated (v)	LDai
	debeauxii subsp. ***nemoralis***	LDai
	fischeri Willd.	CDes EBee WPGP
	glastifolia	EBee GCal MBel MSpe NBre WPGP
	gymnocarpa	see *C. cineraria*
	hypoleuca	NBid
	jacea	CSam EShb GAbr MSpe NBid NLar WCot WOut WPer
	'Jody' **new**	WCAu
	'John Coutts'	Widely available
	'Jordy'	EBee ECtt IPot LDai
	kotschyana	CDes EBee NBre WPGP
	macrocephala	Widely available
	maculosa	LDai
	mollis	NBid
	montana	Widely available
	- 'Alba'	Widely available
§	- 'Carnea'	CCVN CElw CPom CSam EBee EBla ECha GCra GMaP GMac LLWP LRHS MAvo MSpe NBir NChi NLar SAga SMeo SPhx STes WCAu WMoo WSHC WWEG
	- 'Gold Bullion'	CDes CSpe CWGN EBla ECtt ELan ELon EPfP EWes EWll GBuc GKir GMaP LDai LRHS MBri MCCP MRav MSpe NBid NBir NLar NPro SMad SMrm WCAu WWEG
	- 'Gold Strike'	EBee
	- 'Grandiflora'	EBee MBri
	- 'Joyce'	CDes CElw CPom EBee EBla LDai MAvo NBid NLar
	- 'Lady Flora Hastings'	CBre CDes CElw CKno CMdw CPom CSam CSpe EBee EBla LDai LEdu MAvo MSpe NBid SUsu WPGP WWEG
	- lilac-flowered	NBid
	- 'Ochroleuca'	CDes EBee EGoo GBuc LDai MBel NBid NBre
	- pale pink-flowered	NChi
	- 'Parham'	CElw CPrp CSev EBee EBla ECtt ELan EPPr GBuc GCal LBMP LHop LLWG LLWP LRHS LSRN MBel MCot MRav MWat NEgg NSti SPer SPlb SPoG WFar WMnd WWEG
	- 'Purple Heart'	EBee EBla EKen IPot MBNS MBri NBPC NPri SMrm
	- 'Purple Prose'	MAvo WWEG
	- 'Purpurea'	CDes CPom EBee MSpe
	- 'Rosea'	see *C. montana* 'Carnea'
*	- ***violacea***	NBid
	- 'Violetta'	EBee NBir WCAu WFar WMoo
	montana × ***triumfettii***	CDes WCot
	moschata	see *Amberboa moschata*
	nervosa	see *C. uniflora* subsp. *nervosa*
	nigra	CArn COld CRWN EBWF EBee EBla GJos NBre NLan NMir NSco SECG SMrm WMoo WSFF
	- var. ***alba***	CArn CBre NBid
	- subsp. ***rivularis***	ECha LDai NBid NBre
	nogmovii **new**	EBee
	orientalis	CSpe EBee EWes GCal LBMP LLWG LRHS MNFA NBre SMeo SPhx SPoG WHal WPer
	pannonica subsp. ***pannonica***	NBid WSHC
	phrygia	COIW GAbr NBre WPer
	pulcherrima	EBee LRHS MBel NBre NChi WCom WPer
	'Pulchra Major'	see *Stemmacantha centaureoides*
	rothrockii	LDai
	rupestris	EBee EPfP MAvo NBre SGar SPhx WPer
	ruthenica	CAby EBee EWTr GMac GQue NBre NGdn NLar SMad SPer SPhx SPlb WCot WHil
	scabiosa	CArn CRWN CWib EBWF GPWP MHer NBid NBre NLan NMir NPri NSco SECG WPer
	- f. ***albiflora***	EBee ECtt LRHS
	simplicicaulis	CDes CSam CWan EBee ECrN GAbr MSpe MTho NChi SMrm SRms WCom WEas WHoo WPer WSHC
	thracica	EBee LDai SAga WCot
	'Totnes Fat Lemon' **new**	CDes
	triumfettii	CPBP
	- 'Blue Dreams'	LDai
	- 'Hoar Frost'	CDes EBee MSpe WCot WPGP
I	- subsp. ***cana*** 'Rosea'	WBrk
	- subsp. ***stricta***	CPrp EBee GBuc MSpe WFar
	uniflora	CDes EBee LDai
§	- subsp. ***nervosa***	NBid NBre NBro WPer
	woronowii	LDai

Centaurium (*Gentianaceae*)

	erythraea	CArn EBWF GPoy MHer
*	***littorale*** 'Album'	WSFF
	scilloides	CPBP MTho NLAp NMen NSla NWCA WAbe

Centella (*Apiaceae*)

§	***asiatica***	CArn EOHP GPoy ILis WJek

Centradenia (*Melastomataceae*)

	floribunda	LAst
	inaequilateralis	CCCN
	- 'Cascade'	MBri SPet

Centranthus (*Valerianaceae*)

§	***lecoqii***	EBee ECtt EWes LPla SPhx WCot
§	***ruber***	Widely available
*	- 'Alba Pura'	NBPC
§	- 'Albus'	Widely available
	- 'Atrococcineus'	ECha SPoG WPer
	- 'Clair' **new**	CNat
	- var. ***coccineus***	CBcs CHrt CKno EBee EGoo ELan EPfP EWTr GAbr GMaP LAst LBMP LRHS MCot MNHC MRav MWat NBlu NPri NVic SBch SEND SMrm SPer SPhx SRot WCAu WCot WFar WWEG
	- mauve-flowered misapplied	see *C. lecoqii*
	- mauve-flowered	NBir
	- 'Roseus'	WMoo
	- 'Snowcloud'	CSev ECtt EPfP MNHC WClo WHil
	'White Cloud'	WJek

Centropogon (*Campanulaceae*)

§	***ayavacensis*** subsp. ***ayavacensis*** B&SWJ 10663 **new**	WCru
	cordifolius B&SWJ 10282 **new**	WCru
	costaricae B&SWJ 10455	WCru
	hirsutus B&SWJ 10657 **new**	WCru
	willdenowianus	see *C. ayavacensis* subsp. *ayavacensis*

Cephalanthera (*Orchidaceae*)

	falcata	EFEx GEdr WWst
	longibracteata	EFEx GEdr WWst

Cephalanthus (*Rubiaceae*)

occidentalis CMac CWib EBee ELon EMil LRHS LSou MBNS MBlu MBri MGos NLar SHGN SLim SMad SPer SPoG SRms WBVN WFar

Cephalaria (*Dipsacaceae*)

HWJ 695 SPhx
§ ***alpina*** COlW EBee EBla EHrv EPfP LBMP LRHS MHer MNrw MRav NLar SBch SPhx SRms SWat WCot WFar WPer
- RCB/TQ E-1 WCot
- 'Nana' NWCA
ambrosioides MBel
- MESE 503 EBee
anatolica KM T-04-72 **new** EBee
caucasica see *C. gigantea*
dipsacoides CEnt CFee CSam EBee EBla ECha LDai LPio NBre NLar SPhx SPoG STes WHal WMoo
§ ***flava*** EBee NBre
galpiniana SPlb
- subsp. ***simplicior*** EBee
§ ***gigantea*** Widely available
graeca see *C. flava*
leucantha CArn GBuc MBel NBid NBre SPhx STes WFar WMoo
litvinovii CElw EBee SPhx
radiata CSam EBee GBin LPio
tatarica hort. see *C. gigantea*
tchihatchewii EBee MBel
uralensis EBee

Cephalaria × *Scabiosa* (*Dipsacaceae*)

C. alpina × ***S. cinerea*** LRHS

Cephalotaxus (*Cephalotaxaceae*)

fortunei CDul SPer
- 'Prostrate Spreader' EHul SLim
harringtonii ECho ERom GKir LEdu WPGP
- var. ***drupacea*** CDoC NWea
- 'Fastigiata' CBcs CDoC CDul ECho EHul EOrn GKir IArd IDee IFFs LRHS MAsh MBar MBri MGos NPal SCoo SLim SPoG WDin WFar
- 'Gimborn's Pillow' IDee MBar
- 'Korean Gold' CKen GKir LRHS NLar SLim SPoG
- 'Prostrata' LRHS MBar SPoG
sinensis CBcs CMCN

Cephalotus (*Cephalotaceae*)

follicularis SHmp

Cerastium (*Caryophyllaceae*)

alpinum ECho IFoB SRms
- var. ***lanatum*** ECho EDAr EWes LRHS
arvense NDlv
candidissimum EWes NLar
tomentosum EAlp ECho EPfP GKir LRHS NBlu NDlv NPri SPer SPet SPlb SPoG WFar
- var. ***columnae*** ECha ECho EHoe EPfP EWes SIng
- 'Silberteppich' LBMP
- 'Yo Yo' WFar

Ceratonia (*Caesalpiniaceae*)

siliqua CBcs SEND

Ceratophyllum (*Ceratophyllaceae*)

demersum CBen CRow CWat EHon EMFW EPfP MSKA NSco SWat WMAq

Ceratostigma ✿ (*Plumbaginaceae*)

abyssinicum ELan
asperrimum WCru
B&SWJ 7260 **new**
'Autumn Blue' EPfP
griffithii CBot CChe CDoC CDul CHll CMac CWSG EBee ECtt EHoe ELan EPfP LAst LBMP LRHS MCCP MRav MSwo NBlu SBch SMad SPer SPoG SWal WDin WFar WKif WSHC
- SF 149/150 ISea
§ ***plumbaginoides*** ♀H3-4 Widely available
willmottianum ♀H3-4 Widely available
- BWJ 8140 WCru
- Desert Skies = 'Palmgold'PBR CBcs EBee ELan EPfP ERas GBuc LAst LRHS MBlu MGos NLar SBch SCoo SLim SMad SPer SSta SWvt
- Forest Blue = 'Lice'PBR CAbP CDoC CMac CSBt CSpe CWSG EBee ELan EPfP LAst LHop LRHS LSRN LSqu MAsh MBri MGos NPri SBch SCoo SLim SPer SPoG SReu WDin WPat

Cercidiphyllum ✿ (*Cercidiphyllaceae*)

japonicum ♀H4 Widely available
- 'Boyd's Dwarf' LRHS MBri NLar SPoG SSpi WAbe
- 'Herkenrode Dwarf' MBri NLar
- 'Heronswood Globe' CPMA EPfP MBlu NLar SSta WSpi
- 'Kreukenberg Dwarf' CPMA
- 'Morioka Weeping' CTho SMad SSta WPGP
- 'Peach' **new** NLar
§ - f. ***pendulum*** ♀H4 CBcs CDul CEnd CLnd CMCN CPMA CTri CWSG EBee EPfP GKir LRHS MAsh MBlu MGos NEgg NLar SCoo SLim SPoG SSpi WDin
- - 'Amazing Grace' CTho LLHF MBlu SSta
- 'Raspberry' MBri NLar
- Red Fox see *C. japonicum* 'Rotfuchs'
§ - 'Rotfuchs' CBcs CEnd CMCN CPMA EBee EPfP EWTr GKir LRHS MAsh MBlu MBri MGos NCGa NLar NPCo NPal SCoo SLim SMad SPoG SSpi SSta WPGP
- 'Ruby' CPMA MBlu MBri NLar
- 'Strawberry' CBcs EBee MBlu MBri NLar
- 'Tidal Wave' MBri NLar
magnificum CBcs CDoC CDul CEnd CMCN EPfP IDee NEgg NLar WCru WPGP
- f. ***pendulum*** see *C. japonicum* f. *pendulum*

Cercis (*Caesalpiniaceae*)

sp. WFoF
canadensis CBcs CDul CMCN CWGN EPfP IFFs MGos NEgg NHol NLar NWea SCoo SLim SPer WPat
- f. ***alba*** ESwi LRHS LSRN
- - 'Royal White' CPMA EPfP IArd MBlu
- 'Appalachian Red' CPMA LSRN MBlu NBhm NLar
- 'Cascading Hearts' **new** ESwi
- 'Flame' CPMA NBhm WPat
- 'Floating Clouds' (v) **new** MGos
- 'Forest Pansy' ♀H4 Widely available
- 'Hearts of Gold' MBlu MGos
- Lavender Twist = 'Covey' ESwi LRHS LSRN MBlu MBri MGos NLar SGol SPoG
§ - var. ***occidentalis*** NLar NMun
- 'Pauline Lily' NLar
- 'Rubye Atkinson' CPMA NLar SSpi

- 'Tennessee Pink'	CPMA NLar
- 'Texan White' **new**	SSpi
- var. ***texensis***	NLar
'Traveller' **new**	
chinensis	CBcs NLar SPer WDin
- 'Avondale'	CAbP CBcs CDoC CEnd CPMA CTho CWib EBee EPfP ERas EWTr EWes IArd LRHS LSRN MAsh MBlu MBri MGos MMuc NHol NLar NPCo SBch SCoo SLim SSpi SWvt WPGP WPat
- 'Don Egolf'	CPMA LRHS LSRN MGos MPkF NLar
gigantea	NLar
griffithii	EGFP LLHF NLar NMun
occidentalis	see *C. canadensis* var. *occidentalis*
racemosa	IDee NLar WPGP
reniformis 'Oklahoma'	CPMA EBee ESwi LSRN MGos NLar NPCo
- 'Texas White'	CBcs CPMA EBee LRHS NLar SLim WPat WSpi
siliquastrum ♀H4	Widely available
- f. ***albida***	CBcs CBot ECrN EPfP LHop LRHS SPoG SSpi WCFE WSpi
- 'Bodnant'	EBee EPfP EWes LAst LLHF LSRN MBlu MBri MGos NLar
- 'White Swan'	CPMA EWes
yunnanensis	LRHS NLar

Cerinthe (*Boraginaceae*)

glabra	LBMP NBre SPlb
major	LEdu WEas
- 'Kiwi Blue'	CHll MDKP
- 'Purpurascens'	CMea CSpe EBee EGoo EHrv ELan EPfP IFoB LBMP MCot MSCN NLar SGar SMad SMrm SPer SPoG WWEG
- 'Yellow Gem'	NLar
retorta	CSpe LDai

Ceropegia (*Asclepiadaceae*)

fusca	EShb
§ ***linearis***	EShb LRHS MBri SRms STre
subsp. ***woodii*** ♀H1	
§ - - 'Lady Heart' (v)	EShb
- - 'Variegata'	see *C. linearis* subsp. *woodii* 'Lady Heart'
pubescens GWJ 9441	WCru
sandersonii ♀H1	LRHS
woodii	see *C. linearis* subsp. *woodii*

Ceroxylon (*Arecaceae*)

alpinum	LPJP LPal
ventricosum	LPal

Cestrum (*Solanaceae*)

aurantiacum	ERea EShb
× ***cultum***	CHll EShb
- 'Cretan Purple'	CBcs CHid CHll CWan EBee ELan ELon EPfP ERea EShb EWTr LHop MBri SEND SMad SPoG WCFE WSHC
diurnum × ***nocturnum***	EShb
§ ***elegans***	CDoC CHEx CHll CPLG CSev CTsd EBee ELon LRHS NEgg SEND SLon WDin WWlt
fasciculatum	EShb MBri SMad
'Newellii' ♀H2	CBcs CMHG CPLG CSev CStu CWib EBak EBee ELan ELon EPfP ERea EShb LRHS SDnm SEND SGar WBor WSHC
nocturnum	CCCN CDoC CHll EBak EOHP ERea EShb IDee NExo WCFE
parqui ♀H3	CAbb CBcs CHEx CHll CMHG CWib EBee ELan EPfP ERea EShb IDee LRHS SDix SDnm SEND SGar SLon SMad SMrm SUsu WKif WSHC WWlt
- 'Orange Essence'	WCot
psittacinum	CPLG
purpureum (Lindl.) Standl.	see *C. elegans*
roseum	CPLG
- 'Ilnacullin'	CFee ERea

Ceterach (*Aspleniaceae*)

officinarum	see *Asplenium ceterach*

Chaenomeles (*Rosaceae*)

cathayensis	CTho LEdu NLar
§ ***japonica***	MBar SHlg WDin WFar
- 'Chojubai'	CMen
- 'Cido'	CAgr LBuc
- 'Orange Beauty'	LRHS WFar
- 'Sargentii'	CMac EBee EPfP MGos NBro
'John Pilger'	NHol
lagenaria	see *C. speciosa*
'Madame Butterfly'	CDoC EBee GKir LRHS LSRN MAsh MBri MRav NEgg NLar SBch SPer SPoG WClo WGrn
maulei	see *C. japonica*
'Orange Star'	CEnd EBee MNHC
sinensis	see *Pseudocydonia sinensis*
§ ***speciosa***	CSam MBar MGan NWea
- 'Apple Blossom'	see *C. speciosa* 'Moerloosei'
- 'Brilliant'	EPfP
- 'Contorta'	CDoC LRHS SPoG
- 'Eximia' **new**	LRHS
- 'Falconnet Charlet' (d)	MRav
- 'Friesdorfer' **new**	LRHS
- 'Geisha Girl' (d) ♀H4	Widely available
- 'Grayshott Salmon'	NHol NPro WFar
- 'Kinshiden' **new**	LRHS
§ - 'Moerloosei' ♀H4	CDoC CDul CPMA CSBt CSam ELan EPfP EWTr IMGH LAst LRHS MBlu MBri MGos MRav MSwo MWat NLar NScw SAga SLim SPer SSta WDin WMoo WPat WTin
- 'Nivalis'	Widely available
- 'Port Eliot'	LRHS
- 'Rubra Grandiflora'	LRHS WBVN
- 'Simonii' (d)	CBcs EBee EPfP MGos MRav NHol NWea SPer WFar
- 'Snow'	MSwo NHol
- 'Umbilicata'	SPer SRms
- 'Yukigoten'	CDoC CWib EBee LRHS NLar SBch WClo
× ***superba***	STre
- 'Boule de Feu'	CTri CWib EBee ECtt MCoo
- 'Cameo' (d)	CAbP CBot CChe CEnd CSBt EBee ELon EPfP LHop MBNS MBri MHav MRav NCGa NLar SLPl WRHF
- 'Clementine'	CWib EBee
- 'Crimson and Gold' ♀H4	Widely available
- 'Elly Mossel'	CMac CWib WFar
- 'Ernst Finken'	EBee NLar
- 'Etna'	EBee
- 'Fascination'	EBee NLar
- 'Fire Dance'	CDul CWib EBee ECtt MSwo NHol NLar SPer
- 'Hollandia'	MGos
- 'Issai White'	MRav
- 'Jet Trail'	CBcs CSBt EBee ELan EPfP LAst LRHS LSRN MAsh MGos MRav MSwo NBlu NLar NPro SLPl SPoG SSta WFar

	- 'Knap Hill Scarlet' ♀H4	CDoC CDul EBee EPfP GGal GKir LHop LRHS MAsh MGos NHol SLim SPer SPoG SRms WDin WFar
	- 'Lemon and Lime'	ELan EPfP LRHS MGos MRav NSti SLon
	- 'Nicoline' ♀H4	CBcs CDoC CDul EBee EPfP GKir MBri NEgg NPri WDin WFar
	- 'Pink Lady' ♀H4	Widely available
	- 'Pink Trail'	NBlu
	- 'Red Joy'	EMil MAsh NLar SPoG
	- 'Red Trail'	MRav
	- 'Rowallane' ♀H4	EBee ELan EPfP ERas LOck MRav
	- 'Salmon Horizon'	EPfP MGos NLar
	- 'Tortuosa'	EBee LHop SPoG
	- 'Vermilion'	MAsh
	'Toyo-nishiki'	MBlu NLar

Chaenorhinum (*Scrophulariaceae*)

§	***origanifolium***	ECho EShb GKev NRya SBch SPlb
	- 'Blue Dream'	CEnt CSpe EBee ECho ECtt EPfP GKev LRHS NVic SPoG SWvt WFar WMoo WPer WWEG
	- 'Dreamcatcher' new	EPfP
	- 'Summer Skies'	NPri SPet WFar

Chaerophyllum (*Apiaceae*)

	hirsutum	CRow IMou
	- 'Roseum'	Widely available
	temulum	CArn

Chamaebatiaria (*Rosaceae*)

	millefolium	NLar

Chamaecyparis ✿ (*Cupressaceae*)

	'Erecta Viridis'	CSBt MHav
	formosensis	CKen
	lawsoniana	CDul EHul EMac MBar NWea WBVN WDin WMou
	- SIN 1820	GLin
	- 'Albospica' (v)	GKir MBar WFar
	- 'Albovariegata' (v)	MBar
	- 'Allumii Aurea'	see *C. lawsoniana* 'Alumigold'
	- 'Allumii Magnificent'	CDul MAsh NLar
§	- 'Alumigold'	CSBt CWib GKir MAsh MBar MGos NBlu SCoo WDin
	- 'Alumii'	EHul GKir IFFs MAsh MBar MGos NWea
	- 'Argentea'	see *C. lawsoniana* 'Argenteovariegata'
§	- 'Argenteovariegata' (v)	CDoC GKir
	- 'Aurea'	CDul
	- 'Aurea Densa' ♀H4	CKen CMac CSBt CTri ECho EHul EOrn EPfP MAsh MBar MGos NEgg SCoo STre WEve WGor
	- 'Aureovariegata' (v)	GKir MBar
§	- 'Barabits' Globe'	MBar
	- 'Bleu Nantais'	CKen ECho EHul GKir LBee LRHS MAsh MBar MGos NBlu SCoo SLim SPoG WCFE WEve WFar
	- 'Blom'	CKen EHul MBri
§	- 'Blue Gown'	EHul MBar MGos SRms
§	- 'Blue Jacket'	NWea
	- 'Blue Surprise'	CKen EHul MBar WFar
	- 'Brégéon'	CKen NLar
	- 'Broomhill Gold'	CDoC CSBt ECho EHul GKir LRHS MAsh MBar MGos NHol SCoo SLim SPer SPoG WDin WEve
*	- 'Burkwood's Blue'	MBar
	- 'Caudata'	CKen MBar NLar
	- 'Chantry Gold'	EHul SCoo WEve
§	- 'Chilworth Silver' ♀H4	CSBt EHul GKir IFFs LBee LRHS MAsh MBar NBlu SCoo SLim SPer SPoG SRms WBVN WDin WFar
	- 'Columnaris'	CBcs CDoC CMac ECho EPfP GKir IFFs LBee LMaj LRHS MBar MBri MGos NBlu NEgg NWea SCoo SPoG WFar
	- 'Columnaris Aurea'	see *C. lawsoniana* 'Golden Spire'
N	- 'Columnaris Glauca'	CSBt CWib EHul GKir MAsh MGos NEgg NWea SBod SCoo SPer WDin WFar
	- 'Crawford's Compact'	CMac
	- 'Cream Crackers'	EHul
	- 'Cream Glow'	CDoC CKen CSBt GKir LRHS MGos NLar SCoo SLim SPoG WFar WGor
	- 'Croftway'	EHul
	- 'Dik's Weeping'	CDoC GKir NLar NWea SLim WEve
	- 'Duncanii'	ECho EHul
	- 'Dutch Gold'	EHul MAsh
	- 'Dwarf Blue'	see *C. lawsoniana* 'Pick's Dwarf Blue'
	- 'Eclipse'	CKen
	- 'Elegantissima' ambig.	CKen MGos
	- 'Ellwoodii' ♀H4	CDul CMac CSBt CTri CWib ECho EHul EPfP GKir IFFs LAst MAsh MBar MGos NBlu NWea SCoo SLim SPer SPoG WDin WFar WMoo
I	- 'Ellwoodii Glauca'	SPlb
	- 'Ellwood's Empire'	EHul GKir
	- 'Ellwood's Gold' ♀H4	CBcs CDoC CMac CSBt CWib ECho EHul ELan EPfP GKir IFFs LBee LRHS MAsh MBar MBri MGos NBlu NHol NWea SPer SPlb SPoG STre WBVN WDin WEve WFar WMoo
	- 'Ellwood's Gold Pillar'	ECho EHul GKir LBee LRHS MAsh MGos NHol SCoo SLim SPoG WFar
§	- 'Ellwood's Nymph'	CKen ECho GKir LRHS MAsh MBar SCoo SLim WFar WGor
	- Ellwood's Pillar = 'Flolar'	CDoC CMac EHul GKir LAst LBee LRHS MAsh MBar MBri MGos NBlu NHol NLar SCoo SLim WCFE WDin WFar
	- 'Ellwood's Pygmy'	CMac ECho GKir MBar
	- 'Ellwood's Silver'	ECho MAsh WFar
	- 'Ellwood's Silver Threads'	CMac
	- 'Ellwood's Variegata'	see *C. lawsoniana* 'Ellwood's White'
§	- 'Ellwood's White' (v)	CKen CSBt ECho EHul EPfP MBar WFar
I	- 'Emerald'	CKen MBar
	- 'Emerald Spire'	MAsh NHol
	- 'Empire'	WFar
	- 'Erecta Aurea'	ECho EHul MBri MGos SCoo
	- 'Erecta Filiformis'	MBar
	- 'Erecta Viridis'	CTrG GKir MBar MBri NEgg NWea WDin WFar
	- 'Ericoides'	EHul
	- 'Erika'	ECho MBar
	- 'Filiformis Compacta'	EHul
	- 'Fleckellwood'	CWib EHul MAsh MBar
	- 'Fletcheri' ♀H4	CMac CWib EHul GKir MBar NWea SBod WDin WFar
	- 'Fletcheri Aurea'	see *C. lawsoniana* 'Yellow Transparent'
	- 'Fletcher's White'	ECho EHul MBar
	- 'Forsteckensis'	CKen ECho EHul EOrn GKir MBar NLar NWea SCoo SRms WEve WFar WGor
I	- 'Forsteckensis Aurea'	NLar
	- 'Fraseri'	MBar NWea
	- 'Gimbornii' ♀H4	ECho EHul GKir LBee LRHS MAsh MBar NBlu SCoo SLim SRms WFar
	- 'Glauca'	CDul
	- 'Globosa'	MGos
	- 'Globus'	see *C. lawsoniana* 'Barabits' Globe'

	- 'Gnome'	CDoC CMac ECho EHul EOrn GEdr LAst LRHS MBar MGos SCoo SLim SPoG WEve WGor
	- 'Gold Flake'	MBar MGos
	- 'Gold Splash'	MBar
	- 'Golden King'	MBar
§	- 'Golden Pot'	CDoC CMac CSBt CWib EHul GKir LBee LRHS MBar MGos NBlu NHol SCoo SPoG WDin WFar
§	- 'Golden Queen'	EHul
	- 'Golden Showers'	EHul
§	- 'Golden Spire'	MBar NLar WFar
	- 'Golden Triumph'	EHul
	- 'Golden Wonder'	EHul MBar MGos NEgg NLar NWea SCoo SRms WDin WEve WFar
	- 'Goldfinger'	CDoC NLar
	- 'Grant's Gold'	EHul
	- 'Grayswood Feather'	CDoC CSBt EHul GKir LBee LRHS MAsh MBar MGos SCoo SLim SPlb WEve
	- 'Grayswood Gold'	EHul GKir LBee LRHS MBar WEve
	- 'Grayswood Pillar' ♀H4	CDul EHul MBar MGos
	- 'Green Globe'	CDoC CKen CMen CSBt EHul LBee LRHS MAsh MBar MGos NLar SCoo SLim WAbe WDin WEve
§	- 'Green Hedger' ♀H4	CSBt MBar MHav NBlu NWea SCoo SRms WFar
§	- 'Green Pillar'	CWib ECho IFFs LAst LBee LRHS MBar NEgg SCoo
	- 'Green Spire'	see *C. lawsoniana* 'Green Pillar'
	- 'Hillieri'	MBar
	- 'Hogger's Blue Gown'	see *C. lawsoniana* 'Blue Gown'
	- 'Imbricata Pendula'	CDoC CKen GKir IDee LRHS NLar SLim
	- 'Intertexta' ♀H4	EHul WEve
	- 'Ivonne'	EHul GKir MGos WEve
	- 'Jackman's Green Hedger'	see *C. lawsoniana* 'Green Hedger'
	- 'Jackman's Variety'	see *C. lawsoniana* 'Green Pillar'
	- 'Jeanette'	MGos
	- 'Kelleriis Gold'	EHul MBar
	- 'Kilmacurragh' ♀H4	CDul CMac GKir MBar MGos NWea WCFE
	- 'Kilworth Column'	CDoC MGos NLar NWea SCoo
	- 'Knowefieldensis'	CMac ECho EHul
	- 'Lane' misapplied	see *C. lawsoniana* 'Lanei Aurea'
	- 'Lanei' misapplied	see *C. lawsoniana* 'Lanei Aurea'
	- 'Lanei'	CSBt CWib ECho MGos MRav NEgg SCoo WDin WFar
§	- 'Lanei Aurea' ♀H4	EHul MBar MGos NWea WFar
	- 'Lemon Pillar'	NHol WDin WEve
	- 'Lemon Queen'	CSBt EHul LBee LRHS
	- 'Limelight'	MGos
	- 'Little Spire' ♀H4	CDoC ECho EOrn EPla GKir LBee LRHS MBar MBri MGos NHol NLar SBch SCoo SLim SPoG WEve WGor
	- 'Lombartsii'	WFar
	- 'Lutea' ♀H4	CMac EHul GKir MGos NWea
§	- 'Lutea Nana' ♀H4	CMac EHul MAsh MBar MGos NLar SCoo
§	- 'Lutea Smithii'	MBar NWea
	- 'Luteocompacta'	LBee LRHS
	- 'Lycopodioides'	ECho MBar
*	- 'MacPenny's Gold'	CMac
	- 'Milford Blue Jacket'	see *C. lawsoniana* 'Blue Jacket'
§	- 'Minima'	MBar SRms
	- 'Minima Argentea'	see *C. lawsoniana* 'Nana Argentea'
	- 'Minima Aurea' ♀H4	Widely available
	- 'Minima Densa'	see *C. lawsoniana* 'Minima'
	- 'Minima Glauca' ♀H4	CDul CSBt ECho EHul EPfP GEdr GKir IFFs LRHS MAsh MBar MGos NEgg NHol NWea SCoo SLim WDin WEve WFar
	- 'Moonlight'	MBar MGos
*	- 'Moonsprite'	ECho NLar SCoo SLim SPoG
	- 'Naberi'	GKir
	- 'Nana'	MBar
	- 'Nana Albospica' (v)	ECho EHul EOrn LBee LRHS MBar SCoo SPoG WFar WGor
§	- 'Nana Argentea'	CKen CMac EHul EPfP SCoo WFar WGor
	- 'Nana Lutea'	see *C. lawsoniana* 'Lutea Nana'
	- 'New Silver'	MGos
	- 'Nicole'	ECho MAsh SCoo SPoG WGor
	- 'Nidiformis'	EHul MBar NWea SCoo SRms
	- 'Nyewoods'	see *C. lawsoniana* 'Chilworth Silver'
	- 'Nymph'	see *C. lawsoniana* 'Ellwood's Nymph'
§	- 'Pelt's Blue' ♀H4	CBcs CDoC CDul CKen CSBt EHul IFFs LBee LRHS MBar MGos NLar SCoo SLim SPoG WDin WFar
	- 'Pembury Blue' ♀H4	CDoC CDul CSBt CWib ECho EHul EPfP GKir LBee LRHS MAsh MBar MGos NEgg NLar NWea SBod SCoo SLim SPer SPoG WDin WFar
	- 'Pendula'	CDoC MBar
§	- 'Pick's Dwarf Blue'	LRHS MBar MGos NHol SCoo WEve WGor
	- Pot of Gold	see *C. lawsoniana* 'Golden Pot'
	- 'Pottenii'	CMac CSBt ECho EHul GKir LBee LRHS MAsh MBar MGos NWea SCoo WDin WFar
	- 'Pygmaea Argentea' (v) ♀H4	CKen CMac CSBt CWib ECho EHul ELan EOrn EPfP EPla GKir LBee LRHS MAsh MBar MBri MGos NBlu NEgg NHol SLim SPoG SRms WBor WCFE WDin WFar
	- 'Pygmy'	EHul GKir LRHS MBar NHol NLar SCoo SLim WEve
	- 'Rijnhof'	EHul LBee
	- 'Rimpelaar'	CDoC MGos
	- 'Rogersii'	MBar SRms WFar
	- 'Romana'	MBri
	- 'Royal Gold'	EHul NBlu
	- 'Silver Queen' (v)	CKen MBar
	- 'Silver Threads' (v)	CMac ECho EHul GKir LBee LRHS MAsh MBar NHol WFar
	- 'Silver Tip' (v)	ECho EHul LRHS SCoo SLim
	- 'Smithii'	see *C. lawsoniana* 'Lutea Smithii'
	- 'Snow Flurry' (v)	CKen ECho EHul WFar
	- 'Snow White' PBR (v)	ECho EHul GKir LBee LRHS MAsh MBar MBri MGos NHol SCoo SLim SPoG WFar WGor
	- 'Somerset'	MBar MGos
	- 'Springtime' PBR	CDoC CSBt EHul LBee LRHS SCoo SLim SPoG WGor
	- 'Stardust' ♀H4	CBcs CDoC CDul CMac CSBt CTri CWib EHul ELan GKir IFFs LRHS MAsh MBar MBri NBlu NEgg SBod SCoo SLim SPer SPoG WDin
	- 'Stewartii'	CDul CTri MBar NEgg NWea SBod SCoo
	- 'Stilton Cheese'	MBar NHol SCoo
*	- 'Summer Cream'	EHul
	- 'Summer Snow' (v)	CDoC CDul CMac ECho EHul EPfP GKir LBee LRHS MBar MGos NBlu NHol SCoo SLim SRms WFar
	- 'Sunkist'	CSBt SCoo SLim WFar
	- 'Tamariscifolia'	CDoC EHul MBar WCFE WDin WFar
	- 'Tharandtensis Caesia'	EOrn MBar WFar
	- 'Tilford'	EHul
	- 'Treasure' (v)	CSBt CSli ECho EHul EPfP LBee LRHS MAsh MBar NBlu NHol SCoo SLim SPoG WFar

- 'Triomf van Boskoop' MBar
- 'Van Pelt' see *C. lawsoniana* 'Pelt's Blue'
- 'Versicolor' (v) MBar
- 'Waterfall' SMad
- 'Westermannii' (v) CMac EHul LRHS SCoo
- 'White Edge' WFar
- 'White Spot' (v) ECho EHul GKir LBee LRHS MBar MBri SCoo SPoG WBVN WFar
- 'White Wonder' MGos
- 'Winston Churchill' CSBt MBar MGos NWea SBod
- 'Wisselii' ♀H4 CDoC CKen CMac CTrG ECho EHul GKir IFFs LBee MBar MBri NLar NWea SCoo SRms WDin WFar WMoo
- 'Wisselii Nana' CKen EHul
- 'Wissel's Saguaro' CDoC CKen MGos NLar SLim
- 'Witzeliana' CDul CSBt ECho EOrn MBar MGos NLar
- 'Wyevale Silver' MBar
- 'Yellow Queen' see *C. lawsoniana* 'Golden Queen'
- 'Yellow Success' see *C. lawsoniana* 'Golden Queen'

§ - 'Yellow Transparent' MBar SCoo
- 'Yvonne' CDul ECho GKir LRHS MAsh MBar MGos NEgg NHol NLar SCoo SLim SPoG WEve

leylandii see × *Cupressocyparis leylandii*

nootkatensis ECho MBar
- 'Aurea' GKir IFFs WDin WEve
- 'Aureovariegata' (v) EHul
- 'Compacta' CTri MBar
- 'Glauca' CTho IFFs MBar
- 'Gracilis' EHul
- 'Green Arrow' CKen ECho LRHS SCoo SLim
- 'Jubilee' NPCo SCoo SLim WMou
- 'Kanada' NLar
- 'Lutea' CTri LRHS MBar NWea
- 'Nidifera' MBar
- 'Nordkroken' NLar
- 'Pendula' ♀H4 CDoC CDul CKen ECho ELan EOrn EPfP EPla GKir LMaj LRHS MAsh MBar MBlu MBri MGos NBlu NEgg NPCo NWea SCoo WCFE WDin WEve WFar
- 'Strict Weeper' CKen NLar SLim SPoG
- 'Variegata' (v) MBar

obtusa 'Albospica' (v) EHul
- 'Albovariegata' (v) CKen
- 'Arneson's Compact' CKen
- 'Aurea' CDoC SCoo WEve
- 'Aureovariegata' see *C. obtusa* 'Opaal'
- 'Aurora' CKen ECho ELan EMil EOrn MBri MGos SLim WEve

* - 'Autumn Gold' MBar
- 'Bambi' CDoC CKen EOrn MGos NLar WAbe WEve WThu
- 'Barkenny' CKen
- 'Bartley' CKen
- 'Bassett' CKen
- 'Bess' CKen
- 'Brigitt' CKen
- 'Buttonball' CKen MGos
- 'Caespitosa' CKen WAbe
- 'Chabo-yadori' CDoC ECho EHul EOrn GKir LRHS MBar MGos SCoo SLim SPoG WFar
- 'Chilworth' CDoC CKen MBar MGos NHol NLar
- 'Chima-anihiba' CKen
- 'Chirimen' CDoC CKen MGos NHol NLar
- 'Clarke's Seedling' CDoC NLar
- 'Confucius' CDoC EHul MGos NHol
- 'Contorta' EOrn MBar

§ - 'Coralliformis' ECho EOrn MBar
- 'Corley Gold' **new** MGos

§ - 'Crippsii' ♀H4 CBcs CDoC CDul EHul EOrn GKir LRHS MBar MGos SCoo SLim
- 'Crippsii Aurea' see *C. obtusa* 'Crippsii'
- 'Dainty Doll' CDoC CKen EOrn MGos NLar
- 'Densa' see *C. obtusa* 'Nana Densa'
- 'Draht' CDoC MBar MGos NLar SCoo
- 'Draht Hexe' CKen
- 'Elf' CKen
- 'Ellie B' CKen EOrn
- 'Ericoides' CKen ECho EOrn
- 'Erika' ECho EOrn
- 'Fernspray Gold' CDoC CKen CTri ECho EHul EOrn GKir IFFs LRHS MAsh MBar NEgg SBch SBod SCoo SLim SPer SPoG WFar
- 'Flabelliformis' CKen
- 'Gimborn Beauty' CDoC
- 'Gnome' CKen CMen GKir
- 'Gold Fern' CKen MGos WFar
- 'Gold Tip' EOrn
- 'Golden Fairy' CDoC CKen EOrn MGos WAbe WEve
- 'Golden Filament' (v) CKen
- 'Golden Nymph' CKen EOrn MGos NLar
- 'Golden Sprite' CDoC CKen MGos NLar WAbe WEve
- 'Goldilocks' EHul
- 'Gracilis Aurea' CKen
- 'Graciosa' see *C. obtusa* 'Loenik'
- 'Green Diamond' CKen
- 'Hage' CKen EOrn
- 'Hypnoides Nana' CKen EOrn
- 'Intermedia' CDoC CKen EOrn MGos WAbe
- 'Ivan's Column' CKen
- 'Junior' CKen
- 'Juniperoides' CKen EOrn WThu
- 'Juniperoides Compacta' CKen WAbe
- 'Kamarachiba' CDoC CKen CSBt ECho LBee LRHS NLar SCoo SLim SPoG WEve WFar
- 'Kanaamihiba' MBar
- 'Kerdalo' LRHS NLar SLim SPoG
- 'Konijn' ECho EHul EOrn
- 'Kosteri' CDoC CKen CMac ECho EHul ELan EOrn LBee MAsh MBar NBlu NEgg NHol SCoo SLim WEve
- 'Kyoto Creeper' CKen
- 'Laxa' MGos
- 'Leprechaun' MGos NHol NLar
- 'Limerick' CKen
- 'Little Markey' CKen EOrn

§ - 'Loenik' EOrn MBar SCoo
- 'Lycopodioides' ECho EOrn MGos
- 'Lycopodioides Aurea' SCoo
- 'Marian' CKen MGos NLar

§ - 'Mariesii' (v) CKen EOrn LBee SCoo
- 'Melody' CKen NLar
- 'Meroke' **new** NLar
- 'Minima' CKen MGos
- 'Nana' ♀H4 CDoC CKen CMac CMen LBee MBar MGos NHol WEve
- 'Nana Aurea' ♀H4 CDoC CMac CMea CSBt ECho EHul EOrn EPfP GKir MAsh MBar MGos NHol WBrE WEve WFar
- 'Nana Compacta' EOrn

I - 'Nana Confucius' MGos

§ - 'Nana Densa' CDoC CKen CMac NLar
- 'Nana Gracilis' ♀H4 CDoC CDul CKen CMen CSBt CSli ECho EHul ELan EOrn EPfP GEdr GKir MAsh MBar MBri MGos NBlu NEgg NHol NWea SCoo SLim SPoG STre WDin WEve WFar

I - 'Nana Gracilis Aurea' CMen EHul WEve
I - 'Nana Lutea' CDoC CKen CSBt ECho EHul EOrn EPfP GKir LBee LRHS MAsh MBar MGos NBlu NDlv NHol NWea SCoo SLim SPoG
- 'Nana Pyramidalis' LBee
- 'Nana Rigida' see *C. obtusa* 'Rigid Dwarf'
- 'Nana Variegata' see *C. obtusa* 'Mariesii'
§ - 'Opaal' (v) MBar
- 'Pygmaea' CSBt ECho EHul EOrn MBar MGos SCoo SLim WEve
- 'Pygmaea Aurescens' MBar
§ - 'Rigid Dwarf' CDoC CKen ECho EHul EOrn LBee LRHS MBar NLar SCoo SPoG WEve
- 'Saffron Spray' CKen LRHS SLim
- 'Snowflake' (v) CDoC CKen ECho SBch WEve WFar
- 'Snowkist' (v) CKen
- 'Spiralis' CKen MBar
- 'Stoneham' CKen MBar
- 'Suirova-hiba' SLim
- 'Tempelhof' CKen CSBt ECho EHul EOrn GKir LRHS MAsh MBar MGos MHav NEgg NLar SCoo SLim WEve
- 'Tetragona Aurea' CBcs CMac ECho EHul EOrn MBar MGos NLar SCoo SLim WEve
- 'Tonia' (v) CKen EHul EOrn GKir NHol NLar SCoo SLim SPoG WEve WGor
- 'Topsie' CKen NLar
- 'Torulosa' see *C. obtusa* 'Coralliformis'
- 'Tsatsumi' CDoC EMil SCoo
- 'Tsatsumi Gold' CDoC CKen ECho NLar SCoo SLim SPoG
- 'Verdon' CKen
- 'Winter Gold' WEve
- 'Wissel' CKen EOrn MGos
- 'Wyckoff' CKen
- 'Yellowtip' (v) CKen ECho EHul MBar MGos NLar WEve
pisifera 'Aurea Nana' misapplied see *C. pisifera* 'Strathmore'
- 'Avenue' EHul
- 'Baby Blue' ECho ELan EPfP LRHS MGos SCoo SLim
- 'Blue Globe' CKen
- 'Boulevard' ♀H4 CBcs CDoC CDul CMac CSBt CWib ECho EHul ELan EPfP GKir IFFs LBee LRHS MAsh MBar MGos MHav NBlu NEgg NWea SLim SPer SRms STre WBVN WDin WEve WFar WMoo
- 'Compacta' EOrn
- 'Compacta Variegata' (v) ECho EOrn MBar NDlv NEgg
- 'Curly Tops' CSBt ECho GKir LRHS MGos SCoo SLim WEve
- 'Devon Cream' ECho LBee LRHS MAsh MBar MGos NEgg SCoo WFar
- 'Filifera' CMac CSBt GKir MBar SCoo WFar
- 'Filifera Aurea' ♀H4 CKen CMac CWib ECho EHul EOrn GKir LBee LRHS MAsh MBar MGos NEgg NHol NWea SCoo SRms WCFE WDin WEve WFar
- 'Filifera Aureovariegata' (v) EHul MBar SCoo
- 'Filifera Nana' ECho EHul ELan MBar SLim SPoG STre WDin WFar
- 'Filifera Nana Aurea' see *C. pisifera* 'Golden Mop'
- 'Filifera Sungold' see *C. pisifera* 'Sungold'
- 'Fuiri-tsukomo' CKen
* - 'Gold Cascade' MGos
- 'Gold Cushion' CKen
- 'Gold Dust' see *C. pisifera* 'Plumosa Aurea'
- 'Gold Spangle' CKen ECho EHul MBar WFar
§ - 'Golden Mop' ♀H4 CKen EHul GKir MAsh NLar
- 'Green Pincushion' CKen CMen
- 'Hime-himuro' CKen
- 'Hime-sawara' CKen CMen EOrn
- 'Margaret' CKen
- 'Nana' CKen CMen ECho EHul EPfP MAsh MBar MGos NDlv NHol WFar
I - 'Nana Albovariegata' (v) CDoC ECho EOrn MAsh MBar SPoG WFar WThu
- 'Nana Aureovariegata' (v) CDoC CSBt ECho EHul LBee LRHS MAsh MBar NBlu NDlv SCoo SLim SPer WEve WFar
I - 'Nana Compacta' CMac SRms
- 'Nana Variegata' (v) CMac LBee LRHS MBar SCoo SLim WFar
I - 'Parslorii' CKen
- 'Pici' CKen
- 'Plumosa Albopicta' (v) MBar
§ - 'Plumosa Aurea' CKen EHul GKir MBar WDin WFar
- 'Plumosa Aurea Compacta' CKen NDlv
- 'Plumosa Aurea Nana' ECho MBar MGos NDlv NHol WFar
I - 'Plumosa Aurea Nana Compacta' CMac
- 'Plumosa Aurescens' CDoC CMac
§ - 'Plumosa Compressa' CDoC CKen ECho EHul EOrn MAsh MBar SCoo SLim WFar WGor
- 'Plumosa Densa' see *C. pisifera* 'Plumosa Compressa'
- 'Plumosa Flavescens' EHul MBar SCoo
I - 'Plumosa Juniperoides' CKen ECho EHul EOrn MBar SCoo SLim WFar WGor
- 'Plumosa Purple Dome' see *C. pisifera* 'Purple Dome'
I - 'Plumosa Pygmaea' MGos NDlv WGor
§ - 'Plumosa Rogersii' EHul EOrn MBar NHol WGor
§ - 'Purple Dome' EHul EOrn MBar
I - 'Pygmaea Tsukumo' MGos NLar
- 'Rogersii' see *C. pisifera* 'Plumosa Rogersii'
- 'Silver and Gold' (v) EHul MBar
- 'Silver Lode' (v) CKen EOrn
- 'Snow' (v) CKen EOrn MBar
- 'Snowflake' CKen ECho EHul MGos NHol NLar
- 'Spaan's Cannon Ball' CKen ECho
§ - 'Squarrosa' MBar WDin WFar
- 'Squarrosa Dumosa' CKen EHul MBar
- 'Squarrosa Intermedia' MBar
I - 'Squarrosa Lombarts' CSBt ECho EHul GKir IFFs MBar SCoo
- 'Squarrosa Lutea' CKen MBar
- 'Squarrosa Sulphurea' CSBt ECho EHul EPfP LRHS MAsh MBar SLim SPer STre WBVN WDin WFar
- 'Squarrosa Veitchii' see *C. pisifera* 'Squarrosa'
§ - 'Strathmore' CKen EHul MBar NHol WDin
§ - 'Sungold' CDoC CKen CSBt ECho EHul EPla GKir LRHS MAsh MBar NBlu SCoo SLim SPoG WEve
- 'Tama-himuro' CKen
- 'Teddy Bear' MBri NLar NScw
- 'True Blue' MBri MGos NLar
- 'White Beauty' (v) SLim
- 'White Pygmy' EOrn
- 'Winter Beauty' **new** LRHS
thyoides 'Andelyensis' CMac CSBt ECho EHul EOrn GKir MBar NBlu NEgg SCoo WFar
- 'Andelyensis Nana' CKen
- 'Aurea' EHul MBar
- 'Conica' CKen
- 'Ericoides' ♀H4 CKen CTri ECho EHul EOrn GKir LBee MBar SPlb WDin WFar
§ - 'Glauca' EOrn
- 'Kewensis' see *C. thyoides* 'Glauca'
- 'Little Jamie' CKen
- 'Red Star' see *C. thyoides* 'Rubicon'

§ - 'Rubicon'	CMac CSBt ECho EHul EOrn EPfP EPla GKir IFFs LBee LRHS MAsh MBar MGos NEgg SBch SLim SPoG WBor WFar
- 'Top Point'	ECho LBee LRHS MAsh MGos SCoo SLim SPoG
- 'Variegata' (v)	EHul MBar

Chamaecytisus (*Papilionaceae*)

§ ***albus***	GQui SPer WDin
§ ***hirsutus***	MBri WPGP
prolifer	CPLG NLar
§ ***purpureus***	CBgR CSBt EBee ELan EPfP GKir LHop LRHS MRav NLar NPri NWea SBod SPer WBVN WCFE WDin WFar WPat
- f. ***albus***	EPfP SPer
§ - 'Atropurpureus' ♀H4	SPer
- 'Incarnatus'	see *C. purpureus* 'Atropurpureus'
- 'Lilac Lady'	LRHS
§ ***supinus***	CPLG SRms

Chamaedaphne (*Ericaceae*)

calyculata	CBcs SPer WSHC
- 'Nana'	CMHG

Chamaedorea (*Arecaceae*)

elegans ♀H1	CTsd LPal LRHS MBri
erumpens	see *C. seifrizii*
metallica misapplied	see *C. microspadix*
metallica O.F. Cook ex H.E. Moore ♀H1	LPal
§ ***microspadix***	CPHo EAmu LPJP LPal SChr
radicalis	CBrP CPHo EAmu LPJP LPal
§ ***seifrizii*** ♀H1	LPal

Chamaemelum (*Asteraceae*)

§ ***nobile***	CArn CHby CPrp CSev CTri CWan ECho ELau EPfP GBar GKir GMac GPoy MBri MHer MNHC NGHP NGdn NPri SBch SECG SPlb SRms SVic WJek WPer
- dwarf	GBar LMor SVic
- dwarf, double-flowered (d)	GBar
- 'Flore Pleno' (d)	Widely available
- 'Treneague'	Widely available

Chamaenerion see *Chamerion*

Chamaepericlymenum see *Cornus*

Chamaerops (*Arecaceae*)

excelsa misapplied	see *Trachycarpus fortunei*
excelsa Thunb.	see *Rhapis excelsa*
humilis ♀H3	CAbb CBcs CBrP CHEx CTrC CWSG EPfP EPla IFFs LPJP LPal LRHS MGos MREP NMoo NPal NScw SAPC SArc SBch SChr SEND SPlb SPoG STrG WCot WPGP
§ - var. ***argentea***	CBrP CDTJ CPHo CTrC EAmu EGxp ETod LPJP LRHS MGos NPal SBch WCot
- var. ***cerifera***	see *C. humilis* var. *argentea*
- 'Vulcano'	CDTJ EAmu LRHS MBri MGos SChr

Chamaespartium see *Genista*

Chamaesphacos (*Lamiaceae*)

ilicifolius misapplied	see *Siphocranion macranthum*

Chambeyronia (*Arecaceae*)

macrocarpa	EAmu LPal NExo

Chamelaucium (*Myrtaceae*)

uncinatum	LRHS

Chamerion (*Onagraceae*)

§ ***angustifolium***	EBWF GBar NSco SWat WSFF
§ - 'Album'	Widely available
- 'Isobel'	CSpe MRav WCot
- 'Stahl Rose'	CBot CHid CMea EBee EWes NSti SMrm SPhx SSvw STes SWat WPGP WSHC
§ ***dodonaei***	ELan EWld IMou MTho SPhx WFar

Chasmanthe (*Iridaceae*)

aethiopica	CPou EBee GGar
bicolor	CDes CPLG CPou EBee IDee
floribunda	CAbb CHEx CPrp EBee EBrs WOut
- var. ***duckittii***	CFir CPrp EBee EBrs ECho EPfP WPGP
- - 'Golden Wave'	EBrs
- 'Saturnes'	EBee
- 'Venus'	EBee EBrs

Chasmanthium (*Poaceae*)

§ ***latifolium***	Widely available

Cheilanthes (*Adiantaceae*)

argentea	CLAP WAbe WRic
cucullans new	WAbe
distans	SRms WAbe WRic
eatonii	WAbe
eckloniana	WAbe
grisea new	WAbe
lanosa	CBty CCCN CLAP EBee EFer EShb EWes LRHS NMyG SGSe SRms WCot
lindheimeri	WAbe
microphylla	LRHS WAbe
myriophylla	WAbe
nivea	WAbe
sieberi	WAbe
siliquosa	WAbe
sinuata	CLAP WAbe
tomentosa	CBty CCCN CLAP EBee LRHS SRms WRic
wootonii new	WAbe

Cheiranthus see *Erysimum*

Cheirolophus (*Asteraceae*)

benoistii misapplied	see *Centaurea atropurpurea*

Chelidonium (*Papaveraceae*)

japonicum	see *Hylomecon japonica*
majus	CArn CRWN EBWF GPoy GQui MHer MNHC WCHb WHer WSFF
- 'Flore Pleno' (d)	CBre MMHG NBid NBro WCFE WCHb WHer WTou
- var. ***laciniatum***	GBar WCot

Chelone (*Scrophulariaceae*)

barbata	see *Penstemon barbatus*
§ ***glabra***	Widely available
lyonii	EBee GGar LEdu MDKP NBre NGdn NLar SPad SPet WMoo WPer WPnP WShi
- 'Hot Lips'	WCAu
- 'Pink Temptation'	EBee GJos SPet
obliqua	Widely available
- var. ***alba***	see *C. glabra*

- 'Forncett Foremost' GQui
- 'Forncett Poppet' NBre
- 'Pink Sensation' EBee MBri NBre WFar
* - ***rosea*** EBee MBel MMHG NBPC WGwG

Chelonopsis (*Lamiaceae*)

moschata CLAP CPom EBee LEdu SMad WMoo WPGP WPrP
yagiharana EBee ELon GGar MBri MCCP MDKP MWea NBPC NBhm NBid WMoo

Chengiopanax (*Araliaceae*)

sciadophylloides B&SWJ 4728 WCru

Chenopodium (*Chenopodiaceae*)

bonus-henricus CAgr CArn CBod CHby CWan GBar GPoy ILis MHer MNHC SBch SIde WCHb WHer
giganteum ILis MNHC WJek

cherimoya see *Annona cherimola*

cherry, Duke see *Prunus* × *gondouinii*

cherry, sour or morello see *Prunus cerasus*

cherry, sweet see *Prunus avium*

chervil see *Anthriscus cerefolium*

chestnut, sweet see *Castanea sativa*

Chiastophyllum (*Crassulaceae*)

§ ***oppositifolium*** ♀H4 CBcs CHrt CSam CStu CTri EBee ECha ECho EDAr ELan EPfP GAbr GEdr GGar GJos GKev LAst LRHS MLHP MRav NBid NCob NHol NMen NWCA SPlb SRms WCot WMoo WSHC
- 'Frosted Jade' see *C. oppositifolium* 'Jim's Pride'
- 'Jane's Reverse' EBee WCot
§ - 'Jim's Pride' (v) Widely available
simplicifolium see *C. oppositifolium*

Chiliotrichum (*Asteraceae*)

diffusum (G. Forst.) Kuntze CWib GGar
- dark-leaved **new** GGar
- 'Siska' CBcs GBin IFFs SMad WCot

Chilopsis (*Bignoniaceae*)

linearis (Cav.) Sweet CArn

Chimonanthus ✿ (*Calycanthaceae*)

fragrans see *C. praecox*
nitens CBcs CMCN NLar
§ ***praecox*** Widely available
- 'Brockhill Goldleaf' NLar
- 'Grandiflorus' ♀H4 CEnd CPMA EPfP LRHS MAsh MBri SPoG SSpi SSta WPGP WPat
- 'Luteus' ♀H4 CEnd CPMA ECrN ELan EPfP LRHS LSRN MAsh MBri MGos MRav NLar SPer SPoG SSpi SSta WPGP WPat
- 'Sunburst' CPMA
- 'Trenython' CEnd CPMA
salicifolius **new** NLar
yunnanensis CBcs CPne NLar

Chimonobambusa (*Poaceae*)

falcata see *Drepanostachyum falcatum*
hejiangensis EPla
hookeriana misapplied see *Himalayacalamus falconeri* 'Damarapa'
macrophylla EPla
f. ***intermedia***
§ ***marmorea*** CDTJ CMCo EAmu EPla ERod LPal MMoz MWht NPal SBig WDyG WJun WPGP
- 'Variegata' (v) CDTJ EPla ERod MMoz SLPl WJun WPGP
§ ***quadrangularis*** CBcs CDTJ CDoC CGHE CHEx CMCo CTrG EBee EPfP EPla ERod ESwi IMou LEdu LRHS MAvo MMoz MWht NPal SBig WJun WPGP
- 'Nagaminei' (v) EPla WJun
- 'Suow' (v) CDTJ CGHE EPla WPGP
- 'Tatejima' EPla WJun
tumidissinoda CAbb CDTJ CGHE CMCo EPla ERod ESwi IMou MMoz MWht NPal SBig WDyG WJun WPGP

Chinese chives see *Allium tuberosum*

Chiogenes see *Gaultheria*

Chionanthus (*Oleaceae*)

foveolatus EShb
retusus CBcs CDul CMCN EPfP IDee LRHS MBri MPkF NLar SSpi WDin
virginicus CBcs CDoC CDul CEnd CMCN CPMA EBee ELan EPfP ERas EWTr IArd IDee IFFs IMGH MBlu MBri MMuc MRav NEgg SPlb SSpi SSta WDin WPGP WSpi

Chionochloa (*Poaceae*)

beddiei **new** GBin
conspicua CAby CGHE CHrt CKno EBee EKen GCal GQue LBMP MAvo NBir NLar NWsh SBod SGSe SMad WPGP
- subsp. ***conspicua*** GGar
- 'Rubra' see *C. rubra*
flavescens EHoe GBin LRHS MAvo
flavicans CHrt CKno EBee GBin IMou MMuc SGar
rigida EBee
§ ***rubra*** CElw CGHE CKno CSpe EBee EHoe ELan EPla EWes GCal GMaP IMou LEdu LHop LRHS MAvo MMoz MRav NChi SApp SGSe WCot WMoo WPGP WTin WWEG
- subsp. ***cuprea*** EBee GBin GGar SMad

Chionodoxa ✿ (*Hyacinthaceae*)

cretica see *C. nana*
§ ***forbesii*** CBro CWCL EBrs ECGP ECho EPfP EPot LRHS NBir SMrm SPer SRms WFar WShi
- 'Alba' ECho LAma
- 'Blue Giant' EBrs ECho EPot ERCP LRHS
- 'Rosea' EBrs ECho LAma
- Siehei Group see *C. siehei*
- 'Tmoli' **new** ECho
- 'Violet Beauty' **new** ECho
- 'Zwanenburg' **new** ECho
gigantea see *C. luciliae* Gigantea Group
lochiae EBrs
luciliae misapplied see *C. forbesii*
luciliae ambig. ECho IHer
luciliae Boiss. ♀H4 CAvo CBro EPfP EPot LAma MBri SPer
- 'Alba' CBro EBrs ECho GGar LRHS SMrm SPer

§ - Gigantea Group — EBrs ECho ELan EPot GKev LAma
- - 'Alba' — EPot GKev
§ ***nana*** — ECho
'Pink Giant' — CAvo CBro EBrs ECho ELan EPfP EPot ERCP EWTr GGar LAma LHop LRHS SMrm WCot WHil
sardensis 🏆^{H4} — CBgR CBro EBrs ECho EPot ERCP LAma LHop LRHS SPhx WCot WShi
§ ***siehei*** 🏆^{H4} — CBro
'Valentine Day' — EPot

Chionographis (*Melanthiaceae*)

japonica — EBee EFEx WCru

× *Chionoscilla* (*Hyacinthaceae*)

§ ***allenii*** — CAvo EBrs ECho EPot SPhx
- 'Frà Angelico' 🏆^{H4} **new** — LRHS

Chirita (*Gesneriaceae*)

'Aiko' — WDib
'Chastity' — CSpe WDib
'Diane Marie' — WDib
flavimaculata **new** — WDib
heterotricha — WDib
'Keiko' — CSpe WDib
* ***latifolia*** × ***linearifolia*** — WDib
linearifolia — WDib
linearifolia × ***sinensis*** — WDib
longgangensis — WDib
'New York' — CSpe WDib
sinensis 🏆^{H1} — WDib
- 'Hisako' — CSpe WDib
speciosa 'Crûg Cornetto' — WCru
'Stardust' — WDib
tamiana — CSpe WDib

Chironia (*Gentianaceae*)

baccifera — SPlb

× *Chitalpa* (*Bignoniaceae*)

tashkentensis — CBcs CEnd CMCN EBee EPfP IDee MBri NLar WPGP WPat
- 'Morning Cloud' **new** — MBlu
- 'Pink Dawn' — IFFs MBri NLar
- Summer Bells = 'Minsum' — CDoC EMil LHop LRHS MAsh MGos MREP SBig SCoo WCot

chives see *Allium schoenoprasum*

Chlidanthus (*Amaryllidaceae*)

fragrans — CCCN CMdw CStu EBrs ECho EShb GGar

Chloranthus (*Chloranthaceae*)

fortunei — CDes CLAP EBee LFur WPGP
japonicus — CLAP LFur WCru
oldhamii — CLAP EWld LEdu LFur
- B&SWJ 2019 — WCru
serratus — CLAP EBee WCru

Chloris (*Poaceae*)

distichophylla — see *Eustachys distichophylla*

Chlorophytum (*Anthericaceae*)

comosum — EShb SEND SVic
- 'Aureomarginata' — SEND
- 'Variegatum' (v) 🏆$^{H1+3}$ — CDTJ LRHS MBri SEND SRms
- 'Vittatum' (v) 🏆$^{H1+3}$ — EShb SRms SWal
krookianum — CFir EBee WCot
macrophyllum — EShb
majus — WCot
nepalense — WCot
- B&SWJ 2393 — WCru
- B&SWJ 2528 — WCru
orchidastrum — EShb
saundersiae — CPLG SHom

Choisya (*Rutaceae*)

× ***dewitteana*** — Widely available
'Aztec Pearl' 🏆^{H4}
dumosa — LHop
Goldfingers = 'Limo'^{PBR} — CBcs CDul EBee ELan EPfP LAst LHop LRHS LSRN MAsh MBri MGos MRav MSwo NEgg NHol NLar NPri SBch SCoo SLim SLon SPad SPer SPoG SSta SWvt
ternata 🏆^{H4} — Widely available
- Moonshine = 'Walcho'^{PBR} — GBin NHol NLar WCot
- Moonsleeper^{PBR} — see *C. ternata* Sundance
§ - Sundance = 'Lich'^{PBR} 🏆^{H3} — Widely available

Chondropetalum (*Restionaceae*)

* ***elephantinum*** — CSpe
hookerianum — NEgg
mucronatum — CTrC WPGP
tectorum — CAbb CBcs CBct CDoC CFir CHEx CKno CPen CSpe CTrC EAmu EBee EPfP IDee LRHS LSRN MGos NOak NScw SApp SBch SHDw SPer SPlb SPoG WHal WPGP WPrP
- dwarf — CTrC WPGP

Chondrosum (*Poaceae*)

gracile — see *Bouteloua gracilis*

Chordospartium see *Carmichaelia*

Chorisia (*Bombacaceae*)

speciosa — CCCN EAmu

Chorizema (*Papilionaceae*)

cordatum 🏆^{H1} — ECou
ilicifolium — CBcs CCCN CSPN ERea

Chromolaena (*Asteraceae*)

arnottiana RCB/Arg L2 — CDes
- 'Salsipuede' — WCot

Chronanthus see *Cytisus*

Chrysalidocarpus see *Dypsis*

Chrysanthemopsis see *Rhodanthemum*

hosmariense — see *Rhodanthemum hosmariense*

Chrysanthemum ✿ (*Asteraceae*)

'Agnes Ann' (21d) — MNrw
'Alehmer Rote' (21) — LDai MNrw WWEG
'Aline' (21) — MNrw SPhx
'Allison '88' (21) — MNrw
alpinum — see *Leucanthemopsis alpina*
'Anastasia' (21c) — CHid EBee ECtt EPPr LDai MNrw MRav NSti SPhx SRms WFar WIvy WPer
N 'Anastasia Variegated' (28/v) — EBee
'Anastasia White' (28) — WIvy WWEG
'Angela Blundell' — WCot
'Anja's Bouquet' — EBee
'Anne Ratsey' (21) — CSam MNrw
'Anne, Lady Brocket' (21d) — ECtt MNrw NCGa NWsh SSvw
'Apollo' (21) — EBee EWll LDai SPhx SSvw WCot WHoo
'Apricot' (21) — EBee EPPr MRav SSvw

Name	Suppliers
arcticum L.	see *Arctanthemum arcticum*
argenteum	see *Tanacetum argenteum*
'Aunt Millicent' (21d)	LLHF MNrw SPhx
balsamita	see *Tanacetum balsamita*
Barbara = 'Yobarbara'[PBR] (22)	EPfP
'Belle' (21d)	SSvw
'Blenda'	ECtt
Bravo = 'Yobra' (22c) ♀H3	EPfP
* 'Breitner's Supreme'	MNrw WCAu WWEG
'Brennpunkt'	SMrs
'Bright Eye' (21b)	MNrw WMnd
'Brightness' (21)	SSvw SUsu
'Bronze Beauty' (25b)	WFar
§ 'Bronze Elegance' (28b)	EBee EBrs LDai MBel MNrw NBir NGdn NSti SMrs SRms SSvw WEas WIvy WMnd
'Bronze Mei-kyo'	see *C.* 'Bronze Elegance'
'Burnt Orange' **new**	MNrw
'Capel Manor'	EBee WCot
'Carmine Blush' (21)	EBee MNrw SPhx WBrk WCot
'Chelsea Physic Garden'	EBee MNrw SPhx SSvw WCot
'Christine's Pink'	MAvo
'Cinderella'	WMnd
cinerariifolium	see *Tanacetum cinerariifolium*
'Clara Curtis' (21d))	Widely available
coccineum	see *Tanacetum coccineum*
corymbosum	see *Tanacetum corymbosum*
'Cottage Apricot'	EBrs LDai LHop MBNS MLHP MNrw WEas
'Cottage Bronze'	MNrw
'Cottage Lemon'	MNrw
'Cottage Pink'	see *C.* 'Emperor of China'
'Cottage Yellow'	SSvw WHoo
'Cousin Joan'	EBee LDai MNrw WCot
'Daniel Cooper' (21)	MNrw
Debonair = 'Yodebo'[PBR] (22c) ♀H3	EPfP
§ 'Doctor Tom Parr' (21c)	CPLG EBee ELan GCal IGor LAst LHop MNrw SUsu
'Duchess of Edinburgh' (21d)	CPrp EBee EBrs ECtt ELan EPfP EShb MNrw SBch SSvw WCAu WMnd
'Early Yellow' **new**	MAvo
'Edelweiss' (21)	CAby WCot
§ 'Emperor of China' (21)	CAby CElw CSam EBee ECha ECtt EPPr GCal IGor MNrw MRav NCGa SSvw WBor WCot WFar WMnd WWEG
'Esther' (21d)	MNrw
foeniculaceum misapplied	see *Argyranthemum foeniculaceum* misapplied
foeniculaceum (Willd.) Desf.	see *Argyranthemum foeniculaceum* (Willd.) Webb & Sch. Bip.
'Fred Raynor'	MNrw
frutescens	see *Argyranthemum frutescens*
'Gladys' (24b)	ELan SRGP
'Golden Wedding' (21)	MNrw
'Goldengreenheart' (21)	MAvo MNrw WHoo
'Goldmarianne' (21)	GBin
'Grandchild' (21c)	LLHF MNrw SPhx
§ × ***grandiflorum***	SRms
– 'Corinna'	GBin
haradjanii	see *Tanacetum haradjanii*
'Hebe'	EBee
'Horningsea Pink' (19d)	ECGP WBor
hosmariense	see *Rhodanthemum hosmariense*
indicum **new**	LRHS
'Innocence' (21)	CAby CSam EBee ECtt ELan IGor MNrw MRav NGdn NSti SAga SSvw WHoo
'Jante Wells' (21b)	WEas
'Jessie Cooper'	see *C.* 'Mrs Jessie Cooper'
'Julia' (28)	EPPr SRGP
'Julia Peterson'	WCot
Julia = 'Yojulia'	EBee
'Julie Lagravère' (28)	MNrw
× ***koreanum***	see *C.* × *grandiflorum*
'Lady in Pink' (21)	LDai MAvo
leucanthemum	see *Leucanthemum vulgare*
'Louise' (25b)	MNrw
'Lucy Simpson' (21d)	MNrw
macrophyllum	see *Tanacetum macrophyllum* (Waldst. & Kit.) Sch.Bip.
maresii	see *Rhodanthemum hosmariense*
'Margaret' (29c) ♀H3	WCot
'Marion' (25a)	LDai SPhx WCot
'Mary' (21f)	LDai MNrw
'Mary Stoker' (21d))	CHrt CPrp CSam EBee EBrs ECtt ELan EPfP EShb MLHP MNFA MNrw MRav NCGa NSti SRGP SSvw WAul WCAu WFar WMnd WWEG
'Mauve Gem' (21f)	MNrw
mawii	see *Rhodanthemum gayanum*
maximum misapplied	see *Leucanthemum* × ***superbum***
maximum Ramond	see *Leucanthemum maximum* (Ramond) DC.
'Mei-kyo' (28b)	CMea EBee ECtt IGor MNrw SPhx SRms WBor WCot WFar WHil WWEG
'Moonlight' (29d/K)	MRav
§ 'Mrs Jessie Cooper' (21)	CAby ELan GQue LDai MNrw NBir NLar NWsh SSvw WCom WCot WHil WHoo WPtf WTin
'Mrs Jessie Cooper No 2'	MNrw
'Nancy Perry' (21d)	CSam ELan MNrw MRav SSvw
nankingense	WFar
'Nantyderry Sunshine' (28b) ♀H4	CPrp CSam EBee LLHF MNrw SPhx SSvw WCot WEas WMnd WPer WWEG
'Nell Gwyn' (21d)	MNrw
'Netherhall Moonlight'	MNrw
nipponicum	see *Nipponanthemum nipponicum*
pacificum	see *Ajania pacifica*
parthenium	see *Tanacetum parthenium*
'Paul Boissier' (30Rub)	CAby ECtt LDai MNrw NSti SPhx SSvw WCot WMnd
'Penny's Yellow' **new**	LLHF
'Perry's Peach' (21a)	LDai LLHF MNrw NPer SPhx SSvw
'Peterkin'	CPrp ECGP ECtt MNrw WWEG
'Pink Progression'	NBir
'Primrose Blanche Poitevene' (5b) **new**	EMal
'Princess' (21d)	LLHF
ptarmiciflorum	see *Tanacetum ptarmiciflorum*
'Purleigh White' (28b)	CPrp ECtt LDai MNFA MNrw NSti SSvw WCot
'Raquel' (21)	EPfP MNrw
'Romany' (2)	CElw WEas
'Rose Madder'	WCot
roseum	see *Tanacetum coccineum*
'Royal Command' (21)	MNrw WCot
rubellum	see *C. zawadskii*
'Ruby Enbee Wedding' (29d) ♀H3	WPtf
'Ruby Mound' (21c) ♀H3	LLHF MNrw SDys SPhx SSvw WCot WEas
'Ruby Raynor' (21) ♀H4	MNrw SPhx SSvw
'Rumpelstilzchen' (21d)	CElw CMea ECtt MNrw WPer
'Sarah's Yellow'	CAby
'Sea Urchin' (21f) ♀H3	MNrw

'Shining Light' (21f) LLHF MNrw
sinense see *C.* × *grandiflorum*
'Skylark' (22a) NPri
'Sonnenschein' LHop
'Spartan Canary' new SWal
'Spartan Display' new SWal
'Spartan Fire' SWal
'Spartan Glory' (25b) SWal
'Spartan Linnet' SWal
'Spartan Raspberry' (21d) SWal
'Spartan Seagull' (21d) MNrw SSvw SWal
'Spartan Star' (29d) SWal
'Spartan Sunrise' (29c) SWal
'Starlet' (21f) LLHF MNrw SSvw
'Sunbeam' (28) EBee
'Syllabub' ♀H3 ECtt
'Tapestry Rose' (21d) CMea IGor LDai MCot MNrw NCGa SPhx SSvw WBor
'Tom Parr' see *C.* 'Doctor Tom Parr'
'Tommy Trout' (28/K) MNrw
uliginosum see *Leucanthemella serotina*
'Uri' LPla SAga SPhx
'Vagabond Prince' MNrw SPhx WCot WHoo
'Venus' (21) WCot
'Venus One' LDai SPhx
'Wedding Day' (21) EBee MNrw NCGa WCAu WTin
'Wedding Sunshine' (21) LDai MNrw
welwitschii see *Glebionis segetum*
'Wendy Tench' (21d) ECtt
weyrichii EBee ECho ECtt EShb LEdu MTho NRya SAga SRms
'White Gloss' (21e) LLHF MNrw SSvw
'White Tower' MNrw
'Winning's Red' (21) LHop SMad SSvw
'Yellow Starlet' (21f) LLHF MNrw SSvw
yezoense ♀H4 CSam CStu ELan LRHS MNrw
- B&SWJ 10872 WCru
- 'Roseum' CSam ECtt NSti WBor
§ ***zawadskii*** CMac WFar

Chrysocephalum (*Asteraceae*)

'Desert Flame' LSou

Chrysocoma (*Asteraceae*)

ciliata JJH 9401633 NWCA

Chrysogonum (*Asteraceae*)

australe EBee
virginianum CMea CPrp EBee ECha EShb EWes LRHS MAvo MRav SBch SPer WFar WMoo WWEG
- 'Allen Bush' new EBee

Chrysopogon (*Poaceae*)

gryllus EBee SApp WPGP

Chrysopsis (*Asteraceae*)

§ ***mariana*** WOld
villosa (Pursh) Nutt. ex DC. see *Heterotheca villosa*

Chrysosplenium (*Saxifragaceae*)

alternifolium EMFW
davidianum CBre CSam EBee ECha EPot EWld GEdr GGar GJos GKev IMou NBir NSla WBor WCot WCru WFar WMoo WPrP WPtf
flagelliferum B&SWJ 8902 WCru
lanuginosum var. ***formosanum*** B&SWJ 6979 WCru
macrophyllum CBct CDes EWld IMou WBor WCot WCru
macrostemon var. ***shiobarense*** B&SWJ 6173 WCru
oppositifolium EBWF EBee GPWP WHer WShi

Chusquea (*Poaceae*)

breviglumis misapplied see *C. culeou* 'Tenuis'
breviglumis Phil. NMoo
culeou ♀H4 CAbb CBcs CDoC CEnd CEnt CGHE CHEx CHid EBee ENBC EPfP EPla LAst LEdu LPal MGos MMoz MWht NBea NMoo SBig SDix SSta WJun WPGP WPnP
- 'Breviglumis' see *C. culeou* 'Tenuis'
- 'Purple Splendour' EPla WJun WPGP
§ - 'Tenuis' EPla ERod WJun
- weeping CDTJ WPGP
cumingii CBcs EBee WJun WPGP
delicatula from Machu Picchu, Peru WPGP
gigantea CDTJ CEnt EPla MMoz MWht SBig WJun WPGP
- 'Bracken Hill' MMoz
macrostachya EBee EPla WPGP
montana CBcs CDTJ EBee EPla
mulleri F&M 104A from Mexico WPGP
quila EPla MMoz WPGP
valdiviensis EPla WJun WPGP

Cibotium (*Dicksoniaceae*)

glaucum WRic

Cicerbita (*Asteraceae*)

sp. ECtt
BWJ 7891 from China WCru
§ ***alpina*** EBee NBid NLar SGar SPlb
plumieri EWes GAbr IFro MHer SPhx WCot WFar WHrl

Cichorium (*Asteraceae*)

intybus Widely available
- f. ***album*** CBod CPrp EBee EBla ECha ECtt EPfP LHop LRHS MAvo MBel MRav NBir NCGa NCob NGdn SBch SWat WCAu WCHb
- var. ***foliosum*** EBee
- 'Roseum' CBod CPrp CSpe CWCL EBee EBla ECha ECtt ELan EPfP GMac LHop LRHS MAvo MBel MCot MRav NBir NCGa NCob NGdn SBch SPer SWat WCAu WCHb WHrl

Cimicifuga see *Actaea*

acerina see *Actaea japonica*
americana see *Actaea podocarpa*
cordifolia Pursh see *Actaea podocarpa*
cordifolia (DC.) Torrey & A.Gray see *Actaea cordifolia*
foetida see *Actaea cimicifuga*
racemosa var. ***cordifolia*** see *Actaea cordifolia*
- 'Purpurea' see *Actaea simplex* Atropurpurea Group
ramosa see *Actaea simplex* 'Prichard's Giant'
rubifolia see *Actaea cordifolia*
simplex var. ***matsumurae*** see *Actaea matsumurae*

Cineraria (*Asteraceae*)

× ***hybrida*** see *Pericallis* × *hybrida*
maritima see *Senecio cineraria*

saxifraga EShb

Cinnamomum (*Lauraceae*)

camphora CBcs CHEx CPLG CTrG
japonicum WPGP
micranthum WPGP

Cionura (*Asclepiadaceae*)

oreophila WPGP WSHC

Circaea (*Onagraceae*)

alpina EBee
lutetiana EBWF NSco WHer
- 'Caveat Emptor' (v) CBow CHid EBee NBid WCot WHer

Cirsium (*Asteraceae*)

acaule NLar
anartiolepis F&M 252 new WPGP
arvense WSFF
* *atroroseum* SWat
diacantha see *Ptilostemon diacantha*
eriophorum LDai
falconeri NBur
helenioides see *C. heterophyllum*
§ *heterophyllum* CPom EBee EWld LDai LEdu NBre NBur NChi NLar SHar SPhx SUsu WCot WPGP
japonicum GKir
- 'Early Pink Beauty' LDai NBre
- 'Early Rose Beauty' ILad NBre
- 'Pink Beauty' WWEG
- 'Rose Beauty' EBee ECrN SPur
kamtschaticum B&SWJ 10927 WCru
'Mount Etna' CDes CPrp CSam EBee EBla LLWG LRHS MBNS MSpe NCob NGdn WCAu
oleraceum LEdu NBid NBre NLar
palustre EBWF
- 'Love and Hate' WAlt
purpuratum EBee MNrw WCot WPGP
rivulare CSam GKir
- 'Atropurpureum' Widely available
tuberosum CAby SPhx
vulgare WSFF

Cissus (*Vitaceae*)

antarctica ♀H1 CCCN CTrC EShb SEND
pedata B&SWJ 2371 WCru
quadrangularis new SBch
rhombifolia ♀H1 EOHP SEND
§ *striata* CBcs CDoC CHEx CMac CTrC CWCL EBee ELon EShb LRHS MRav SBch SEND SLim SWvt WSHC

Cistus ✿ (*Cistaceae*)

acutifolius misapplied see *C. inflatus*, *C.* × *pulverulentus*
× *aguilarii* CBcs CHEx CSBt CTri EPfP LAst MRav WOut WSHC
- 'Maculatus' ♀H3 CBot CDoC CDul CPLG CSam EBee ELan EPfP GGar GKir LRHS LSRN NPri SBch SCoo SLPl SPer SPoG SWvt WAbe WCFE WHCG WKif
albidus CArn EBee EGoo
algarvensis see *Halimium ocymoides*
'Ann Baker' EBee MBrN SLPl WAbe
'Anne Palmer' see *C.* × *fernandesiae* 'Anne Palmer'
× *argenteus* 'Blushing Peggy Sammons' CDoC WAbe
- Golden Treasure = 'Nepond' (v) CBow EPfP EQua SWvt
- 'Paper Moon' LSRN
§ - 'Peggy Sammons' ♀H3 CBgR CBot CDoC EBee ECha ECrN ELan EPfP EWTr GKir LAst LBMP LRHS LSRN MAsh MGos MWte SCoo SLim SPer SPoG SWvt WBrE WFar WHar WSHC
- 'Silver Ghost' WAbe
- 'Silver Pink' ambig. Widely available
'Blanche' see *C. ladanifer* 'Blanche'
× *bornetianus* 'Jester' CSBt EBee LRHS MAsh
× *canescens* EBee
- f. *albus* CWib EBee EQua WEas WHCG WKif
§ *clusii* NLar
× *corbariensis* see *C.* × *hybridus*
creticus CDoC CPLG CSam ELau EQua LAst LRHS MAsh MBri MGos MLHP NMun SGar SLon SPoG WKif WPGP
§ - subsp. *creticus* EBee ELan ELon EPfP LRHS MRav SCoo SPer WAbe
§ - - f. *albus* 'Tania Compton' WAbe
- - 'Lasithi' WAbe
§ - subsp. *incanus* LRHS SHlg WHCG WPat
× *crispatus* WAbe
§ - 'Warley Rose' GMaP LRHS WAbe WKif
crispus misapplied see *C.* × *pulverulentus*, *C.* × *purpureus*
§ *crispus* L. EBee SEND WEas
- 'Prostratus' see *C. crispus* L.
- 'Sunset' see *C.* × *pulverulentus* 'Sunset'
§ × *cyprius* ♀H4 CArn CDul EBee ECtt ELan EPfP MCot MGos MNHC MRav MWat SDix SEND SPer SRms WDin WFar
§ - var. *ellipticus* 'Elma' ♀H3 EBee ELan EPfP ERas LRHS MAsh MCot SPer WEas WHCG WPGP
§ × *dansereaui* CMHG CSBt CWib EBee LRHS MGos MRav WAbe WFar WSpi
- 'Albiflorus' see *C.* × *dansereaui* 'Portmeirion'
- 'Decumbens' ♀H4 CBcs CChe CDul CMHG CTri EBee ELan EPfP LHop LRHS MAsh MBNS MRav MSwo SArc SCoo SPer SPoG SWvt WAbe WClo WDin WHCG WPGP
- 'Jenkyn Place' CDoC EBee GMaP LRHS LSRN MBNS MBri MGos SLPl SPer SPoG SUsu WKif
§ - 'Portmeirion' WAbe WFar
× *dubius* EBee
'Elma' see *C.* × *cyprius* var. *ellipticus* 'Elma'
'Enigma' CDoC CSam EBee
§ × *fernandesiae* 'Anne Palmer' CBgR EBee EPfP LHop LLHF LRHS LSRN MAsh SEND SPoG SRGP WFar
× *florentinus* misapplied see × *Halimiocistus* 'Ingwersenii'
§ × *florentinus* Lam. CAbP EBee GMaP
- 'Fontfroide' EBee WAbe
formosus see *Halimium lasianthum* subsp. *formosum*
'Gordon Cooper' CWan EBee LRHS LSRN MMuc SCoo WAbe
× *heterocalyx* 'Chelsea Bonnet' EBee GMaP LRHS MBNS SCoo SLim SPoG WAbe WPGP WPen
hirsutus Lam. 1786 see *C. inflatus*
- var. *psilosepalus* see *C. inflatus*
§ × *hybridus* Widely available
- Gold Prize = 'Wyecis' (v) CWGN CWit EBee ELan MBri MGos NEgg NLar SBch SPoG SWvt WFar WGrn WHar
- Rospico = 'Rencis' (v) new EMil LRHS
incanus see *C. creticus* subsp. *incanus*
§ *inflatus* WAbe
ingwerseniana see × *Halimiocistus* 'Ingwersenii'

	'Jessamy Beauty'	SLPl WAbe
	'Jessamy Bride'	SLPl
	'Jessamy Charm'	SPhx
	ladanifer misapplied	see *C.* × *cyprius*
	ladanifer ambig.	CMac ERas
	- SDR 5611	GKev
	ladanifer L. 𝕐H3	CDoC CSBt CTri ECha ELan EPfP EWTr GCra GPoy MRav MSwo SBch SGar SPer WEas WFar WHar WSHC
	- var. ***albiflorus***	EQua
§	- 'Blanche'	CBgR EBee LLHF LSRN SSpi WKif
	- 'Minstrel' **new**	LRHS
§	- 'Paladin'	EBee SBch WAbe
	- Palhinhae Group	see *C. ladanifer* var. *sulcatus*
	- 'Pat'	EBee ELan EPfP LRHS LSRN MAsh NBir SPoG SSpi
§	- var. ***sulcatus***	CDoC EBee ELan EPfP GKev LRHS SPoG WFar
	- - SDR 5620	GKev
	- - f. ***bicolor***	EBee
	lasianthus	see *Halimium lasianthum*
	laurifolius 𝕐H4	CDoC EBee EPfP LRHS MGos MNrw NBir NEgg NLar SLPl SPer SPoG
	× ***laxus***	WAbe
	- 'Snow White'	CAbP CDoC EBee EPfP LAst LRHS MGos NPer NPro SLPl SLim SLon SPoG SRms WGrn WKif
	× ***ledon***	SLPl
§	× ***lenis*** 'Grayswood Pink' 𝕐H4	Widely available
	× ***loretii*** misapplied	see *C.* × *dansereaui*
	× ***loretii*** Rouy & Foucaud	see *C.* × *stenophyllus*
	× ***lusitanicus*** Maund	see *C.* × *dansereaui*
	'May Snow'	LRHS MBNS
	'Merrist Wood Cream'	see × *Halimiocistus wintonensis* 'Merrist Wood Cream'
	monspeliensis	CAbP CMac EBee EPfP EQua GGar LRHS MAsh MBNS SLon SPer SPoG WFar
	- CMBS 62	WPGP
	- 'Vicar's Mead'	CCCN CDoC EBee ELan EPfP LRHS MBNS SEND SRms
	× ***oblongifolius***	EBee
	× ***obtusifolius*** ambig.	EBee LRHS
	× ***obtusifolius*** Sweet	CAbP EPfP EWes SLPl WEas
§	- 'Thrive'	LRHS MBri SCoo
	ochreatus	see *C. symphytifolius* subsp. *leucophyllus*
	ocymoides	see *Halimium ocymoides*
	'Paladin'	see *C. ladanifer* 'Paladin'
	palhinhae	see *C. ladanifer* var. *sulcatus*
	parviflorus misapplied	see *C.* × *lenis* 'Grayswood Pink'
	parviflorus Lam.	CBot WSHC
	'Peggy Sammons'	see *C.* × *argenteus* 'Peggy Sammons'
	× ***platysepalus***	EBee SLPl SPhx
	populifolius	CMHG CMac ECha LLHF LRHS SPer WAbe WPGP
	- var. ***lasiocalyx***	see *C. populifolius* subsp. *major*
§	- subsp. ***major*** 𝕐H3	CBgR EBee EPfP LRHS LSRN WPGP
	psilosepalus	see *C. inflatus*
§	× ***pulverulentus***	CPLG CTri EBee ECha EPfP MMHG SWal WDin WSHC
§	- 'Sunset' 𝕐H3	Widely available
	- 'Warley Rose'	see *C.* × *crispatus* 'Warley Rose'
§	× ***purpureus*** 𝕐H3	Widely available
	- 'Alan Fradd'	CBcs CMac EBee ECrN EPfP ERas EWTr GGar LAst LBMP LHop LRHS LSRN MAsh MDun MGos MSwo SCoo SEND SLim SMrm SPoG SRGP SWvt WBor WFar
	- var. ***argenteus*** f. ***stictus***	EBee LRHS LSRN WAbe
	- 'Betty Taudevin'	see *C.* × *purpureus*
	- var. ***holorhodos***	EBee
	× ***rodiaei*** 'Jessabel'	CBgR EBee LRHS MAsh SCoo SEND SPoG WAbe WGrn
	- 'Jessica'	EBee NLar WAbe
	rosmarinifolius	see *C. clusii*
	'Ruby Cluster'	CCCN EBee LRHS LSRN SRms WClo
	sahucii	see × *Halimiocistus sahucii*
	salviifolius	CAbP CArn CCCN ERas LRHS WFar WHCG WKif
	- 'Avalanche'	EBee MRav WAbe
	- 'Gold Star'	EBee
	- 'Prostratus'	ELan WPGP
	salviifolius × ***monspeliensis***	see *C.* × *florentinus* Lam.
	'Silver Pink' misapplied	see *C.* × *lenis* 'Grayswood Pink'
	× ***skanbergii*** 𝕐H3	CBcs CBgR CHEx CSBt CTri CWib EBee ELan EPfP ERas GGar LHop LIMB LRHS MGos MLHP MRav MWat NBir SCoo SDix SEND SMrm SPer SPoG WEas WFar
	'Snow Fire' 𝕐H4	CAbP CBgR CCCN CDoC EBee EPfP LRHS LSRN MAsh MGos MMuc NPro SBch SCoo SLPl SPoG SSpi WAbe WClo WGrn
§	× ***stenophyllus***	CMac CWib SPer
	symphytifolius	WPGP
§	- subsp. ***leucophyllus*** MSF 98.019	WPGP
	'Tania Compton'	see *C. creticus* subsp. *creticus* f. *albus* 'Tania Compton'
	'Thornfield White'	EBee
	'Thrive'	see *C.* × *obtusifolius* 'Thrive'
	tomentosus	see *Helianthemum nummularium* subsp. *tomentosum*
	× ***verguinii***	LHop SDix
	- var. ***albiflorus*** misapplied	see *C.* × *dansereaui* 'Portmeirion'
	villosus	see *C. creticus* subsp. *creticus*
	wintonensis	see × *Halimiocistus wintonensis*

Citharexylum (*Verbenaceae*)

	spicatum	CPLG WBor WPGP

× *Citrofortunella* (*Rutaceae*)

	sp.	CCCN
§	***microcarpa*** (F) 𝕐H1	CBcs CCCN CDoC EMui EPfP ERea LRHS MBri NLar SPoG
§	- 'Tiger' (v/F) 𝕐H1	EPfP
	- 'Variegata'	see × *C. microcarpa* 'Tiger'
	mitis	see × *C. microcarpa*

citron see *Citrus medica*

Citrullus (*Cucurbitaceae*)

	colocynthis	CArn

Citrus ✿ (*Rutaceae*)

	amblycarpa djeruk lime (F)	ERea
I	***aurantiata*** 'Chinese Citron' (F)	ERea
	aurantiifolia (F)	CCCN EPfP ERea SVic
	- key lime (F)	ERea
	- 'Paduk' (F)	ERea
	aurantium	ERea
	- 'Bouquet de Fleurs' (F)	CCCN ERea
	- var. ***myrtifolia*** 'Chinotto' (F)	ERea
	- 'Seville' (F)	ERea
	bergamia bergamot	ERea

calamondin see × *Citrofortunella microcarpa*
'Fukushu' (F) CCCN EMui ERea
hystrix CCCN CDoC EMui ERea LSRN NScw
japonica see *Fortunella japonica*
'Kulci' (F) CCCN
kumquat see *Fortunella margarita*
'La Valette' (F) EPfP ERea LSRN SEND
latifolia (F/S) CCCN CDoC EMui EPfP LRHS MREP
limetta CCCN
- 'Romnya' (F) ERea
limettoides (F) CArn ERea
limon (F) CHEx CTsd EPfP LRHS MREP SPoG STrG SVic
- 'Amalfitanum' (F) ERea
- 'Four Seasons' (F) CCCN ERea NLar
§ - 'Garey's Eureka' (F) CDoC EPfP ERea
- 'Genova' (F) ERea
- 'Imperial' (F) ERea
- 'Lemonade' (F) ERea
- 'Mosquito' (v) CHll ERea
- 'Quatre Saisons' see *C. limon* 'Garey's Eureka'
- 'Toscana' (F) EPfP ERea
- 'Variegata' (F/v) ♀H1 CCCN EMui ERea
- 'Villa Franca' (F) ERea
- 'Yen Ben' (F) ERea
× ***limonia*** 'Rangpur' (F) ERea
'Lipo' CCCN NLar
macrophylla ERea
madurensis see *Fortunella japonica*
maxima (F) ERea
medica (F) CHll ERea
- 'Cidro Digitado' see *C. medica* var. *digitata*
§ - var. ***digitata*** (F) EMui ERea
- 'Ethrog' (F) ERea
- var. ***sarcodactylis*** see *C. medica* var. *digitata*
× ***meyeri*** CHEx
- 'Improved Meyer' (F) EMui ERea
- 'Meyer' (F) ♀H1 CBcs CCCN CHll CTri CTsd EPfP ERea LRHS NLar SPer
microcarpa Philippine lime see × *Citrofortunella microcarpa*
mitis see × *Citrofortunella microcarpa*
× ***nobilis*** Ortanique Group (F) EPfP
- 'Silver Hill Owari' (F) ERea
- Tangor Group (F) ERea
× ***paradisi*** (F) CCCN MREP SPoG SVic
- 'Foster' (F) ERea
- 'Golden Special' (F) ERea
- 'Marsh' (F) ERea
- 'Red Blush' (F/S) ERea
- 'Star Ruby' (F/S) EMui ERea
'Ponderosa' (F) ERea
'Pursta' (F) CCCN ERea
reticulata (F) CCCN MREP
- Mandarin Group (F) CDoC EMui EPfP
- - 'Clementine' (F) CDoC ERea LRHS
- - 'De Nules' (F/S) EMui ERea
- 'Orogrande' ERea
sinensis (F) CCCN LRHS SPoG SVic
- 'Egg' (F) ERea
- 'Harwood Late' (F) ERea
- 'Jaffa' see *C. sinensis* 'Shamouti'
- 'Lane Late' (F) ERea
- 'Malta Blood' (F) ERea
- 'Moro Blood' (F) ERea
- 'Navelate' (F) ERea
- 'Navelina' (F/S) CDoC CTri
- 'Newhall' (F) ERea
- 'Saint Michael' (F) ERea
- 'Sanguinelli' (F) ERea
§ - 'Shamouti' (F) ERea
- 'Tarocco' (F) ERea
- 'Trovita' (F) ERea
- 'Valencia' (F) EMui
- 'Valencia Late' (F) ERea
- 'Washington' (F/S) EPfP ERea
× ***tangelo*** 'Minneola' (F) ERea
- 'Seminole' (F) ERea
- 'Ugli' (F) ERea
unshiu 'Miyagawa' CCCN ERea

Cladanthus (*Asteraceae*)

B&F MA 20 new WCot

Cladothamnus see *Elliottia*

Cladrastis (*Papilionaceae*)

§ ***kentukea*** CArn CBcs CDul CLnd CMCN ELan EPfP EWTr LRHS MBlu MBri MRav NLar SSpi WDin
§ - 'Perkins Pink' MBlu MBri SSpi
- 'Rosea' see *C. kentukea* 'Perkins Pink'
lutea see *C. kentukea*
sinensis CBcs CDul CGHE CPLG EBee EPfP EPla IDee IFFs MBlu SSpi WPGP

Clarkia (*Onagraceae*)

* ***repens*** CSpe

Clavinodum (*Poaceae*)

§ ***oedogonatum*** EPla MWht

Claytonia (*Portulacaceae*)

alsinoides see *C. sibirica*
australasica see *Neopaxia australasica*
caroliniana EBee NLar
§ ***perfoliata*** CArn GPoy ILis WCHb WHer
§ ***sibirica*** CAgr CArn CElw IMou LSou
- f. ***albiflora*** CElw WCot WMoo
virginica EBee EHrv LAma WFar WMoo

Clematis ✿ (*Ranunculaceae*)

BWJ 7630 from China WCru
BWJ 8169 from China WCru
CC 711 CPLG
CC 4710 CPLG
WJS 8910 from Japan WCru
'Abundance' (Vt) ♀H4 CDoC CElw CRHN CSPN CWCL EBee EPfP ESCh ETho LOck LRHS LSRN MBri MRav NBea NHol NTay SBch SDix SPer SPet
acuminata var. ***sikkimensis*** B&SWJ 7202 WCru
addisonii CBcs CSPN CWGN EBee ESCh LRHS MWhi NHaw WSHC
aethusifolia CSPN
afoliata CSPN ECou GKev WThu
afoliata × ***forsteri*** ECou
'Ai-Nor' (EL) ETho
'Akaishi' (EL) CWGN EBee ESCh ETho NTay
akebioides LRHS
Alabast = 'Poulala'PBR (EL) ♀H4 CSPN EBee ESCh ETho LRHS MAsh NBea NHaw NPri NTay SCoo SPoG SWCr
'Alba Luxurians' (Vt) ♀H4 Widely available
'Albatross' ESCh LSRN
'Albiflora' (A) CSPN ECtt ESCh NSti
'Albina Plena' (A/d) ESCh ETho MGos
'Aleksandrit' (EL) NHaw

	Name	Suppliers
	'Alice Fisk' (EL)	CSPN EBee EPfP ESCh ETho LSRN MSwo NBea NHaw WGor
	'Alionushka' (I) ♀H4	CRHN CSam EBee ELan ELon EPfP ESCh ETho LOck LRHS LSRN MAsh MBri MGos NBea NPri NTay SAga SPer SPet SPoG SWCr WCot
	'Allanah' (LL)	EBee ELon EPfP ETho LOck LRHS LSRN MGos NHaw SCoo SPet SPoG WFar
	alpina ♀H4	CBot ECtt EPfP GGal GKev GKir LSRN MBar MRav MWhi NBlu NHaw NPer SPlb WBVN WFar
	- SDR 3611	GKev
	- 'Albiflora'	see *C. sibirica*
	- 'Columbine White'	see *C.* 'White Columbine'
I	- 'Odorata'	CSPN MGos NHaw
§	- 'Pamela Jackman' ♀H4	CDoC CSPN CWSG EBee ELan ESCh GKir IBal LOck LRHS LSRN MAsh MGos NBea NEgg NHol NSti NTay SBod SCoo SDix SPer SPet SPoG SWvt WFar
	- pink-flowered	GKir
	- 'Stolwijk Gold'	ESCh ETho MBlu MGos NTay
	alternata	CWGN EBee ESCh ETho
	'Amelia Joan' (Ta)	MWat
	'Ameshisuto' (EL)	ESCh ETho
	'Andromeda' (EL)	CSPN EBee ESCh ETho LRHS NBea NHaw NTay SGar WFar
	'Angela's Double' (A/d) **new**	ESCh
	Angelique = 'Evipo017' (EL)	ETho LBuc LRHS LSqu MAsh NTay SLon SPoG SWCr
	'Anita' (Ta)	EPfP ESCh ETho LSRN NHaw SMDP
	'Anna' (EL)	ESCh
	'Anna Carolina'	ESCh
	Anna Louise = 'Evithree'PBR (EL) ♀H4	CLng CSPN CWCL EBee ESCh ETho IBal LBuc LRHS LSRN LSqu MAsh MBri NPri NTay SCoo SPoG SWCr
	'Annabel' (EL)	CSPN LSRN
	'Annemieke' (Ta)	MGos
	Anniversary = 'Pynot' (EL)	ESCh LSRN SCoo
	'Anti' (LL)	ESCh NBea
	'Aotearoa' (LL)	EBee ESCh NHaw
	Aphrodite = 'Aphrodite Elegafumina'	CRHN EBee ESCh LRHS MAsh NBea NHaw
	apiifolia	MWhi
	- B&SWJ 4838	WCru
	'Apple Blossom' (Ar) ♀H4	Widely available
	'Arabella' (I) ♀H4	CElw CPou CRHN CSPN CSam CWCL EBee ELan ELon EPfP ESCh EShb ETho LAst LBMP LOck LRHS LSRN MAsh MBri NBea NPri NTay SPer SPet SPoG SWCr SWvt WFar
§	Arctic Queen = 'Evitwo'PBR (EL) ♀H4	CLng CSPN CWCL EBee ESCh ETho LBuc LRHS LSRN LSqu MAsh NPri NTay SCoo SPer SPoG SWCr WFar
	armandii	Widely available
	- 'Enham Star'	LBuc LRHS MBri MGos
§	- 'Little White Charm'	CAlb CSPN LRHS NLar SBch SPoG
	- 'Meyeniana'	see *C. armandii* 'Little White Charm'
§	- 'Snowdrift'	CAlb CBcs CSBt CSPN CSam CWSG EBee ELan ELon EPfP ESCh ETho LRHS MAsh MGos MSwo NEgg NSti NTay SBch SPer SPoG SRms WSpi
	× ***aromatica***	CBcs CFir CSPN CSam CWGN EAEE EBee ELan EPfP ESCh ETho LFol LOck LPio LRHS MBNS MCot MRav NBea NSti NTay SCoo SPoG WSpi
§	'Asagasumi' (EL)	ESCh ETho NTay
	'Asao' (EL)	CElw CFir CRHN EBee ELan EPfP ESCh ETho LAst LOck LRHS MAsh MGos MRav NTay SCoo SPer SPet SPoG SWCr
	'Ascotiensis' (LL)	CBcs CRHN CSPN EBee EPfP ESCh ETho LRHS MAsh NHaw NTay SCoo SPer SWCr WFar
	'Ashva'	CAlb CWGN ESCh LRHS MGos
	'Aureolin' (Ta)	CSPN CWSG EBee EPfP ETho MBar NHol SCoo WPGP
	Avant-garde = 'Evipo033'PBR (Vt)	CLng CWGN EBee ESCh ETho LRHS LSqu MAsh SLon SPoG SWCr
§	'Bagatelle' (LL)	CLng CRHN CSPN ESCh LRHS LSRN NHaw SMDP SPad WFar
	'Bal Maiden' (Vt)	CRHN
§	'Ballerina in Blue' (A/d)	NHaw
	'Ballet Skirt' (A/d) ♀H4	ESCh MGos NHaw
	'Bałtyk' (EL)	CSPN ESCh
	'Barbara' (LL)	ETho MRav NHaw NTay
	'Barbara Dibley' (EL)	CTri CWSG EBee ELon ESCh LOck LRHS NBea NHaw SCoo SDix SPet
	'Barbara Harrington'PBR (LL)	CLng ESCh LRHS LSRN MAsh NHaw
	'Barbara Jackman' (EL)	EBee ECtt ETho GKir LOck LRHS LSRN MAsh MBar MGos MRav MSwo NBea NTay SCoo SLim SPer SPoG SWCr WFoF
	'Basil Bartlett' (Fo)	ECou
	'Beata' (LL)	ESCh MGos NBea
	'Beauty of Richmond' (EL)	CWSG ESCh
	'Beauty of Worcester' (EL)	CFir CSPN CWSG ELan ELon EPfP ESCh ETho GKir LOck LRHS LSRN MBar MSwo NBea NHaw NTay SCoo SDix SPer SPet SPoG WFar
	'Bees' Jubilee' (EL)	CBcs CMac CRHN CWSG EBee ECtt ELan EPfP ESCh ETho GKir LRHS LSRN MAsh MBar MGan MGos MRav MSwo NBir NBlu NTay SDix SLim SPer SPet SPoG SWCr SWvt WFar
	'Bella' (EL)	EBee ESCh NHaw
	'Belle Nantaise' (EL)	EBee LRHS SCoo SPet
	'Belle of Woking' (EL)	CRHN CSPN CWSG EBee ECtt ELan ELon EPfP ESCh ETho LOck LRHS LSRN MAsh MBar MRav NBea NTay SCoo SDix SLim SPet SPoG SWCr WBVN
	'Bells of Emei Shan' **new**	ETho WCru
	'Benedictus' (EL)	ESCh
	'Berry Red' (A)	CWGN
§	'Beth Currie' (EL)	CLng CSPN EBee EPfP ESCh LRHS MAsh NPri
	'Betina'	see *C.* 'Red Beetroot Beauty'
	'Betty Corning' (Vt) ♀H4	CRHN CSPN CWGN EBee ELan ELon EPfP ESCh ETho LFol LRHS LSRN MAsh MBri MGos NBea NPri NTay SCoo SLim SLon SWCr WFar WGwG
	'Betty Risdon' (EL)	ESCh ETho LRHS NTay
	'Bill MacKenzie' (Ta) ♀H4	Widely available
	'Black Prince' (Vt)	CRHN CWGN EBee ELan ESCh ETho LOck LRHS LSRN MGos NBea NHaw NHol NLar NTay SLon SMDP
	'Black Tea' (LL)	ESCh LSRN NHaw NTay
§	'Błękitny Anioł' (LL) ♀H4	CElw CLng CRHN CSPN ESCh ETho LOck LRHS MAsh MGos NBea NLar NPri NTay SCoo SPer SPet SPoG WFar
	Blue Angel	see *C.* 'Błękitny Anioł'
	'Blue Belle' (Vt)	CPou CRHN ELan LRHS NSti SLon SMDP SPoG WFar
	'Blue Bird' (A/d)	CBcs CWCL CWSG EBee ECtt ESCh GKir LRHS MBlu NHol SMDP SPoG
	Blue Blood	see *C.* 'Königskind'

'Blue Boy' (I) — see *C.* × *diversifolia* 'Blue Boy' (I)
'Blue Boy' — see *C.* 'Elsa Späth'
'Blue Dancer' (A) — CElw CLng EBee EPfP ESCh EShb ETho IBal LRHS MAsh MGos NBea NLar NTay SWCr
'Blue Eclipse' (A) — CSPN CTri CWGN LRHS MBri MGos NHaw
'Blue Eyes' (EL) — CSPN EBee ELon ESCh ETho LRHS LSRN NHaw NTay
§ 'Blue Light'PBR (EL/d) — CSPN ELan ESCh ETho LRHS MGos NLar NTay WFar
Blue Moon = 'Evirin'PBR (EL) — CLng EBee EPfP ESCh ETho LAst LRHS LSRN MAsh NLar NPri NTay SCoo SPoG SWCr WFar
Blue Pirouette = 'Zobluepi'PBR (I) — CWGN EBrs ESCh LRHS MAsh NLar SMDP SPoG
Blue Rain — see *C.* 'Sinii Dozhd'
'Blue Ravine' (EL) — EBee EPfP ESCh LRHS MGos NLar NTay SCoo
'Blue Tapers' (A) — ESCh NHaw
§ 'Blushing Ballerina' (A/d) — ESCh
Bonanza = 'Evipo031'PBR — CLng ESCh ETho LBuc LRHS LSqu MAsh SPoG SWCr
§ × ***bonstedtii*** 'Campanile' (H) — NBir
- 'Crépuscule' (H) — MCot SMDP SRms
'Boskoop Beauty' (EL) — ESCh NHaw NTay
Bourbon = 'Evipo018'PBR — ETho LBuc LMor LRHS LSqu MAsh NPri SPoG SWCr
'Bowl of Beauty' (Ar) — MGos
'Bracebridge Star' (EL) — ECtt ESCh NBea
brachiata — CPne
'Brocade' (Vt) — CRHN CSPN ESCh ETho NHaw
'Broughton Bride' — CSPN CTri CWGN ESCh LRHS MBri NHol
'Broughton Star' (M/d) ♀H4 — CElw CPou CRHN CSBt CSPN CWib EBee ELan EPfP ESCh ETho GKir LRHS LSRN MBlu MBri MGos MRav MSwo NBea NBir NHol NSti SBod SLim SPet SPoG WFar
'Brunette' (A) — CSPN EBee ELan EPfP ESCh ETho LRHS MAsh MGos NHaw NLar NTay SPoG SWCr
buchananiana Finet & Gagnep. — see *C. rehderiana*
buchananiana DC. — EBee
- B&SWJ 8333a — WCru
'Buckland Beauty' (V) — ESCh GMac NBea
'Buckland Longshanks' (H) — SMDP
'Burford Princess' (Vt) — NHaw
I 'Burford Variety' (Ta) — ESCh
'Burford White' (A) — CSPN EBee EPfP NLar
'Burma Star' (EL) — CWGN EPfP ESCh ETho LOck LRHS NBea NHaw NTay
Caddick's Cascade = 'Semu' — CSPN CWGN ESCh ETho NHaw
'Caerulea Luxurians' (Vt) — CRHN CWGN ESCh NHaw NTay WSHC
calycina — see *C. cirrhosa* var. *balearica*
campaniflora — see *C. viticella* subsp. *campaniflora*
'Campanile' — see *C.* × *bonstedtii* 'Campanile'
'Candida' (EL) — EBee ESCh
'Candleglow' (A) — CSPN EBee LRHS MBri
'Candy Stripe' — CLng EBee ESCh LRHS MAsh NTay SCoo SWCr
'Capitaine Thuilleaux' — see *C.* 'Souvenir du Capitaine Thuilleaux'
'Cardinal Wyszynski' — see *C.* 'Kardynał Wyszyński'
'Carmencita' (Vt) — CRHN CSPN EBee ESCh ETho LRHS NBea NHaw SCoo SDix SLon SPet WFar
'Carnaby' (EL) — CSPN CWCL CWSG EBee ELan EPfP ESCh ETho LOck LRHS LSRN MAsh MBar MBri MGos NBea NTay SCoo SLim SPoG SWCr WPGP
'Carnival Queen' — CSPN CWSG ESCh
'Caroline' (LL) — CSPN CWGN EBee ESCh ETho LSRN NHaw NTay SMDP
* × ***cartmanii*** hort. (Fo) — SAga
- 'Avalanche'PBR (Fo/m) ♀H3 — CSPN ELan ESCh ETho GBin LBuc LRHS MGos NLar NPri NTay SBch SCoo SLim SPoG
- 'Joe' (Fo/m) — CBcs CWCL EBee ELan EPfP EPot ESCh ETho EWes ITim LRHS LSRN MAsh MGos NHol SBch SCoo SMrm SPoG SWCr WHil
- 'Joe' × ***marmoraria*** (Fo) — ECho MGos
- 'Joe' × 'Sharon' — LSRN
- 'Snow Valley'PBR (Fo) — LRHS
- 'White Abundance'PBR (Fo/f) — CAlb ESCh ETho LRHS NLar SPoG
× ***cartmanii*** hort. × ***petriei*** (Fo) — ECho
Cassis = 'Evipo020'PBR — CWGN ESCh ETho LBuc LRHS LSRN LSqu MAsh NTay SLon SPoG SWCr
Cezanne = 'Evipo023'PBR (EL) — ETho LBuc LRHS LSqu MAsh NTay SLon SPoG SWCr
'Chacewater' (Vt) — CRHN
'Chalcedony' (EL) — CSPN CWGN ESCh ETho LRHS MGos
Chantilly = 'Evipo021'PBR **new** — ETho LBuc LRHS LSqu MAsh SWCr
'Charissima' (EL) — CBcs CSPN CWGN EPfP LRHS MAsh MGos NLar NTay SCoo SPet SWCr WFar
'Chatsworth' (Vt) — EPfP LRHS MAsh
chiisanensis — CSPN MWhi
- B&SWJ 4560 — WCru
- B&SWJ 8706 — WCru
- 'Korean Beauty' — GKev
- 'Lemon Bells' (A) — ELan EPfP ETho LOck LRHS MAsh SCoo SPoG SWCr
- 'Love Child' (A) — CElw CSPN EBee ELan ESCh LRHS SLim SPer
'China Blue' — SMDP
chinensis misapplied — see *C. terniflora*
chinensis Osbeck RWJ 10042 — WCru
Chinook = 'Evipo013'PBR — CLng EBee LRHS NTay
'Christian Steven' (LL) — CSPN ESCh
chrysantha — see *C. tangutica*
chrysocoma misapplied — see *C. spooneri*, *C.* × *vedrariensis*
N ***chrysocoma*** Franch. — EPfP LRHS MBar NHol SMDP WCru WSpi
- ACE 1093 — CPou
- B&L 12237 — NBea
'Cicciolina' (Vt) — CRHN ETho NHaw
cirrhosa — CBot CTri ELan GKir LOck LRHS MAsh MGos MWhi NHol NTay SArc SWCr
§ - var. ***balearica*** — Widely available
- 'Ourika Valley' — EBee EPfP ESCh ETho LRHS MAsh NBea NLar NTay SWCr WFar
- var. ***purpurascens*** 'Freckles' ♀H3 — Widely available
- - 'Jingle Bells' — CRHN EBee EGxp EPfP ESCh ETho LOck LRHS LSRN MAsh NBea NHol SCoo SLim SPoG SWCr WFar WSpi
- - 'Lansdowne Gem' — CSPN CWGN CWib LRHS NBea NHol SMDP WSpi
- 'Wisley Cream' ♀H3 — CBcs CDul CSPN CWCL CWib EBee ECtt ELan EPfP ESCh ETho LOck

	LRHS LSRN MAsh MGos MSwo NBea NHol NPri NSti NTay SCoo SLim SPer SPoG SWCr SWvt WFar WPGP
clarkeana misapplied	see *C. urophylla* 'Winter Beauty'
'Clochette Pride' (A/d)	ESCh
coactilis	EBee
'Colette Deville' (EL)	NTay
columbiana	WAbe
var. ***tenuiloba*** 'Ylva' (A)	
'Columbine' (A)	CWSG EBee ETho GGar LRHS MBar MSwo NBea NHol SDix SPer SPoG
'Columella' (A)	ESCh ETho MGos NHaw NLar
'Comtesse de Bouchaud' (LL) ♀H4	Widely available
Confetti = 'Evipo036'^{PBR}	CLng ESCh ETho LRHS LSRN NTay
confusa HWJK 2200	WCru
'Congratulations' **new**	LOck
connata	GQui
- GWJ 9386	WCru
- HWJCM 132	WCru
aff. ***connata*** GWJ 9431 from West Bengal	WCru
- HWJK 2176 from Nepal	WCru
'Constance' (A) ♀H4	CElw CRHN CSPN CWCL EBee EPfP ETho IBal LRHS LSRN MAsh NBea NHaw NPri NSti NTay SCoo SPer SPoG SRms SWCr WBor WPGP
'Continuity' (M)	CWGN EBee LRHS SDix
'Corona' (EL)	CLng CSPN ELan EPfP ETho LRHS MBar NHaw SBod SCoo WFar
'Corry' (Ta)	ESCh NLar
'Côte d'Azur' (H)	CMdw ECtt GCal MCCP MCot SPer
'Countess of Lovelace' (EL)	CBcs CSPN CWSG EBee ELan EPfP ESCh ETho LRHS LSRN MAsh MBar MBri MGos MRav NBea NTay SCoo SLim SPet SWCr WFar
County Park hybrids (Fo)	ECou
'Cragside' (A)	EBee ESCh ETho NBea
crassifolia B&SWJ 6700	WCru
§ 'Crimson King' (LL)	ESCh ETho NHaw WGor
'Crinkle' (M)	CCCN
§ ***crispa***	CElw CPou CSPN ESCh GAuc IFro MWhi NBea NHaw WSHC
§ Crystal Fountain = 'Evipo038'^{PBR} (EL)	CLng CWCL CWGN ESCh ETho LRHS LSqu MAsh NPri NTay SCoo SPoG SWCr
× ***cylindrica***	CSPN EBee
'Daan' (A) **new**	ESCh
'Danae' (Vt)	CRHN NHaw
'Daniel Deronda' (EL) ♀H4	CDoC CDul CSPN CWSG ECtt ELan ESCh ETho GKir LOck LRHS LSRN MAsh MGos MRav NBea NBir NPri NTay SCoo SDix SLim SPoG SWCr WFar
'Darius' (EL)	ESCh
'Dark Eyes' (Vt) **new**	CWGN ESCh
'Dark Secret' (A)	CSPN EPfP LRHS MBri
'Dawn' (EL)	CCCN CLng CSPN ELon ESCh ETho LOck LRHS LSRN MAsh NBea NTay SCoo SPoG SWCr
'Débutante' (EL)	ESCh NHaw
'Denny's Double' (EL/d)	CSPN CWGN CWSG ESCh ETho LRHS NTay
'Diana' (LL)	ESCh ETho
dioica F&M 100	WPGP
dioscoreifolia	see *C. terniflora*
§ × ***diversifolia***	CRHN EBee ESCh MBNS MGos NHaw NHol SDix SGar WSpi
§ - 'Blue Boy' (I)	CElw CMoH CRHN CSPN EBee ESCh MGos NHaw NTay
- 'Floris V' (I)	ESCh IPot LPio NHaw NLar
- 'Heather Herschell' (I)	CElw CRHN CSPN EBee ELon ESCh NBea NHaw SMDP
§ - 'Hendersonii' (I)	EAEE EBee ELan ELon EPfP ESCh ETho GGar GKir LHop LOck LPio LRHS LSRN MRav MSwo NBea NBir NHol NSti NTay SDix SWat WKif WSpi
§ - 'Olgae' (I)	CMoH CPLG CSPN NBea NHaw NTay SMDP WGwG
'Doctor Ruppel' (EL)	CMac CSPN CWCL CWSG ECtt EPfP ESCh ETho GKir LOck LRHS LSRN MAsh MBar MBri MGos MRav MSwo NBea NBir NPri NTay SDix SLim SPer SPet SPoG SWCr WBVN WFar
'Dominika' (LL)	CSPN CWGN ESCh NHaw NTay
'Dorath'	ELon ESCh
'Dorothy Tolver' (EL)	ESCh ETho
'Dorothy Walton'	see *C.* 'Bagatelle'
'Double Cross'	ECou
'Dubysa'	ESCh
'Duchess of Albany' (T)	CSPN CTri CWSG CWib EBee ELan EPfP ESCh ETho IBal LAst LOck LRHS LSRN MAsh MBar MGos NBea NEgg NHol NSti NTay SLim SPer SPet SWCr WFar WSHC
'Duchess of Edinburgh' (EL)	CBcs CFir CMac CRHN CWSG EBee ECtt ELan EPfP ESCh ETho GKir GMac LAst LRHS LSRN MAsh MBar MGos MSwo NBea NEgg NTay SDix SLim SPet SPoG SWCr WFar
'Duchess of Sutherland' (EL)	MGos NHaw SDix SPet
'Dulcie'	NHaw
× ***durandii*** ♀H4	CBcs CBot CRHN CSPN CWCL EBee ELan EPfP ESCh ETho LRHS LSRN MAsh MBar MBri MRav NBea NHol NPri NSti SCoo SLim SPer SPoG SWCr WFar WSpi
'Dusky' **new**	ESCh
'Dusky Star' (M)	CWGN
'Dutch Sky' **new**	ESCh MBri
'Dymchatyi' (EL) **new**	ECou
'Early Sensation' (Fo/f)	Widely available
'East Malling' (M)	NHaw
'Edith' (EL) ♀H4	ECtt ESCh ETho LRHS LSRN NBea NHaw NTay WGor
'Edomurasaki' (EL)	ESCh
'Edouard Desfossé' (EL)	CLng ESCh
'Edward Prichard'	CMoH CSPN EBee EPfP ESCh ETho MGos MWea NBea NHaw SMDP
'Eetika' (LL)	CRHN ESCh ETho NBea
'Ekstra' (LL)	EBee ESCh ETho
'Eleanor' (Fo/f)	ECou GEdr
'Elfin' (Fo/v)	ECou
'Elizabeth' (M) ♀H4	Widely available
§ 'Elsa Späth' (EL)	CElw CPLG CRHN CSPN CTri EBee ELan EPfP ESCh ETho GKir LAst LRHS LSRN MAsh MBar MBri MGan MGos MRav NBea NTay SDix SPer SPoG SWCr WFar
'Elten' (M)	CSPN CWGN SMDP
'Elvan' (Vt)	CRHN NHaw NLar SPet
'Emajõgi' (LL)	ESCh
'Emilia Plater' (Vt)	CRHN CSPN ESCh ETho LOck MGos NBea NHaw NTay SLon
Empress = 'Evipo011'^{PBR} (EL)	ETho LBuc LRHS LSqu MAsh NTay SLon SWCr
'Entel' (Vt)	CRHN CWGN ETho NHaw
'Erik' (A)	ESCh NBea
× ***eriostemon***	see *C.* × *diversifolia*
'Ernest Markham' (LL) ♀H4	Widely available
'Esperanto' (LL)	EBee ESCh MGos NBea SMDP

'Essex Star' (Fo) ECou
'Étoile de Malicorne' (EL) ESCh WGor
'Étoile de Paris' (EL) ESCh
Étoile Nacrée see *C.* 'Sakurahime'
'Étoile Rose' (Vt) CRHN CSPN CTri CWCL ELan EPfP ESCh ETho GKir IBal LAst LOck LRHS LSRN MAsh MGos MRav NBea NHol NTay SCoo SDix SLim SPer SWCr WBor WFar WPGP
'Étoile Violette' (Vt) ♀H4 Widely available
'Eva' (LL) ESCh NBea
Evening Star = 'Evista'PBR EPfP NTay WFar
'Eximia' see *C.* 'Ballerina in Blue'
'Fair Rosamond' (EL) EBee EPfP ESCh LRHS MGos NBea NHaw NTay SPet
'Fairy' (Fo/f) ECou
Fairy BluePBR see *C.* Crystal Fountain
'Fairy Queen' (EL) ESCh
fargesii var. ***souliei*** see *C. potaninii* var. *potaninii*
× ***fargesioides*** see *C.* 'Paul Farges'
fasciculiflora CBot CMHG CRHN CSPN EBee IDee LRHS SSpi
- L 657 WCru WPGP
'Fascination'PBR (I) CWGN EBrs EPfP ESCh ETho NHaw SMDP
fauriei WSHC
Filigree = 'Evipo029'PBR **new** LRHS MAsh
finetiana misapplied see *C. paniculata* J.G. Gmel.
'Firefly' (EL) ESCh MGos
'Fireworks' (EL) CAlb CSPN CWGN EBee ECtt EPfP ESCh ETho LOck LRHS LSRN MAsh MBri MGos MRav NBea NEgg NPri NTay SWCr WFar WFoF WGor
'Flamingo' (EL) CWCL CWSG
flammula Widely available
- 'Rubra Marginata' see *C.* × *triternata* 'Rubromarginata'
Fleuri = 'Evipo042' **new** LBuc LRHS MAsh
§ 'Floral Feast' (A/d) CSPN ESCh LRHS NBea SPoG
'Floralia' see *C.* 'Floral Feast'
florida CSPN CWGN ESCh
- 'Bicolor' see *C. florida* var. *sieboldiana*
'Florida Blue' ESCh
florida var. ***flore-pleno*** (d) CCCN CFir CSPN CWCL EBee ELan EPfP ESCh ETho GMac LAst LOck LRHS LSRN MAsh NBea NEgg NTay SPer SPoG SWCr WFar WGwG
- Pistachio = 'Evirida'PBR (LL) CCCN CLng CSPN CWCL CWGN EBee EPfP ESCh ETho IBal LBuc LRHS LSRN LSqu MAsh NLar NTay SWCr WFar
§ - var. ***sieboldiana*** (d) CBcs CSPN CWCL CWSG EBee ELan EPfP ESCh ETho GMac IBal LAst LBMP LRHS LSRN MBri MGos NBea NLar NTay SLim SPer SPoG SRkn SWCr WFar WGwG WPGP
- 'Thorncroft' (LL) ETho
'Flutter' (M) **new** LRHS
foetida CBcs CSPN
foetida × 'Lunar Lass' (Fo) ECho ECou
foetida × ***petriei*** ECho ECou
'Fond Memories' (EL) ESCh ETho LSRN NTay WHlf
'Forever' ESCh
I 'Forget-me-not' ESCh LSRN WHlf
forrestii see *C. napaulensis*
§ ***forsteri*** CBcs CSPN ESCh ETho LFol WPGP WSHC
'Foxtrot' (Vt) CRHN ESCh NBea NHaw
'Foxy' (A) ♀H4 CBcs EBee LRHS NHaw NTay SLon WGob
'Fragrant Joy' (Fo/m) ECou
'Fragrant Oberon' ECou
'Fragrant Spring' (M) CSPN CWGN ECtt ELon ETho LOck LRHS MGos NHaw NLar SBod SMDP WFar WGwG
'Frances Rivis' (A) ♀H4 Widely available
'Francesca' (A) ESCh LSRN MGos NBea
'Frankie' (A) ♀H4 CSPN EBee ELan EPfP ESCh ETho LRHS LSRN MAsh NTay SCoo SPoG SWCr
Franziska Marie = 'Evipo008' (EL) CLng ETho LBuc LRHS LSqu MAsh NPri NTay SLon SWCr
'Frau Mikiko' (EL) ESCh ETho MGos
'Freda' (M) ♀H4 CRHN CTri CWSG EBee ECtt ELan EPfP ESCh ETho LRHS LSRN MAsh MBlu MBri MGos MRav NBea NHol NSti NTay SDix SPer SPoG SWCr WCru
fruticosa 'Mongolian Gold' **new** CWGN ESCh
'Fryderyk Chopin' (EL) CSPN ESCh NHaw NLar
'Fuji-musume' (EL) ♀H4 CSPN CWGN ESCh ETho LOck LRHS NBea NHaw NLar NTay SPet SPoG SWCr WFar
'Fujinami' (EL) ESCh MAsh
'Fukuzono' ETho LOck LRHS LSRN MAsh NHaw
fusca misapplied see *C. japonica*
fusca Turcz. WIvy WSHC
- dwarf CWGN NHaw
§ - var. ***fusca*** ESCh ETho WSHC
- var. ***kamtschatica*** see *C. fusca* Turcz. var. *fusca*
'Fuyu-no-tabi' (EL) ESCh
'G. Steffner' (A) ESCh MGos
'Gabrielle' (EL) CSPN ESCh LRHS LSRN NHaw NTay
GalorePBR see *C.* Vesuvius
Gazelle = 'Evipo014'PBR CLng LRHS NTay SPoG
'Gemini' (EL) ESCh MGos
'General Sikorski' (EL) CBcs CMac CRHN CSPN CWSG ECtt ELan EPfP ESCh ETho LOck LRHS LSRN MAsh MBri MGos NBea NTay SCoo SDix SLim SPer SPoG SWCr
gentianoides ETho LSRN WCot
'Geoffrey Tolver' (LL) **new** ETho
'Georg' (A/d) ESCh MGos NHaw
'Georg Ots' (LL) ESCh
Giant Star = 'Gistar'PBR (M) CWGN ESCh LRHS MGos NEgg NLar NPer SPoG
'Gillian Blades' (EL) ♀H4 CLng CRHN CSPN EBee ELan EPfP ESCh ETho LOck LRHS LSRN MAsh NBea NHaw NPri NTay SCoo SPer SPet SPoG SWCr
§ 'Gipsy Queen' (LL) ♀H4 CBcs CSPN CWCL CWSG EBee ECtt ELan EPfP ESCh ETho GKir LRHS LSRN MAsh MBar MRav NBea NPri NTay SDix SPoG SWCr WFar
'Girenas' ESCh
'Giuseppi Verde' (A) **new** ESCh
'Gladys Picard' (EL) ESCh NHaw NTay WFar
glauca Turcz. see *C. intricata*
glauca ambig. GAuc
glaucophylla WCru WSHC
'Glynderek' (EL) ESCh
'Golden Harvest' (Ta) NHol NLar WFar
Golden Tiara = 'Kugotia'PBR (Ta) ♀H4 CSPN CWGN ESCh ETho MGos NBea NLar NTay
'Gothenburg' (M) EBee ESCh NBea NHaw WFar
I 'Gothenburg Superba' SMDP
'Grace' (Ta) CRHN CSPN EBee ESCh NBea NHaw NLar SMDP
I 'Grandiflora' (F) WFar
'Grandiflora Sanguinea' Johnson see *C.* 'Södertälje'

grata misapplied	see *C.* × *jouiniana*
grata Wall. B&SWJ 6774	WCru
'Gravetye Beauty' (T)	CRHN CSPN ELan EPfP ESCh ETho GMac IBal LAst LOck LRHS LSRN MAsh MBri MGos MRav NBea NHol NPri NSti NTay SDix SLim SPer SPoG SRkn SRms SWCr WGwG WSpi
§ 'Grażyna'	ESCh NTay
'Green Velvet' (Fo/m)	ECou
grewiiflora B&SWJ 2956	WCru
'Guernsey Cream' (EL)	CFir CSPN CSam CWSG EBee ESCh ETho LAst LOck LRHS LSRN MAsh MBri MGos NBea NTay SCoo SDix SLim SPet SPoG SWCr WFar
'Guiding Star' (EL)	ETho NHaw
'H.F. Young' (EL)	CSPN CWSG EBee ELan EPfP ESCh ETho GKir GMac LOck LRHS LSRN MAsh MBar MBri MGos NBea NTay SCoo SDix SLim SPer SPet SPoG SWCr
'Hagley Hybrid' (LL)	CDoC CMac CSPN EBee ECtt ELan EPfP ESCh ETho GKir LAst LRHS LSRN MAsh MBar MBri MGos MRav NBea NBlu NEgg NTay SDix SLim SPer SPet SPoG SWCr WFar WGwG
'Haku-ōkan' (EL)	CSPN EBee EPfP ESCh ETho LOck LRHS LSRN NBea NLar NTay SCoo SPoG
'Hakuree' (I)	ESCh ETho LOck LRHS SMDP
'Hanaguruma' (EL)	CSPN ESCh ETho LSRN NBea NHaw NTay WFar
'Hanajima' (I)	ESCh ETho SMDP
'Hania'	CWGN ESCh ETho
'Happy Anniversary' (EL)	ETho LBuc LSRN NTay
Harlow Carr = 'Evipo004'[PBR]	CLng CWGN EPfP ESCh LRHS MAsh SCoo SWCr
'Harmony' (EL/d)	ESCh
'Haruyama' (EL)	ESCh
Havering hybrids (Fo)	ECou
'Helen Cropper' (EL)	ESCh ETho
'Helios' (Ta)	CSPN EPfP ESCh ETho LRHS MGos NBea NSti NTay SCoo SPer SPoG
'Helsingborg' (A) ♀H4	CBcs CLng CSPN EBee ECtt ELan EPfP ESCh ETho LAst LRHS MAsh NBea NHol NSti NTay SCoo SPoG SWCr
hendersonii Koch	see *C.* × *diversifolia* 'Hendersonii'
hendersonii Stand.	see *C.* × *diversifolia*
I 'Hendersonii' (I)	CSam LRHS LSRN MAvo MNFA NHol NTay SRkn
'Hendersonii Rubra' (Ar)	CSPN NLar SPoG
'Hendryetta'[PBR] (I)	CWGN EBrs EPfP ESCh ETho LBMP LRHS MAsh NTay SMDP SPoG SRkn
henryi	EShb LSRN MAsh SBod
- B&SWJ 3402	WCru
'Henryi' (EL) ♀H4	CDul CRHN CSPN CTri CWCL CWSG EBee ELan EPfP ESCh ETho LRHS LSRN MBar MBri MGos MRav MSwo NBea NEgg SDix SPer SPet SPoG SWCr WFar WGwG
henryi var. ***morii*** B&SWJ 1668	WCru
heracleifolia	CAby CBcs CBot CFir CPou ECtt ESCh GAuc LRHS MWhi NHol NLar SGSe WCom WPer WWEG
- Alan Bloom[PBR]	see *C. tubulosa* Alan Bloom
I - 'Alba' (H)	LPio
- 'Blue Dwarf'	ESCh ETho MGos SMDP
- 'Campanile'	see *C.* × *bonstedtii* 'Campanile'
- 'Cassandra'	CSam EAEE ECGP ECtt EPfP ESCh EShb ETho GCal LHop LRHS MAvo MCot MGos NCGa NHol NLar NOrc SAga SMDP SPoG
- 'China Purple'	CSpe EBee ESCh LPio LSou MBNS MNrw NLar WHoo
- var. ***davidiana***	see *C. tubulosa*
- 'Pink Dwarf'	CWGN ETho NLar SMDP
- 'Roundway Blue Bird'	CBot ESCh LHop LRHS NHaw SMDP
'Herbert Johnson' (EL)	ESCh
hexapetala misapplied	see *C. recta* subsp. *recta* var. *lasiosepala*
hexapetala Forster	see *C. forsteri*
hexasepala	see *C. forsteri*
'Hikarugenji' (EL)	CSPN ESCh NHaw
hirsutissima var. ***scottii***	EBee
'Honora' (LL)	CSPN CWGN EGxp ESCh LOck LRHS NTay SCoo SPoG
'Horn of Plenty' (EL)	ELon LOck NHaw SPet
'Huldine' (LL) ♀H4	CBcs CElw CRHN CSPN EBee ELan EPfP ESCh ETho LRHS LSRN MAsh MBar MRav NBea NSti NTay SDix SPer SPet SPoG SWCr
'Huvi' (LL)	CWGN ESCh ETho NBea NHaw
'Hybrida Sieboldii' (EL)	CRHN EBee ESCh NTay SCoo
Hyde Hall = 'Evipo009'[PBR]	CLng CWGN EBee EPfP ESCh ETho IBal LRHS LSqu MAsh SLon SPoG SWCr
'Hythe Egret' (Fo)	ECho ESCh LLHF SIng
I Am a Little Beauty = 'Zolibe' (Vt)	CWGN ESCh NHaw
I Am Lady Q = 'Zoiamladyq' (Vt) **new**	CWGN ESCh
I Am Red Robin = 'Zorero'[PBR] (A)	ESCh
'Ialtinskii Etiud' (LL)	ESCh
ianthina	ESCh WPGP
- var. ***ianthina***	CRHN
- var. ***kuripoensis*** B&SWJ 700	WCru
'Ibi' (EL)	CWGN ESCh
Ice Blue = 'Evipo003'[PBR] (Prairie Series) (EL)	ETho LBuc LRHS LSqu MAsh NPri SLon SPoG SWCr
'Ice Maiden' (EL)	NTay
'Ice Queen' (EL)	LRHS
'Ideal' (EL)	ESCh
'Ilka' (EL)	ESCh
'Imperial' (EL)	ESCh NHaw
indivisa	see *C. paniculata* J.G. Gmel.
Inspiration = 'Zoin'[PBR] (I)	CSPN EBrs ELan EPfP ESCh ETho LRHS MGos NLar NTay SCoo
integrifolia	Widely available
I - 'Alba'	CBcs CBot CElw CSPN EBee ECtt ELon ESCh ETho GBuc LHop LPio LSRN MBNS MDKP NBea NBir NHaw NSti NTay SCoo SPer SPoG
- blue-flowered	ITim
- 'Budapest'	ESCh NHaw
- 'Cora' (I)	CWGN
- 'Hendersonii' Koch	see *C.* × *diversifolia* 'Hendersonii'
- var. ***latifolia***	CElw ESCh
- mid-blue-flowered	ESCh MGos
- 'Olgae'	see *C.* × *diversifolia* 'Olgae'
- 'Ozawa's Blue'	EAEE EBee ESCh ETho LPio LRHS MBNS MCot
- white-flowered	see *C. integrifolia* 'Alba'
§ ***intricata***	CBcs CPLG CSPN EBee MGos SGar
'Iola Fair' (EL)	CSPN ESCh ETho NHaw NTay
ispahanica	SGar
'Iubileinyi-70' (LL)	ESCh
'Ivan Olsson' (EL)	CSPN ESCh ETho MGos NBea
'Izumi' (LL) **new**	ESCh

'Jackmanii' (LL) ♀H4 CBcs CMac CTri EBee EPfP ESCh EТho GKir LOck LRHS LSRN MAsh MGos NBea NBlu NWea SCoo SLim SPer SPet SPoG SWCr WFar
'Jackmanii Alba' (EL) ELan ELon EPfP ETho LRHS LSRN MAsh MBar NBea NTay SCoo SLim SPet SWCr
Jackmanii Purpurea = 'Zojapur' **new** ESCh
'Jackmanii Rubra' (EL) ETho LRHS NBea
'Jackmanii Superba' misapplied see *C.* 'Gipsy Queen'
'Jackmanii Superba' ambig. (LL) CDul CMac CSPN CWCL CWSG EBee ECtt ELan EPfP ETho GGar LAst LRHS MAsh MBar MBri MGan MGos MRav MSwo NBea NEgg NPer NPri NTay SDix SLim SPer SPoG WFar
'Jacqueline du Pré' (A) ♀H4 CAlb CBcs CSPN CWCL EBee ELan EPfP ESCh ETho LOck MGos NBea NHaw NTay SMDP
'Jacqui' (M/d) ETho MGos NHaw NLar
'James Mason' (EL) CSPN ESCh ETho NBea NHaw NTay
'Jan Fopma'PBR (I) CWGN ESCh ETho SMDP
'Jan Lindmark' (A/d) CLng EBee EPfP ESCh ETho LRHS MAsh MGos NBea NHol NLar NSti NTay SCoo SWCr WFar
§ 'Jan Paweł II' (EL) CWSG EBee ECtt EGxp ELan EPfP ETho GKir LOck LRHS NBea SBod SCoo SPer
'Janina' CWGN ESCh
'Jānis Ruplēns Number 1' ESCh
'Janny' (A) ESCh
§ ***japonica*** CElw CSPN ESCh NHaw SMDP
- B&SWJ 11204 WCru
§ - var. ***obvallata*** B&SWJ 8900 WCru
'Jasper' ESCh
'Jefferies' (Ar) LRHS NLar
'Jenny' (M) CWGN EBee ESCh ETho LRHS MAsh MGos NHaw NLar SMDP
'Jenny Caddick' (Vt) CSPN ESCh ETho NHaw NTay SMDP
'Jerzy Popiełuszko' (EL) ETho LRHS
'Joan Gray' (EL) ESCh
'Joan Picton' (EL) CWSG ESCh LRHS NTay
'John Gudmundsson' (EL) ESCh
'John Huxtable' (LL) ♀H4 CDoC CLng CRHN EPfP ESCh ETho LRHS MAsh NBea NHaw NPri NTay SPoG WGor
John Paul II see *C.* 'Jan Paweł II'
'John Treasure' (Vt) CRHN EBee ETho LOck LRHS NHaw NLar
'John Warren' (EL) CWSG EBee ESCh ETho LRHS MAsh NHaw NTay SCoo SPer SPoG SWCr WFar
Jolly Good = 'Zojogo' **new** CWGN ESCh ETho
'Jorma' (LL) ESCh
Josephine = 'Evijohill'PBR (EL) ♀H4 CLng CSPN CWCL EBee EPfP ESCh ETho LAst LOck LRHS LSRN LSqu MAsh NLar NPri NTay SCoo SPer SPoG SWCr WFar
§ × ***jouiniana*** EBee MRav NHol WSHC
- 'Chance' (H) ESCh NHaw NTay
'Julka' (EL) ESCh ETho NHaw
'June Pyne' ETho
'Justa' (Vt) CWGN ESCh NHaw
'Juuli' (I) ESCh LSRN NTay
'Kaaru' (LL) CRHN CSPN ESCh ETho
'Kacper' (EL) CSPN ESCh ETho MGos NHaw
'Kaen' **new** CWGN ESCh ETho
'Kaiu' (V) ESCh LOck LRHS NHaw SPoG
§ 'Kakio' (EL) CLng EBee ESCh ETho LOck LRHS LSRN MAsh MGos NBea NTay SPet SPoG WFar
'Kalina' (EL) ESCh ETho NHaw
'Kamilla' (EL) CWGN ESCh
§ 'Kardynał Wyszyński' (EL) EBee ETho GKir MGos NBea SCoo SMDP
'Karin' ESCh
§ 'Kasmu' (Vt) ESCh NHaw
'Katharina' (EL) ESCh
'Kathleen Dunford' (EL) LRHS LSRN NBea NHaw SCoo SMDP SPoG
'Kathleen Wheeler' (EL) NTay
'Kathryn Chapman' (Vt) CRHN ESCh NHaw
'Keith Richardson' (EL) ESCh NTay
'Ken Donson' (EL) ♀H4 EBee EPfP ESCh MGos NTay SCoo
'Ken Pyne' **new** ESCh
'Kermesina' (Vt) ♀H4 CElw CFir CRHN CWCL EBee ELan EPfP ESCh ETho GKir LHop LOck LRHS MAsh MBri MGos MHer MRav NBea NHol NSti NTay SCoo SDix SPer SPet SPoG SWCr WSHC
'Kiev' (Vt) ESCh NHaw
'Killifreth' (Vt) CRHN
'King Edward VII' (EL) EBee EPfP ESCh LRHS NBea NTay WGor
'King George V' (LL) ESCh
Kingfisher = 'Evipo037' ETho LBuc LRHS LSqu MAsh SLon SPoG SWCr
'Kiri Te Kanawa' (EL) CSPN EBee ELon ESCh ETho LOck LRHS LSRN MGos NBea NHaw NTay SMDP
'Kirimäe' (LL) ESCh
'Kirsten Creed' **new** LRHS
'Kjell' (EL) ESCh
'Kommerei' (LL) ESCh ETho NHaw
§ 'Königskind' (EL) CSPN ESCh ETho MGos NBea NTay NHol WCru
koreana NHol WCru
- var. ***lutea*** GGar WCru
'Kosmicheskaia Melodiia' (LL) CSPN ESCh NTay
'Kuba' (LL) ESCh
'Küllus' (LL) CWGN ESCh ETho NTay
'Kunpü' ESCh
ladakhiana CSPN GQui MWhi NHaw SMDP WPtf
'Lady Betty Balfour' (LL) CElw CLng CSPN CWSG ESCh ETho LRHS MBNS NTay SCoo SDix SPet SPoG WFar
'Lady Bird Johnson' (T) EBee ELon EPfP ESCh ETho LOck LRHS LSRN MAsh NPri SCoo SPoG
'Lady Caroline Nevill' (EL) CRHN ESCh NBea NTay
'Lady Londesborough' (EL) EBee EPfP ESCh LRHS NBea NHaw NTay SCoo SDix SPoG
'Lady Northcliffe' (EL) CLng CSPN CTri CWSG EPfP ESCh ETho LRHS MAsh NBea NTay SDix SPet SWCr
'Lambton Park' (Ta) ♀H4 CAlb CFir CRHN EBee EPfP ETho LOck LRHS LSRN NBea NHaw NLar SMDP
'Lantern Light' (A) **new** LRHS
lasiandra NHaw
- B&SWJ 6252 WCru
- B&SWJ 6775 WCru
'Last Dance' (Ta) CRHN
Lasting Love see *C.* 'Grażyna'
'Lasurstern' (EL) ♀H4 CBcs CPLG CRHN CSPN CTri EBee ECtt ELan EPfP ESCh ETho GKir GMac LAst LRHS LSRN MAsh MBar MBri MRav NTay SDix SWCr WFar
'Laura' (LL) ESCh NHaw
'Laura Denny' (EL) ESCh ETho LRHS

	Name	Suppliers
	'Lavender Lace'	ESCh
	'Lawsoniana' (EL)	CElw CRHN CWSG LAst MBar NTay
	'Lech Wałęsa'	CWGN
	'Lemon Chiffon' (EL)	CSPN EBee ESCh ETho LRHS MAsh NHaw NTay SPoG SWCr
	'Leoni'	ESCh
	aff. ***leschenaultiana***	ESCh
	Liberation = 'Evifive'PBR (EL)	CLng ESCh LRHS MAsh SCoo SPoG SWCr
§	***ligusticifolia***	NHaw
	'Liisu' (LL)	ESCh
	'Lilacina Floribunda' (EL)	CBcs EBee MBar NHaw
	'Lilactime' (EL)	ESCh NHaw
	'Lincoln Star' (EL)	CLng CRHN ELon EPfP ESCh GKir LOck LRHS MBar MGos NBea NTay SDix SPer SPet SPoG
	'Little Bas' (Vt)	CRHN CSPN ESCh MBri NHaw NLar NTay SLon
	'Little Butterfly' (Vt)	CRHN ESCh MGos NBea NHaw NTay
	'Little Mermaid' (EL) **new**	CWGN ESCh
	'Little Nell' (Vt)	CCCN CElw CRHN CSPN ELan EPfP ESCh ETho GKir LOck LRHS MRav NBea NHol NTay SCoo SDix SPer SPet SPoG WFar WSpi
	'Lord Herschell'	ETho LOck LRHS SMDP
	'Lord Nevill' (EL)	CRHN CWSG EPfP ESCh ETho LOck LRHS NBea SPoG WFar
	'Louise Pummell'	ECou
	'Louise Rowe' (EL)	CElw CLng EBee ELan ESCh ETho LOck LRHS LSRN MAsh MGos NBea NHaw NTay SPoG
	loureiroana HWJ 663	WCru
	'Love Jewelry'	CWGN ESCh ETho NHaw NTay
	'Lunar Lass' (Fo/f)	CAlb ECho EPfP EPot ETho ITim LRHS NBea NLAp NSla SBch SIng WPGP
I	'Lunar Lass Variegata' (Fo/v)	ECho LLHF
	'Luther Burbank' (LL)	NTay
	'M. Koster' (Vt)	CDoC CRHN CSam EBee EPfP ESCh ETho LOck LRHS NBea NHaw SPer
	macropetala (d)	CBcs CSBt EBee ELan EPfP ESCh ETho LAst LRHS MAsh MBar MGan MGos MRav MWhi NBea SDix SPer SPet SWCr WBrE WFar
	- 'Alborosea'	see *C.* 'Blushing Ballerina'
	- 'Blue Lagoon'	see *C. macropetala* 'Lagoon' Jackman 1959
	- 'Lagoon' Jackman 1956	see *C. macropetala* 'Maidwell Hall' Jackman
	- 'Lagoon' ambig.	LSRN MAsh SPet
§	- 'Lagoon' Jackman 1959 (A/d) ♀H4	CSPN EBee ETho LRHS LSRN MSwo NBea NHol NSti NTay SCoo SLim SPoG SWCr
§	- 'Maidwell Hall' Jackman (A/d)	CSPN CTri CWSG EBee ECtt EPfP ESCh ETho LRHS LSRN MGos NBea NHol WPGP
	- 'Maidwell Hall' O.E.P. Wyatt (A)	MRav SCoo
	- 'Wesselton' (A/d) ♀H4	CSPN CTri EPfP ESCh ETho LRHS MAsh MBri MGos NBea NHaw NHol WFar
	- 'White Moth'	see *C.* 'White Moth'
	'Madame Baron-Veillard' (LL)	CLng ECtt ESCh LAst LRHS MBar NEgg NTay SCoo SDix SPoG WFar
	'Madame Edouard André' (LL)	CLng CRHN CSPN EPfP ESCh LRHS MAsh NBea NTay SCoo SPet SPoG SWCr WFar
	'Madame Grangé' (LL) ♀H4	CSPN EPfP ESCh LRHS MAsh NBea NHaw NTay SCoo SPoG SWCr
	'Madame Julia Correvon' (Vt) ♀H4	Widely available
	'Madame le Coultre'	see *C.* 'Mevrouw Le Coultre'
	'Madeleine' (A)	ESCh
	'Majojo' (Fo)	GEdr LLHF
	mandschurica	ETho GCal NHaw
	- B&SWJ 1060	WCru
	'Marcel Moser' (EL)	NTay
	'Marcelina' (EL)	ESCh
	'Margaret Hunt' (LL)	CSPN EGxp ELan ESCh ETho LSRN NBea NHaw
	'Margaret Jones' (M/d)	EBee ESCh NHaw
	'Margaret Wood' (EL)	NTay
	'Maria Cornelia' (Vt) **new**	CWGN ESCh
	'Maria Louise Jensen' (EL)	NTay
	'Marie Boisselot' (EL) ♀H4	Widely available
	'Marinka' (H)	ESCh SMDP
	'Märjamaa' (LL)	ESCh
	'Marjorie' (M/d)	CBcs CDoC CSPN CTri CWSG EBee ECtt ELan EPfP ESCh ETho LOck LRHS MAsh MGos MRav NBea NEgg NHol NTay SAga SBod SPer SPet SPoG SWCr WBVN WCru WFar WSHC
	'Markham's Pink' (A/d) ♀H4	Widely available
	marmoraria ♀H2-3	CMoH EAEE ECho LHop LRHS SIng WFar
	- hybrid (Fo)	ITim
	marmoraria* × *petriei	ECho SIng
	'Marmori' (LL)	CWGN ESCh ETho LRHS MAsh NHaw
	'Mary Whistler' (A)	ESCh MGos
	'Mary-Claire' (EL/d)	ESCh
§	'Maskarad' (Vt)	CSPN ESCh
	Masquerade (Vt)	see *C.* 'Maskarad'
I	'Masquerade' (EL)	ETho MBri NTay
	'Matilda' (EL)	ESCh
	'Matka Siedliska' (EL)	CSPN NBea NTay
	'Maureen' (LL)	CSPN CWGN CWSG
	maximowicziana	see *C. terniflora*
	'Mayleen' (M) ♀H4	CPou CSBt CTri CWSG EBee ECtt EPfP ESCh ETho EWTr LOck LRHS MAsh MBri MGos MRav NBea NEgg NTay SAga SBch SBod SCoo SLim SPer SPet SPoG SWCr WFar
	Medley = 'Evipo012'PBR	CLng ESCh LRHS NTay
	'Meeli' (LL)	EBee ESCh
	'Meloodia' (LL)	NBea
§	'Mevrouw Le Coultre' (EL)	MBlu MCot MGan NBlu
	microphylla	ECou
	Mienie Belle = 'Zomibel' (T) **new**	ESCh ETho
	'Mikelite' (Vt)	ESCh NHaw
	'Miniseelik' (LL)	ESCh NTay SMDP
	'Minister' (EL)	ESCh LRHS
	'Minuet' (Vt) ♀H4	CRHN CSPN ELon EPfP ESCh ETho GKir LOck LRHS MSwo NBea NTay SCoo SDix SPer WSpi
	'Miriam Markham' (EL)	ESCh NBea NHaw
	'Miss Bateman' (EL) ♀H4	CDoC CMac CRHN CSPN CTri CWSG EBee ECtt ELan EPfP ESCh ETho GKir LBMP LRHS LSRN MAsh MBar MBri NBea NPri NTay SDix SLim SPer SPet SPoG SWCr WBor
	'Miss Christine' (M)	ESCh ETho LSRN NTay SMDP WFar
	'Miss Crawshay' (EL)	NHaw
	'Moniuszko'	CWGN ESCh
N	***montana***	CBcs CPLG CSBt EBee ECtt GGal MBar MGos NBea NHol SBch SBod SDix SPet SSta WFar
	- B&SWJ 6724 from Taiwan	WCru
	- B&SWJ 6930	WCru
	- BWJ 8189b from China	WCru

	- HWJK 2156 from Nepal	WCru
	- 'Alexander'	CPou CWSG EPfP LRHS MAsh MGos SWCr
	- var. ***grandiflora*** ♀H4	Widely available
I	- 'Lilacina'	ESCh
	- 'Peveril'	CSPN ESCh ETho
	- 'Prosperity'	ESCh
	- var. ***rubens*** E.H.Wilson	CDoC CSBt CTri ELan EPfP ESCh ETho GGal GGar LOck LRHS MBar MBri MSwo NBea NHol NWea SDix SPet SPlb SPoG SReu SWCr WFar
I	- - 'Odorata'	EBee ETho LFol MGos MRav SBod SCoo SLim SPoG WGor WGwG
	- - 'Pink Perfection'	CDoC CWSG EBee ECtt ELan EPfP ESCh EWTr LAst LBMP LRHS LSRN MAsh NBea NEgg NHol NTay SCoo SPer SPoG SWCr WFar
	- - 'Tetrarose' ♀H4	Widely available
	- - 'Veitch'	CBot MWhi
I	- 'Rubens Superba'	CMHG CTri CWSG EBee ECtt ESCh LBuc MAsh MGan NPri SLim WBVN WFar
	- var. ***sericea***	see *C. spooneri*
§	- var. ***wilsonii***	CElw CSPN CSam EBee ECtt ELan EPfP ESCh ETho GGar LOck LRHS LSRN MAsh MBar MGos MNHC MRav MSwo NBea NTay SDix SMDP SPet SWCr WFar
	'Monte Cassino' (EL)	CRHN CSPN CWGN EBee ESCh ETho LRHS NBea SMDP
	'Moonbeam' (Fo)	CMHG EAEE EBee ECou ELan EPot ESCh GEdr ITim LRHS MGos MRav NBea NOrc NTay WCot
§	'Moonlight' (EL)	CElw CSPN ESCh LRHS NTay
	'Moonman' (Fo)	LLHF
	Morning Cloud	see *C.* 'Yukikomachi'
	Morning Star = 'Zoklako' **new**	CWGN ETho
	'Morning Yellow' (M)	CCCN ESCh EWTr LHop LRHS NEgg
	'Mrs Cholmondeley' (EL) ♀H4	CMac CRHN CSPN CWSG EBee ELan ELon EPfP ESCh ETho GKir LOck LRHS LSRN MAsh MBar MBri MGan MGos MSwo NBea NBlu NPri NTay SDix SLim SPoG SWCr WFar
	'Mrs George Jackman' (EL) ♀H4	CSPN ESCh ETho LRHS MGos NBea NLar NTay SCoo
	'Mrs Hope' (EL)	ESCh
	'Mrs James Mason' (EL)	ELon ESCh LRHS NBea NHaw NTay SMDP
	'Mrs N.Thompson' (EL)	CMac CSPN CTri EBee ELan ESCh ETho LOck LRHS LSRN MAsh MBar MBri MGos NBea NBir NEgg NPer NTay SDix SPer SPet SPoG WFar
	'Mrs P.B.Truax' (EL)	ESCh LRHS NBea NTay SMDP
	'Mrs P.T.James' (EL)	ESCh
	'Mrs Robert Brydon' (H)	ECtt IPot LRHS MBNS NBPC NCGa NHol NLar NSti NTay SRGP STes WCot WFar
	'Mrs Spencer Castle' (EL)	CSPN ESCh ETho LRHS NBea NTay
	'Mrs T. Lundell' (Vt)	CRHN CSPN EBee ESCh MGos NHaw NTay
	'Multi Blue' (EL)	CBcs CElw CRHN CWSG EBee ECtt ELan EPfP ESCh ETho LAst LOck LRHS LSRN MAsh MBri MGos MRav NBea NTay SBod SLim SPer SPet SPoG SWCr WBrE WFar WGwG
	'My Angel'PBR (Ta)	CSPN ELan ESCh MGos NHaw NLar NTay WSpi
	'Myōjō' (EL)	CSPN EBee ESCh SPoG
	'Nadezhda' (LL)	ESCh NBea SMDP
§	***napaulensis***	CSPN CTri ESCh ETho LFol LRHS MNrw NTay WCru WFar WSHC WSpi
I	'Natacha' (EL)	EBee ESCh LOck MAsh NBea NHaw NTay SCoo
	'Natascha' (EL)	CLng LRHS LSRN
	'Neapolitan'	ESCh
	'Negritianka' (LL)	CSPN EBee EPfP ESCh LRHS LSRN NBea NHaw NTay SPoG
	'Negus' (LL)	ESCh MGos
	'Nelly Moser' (EL) ♀H4	Widely available
	'Nelly Moser Neu' (EL)	NTay
	'New Dawn' (M)	CSPN NHaw
	'New Love'PBR (H)	CSPN ESCh ETho LHop LSRN MGos NHaw NLar
	New Zealand hybrids (Fo)	ECou
	'Night Veil' (Vt)	ETho
	'Nikolai Rubtsov' (LL)	CSPN ESCh SMDP
	'Niobe' (EL) ♀H4	Widely available
	'Norfolk Queen' (EL)	ESCh
	'North Star' (EL)	LRHS NTay
	North Star (LL)	see *C.* 'Põhjanael'
	'Nuit de Chine' (EL)	ESCh
	nutans var. ***thyrsoidea***	see *C. rehderiana*
	obvallata	see *C. japonica* var. *obvallata*
	'Ocean Pearl' (A)	ETho NLar NTay
	ochotensis	CSPN SDys
	ochroleuca	GAuc
	Octopus = 'Zooct' (A) **new**	ESCh
	'Odoriba' (V)	CWGN ESCh ETho NHaw NLar
	'Ola Howells' (A/d)	ESCh NBea
	'Olga' (M)	ESCh
	'Olimpiada-80' (EL)	ESCh
	'Omoshiro' (EL)	CAlb CWGN ESCh ETho LRHS MGos NBea NHaw NTay
	Ooh La La = 'Evipo041' **new**	LBuc LRHS MAsh
	'Oonagare Ichigoo' (Vt)	ESCh MGos
	Opaline	see *C.* 'Asagasumi'
	orientalis misapplied	see *C. tibetana* subsp. *vernayi*
	orientalis L.	CElw EBee GCra NHol SCoo WFar
	- 'Orange Peel'	see *C. tibetana* subsp. *vernayi* var. *vernayi* 'Orange Peel'
	'Otto Fröbel' (EL)	CSPN ESCh NTay
	'Paddington' (EL)	ETho
	'Pagoda' (Vt) ♀H4	CDoC CRHN EBee EPfP ESCh ETho LRHS MAsh MBri MRav NBea NHol NSti NTay SCoo SRms SWCr
	Palette = 'Evipo034'PBR	CLng ESCh LRHS SPoG
	'Pamela' (F)	CSPN ESCh ETho NHaw NTay
	'Pamela Jackman'	see *C. alpina* 'Pamela Jackman'
	'Pamiat Serdtsa' (I)	EBee ESCh ETho NHaw
	'Pamina' (EL)	CWGN ETho
	'Pangbourne Pink' (I) ♀H4	CSPN CWCL EBee EPfP ESCh ETho GBuc LRHS MAsh NBea NHaw NTay SCoo
	paniculata Thunb.	see *C. terniflora*
§	***paniculata*** J.G. Gmel.	CSPN WPGP
	- (f)	ETho
	- var. ***lobata***	NLar
	'Paola' (EL/d)	CWGN ESCh
	'Paradise Queen' (EL)	ESCh LBuc NLar WFar
	'Parasol' (EL)	CSPN ESCh
	Parisienne = 'Evipo019'PBR	ETho LBuc LRHS LSqu MAsh NTay SLon SPoG SWCr
	parviflora DC.	see *C. viticella* subsp. *campaniflora*
	parviloba var. ***bartlettii*** B&SWJ 6788	WCru
	'Pastel Blue' (I)	ESCh ETho NBea SMDP
	'Pastel Pink' (I)	ESCh ETho SMDP
	'Pastel Princess' (EL)	NHaw NTay
	'Pat Coleman' (EL)	ETho

	Name	Suppliers
	patens	CElw
	- 'Korean Moon' (EL)	WCru
§	- 'Manshuu Ki' (EL)	CDoC CRHN CSPN CWSG EBee ECtt EPfP ESCh ETho GKir LRHS NBea NTay
	- 'Nagoya' (EL)	ESCh
	- 'Sanda' (EL)	ESCh
	- 'Yukiokoshi' (EL)	ESCh ETho NTay
	Patricia Ann Fretwell = 'Pafar' (EL)	CSPN
§	'Paul Farges' (Vt) ♀H4	CSPN CWGN EBee ETho NHaw NHol NSti NTay SMDP
	'Pauline' (A/d) ♀H4	CBcs CLng CWSG EBee ESCh ETho LRHS LSRN MAsh MGos NBea NTay SCoo SWCr
	'Pearl Rose' (A/d)	CWSG
	'Pendragon' (Vt)	CRHN CWGN ESCh NHaw
	'Pennell's Purity' (LL)	NBea NHaw NTay
	Peppermint = 'Evipo005'PBR **new**	ETho LBuc LRHS LSqu MAsh
	'Percy Picton' (EL)	LRHS
	'Perle d'Azur' (LL)	Widely available
	'Perrin's Pride' (Vt)	CLng ESCh LRHS MAsh MGos NBea NLar NTay SCoo
	Petit Faucon = 'Evisix'PBR (I) ♀H4	CLng EBee ECtt EPfP ETho LAst LOck LRHS LSRN LSqu MAsh MBri NBea NPri NSti NTay SCoo SLim SPer SPoG SWCr WPGP
	petriei	ECou GBBs GGar
	- 'Princess' (Fo/f)	ECou SIng
	- 'Steepdown' (Fo/f)	ECou
	'Peveril Pearl' (EL)	ESCh ETho NTay
	'Peveril Profusion' (T)	LRHS MAsh
	'Phoenix' (EL)	ESCh NTay
	Picardy = 'Evipo024'PBR (EL)	ETho LBuc LRHS LSqu MAsh NTay SPoG SWCr
I	'Picton's Variety' (M)	CTri EBee NHaw NHol SMDP WFar
	pierotii B&SWJ 6281	WCru
	'Piilu' (EL)	CSPN CWGN ELan ESCh ETho LBuc LOck LRHS LSRN MAsh MBNS MBri MGos MWea NBea NHaw NPri NTay SCoo SMDP SPad SPoG SWCr
	'Pink Celebration'	CWGN ESCh ETho
	'Pink Champagne'	see *C.* 'Kakio'
	'Pink Delight'PBR	CWGN
	'Pink Fantasy' (LL)	CLng CRHN CSPN CTri CWSG ESCh ETho LRHS MAsh MBar MGos NBea NTay SCoo SLim SRkn SWCr
	'Pink Flamingo' (A) ♀H4	CLng CSPN CWCL EBee ECtt EGxp ELan EPfP ESCh ETho LRHS MAsh NSti NTay SBod SCoo SPet SPoG SRkn SWCr WBrE
	'Pink Ice' (I)	ESCh LOck LRHS
	'Pink Pearl' (EL)	ESCh NTay
	'Pirko' (Vt)	ESCh NHaw
§	***pitcheri***	GAuc WSHC
	'Pixie' (Fo/m)	CSPN ECou ELan EPfP ETho GGar IMon ITim LRHS MGos NHaw NHol NLar NTay SBod SCoo SPoG
I	'Pleniflora' (M/d)	ESCh MGos NHaw
§	'Plum Beauty' (A)	CSPN ESCh MGos NHaw
§	'Põhjanael' (LL)	CSPN CWSG ESCh MGos NBea
	'Pointy' (A)	ESCh
	Polar BearPBR	see *C.* Arctic Queen
	'Poldice' (Vt)	CRHN
	'Polish Spirit' (LL) ♀H4	CDoC CElw CRHN CSPN CSam CTri CWCL EBee ECtt ELan EPfP ESCh ETho GKir LOck LRHS LSRN MAsh MBlu MGos NBea NBlu NHol NPri NTay SPer SPoG SRkn WFar WSHC
	'Polonez' (Vt)	ETho
	potaninii	CSPN ECtt GCra MWhi WPtf WSHC
§	- var. ***potaninii***	NTay
	- var. ***souliei***	see *C. potaninii* var. *potaninii*
	- 'Summer Snow'	see *C.* 'Paul Farges'
	'Praecox' (H) ♀H4	CRHN CSam CWCL EAEE EBee ECtt ELan EPfP ESCh ETho LHop LRHS MAsh MBar MBri MWhi NBea NBir NHol SDix SWCr WCot
	'Prairie River' (A)	ETho
	Pretty in Blue = 'Zopre'PBR (F)	EBee ESCh
	'Pribaltika' (LL)	ESCh
	'Primrose Star'PBR	see *C.* 'Star'
	'Prince Charles' (LL) ♀H4	CElw CPou CRHN CSPN CTri EBee ELan EPfP ESCh ETho LOck LRHS LSRN MGos NBea NTay SCoo SDix SLim SPer SPet SPoG WFar WGwG
	'Prince Philip' (EL)	ESCh NTay WFar
§	'Princess Diana' (T) ♀H4	Widely available
§	'Princess of Wales' (EL)	CWCL EPfP ESCh LRHS LSRN MBNS NLar NPri NSti WFar
	'Prins Hendrik' (EL)	WGor
	'Prinsesse Alexandra'PBR	EBee ESCh ETho NTay SPad
	'Propertius' (A)	CWGN EBee ESCh ETho LRHS MAsh MGos NBea NHaw SMDP SPoG
	'Proteus' (EL)	CLng CSPN ELan ELon EPfP ESCh ETho LRHS MAsh MGos NBea NTay SCoo SDix SPet
	'Pruinina'	see *C.* 'Plum Beauty'
	psilandra	SMDP
	'Purple Haze' (Vt)	CRHN
	'Purple Princess' (H)	ESCh LRHS MAvo
	'Purple Rain' (A)	CTri ESCh LRHS NHol
	'Purple Spider' (A/d)	CSPN EBee ESCh ETho LRHS MBlu NHaw NHol NLar NTay SCoo SPer SPoG
	'Purpurea Plena Elegans' (Vt/d) ♀H4	Widely available
	quadribracteolata	ECou
	- 'Nancy's Lookout'	ECou
	'Queen of Holland'PBR	CWGN ESCh
	'Radar Love' (Ta)	GMaP LLHF NLar WBrE
	'Radost' (EL)	ESCh
	'Ragamuffin' (EL/d)	ESCh MGos
	'Rahvarinne' (LL)	ESCh ETho
	'Ramona' (LL)	ESCh LRHS LSRN MAsh NHaw
	Rebecca = 'Evipo016' **new**	ETho LBuc LRHS LSqu MAsh SLon
	recta	CSPN ECtt ETho GKir LPio MCot MNrw MWhi NBea NLar WPer WTin
§	- 'Lime Close' (F)	LPio
I	- 'Peveril' (F)	ESCh NBea SMDP
	- 'Purpurea' (F)	CBcs CBot CSpe EBee EHoe ELan EPfP ETho EWTr GCra LHop LOck LPio LRHS MAsh MAvo MWhi NBPC NBea NBir NSti SAga SBod SDix SPer SPhx SWCr WCot WHoo WTin
§	- subsp. ***recta*** var. ***lasiosepala***	CSPN
	- Serious Black	see *C. recta* 'Lime Close'
	- 'Velvet Night' (F)	CMHG CPrp CWGN ECtt ESCh LRHS MAvo MBel MCot MGos NBea NEgg NLar SDix SMDP SPoG
	'Red Ballon' (Ta)	SMDP
§	'Red Beetroot Beauty' (A)	CSPN ESCh LRHS
	'Red Cooler'	see *C.* 'Crimson King'
	'Red Pearl' (EL)	ESCh ETho MGos NTay
§	***rehderiana*** ♀H4	CBgR CBot CDul CFir CRHN CSPN CSam CTri EBee ELan EPfP ESCh ETho GAuc GMac IDee LRHS MBlu

		MRav MWhi NBea NBir NHol NSti NTay SDix SPer WGwG WPGP WSHC
	- BWJ 7700	WCru
	'Remembrance' (LL)	ESCh ETho LSRN
	repens Veitch	see *C. montana* var. *wilsonii*
	repens Finet & Gagn. DJHC 795	SMDP
I	'Rhapsody' B. Fretwell (EL)	CSPN LSRN NHaw
	'Rhapsody' ambig.	CLng EPfP ETho LRHS MAsh MGos NTay SCoo SPoG SWCr WFar
	'Richard Pennell' (EL) ♀H4	EBee ESCh ETho LOck LRHS MAsh NBea NTay SDix SWCr
	'Rodomax' (A)	ESCh
	'Roko-Kolla' (LL)	CSPN EBee ESCh ETho NBea
	'Romantika' (LL)	CSPN EBee ELan ELon ESCh ETho LRHS NBea NHaw NTay SCoo SPer SPoG
	'Roogoja' (LL)	ESCh
	'Rooguchi' (I)	CWGN EBee ESCh ETho LRHS MAsh SMDP SPoG SWCr
	'Rosa Königskind' (EL)	ESCh ETho
	'Rose Supreme' (EL)	ESCh ETho
I	'Rosea' (I) ♀H4	CBcs CSPN EAEE EBee EPfP ESCh ETho LHop LOck LRHS LSRN MTho NBea NSti NTay SPoG
	'Rosea' (Vt)	ESCh
	Rosebud = 'Robud'PBR (M/d)	EBee ESCh NLar NPer SMDP
	Rosemoor = 'Evipo002'PBR	CLng CWCL CWGN EPfP ETho IBal LRHS LSqu MAsh MBri SCoo SWCr
	'Rosy O'Grady' (A) ♀H4	CWCL EBee ELan ETho LRHS MBar MBri MGos NHol NLar NSti
	'Rosy Pagoda' (A)	EBee ELan ELon EPfP ESCh LOck MBri NBea NBir NHaw NLar
	'Rouge Cardinal' (LL)	CElw CRHN CSPN CWSG EBee ECtt ELan EPfP ESCh ETho IBal LOck LRHS LSRN MAsh MBar MBri MCot MGos NBea NBlu NEgg SDix SPad SPer SPet SPoG SWCr WBVN WFar
	'Royal Velours' (Vt) ♀H4	CDoC CElw CRHN CSPN CTri EBee ELan EPfP ESCh ETho GKir LOck LRHS LSRN MAsh MGos MWhi NBea NHol NSti SCoo SDix SLim SPer SWCr
	Royal Velvet = 'Evifour'PBR (EL)	CLng CSPN CWCL EPfP ESCh ETho IBal LAst LRHS LSRN MAsh MBri NTay SCoo SLim SPoG
	'Royalty' (EL) ♀H4	CElw CLng CSPN ELan EPfP ESCh IBal LOck LRHS LSRN MAsh NBir NPri NTay SCoo SLim SPer SPoG SWCr
	'Rozalia' (EL)	ESCh
	'Rubens Superba'	see *C. montana* 'Rubens Superba'
	'Rubra' (Vt)	MBlu
	'Ruby' (A)	CMHG CSPN CWSG EBee ELon EPfP ETho LOck LRHS LSRN MGos NBea NBlu NHol NSti SCoo SPer SPoG
	'Ruby Glow' (EL)	CLng EPfP ESCh LRHS LSRN MAsh NTay SCoo
	'Rüütel' (EL)	ESCh ETho LOck LRHS MGos NBea NHaw NTay SCoo SMDP SPoG
	'Saalomon' (LL)	ESCh
	'Sakala' (EL)	ESCh
§	'Sakurahime' (EL)	EBee ESCh
	'Sally Cadge' (EL)	ESCh NHaw NTay
	'Samantha Denny' (EL)	CSPN ESCh NBea NHaw
	'Sander' (H)	CSPN ESCh ETho SMDP
	'Sandra Denny' (EL)	ETho
	'Sano-no-murasaki' (EL)	ESCh
	Saphyra Indigo = 'Cleminov51'	MAsh
	'Satsukibare' (EL)	ESCh MGos
I	'Saturn' (LL)	ESCh
	'Saturn' (EL)	ESCh
	Savannah = 'Evipo015'PBR (Vt)	CLng LRHS NTay
	'Scartho Gem' (EL)	CLng EPfP ESCh LRHS MAsh NTay SCoo
	'Sealand Gem' (EL)	ESCh NBea NHaw NTay
	'Serenata' (EL)	ESCh
	serratifolia	ETho MBel MDKP MWhi SDix SWal WBVN WFar
	- B&SWJ 8458 from Korea	WCru
	'Sheila Thacker' (EL)	ETho
	'Shin-shigyoku' (EL)	CWGN ESCh MGos NTay
	'Shirayukihime' (LL)	CSPN ESCh
§	'Shiva' (A)	LRHS MBri
	'Sho-un' (EL)	EBee ESCh
	'Sialia' (A/d)	ESCh MGos
§	***sibirica***	EPfP NBea
	'Signe' (EL)	ETho
	'Signe' (Vt)	see *C.* 'Kasmu'
	'Silmakivi' (EL)	ESCh
	'Silver Moon' (EL)	CSPN ESCh ETho LOck LRHS NBea NLar NTay SCoo
	'Simplicity' (A)	CSPN EBee LRHS MBri
	simsii Small	see *C. pitcheri*
	simsii Sweet	see *C. crispa*
	'Sinee Plamia' (LL)	ESCh NHaw
§	'Sinii Dozhd' (I)	CSPN ESCh
	'Sir Eric Savill' (M)	ESCh
	'Sir Garnet Wolseley' (EL)	ESCh LRHS SDix
	'Sir Trevor Lawrence' (T)	CSPN EBee ESCh ETho LRHS MAsh NBea NHaw NHol NSti NTay SCoo SPer SPoG SWCr WFar
	'Sizaia Ptitsa' (I)	ESCh ETho
	'Snow Queen' (EL)	CSPN EBee EPfP ESCh ETho LOck LRHS MAsh MBri MGos NBea NTay SPet
	'Snowbells' **new**	EGxp
	'Snowbird' (A/d)	CSPN ELon EPfP ESCh LRHS MAsh NHaw NHol SPoG
	'Snowdrift'	see *C. armandii* 'Snowdrift'
§	'Södertälje' (Vt)	CRHN ESCh ETho LRHS NBea SCoo SPoG WFar
	'Solidarność' (EL)	ETho LRHS
	songarica	NHol
	'Sonnette'	ESCh
	'Southern Cross' **new**	LRHS
	'Souvenir de J.L. Delbard' (EL)	ESCh
§	'Souvenir du Capitaine Thuilleaux' (EL)	ESCh GKir MGos NBea NTay
	'Special Occasion' (EL)	CLng CSPN CWGN EBee ESCh ETho LRHS LSRN MAsh NBea NHaw NLar NPri NTay SCoo SPoG WFar
§	***spooneri***	CTri CWSG ECtt EPfP GQui MGan NHol SCoo SRms WFoF
	'Sputnik' (I)	CSPN CWGN NHaw NTay
	stans	CPLG CPou EPfP ESCh IFro LRHS MAsh NBea NLar NWCA SIng SMDP
	- B&SWJ 5073	WCru
	- B&SWJ 6345	WCru
§	'Star'PBR (M/d)	CDoC CSPN CWGN EBee EPfP ESCh ETho LOck LRHS MAsh MGos MRav MSwo NHol NLar SPoG WFar
	'Star of India' (LL)	CElw CLng CRHN EBee EPfP ESCh ETho LRHS MAsh MGos MRav NBea NTay SCoo SPer SPoG SWCr WFar

	Name	Suppliers
	'Starfish' (EL)	ESCh MGos NHaw
	'Starlight' (M) **new**	LRHS
	'Stasik' (LL)	ESCh NHaw
	'Stephanie' (A)	ESCh
	Still Waters = 'Zostiwa' **new**	CWGN ETho
	'Strawberry Roan' (EL)	ESCh
	Sugar Candy = 'Evione'PBR (EL)	CLng ESCh IBal LRHS MAsh MBri NTay SCoo SPoG
	Summer Snow	see *C.* 'Paul Farges'
	'Sundance'	CSPN EBee ESCh SMDP
	'Sunrise'PBR (M/d)	CSPN CWGN EBee ELon ESCh ETho LOck LRHS MSwo NHaw NLar WFar
	'Sunset' (EL) ♀H4	CLng ESCh LRHS LSRN MAsh MBri NBea NLar NPri NTay SCoo SPoG SWCr WFar
	'Sunstar'	SWal
	'Swedish Bells' (I)	ETho
	'Sylvia Denny' (EL)	CWSG EBee ELan EPfP ESCh ETho GKir LRHS MBar MRav NBea NTay SPet
	'Sympatia' (LL)	ESCh NHaw
	'Syrena' (LL)	NBea NHaw
	szuyuanensis B&SWJ 6791	WCru
	'Tage Lundell' (A)	CLng CSPN EBee EPfP LRHS MGos NBea SMDP
	'Tamula'	ESCh
	'Tango' (Vt)	CElw CRHN EBee ESCh NBea NHaw NTay SMDP
§	***tangutica***	Widely available
	'Tapestry' (I)	SMDP
	'Tartu' (EL)	CSPN ESCh ETho
	tashiroi purple-flowered B&SWJ 7005	WCru
	- 'Yellow Peril'	WCru
	'Teksa' (LL)	ESCh
	'Tentel' (LL)	ESCh
§	***terniflora***	CBcs EBee EPfP ESCh ETho LFol LRHS NHaw NSti
	- B&SWJ 5751	WCru
	- var. ***robusta***	see *C. terniflora* var. *terniflora*
§	- var. ***terniflora***	LFol
	'Teshio' (EL)	CSPN EBee ESCh LRHS NHaw SPoG
	texensis	CBcs CElw IFro WSHC
	- 'The Princess of Wales'	see *C.* 'Princess Diana'
	'The Bride' (EL)	CSPN CWGN ESCh ETho LRHS LSRN MGos NBea NHaw NTay
	'The First Lady' (EL)	CSPN ESCh ETho LRHS NTay
	'The President' (EL) ♀H4	Widely available
	'The Princess of Wales' (EL)	see *C.* 'Princess of Wales' (EL)
	'The Princess of Wales' (T)	see *C.* 'Princess Diana' (T)
	'The Vagabond' (EL)	CSPN CWSG ELan ELon ESCh ETho LOck LRHS LSRN MGos NBea NHaw NLar NTay SCoo SPet
	'Theydon Belle' (EL)	ESCh
	Thumbelina = 'Evipo030'PBR **new**	LRHS MAsh
	thunbergii misapplied	see *C. terniflora*
	'Thyrislund' (EL)	CSPN EBee ESCh
	'Tibetan Mix' (Ta)	CSPN SMDP
	tibetana	MBar MNrw NHaw
	- 'Black Tibet'	ESCh SMDP
§	- subsp. ***vernayi***	CMHG GKir
	- - SDR 3060	GKev
	- - var. ***laciniifolia***	NHol
§	- - var. ***vernayi*** 'Orange Peel' LS&E 13342	CBcs CDoC ESCh ETho GKir LRHS MRav NHol SGar SLim WFar WSpi
	Timpany NZ hybrids (Fo)	ITim
	'Tinkerbell'	see *C.* 'Shiva'
	'Titania' (EL)	ESCh
	'Toki' (EL)	CWGN EBee ESCh
	tongluensis GWJ 9358	WCru
	- HWJK 2368	WCru
	'Treasure Trove' (Ta)	CSPN LRHS NHol SMDP
	'Trianon' (EL)	ESCh
	'Triibu' (LL)	ESCh
	'Trikatrei' (LL)	ESCh
	× ***triternata*** **new**	LRHS
§	- 'Rubromarginata' ♀H4	CDoC CFir CRHN CSPN CWGN EBee ELan ELon EPfP ESCh ETho GMac LFol LOck LRHS LSRN MAsh MBri MGos MRav NBea NHol NSti SDix SPer SPoG SRkn SWCr
	'True Blue'	ESCh
	'Tsuzuki' (EL)	CSPN EBee ESCh NBea
§	***tubulosa***	CSPN EBee ESCh ETho MGos NHol SBch SMDP SRms
§	- Alan Bloom = 'Alblo'PBR (H)	EBrs GKir LRHS
	- 'Wyevale' (H) ♀H4	CSPN EAEE ELan EPfP ETho GGar LHop LRHS MAvo MCot MRav NHol NTay SAga SCoo SDix SMad SPoG WEas
	'Tuchka' (EL)	ESCh
	'Twilight' (EL)	CLng CSPN EPfP ESCh LRHS MAsh NTay WFar
	uncinata B&SWJ 1893	WCru
§	***urophylla*** 'Winter Beauty'	ETho MGos MRav SPoG
	urticifolia B&SWJ 8651	WCru
	- B&SWJ 8852	WCru
	'Valge Daam' (LL)	CWGN ESCh ETho NHaw NTay
	'Vanessa' (LL)	CRHN ESCh
	'Vanilla Cream' (Fo)	ECou
	'Vanso'PBR	see *C.* 'Blue Light'
	× ***vedrariensis*** 'Hidcote' (M)	NHaw SMDP
	'Venosa Violacea' (Vt) ♀H4	CElw CRHN CSPN CSam EBee ELan EPfP ESCh EShb ETho LOck LRHS LSRN MAsh MRav NBea NHol NSti NTay SCoo SDix SPer SPoG SWCr WFar
	'Vera' (M)	CSPN EBee ECtt ESCh ETho LRHS LSRN NTay SCoo WFar
	vernayi	see *C. tibetana* subsp. *vernayi*
	'Veronica's Choice' (EL)	CRHN CSPN ELan ESCh LOck MGos MRav NBea NHaw NTay SPet
	Versailles = 'Evipo025'PBR (EL)	ETho LRHS MAsh NTay
	versicolor	ESCh
§	Vesuvius = 'Evipo032'PBR	CLng ESCh LBuc LRHS LSqu MAsh SLon SPoG SWCr
	Victor Hugo = 'Evipo007'PBR	CLng EPfP ESCh ETho IBal LBuc LRHS MAsh NLar NTay SCoo
N	'Victoria' (LL) ♀H4	CRHN CSPN ESCh ETho LRHS LSRN MAsh MGos MRav NBea NHaw NTay SCoo SDix SPoG SWCr
	Viennetta = 'Evipo006'PBR **new**	ETho LBuc LRHS LSqu MAsh SLon SWCr
	'Vilhelmīne'	CWGN ESCh
	'Ville de Lyon' (LL)	CBcs CElw CMac CRHN CSPN CWCL EBee ELan EPfP ESCh GKir LRHS LSRN MAsh MBar MBri MGan MGos NBea NBlu NEgg NPri SDix SLim SPer SPet SPoG SWCr WFar
	'Vince Denny' (Ta)	ESCh ETho SMDP
	Vino = 'Poulvo'PBR (EL)	CLng IBal LRHS MAsh NHaw NTay SCoo SPoG
I	'Viola' (LL)	CSPN EBee ESCh ETho LRHS MBri MGos NBea NHaw NTay WFar
	'Violet Charm' (EL)	CWSG NTay
	'Violet Elizabeth' (EL)	ESCh MRav
	'Violet Purple' (A)	MGos NHaw

	'Violetta' (EL)	ESCh
	viorna	ESCh WSHC
	virginiana misapplied	see *C. vitalba*
	virginiana Hook.	see *C. ligusticifolia*
	virginiana L.	CElw
§	***vitalba***	CArn CRWN EBWF ESCh ETho MBar NHaw SECG WGwG WHer
	viticella ♀H4	CElw CRHN CWib ESCh ETho MBri NBea NHaw SDix WSHC
§	- subsp. ***campaniflora***	CBot CElw CMea CRHN CSPN EShb ETho GCal GMac NBea NHaw NWCA WCru WPGP
§	- 'Flore Pleno'	CRHN ELon EPfP ESCh ETho LOck LRHS LSRN MAsh NHaw
	- 'Hågelby Pink'	CRHN CWGN ESCh
	- 'Hågelby White'	CWGN ESCh ETho NHaw
	- 'Hanna' (Vt)	ESCh ETho LSRN NHaw
	- 'Mary Rose'	see *C. viticella* 'Flore Pleno'
	'Vivienne'	see *C.* 'Beth Currie'
	'Vivienne Lawson' (LL)	ESCh LRHS
	'Voluceau' (Vt)	CLng CPou CRHN ELan ESCh GKir LRHS LSRN MAsh MGos MRav NBea SPer
	'Vostok' (LL)	ESCh MGos
	'Vyvyan Pennell' (EL)	CBcs CSPN CTri EBee ECtt ELan EPfP ESCh ETho GKir LHop LRHS LSRN MAsh MBar MBri MGan MGos MSwo NBea NEgg NPri NTay SLim SPer SPet SPoG SWCr WBor WFar
	'W.E. Gladstone' (EL)	CRHN ETho GKir LRHS NBea NTay SDix
	'Wada's Primrose'	see *C. patens* 'Manshuu Ki'
	'Walenburg' (Vt)	CRHN CWGN ESCh ETho NBea NHaw SLon
	'Walter Pennell' (EL)	CBcs CLng CWSG EBee ESCh ETho IBal LRHS MAsh NBea NTay SCoo SLim WGor
	'Warsaw' (Ta)	NPri
	'Warszawska Nike' (EL) ♀H4	CLng CRHN EBee ELan EPfP ESCh ETho LOck LRHS MAsh MBri MGos NBea NTay SCoo SPad SPer SPet
	'Warwickshire Rose' (M)	CLng CRHN CSPN CTri CWGN CWSG ECtt ESCh ETho EWTr GKir LOck LRHS LSRN MAsh MGos MWat NBea NHaw NHol NTay SPoG WFar WPGP
	'Waterperry Star' (Ta)	MWat
	'Wedding Day' (EL)	ESCh ETho LSRN NLar NTay WHlf
	'Wee Willie Winkie' (M)	CWGN LRHS SCoo SPoG
	'Westerplatte' (EL)	CLng CRHN CSPN CWGN EPfP ESCh ETho LOck LRHS MAsh MGos NBea NHaw NTay SMDP WFar
	'Whirligig' (A)	CSPN
§	'White Columbine' (A) ♀H4	EBee EPfP ESCh ETho LOck LRHS MGos NBea NSti SDix SPet
	'White Lady' (A/d)	ESCh NHaw NTay
	'White Magic' (Vt)	CRHN CWGN ETho MGos
§	'White Moth' (A/d)	CSPN CWSG EBee ELan ETho LRHS LSRN MGos MRav NHaw NHol SPer SPoG SRms
	'White Swan' (A/d)	CSPN EPfP ESCh MBri MGos NHol NSti SCoo WFoF
	'White Tokyo' (A/d)	MGos
	'White Wings' (A/d)	EBee SPet
	'Wilhelmina Tull' (EL)	CSPN ESCh
	'Will Goodwin' (EL) ♀H4	CBcs CLng CWCL EBee ELan EPfP ETho LRHS MAsh MBri NBea SWCr
	'William Kennett' (EL)	CWSG EBee ELan EPfP ESCh ETho LRHS MBar MBri MGan MGos NTay SDix
	williamsii	ESCh
	'Willy' (A)	CBcs CSPN EBee ECtt ELan EPfP ESCh ETho GKir GQui LOck LRHS MAsh MBar MBri MGos MSwo NBea NHol NSti NTay SDix SLim SPer SPet SPoG SWCr WBVN
	Wisley = 'Evipo001'PBR	CBcs CLng EPfP ESCh IBal LRHS MAsh MBri NLar SLon SPer SPoG SWCr
	'Xerxes' misapplied	see *C.* 'Elsa Späth'
	'Yaichi' (EL)	ESCh
	'Yatsuhashi'	CFir
	'Yellow Jester' (A)	CWGN
	'Yellow Queen' Holland	see *C. patens* 'Manshuu Ki'
	'Yellow Queen' Lundell/Treasures	see *C.* 'Moonlight'
§	'Yukikomachi' (EL)	CSPN ESCh ETho NBea NHaw NTay
	'Yvette Houry' (EL)	ESCh NHaw NLar NTay

Clematopsis see *Clematis*

Clementsia see *Rhodiola*

Cleome (*Capparaceae*)

	'Senorita Rosalita'	SVil

Clerodendrum (*Verbenaceae*)

	bungei	Widely available
	- 'Herfstleu'	MGos
	- 'Pink Diamond' (v)	CCCN CDoC CDul CWGN EBee ELon EMil EPfP EWes LAst LBuc LHop LRHS LSRN MAsh MGos MPkF NLar NPri NSti SPer SPoG WCot WFar
§	***chinense***	CCCN ERea
	var. ***chinense*** (d) ♀H1	
	- 'Pleniflorum'	see *C. chinense* var. *chinense*
	fragrans var. ***pleniflorum***	see *C. chinense* var. *chinense*
*	***mutabile*** B&SWJ 6651	WCru
	myricoides 'Ugandense' ♀H1	CCCN CHll CRHN CSpe CTsd ELan ERea EShb LPio LRHS SAga SMrm WSFF
	philippinum	see *C. chinense* var. *chinense*
	quadriloculare	CCCN
	aff. ***serratum*** DJHV 06074 **new**	WCru
	× ***speciosum***	ERea
	aff. ***subscaposum*** WWJ 11735 **new**	WCru
	thomsoniae ♀H1	ELan ERea MBri WSFF
	trichotomum	Widely available
	- 'Carnival' (v)	CAbP CBcs CCCN CDul CMac CPLG CPMA EBee ELan EPfP EPla EWes IArd LRHS MAsh MBri MCCP NCGa NLar SLim SMad SPer SPoG WPat
	- var. ***fargesii*** ♀H4	Widely available
	- 'Purple Haze'	MBri
	- white calyx B&SWJ 4896	WCru
	wallichii	CSpe EShb

Clethra ✿ (*Clethraceae*)

	acuminata	EPfP
	alnifolia	CBcs CDul CEnd CMCN CMHG CPLG CTrC CTrG EBee EPfP IDee MBar SRms WBor WCFE WDin WFar
	- 'Anne Bidwell'	MBri NLar
	- 'Creel's Calico' (v)	MBri NLar
	- 'Fern Valley Pink'	CCCN CSBt EBee LLHF LRHS MBri MDun NLar
	- 'Hokie Pink'	MBri NLar

- 'Hummingbird' CCCN CDoC CEnd CMac CPLG CWib EBee ELan EPfP GGGa GKir LRHS MAsh MBlu MBri MGos MWat NLar NPCo SLim SPoG SSpi SWvt WBVN WFar WSHC
- 'Paniculata' ♀H4 CDoC EPfP GKir LRHS MMuc SAga SPoG SPur WFar
- 'Pink Spire' CBcs CDoC CDul EBee ECrN ELon EPfP GGGa MMHG MRav NBlu NEgg NLar NPal SCoo WDin WFar
- 'Rosea' CBot CTri GQui IMGH MBar MGos MMHG SPer WFar
- 'Ruby Spice' Widely available
- 'September Beauty' MBri NLar
- 'Sixteen Candles' GGGa NLar

arborea CBcs CHEx CMHG CTrC NLar SSpi
barbinervis ♀H4 CBcs CMCN CPLG EBee EPfP GAuc IDee LRHS MBlu MBri NLar SPer WFar WSHC
- B&SWJ 11562 WCru
- B&SWJ 5416 WPGP
- B&SWJ 8915 WCru

delavayi Franch. CBcs CCCN CDoC EPfP EWes GGGa GQui NLar
fargesii EBee EPfP IMGH MBri MGos NLar WBVN
monostachya NLar
pringlei NLar WSHC
tomentosa 'Cottondale' MBri NLar

Cleyera (*Theaceae*)

fortunei see *C. japonica* 'Fortunei'
- 'Variegata' see *C. japonica* 'Fortunei'

japonica EGFP
§ - 'Fortunei' (v) CCCN CMac CWib LRHS SSta WFar
- var. ***japonica*** CGHE WPGP
- 'Tricolor' (v) CBcs IDee
- var. ***wallichii*** EBee WPGP

Clianthus (*Papilionaceae*)

maximus ECou
§ ***puniceus*** ♀H2 CAbb CHEx CHll CPLG CPne CSBt CSpe CStu CTsd CWib EBee ECou EPfP GGar LHop LRHS SAga SEND SPer SPlb SPoG WCru WPGP WSHC
§ - 'Albus' ♀H2 CBcs CBot CHEx CHll CPLG CTsd CWib EBee EPfP LRHS SPer SPoG WPGP
- 'Flamingo' see *C. puniceus* 'Roseus'
- 'Kaka King' CBcs EWes
- 'Red Admiral' see *C. puniceus*
- 'Red Cardinal' see *C. puniceus*
- 'Red Kakatoo' **new** EGxp
§ - 'Roseus' CBcs CPLG SPer SPoG WPGP
- 'White Heron' see *C. puniceus* 'Albus'

Clinopodium (*Lamiaceae*)

acinos see *Acinos arvensis*
ascendens see *Calamintha ascendens*
calamintha see *Calamintha nepeta*
grandiflorum see *Calamintha grandiflora*
§ ***vulgare*** CArn CRWN EBWF EBee GBar MHer MNHC NGHP NMir NSco SGar SIde WDyG WFoF WMoo WOut WPtf

Clintonia (*Convallariaceae*)

andrewsiana CLAP EBee ECho EHrv EWes GBuc GEdr GGGa GGar MNrw WCot WCru
borealis WCru
udensis WCru
- HWJK 2339 from Nepal WCru

umbellulata CLAP GCal WCru
uniflora CLAP EBee EBrs ECho EHrv EWes GBuc GEdr GGar MNrw WCru

Clivia ✿ (*Amaryllidaceae*)

caulescens ERea WCot
× ***cyrtanthiflora*** ERea
gardenii ERea WCot
gardenii × ***miniata*** **new** WCot
miniata ♀H1 CBcs CBgR CSpe CTsd ECho ERea EShb LRHS SMrm SRms WCot
- 'Aurea' ♀H1 CSpe
- var. ***citrina*** ♀H1 CFwr ECho LAma LRHS WCot
- - 'Butterball' **new** ERea
- - 'New Dawn' ERea
- 'Citrina Spider' CFwr
- 'Daruma' **new** WCot
- hybrids MBri NPal SEND
- 'Light of Buddha' (v) **new** WCot
- 'Orange Spider' CFwr
- pastel shades CFwr
- 'Striata' (v) CFwr ERea WCot
- 'Vico Yellow' **new** ERea
- 'Viscy Yellow' CTsd
- 'Wide Leaf Monk' WCot

nobilis ♀H1 ERea WCot
'San Marcus Yellow' WCot
× 'Solomone Yellow' **new**
'Solomone Yellow' ERea

Clusia (*Clusiaceae*)

rosea CCCN

Clypeola (*Brassicaceae*)

jonthlaspi WCot

Clytostoma (*Bignoniaceae*)

§ ***calystegioides*** CHll CRHN ERea EShb

Cneorum (*Cneoraceae*)

tricoccon WSHC

Cnicus (*Asteraceae*)

§ ***benedictus*** CArn MHer SIde SPav

Cnidium (*Apiaceae*)

japonicum **new** GLin
officinale **new** GPoy

Coaxana (*Apiaceae*)

purpurea B&SWJ 9028 WCru

Cobaea (*Cobaeaceae*)

lutea B&SWJ 9142A WCru
pringlei WPGP WSHC
- CD&R 1323 WCot

scandens ♀H3 CCCN CDTJ CSpe EBee ELan EShb IFoB SBch SGar SPer
- f. ***alba*** ♀H3 CSpe SPer

cobnut see *Corylus avellana*

Cocculus (*Menispermaceae*)

§ ***orbiculatus*** CPLG
- B&SWJ 535 WCru

trilobus see *C. orbiculatus*

Cochlearia (*Brassicaceae*)

armoracia see *Armoracia rusticana*
officinalis CArn EBWF MHer SECG WHer

Cocos (*Arecaceae*)

	plumosa	see *Syagrus romanzoffiana*
	weddelliana	see *Lytocaryum weddellianum*

Codiaeum ✿ (*Euphorbiaceae*)

	variegatum	LRHS
	var. ***pictum*** 'Excellent' (v)	
	- - 'Petra' (v)	LRHS MBri

Codonanthe (*Gesneriaceae*)

	gracilis	WDib
	'Paula'	WDib

× *Codonatanthus* (*Gesneriaceae*)

	'Golden Tambourine'	WDib
	'Sunset'	WDib
	'Tambourine'	WDib

Codonopsis ✿ (*Campanulaceae*)

	GWJ 9442 from India	WCru
	HWJK 2105 from Nepal	WCru
	SDR 4718	GKev
	from Chollipo, Korea	EWld
	affinis HWJCM 70	WCru
	- HWJK 2151	WCru
	benthamii	EBee GKev
	- GWJ 9352	WCru
	bhutanica	EBee NEgg
	bulleyana	GKir IGor
	cardiophylla	EBee EWld GCal
	celebica HWJ 665	WCru
	clematidea	CHar CSpe EBee ECha ECho ECtt EPfP GCal GKev LHop LRHS MCCP MTho MWhi NChi NEgg NSum SAga SBch SGSe SMrm SPhx SPlb SRms SWvt WCru WKif WSpi WWEG
	- 'Lilac Eyes'	MCCP SGSe SPad
	convolvulacea misapplied	see *C. grey-wilsonii*
	convolvulacea Kurz	CPne CStu GBuc IGor ITim MTho NSla
	- J&JA 4.220.705	NWCA
	- 'Alba'	see *C. grey-wilsonii* 'Himal Snow'
	- Forrest's form	see *C. forrestii* Diels
	- var. ***hirsuta*** B&SWJ 7812	WCru
	'Dangshen'	see *C. pilosula*
	dicentrifolia HWJCM 267	WCru
	forrestii misapplied	see *C. grey-wilsonii*
§	***forrestii*** Diels	EBee GKir
	- BWJ 7776	WCru
	- BWJ 7847	WCru
§	***grey-wilsonii*** ♀H4	CAby CLAP EBee EBrs ECho EWld GEdr IGor ITim WFar WIvy
	- B&SWJ 7532	WCru
§	- 'Himal Snow'	CAby CLAP EWld GEdr MDKP
	javanica B&SWJ 8145	WCru
	kawakamii	EBee
	- B&SWJ 1592	WCru
	- RWJ 10007	WCru
§	***lanceolata***	CAby CPne EBee EWld IGor LFur SGSe
	- B&SWJ 562	WCru
	lancifolia B&SWJ 3835	WCru
	meleagris Diels	IGor
	mollis	ECho NGby NLar NSum WFar
	nepalensis Grey-Wilson	see *C. grey-wilsonii*
	obtusa	EBee GKir
	ovata	CBot CFir GBuc IGor MTho NBro NChi SRms
§	***pilosula***	EBee EWld GPoy IGor MNrw MTho SGSe
	- BWJ 7910	WCru
§	***rotundifolia***	EBee EWld IGor MDKP WCru
	var. ***angustifolia***	
	- var. ***grandiflora***	EBee
	silvestris	see *C. pilosula*
	subscaposa	EBee
	subsimplex BWJ 7502	WCru
	tangshen misapplied	see *C. rotundifolia* var. *angustifolia*
	tangshen Oliv.	CArn EBee GKev GKir MNrw MTho
	thalictrifolia MECC 93	WCru
	ussuriensis	see *C. lanceolata*
	vinciflora	CPne GEdr GKev IGor WBVN WIvy
	viridiflora	WCru
	viridis HWJK 2435	WCru

Coffea (*Rubiaceae*)

	arabica	CCCN LRHS

coffee see *Coffea*

Coix (*Poaceae*)

	lacryma-jobi	SWal

Colchicum ✿ (*Colchicaceae*)

	agrippinum ♀H4	CAvo CBro CFee EBla EBrs ECha ECho EPot GGar ITim MRav NBir NMen NRya WHoo WTin
	'Antares'	ECha NBir
	atropurpureum	EBrs ECho EPot LAma
	- Drake's form	ECho
	'Attlee'	LAma
	'Autumn Herald'	EBrs ECho LAma LRHS
N	'Autumn Queen'	EBrs ECho LAma LRHS
§	***autumnale***	CArn CAvo CBro CFee EBrs ECho EPot GAuc GKir GPoy ITim LAma LRHS NMen NRya WFar WShi
*	- 'Albopilosum'	NBir
	- 'Alboplenum'	CBro EBrs ECho EPot ERCP LAma LRHS WTin WWst
	- 'Album'	CAvo CBro EBrs ECho EPot ERCP GGar LAma LRHS NBir SPer SPhx WGwG WHoo WShi WTin
	- 'Atropurpureum'	ECho
	- 'Drama Bunch' **new**	WWst
	- var. ***major*** hort.	see *C. byzantinum* Ker Gawl.
	- var. ***minor*** hort.	see *C. autumnale*
§	- 'Nancy Lindsay' ♀H4	CBro EBla EBrs ECho EPot LRHS SCnR WCot
	- 'Pannonicum'	see *C. autumnale* 'Nancy Lindsay'
§	- 'Pleniflorum' (d)	EBrs ECho EPot LAma MMHG
*	- ***roseum***	ECho
	- 'Roseum Plenum'	see *C. autumnale* 'Pleniflorum'
	baytopiorum	ECho GAuc
	- from Turkey	ECho
§	***bivonae***	EBrs ECho EPot LAma
	- Hoa 9139	WWst
	- 'Apollo'	EBrs ECho GKev WWst
	Blom's hybrid	WTin
§	***boissieri***	EBrs ECho EPot ERos WWst
	bornmuelleri misapplied	see *C. speciosum* var. *bornmuelleri* hort.
	bornmuelleri Freyn	CBro ECho EPot GAuc LAma
	bowlesianum	see *C. bivonae*
§	***byzantinum*** Ker Gawl. ♀H4	CBro EBrs EPot LAma LRHS NBir WTin
	- ***album***	see *C. byzantinum* 'Innocence'
§	- 'Innocence'	CBro EBla EBrs ECho EPot GAuc
	cilicicum	CBro ECho EPot LAma WHoo
	- Bowles's form	ECho

	- 'Purpureum'	EBrs ECho LAma LRHS WWst
	'Conquest'	see *C.* 'Glory of Heemstede'
	corsicum	EBrs ECho ERos NMen WThu
	crocifolium	EBrs
	cupanii	CPBP EBrs ECho EPot WWst
	- prostrate-leaved **new**	WWst
	- var. ***pulverulentum***	EBrs ECho
	'Daendels'	LAma
	davisii	ECho WWst
	'Dick Trotter'	EBrs ECho EPot LAma LRHS MBri
	'Disraeli'	EBrs ECho
	doerfleri	see *C. hungaricum*
	'E.A. Bowles'	LAma
	falcifolium	ECho WWst
§	***giganteum***	EBrs ECho EPot GAuc LAma LRHS
§	'Glory of Heemstede'	EBrs ECho GKev LRHS
	'Gracia'	EBrs
	graecum	EBrs ECho WWst
	'Harlekijn'	EBrs ECho ERCP
§	***hungaricum***	CFee EBrs ECho
	- f. ***albiflorum***	EBrs ECho EPot GAuc WWst
	illyricum	see *C. giganteum*
	'Jochem Hof'	EBrs ECho LRHS
	'Jolanthe'	WWst
	kesselringii	GAuc WWst
	kotschyi	EPot WWst
	laetum misapplied	see *C. parnassicum*
	laetum Stev.	GAuc
	'Lilac Bedder'	EBrs ECho EPot
	'Lilac Wonder'	EBrs ECho EPfP GKev LAma LRHS MRav SPer WCot WFar
	lusitanum	GAuc LAma
	luteum	EBrs ECho GAuc WWst
	macrophyllum	EBrs ECho GAuc LAma WWst
	micranthum	ECho
	minutum **new**	ECho
	munzurense **new**	WWst
	'Oktoberfest'	EPot
	parlatoris	EBrs ECho
§	***parnassicum***	CBro EBrs ECha ECho WWst
	- CH 835	WWst
	- Hoa 8942	WWst
	peloponnesiacum	EBrs
	'Pink Goblet' ♀H4	CBro LAma
	'Poseidon'	EBrs ECho
	procurrens	see *C. boissieri*
	pusillum	EBrs WWst
	'Rosy Dawn' ♀H4	CAvo CBro EBrs ECha ECho GGar LAma LRHS NRya
	sfikasianum	EBrs ECho
	sibthorpii	see *C. bivonae*
	speciosum ♀H4	CAvo CBro EBrs ECho EPot GKir LAma LRHS NBir WCot
	- 'Album' ♀H4	CAvo CBro CFee EBla EBrs ECha ECho EPfP EPot LAma LRHS MBri NBir SPhx
	- 'Atrorubens'	CAvo ECha ECho LAma MBri
I	- var. ***bornmuelleri*** hort.	ECho WWst
	- var. ***illyricum*** hort.	see *C. giganteum*
	- 'Maximum'	LAma MBri
	- 'Ordu'	EBrs ECho LRHS
	- 'Rubrum'	ECho
	szovitsii Fisch. & B. Mey.	EBrs ECho
	- 'Tivi' **new**	WWst
	- white-flowered	ECho
	tenorei ♀H4	EBrs ECho EPot GAuc GKev LAma LLHF NBir SPhx
	'The Giant'	CAvo CBro EBrs ECho EPot GKev LAma LRHS WCot
	triphyllum	EBrs ECho WWst
	troodi ambig.	ECho ERos WWst
	variegatum	ECho LAma WWst
	'Violet Queen'	EBrs ECho EPot LAma LRHS
	'Waterlily' (d) ♀H4	CAvo CBro EBla EBrs ECho ELan EPfP EPot ERCP GGar GKev ITim LAma LRHS NBir SPhx WGwG WHoo
	'William Dykes'	EBla EBrs ECho LAma
	'Zephyr'	ECho LAma

Coleonema (*Rutaceae*)

§	***pulchellum***	CCCN CHEx CSpe NSti
	pulchrum misapplied	see *C. pulchellum*
	'Sunset Gold'	CSpe CTrC CWit LHop SPlb

Coleus see *Plectranthus, Solenostemon*

Colignonia (*Nyctaginaceae*)

	ovalifolia B&SWJ 10644	WCru

Colletia (*Rhamnaceae*)

	armata	see *C. hystrix*
	cruciata	see *C. paradoxa*
§	***hystrix***	CBcs CHEx CMac CTrG CTri CTsd EBee GGar SAPC SArc SLon SMad WBor WSHC
	- RCB RA S-3	WCot
	- 'Rosea'	CTrC GCal LRHS
§	***paradoxa***	CBcs CCCN CHEx CWib GCal LPJP MBri NLar SAPC SArc SMad
	paradoxa* × *spinosissima	SMad

Colliguaja (*Euphorbiaceae*)

	odorifera **new**	EBee

Collinsonia (*Lamiaceae*)

	canadensis	CArn ELan

Collomia (*Polemoniaceae*)

	debilis	NPol
	- var. ***larsenii***	see *C. larsenii*
	grandiflora	CSpe LFur NPol WCot
§	***larsenii***	NPol
	mazama	NPol

Colobanthus (*Caryophyllaceae*)

	canaliculatus	CPBP
§	***quitensis***	ECho

Colocasia (*Araceae*)

	affinis var. ***jeningsii***	CDTJ EAmu
	antiquorum	see *C. esculenta*
§	***esculenta*** ♀H1	CBct CDTJ CHEx EAmu EBrs EGxp EShb LPio MSKA SDix XBlo
	- 'Black Beauty' **new**	EAmu
	- 'Black Magic'	Widely available
	- 'Black Ruffles'	CDTJ
	- burgundy-stemmed	CDTJ SBig
	- 'Chicago Harlequin'	CDTJ
	- 'Fontanesii'	CDTJ CHEx EAmu WCot
	- 'Hilo Beauty'	EAmu XBlo
	- 'Illustris'	CDTJ SGar WClo
	- 'Nigrescens'	EAmu
	fallax	CFir CHEx EAmu WPrP
	formosana B&SWJ 6909	WCru
	gigantea	CDTJ EAmu MSKA SBst

Colquhounia (*Lamiaceae*)

	coccinea	CArn CHll CTrC EShb GQui MBlu MRav NLar SGar SLon SSpi WCom WCru WSHC
	- Sch 2458	WPGP

§ - var. **mollis** B&SWJ 7222 WCru
- var. **vestita** misapplied see *C. coccinea* var. *mollis*
- var. **vestita** ambig. CBcs CTsd CWib EBee EPfP GGar IMGH LHop LRHS MWea SEND WBor

Columnea (*Gesneriaceae*)

'Aladdin's Lamp' WDib
'Apollo' WDib
× **banksii** ♀H1 EOHP WDib
'Bold Venture' WDib
§ 'Broget Stavanger' (v) WDib
'Chanticleer' ♀H1 MBri WDib
I 'Firedragon' WDib
'Gavin Brown' EOHP WDib
gloriosa EBak
hirta ♀H1 MBri WDib
- 'Variegata' see *C.* 'Light Prince'
'Inferno' WDib
'Katsura' MBri WDib
I 'Kewensis Variegata' (v) ♀H1 MBri
§ 'Light Prince' (v) WDib
'Merkur' WDib
microphylla 'Variegata' (v) MBri
I 'Midnight Lantern' WDib
'Rising Sun' WDib
'Robin' WDib
schiedeana EOHP EShb MBri WDib
'Stavanger' ♀H1 WDib
'Stavanger Variegated' see *C.* 'Broget Stavanger'

Colutea (*Papilionaceae*)

arborescens CArn CBcs CMac CPLG CWib EBee ELan GKir LHop MBlu MGos NWea SEND SPer SPlb SPoG WDin
× **media** GKir MBlu SGar SHGN
- 'Copper Beauty' CBcs EBee GKir LRHS MBri MGos NLar SPer WPat
orientalis CCCN LHop

Colysis (*Polypodiaceae*)

wrightii f. **laciniata** EBee

Comarum see *Potentilla*

Combretum (*Combretaceae*)

fruticosum CCCN

Commelina (*Commelinaceae*)

coelestis see *C. tuberosa* Coelestis Group
dianthifolia EBee GCal LPio MTho SRms WPer
robusta EBee LPio WCot
tuberosa EBrs ELan EPfP LPio WBrE
- B&SWJ 10353 WCru
- 'Alba' ELan GCal LPio WPer
- 'Axminster Lilac' WPer
§ - Coelestis Group CEnt CSpe CStu EBee ECha ELon EPfP IGor LHop LRHS MAvo MCot SGar SRkn SRms WKif WPer WSHC
- - 'Hopleys Variegated' (v) CBow
- - 'Sleeping Beauty' LRHS MSpe

Comptonia (*Myricaceae*)

peregrina NLar WCru

Conandron (*Gesneriaceae*)

ramondoides B&SWJ 8929 WCru

Conanthera (*Tecophilaeaceae*)

bifolia ECho
campanulata EBee ECho

Conicosia (*Aizoaceae*)

pugioniformis CTrC

Coniogramme (*Adiantaceae*)

emeiensis WCot
intermedia WRic

Conium (*Apiaceae*)

maculatum CArn

Conoclinium (*Asteraceae*)

§ **coelestinum** EBee EShb EWes GKir LBMP LHop MDKP NBre SMad WMoo WSFF
dissectum WSFF

Conopodium (*Apiaceae*)

majus CRWN EBWF LFur WShi

Conostylis (*Haemodoraceae*)

candicans new ECou

Conradina (*Lamiaceae*)

verticillata NLAp WPat

Consolida (*Ranunculaceae*)

§ **ajacis** MNHC
ambigua see *C. ajacis*

Convallaria ✿ (*Convallariaceae*)

japonica see *Ophiopogon jaburan*
keiskei EBla EPPr GAuc WWEG
majalis ♀H4 Widely available
- 'Albostriata' (v) Widely available
- 'Berlin Giant' EBla NBre NRya
- 'Bordeaux' CHid EBee ELon
- 'Dorien' CBct CBre EBee EPPr MAvo WCom
- 'Flore Pleno' (d) EHrv MTho SGSe WWEG
- 'Fortin's Giant' see *C. majalis* 'Géant de Fortin'
- 'Géant de Fortin' CBct CBro CFir CLAP CRow EBla EPla EPot GCal GEdr MRav NBir NBre NGby SMad WCom WCot WFar
- 'Gerard Debureaux' see *C. majalis* 'Green Tapestry'
§ - 'Green Tapestry' (v) CBct CBow CLAP CRow
- 'Haldon Grange' (v) CLAP SMad
- 'Hardwick Hall' (v) CAvo CBct CBow CLAP CMdw CRow EBee EBla ECha ECho EHoe EHrv EPla EPot MAvo NBre WCot WFar WTin WWEG
- 'Hofheim' (v) CLAP CRow WWEG
- 'Marcel' (v) CLAP WCom
- 'Prolificans' CAvo CBct CBgR CBro CFir CLAP CMdw EBee EBrs ECho EPPr ERos MAvo MBel MRav NBir NMyG NSti SSvw WCom WCot WFar WWEG
- var. **rosea** Widely available
- 'Variegata' (v) CAvo CBgR CHar CStu EBee EBla EPla LHop NMen NMyG SBch SMad SSvw WCom WHil WWEG
- 'Vic Pawlowski's Gold' (v) CBct CLAP CMac CPLG CRow CStu EBee ELon EPPr MAvo WCHb
montana NLar
transcaucasica EBee ECho EPot WCot

Convolvulus (*Convolvulaceae*)

althaeoides CBot CMea ECGP ECho ELan EShb MCot NBir SEND SPhx WAbb WEas
§ - subsp. **tenuissimus** CSWP CSpe EBee ECtt EWes WCFE WCom WSHC
- - 'Pink Fanfare' WSpi
§ **boissieri** EPot

	cantabricus	CHll MDKP SGSe WHil WSHC
	chilensis	CCCN LSou
	cneorum ♀H3	Widely available
	- 'Snow Angel'	EBee GBin LBuc LRHS LSou NCGa SWvt WSpi
	compactus	GKev
	elegantissimus	see *C. althaeoides* subsp. *tenuissimus*
	humilis	ECho
	lineatus	ECho EWes MTho NMen NWCA
	mauritanicus	see *C. sabatius*
	nitidus	see *C. boissieri*
§	***sabatius*** ♀H3	CCCN CHEx CHrt CSam CTri ECho ECtt ELan EPfP EPot LAst LHop MCot NBlu NMen NWCA SAga SBch SGar SIng SPer SPoG WCFE WEas WFar
	- 'Compton Lane'	WCom
	- dark-flowered	CCCN CSpe ECho ELan GCal SMrm SUsu
	- 'Moroccan Beauty'PBR	WSpi

× *Cooperanthes* see *Zephyranthes*

Cooperia see *Zephyranthes*

Copernicia (*Arecaceae*)

alba	LPal

Coprosma ✿ (*Rubiaceae*)

	acerosa	CTrC
	- 'Hawera'	CBcs
	- 'Live Wire' (f)	ECou
	- 'Red Rocks'	CBcs CTrC EBee
	areolata (m)	ECou
	atropurpurea (f)	ECou NWCA
	- (m)	ECou
	'Autumn Orange' (f)	ECou
	'Autumn Prince' (m)	ECou
	baueri misapplied	see *C. repens*
	'Beatson's Gold' (f/v)	CBcs CBgR CBot CDTJ CHll CTrG CTsd EBee ELan EPfP GGar ISea LRHS MSCN SEND SLim STre SWvt WDin WGrn WSHC
	'Black Cloud'	CTrC
	'Blue Pearls' (f)	ECou
	'Brunette' (f)	ECou
	brunnea	ECou
	- 'Blue Beauty' (f)	ECou
	- 'Violet Fleck' (f)	ECou
	'Bruno' (m)	ECou
	'Cappuccino'	CBcs EBee GBin IFFs IMon LSou
	cheesemanii (f)	ECou
	- (m)	ECou
	- 'Hanmer Red' (f)	ECou
	- 'Mack' (m)	ECou
	- 'Red Mack' (f)	ECou
	'Chocolate Soldier' (m)	ECou
	'Clearwater Gold'	CTrC
	'Coppershine'	CPLG CTrC
	crassifolia × ***repens*** (m)	ECou
	× ***cunninghamii*** (f)	ECou
	- ***macrocarpa*** (m)	ECou
	'Cutie' (f)	CTrC ECou
	depressa	ECou
	- 'Orange Spread' (f)	ECou
	'Evening Glow'PBR (f/v)	CBgR CCCN CDTJ CDoC CSBt EBee ECou ELan EPfP ERas IFFs IMon LSou MGos SLim
	'Fire Burst'PBR	CBcs CCCN CDoC CWit ELan EPfP ERas GGar IFFs IMon LSou MRav SLim WCFE
	grandifolia **new**	ECou
	'Green Girl' (f)	ECou
	'Green Globe'	CHll
	'Hinerua' (f)	ECou
	'Indigo Lustre' (f)	ECou
	'Jewel' (f)	ECou
	'Karo Red'PBR (v)	CDoC CTrC ELan EPfP IFFs IMon MGos SLim
	× ***kirkii*** 'Gold Edge'	ECou
I	- 'Kirkii' (f)	CHll ECou STre
I	- 'Kirkii Variegata' (f/v)	CBcs CBot CDoC CTrC CTsd EBee ECou LRHS STre WSHC
	'Kiwi' (m)	ECou
	'Kiwi Red'	GGar
	'Kiwi-gold' (m/v)	ECou
	'Lemon Drops' (f)	ECou
	linariifolia (m)	ECou
	lucida (f)	ECou
	- 'Mount White' (m)	ECou
	- 'Wanaka' (f)	ECou
	macrocarpa (f)	ECou
	- (m)	CTrC ECou
	nitida (f)	ECou
	parviflora (m)	ECou
	- purple-fruited (f)	ECou
	- red-fruited (f)	ECou
	- white-fruited (f)	ECou
	'Pearl Drops' (f)	ECou
	'Pearl's Sister' (f)	ECou
	'Pearly Queen' (f)	ECou
	petriei	ECou WThu
	- 'Don' (m)	ECou
	- 'Lyn' (f)	ECou
	'Pride'	CDoC CTrG MHav
	propinqua	WSHC
	- (f)	ECou
	- (m)	ECou
	- var. ***latiuscula*** (f)	ECou
	- - (m)	ECou
	'Prostrata' (m)	ECou
	pseudocuneata (m)	ECou
	quadrifida	ECou
	'Rainbow Surprise'PBR (v)	CCCN CDoC CSBt EBee ELan ERas IFFs LSou MGos MRav SLim SPoG
§	***repens***	CPLG EShb
	- (f)	ECou
	- (m)	ECou
	- 'Apricot Flush' (f)	ECou
	- 'County Park Plum' (v)	ECou
	- 'County Park Purple' (f)	ECou
	- 'County Park Red'	ECou
	- 'Exotica' (f/v)	ECou
	- 'Marble King' (m/v)	ECou
	- 'Marble Queen' (m/v) ♀H1-2	CBcs CHll ECou MGos
	- 'Orangeade' (f)	ECou
	- Pacific Night = 'Hutpac'	CDoC CSBt ECou ELan EPfP LBuc MDKP MGos SPoG
	- 'Painter's Palette' (m)	CBcs EBee ECou EMil GGar SLim WDin
	- 'Picturata' (m/v) ♀H1-2	ECou EShb
	- 'Pink Splendour' (m/v)	CBcs CDoC ECou GGar MGos MHav
	- 'Rangatiri' (f)	ECou
	- 'Silver Queen' (m/v)	ECou
	- 'Variegata' (m/v)	ECou MSCN
	rigida	ECou
	- 'Ann' (f)	ECou
	- 'Tan' (m)	ECou
	robusta	ECou
	- 'Cullen's Point' (f)	ECou

- 'Sally Blunt' (f)	ECou
- 'Steepdown' (f)	ECou
- 'Tim Blunt' (m)	ECou
- 'Variegata' (m/v)	ECou
- 'William' (m)	ECou
- 'Woodside' (f)	ECou
rotundifolia	ECou
'Roy's Red' (m)	CBgR CDoC EBee ECou GGar LSRN
rugosa	CPLG
- (f)	ECou
'Snowberry' (f)	ECou
'Taiko'	CTrC
tenuifolia (m)	ECou
'Translucent Gold' (f)	ECou
'Violet Drops' (f)	ECou
virescens (f)	ECou
'Walter Brockie'	CHll CTrC SEND
'White Lady' (f)	ECou
'Winter Bronze' (f)	ECou
'Yvonne'	MGos

Coptis (*Ranunculaceae*)

japonica	WCru
- var. ***dissecta***	EBee WCru
- var. ***major***	CDes EBee WCru WSHC
omeiensis	WCru
quinquefolia	EBee
- B&SWJ 1677	WCru
ramosa B&SWJ 6000	WCru
- B&SWJ 6030	WCru

Corallospartium see *Carmichaelia*

Cordyline ✿ (*Agavaceae*)

australis 🏆H3	Widely available
- 'Albertii' (v) 🏆H3	CBcs CCCN CTrC MBri NMoo SAPC SArc SEND
- 'Atropurpurea'	CCCN CDoC COlW IFoB WDin WFar
- 'Black Night'	CCCN CTrC
- 'Black Tower'	CDoC MGos
- 'Claret'	CBcs CTrC
- 'Coffee Cream'	CBcs CCCN ELan EPfP SBch SPer WDin WFar
- 'Olive Fountain'	CCCN EBee
- 'Peko'[PBR]	CCCN MGos
- 'Pink Champagne'	CBcs CCCN EBee LBuc LRHS LSRN MGos NEgg SLim SPoG
- 'Pink Stripe' (v)	CBcs CCCN CDoC ELan EPfP ISea LRHS LSRN MBri MCCP NScw SEND SLim SWvt
- 'Purple Heart'	CCCN CTrC MSwo
- Purpurea Group	CBcs CBot CChe CDTJ CMHG CTrC CWSG EAlp EBee ELan ELon EPfP GKir ISea LAst LRHS MGos NBlu SEND SPer SPlb WClo WFar
- 'Red Sensation'	CCCN CHEx COlW CTrC CTsd LRHS SWvt
- 'Red Star'	CAbb CBcs CCCN CDoC CMac CSBt CTrC CWSG CWib EBee ELan EPfP GKir LAst LRHS MCCP MSwo NBlu NPer SPoG SWvt WBVN WBrE WCot WFar WGwG
- 'Sparkler'	CBcs CCCN ESwi LRHS MGos
- 'Sundance' 🏆H3	CBcs CDoC CEnd CMac CSBt CTrC CWSG CWib EPfP IFFs LAst LRHS MBri MCCP MGos MSwo NPer NPri SLim SPad SPoG SRms SWvt WFar
- 'Torbay Dazzler' (v) 🏆H3	CAbb CDoC CEnd CHEx CMHG CMac CSBt CWSG EBee ELan EPfP GKir LRHS LSRN MAsh MBri MGos MREP NEgg NPal NPri NScw SBch SEND SLim SPer SPoG SWvt WDin
- 'Torbay Red' 🏆H3	CAbb CBcs CCCN CDoC CDul CMHG CMac CWSG ELan ELon EPfP LRHS LSRN MAsh MBri NPri SBch SWvt WFar
- 'Torbay Sunset'	CCCN CDoC CTrC ELan
- 'Variegata' (v)	CBot
'Autumn'	CCCN IFFs
banksii	CTsd GCal GGar ISea
'Cardinal'[PBR]	CBcs CWit
'Dark Star'	CBcs CCCN CDTJ CDoC CMac SLim
Festival Grass = 'Jurred' **new**	IMon
fruticosa 'Atom'	MBri
- 'Baby Ti' (v)	MBri
- 'Calypso Queen'	MBri
- 'Kiwi'	MBri
- 'Orange Prince'	MBri
- 'Red Edge' 🏆H1	LRHS MBri XBlo
- 'Yellow King'	MBri
'Green Goddess'	GGar SBch SLim
§ ***indivisa***	CDTJ CTsd EAmu EBak EBee GCal GGar LMaj LRHS MBri SPlb WPGP
'Jurassic Jade'	CBcs CTrC
'Jurassic Jasper'	CTrC
kaspar	CCCN CHEx CTsd SAPC SArc
obtecta	CCCN CTsd
- bronze-leaved **new**	CTsd
'Pacific Coral'	LBuc
'Pacific Dawn' **new**	EGxp
pumilio	LRHS
'Purple Passion' **new**	LRHS
'Purple Sensation'	CBcs CCCN CTrC LRHS NPri
'Purple Tower' 🏆H3	CDoC CHEx EPfP MGos SLim SPad
'Red Bush'	XBlo
'Red Fountain'[PBR]	ESwi
§ ***stricta***	CHEx MBri
terminalis	see *C. fruticosa*

Coreopsis (*Asteraceae*)

'Astolat'	EAEE EBee LHop LRHS MNFA MWea SPer
auriculata Cutting Gold	see *C.* 'Schnittgold'
- 'Elfin Gold'	EBee EDAr LBMP WFar
- 'Nana'	EBee NBre WFar WWEG
- 'Zamphir'	EBee EPfP MNrw NBhm NBre NCGa
'Autumn Blush'	EBee NBhm NBre NCGa SBch
'Baby Gold'	see *C. lanceolata* 'Sonnenkind' (unblotched)
Baby Sun	see *C.* 'Sonnenkind' (red-blotched)
basalis 'Sunshine'	WPer
'Butterfly Flame' **new**	LRHS
'Caluroso' **new**	LRHS
'Calypso' (v)	ECtt EWes LBuc LRHS SCoo SMad
'Cutting Edge'	CEnt
'Golden Ballerina' **new**	LRHS
grandiflora	NEgg
- 'Badengold'	EBee
- 'Bernwode' (v)	CMac EBee LSou NLar SPoG SWvt
- 'Domino'	EBee LRHS NBre SMrm
- 'Early Sunrise' 🏆H4	CSBt EBee ECtt EPfP GMaP LBMP LDai LRHS MBri MHer NBir NGBl NMir NPer SAga SGar SPet SPoG STes SWvt WFar WPer WWEG WWFP
- Flying Saucers = 'Walcoreop'[PBR]	EBee GKir LBuc LRHS SCoo SPoG
- 'Heliot'	SAga
- 'Illico' **new**	LRHS

	- 'Mayfield Giant'	CSBt EBee EShb LHop LRHS MNrw MWea NPri SPer SPoG SRms SWvt WWEG
	- 'Presto' **new**	LRHS WHil
	- 'Rising Sun'	EBee MBri NPri SPet WPer
	- 'Sunburst'	EBee EPfP LRHS NBre WPer
	- 'Sunfire'	EBee MHer STes WHil
	- 'Sunray'	CBcs CDoC CSBt CWib EBee ECtt ELon EPfP EShb GKir LAst LRHS LSRN MBri NBlu NGdn NPri SBch SMrm SPlb SPoG SRms SWvt WMoo WPer WWEG
	- 'Tetra Riesen'	NBre
	heterophylla	see *Iostephane heterophylla*
	'Jethro Tull' **new**	EBee MAsh MBri
	lanceolata	NBre NSti
	- 'Goldfink'	GKir MRav SRms
	- 'Goldteppich' **new**	LRHS
	- 'Little Sundial'	EBee EPPr LSou
§	- 'Sonnenkind' (unblotched)	EBee EPfP NNor WWEG
	- 'Walter'	EAEE EBee ECtt GGar LRHS MBri MWea NEgg SPoG
	'Limerock Dream' **new**	LRHS
	'Limerock Passion'PBR **new**	LRHS LSou MWea NLar NPri SBch SRkn SUsu WSpi
	'Limerock Ruby'PBR	CCVN CPrp EBee ECtt EKen ELon EShb GQue LLWG LRHS LSou MAvo MCot MNrw MWea NBPC NEgg NLar NPri SBch SMrm SPer SPoG SPur SRkn SWvt WCot WFar WSpi WWEG
	major	CSam EBee
	maximiliani	see *Helianthus maximiliani*
	palmata	MDKP
	'Pinwheel'	EBee SBch
	pubescens	LSou
	- 'Sunshine Superman'	EDAr LSou WWEG
	rosea	NLar WFar WPer
	- 'American Dream'	CSBt EBee ELan EPfP EShb GKir LAst LBMP LRHS LSRN NGdn NPri SBch SGSe SGar SMrm SPad SPer SPlb SPoG SRms SWal SWvt WBrE WFar
	- 'Heaven's Gate'PBR	EBee EPfP EWll MBri NBPC NBre
	- 'Sweet Dreams'PBR	EBee EBrs LRHS LSou MWea SPer SPoG SRkn WFar
	'Sangria' **new**	LAst
§	'Schnittgold'	CWan EBee NBre WPer
	'Snowberry'	EBee NBhm SBch
I	'Sonnenkind' (red-blotched)	EBee ECtt LBMP LRHS NBlu NBre WPer
	'Sterntaler'	CFir CPrp EBee EPPr EPau EPfP EShb GKir IMon LRHS MBri MWat NCGa NPri NVic SBch SMad SMrm SPet SWvt WPer
	Sun Child	see *C.* 'Sonnenkind' (red-blotched)
	'Tequila Sunrise' (v)	MBNS NMoo SMrm SPad
	tinctoria 'Tiger Stripes'	LRHS
	tripteris	CAby CPou EBee LPla LRHS MDKP MMuc NBre SAga SGSe SMad SPhx WMoo WPer
	- 'Mostenveld'	EBee
	- 'Pierre Bennerup'	EPPr MAvo SUsu
	'Turkish Delight' **new**	LRHS
	verticillata	CMac EBee ECha EHrv EPfP GCal MBrN MDun MGos MHer MWat NPer SBch SDix SRms WFar WHal
	- Crème Brûlée = 'Crembru'PBR	EBee EBrs ECtt EWes LLWG LRHS LSou MAvo MWea NBPC NEgg NLar SCoo SMrm SPer SRkn SUsu WCot WSpi WWEG
I	- 'Golden Gain'	EBee ECtt LHop LRHS MArl MBel NGdn SBch WFar WMnd WWEG
	- 'Golden Shower'	see *C. verticillata* 'Grandiflora'
§	- 'Grandiflora' ♀H4	CBcs COlW CPrp EAEE EBee EBrs ELan EPfP GMaP LRHS MBel MNFA MRav NCGa NGdn NHol NVic SMad SPer WCAu WFar WMnd
	- 'Moonbeam' ♀H4	Widely available
	- 'Old Timer' ♀H4	SDix SUsu
	- 'Ruby Red'	CAbP CCVN CMac EBee ECtt LHop LSou NLar SMad SUsu
	- 'Zagreb' ♀H4	Widely available

Corethrogyne (*Asteraceae*)

californica KM C-27-02	EBee

coriander see *Coriandrum sativum*

Coriandrum (*Apiaceae*)

sativum	CArn CSev GPoy ILis LRHS MHer MNHC NVic SBch SIde SPoG
- 'Confetti' **new**	MNHC
- 'Leisure'	NPri SVic
- 'Santo'	ELau NGHP
- 'Slobolt'	NGHP

Coriaria ✿ (*Coriariaceae*)

	arborea	WCru
	intermedia B&SWJ 019	WCru
	japonica	IDee IFFs NLar WCru
	- B&SWJ 2833	WCru
	- subsp. ***intermedia*** B&SWJ 3877	WCru
	kingiana	CDes EBee ECou WCru WPGP
§	***microphylla***	WCru
	- B&SWJ 8999	WCru
	myrtifolia	EBee EWld NLar WCru WFar
	nepalensis	NLar WCru
	- BWJ 7755	WCru
	pteridoides	WCru
	ruscifolia	WCru
	- HCM 98178	WCru
	sarmentosa	WCru
	terminalis	CBcs CDes CMdw CTrG EBee EPfP
	var. ***xanthocarpa***	GBuc GCal GGar LSou NLar WCot WCru
	- - GWJ 9204	WCru
	- - HWJK 2112c	WCru
	thymifolia	see *C. microphylla*

Cornus ✿ (*Cornaceae*)

alba L.	CCVT CDoC CDul CLnd CTrG ECrN EMac ISea MHer MRav NWea SRms WDin WMou
- 'Alleman's Compact'	CPMA
- 'Argenteovariegata'	see *C. alba* 'Variegata'
- 'Aurea' ♀H4	Widely available
- Baton Rouge = 'Minbat' **new**	EMil LRHS MAsh
- Chief Bloodgood = 'Chblzam'	CPMA
- 'Cream Cracker'PBR (v)	MGos NHol WPat
- 'Elegantissima' (v) ♀H4	Widely available
- 'Gouchaultii' (v)	CAlb CBcs CPMA EBee ECrN EMac GKir IFFs LBMP LRHS MAsh MBar MRav MWat NLar SBch SLim SPer SRms WDin WFar
- 'Hessei' misapplied	see *C. sanguinea* 'Compressa'
- 'Hessei'	WPat
- Ivory Halo = 'Bailhalo'PBR	EBee EMil EPfP LHop LSRN MBri MGos MRav NWea SPer SPoG SRms
- 'Kesselringii'	Widely available

	- Red Gnome = 'Regnzam'	CPMA LLHF WPat
	- 'Ruby'	CPMA
	- 'Siberian Pearls'	CBcs CPMA EBee ELan MBlu MGos SSta
§	- 'Sibirica' ♀H4	Widely available
	- 'Sibirica Variegata' (v)	CAlb CBow CDoC CMac CPMA EBee EPfP EPla GCra LRHS LSRN MAsh MBar MBlu MGos NCGa NEgg NPri SBch SLim SPer SPoG SSpi SSta SWvt WCFE WFar
	- 'Snow Pearls'	CPMA
	- 'Spaethii' (v) ♀H4	Widely available
§	- 'Variegata' (v)	CBcs ECho EQua LAst MGos
	- 'Westonbirt'	see *C. alba* 'Sibirica'
	alternifolia	CBcs CMCN ELan MDun WPat
§	- 'Argentea' (v) ♀H4	Widely available
	- 'Brunette'	NLar
	- 'Silver Giant' (v)	CPMA MBri NLar WSpi
	- 'Variegata'	see *C. alternifolia* 'Argentea'
	- 'Yellow Spring' **new**	NLar
	amomum	CAbP EBtc NHol NLar WFar
	- 'Blue Cloud'	CPMA MAsh
	- 'Lady Jane'	NLar
	- subsp. ***obliqua***	WPGP
	angustata	SSpi
	'Ascona'	CBcs CEnd CPMA ELan EPfP LRHS NLar SSpi SSta WPat
	Aurora = 'Rutban' (Stellar Series)	CPMA MBlu MPkF NLar SSpi
	australis	GAuc
	canadensis ♀H4	Widely available
	candidissima Marshall	see *C. racemosa*
	capitata	CAgr CBcs CBgR CDoC CDul CEnd CMac CPne CTho CTrG CTsd EPfP GGar GKev ITim LHop SEND SGar SPoG SSpi WBVN WCru WFar WPGP WPat WSpi
	capitata* × *florida **new**	CSam
§	Celestial = 'Rutdan' (Stellar Series)	CPMA MPkF NLar
	'Centennial'	LRHS SSpi
	chinensis	LMil SWvt
	'Constellation' (Stellar Series)	CPMA
	controversa	CBcs CCVT CDul CLnd CMCN CTri ECho ECrN ELan EPfP GKir IFFs MBar MBlu MDun MMuc NLar NWea SEND SLPl SLim SReu SSpi SSta SWvt WDin WFar WHar WPGP
	- 'Candlelight'	MBlu MBri NLar
§	- 'Frans Type' (v)	CBcs CBot CEnd CPMA ECho ELan ERom LSRN SReu SSta WDin WHCG
	- 'Green Carpet' **new**	NLar
I	- 'Marginata Nord'	NLar NPal WPGP
	- 'Pagoda'	EPfP MBlu MBri NBhm NLar NPal
	- 'Troya Dwarf'	CPMA
	- 'Variegata' (v) ♀H4	Widely available
	- 'Variegata' Frans type	see *C. controversa* 'Frans Type'
	- 'Winter Orange'	CPMA NLar
	'Eddie's White Wonder' ♀H4	Widely available
	excelsa F&M 057	WPGP
	florida	CCVT CDul CLnd CMCN CTho EBee EWTr IFFs LAst LRHS MBar MMuc MSnd NBlu SPer WDin WHCr
	- 'Alba Plena' (d)	CPMA NLar
	- 'Andrea Hart'	CPMA
	- 'Appalachian Spring' **new**	LRHS MGos
	- 'Apple Blossom'	CMac CPMA CSBt ECho NPCo
	- 'Autumn Gold'	CPMA
	- Cherokee Brave = 'Comco No 1'	CPMA CWib ECho ESwi LMil LRHS MGos MPkF NLar NPCo SBch SSpi
	- 'Cherokee Chief' ♀H4	CAbP CBcs CDul CEnd CPMA CTri CWib CWit ECho IMGH LAst LSRN MGos MPkF NLar NPCo SBch SLim SPer SSpi WDin WFar WGob WHar WPat WSpi
	- 'Cherokee Daybreak'	see *C. florida* 'Daybreak'
	- 'Cherokee Princess'	CPMA ECho LRHS MPkF
	- 'Cherokee Sunset'	see *C. florida* 'Sunset'
	- 'Cloud Nine'	CBcs CDoC CPMA CWGN EBee ECho MGos MPkF NLar NPCo WSpi
	- 'Daniela' (v)	NLar
§	- 'Daybreak' (v)	CBcs CEnd CPMA CWib ECho ESwi LRHS LSRN MAsh MBri MGos MPkF SBch SSta
	- 'Eternal Dogwood' (d)	ESwi LRHS LSRN MGos
	- 'Firebird'	LRHS MGos
	- 'First Lady' (v)	CMac CPMA CWit ECho NPCo
	- 'Fragrant Cloud'	ECho
	- 'G.H. Ford' (v)	CPMA NLar
	- 'Golden Nugget' (v)	CPMA ECho
	- 'Junior Miss'	CEnd CPMA
	- 'Junior Miss Variegated' (v)	CPMA
	- 'Moonglow'	CPMA LMaj
	- 'Pendula'	CBcs CPMA MPkF
	- 'Pink Flame' (v)	NLar
	- f. ***pluribracteata*** (d)	NLar
	- var. ***pringlei***	CPMA
	- 'Purple Glory'	CBcs CPMA ECho NLar
	- 'Pygmaea'	NLar
	- 'Rainbow' (v)	CAbP CBcs CPMA CWib EBee GKir LAst LRHS MBri MGos MPkF SBch SBod SLim SPer SSpi WDin
	- 'Red Giant'	CAbP CBcs CPMA ELan LMil LRHS NLar
	- f. ***rubra***	CAlb CBcs CSBt CTri CWib ECho ELan EWTr GKir LAst LMaj LRHS MGos MMuc MWea NPCo SPer SPoG WDin WFar WSpi
	- 'Spring Day'	CSBt ECho NPCo
	- 'Spring Song'	CMac CPMA CSBt ECho NLar NPCo
	- 'Springtime'	CPMA ECho NLar
	- 'Stoke's Pink'	CEnd CPMA CSBt CWit ECho NPCo WSpi
§	- 'Sunset' (v)	CEnd CPMA CWib ECho LRHS MBri MGos MPkF NLar NPCo SPer SSta SWvt
	- 'Sweetwater'	CBcs CEnd CPMA
	- 'Tricolor'	see *C. florida* 'Welchii'
	- 'Weaver's White'	CBcs ECho MPkF
§	- 'Welchii' (v)	CEnd CPMA
	- 'White Cloud'	CPMA ELan MBri MPkF
	- 'Xanthocarpa'	MPkF
	aff. ***gigantea*** HWJ 834 **new**	WCru
	'Gloria Birkett'	CAbP ECho LMil LRHS NPCo SSpi WGob
	hemsleyi	EPla
	hessei misapplied	see *C. sanguinea* 'Compressa'
	hongkongensis	SSpi
	- HWJ 1033	WCru
	- WWJ 11700	WCru
	- subsp. ***tonkinensis*** B&SWJ 11791	WCru
	- - HWJ 1022	WCru
	'Kelsey Dwarf'	see *C. sericea* 'Kelseyi'
	'Kenwyn Clapp'	CPMA
	kousa	CDoC CDul CMCN CMac CPne CTho ECho ELan EMac EPfP ERom GKir IFFs ISea LMaj LRHS MBar

	Name	Suppliers
		MDun MSnd NBlu NEgg NLar SBch SLim SPer SPlb WDin WFar WHCG WHar
	- B&SWJ 5494	WCru
	- 'Aget'	CPMA
	- 'Akabana'	CPMA
	- 'Akatsuki'	CPMA
	- 'All Summer'	CPMA
	- 'Angyo Issai' **new**	NLar
	- 'Autumn Rose'	CPMA EPfP NLar
	- 'Beni-fuji'	CPMA NLar
	- 'Big Apple'	CPMA NLar
	- 'Blue Shadow'	CPMA IDee MBri NLar
	- 'Boldre Beauty' **new**	SSpi
	- 'Bonfire' (v)	CPMA
	- 'Bultinck's Beauty'	NLar
	- 'Bush's Pink'	CPMA
	- 'Cherokee'	CPMA SLim
	- 'China Dawn' (v)	CPMA
	- var. ***chinensis*** ♀H4	Widely available
	- - 'Bodnant Form'	CEnd CPMA ECho GKir NPCo WPGP
	- - 'China Girl'	CAbP CDul CEnd CPMA CWib EBee ELan EPfP EWTr GKir LBuc LMil LRHS LSRN MBlu MBri MGos MSwo NLar SLim SPer SSpi SSta WDin WPGP WPat
	- - 'Claudia'	NLar
	- - 'Great Star' **new**	MAsh
	- - 'Greta's Gold' (v)	CPMA
	- - 'Milky Way'	CMCN CPMA CWib EBee ECho LBuc LRHS LSRN MBlu MGos MPkF NLar NPCo SSpi WPat WSpi
	- - 'Snowflake'	CPMA NLar
	- - 'Spinners'	CPMA
	- - 'Summer Stars'	CPMA NLar WPat
	- - 'White Dusted' (v)	CPMA EPfP NLar
	- - 'White Fountain'	MBri MPkF NLar
	- - 'Wieting's Select'	CPMA MPkF
	- - 'Wisley Queen'	CAbP CPMA LMil LRHS MAsh SPoG SSpi
	- 'Claudine'	CPMA
	- 'Doctor Bump'	CPMA NLar
	- 'Doubloon'	CPMA ECho
	- 'Dwarf Pink'	CPMA
	- 'Ed Mezitt'	CPMA NLar
	- 'Elizabeth Lustgarten'	CPMA SSta
	- 'Fanfare'	CPMA NLar
	- 'Fernie's Favourite' **new**	CPMA
	- Galilean = 'Galzam'	CPMA
	- 'Gay Head'	CPMA
I	- 'Girard's Nana'	CPMA
	- 'Gold Cup' (v)	CPMA MPkF
	- 'Gold Star' (v)	CAbP CBcs CEnd CMac CPMA CWGN EBee ECho ELan EPfP LMil LRHS MBlu MBri MGos NLar NPCo SPoG SSpi
	- 'Greensleeves'	CPMA
	- 'Heart Throb'	CPMA LRHS MGos NLar
	- 'Highland'	CPMA
	- 'Kim' **new**	NLar
	- 'Kreus Dame'	CPMA MBri MPkF
	- 'Laura' **new**	MBri
	- 'Little Beauty'	CPMA
	- 'Lustgarten Weeping'	CPMA NLar
	- 'Madame Butterfly'	CEnd CPMA LRHS MBlu NLar NPCo
	- 'Milky Way' **new**	ESwi
	- 'Milky Way Select'	CBcs CPMA ECho LMaj MGos
	- 'Minuma'	NLar
	- 'Miss Petty'	CPMA MPkF NLar
	- 'Miss Satomi' ♀H4	Widely available
	- 'Moonbeam'	CPMA MBri MPkF NLar WPat
	- 'Mount Fuji'	CPMA MBri NLar
	- 'National'	CPMA ECho EPfP LMil MGos MPkF SSpi WPat
	- 'Nicole'	CDoC LRHS WDin WGob WPat
	- 'Pevé Limbo' (v)	CPMA MPkF NLar
	- 'Pevé Satomi Compact' **new**	NLar
	- 'Polywood'	CPMA NLar
	- 'Radiant Rose'	CPMA LRHS MBri MPkF NLar SSpi
	- 'Rasen'	CPMA MBri NLar
	- 'Rel Whirlwind'	CPMA NLar
	- 'Rosea'	CPMA
	- Samaratin = 'Samzam' (v)	CEnd CPMA ESwi LRHS LSRN MBri MGos MPkF
	- 'Schmetterling'	CPMA LRHS NLar WPat
	- 'Silver Pheasant' (v) **new**	NLar
	- 'Snowbird'	CPMA
	- 'Snowboy' (v)	CBcs CEnd CPMA LRHS NPCo SMad
	- 'Snowflurries' **new**	CPMA
	- 'Southern Cross'	CPMA
	- 'Square Dance'	CPMA
	- 'Steeple'	CPMA
	- 'Summer Fun'	CPMA
	- 'Summer Majesty'	CPMA
	- 'Sunsplash' (v)	CPMA NLar
	- 'Temple Jewel' (v)	CPMA
	- 'Teutonia'	CPMA LRHS MBri MPkF NLar
	- 'Tinknor's Choice'	CPMA
	- 'Trinity Star'	CPMA SSpi
	- 'Triple Crown'	CPMA
	- 'Tsukubanomine'	CPMA NLar
	- 'U.S.A.'	MPkF
	- 'Vale Milky Way' (v)	NLar
	- 'Weaver's Weeping'	CPMA MPkF
	- 'Weisse Fontäne'	CPMA LRHS NLar
	- 'White Dream'	CPMA NLar
	- 'White Giant'	CPMA
	- 'Wolf Eyes' (v)	CPMA LRHS MBlu MPkF NLar SSpi SSta WPat
	kousa* × *florida 'Aurea'	MPkF
	macrophylla Wall.	CMCN EPfP WPGP
	mas	Widely available
	- 'Aurea' (v)	CAbP CDul CPMA EBee ELan EPfP EPla LHop LRHS MAsh MBri MGos MRav NEgg NLar NPCo SLim SPer SPoG SSpi SSta WDin WPat
§	- 'Aureoelegantissima' (v)	CEnd CGHE CMac CPMA EPla LRHS MBri NEgg NLar SPoG SSpi WFar WPGP WPat WSHC
	- 'Devin'	NLar
	- 'Elegantissima'	see *C. mas* 'Aureoelegantissima'
	- 'Golden Glory' ♀H4	CBcs CPMA EPfP MBri NLar
	- 'Happy Face' **new**	NLar
	- 'Hillier's Upright'	CPMA
	- 'Jolico'	CPMA NLar
	- 'Kasanlaker' **new**	MBri NLar
	- 'Pioneer'	CPMA
	- 'Redstone'	CPMA
	- 'Spring Glow'	CPMA NLar
	- 'Titus'	NLar
	- 'Variegata' (v) ♀H4	CAbP CBcs CBot CMCN CMac CPMA EBee EPfP EPla LRHS MAsh MBlu MBri MGos NLar NPCo NPal SPer SPoG SSpi WDin WFar WPat
	- 'Xanthocarpa'	CPMA
N	'Norman Hadden' ♀H4	Widely available
	nuttallii	CCVT CDul CSBt CTho CTri CWib ECho ELan EPfP EWTr GAuc GLin IMGH MGos SPer SWvt WDin WFar
	- 'Colrigo Giant'	CPMA MPkF WPat

- 'Gold Spot' (v) — CMac CPMA ECho MGos NPCo NWea
- 'Monarch' — CPMA CTho NLar SSpi
- 'North Star' — CPMA ECho NLar
- 'Osmunda' — ECho
- 'Pink Blush' — MPkF NLar
- 'Portlemouth' — CEnd CPMA SSpi WGob WPat WSpi
- 'Zurico' — CPMA MPkF NLar

officinalis — CAgr CDul CMCN CMac EBee EMil EPfP LHop LRHS MAsh MBri MMuc MWea NLar WDin
'Ormonde' — CPMA CWGN CWit ECho ISea LRHS NLar NPCo SSpi
'Pink Blush' — CPMA
'Porlock' ♀H4 — CDul CMCN CPMA EPfP GKir ITim LRHS LSRN MBri NLar SSpi WDin
pumila — CPMA NLar
§ ***racemosa*** — MBri NLar WFar
rugosa — EBtc NLar
x ***rutgersiensis*** Galaxy — see *C.* Celestial
Ruth Ellen = 'Rutlan' (Stellar Series) — CPMA NLar
sanguinea — CBcs CCVT CDul CLnd CRWN CTri ECrN EMac EPfP IFFs LBuc LMaj MRav MSwo NWea SPer SVic WBVN WDin WHar WMou
- 'Anny' — MAsh MBlu
- 'Anny's Winter Orange' **new** — CPMA
§ - 'Compressa' — EBee EPfP MRav NLar WFar
- 'Magic Flame' — CPMA MAsh MBri
- 'Midwinter Fire' — Widely available
- 'Winter Beauty' — CAlb CDoC CPMA CSBt CWib EBee EPfP ERas LRHS LSou MAsh MBlu NEgg NLar NWea SLon SWvt WCFE WFar WHar WPat
§ ***sericea*** — CArn EMac EPla GKir SRms WMoo
- 'Budd's Yellow' — GKir LRHS MBlu MBri
- 'Cardinal' — EPfP LRHS MBri NLar
- 'Coral Red' — CPMA
- 'Flaviramea' ♀H4 — Widely available
- 'Hedgerows Gold' (v) — CPMA CSBt ELan EMil LHop LRHS MAsh NPri SPoG SPur WPat
- 'Isanti' — CPMA
§ - 'Kelseyi' — CAlb CMac CPMA EBee EPla MBNS MBar MRav SBod SLPl SPer WDin WMoo
- Kelsey's Gold = 'Rosco' — MAsh WPat
- subsp. ***occidentalis*** 'Sunshine' — CPMA NLar NPro
§ - 'White Gold' (v) ♀H4 — CBow CDoC CPMA EBee EHoe MAsh MBri MRav MSwo NPro SLon SPer SPoG WDin WFar WMoo
- 'White Spot' — see *C. sericea* 'White Gold'
Stardust = 'Rutfan' (Stellar Series) — CPMA
Stellar Pink = 'Rutgan' (Stellar Series) — CPMA CWib LRHS MBri MGos MPkF NLar SSpi
stolonifera — see *C. sericea*
Venus = 'Kn30-8' — CPMA LRHS MBri MPkF SPoG
walteri — CBcs CMCN WFar
- B&SWJ 876 — WCru

Corokia (*Escalloniaceae*)

buddlejoides — CBcs CDoC CMHG CTsd CWib EBee ECou GGar GKir LRHS SEND SPoG WFar
'Coppershine' — CMHG
cotoneaster — CAbP CMac CTri EBee ECho ECou ELan EPfP LRHS MAsh MGos SBch SMad SPer SPoG SWvt WBrE WCot WFar WPat WSHC
- 'Boundary Hill' — ECou
- 'Brown's Stream' — ECou
- 'Hodder River' — ECou
- 'Little Prince' — GGar
- 'Ohau Scarlet' — ECou
- 'Ohau Yellow' — ECou
- 'Swale Stream' — ECou
- 'Wanaka' — ECou
macrocarpa — CDoC ECou ISea SDix
* ***parviflora*** — CTrC
x ***virgata*** — CAbP CBcs CDoC CMHG CMac CTrC CTri ECou ELan EPfP GGal ISea MCCP NScw SAPC SArc SPer SWvt WBVN WHar WSHC
- 'Bronze King' — CDoC CSam CWit EBee LRHS SPer
- 'Bronze Lady' — ECou
- 'Cheesemanii' — ECou GGar
- 'County Park Lemon' — ECou
- 'County Park Orange' — ECou
- 'County Park Purple' — ECou
- 'County Park Red' — ECou
- 'Envy' — ECou
- 'Everglades' — ECou
- 'Frosted Chocolate' — CBcs CDoC CSam CTrC CTsd EBee ECou ELan EPfP ETod LBMP LHop LLHF LRHS MAsh MGos SPoG SSta SWvt WCot WDin WFar
- 'Geenty's Green' — CTrC ECou LRHS
- 'Havering' — ECou
- 'Mangatangi' — CTrC MGos
- 'Pink Delight' — CDoC ECou EPfP LBMP MAsh MRav SSta
- 'Red Wonder' — CDoC CMHG CMac CPen CTrC EBee ELan EPfP GGar LRHS MMHG SEND SPoG WDin WFar
- 'Sandrine' — ECou
- 'Silver Ghost' — CDoC ECou
- 'Sunsplash' (v) — CBcs CDoC CMac CTrC CTsd EBee ECou EPfP LBMP LHop LLHF LRHS MAsh MGos SEND SPoG SWvt WFar WHar
I - 'Virgata' — CChe ECou MGos
- 'Wingletye' — ECou
- 'Yellow Wonder' — CBcs CDoC CMHG CPen CTrC EBee ECou GGar LRHS MGos NLar SBod SPoG SWvt WDin

Coronilla (*Papilionaceae*)

comosa — see *Hippocrepis comosa*
coronata — WCot
emerus — see *Hippocrepis emerus*
glauca — see *C. valentina* subsp. *glauca*
valentina — CDoC CRHN CSPN LHop SDix WSHC
- 'Creamed Corn' **new** — WCot
§ - subsp. ***glauca*** ♀H3 — CAlb CBgR CBot CDul CFee CMac CSBt CTri CWib EBee ELan ELon EPfP LAst LRHS LSRN NPri SBch SEND SGar SPer SPoG SRms SWvt WAbe WFar WHCG WPat
- - 'Brockhill Blue' — CWGN LRHS
- - 'Citrina' ♀H3 — Widely available
* - - 'Pygmaea' — WCot WWFP
- - 'Variegata' (v) — CBcs CBot CDoC CMac CSPN CTri CWCL CWib EBee ELan ELon EPfP LRHS MAsh MCot SBch SBod SLim SLon SMrm SPer SPoG WCot WFar
varia — CArn EBee LHop NLar NPri SEND SRms

Correa (*Rutaceae*)

alba — CCCN CDoC CPLG CTrC EBee

	ECou EPfP LBMP LRHS MAsh WGwG WHar
- 'Pinkie' ♀H2	CBcs CPLG ECou MAsh SAga SHGN
backhouseana ♀H2	CAbb CBcs CBgR CDoC CMac CPLG CTrC CTrG CTri CWit EBee ECou ELan EPfP GGar IDee LHop LRHS MAsh NLar SAga SBod SGar SMrm WGwG WHar WSHC
- 'Peaches and Cream'	CSBt SRkn
baeuerlenii	ECou
decumbens	CAbb CTrC ECou MAsh SEND
'Dusky Bells' ♀H2	CBcs CCCN CDoC CHll CSWP CTrC CTri ECou EPfP GGar LBMP LHop LRHS MAsh SAga SEND SHGN SMrm SPoG SRkn
'Dusky Maid'	CCCN CPLG WAbe
'Federation Belle'	CDoC ECou
glabra red-flowered	ECou
'Gwen'	CDoC ECou
'Harrisii'	see *C.* 'Mannii'
'Inglewood Gold'	ECou
'Ivory Bells'	ECou
lawrenceana	CDoC ECou SEND WAbe
§ 'Mannii' ♀H2	CBcs CDoC CPLG CPom CTsd EBee ECou ELan EPfP LRHS WSHC
'Marian's Marvel' ♀H2	CBgR CCCN CDoC CMHG CPLG CTrC ECou LBMP MAsh SEND SGar SPoG SRkn WAbe
'Peachy Cream'	CDoC EPfP LRHS
'Pink Mist'	CDoC ECou
'Poorinda Mary'	ECou
pulchella ♀H2	CDoC CPLG CTri LBMP MAsh
- orange-flowered	ECou
reflexa ♀H2	CDoC CPLG ECou WAbe
- var. ***nummulariifolia***	ECou LBMP MAsh WAbe WCot
- var. ***reflexa***	CPLG
- - 'Mary's Choice'	CDoC
- var. ***scabridula*** 'Yanakie'	ECou
* - ***virens***	CPLG WEas
schlechtendalii	ECou

Cortaderia ✿ (*Poaceae*)

sp.	EBee
argentea	see *C. selloana*
fulvida misapplied	see *C. richardii* (Endl.) Zotov
§ ***fulvida*** (Buchanan) Zotov	CBcs CHrt CKno EBee EWes IDee MNrw NWsh SMad WDin
jubata 'Candy Floss'	CKno
'Point du Raz'	CKno
richardii misapplied	see *C. fulvida* (Buchanan) Zotov
richardii ambig.	CFir EHoe EPau IMou WWEG
§ ***richardii*** (Endl.) Zotov ♀H3-4	CAby CBcs CKno EPPr EWes GGar GMaP IBlr IMou MAvo NVic NWsh SAPC SArc WCot WCru WMnd
- BR 26	GGar
§ ***selloana***	CBcs CDul CHEx CSBt CTrG CTri CWib EHul EPfP GKir LRHS MAvo MBar MGos MRav NBir NBlu NGBl SAPC SArc SBch SPlb SWal WBVN WFar WMoo
§ - 'Albolineata' (v)	CBcs CBct EHoe ELon EWes MSCN MWht NOak NWsh SEND SLim SPer SPoG SWvt WFar WGrn WPat
§ - 'Aureolineata' (v) ♀H3	CBcs CBct CDoC CHrt CMac EBee EHoe ELan EPfP GKir MAsh MGos MMoz MWhi NBid NLar NOak NWsh SBch SEND SLim SPer SPoG SWvt WFar WGrn WPGP WPat
- 'Cool Ice'	CKno CPen
- 'Evita'PBR	CKno LHop WCot
- 'Gold Band'	see *C. selloana* 'Aureolineata'
- 'Golden Comet'	GKir
- 'Icalma'	CPen CPrp LRHS
- 'Monstrosa'	SEND
- 'Patagonia'	EHoe EPPr
- 'Pink Feather'	EPfP GKir IFFs NPri SApp SEND SPer
- 'Pumila' ♀H4	Widely available
- 'Rendatleri'	CBcs CDoC ELan EPfP GKir LRHS LSRN SCoo SLim SPer SPoG WDin
- 'Rosea'	EAlp EBee EGxp EPfP MBar MGos NBPC NBlu NGdn WBrE WFar WWEG
- 'Silver Comet'	GKir
- Silver Feather = 'Notcort' (v)	NWsh
- 'Silver Fountain' (v)	ELan EPfP LRHS MAsh SPer
- 'Silver Stripe'	see *C. selloana* 'Albolineata'
- 'Splendid Star'PBR (v)	CBcs CDoC CKno EBee EGxp EHoe GBin LBuc LHop LRHS MAsh MBri MGos MREP NLar NOak SBch SMad SPoG SWvt WCot
- 'Sunningdale Silver' ♀H3	CDoC CDul CMac EBee ECha ECtt EHoe EHul ELan EPfP GKir LRHS LSRN MAsh MBri MGos SBch SLim SMad SPer SPoG SWvt WDin WFar
* - 'White Feather'	CChe IFFs MWhi NGdn NPri SApp SLim WFar WMoo WWEG
Toe Toe	see *C. richardii* (Endl.) Zotov

Cortia (*Apiaceae*)

SDR 3922	EBee
SDR 3952	EBee

Cortiella (*Apiaceae*)

aff. ***hookeri*** HWJK 2291	WCru

Cortusa (*Primulaceae*)

altaica	EBee GKev
brotheri	ECho
- CC 2987	EBee
- CC 5247	GKev
matthioli	CElw CPom EBee ECho EPfP EWld GBBs GKev GKir LRHS NMen NWCA SRms WBVN WFar
- BWJ 7740	WCru
- 'Alba'	CElw EBee ECho GBuc GEdr GKev GKir NMen NWCA SRms
- subsp. ***pekinensis***	CFir ECho GBuc GEdr GGar GKir NHol NLar NMen NWCA SGSe SPet SRms WCot WFar
turkestanica	ECho GAuc LLHF

Corydalis ✿ (*Papaveraceae*)

from Sichuan, China	CPom MDKP NCot
ambigua misapplied	see *C. fumariifolia*
angustifolia	NDlv WWst
- white-flowered	WWst
anthriscifolia	CLAP LFur MDKP WCot
'Berry Exciting'	CBow
'Blackberry Wine'	CSpe EBee ECtt EWTr GBuc MDKP NPri WFar
'Blue Panda'	see *C. flexuosa* 'Blue Panda'
bracteata	NCot
'Bronze Beauty' **new**	CBow
bulbosa misapplied	see *C. cava*
bulbosa (L.) DC.	see *C. solida*
buschii	CLAP EBee EBrs ECho ERos GBuc GEdr NCot NRya SCnR WHil WPGP
'Canary Feathers' **new**	EBee
caseana	LFur
subsp. ***caseana*** **new**	
cashmeriana	CLAP GEdr GKir LRHS NBid NMen WAbe WHal

	Name	Suppliers
	- 'Kailash'	CLAP GBuc
	cashmeriana × ***flexuosa***	CBro CLAP LRHS WAbe
	caucasica	ECho ERos GBuc NMen
	- var. ***alba*** misapplied	see *C. malkensis*
§	***cava***	CHid CLAP CPom EBee EBrs ECho EPot LAma SPhx WShi
	- 'Albiflora'	CLAP CSsd EBrs ECho EPot SPhx
	- subsp. ***cava***	ECho
	chaerophylla	IBlr
	cheilanthifolia	CPLG CRow CSpe EBee ECha EDAr EHrv EPfP LBMP LRHS MSCN SGar SPhx SRms WEas WFar WPGP WTin
	chionophila	EBee WWst
	'Craigton Blue'	GBuc
	curviflora	EWes SSvw WCot
	subsp. ***rosthornii***	
	- - 'Blue Heron'	IPot
	darwasica	WWst
	davidii	CPLG
	decipiens Schott, Nyman & Kotschy	see *C. solida* subsp. *incisa*
I	***decipiens*** misapplied ♀^{H4}	CPom EBrs ECho EPPr EPot
I	- purple-flowered	EBee EBrs ECho WWst
	decumbens	WCru
	B&SWJ 11142 **new**	
	densiflora	ECho WWst
	'Early Bird'	EBee EWes
	elata	Widely available
	- 'Blue Summit'	CLAP EBee EBrs EPPr IMou LRHS
	elata × ***flexuosa***	IMou
	elata × ***flexuosa*** clone 1	CLAP CMdw CPom GEdr WPrP
	erdelii	EBrs ECho WWst
	flexuosa ♀^{H4}	CFee CSpe EBee ECho EPfP IFro MArl MLHP MNrw MTho NCob SGar WAbe WBor WFar WSHC
	- CD&R 528	NRya
	- 'Balang Mist'	CLAP
	- 'Blue Dragon'	see *C. flexuosa* 'Purple Leaf'
§	- 'Blue Panda'	CPLG EBee EPPr EWes GBuc GMaP LRHS MDun NLar WFar
	- 'China Blue'	Widely available
	- 'Copperhead'	ECho
	- 'Golden Panda'^{PBR} (v)	CBct CBow CHid EBee ECho LRHS MCCP NLar WCot
	- 'Hale Cat'	ECtt EPPr
	- 'Hidden Purple'	CHid
	- 'Nightshade'	ECtt GBuc NBid NCob WCot WFar WPrP
I	- 'Norman's Seedling'	ECtt EPPr WPGP
	- 'Père David'	Widely available
§	- 'Purple Leaf'	Widely available
§	***fumariifolia***	EBrs ECho GKev MTho
	glauca	see *C. sempervirens*
	glaucescens	ECho WWst
	- 'Early Beauty'	EBrs ECho WWst
	gracilis	WWst
	henrikii	NMen WWst
	heterocarpa	IMou
	incisa	ECho ERCP NMen
	- B&SWJ 4417	WCru
	integra	WWst
	'Kingfisher'	CDes CLAP EWes IPot NLar SBch WAbe WFar
	kusnetzovii	WWst
	ledebouriana	EBrs ECho EPot WWst
	leucanthema	CLAP CPLG EBee
	- DJHC 752	CDes WPrP
	- 'Silver Spectre' (v)	CBow CPLG EBee ECtt LLHF LRHS MNrw NSti SPoG WFar
	linstowiana	CPLG
	- CD&R 605	CLAP
§	***lutea***	CBcs CRWN EBee EPfP GBuc IBlr IFoB IFro MMuc MSCN NBir NCob NPer NVic SEND SRms WCot WMoo
	magadanica	LFur
§	***malkensis*** ♀^{H4}	CAvo EBee ECho ERos GBin GBuc NBir NRya SCnR WFar WThu
	maracandica	WWst
	moorcroftiana	CPLG
	nariniana	WWst
	nobilis	CPom CSpe EBrs ECho IFro SPhx WFar WWst
	nudicaulis	EBrs ECho WWst
	ochotensis	IMou
	- B&SWJ 917	WCru
§	***ochroleuca***	CElw CMac CRow CSpe EBee GCal GKir LPla MSCN MTho NPol WFar WMoo
	ophiocarpa	CSpe CSsd EGoo EHoe ELan GCal IBlr LFur MBNS NBur WMoo
	oppositifolia	WWst
	- subsp. ***kurdica***	WWst
	ornata	WWst
	pachycentra	CPLG
	paczoskii	EBrs ECho ERos GBuc GGar GKev GKir LRHS NDlv NMen
	- RS 12180	EBee
	paschei	WWst
	popovii	MTho SCnR WWst
	pseudofumaria alba	see *C. ochroleuca*
	pumila	EBee ECho
	quantmeyeriana 'Chocolate Stars'	CBow CSpe CWGN EBee ECtt ELon LLHF LPla LSou MAvo MBNS SBch SMrm SPhx SPoG WFar
	raddeana B&SWJ 11057	WCru
	repens	WWst
	rosea 'American Dream'	CWCL
§	***saxicola***	EBee
	scandens	see *Dicentra scandens*
	schanginii subsp. ***ainii*** ♀^{H2}	EBrs ECho WWst
	- subsp. ***schanginii***	EBrs ECho
	scouleri	NBir
	seisumsiana	WWst
§	***sempervirens***	CBod LRHS WWEG
	- 'Alba'	CBow ECho WFoF
	sewerzowii	WWst
	siamensis	IMou
	- B&SWJ 7200	WCru
	smithiana	WFar
§	***solida***	CAvo CBro CPom CStu EBee EBrs ECho ECtt ELan EPfP EPot GAbr IBlr ITim LAma LEdu LRHS MRav NMen NRya SIng SMrm SPad SPhx WBVN WCot WFar WPnP WShi WTin
	- 'Alcombe'	MPoH
	- 'Firecracker'	CBro EBrs ECho LRHS
	- 'First Kiss'	WWst
	- 'Grove Seedling'	MPoH
	- 'Harkov'	MPoH WFar WWst
	- 'Ice Pink'	NMen
§	- subsp. ***incisa*** ♀^{H4}	EBee EBrs ECho GKev MNrw MTho SPhx WCot WShi
	- - CH 850	WWst
	- - Hoa 8943	WWst
	- lilac-flowered **new**	IFoB
	- 'Margaret'	WWst
	- 'Maxima'	NMen
	- 'Merlin'	WWst
	- Nettleton seedlings	EPot
	- 'Pink Discovery'	WWst

- 'Purple Beauty' EBrs ECho EPot WWst
- 'Snowlark' WWst
§ - subsp. ***solida*** CLAP CMil EBrs ECho EPot GGar LRHS NBir NRya SPhx
- - from Penza, Russia GBuc ITim LRHS MPoH NCot WWst
- - 'Alba' NSla
- - 'Beth Evans' CAvo CWCL EBee EBrs ECha ECho ECtt EPPr EPot ERCP GBin GEdr GKev IPot LAma LEdu LLHF MCot NCGa NHol NMen SCnR SPhx WCot WFar
- - 'Blue Giant' MPoH
- - 'Blushing Girl' ECho
- - 'Dieter Schacht' ♀H4 EBee ECho EPot GBin ITim LAma NLar NMen WCot
- - 'Evening Shade' ECho
- - 'George Baker' ♀H4 CAvo CBro CPom EBee EBrs ECho EPot ERCP GBuc GEdr GGar IFoB IPot LAma LEdu LFur LLHF LRHS MTho NHol NMen NSla SPhx SUsu WCom WCot WFar WHil WWst
- - 'Lahovice' NMen WCot WFar
- - 'Nettleton Pink' EBrs
- - Prasil Group EBrs EPot IPot SPhx
- - 'Snowstorm' MPoH
- - 'White Knight' EPot WCot
- f. ***transsylvanica*** see *C. solida* subsp. *solida*
- 'White King' WWst
- 'White Swallow' EBrs ECho WWst
- 'Zwanenberg' new WWst
'Spinners' CDes CElw CLAP CMea ECtt EPPr GCal GKev IPot SBch SMeo SSvw SUsu WPGP WPrP WSHC
stipulata B&SWJ 2951 new WCru
taliensis EBee MCot SBch
tauricola EPot NMen WWst
thalictrifolia Franch. see *C. saxicola*
tomentella LFur
'Tory MP' CDes CEnt CHid CLAP CPne CPom CSam EBee GAbr GBuc GEdr MDKP MNrw NBid NChi WHoo WMnd WPGP WPrP
transsylvanica see *C. solida* subsp. *solida*
triternata ♀H4 EPot
vittae ECho WWst
vivipara ECho EPot
wendelboi EBrs ECho
- subsp. ***congesta*** WWst
- Jonus form new NMen
'Wildside Blue' CLAP
wilsonii GEdr IGor WCru WEas
zetterlundii GBuc NDlv WWst

Corylopsis ✿ (*Hamamelidaceae*)

glabrescens CPMA LRHS
- var. ***gotoana*** EPfP NLar SSpi SSta
- - 'Chollipo' CBcs LRHS SSta
glandulifera NLar
himalayana NLar
pauciflora ♀H4 CBcs CDoC CDul CEnd CPMA CTri CWib EBee ELan EPfP LRHS LSRN MAsh MBlu MBri MDun MGos MRav NEgg NLar NPCo NPri SLim SPer SPoG SReu SSpi SSta WDin WFar
platypetala see *C. sinensis* var. *calvescens*
- var. ***laevis*** see *C. sinensis* var. *calvescens*
sinensis WPGP
§ - var. ***calvescens*** CBcs CPMA MBri NLar WPGP
§ - - f. ***veitchiana*** ♀H4 CPMA CSam ELan EPfP IDee LRHS NLar SSpi WDin
- - - purple-leaved CPMA
§ - var. ***sinensis*** ♀H4 CDoC CPMA EBee ELon EPfP IDee LAst LRHS MAsh MBlu SLon SPoG SReu WAbe WDin WFar WSpi
- - 'Spring Purple' CAbP CBcs CEnd CGHE CMac CPMA EBee EPfP LRHS NLar SSpi SSta WDin WFar WPGP
spicata CBcs CDul CPMA EBee IDee LRHS MBlu MGos MRav NEgg NLar SLim SSpi WBVN
- 'Golden Spring' MBlu NLar
- 'Red Eye' NLar
veitchiana see *C. sinensis* var. *calvescens* f. *veitchiana*
willmottiae see *C. sinensis* var. *sinensis*

Corylus ✿ (*Corylaceae*)

avellana (F) CBcs CCVT CDoC CDul CLnd CRWN CTri ECrN EMac EPfP EWTr GAbr GKir IFFs LAst LBuc LRHS MAsh MBar MBri MGos NEgg NLar NWea SBch SPer SVic WDin WHar WMou
- 'Anny's Compact Red' NHol
- 'Anny's Red Dwarf' WPat
- 'Aurea' CBcs CDul CEnd CLnd CSBt CTho CTri EBee ECrN ELan EPfP EWTr GKir LBuc LRHS MAsh MBlu MBri MGos MRav NHol NWea SLim SPer SSta SWvt WDin WFar
- 'Bollwylle' see *C. maxima* 'Halle'sche Riesennuss'
- 'Casina' (F) CAgr CTho
- 'Contorta' Widely available
- 'Corabel' (F) CAgr MCoo
- 'Cosford Cob' (F) CAgr CCVT CDoC CDul CSBt CTho CTri ECrN EMui ERea GKir GTwe LBuc MBlu MBri MGos SDea SKee SPer
- Emoa Series MCoo
- 'Fortin' (F) ECrN
§ - 'Fuscorubra' (F) CPMA ECrN GKir MRav MWat
- 'Gustav's Zeller' (F) CAgr LRHS MBri MCoo
§ - 'Heterophylla' CEnd CTho EPfP GKir IFFs MBri WMou
- 'Laciniata' see *C. avellana* 'Heterophylla'
§ - 'Lang Tidlig Zeller' (F) CAgr MCoo
- 'Merveille de Bollwyller' see *C. maxima* 'Halle'sche Riesennuss'
- 'Nottingham Prolific' see *C. avellana* 'Pearson's Prolific'
- 'Pauetet' (F) CAgr
§ - 'Pearson's Prolific' (F) CAgr CSBt GTwe LBuc SDea SKee
- 'Pendula' GKir LRHS MBlu MBri SCoo SLim WPat
- 'Purpurea' see *C. avellana* 'Fuscorubra'
- 'Red Majestic' PBR Widely available
- 'Tonda di Giffoni' CAgr MCoo
- 'Webb's Prize Cob' (F) CAgr CDoC CDul ECrN ERea GTwe MBlu NLar SDea SEND SKee SVic WMou
colurna ♀H4 CAgr CCVT CDul CLnd CMCN CTho EBee ECrN EPfP EWTr GKir IFFs LRHS MGos MWat NLar NWea SCoo SPer WBVN WDin WMou
'Te Terra Red' CMCN CPMA EBee GKir MAsh MBlu MBri NLar SMad SSpi WMou
× ***colurnoides*** 'Chinoka' (F) MCoo
- 'Laroka' (F) ECrN

Early Long Zeller	see *C. avellana* 'Lang Tidlig Zeller'
'Freeoka' (F) new	MCoo
ferox GWJ 9293	WCru
maxima (F)	CLnd CTri EMac EMui ERea GTwe MSwo NWea SDea WDin
- 'Butler' (F)	CAgr CTho CTri ERea GTwe MBri SKee
- 'Ennis' (F)	CAgr ERea GTwe SDea SKee
- 'Fertile de Coutard'	see *C. maxima* 'White Filbert'
- 'Frizzled Filbert' (F)	ECrN
- 'Frühe van Frauendorf'	see *C. maxima* 'Red Filbert'
- 'Garibaldi' (F)	NLar
- 'Grote Lambertsnoot'	see *C. maxima* 'Kentish Cob'
- 'Gunslebert' (F)	CAgr CCVT CSBt CTho ECrN ERea GTwe MBri SDea SKee
- Halle Giant	see *C. maxima* 'Halle'sche Riesennuss'
§ - 'Halle'sche Riesennuss' (F)	CAgr ECrN EPfP GTwe MAsh MMuc NLar SEND SKee
§ - 'Kentish Cob' (F)	CAgr CBcs CDoC CDul CSBt CTho CWSG ECrN ELan EPfP ERea GTwe LBuc MAsh MBlu MBri MGan MGos SBch SDea SFam SKee SPer SRms WHar
- 'Lambert's Filbert'	see *C. maxima* 'Kentish Cob'
- 'Longue d'Espagne'	see *C. maxima* 'Kentish Cob'
- 'Monsieur de Bouweller'	see *C. maxima* 'Halle'sche Riesennuss'
- 'Purple Filbert'	see *C. maxima* 'Purpurea'
§ - 'Purpurea' (F) ♀H4	Widely available
§ - 'Red Filbert' (F)	CEnd CTho CWSG EMil ERea GTwe IFFs LRHS MAsh MBlu MBri NLar SCoo SKee SLim WPat
- 'Red Zellernut'	see *C. maxima* 'Red Filbert'
- 'Spanish White'	see *C. maxima* 'White Filbert'
§ - 'White Filbert' (F)	CDoC ERea GTwe MAsh SKee WHar
- 'White Spanish Filbert'	see *C. maxima* 'White Filbert'
- 'Witpit Lambertsnoot'	see *C. maxima* 'White Filbert'
'Nottingham Early' (F) new	NLar

Corymbia see *Eucalyptus*

Corynabutilon see *Abutilon*

Corynephorus (*Poaceae*)

canescens	CKno EBee GFor GQue MBar NBir WWEG

Corynocarpus (*Corynocarpaceae*)

laevigatus	CHEx ECou MBri

Cosmos (*Asteraceae*)

§ ***atrosanguineus***	Widely available
- 'Chocamocha'	CAvo CBcs CCCN CHar CSpe CWCL EBee ECtt EPfP GBin LAst LHop LRHS LSRN LSou NBhm NPri SBch SMrm SRot STes SUsu
bipinnatus Bright Lights mixed (d)	CSpe
- 'Purity'	CSpe
- 'Sonata Carmine'	LSou NBlu NPri
- 'Sonata Pink'	LSou NBlu NPri SPoG
- 'Sonata White'	CSpe LAst LSou NBlu NPri SPoG
peucedanifolius	CAvo CSpe SUsu
- 'Flamingo'	EBee GMac LSou NBhm NCGa

Cosmos × *Dahlia* (*Asteraceae*)

'Mexican Black'	WCot

costmary see *Tanacetum balsamita*

Costus (*Costaceae*)

from Uganda new	GCal

Cotinus ✿ (*Anacardiaceae*)

americanus	see *C. obovatus*
§ ***coggygria*** ♀H4	Widely available
- Golden Spirit = 'Ancot'PBR	Widely available
- Green Fountain = 'Kolcot'PBR	LRHS
- 'Kanari'	CPMA EBee NLar WPat
- 'Nordine'	NLar
- 'Notcutt's Variety'	ELan EPfP GKir MGos MRav NSti
- 'Pink Champagne'	CPMA EPfP MBri NLar SSpi WPat
- Purpureus Group	GKir LRHS
- 'Red Beauty'	CPMA NLar
- Red Spirit = 'Firstpur'	NLar
- 'Royal Purple' ♀H4	Widely available
- Rubrifolius Group	CBcs CMac EBee EPfP LRHS MAsh NHol SPer SWvt WDin WFar
- Smokey Joe = 'Lisjo'	EPfP LRHS MAsh NCGa SBch SLon SPoG SSta
- 'Smokey Joe Purple'	LSou
- 'Velvet Cloak'	CAbP CPMA EBee ELan EPfP GKir LBuc LRHS MBri MGos MRav NLar SLon SWvt WHCG
- 'Young Lady'PBR	Widely available
Dusky Maiden = 'Londus' new	EBee EPfP
'Flame' ♀H4	CAbP CBcs CDul CPMA EBee ELan EPfP GKir LHop LRHS MAsh MBri MGos MRav NLar SLim SPer SPoG SSpi WHCG WPat
'Grace'	Widely available
§ ***obovatus*** ♀H4	EBee EBtc EPfP IArd IDee LRHS MBlu MPkF MRav NLar WPat

Cotoneaster ✿ (*Rosaceae*)

acuminatus	EMac SRms
adpressus ♀H4	EPfP MGos MSwo
§ - 'Little Gem'	ECho MGos NLar
- var. ***praecox***	see *C. nanshan*
- 'Tom Thumb'	see *C. adpressus* 'Little Gem'
affinis	SRms SSpi
albokermesinus	SRms
amoenus	SLPl SRms
- 'Fire Mountain'	NPro
§ ***apiculatus***	MAsh SRms
§ ***ascendens***	SRms
assamensis	SRms
§ ***astrophoros***	CMac GKir MBlu
atropurpureus	SRms
§ - 'Variegatus' (v) ♀H4	CBcs CBot CDul CSBt CWSG CWib EBee EHoe ELan EPfP GKir ISea LBMP LRHS MAsh MBar MGos NEgg NPer SBch SCoo SLim SPer SPoG SRms SWvt WDin WFar WMoo
boisianus	SRms
bradyi	SRms
§ ***bullatus*** ♀H4	CDul CLnd CTri EMac EPfP GKir IFFs MGos MMuc NLar SPer SRms
- 'Firebird'	see *C. ignescens*
- f. ***floribundus***	see *C. bullatus*
- var. ***macrophyllus***	see *C. rehderi*
- 'McLaren'	SRms
bumthangensis	SRms
buxifolius blue-leaved	see *C. lidjiangensis*
- 'Brno'	see *C. marginatus* 'Brno'
- f. ***vellaeus***	see *C. astrophoros*
camilli-schneideri	SRms

	canescens	SRms
§	***cashmiriensis*** ♀H4	MGos
	cavei	MBlu SRms
	cinnabarinus	SRms
§	***cochleatus***	CDul EBee LAst MBar MGos NMen SRms
§	***congestus***	CSBt CWib EBee GKir MBar MGos MSwo MWat NHol SPlb SRms WDin WHar
	- 'Nanus'	CMea CTri ELan EOrn MGos NDlv NHol NLAp WPat
	conspicuus	CBcs EWTr SRms
	- 'Decorus' ♀H4	CAlb CCVT CDoC CDul CSBt CWSG EBee ECrN EPfP GKir IFFs LHop LRHS MBar MGan MGos MMuc MSwo NEgg NHol NPri NWea SBch SLim SPer SPlb SPoG WDin WMoo
	- 'Leicester Gem'	SRms
	- 'Red Glory'	CMac
	cooperi	SRms
	cornifolius	SRms
	cuspidatus	MBlu
N	***dammeri*** ♀H4	Widely available
§	- 'Major'	CAlb LBuc
§	- 'Mooncreeper'	LRHS MBri
	- 'Oakwood'	see *C. radicans* 'Eichholz'
	- var. ***radicans*** misapplied	see *C. dammeri* 'Major'
	- var. ***radicans*** C.K.Schneid.	see *C. radicans*
	dielsianus	EMac IFFs NWea SRms
	distichus var. ***tongolensis***	see *C. splendens*
	divaricatus	EMac EPfP IFFs NLar NWea SPer SRms WFar
	duthieanus 'Boer'	see *C. apiculatus*
	elatus	SRms
	elegans	SRms
	emeiensis	SRms
	'Erlinda'	see *C.* × *suecicus* 'Erlinda'
	'Exburiensis'	CBcs CDoC CDul EBee EPfP ERas GKir LAst LRHS MAsh MBri MGos MMuc MRav NLar SEND WDin WFar WHCG
	falconeri	EBee SRms
	fangianus	EMac
	fastigiatus	SRms
	flinckii	SRms
	floccosus	NWea
	floridus	SRms
	forrestii	SRms
	franchetii	CBcs CCVT CDul CMac CSBt EBee ECrN ELan EPfP GKir IFFs LBuc LHop LRHS MGos MMuc MSwo MWat NWea SCoo SLim SPer SPoG SRms SVic WCFE WDin WFar WHar
	- var. ***cinerascens***	SRms
	frigidus	SRms WDin
N	- 'Cornubia' ♀H4	Widely available
	- 'Notcutt's Variety'	EPfP
	- 'Saint Monica'	MBlu
	gamblei	SRms
	ganghobaensis	SRms
	glabratus	SLPl SRms
	glacialis	SRms
	glaucophyllus	IArd SEND SRms
§	***glomerulatus***	MBar SRms
	gracilis	SRms
	granatensis	SRms
	harrovianus	SLPl SRms
	harrysmithii	GAuc GKir
I	***hedegaardii*** 'Fructu Luteo'	SRms
	henryanus	CDoC SRms
	'Herbstfeuer'	see *C. salicifolius* 'Herbstfeuer'
	'Highlight'	see *C. pluriflorus*
§	***hjelmqvistii***	LBuc SRms
	- 'Robustus'	see *C. hjelmqvistii*
	- 'Rotundifolius'	see *C. hjelmqvistii*
	hodjingensis	SRms
	horizontalis ♀H4	Widely available
	- 'Variegatus'	see *C. atropurpureus* 'Variegatus'
	- var. ***wilsonii***	see *C. ascendens*
	hualiensis	SRms
	humifusus	see *C. dammeri*
	hummelii	SRms
§	'Hybridus Pendulus'	Widely available
§	***hylmoei***	SLPl SRms
	hypocarpus	SRms
	ignavus	SLPl SRms
§	***ignescens***	NWea SRms
	ignotus	SRms
	induratus	SLPl SRms
	insculptus	SRms
	integerrimus	SRms
§	***integrifolius*** ♀H4	EPfP EPla LRHS MBar NMen SCoo SRms STre WMoo
	- 'Silver Shadow'	NLar
	kangdingensis	SRms
	lacteus ♀H4	CBcs CCVT CDul CTri EBee ECrN ELan EMac EPfP EWTr GKir LBuc LHop LRHS MBri MGos MMuc MRav NBlu NEgg NWea SCoo SEND SLon SPer SPoG SRms WDin WFar
	lancasteri	SRms
	langei	SRms
	laxiflorus	SRms
§	***lidjiangensis***	SRms
§	***linearifolius***	GCra GKir LRHS
	lucidus	SPer SRms
	ludlowii	SRms
	magnificus	SRms
§	***mairei***	SRms
	marginatus	SRms
§	- 'Blazovice'	SRms
§	- 'Brno'	SRms
	marquandii	GKir SRms
§	***meiophyllus***	MBlu
	meuselii	SRms
	microphyllus misapplied	see *C. purpurascens*
	microphyllus Wall. ex Lindl.	CDul CTri EBee LRHS MBar MGos NBlu NScw NWea SDix SPer SPoG STre WDin WMoo
	- NICE 004	WCFE
	- var. ***cochleatus*** misapplied	see *C. cashmiriensis*
	- var. ***cochleatus*** (Franch.) Rehd. & Wils.	see *C. cochleatus*
	- 'Donard Gem'	see *C. astrophoros*
	- 'Ruby'	SRms
	- 'Teulon Porter'	see *C. astrophoros*
	- var. ***thymifolius*** misapplied	see *C. linearifolius*
	- var. ***thymifolius*** (Lindl.) Koehne	see *C. integrifolius*
	milkedandai	SRms
	miniatus	SRms
	mirabilis	SRms
	monopyrenus	SRms
	'Mooncreeper'	see *C. dammeri* 'Mooncreeper'
	morrisonensis	SRms
	moupinensis	SRms
	mucronatus	SRms
	multiflorus Bunge	SRms
§	***nanshan***	CAbP NLar NWea SRms

- 'Boer'	see *C. apiculatus*
newryensis	SRms
nitens	SRms
nitidifolius	see *C. glomerulatus*
nohelii	SRms
notabilis	SRms
nummularioides	SRms
nummularius	SRms
obscurus	SRms
obtusus	SRms
pangiensis	SRms
pannosus	SLPl SRms WFar
- 'Speckles'	SRms
paradoxus	SRms
parkeri	SRms
pekinensis	SRms
permutatus	see *C. pluriflorus*
perpusillus	SRms WFar
§ ***pluriflorus***	SRms
poluninii	SRms
polycarpus	SRms
praecox 'Boer'	see *C. apiculatus*
procumbens	SLon SRms WDin
- 'Queen of Carpets'	CDoC CDul EBee EPfP EQua ERas GKir LHop LRHS LSRN MAsh MGos MRav MWhi NLar SBch SCoo SLim SPoG SRms SWvt WMoo
- 'Streib's Findling'	see *C.* 'Streib's Findling'
prostratus	SRms
przewalskii	SRms
pseudo-obscurus	SRms
§ ***purpurascens***	CSBt ELau GKir MGos NPri WFar
pyrenaicus	see *C. congestus*
qungbixiensis	SRms
racemiflorus	SRms
§ ***radicans***	IFFs MWat
§ - 'Eichholz'	EBee MGos NHol NLar SBch SPoG WDin
§ ***rehderi***	CMHG NLar SRms
roseus	SRms
'Rothschildianus' ♀H4	Widely available
rotundifolius	SLon
rubens	GKir
rugosus	SRms
salicifolius	EBee GKir MSwo SPer SRms WDin WFar
- Autumn Fire	see *C. salicifolius* 'Herbstfeuer'
§ - 'Avonbank'	CDoC CEnd NLar
- 'Bruno Orangeade'	SRms
- 'Gnom'	CChe CDul CMac EBee ELan EPfP EQua LRHS MAsh MBar MBlu MGos MRav NBir NEgg SPer SPoG SRms WDin WFar WMoo
§ - 'Herbstfeuer'	MGos MRav MSwo SRms WFar
- 'Merriott Weeper'	CDoC
- 'Pendulus'	see *C.* 'Hybridus Pendulus'
- 'Repens'	CDoC CWib EPfP EWTr LRHS MGan MWhi NHol NScw NWea SLim SPer SPoG SRms WDin WFar
- var. ***rugosus*** hort.	see *C. hylmoei*
- 'Scarlet Leader'	CMac
salwinensis	SLPl SRms
sandakphuensis	SRms
scandinavicus	SRms
schantungensis	SRms
schlechtendalii 'Blazovice'	see *C. marginatus* 'Blazovice'
- 'Brno'	see *C. marginatus* 'Brno'
schubertii	SRms
serotinus misapplied	see *C. meiophyllus*
serotinus Hutchinson	NLar SLPl SRms
shannanensis	SRms
shansiensis	SRms
sherriffii	SRms
aff. ***sichuanensis***	GAuc
sikangensis	GBin SLon SRms
simonsii ♀H4	CCVT CDoC CDul CLnd CMac CTri EBee ELan EMac EPfP GKir IFFs LAst LBuc MBar MGos NHol NScw NWea SCoo SPer SPoG SRms WDin WFar WHar
§ ***splendens***	GKir SRms WFar
- 'Sabrina'	see *C. splendens*
spongbergii	SRms
staintonii	SRms
sternianus ♀H4	EBee EPfP MBar SLPl SRms
§ 'Streib's Findling'	EBee MAsh NLar
suavis	SRms
subacutus	SRms
subadpressus	SRms
× ***suecicus*** 'Coral Beauty'	Widely available
§ - 'Erlinda' (v)	CWib NBlu NLar SCoo SRms
- 'Ifor'	SLPl SRms
- 'Juliette' (v)	CWib EHoe ERas LAst LSRN MAsh MBar NBlu NLar SCoo SPoG WFar
- 'Skogholm'	CBcs CDul CWSG CWib EBee GKir IFFs LRHS MBar MGos SCoo SPer SRms WDin WFar WHar
taoensis	SRms
tardiflorus	SRms
tauricus	SRms
teijiashanensis	SRms
tengyuehensis	SRms
thimphuensis	SRms
tomentellus	WCFE
tomentosus	SRms
turbinatus	SLPl SRms
'Valkenburg'	SRms
vandelaarii	SLPl SRms
veitchii	MBri NLar SRms
verruculosus	SRms
villosulus	SRms
vilmorinianus	SRms
wardii misapplied	see *C. mairei*
wardii W.W. Sm.	GGal SRms
× ***watereri***	CCVT CWib EBee LRHS MSwo NWea SBch SEND WDin WJas
- 'Avonbank'	see *C. salicifolius* 'Avonbank'
- 'Corina'	SRms
- 'Cornubia'	see *C. frigidus* 'Cornubia'
- 'John Waterer' ♀H4	EPfP LRHS MGos SPer SPoG WFar
- 'Pendulus'	see *C.* 'Hybridus Pendulus'
- 'Pink Champagne'	CMac EQua MRav
wilsonii	SRms
yallungensis	SRms
yinchangensis	SRms
zabelii	SRms

Cotula (*Asteraceae*)

C&H 452	NWCA
atrata	see *Leptinella atrata*
coronopifolia	CBen CWat EHon EMFW LPBA NPer SWat
§ ***hispida*** (DC.) Harv.	CMea CTri EAlp EBee ECho EDAr EHoe EPot GAbr GKev GMaP LRHS MAvo MBar MHer MSCN MTho MWat NPer NRya NWCA SIng SPoG SRms WCom WEas WFar WPat WPer
lineariloba (DC.) Hilliard	ECha ECho EWes LBee LRHS
minor	see *Leptinella minor*
'Platt's Black'	see *Leptinella squalida* 'Platt's Black'
potentilloides	see *Leptinella potentillina*

	pyrethrifolia	see *Leptinella pyrethrifolia*
	rotundata	see *Leptinella rotundata*
	sericea	see *Leptinella albida*
	serrulata	see *Leptinella serrulata*
	squalida	see *Leptinella squalida*

Cotyledon (*Crassulaceae*)

	chrysantha	see *Rosularia chrysantha*
	gibbiflora var. ***metallica***	see *Echeveria gibbiflora* var. *metallica*
	oppositifolia	see *Chiastophyllum oppositifolium*
	orbiculata	CHEx ETod SDix
	- var. ***oblonga***	EBee WEas
	- var. ***orbiculata***	EShb
	- 'Silver Waves'	MCot
	simplicifolia	see *Chiastophyllum oppositifolium*
	tomentosa subsp. ***ladismithensis***	EShb LRHS

Cowania see *Purshia*

Crambe (*Brassicaceae*)

	cordifolia ♀H4	Widely available
	maritima ♀H4	CArn CSev CSpe EBWF EBee ECGP ECha EPfP GMaP GPoy LRHS MBel MCot MRav NEgg NSti SMad SPer SWat WFar WJek WMnd WPer WSpi WWEG
	- 'Lilywhite'	CAgr ILis SVic WCom WCot
	tatarica	SHar WPer

cranberry see *Vaccinium macrocarpon*, *V. oxycoccos*

Crassula (*Crassulaceae*)

	anomala	see *C. atropurpurea* var. *anomala*
	arborescens	EShb SRms STre
	argentea	see *C. ovata*
§	***atropurpurea*** var. ***anomala***	SChr
	- subsp. ***arborescens*** 'Blue Mist'	SEND
	coccinea	EShb
	dejecta	EShb
§	***exilis*** subsp. ***cooperi***	STre
	lactea	STre
	lycopodioides variegata	see *C. muscosa* 'Variegata'
	multicava	CHEx
	muscosa	EShb SChr SRot STre
§	- 'Variegata' (v)	EShb
	obtusa	SRot
§	***ovata*** ♀H1	CHEx CTsd EBak EOHP EPfP MBri NPer NScw SEND SWal WCor WThu
	- 'Gollum'	STre
	- 'Hummel's Sunset' (v) ♀H1	STre SWal
*	- ***nana***	SEND STre
	- 'Obliqua'	STre
	- 'Variegata' (v)	EBak STre
	perfoliata var. ***falcata*** ♀H1	CTsd EShb MBri SRot
	perforata	WCor
	- 'Variegata' (v)	CBow EWll LSou SRot
	picturata	see *C. exilis* subsp. *cooperi*
	portulacea	see *C. ovata*
	rupestris ♀H1	MBri STre
§	***sarcocaulis***	CHEx CTri EAlp ECho ELan ELon EPot EWll GEdr GMaP MTho NLAp NMen NVic NWCA SEND SGar SIng SPlb SPoG SRms SRot STre SWal WAbe WEas WFar WPat WSHC
I	- ***alba***	GEdr NLAp STre WPer
	- 'Ken Aslet'	STre
	schmidtii	MBri
	sedifolia	see *C. setulosa* 'Milfordiae'
	sediformis	see *C. setulosa* 'Milfordiae'
§	***setulosa*** 'Milfordiae'	CTri ECho EDAr GKir NBir
	socialis	EPot STre
	- 'Major'	SChr
	tetragona	SEND
*	***tomentosa*** 'Variegata' (v)	EShb
	'Très Bon'	STre

+ *Crataegomespilus* (*Rosaceae*)

	'Dardarii'	MBri
	'Jules d'Asnières'	MBri NLar

× *Crataegosorbus* (*Rosaceae*)

§	'Granatnaja'	IArd
	miczurinii 'Ivan's Belle'	CAgr

Crataegus ✿ (*Rosaceae*)

	F&M 196	WPGP
	altaica	GKir
	arnoldiana	CAgr CDul CEnd CLnd CTri EBee ECrN EPfP GKir LRHS MCoo NWea SCoo SEND SFam SLPl SPer
	'Autumn Glory'	CEnd CLnd EBee ECrN GKir WFar
	azarolus	CAgr CLnd CTho EPfP MBri
	champlainensis	CLnd
	chrysocarpa	EPfP
	chungtienensis	SSpi WSpi
N	***coccinea*** misapplied	see *C. intricata*
N	***coccinea*** ambig.	NWea
§	***coccinea*** L.	CAgr CLnd CTho EBee EPfP GKir LRHS MAsh MBri MCoo SCoo
	coccinioides	EPfP
	cordata	see *C. phaenopyrum*
	crus-galli misapplied	see *C. persimilis* 'Prunifolia'
	crus-galli L.	CCVT CDoC CDul CLnd CTho EBee ECrN EPfP LAst MAsh NWea SPer WDin WFar WJas
	dahurica	EPfP
	× ***dippeliana***	EPfP
	douglasii	EPfP GAuc
	dsungarica	EPfP
	× ***durobrivensis***	CAgr CDul CLnd EPfP GKir MBri MCoo NLar
	ellwangeriana	CAgr ECrN EPfP
	eriocarpa	CLnd
	flabellata	GKir
	gemmosa	CEnd GKir MAsh MBri MCoo NLar NWea
	greggiana	EPfP
	× ***grignonensis***	CBcs CCVT CDul CLnd CTho ECrN LMaj LRHS MAsh SEND SPer WJas
§	***intricata***	EPfP NWea
	irrasa	EPfP
	jonesiae	ECrN EPfP
	laciniata Ucria	see *C. orientalis*
§	***laevigata***	GKir NWea
	- 'Coccinea Plena'	see *C. laevigata* 'Paul's Scarlet'
	- 'Crimson Cloud'	CDoC CDul CEnd CLnd CWSG CWib EBee ECrN ELan EMui EPfP GKir LBuc LRHS MAsh MBri MGos MSwo NWea SBch SCoo SCrf SEND SLim SLon SPer SPoG WFar WHar WJas
	- 'Gireoudii'	CBcs CDul CEnd CPMA CWib LAst MGos NLar WPat
	- 'Mutabilis'	CLnd CTri

§ - 'Paul's Scarlet' (d) ♀H4 Widely available
- 'Pink Corkscrew' EPfP GKir LLHF MBlu MBri MGos NHol SMad WPat
- 'Plena' (d) CBcs CDoC CDul CLnd CMac CSBt CTho CTri CWib EBee ECrN GKir LAst LRHS MGos MSwo MWat NWea SBch SCrf SLim SPer WDin WFar WHar
- 'Punicea' GKir
- 'Rosea' GKir
- 'Rosea Flore Pleno' (d) ♀H4 Widely available
× ***lavalleei*** CCVT CDul CLnd CTri EBee ECrN ELan EPfP GKir LAst LMaj MAsh MSwo NWea SCoo SFam SPer SPur WDin
- 'Carrierei' ♀H4 CDoC CMac CTho EPfP EWTr GKir LHop LMaj LRHS MAsh MBri NWea SCoo
lobulata EPfP
mexicana see *C. pubescens* f. *stipulacea*
mollis CAgr CTho ECrN EPfP MBri WSpi
monogyna Widely available
§ - 'Biflora' CDul CEnd CLnd CTho CTri EBee ECrN GKir LRHS MAsh MCoo MGos NWea SCoo SLim SPoG
- 'Compacta' MBlu NLar WPat
- 'Flexuosa' MGos WCot
- 'Praecox' see *C. monogyna* 'Biflora'
- 'Stricta' CCVT CDul CLnd CSBt EBee ECrN EPfP GKir LMaj SPoG
- 'Variegata' (v) ECrN
× ***mordenensis*** 'Toba' (d) CDul CLnd EPfP MBri
nigra EPfP
§ ***orientalis*** CCVT CDul CEnd CLnd CMCN CTho CTri EBee EPfP GKir IArd IDee IFFs LRHS MAsh MBlu MBri MCoo MGos NWea SCoo SLPl SLim SSpi WJas WMou WSpi
oxyacantha see *C. laevigata*
pedicellata see *C. coccinea* L.
pentagyna EPfP
§ ***persimilis*** 'Prunifolia' ♀H4 Widely available
- 'Prunifolia Splendens' CCVT EWTr GBin GKir LRHS MBri MCoo SCoo WPat
§ ***phaenopyrum*** CDul CLnd CTho EBee EPfP IDee LRHS MGos SLPl SMad
pinnatifida EPfP GKir
- var. ***major*** CDul CEnd EBee EPfP LRHS MBri MCoo NWea SCoo
- - 'Big Golden Star' CAgr CLnd CTho ECrN GKir LRHS MAsh MBri MCoo NLar SCoo
'Praecox' see *C. monogyna* 'Biflora'
prunifolia see *C. persimilis* 'Prunifolia'
pseudoheterophylla EPfP
* ***pubescens*** f. ***major*** CAgr
§ - f. ***stipulacea*** CDul CTho ECrN EPfP LRHS MBri
punctata CTho LRHS SLPl
- f. ***aurea*** EPfP
sanguinea EPfP
schraderiana CAgr CDul CLnd CTho EBee EBtc EPfP GKir LRHS MBri MCoo NWea SCoo SPoG
songarica new GAuc
sorbifolia EPfP
succulenta EPfP GKir
- var. ***macracantha*** EPfP GKir
suksdorfii EPfP
tanacetifolia CAgr CDul CPMA CTho EPfP GKir LLHF LRHS MBlu MBri SPer
* - 'Fructu Albo' GKir
turkestanica EPfP
viridis 'Winter King' CDoC CPMA EPfP GKir MBlu MCoo SLim
wattiana EBee ELan EPfP

× *Crataemespilus* (*Rosaceae*)

grandiflora CBcs CDul CEnd CLnd CTho WSpi

Crawfurdia (*Gentianaceae*)

speciosa B&SWJ 2138 WCru

Cremanthodium (*Asteraceae*)

angustifolium EBee
- SDR 1831 GKev
arnicoides EBee GKev
ellisii GKev
- CC 4642 EBee
helianthus new GKev
nepalense new GKev
pleurocaule new GKev

Cremastra (*Orchidaceae*)

variabilis WWst

× *Cremnosedum* (*Crassulaceae*)

§ 'Little Gem' CStu EPot NMen

Crenularia see *Aethionema*

Crepis (*Asteraceae*)

aurea EBee WCom
incana ♀H4 CMea CMoH EBee ECho ECtt MAvo MTho NChi NMen NSla NWCA SIng SPhx SRms WPat
- 'Pink Mist' GBin LRHS MBri NLar SDix
rubra LRHS

Crinitaria see *Aster*

Crinodendron (*Elaeocarpaceae*)

hookerianum ♀H3 Widely available
- 'Ada Hoffmann' CBcs CDoC CMac EBee ELan ELon GBin ISea LRHS LSRN MBlu MBri MGos MREP NDlv NLar NMun SBch SLim SPoG
patagua CBcs CCCN CSam CWib EBee EQua GGar GQui IArd ISea MBri NEgg NLar SLon WAbe WFar WSHC

Crinum (*Amaryllidaceae*)

amoenum CCCN EBee EBrs ECho WCot
asiaticum WCot
- DJHC 970606 WCot
- var. ***sinicum*** WCot
§ ***bulbispermum*** CFir EBee ELan WCot
capense see *C. bulbispermum*
'Carolina Beauty' WCot
'Elizabeth Traub' WCot
'Ellen Bosanquet' CCCN CDes CFir EBee WCot
'Emma Jones' WCot
erubescens WCot
'Hanibal's Dwarf' CDes EBee WCot
'Heja Lodge' WCot
macowanii WCot
moorei CAvo CBro CDes CFir EBrs ECho LEdu LPio LRHS SChr WCot WPGP
- f. ***album*** CCCN CStu EBee LPio LRHS WCot
'Ollene' WCot
§ × ***powellii*** ♀H3 Widely available
- 'Album' ♀H3 CAvo CBro CHEx CTri EBee EBrs ECha ECho ELan ELon EShb EWes GCra GKir LAma LEdu LHop LPio

Plant	Suppliers
	LRHS MBri MRav MWte SEND SSpi WCot WFar WHil WPGP
- 'Harlemense'	SSpi
- 'Longifolium'	see *C. bulbispermum*
- 'Roseum'	see *C.* × *powellii*
'Regina's Disco Lounge'	WCot
variabile	EBee WCot
yemense	IMou WCot

Criogenes see *Cypripedium*

Crithmum (*Apiaceae*)

Plant	Suppliers
maritimum	CArn EBWF SPlb WJek

Crocosmia ✿ (*Iridaceae*)

Plant	Suppliers
'Alistair'	ECtt
'Anniversary'	IBlr
'Apricot'	ECrc IBal
aurea misapplied	see *C.* × *crocosmiiflora* 'George Davison' Davison
aurea ambig.	EShb GCal
aurea (Pappe ex Hook.f.) Planch.	CDes CPne CPou ECtt IBlr NHol
- subsp. ***aurea***	IBlr
- - 'Maculata'	ECrc IBlr
- subsp. ***pauciflora***	IBlr
'Auricorn'	IBlr NCot NHol
'Auriol'	IBlr
'Aurora'	CHVG CPrp NGdn
'Beth Chatto'	CPrp ECrc IBal
Bressingham Beacon = 'Blos'	IBlr WRHF
'Bressingham Blaze'	CBre CMHG CPrp EBee EBla EBrs ECrc ECtt GKir IBlr LRHS NBre NGdn NHol WCot WHil
Bridgemere hybrid	ECrc NHol
Bright Eyes = 'Walbreyes' **new**	LRHS
'Cadenza'	IBal IBlr NCot NHol
'Carnival'	ECtt IBlr
'Cascade'	IBal IBlr NCot
'Chinatown'	IBal IBlr MAvo NCot NHol
'Citronella' misapplied	see *C.* × *crocosmiiflora* 'Honey Angels'
'Comet' Knutty	CPrp EBrs ECrc GBuc GCal IBlr MAvo NCot NHol
§ × ***crocosmiiflora***	CHEx CTri EBee EPla IBlr LAst LRHS MCot NBPC NBlu NHol SEND SIng SPlb SRms WBrk WCot WFar WMoo WShi
- 'A.E. Amos'	ECrc ECtt
- 'A.J. Hogan'	CPrp GBin IBal IBlr NHol SMrs
- 'African Glow'	EBee ECrc IBal
- 'African Gold' **new**	LRHS
- 'Amber Sun'	IBlr
- 'Amberglow'	CBgR CElw CMea CPrp ECho GKir IBal IBlr NBre NHol NPer WFar
- 'Apricot Queen'	IBlr MAvo NHol
- 'Autumn Gold'	IBlr
- 'Baby Barnaby'	CBre CDes EBee ECtt IBlr NHol SBch WPGP
- 'Babylon'	Widely available
- 'Best of British'	CHVG
- 'Bicolor'	CPrp IBal IBlr NHol WHil
- 'Burford Bronze'	CAbx CPrp IBal IBlr MAvo NCot NHol WHil
- 'Buttercup'	CSam EBee ECrc ERCP EWll GKev IBal IBlr MAvo MBel MCot NBre NHol STes WBor WFar WMoo WWEG
- 'Canary Bird'	CBro CPne CPrp CRow CSam ECho ECtt GAbr GMac IBal IBlr NBPC NGdn NHol WBrk WRHF
- 'Cardinale'	IBlr
§ - 'Carmin Brillant' ♀H3-4	Widely available
- 'Challa'	EBee ECrc
- 'Citrina'	GKir
- 'Citronella' J.E. Fitt	CBgR CBro CPLG CPrp CSam CTri EBee EBla EBrs ECha ECrc EPfP GKev GMaP GQue LBMP LRHS MBel MRav NCob NGdn NHol SAga WBVN WBrk WCot
§ - 'Coleton Fishacre'	Widely available
§ - 'Columbus'	CPar CPrp CSam EBee ECrc EPfP EWld GBin IBal IBlr LHop LRHS MAvo NHol SGar WBor WFar WMnd WWEG
- 'Colwall'	IBal IBlr MAvo NCot
- 'Constance'	CBgR CBro CElw CPrp CSam EBee EBrs ECrc GGar GKir IBal IBlr LRHS MAvo MBri MNrw NBid NGdn NHol SRGP SRos WFar
- 'Corona'	CPrp IBal IBlr MAvo NCot NHol
- 'Corten'	IBlr
§ - 'Croesus'	ECrc IBal IBlr MAvo MRav NCot
- 'Custard Cream'	CAbx CPrp CSpe ECrc ECtt IBlr MAvo NHol SRos WCon WFar WRHF
- 'D.H. Houghton'	IBlr
- 'Debutante'	CDes CPrp EBee EBrs ECrc ECtt IBal IBlr LRHS MAvo NHol SUsu WHoo WPGP WSHC
§ - 'Diadème'	CSam MAvo NHol
- 'Dusky Maiden'	Widely available
§ - 'E.A. Bowles'	CPou CPrp EBee ECrc IBlr WCot
- 'Eastern Promise'	CAbx CBre CPrp EBee ELon IBal IBlr MAvo NCot SMrm WHil
- 'Eclatant'	IBlr
- 'Elegans'	CBre CElw EBrs ECrc ECtt IBal IBlr LRHS
§ - 'Emily McKenzie'	Widely available
- 'Etoile de Feu'	IBlr
- 'Fantasie'	CBgR ECrc IBal MAvo
- 'Festival Orange'	ECrc IBlr MAvo
- 'Fire Jumper'	CDes EBee MAvo WPGP
- 'Firebrand'	IBlr NCot
- 'Fireglow'	ECho ECtt GKir IBal IBlr IFFs NCot WFar WPer
- 'Flamethrower'	IBlr MAvo
- 'George Davison' misapplied	see *C.* × *crocosmiiflora* 'Golden Glory' ambig., *C.* 'Sulphurea'
§ - 'George Davison' Davison	Widely available
- 'Gloria'	ECrc IBal IBlr SUsu WHil
- 'Golden Glory' misapplied	see *C.* × *crocosmiiflora* 'Diadème'
§ - 'Golden Glory' ambig.	CPLG CWCL EHrv ELan IBal IBlr LSou MSwo NBir NHol SPlb SRos WCot WFar WHil
- 'Goldfinch'	CPrp ECrc IBlr NCot NHol WHil WWEG
- 'Goldie'	ECrc
- 'Hades'	CPrp IBlr MAvo NCot WHil
- 'Harvest Sun'	IBlr
- 'Heligan' **new**	EBee EPfP
- 'His Majesty'	CAbx CBro CPne CPrp CSam CSpe ECrc ECtt IBal IBlr NHol SDys WFar WHil WPer
- 'Hoey Joey'	ECrc GMac
§ - 'Honey Angels'	Widely available
- 'Honey Bells'	CElw ECrc WBrk
- 'Irish Dawn'	CPrp ECrc IBal IBlr NBre NCot NHol
§ - 'Jackanapes'	CPne CPrp CRow CWCL EBrs ECtt EHrv ELan ELon GCal GGar GKir IBal IBlr LRHS MBri MGos MLHP

		NHol SBch SDys SUsu WFar WHil WPGP
	- 'James Coey' misapplied	see *C.* × *crocosmiiflora* 'Carmin Brilliant'
	- 'James Coey' J.E. Fitt	CHar COlW CPrp CRow EAEE EBee EBla ECha EHoe EHrv EPfP IFoB LRHS MLHP NGdn NHol SIng SPhx SRGP SWvt WFar WMoo
	- 'Jesse van Dyke'	IBlr
§	- 'Jessie'	CElw ECrc IBlr MAvo SMrm WHil WPer
	- 'Judith'	ECrc IBlr NCot
	- 'Kapoor'	IBlr
	- 'Kiautschou'	CHVG CWCL EBee EBrs ECtt GMac IBal IBlr MAvo NBre NHol SDys
	- 'Lady Hamilton'	Widely available
	- 'Lady McKenzie'	see *C.* × *crocosmiiflora* 'Emily McKenzie'
	- 'Lady Oxford'	CPrp ECrc IBlr LRHS NHol SMrm WHil
	- 'Lambrook Gold'	CAvo ECrc IBlr SUsu
	- 'Lord Nelson'	CPrp IBal MAvo NHol
	- 'Loweswater'	ECrc MAvo
	- 'Lutea'	EBee ECtt IBal IBlr NCob NHol
	- 'Marjorie'	ECrc LRHS
	- 'Mars'	CElw CPrp EBla ECrc EWes EWll GAbr GBuc GCal GGar GMac IBal IBlr IFoB LPio LRHS MWhi NHol SBch SPlb SRGP WFar WPGP WPer WWEG
	- 'Mephistopheles'	CPrp IBlr MAvo NCot NHol WHil
	- 'Merryman'	ECrc GAbr GMac MAvo
	- 'Météore'	CBgR CPrp EBee EBrs ELon EPot GAbr GGar IBal LRHS MBNS NBre NHol NPri SBch WCon WPrP WWEG
	- 'Morgenlicht'	ECtt IBal IBlr NHol WBrk WCot
	- 'Moses' **new**	ECrc
	- 'Mount Usher'	CFir CMdw CPrp ECrc ECtt GCal IBal IBlr MAvo NHol SGar WFar WHil WOut
	- 'Mrs David Howard'	SApp
§	- 'Mrs Geoffrey Howard'	CDes CPrp CSam EBee ECtt GGar IBal IBlr MAvo NHol SUsu WBrk WCru WPGP WPrP
	- 'Mrs Morrison'	see *C.* × *crocosmiiflora* 'Mrs Geoffrey Howard'
	- Newry seedling	see *C.* × *crocosmiiflora* 'Prometheus'
	- 'Nigricans'	ECrc
	- 'Nimbus'	CPrp EBee IBal IBlr WHil
§	- 'Norwich Canary'	CBgR CMHG COlW CPrp EBee EBla ECha EPPr EPfP EShb GBuc GCra IBal IBlr LEdu LRHS MRav NBir NGdn NHol NPri NSti SMrm SUsu WBrk WCot WMoo WSpi WWEG
	- 'Olympic Fire'	ECrc IBlr MAvo NCot NHol
	- 'Pepper'	ECrc IBlr
	- 'Plaisir'	IBal IBlr MAvo NBid NHol WFar WPrP WWEG
	- 'Polo'	CBgR CSam
	- 'Princess'	see *C. pottsii* 'Princess'
§	- 'Princess Alexandra'	IBlr
	- 'Prolificans'	IBlr
§	- 'Prometheus'	CPrp IBal IBlr NHol SMrs WHil
	- 'Queen Alexandra' misapplied	see *C.* × *crocosmiiflora* 'Princess Alexandra'
§	- 'Queen Alexandra' J.E. Fitt	ECha IBlr LEdu LHop NHol SPer WHal WMoo WPer
	- 'Queen Charlotte'	CPrp ECrc IBal IBlr
	- 'Queen Mary II'	see *C.* × *crocosmiiflora* 'Columbus'
	- 'Queen of Spain'	CPrp EBrs GKir IBal IBlr LRHS MBel MDKP NHol WHil
	- 'Rayon d'Or'	CDes ECrc IBlr WPGP
	- 'Red King'	CPrp EBee EBla EBrs EPfP EPot IBal IBlr LHop MBNS MWea SGar WFar WHil WRHF WSpi WWEG
	- 'Red Knight'	CBgR CHVG CMMP GAbr IBlr NHol
	- 'Rheingold' misapplied	see *C.* × *crocosmiiflora* 'Diadème'
	- 'Rose Queen'	IBlr NCot
	- 'Saint Clements'	ECrc IBlr NCot NHol
	- 'Saracen'	Widely available
	- 'Severn Seas' **new**	ECrc
	- 'Sir Mathew Wilson'	CDes EBee EBrs GKir IBal IBlr MAvo WCot WPGP
	- 'Solfatare' ♀H3	Widely available
	- 'Solfatare Coleton Fishacre'	see *C.* × *crocosmiiflora* 'Coleton Fishacre'
	- 'Star of the East' ♀H3	Widely available
	- 'Starbright'	IBlr
	- 'Starfire'	ECrc ECtt
	- 'Sultan'	CDes CElw EBee ECrc IBlr NCot WCot WFar WMoo WPGP
	- 'Venus'	CAbx CBgR CBre CPen CPou CPrp EBee EBrs ECtt EShb EWll GBuc IBal IBlr IFFs LRHS MAvo NBre NHol NLar SRGP SRos WFar WHil WMoo WPrP
	- 'Vesuvius'	ECrc GCal IBlr WFar
	- 'Vic's Yellow'	ECrc SGar SMrm
	- 'Voyager'	CPrp EBee EBrs ECtt ELon EPot ERCP GAbr IBal IBlr LHop LRHS MBri NHol SGar SWal WBor WHil WPer
	- Wasdale strain **new**	ECrc
	- 'Zeal Tan'	CElw CPar CPen CPrp CSam EBee ECGP ECtt ELan ELon EPPr GCal GKir IBlr LRHS MAvo MBNS MDKP NCGa NEgg SBch SMrm SPoG SUsu WBrk WCot
§	× ***crocosmioides***	IBlr
	- 'Castle Ward Late'	CBgR CPou CRow EAEE ECha ECrc GAbr GBuc GCal IBal IBlr NBre NCGa NHol SUsu WMoo WSHC
	- 'Mount Stewart Late'	IBlr
§	- 'Vulcan' Leichtlin	IBlr LRHS NHol WHil
	'Cylvia' **new**	ECrc
	'Darkleaf Apricot'	see *C.* × *crocosmiiflora* 'Coleton Fishacre'
	'Devil's Advocate'	MAvo
	'Doctor Marion Wood'	ECrc MAvo NCot
	'Eldorado'	see *C.* × *crocosmiiflora* 'E.A. Bowles'
	'Elegance'	IBlr
	'Elizabeth'	NHol
	'Ellenbank Canary'	CBgR GMac MAvo
	'Ellenbank Firecrest'	CBgR CDes GMac MAvo NCGa WOut
	'Ellenbank Skylark'	CBgR GMac MAvo
	'Emberglow'	Widely available
	'Fandango'	IBal IBlr NCot NHol
	'Fernhill'	ECrc IBlr
*	'Feuerser'	ECtt
	'Fire King' misapplied	see *C.* × *crocosmiiflora* 'Jackanapes'
	'Fire King' ambig.	WHil WSpi
	'Fire King'	CBgR EBee ECrc ERCP GAbr IBal IFFs LRHS NBPC
	'Fire Sprite'	IBlr
	'Firefly'	IBlr NHol
	'Fireworks' **new**	NCot
	'Flaire'	IBlr
	'Fleuve Jaune'	CPne ECrc ECtt
	fucata	IBlr

- 'Jupiter'	see *C.* 'Jupiter'
fucata* × *paniculata	CPrp NHol
'Fugue'	IBlr
'Fusilade'	IBlr
'Gold Sprite'	IBlr NCot
'Golden Ballerina' PBR **new**	EBee LRHS LSou SGSe
'Golden Dew'	EBee ECrc ECtt GAbr GKir GQue LSou MBNS NCGa NChi NEgg SBch WBrk WCot WGor WHil
Golden Fleece *sensu* Lemoine	see *C.* × *crocosmiiflora* 'Coleton Fishacre'
'Harlequin'	CElw
'Hellfire' **new**	CSpe LLWG MAvo MBNS NGdn WCot
'Highlight'	ECrc IBal IBlr MAvo NCot NHol
'Hill House'	MAvo
'Irish Flame'	ECrc GKir NHol
'Irish Sunset'	GKir NHol
'Jennine'	CAbx EBee ECrc IBal NCot NHol SRGP WHil
Jenny Bloom = 'Blacro' PBR	COlW CPrp EBrs ECrc GBuc GKir NBir NChi SMrs
'John Boots'	CPrp EBee EBrs EHrv ELon GAbr GBuc IBal IBlr LPio MCot NCGa NHol SRGP WFar WHil
§ 'Jupiter'	CAbx CBre CPou CPrp CSam CWCL GAbr GBuc GMac IBal IBlr MAvo MMuc MRav NChi NHol SApp WFar WHil
'Kathleen'	ECrc GSec
'Krakatoa'	CPrp EBee ECrc EPfP IBal LLHF MWea SGSe SPoG SRkn
'Lady Wilson' misapplied	see *C.* × *crocosmiiflora* 'Norwich Canary'
'Lana de Savary'	CPrp GBin GCal IBal IBlr NBid NCot NHol
'Late Cornish'	see *C.* × *crocosmiiflora* 'Queen Alexandra' J.E. Fitt
'Late Lucifer'	CHEx CTri GCal IBlr LSRN SDix
× ***latifolia***	see *C.* × *crocosmioides*
'Limpopo'	CMac EBee ECtt ELon GAbr GQue LSou MAvo MBNS NCot NEgg SHar SMrm SPer SPoG WCot WWlt
'Lucifer' ♀H4	Widely available
'Mandarin'	ECrc IBlr
'Marcotijn'	ECtt GGar IBal IBlr IGor LPio NHol WOut
masoniorum ♀H3	Widely available
- 'African Dawn'	CPen ECrc ECtt GQue MAvo NCot
- 'Amber'	IBlr
- 'Dixter Flame'	ECtt IBlr IFoB LPio SDix WOut
- 'Firebird'	EBrs GBuc GCra IBlr IGor MAvo MBri NBre NHol SRos
- 'Flamenco'	IBlr
- 'Golden Swan'	ECtt
- Holehird strain **new**	ECrc
- 'Kiaora'	ECrc IBlr
- 'Moira Reid'	ECrc IBlr NHol
- red-flowered	IBlr
- 'Rowallane Apricot'	IBlr
- 'Rowallane Orange'	GAbr IBlr NHol WHil
- 'Rowallane Yellow' ♀H3-4	CDes EBrs ECtt GCal GKir GMac IBlr IGor IMou ITim MAvo MBri NCGa NHol SMrm SRos WCot WOut
- Slieve Donard selection **new**	ECrc
- 'Tropicana'	IBlr
mathewsiana	IBlr
'Mex'	MAvo WCot
'Minotaur'	IBlr
'Mistral'	CAbx CBgR CMea CPrp EBee EBrs EPfP EPot EWll GBuc GMac IBal IBlr MAvo MBel MNrw NBre NHol WBor WFar WMoo
'Moorland Blaze' **new**	WMoo
'Mount Stewart'	see *C.* × *crocosmiiflora* 'Jessie'
'Mr Bedford'	see *C.* × *crocosmiiflora* 'Croesus'
'Mullard Pink'	ECrc MAvo
'Okavango' PBR	CBgR CBre CBro CMac CPen CSpe EBee ECGP ECtt ELon GAbr GQue LSou MAvo MBNS NBPC NCot NGdn NLar SHar SMrm SPoG WCot WRHF
Old Hat	see *C.* 'Walberton Red'
'Orange Devil'	CBre EBee ECtt IBal IBlr LRHS MAvo MBNS MBri MWea SMrm
'Orange Lucifer'	NBre WPrP
'Orange River' **new**	WCot
'Orange Spirit'	WFar
'Orangeade'	EBrs ECtt GBin IBal IBlr NCot NHol SMrm SMrs SUsu
'Out of the West'	ECrc
'Pageant'	ECrc NCot
§ ***paniculata***	CMac CPne CPou EBla ECtt GAbr GGar LPla MNFA MNrw NBid NHol NOrc SAPC SBch SPet WBor WBrk WMoo WPen WShi WTin
- brown/orange-flowered	IBlr
- 'Cally Greyleaf'	EWld GCal
- 'Cally Sword'	GCal
- 'Major'	CTri IBlr
- 'Natal'	CPrp ECtt IBal NHol WFar
- red-flowered	IBlr SWvt
- triploid	IBlr
aff. ***paniculata***	ECtt IBlr
'Paul's Best Yellow' **new**	EBee LLWG MAvo MBNS WCot
pearsei	IBlr
'Phillipa Browne'	EBee IBal LSou MAvo NCot NEgg SRGP WCot WMoo
§ ***pottsii***	CBgR CHVG CRow ECtt EPla GBin IBal IBlr NHol WFar WWEG
- CD&R 109	CPou
- 'Culzean Pink'	CBgR CHVG CPrp EBee GAbr GBin GBuc GCal GMac IBal IBlr MAvo MLHP MRav NBir NCob NCot NHol SMrm SMrs WCot WOut WPGP WWEG
- deep pink-flowered	IBlr IGor WMoo
- 'Grandiflora'	IBlr
§ - 'Princess'	ECrc IBal MAvo
'Quantreau'	ECrc IBlr NCot
'R.W. Wallace'	CPrp ECrc IBal NHol
'Red Devils'	NHol
'Red Star'	IBal
'Roman Gold'	IBlr
rosea	see *Tritonia disticha* subsp. *rubrolucens*
'Rowden Bronze'	see *C.* × *crocosmiiflora* 'Coleton Fishacre'
'Rowden Chrome'	see *C.* × *crocosmiiflora* 'George Davison' Davison
'Ruby Velvet'	IBlr
'Rubygold'	CPrp IBlr
'Sabena'	MAvo
'Saffron Queen'	IBlr
'Salsa' **new**	WCot
'Saturn'	see *C.* 'Jupiter'
'Scarlatti'	GAbr IBal IBlr NCot NHol
'Severn Sunrise' ♀H3-4	Widely available
'Shocking'	ECrc IBlr NCot NHol
'Son of Lucifer'	WFar
'Sonate'	MBel NHol SPlb WPer
'Spitfire'	Widely available
§ 'Sulphurea'	CPou CPrp CRow CSam ECtt IBal

	Name	Suppliers
		IBlr MCot NHol SDix SIng SMrm WBrk WCot WEas WHal WHil WPer
	'Sunset'	MAvo
	'Sunzest'	ECrc WFar
	'Tangerine' **new**	ECrc
	'Tangerine Queen'	CAbx EBrs ECrc ECtt IBal IBlr NCot NHol SMrm SUsu WHil WMoo
	'Tiger'	CElw ECrc IBlr
	'Vulcan' Leichtlin	see *C.* × *crocosmioides* 'Vulcan' Leichtlin
I	'Vulcan' A. Bloom	CPen CPrp EBrs ECtt GAbr GGar IBal IBlr MAvo NHol SAga WCot WFar
§	'Walberton Red'	CAbx ECrc EWes IBal IBlr MAvo MBri SAga SApp SMad SUsu WCot WHil
	Walberton Yellow = 'Walcroy'PBR	LRHS SApp SUsu WCot WHil
	'Zambesi'PBR	CBro CDes CKno EBee ECtt EHrv ELon GAbr GQue LHop LRHS LSou MAvo MBNS NBPC NCGa NCot NLar SBch SPer WCot
	'Zeal Giant'	CRow ECrc ECtt IBlr MAvo NHol
	Zeal unnamed	CPrp EBee ECrc GMac IBal IBlr NHol WFar

Crocus ✿ (*Iridaceae*)

	Name	Suppliers
	abantensis	ECho ERos
	adanensis	ERos
	'Advance'	CBro EBrs ECho EGoo EPfP EPot LAma LRHS MBri MCot SPer
	alatavicus	ECho WWst
	albiflorus	see *C. vernus* subsp. *albiflorus*
	ancyrensis	ECho EPot LAma
	- 'Golden Bunch'	EBrs ECho EPfP LRHS WShi
§	***angustifolius*** ♀H4	ECho ERos
	- 'Berlin Gold' **new**	ECho
	- bronze-tinged	NMin
	- 'Minor'	EBrs ECho
	antalyensis	ECho
	'Ard Schenk'	EBrs ECho EPot GKev LAma LRHS
	asturicus	see *C. serotinus* subsp. *salzmannii*
	- var. ***atropurpureus*** **new**	LRHS
	asumaniae	EBrs ECho ERos
	'Aubade'	EBrs ECho EPot
	aureus	see *C. flavus* subsp. *flavus*
	banaticus ♀H4	CBro EBrs ECho EPot ERos LLHF MSSP NMen WWst
	- 'Albus'	ERos
	baytopiorum	ECho ERos NMen
	biflorus	ECho
	- subsp. ***adamii***	EBrs ERos
	- subsp. ***alexandri***	ERos
	- subsp. ***biflorus***	EBrs ECho ERos
§	- - 'Parkinsonii'	ERos
	- 'Bowles's Blue' **new**	ECho
	- subsp. ***crewei***	ECho ERos
	- subsp. ***isauricus***	EBrs ECho ERos
	- subsp. ***melantherus***	EBrs ECho ERos WWst
	- 'Miss Vain'	EBrs ECho EPfP EPot GKev LAma LRHS MBri
	- var. ***parkinsonii***	see *C. biflorus* subsp. *biflorus* 'Parkinsonii'
	- 'Serevan'	NMin
	- subsp. ***tauri***	ECho WWst
	- subsp. ***weldenii***	ECho
	- - 'Albus'	EBrs ECho EPot ERos LAma
	- - 'Fairy'	EBrs ECho ERos LAma LRHS
	'Blue Bird'	CBro EBrs ECho EPot LAma LRHS
	'Blue Pearl' ♀H4	CAvo CBro CFFs CMea EBrs ECho EPfP EPot GKev LRHS MBri NBir SBch SPer SPhx WShi
	boryi	EBrs ECho LLHF LRHS WCot
	cambessedesii	EBrs ECho ERos SCnR
§	***cancellatus*** subsp. ***cancellatus***	EBrs ECho ERos LAma
	- var. ***cilicicus***	see *C. cancellatus* subsp. *cancellatus*
	- subsp. ***lycius***	EBrs ECho
	- subsp. ***mazziaricus***	ERos
	- - large-flowered **new**	WWst
	- - 'Rendina' **new**	WWst
	- subsp. ***pamphylicus***	ECho ERos
	candidus	ECho WWst
	- var. ***subflavus***	see *C. olivieri* subsp. *olivieri*
	cartwrightianus ♀H4	ECho LRHS
	- CE&H 613	WWst
	- 'Albus' misapplied	see *C. hadriaticus*
N	- 'Albus' Tubergen ♀H4	EBrs ECho EPot ERos LRHS
	- 'Halloween' **new**	WWst
	- white-flowered clone **new**	WWst
	chrysanthus 'Blue Peter'	ECho
	- 'Cream Beauty' ♀H4	CAvo CBro CFFs CMea EBrs ECho EPfP EPot EWal GKev LAma LRHS MBri NBir SPhx
	- 'E.A. Bowles' ♀H4	ECho
	- 'E.P. Bowles'	CAvo EBrs LAma MBri
	- 'Early Gold'	WWst
	- 'Eye-catcher'	MCot
	- var. ***fuscotinctus***	EBrs ECho EPfP EPot LAma MBri MCot
	- 'Milea'	EBrs ECho
	- 'Moonlight'	LAma
	- 'Skyline'	EBrs ECho
	- 'Sunspot'	EPot
	- 'Uschak Orange'	EBrs WWst
	- 'Warley'	ECho
	- 'Zwanenburg Bronze' ♀H4	EBrs ECho EPfP EPot LAma LRHS MCot SPhx
	'Cloth of Gold'	see *C. angustifolius*
	clusii	see *C. serotinus* subsp. *clusii*
	corsicus ♀H4	EBrs ECho EPot ERos LRHS WWst
	cvijicii	ECho EPot
	- white-flowered	ECho
	dalmaticus	ECho EPot
	- 'Petrovac'	ECho
	danfordiae	ERos
	'Dorothy'	EBrs ECho EPot LAma
	'Dutch Yellow'	see *C.* × *luteus* 'Golden Yellow'
	'Ego'	WWst
	'Elegance'	EBrs LRHS
	etruscus ♀H4	ERos
	- 'Rosalind'	EBrs ECho
	- 'Zwanenburg'	EBrs ECho EPot LAma MCot
	flavus	ECho WWst
§	- subsp. ***flavus*** ♀H4	EBrs ECho EPot LAma LRHS WShi
	fleischeri	EBrs ECho EPot ERos LAma LRHS
	gargaricus	ERos SCnR WWst
	- subsp. ***gargaricus***	ERos
	- subsp. ***herbertii***	ERos
	'Geel' **new**	LRHS
	'Golden Mammoth'	see *C.* × *luteus* 'Golden Yellow'
	'Goldilocks'	EBrs ECho GKev LAma LRHS
	goulimyi ♀H4	CBro EBrs ECho EPot ERos LAma LRHS WCot
	- 'Albus'	see *C. goulimyi* subsp. *goulimyi* 'Mani White'
§	- subsp. ***goulimyi*** 'Mani White' ♀H4	ECho EPot ERos LRHS SCnR
	- subsp. ***leucanthus***	ERos
	- - Hoa 0183	WWst
	'Gypsy Girl'	CAvo CBro CFFs EBrs ECho EPot LAma MBri SPhx
§	***hadriaticus*** ♀H4	EBrs ECho ERos LAma LRHS NMin

Name	Suppliers
- var. ***chrysobelonicus***	see *C. hadriatícus*
- 'Crystal' **new**	WWst
- 'Elysean Pearl' **new**	WWst
- 'Indian Summer' **new**	WWst
'Herald'	CAvo EBrs EPot LAma MCot
imperati $\mathbb{Y}^{H4}$	ERos
- subsp. ***imperati*** 'De Jager'	ECho EPot ERCP LAma
- subsp. ***suaveolens***	EBrs ERos
'Jeanne d'Arc'	CAvo CBro CFFs EBrs ECho EPfP EPot LAma LRHS MBri MCot NBir WShi
'Jeannine'	EBrs ECho EPot
× ***jessoppiae***	EBrs ECho ERos WWst
karduchorum	ECho LAma
korolkowii	CGrW EBrs ECho ERos LAma LRHS
- 'Kiss of Spring'	EBrs ECho EPot LRHS
- 'Lemon Queen'	ECho
kosaninii	EBrs ECho EPot ERos NMin
- CH 801	WWst
kotschyanus $\mathbb{Y}^{H4}$	ECho LRHS NRya SPer
- HKEP 9205	WWst
- 'Albus'	EBrs ECho
§ - subsp. ***kotschyanus***	CBro EBrs ECho EPot LAma
- var. ***leucopharynx***	EBrs ECho LRHS
- 'Reliance'	EBrs ECho WWst
- stoloniferous HKEP 9317 **new**	WWst
kotschyanus* × *ochroleucus	EBrs ECho WWst
'Ladykiller' $\mathbb{Y}^{H4}$	CAvo CBro CFFs EBrs ECho EPot ERCP GKev LAma LRHS MBri SPhx
laevigatus $\mathbb{Y}^{H4}$	ECho
- Hoa 0138	WWst
- from Crete	EBrs
- 'Fontenayi'	CBro EBrs ECho EPot ERCP
- white-flowered	EBrs ECho
'Large Yellow'	see *C.* × *luteus* 'Golden Yellow'
ligusticus	EBrs ECho
longiflorus $\mathbb{Y}^{H4}$	CBro EBrs ECho ERos GEdr LLHF LRHS WWst
- Hoa 9703	WWst
§ × ***luteus*** 'Golden Yellow' $\mathbb{Y}^{H4}$	CAvo CFFs EBrs EPfP LAma WShi
§ - 'Stellaris'	EBrs ECho ERos
malyi $\mathbb{Y}^{H2-4}$	EBrs ECho ERos NMin
- 'Ballerina'	ECho LRHS WWst
- 'Sveti Roc'	EPot
mathewii	EBrs ECho EPot WCot
medius $\mathbb{Y}^{H4}$	CBro EPot ERos LAma
michelsonii	WWst
minimus	EBrs ECho EPot ERCP ERos LAma
'National Park'	LRHS
niveus	CBro EBrs ECho EPot ERos LAma LRHS WCot
- MK 3085 **new**	WWst
- pale blue-flowered **new**	WWst
nudiflorus	CBro EBrs ECho EPot ERos LAma NMen
ochroleucus $\mathbb{Y}^{H4}$	EBrs ECho EPot ERos SPhx
olivieri	ECho ERos
- subsp. ***balansae***	EBrs ECho ERos
- - 'Zwanenburg'	CMea EBrs ECho EPot
§ - subsp. ***olivieri***	EBrs ECho ERos
- - 'Little Tiger'	EBrs ECho WWst
oreocreticus	EBrs ECho
pallasii	EBrs ECho
- subsp. ***pallasii***	ECho ERos
pestalozzae	EBrs ECho ERos WWst
- var. ***caeruleus***	ECho ERos SCnR
- - CRO 401	WWst
'Prins Claus'	EBrs ECho EPot LAma LRHS MBri SPer
'Prinses Beatrix'	ECho
pulchellus $\mathbb{Y}^{H4}$	EBrs ECho EPot ERCP ERos LAma LRHS NWCA SPhx WCot
- ***albus***	EBrs ECho EPot LRHS
- 'Inspiration'	EBrs ECho
- 'Michael Hoog'	EBrs ECho
'Purpureus'	see *C. vernus* 'Purpureus Grandiflorus'
reticulatus	ECho WWst
- subsp. ***reticulatus***	ECho EPot
'Romance'	CAvo CFFs EBrs EPot LAma LRHS MBri MCot SPer
'Ruby Giant'	CAvo CBro EBrs ECho EPfP EPot LAma LRHS MBri MCot NBir SPer SPhx WShi
rujanensis	ECho ERos WWst
salzmannii	see *C. serotinus* subsp. *salzmannii*
sativus	CArn CAvo CBod CBro CGrW CPrp EBrs ECho ELan EOHP EPot ERCP GPoy IHer LAma LRHS MCot MMHG NBir NGHP SPer
'Saturnus'	EBrs EPot LAma
scepusiensis	see *C. vernus* subsp. *vernus*
§ ***serotinus*** subsp. ***clusii***	CBro EBrs ECho LAma LRHS
- - 'Poseidon' **new**	WWst
§ - subsp. ***salzmannii***	CBro EBrs ECho ERos LAma
- - Hoa 9911	WWst
- - KPW 9425	WWst
- - f. ***albus***	ECho
- - 'Erectophyllus'	EBrs ECho WWst
sibiricus	see *C. sieberi*
§ ***sieberi*** $\mathbb{Y}^{H4}$	EPot ERos
§ - 'Albus' $\mathbb{Y}^{H4}$	CBro CFFs EBrs ECho EPot LRHS MBri
- subsp. ***atticus***	EBrs ECho LAma LRHS
- - 'Firefly'	EBrs ECho EPot LAma LRHS SPhx
- 'Bowles's White'	see *C. sieberi* 'Albus'
- 'Hubert Edelsten' $\mathbb{Y}^{H4}$	EBrs ECho ERos LAma
- 'Ronald Ginns'	EPot
- subsp. ***sublimis*** 'Tricolor' $\mathbb{Y}^{H4}$	CAvo CBro CFFs CGrW EBrs ECho EPfP EPot ERos GKev LAma LRHS MBri NBir SBch
- 'Violet Queen'	EBrs ECho LAma MBri
'Snow Bunting' $\mathbb{Y}^{H4}$	CAvo CBro CFFs EBrs ECho EGoo EPfP EPot EWal LAma LRHS NBir SPer SPhx WShi
speciosus $\mathbb{Y}^{H4}$	CAvo CBro EBrs EPot LAma LRHS MLHP NBir SPer WHoo WShi
- 'Aino'	EBrs ECho WWst
- 'Aitchisonii'	CGrW EBrs ECho EPot LAma LRHS SPhx
- 'Albus' $\mathbb{Y}^{H4}$	CAvo CBro EBrs ECho EPot LRHS SPhx
- 'Artabir'	EBrs ECho EPot GKev LRHS
- 'Cassiope'	EBrs ECho EPot GKev LAma LRHS
- 'Conqueror'	CBro EBrs ECho EPot GKev LAma LRHS MCot WBor
- 'Lithuanian Autumn'	WWst
- 'Oxonian'	EBrs ECho EPot LAma LRHS MCot SPhx
- subsp. ***speciosus***	EBrs ECho
- subsp. ***xantholaimos*** **new**	WWst
× ***stellaris***	see *C.* × *luteus* 'Stellaris'
susianus	see *C. angustifolius*
suterianus	see *C. olivieri* subsp. *olivieri*
thomasii BM 7589	WWst
tommasinianus $\mathbb{Y}^{H4}$	CAvo CBro CFFs CGrW EBrs ECho EPot LAma LLWP LRHS MBri MRav NBir SPhx SRms WShi

- 'Albus'	EBrs EPot LAma LRHS
- 'Barr's Purple'	EBrs ECho EGoo EPot LAma LRHS
- 'Claret'	ECho
- 'Eric Smith'	ECho
- 'Lilac Beauty'	EBrs ECho EPfP EPot LAma SPer
- 'Pictus'	EBrs ECho EPot ERos LAma NMen
- 'Roseus'	CAvo CMea EBrs ECho EPot ERos LAma NMen
- 'Whitewell Purple'	CAvo CBro CFFs EBrs ECho EPot GKev LAma LRHS MBri NBir SPhx WShi
tournefortii ♀H2-4	CBro EBrs ECho ERos LRHS SCnR
* - 'Albus'	ECho
'Vanguard' ♀H4	CBro EBrs EPot ERCP LAma LRHS MCot SBch
veluchensis	EBrs ECho EPot NMin WWst
veneris	EBrs ECho
§ ***vernus*** subsp. ***albiflorus***	CGrW EBrs ECho EPot ERos
- 'Fantasy'	EBrs ECho LRHS
- 'Flower Record'	EBrs EPfP GKev LRHS MBri NBir
- 'Graecus'	EBrs ECho EPot ERos WWst
- 'Grand Maître'	CAvo CFFs EBrs LAma LRHS MBri
- 'Haarlem Gem'	EBrs ECho
- 'King of the Striped'	EBrs ECho LRHS SPer
- 'Michael's Purple'	EBrs ECho WWst
- 'Negro Boy'	EBrs EPot
- 'Pickwick'	CAvo CFFs EBrs EPfP EPot LAma LRHS MBri MCot NBir WShi
§ - 'Purpureus Grandiflorus'	CBro EPot
- 'Queen of the Blues'	CAvo CBro CFFs EBrs EPot WShi
- 'Remembrance'	EBrs EPfP EPot LAma NBir WShi
- 'Tatra Shades' **new**	WWst
- Uklin strain	ECho WWst
§ - subsp. ***vernus***	EBrs ECho ERos
- - 'Grandiflorus'	see *C. vernus* 'Purpureus Grandiflorus'
- - Heuffelianus Group	EBrs EPot WWst
- - - 'Dark Eyes'	WWst
- - var. ***neapolitanus***	ERos
- - 'Oradea'	WWst
versicolor	ECho ERos
- 'Picturatus'	EBrs ECho EPot ERCP ERos LAma LLHF LRHS
vitellinus	EBrs ECho
'White Triumphator'	LAma
'Yalta' **new**	ECho
'Yellow Mammoth'	see *C.* × *luteus* 'Golden Yellow'
'Zenith'	ECho EPot
'Zephyr' ♀H4	CBro ECho EPot ERos LAma LRHS
zonatus	see *C. kotschyanus* subsp. *kotschyanus*

Croomia (*Stemonaceae*)

heterosepala	WCru

Crotalaria (*Papilionaceae*)

laburnifolia	CCCN

Crowea (*Rutaceae*)

exalata × ***saligna***	CPLG

Crucianella (*Rubiaceae*)

stylosa	see *Phuopsis stylosa*

Cruciata (*Rubiaceae*)

§ ***laevipes***	EBWF NMir

Crusea (*Rubiaceae*)

coccinea B&SWJ 10254 **new**	WCru

Cryptanthus (*Bromeliaceae*)

bromelioides	MBri

Cryptocarya (*Lauraceae*)

alba	IDee

Cryptogramma (*Adiantaceae*)

crispa	SRms WHer WRic

Cryptomeria (*Cupressaceae*)

fortunei	see *C. japonica* var. *sinensis*
japonica ♀H4	CDul CMen CTho GKir IFFs ISea STre WEve
- Araucarioides Group	CDoC EHul NLar
- 'Aritaki'	LRHS
- 'Atawai'	NLar
- 'Bandai'	LBuc
- 'Bandai-sugi' ♀H4	CKen CMac CMen ECho EHul EOrn EPfP GKir IFFs LRHS MBar MGos NHol SCoo SLim WGor
- 'Barabits Gold'	MBar MGos WEve
- 'Compressa'	CDoC CKen CSli ECho EHul EPfP LBee MAsh MBar MGos SCoo SLim WGor
§ - 'Cristata'	CBcs CDoC CMac ECho ELan EOrn LRHS MBar MGos NPal SCoo SLim SPoG
* - 'Cristata Compacta'	EOrn
- 'Dacrydioides'	CDoC SLim
- Elegans Group	CBcs CDul CMac CSBt CTri ECrN EHul ELan EOrn EPfP GKir LAst LRHS MBar MBri MGos NEgg NWea SBch SCoo SLim SPer SPoG WBVN WDin WFar
- 'Elegans Aurea'	CBcs CDoC CTri ECho ECrN EHul EMil MAsh MBar STre WDin WEve
- 'Elegans Compacta' ♀H4	CDoC CMac CSBt CWib ECho EHul ELan EOrn GBin IMGH LBee LRHS MAsh MBar MBri SCoo SLim SPoG WBVN WEve
- 'Elegans Nana'	IFFs LBee LRHS NEgg SEND SRms WBor
- 'Elegans Viridis'	ELan LRHS MBar NEgg SCoo SLim SPer SPoG
- 'Globosa'	EOrn
- 'Globosa Nana' ♀H4	CDoC ECho EHul EPfP ERom LAst LBee LRHS MAsh MBar MBri MGos NEgg NLar SCoo SLim SPoG WFar WGor
- 'Golden Promise'	CDoC EOrn LRHS MAsh NHol SCoo SLim SPer SPoG WEve WGor
- Gracilis Group	CDoC
- 'Jindai-sugi'	ECho MBar NLar
- 'Kilmacurragh'	CDoC CKen EHul MBar NWea SLim WThu
- 'Knaptonensis' (v)	CDoC MGos WEve
- 'Kohui-yatsubusa'	CKen
* - 'Konijn-yatsubusa'	CKen
- 'Koshiji-yatsubusa'	EOrn MBar MGos
- 'Koshyi'	CKen NLar
- 'Little Champion'	CDoC CKen NLar SCoo SLim
- 'Little Diamond'	CKen
- 'Littleworth Dwarf'	see *C. japonica* 'Littleworth Gnom'
§ - 'Littleworth Gnom'	NLar
- 'Lobbii Nana' hort.	see *C. japonica* 'Nana'
§ - 'Mankichi-sugi'	MBri NHol NLar WEve
- 'Monstrosa'	MBar
- 'Monstrosa Nana'	see *C. japonica* 'Mankichi-sugi'
- 'Mushroom'	MGos WFar
§ - 'Nana'	CDoC CMac CTri EHul EOrn EPfP SPoG WCor WFar

- 'Osaka-tama' CKen
- 'Pipo' CKen NLar
- 'Pygmaea' MBar MGos NHol SCoo SRms
- 'Rasen' IFFs
- 'Rasen-sugi' LBuc LRHS MBar MBri MGos NLar NPal SCoo SLim SMad SPoG
- 'Sekkan-sugi' CBcs CCVN CDoC CDul CSli ECho EHul EOrn EPfP GBin IDee LAst LBee LRHS MAsh MBar MGos NHol NLar SBch SCoo SLim SPoG WEve WFar
- 'Sekka-sugi' see *C. japonica* 'Cristata'
§ - var. ***sinensis*** CMCN
* - - 'Vilmoriniana Compacta' EOrn
§ - 'Spiralis' CDoC CKen CMac ECho EHul EOrn EPfP IFFs LBee LRHS MAsh MBar MGos NEgg NHol NPal SCoo SLim SPer SPoG WCor WEve WFar
§ - 'Spiraliter Falcata' CDoC MBar NLar
§ - 'Tansu' CDoC CKen ECho EOrn MBar MGos NHol
- 'Tenzan-sugi' CDoC CKen MGos SLim WThu
- 'Tilford Cream' ECho
- 'Tilford Gold' ECho EHul EOrn IFFs LRHS MBar MGos NEgg NHol WEve WFar WGor
- 'Toda' CKen
- 'Vilmorin Gold' CKen EMil EOrn MGos NHol WFar
- 'Vilmoriniana' ♀H4 CDoC CKen CMen CSli CTri ECho EHul EOrn EPfP EPla GKir IFFs IMGH LBee LRHS MBar MGos NBlu NEgg NHol SCoo SIng SLim SPer SPoG WDin WEve WFar WMoo
- 'Viminalis' NHol
- 'Winter Bronze' CKen
- 'Yatsubusa' see *C. japonica* 'Tansu'
- 'Yore-sugi' see *C. japonica* 'Spiralis', 'Spiraliter Falcata'
- 'Yoshino' CKen LRHS SLim
sinensis see *C. japonica* var. *sinensis*

Cryptostegia (*Asclepiadaceae*)
grandiflora CCCN

Cryptotaenia (*Apiaceae*)
japonica CPou MHer MNHC WHer WJek
- f. ***atropurpurea*** CArn CSpe CSpr EBee EHoe GGar LEdu NSti SGSe WCHb WFar

Ctenanthe (*Marantaceae*)
lubbersiana ♀H1 XBlo
§ ***oppenheimiana*** XBlo

Cucubalus (*Caryophyllaceae*)
baccifer EWld NLar WPer WPrP

Cudrania see *Maclura*

cumin see *Cuminum cyminum*

Cuminum (*Apiaceae*)
cyminum CArn ELau MNHC SIde SVic

Cunninghamia (*Cupressaceae*)
§ ***lanceolata*** CBcs CDTJ CDoC CDul CGHE CMCN CTho ECho EPla GKir IArd IDee IFFs LRHS MBlu NMun SCoo SLim SMad SPoG SSta STre WBor WEve WMou WPGP WSpi
§ - 'Bánó' EOrn
- 'Compacta' see *C. lanceolata* 'Bánó'
- 'Glauca' CTho WPGP
- 'Grounded' **new** STre
- 'Little Leo' CDoC CKen ECho
sinensis see *C. lanceolata*
unicaniculata see *C. lanceolata*

Cunonia (*Cunoniaceae*)
capensis CPLG CTrC EShb GKir

Cuphea (*Lythraceae*)
caeciliae SGar WWlt
* ***compacta*** LAst
cyanea CMHG SDix SUsu WWlt
'Harlequin' NPri
hirtella LHop
hyssopifolia ♀H1 CHll EShb LRHS SBch SWvt
- 'Alba' CCCN SBch SWvt
- Lemon Squash = 'Kkcuphls' **new** SVil
- pink-flowered CCCN SBch
- red-flowered CCCN
- 'Rosea' SEND SWvt
§ ***ignea*** ♀H1 CWib MBel MBri SUsu WWlt
§ ***llavea*** 'Georgia Scarlet' CCCN LAst LSou NPri WWlt
- 'Tiny Mice' see *C. llavea* 'Georgia Scarlet'
I ***macrophylla*** hort. CHll
platycentra see *C. ignea*
viscosissima MCot

× *Cupressocyparis* ✿ (*Cupressaceae*)
§ ***leylandii*** ♀H4 CBcs CCVT CChe CDoC CDul CMac CTri EHul EPfP LBuc LSRN MAsh MBar MBri MGos NBlu NEgg NWea SBch SLim SPer SPoG SWvt WDin WEve WHar WMou
I - '2001' **new** WMou
- 'Blue Jeans'PBR **new** SEND
§ - 'Castlewellan' CBcs CCVT CChe CDoC CDul CMac CTri EHul EPfP ERom LBuc LRHS LSRN MAsh MBar MBri MGos NBlu NWea SBch SEND SLim SPer SPoG SWvt WDin WEve WFar WHar WMou
- 'Galway Gold' see × *C. leylandii* 'Castlewellan'
- 'Gold Rider' ♀H4 CDoC EHul MAsh MBar MGos NEgg NWea SCoo SEND SPer SPoG STre SWvt WDin WEve WHar
§ - 'Harlequin' (v) CBcs CMac SEND SWvt
- 'Herculea' CDoC MAsh
- 'Naylor's Blue' CMac
- 'Olive's Green' EHul SWvt
- 'Robinson's Gold' ♀H4 CMac EHul GQui LRHS MBar MMuc NWea SLim WFar
- 'Silver Dust' (v) WFar
- 'Variegata' see × *C. leylandii* 'Harlequin'
- 'Winter Sun' WCFE
ovensii EHul

Cupressus (*Cupressaceae*)
arizonica var. ***arizonica*** MGos
- - 'Arctic' CDoC SLim
- 'Conica Glauca' WEve
§ - var. ***glabra*** WPGP
- - 'Aurea' CMac ECho EHul LRHS MBar MGos NPCo SLim WFar
- - 'Blue Ice' ♀H3 CBcs CDoC CDul CMac CTho ECho EHul EMil EOrn LRHS MAsh MBar MGos NPCo SCoo SLim SPer SPoG SWvt WEve WFar
- - 'Compacta' CKen
- - 'Conica' CKen

I - - 'Fastigiata'	CCVT CDoC ECrN EHul EPfP LMaj MBar SBch SCoo
- - 'Glauca'	ECho EPfP IFFs MBlu WBVN
* - - 'Lutea'	ECho EOrn SPoG
- var. ***nevadensis***	GAuc
- 'Pyramidalis' ♀H3	CMac ECrN EPfP SEND WEve
I - 'Sulfurea'	MAsh NLar
cashmeriana ♀H2	CBcs CDTJ CDoC CTho ELan ERea LRHS NPCo SLim WFar
glabra	see *C. arizonica* var. *glabra*
lusitanica 'Brice's Weeping'	CKen SLim
- 'Brookhall'	IDee
- 'Glauca Pendula'	CDoC CKen EPfP WEve
- 'Pygmy'	CKen
macrocarpa	CBcs CCVT CDoC CDul CTho EHul IFFs SEND
- 'Compacta'	CKen
- 'Conybearii Aurea'	NPCo
- 'Donard Gold'	CMac MBar
- 'Gold Spread'	ECho EHul SCoo SLim SPoG WFar
- 'Goldcrest' ♀H3	Widely available
- 'Golden Cone'	CKen CSBt ECho NPCo WEve
- 'Golden Pillar' ♀H3	CDoC EHul MBar SPoG SWvt WDin WFar
- 'Golden Spire'	WFar
- 'Greenstead Magnificent'	ECho LRHS MAsh SCoo SLim
- 'Horizontalis Aurea'	EHul MBar
- 'Lohbrunner'	CKen
- 'Lutea'	CDoC CMac ECho NPCo WFar
- 'Pygmaea'	CKen
- 'Sulphur Cushion'	CKen
- 'Wilma'	ECho EHul LAst LBee LRHS MAsh MGos NBlu NEgg SBch SCoo SLim SPoG SWvt
- 'Woking'	CKen
sargentii	GKir
sempervirens	CDul CMCN CPMA ECrN EHul ELan ERom ETod ISea LRHS NLar SBch SPlb STrG WEve WFar
- 'Agrimed'	LMaj
- 'Bolgheri'	SBig
- 'Garda'	CDoC
- 'Green Pencil'	CKen EPfP WEve
- 'Pyramidalis'	see *C. sempervirens* Stricta Group
- var. ***sempervirens***	see *C. sempervirens* Stricta Group
§ - Stricta Group ♀H3	CArn CBcs CCVT CKen CMCN CSWP CTho ECho EHul EPfP LRHS MAsh NBlu NLar SAPC SArc SBch SCoo WCFE WEve
- 'Swane's Gold'	CBcs CDoC CFee CKen ECho EHul EOrn EPfP LRHS NPCo NPal SCoo SLim SPoG WCFE WEve WFar
- 'Totem Pole'	CDoC CKen CSBt CTho CTri ECho ECrN EHul EOrn EPfP LAst LBee LRHS MGos NEgg NScw SCoo SEND SLim SPer SPoG WEve
torulosa	IDee

× *Cuprocyparis* see × *Cupressocyparis*

Curculigo (*Hypoxidaceae*)

capitulata	XBlo
crassifolia B&SWJ 2318	WCru

Curcuma (*Zingiberaceae*)

alismatifolia	EPfP
longa	CArn
roscoeana	LAma
'Siam Silver'	LRHS
'Siam Suzy'	LRHS
zedoaria	EShb LAma LRHS
- 'Bicolor Wonder'	CCCN
- 'Pink Wonder'	CCCN
- 'White Wonder'	CCCN

Curtonus see *Crocosmia*

Cussonia (*Araliaceae*)

paniculata	CDTJ CPne CWit EBee EShb WCot
spicata	EShb
transvaalensis	EShb

custard apple see *Annona cherimola*, *A. reticulata*

Cyananthus (*Campanulaceae*)

SDR 4734	GKev
SDR 4908	GKev
incanus	GKev
integer misapplied	see *C. microphyllus*
lobatus ♀H4	ECho GBuc GKev GMaP NSla
- 'Albus'	EPot EWes WAbe
- dark	WAbe
- 'Dark Beauty'	ECho
- giant	EPot GEdr
- 'Midnight'	GEdr
lobatus × ***microphyllus***	NWCA WAbe
macrocalyx	GKev
§ ***microphyllus*** ♀H4	CPBP ECho EPot GEdr GJos GMaP IFoB NLAp NSla WAbe
sherriffii	EPot GJos IFoB WAbe WFar

Cyanella (*Tecophilaeaceae*)

lutea	ECho
orchidiformis	ECho

Cyathea (*Cyatheaceae*)

atrox	CDTJ
australis	CBty CDTJ EAmu ESwi ETod IDee LPal LRHS MAsh MGos NPal WFib WPGP WRic
brownii	WRic
cooperi	CDTJ EAmu EFtx LRHS WFib WRic
* - 'Brentwood'	WRic
cunninghamii	CDTJ EAmu
dealbata	CBcs CDTJ CTrC CWit EAmu LPal MGos WRic
dregei	SPlb WRic
incisoserrata	WRic
medullaris	CBcs CDTJ CTrC CWit EAmu LRHS MGos WRic
milnei	CDTJ WRic
robusta	WRic
smithii	CBcs CDTJ CTrC CWit EAmu WRic
tomentosissima	CDTJ EFtx WRic

Cyathodes (*Epacridaceae*)

colensoi	see *Leucopogon colensoi*
fasciculata	see *Leucopogon fasciculatus*
fraseri	see *Leucopogon fraseri*
juniperina	see *Leptecophylla juniperina*
parviflora	see *Leucopogon parviflorus*
parvifolia	see *Leptecophylla juniperina* subsp. *parvifolia*

Cycas (*Cycadaceae*)

circinalis	LPal
media	LPal SBst
panzhihuaensis	CBrP LPal NExo SPlb
revoluta ♀H1	CAbb CBrP CCCN CDoC CHEx CTrC EAmu EPfP LPal LRHS MBri MREP NLar NPal SAPC SArc SBst SChr SEND SMad STrG WCot

	Name	Suppliers
	revoluta* × *taitungensis	CBrP
§	***rumphii***	CBrP EAmu LPal
	taitungensis	CBrP
	thouarsii	see *C. rumphii*

Cyclamen ✿ (*Primulaceae*)

	Name	Suppliers
	africanum	CBro EBrs ECho EJWh EPot ITim LAma LRHS MAsh NWCA STil WCot
	africanum* × *hederifolium	CWCL ECho
§	***alpinum***	CBro EBrs ECho EJWh EPot GKev LAma LLHF LRHS MAsh STil
	balearicum	CBro CPBP EBrs ECho EJWh LAma LRHS MAsh NMen STil
	cilicium ♀H2-4	CBro CLAP EBrs ECho EJWh EPot ERCP ERos LAma LRHS MAsh MCot MHer MTho NMen STil WCom WFar WHoo WIvy WPat WShi
	- f. ***album***	CBro EBrs ECho EJWh EPot ERos GKir LAma LRHS MAsh NMen STil WCom
	- patterned-leaved	ECho NBir
	colchicum	ECho MAsh STil
§	***coum*** ♀H4	Widely available
	- from Turkey	ERos
	- var. ***abchasicum***	see *C. coum* subsp. *caucasicum*
§	- subsp. ***caucasicum***	ERos GBuc MAsh STil
	- subsp. ***coum***	CBro ECho MAsh
	- - f. ***albissimum***	WCom
	- - - 'George Bisson'	MAsh
	- - - 'Golan Heights'	MAsh STil WIvy
	- - f. ***coum*** Nymans Group	MAsh WFar
	- - - Pewter Group ♀H2-4	CPMA EBrs ECGP ECho ELon ERos GKev MAsh MTho WCom WFar WIvy
	- - - - bicoloured	EJWh
	- - - - 'Blush'	CPMA GBuc STil
	- - - - 'Maurice Dryden'	CAvo CBro CLAP CPMA CWCL EBrs ECGP ECho EHrv GBuc LAma LRHS MAsh STil
	- - - - red-flowered	LAma WPat
	- - - - 'Tilebarn Elizabeth'	CDes CSsd EHrv MAsh NBir STil WHoo
	- - - - white-flowered	GBuc MAsh
	- - - plain-leaved red-flowered	STil
	- - - 'Roseum'	CWCL EBrs GBuc STil
	- - - Silver Group	CBro CPMA ECho EHrv GEdr GKir LHop LRHS NRya NSla WCot WFar WHoo WPGP
	- - - - red-flowered	CAvo EPot MTho STil WHoo
	- - magenta-flowered	CWCL WHoo
	- - f. ***pallidum*** 'Album'	CAvo CPMA CWCL EBrs ECho EPot ERos LAma MAsh SIng SMrm STil WAbe WHoo WPat WSpi
	- - - 'Marbled Moon'	MAsh STil
	- dark pink-flowered	CAvo CLAP ECho WAbe WHoo
	- hybrid	ERCP
	- marble-leaved	CWCL ECho LHop WHoo
	- 'Meaden's Crimson'	EPot
	- plain-leaved	CLAP EBla EPot WAbe WCom
	- red-flowered	CLAP ECho
I	- 'Rubrum'	EBrs
	- 'Tilebarn Graham'	MAsh
	creticum	ECho EJWh LRHS MAsh STil
	creticum* × *repandum	see *C.* × *meiklei*
	cyprium	CBro EBrs ECho EJWh LRHS MAsh STil WIvy
	- 'E.S.'	ECho MAsh STil WFar
	× ***drydeniae***	CPMA
	elegans	EJWh MAsh STil
	europaeum	see *C. purpurascens*
	fatrense	see *C. purpurascens* subsp. *purpurascens* from Fatra, Slovakia
	graecum	CBro EBrs ECho EDAr EJWh EPot LRHS MAsh NMen STil WCot WIvy
	- f. ***album***	CBro EBrs ECho EJWh EPot LRHS MAsh STil
	- subsp. ***anatolicum***	MAsh STil
	- subsp. ***candicum***	MAsh STil
	- subsp. ***graecum*** f. ***graecum*** 'Glyfada'	STil
	- 'Rhodopou' **new**	EPot
§	***hederifolium*** ♀H4	Widely available
	- SL 175/1	WCot
	- 'Amaze Me' **new**	EWTr LRHS
	- arrow-head	CLAP ECho
	- var. ***confusum***	MAsh STil WCot
	- var. ***hederifolium*** f. ***albiflorum***	CAvo CBro CSWP CSam CStu CTri ECho EDAr EHrv EPot ERCP ERos GBuc LAma MBar MBri NHol NMen NMyG SIng SPhx STil WAbe WCom WHoo WPat WPnP
	- - - 'Album'	CWCL EBrs
	- - - Bowles's Apollo Group	GBuc WCom
§	- - - - 'Artemis'	MAsh STil
	- - - - 'White Bowles's Apollo'	see *C. hederifolium* var. *hederifolium* f. *albiflorum* (Bowles's Apollo Group) 'Artemis'
	- - - 'Nettleton Silver'	see *C. hederifolium* var. *hederifolium* f. *albiflorum* 'White Cloud'
	- - - 'Perlenteppich'	GBuc GMaP
	- - - 'Tilebarn Helena'	STil
§	- - - 'White Cloud'	CLAP EBla ECho EPot MAsh NSla STil WCot WHoo WIvy
	- - f. ***hederifolium*** Bowles's Apollo Group	CHid CLAP CWCL ECGP GBuc MAsh STil WCom
	- - - 'Fairy Rings'	MAsh
	- - - 'Rosenteppich'	GBuc GMaP
	- - - 'Ruby Glow'	CWCL GBuc LRHS MAsh NBir WPat
	- - - 'Silver Cloud'	CBro CHid CLAP EHrv GBuc MAsh NBir STil WAbe WCom WCot WHoo WIvy WPGP WPat
	- - - 'Silver Shield'	MAsh
	- - - 'Stargazer'	MAsh
	- - 'Tilebarn Silver Arrow'	CPMA MAsh STil
	- long-leaved	CPMA WCom
	- 'Pewter Mist'	ELon LAma
	- 'Rose Pearls'	EAlp
	- 'San Marino Silver'	GEdr
	- scented	NHol STil WCom
	- 'Silver Mist' **new**	LRHS
	- Silver-leaved Group	CAvo CPMA EBla EBrs ECGP ECho EPot LHop LRHS MAsh NWCA SRot STil WFar
	- 'Turkish Delight' **new**	EDAr
	× ***hildebrandii***	WIvy
	ibericum	see *C. coum* subsp. *caucasicum*
	intaminatum	CBro EBrs ECho EJWh EPot ERos GKir LAma LRHS MAsh NMen STil WIvy
	- patterned-leaved	EJWh MAsh STil
	- pink-flowered	MAsh NMen STil
	- plain-leaved	MAsh STil WThu
	latifolium	see *C. persicum*
	libanoticum	CBro CPBP EBrs ECho EJWh LAma LRHS MAsh NMen STil WFar
§	× ***meiklei***	CBro
	mirabile ♀H2-3	CBro CPBP EBrs ECho EJWh EPot LAma LRHS MAsh NMen STil WIvy WThu

	- f. ***niveum***	EJWh
	- 'Tilebarn Anne'	MAsh STil
	- 'Tilebarn Jan'	CPMA ECho MAsh STil
	- 'Tilebarn Nicholas'	ECho MAsh STil
	neapolitanum	see *C. hederifolium*
	orbiculatum	see *C. coum*
	parviflorum	EJWh MAsh STil
	peloponnesiacum ♀H2-3	EJWh EPot ERos MAsh WCot
§	- subsp. ***peloponnesiacum***	CBro STil
	- subsp. ***rhodense***	MAsh STil
	- subsp. ***vividum***	MAsh STil
	- white-flowered	STil
§	***persicum***	CBro CWCL EBrs ECho EJWh LRHS MAsh NBlu STil
	- CSE 90560	STil
	- var. ***persicum*** f. ***puniceum*** from Lebanon	STil
	- - - 'Tilebarn Karpathos'	MAsh STil
	- white-flowered	ECho MAsh
	pseudibericum ♀H2-3	CBro CPBP EBrs ECho EJWh EPot LAma LHop LRHS MAsh STil
	- AC&W 664	ITim
	- 'Roseum'	MAsh NMen STil
§	***purpurascens*** ♀H4	CBro ECho EJWh EPot GBuc GKir LLHF LRHS MAsh NMen NWCA STil WHoo WIvy WPat
	- var. ***fatrense***	see *C. purpurascens* subsp. *purpurascens* from Fatra, Slovakia
	- 'Lake Garda'	MAsh WPGP
§	- subsp. ***purpurascens*** from Fatra, Slovakia	MAsh STil
	- silver-leaved	STil
	repandum	CAvo CBro CDes CWCL EBrs ECho EHrv EJWh ERos LAma LRHS MAsh NMen STil WHer
	- 'Pelops' misapplied	see *C. peloponnesiacum* subsp. *peloponnesiacum*
	- subsp. ***repandum*** f. ***album***	CLAP EJWh MAsh STil
	rohlfsianum	CBro ECho EJWh LRHS MAsh STil WThu
	× ***saundersii***	EJWh MAsh STil
	trochopteranthum	see *C. alpinum*
	× ***wellensiekii***	MAsh STil
	× ***whiteae***	MAsh

Cyclanthera (*Cucurbitaceae*)

pedata 'Fat Baby'	WTou

Cydonia ✿ (*Rosaceae*)

	japonica	see *Chaenomeles speciosa*
	oblonga (F)	ECrN GKev LMaj
	- 'Agvambari' (F)	SKee
	- 'Aromatnaya' (F)	ERea
	- 'Champion' (F)	CAgr CBcs ECrN ERea GTwe LBuc MCoo NEgg NLar SKee SVic
	- 'Early Prolific' (F)	ECrN LAst
	- 'Ekmek' (F)	SKee
	- 'Isfahan' (F)	SKee
	- 'Krymsk' (F)	CAgr
	- 'Leskovac' (F)	CAgr ERea NLar
§	- 'Lusitanica' (F)	CAgr CDoC ERea GTwe MCoo NLar SKee SPer
	- 'Meech's Prolific' (F)	CAgr CDul CLnd CTho CTri ECrN EMil EMui ERea GTwe IFFs LAst MAsh MBlu MBri MGos MRav MWat NLar SDea SFam SKee SPer SPoG
	- pear-shaped (F)	ECrN MCoo NEgg
	- Portugal	see *C. oblonga* 'Lusitanica'
	- 'Rea's Mammoth' (F)	NLar
	- 'Serbian Gold' (F) **new**	GTwe LRHS MBri
	- 'Shams' (F)	SKee
	- 'Sobu' (F)	SKee
	- 'Vranja' (F) ♀H4	Widely available

Cymbalaria (*Scrophulariaceae*)

	aequitriloba 'Alba'	GGar
§	***hepaticifolia***	WPer
§	***muralis***	EAlp EBWF ECho ECtt EWll GGar LRHS MHer NPri SECG WCom WGor
	- 'Albiflora'	see *C. muralis* 'Pallidior'
	- 'Kenilworth White'	WMoo
	- 'Nana Alba'	MMuc NPri SEND WPer
§	- 'Pallidior'	ECho
§	***pallida***	CEnt CMea CPBP LRHS MMuc NSla SBch SPlb WMoo WPer
§	***pilosa***	ECtt NLar

Cymbopogon (*Poaceae*)

citratus	CArn CBod CCCN CHby COld CSev ERea GPoy MNHC NGHP SBch SHDw SIde SPoG SVic WCHb WCot WJek
flexuosus	CCCN ELau MHer
martini	CArn GPoy
nardus	CArn GPoy

Cymophyllus (*Cyperaceae*)

§	***fraserianus***	CDes CHEx GBin

Cymopterus (*Apiaceae*)

terebinthinus var. ***albiflorus*** **new**	LFur

Cynanchum (*Asclepiadaceae*)

acuminatifolium	GCal

Cynara (*Asteraceae*)

§	***baetica*** subsp. ***maroccana***	LDai
	cardunculus ♀H3-4	Widely available
	- ACL 380/78	SWat
I	- 'Cardy'	CBot EBee LRHS NBre NCGa SWat WBrE
	- var. ***ferocissima***	LRHS
I	- 'Florist Cardy'	IGor NLar
	- 'Gobbo di Nizza'	EBee ELau ERea WHer
§	- Scolymus Group	Widely available
	- - 'Carciofo Violetto Precoce'	WHer
	- - 'Gigante di Romagna'	WHer
	- - 'Gros Camus de Bretagne'	MAvo WCot
	- - 'Gros Vert de Lâon'	CBcs ECha ELan NBhm WCot WPGP
	- - 'Imperial Star'	ELau WHil
	- - 'Large Green'	NLar
	- - 'Purple Globe'	CArn CPrp ELau SMrm
	- - 'Romanesco'	EBee ELau SVic
	- - 'Vert Globe'	CBod CBot CHar CPrp CSBt CSev ELau ERea IFoB MWat NPer NVic SMrm SVic
	- - 'Violetto di Chioggia'	CSev EBee ELau ERea WHer
	hystrix misapplied	see *C. baetica* subsp. *maroccana*
	scolymus	see *C. cardunculus* Scolymus Group
	'Violet de Provence'	CSBt ELau

Cynodon (*Poaceae*)

aethiopicus	CMHG EBee EHoe EPPr GBin LEdu SBch SGar SHDw

Cynoglossum (*Boraginaceae*)

amabile ♀H4 NCGa SEND
- f. ***roseum*** 'Mystery Rose' WPGP
coelestinum new WCot
dioscoridis CBot WPer
nervosum CBot EBee ECtt ELan EPPr EPfP GKir LAst LHop LRHS MCot MLHP MRav NChi NEgg NGdn NWCA SPer SWat WCAu WCHb WCot WFar WWEG
officinale CArn EBWF MHer WCHb WHer

Cynosurus (*Poaceae*)

cristatus EBWF NMir
- viviparous CNat

Cypella (*Iridaceae*)

aquatilis LLWG
herbertii EDif EWTr
peruviana WHil
plumbea see *Phalocallis coelestis*

Cyperus (*Cyperaceae*)

§ ***albostriatus*** CCCN CHEx EShb MBri
alternifolius misapplied see *C. involucratus*
alternifolius L. CBen EAmu EBee LPBA MSKA SAPC WMAq
- 'Compactus' see *C. involucratus* 'Nanus'
'Cally Proliferous' new GCal
'Chira' CHrt EKen MBNS NWsh WGwG
§ ***cyperoides*** MBri
diffusus misapplied see *C. albostriatus*
§ ***eragrostis*** CArn CMil CPom CRow CWit EHoe GCal MCCP MMuc NWsh SDix SPlb SWat WAbb WGrn WMAq WMoo
esculentus CArn SWal
fuscus EKen MDKP WFar WHal WMoo
glaber EBee LDai MBNS MBar NBre WWEG
haspan misapplied see *C. papyrus* 'Nanus'
haspan L. EShb MSKA
§ ***involucratus*** ♀H1 CHEx CRow EBak EHon EShb LPBA MBri MMuc MSKA SArc SGSe SMad SWal SWat WFar WMnd WMoo
- 'Gracilis' EBak MBri
§ - 'Nanus' LPBA MSCN SWal
longus CBen CWat EHoe EHon EMFW EPPr GAuc GCal LPBA MBar MLHP MMuc NNor NPer NWsh SWal SWat WFar WHal WMAq WPnP WPrP
papyrus ♀H1 CDTJ CHEx CKno CMCo CSpr EAmu ERea GKir LRHS MBri MSKA SAPC SArc SBig SMad XBlo
§ - 'Nanus' ♀H1 CHEx LPal XBlo
prolifer LLWG
rotundus CRow MCCP NLar SBch WTou
sumula hort. see *C. cyperoides*
ustulatus CKno MDKP
vegetus see *C. eragrostis*

Cyphomandra (*Solanaceae*)

betacea (F) CCCN SVic

Cypripedium (*Orchidaceae*)

acaule WWst
Aki gx GEdr NLAp WWst XFro
- 'Pastel' GEdr NLAp WWst XFro
× ***andrewsii*** NLAp
× ***barbeyi*** see *C.* × *ventricosum*
calceolus CFir EBee EHrv MDun NLAp WWst
- from Korea NLAp
- from Kurilen Island NLAp
- from Lake Baikal NLAp
calcicolum NLAp
californicum NLAp
cordigerum NLAp
corrugatum see *C. tibeticum*
debile GEdr
Emil gx GEdr NLAp WWst XFro
fasciolatum NLAp
flavum CFir GBin GEdr MDun NLAp
- white-flowered CFir WCot
formosanum EBee GAuc LAma WWst
Gisela gx GEdr LAma WWst XFro
- 'Pastel' GEdr NLAp WWst XFro
- 'Yellow' LAma
guttatum NLAp WWst
guttatum × ***flavum*** new WFut
Hank Small gx GEdr NLAp WWst XFro
henryi LAma NLAp
himalaicum NLAp
Inge gx NLAp WWst XFro
Ingrid gx GEdr NLAp WWst XFro
japonicum GBin GEdr NLAp WWst
kentuckiense CCCN CFir GEdr MDun NLAp
macranthos EHrv GEdr NLAp WWst
- f. ***albiflorum*** NLAp
- from Lake Baikal NLAp
manchuricum NLAp
red-flowered
- white-flowered NLAp
Maria gx XFro
Michael gx GEdr NLAp WWst XFro
parviflorum NLAp
- var. ***makasin*** NLAp
§ - var. ***pubescens*** GBin LAma NLAp
- var. ***pubescens*** GEdr
× ***reginae*** new
Philipp gx GEdr NLAp WWst XFro
pubescens see *C. parviflorum* var. *pubescens*
reginae CCCN EBee EHrv EPot EWes GAuc GEdr GKev LAma MDun MREP NLAp WClo WCot WHlf
- f. ***albolabium*** GEdr
Sabine gx GEdr NLAp WWst XFro
Sebastian gx new WWst XFro
segawae LAma
§ ***tibeticum*** NLAp
Ulla Silkens gx EBee GEdr GKev LAma NLAp WWst XFro
§ × ***ventricosum*** GEdr NLAp WWst XFro
- 'Pastel' new WWst XFro

Cyrilla (*Cyrillaceae*)

racemiflora CMac MBri

Cyrtanthus (*Amaryllidaceae*)

from high altitude WCot
'Alaska' EBrs ECho
§ ***brachyscyphus*** CDes CSpe EBee EBrs ECho ERos EShb GGar WCot WPrP
breviflorus CDes EBee ECho NMen WPGP
contractus CDes
'Edwina' CCCN ECho EShb LRHS SPer
§ ***elatus*** ♀H1 CPne CSev CSpe CStu EBrs ECho EShb LAma LEdu LRHS MCCP SEND SIng WCot WGwG WHer
- 'Cream Beauty' EBrs ECho WCot
- 'Pink Diamond' EBrs ECho WCot
'Elizabeth' CCCN ECho LRHS SPer
falcatus ♀H1 CLak EBrs
luteus WAbe

mackenii	CDes CPne EBee ECho WGwG WPGP
- cream-white-flowered	CCCN
- 'Himalayan Pink'	CCCN EBee
- pink-flowered	WPrP
- red-flowered	CCCN EBee
- white-flowered	EBee EBrs
- yellow-flowered	WPrP
montanus	EBee EBrs ECho WCot
parviflorus	see *C. brachyscyphus*
purpureus	see *C. elatus*
rhodesianus new	GCal
sanguineus	ECho WCot WPGP
smithiae	ECho
speciosus	see *C. elatus*

Cyrtomium (*Dryopteridaceae*)

§ ***caryotideum***	CLAP GQui WRic
§ ***falcatum*** ♀H3	CBty CFir CFwr CHEx CLAP CMHG CTrC EBee ELan EPfP EWTr GCal GMaP IBal LBMP LRHS NHol NMoo NOrc SBch SEND SPad SPoG SRms SRot WFar WMoo WPnP WRic
- 'Rochfordianum'	CBcs CBty CCCN EBee LRHS WFib
§ ***fortunei*** ♀H4	Widely available
- var. ***clivicola***	CBty CPrp CWCL EBee EPfP EShb GCal LRHS MAsh MGos MRav NDlv NHol NLar NMoo SBch WRic
lonchitoides	CLAP
macrophyllum	CLAP GLin

Cystopteris ✿ (*Woodsiaceae*)

bulbifera	CLAP GQui
dickieana	CLAP GBin GGar NHol NVic SRms WCot WFib WRic
fragilis	EBee ECha EFer GQui SRms WFib
- 'Cristata'	CLAP
moupinensis B&SWJ 6767	WCru
tennesseensis	WAbe WRic

Cytisus (*Papilionaceae*)

albus misapplied	see *C. multiflorus*
albus Hacq.	see *Chamaecytisus albus*
'Amber Elf'PBR	MBri SRms
'Andreanus'	see *C. scoparius* f. *andreanus*
'Apricot Gem'	LRHS MBar MGos NLar NPri SPoG WFar
battandieri ♀H4	Widely available
- 'Yellow Tail' ♀H4	CEnd LRHS MBri WPGP
× ***beanii*** ♀H4	CDul EBee ELan EPfP GKir LRHS MAsh SLon SRms WDin WFar
- 'Osiris'	CDul
'Boskoop Glory'	GKir NLar
'Boskoop Ruby' ♀H4	CBgR CDoC CSBt EPfP EWTr GGar GKir LAst LRHS LSRN MAsh NEgg NPri SBch SPer SPoG SWvt WBor WFar WHar
'Burkwoodii' ♀H4	CBcs CDoC CDul CWSG EBee ELan EPfP GKir LAst LRHS LSRN MRav MSwo MWat NEgg NHol SBch SPoG WFar
canariensis	see *Genista canariensis*
'Compact Crimson'	CDoC LRHS SBch
'Cottage'	EPot WAbe
§ ***decumbens***	MAsh
'Donard Gem'	CDoC EBee SBch
'Dorothy Walpole'	WFar
'Dukaat'	EBee GKir
'Firefly'	CBcs NBro
'Fulgens'	EPfP MBar
'Golden Cascade'	CBcs CDoC EBee ELan LAst LRHS MAsh NEgg SBch
'Golden Sunlight'	CSBt EBee EPfP MSwo
'Goldfinch'	CDoC CSBt CWSG EBee ELan GKir LRHS MAsh MBri MNHC MSwo NLar NPri SPad SWal
hirsutus	see *Chamaecytisus hirsutus*
'Hollandia' ♀H4	CBcs CDoC CSBt CTsd CWSG EBee EPfP GKir LBMP LRHS MAsh MBar MGos MMuc MRav NBro NHol NPri SPer WDin WFar
× ***kewensis*** ♀H4	CWSG EBee ELan EPfP GKir LRHS MAsh MBar MGos MMuc MRav NHol SRms WDin WSpi
- 'Niki'	EBee EPfP LRHS MAsh MGos SPoG WRHF
'Killiney Red'	ELan MBri MGos MMuc
'Killiney Salmon'	GGar LRHS LSRN MRav WFar
'La Coquette'	CDoC EBee EPfP LRHS MAsh MBar SBch SPlb
'Lena' ♀H4	CDoC CHar CSBt EBee EPfP GGar GKir LAst LRHS LSRN MAsh MBar MBri MGos MWat NEgg NHol NLar NPri WBor WClo WFar WHar
leucanthus	see *Chamaecytisus albus*
'Luna'	EBee WFar
maderensis	see *Genista maderensis*
'Maria Burkwood'	EPfP MGos NLar
'Minstead'	CDoC ELan EPfP GGar LRHS NEgg WAbe WClo
monspessulanus	see *Genista monspessulana*
'Moonlight'	NBro
'Moyclare Pink'	CMHG
'Mrs Norman Henry'	NLar
§ ***multiflorus*** ♀H4	SRms
nigricans	WPGP
- 'Cyni'	CBgR CTsd ECrN ELan ELon IArd LAst LRHS MAsh SEND SPer SPoG SSpi
'Palette'	MBar
'Porlock'	see *Genista* 'Porlock'
× ***praecox***	EWTr LAst LRHS MAsh NBlu NEgg NHol SPlb SPoG WFar WHar
- 'Albus'	CDoC CDul CHar CSBt EBee ECrN ELan EPfP GGar GKir LAst LRHS LSRN MAsh MBar MGos MRav NBlu NHol NPri SBch SPer WFar WHar
- 'Allgold' ♀H4	Widely available
- 'Canary Bird'	see *C.* × *praecox* 'Goldspeer'
- cream-flowered new	MMuc
- 'Frisia'	MBar NBro WFar
§ - 'Goldspeer'	MMuc SEND
- 'Lilac Lady'	LRHS
- 'Warminster' ♀H4	EPfP MBar MBri MRav MWat NBlu NWea SBch SPer SRms
purpureus	see *Chamaecytisus purpureus*
- 'Atropurpureus'	see *Chamaecytisus purpureus* 'Atropurpureus'
racemosus	see *Genista* × *spachiana*
Red Favourite	see *C.* 'Roter Favorit'
'Red Wings'	LRHS MAsh NHol SPer
§ 'Roter Favorit'	EPfP MBar MGos MNHC NScw WGor
scoparius	CArn CDul CRWN EBWF NWea SRms WDin
§ - f. ***andreanus*** ♀H4	CDoC EPfP MGos NWea SPer WFar
- - 'Splendens'	CBgR
- 'Cornish Cream'	CDoC CDul EPfP GKir LRHS WFar
§ - subsp. ***maritimus***	SLPl
- Monarch strain	GJos
- var. ***prostratus***	see *C. scoparius* subsp. *maritimus*
× ***spachianus***	see *Genista* × *spachiana*
supinus	see *Chamaecytisus supinus*

'Windlesham Ruby'	CDoC CPLG EBee ELan EPfP GKir LRHS LSRN MBar NLar NPri SBch SPad SPer WBVN WDin WFar
'Zeelandia' ♀H4	EBee EPfP GKir LRHS MBar MRav MWat NEgg NHol NPri SPer WFar

D

Daboecia ✿ (*Ericaceae*)

§ ***cantabrica*** f. ***alba***	CSBt MBar MBri NHol SHeS SPer SRms
- - 'Alba Globosa'	CCCN MBar SHeS
- - 'Creeping White'	SHeS
- - 'David Moss' ♀H4	MBar SHeS
- - 'Early Bride'	SHeS
- - 'Snowdrift'	MBar SHeS
- - 'White Carpet'	SHeS
- 'Arielle' ♀H4	SHeS
- 'Atropurpurea'	CCCN CSBt NHol SHeS SPer
- 'Barbara Phillips' ♀H4	MBar SHeS
- 'Bellita'	SHeS
- 'Bicolor' ♀H4	SHeS
- 'Blueless'	SHeS
- f. ***blumii*** 'Pink Blum'	SHeS
- - 'Purple Blum'	SHeS
- - 'White Blum'	SHeS
- 'Bubbles'	SHeS
- 'Celtic Star'	SHeS
- 'Chaldon'	SHeS
- 'Charles Nelson' (d)	MBar SHeS
- 'Cherub'	SHeS
- 'Cinderella'	MBar SHeS
- 'Cleggan'	SHeS
- 'Clifden'	SHeS
- 'Covadonga'	MBar SHeS
- 'Cupido'	CTsd SHeS
§ - 'Donard Pink'	MBar SHeS
- 'Eskdale Baron'	SHeS
- 'Eskdale Blea'	SHeS
- 'Eskdale Blonde'	SHeS
- 'Glamour'	SHeS
- 'Globosa Pink'	SHeS
- 'Harlequin'	SHeS
- 'Heather Yates'	SHeS
- 'Heraut'	SHeS
- 'Hookstone Purple'	CCCN MBar NHol SHeS
- 'Irish Shine'	SHeS
- 'Johnny Boy'	SHeS
- 'Lilac Osmond'	MBar SHeS
- 'Pink'	see *D. cantabrica* 'Donard Pink'
- 'Pink Lady'	MBar SHeS
- 'Polifolia'	SHeS SRms
- 'Porter's Variety'	MBar SHeS
- 'Praegerae'	CCCN CTri MBar SHeS
- 'Purpurea'	MBar SHeS
- 'Rainbow' (v)	MBar SHeS
- 'Rodeo' ♀H4	SHeS
- 'Rosea'	MBar SHeS
- 'Rubra'	SHeS
- subsp. ***scotica*** 'Bearsden'	MBar SHeS
- - 'Ben'	SHeS
- - 'Cora'	MBar SHeS
- - 'Golden Imp'	SHeS
- - 'Goscote'	MGos SHeS
- - 'Jack Drake' ♀H4	MBar MBri SHeS
- - 'Katherine's Choice'	CBcs SHeS
- - 'Red Imp'	SHeS
- - 'Robin'	SHeS
- - 'Silverwells' ♀H4	CBcs MBar MBri SHeS
- - 'Tabramhill'	MBar SHeS
- - 'William Buchanan' ♀H4	GGar MBar MBri NHol SHeS
- - 'William Buchanan Gold' (v)	CCCN MBar MBri SHeS
- 'Tom Pearce'	CCCN
- 'Waley's Red' ♀H4	GQui MBar NHol SHeS
- 'Wijnie'	SHeS

Dacrycarpus (*Podocarpaceae*)

§ ***dacrydioides***	CBcs ECou LEdu
- 'Dark Delight'	ECou

Dacrydium (*Podocarpaceae*)

bidwillii	see *Halocarpus bidwillii*
cupressinum	CAbb CBcs CDoC CTrC SMad
franklinii	see *Lagarostrobos franklinii*
laxifolium	see *Lepidothamnus laxifolius*

Dactylis (*Poaceae*)

glomerata	WSFF
- 'Variegata' (v)	EBee EPPr LRHS MCCP MMuc NBid NHol SBch SEND SHDw WCot WFar

Dactylorhiza (*Orchidaceae*)

alpestris	CFir EBee GEdr MAvo MDun NLAp WClo WCot
aristata	EFEx WWst
× ***braunii***	ECha
§ ***elata*** ♀H4	GAbr GQui IBlr LAma MBri NLAp SMrm SPhx SUsu WWst
- 'Lydia'	GCra SPhx
Foliorella gx	NLAp
§ ***foliosa*** ♀H4	CBro CCCN CTsd EBee ERos GCra GKir IBlr LLWG MDun MNrw MTho NLAp NSum WFar WOld
§ ***fuchsii***	CBro CCCN CMil CPrp EBee EBla EPot ERos GBuc GEdr GKev MAvo MDun MNrw NLAp NMen NRya NSla NSum SCnR SUsu WClo WCot WFar WHer WPnP WTin
- pink-flowered	CFir
- white-flowered	CFir NLAp
× ***grandis***	EBla IBlr SCnR
hybrids	GKir NLAp
incarnata	CFir CPrp EBee EBla GAuc GEdr MDun MREP NBid NLAp WPnP WSpi
§ ***maculata***	CFir CHid EBee EBla EHrv ELan EPfP GAbr GAuc GEdr GKir LAma MDun MREP NLAp NMen NSum WBor WClo WCot WFar WHer WHlf WPnP
- subsp. ***ericetorum***	NLAp
maderensis	see *D. foliosa*
§ ***majalis***	CFir CLAP CPrp EBee EBla GAuc LAma MDun MREP NLAp WFar WPnP
- subsp. ***sphagnicola***	EBee GEdr MDun NLAp WClo WCot
mascula	see *Orchis mascula*
praetermissa	CCCN CFir CLAP CPBP CPrp EBee EBla GEdr GKev MDun MREP NLAp NMen WClo WCot WFar WPnP
- 'Copenhaven'	NLAp
- subsp. ***praetermissa*** hybrid **new**	EBee GEdr
purpurella	CFir CLAP CPrp EBee EBla GEdr MDun MREP NLAp NMen NRya WCot WFar WPnP
- 'Palmengarten'	NLAp
sambucina	GAuc NLAp

	traunsteineri	EBee

Dahlia ✿ (*Asteraceae*)

	NJM 05.008	WPGP
	NJM 05.085	WPGP
	'Abba' (SD)	ECtt
	'Admiral Rawlings' (SD)	MWea WHal WWlt
	'Akita' (Misc)	LRHS MBri SPer WAba
	'Alauna Clair-Obscur' (MC/Fim) **new**	ERCP
	'Alfred Grille' (MS-c)	CSut LRHS SPer
	'Alf's Mascot' (MD)	WAba
	'Allan Snowfire' (MS-c)	LAyl WAba
	'Almand's Climax' (GD) ♀H3	WAba
	'Alva's Doris' (SS-c) ♀H3	LAyl WAba
	'Alva's Supreme' (GD) ♀H3	LAyl WAba
I	'Amazone' (DwB)	LAst LRHS
	'Amberglow' (MinBa)	LAyl
	'Ambition' (SS-c)	ERCP
	'Amira' (SBa)	WAba
	'Ananda' (S-c)	CFir
	'Andrew Magson' (SS-c) ♀H3	WAba
	'Andrew Mitchell' (MS-c)	WAba
	'Andries' Amber' (MinS-c)	LYaf
	'Andries' Orange' (MinS-c)	LYaf
	'Angard Coronet' **new**	WAba
	'Ann Breckenfelder' (Col) ♀H3	EBee ECtt EHrv LOck LRHS MAvo NEgg SDix SMrm WCot
	'Anniversary Ball' (MinBa)	LAyl
	'Apache' (MS-c/Fim)	LRHS SPer WAba
	'Apache Blauw' **new**	LRHS
	'Apricot Honeymoon Dress' (SD)	WAba
	'Arabian Night' (SD)	Widely available
	'Aspen' (Dwf)	MWea NBPC
	'Audacity' (MD)	LAyl
	'Aurora's Kiss' (MinBa)	LYaf
	'Aurwen's Violet' (Pom)	LAyl
	australis	EBee WPGP
	- B&SWJ 10208	WCru
	- B&SWJ 10358	WCru
	- B&SWJ 10389	WCru
	'Autumn Choice' (MD)	LAyl
	'Autumn Fairy' (D) **new**	ERCP
	'B.J. Beauty' (MD)	LAyl
	'Babette' (S-c)	LYaf
	'Babylon' (GD)	EPfP
	'Babylon Bronze'	CSut
	'Bagley Blush' (MinD)	WAba
	'Bantling' (MinBa)	ECtt ERCP
	'Barbarry Banker' (MinD)	LAyl
	'Barbarry Carousel' (SBa)	WAba
	'Barbarry Coronet' (MinD)	WAba
	'Barbarry Orange' (SD)	WAba
	'Barbarry Ticket' (SD)	WAba
	'Baret Joy' (LS-c)	WAba
	'Barton Memory' (S-c)	LAyl
	'Bayou'^{PBR} (Misc) **new**	LRHS WAba
I	'Bea' (SWL)	WAba
	'Bednall Beauty' (Misc/DwB) ♀H3	CBgR CHVG CHll CMoH COIW CSpe EBee ECtt EHrv ELan EShb EWes LHop LRHS MBri MRav NEgg SAga SDnm SDys SMrm SPav SUsu WAba WBrk WClo WCot WDyG WSpi WWEG
	'Bell Boy' (MinBa)	ECtt
	'Berger's Rekord' (S-c)	CSut EPfP LRHS WAba
	'Berliner Kleene' (MinD/DwB)	SBch
	'Berliner Orange' (MD) **new**	ERCP
	'Beth's Chaplet' **new**	WCot
	'Bishop of Auckland'^{PBR} (Misc)	CAvo CBgR CSpe EBee ECtt ERCP LPio LRHS MCot NEgg WCot WWEG
	'Bishop of Canterbury'^{PBR} (Misc)	CBgR EBee ECtt EPfP LRHS NGdn
	'Bishop of Lancaster' (Misc)	LPio LRHS
	'Bishop of Leicester' (Misc)	CAvo CBgR CSpe ECtt EPfP LPio LRHS LSou MWea SPet
	'Bishop of Llandaff' (Misc) ♀H3	Widely available
	'Bishop of Oxford' (Misc)	CBgR CSpe EBee EPfP LPio LRHS LSou MWea NBPC NGdn SAga SPet
	'Bishop of York' (Misc)	CAvo CBgR CFFs CSpe EBee ECtt EPfP EPot ERCP LPio LRHS LSou MWea NBPC NGdn SPet WBrk
	'Bishop Peter Price' (Sin)	CHar CMil
	'Bishop's Children'	CSpr
	'Black Fire' (SD)	LAyl
	'Black Narcissus' (MC)	CHVG WWlt
	'Black Wizard' (MS-c) **new**	SMrm SWal
	'Bliss' (SWL)	WAba
	'Blue Bell' (MD) **new**	LRHS
	'Bluesette' (SD)	LRHS
	'Bonesta' (MinD)	CSut
	'Boogie Woogie' (Anem)	CSut
	'Bora Bora' (SS-c)	LRHS
	'Bracken Ballerina' (SWL) **new**	WAba
	'Brackenhill Flame' (SD)	WAba
	'Brackenridge Ballerina' (SWL)	CSam LAyl WAba
	'Brian's Dream' (MinD)	LAyl
	'Bride's Bouquet' (Col)	ERCP
	'Bridge View Aloha' (MS-c) ♀H3	EPfP LRHS SMrm WAba
	'Bridge View Madlyn' **new**	WAba
	'Bronze Glints' (MS-c)	WAba
	'Brookfield Delight' (Sin/Lil) ♀H3	SUsu
	'Bryn Terfel' (GD)	WAba
	'Café au Lait' (GD)	CBgR LRHS SEND SPer WAba WSpi
	'Cameo' (WL)	CSam LAyl LYaf
*	'Canary Fubuki' (MD)	ERCP
	'Candy Cupid' (MinBa) ♀H3	LYaf WAba
	'Candy Eyes'	CBcs EBee EKen EPfP LRHS LSRN LSou NSti
	'Candy Pink' **new**	MAsh
	'Caribbean Cocktail' **new**	LRHS
	'Caribbean Delight' **new**	LRHS
	'Caribbean Fantasy'	CSut EBee LRHS NGdn SPer WAba
	'Caribbean Sunset' **new**	LRHS
	'Carmen' **new**	WAba
	'Carolina Moon' (SD)	CSam LAyl
	'Catherine Deneuve' (Misc)	ECtt
	'Charlie Dimmock' (SWL) ♀H3	WAba
	'Chat Noir' (MS-c)	CAvo CFFs CSut EBee ERCP LRHS
	'Cherwell Goldcrest' (SS-c)	WAba
	'Cherwell Siskin' (MD)	WAba
	'Chic' (MinBa)	ECtt LRHS
	'Chic en Rouge'	NBPC
	'Chic White' **new**	LRHS
	'Chimborazo' (Col)	LAyl SDix
	'Chocolate Orange' (Sin)	WCot
	'Christine' (SD)	LRHS SPer WAba
	'Christmas Carol' (Col)	ECtt
	'Christopher Taylor' (SWL)	WAba
I	'Cindy' (MinD)	WAba
	'Citizen' **new**	ERCP
	'City of Alkmaar' (SC) **new**	LRHS SMrm

'City of Leiden' (MinS-c) **new**	LRHS
'City of Rotterdam' **new**	LRHS
'Clair de Lune' (Col) 🏆H3	CWCL EBee ECtt LAst LOck MCot SMrm SPav WAba WCot WHrl WSpi
'Clarion' (MS-c)	CSpe EBee LRHS NPri
'Clarion 79' (DwB)	SUsu
(Classic Series) 'Classic Masquerade'[PBR] (Misc)	CBgR
- 'Classic Poème'[PBR] (Misc)	CBgR LRHS
- 'Classic Rosamunde'[PBR] (Misc)	CBgR NGdn SWal
- 'Classic Summertime' (Misc)	CBgR EBee
- 'Classic Swanlake'[PBR] (Misc)	CBgR
'Claudette' (D) **new**	LRHS
'Clint's Climax' (LD)	WAba
coccinea (B)	CBgR CGHE CHll CSpe EBee EBrs EHrv EPfP GCal IHer LAst LPio MCot NCob SDix SHGN SPav WAba WCot WDyG WHrl WPGP
- B&SWJ 9126	WCru
- NJM 05.072	WPGP
- var. ***palmeri***	CAvo CBgR CSpe EBee LFur LPio LRHS WPGP
coccinea* × *merckii (B)	EWes
'Color Spectacle' (LS-c)	ERCP LRHS
'Cornel' (SBa)	LAyl LRHS LYaf WAba
'Cornel Brons' (MinBa) **new**	ERCP
'Corrine' (SWL)	WAba
'Crazy Love' (SD) **new**	LRHS WAba
'Cream Moonlight' (MS-c)	WAba
'Czardas'	GCal
'Daleko Jupiter' (GS-c)	WAba
'Danum Gail' (LD)	WAba
'Danum Meteor' (GS-c)	WAba
'Dark Angel' **new**	LRHS
'Dark Desire'[PBR] (Sin/DwB)	CAvo CBct CBgR CFir CSpe CWCL ECtt LAst LHop MBri SCoo SDnm SMrm
'Dave's Snip' (MinD)	WAba
'David Howard' (MinD) 🏆H3	Widely available
'Dawn Sky' (SD)	LAyl
'Deborah's Kiwi' (SC)	WAba
'Debra Anne Craven' (GS-c)	WAba
'Denise Willow' (Pom)	WAba
dissecta	WPGP
- F&M 191	WPGP
'Doctor John Grainger' (MinD)	CHVG
'Doktor Hans Ricken' (SD)	WAba
'Doris Day' (SC)	LYaf WAba
'Doris Knight' (SC)	LYaf
'Downham Royal' (MinBa)	ERCP WAba
'Duet' (MD)	ECtt EPfP LRHS WAba
'Dutch Baby' (Pom)	WAba
'Eastwood Moonlight' (MS-c)	WAba
'Eastwood Star' (MS-c)	WAba
'Edge of Joy' **new**	LRHS
'Edinburgh' (SD)	ERCP SWal WAba
'El Paso' (SD)	MBri WAba
'Electric Haze' **new**	NGdn
'Elga' **new**	ERCP
'Elise' (MinD)	SPer
'Elizabeth Hammett' (MinD)	WAba
'Elizabeth Snowden' (Col)	WAba
'Ellen Huston' (Misc/DwB) 🏆H3	CBgR EBee EBrs ECtt ERCP LOck LPio LRHS MBri SBch SMrm WCot

	'Elma E' (LD)	LAyl WAba
	'Embrace' (SC)	LAyl WAba
	'Emile Rose' (MinS-c)	WAba
	'Emma's Coronet' (MinD)	WAba
	'Engelhardt's Matador' (MD)	CBgR EBee ECtt LAst LOck LRHS LSou SBch WCot WHrl
	'English Breakfast' **new**	LRHS
	'Eveline' (SD)	CBgR EBrs EPfP ERCP LRHS MBri
	excelsa (B)	CHEx CHll
	- B&SWJ 10233	WCru
	- B&SWJ 10238	WCru
	'Excentrique' (Misc)	ECtt
	'Exotic Dwarf' (Sin/Lil)	EBee ECtt LOck LRHS LSou NGdn WCot
	'Explosion' (SS-c)	LRHS
	'Eye Candy'	LRHS
	'Fabula' (Col)	LRHS
	'Famoso' (Col) **new**	ERCP LRHS
	'Fantastico' (Col) **new**	ERCP
	'Fascination' (SWL/DwB) 🏆H3	CBgR CHVG CHar COIW CSam EBee EBrs ECtt EWll LAyl LPio LRHS LSou MCot MWea NEgg NGdn SBch SMrm WHoo WSpi WWEG
I	'Fascination' (Misc)	SPet
	'Fascination' ambig.	ERCP
	'Fashion Monger' (Col)	EBee ECtt EHrv LOck MAvo NEgg NGdn SMrm WCot
	'Ferncliffe Illusion' (LD)	ERCP
	'Festivo' (Col)	LRHS
	'Fidalgo Magic' (MD)	WAba
	'Fidalgo Supreme' (MD)	LAyl
	'Figurine' (SWL) 🏆H3	WAba
	'Finchcocks' (SWL) 🏆H3	LAyl
	'Fire and Ice' **new**	LRHS WAba
	'Fire Mountain' (MinD)	CSam EBee WCot
	'Firebird' (Sin)	WAba
	'Firebird' (MS-c)	see *D.* 'Vuurvogel'
	'Fleur' (MinD/Fim)	LRHS SPer WAba
	'Floorinoor' (Anem)	LRHS SPer
	'Florence Li Tim-Oi' (Sin) **new**	CHar
	'Forncett Furnace' (B)	GCal
	'Fortuna' (Col) **new**	ERCP
	'Frank Holmes' (Pom)	WAba
	'Franz Kafka' (Pom)	ECtt ERCP
	'Freak of Nature' **new**	WAba
§	'Freya's Paso Doble' (Anem) 🏆H3	LAyl
*	'Friquolet'	ERCP LRHS
	'Funny Face' (Misc)	WAba
	'Fusion' (MD) 🏆H3	WCot
	'Fuzzy Wuzzy' (MD)	CSut
	(Gallery Series) 'Gallery Art Deco'[PBR] (SD) 🏆H3	ERCP LRHS SBch SUsu
	- 'Gallery Art Fair'[PBR] (MinD) 🏆H3	LRHS
	- 'Gallery Art Nouveau'[PBR] (MinD) 🏆H3	ERCP LOck LRHS MBri SBch SUsu WCot
	- 'Gallery Matisse'[PBR] (SD)	ERCP SPer
	- 'Gallery Salvador'[PBR] (SD) **new**	ERCP
	'Garden Festival' (SWL)	LRHS WAba
	'Garden Party' (MC/DwB) 🏆H3	LAyl
	'Garden Wonder' (SD)	EPfP LRHS SBch
	'Gay Princess' (SWL)	LAyl
	'Geerlings' Cupido' (SWL)	WAba
	'Geoffrey Kent' (MinD) 🏆H3	WAba
	'Gerrie Hoek' (SWL)	CSam ERCP LYaf MWea WSpi
	'Gill's Pastelle' (MS-c)	WAba
	'Gina Lombaert' (MS-c)	SEND WAba

	Name	Suppliers
	'Giselle'	LRHS SPer SPet
	'Glorie van Heemstede' (SWL) ♀H3	CSam ERCP LAyl LPio LYaf MWte SEND WHrl
	'Glorie van Naardwijk' (SD)	SWal
	'Glorie van Noordwijk' (MinS-c)	ERCP LRHS WAba
	'Glow' **new**	LRHS WAba
	'Gold Crown' (LS-c)	EPfP
	'Golden Crown' (LC) **new**	WAba
	'Golden Emblem' (MD)	ECtt SWal
	'Golden Jubilee' (D)	EPfP SPer
	'Golden Scepter' (MinD)	LRHS WAba
	'Golden Symbol' (MS-c)	WAba
	'Golden Torch' **new**	LRHS
	'Good Earth' (MC)	LRHS SMrm
	'Grand Willo' (Pom)	WAba
	'Grenadier' (SWL) ♀H3	CBgR EBee ECtt LRHS LSou SDix SDys SPav WAba WBor WCot WWEG
	'Gwyneth' (SWL)	WAba
	'Gypsy Boy' (LD)	LAyl
	'Hamari Accord' (LS-c) ♀H3	LAyl WAba
	'Hamari Bride' (MS-c) ♀H3	LAyl
	'Hamari Gold' (GD) ♀H3	WAba
	'Hamari Katrina' (LS-c)	WAba
	'Hamilton Lillian' (SD) ♀H3	WAba
	'Hans Radi' (Misc)	WAba
	(Happy Single Series)	EBee ERCP LSou
	Happy Single First Love = 'Hs First Love'PBR (Sin)	
	- Happy Single Juliet = 'HS Juliet'PBR (Sin)	EBee
	- Happy Single Kiss = 'HS Kiss'PBR	EBee LSou NOrc
	- Happy Single Party = 'HS Party'PBR	EBee ERCP LSou
	- Happy Single Romeo = 'HS Romeo'PBR **new**	LSou
	- Happy Single Wink = 'HS Wink'PBR (Sin) **new**	LSou
	'Haresbrook' (Sin)	EShb NGdn SPav WAba WSpi
	'Hayley Jayne' (S-Sc)	ERCP SPer WAba
	'Heartbreaker' (MD) **new**	LRHS
	'Helga' (MS-c)	ECtt ERCP
	'Herbert Smith' (D)	LRHS SEND
	'Hillcrest Desire' (SC) ♀H3	LAyl WAba
	'Hillcrest Heights' (LS-c)	WAba
	'Hillcrest Kismet' (MD)	LAyl
	'Hillcrest Margaret' (MinD)	WAba
	'Hillcrest Regal' (Col) ♀H3	WAba
	'Hillcrest Royal' (MC) ♀H3	SDix
	'Honka' (Misc) ♀H3	CBgR ERCP LAyl LRHS WAba WCot
	'Honka Red' (Misc) **new**	ERCP
	'Honka Surprise' (Misc) **new**	CBgR ERCP WCot
	'Honka White' (Misc) **new**	ERCP
	'Hot Chocolate' (MinD)	EPfP WBrk WCot WHoo
	'Hugs and Kisses' **new**	WHlf
	'Ibis' **new**	LRHS
	'Icarus' (SS-c) **new**	WAba
	imperialis (B)	CDTJ CHEx CHll EBee EShb EWes LRHS SBig WBVN WDyG WHal
	- B&SWJ 8997	WCru
I	- 'Tasmania' (B)	GCal
	'Impression Famosa'	MBri
	'Impression Fantastico'	MBri
	'Impression Festivo'	MBri
	'Inca' (Anem) **new**	ERCP
	'Inca Matchless' (MD)	WAba
	'Indian Summer' (SC)	WAba
	'Irene Ellen' (SD)	WAba
	'Iris' (Pom)	WAba
	'Ivanetti' (MinBa)	EPfP WAba
	'Jackie Magson' (SS-c)	WAba
	'Jackie's Baby' (MinD)	WAba
	'Janal Amy' (GS-c)	WAba
	'Jason' (SS-c)	WAba
	'Jean Fairs' (MinWL) ♀H3	LYaf
	'Jean McMillan' (SC)	WAba
	'Jeanne d'Arc' (GC)	CSut EPfP
	'Jennie' (MS-c/Fim)	LRHS
	'Jescot Jess' (MinD)	LYaf
	'Jescot Julie' (O)	LAyl
	'Jescot Lingold' (MinD)	LRHS WAba
	'Jill Day' (SC)	LYaf
	'Jim Branigan' (LS-c)	WAba
	'Jim's Jupiter' (LS-c)	WAba
	'John Street' (SWL) ♀H3	WSpi
	'Jomanda' (MinBa) ♀H3	LYaf
	'Jo's Choice' (MinD)	LYaf
	'Judy Tregidden' (MWL)	CSam
	'Jules Dyson' (Misc)	SDys
	'Jura' (SS-c)	EPfP ERCP LRHS
	'Karenglen' (MinD) ♀H3	LYaf WAba
	'Karma Amanda' (SD)	LRHS WAba
	'Karma Corona'PBR (SC)	WAba
	'Karma Fuchsiana' (SD)	ERCP SBch
	'Karma Lagoon'PBR	LRHS SBch WAba
	'Karma Maarten Zwaan'PBR (SWL)	WAba
	'Karma Naomi'PBR	ERCP WAba
	'Karma Pink Corona'PBR (SC) **new**	WAba
	'Karma Prospero'PBR (SD) **new**	SBch
	'Karma Red Corona'PBR (SC) **new**	WAba
	'Karma Sangria'PBR (SC)	WAba
	'Karma Serena'PBR	WAba
	'Karma Ventura'PBR (SD)	SBch
	'Karma Yin Yang' (SD)	WAba
	'Kate's Pastelle' (Ms-c)	WAba
	'Kathryn's Cupid' (MinBa) ♀H3	SWal WAba
	'Kayleigh Spiller' (Col)	CBgR
	'Keith's Choice' (MD)	WAba
	'Kelsea Carla' (SS-c) ♀H3	WAba
	'Kenn Emerland' (MS-c)	EPfP
	'Kenora Canada' (MS-c)	WAba
	'Kenora Challenger' (LS-c)	WAba
	'Kenora Lisa' (MD)	WAba
	'Kenora Macop-B' (MC/Fim)	CSut ERCP LRHS
	'Kenora Sunset' (MS-c) ♀H3	LAyl LYaf
	'Kenora Valentine' (LD) ♀H3	LAyl
	'Kidd's Climax' (GD) ♀H3	WAba
	'Kidd's Delight' **new**	CSut
	'Kiss Me' (SD) **new**	LRHS
	'Klankstad Kerkrade' (SC)	WAba
	'Klondike' (MS-c)	WAba
I	'Knockout' (Sin)	EPfP LRHS LSRN LSou MAsh MWea NSti
I	'Kyoto' (SWL)	WAba
	'L.A.T.E.' (MinBa)	WAba
	'La Gioconda' (Col)	LRHS
	'Lady Linda' (SD)	LYaf WAba
	'Lambada' (Anem) **new**	LRHS
	'L'Ancresse' (MinBa)	LAyl WAba
	'Last Dance' (MD)	LRHS
	'Lavender Perfection' (GD)	CSut LRHS
	'Lemon Cane' (Misc)	WAba
	'Lemon Elegans' (SS-c) ♀H3	LYaf WAba

	'Lemon Zing' (MinBa)	LAyl
	'Lilac Taratahi' (SC) ♀H3	CSam LAyl
	'Lilac Time' (MD)	SPer
	'Linda's Chester' (SC)	LYaf
	'Lismore Canary' (SWL)	CSam WAba
	'Lismore Moonlight' (Pom)	LAyl
	'Lismore Willie' (SWL) ♀H3	LYaf WAba
	'Little Robert' (MinD)	WAba
	'Little Tiger' (MinD)	ERCP LRHS MBri
	'Little Treasure'	EPfP SMrm
I	'Little William' (MinBa)	LRHS WAba
	'Ludwig Helfert' (S-c)	ERCP SEND SWal
	'Mabel Ann' (GD)	LAyl WAba
	'Madame J. Snapper'	WSpi
	'Madame Simone Stappers' (WL)	LPio LRHS MMHG
	'Madame Vera' (SD)	LYaf
	'Malham Portia' (SWL)	WAba
	'Marble Ball' (MinD)	ERCP
	'Margaret Haggo' (SWL)	CSam
	'Margareth Kleene' (MD) **new**	LRHS
	'Mark Lockwood' (Pom)	WAba
	'Marlene Joy' (MS-c/Fim)	LRHS WAba
	'Martin's Yellow' (Pom)	WAba
	'Mary Eveline' (Col)	ECtt LAyl LRHS
	'Mary Hammett' (MinD)	WAba WSpi
	'Mary's Jomanda' (SBa) ♀H3	WAba
	merckii (B)	CBgR CFir CGHE CMdw CSpe EBee EGoo EWes LAyl LFur LPio LRHS MNrw MRav SAga SUsu WAba WCom WDyG WPGP WSHC
	- F&M 222	WPGP
	- ***alba*** (B)	CSpe LPio SUsu WCom WCru
	- compact (B)	WPGP
	'Mermaid of Zennor' (Sin)	CFir EBee MCot
	'Minley Carol' (Pom) ♀H3	LAyl WAba
	'Minnesota' (MD)	WAba
	'Miss Campbell' **new**	ERCP
	'Mistral' (MS-c/Fim)	ECtt
	'Molly Trotter' (Sin)	CHar
	'Mom's Special' (LD)	CSut WHlf
	'Moonfire' (Misc/DwB) ♀H3	Widely available
	'Moonglow' (LS-c)	ERCP
	'Moor Place' (Pom)	WAba
	'Moray Susan' (SWL)	WAba
	'München' (MinD)	NGdn
	'Murdoch'	CBgR EBee ECtt EPfP LOck LRHS MCot SDys SPav WAba WCot WHrl WSpi
	'Murillo'	LAyl MBri WCot
	'Musette' (MinD)	ECtt SMrm
	'My Beverley' (MS-c/Fim)	LAyl
	'My Love' (SS-c)	CSut EPfP ERCP LAst LRHS MWea SEND SPer WAba
	'Mystery Day' (MD)	CBgR ECtt EPfP MBri NBPC NGdn SBch
	'Nargold' (MS-c/Fim)	LAyl
	'Natal' (MinBa)	ECtt EPfP ERCP LRHS SPer WAba
	'Nationwide' (SD)	WAba
	'Nepos' (SWL)	LYaf
	'Nescio' (Pom)	EPfP ERCP
	'New Baby' (MinBa)	ERCP WAba
	'New Dimension' (SS-c)	EPfP ERCP SPer SWal
I	'Night Queen' (Pom)	EPfP
	'Nippon' (Sin)	EBee LRHS NGdn
	'Nonette' (SWL)	CBgR EBee ECtt LAst LOck LRHS NEgg WAba WClo WCot
*	'Nuit d'Eté' (MS-c)	EBee ERCP LPio LRHS MWea SEND
	'Oakwood Diamond' (SBa)	LYaf

	'Onesta' (SD)	CSam
	'Optic Illusion' (SD)	LRHS
	'Orange Fubuki' (SD) **new**	LRHS
	'Orel' (Col)	WAba
	'Orfeo' (MC)	ECtt ERCP SWal WAba
	'Osaka' (SD)	LRHS
	'Osirium' (SD) **new**	LRHS
	'Otto's Thrill' (LD)	SMrm
	'Palm Springs' (SD)	EPfP LRHS WAba
	'Park Princess' (SC/DwB)	CSut LRHS NGdn SMrm
	'Paso Doble' misapplied	see *D.* 'Freya's Paso Doble'
	'Peace Pact' (SWL)	WAba
	'Peach Cupid' (MinBa) ♀H3	LYaf WAba
	'Peaches and Cream'[PBR] (MinD)	LRHS SBch WAba
	'Pearl of Heemstede' (SD) ♀H3	LAyl
	'Pearl Sharowean' (MS-c)	WAba
	'Pensford Marion' (Pom)	WAba
	'Peter' (MinD)	ECtt
I	'Peter' (SS-c)	EPfP
	'Pfitzer's Joker' **new**	WAba
I	'Phoenix' (MD)	WAba
	'Pink Giraffe' (O) ♀H3	CBgR ERCP
	'Pink Pastelle' (MS-c) ♀H3	WAba
	'Pink Shirley Alliance' (SC)	LAyl
	'Pink Skin' (MD) **new**	ERCP
	'Pink Suffusion' (SD)	WAba
	pinnata	WAba
	- B&SWJ 10240	WCru
	'Piper's Pink' (SS-c/DwB)	LAyl
	'Poème'	CSpe LRHS MWea SPer
	'Pontiac' (SC)	LAyl
	'Pooh' (Col)	ERCP LAyl
I	'Poppet' (Pom)	WAba
	'Porcelain' (SWL) ♀H3	LYaf WSpi
	'Preference' (SS-c)	ERCP
	'Preston Park' (Sin/DwB) ♀H3	CSam LAyl
	'Pretty in Pink'	CSut WAba
	Pride of Berlin	see *D.* 'Stolz von Berlin'
	'Primrose Diane' (SD)	WAba
	'Procyon' (SD)	CBgR EPfP ERCP MWea WAba
	'Promise' (MS-c/Fim)	ECtt WAba
	'Pumpkin Pie' **new**	WCot
	'Purple Gem' (SS-c)	ERCP LRHS SMrm WAba
	'Purple Puff' (Anem) **new**	LRHS
	aff. ***purpusii*** B&SWJ 10321	WCru
	'Radfo' (SS-c)	WAba
	'Raffles' (SD)	LAyl
	'Ragged Robin'[PBR] (Misc)	CBgR CSpe CWCL EBee ECtt ERCP LOck LRHS MBri MCot WCot WWlt
	'Red Bird'	CMoH
	'Red Majorette' (SS-c)	ERCP SWal
	'Red Pygmy' (SS-c)	LRHS MBri
	'Rembrandt USA' (DwSin)	MBri
	'Requiem' (SD)	CSut ERCP LRHS WAba
	'Riisa' (MinBa)	WAba
	'Rip City' (SS-c)	CSpe MCot
	'Risca Miner' (SBa)	WAba
	'River Dance' (Anem) **new**	LRHS
	'Robin Hood' (SBa)	WAba
	'Rocco' (MinBa) **new**	ERCP
	'Rockcliffe' (MinD)	WAba
	'Romeo'	LRHS NPri
	'Rosella' (MD)	EPfP SWal
	'Rosendale Joshua' **new**	WAba
	'Rossendale Luke' (SD)	WAba
	'Rothesay Robin' (SD)	WAba
I	'Roxy' (Sin/DwB)	CBgR CMMP CSam EBee ECtt EHrv ELan EPfP LAst LAyl LRHS MBri

	Name	Suppliers
		NEgg NGdn NVic SBch SMrm SPav WCot WHoo WSpi WWEG
	'Royal Blood'[PBR] (Misc)	CSpe MBri
	'Ruskin Charlotte' (LS-c)	LAyl WAba
	'Ruskin Diana' (SD)	LYaf
	'Ruskin Impact' (SD)	WAba
	'Ruskin Marigold' (SS-c)	LAyl LYaf
	'Ruskin Myra' (SS-c)	LAyl WAba
	'Ruskin Penelope' (SS-c) **new**	LRHS
	'Rustig' (MD)	WAba
	'Ryedale Sunshine' (SD)	WAba
	'Saint-Saëns' (S-c)	LRHS SEND WAba
	'Sakura Fubuki'	ERCP
	'Salmon Keene' (LS-c)	WAba
	'Salmon Symbol' (MS-c)	WAba
	'Sam Hopkins' (SD)	CSam
	'Sam Huston' (GD)	WAba
	'Sandra' ambig. **new**	ERCP
	'Sarah G' (LS-c)	EBee
	'Sascha' (SWL) ♀H3	LAyl
	'Scarlet Fern'	CBcs EBee LSRN LSou NSti
	'Scaur Swinton' (MD)	LAyl
	'Seattle' (SD)	WAba
	'Seawood Glory' **new**	ERCP
	'Seduction' (MinD) **new**	ERCP
	'Seikeman's Feuerball' (MinD)	WAba
	'Shandy' (SS-c)	LAyl
	'Shannon' (SD)	LRHS SPer
	sherffii	MWea SIng
	'Shirley Alliance' (SC)	WAba
	'Shooting Star' (LS-c)	SPer WAba
	'Siberia'[PBR] (MinD) **new**	ERCP
	'Sights of Summer' (MinD) **new**	ERCP
	'Sir Alf Ramsey' (GD)	LAyl WAba
	'Small World' (Pom) ♀H3	LAyl WAba
	'Smokey'	EPfP SEND SPer
	'Sneezy' (Sin)	ELan LRHS
	'Snip' (MinS-c)	WAba
	'Snowflake' (SWL)	ERCP LRHS SMrm WAba
	'Snowstorm' (MD)	CSut SBch
	'So Dainty' (MinS-c) ♀H3	LAyl WAba
	sorensenii	SMad
	'Sorrento Fiesta' (SS-c)	WAba
	'Soulman' (Anem)	LRHS
	'Souvenir d'Eté' (Pom)	LRHS
	'Starburst'	LRHS
	'Star's Favourite' (MC)	ERCP
	Starsister Series **new**	NPri
§	'Stolz von Berlin' (MinBa)	ECtt EPfP ERCP LRHS WAba
	'Stoneleigh Cherry' (Pom)	LAyl
	'Suffolk Punch' (MD)	LAyl LYaf SPer
I	'Summer Night' (SC)	ECGP LAyl LRHS MCot SPer
	'Summertime'	SPer
	'Sunlight Pastelle' (MS-c)	WAba
	'Sunny Boy' (MinD)	LRHS WAba
	'Sunray Glint' (MS-c)	WAba
	'Sunset' (SD)	WAba
I	'Sunshine' (Sin)	ECtt LAyl LRHS
	'Superfine' (SC)	WAba
	'Suzette' (SD/DwB)	LRHS
	'Swan Lake' (SD)	EShb SPer SPet
	'Sweetheart' (SD)	EBrs ERCP
I	'Sylvia' (SBa)	EPfP LRHS WAba
	'Tae Bo' (SD) **new**	LRHS
	'Tally Ho' (Misc) ♀H3	CBgR CMMP CSam EBee ECtt EHrv GCal LRHS MBri MRav SDys SMad SPav WCot WWEG
	'Tam Tam'	SMrm
	'Taratahi Ruby' (SWL) ♀H3	LAyl LYaf WAba
	'Taxi Driver' **new**	CMoH
	'Teesbrooke Audrey' (Col)	ECtt LAyl WAba
	tenuicaulis	CDTJ EBee SBig
	– F&M 99	WPGP
	– F&M 355	WPGP
	'The Phantom' (Anem) **new**	ERCP
	'Thomas A. Edison' (MD)	CSut EPfP ERCP
	'Tiptoe' (MinD)	LAyl
	'Tommy Doc' (SS-c)	WAba
	'Tomo' (SD)	LAyl
	'Topmix White' (DwB) **new**	LRHS
	'Topmix Yellow' (DwB) **new**	LRHS
	'Toto' (Anem)	ERCP SBch
	'Trelyn Kiwi' (SS-c) ♀H3	WAba
	'Tropical Sunset' (SD)	EPfP SPer
	'Troy Dyson' (Misc)	SDys
	'Tsuki-ytori-no-shisha' (MC)	WAba
	'Tui Orange' (SS-c)	WAba
	'Twyning's After Eight' (Sin) ♀H3	CSam CSpe EBee ECtt LRHS MAvo MBNS MBri MCot MMHG NEgg SDix SMad SMrm SUsu WCot WHoo
	'Twyning's Chocolate' (Sin) ♀H3	CSam
	'Unwins' Centennial' (Anem) **new**	LRHS
	'Vancouver' (Misc)	CBgR ERCP LRHS NBPC
	'Veritable' (MS-c)	WAba
	'Vicky Crutchfield' (SWL)	LYaf
§	'Vuurvogel' (MS-c)	SWal
	'Wanda's Capella' (GD)	WAba
	'Wandy' (Pom) ♀H3	WAba
	'War of the Roses'	SGar SWal WHer
	'Welcome Guest' (MS-c)	WAba
	'Weston Dove' (MinS-c)	WAba
	'Weston Nugget' (MinC)	WAba
	'Weston Spanish Dancer' (MinC) ♀H3	LAyl LYaf WAba
	'Wheel' (Col)	WAba
	'White Alva's' (GD) ♀H3	LAyl
	'White Aster' (Pom)	LRHS
	'White Ballerina' (SWL)	CSam LAyl
	'White Ballet' (SD) ♀H3	LAyl
	'White Katrina' (LS-c)	WAba
	'White Moonlight' (MS-c)	LAyl LYaf WAba
	'White Pastelle' (MS-c)	WAba
	'White Perfection' (LD)	ECtt EPfP LRHS WSpi
	'White Star' (MS-c)	ERCP SWal
	'Willo's Flecks' (Pom)	WAba
	'Willo's Violet' (Pom)	WAba
	'Willowfield Kay' (MS-c)	WAba
	'Willowfield Mick' (LD)	WAba
	'Winholme Diane' (SD)	WAba
	'Winston Churchill' (MinD)	LYaf WSpi
	'Winter Springs' (S-Sc) **new**	ERCP
	'Wittem' (MD)	LRHS
	'Wittemans Superba' (SS-c) ♀H3	SDix
	'Wootton Cupid' (MinBa) ♀H3	LYaf WAba
	'Yellow Frank Hornsey' (SD)	WAba
	'Yellow Hammer' (Sin/DwB) ♀H3	LAyl
	'Yellow Happiness' **new**	LRHS
	'Yellow Star' (MS-c)	ERCP LRHS
	'Yellow Symbol' (MS-c)	LYaf
	'Yellow Twist'	CAvo
	'Yelno Enchantment' (SWL)	LAyl
	'Yelno Harmony' (SD) ♀H3	LYaf
	'Yin Yang'	ERCP
	'York and Lancaster' (MD)	CBgR IGor

'Yorkie' (MS-c) WAba
I 'Yvonne' (MWL) LRHS WAba
'Zorro' (GD) ♀H3 WAba

Dais (*Thymelaeaceae*)

cotinifolia EShb

Daiswa see *Paris*

Dalea (*Papilionaceae*)

candida EBee
purpurea EBee

Dalechampia (*Euphorbiaceae*)

dioscoreifolia CCCN EShb
spathulata CCCN

Damasonium (*Alismataceae*)

alisma CNat

damson see *Prunus insititia*

Danae (*Ruscaceae*)

§ ***racemosa*** CBcs CTri EBee ELan EPfP EPla GKir IMon LHop MGos MRav SAPC SArc SEND SMac SPer SRms SSpi SWvt WCot WDin WPGP WPat WSpi

Daphne ✿ (*Thymelaeaceae*)

DJHC 98164 from China WCru
acutiloba CPMA ECho GKev WPGP WSHC
- 'Fragrant Cloud' CPMA EWes SChF
albowiana CPMA EWes LLHF LRHS SAga SChF SCoo
alpina CPMA GKev NEgg WThu
altaica CPMA
arbuscula ♀H4 CPMA ECho EPot LLHF MWat NMen
- subsp. ***arbuscula*** f. ***albiflora*** CPMA
- 'Muran Pride' CPMA
- f. ***radicans*** CPMA
arbuscula × ***cneorum*** var. ***verlotii*** CPMA
arbuscula × 'Leila Haines' see *D.* × *schlyteri*
arisanensis B&SWJ 6983 **new** WCru
bholua CAbP CHll CPMA EPfP GGal LRHS MGos SReu SSpi SSta WAbe WCru WSpi
I - 'Alba' CLAP CPMA ECho ELan EPfP GGGa LRHS MGos SCoo SSpi SSta WGob WPGP
- 'Darjeeling' CBcs CLAP CPLG CPMA EPfP LBuc LRHS SCoo SSpi SSta WGob WPGP
- var. ***glacialis*** 'Gurkha' CGHE CPLG CPMA EBee ELan EPfP LRHS SChF SSpi WPGP WSpi
- 'Glendoick' EPfP GGGa
- 'Jacqueline Postill' ♀H3 Widely available
- 'Limpsfield' LRHS SCoo
- 'Peter Smithers' CLAP CPLG CPMA GGGa LRHS SChF SCoo SReu SSpi SSta WGob WPGP
blagayana CPMA ECho EPot GKev NBir SRms WPGP
- 'Brenda Anderson' CPMA
'Bramdean' see *D.* × *napolitana* 'Bramdean'
× ***burkwoodii*** ♀H4 CMea SAga WDin
- 'Albert Burkwood' CPMA
- 'Astrid' (v) CBcs CBow CPMA EBee LRHS MMHG MWea SIng SPoG SSta WDin
§ - 'Carol Mackie' (v) CPMA
- 'G.K.Argles' (v) ♀H4 CPMA MAsh
I - 'Gold Sport' CPMA
- 'Gold Strike' (v) CPMA
- 'Golden Treasure' CPMA LRHS MAsh SChF
- 'Lavenirei' CPMA
- 'Somerset' CBcs CPMA ELan EPfP LRHS MRav MSwo NWea SAga SLim WDin
§ - 'Somerset Gold Edge' (v) CPMA
- 'Variegata' broad gold edge see *D.* × *burkwoodii* 'Somerset Gold Edge'
- 'Variegata' narrow gold edge see *D.* × *burkwoodii* 'Carol Mackie'
calcicola 'Gang-ho-ba' CPMA
- 'Sichuan Gold' CPMA
caucasica CPMA
circassica CPMA
cneorum CBcs CPMA MMHG NMen WDin
- f. ***alba*** CPMA SChF
- 'Benaco' CPMA
- 'Blackthorn Triumph' CPMA WAbe
- 'Eximia' ♀H4 CPMA CTri ECho EPot MDun SIng SRms WAbe
- 'Klaus Patzner' **new** CPMA
- 'Lac des Gloriettes' CPMA
- 'Puszta' CPMA SAga WAbe
- var. ***pygmaea*** CPMA EPot WAbe
- - 'Alba' CPMA
- 'Rose Glow' CPMA ECho
- 'Ruby Glow' CPMA ECho
- 'Variegata' (v) CPMA ECho EPot NWCA WAbe
- 'Velký Kosír' CPMA SChF WAbe
collina see *D. sericea* Collina Group
× ***eschmannii*** 'Jacob Eschmann' CPMA
'Forarch' CPMA
giraldii CPMA
aff. ***giraldii*** NMen
× ***hendersonii*** CPMA
- 'Appleblossom' CPMA ECho WAbe
- 'Aymon Correvon' CPMA
- 'Blackthorn Rose' CPMA
- 'Ernst Hauser' CPMA ECho GKev LLHF WAbe
- 'Fritz Kummert' CPMA WAbe
- 'Jeanette Brickell' CPMA WAbe
- 'Kath Dryden' CPMA
- 'Marion White' CPMA
- 'Rosebud' CPMA
- 'Solferino' CPMA
'Hinton' CPMA WAbe
× ***houtteana*** CPMA ECho NBir
× ***hybrida*** CPMA
japonica 'Striata' see *D. odora* 'Aureomarginata'
jasminea CPMA ECho NMen
jezoensis CPMA LRHS SSta WCru
× ***jintyae*** 'Pink Cascade' CPMA
juliae CPMA
kamtschatica CPMA
'Kilmeston Beauty' CPMA
kosaninii CPMA
× ***latymeri*** CPMA
- 'Spring Sonnet' CPMA
laureola CPMA CSWP EPfP GKev GPoy MBri MMHG NBir NPer WCFE WPGP
- 'Kingsley Green' CPMA
- 'Margaret Mathew' CPMA EPfP EPot SChF
- subsp. ***philippi*** CPMA CWSG EBee ELan EPfP EWTr GKev LHop LRHS MBlu MBri NDlv NMen SSta WSpi
'Leila Haines' CPMA
longilobata 'Peter Moore' CPMA
× ***mantensiana*** 'Audrey Vockins' CPMA SChF
- 'Manten' CPMA ECho

Name	Suppliers
× ***mauerbachii*** 'Perfume of Spring'	CPMA ECho
'Meon'	see *D.* × *napolitana* 'Meon'
mezereum	CBot CSBt CTri ECho GAbr GGal GKev GKir IFFs IFoB ITim LRHS MBar MBri MGos NChi NPri NWea SBch SLim SWvt WDin WFar WHar WPGP
- f. ***alba***	CPMA CWib ECho ELon ERas GKir LHop MGos NChi SPer SRms SWvt WAbe WSpi
- - 'Bowles's Variety'	CBot CPMA
- 'Rosea'	ECho SRms
- var. ***rubra***	CBcs CPMA CWSG CWib ECho ELan EWTr GKir LRHS LSou MGan MGos MRav MSwo NBlu SPer SPoG WAbe WDin WFar
× ***napolitana*** ♀H4	CBcs CPMA ECho EPfP EPot SChF WPat
§ - 'Bramdean'	CPMA ECho
§ - 'Meon'	CPMA ECho MAsh WAbe
odora	CBcs CPMA EBee EPot LRHS MSwo NMen SLim SSta WDin WSpi
§ - f. ***alba***	CCCN CPMA ECho GAbr GKir NLar SPer
- - 'Sakiwaka'	CCCN CPMA ECho
§ - 'Aureomarginata' (v) ♀H3-4	Widely available
- 'Clotted Cream' (v)	CPMA
- 'Geisha Girl' (v)	CPMA ELan MAsh MGos SPoG
- var. ***leucantha***	see *D. odora* f. *alba*
- 'Limelight'	CPMA
- 'Mae-jima' (v)	CPMA ELan EPfP LLHF LRHS MAsh MBri SLon SPoG
- 'Marginata'	see *D. odora* 'Aureomarginata'
- var. ***rubra***	CCCN CFir CPMA ECho GAbr LLHF NLar SPer WGob
- 'Walberton' (v)	GKir LRHS MGos
oleoides	CPMA
papyracea	GGGa
petraea 'Cima Tombea'	CPMA
- 'Corna Blacca'	CPMA
- 'Garnet'	WAbe
- 'Grandiflora'	CPMA SChF
- 'Lydora'	CPMA
- 'Michele'	CPMA
- 'Persebee'	CPMA
- 'Punchinello'	CPMA
- 'Tuflungo'	CPMA
petraea × ***sericea*** Collina Group	SSta
'Pink Star'	CPMA
pontica ♀H4	CBcs CGHE CPMA EBee ECho EPfP GKir LRHS MBri NLar NMen NWCA SDix SPer SPoG SSpi WPGP
pseudomezereum	WCru
retusa	see *D. tangutica* Retusa Group
'Richard's Choice'	CPMA
× ***rollsdorfii*** 'Arnold Cihlarz'	CPMA EPot LRHS MAsh WAbe
- 'Wilhelm Schacht'	CPMA ECho ELon EPot SAga SChF WAbe
'Rossetii'	CPMA
'Rosy Wave'	CPMA SChF
§ × ***schlyteri***	CPMA
- 'Lovisa Maria'	CPMA EPot WAbe
sericea	CPMA
§ - Collina Group	CPMA EPfP SRms
'Spring Beauty' **new**	CPMA
'Spring Herald'	CPMA
'Stasek' (v)	CPMA WThu
sureil GWJ 9200	WCru
× ***susannae*** 'Anton Fahndrich'	EPot
- 'Anton Fahndrich' × ***sericea*** Collina Group	CPMA
- 'Cheriton'	CPMA ECho EPfP EPot LRHS SChF WAbe
- 'Tichborne'	CPMA EPot MAsh NMen SChF WAbe WThu
tangutica ♀H4	Widely available
- compact **new**	MAsh
§ - Retusa Group ♀H4	CPLG CPMA ECho ELan ELon EPot GGar GKev GKir GMaP LHop MAsh MBri NLAp NMen NRya SRms WAbe WCru WSpi
- - SDR 3024	GKev
× ***thauma***	NMen
× ***transatlantica*** 'Beulah Cross' (v)	CAbP CPMA ELan LLHF LRHS MAsh MBri SPoG SSpi
- Eternal Fragrance = 'Blafra'PBR	CAbP ELan EPfP EPot LLHF LRHS LSqu MAsh MBri MGos NCGa SLon SPer SPoG SSpi
- 'Jim's Pride'	SChF
'Valerie Hillier'	CPMA LRHS
velenovskyi	CPMA
× ***whiteorum*** 'Beauworth'	CPMA ECho LLHF LRHS WAbe
- 'Kilmeston'	CPMA NMen
- 'Warnford'	CPMA
wolongensis 'Kevock Star'	GKev

Daphniphyllum (*Daphniphyllaceae*)

Name	Suppliers
calycinum B&SWJ 4058	WCru
chartaceum	see *D. himalaense* subsp. *himalaense*
glaucescens	WCru
subsp. ***oldhamii*** var. ***kengii*** B&SWJ 6872	
- - B&SWJ 7119	WCru
- - var. ***oldhamii*** B&SWJ 7056	WCru
§ ***himalaense***	WCru
subsp. ***himalaense*** B&SWJ 8225 **new**	
humile	see *D. macropodum* var. *humile*
macropodum	CBcs CCCN CGHE CHEx CWib EPfP EPla LRHS MBri NLar SAPC SArc SDix SMad SSpi WCru WFar WPGP WSpi
- B&SWJ 581	WCru
- B&SWJ 2898	WCru
- B&SWJ 6809 from Taiwan	WCru
- B&SWJ 8763 from Cheju-do, Korea	WCru
- B&SWJ 8507 from Ulleungdo, South Korea **new**	WCru
- dwarf	WCru
§ - var. ***humile*** B&SWJ 11232 **new**	WCru
aff. ***paxianum*** B&SWJ 9755 **new**	WCru
pentandrum B&SWJ 6888 **new**	WCru
teijsmannii B&SWJ 3805	WCru
-B&SWJ 11110 from Japan	WCru
- B&SWJ 11112	WCru

Darlingtonia (*Sarraceniaceae*)

Name	Suppliers
californica ♀H1	CSWC EFEx LRHS MCCP NChu SHmp WSSs

Darmera (*Saxifragaceae*)

Name	Suppliers
peltata ♀H4	Widely available

- 'Nana' CHEx EBee ECha GBuc NBid NHol NLar SWat WFar WMoo WPnP

Dasylirion (*Dracaenaceae*)

§ ***acrotrichum*** CDTJ SAPC SArc SChr
berlandieri NJM 05.048 new WPGP
cedrosanum CDTJ
glaucophyllum EAmu MREP
gracile Planchon see *D. acrotrichum*
leiophyllum WPGP
longissimum CAbb CBrP CTrC EAmu EShb SChr
miquihuanense F&M 321 WPGP
- NJM 05.062 WPGP
quadrangulatum NJM 05.064 new WPGP
serratifolium EAmu
texanum CTrC LEdu
wheeleri ♀H1 CBrP CTrC EAmu SChr

Dasyphyllum (*Asteraceae*)

diacanthoides WPGP

date see *Phoenix dactylifera*

Datisca (*Datiscaceae*)

cannabina CArn CDTJ CDes CFir CHid EBee ECha GBin GCal IMou NChi NLar SDix SMad SMrm SPhx WMoo WPGP

Datura (*Solanaceae*)

arborea see *Brugmansia arborea*
chlorantha see *Brugmansia chlorantha*
cornigera see *Brugmansia arborea*
metel 'Double Eryngium Blue' new WHil
rosea see *Brugmansia* × *insignis* pink-flowered
rosei see *Brugmansia sanguinea*
sanguinea see *Brugmansia sanguinea*
stramonium CArn
suaveolens see *Brugmansia suaveolens*
versicolor see *Brugmansia versicolor* Lagerh.
- 'Grand Marnier' see *Brugmansia* × *candida* 'Grand Marnier'

Daubenya (*Hyacinthaceae*)

alba new ECho
aurea new ECho
- var. ***coccinea*** new ECho
marginata new ECho
namaquensis new ECho

Daucus (*Apiaceae*)

carota CArn CHrt CRWN EBWF NMir NSco SECG
- 'Jane's Lace' CNat

Davallia (*Davalliaceae*)

canariensis ♀H1 SEND
mariesii ♀H3 CMen CTsd SMad WAbe WCot
- var. ***stenolepis*** CMen WRic
tasmanii WRic
trichomanoides CMen
- f. ***barbata*** CMen

Davidia (*Cornaceae*)

involucrata ♀H4 Widely available
- 'Sonoma' MBlu
- var. ***vilmoriniana*** ♀H4 CBcs CDoC CWCL EBee ELan EPfP GKir IMGH LRHS MAsh MBlu MCCP MGan MGos SLim SPer

Daviesia (*Papilionaceae*)

* ***ovalifolia*** SPlb
pectinata new SPlb

Debregeasia (*Urticaceae*)

longifolia WWJ 11686 WCru

Decaisnea (*Lardizabalaceae*)

fargesii Widely available
- B&SWJ 8070 WCru
insignis WPGP

Decumaria (*Hydrangeaceae*)

barbara CMac EBee LRHS MMuc NLar NSti SLim SSta WCru WFar WSHC
- 'Vicki' EBee NLar
sinensis EBee EPfP LRHS MAsh MMuc SLon SPoG SSpi WCru WSHC

Deinanthe (*Hydrangeaceae*)

bifida CDes CLAP CMil EBee EWes GEdr LEdu LFur WCru WPGP
- B&SWJ 5012 WCru
- B&SWJ 5436 EWld GEdr SBig
- B&SWJ 5655 WCru
- 'Pink Kii' WCru
- 'Pink-Shi' CLAP WCru
bifida × ***caerulea*** CLAP
'Blue Blush' WCru
caerulea CLAP CMil EBee GEdr IGor IMou LEdu NLar WCru WPGP
- 'Blue Wonder' CLAP EBee EPPr
- pale-flowered GEdr

Delonix (*Caesalpiniaceae*)

regia EShb SPlb

Delosperma (*Aizoaceae*)

§ ***aberdeenense*** ♀H1 CHEx
ashtonii CCCN EDAr GEdr WPer
basuticum NSla
'Basutoland' see *D. nubigenum*
brunnthaleri new LRHS
congestum CMea EAlp ECho EDAr EPot EShb EWll GEdr NWCA SMad WClo
- 'Gold Nugget' LRHS
cooperi CBgR CCCN EAlp ECho ECtt EDAr EPfP EPot EWll ITim LRHS MSCN NLAp NWCA SBch SEND SIng SPlb WDyG WFar WPer
floribunda 'Stardust' new SGar
harazianum CPBP EDAr
lineare NBir
lydenburgense SChr
§ ***nubigenum*** CTri EAlp ECho ECtt EDAr ELan EPfP EPot GEdr GGar GKev ITim LRHS MSCN SEND SIng SPoG WFar WPer
sutherlandii EAlp ECho EDAr EShb EWll GGar
- 'Peach Star' EAlp EDAr NWCA

Delphinium ✿ (*Ranunculaceae*)

SDR 4817 GKev
HWJK 2179 from Nepal WCru
HWJK 2263 from Nepal WCru
from Nepal GKir
'After Midnight' CNMi
'Ailsa' CNMi

'Alice Artindale' (d)	EWes IFoB MWte SAga SMrm WCot WPGP
ambiguum	see *Consolida ajacis*
'Angela Harbutt'	CNMi
'Ann Woodfield'	CNMi
'Anne Kenrick'	CNMi
'Ariel' ambig.	LRHS WSpi
Astolat Group	CBcs CBot CSBt CTri CWCL CWib EBee ELan EPfP GKir GMaP LBMP LRHS MBri MWat NBPC NBir NCob NLar NPri SBch SMrm SPer SPoG WCAu WFar WHoo WWEG
'Atholl' ♀H4	ELar
'Atlantic Blue' **new**	LSou
'Augenweide'	EBee
beesianum	GKev
Belladonna Group	IFoB
- 'Atlantis' ♀H4	EBee ECha ELar LRHS NGby NLar SMrm SWat
- 'Balaton'	ELar
- 'Blue Shadow'	CWCL
- 'Capri'	EBee
- 'Casa Blanca'	EBee ELar GMaP NLar SBch SMrm SWat WPer WWEG
- 'Cliveden Beauty'	EBee EPfP GMaP LHop NLar SBch SMrm SPoG SWat WPer WSpi WWEG
- 'Delft Blue'PBR	EBee EPfP NMoo
§ - 'Janny Arrow'PBR	LRHS
- 'Moerheimii'	NGby SMrm WSpi
- 'Piccolo'	ECha NLar
- 'Pink Sensation'	see *D.* × *ruysii* 'Pink Sensation'
- 'Völkerfrieden' ♀H4	ELar MRav NGby NPro WSpi
Bellalightblue = 'Barfifteen'PBR **new**	LRHS
× ***bellamosum***	CBot ILad NLar SBch WPer WWEG
'Berghimmel'	EBee NGby
'Beryl Burton'	CNMi
bicolor	LFur
Black Knight Group	Widely available
'Black Velvet'	CBcs LRHS
'Blauwal'	GBin WSpi
'Blue Arrow'	see *D.* 'Blue Max Arrow', *D.* (Belladonna Group) 'Janny Arrow', *D.* 'Kings Blue Arrow'
Blue Bird Group	CBcs CSBt CTri EBee ELan EPfP GMaP LBMP LRHS MRav MWat NBPC NLar NMir NPri SBch SPer SPoG WCAu WFar WHoo WWEG
'Blue Butterfly'	see *D. grandiflorum* 'Blue Butterfly'
'Blue Dawn' ♀H4	CNMi ELar
Blue Fountains Group	CSBt EPfP GKir LSRN SPer SPet SPoG SRms
'Blue Jay'	CBcs CTri EBee ECtt EPfP GKir LRHS LSRN MWat NBir NLar NPri SBch SPer WWEG
§ 'Blue Max Arrow'	LRHS
'Blue Mirror'	SRms
'Blue Nile' ♀H4	CNMi
'Blue Oasis'	CNMi
Blue River	CBcs LRHS SPoG
'Blue Skies'	ECtt GKir NLar
Blue Springs Group	NGdn NLar
'Blue Tit'	CNMi ELar
'Blue Triumphator'	EBee
'Bruce' ♀H4	CNMi ELar WCFE
brunonianum	WThu
bulleyanum	GAuc
'Butterball'	ELar
caeruleum **new**	GKev
californicum	EBee
Cameliard Group	CBcs CSBt EBee ECtt ELan EPfP GKir LBMP LRHS MWat NBPC NLar NPri SPer SPoG WCot WWEG
'Cameliard' (Pacific Hybrid Series) **new**	WCAu
'Can-Can' ♀H4	CNMi ELar
cardinale	EHrv
cashmerianum	EBee GKev
'Cassius' ♀H4	CNMi
caucasicum	see *D. speciosum*
'Centurion Sky Blue' (Centurion Series)	LRHS
ceratophorum var. ***ceratophorum*** BWJ 7799	WCru
'Chelsea Star'	CNMi GBin
'Cher'	CNMi
'Cherry Blossom'	EPfP NLar
'Cherub' ♀H4	ELar
chinense	see *D. grandiflorum*
'Christel'	EWTr LRHS LSRN NGby
'Christine Harbutt' **new**	ELar
chrysotrichum var. ***tsarongense***	EBee GKev
'Clack's Choice'	CNMi
'Claire' ♀H4	CNMi ELar
Clear Springs Series	SGar
'Clifford Sky' ♀H4	ELar LRHS MBri
Connecticut Yankees Group	SMrm SRms
'Conspicuous' ♀H4	CNMi ELar
'Constance Rivett' ♀H4	ELar
'Coral Sunset'PBR (d)	NMoo
Cottage Garden mixed **new**	SWal
'Crown Jewel'	ELar WCFE
'Cupid'	ELar
'Darling Sue'	CNMi
'Darwin's Blue Indulgence'PBR	EPfP LRHS
delavayi	EBee GKev
- B&SWJ 7796	WCru
densiflorum **new**	GKev
'Diamant'PBR	LRHS
'Dreaming Spires'	SRms
drepanocentrum HWJK 2263	WCru
'Dunsden Green'	CNMi
'Dusky Maidens Group	IFoB STes
dwarf, dark blue-flowered	LRHS
dwarf, lavender-flowered	LRHS
elatum	GCal IFoB NGdn SRms
- 'Double Innocence' (New Millennium Series) (d) **new**	LRHS
- 'Morning Lights' (New Millennium Series) **new**	LRHS
'Elisabeth Sahin' ♀H4	CNMi ELar
'Elizabeth Cook' ♀H4	CNMi ELar
'Elmfreude'	LRHS WSpi
'Elmhimmel'	GKir
'Emily Hawkins' ♀H4	CNMi
exaltatum	EBee
'F.W. Smith'	EBee
'Fanfare'	CNMi ELar
'Faust' ♀H4	CNMi ELar
'Fenella' ♀H4	CNMi ELar WCFE
'Finsteraarhorn'	EBee GBin LRHS NGby WSpi
'Florestan'	CNMi
forrestii **new**	GKev
cf. ***forrestii***	EBee
'Foxhill Nina'	CNMi ELar
'Franjo Sahin'	ELar

	Name	Suppliers
	Galahad Group	Widely available
	'Galileo' ♀H4	CNMi
	'Gemma'	CNMi
	'Gillian Dallas' ♀H4	ELar
	'Giotto' ♀H4	CNMi
	glaciale HWJK 2299	WCru
	'Gordon Forsyth'	CNMi
	'Gossamer'	CNMi EWTr IKil
§	***grandiflorum***	CWCL GKev
§	- 'Blauer Zwerg'	SPoG
§	- 'Blue Butterfly'	CBot CSpe EBrs EBur EPfP LRHS MBNS SCoo SPlb SPoG WPer WSHC WWEG
	- Blue Dwarf	see *D. grandiflorum* 'Blauer Zwerg'
	- 'Blue Wave' **new**	LRHS
	- 'Delfix' **new**	LRHS
	- 'Summer Blues' (Summer Series) **new**	LRHS
	'Green Twist' (New Millennium Series) **new**	STes
	(Guardian Series) 'Guardian Blue'	LRHS NPri
	- 'Guardian Lavender'	LRHS NPri
	- 'Guardian White'	CWCL LRHS NPri
	Guinevere Group	CBcs CSBt CWCL CWib EBee ECtt EPfP LBMP LRHS MBri NBPC NBir NLar NPri SBch SPad SPer SPoG WCAu WFar WWEG
	'Guy Langdon'	CNMi
	hansenii	LLHF
	'Harlekijn'	NLar
	'Heavenly Blue'	NLar
I	'Independence'	EWTr LRHS
	Ivory Towers Group	ECtt
	'Jenny Agutter'	CNMi
	'Jill Curley' ♀H4	CNMi ELar
	'Kathleen Cooke'	CNMi
	'Kennington Calypso'	CNMi
	'Kestrel' ♀H4	CNMi ELar
	King Arthur Group	CBcs CSBt EBee ECtt ELan EPfP LBMP LHop LRHS LSRN MRav MWat NBPC NLar NPri SBch SMrm SPer SPoG WCAu WFar WWEG
§	'Kings Blue Arrow' PBR **new**	LRHS
	'Lady Guinevere'	EBee
§	'Langdon's Royal Flush' ♀H4	CNMi ELar
	'Lanzenträger'	LRHS WSpi
	'Leonora'	CNMi ELar
	'Lily Radley'	ELar
	'Loch Leven' ♀H4	CNMi GBin
	'Lord Butler' ♀H4	CNMi ELar LRHS
	'Lucia Sahin' ♀H4	CNMi ELar LRHS
	maackianum	EWld GAuc GCal
	Magic Fountains Series	CSam GMaP IFoB LRHS MRav SPlb SPoG SRot WFar WGor WRHF
	- 'Magic Fountains Cherry Blossom'	SBch SPoG WFar
	- 'Magic Fountains Dark Blue'	EPfP GMaP LSRN NEgg NLar SBch SMrm SPoG STes WFar
	- 'Magic Fountains Deep Blue'	NLar SBch
	- 'Magic Fountains Lavender'	EPfP SBch
	- 'Magic Fountains Lilac Pink'	SBch SPoG
	- 'Magic Fountains Lilac Rose'	NLar NVic WFar
	- 'Magic Fountains Pure White'	EPfP NEgg NLar SBch WFar
	- 'Magic Fountains Sky Blue'	EPfP NVic SBch SPoG STes WFar
	'Margaret' **new**	ELar
	'Merlin' ambig.	LRHS LSRN WSpi
	'Michael Ayres' ♀H4	CNMi ELar
	micropetalum CNDS 031	WCru
	'Mighty Atom'	CNMi
	'Min' ♀H4	CNMi ELar
	'Misty Mauves' (New Millennium Series) (d) **new**	EWTr
	'Moonbeam'	ELar
	'Mrs Newton Lees'	IKil LRHS
	'Ned Wit'	IKil
	nelsonii	LFur
	New Century hybrids	CBcs
	'New Millennium Pagan Purple' **new**	LRHS
	'Nicolas Woodfield'	CNMi
	'Nobility'	ELar
	nudicaule	CBot ECho SPoG
	- 'Laurin'	ECho LRHS WFar
	'Olive Poppleton' ♀H4	CNMi SAga
	'Oliver' ♀H4	CNMi ELar
	'Our Deb' ♀H4	ELar
	Pacific hybrids	EPfP LHop LRHS LSRN MHer MLHP NBlu NLar SBch SPet SRms SWal SWvt WFar
	'Pagan Purples' (d)	ELar IFoB LRHS
	'Pandora'	CNMi ELar
	'Patricia Johnson'	ELar
	Percival Group	LRHS NLar
	Pink River = 'Barfourtythree' PBR	CBcs
	'Pink Ruffles'	CNMi ELar
	Princess Caroline = 'Odabar' PBR	CBcs
	'Purple Passion' (New Millennium Series) **new**	LRHS STes
	'Purple Ruffles'	EPfP
	'Purple Velvet' ♀H4	CNMi ELar
	'Red Caroline'	CBcs LRHS
	requienii	CBgR CBot CSpe EWld LFur NSti SBHP SBch WCot
	'Rona'	CNMi
	'Rosemary Brock' ♀H4	ELar
	Round Table Mixture	CTri
	'Royal Aspirations' (New Millennium Series)	ELar STes
	'Royal Flush'	see *D.* 'Langdon's Royal Flush'
§	× ***ruysii*** 'Pink Sensation'	CBot NCGa NLar NPro WPGP WSpi
	'Sandpiper' ♀H4	CNMi
	'Sarita'	SUsu
	'Secret' PBR	LRHS
§	***semibarbatum***	CBot
	'Sentinel'	CNMi
	siamense B&SWJ 7278	WCru
	'Silver Jubilee'	CNMi ELar
	'Sky Sensation'	NLar
	'Snow Queen Arrow'	LRHS
	'Snowdon'	CNMi
§	***speciosum***	EBee
	'Spindrift' ♀H4	CNMi ELar
	stapeliosmum B&SWJ 2954	WCru
	staphisagria	CArn ECGP EOHP MCot SSth
	'Starmaker'	EPfP
	'Strawberry Fair'	CNMi WSpi
	Summer Skies Group	CBcs CSBt CTri EBee ECtt ELan EPfP LBMP LHop LRHS MBri MWat NBir NLar NPri SBch SPer SPoG WBor WBrE WCAu WFar WHoo WWEG
	'Summer Wine'	ELar

'Summerfield Miranda' ♀H4	CNMi
'Summerfield Oberon'	CNMi ELar WCot
'Sungleam' ♀H4	ELar IKil NLar
'Sunkissed' ♀H4	CNMi ELar
'Sunny Skies' (New Millennium Series)	ELar
'Susan Edmunds'PBR (d) ♀H4	LRHS
sutchuenense	NCGa WWlt
- BWJ 7867	WCru
tatsienense	SRms WCru
tenii BWJ 7693	WCru
- BWJ 7906	WCru
'Tiddles' ♀H4	ELar
'Tiger Eye'	CNMi ELar
'Tiny Tim'	CNMi
tricorne	CLAP
'Turkish Delight'	ELar
'Vanessa Mae'	CNMi
'Vespers'	ELar
vestitum	ECtt EWld SBch
viscosum HWJK 2268	WCru
'Walton Beauty'	CNMi
'Walton Benjamin'	CNMi
'Walton Gemstone' ♀H4	CNMi ELar
White River	CBcs LRHS
'White Ruffles'	ELar
'White Swan' **new**	EPfP
Woodfield strain	WHrl
yunnanense	EBee
'Yvonne'	LRHS LSRN NLar
zalil	see *D. semibarbatum*

Dendranthema see *Chrysanthemum*

pacificum	see *Ajania pacifica*

Dendriopoterium see *Sanguisorba*

Dendrobenthamia see *Cornus*

Dendrocalamus (*Poaceae*)

asper	XBlo
calostachys	SPlb
giganteus	XBlo
§ ***strictus***	XBlo

Dendromecon (*Papaveraceae*)

rigida	CBcs EPfP LRHS MBri NLar SAga WCot WPGP WSHC

Dendropanax (*Araliaceae*)

trifidus B&SWJ 11230	WCru

Dennstaedtia (*Dennstaedtiaceae*)

punctilobula	CLAP EBee WCot WRic

Dentaria see *Cardamine*

pinnata	see *Cardamine heptaphylla*
polyphylla	see *Cardamine kitaibelii*

Dermatobotrys (*Scrophulariaceae*)

saundersii	ECre

Derwentia see *Parahebe*

Deschampsia (*Poaceae*)

cespitosa	CHrt CKno COIW CRWN CSam CWib EBWF EPPr EPfP GFor LRHS MBar MWat SMrm SPlb WCFE WCot WDin WGwG WMnd WMoo WPnP WTin WWEG
- subsp. ***alpina***	LEdu
- Bronze Veil	see *D. cespitosa* 'Bronzeschleier'
§ - 'Bronzeschleier'	CKno CMea CSam CWCL EAEE EBee EBrs EHoe ELan EPPr EPfP EPla GCal GKir GMaP LEdu LRHS MAvo MBrN NGdn NOak NWsh SApp SPer SPhx SSvw WMoo WPtf WTin WWEG
- brown	SApp
- 'Fairy's Joke'	see *D. cespitosa* var. *vivipara*
- 'Fose'	SApp
- Gold Dust	see *D. cespitosa* 'Goldstaub'
- Golden Dew	see *D. cespitosa* 'Goldtau'
- Golden Pendant	see *D. cespitosa* 'Goldgehänge'
- Golden Shower	see *D. cespitosa* 'Goldgehänge'
- Golden Veil	see *D. cespitosa* 'Goldschleier'
§ - 'Goldgehänge'	CSam EHoe EHul EPfP EPla MMHG NBir NLar NPro SLPl WWEG
- 'Goldschatt'	EBee
§ - 'Goldschleier'	CPrp CSam EBee EBrs ECha EPPr EPla GCal GGar GKir GMaP GQue LEdu LRHS NGdn NWsh SApp SPhx WMoo WPGP
§ - 'Goldstaub'	EPPr
§ - 'Goldtau'	Widely available
- 'Morning Dew'	WFar
- 'Northern Lights' (v)	CWCL EAlp EBee ELan EPfP GGar GKir LEdu LHop LRHS MAvo MBri MWhi SApp SBch SLim SPer SPoG SRms SWvt WCot WPGP WWEG
- 'Schottland'	EBee GBin
- 'Tardiflora'	EBee
§ - var. ***vivipara***	EBee EHoe EPPr EPla NBro NHol NLar SGSe
- 'Waldschatt'	EBee
- 'Willow Green'	GCal MRav SCoo
flexuosa	COIW EHoe GFor NBir NWsh SMrm
- 'Tatra Gold'	Widely available
media	EHoe

Desfontainia (*Loganiaceae*)

§ ***spinosa*** ♀H3	Widely available
- 'Harold Comber'	CMac MDun WCru
- f. ***hookeri***	see *D. spinosa*

Desmodium (*Papilionaceae*)

callianthum	CMac EBee EPfP WSHC
canadense	EBee NLar SBHP
§ ***elegans*** ♀H4	CBcs CHEx EBee ELan EPfP MBri NLar WHer WPGP WSHC
praestans	see *D. yunnanense*
tiliifolium	see *D. elegans*
§ ***yunnanense***	CHEx EPfP WSHC

Deuterocohnia (*Bromeliaceae*)

brevifolia ♀H1	WCot

Deutzia ✿ (*Hydrangeaceae*)

CC 4548	CPLG
CC 4550	CPLG
calycosa	GQui WPat
- BWJ 8007	WCru
- 'Dali'	CDoC CPLG SDys WPGP
chunii	see *D. ningpoensis*
compacta	SLon WFar WPGP
- GWJ 9202	WCru
- 'Lavender Time'	CDoC CMac CPLG EBee EWTr LRHS WCFE
cordatula B&SWJ 6917	WCru
coreana BWJ 8588	WCru
corymbosa	CDoC
crenata B&SWJ 8896	WCru
- 'Flore Pleno'	see *D. scabra* 'Plena'

	Name	Suppliers
	- var. ***heterotricha*** B&SWJ 5805	WCru
	- 'Nakaiana'	MAsh SIng WPat
	- - B&SWJ 8879	WCru
	- var. ***nakaiana*** 'Nikko'	see *D. gracilis* 'Nikko'
§	- 'Pride of Rochester' (d)	CBcs CMCN CWib EBee ECrN GKir LSou MBar MGos MMuc MRav NLar SLim SPad SPoG SWvt WDin WGrn WHar
	'Dark Eyes'	GGGa
	discolor 'Major'	CPLG
	× ***elegantissima***	SRms
	- 'Fasciculata'	EPfP LRHS SPer WGrn
	- 'Rosealind' ♀H4	CBcs CMac CPLG CTri EBee ECrN EPfP EWTr LHop LRHS MBri MGos MRav NCGa SPer SPoG SRms SSpi SWvt WCFE WCom WKif WSHC WSpi
	glabrata B&SWJ 617	GQui WCru
	glomeruliflora BWJ 7742	WCru
	gracilis	CDoC CHar CSBt EBee ELan EPfP EWTr GGal GQui MBar MGos MRav MSwo SPad SPer SPoG WDin WFar WSpi
	- B&SWJ 8927	WCru
	- 'Aurea'	CBcs EPfP
	- 'Carminea'	see *D.* × *rosea* 'Carminea'
§	- 'Marmorata' (v)	CBow CPMA EBee NLar SLon WCom WCot WHCG
§	- 'Nikko'	CAbP CBcs CMCN CMac CPBP CPLG CTri EBee ECho EWes LRHS MBar MGos MHer MMuc MWhi NBlu NHol NLar NPro SPlb WDin WHCG WKif WSHC
	- var. ***ogatae*** B&SWJ 8911	WCru
	- 'Rosea'	see *D.* × *rosea*
	- 'Variegata'	see *D. gracilis* 'Marmorata'
	hookeriana	WFar
	- KW 6393	WPGP
	× ***hybrida*** 'Contraste'	CMac SPer
	- 'Joconde'	CPLG GKir WFar WKif
	- 'Magicien'	CDoC CDul CMHG CMac CPLG CSBt CSam CWib EBee ECrN ELan EPfP GQui LHop LRHS MAsh MBri MRav MSwo NBir SLon SMrm SPer SWvt WCom WFar WHCG WHar WPat
	- 'Mont Rose' ♀H4	Widely available
§	- 'Strawberry Fields' ♀H4	CBcs CGHE CMCN CPLG CTri EBee ELan EPla EWTr GKir LAst LBMP LBuc LRHS LSRN LSou MAsh MBar MBlu MBri MGos NEgg SBod SLon SPad SPoG WBVN WFar WKif WPGP
	'Iris Alford'	CGHE LRHS SLon
	× ***kalmiiflora***	CMac CPLG CPMA CSBt CTri EBee GQui LRHS MAsh MBar MBri SLPl SPer SPoG SRms
	× ***lemoinei***	CBot
	longifolia 'Veitchii' ♀H4	CSBt ERas GQui MRav WCFE
	- 'Vilmoriniae'	CDul MRav
	× ***magnifica***	CBcs CDul EBee ELan EPfP GQui MBri SRms WDin WHCG WHar WSpi
	- 'Rubra'	see *D.* × *hybrida* 'Strawberry Fields'
	monbeigii	CDoC CPLG GKir WKif
	- BWJ 7728	WCru
	multiradiata new	WPGP
§	***ningpoensis*** ♀H4	CAbP CPLG EBee GBin GQui SLPl SMrm SPer WPGP
	parviflora var. ***barbinervis*** B&SWJ 8478	WCru
	'Pink Pompon'	see *D.* 'Rosea Plena'
	pulchra	CAbP CDoC CHar CMCN CPom EBee EPfP IDee LRHS MBri MRav NPro SLon SMrm SPer SSpi WFar WHCG WPGP WSpi
	- B&SWJ 3870	WCru
	- B&SWJ 6908	WCru
	purpurascens BWJ 7859	WCru
§	× ***rosea***	CDul CWib EBee ECrN EPfP LAst LRHS MBar SPoG SRms WFar WKif
	- 'Campanulata'	CPLG EPfP MSwo
§	- 'Carminea'	SPlb SRms WCom WDin WFar WMoo WPat
	- 'Multiflora' new	LRHS
§	'Rosea Plena' (d)	CDoC CMac CPLG CSBt CWib EBee ECrN EPfP LRHS MAsh MGos MMuc NBlu NEgg NLar SLim SPoG WCom WFar WPat WRHF
	scabra	CDul CTri IFFs
	- B&SWJ 8924	WCru
§	- 'Candidissima' (d)	CMac ECrN GQui MRav NLar SPer
	- 'Codsall Pink'	MRav
§	- 'Plena' (d)	CPLG EBee ECrN ECtt ELan EPfP GKir LRHS SPer WCFE
	- 'Pride of Rochester'	see *D. crenata* 'Pride of Rochester'
	- 'Punctata' (v)	EBee EHoe MMuc SRms WFar
	- 'Robert Fortune' new	SPlb
	- 'Variegata' (v)	CDul CMac
	setchuenensis	CMac EPfP GQui SSpi WHCG WPat WSHC
	- var. ***corymbiflora*** ♀H4	CBcs CBot CDoC CDul CGHE CPLG CSam CTri EBee EPfP ERas GKir IDee LHop LRHS MBri MSwo SPoG WCom WFar WKif WPGP
	taiwanensis	EBee NLar
	- B&SWJ 6858	WCru
	'Tourbillon Rouge'	CDoC EBee EQua LRHS SBch WDin WSpi
*	***vidalii***	GGal
	× ***wellsii***	see *D. scabra* 'Candidissima'
	× ***wilsonii***	SRms

Dianella ✿ (*Phormiaceae*)

	Name	Suppliers
	brevicaulis	ECou
	caerulea	CMac ECha ECou ELan GBuc IFoB IGor IMou NBir
	- Breeze = 'Dcnco'	ECou ELan EPPr IFFs NOak
	- Cassa Blue = 'Dbb03'	CBgR EBee ELan EWes GEdr GGar IFFs LAst LHop LRHS MMHG NBhm NOak SHar SPoG
	- 'Kulnura'	ECou
	- Little Jess = 'Dcmp01'	CBgR CPrp EBee EPPr EPla GEdr GGar IFFs LRHS MMHG NOak SPoG
	- var. ***petasmatodes***	EPPr WCot
	- 'Variegata'	see *D. tasmanica* 'Variegata'
	intermedia	CTrC EBee EWld IBlr
	- 'Variegata' (v)	IBlr
	nigra	CBcs CPou CTrC EBee ECou IFro IMou LEdu NCGa WFar
	- 'Margaret Pringle' (v)	CTrC NOak
	- 'Taupo'	ECou
	prunina Utopia = 'DP303' new	CBow
	revoluta	CFir ECou
	- 'Baby Bliss'	ECou NOak
	- 'Hartz Mountain'	ECou
	- Little Rev = 'Dr5000'PBR	EBee ECou ELan EPPr EPfP GEdr GGar IFFs LHop MMHG MMuc NOak SMrm
	tasmanica	Widely available

	- 'Emerald Arch'	ELan NOak
	- 'Prosser'	ECou
	- Tasred = 'Tr20'PBR	EBee ELan EPPr EPfP GBin GEdr IFFs LHop LRHS MCot MMHG NOak SHar WAul
§	- 'Variegata' (v)	CBct CBod CDTJ CFir CSpe CStu EBee ECou ELan GBuc LHop SGSe

Dianthus ✿ (*Caryophyllaceae*)

	AC&W 2116	LBee GEdr
	SDR 5460	GKev
	'Acton's Propellor' **new**	WEas
	'Admiral Crompton' (pf)	CNMi
	'Alan Titchmarsh' (p)	EBee ECGP ECtt EPfP EWll LRHS LSRN MMHG NCGa NEgg NPri SPoG SWvt
	'Aldridge Yellow' (b)	SAll
	'Alegro'	SAll
	'Alfriston' (b) ♀H4	SAll
	'Alice' (p)	LSRN SAll
	'Alice Lever' (p)	WAbe
	'Allspice' (p)	MRav SBch SSvw WEas WHoo
	Allwoodii Alpinus Group (p)	SRms WFar
	'Allwood's Crimson' (pf)	SAll
	alpinus ♀H4	ECho GJos GKev LRHS NMen SRms WFar WPer
	- 'Albus'	ECho LRHS NHol WAbe
	- 'Joan's Blood' ♀H4	CPBP GBuc LSRN NHol SMad WAbe WCom WFar WHoo WRHF
	'Alyson' (p)	SAll
	Amazon Series **new**	LRHS
	amurensis	ECho EDAr EPPr LFur SSvw WGwG WPer
	anatolicus	CTri ECho LRHS MHer NDlv NGdn NWCA SSvw WCom WPer
	'Andrew Morton' (b)	SAll
	'Angelo' (b)	SAll
	'Annabelle' (p)	ECho
	'Anne Jones' (b)	EPfP
	'Annette' (pf)	EBee ECho ECtt GKev LRHS LSRN MWat SWvt WClo
	'Annie Claybourne' (pf)	CNMi
	'Apricot Sue' (pf)	CNMi
	'Arctic Star' (p)	CMea CTri EBee ECho GMaP LRHS NEgg NLar SPet SPoG SRot SSvw SWvt WFar
	arenarius	EWTr GKev SPlb SSvw WPer
	'Argus'	IGor SSvw
	armeria	WHer WOut WTou
	'Arthur Leslie' (b)	SAll
§	× ***arvernensis*** (p) ♀H4	EAlp ECha ECho EPot
	- 'Albus'	ECho
	'Aurora' (b)	SAll
	'Auvergne'	see *D.* × *arvernensis*
	'Averiensis'	see *D.* 'Berlin Snow'
	'Baby Treasure' (p)	ECho SRot
	'Badenia' (p)	ECha LRHS
	'Bailey's Anniversary' (p)	SEND
	'Bailey's Celebration' (p)	CBgR EPfP SRGP
§	'Bailey's Daily Mail' (p) ♀H4	CBcs EBee SPoG
	'Barbara Norton' (p)	ECtt WSHC
	barbatus	GAuc SECG
	- 'Black Adder'	CSpe
	- Nigrescens Group (p,a) ♀H4	CBre CHrt CMea CSpe SAga SPhx
I	- 'Sooty' (p,a)	EBee ELan NDlv NGdn NHol SMad WCFE WFar
	- 'Super Parfait Strawberry' (Super Parfait Series) ♀H3 **new**	LRHS
	- 'Tuxedo Black'	MWea
§	'Bat's Double Red' (p/d)	IGor SAll SSvw
	'Becky Robinson' (p) ♀H4	SAll
	'Bedfordshire Belle' (b)	SAll
	'Bella' (p)	CPBP
§	'Berlin Snow' (p)	CPBP ECho ELan EPot EWes LRHS SAll
	'Betty Miller' (b)	SAll
	'Betty Morton' (p) ♀H4	ECtt IFoB MWea SSvw WFar WKif
	'Binsey Red' (p)	SSvw
	'Blue Hills' (p)	ECho GKev MWea
	'Blue Ice' (b)	SAll
	'Blush'	see *D.* 'Souvenir de la Malmaison'
	'Bobby' (p)	SAll
	'Bob's Highlight' (pf)	CNMi
	'Bombardier' (p)	ECtt
	'Bookham Gleam' (b) **new**	SAll
	'Bookham Grand' (b)	SAll
	'Bookham Heroine' (b)	SAll
	'Bookham Lad' (b)	SAll
	'Border Special' (b)	SAll
	'Bouquet Purple' (p)	CSpe
	'Bovey Belle' (p) ♀H4	CBcs
	'Bressingham Pink' (p)	ECtt
	'Brian Tumbler' (b) ♀H4	SAll
	'Bridal Veil' (p)	SAll SBch SSvw WHer
	'Brigadier' (p)	ECho
	'Brilliance' (p)	ECho WMoo
	'Brilliant'	see *D. deltoides* 'Brilliant'
	'Brilliant Star' (p) ♀H4	CBgR ECho LBee LRHS SPet SWvt WWFP
	'Brympton Red' (p)	ECha MRav SAll SSvw WCom WEas
	'Bryony Lisa' (b) ♀H4	SAll
	caesius	see *D. gratianopolitanus*
	callizonus	EPot NMen
	'Calypso' (pf)	CTri
	'Calypso Star' (p) ♀H4	CPBP EBee ECho ECtt GBuc GMaP SPet SPoG STes
	'Camilla' (b)	SSvw WCom
	'Can-can' (pf)	ECho ECtt
	'Candy Clove' (b)	SAll
	Candy Floss = 'Devon Flavia'PBR (p)	CBgR ECtt GKir LBMP LRHS MAvo MWat NEgg SBch SPoG
	'Candy Spice'PBR (p)	MRav
	'Carmine Letitia Wyatt'PBR (p) ♀H4	EBee SPoG
	carthusianorum	CArn CKno EWTr IGor LDai LPla MAvo MCot MNFA NDlv SAga SAll SGSe SGar SMeo SPhx SPlb SSvw STes SWat WCom WOut WPGP WPer
	- SDR 5414	GKev
I	- 'Rupert's Pink' **new**	EDAr MAvo
	caryophyllus	CArn GBar MNHC
	'Casser's Pink' (p)	GBuc WCom
	'Charles' (p)	SAll
	'Charles Edward' (p)	SAll
	'Charles Musgrave'	see *D.* 'Musgrave's Pink'
	'Chastity' (p)	WHoo
	Cheddar pink	see *D. gratianopolitanus*
	'Cheerio' (pf) ♀H2	SAll
	'Cherly'	LSRN
	'Cherry Clove' (b)	SAll
	'Cherry Pie' (p)	EAEE EBee ECtt EPfP LRHS SPoG WMnd
	'Cheryl'	see *D.* 'Houndspool Cheryl'
	'Chianti' (pf)	NGdn
	'Chianti Double' (p) **new**	SAll
	chinensis (p,a)	CArn
	- 'Black and White'	CSpe
	'Chris Crew' (b) ♀H4	SAll
	'Christopher' (p)	SAll

	Name	Suppliers
	'Clara' (pf)	CNMi
	'Clara's Lass' (pf)	CNMi
	'Clare' (p)	SAll
	'Claret Joy' (p) ♀[H4]	CBcs CFir EPfP MMuc NEgg SAll SEND
§	'Cockenzie Pink' (p)	IGor SAll SSvw WEas
	'Coconut Sundae' (p)	CBgR ECtt EWll LBMP MWat SBch WBor
	'Constance' (p)	SAll
	'Constance Finnis'	see *D.* 'Fair Folly'
	'Consul' (b)	SAll
	'Conwy Silver'	NMen WAbe
	'Conwy Star'	CPBP NMen WAbe
	'Copperhead' (b)	SAll
	'Coral Reef' (p) **new**	LRHS
	'Corona Cherry Magic' ♀[H3]	LRHS
	'Coronation Ruby' (p) ♀[H4]	CBcs SAll
	'Coste Budde' (p)	IGor WEas WSHC
	'Cranmere Pool' (p) ♀[H4]	CMea EBee ECtt ELan EPfP MWat NPri SBch SPoG SWvt WFar WMnd
	cretaceus	NWCA
	'Crimson Chance' (p)	EPot NSla
	'Crimson Tempo'[PBR] (pf)	SAll
	'Crock of Gold' (b) **new**	SAll
	'Crompton Classic' (pf)	CNMi
	cruentus	SPhx SSvw WPer WWEG
	'D.D.R.'	see *D.* 'Berlin Snow'
	'Dad's Favourite' (p)	CEnt IGor SAll SRms SSvw WEas
	'Daily Mail'	see *D.* 'Bailey's Daily Mail'
	'Dainty Dame' (p) ♀[H4]	CPBP CSpe CTri ECho GBuc LRHS MNHC MWea SPoG SRot WFar
	'Damask Superb' (p)	IGor
	'Daphne' (p)	SAll
	'Dark Star' (p)	ECho
	'Dartington Double' (p)	ECho
	'David' (p)	LSRN SAll
	'David Russell' (b) ♀[H4]	SAll
	'David Saunders' (b) ♀[H4]	SAll
	'Dawlish Joy' (p)	EBee SPoG SRGP
	'Dawn' (b)	SAll
	'Dawn' (pf)	ECho
	'Dedham Beauty'	WCot
	deltoides ♀[H4]	CArn CEnt CSev EBWF ECha ECho EPfP GBar NSco SECG SHGN SPlb SRms WFar WJek
	- 'Albus'	ECha EPfP GBar LRHS MNHC NBlu NGdn NPri SSvw SWat WMoo
	- 'Arctic Fire'	CWib ECho EPfP LBMP LRHS NBlu NGdn WFar WMoo
	- 'Bright Eyes'	ECho
§	- 'Brilliant'	CTri ECho EPau GJos MDun MNHC NPri NVic SAll SRms SWat WCom WFar WGor WWEG
	- 'Canta Libra'	SWal
	- 'Dark Eyes' (p)	EWes
	- 'Erectus'	EPfP
	- Flashing Light	see *D. deltoides* 'Leuchtfunk'
§	- 'Leuchtfunk'	CHrt EAlp ECho ECtt EPfP GGar IBal LAst LBMP LRHS MWat NChi NGdn NNor SPoG SWal WFar WMoo WWEG
I	- 'Luneburg Heath Maiden Pink'	SSvw
	- 'Microchip'	WClo WFar WMoo
	- 'Nelli' (p)	ECho MBNS SSvw
	- red-flowered	NBlu SVic
	- 'Shrimp'	NGdn
	'Denis' (p)	LSRN SAll
	'Desert Song' (b)	SAll
	'Devon Cream'[PBR] (p)	EAEE EBee ECtt LRHS NEgg NPri SPoG WMnd
	'Devon Dove'[PBR] (p) ♀[H4]	CBgR CMea CSBt EAEE EBee ECtt EPfP MRav NCGa NEgg SBch SPoG WWFP
§	'Devon Flores' (p)	LRHS
	'Devon General'[PBR] (p)	CTri EBee ECtt SBch SPoG
	'Devon Glow' (p) ♀[H4]	EBee EPfP SPoG
	'Devon Magic'[PBR] (p)	EBee ECtt ELan MWat SPoG WFar
	'Devon Pearl'[PBR] (p)	EBee WMnd
	'Devon Wizard'[PBR] (p) ♀[H4]	CBgR CMea CSBt EAEE EBee ECtt EPfP LRHS MRav MWat NCGa NEgg SBch SPoG WFar
	'Devon Yvette'[PBR]	LRHS
	'Dewdrop' (p)	CMea CTri EBee ECho ECtt EPfP EPot LRHS MHer MMuc NBir NGdn NPro SAll SEND WAbe WFar WPer
	'Diana'	see *D.* Dona
	'Diane' (p) ♀[H4]	EBee ECtt ELan EPfP GKir LRHS NEgg SAll SPoG SWvt WMnd
*	'Diane Cape'	SAll
	'Diplomat' (b)	SAll
§	Dona = 'Brecas' (pf)	EAEE LSRN SRGP
	'Dora' (p)	LAst LRHS
	'Doris' (p) ♀[H4]	CBcs CMea CTri CWan EBee ECtt EPfP GKir LAst LBMP LHop LRHS LSRN MRav MWat NEgg NPri SAll SBch SPer SPlb SPoG SRGP SRms SSvw SWvt WCAu WKif WMnd WWEG
	'Doris Allwood' (pf)	CNMi CSBt EMal SAll
	'Doris Elite' (p)	SAll
	'Doris Galbally' (b)	SAll
	'Doris Majestic' (p)	SAll WFar
	'Doris Ruby'	see *D.* 'Houndspool Ruby'
	'Doris Supreme' (p)	SAll
	'Double North'	ELon NWCA
	'Dubarry' (p)	CTri CWan ECho ECtt WGor WPer
	'Duchess of Fife' (p)	ECtt
	'Duchess of Westminster' (M)	EMal SAll
	'Duke of Norfolk' (pf)	EMal
	'Earl of Essex' (p)	SAll SSvw
	'Edenside Scarlet' (b)	SAll
	'Edenside White' (b)	SAll
	'Edna' (p)	SAll
	'Edward Allwood' (pf)	SAll
	'Eileen' (p)	SAll
	'Eileen Lever' (p)	CPBP EPot WAbe WFar
	'Eleanor Parker' (p)	WAbe
	'Eleanor's Old Irish' (p)	MWhi WCot WHoo WTin
	'Elfin Star' (p)	ECho SPet
	'Elizabeth' (p)	CEnt WEas
	'Elizabethan' (p)	CDes CFee GMac
*	'Elizabethan Pink' (p)	SAll
	'Emile Paré' (p)	WCom
	'Emma James' (b)	SAll
	'Emperor'	see *D.* 'Bat's Double Red'
	erectaceaus **new**	GAuc
	erinaceus	ECho EPot NWCA SRot WAbe WPat
	- var. ***alpinus***	EPot
	'Erycina' (b)	SAll
	'Ethel Hurford' (p)	WHoo
	'Eva Humphries' (b)	SAll
	'Evening Star' (p) ♀[H4]	CBgR CTri EAlp EBee ECho LBee LRHS MAsh NEgg SPet SPoG SWvt
	'Excelsior' (p)	SSvw
	'Exquisite' (b)	SAll
§	'Fair Folly' (p)	SAll SSvw
	'Fanal' (p)	NBir
	'Farida'[PBR] (pf)	SAll
	'Farnham Rose' (p)	SAll SSvw
	'Fenbow Nutmeg Clove' (b)	MBrN SDix WMnd

'Fettes Mount' (p) SSvw WCom WCot
'Feuerhexe' (p) EPot
'Fimbriatus' (p) WHoo
'Fiona' (p) SAll
'Fireglow' (b) SAll
'Firestar' (p) CTri EAlp GAbr LBee LRHS MWat SPet SWvt
'First Lady' (b) ECho SAll
Fizzy (Early Bird Series) new SBch
'Flanders' (b) ♀H4 SAll
'Fleur' (p) SAll
'Forest Princess' (b) SAll
'Forest Sprite' (b) SAll
'Forest Treasure' (b) SAll
'Forest Violet' (b) SAll
'Fortuna' (p) SAll
'Fountain's Abbey' (p) IGor
'Fragrant Ann' (pf) ♀H1 CNMi
'Frances Isabel' (p) SAll
'Freda' (p) SAll
freynii ECho EPot EWes WAbe
* - var. ***nana*** GKev
N fringed pink see *D. superbus*
'Fusilier' (p) CElw CMea CTri EAlp EBee ECho EDAr EPfP GMaP LHop LRHS MAsh MBar NWCA SAll SRot SWvt WFar
'Gail Graham' (b) SAll
'Gail Tilsley' (b) SAll
'Garland' (p) CMea CTri WGor
'Gaydena' (b) SAll
giganteus CSpe MWea WGwG WSHC
'Gingham Gown' (p) CPBP EPot NBir SAll SPoG
glacialis SSvw
'Gold Fleck' ECtt EPot LRHS SBch SIng
'Golden Cross' (b) ♀H4 SAll
'Grandma Calvert' (p) SAll
graniticus EPot
'Gran's Favourite' (p) ♀H4 CEnt CMea CSBt CTri EAEE EBee ECtt EPfP LAst LBMP LHop LRHS LSRN MAvo MMuc MWat NEgg NPri SAll SBch SEND SPlb SPoG SRGP SRms SWvt WBor WEas WFar
§ ***gratianopolitanus*** ♀H4 CArn CBod CTri EPfP EPot GJos GKev MHer MNHC MRav NBid NWCA SRms WGwG
- 'Albus' EPot MHer
- 'Compactus Eydangeri' (p) GBin
- dwarf new NWCA
- 'Emmen' (p) ELon
- 'Flore Pleno' (d) SHGN SSvw
- 'Grandiflorus' SHGN WFar
* - 'Karlik' (p) GKev
'Gravetye Gem' (b) SRms
'Green Lane' (p) CHll
'Grenadier' (p) ECho
'Grey Dove' (b) ♀H4 SAll
'Greytown' (b) GCal
'Gypsy Star' (p) EBee ECho GMaP SPet SPoG
haematocalyx EPot GKev NMen NWCA SSvw WCom WFar WPer
- 'Alpinus' see *D. haematocalyx* subsp. *pindicola*
§ - subsp. ***pindicola*** GAuc GKev LLHF NMen
'Harkell Special' (b) SAll
'Harlequin' (p) WPer
'Haytor Rock' (p) ♀H4 EBee EPfP WWEG
'Haytor White' (p) ♀H4 CWib EPfP GKir LAst MRav SAll SRms WCot WEas WWEG
'Hazel Ruth' (b) ♀H4 SAll
'Heidi' (p) SHGN
'Helen' (p) LSRN SAll
'Helena Hitchcock' (p) SAll
'Helix' (pf) SAll
'Hereford Butter Market' (p) EBee
'Hidcote' (p) CTri LRHS MWat NMen WFar
'Hidcote Red' ECho LBee MWat
'Highland Fraser' (p) SRms WEas WKif
'Hope' (p) SSvw
'Horsa' (b) SAll
'Hot Spice'PBR (p) ♀H4 SPoG
§ 'Houndspool Cheryl' (p) ♀H4 CTri EBee EPfP MWat SAll SRGP SRms WFar
§ 'Houndspool Ruby' (p) ♀H4 CBgR EPfP SAll SBch WEas
'Ian' (p) LSRN SAll
'Iceberg' (p) ECho
Iced Gem = 'WP06 Fatima' (Scent First Series) (p) new SBch
'Icomb' (p) SRms WHoo WPer
'Imperial Clove' (b) SAll
'Ina' (p) EGoo SRms
'Inchmery' (p) SAll SHGN SSvw WEas WHoo
'India Star'PBR (p) ♀H4 CBgR CTri EAlp EBee ECho LRHS NEgg STes WPat
'Inglestone' (p) CTri NHol WPer
'Inshriach Dazzler' (p) ♀H4 CPBP EAlp ECho ECtt GAbr GGar GMaP LBee LRHS MAsh MHer NDlv NEgg NHol NRya SIng SRot WCom
'Inshriach Startler' (p) CMea
'Ipswich Pink' (p) LRHS MNHC SRms
I 'Ivonne' (pf) SAll
'Ivonne Orange' (pf) SAll
'Jacqueline Ann' (pf) ♀H1 CNMi
'James Portman' (p) CBcs CBgR EBee ELon WMnd
'Jane Austen' (p) WPer
'Janelle Welch' (pf) CNMi
'Janet Walker' (p) GMaP
japonicus f. ***albiflorus*** GKev LFur
'Jess Hewins' (pf) CNMi SAll
* 'Jewel' ECho ECtt
'Joan Schofield' (p) ECho LRHS SBch SPoG
'Joanne's Highlight' (pf) CNMi
'Joe Vernon' (pf) CNMi
'John Ball' (p) SSvw
'Joy' (p) ♀H4 EBee ECho ECtt EPfP GKir LAst LRHS SAll SPoG SSvw WWEG
'Julian' (p) SAll
'Julie Ann Davis' (b) SAll
'Kathleen Hitchcock' (b) ♀H4 SAll
'Kessock Charm' MNrw
'Kesteven Chamonix' (p) WPer
'Kesteven Kirkstead' (p) ♀H4 CSWP MNrw
kitaibelii see *D. petraeus* subsp. *petraeus*
'Kiwi Far North' SHGN
knappii EBee LDai NLar NVic SMeo SRms SSvw WMoo WPer
- 'Yellow Harmony' (p,a) GJos SGar
kusnezovii LFur
'La Bourboule' (p) ♀H4 CMea CTri ECho EDAr EPot GAbr LRHS MBar MWat NHol NMen NPri SRms WCom WFar WPat
'La Bourboule Alba' (p) CTri ECho ECtt EDAr EPot WFar WGor
'Laced Hero' (p) IGor NWCA
'Laced Joy' (p) SAll
'Laced Monarch' (p) CBcs EAEE EBee ECtt EPfP GCra GKir LAst MAvo MCot MMuc NCGa NEgg NLar SAll SEND SMrm SPlb SPoG SSvw WWEG

	Name	Suppliers
	'Laced Mrs Sinkins' (p)	SAll SHGN
	'Laced Prudence'	see *D.* 'Prudence'
	'Laced Romeo' (p)	SAll
	'Laced Treasure' (p)	SAll
	'Lady Granville' (p)	IGor SAll SBch SHGN SSvw
	Lady in Red = 'WP04 Xanthe'PBR (p)	CBgR CSBt LRHS SSvw
	'Lady Madonna' (p)	LRHS MWat SSvw
	'Lady Wharncliffe' (p)	IGor SBch
	'Lancing Monarch' (b)	SAll
	langeanus NS 255	NWCA
	'Laura' (p)	SAll
	'Lemsii' (p) ♀H4	ECho ECtt NMen WPer
	'Leslie Rennison' (b)	SAll
	'Letitia Wyatt' (p) ♀H4	CMea EBee EPfP MRav SBch SPoG SRGP
	'Leuchtkugel'	ECho LLHF NMen
	leucophaeus var. ***leucophaeus***	EPot
	'Liberty' (pf)	SAll
	'Lily Lesurf' (b)	SAll
I	'Lily the Pink' (p)	LRHS
	'Linfield Annie's Fancy' (pf)	CNMi
	'Linfield Dorothy Perry' (p) ♀H4	SAll
	'Linfield Isobel Croft' (p)	SAll
	'Linfield Julie' **new**	SAll
	'Lionheart' (p)	LRHS
	'Little Ben' (p)	SAll
	'Little Jock' (p/d)	CPBP ECho ECtt EDAr EPot GGar LRHS MBar MHer MWat SAll SIng SPlb SPoG SRms WEas WFar
	'Little Miss Muffet' (p)	CHll
	'London Brocade' (p)	SHGN SSvw
	'London Glow' (p)	SAll
	'London Lovely' (p)	SAll SHGN SSvw
	'London Poppet' (p)	NDlv SAll SSvw
	'Loveliness' (p,a)	CBre
	lumnitzeri	ECho LLHF WPer
	'Lustre' (b)	SAll
	'Madonna' (pf)	EPfP SSvw
	'Maggie' (p)	LSRN
	'Maisie Neal' (b) ♀H4	SAll
	'Mambo' (pf) ♀H4	SAll
	'Mandy' (p)	SAll
	'Marjery Breeze'	SAll
	'Marmion' (M)	EMal SAll
	'Mars' (p)	ECho ECtt NDlv
	'Matthew' (p)	WHoo
	'Maudie Hinds' (b)	SAll
	'Maybole' (b)	SAll
	'Maythorne' (p)	SRms
	'Melody' (pf) **new**	LRHS
	'Mendip Hills' (b)	SAll
	Mendlesham Minx = 'Russmin'PBR (p)	EBee ECho EDAr GBuc GGar LRHS SAll SBch SWvt
	'Merlin' ♀H4	NEgg
	'Messines Pink' (p)	SAll SSvw
	'Michael Saunders' (b) ♀H4	SAll
	microlepis	ECho ITim MAvo NGdn
	- ED 791562	NGdn
	- 'Leuchtkugel'	ECho WAbe
	- var. ***musalae***	ECho ITim LLHF NMen
	'Mike Briggs' (b)	SAll
	'Miss Sinkins' (p)	CTri SPet
	monadelphus subsp. ***pallens*** **new**	GAuc
	'Monica Wyatt' (p) ♀H4	EAEE EBee ECtt EPfP GKir LRHS NCGa NEgg SPoG WWEG
	monspessulanus	GKev NDlv SSvw WMoo WPer
	'Montrose Pink'	see *D.* 'Cockenzie Pink'
	Morning Star = 'Devon Winnie'PBR	LBee LRHS
	'Moulin Rouge' (p) ♀H4	CBgR EBee ECtt GCra MWat SHGN SPoG SSvw WWFP
	'Mr Chumleigh' **new**	CSpe
	'Mrs Clark'	see *D.* 'Nellie Clark'
	'Mrs Macbride' (p)	SAll
	'Mrs Perkins' (b)	SAll
	'Mrs Roxburgh' (p)	CSam
	'Mrs Sinkins' (p)	Widely available
	'Murray Douglas' (p)	SSvw
N	'Musgrave's Pink' (p)	ECha MRav SAll SBch SSvw WEas
	'Musgrave's White'	see *D.* 'Musgrave's Pink'
	myrtinervius	ECho GKev MAvo NLar SHGN SRms WHoo
	'Mystic Star'	CMea EAlp ELan SBch SSvw
	'Napoleon III' (p)	SAll SSvw WCom
	nardiformis	SPhx SSvw WPer
	'Nautilus' (b)	SAll
	neglectus	see ***D. pavonius***
§	'Nellie Clark' (p)	ECho MWat
	'Nelson'PBR	SAll
	'Neon Star'PBR (p) ♀H4	CTri EBee ECho EDAr ELan GKev LRHS MAsh NPri SPoG WFar
	'Night Star' (p) ♀H4	CBgR EAlp EBee ECho ELan EPfP GKev GMaP LAst LSou MAsh MNrw NEgg SPet SRot SSvw WFar
	nitidus	NBir NWCA SSvw WPer
	nivalis	EPot
	noeanus	see ***D. petraeus*** subsp. ***noeanus***
	'Northland' (pf)	CNMi EMal SAll
	'Nyewoods Cream' (p)	CMea CTri ECho LRHS MBar MHer NMen NPri SIng WPer
§	'Oakington' (p)	CTri LRHS MRav NPri NWCA
	'Oakington Rose'	see *D.* 'Oakington'
	'Odessa' (pf) **new**	LRHS
	'Old Blush'	see *D.* 'Souvenir de la Malmaison'
	'Old Dutch Pink' (p)	IGor SSvw
	'Old Irish' (p)	IGor
	'Old Mother Hubbard' (p)	CFee CHll
	'Old Red Clove' (p)	WCot WEas
§	'Old Square Eyes' (p)	MNrw SAll SSvw WCom WEas WFar
	'Old Velvet' (p)	GCal MNrw SAll
	'Oliver' (p)	SAll
	'Orange Maid' (b)	SAll
	'Oscar' (b)	SAll
	'Painted Lady' (p)	IGor SAll
	'Paisley Gem' (p)	SAll SSvw
	Passion = 'WP07 Walberg' (Scent First Series) **new**	SBch
§	***pavonius*** ♀H4	EWTr EWes MAvo NGdn NLar NWCA WPer
	- 'Nancy Lindsay' (p)	SSvw
	'Pax' (pf)	SAll
	'Peach' (p)	SEND
§	***petraeus***	EWes MAvo
§	- subsp. ***noeanus***	EPot GKev LLHF WHal WPer
§	- subsp. ***petraeus***	WPer
	'Petticoat Lace' (p)	SAll
	'Pheasant's Eye' (p)	SAll SSvw WHer
*	'Picton's Propeller' (p)	GBuc
	'Pike's Pink' (p/d) ♀H4	CSpe CTri EBee ECho ECtt EDAr ELan EPfP GGar LHop LRHS MHer MMuc MRav MWat NMen SAll SEND SIng SPet SPoG SRms SSvw WClo WCom WEas
	pindicola	see ***D. haematocalyx*** subsp. ***pindicola***
	'Pink Devon Pearl'PBR	CBgR SAll
	'Pink Fantasy' (b)	SAll
	'Pink Jewel' (p)	CMea CPBP EAlp ECho ECtt EPot LRHS NMen SAll SIng WEas

	Name	Suppliers
	'Pink Mrs Sinkins' (p)	ECha MHer MLHP SAll
	'Pixie' (b)	EPot
	'Pixie Star'[PBR] (p) ♀H4	ECho EPfP SPoG SRot
	plumarius	CArn SAll SECG SRms SSvw WHer WMoo
	- 'Ipswich Pinks' **new**	GJos
	- 'Sonata' **new**	GJos
	pontederae	WPer
	'Popstar'	EWll LRHS
	'Prado' (pf) ♀H4	SAll
	'Pretty Lady' (p)	ECho
	'Prince Charming' (p)	EAlp ECho ECtt EPot NPri SIng SRms WPer
	'Princess of Wales' (M)	EMal SAll
	'Priory Pink' (p)	SAll
§	'Prudence' (p)	SAll
	'Pudsey Prize' (p)	CPBP EPot WAbe
	'Pummelchen' (p)	CPBP EPot ITim
	'Purple Jenny' (p)	SAll
	'Queen of Hearts' (p)	CTri ECho MMuc NWCA SEND WPer
§	'Queen of Henri' (p)	ECho ECtt GEdr LRHS MHer SHGN WFar
	'Queen of Sheba' (p)	SAll SHGN SSvw WKif
	'Rachel' (p)	ECtt WPat
	'Rainbow Loveliness' (p,a)	SAll SRms WHil
	'Ralph Gould' (p)	ECho
	'Raspberry Sundae' (p)	CBgR ECtt LBMP LRHS MWat SBch
	'Rebecca' (b)	SAll
	'Red Star'[PBR] (p) ♀H4	EAlp ELan GGar LRHS NPri SPet SRot
	'Red Velvet'	LRHS
	'Reine de Henri'	see *D.* 'Queen of Henri'
	'Richard Pollak' (b)	SAll
	'Rivendell' (p)	CPBP ECho NMen WAbe
	'Robert Allwood' (pf)	SAll
	'Robin Ritchie' (p)	WHoo
	'Roodkapje' (p)	SSvw
	'Rose de Mai' (p)	CSam SAll SBch SHGN SSvw WHoo
	'Rose Devon Pearl'[PBR]	EAEE EPfP LRHS
	'Rose Joy' (p) ♀H4	EBee EPfP NLar
	'Roysii' (p)	WPer
	'Rubin' (pf)	WEas
	'Ruby'	see *D.* 'Houndspool Ruby'
	'Ruby Doris'	see *D.* 'Houndspool Ruby'
	'Saint Nicholas' (p)	SSvw
	'Sam Barlow' (p)	SAll SSvw
	'Santa Claus' (b)	SAll
	scopulorum perplexans	ITim
	seguieri	SSvw WHrl
	serotinus	EPot SSvw WCot
	shinanensis	GKev
	Shooting Star	see *D.* 'Devon Flores'
	'Shot Silk' (pf)	SAll
	'Show Aristocrat' (p)	SAll
	'Show Beauty' (p)	ECtt SAll
	'Show Glory' (p)	SAll
	'Show Harlequin' (p)	SAll
	'Show Satin' (p)	ECtt SAll
	'Shrimp' (b)	CWib
*	'Six Hills'	NHol WCom WPat
	'Slap 'n' Tickle'	LRHS LSRN SBch
	'Snowflake' (p)	ECho
	'Snowshill Manor' (p)	WPer
	'Solomon' (p)	SSvw
	'Sops-in-wine' (p)	CSam ECha ECtt GBuc MSCN SAll
	'Southmead' (p)	ECho
§	'Souvenir de la Malmaison' (M)	EMal SAll
	'Spangle' (b)	SAll
	'Spencer Bickham' (p)	MNrw SHGN
	spiculifolius	EDAr EPot GAuc ITim MAvo MBNS SPhx SSvw WFar
	'Spirit' (pf)	SAll
	'Spring Beauty' (p)	NBir
	'Spring Star' (p)	ECtt MSCN SRot
	'Square Eyes'	see *D.* 'Old Square Eyes'
	squarrosus	ECho EPot NWCA
*	- ***alpinus***	ECho
	- 'Nanus'	see *D.* 'Berlin Snow'
	'Starburst'	CMea EAlp LRHS SBch
	'Stardust'	EAlp
	Starlight = 'Hilstar'	CMea LRHS
	'Starry Eyes' (p) ♀H4	CMea EAlp ELan EPfP GMaP LRHS MWat MWea NEgg NPri SRot STes SWvt WFar
	'Storm' (pf)	EMal SAll
	'Strawberries and Cream' (p)	EAEE EBee ECtt GKir LRHS NEgg NOrc SPoG WMnd
	'Strawberry Kiss'	LRHS
*	***strictus*** subsp. ***pulchellus***	CPBP
	subacaulis	EDAr EWTr NGdn NLar
	- subsp. ***brachyanthus***	NMen WAbe
	- - 'Murray Lyon'	NMen WThu
	suendermannii	see *D. petraeus*
	'Suffolk Hussar' (p) **new**	LRHS
	Sugar Plum = 'WP08 Ianthe' (Scent First Series) **new**	SBch
	'Summerfield Adam' (p)	SAll
	'Summerfield Amy Francesca' (p)	SAll
	'Summerfield Blaze' (p)	SAll
	'Summerfield Debbie' (p)	SAll
	'Summerfield Emma Louise' (p)	SAll
	'Summerfield Rebecca' (p)	SAll
	'Sunburst' (P) **new**	MAsh
	(Sunflor Series) 'Sunflor Althea'	NBlu
	- 'Sunflor Campari'	NBlu
	- 'Sunflor Odessa Purple' **new**	SGar
	- 'Sunflor Pink Campari'	NBlu
	'Sunray' (b)	SAll
	'Sunstar' (b)	SAll
§	***superbus***	EGoo LHop MBNS WHer WMoo WPer WRHF
	- 'Crimsonia'	MBrN WOut
	- var. ***longicalycinus***	MNrw
I	- 'Primadonna'	GQue WPer
	- subsp. ***speciosus***	GKev LFur
	'Susan' (p)	SAll
	'Susannah' (p)	SAll
*	'Susan's Seedling' (p)	SAll
	'Swanlake' (p)	SAll
	'Sway Lass' (p)	MMuc SEND
	'Sweet Sophie' (pf)	CNMi
	'Sweet Sue' (b)	SAll
	'Sweetheart Abbey' (p)	GBuc IGor SSvw
	'Sweetness Mix' **new**	GJos
	sylvestris	SSvw
	- dwarf	EPot
	'Tamsin Fifield' (b) ♀H4	SAll
	'Tatra Blush' (p)	GCal
	'Tatra Fragrance' (p)	CMdw GCal SAll
	'Tatra Ghost' (p)	GCal GMac SAll
	'Tayside Red' (M)	EMal SAll
	'Tempo' (pf) ♀H1	SAll
	'Thora' (M)	EMal SAll
	Tickled Pink = 'PP11'	CBgR ECtt ELan GKir LBMP LRHS LSRN MWat SBch SPoG WClo
	'Tony's Choice' (pf)	CNMi

'Treasure' (p)	ECho
'Trevor' (p)	SAll
turkestanicus	NBir WGwG WPtf
Tyrolean trailing carnations	SAll
'Uncle Teddy' (b) ♀H4	SAll
'Unique' (p)	MNrw SAll SBch SSvw
'Ursula Le Grove' (p)	IGor SSvw
'Valda Wyatt' (p) ♀H4	CBcs EAEE EBee ELan EPfP GKir LAst LRHS MWat NCGa NEgg SAll SBch SPoG SRGP SWvt WMnd
'Vic Masters'	SPhx
'Violet Clove' (b)	SAll
'W.A. Musgrave'	see *D.* 'Musgrave's Pink'
'W.H. Brooks' (b)	SAll
'Waithman Beauty' (p)	CTri ECtt MBar SAll WHoo WPer WTin
'Waithman's Jubilee' (p)	SAll SRms WSHC
'Warden Hybrid' (p)	CMea CTri ECho ECtt EPfP GMaP LAst LRHS MWea SHGN SPoG SWvt WAbe WFar
'Waterloo Sunset'	CMea CSBt
'Wedding Bells' (pf)	SAll
'Weetwood Double' (p)	CFee SBch
weyrichii	ECho EPot
'Whatfield Anona' (p)	SAll
'Whatfield Beauty' (p)	ECho ECtt ELan
'Whatfield Brilliant' (p)	ECho
'Whatfield Cancan' (p) ♀H4	CElw CMea ECho ECtt GMaP LHop LRHS MNHC MWat NEgg NPri NWCA SAll SBch SMrm SPoG SWvt WAbe WWFP
'Whatfield Cream Lace'	NWCA
'Whatfield Cyclops' (p)	ECho SAll
'Whatfield Dawn' (p)	ECho
'Whatfield Dorothy Mann' (p)	ECho SAll
'Whatfield Fuchsia Floss' (p)	SAll
'Whatfield Gem' (p)	ECho ECtt ELan GEdr LRHS MWat NPri SAll SPoG SWvt WFar WPer
'Whatfield Joy' (p)	ECho ECtt ELan EPfP GMaP LBee LRHS MHer NMen SAll SPoG WFar WHoo WPat
'Whatfield Magenta' (p) ♀H4	ECho ELan EPfP EPot LBee LRHS MWat NMen NWCA SAll SPoG WAbe WEas
'Whatfield Mini' (p)	SAll SRms WPer
'Whatfield Miss' (p)	SAll
'Whatfield Misty Morn' (p)	ECho SAll
'Whatfield Peach' (p)	SAll
'Whatfield Pretty Lady' (p)	ECho SAll
'Whatfield Rose' (p)	ECho EPot
'Whatfield Ruby' (p)	ECho ELan LRHS NWCA SAll WFar WPer
'Whatfield Supergem' (p)	ECho ECtt EPot
'Whatfield White' (p)	ECho ECtt SAll SRms
'Whatfield White Moon' (p)	ECho
'Whatfield Wisp' (p)	CPBP CTri EAlp ECho EPfP EPot GEdr MRav NBir NMen NWCA SPoG
'White and Crimson' (p)	SAll
'White Joy' ^{PBR} (p) ♀H4	MRav
'White Ladies' (p)	ELan LRHS MRav SAll
'Whitecliff' (b)	SAll
'Whitehill' (p) ♀H4	ECho EPot MHer NMen
'Whitesmith' (b) ♀H4	SAll
'Widecombe Fair' (p) ♀H4	CTri CWan EBee ECtt ELan SAll SBch SPoG SRms
'William Brownhill' (p)	SSvw
'Winnie Lesurf' (b)	SAll
'Yorkshireman' (b)	SAll
'Zebra' (b)	SAll
zonatus	NWCA

Diarrhena (*Poaceae*)

americana	GFor
japonica	EPPr GFor
* ***mandschurica***	EPPr
obovata	EPPr

Diascia ✿ (*Scrophulariaceae*)

'Alice Car' **new**	SBch
anastrepta	EBee
'Andrew'	SBch
'Appleby Appleblossom'	SBch
'Apricot'	see *D. barberae* 'Hopleys Apricot'
Apricot Delight = 'Codicot' (Sun Chimes Series)	WFar
barberae 'Belmore Beauty' (v)	ECtt EWes LIMB LSou WAbe WWEG
- 'Blackthorn Apricot' ♀H3-4	CBot EAEE EBee ECha ECtt ELan EPfP EShb GBuc GMaP LRHS MRav SMrm SPav SPer SPlb SPoG SWvt WFar WPer WWEG
§ - 'Fisher's Flora' ♀H3-4	EPyc WFar
- 'Fisher's Flora' × 'Lilac Belle'	ECtt
§ - 'Hopleys Apricot'	EPfP MSCN
§ - 'Ruby Field' ♀H3-4	CMea EBee ECha ECtt ELan EPfP LHop LRHS MRav NEgg SPer SPoG SRms SWvt WCFE WFar WWEG
Blue Bonnet = 'Hecbon'	ECtt GBee SWvt WFar
'Blush'	see *D. integerrima* 'Blush'
Blush Delight = 'Codiush' (Sun Chimes Series)	WFar
'Candy Floss' **new**	SBch
'Coldham'	CMdw
Coral Belle = 'Hecbel' ^{PBR} ♀H3-4	EBee ECtt EPfP EWes LHop LSou SBch SIng SMrm SPav WFar
cordata misapplied	see *D. barberae* 'Fisher's Flora'
cordifolia	see *D. barberae* 'Fisher's Flora'
Eclat = 'Heclat'	ECtt WFar
elegans misapplied	see *D. fetcaniensis*, *D. vigilis*
'Elizabeth' ♀H3-4	WHrl
'Emma'	SWvt
felthamii	see *D. fetcaniensis*
§ ***fetcaniensis***	CMHG CMea EBee EPfP EShb LRHS MHer NEgg SPer WBrk WCFE WClo WHal WKif WWEG
- 'Daydream'	LBuc LRHS WHrl
flanaganii misapplied	see *D. vigilis*
(Flying Colours Series) Flying Colours Appleblossom = 'Diastara'	EPfP SPoG
- Flying Colours Apricot = 'Diastina'	EPfP SPoG
- Flying Colours Coral = 'Diastis' ^{PBR}	SPoG
- Flying Colours Red = 'Diastonia' ^{PBR}	EPfP SPoG
'Frilly' ♀H3-4	ECtt
'Hector Harrison'	see *D.* 'Salmon Supreme'
Ice Cracker = 'Hecrack'	CMea ECtt ELan LHop LRHS SHGN SPav
Ice Cream = 'Icepol'	IMon LHop NLar SCoo
Iceberg = 'Hecice' ^{PBR}	SWvt
§ ***integerrima*** ♀H3-4	CSam ECha ELan ELon LLWP
- from Lesotho	SMrm
- 'Alba'	see *D. integerrima* 'Blush'
§ - 'Blush'	CSpe EGoo
- 'Ivory Angel'	see *D. integerrima* 'Blush'
integrifolia	see *D. integerrima*
'Isabel' **new**	SBch

'Jacqueline's Joy' CMea NPer SBch WFar
'Joyce's Choice' ♀H3-4 EWes LRHS WFar
'Katherine Sharman' (v) ECtt EWes LSou SAga WAbe
'Lady Valerie' ♀H3-4 EWes WPer
'Lilac Belle' ♀H3-4 CMea EBee ECtt ELan EPfP IMon LHop LRHS NBir NEgg NGdn SBch SPlb SPoG WFar WPer WWEG
'Lilac Mist' ♀H3-4 NPer
lilacina* × *rigescens GBee
Little Dancer = 'Pendan'PBR IMon LAst LSou SBch SCoo SIng SMrm SVil
Little Dreamer = 'Pender'PBR LAst SBch SVil
Little Drifter LSou SVil WRHF
Little Gem **new** SBch
Little Maiden = 'Penmaid' LSou SVil WGor
Little Tango LHop LSou SIng SMrm SVil
'Miracle Carmine' **new** WGor
'Miro' NLar
patens CHll
personata CPrp LHop LPla SDys
Pink Delight = 'Codiink' WFar
Pink Panther = 'Penther'PBR ECtt NLar SBch SCoo SPav SPoG SWvt
'Pink Queen' ECtt SRms
'Pink Spires' CElw
Prince of Orange = 'Hopor' NLar
Red Ace = 'Hecrace'PBR EPfP LAst LHop NPer SPav SPoG SWvt
Redstart = 'Hecstart' ECtt EPfP NGdn SWvt WFar
rigescens ♀H3 CBot CHEx COlW CPrp CSpe CWCL ECtt ELan EPfP EShb GGar ISea MHer MRav MWte NPer SAga SPlb SUsu SWvt WAbe WCFE WClo WCom WFar WPGP WSHC WSpi
§ - 'Anne Rennie' EBee ECtt LRHS SPoG SWvt
- pale-flowered see *D. rigescens* 'Anne Rennie'
'Ruby Field' see *D. barberae* 'Ruby Field'
'Rupert Lambert' ♀H3-4 GBuc LLWP WPer
§ 'Salmon Supreme' ECtt ELan EPfP GBee LAst LRHS NGdn NPer SPoG SRms WFar WMoo WPer
Susan = 'Winsue'PBR WFar
tugelensis WFar
'Twinkle' ♀H3-4 ECtt EPfP LAst LRHS NBir NGdn NPer WFar
* 'Twins Gully' GCal SMrm
§ ***vigilis*** ♀H3 CBot CMHG CMea CPLG ECha EPfP GBee LHop LRHS MCot NBro SBch WCom WHal
- 'Jack Elliott' MAvo MRav WCFE
(Whisper Series) Whisper Apricot Improved = 'Balwhisaptim'PBR NPri SCoo
- Whisper Cranberry Red = 'Balwhiscran'PBR SCoo SGar
- Whisper Pumpkin = 'Balwhispum'PBR **new** LAst
- Whisper Tangerine = 'Balwhistang' LSou SGar
- Whisper White = 'Balwhiswhit'PBR LAst NPri SGar
White Belle = 'Penbel' LSou SBch SMrm SVil
Wink Garnet = 'Balwingarn'PBR (Wink Series) SGar

Dicentra ✿ (*Papaveraceae*)

CC 4452 CPLG
'Adrian Bloom' EBee EBrs ECtt EHrv EPfP EWTr MBNS MCot MWat NBPC NCob NPri SCoo SMrm SPer SWvt WBrE WFar WMoo WWEG
'Bacchanal' ♀H4 Widely available
'Boothman's Variety' see *D.* 'Stuart Boothman'
'Bountiful' CMac EBee LRHS MBNS MRav NCob NGdn SWvt WWEG
'Brownie' CMoH GBuc
canadensis CLAP EBee EPot GBuc MAvo MTho NLar WCot WCru WHal
'Candy Hearts'PBR CBct EBee ECtt ELan EPfP IPot LAst LHop MBNS NBPC NBro NCob NGdn NLar SMrm WFar
'Coldham' ELon WCru WSHC
cucullaria CElw CLAP CMea CRow CStu CWCL EBee EBrs ECho EPot ERos GBuc GGar LRHS MRav MTho NHol NMen NWCA WAbe WBVN WCru WFar
- 'Pittsburg' CDes EBee EPPr GBuc SCnR WCot
* 'Dark Stuart Boothman' ECho
'Double Decker' **new** MCot
eximia misapplied see *D. formosa*
eximia (Ker Gawl.) Torr. CSpe EBee LBMP WClo
- 'Alba' see *D. eximia* 'Snowdrift'
- 'Percy Picton' **new** EBee
§ - 'Snowdrift' CLAP EBee ECtt EHrv ELan EPfP MCot MDun MTho NGdn SMrm SRms WFar WMoo WPrP WWEG
§ ***formosa*** Widely available
- ***alba*** CTri ECha GCra GMaP NBir SRms WCru WFar
- 'Aurora' EBee EBrs ECtt ELon EPPr EPfP GBin LAst LRHS MRav NBPC NGdn NSti SBch SPer SPet SPoG SWvt WCAu WFar WMoo WPnP
- 'Cox's Dark Red' CLAP EBee EWes GBuc LLHF NMen
- dark-flowered WMoo
- 'Furse's Form' CMoH
- subsp. ***oregana*** CLAP EBee EPPr GBuc GGar NBre NChi NMen WCru WHal
- - 'Rosea' EPPr
- 'Spring Gold' ECha ELon WMoo
'Ivory Hearts'PBR CWGN EBee ECtt ELan EPfP LAst LHop LRHS LSRN MAvo MBNS NBPC NBro NCGa NCob NGdn NLar SMrm SPer
'Katy' EPPr
'King of Hearts' Widely available
'Langtrees' ♀H4 CHar CMac CMil CRow CSam CSev EBee ECha EPau EPfP LHop MLHP MRav MWte NBro NCob SGSe SGar SPer SRms SWvt WCru WEas WFar WMoo WPtf WSpi WWEG
lichiangensis CAby EWld WCru WSHC
'Luxuriant' ♀H4 CBcs CSBt EAEE EBee EBrs ECtt ELan EPfP EShb LRHS MBel MCot MRav NBPC NCob NPri SBch SMrm SPer SPoG SRms SWvt WBor WCAu WFar WMoo WPnP WWEG
macrantha CDes CEnt CLAP CMoH CRow EBee ECha EPfP GBuc GCra LAma LHop MTho SMad WCru WPGP WSHC
macrocapnos CFir CRow EPfP GBuc GCal GQui IFro LRHS MDKP MTho WCru WTou
'Pearl Drops' CElw CRow EHrv ELan GAbr GBuc GGar GMaP MCot MRav NBid NGdn NMen SRms WAbb WMoo
peregrina GEdr WWSt
- ***alba*** GEdr
- 'Yubae' **new** WWSt

§ ***scandens***	CRHN CRow CSam CSpe ECho EPfP GCal ITim LAst MCCP MSCN MTho NCob NLar SGSe SHGN SUsu WSHC
- GWJ 9438	WCru
- 'Shirley Clemo'	CPLG
'Silver Beads'	EBee ECho
Snowflakes = 'Fusd'	EWes MRav NBre
spectabilis ♀H4	Widely available
- 'Alba' ♀H4	Widely available
- 'Gold Heart' PBR	CBow EBee EBrs EPfP LRHS MGos MRav SBch SGol SPoG
'Spring Morning'	CElw CMHG CMoH CSam ECtt EHrv EPPr LRHS NBre NSti WRHF
§ 'Stuart Boothman' ♀H4	Widely available
thalictrifolia	see *D. scandens*
torulosa	WTou
- B&SWJ 7814	WCru
ventii GWJ 9376 **new**	WCru

Dichelostemma (*Alliaceae*)

§ ***capitatum*** NNS 95-213	WCot
congestum	CAvo CFFs EBee EBrs ECho ERos GAuc WCot
§ ***ida-maia***	CAvo CBro CFFs CGrW EBee EBrs ECho GAuc ILad LRHS MWea WCon
- 'Pink Diamond'	CBro EBee EBrs ECho SPad WCot
multiflorum	WCot
pulchellum	see *D. capitatum*
volubile	EBee ECho WCot WWst

Dichondra (*Convolvulaceae*)

argentea 'Silver Falls'	CSpe CSpr EShb LAst LSou NPri SCoo SGar SPoG
§ ***micrantha***	EShb
repens misapplied	see *D. micrantha*

Dichopogon (*Anthericaceae*)

strictus	ECou

Dichroa (*Hydrangeaceae*)

febrifuga	CAbb CBcs CDoC CHEx CHll CMil CTsd CWGN CWib EBee ELan EWes LRHS WCot WCru WPGP
- B&SWJ 2367	WCru
- HWJK 2430	WCru
- pink-flowered	CHEx
aff. ***hirsuta*** B&SWJ 8207 from Vietnam	WCru
- B&SWJ 8371 from Lao	WCru
versicolor B&SWJ 6565	WCru
- B&SWJ 6605 from Thailand	WCru
aff. ***versicolor***	WPGP
- Guiz 48	WPGP
aff. ***yunnanensis*** B&SWJ 9734	WCru

Dichromena see *Rhynchospora*

Dicksonia ✿ (*Dicksoniaceae*)

antarctica ♀H3	Widely available
berteriana	WRic
fibrosa ♀H3	CBcs CDTJ CTrC CWit EAmu GLin IDee MAsh SPoG WRic
sellowiana	CDTJ WRic
squarrosa ♀H2	CBcs CBty CCCN CDTJ CTrC CWit EAmu MGos NMoo SAPC SArc SPoG WRic

Dicliptera (*Acanthaceae*)

§ ***sericea***	CDes CHll CMdw EBee EShb GCal IKil LHop LSou MWea SEND SRkn WCom WCot WDyG WFar WHil WPGP WSHC
suberecta	see *D. sericea*

Dicoma (*Asteraceae*)

anomala	SPlb

Dicranostigma (*Papaveraceae*)

leptopodum	CSpe

Dictamnus ✿ (*Rutaceae*)

albus	Widely available
§ - var. ***purpureus*** ♀H4	Widely available
* - ***turkestanicus***	GCal
fraxinella	see *D. albus* var. *purpureus*

Didymochlaena (*Dryopteridaceae*)

lunulata	see *D. truncatula*
§ ***truncatula***	MBri XBlo

Dieffenbachia (*Araceae*)

'Camille' (v) ♀H1	LRHS

Dierama ✿ (*Iridaceae*)

adelphicum **new**	GAbr
ambiguum	GAbr WCot
argyreum	CBgR CCCN CElw CWCL EBee GAbr GKev LFur MCot NChi NFir SGSe SWal WBrE WCot WKif WPtf
'Ariel'	IBlr
'Ballerina'	CFir ECho
'Ballyrogan Red' **new**	IBlr
'Black Knight'	CPLG CPrp IBlr
'Blush'	IBlr
'Buckland White' **new**	WPGP
'Candy Stripe'	CRow EBee STes
'Cherry Chimes'	LRHS MGos
cooperi	CElw CPou CPrp EBee IBlr LFur NBir WCot
'Coral Bells'	CDes EBee GCal WPGP
'Cosmos' **new**	GKev
'Delicacy' **new**	IBlr
'Desire' **new**	IBlr
dissimile	EBee NFir
'Donard Legacy'	IBlr
§ ***dracomontanum***	Widely available
- JCA 3.141.100	WPGP
- dwarf pale pink-flowered	LRHS
- Wisley Princess Group	LRHS MBri
dracomontanum* × *pulcherrimum	SMad
dubium	IBlr
ensifolium	see *D. pendulum*
erectum	CBcs CBgR CCCN CHid CWCL EBee GAbr GKev IBlr MCot SBch SGSe WCot
'Fairy Bells'	CPen IPot NCob
'Fireworks'	CWCL GEdr
floriferum	CBro IBlr LRHS
formosum	CGHE WPGP
galpinii	CGHE CWCL ELan GAbr GBin GEdr LRHS NFir NLar STes WPGP
grandiflorum	CPBP CPou ECho IBlr WCru
'Guinevere'	Widely available
igneum	Widely available
- CD&R 278	CPou
insigne	EBee
'Iris'	IBlr
jucundum	EBee GBuc MBel
'Knee-high Lavender'	CDes EPla SAga WPGP
'Lancelot'	Widely available
latifolium	CGHE CHid IBlr LRHS NFir

luteoalbidum	EBee GAbr WPGP
'Mandarin'	CDes IBlr WPGP
medium	CGHE CPen EBee ELon LPio NCGa SUsu SWat WCot WPGP
'Milkmaid'	CPLG CPrp IBlr NCot
'Miranda'	CAby CPen CSpe EBee ECtt GBuc GEdr GKev GQue LFur LRHS MBNS NCGa NCob NCot NEgg NGdn NSti SDix SDnm SMad SMrm WCot WPtf WSpi
mossii	CBcs CCCN CPLG CWCL EBee ELan GBin GEdr GKev IBlr LFur LHop LRHS MCot NBre NLar SBch SGSe SPlb SPoG WPGP
nixonianum	IBlr
'Oberon'	MRav
'Pamina'	CPLG CPrp IBlr
'Papagena'	IBlr
'Papageno'	IBlr
pauciflorum	CBgR CFir CGHE CHid CPLG CPrp CWCL CWib EBee ECho EDAr ERos GEdr LPio MHer NBir NFir NLAp NLar SMrm SRot SUsu SWat WPGP WSHC WWEG
- CD&R 197	CPBP MDKP
§ ***pendulum***	Widely available
- 'Album' **new**	WHlf
- var. ***pumilum***	CMoH
'Petite Fairy'	CPen
pictum	EBee IBlr
Plant World hybrids	GGar SGSe
'Pretty Flamingo'	CPrp IBlr
'Puck'	CDes CPen EBee GCal IBlr IGor MRav WPGP
pulcherrimum	Widely available
- var. ***album***	CBro CCCN CGHE CHar CLAP CWCL EBee ECho ELan GBuc GEdr IBlr IPot LFur LPio MHer MNrw NCGa NCob STes SWal WPGP WSpi WWEG
- 'Angel Gabriel'	LRHS
- 'Blackbird'	Widely available
- dark pink-flowered	GKev SGSe
- dwarf	ELon GKev IPot
- 'Falcon'	IBlr
- 'Flamingo'	IBlr
- 'Flaring Tips'	IPot
- giant form **new**	CPne
- lilac-flowered	LHop
- 'Merlin'	Widely available
- 'Pearly Queen'	CRow EBee
- 'Peregrine'	WPGP
- 'Redwing'	IBlr
- Slieve Donard hybrids	CLAP CWCL EBee ECho ECtt EDAr IPot ITim LAst LHop LRHS MHer NEgg SBch SPet WFar WHrl WMnd WSpi WWEG
pumilum misapplied	see *D. dracomontanum*
'Purple Passion'	CPen LRHS NCGa
'Queen of the Night'	IBlr
reynoldsii	Widely available
robustum	CGHE CPLG CPou CSpe GAbr IBlr NFir WBVN WPGP
'Sarastro'	CPLG CPrp IBlr
'September Charm'	IBlr
sertum	CBro EBee
'Spring Dancer'	CWCL GEdr GKev SGSe
'Tamino'	IBlr
'Tiny Bells'	CDes EBee ECha EDAr GCal WPGP
'Titania'	IBlr
trichorhizum	CBgR CCCN CFir CGHE CPBP CPLG CWCL EBee ECho EKen ELan GAbr IBlr LFur LHop NFir SAga SBch SGSe SPoG WSHC
'Tubular Bells'	IBlr
tyrium	NFir
'Violet Ice'	IBlr
'Westminster Chimes'	CDes IBlr WPGP
'Zulu Bells'	ELon

Diervilla ✿ (*Caprifoliaceae*)

lonicera	CHar
middendorffiana	see *Weigela middendorffiana*
rivularis 'Troja Black'	NLar
§ ***sessilifolia***	CBcs CHar CMac EBee GAuc IDee LAst MAsh MRav SGar SLon WBVN WCot WFar WMoo
- 'Butterfly'	CMac WMoo
× ***splendens***	CAbP CMHG CPLG CWib EBee EHoe ELan EPfP LHop LRHS MBNS MBar MBlu MGos MRav MSwo NHol SEND SGar SLPl SPer SPoG WDin

Dietes (*Iridaceae*)

bicolor	CAbb CBod CDes CHEx CPen CPne CTrC ERea EShb LEdu LPio LSou SDnm SGSe SHom
grandiflora	CAbb CArn CDes CFee CMdw CPen CPne EBee ECho EDif ERea EShb LEdu LPio SBch SGSe SHom WBor WCot WPrP WThu
§ ***iridioides***	CDes CPne CSWP CStu EBee EBrs ECho EShb GBin LPio WCot WPGP

Digitalis ✿ (*Scrophulariaceae*)

RCB/TQ 059 from İkizdere	WCru
ambigua	see *D. grandiflora*
apricot hybrids	see *D. purpurea* 'Sutton's Apricot'
cariensis	EBee GKev SPav
ciliata	ELan GCal MBel SPav
davisiana	CBot CPLG GBuc MCot MNHC SPav SPhx STes WCHb WMoo
dubia	CBot EPfP MBel NBir NBre SDnm SPav
'Elsie Kelsey'	CEnt ECtt EShb LRHS SDnm SPav SWvt WHil
eriostachya	see *D. lutea*
ferruginea ♀H4	Widely available
- 'Gelber Herold'	CBot EBee GAbr GMaP LBMP LRHS MDKP NBre NLar SMrm
- 'Gigantea'	EBee GQue LRHS MBri NBPC NPri SWat WCot WWEG
- subsp. ***schischkinii***	SDnm SPav
* ***floribunda***	SPav
fontanesii	CEnt EPPr GAbr GBuc GKev LFur NBur WCot
× ***fulva***	MBel NBir
'Glory of Roundway'	CBot CDes EBee EBla MHer WCot
§ ***grandiflora*** ♀H4	Widely available
- 'Carillon'	CWan EBee EPau EPfP EShb GAbr IFoB LAst LBMP LDai LRHS NBir NGHP NLar NPri SGSe WGor WPer
- 'Cream Bell'	EPfP LRHS
- 'Dwarf Carillon'	ECtt EWld
- 'Temple Bells'	WPer
heywoodii	see *D. purpurea* subsp. *heywoodii*
'John Innes Tetra'	EShb WPGP
kishinskyi	see *D. parviflora*
laevigata	CBot CEnt CFir CHar CSam EBee EBla EBrs GKev LRHS MCot MWea NBro NGHP SDnm SMeo SPav SPet WCHb WCot WMnd WMoo WPer
lamarckii misapplied	see *D. lanata*

lamarckii Ivanina	NBPC
§ ***lanata***	Widely available
- 'Café Crème'	LRHS LSou MCot MNHC NBPC
§ ***lutea***	Widely available
§ - subsp. ***australis***	EBla LDai MAvo SDnm SPav
- 'Flashing Spires' (v)	CBow LRHS
- 'Yellow Medley'	EBee
× ***mertonensis*** ♀H4	Widely available
- 'Summer King'	ECtt LRHS LSRN NBre
micrantha	see *D. lutea* subsp. *australis*
nervosa	SPav
obscura	CBot ECho EHrv EShb IFoB LBMP LFur MAvo MCot NBir NCob NGHP NPri SDnm SIde SPav SPet WCHb WMnd
orientalis	see *D. grandiflora*
§ ***parviflora***	Widely available
- 'Milk Chocolate'	CBcs CMHG ECtt EPfP GQue LFur LRHS LSRN LSou MCot MHer MNHC NBre NEgg SBHP SGSe SIde SMrm SPet WFar WPnP WWEG
purpurea	CArn EBWF EBee ECtt EDAr GKir GPoy MHer MLHP MNHC NCob NLan NMir NPri SBch SECG SIde SMrm SPlb SPoG WClo WMoo WWFP
- 'Alba'	see *D. purpurea* f. *albiflora*
§ - f. ***albiflora***	Widely available
- - 'Anne Redetzky'[PBR]	CBow IFoB LRHS WMnd
- - unspotted	CWan
- Camelot Series	LRHS NGHP WHil
- - 'Camelot Cream'	EAEE EPfP LRHS NPri SWvt
- - 'Camelot Lavender'	EPfP LRHS NEgg NPri SWvt WCot
- - 'Camelot Rose'	EPfP LRHS NEgg NPri SWvt
- - 'Camelot White'	EPfP LRHS NEgg WBor
- 'Candy Mountain' new	EWll
- Excelsior Group	CBcs CBot CCVT CSBt CSam CTri EAEE ECtt EPfP GJos GKir GMaP LAst LRHS MBri MNHC NBlu NMir NVic SBch SPer SPoG SRms SWal SWvt WFar WGor
- - (Suttons; Unwins) ♀H4	ECtt MRav
- Foxy Group	CBot CWib ECtt EHrv LRHS SBch SPet SPoG SRms WFar WWEG
- - 'Foxy Apricot'	CBcs SWvt
- - 'Foxy Primrose'	NPri
- Giant Spotted Group	CBot ECtt EHrv EPfP LRHS SCoo
- Glittering Prizes Group	SWat
- Gloxinioides Group	ELan NCob WFar
- - 'Isabellina'	CBot
- - 'The Shirley' ♀H4	ECtt SGar WGor
§ - subsp. ***heywoodii***	CBot EBee ELan GBuc SDnm SPav WCHb WMoo
- - 'Pink Champagne'	LRHS
- - 'Silver Fox'	ECtt LSRN
- 'Jellito's Apricot'	CSam
- subsp. ***nevadensis***	CBot
- 'Pam's Choice'	CPLG CSpe EBee EBla ECtt EPfP GAbr IPot LAst LBMP LHop LRHS LSRN MGos MWat NBPC NEgg NGBl SBch SMad SRGP WFar WHrl WMnd WMoo WWEG WWlt
- peloric	WCHb
- 'Primrose Carousel'	EBee ECrN ECtt ILad LRHS NEgg WWlt
- 'Snow Thimble'	EBee ECtt LRHS MBNS MBri NLar NVic SMrm WWEG
§ - 'Sutton's Apricot' ♀H4	Widely available
* - 'Sutton's Giant Primrose'	CBot
- 'Torpedo Lilac Rose'	LRHS
purpurea × ***thapsi***	CBot
'Red Skin'	CPom SGSe
'Saltwood Summer'	IFoB LRHS
× ***sibirica***	EBee LFur MBel SPhx WCHb
* ***spaniflora***	SPhx
'Spice Island'[PBR]	EBee LBuc LRHS SPoG
* ***stewartii***	CHar ECtt ELan EWes GCra LDai LFur NBPC NBur SPad SPav WMoo
thapsi	CArn ECtt EPfP GAbr LRHS NBPC NBur NPri SDnm SIde SPav WCHb WMoo WPer WWFP
- JCA 410.000	EBee
- 'Spanish Peaks'	EBee LRHS LSou
trojana	ECtt SGar
Vesuvius Group	CEnt
viridiflora	CPLG ECtt EShb MCot NBro SBHP SGar SPav SPhx SWat WCHb WFar WPer

dill see *Anethum graveolens*

Dionaea ✿ (*Droseraceae*)

muscipula	CHew CSWC LRHS MCCP NChu SHmp SPlb WSSs
- 'Akai Ryu'	CSWC EECP NChu WSSs
- 'Red Piranha' new	NChu
- 'Royal Red'	CHew CSWC NChu
- shark-toothed	CSWC EECP NChu
- 'Spider'	CSWC EECP NChu

Dionysia (*Primulaceae*)

'Annielle'	WAbe
aretioides ♀H2	WAbe
- 'Bevere'	WAbe
- 'Gravetye'	ECho
- 'Phyllis Carter'	ECho
bazoftica	WAbe
'Bernd Wetzel'	WAbe
bryoides	WAbe
'Charlson Primrose'	WAbe
'Charlson Terri'	WAbe
curviflora	WAbe
'Emmely'	WAbe
'Eric Watson'	WAbe
'Ewesley Iota'	WAbe
'Ewesley Kappa'	WAbe
'Ewesley Mu'	WAbe
'Ewesley Theta'	WAbe
freitagii	WAbe
gaubae	WAbe
'Harlekin'	WAbe
janthina	WAbe
'Monika'	WAbe
'Schneeball'	WAbe
tapetodes	WAbe
- 'Brimstone'	WAbe
- farinose	ECho

Dioon (*Zamiaceae*)

califanoi	CBrP
caputoi	CBrP
edule ♀H1	CBrP LPal SBst
- var. ***angustifolium***	CBrP
mejiae	CBrP LPal
merolae	CBrP
rzedowskii	CBrP LPal
spinulosum	CBrP LPal SBig

Dioscorea (*Dioscoreaceae*)

CC 5622	EWld
araucana	LSou
batatas	LEdu
caucasica 'Zojugre' new	EBee

deltoidea	CPLG EWld
japonica	CAgr EShb WBVN
sylvatica new	WHil
villosa	CArn

Diosma (*Rutaceae*)

ericoides	SEND SWvt
- 'Pink Fountain'	EBee LBuc SPoG
- 'Sunset Gold'	CWGN EBee LBuc MAsh SCoo SPoG
hirsuta 'Silver Flame'	EBee LRHS

Diospyros (*Ebenaceae*)

austroafricana	SPlb
* ***hyrcanum***	EGFP NLar
kaki (F)	CBcs CMCN CTho EPfP ERom LRHS MREP NLar WDin WPGP
- 'Fuyu'	CAgr
- 'Kostata'	CAgr
- 'Mazelii'	CAgr
lotus	CAgr CBcs CMCN CMac CTho LEdu LRHS MBri NLar SPlb WPGP
- (f)	CAgr
- (m)	CAgr
lycioides	EShb SPlb
'Nikita's Gift' new	CAgr
rhombifolia	WPGP
'Russian Beauty' new	CAgr
virginiana (F)	CAgr CBcs CMCN CTho EPfP LRHS NLar SSpi

Dipcadi (*Hyacinthaceae*)

ciliare new	CLak
serotinum	ITim
- subsp. ***lividum***	WPGP
white-flowered new	CLak

Dipelta (*Caprifoliaceae*)

floribunda ♀H4	CBcs CBot CDul CMCN CMac CPLG CPMA ELan EPfP ERas MBlu MBri NLar WPGP WPat WSHC
ventricosa	CAbP CBcs CGHE CPLG CPMA EPfP LRHS MAsh MBlu MBri NLar SSpi WPGP WPat
yunnanensis	CBcs CPLG CPMA CTri ELan EPfP MBri NLar SSpi SSta WPGP WPat
- SDR 4334	GKev

Diphylleia (*Berberidaceae*)

cymosa	CLAP ECha GEdr MRav WCot WCru WTin
grayi	CLAP EBee GEdr WCru
sinensis	CLAP GEdr WCru

Dipidax see *Onixotis*

Diplacus see *Mimulus*

Dipladenia see *Mandevilla*

Diplarrhena (*Iridaceae*)

§ ***latifolia***	CFir GBBs GCal GGar IBlr LRHS SGSe
- Helen Dillon's form	IBlr
moraea	CAbP CMac CMea CWCL ECha ECho GBBs GCal GKir GMac IBlr IFoB IKil ITim MDun NCGa NLAp SAga WAbe WBrE WPGP WSHC
- ***minor***	IBlr
- 'Slieve Donard'	IBlr
- West Coast form	see *D. latifolia*

Diplazium (*Woodsiaceae*)

tomitaroanum	EBee
wichurae	EBee EPPr

Diplostephium (*Asteraceae*)

alveolatum B&SWJ 10686	WCru

Diplotaxis (*Brassicaceae*)

muralis	CArn ELau WJek
tenuifolia	ELau MNHC NGHP NPri

Dipsacus (*Dipsacaceae*)

§ ***fullonum***	CArn CMac CPrp CWan EBWF EPfP GBar GPWP IFro MBri MHer MNHC NBid NMir NPri NVic SBch SECG SIde WHer WHil WJek WSFF
inermis	CSam EBee ECha NBid NLar WFar
japonicus	CArn
- HWJ 695	WCru
pilosus	CPom EBWF
sativus	GPWP NLar
strigosus	SPhx
sylvestris	see *D. fullonum*

Dipteracanthus see *Ruellia*

Dipteronia (*Aceraceae*)

sinensis	CGHE CMCN EBee EPla MBri NLar WPGP

Disanthus (*Hamamelidaceae*)

cercidifolius ♀H4	CAbP CBcs CMCN CMac CPMA EPfP GKir IDee LRHS MBlu MBri NLar SSpi WPGP
- 'Ena-nishiki' (v)	NLar
- 'Rikiv' new	SSpi

Discaria (*Rhamnaceae*)

chacaye	LEdu WPGP

Diselma (*Cupressaceae*)

archeri	CDoC CKen GKir MBar SCoo
- 'Read Dwarf'	CKen

Disphyma (*Aizoaceae*)

crassifolium	SChr

Disporopsis (*Convallariaceae*)

aspersa	CDes CLAP EBee ECho EPPr EWld LEdu MAvo WCru WPGP
- tall	CBct WCru
fuscopicta	CBct CLAP EBee EHrv EPPr MAvo WCru WTin
longifolia	CLAP
- B&SWJ 5284	WCru
* ***luzoniensis***	CBct GEdr
- B&SWJ 3891	WCru
'Min Shan'	ELon
* ***nova***	EBee EPPr
§ ***pernyi***	Widely available
- B&SWJ 229	WCru
- B&SWJ 1864	CBct EPPr WCru
- 'Bill Baker'	EBee LEdu MAvo
taiwanensis	CBct
- B&SWJ 3388	WCru
undulata	LEdu NBid WCru WPrP

Disporum (*Convallariaceae*)

austrosinense B&SWJ 9777	WCru
bodinieri	CDes EBee LEdu WPnP

	Name	Suppliers
	- DJHC 765	WCru
	aff. ***bodinieri***	WPGP
	cantoniense	CDes CFir CLAP CPom EBee EPPr GEdr IFoB LEdu WCru WFar WPGP WPrP WWst
	- B&L 12512	CLAP
	- B&SWJ 1424	WCru
	- B&SWJ 9715	WCru
	- DJHC 98485	CDes
I	- 'Aureovariegata'	CBct CDes EBee WCot
	- var. ***cantoniense*** f. ***brunneum*** B&SWJ 5290	WCru
	- 'Green Giant'	CDes CLAP EBee IFoB WFar WPnP
	- var. ***kawakamii*** B&SWJ 350	WCru
	- - RWJ 10103	WCru
	- var. ***multiflorum*** B&SWJ 11252 new	WCru
	- - B&SWJ 11291	WCru
	- 'Night Heron'	CLAP EBee IFoB MWea WCot WFar
	- var. ***sikkimense*** B&SWJ 2337 new	WCru
*	***flavum***	CAvo ECho GKir SUsu
	hookeri	CLAP CPom EBee EBrs ECho GGar GKir MAvo NMen WCot WCru
	- var. ***oreganum***	EBee EPPr IBlr IFoB WCru
	lanuginosum	CBct EPPr GEdr MAvo WCot WCru
	leschenaultianum B&SWJ 9484	WCru
	- B&SWJ 9505	WCru
	leucanthum	WFar
	- B&SWJ 2389	WCru
	longistylum L 1564	WCru
	lutescens	EBee LFur WCru
	maculatum	CAby CBct CLAP IFoB SMac WCru
	megalanthum	CLAP EBee EHrv IFoB LFur WCot WCru
	- CD&R 2412B	EPPr
	nantouense	IFoB LEdu WCot WFar WPGP
	- B&SWJ 359	CBct WCru
	- B&SWJ 6812	WCru
	sessile	EBee ECho GGar LEdu MSCN WCru
	- AGSJ 146	NMen
	- B&SWJ 2824	WCru
I	- 'Aureovariegatum' (v)	ECho MAvo WCru
	- 'Cricket'	EBee GEdr WFar
	- 'Kinga' (v)	EBee GEdr
I	- 'Robustum Variegatum'	EBee MAvo
	- variegated (v)	CBct
	- 'Variegatum' (v)	CAvo CHEx CRow CStu EBee EBrs ECha ECho ELan EPPr EPfP EPla EPot GEdr GGar GMaP IMou LEdu LRHS MRav NBid WBor WCot WCru WFar WHil WPGP WPnP
	- 'White Lightning' (v)	WCot
	- var. ***yakushimense***	ECho
	shimadae B&SWJ 399	WCru
	smilacinum	NLar WCru WFar
	- B&SWJ 713	WCru
*	- 'Aureovariegatum' (v)	LEdu WCot WCru
	- double-flowered (d)	EBee GEdr
	- 'Kino-tsukasa'	EBee
	- pink-flowered	WCru
	smithii	CBct CPom CStu EBee EBrs ECho EPfP EPot ERos GAbr GBuc GEdr GGar GKev GKir LEdu NBir NMen WCot WCru WFar WPGP
	taiwanense B&SWJ 1513	WCru
	- B&SWJ 2018	WCru
	trabeculatum new	WCru
	- 'Nakafu'	WCru
	trachycarpum	CLAP
	uniflorum	CBct CDes CGHE CLAP CPom CStu EBee EBrs ECho EPfP EPla GKir IFoB LEdu NBid SBch WFar WHil WPGP WPnP WSHC WTin
	- B&SWJ 651	WCot WCru
	- B&SWJ 872	WCru
	- B&SWJ 4100	WCru
	viridescens	CAby CBct LEdu WCru
	- B&SWJ 4598	WCru

Distictis (*Bignoniaceae*)

	Name	Suppliers
	buccinatoria	EShb

Distylium (*Hamamelidaceae*)

	Name	Suppliers
	myricoides	CMCN NLar WFar
	racemosum	CBcs CMac EPfP MBlu MBri NLar SLPl SReu SSta WSHC

Diuranthera see *Chlorophytum*

Dizygotheca see *Schefflera*

Dobinea (*Podoaceae*)

	Name	Suppliers
	vulgaris B&SWJ 2532	WCru

Dodecatheon (*Primulaceae*)

	Name	Suppliers
	alpinum	EBee GKev SRms WAbe
	- subsp. ***alpinum*** NNS 02-132	GKev
	- - NNS 04-128	GKev
	- subsp. ***majus***	EBee
	amethystinum	see *D. pulchellum*
	'Aphrodite'PBR	EBee EKen MBri NLar
	austrofrigidum	GKev
	clevelandii	MDKP
	- subsp. ***insulare***	EBee LLHF LRHS NWCA
	- subsp. ***patulum***	GBuc LRHS
	cusickii	see *D. pulchellum* subsp. *cusickii*
	dentatum ♀H4	CElw EBee GBuc GEdr GKev MDKP MTho WAbe WFar
	frigidum	WAbe
§	***hendersonii*** ♀H4	GAuc GBuc NMen SRms
	integrifolium	see *D. hendersonii*
§	***jeffreyi***	EBee EBrs EPPr GEdr GGar GKev LRHS MBri NBPC NLAp NLar NMen NMyG WAbe WBor WFar
	- NNS 05-250	NWCA
	- NNS 06-195	GKev
	- 'Rotlicht'	SRms WPer
*	× ***lemoinei***	WAbe
§	***meadia*** ♀H4	Widely available
	- from Cedar County	WAbe
	- f. ***album*** ♀H4	CBro CFwr CSWP CTri EBee EBrs ECho ELan EPfP EPot GAuc GEdr GGar LAma LHop LRHS MTho NHol NMen NMyG NWCA SPer SRms SWvt WPnP WSpi
	- 'Aphrodite'	WBor
*	- 'Goliath'	EBee
	- membranaceous	WAbe
	- 'Queen Victoria'	EBee EBrs ECho LEdu SMeo SRGP WFar WPnP
	pauciflorum (Dur.) E. Greene	see *D. meadia*
	pauciflorum misapplied	see *D. pulchellum*
	poeticum	EBee
	- NNS 00-259	GKev
§	***pulchellum*** ♀H4	CBro EBee GEdr GGar GKev LHop LLWG LRHS MNrw NLAp NMen NWCA SIng WPer

§ - subsp. ***cusickii***	SRms
- subsp. ***pulchellum*** 'Red Wings'	EBee EBla EBrs ECho EPot LRHS MDKP NBir NMen SMeo SPoG WFar WHoo WPnP
- ***radicatum***	see *D. pulchellum*
- 'Sooke's Variety'	CStu WAbe
radicatum	see *D. pulchellum*
redolens	EBee
tetrandrum	see *D. jeffreyi*

Dodonaea (*Sapindaceae*)

viscosa	CArn CTrC ECou ISea SPlb
- (f)	ECou
- (m)	ECou
- 'Purpurea'	CAbb CBcs CDoC CPLG CPne CTrC CWit EAmu EBee ECou EShb GLin IMon ISea LRHS LSou MAsh
- - (f)	ECou
- - (m)	ECou

Doellingeria (*Asteraceae*)

scabra	see *Aster scaber*

Dolichandra (*Bignoniaceae*)

cynanchoides RCB RA Q-4	WCot

Dolichos (*Papilionaceae*)

purpureus	see *Lablab purpureus*

Dombeya (*Sterculiaceae*)

calantha	CCCN
× ***cayeuxii***	CCCN
wallichii new	CCCN

Dondia see *Hacquetia*

Doodia (*Blechnaceae*)

aspera	WRic
§ ***caudata***	EFtx WRic
media	CBty GBin LLHF MGos WRic
squarrosa	see *D. caudata*

Doronicum (*Asteraceae*)

austriacum	MSCN NBid NBre
cataractarum	NBre
caucasicum	see *D. orientale*
§ ***columnae***	CBcs EBee GKev
cordatum	see *D. columnae*
§ × ***excelsum*** 'Harpur Crewe'	CPrp EBee LEdu MRav NBre NPer NVic WCAu
'Finesse'	GBuc GCal LRHS NBre SPoG SRms WMoo
'Little Leo'	EBee ELan EPfP GJos GMaP LHop LRHS LSRN MAvo NLar NPri NVic SAga SBch SPet SPoG SRGP WBVN WBrE WWEG
§ ***orientale***	CWan EBee EPfP GJos GKir NBid NBlu SEND SPer SPoG SWat
- 'Goldcut'	NBre NGdn
- 'Magnificum'	CSBt EBee EDAr EPfP GMaP LRHS MBri NEgg NGBl NMir SMrm SPoG SRms SWal WFar WWEG
pardalianches	CMea ECha NBre NSco WCot WRHF
- 'Goldstrauss'	EBee
plantagineum 'Excelsum'	see *D.* × *excelsum* 'Harpur Crewe'

Doryanthes (*Doryanthaceae*)

excelsa	CHEx CTrC
palmeri	CBrP CHEx

Dorycnium see *Lotus*

Doryopteris (*Adiantaceae*)

pedata	MBri

Douglasia see *Androsace*

vitaliana	see *Vitaliana primuliflora*

Dovea (*Restionaceae*)

macrocarpa	CCCN

Dovyalis (*Flacourtiaceae*)

caffra (F)	XBlo

Doxantha see *Macfadyena*

Draba (*Brassicaceae*)

aizoides	ECho LRHS MWat SPlb SPoG SRms WFar
aizoon	see *D. lasiocarpa*
athoa	EDAr
bruniifolia	EBur ECho EWes LRHS
- subsp. ***olympica***	WFar
bryoides	see *D. rigida* var. *bryoides*
compacta	see *D. lasiocarpa* Compacta Group
crassifolia	ECho
cretica	ECho NMen
cusickii	GKev
cuspidata	EPot
dedeana	ECho EWes
densifolia	GAuc
dubia	EDAr
glacialis new	EDAr
hispanica	EDAr
hoppeana	EDAr
§ ***lasiocarpa***	SGar
§ - Compacta Group	ECho NWCA
longisiliqua 🏆H2	ITim
- EMR 2551	EPot
magadanensis new	GAuc
mollissima	EPot WAbe
oligosperma subsp. ***subsessilis***	NWCA
ossetica	WAbe
parnassica	EDAr GAuc
polytricha	GAuc WAbe
§ ***rigida*** var. ***bryoides***	ECho WThu
- var. ***imbricata*** f. ***compacta***	EPot
rosularis	GAuc
× ***salomonii***	EPot
scardica	see *D. lasiocarpa*
ventosa	WAbe

Dracaena ✿ (*Dracaenaceae*)

congesta	see *Cordyline stricta*
draco 🏆H1	CArn CTrC EShb SBch XBlo
fragrans	MBri
- (Compacta Group) 'Compacta Purpurea'	MBri
- - 'Compacta Variegata' (v)	MBri
- (Deremensis Group) 'Lemon Lime' (v) 🏆H1	MBri
- - 'Warneckei' (v) 🏆H1	MBri
- - 'Yellow Stripe' (v) 🏆H1	MBri
* - ***glauca***	MBri
- 'Janet Craig'	MBri
- 'Massangeana' (v) 🏆H1	MBri
indivisa	see *Cordyline indivisa*
'Lemon Lime Tips'	XBlo
marginata (v) 🏆H1	MBri XBlo
- 'Colorama' (v)	MBri
- 'Tricolor' (v) 🏆H1	EShb XBlo

sanderiana (v) ♀H1	EShb MBri
* ***schrijveriana***	MBri
steudneri	MBri
stricta	see *Cordyline stricta*

Dracocephalum (*Lamiaceae*)

sp.	LLHF
argunense	CAby LRHS NLAp SAga SPhx SRms WPat WPer
* - 'Album'	GKev
- 'Fuji Blue'	CEnt EBee EPfP LRHS LSRN NBre NLar
- 'Fuji White'	CEnt EBee LSRN SPad SPhx WPer
austriacum	WPer
botryoides	LLHF NWCA WPer
forrestii	GKev
aff. ***forrestii***	LLHF
grandiflorum	CAby CBod CEnt CMea GKev GKir LLHF MMHG SAga SBHP SPhx WFar WPer
hemsleyanum	LLHF
isabellae	EBrs
mairei	see *D. renatii*
moldavica	SIde
nutans	NLar
peregrinum 'Blue Dragon'	NPri
prattii	see *Nepeta prattii*
§ ***renatii***	CEnt LLHF SPhx WPer
rupestre	CAby EBee EWld MBri NBre
ruyschiana	ELan GEdr MRav NLar NWCA SEND
- 'Blue Moon'	EBee NBPC NBre SPad
sibiricum	see *Nepeta sibirica*
virginicum	see *Physostegia virginiana*
wendelboi	EBee NBir

Dracophyllum (*Epacridaceae*)

muscoides new	GKev
traversii	GKev

Dracunculus (*Araceae*)

canariensis	CStu WCot
muscivorus	see *Helicodiceros muscivorus*
§ ***vulgaris***	CArn CHid CPom CSpe CStu EBee EBrs ECho EHrv EPfP EPot GGar LEdu LFur LRHS MAvo MCCP MRav NWCA SDix SEND SPad WCot WFar WHil WPnP
- white-flowered	WPnP

Dregea (*Asclepiadaceae*)

sinensis	CBot CCCN CHll CRHN CStu CWGN EBee ELan EPfP ERea EWes LRHS MAsh MRav SEND SPer SPoG WCot WPGP WSHC
- 'Brockhill Silver'	WSHC
- 'Variegata' (v)	EShb EWes MAvo WCot

Drepanostachyum (*Poaceae*)

§ ***falcatum***	GKir
falconeri J.J.N. Campbell. ex D. McClintock	see *Himalayacalamus falconeri*, *Himalayacalamus falconeri* 'Damarapa'
hookerianum	see *Himalayacalamus hookerianus*
§ ***khasianum***	CDTJ CGHE EPla WPGP
§ ***microphyllum***	EPla IMou WJun WPGP

Drimia (*Hyacinthaceae*)

anomala new	CLak

Drimiopsis (*Hyacinthaceae*)

maculata	CStu WCot

Drimys (*Winteraceae*)

aromatica	see *D. lanceolata*
colorata	see *Pseudowintera colorata*
granadensis var. ***grandiflora*** B&SWJ 10777	WCru
granatensis	CGHE WPGP
§ ***lanceolata***	Widely available
- (f)	CTrC ECou GGar NCGa SPer
- (m)	CDoC CTrC ECou GGar SPer
- 'Inverewe Prolific' (f)	GGar
- 'Mount Wellington'	GCal
- 'Suzette' (v)	MBlu MGos
* ***latifolia***	CBcs CHEx
winteri ♀H4	Widely available
- var. ***andina***	CPLG EPfP WPGP
§ - var. ***chilensis***	CPLG EPfP GGar ISea LRHS SPoG SSpi WCru WPGP
- Latifolia Group	see *D. winteri* var. *chilensis*

Drosanthemum (*Aizoaceae*)

hispidum	EAlp ECho ELan EPfP EPot GMaP ITim LRHS MTho NMen NWCA SBHP SIng SPlb SPoG
speciosum	ECho
* ***sutherlandii***	ECho

Drosera ✿ (*Droseraceae*)

admirabilis	CHew CSWC
aliciae	CHew CSWC EECP NChu SHmp
andersoniana	EFEx
androsacea	CHew
anglica	CSWC NChu
ascendens	CHew
binata	CHew EECP SHmp
§ - subsp. ***dichotoma***	CHew CSWC
- 'Extrema'	CHew
- 'Multifida'	CHew MCCP
browniana	EFEx
bulbigena	EFEx
bulbosa subsp. ***bulbosa***	EFEx
- subsp. ***major***	EFEx
callistos	CHew EECP
capensis	CHew CSWC LRHS MCCP NChu SHmp
- 'Albino'	CHew EECP MCCP
- red	CSWC NChu
cuneifolia	CHew
dichotoma	see *D. binata* subsp. *dichotoma*
dichrosepala	CHew EECP
echinoblastus new	CHew
enodes new	CHew
ericksoniae	CHew
erythrorhiza	EFEx
- subsp. ***collina***	EFEx
- subsp. ***erythrorhiza***	CHew EFEx
- subsp. ***magna***	EFEx
- subsp. ***squamosa***	EFEx
filiformis new	NChu
- var. ***filiformis***	CHew CSWC EECP
gigantea	EFEx
graniticola	EFEx
helodes	CHew
heterophylla	EFEx
lasiantha	CHew
leioblastus new	CHew
loureiroi	EFEx

macrantha	EFEx
- subsp. ***macrantha***	EFEx
macrophylla subsp. ***macrophylla***	EFEx
mannii	CHew
marchantii subsp. ***prophylla***	EFEx
menziesii subsp. ***basifolia***	EFEx
- subsp. ***menziesii***	EFEx
- subsp. ***thysanosepala***	EFEx
modesta	EFEx
nidiformis	CHew
orbiculata	EFEx
paleacea subsp. ***trichocaulis***	CHew
peltata	CSWC EFEx
platypoda	EFEx
pulchella	CHew
pycnoblasta new	CHew
pygmaea	CHew
ramellosa	EFEx
roseana	CHew
rosulata	EFEx
rotundifolia	CSWC SHmp WHer
salina	EFEx
sargentii	CHew
scorpioides	CHew CSWC EECP SHmp
slackii	CHew CSWC NChu
spatulata	CSWC SHmp
stelliflora	CHew
stolonifera subsp. ***compacta***	EFEx
- subsp. ***humilis***	EFEx
- subsp. ***porrecta***	EFEx
- subsp. ***rupicola***	EFEx
- subsp. ***stolonifera***	EFEx
tubaestylus	EFEx
zonaria	EFEx

Drosophyllum (*Droseraceae*)

lusitanicum	CHew

Dryandra (*Proteaceae*)

formosa	SPlb

Dryas (*Rosaceae*)

	drummondii	ECho LLHF WAbe WFar
§	***integrifolia***	NMen
	- subsp. ***crenulata*** new	GKev
	- 'Greenland Green'	WAbe
	octopetala ♀H4	CMea CSam EAlp ECho EPfP GJos GKev LHop LRHS MWat NChi NLAp NVic SIng SPoG SRms WAbe
§	- dwarf	EWTr
	- 'Harry Bush'	GJos
	- subsp. ***hookeriana*** new	LLHF
	- 'Minor' ♀H4	ECho LRHS NMen WAbe
	× ***suendermannii*** ♀H4	EPfP EPot GMaP NMen WAbe
	tenella misapplied	see *D. octopetala* dwarf
	tenella Pursh	see *D. integrifolia*

Dryopteris ✿ (*Dryopteridaceae*)

	from Emei Shan, China	WPGP
	aemula	SRms WRic
§	***affinis*** ♀H4	CBty CLAP EBee ECha EMFW EPfP ERod GMaP IFFs LBuc LPBA MAsh MCot MGos MMoz MRav NHol NMoo SRms WFib WRic WShi WWEG
§	- subsp. ***borreri***	SRms STre
	- subsp. ***cambrensis*** 'Crispa Barnes'	WPGP
	- - 'Insubrica'	EFer
	- 'Congesta'	CLAP EBee WWEG
	- 'Congesta Cristata'	CLAP CWCL EFer EPfP GMaP LPBA MAsh NHol SRot WBrE
	- Crispa Group	CLAP LAst LRHS MMoz WWEG
§	- 'Crispa Gracilis' ♀H4	CLAP CPrp EFer EFtx ELan EPPr ERod GBin LRHS MAvo MCCP NBir NEgg WRic WWEG
*	- 'Crispa Gracilis Congesta'	CBty NGdn NHol SBch SGSe WFib WPat
§	- 'Cristata' ♀H4	Widely available
	- 'Cristata Angustata' ♀H4	CBty CChe CLAP EBee EFer ELan EPfP ETod GBin LRHS MAsh MMoz NBid NDlv NGdn NHol SRms WFib WMoo WPGP WRic WSpi
	- 'Cristata The King'	see *D. affinis* 'Cristata'
	- 'Grandiceps Askew'	EFer SRms WFib
	- 'Pinderi'	CBty CLAP EBee EFer ELan GBin LRHS MAsh MMuc NHol SEND SRms WRic WWEG
	- Polydactyla Group	CLAP GQui MDun SPer WFar
	- - 'Polydactyla Dadds'	CBty CLAP EFtx EQua LLHF NLar NMyG SMac
	- - 'Polydactyla Mapplebeck' ♀H4	CLAP GBin LPBA NBid NHol SRms WFib WRic
	- 'Revoluta'	SGSe
	- 'Revolvens'	CLAP EBee EFer SRms
	atrata misapplied	see *D. cycadina*
	atrata	CDTJ CWCL EBee EWTr LRHS MAsh MMuc NMoo SBch SPoG
	× ***australis***	CLAP MAsh WRic
	austriaca	see *D. dilatata*
	bissetiana	WRic
	blanfordii	WPGP WRic
	borreri	see *D. affinis* subsp. *borreri*
	buschiana	CBty CDTJ CLAP EFtx MRav NLar
	carthusiana	CLAP EBee EFer GBin NLar SRms WPtf WRic
	- 'Cristata'	EFer
	celsa	WRic
	championii	CCCN CLAP EBee LRHS WRic
	clintoniana	CLAP EBee EFer GBin WPGP WRic
	× ***complexa*** 'Stablerae'	CLAP EBee EFtx GBin WFib WPGP WRic
	- - crisped	WFib
	crassirhizoma	CCCN CLAP EBee GBin WRic
	cristata	CLAP CWCL EBee EFer EPfP WMoo WRic
§	***cycadina*** ♀H4	CCVT CHEx CLAP EBee EFer EFtx ELan EPfP ERod EShb GBin LPBA LRHS MBri MCCP MDun MGos MMoz MWat NBir NHol NWsh WFib WMoo WPnP WRic
	dickinsii	GLin
§	***dilatata*** ♀H4	CBgR CRWN ECha EFer EFtx ELan EPfP ERod LRHS MAsh MRav NHol SGSe SRms WFib WHal WRic WShi
	- 'Crispa Whiteside' ♀H4	CBgR CBty CLAP CPrp CWCL EBee EFer EFtx EPfP ERod MAsh MBri NHol NLar NMyG SMac SPlb SRms WFib WMoo WPGP WRic WWEG
	- 'Grandiceps'	CLAP EFer NHol WFib
	- 'Jimmy Dyce'	CLAP
	- 'Lepidota Crispa Cristata'	CLAP EBee
	- 'Lepidota Cristata' ♀H4	CBty CChe CLAP CMHG CWCL EFtx ELan ERod GBin MAsh NGdn NHol NMyG NVic SGSe SMac SRms WFar WFib WMoo WPrP WRic
	- 'Lepidota Grandiceps'	CLAP

*	- 'Recurvata'	CBty CLAP EBee LLHF MAsh NLar WRic
	- recurved	CMil
	erythrosora ♀H4	Widely available
	- 'Brilliance'	CCCN CLAP EBee LRHS MAsh NLar
	- 'Prolifera'	see *D. erythrosora* var. *prolifica*
§	- var. ***prolifica*** ♀H4	CBty CChe CLAP EBee EFtx GKev GMaP LRHS MAsh MGos MMoz NBir NDlv NEgg NHol NLar NMyG WCot WFib WRic
	expansa	EBee
	filix-mas ♀H4	Widely available
	- 'Barnesii'	CLAP CWCL EBee EFer ERod ETod GBin GCal MAsh MMuc NDlv NLar NMoo NWsh SEND SPlb SPoG WRic WWEG
	- 'Crispa'	CBty CLAP EBee EHon LRHS NHol SRms WFib
	- 'Crispa Congesta'	see *D. affinis* 'Crispa Gracilis'
	- 'Crispa Cristata'	CBgR CBty CChe CLAP CWCL EBee EFer EFtx ELan EPfP ERod GMaP LHop LRHS MAsh MBri MDun MMuc NBid NBir NHol SEND SGSe SPoG SRms SWat WFib WGor WRic WWEG
	- 'Cristata' ♀H4	CLAP EBee EFer ELan GKir MMoz NMyG NOrc SRms SWat WBVN WMoo
	- Cristata Group	EFer WRic
	- - 'Cristata Jackson'	CLAP SPlb
	- - 'Cristata Martindale'	CLAP NBid NHol SRms WFib
	- - 'Fred Jackson'	CLAP NHol WFib
	- 'Cristata Grandiceps'	EFer
	- 'Depauperata'	CLAP WPGP
	- 'Euxinensis'	CLAP
	- 'Furcans'	CLAP WRic
	- 'Grandiceps Wills' ♀H4	NBid NHol WFib
	- 'Linearis'	CMHG EBee EFer EHon ELan LAst LPBA MCot MGos NHol NWsh SGSe SRms WFib
	- 'Linearis Congesta'	WPGP
	- 'Linearis Cristata'	WRic
	- 'Linearis Polydactyla'	CBgR CBty CLAP CWCL EBee EFer EFtx EPfP GBin GKir LBMP LRHS MAsh MMoz MMuc NGdn NHol NMoo NMyG SEND SPoG WAbe WFar WIvy WMoo WPnP WPtf
	- 'Parsley'	CLAP
*	- Polydactyla Group	MGos MRav NEgg
I	***filix-mas*** 'Revolvens'	WFib
	goldieana	CDTJ CFwr CLAP CMHG EBee EFer EFtx EWTr GBin GMaP LRHS MAsh NBir NCob NGdn NLar NMyG WCot WFar WFib WMoo WPnP WRic WSpi WWEG
	hirtipes misapplied	see *D. cycadina*
	hondoensis	EFtx WRic
	intermedia	WRic
	lacera	WRic
	lepidopoda	EFtx GLin WAbe
	ludoviciana	EFtx WRic
	marginalis	CDTJ CLAP EBee EKen GBin LRHS MMoz NHol NLar SBch WMoo WRic
	oreades	SRms WAbe
	pacifica	CLAP
	paleacea	CLAP
	pseudofilix-mas	WRic
	pseudomas	see *D. affinis*
	pycnopteroides	EFtx WRic
	× ***remota***	SRms WRic
	sieboldii	CBty CHEx CLAP CPrp CWCL EBee EFer ELan ERod EShb GAbr GEdr LRHS MAsh MAvo NDlv NGdn NHol NMyG SBch SGSe SRms WAbe WBor WCot WMoo WPGP WRic WWEG
	stewartii	CLAP EBee GBin LLHF MAsh NMyG WRic
	tokyoensis	CDTJ CDes CFwr CLAP EBee EFtx GBin NHol NLar WPGP WRic WSpi
	uniformis	CLAP ELan
	wallichiana ♀H4	Widely available
	- F&M 107	WPGP

Duchesnea (*Rosaceae*)

	chrysantha	see *D. indica*
§	***indica***	CSWP GAbr IGor LEdu MRav WMoo WOut
§	- 'Harlequin' (v)	CPLG EBee GBar MCCP MTho
*	- 'Snowflake' (v)	CRow WMoo
	- 'Variegata'	see *D. indica* 'Harlequin'

Dudleya (*Crassulaceae*)

	farinosa	CHEx

Dugaldia (*Asteraceae*)

	hoopesii	see *Hymenoxys hoopesii*

Dulichium (*Cyperaceae*)

	arundinaceum	GKir LLWG LSRN

Dunalia (*Solanaceae*)

	australis	see *Iochroma australe*
	- blue-flowered	see *Iochroma australe* 'Bill Evans'
	- white-flowered	see *Iochroma australe* 'Andean Snow'

Duranta (*Verbenaceae*)

§	***erecta***	CCCN EShb
§	- 'Geisha Girl'	CCCN EShb
	- 'Sapphire Swirl'	see *D. erecta* 'Geisha Girl'
	- 'Variegata' (v)	CCCN EShb
	plumieri	see *D. erecta*
	repens	see *D. erecta*
	serratifolia	CCCN

Duvalia (*Asclepiadaceae*)

	from Mierenfontein	CFwr
	hybrid	CFwr
*	***speciosa***	CFwr

Duvernoia see *Justicia*

Dyckia (*Bromeliaceae*)

	frigida	EBee WCot
	leptostachya new	WGrn
	marnier-lapostollei	WCot
	'Morris Hobbs'	WCot
	remotiflora	CBrP SChr
	velascana	CHEx

Dymondia (*Asteraceae*)

	margaretae	CFee CPBP CStu WAbe

Dypsis (*Arecaceae*)

§	***decaryi***	CCCN EAmu LPal XBlo
	decipiens	CBrP
	lutescens ♀H1	LPal LRHS MBri XBlo

Dyschoriste (*Acanthaceae*)

	aff. ***rogersii*** new	WHil

Dysosma see *Podophyllum*

E

Ebenus (*Papilionaceae*)

	cretica	LEdu

Ecballium (*Cucurbitaceae*)

	elaterium	CArn CDTJ LEdu SGar SIde WPGP

Eccremocarpus (*Bignoniaceae*)

	scaber	CBcs CDul CEnt CRHN CTrG ELan EPfP LBMP LRHS MBri MNrw NPer SBch SGar SLim SRms WBrE
	- 'Aureus'	EPfP SPoG
	- 'Carmineus'	EPfP EWld GGar SGar SPoG
	- orange-flowered	EBee SPoG
I	- 'Roseus'	NLar SPoG
	- 'Tresco Cream'	CSpe IDee LBMP
	- Tresco Series	CTsd

Echeandia (*Anthericaceae*)

	formosa B&SWJ 9147	WCru

Echeveria ✿ (*Crassulaceae*)

	affinis	EBrs MBri
	agavoides 𝕐H1	MRav
*	- 'Metallica'	MBri
*	'Black Prince'	CAbb CBow CDoC CStu NPer SMrm SPlb SRot STre WCom WCot WDyG WEas WFar
	'Blue Waves' **new**	WCot
*	***cana***	CBct EWll SRot
	coccinea	ELan
	'Crûg Ice'	WCru
	derenbergii 𝕐H1	STre
	× ***derosa***	EPfP
	- 'Worfield Wonder' 𝕐H1	MWte STre WEas
	'Duchess of Nuremberg'	CDoC SMrm SRot WCot WFar
	elegans 𝕐H1	CHEx EPfP GAbr LSou MBri SAPC SIng WBrE WCom WCot WDyG WGwG
§	***gibbiflora*** var. ***metallica*** 𝕐H1	EPfP WEas
*	× ***gilva*** 'Red' 𝕐H1	WCot WEas
	glauca Baker	see *E. secunda* var. *glauca*
	harmsii 𝕐H1	CDoC CSWP STre WGwG
	'Hens and Chicks'	CHEx
	'Little Rose'	STre
	'Mahogany'	MAvo SUsu WCot WGrn
	'Mauna Loa'	EBee WCot
	maxonii B&SWJ 10396 **new**	WCru
	'Meridian'	CHEx
	montana B&SWJ 10277 **new**	WCru
	multicaulis **new**	MSCN
	nodulosa	STre WCot
	peacockii	EOHP MSCN SMrm SPet SWal
	'Perle d'Azur'	CHEx WCom WCot
	'Perle von Nürnberg' 𝕐H1	CAbb SMad SPet
	'Pinky'	WCot
	prolifica	STre
	pulidonis 𝕐H1	EPfP WCot
	rosea	WCot
	runyonii 'Topsy Turvy'	CDoC CHEx EOHP EPfP SMrm SPet SRot
	secunda	CAbb STre SWal
§	- var. ***glauca*** 𝕐H1	CDTJ CDoC CHEx CTsd EAmu EBee ELan EPfP EShb ETod GAbr LPJP MAvo NBir SArc STre SUsu WCom WCot
*	- - 'Gigantea'	NPer
	setosa 𝕐H1	EPfP MSCN
	- var. ***ciliata***	EShb
	shaviana	CBow EWll
	'Violet Queen'	CAbb

Echidnopsis (*Asclepiadaceae*)

	cereiformis	CFwr
	dammanniana	CFwr

Echinacea ✿ (*Asteraceae*)

	After Midnight	see *E.* 'Emily Saul'
	angustifolia	CArn CBod EBee EBla EPfP GMac GPoy LPio MHer NGHP SUsu
§	'Art's Pride' PBR	Widely available
	'CBG Cone3'	EBee NBhm
§	'Emily Saul' (Big Sky Series)	CBcs CPar IPot LRHS MAsh NGHP SMrm STes
	'Evan Saul' (Big Sky Series)	CBcs CCVN CPar CWGN EPfP IPot LBMP LRHS LSou MBNS MCot MWea NBhm NCGa NGHP NGdn NMoo NOrc SMrm SPhx SPoG SRkn WCAu WCot
	'Green Envy'	CBcs CBct CKno CMea CMil CPar CWGN EBee ECtt EKen ELon GQue LRHS LSou MAvo MBNS MBel MNrw NEgg NGHP NGdn NSti SHar SMrm SPhx SPoG WClo WCot WFut WPrP
	'Katie Saul' (Big Sky Series) **new**	IPot LRHS MBNS NGHP SPhx STes
	laevigata	NGdn
	'Matthew Saul' (Big Sky Series)	Widely available
	Orange Meadowbrite PBR	see *E.* 'Art's Pride'
	pallida	Widely available
	- 'Hula Dancer'	EBee EPfP NPri WHil WWEG
	paradoxa	Widely available
	- 'Yellow Mellow'	EPfP LSRN NLar
	'Pink Shuttles' **new**	SHar SPhx
	Pixie Meadowbrite = 'CBG Cone 2'	CWGN EBee ECtt IKil LFur NSti WCot
§	***purpurea***	Widely available
	- 'After Midnight' **new**	NBhm
	- 'Alaska' PBR	LRHS NGdn
	- 'Alba'	EBla ECtt EShb GKir LBMP LRHS MNHC NVic SHlg
	- 'Augustkönigin'	EBee EHrv LRHS NBir
	- 'Avalanche' **new**	LRHS
	- 'Baby Swan White' **new**	LRHS STes WCot WHil WWEG
	- Bressingham hybrids	EBee EBla ELan LAst LRHS MRav NCGa SPer SPhx SPoG WFar
	- 'Coconut Lime'	CBod CMil CWGN ECtt LRHS MBNS NGHP NGdn NSti SPhx SPoG SUsu WCot WHlf
	- dark-stemmed	SAga SPhx
	- Doppelganger	see *E. purpurea* 'Doubledecker'
§	- 'Doubledecker'	CHll EBee ECtt EPfP ILad LBMP LLHF LRHS MBNS MDKP NGHP NGdn SBch SMad SPhx SPoG STes WFar WHil WPer WWEG
	- Elton Knight = 'Elbrook' 𝕐H3	EBee EKen IPot LFCN LRHS MAsh MBNS MBri MWea NGHP SDix SPoG SRkn SWvt
	- 'Fancy Frills'	EBee EBla ECtt GAbr IPot LSou MBNS NBhm NGHP NGdn SPoG WCot
	- 'Fatal Attraction' PBR	CBod CKno CPar CWGN EBee ECtt EHrv ELon GAbr GQue IPot LPio LRHS LSou MAvo MBNS MNrw MWea NCGa NEgg NGHP NGdn NMoo SMrs SPhx SPoG SUsu SWvt WCot WWEG

- 'Fragrant Angel'[PBR]	CKno CMac CWGN EBee EBla ECtt ELon IPot LRHS LSRN LSou MAvo MBel MCot MDKP MWea NGHP SHar SMrm SMrs SPhx SPoG SUsu SWvt WCot
- 'Green Eyes'[PBR]	NBhm
- 'Hope'[PBR]	IPot MMHG WCAu
- 'Indiaca'	EBee MBNS NGHP SMrm WSpi
- 'Jade'	CKno CMea CWGN EBee ECtt EHrv EPfP GQue LPio LRHS LSRN LSou MBNS MBri MCot NCGa NEgg NGdn NLar SMrm SMrs SPhx SUsu WCot WWlt
- 'Kim's Knee High'[PBR]	Widely available
- 'Kim's Mop Head'	CKno CMac EBee EBla EBrs ECtt EHrv ELon EWes GKir LAst LRHS LSou MRav NOrc SHar SPav SPoG SUsu WCot WFar WWEG
§ - 'Leuchtstern'	CKno EBee LRHS NBir NBre NGHP NGdn NLar SWat WHal WMnd WPer WWEG
- 'Lilliput' **new**	LRHS
- 'Little Giant'	EBee LRHS NBhm
- 'Magnus' ♀H4	Widely available
- 'Maxima'	CAbP EBee EBrs ECtt EHrv LPio LRHS MBel WCot WGwG WWEG
- 'Merlot' **new**	NBhm
- 'Pica Bella'	EBee EPfP LRHS MAvo NGdn
- 'Pink Double Delight'	LHop LRHS MRav NCGa NGHP NGdn WHlf
- 'Prairie Frost' (v)	NGHP
- 'Prairie Splendor' **new**	EPfP LRHS
- 'Primadonna Deep Rose'	CEnt EBee ECGP NBre NGBl NGHP
- 'Razzmatazz'[PBR] (d)	Widely available
- 'Robert Bloom'	CAbP EBee EBla ECtt EHrv GQue LHop LRHS MBel MCot MNFA NBir NGdn SMrm SWvt WCAu WCot WGwG WWEG
- 'Rubinglow'	CElw CHar CWCL EBee EBla ECtt EHrv IBal IPot LAst LSou MBel MDKP NBir NGHP NGdn NLar SMrs SPer SPoG SWvt WCot
- 'Rubinstern' ♀H4	Widely available
- 'Ruby Giant' ♀H4	Widely available
- 'Sparkler' (v)	CWGN MBNS SPoG WCot
- 'The King'	EBee ECtt IBal MAvo NGHP NGdn
- 'Verbesserter Leuchtstern'	NBre NGHP NLar
- 'Vintage Wine'[PBR]	CKno CWCL CWGN EBee EBrs ECtt EHrv ELan ELon GQue IBal IKil IPot LOck LRHS LSou MBel NEgg NGHP NGdn NSti SMad SMrs SPhx SPoG SUsu SWvt WCAu WCot WWEG
- 'White Lustre'	EBee ECha EPfP LPio LRHS NBre NMoo SPav WFar
- White Natalie = 'Norwhinat' **new**	NGHP
- 'White Swan'	Widely available
'Raspberry Tart' **new**	NGHP
'Starlight'	see *E. purpurea* 'Leuchtstern'
Summer Sky	see *E.* 'Katie Saul'
'Sunrise'[PBR] (Big Sky Series)	Widely available
'Sunset'[PBR] (Big Sky Series)	Widely available
tennesseensis	CArn EShb
- 'Rocky Top'	CBcs CMac CMea CSpe EBee ECtt EHrv EShb IBal LBMP LFur LRHS LSRN MBel MNFA NBhm NBre NGHP NGdn NLar SBch SMad SPhx SSvw STes SUsu WCot
'Tiki Torch' **new**	NBhm NGHP STes WCot
'Twilight' (Big Sky Series)	CPar EBee EPfP GQue IPot LSou MAsh MWea NBhm NGHP NOrc SPhx SUsu

Echinops (*Asteraceae*)

RCB AM -14	WCot
albus	see *E.* 'Nivalis'
babatagensis	EBee
§ ***bannaticus***	CBcs CSBt EBee GKir NBid WFar
* - 'Albus'	EPfP EWll LAst NBre NGdn
- 'Blue Globe'	CElw CMHG EBee EHoe EPfP EShb GCal GKir GMaP LAst LRHS LSRN MBri NBPC NChi NGdn SBch SCoo SMrm SPoG STes WBrE WFar WMnd WPer WWEG
- 'Blue Pearl'	EBee
- 'Taplow Blue' ♀H4	Widely available
commutatus	see *E. exaltatus*
§ ***exaltatus***	LPla NBir NBre WGwG
maracandicus	EBee GCal
§ 'Nivalis'	CBre EBee SEND WCAu
ritro misapplied	see *E. bannaticus*
§ ***ritro*** L. ♀H4	Widely available
- 'Moonstone'	CRow
- subsp. ***ruthenicus*** ♀H4	ECGP ELan IGor MRav NBre SDix SUsu WPGP
- - 'Platinum Blue'	CWCL EBee GKir LRHS NBPC NEgg NLar SPet SPoG WCAu WMnd WPer
- 'Sea Stone'	EBee
- 'Veitch's Blue' misapplied	see *E. ritro* L.
- 'Veitch's Blue'	Widely available
sphaerocephalus	GQue NBid NBir NBre NBur SMrm SPlb WPer
- 'Arctic Glow'	CMac CPou CSam EBee ECha ECtt EHoe ELan EPfP EShb GKir GMac LAst LRHS MBri MWhi NBro NGdn NLar NPri NVic SMrm SPer SPlb SWvt WCAu WFar WMnd WWEG
strigosus	EBee NBre
terscheckii	EAmu
tjanschanicus	LDai LRHS NLar NMoo WWEG
tournefortii	GBin

Echium (*Boraginaceae*)

acanthocarpum	XPde
aculeatum	XPde
- 'Bicolor'	XPde
- 'Rosea'	XPde
amoenum	NWCA
boissieri	CCCN ELan XPde
brevirame	XPde
callithyrsum	XPde
§ ***candicans*** ♀H2-3	CAbb CBcs CCCN CFir CHEx CHrt CTrC CTsd ECre EShb GGal IDee LRHS NBur SAPC SArc WCHb WFar WSpi XPde
decaisnei subsp. ***decaisnei***	XPde
famarae	XPde
fastuosum	see *E. candicans*
- 'Ciel'	XPde
- 'Death Star' (v) **new**	CSpe
- 'Marine'	XPde
- 'Rouge'	XPde
gentianoides	XPde
- 'Dark Globe'	XPde
- 'Maryvonne'	XPde
- 'Pablina'	XPde
giganteum	CHll XPde
handiense	XPde
italicum	CCCN EBee NLar SIde XPde
lusitanicum	CCCN
- subsp. ***polycaulon***	WHil XPde

onosmifolium	CHll XPde
pininana ♀H2-3	Widely available
- 'Snow Tower'	CBcs CCCN CDTJ CTsd EBee ELan SBst XPde
'Pink Fountain'	CCCN CDTJ ECre ELan ILad NLar SBst XPde
plantagineum	CCCN XPde
rosulatum	CCCN XPde
russicum	CCCN CSpe CTsd EBee GAuc IDee IFro LAst LHop NBPC NChi NLar SDnm SIde SPad SPav SPhx SPlb WAul WCHb WCot WPer XPde
simplex	CCCN WSpi XPde
strictum	CCCN XPde
sventenii	XPde
tuberculatum	CCCN CFir SBod SPhx WMoo XPde
vulgare	CArn CCCN EBWF EGoo ELan EOHP GPWP MHer MNHC NLar NMir NPri NSco SBch SECG SIde WBrE WCHb WHer WJek
- 'Blue Bedder'	WSFF
- Drake's form	SGar
webbii	MMHG XPde
wildpretii ♀H2-3	CBow CCCN CDTJ ELan ILad SBch XPde
- subsp. ***wildpretii***	SPav

Edgeworthia (*Thymelaeaceae*)

§ ***chrysantha***	CBcs CFwr CHll CPMA CTri CWib EPfP LBuc LRHS MBri MGos NPal SBig SChF SPer SPoG WSHC WSpi
- B&SWJ 1048	WCru
I - 'Grandiflora'	CPMA MBri MGos NLar NPal
§ - 'Red Dragon'	CBcs CPMA NLar
- f. ***rubra*** hort.	see *E. chrysantha* 'Red Dragon'
papyrifera	see *E. chrysantha*

Edraianthus (*Campanulaceae*)

croaticus	see *E. graminifolius*
dalmaticus	GKev
- ***albus***	EPot GKev
dinaricus	EPot GKev NMen
§ ***graminifolius***	EBee ECho EPot GKev NLAp NMen WFar
owerinianus	EPot WAbe
§ ***pumilio*** ♀H4	ECho EPot GKev NLAp NMen SRms WAbe
§ ***serpyllifolius***	ECho NMen
- 'Major'	GKev NMen WAbe
wettsteinii **new**	GKev

Ehretia (*Boraginaceae*)

anacua	CBcs
dicksonii	CBcs CHEx MBri WPGP

Ehrharta (*Poaceae*)

thunbergii	EPPr

Eichhornia (*Pontederiaceae*)

crassipes	CBen CWat EMFW LPBA MSKA SCoo
- 'Major'	NPer

Elaeagnus ✿ (*Elaeagnaceae*)

angustifolia	CAgr CBot CDul EBee ECrN EMac EPfP LMaj MBar MBlu MCoo MGos NLar NWea SPer SRms WDin WFar
- Caspica Group	see *E.* 'Quicksilver'
argentea	see *E. commutata*
§ ***commutata***	CBcs CBot CMCN CMac EBee ECrN EHoe EPfP IMGH LEdu LHop MBlu MWhi NLar SPer WDin WPen WSpi
- 'Zempin'	ECrN MAsh MBri
§ × ***ebbingei***	Widely available
- 'Coastal Gold' (v)	CAbP CBcs CDoC CDul CSBt EBee EQua LBMP LRHS LSRN MAsh MGos SLim SPoG SRms
- 'Gilt Edge' (v) ♀H4	Widely available
* - 'Gold Flash'	LAst
- Gold Splash = 'Lannou' (v)	CDoC CTrC CWSG EBee EMil EPfP EQua ERas LRHS MAsh MBri SPoG SWvt
- 'Lemon Ice' (v)	NLar
- 'Limelight' (v)	Widely available
- 'Moonlight' **new**	LRHS MBri
- 'Salcombe Seedling'	CCCN NLar
glabra	EPfP GGal
- 'Reflexa'	see *E.* × *reflexa*
macrophylla	CMac EPfP WMoo
multiflora	CDul MBri SPer WPGP
parvifolia	CCCN EBee EPfP
pungens	ERom NBir
- 'Argenteovariegata'	see *E. pungens* 'Variegata'
- 'Aureovariegata'	see *E. pungens* 'Maculata'
- 'Dicksonii' (v)	CBcs CBow CWib EBee LRHS NLar SLon SPer SRms WFar
- 'Forest Gold' (v)	CAbP ELan EPfP LRHS MAsh
- 'Frederici' (v)	CBcs CDoC CMHG CMac CTrC EBee EHoe ELan EPfP EPla ERas LBMP LHop LRHS MAsh MRav SPer SPoG WBor WDin WHCG WPat
- 'Goldrim' (v) ♀H4	CMac EPfP LRHS MGos SLim WDin WMoo
- 'Hosuba-fukurin' (v)	LLHF LRHS SLon SPoG
§ - 'Maculata' (v)	Widely available
§ - 'Variegata' (v)	CBcs CMac EPla EQua NBir SPer WHCG
§ 'Quicksilver' ♀H4	Widely available
§ × ***reflexa***	CBcs EPla WHCG WPGP
× ***submacrophylla***	see *E.* × *ebbingei*
umbellata	CBcs CPLG EBee ECrN EMac EPfP MAsh MBlu MBri NLar SPer WHCG WSHC
- 'Big Red' (F) **new**	CAgr
- var. ***borealis*** 'Polar Lights'	MBri
- 'Brilliant Rose' (F) **new**	CAgr
- 'Hidden Springs' (F) **new**	CAgr
- 'Jewel' (F) **new**	CAgr
- 'Newgate' (F) **new**	CAgr
- 'Red Cascade' (F) **new**	CAgr
- 'Sweet 'n' Tart' (F) **new**	CAgr

Elatostema (*Urticaceae*)

repens var. ***pulchrum*** ♀H1	MBri
rugosum	CHEx

elderberry see *Sambucus nigra*

Elegia (*Restionaceae*)

capensis	CAbb CBcs CBct CCCN CDTJ CDoC CFir CHEx CPen CTrC EAmu EBee EShb ESwi IDee MAvo SPlb WDyG WPGP
cuspidata	EShb
spathacea	CFir

Eleocharis (*Cyperaceae*)

acicularis	CWat EMFW EPfP WPnP
dulcis variegated (v)	CRow
palustris	CRWN EBWF EMFW

Elettaria (*Zingiberaceae*)

cardamomum	CArn EOHP EShb GPoy LEdu MBri SBch SHDw WJek

Eleutherococcus (*Araliaceae*)

aff. ***cissifolius*** BWJ 7713 new	WCru
hypoleucus B&SWJ 5532	WCru
nakaianus B&SWJ 5027	WCru
pictus	see *Kalopanax septemlobus*
senticosus	GPoy
- B&SWJ 4528	WCru
- B&SWJ 4568	WCru
septemlobus	see *Kalopanax septemlobus*
sessiliflorus B&SWJ 8457	WCru
sieboldianus	CBcs MGos MRav WDin WFar
- 'Variegatus' (v)	CBcs CBot CSpe EBee EHoe ELan ELon EPfP EQua IDee LAst MGos MRav NEgg NLar NMun WHer WSHC
trifoliatus RWJ 10108	WCru

Elingamita (*Myrsinaceae*)

johnsonii	ECou

Elisena (*Amaryllidaceae*)

longipetala	see *Hymenocallis longipetala*

Elliottia (*Ericaceae*)

bracteata	see *Tripetaleia bracteata*
* ***paniculata latifolia***	NLar

Ellisiophyllum (*Scrophulariaceae*)

pinnatum	CDes CFee EBee WBor WMoo WPGP
- B&SWJ 197	WCru WPrP

Elmera (*Saxifragaceae*)

racemosa	EDif WPtf

Elodea (*Hydrocharitaceae*)

canadensis	EMFW MSKA NBir WMAq
crispa	see *Lagarosiphon major*

Elsholtzia (*Lamiaceae*)

fruticosa	CArn
stauntonii	CArn CBcs CBot EBee ECha LRHS MBri MHer SEND SPer SPoG WBor
- 'Alba'	CArn CBot

Elymus (*Poaceae*)

arenarius	see *Leymus arenarius*
canadensis	CRWN EHoe EPPr
- f. ***glaucifolius***	CFir GCal
cinereus from Washington State, USA	CDes EBee WPGP
elongatus	SApp
giganteus	see *Leymus racemosus*
glaucus misapplied	see *E. hispidus*
§ ***hispidus***	CMoH EAlp EBee EHoe EPPr EPau MBlu MBri MLHP MMoz NPri SBod SPer WCFE WCot
magellanicus	Widely available
- 'Blue Sword'	COIW LRHS MGos NBPC SRms WPtf
riparius	EPPr
sibiricus	EPPr
solandri	EHoe EWes GBin GFor NNor
- JCA 5.345.500	WPGP
villosus	EPPr MAvo
- var. ***arkansanus***	EPPr
virginicus	EBee EPPr

Elytrigia (*Poaceae*)

atherica	EBWF

Embothrium ✿ (*Proteaceae*)

coccineum	CBcs CGHE CPne CTrG CTri EBee ELon EPfP LRHS MGos MPhe SPlb SReu WBrE WPGP WPat
- Lanceolatum Group	CDoC CDul CEnd CHid EBee ELan EPfP GCal GGar ISea LRHS MBlu MDun NPal SAPC SArc SBch SLim SMad SPer SPoG SSpi SSta WAbe WDin
- - 'Inca Flame'	CBcs CCCN CDoC CPMA ELan ELon EPfP ISea MAsh MDun MGos NCGa NLar SBch SPoG SSta SWvt
* - - 'Inca King'	EBee
- - 'Ñorquinco' ♀H3	CBcs CDoC GGal GGar WHil
- Longifolium Group	CCCN GGal IBlr ISea MMHG

Eminium (*Araceae*)

albertii	EBrs ECho
spiculatum LB 374/5	WCot

Emmenopterys (*Rubiaceae*)

henryi	CBcs CCCN CGHE CMCN EBee EPfP EWTr IArd IFFs MBri NLar WPGP

Empetrum (*Empetraceae*)

luteum	MBar
nigrum	GAuc GPoy MBar WThu
rubrum 'Tomentosum'	WThu

Empodium (*Hypoxidaceae*)

plicatum	EBrs ECho

Enantiophylla (*Apiaceae*)

B&SWJ 10318 from Guatemala	WCru
heydeana B&SWJ 9114	WCru

Enceliopsis (*Asteraceae*)

covillei NNS 04-136	WCot

Encephalartos ✿ (*Zamiaceae*)

altensteinii	CBrP
caffer	CBrP
cycadifolius	CBrP LPal
ferox	CBrP
friderici-guilielmi	CBrP
ghellinckii	LPal
horridus	CBrP
kisambo	LPal
lanatus	CBrP
lebomboensis	CBrP
lehmannii	CBrP LPal
natalensis	CBrP LPal
senticosus	LPal
umbeluziensis	CBrP
villosus	CBrP LPal

Endymion see *Hyacinthoides*

Enkianthus ✿ (*Ericaceae*)

SDR 5144 new	GKev
campanulatus ♀H4	Widely available
- var. ***campanulatus*** f. ***albiflorus***	CBcs LRHS NLar
I - 'Hollandia'	CBcs CPMA MBri
- var. ***palibinii***	CBcs EPfP GGGa MAsh MGos NLar SSpi SSta WBrE

- 'Red Bells'	CBcs CDoC CDul CMac EPfP GBin LRHS MAsh MGos MMHG NLar SPoG SSpi SSta SWvt WFar
- 'Red Velvet'	CBcs NLar
- 'Ruby Glow'	CBcs MBri NLar
- var. ***sikokianus***	EPfP GGGa NLar
- 'Tokyo Masquerade'	CPMA
* - 'Variegatus' (v)	LRHS MAsh SPoG
- 'Venus'	CBcs NLar
- 'Victoria'	CBcs NLar
- 'Wallaby'	CBcs MBri NLar
cernuus f. ***rubens*** ♀H4	CBcs EPfP GGGa MBri NBea WDin
chinensis	EPfP GGGa IMGH LRHS MAsh
deflexus	CMCN SSpi WPGP
- GWJ 9225	WCru
perulatus ♀H4	CBcs CDul CMac EBee EPfP LRHS MRav WFar

Ensete (*Musaceae*)

gilletii	XBlo
glaucum	CDTJ EAmu NExo SBst WCot
superbum	NExo
§ ***ventricosum*** ♀H1+3	CBot CCCN CDTJ CDoC CHll EAmu LPal NExo SAPC SArc SBst SChr XBlo
- from Uganda **new**	GCal
§ - 'Maurelii'	CBrP CCCN CDTJ CDoC CHEx CHll CSpe CTsd EAmu EShb ESwi ETod LRHS NScw SAPC SArc SDix SPad SPoG WCot WPGP
- 'Montbeliardii'	EAmu
- 'Rubrum'	see *E. ventricosum* 'Maurelii'

Entelea (*Tiliaceae*)

arborescens	CHEx ECou EShb

Eomecon (*Papaveraceae*)

chionantha	CDes CFir CHEx CHid CPLG CSam CSpe EBee ECho EHrv ERos GAbr GBuc GCal GCra LEdu MLHP MRav MWhi NBid SMad SMrm WFar WHer WMoo WPGP WPnP WWEG

Epacris (*Epacridaceae*)

paludosa	ECou
serpyllifolia	ECou WThu

Ephedra (*Ephedraceae*)

sp.	SAPC SArc
chilensis 'Mellow Yellow'	EBee
- 'Quite White'	EBee
distachya	GPoy
equisetina	IFro
gerardiana	GEdr IFro
- var. ***sikkimensis***	WOld WPer
intermedia RCB/TQ K-1	WCot
§ ***major***	WHer
minima	GEdr NWCA WThu
minuta	CKen MSCN
nebrodensis	see *E. major*
nevadensis	GPoy
sinica	CArn
viridis	CArn

Epigaea (*Ericaceae*)

gaultherioides	GGGa

Epilobium (*Onagraceae*)

angustifolium	see *Chamerion angustifolium*
- f. ***leucanthum***	see *Chamerion angustifolium* 'Album'
californicum misapplied	see *Zauschneria californica*
canum	see *Zauschneria californica* subsp. *cana*
crassum	GBuc
dodonaei	see *Chamerion dodonaei*
garrettii	see *Zauschneria californica* subsp. *garrettii*
N ***glabellum*** misapplied	CSpe LRHS MWat SUsu WEas WWlt
hirsutum	EBWF
- 'Album'	SPoG WAlt
- 'Caerphilly Castle' (d)	WAlt
- 'Cheryl's Blush'	CRow
- 'Spring Lime'	WAlt
- 'Well Creek' (v)	WAlt WCHb WCot WHrl
microphyllum	see *Zauschneria californica* subsp. *cana*
rosmarinifolium	see *Chamerion dodonaei*
septentrionale	see *Zauschneria septentrionalis*
villosum	see *Zauschneria californica* subsp. *mexicana*

Epimedium ✿ (*Berberidaceae*)

from Yunnan, China	CDes CLAP CPom
acuminatum	CDes CElw CGHE CLAP CMoH CPLG EBee EFEx LPio SMac SUsu WPGP WSHC
- L 575	EHrv
- 'Galaxy'	CLAP CPMA EBee
'Akakage'	CHid CLAP EBee EWTr GBuc
'Akebono'	CDes CLAP CMil CPMA EBee NLar WCon
alpinum	CMac EBee EBla EPPr GBuc GKir NHol WMoo
'Amanogawa'	CDes CLAP CPMA CPom IFoB
'Amber Queen' PBR	EBee EWTr LLHF LPio SPhx WHlf
'Asiatic hybrid'	CElw CLAP CPMA WHal WPnP
'Beni-chidori'	CLAP EBee GEdr
'Beni-kujaku'	CLAP CPMA EBee GBuc GEdr
brachyrrhizum	CDes CLAP CMil CPLG CPMA CPom EBee LLHF WPGP
brevicornu	CLAP CPMA CPom WPGP
'Buckland Spider'	CDes CLAP EBee WPGP
campanulatum	CGHE CPMA LLHF
× ***cantabrigiense***	CBro CMac ECtt EPla GEdr GGar GMaP MCot MRav NBre NHol SPur WPnP
chlorandrum	CDes CLAP EBee IFoB SUsu WPGP
cremeum	see *E. grandiflorum* subsp. *koreanum*
davidii	CDes CGHE CMoH CPLG CPMA EBee ECha EWld GEdr MNFA NLar SMac WFar WHal WHoo WPGP WSHC
- EMR 4125	CElw CLAP EHrv
diphyllum	CGHE CPom CPrp EBee EHrv ELan SAga WBVN WHal
- 'White Splash'	EBee GEdr
dolichostemon	CElw CLAP CPMA
ecalcaratum	CDes CLAP CPLG CPMA CPom EBee WPGP
elongatum	CLAP GEdr
'Enchantress'	CLAP CPMA CPom ECha EHrv EWld GBuc SAga WHal WHoo
epsteinii	CDes CLAP CMil CPLG CPMA CPom EBee EPPr LLHF WPGP
fangii	CPLG
fargesii	CDes CMil CPLG EBee EHrv GEdr WCot WPGP
- 'Pink Constellation'	CDes CLAP CPMA CPom SBch WPGP
'Fire Dragon'	CBct EBee EPfP EWTr GEdr LLHF
flavum	CDes CLAP CPMA EBee EHrv WPGP

franchetii	CGHE CPLG CPom
- 'Brimstone Butterfly'	CDes CLAP CPLG CPMA EBee WHoo WPGP
'Fukujuji'	CLAP EBee LFur
'Golden Eagle'	CBow CLAP CPLG CPMA EBee EWes EWld
§ ***grandiflorum*** ♀H4	CBcs CElw CTri EBee EHrv ELan ELon EPfP EWTr GEdr GKev GKir LBMP NBir NLar NMen SAga SPer WCAu WFar WPnP WPtf WWEG
- 'Album'	CLAP EBee
- 'Crimson Beauty'	CLAP CPMA GBuc MRav WCon WHal WHoo WSHC
- 'Crimson Queen'	CBow CDes WPGP
- 'Freya'	CDes
§ - var. ***higoense***	CDes CPMA EBee WCot WHal
- 'Jennie Maillard'	SUsu
- 'Koji'	CLAP NLar WSHC
§ - subsp. ***koreanum***	CLAP EBee ECha EFEx
- 'La Rocaille'	CDes CLAP EBee
- lilac-flowered	CLAP WFar WHal
- 'Lilacinum'	EBee
- 'Lilafee'	Widely available
- 'Mount Kitadake'	CLAP
- 'Nanum' ♀H4	CDes CMil CPMA CPom EBee ECho EHrv GKir NMen NWCA WAbe WPGP
- pink-flowered	EHrv
- 'Purple Prince'	CDes CLAP
- 'Queen Esta'	CDes CLAP CPMA WPGP
- 'Red Beauty'	CLAP GAbr NLar
- 'Rose Queen' ♀H4	CMMP CPrp CSam EBee ECha EHrv ELan EPfP GBuc GEdr GGar GMaP MAvo MBri MRav NBir NMyG NSti SPoG SUsu SWvt WMoo WWEG
- 'Roseum'	CHid CLAP CMac CMil NMen SGSe SWvt WSHC
- 'Rubinkrone'	EBee GEdr GMaP
- 'Sirius'	CDes CLAP CPMA
- f. ***violaceum***	CFir CLAP CPMA CPrp WSHC
- 'White Beauty'	WSHC
- 'White Queen' ♀H4	CElw CFir CPMA CPrp EBee EHrv EPPr MRav NMyG WHal
- 'Wildside Red'	CPMA
- 'Yellow Princess'	CDes CElw CLAP CPMA EBee WCot
- 'Yubae'	EBee GEdr WWst
'Hagoromo'	EBee LFur
'Hakubai'	EBee GEdr
higoense	see *E. grandiflorum* var. *higoense*
ilicifolium	CDes WPGP
'Jean O'Neill'	CDes EBee WPGP
'Jenny Pym' **new**	EBee
'Kaguyahime'	CBow CLAP CPMA EHrv EPPr IFoB WCon
'Koki'	EBee GEdr
latisepalum	CBow CDes CLAP CMil CPMA CPom EBee EHrv GEdr MNrw WCot WPGP
leptorrhizum	CDes CElw CGHE CLAP CPLG CPMA EBee EHrv EPPr EWTr GBuc MNFA MNrw NCGa SUsu WCot WHal WSHC
- 'Mariko'	CDes CLAP CPMA CPom
lishihchenii	CDes CLAP WPGP
'Little Shrimp'	CPMA CTri EBee ELon GBuc LLHF MNFA NLar WPat
macranthum	see *E. grandiflorum*
'Madame Butterfly' **new**	WHlf
membranaceum	CDes CGHE CLAP CPMA GEdr LLHF SUsu WHal WPGP
mikinorii **new**	CPom
myrianthum	CBow CDes CPMA WPGP
ogisui	CDes CLAP CMil CPLG CPMA CPom EBee EHrv WPGP WThu
§ × ***omeiense*** 'Akame'	CBow CDes CGHE CLAP CMil CPLG CPMA EBee EPPr WPGP
- 'Emei Shan'	see *E.* × *omeiense* 'Akame'
- 'Pale Fire'	EWld
- 'Pale Fire Sibling'	CDes CPMA CPom
- 'Stormcloud'	CDes CGHE CLAP CMil CPLG CPMA CPom EBee EPPr SMac WPGP
pauciflorum	CHid CLAP CPMA EBee EPPr EWTr
× ***perralchicum*** ♀H4	CBro CMac CPMA CTri ECha GBuc GKev GKir LRHS MLHP NLar SGar SLPl WBVN WCAu WPnP
- 'Frohnleiten'	Widely available
- 'Lichtenberg'	CDes EBee SUsu
- 'Nachfolger'	EBee
- 'Wisley'	CElw CPMA CSam EHrv EWes
perralderianum	CHEx CMac CSam ELan GEdr GMaP MBel MCot SMrm SRms WHal WHoo WPnP
- 'Weihenstephan'	WPnP
'Pink Elf'	EPfP EWTr GBuc LLHF LRHS NOrc
pinnatum	EBee EBrs ECho GMaP WHal
§ - subsp. ***colchicum*** ♀H4	CLAP CMac CPMA CPom EBee EBrs ELan EPfP EWTr GAbr GBBs GEdr LRHS MCot MRav NGdn NHol NWsh SAga SDix SPoG WCAu WCot WFar WHoo WPnP WTin
- - L 321	CDes
- - 'Black Sea'	CLAP CPMA EBee EHrv GMac LHop MNrw NCGa NLar
- ***elegans***	see *E. pinnatum* subsp. *colchicum*
platypetalum	CBow CLAP CPMA WCot WPGP
pubescens	CMil CPMA EBee EHrv SAga
pubigerum	CHid CPMA CSam EBee ECha EHrv EWTr GAbr GBuc GEdr GKir LRHS MNFA NHol NMRc NMyG NPri SBch SWvt WCAu WHal WPtf WSpi
rhizomatosum	CDes CLAP CPom EBee EPPr LLHF WCot WPGP WSHC
- Og 92.114	CPMA
× ***rubrum*** ♀H4	Widely available
sagittatum	CLAP EFEx
'Sakura-maru'	GEdr
'Sasaki'	CLAP EBee GBuc MBri NMyG
sempervirens	CLAP CPMA EBee WHal
- var. ***sempervirens***	CLAP
× ***setosum***	CPMA CPom EBee ECha EHrv NLar SMac WHal
stellulatum 'Wudang Star'	CDes CGHE CLAP CMil CPLG CPMA CPom EBee EHrv EWes GEdr IMou WPGP WSpi
sutchuenense	CLAP
'Suzuka'	CBow EBee GEdr
'Tama-no-genpei'	CPMA CPom
× ***versicolor***	CBow CPLG LRHS
- 'Cupreum'	CLAP CPMA CPom EBee SMac
§ - 'Discolor'	CDes CLAP CPom EBla ECha EHrv EWld NBir SAga
- 'Neosulphureum'	CBro CDes CLAP CMMP SLPl SMac WPGP WThu
- 'Sulphureum' ♀H4	Widely available
- 'Versicolor'	see *E.* × *versicolor* 'Discolor'
× ***warleyense***	Widely available
- 'Orangekönigin'	CElw CMoH CPom CWCL EBee EBla ELon GBBs GBuc LBMP LPio LRHS LSRN MBri MCot MNFA MRav NBro NLar NMyG NSti SEND WBor WCAu WFar WHal WPnP
'William Stearn'	CLAP
wushanense	CLAP CPMA LEdu

- 'Caramel'	CBow CDes CFee CLAP CMil CPLG CPMA CPom EBee EHrv LEdu WPGP
× ***youngianum***	CBcs CMac NEgg
- 'Merlin'	CLAP CMil CPMA EBee ECha EHrv EPfP NLar NMyG NSti WHal WSHC
- 'Niveum' ♀H4	Widely available
- 'Roseum'	CBcs CElw CWCL EBee EPfP ERos GBBs IFoB LBMP LRHS LSRN MCot MRav NCGa NCob NMen NMoo NPri NSti SBch SBod SGSe SPer SPlb SWvt WBor WCAu WFar WPnP WWEG
- 'Shikinomai'	CLAP CPMA
- 'Tamabotan'	CBow CDes CLAP GBuc MRav
§ - 'Typicum'	CLAP WSHC
- white-flowered	NMen
- 'Yenomoto'	CLAP CPMA
- 'Youngianum'	see *E.* × *youngianum* 'Typicum'
zhushanense	EBee GEdr

Epipactis (*Orchidaceae*)

gigantea	Widely available
gigantea × ***veratrifolia***	see *E.* Lowland Legacy gx
helleborine	WHer
§ **Lowland Legacy gx**	NLAp
- 'Irène'	WWst
mairei	WWst
palustris	CPrp EBee EBla GEdr IPot LRHS MREP NLAp NLar NWCA WHer WHlf WPnP WPrP
purpurata	EBee
'Renate'	WWst
Sabine gx	NLAp WFar WWst
* - 'Frankfurt'	NMen
thunbergii	EFEx GEdr NLAp WWst
- yellow-flowered	GEdr WWst
veratrifolia	NLAp WWst

Epipremnum (*Araceae*)

§ ***aureum*** ♀H1	LRHS MBri
§ ***pinnatum***	MBri
- 'Marble Queen' (v)	LRHS XBlo

Episcia (*Gesneriaceae*)

dianthiflora	SRms WDib
'San Miguel'	WDib

Equisetum ✿ (*Equisetaceae*)

arvense	CArn
'Bandit' (v)	CBow CRow MSKA SMad WMoo
× ***bowmanii***	CNat
* ***camtschatcense***	CBgR CDes CMCo EBee SBig SMad
× ***dycei***	CNat
fluviatile	CNat EBee MSKA NLar
hyemale	CChe CKno CMil CTrC EHoe EPfP EPla MSCN MSKA NOak NPer NSti SAPC SArc SPlb WDyG WFar WMoo WPnP WPrP
§ - var. ***affine***	CBgR CHid CNat CRow EBee ELan EPla GCal LEdu LSou MBlu MSKA NVic SMad WMAq
- var. ***robustum***	see *E. hyemale* var. *affine*
pratense	CNat
ramosissimum	CNat
- var. ***japonicum***	EBee EMFW LEdu LPBA MCCP NScw SBod SWat WPnP
robustum	CTrC
scirpoides	CTrC EBee EFer EHoe EMFW EPfP LPBA MCCP MSKA NHol NPer SPlb SWat WMAq WMoo WPnP WPrP
sylvaticum	CNat
telmateia	SMad
variegatum	EBee EFer EWll NVic

Eragrostis (*Poaceae*)

sp.	EBee
RCB/Arg S-7	WCot
airoides misapplied	see *Agrostis montevidensis*
airoides ambig.	CHar CHrt EBee EKen GQui SPoG WMnd WMoo
chloromelas	EPPr WPGP
curvula	Widely available
- S&SH 10	WPGP
- 'Totnes Burgundy'	CAby CDes CKno CPen CWCL EAlp EBee ECha EHoe EPPr LEdu LHop MAvo MMoz MNrw NOak SPhx SRms SUsu WHal WHrl WMoo WPGP WPrP WWEG
elliottii	CKno EBee ECha EGoo EPPr GFor LBMP LHop LRHS MAvo MWea NBPC NCGa SBch SHDw SPad WFar WHrl WWEG
- 'Wind Dancer' **new**	EPPr LRHS
'Silver Needles'	see *Agrostis canina* 'Silver Needles'
spectabilis	CFir CHrt CKno CMea CSBt EBee EHoe GFor ILad LBMP LDai LRHS MDKP MMHG MWea MWhi NBPC NCGa NGdn NLar SBch SMad SPur WClo WFar WMoo WWEG
trichodes	CFir CKno EBee EGoo EHoe LDai LEdu LRHS MAvo NBPC NBre SMad SUsu WHrl WPer

Eranthemum (*Acanthaceae*)

pulchellum ♀H1	ECre

Eranthis (*Ranunculaceae*)

cilicica	see *E. hyemalis* Cilicica Group
§ ***hyemalis*** ♀H4	CBro CMea CTri EBrs ECho EHrv ELan EPfP EPot ERCP GKev IHer LAma LRHS MBri MCot MRav MWat SGar SMrm SPer SPhx WBVN WCot WFar WGwG WShi
§ - Cilicica Group	CBro EBrs ECho EHrv ELan EPot ERCP GKev GMaP LAma LRHS SPhx
- 'Flore Pleno' (d)	ECho EPot
§ - Tubergenii Group	ECho EPot WAbe WWst
- - 'Guinea Gold' ♀H4	CBro EBrs ECho
longistipitata **new**	WWst
pinnatifida	EBrs ECho EFEx GEdr WCru WWst
stellata	WCot
× ***tubergenii***	see *E. hyemalis* Tubergenii Group

Ercilla (*Phytolaccaceae*)

volubilis	CPLG CRHN CWGN EBee EWes LHop NSti WCot WCru WSHC

Eremophila (*Myoporaceae*)

§ ***debilis***	ECou
glabra orange-flowered	ECou
'Kilbara Carpet'	ECou
maculata	ECou
'Yellow Trumpet'	ECou

Eremurus (*Asphodelaceae*)

altaicus JCA 0.443.809	WCot
'Brutus'	EBee EBrs LAma
bungei	see *E. stenophyllus* subsp. *stenophyllus*
cristatus	WCot
JCA 0.444.029 **new**	
'Disco' **new**	EBee

'Emmy Ro' EBee EBrs LAma NLar SPhx WCot
'Flamengo' new EBee
fuscus JCA 0.444.043 WCot
'Helena' EBee LAma NLar
himalaicus CAvo CBot CBro CFFs CMea EBee EBrs ECho EHrv ELan EPot ERCP LAma LAst LRHS MHer SPer SPhx WCot WWEG
'Image' EBee EBrs LFur LRHS
× ***isabellinus*** new SEND
- 'Cleopatra' CAvo CBcs CSWP CSpe CWGN EBee EBrs ECho EHrv EPot ERCP GMaP LAma LRHS MBNS MGos MHer NMoo SBch SPad SPoG WWEG
- 'Obelisk' EBee EBrs ELan ERCP LAma SPhx
- 'Pinokkio' CAvo EBee EBrs ECho EGoo EPot LAma LRHS MHer SPhx
- Ruiter hybrids CMea CSWP EBee EBrs ELan EPfP LAma LAst LFur LRHS MGos MWat SPer SPet SPhx SPoG WBVN WClo WFar
- Shelford hybrids CAvo CBcs CFFs EBee EBrs ECho ELan LAma LRHS MCot MNrw SPhx WBVN
'Jeanne-Claire' EBee LAma NLar
'Joanna' EBee LAma LSRN NLar
lactiflorus EBee ECho
'Line Dance' LAma
'Luca Ro' EBee
'Moneymaker' EBee EBrs EPot LAma LRHS NLar
'Oase' CAvo CBro EBee EBrs ECho EHrv ELan EWll LAma LFur NLar WWEG
'Paradiso' EBee LRHS SPhx
regelii JCA 444.083 new WCot
'Rexona' EBee EBrs EWll LAma LRHS MBNS
robustus ♀H4 CAvo CBcs CBot CBro CMea EBee EBrs ECho EHrv ELan EPot ERCP LAma LAst LFur LRHS MAvo MBel MCot MHer NLar SMad SPhx SPlb WFar WWEG WWFP
'Roford' CMea EBee EBrs ECho LAma NMoo
'Romance' CAvo EBee EBrs ELon EPot ERCP EWll LAma LRHS MBNS MNrw WWEG
'Rumba' EBee LAma NLar SPhx
'Samba' EBee LAma
sogdianus EBee EBrs
stenophyllus ♀H4 CBro CFFs CTri CWib EBrs ECho EPot ERCP LHop LRHS SBch SPhx WFar WWEG
§ - subsp. ***stenophyllus*** CAvo CBcs CMea EBee EHrv EPfP EShb GMaP LAma LRHS MBel MHer MNrw NBPC NPer NPri SPer WBVN WFar
'Tango' new EBee
'Tap Dance' EBee LAma
tauricus EBee EBrs ECho
'Yellow Giant' EBee EBrs ECho
zenaidae WCot

Erianthus see *Saccharum*

Eriastrum (*Polemoniaceae*)

densifolium 'Tetra Riesen' NNS 05-271 WCot

Erica ✿ (*Ericaceae*)

abietina subsp. ***aurantiaca*** new CDes
'African Fanfare' SHeS
× ***afroeuropaea*** SHeS
alopecurus SPlb
arborea CTrG SPlb
- var. ***alpina*** ♀H4 CDoC CTri EPfP LRHS MBar NHol SHeS SPer SPoG SRms SSpi
§ - - 'Albert's Gold' ♀H4 CBcs CSBt CTri ELan EPfP LRHS MAsh MBar MBri MGos MSwo NHol SHeS SPer SPoG SRms WFar
- 'Arbora Gold' see *E. arborea* var. *alpina* 'Albert's Gold'
- 'Arnold's Gold' see *E. arborea* var. *alpina* 'Albert's Gold'
- 'Estrella Gold' ♀H4 CBcs CDoC CSBt CTri ELan EPfP LRHS MAsh MBar MGos NHol SBch SHeS SLon SPer SRms
- 'Great Star' new EMil
- 'Picos Pygmy' SHeS
- 'Spanish Lime' SHeS
- 'Spring Smile' SHeS
australis ♀H4 MBar
- 'Castellar Blush' LRHS SHeS
- 'Holehird' SHeS
- 'Mr Robert' ♀H3 EPfP MBar SHeS
- 'Riverslea' ♀H4 CTri LRHS MBar SHeS
caffra SHeS SPlb
canaliculata ♀H3 CBcs SHeS
carnea ELan
- 'Accent' SHeS
- 'Adrienne Duncan' ♀H4 LRHS MBar NDlv NHol SHeS
- 'Alan Coates' MBar SHeS
- 'Alba' SHeS
- 'Altadena' MBar SHeS
- 'Amy Doncaster' see *E. carnea* 'Treasure Trove'
- 'Ann Sparkes' ♀H4 CSBt CTri EPfP MBar MSwo NHol SHeS SRms
- 'Atrorubra' MBar SHeS
- 'Aurea' LRHS MBar NHol SHeS SRms
- 'Barry Sellers' SHeS
§ - 'Bell's Extra Special' EPfP SHeS
- 'Beoley Pink' SHeS
- 'C.J. Backhouse' SHeS
I - 'Carnea' MBar SHeS
- 'Catherine Kolster' SHeS
- 'Cecilia M. Beale' MBar SHeS
- 'Challenger' ♀H4 EPfP LRHS MBar MGos NHol SCoo SHeS SPer SRms
- 'Christine Fletcher' SHeS
- 'Clare Wilkinson' SHeS
- 'David's Seedling' SHeS
- 'December Red' CSBt EPfP MBar MSwo NHol SHeS SPer SRms
- 'Dømmesmoen' SHeS
- 'Dwingeloo Pride' SHeS
- 'Early Red' SHeS
- 'Eileen Porter' MBar NHol SHeS
- 'Eva' CBcs SHeS
- 'Foxhollow' ♀H4 CBcs CTri EPfP IArd MBar MGos MSwo NHol SHeS SRms
- 'Foxhollow Fairy' MBar SHeS SRms
- 'Gelber Findling' SHeS
- 'Gelderingen Gold' SHeS
- 'Golden Starlet' ♀H4 CSBt CTri EPfP MBar MGos NBlu NHol NPri SHeS SPer SRms
- 'Gracilis' MBar SHeS
- 'Hamburg' SHeS
- 'Heathwood' LRHS MBar NHol SCoo SHeS SRms
- 'Hilletje' SHeS SRms
- 'Ice Princess' ♀H4 EPfP NHol NPri SCoo SHeS SPer SRms
- 'Isabell' ♀H4 CBcs EPfP NPri SCoo SHeS SRms
- 'Jack Stitt' MBar SHeS
- 'James Backhouse' CTri SHeS
- 'January Sun' SHeS

	Name	Suppliers
	- 'Jason Attwater'	SHeS
	- 'Jean'	SHeS
	- 'Jennifer Anne'	MBar SHeS
	- 'John Kampa'	MBar NHol SHeS
	- 'John Pook'	SHeS
	- 'King George'	CTri MBar NHol SHeS
§	- 'Kramer's Rubin'	SHeS
	- 'Lake Garda'	SHeS
	- 'Late Pink'	SHeS
	- 'Lena'	see *E.* × *darleyensis* 'Lena'
	- 'Lesley Sparkes'	CSBt MBar SHeS
	- 'Little Peter'	SHeS
	- 'Lohse's Rubin'	NHol SHeS
	- 'Lohse's Rubinfeuer'	SHeS
	- 'Lohse's Rubinschimmer'	SHeS
	- 'Loughrigg' $\mathbb{Y}^{H4}$	CSBt CTri MBar NHol SHeS SRms
	- Madame Seedling	see *E. carnea* 'Weisse March Seedling'
	- 'March Seedling'	EPfP MBar NHol NPri SHeS SRms
	- 'Margery Frearson'	SHeS
	- 'Martin'	SHeS
	- 'Moonlight'	SHeS
	- 'Mrs Sam Doncaster'	MBar SHeS
	- 'Myretoun Ruby' $\mathbb{Y}^{H4}$	CBcs CSBt CTri EBrs EPfP MBar MGos NBlu NDlv NHol NPri SHeS SPer SRms
	- 'Nathalie' $\mathbb{Y}^{H4}$	CSBt MSwo NHol SCoo SHeS SRms
	- 'Netherfield Orange'	SHeS
	- 'Oriënt'	SHeS SRms
	- 'Pallida'	SHeS
	- 'Pink Beauty'	see *E. carnea* 'Pink Pearl'
	- 'Pink Cloud'	SHeS
	- 'Pink Mist'	SHeS SPer SRms
§	- 'Pink Pearl'	MBar SHeS
	- 'Pink Spangles' $\mathbb{Y}^{H4}$	CBcs CSBt CTri MBar MGos MSwo NHol SHeS SRms
	- 'Pirbright Rose'	SHeS SRms
	- 'Polden Pride'	SHeS
	- 'Porter's Red'	MBar SHeS
	- 'Praecox Rubra' $\mathbb{Y}^{H4}$	EPfP MBar NHol SHeS
	- 'Prince of Wales'	SHeS
	- 'Queen Mary'	SHeS
	- 'Queen of Spain'	SHeS
	- 'R.B. Cooke' $\mathbb{Y}^{H4}$	EPfP MBar SCoo SHeS SRms
	- 'Red Rover'	SHeS
	- 'Robert Jan'	SHeS
	- 'Romance'	SHeS
	- 'Rosalie' $\mathbb{Y}^{H4}$	CBcs EPfP IArd MMuc MSwo NPri SCoo SHeS SPer SRms
	- 'Rosalinde Schorn'	SHeS
	- 'Rosantha'	SHeS SRms
	- 'Rosea'	SPlb
	- 'Rosy Gem'	MBar SHeS
	- 'Rosy Morn'	SHeS
	- 'Rotes Juwel'	SHeS
	- 'Rubinteppich'	SHeS SRms
	- 'Ruby Glow'	MBar MSwo NHol SHeS
	- 'Scatterley'	SHeS
	- 'Schatzalp'	SHeS
	- 'Schneekuppe'	SHeS
	- 'Schneesturm'	SHeS SRms
	- 'Sherwood Creeping'	MBar SHeS
	- 'Smart's Heath'	SHeS
	- 'Sneznik'	SHeS
	- 'Snow Prince'	SHeS
	- 'Snow Queen'	MBar SHeS
	- 'Spring Cottage Crimson'	MBar SHeS
	- 'Spring Day'	MSwo SHeS
	- 'Springwood Pink'	CSBt CTri MBar NHol SHeS SRms
	- 'Springwood White' $\mathbb{Y}^{H4}$	CSBt CTri EBrs EPfP MBar MGos MSwo NHol SHeS SPer SRms
I	- 'Startler'	MBar NHol SHeS
	- 'Sunshine Rambler' $\mathbb{Y}^{H4}$	MBar SHeS
	- 'Thomas Kingscote'	MBar SHeS
§	- 'Treasure Trove'	SHeS
	- 'Tybesta Gold'	SHeS
	- 'Viking'	NHol SHeS
	- 'Vivellii' $\mathbb{Y}^{H4}$	CSBt CTri MBar NDlv NHol SHeS SRms
	- 'Vivellii Aurea'	SHeS
	- 'Walter Reisert'	SHeS
	- 'Wanda'	MBar SHeS
§	- 'Weisse March Seedling'	SHeS
	- 'Wentwood Red'	SHeS
	- 'Westwood Yellow' $\mathbb{Y}^{H4}$	CSBt MBar MGos NHol SHeS SPer SRms
	- Whisky	see *E. carnea* 'Bell's Extra Special'
	- 'Whitehall'	NHol NPri SHeS SRms
	- 'Winter Beauty'	MGos NDlv NHol SHeS
	- 'Winter Gold'	SHeS
	- 'Winter Melody'	SHeS
	- Winter Rubin	see *E. carnea* 'Kramer's Rubin'
	- 'Winter Snow'	CSBt SCoo SHeS SRms
	- 'Winter Sport'	SHeS
	- 'Winterfreude'	SHeS
	- 'Wintersonne'	CBcs EPfP NPri SHeS SRms
	ciliaris 'Aurea'	MBar SHeS SRms
	- 'Bretagne'	SHeS
	- 'Camla'	MBar SHeS
	- 'Corfe Castle'	MBar SHeS
	- 'David McClintock'	MBar SHeS
	- 'Fada das Serras'	SHeS
	- 'Globosa'	SHeS
	- 'Mawiana'	SHeS
	- 'Mrs C.H. Gill' $\mathbb{Y}^{H4}$	SHeS
	- 'Ram'	SHeS
	- 'Rotundiflora'	SHeS
	- 'Stapehill'	SHeS
	- 'Stoborough' $\mathbb{Y}^{H4}$	MBar SHeS
	- 'White Wings'	SHeS
	- 'Wych'	SHeS
	cinerea* f. *alba 'Alba Major'	CSBt MBar SHeS
	- - 'Alba Minor' $\mathbb{Y}^{H4}$	MBar NHol SHeS
	- - 'Celebration'	MBar NBlu NHol SHeS
	- - 'Doctor Small's Seedling'	SHeS
	- - 'Domino'	MBar SHeS
	- - 'Godrevy'	SHeS
	- - 'Hookstone White' $\mathbb{Y}^{H4}$	MBar NDlv SHeS
	- - 'Jos' Honeymoon'	SHeS
	- - 'Marina'	SHeS
	- - 'Nell'	MBar SHeS
	- - 'Snow Cream'	MBar SHeS
	- - 'White Dale'	MBar SHeS
	- 'Alette'	SHeS
	- 'Alfred Bowerman'	SHeS
	- 'Alice Ann Davies'	SHeS
	- 'Angarrack'	SHeS
	- 'Anja Bakker'	SHeS
	- 'Anja Blum'	SHeS
	- 'Anja Slegers'	SHeS
	- 'Ann Berry'	MBar SHeS
	- 'Apple Blossom'	SHeS
	- 'Apricot Charm'	CSBt MBar MSwo SHeS
	- 'Aquarel'	SHeS
	- 'Ashdown Forest'	SHeS
	- 'Ashgarth Garnet'	MBar SHeS
	- 'Atropurpurea'	MBar SHeS
	- 'Atrorubens'	MBar SHeS SRms
	- 'Atrorubens, Daisy Hill'	SHeS
	- 'Atrosanguinea'	MBar
	- 'Atrosanguinea Reuthe's Variety'	SHeS
	- 'Atrosanguinea Smith's Variety'	SHeS

I – 'Aurea'	MMuc
– 'Baylay's Variety'	MBar SHeS
– 'Bemmel'	SHeS
– 'Blossom Time'	MBar SHeS
– 'Bucklebury Red'	SHeS
– 'C.D. Eason' ♀H4	CBcs CSBt CTri EPfP MBar NBlu NHol SHeS SRms
§ – 'C.G. Best' ♀H4	ECho MBar SHeS
– 'Cairn Valley'	SHeS
– 'Caldy Island'	MBar SHeS
– 'Cevennes'	MBar SHeS
– 'Champs Hill' ♀H4	SHeS
– 'Cindy' ♀H4	MBar NHol SHeS
– 'Coccinea'	SHeS
– 'Colligan Bridge'	MBar SHeS
– 'Constance'	MBar SHeS
– 'Contrast'	MBar SHeS
– 'Crimson Glow'	SHeS
– 'Discovery'	SHeS
– 'Duncan Fraser'	MBar SHeS
– 'Eden Valley' ♀H4	MBar NHol SHeS SRms
– 'Eline'	SHeS
– 'England'	SHeS
– 'Felthorpe'	SHeS
– 'Fiddler's Gold' ♀H4	MBar NHol SHeS
– 'Flamingo'	SHeS
– 'Foxhollow Mahogany'	MBar SHeS
– 'Frances'	SHeS
– 'Frankrijk'	SHeS
– 'Fred Corston'	SHeS
– 'G. Osmond'	MBar SHeS
– 'Geke'	SHeS
– 'Glasnevin Red'	MBar SHeS
– 'Glencairn'	MBar NHol SHeS
– 'Golden Charm'	NHol SHeS
– 'Golden Drop'	CSBt MBar NBlu NHol SHeS
– 'Golden Hue' ♀H4	MBar NHol SHeS
– 'Golden Sport'	SHeS
– 'Golden Striker'	SHeS
– 'Golden Tee'	SHeS
– 'Goldilocks'	SHeS
– 'Graham Thomas'	see *E. cinerea* 'C.G. Best'
– 'Grandiflora'	MBar SHeS
– 'Guernsey Lime'	MBar SHeS
– 'Guernsey Pink'	SHeS
– 'Guernsey Plum'	SHeS
– 'Guernsey Purple'	SHeS
– 'Hardwick's Rose'	MBar SHeS
– 'Harry Fulcher'	SHeS
– 'Heatherbank'	SHeS
– 'Heathfield'	SHeS
– 'Heidebrand'	MBar SHeS
– 'Hermann Dijkhuizen'	SHeS
– 'Honeymoon'	MBar SHeS
– 'Hookstone Lavender'	SHeS
– 'Hutton's Seedling'	SHeS
– 'Iberian Beauty'	SHeS
– 'Jack London'	SHeS
– 'Janet'	MBar SHeS
– 'Jersey Wonder'	SHeS
– 'Jiri'	SHeS
– 'John Ardron'	SHeS
– 'John Eason'	SHeS
– 'Jos' Golden'	SHeS
– 'Joseph Murphy'	MBar SHeS
– 'Josephine Ross'	MBar SHeS
– 'Joyce Burfitt'	SHeS
– 'Katinka'	CBcs MBar MSwo NHol SHeS
– 'Kerry Cherry'	SHeS
– 'Knap Hill Pink' ♀H4	MBar SHeS
– 'Lady Skelton'	MBar SHeS
– 'Lavender Lady'	SHeS
– 'Lilac Time'	MBar SHeS
– 'Lilacina'	MBar SHeS
– 'Lime Soda' ♀H4	SHeS
– 'Lorna Anne Hutton'	SHeS
– 'Michael Hugo'	SHeS
– 'Miss Waters'	MBar SHeS
– 'Mrs Dill'	MBar SHeS
– 'Mrs E.A. Mitchell'	NHol SHeS SPlb
– 'Mrs Ford'	MBar SHeS
– 'My Love'	MBar SHeS
– 'Neptune'	SHeS
– 'Newick Lilac'	MBar SHeS
– 'Next Best'	MBar SHeS
– 'Novar'	SHeS
– 'Old Rose'	SHeS
– 'P.S. Patrick' ♀H4	MBar SHeS
– 'Pallas'	SHeS
– 'Pallida'	SHeS
– 'Paul's Purple'	SHeS
– 'Peñaz'	SHeS
– 'Pentreath' ♀H4	MBar SHeS
– 'Pink Foam'	MBar SHeS
– 'Pink Ice' ♀H4	CTri EPfP MBar MSwo NHol SHeS
– 'Plummer's Seedling'	MBar SHeS
– 'Promenade'	SHeS
– 'Prostrate Lavender'	SHeS
– 'Providence'	SHeS
– 'Purple Beauty'	MBar SHeS
– 'Purple Robe'	SHeS
– 'Purple Spreader'	SHeS
– 'Purpurea'	SHeS
– 'Pygmaea'	MBar SHeS
– 'Red Pentreath'	SHeS
– 'Robert Michael'	SHeS
– 'Rock Pool'	MBar NHol SHeS
– 'Rock Ruth'	SHeS
– 'Romiley'	MBar SHeS
– 'Rose Queen'	SHeS
– 'Rosea'	SHeS
I – 'Rosea Splendens'	SHeS
– 'Rosy Chimes'	MBar SHeS
– 'Rozanne Waterer'	SHeS
– 'Ruby'	MBar SHeS
– 'Sandpit Hill'	MBar SHeS
– 'Schizopetala'	MBar SHeS
– 'Screel'	SHeS
– 'Sea Foam'	MBar SHeS
– 'Sherry'	MBar NBlu NHol SHeS
– 'Smith's Lawn'	SHeS
– 'Spicata'	SHeS
– 'Splendens'	SHeS
– 'Startler'	SHeS
– 'Stephen Davis' ♀H4	MBar NHol SHeS
– 'Strawberry Bells'	SHeS
– 'Sue Lloyd'	SHeS
– 'Summer Gold'	NDlv SHeS
– 'Tilford'	SHeS
– 'Tom Waterer'	MBar SHeS
– 'Underwood Pink'	SHeS
– 'Uschie Ziehmann'	SHeS
– 'Velvet Night' ♀H4	CSBt MBar NHol SHeS SRms
– 'Victoria'	MBar SHeS
– 'Violacea'	SHeS
– 'Violetta'	SHeS
– 'Vivienne Patricia'	MBar SHeS
– 'W.G. Notley'	SHeS
– 'West End'	SHeS
– 'Windlebrooke' ♀H4	MBar NHol SHeS
– 'Wine'	SHeS
– 'Yvonne'	SHeS
curviflora	SHeS SPlb

	Name	Suppliers
	× ***darleyensis*** 'Ada S. Collings'	MBar SHeS
	- 'Alba'	see *E.* × *darleyensis* 'Silberschmelze'
	- 'Archie Graham'	SHeS
	- 'Arthur Johnson' ♀H4	CSBt CTri MBar NHol SHeS SRms
	- 'Aurélie Brégeon'	SHeS SRms
	- 'Cherry Stevens'	see *E.* × *darleyensis* 'Furzey'
§	- 'Darley Dale'	CSBt EPfP MBar MMuc NHol NPri SBch SCoo SHeS SPer SRms
	- 'Dunreggan'	SHeS
	- 'Dunwood Splendour'	MBar
	- 'Epe'	SHeS
	- 'Erecta'	SHeS
	- 'Eva' PBR	see *E.* × *darleyensis* 'Eva Gold'
§	- 'Eva Gold' PBR	NHol SHeS SRms
§	- 'Furzey' ♀H4	CSBt EPfP MBar MGos NHol SCoo SHeS SPer SRms
	- 'George Rendall'	CSBt CTri EPfP NHol SCoo SHeS
	- 'Ghost Hills' ♀H4	CSBt EPfP MBar MSwo NHol NPri SBch SCoo SHeS SPer SRms
	- 'J.W. Porter' ♀H4	EPfP MBar MMuc NDlv SCoo SHeS SRms
	- 'Jack H. Brummage'	CSBt CTri IArd MBar MGos MSwo NHol SHeS SRms
	- 'James Smith'	MBar SHeS
	- 'Jenny Porter' ♀H4	CSBt EPfP MBar SHeS
	- 'Kramer's Rote' ♀H4	CBcs CSBt CTri EBrs EPfP MBar MGos MMuc NBlu NDlv NHol NPri SBch SHeS SPer SRms
§	- 'Lena'	SHeS
	- 'Lucie' **new**	NPri
	- 'Margaret Porter'	EPfP SHeS SPer
	- 'Mary Helen'	CSBt EPfP NHol SCoo SHeS SPer SRms
	- Molten Silver	see *E.* × *darleyensis* 'Silberschmelze'
	- 'Moonshine'	NHol
	- 'Mrs Parris' Red'	SHeS
	- 'N.R. Webster'	SHeS
	- 'Pink Perfection'	see *E.* × *darleyensis* 'Darley Dale'
§	- 'Silberschmelze'	CSBt CTri EPfP MBar MGos MMuc MSwo NDlv NHol NPri SHeS SPer SRms
	- 'Spring Surprise' PBR	EPfP NPri SHeS
	- 'Tweety'	CBcs SHeS
	- 'W.G. Pine'	SHeS
	- 'White Fairy'	SHeS
	- 'White Glow'	CTri NBlu SHeS
	- 'White Perfection' ♀H4	CBcs CSBt EPfP IArd MBar NHol NPri SBch SCoo SHeS SRms
	discolor	SHeS
	erigena 'Alba'	MBar SHeS
	- 'Brian Proudley'	MBar SHeS
	- 'Brightness'	CSBt EPfP MBar MSwo NHol SCoo SHeS
	- 'Coccinea'	SHeS
	- 'Ewan Jones'	MBar SHeS
	- 'Glauca'	SHeS
	- 'Golden Lady' ♀H4	CSBt MBar MSwo NHol SCoo SHeS
	- 'Hibernica'	SHeS
	- 'Hibernica Alba'	MBar SHeS
	- 'Irish Dusk' ♀H4	CBcs CSBt CTri EPfP MBar MGos NHol SCoo SHeS SRms
	- 'Irish Salmon'	MBar SHeS
	- 'Irish Silver'	MBar SHeS
	- 'Ivory'	SHeS
	- 'Maxima'	SHeS
	- 'Mrs Parris' Lavender'	SHeS
	- 'Mrs Parris' White'	SHeS
	- 'Nana'	SHeS
	- 'Nana Alba'	MBar SHeS
	- 'Nana Compacta'	SHeS
	- 'Rosea'	MBar SHeS
	- 'Rosslare'	SHeS
	- 'Rubra'	SHeS
	- 'Superba'	MBar MGos SHeS SRms
	- 'Thing Nee'	SHeS
	- 'W.T. Rackliff' ♀H4	CBcs CSBt EPfP MBar MGos MSwo NHol SCoo SHeS SPer SRms
	- 'W.T. Rackliff Variegated' (v)	SHeS
	formosa	CDes
	× ***garforthensis*** 'Tracy Wilson'	SHeS
	glauca var. ***elegans*** **new**	CDes
	- var. ***glauca***	SPlb
	gracilis	SPoG
	× ***griffithsii*** 'Ashlea Gold'	SHeS
	- 'Elegant Spike'	SHeS
§	- 'Heaven Scent'	SHeS
	- 'Jaqueline'	NHol SHeS SRms
	- 'Valerie Griffiths'	MBar NHol SCoo SHeS SRms
	'Heaven Scent'	see *E.* × *griffithsii* 'Heaven Scent'
	'Hélène'	SHeS
	× ***hiemalis*** hort.	SPoG
	- 'Ghislaine'	SHeS
	holosericea **new**	CDes
	× ***krameri*** 'Otto'	SHeS
	- 'Rudi'	SHeS
	lusitanica ♀H3	CTrG LRHS MBar SHeS SPoG
	- 'George Hunt'	ELan EPfP LRHS NHol SHeS SLon SPer SPoG
	- 'Sheffield Park'	ELan LRHS SHeS SSpi
	mackayana	SHeS
	subsp. ***andevalensis***	
	- - f. ***albiflora***	SHeS
	- 'Ann D. Frearson' (d)	SHeS
	- 'Doctor Ronald Gray'	MBar SHeS
	- 'Donegal'	SHeS
	- 'Errigal Dusk'	SHeS
	- 'Galicia'	SHeS
	- 'Lawsoniana'	SHeS
	- 'Maura' (d)	SHeS
	- 'Plena' (d)	MBar SHeS
	- 'Shining Light'	SDys SHeS
	- 'William M'Calla'	SHeS
	mammosa	SPlb
	manipuliflora	MBar
	- 'Aldeburgh'	SHeS
§	- 'Cascades'	SHeS
	- 'Corfu'	SHeS
	- 'Don Richards'	SHeS
	- 'Ian Cooper'	SHeS
	- 'Korçula'	SHeS
	- 'Toothill Mustard'	SHeS
	- 'Waterfall'	see *E. manipuliflora* 'Cascades'
	mediterranea	see *E. erigena*
	micropotamus **new**	CDes
	multiflora 'Formentor'	SHeS
	× ***oldenburgensis*** 'Ammerland'	SHeS
	- 'Oldenburg'	SHeS
	patersonii	CDes SPlb
	plukenetii	CDes
	× ***praegeri***	see *E.* × ***stuartii***
	racemosa	SHeS
	scoparia subsp. ***azorica***	SHeS
	- subsp. ***maderincola*** 'Madeira Gold'	SHeS
	- subsp. ***platycodon***	SHeS
§	- subsp. ***scoparia*** 'Minima'	MBar SHeS
	- - 'Pumila'	see *E. scoparia* subsp. *scoparia* 'Minima'

	spiculifolia	MBar WThu
	– f. ***albiflora***	SHeS
	– 'Balkan Rose'	GCal SHeS
	'Spring Field White'	MMuc
	straussiana	SPlb
§	× ***stuartii***	MBar
	– 'Charles Stuart'	SHeS
	– 'Connemara'	SHeS
	– 'Irish Lemon' ♀H4	CSBt EPfP MBar MSwo NHol SHeS
	– 'Irish Orange'	CSBt MBar NHol SHeS
	– 'Irish Rose'	SHeS
	– 'Nacung'	SHeS
	– 'Pat Turpin'	SHeS
	subdivaricata	SHeS
	terminalis ♀H4	MBar SHeS SRms
	– 'Golden Oriole'	SHeS
	– 'Thelma Woolner'	MBar SHeS
	tetralix	SRms
	– 'Alba'	SHeS
	– 'Alba Mollis' ♀H4	CSBt MBar NHol SHeS
	– 'Alba Praecox'	SHeS
	– 'Allendale Pink'	SHeS
	– 'Ardy'	SHeS
	– 'Bala'	SHeS
	– 'Bartinney'	MBar SHeS
	– 'Con Underwood' ♀H4	CSBt MBar MSwo NHol SHeS SRms
	– 'Curled Roundstone'	SHeS
	– 'Dänemark'	SHeS
	– 'Daphne Underwood'	SHeS
	– 'Darleyensis'	SHeS
	– 'Dee'	SHeS
	– 'Delta'	MBar SHeS
	– 'Foxhome'	MBar SHeS
	– 'George Fraser'	SHeS
	– 'Gratis'	SHeS
	– 'Hailstones'	MBar SHeS
	– 'Helma'	SHeS
	– 'Helma Variegated' (v)	SHeS
	– 'Hookstone Pink'	MSwo SHeS
	– 'Humoresque'	SHeS
	– 'Jos' Creeping'	SHeS
	– 'Ken Underwood'	MBar SHeS
	– 'L.E. Underwood'	MBar NHol SHeS
	– 'Mary Grace'	SHeS
	– 'Melbury White'	MBar SHeS
	– 'Morning Glow'	see *E.* × *watsonii* 'F. White'
	– 'Pink Glow'	SHeS
	– 'Pink Pepper'	SHeS
	– 'Pink Star' ♀H4	MBar NHol SHeS SRms
	– 'Renate'	SHeS
	– 'Riko'	SHeS SRms
	– 'Rosea'	SHeS
	– 'Rubra'	SHeS
§	– 'Ruby's Variety'	MBar SHeS
	– 'Ruby's Velvet'	see *E. tetralix* 'Ruby's Variety'
	– 'Ruth's Gold'	MBar NHol SHeS
	– 'Salmon Seedling'	SHeS
	– 'Samtpfötchen'	SHeS
	– 'Silver Bells'	CSBt MBar SHeS
	– 'Stikker'	SHeS
	– 'Swedish Yellow'	SHeS
	– 'Terschelling'	SHeS
	– 'Tina'	SHeS
	– 'Trixie'	SHeS
	– 'White House'	SHeS
	umbellata	MBar SHeS
	– 'Anne Small'	SHeS
	– 'David Small'	SHeS
	vagans f. ***alba***	MMuc
	– 'Alba Nana'	see *E. vagans* 'Nana'
	– 'Bianca'	SHeS
	– 'Birch Glow' ♀H4	EPfP SHeS
	– 'Carnea'	SHeS
	– 'Charm'	SHeS
	– 'Chittendenii'	SHeS
	– 'Cornish Cream' ♀H4	EPfP MBar NHol SHeS
	– 'Cream'	SHeS
	– 'Diana Hornibrook'	MBar SHeS
	– 'Diana's Gold'	SHeS
	– 'Fiddlestone'	MBar SHeS
	– 'French White'	MBar SHeS
	– 'George Underwood'	MBar SHeS
	– 'Golden Triumph'	MBar SHeS
	– 'Grandiflora'	MBar SHeS
	– 'Holden Pink'	SHeS
	– 'Hookstone Rosea'	MBar SHeS
	– 'Ida M. Britten'	MBar SHeS
	– 'J.C. Fletcher'	SHeS
	– 'Kevernensis Alba' ♀H4	MBar SHeS
	– 'Leucantha'	SHeS
	– 'Lilacina'	MBar SHeS
	– 'Lyonesse' ♀H4	CTri MBar MGos MMuc MSwo NBlu NHol SHeS SRms
	– 'Miss Waterer'	MBar SHeS
	– 'Mrs D.F. Maxwell' ♀H4	CSBt CTri MBar MGos MSwo NHol SHeS SPer SRms
	– 'Mrs Donaldson'	SHeS
§	– 'Nana'	MBar SHeS
	– 'Pallida'	SHeS
	– 'Peach Blossom'	MBar SHeS
	– 'Pyrenees Pink'	MBar SHeS
	– 'Rosea'	SHeS
	– 'Rubra'	MBar SHeS
	– 'Saint Keverne'	CSBt CTri IArd MBar NHol SHeS
	– 'Summertime'	MBar SHeS
	– 'Valerie Proudley' ♀H4	CSBt MBar MGos NHol SHeS SRms
	– 'Valerie Smith'	SHeS
	– 'Viridiflora'	MBar SHeS
	– 'White Lady'	MBar SHeS
	– 'White Rocket'	MBar SHeS
	– 'White Spire'	SHeS
	– 'Yellow John'	CBcs MBar SHeS
	× ***veitchii*** 'Brockhill'	SHeS
	– 'Exeter' ♀H3	CSBt ELan EPfP LRHS MBar NHol SHeS WFar
	– 'Gold Tips' ♀H4	CSBt EPfP LRHS MBar NHol SHeS
	– 'Pink Joy'	LRHS SHeS
	ventricosa	SPoG
	versicolor	SPlb
	verticillata	SHeS
	viridescens	SHeS
	× ***watsonii*** 'Cherry Turpin'	SHeS
	– 'Dawn' ♀H4	MBar SHeS
	– 'Dorothy Metheny'	SHeS
	– 'Dorset Beauty'	SHeS
§	– 'F. White'	MBar SHeS
	– 'Gwen'	MBar SHeS
	– 'H. Maxwell'	SHeS
	– 'Mary'	SHeS
	– 'Pink Pacific'	SHeS
	– 'Rachel'	SHeS
	– 'Truro'	SHeS
	× ***williamsii*** 'Cow-y-Jack'	SHeS
	– 'Croft Pascoe'	SHeS
	– 'David Coombe'	SHeS
	– 'Gew Graze'	SHeS
	– 'Gold Button'	MBar SHeS
	– 'Gwavas'	MBar SHeS
	– 'Jean Julian'	SHeS
	– 'Ken Wilson'	SHeS
	– 'Lizard Downs'	SHeS
	– 'Marion Hughes'	SHeS
	– 'P.D. Williams' ♀H4	CBcs MBar SHeS
I	'Winter Fire' (*oatesii* hybrid)	SHeS

Ericameria (*Asteraceae*)

	discoidea NNS 06-209 **new**	WCot

Erigeron (*Asteraceae*)

	from Big Horn, USA	NMen
	acris	EBWF
	'Adria'	EBee EBla ECtt GBuc LLHF LRHS MBNS SPer WFar WMnd
§	***alpinus***	LRHS NLAp
	aurantiacus	EPfP MBNS NBre NBro NPri
§	***aureus***	LRHS NSla
	- 'Canary Bird' ♀H4	CPBP EPfP NBir NMen NSla SIng WAbe
	- 'The Giant'	CPBP
	'Azure Beauty'	EBee EPfP
	Azure Fairy	see *E.* 'Azurfee'
§	'Azurfee'	CSBt EBee ELan EPfP GKir GMaP LRHS LSqH MBNS MWat NBir NLar NPri SGSe SGar SPer SPoG SWvt WMoo WPer
	Black Sea	see *E.* 'Schwarzes Meer'
	bloomeri var. ***bloomeri*** NNS 05-274	NWCA
	'Blue Beauty'	CMac LRHS SRms
	'Charity'	MRav WBrE
	chrysopsidis 'Grand Ridge'	EPfP LHop LLHF LRHS WAbe
	compositus	CPBP CTri SRms WPer
§	- var. ***discoideus***	EBur GKev NBre NMen SPlb WPer
	- 'Rocky'	ECho SPoG SRot
	concinnus var. ***condensatus*** **new**	LFur
	Darkest of All	see *E.* 'Dunkelste Aller'
	deep pink-flowered	CHEx
	'Dignity'	EBee EBla EKen ELan LLHF MBrN MRav MWat NBro SMrm SPer SUsu WBrk WCot WFar WWEG
	'Dimity'	CMea ECha EDAr NBir NBre SAga WAbe WBrk WClo WFar WHal WSFF
	'Dominator'	EBee GBin
I	'Dunkelste Aller' ♀H3	CPrp CSam EBee EBla ELan EPfP GMaP LBMP LHop LRHS MAvo MBri MRav NMRc SPoG SRms SWvt WBrE WCAu WCot WEas WFar WWEG
	elegantulus	CMea
*	***ereganus***	NBre
	'Felicity'	EBee MAvo
	flettii	EDAr NLAp
	'Foersters Liebling' ♀H4	EBee EBla EPfP GBin NGdn WWEG
	formosissimus	GBin
	'Four Winds'	EBee ECtt ELan EWes GKev LRHS MRav NGdn NMen WPer WWEG
	frigidus	NMen
	'Gaiety'	NBre
	glaucus	CHrt CSBt EBee EWll GAbr GBee GGar GJos LFur LRHS MBNS MRav NBre NGdn NVic SIng SMad WBrk WCot WFar WHoo
	- 'Albus'	EBee EShb LHop LRHS MBNS SAga SMad WFar WPer
	- 'Elstead Pink'	CElw CTri EBee ECtt ELan SAga WFar WSHC
	- 'Roger Raiche'	MRav SMrm
	- 'Roseus'	CBcs
	- 'Sea Breeze'	COIW CPrp EBee ENor GGar GMaP IFFs LHop MBNS MBri NBre NCGa NPri SBch SPoG
	howellii	EBee NBre
	humilis	EDAr
§	***karvinskianus*** ♀H3	Widely available
	leiomerus	EPot LBee LLHF LRHS
	linearis	LLHF NBre NMen NWCA
	'Mrs F.H. Beale'	EBee EBla ECtt LRHS SRGP WSpi
	mucronatus	see *E. karvinskianus*
	multiradiatus	GCal
	'Nachthimmel'	EBla ECtt NBre NGdn
	nanus	WPer
	ochroleucus var. ***scribneri***	LLHF
	'Offenham Excellence'	WCot
§	***peregrinus*** subsp. ***callianthemus***	CPBP
	philadelphicus	CElw CMea IGor NBir NBro
	Pink Jewel	see *E.* 'Rosa Juwel'
	pinnatisectus	GKev WPer
	'Profusion'	see *E. karvinskianus*
	pumilus	CDes
	pygmaeus	LLHF
	pyrenaicus misapplied	see *E. alpinus*
	pyrenaicus Rouy	see *Aster pyrenaeus*
	'Quakeress'	CElw CPrp CSam EBee EBla EBrs ECtt EPfP EShb GMaP GMac IKil LBMP LEdu LHop LRHS MBri MCot MRav NBro NGdn SBch SMrm SPoG SUsu WEas WFar WWEG
§	'Rosa Juwel'	CSBt CTri EBee ECtt ELan EPfP GMaP LBMP LRHS LSqH MBNS MRav NBir NPri SPer SPoG SRms SWvt WCAu WClo WMnd WMoo WPer
	'Rotes Meer'	CPrp EBee EBla ELan MRav WCot WFar
	rotundifolius 'Caerulescens'	see *Bellis caerulescens*
	salsuginosus misapplied	see *Aster sibiricus*, *E. peregrinus* subsp. *callianthemus*
§	'Schneewittchen'	CMMP EBee EBla ELan EPfP GMac MRav MWat NCGa NVic SBch SPet SPoG SWvt WCAu WWEG
§	'Schwarzes Meer'	EBee NGdn SPer WFar
	scopulinus	CPBP ITim LLHF WAbe WPat
	simplex	LRHS
	'Sincerity'	WFar
	'Snow Queen'	WFar
	Snow White	see *E.* 'Schneewittchen'
	'Sommerabend'	EBee
	'Sommerneuschnee'	EBee ECha GBin WMnd
	speciosus 'Grandiflora'	NBre
	'Strahlenmeer'	CPrp EBee MAvo NBre NGdn WFar
	trifidus	see *E. compositus* var. *discoideus*
	uniflorus	LLHF SRms
	'Unity'	LRHS
	untermannii NNS 06.214 **new**	CPBP
	vagus	LLHF
	'Wayne Roderick'	EBee SRGP
	'White Quakeress'	CMea EBee GBuc MRav SIng WCot
	'Wuppertal'	EBee MRav NBro NGdn

Erinacea (*Papilionaceae*)

§	***anthyllis*** ♀H4	SIng
	pungens	see *E. anthyllis*

Erinus (*Scrophulariaceae*)

	alpinus ♀H4	CTri ECho ECtt EPfP GJos GKev GMaP LBMP LRHS MLHP MSCN MWat NHol NLAp NPri NWCA SIng SPet SRms WCom WEas WFar WPer
	- var. ***albus***	ECho GJos NHol NLAp NMen SRms WHoo WPer
	- 'Doktor Hähnle'	ECho EDAr LRHS NMen SRms WFar WHoo WPer WSpi
	- 'Mrs Charles Boyle'	NMen

Eriobotrya (*Rosaceae*)

'Coppertone'	CBcs EMil EPfP LRHS SAPC SArc SCoo
deflexa	CHEx
japonica (F) Υ^{H3}	CAbb CBcs CBot CCCN CDul CHEx CWGN EAmu EBee ELan EPfP ERom EShb ETod GQui LAst LEdu LMaj LRHS MREP NExo SAPC SArc SBst SCoo SPer SVic WHer WPGP WSHC

Eriocapitella see *Anemone*

Eriocephalus (*Asteraceae*)

africanus	SPlb WJek

Eriogonum (*Polygonaceae*)

cespitosum	NLAp
- NNS 03-254	GKev
flavum	GEdr GKev WPer
gracilipes	NLAp
jamesii	NLAp WPat
kennedyi	NLAp
var. ***alpigenum***	
- - NNS 03-259	GKev
siskiyouense	NLAp
umbellatum	ECho EPot EShb LRHS NLAp
- subsp. ***covillei***	CMea
- var. ***humistratum***	WPat
- var. ***porteri*** NNS 06-230	NWCA
- var. ***torreyanum***	CMea GEdr NLAp
- var. ***umbellatum***	LBee
wrightii	GKev
var. ***subscaposum*** NNS 05-307 **new**	

Eriophorum (*Cyperaceae*)

angustifolium	CBen CRWN CWat EBWF EHoe EHon EMFW GFor LPBA MCCP MSKA SPlb SWat WHer WMAq WMoo WPer WPnP WSFF
latifolium	GFor LPBA MSKA SGSe
vaginatum	CRow EHoe GFor MSKA NSco SGSe WSFF

Eriophyllum (*Asteraceae*)

lanatum	EBee ECha EPfP EShb MDKP MWat NBid NBre NGBl SAga WCom WPen WWEG

Eritrichium (*Boraginaceae*)

* ***sibiricum***	EDif LFur

Erodium (*Geraniaceae*)

absinthoides	LRHS MOne
- var. ***amanum***	see *E. amanum*
§ ***acaule***	LLHF WClo WFar
§ ***amanum***	EBee EWes
'Ardwick Redeye'	GCal
balearicum	see *E.* × *variabile* 'Album'
'Bidderi'	MOne WAbe
'Carmel'	MOne NLAp
'Caroline'	WHoo
carvifolium	CElw EBee NLAp NWCA WFar
§ ***castellanum***	EBee LLHF NBro NLAp NMen SHGN SMrm SRms
- 'Dujardin'	SPhx
'Catherine Bunuel'	NMen
celtibericum	EPot MOne NLAp
- 'Peñagolosa'	MOne
'Cézembre'	MOne
chamaedryoides	see *E. reichardii*
- 'Roseum' hort.	see *E.* × *variabile* 'Roseum'
cheilanthifolium 'David Crocker'	EPot NMen
chrysanthum	Widely available
- pink-flowered	CSpe ECha EPot NMen SMrm SRot
corsicum	EBee EBur ECho MTho NMen NWCA WAbe
- 'Album'	EBee ECho LAst LLHF NMen SIng WAbe
'County Park'	CMea EBee ECha ECou MLHP NLAp SHar SRms WCom
daucoides misapplied	see *E. castellanum*
daucoides Boiss.	EBee
'Eileen Emmett'	EPot MOne WAbe
'Elizabeth'	MOne
'Florida'	MAga
foetidum	LFur NMen
- 'Couvé'	NMen
'Fran's Delight'	CMea CSpe ECtt GCal GMaP LRHS MLHP MOne NDlv NLAp NMen WHoo
'Fripetta'	WAbe
N ***glandulosum*** Υ^{H4}	EBee ECho EPfP LHop SEND SRms SRot WCom WFar WPat WSHC
gruinum	CSpe EBee SPhx
guttatum misapplied	see *E.* 'Katherine Joy'
N ***guttatum*** (Desf.) Willd.	ECho EPot EWTr LHop MWat NMen SRms
'Helen'	MOne
hymenodes L'Hér.	see *E. trifolium*
jahandiezianum	NWCA
'Julie Ritchie'	CMea WHoo
§ 'Katherine Joy'	CElw EBee EPot EWes MHer MOne NDlv NLAp SRGP SRot
× ***kolbianum***	NDlv NLAp WAbe WFar WHoo WKif
- 'Natasha'	CMHG EAlp EBee ECtt EPot EWes GBuc GGar GKir GMaP LBee LRHS MHer NLAp NMen SPoG SRGP WAbe WFar
'Las Meninas'	SUsu
'Lilac Wonder'	MOne
× ***lindavicum***	LFur
- 'Charter House'	CMoH
macradenum	see *E. glandulosum*
manescavii	Widely available
'Maryla'	NMen
'Merstham Pink'	CMHG CMoH GMaP NDlv NLAp SMrm SRms
'Mesquita'	CMea
moschatum	ECho
'Nunwood Pink'	NWCA
'Pallidum'	CSam
pelargoniiflorum	CBot CSpe EBee EPfP EWTr LBMP LFur LPio LRHS MCot MTho NBro NLar SBod SEND SMad SMrm SRms STes WEas WFar WKif WPer WPnP WWFP
'Peter Vernon'	MOne NWCA
petraeum hybrids **new**	NWCA
- subsp. ***petraeum***	EPot
'Pickering Pink'	EBee LIMB MOne NDlv NLAp NMen
'Pippa Mills'	CElw
'Princesse Marion'	MLHP NChi
* 'Purple Haze'	CSpe EBee MOne SMrm SRms SRot WFar
§ ***reichardii***	CTri ECho ECtt LRHS MBrN MHer MOne MTho NLAp NWCA SPet SPoG SRms WCFE

	- 'Album'	CEnt CHrt EAlp ECho GEdr LRHS MOne NMen SMrm SPet SPoG WCom WFar WHoo
	- 'Bianca'	EBee SUsu
	- 'Pipsqueak'	NWCA
*	- 'Rubrum'	CElw ECho
	'Robertino'	NMen WAbe
	'Robespierre'	MOne SPhx
	'Robin'	MOne
	rodiei	EBee EPfP EWes WKif
	romanum	see *E. acaule*
§	***rupestre***	CBot EBee ECho ECtt GMaP MWea NDlv NWCA SRms SRot WPat
	'Sarck'	MOne
	sebaceum 'Polly'	NWCA
	'Spanish Eyes'	GKir LAst NEgg NLAp NPri SMrm SRot WAbe WFar WKif
	'Stephanie'	CElw CMHG ECho EPot EWes GMaP LBee LRHS LSRN MHer MOne NDlv NLAp NMen SUsu SWal
	supracanum	see *E. rupestre*
	'Tiny Kyni'	MOne NLAp WAbe WFar
	tordylioides	EBee
	trichomanifolium L'Hér.	EWes LBee LRHS
§	***trifolium***	CBgR CHrt ECho ELan EPfP EPot MHer NSla SGar SIng
	× ***variabile***	ECtt NLAp
§	- 'Album'	CMea EBee ECho EDAr EPfP EPot GBuc LRHS MBar MHer MTho NEgg NPri NWCA SRms SRot WAbe WBrk WFar WPer
I	- 'Bishop's Form'	Widely available
	- 'Candy'	EAlp GEdr GJos MHer
	- 'Derek'	ECho
	- 'Flore Pleno' (d)	EBee ECho EDAr ELan EWes LRHS MHer NLAp NMen SIng SMrm SRms SRot WBrk WFar WPer
	- 'Red Rock'	CTri EBee SIng
§	- 'Roseum' ♀H4	CBot EAlp ECho ECtt EDAr ELan EPfP GGar LBee LRHS MMuc NLAp NWCA SPlb SRms WBrk WFar WPer
I	'Westacre Seedling'	EWes
	'Whitwell Superb'	CDes CElw MOne WPGP
	× ***willkommianum***	MOne NWCA

Erpetion see *Viola*

Eruca (*Brassicaceae*)

vesicaria	CWan NBlu
- subsp. ***sativa***	CSpe ELau GPoy MHer MNHC NGHP SIde WJek

Eryngium ✿ (*Apiaceae*)

	F&M 208	WPGP
	PC&H 268	EKen NLar
§	***agavifolium***	Widely available
	alpinum ♀H4	CSpe EBee EBrs ECha ECho ELan EPfP GGar GKir GMaP LAst LHop MBel MGos MRav MTho NBir NCGa SMrm SPer SPet SRms SRot WCAu WFar
	- 'Amethyst'	EBee GBuc GKev IPot LRHS MBri NBro SMrm WEas
	- 'Blue Jacket'	NSti WBrE
	- 'Blue Star'	CBot CHar CSpe EBee EBla EDAr EHrv ELan EPfP GAbr GMac LRHS MCot MNFA MWat NGBl NHol SMrm SPer SPoG STes WCot WHoo WPer WSpi WTin WWEG
	- 'Holden Blue'	MAvo
	- 'Slieve Donard'	see *E.* × ***zabelii*** 'Donard Variety'
	- 'Superbum'	CBot CSpe ECtt EHrv GBuc GJos LRHS MBri MNrw NCob NLar SRms SWat WGwG
	amethystinum	CBot CMac CMdw EBee EBla EHrv EPfP LPio MCot MNrw WCAu WPer
	biebersteinianum	see *E. caeruleum*
	'Blue Jackpot'	EBee EHrv EWes MBri NBhm NMoo SWat
	'Blue Steel'	LFur MAvo MDKP NChi SBch
	bourgatii	Widely available
	- Graham Stuart Thomas's selection	Widely available
	- 'Oxford Blue' ♀H4	CEnt CSpe EBee EHrv ENor GGar GMaP GMac LAst MHer NLar SGSe SGar SWvt WEas WOld
	- 'Picos Amethyst'	CBcs CMac CWCL CWGN EBee EBrs EKen LHop LRHS LSRN NCGa NLar NSti SCoo SGSe SPhx SVil
	- 'Picos Blue' PBR	Widely available
	bromeliifolium misapplied	see *E. agavifolium*, *E. eburneum*
§	***caeruleum***	GBuc MNrw NChi
	campestre	CBot EWll MDKP NGby NLar WFar WPer WWEG
	caucasicum	see *E. caeruleum*
	'Cobalt Star'	GMac
	creticum	NBro NChi
	cymosum B&SWJ 10267	WCru
	decaisneanum misapplied	see *E. pandanifolium*
	deppeanum NJM 05.031	WPGP
	dichotomum	NChi
	ebracteatum	CSpe EBla IGor LPio MCot
	- CD&R 3248	WCru
	- var. ***poterioides***	LPla
§	***eburneum***	CBcs CBot CFir CGHE CKno EBee EBrs ECha EPfP EWes GBuc GCal GMaP LPio LRHS MAvo NBro NChi NHol NSti SMad SPad WCot WFar WSpi
	aff. ***eburneum***	CMac WPGP
	'Electric Haze' new	NCGa NCob SPoG
	elegans var. ***elegans*** CDPR 3076	WPGP
	foetidum	CArn
§	***giganteum*** ♀H4	Widely available
	- 'Silver Ghost' ♀H4	CBcs CHar CMea CSam CSpe EBee ECtt EHrv EWll GAbr GMac LHop LPio LRHS MNFA NChi NGdn SBch SGar SMeo SUsu SWat SWvt WCot WFar WGwG WSpi WWEG WWlt
	glaciale	EBee
	'Green Jade' new	LRHS
	guatemalense	CGHE WPGP
	- B&SWJ 8989	WCru
	- B&SWJ 10322	WCru
	- B&SWJ 10420	WCru
	horridum misapplied	see *E. eburneum*
	horridum ambig.	EBee EWes GKir LEdu LPio MNrw NChi SAPC SArc WCAu WFar WMnd WPGP
	horridum Malme	GKir WCot
	'Jewel Stone' new	WHlf
	maritimum	CArn CBot CPou EBWF EBee GKev GPoy ITim MDKP MHer NLar SMrm SPlb WAbe WCot WFar WWEG
	Miss Willmott's ghost	see *E. giganteum*
	monocephalum	WPGP
	× ***oliverianum*** ♀H4	Widely available
	palmatum	NChi
§	***pandanifolium*** ♀H4	CFir CHEx CMHG CTrG EBee EPfP EWes GCal LPio NSti SAPC SArc SEND SGSe SGar SMad SPav SPlb

	SPoG SWvt WCot WCru WMnd WPGP WWEG
- 'Physic Purple'	SPhx WCot
paniculatum	EBee WPGP
planum	Widely available
- 'Bethlehem' ♀H4	EBee IPot MBri NLar SWat WSpi
§ - 'Blauer Zwerg'	CKno EBee MGos SWat WFar WHlf WSpi
- 'Blaukappe'	CBot CHar CMea EBee EBrs EDAr ELon EPfP GMac LDai LRHS NLar SEND SMrm SPet SPhx WAul WBrE WHil WSHC WWEG
* - 'Blue Candle'	EBee NLar WFar
- Blue Dwarf	see *E. planum* 'Blauer Zwerg'
- 'Blue Glitter' **new**	ELon
- 'Blue Hobbit' **new**	CChe LBuc LRHS NGdn
- 'Blue Ribbon'	EBee EBla LAst LRHS LSou MRav NGdn SPhx SWat
- 'Flüela'	EBee EBla EShb EWes LRHS LSRN NBro NEgg SCoo SPhx SWat
- 'Hellas'	EBee NLar
- 'Jade Frost'PBR (v)	CDes CWGN EBee ECtt EWes LLHF LOck LPio LRHS LSou MAvo MBNS MBel NSti SPoG WClo WCot WFut
- 'Paradise Jackpot'PBR	EBee IPot MNrw MSCN NGdn SPer
- 'Seven Seas'	CFir CPrp EBee EBla ECtt LRHS MBNS MBri NEgg NGdn SPhx SWat WPer
- 'Silver Stone'	EBee EBla ECtt GMaP LDai LRHS MBri MDKP NGdn NPri SPhx
- 'Tetra Blau' **new**	LRHS
- 'Tetra Petra'	CBcs EBee LRHS MAvo NEgg WPer
- 'Violet Blue'	GCal
proteiflorum	EBee GCal IPot LPio LRHS MAvo MDKP NBPC NCGa SEND SMad SPhx SPlb WHil
- F&M 224	WPGP
serbicum	GCal MAvo WCot WWEG
serra	CAby EBee EBrs EDAr EWes GBuc LDai LRHS MAvo NChi
- RB 90454	MDKP
spinalba	CBot
strotheri B&SWJ 9109	WCru
- B&SWJ 10392	WCru
'Sunny Jackpot' **new**	MAsh
tricuspidatum	EBrs ECtt GKir LRHS WPer WSpi
× ***tripartitum*** ♀H4	Widely available
* ***umbelliferum***	CBcs EDAr GCal GKir LAst MBNS MDKP NBre NChi NPri NSti SPoG WClo WFar
variifolium	Widely available
venustum	CDes LPio LRHS MAvo SMrm WFar WOut
yuccifolium	CArn CKno EBee EBla EBrs EPfP EWes GCal GKir LBMP LEdu LPio LRHS NHol SBch SDix SDnm SMrm SPav SPhx SPlb SWvt WBrE WFar WHoo WTin
× ***zabelii***	CAby CDes ECha GMac LPio NBir NChi SMeo WPGP
- 'Blaue Ritter'	SWat
§ - 'Donard Variety'	EBee EBla ECtt GCal IPot ITim LAst MDKP NLar SWat WWEG
- 'Forncett Ultra'	GCal GMac MAvo NChi SMeo WPGP
- 'Jewel'	MAvo SApp SUsu SWat
- 'Jos Eijking'PBR	EBee EBrs ECtt EKen ELon GBuc GKir GMac IPot LBMP LRHS LSRN MAvo MBel MCot MRav NCGa NHol NLar SMad SPer SPoG SPur SUsu WBrE WClo WCot
- 'Violetta'	ECha ELan GBuc GMac IGor MAvo MBri NGby SWat WFar WHoo

Erysimum ✿ (*Brassicaceae*)

from Madeira	CPLG ELon
allionii misapplied	see *E.* × *marshallii*
amoenum	LLHF
'Anthony Hicks' **new**	CHll
'Apricot Delight'	see *E.* 'Apricot Twist'
§ 'Apricot Twist'	Widely available
arkansanum	see *E. helveticum*
asperum	GJos IFro
bicolor	GGar
'Bowles's Mauve' ♀H3	Widely available
'Bowles's Purple'	NCob SRms SWvt WBVN
'Bowles's Yellow'	GBuc
'Bredon' ♀H3	EPfP NPer WHoo WKif WSpi
brevistylum	GKev
'Butterscotch'	CFee CMea EGoo MMHG NCob WCom WHoo WTin
'Butterscotch Variegated' (v)	NCob
cheiri	CArn MHer NSco WCot
- 'Blood Red'	CSpe SMeo
- 'Bloody Warrior' (d)	CBot CElw ECtt WCom
- 'Deben'	CBot
- 'Fire King'	SMeo
- 'Harpur Crewe' (d)	CBot CFee CHll CTri ELan ELon EPfP EShb GMaP MTho NPer SGar SRms WCot
- 'Orange Bedder' (Bedder Series)	NBir
- Rysi Gold = 'Innrysigol' **new**	CHVG
'Chelsea Jacket'	EPfP SUsu
'Constant Cheer'	Widely available
'Cotswold Gem' (v)	CElw EBee ECtt EHoe ELan ELon EPPr EPfP EShb LBMP LDai LRHS LSou MAsh MHer NBPC NCob NPer SAga SBch SLim SMrm SPoG SWvt WCot WGwG WWEG
'Dawn Breaker'	CElw CWGN EBee ECtt EWes LRHS LSou MAsh MWea NBPC NCob SUsu WCot WWEG
'Devon Gold'	see *E.* 'Plant World Gold'
'Devon Sunset'	SAga
'Dorothy Elmhirst'	see *E.* 'Mrs L.K. Elmhirst'
dwarf lemon-flowered	WHoo
'Ellen Willmott'	CEnt GBin
'Emm's Variety'	ECtt EPot
'Gold Rush' **new**	GJos
'Gold Shot'	GJos
'Golden Gem'	NDlv WCom WPer
'Golden Jubilee'	ECho ECtt ELon GGar LIMB MCot WFar
grandiflorum	GAuc
'Hector's Gatepost'	EBee LRHS LSRN LSou NBPC SRGP SRkn
§ ***helveticum***	CSpr ECho IFro SAga SRms
'Jacob's Jacket'	ECtt MBNS MHer NPer WBVN
'Jenny Brook' **new**	LRHS WHlf
'Joan Adams'	LHop
'John Codrington'	LHop NPer SUsu WKif WSpi WWFP
'Joseph's Coat'	LIMB
'Jubilee Gold'	WWEG
'Julian Orchard'	CHll CSpe SAga SSth
kotschyanum	CPBP ECho ECtt EPot GEdr LBee LRHS NMen NWCA SRms WCom
linifolium	EBur SRms WFar WGor
- 'Little Kiss Lilac' **new**	GJos
§ - 'Variegatum' (v)	CArn CCCN CSBt CWan EBee ECtt ELan EPfP GGar IMon NEgg NPer NPri SAga SBch SPer SPoG SRot WPGP

	- - peach-flowered (v) **new**	MBNS
§	× ***marshallii*** ♀H4	EWTr
	'Mayflower'	NCob
	'Moonlight'	EBee ECtt EPot GBuc GMaP LRHS MHer MTho NBir NCGa SRms WBVN WHoo
§	'Mrs L.K. Elmhirst'	ECtt ELon LSou MDKP MMHG NPer WHoo WWFP
	mutabile	CBgR CTri EBee EGoo MAsh MRav SIde SUsu WHal
	- 'Variegatum' (v)	WCom
	'My Old Mum'	CWGN EAEE EBee ECtt MBNS MRav MWea NCGa
	'Orange Flame'	CMea EBee ECha ECho ECtt EPot LHop LRHS MHer NBlu NPer NWCA WCom WPer
	'Parish's'	CMdw CSpe ECtt MRav SAga
	'Parkwood Gold'	EDAr GJos
	'Pastel Patchwork'	CSpe EBee LRHS LSou NBPC SBch
	Perry's hybrid	NPer
	'Perry's Peculiar'	NPer
§	'Plant World Gold'	CElw
	'Plant World Lemon'	CPLG ECtt LSou MBri NCGa SDnm SRot
§	***pulchellum***	ECha SRot
	- 'Variegatum' (v)	WBrE
	pumilum DC.	see *E. helveticum*
	rupestre	see *E. pulchellum*
	'Rysi Bronze' **new**	LSou
	'Sissinghurst Variegated'	see *E. linifolium* 'Variegatum'
	'Sprite'	CMea CTri ECho ECtt EPot NPer
	'Starbright'	EBee LRHS LSou SPoG
	'Stars and Stripes' (v)	CWGN EBee LBuc LRHS LSou MGos SBch SPoG
	'Sunshine'	SWal
	'Sweet Sorbet'	EBee ECtt EPfP LSou MBri NBPC NEgg NPri SMrm SPav SRkn SWvt
	'Turkish Bazaar'	ECho
	'Valerie Finnis'	WCom
	Walberton's Fragrant Sunshine = 'Walfrasun'	CHll EPfP LRHS SBch SCoo SPoG
	'Wenlock Beauty'	CMea GBin LDai SRms
	'Winter Joy'	CBow LLHF LRHS LSou MAsh MBNS
	'Winter Sorbet' **new**	CBow LAst LSou NCGa SMrm
	'Yellow Bird'	EPfP

Erythraea see *Centaurium*

Erythrina (*Papilionaceae*)

	× ***bidwillii***	CCCN
	crista-galli	CBcs CBot CCCN CDTJ CHEx CSpe EBee ELan EPfP GQui LRHS MWea SPlb WPGP WPat WSHC
	- 'Compacta'	MBri SMad
§	***humeana***	CDTJ
	latissima	CDTJ
	princeps	see *E. humeana*

Erythronium ✿ (*Liliaceae*)

	albidum	CLAP EBee ECho EPot EWTr GAuc GBuc GGar IBlr LAma NMen
	americanum	CAby CArn CLAP EBee EBrs ECho EPot GBuc IBlr LAma MSSP NHol NMen
	'Apple Blossom'	ECho
	'Beechpark'	IBlr
	'Blush'	ECho GBuc IBlr
	'Californian Star'	IBlr
	californicum ♀H4	CAby CFir CLAP EBee EBrs ECho GBuc IBlr ITim SCnR WAbe
	- JCA 1.350.200	WWst
	- J&JA 13216	CLAP
*	- var. ***candidum*** MS 01/009	WWst
	- 'Harvington Snowgoose'	CLAP EBee EHrv LRHS MBri WWst
	- Plas Merdyn form	IBlr
	- 'White Beauty' ♀H4	Widely available
	californicum × ***hendersonii***	IBlr
	caucasicum	CLAP
	citrinum	GBuc MSSP NMen
	- J&JA 13462	CLAP WWst
	citrinum × ***hendersonii***	CAvo IBlr
	'Citronella'	CBro CLAP EHrv GBuc IBlr ITim MSSP NDlv NMen WAbe WCru
	cliftonii hort.	see *E. multiscapoideum* Cliftonii Group
	dens-canis ♀H4	Widely available
	- JCA 470.001	CLAP
	- from Slovenia	CLAP
	- 'Charmer'	CMil EBee ECho GEdr WWst
	- 'Frans Hals'	CLAP CMil EBee EBrs ECho EPot ERos GBuc GEdr GGar LRHS MTho WCru WHal
	- 'Lilac Wonder'	EBee EBrs ECho EPot GEdr GMaP LAma LEdu LRHS MNrw MTho NHol WWst
*	- 'Moerheimii' (d)	CMil EBee ECho IBlr WWst
	- var. ***niveum***	ERos IBlr NEgg
	- 'Old Aberdeen'	CLAP EBee IBlr LRHS MNrw WWst
	- 'Pink Perfection'	EBee EBrs ECho EPot ERos GEdr GGar LEdu LRHS NHol WCru
	- 'Purple King'	EBee EBrs ECGP ECho EPot ERos GBuc GEdr GMaP LAma LRHS MNrw NHol WCru
	- 'Rose Queen'	CAby CFir CMil EBee EBrs ECho EPot ERos GAbr GBuc GGar GMaP LAma LRHS MAvo MTho NHol NLAp SPhx WHal
*	- 'Semi-plenum' (d)	IBlr
	- 'Snowflake'	CLAP EBee EBrs ECha ECho EPot ERos GBuc GEdr GGar LAma LRHS MNrw NBir NMen WAbe WCru
	- white-flowered, from Serbia	ECho
	- 'White Splendour'	CBro ECho ERos IBlr MNrw WWst
	elegans	EBee EBrs ECho EHrv GBuc WWst
	'Flash'	IBlr
§	***grandiflorum***	CLAP EBee EBrs ECho GBuc MSSP NMen
	- M&PS 007	CLAP
	- M&PS 96/024	NMen
	- subsp. ***chrysandrum***	see *E. grandiflorum*
	helenae	CLAP ECho GAuc IBlr
	- J&JA 11678	WWst
	hendersonii	CLAP CPom ECho EHrv GAuc LRHS MSSP WAbe WWst
	- J&JA 12945	CLAP
	howellii	CLAP
	- J&JA 13428	WWst
	- J&JA 13441	CLAP
	japonicum	CBcs EBee EBrs ECho EFEx EPot GAuc GBuc GEdr LAma MNrw NHol NMen WCru WFar WWst
	'Jeanette Brickell'	CLAP IBlr WWst
	'Jeannine'	GBuc IBlr WCru
	'Joanna'	GBuc IBlr MNrw NMen WWst
	klamathense	EPot
	'Kondo'	CTri EBee EBrs ECho EPfP EPot ERos GBuc GEdr GGar GMaP IBlr IFro ITim LAma LEdu LRHS MTho NBir NHol NMen SMrm SPer WAbe WClo WCot WCru WHil
	'Margaret Mathew'	CLAP IBlr WAbe WWst

	'Minnehaha'	WWst
	montanum	ECho EHrv WWst
§	***multiscapoideum***	CLAP ECho GBuc WCot
	- JCA 1.352.100	WWst
	- NNS 99-163	WWst
§	- Cliftonii Group	CLAP EBrs WAbe
	'Oregon Encore'	IBlr
	oregonum	CLAP EBrs ECho EHrv GAuc GBuc GGar IBlr ITim LRHS MBri MNrw MSSP
	- subsp. ***leucandrum***	CLAP WWst
	- - JCA 4.352.400	WWst
	- subsp. ***oregonum***	WCot
I	- 'Sulphur Form'	CLAP
	'Pagoda' ΨH4	Widely available
	pluriflorum	EBrs
	purdyi	see *E. multiscapoideum*
	revolutum ΨH4	CAby CAvo CBro CLAP CMea CPom EBee EBrs ECho EHrv EPot GAuc GBuc GGar GKev GMaP IBlr ITim LRHS MBri MNrw MSSP NMen SCnR SRot WAbe WCru
	- from God's Valley	WWst
	- 'Guincho Splendour'	IBlr
	- Johnsonii Group	ECho WAbe WCru WWst
	- 'Kinfauns' **new**	WWst
	- 'Knightshayes'	EBee LRHS MBri
	- 'Knightshayes Pink'	CLAP EHrv GBuc IBlr NBir WShi WWst
	- 'Pink Beauty'	EBee
	- Plas Merdyn form	IBlr
	- 'Rose Beauty'	CMil EBrs ECho NMen
	- 'Wild Salmon'	CLAP LRHS MBri
	'Rippling Waters'	IBlr
	'Rosalind'	IBlr SCnR
	sibiricum	EBrs ECho NMen WWst
*	- subsp. ***altaicum***	WWst
	- white-flowered	WWst
	'Sundisc'	ECha ECho GBuc IBlr MSSP MTho NMen WAbe WWst
	'Susannah'	WWst
	taylorii	EBee WWst
	tuolumnense ΨH4	CBro CLAP CWCL EBee EBrs ECho EHrv EPot ERos GAuc GBuc GEdr GGar GKev GMaP IBlr IHer LAma LEdu LRHS MCot NMen WAbe
	- EBA clone 2	WAbe WWst
	- EBA clone 3	WAbe
	- 'Edgar Klein' **new**	WWst
	- Plas Merdyn form **new**	IBlr
	- 'Spindlestone'	IBlr WWst
	umbilicatum	IBlr MSSP WWst

Escallonia ✿ (*Escalloniaceae*)

	'Alice'	EBee SLPl SPer
	'Apple Blossom' ΨH4	Widely available
§	***bifida*** ΨH3	CDoC CDul EQua LRHS WFar WPat WSHC
	'C.F. Ball'	CBcs CSBt CTri EBee ELan GGar LBMP LBuc LRHS MAsh MGan MSwo NBlu NEgg NScw NWea SEND SPad SRms WBVN WDin WFar WMoo
	'Compacta Coccinea'	CBcs
	'Dart's Rosy Red'	LBMP NHol SLPl
	'Donard Beauty'	EBee NEgg SRms
	'Donard Radiance' ΨH4	CBcs CDoC CDul CMac CSBt CSam CWib EBee ELan EPfP LHop LRHS LSRN NHol NWea SBod SLim SPer SPoG SRms SWvt WDin WFar WMoo
	'Donard Red'	GGal
	'Donard Seedling'	CBcs CDoC CDul CSBt EBee ELan EPfP LAst LBuc LRHS MAsh MGan MGos MSwo NBlu NHol NPer NWea SBch SBod SLPl SLim SPer SRms STre SWvt WFar WMoo
	'Donard Star'	CWib EBee EPfP NWea SLPl WCFE
	'Edinensis'	EBee EPfP ERas GGar MBar MNHC NLar SBch SEND SLim WDin WFar WMoo WSpi
	'Erecta'	EPfP SHGN
	'Everest'	LBuc LRHS NEgg SLon
	× ***exoniensis***	SRms
	'Gwendolyn Anley'	SLPl WFar
	'Hopleys Gold'PBR	see *E. laevis* 'Gold Brian'
	illinita	EBee LLHF NLar
	'Iveyi' ΨH3	Widely available
§	***laevis***	LRHS WFar
§	- 'Gold Brian'PBR	CDul CMHG EBee EHoe ELan EPau EPfP GGar LRHS LSRN MAsh MGos MWat SCoo SPer SPoG SWal WFar WHar
	- 'Gold Ellen' (v)	CChe CSBt CTri CWSG EBee ELan EPfP LAst LBMP LRHS LSRN MAsh MGos MRav MSwo NEgg NHol SAga SBch SCoo SEND SLim SPer SPoG SRms SWvt WMoo
	'Langleyensis' ΨH4	CBcs CMac CTri CWib GGal NWea WDin WFar WHar
	mexicana	CBot WFar
	montevidensis	see *E. bifida*
	organensis	see *E. laevis*
	'Peach Blossom' ΨH4	CAlb CBcs CDoC CDul CSam CWib EBee ECrN ELan EPfP GGar LHop LRHS MAsh MBri MLHP MSwo NBir NBlu SCoo SLPl SLim SPer SPoG SRms WFar
	'Pink Elf'	MSwo
	'Pink Pyramid' **new**	LRHS
	'Pride of Donard' ΨH4	CBcs CDoC CPLG CSBt EBee EPfP GGar LRHS MGan MGos SRms
	punctata	see *E. rubra*
	Red Carpet = 'Loncar' **new**	WHar
	'Red Dream'	CSBt CWSG EBee ERas LBMP LRHS MAsh MBri MGos MSwo NHol NLar SAga SBch SCoo SPoG SRms SWvt WFar
	'Red Elf'	CAlb CCVT CMac EBee ELan EPfP GGar LAst LRHS MAsh MBar MBri MGos MWat NBlu NEgg NHol SCoo SLPl SPer SPlb SPoG SRms SWvt WBVN WClo WFar
	'Red Hedger'	CDoC CSBt CTrG CTsd CWib ELan GGal MRav SBch SCoo SRms
	'Red Robin'	GGar SPoG
	resinosa	CPLG SAPC SArc WHCG WJek
	revoluta	CTri
§	***rubra***	MLHP
	- 'Crimson Spire' ΨH4	CBcs CChe CDul CSBt CTri CWSG CWib EBee EPfP GGar LRHS LSRN MAsh MGos MNHC MRav MWat NBir NEgg NPri NWea SBch SBod SEND SLim SPer SPlb SPoG SRms WMoo
	- 'Ingramii'	CWib NWea SEND
	- var. ***macrantha***	CBcs CCVT CChe CDoC CDul CMac CSBt CWSG CWib EBee ECrN ELan EPfP GGar IArd LAst LRHS MHer NBir NEgg SBch SCoo SLim SPer SPoG WDin WFar WMoo
*	- - ***aurea***	NScw
	- 'Pygmaea'	see *E. rubra* 'Woodside'

§	- 'Woodside'	ECho EPfP LLHF MLHP NHol SRms WHCG
	'Silver Anniversary'	MSwo
	'Slieve Donard'	CMac EBee EPfP MRav NEgg NHol NWea SLPl SLim SLon SRms WFar

Eschscholzia (*Papaveraceae*)

	californica ♀H4	GKir
	- 'Jersey Cream'	CSpe
	lobbii	CSpe

Espeletia (*Asteraceae*)

	aff. ***summapacis*** B&SWJ 10766 new	WCru

Esterhuysenia (*Aizoaceae*)

	alpina new	CPBP

Eucalyptus ✿ (*Myrtaceae*)

	aggregata	CCVT SAPC SArc
	alpina	SPlb
	archeri	CCVT CDTJ CDoC CDul CTho ECrN EPfP GQui LRHS MMuc MWhi SBch WPGP
	botryoides	GLin
	caesia	SPlb
	camaldulensis	SPlb
	camphora	CCCN CTho
	cinerea	GQui SBig SPlb
	citriodora	CArn CTsd EOHP GQui MHer MNHC NGHP SPlb
	coccifera	CBcs CCVT CDoC CSBt CTho ELan EPfP GGar LMaj LRHS NEgg NPer SBig SPlb SPoG WDin WPGP
	cordata	CCVT CDul
	crenulata	CTrC GLin GQui
	crucis subsp. ***crucis***	SPlb
	cypellocarpa	SPlb
	dalrympleana ♀H3	CAbb CBcs CCVT CDoC CDul CMHG CMac EBee ECrN ELan EPfP EWes LRHS LSRN MGos MSwo NBea NPer SBig SCoo SEND SLim SPer SPoG SRms WDin WHar WPGP
	debeuzevillei	see *E. pauciflora* subsp. *debeuzevillei*
	delegatensis	CMHG GLin NPer
	- subsp. ***tasmaniensis***	GGar
	divaricata	see *E. gunnii* subsp. *divaricata*
	erythrocorys	SPlb
	eximia	SPlb
*	- 'Nana'	SPlb
	ficifolia	CBcs CDTJ
	fraxinoides	SPlb
	gamophylla	SPlb
	glaucescens	CCVT CMHG CTho CWCL ELan EPfP EWes GQui LRHS NPri SAPC SArc SBch WBVN WPGP
	globulus	CArn CHEx GGar ISea MNHC WFar
	goniocalyx	EPfP
§	***gregsoniana***	CCVT CDoC CTho EPfP GGal SPlb WPGP
	gunnii ♀H3	Widely available
§	- subsp. ***divaricata***	CCVT EPfP GQui MBri
	johnstonii	CDul CTrC ECrN NLar SPer
	kruseana	SPlb
	kybeanensis	CCVT GQui MGos
§	***lacrimans***	WPGP
	leucoxylon subsp. ***megalocarpa***	SPlb
*	- - 'Rosea'	MCot
	'Little Boy Blue'	CWib LSRN
	macrocarpa	SPlb
*	***moorei nana***	CDTJ MHer
	neglecta	GLin
	nicholii	CCVT CDul EBee EPfP ERas EWes GQui LRHS MGos NLar SCoo SEND SPoG WPGP
	niphophila	see *E. pauciflora* subsp. *niphophila*
	nitens	CCVT CDTJ CDul CMHG SBig SCoo SEND SPlb
	ovata	GGar
	parviflora	IFFs WBVN
	parvifolia ♀H4	CCCN CCVT CDoC CDul CLnd CMHG CMac EPfP LRHS MWhi SCoo SEND WPGP
	pauciflora	CCCN CCVT CDoC CSBt CTho ELan MGos MMuc NLar SPer
§	- subsp. ***debeuzevillei***	CCVT CDoC CMHG CTho EBee EPfP EWes GQui LMaj LRHS MGos SAPC SArc SBig WPGP
	- subsp. ***hedraia***	NPri
	- var. ***nana***	see *E. gregsoniana*
§	- subsp. ***niphophila*** ♀H4	Widely available
	- - 'Pendula'	see *E. lacrimans*
	perriniana	CBcs CCCN CCVT CDul CLnd CMHG CSBt CWCL EBee ECrN ELan EPfP LRHS MBri MGos MWhi NEgg SBch SBig SCoo SLim SPer SPlb SPoG SWvt WDin WFar WPGP
	pulverulenta	CDul CMac SPlb
	- 'Baby Blue'	LRHS MBri MGos SWvt
	rodwayi	GGar
	rubida	CCCN CMHG
	sideroxylon	SPlb
	- 'Rosea'	SPlb
	subcrenulata	CCVT CMHG EPfP GGar GLin GQui LRHS
	tetraptera	SPlb
	torquata	SPlb
	urnigera	CCVT CDoC LHop LRHS SCoo WDin
	vernicosa	CCVT GGar LRHS
	viminalis	CArn CHEx LRHS WDin

Eucharidium see *Clarkia*

Eucharis (*Amaryllidaceae*)

§	***amazonica*** ♀H1	CCCN EBrs ECho EShb LAma LRHS SPav
	grandiflora misapplied	see *E. amazonica*

Eucodonia (*Gesneriaceae*)

	'Adele'	EABi WDib
	andrieuxii 'Naomi'	WDib
	verticillata	CSpe

Eucomis ✿ (*Hyacinthaceae*)

	'African Beauty' new	LRHS
	autumnalis misapplied	see *E. zambesiaca*
§	***autumnalis*** (Mill.) Chitt. ♀H2-3	CAvo CBgR CBro CDes CFFs CHEx CPou CSWP EBee EBrs ECho EPot ERCP IHer LAma LFur LPio LRHS MCCP SDnm SPav SPer SPlb SWal WBrE WGwG WHil WPGP WTin
	- subsp. ***amaryllidifolia***	WPGP
	- subsp. ***autumnalis***	WPGP
	- - 'Peace Candles'	CPen
	bicolor ♀H2-3	Widely available
	- 'Alba'	CAvo CBgR CPLG EAmu EBee EBrs ECho LPio LRHS SDnm
	- 'Stars and Stripes'	WCru
	'Cabernet Candles'	CPen
§	***comosa***	CAvo CBgR CBro CFFs CHEx CHll CPrp CSam CStu CTrC EBee EBrs

		ERCP EShb GAbr LAma LEdu LPio LRHS SDnm SMad SPav WTin WWEG
	- 'Cornwood'	CAvo CFFs
	- 'First Red'	CDes CPou WPGP
	- 'Kilimanjaro' new	EBee
	- purple-leaved	EShb
	- 'Sparkling Burgundy'	Widely available
	- 'Tarzan's Tail'	WHil
	humilis	CPen
	- 'Twinkle Stars' new	EBee
	hybrid	SDix
	'John Treasure'	WHil
	'Joy's Purple'	CBro CPar CPen LFur LRHS
	montana	CBgR CBro CFwr CPen EBee ERCP LRHS WPGP
	pallidiflora ♀H4	CAvo CDes CGHE CHEx CPen EBee LEdu WHil WPGP
	pole-evansii	CBro CDes CFir CPLG CPen CPne EAEE EAmu EBee EBrs ECGP ELan ERCP EShb LPio LRHS MBel MMHG MRav SMrm WPGP WTin WWEG
I	- 'Purpurea'	GCal
	punctata	see *E. comosa*
*	***reichenbachii***	CDTJ
	'Swazi Pride'	WHil
	undulata	see *E. autumnalis* (Mill.) Chitt.
	vandermerwei	CAvo CBro CDes CFwr CPLG CPen EBee EPot LRHS WPGP WTin
	- 'Octopus'	CPen CPrp CSpr EBee ELan ELon EPfP EShb IPot LLWG LRHS LSou MAvo SPoG SUsu WCot WPrP WWEG
§	***zambesiaca***	CPen GCal LBuc LFur LPio WWEG
	- 'White Dwarf'	CStu ECho EShb LRHS SPer WClo
	'Zeal Bronze'	CDes CGHE CMHG CMil ELan EPfP GCal LPio LRHS NSti WPGP

Eucommia (*Eucommiaceae*)

	ulmoides	CBcs CCCN CDul CMCN EBtc EPfP GKir NLar WPGP

Eucrosia (*Amaryllidaceae*)

	bicolor	EBee LAma

Eucryphia ✿ (*Eucryphiaceae*)

	cordifolia	CAbP CBcs CDul CGHE CMac CWib EBee GKir ISea LAst LRHS NMun SSpi WDin
	- Crarae hardy form	GGGa
§	***cordifolia*** × ***lucida***	CBcs CCCN ELan GGal ISea MSnd SLdr SPer SRot WDin WPGP WPat
	glutinosa ♀H4	CCCN CDul EBee EPfP IMGH LRHS MBri MDun SSpi SSta WDin WFar WPat
	- Plena Group (d)	WPat
	× ***hillieri***	WSpi
	- 'Winton'	CMHG GQui
	× ***intermedia***	CMac CPLG CTrC CTrG CWSG EBee ELan EPfP GGGa LRHS NPal SLdr SPer SRms SRot SSpi WDin WFar WPat
	- 'Rostrevor' ♀H3	Widely available
	'Leatherwood Cream'	WSpi
	lucida	CCCN CDoC CTrC CTsd EBee ELan GGar IArd IMGH ISea MDun NHim NLar WFar WSpi
	- 'Ballerina'	CMHG CMac CPMA ELon GGGa ISea LRHS MAsh MGos NHim SCoo SPoG SRot SSpi SSta WAbe WFar
	- 'Dumpling'	CGHE CPLG EBee WPGP
	- 'Gilt Edge' (v)	CBcs CTrC CWGN LLHF LRHS MMHG
	- 'Pink Cloud'	Widely available
	- 'Pink Whisper'	see *E. milliganii* subsp. *pubescens* 'Pink Whisper'
	- 'Spring Glow' (v)	CTrC CWGN LLHF LRHS MAsh SPoG SSta
	milliganii	CAbP CBcs CDoC CMac CTrC ELan EPfP GGGa GGar GQui LHop LRHS MRav NPal SBod SRms SSpi SSta WAbe WPGP WSpi
§	- subsp. ***pubescens*** 'Pink Whisper'	NHim WPGP
	moorei	CBcs CCCN CMac CPLG EBee GQui LRHS SSpi
	× ***nymansensis***	CTrG CWib LSRN SAPC SArc SDnm SReu SRms SSpi WHCG
	- 'George Graham'	GGGa IMGH
	- 'Nymans Silver' (v)	ELan LLHF LRHS MAsh SPoG SSpi
	- 'Nymansay' ♀H3	Widely available
	- 'Nymansay Variegated' (v)	CPMA
	'Penwith' misapplied	see *E. cordifolia* × *lucida*
	'Penwith' ambig.	CDoC CTsd GQui SPer WBrE WDin WFar

Eugenia (*Myrtaceae*)

	uniflora	CCCN

Eunomia see *Aethionema*

Euodia (*Rutaceae*)

	daniellii	see *Tetradium daniellii*
	hupehensis	see *Tetradium daniellii* Hupehense Group

Euonymus ✿ (*Celastraceae*)

	B&L 12543	EPla EWes
	B&SWJ 4457	WPGP
	CC 4522	CPLG
	alatus ♀H4	Widely available
	- B&SWJ 8794	WCru
	- var. ***apterus***	EPfP
	- Chicago Fire	see *E. alatus* 'Timber Creek'
	- 'Ciliodentatus'	see *E. alatus* 'Compactus'
§	- 'Compactus' ♀H4	Widely available
§	- 'Fire Ball'	CPMA EPfP MBri
	- Little Moses = 'Odom'	NLar
*	- 'Macrophyllus'	CPMA EPfP
	- 'Rudy Haag'	CPMA EPfP MBri NLar
	- 'Select'	see *E. alatus* 'Fire Ball'
	- 'Silver Cloud'	EPfP
§	- 'Timber Creek'	CPMA EPfP GKir MBri NLar WPat
	americanus	EPfP MBlu NLar
	- 'Evergreen'	EPfP
	- narrow-leaved	EPfP
	atropurpureus	EPfP
	'Benkomoki'	EMil MAsh
	bungeanus	EPfP EPla WPat
	- 'Dart's Pride'	CPMA EPfP NLar
	- 'Fireflame'	CPMA EPfP
*	- var. ***mongolicus***	EPfP
	- 'Pendulus'	CPMA EPfP MBlu SCoo
	- var. ***semipersistens***	CPMA
	carnosus	CPMA EPfP
	chibae B&SWJ 11159	WCru
	cornutus var. ***quinquecornutus***	CPMA ELan EPfP GKir IDee LRHS MBlu MBri NBhm NLar WPGP WPat
	'Den Haag'	CPMA EPfP NLar
	echinatus	EPfP EPla
	europaeus	Widely available
	- f. ***albus***	CBot CPMA CTho EPfP EQua LRHS NLar
	- 'Atropurpureus'	CMCN CTho EPfP LRHS MAsh NLar

	Name	Suppliers
	- 'Atrorubens'	CPMA
	- 'Aucubifolius' (v)	CMac EPfP
*	- 'Aureus'	CNat LRHS
	- 'Brilliant'	CPMA EPfP
*	- f. ***bulgaricus***	EPfP
	- 'Chrysophyllus'	EPfP MBlu
	- 'Howard'	EPfP
	- var. ***intermedius***	EPfP MBlu MBri NLar
	- 'Miss Pinkie'	CEnd GKir
	- 'Red Cascade' ♀H4	Widely available
	- 'Scarlet Wonder'	CPMA EPfP
	- 'Thornhayes'	CTho EPfP MBri NLar
I	- 'Variegatus'	EPfP
	europeaus 'Pumilis'	EPfP
	farreri	see *E. nanus*
	fimbriatus	CPMA EPfP
	fortunei	LEdu NHol
	- Blondy = 'Interbolwi'PBR (v)	CAbP CDoC CDul CSBt CTri CWSG CWib EBee ELan EPfP GKir IFoB LAst LRHS MAsh MBar MBri MGos MRav MSwo NEgg NHol NPri SBch SCoo SLim SPer SPoG WDin
	- 'Canadale Gold' (v)	EBee EPfP EPla EQua LRHS MAsh MGos NHol SPoG WDin
	- 'Coloratus'	CMac EBee EPfP MBar MBlu MSwo NHol SEND SLon SPer WDin
	- 'Dart's Blanket'	CDul ECrN ELan MRav WDin WFar
	- 'Emerald Cushion'	CDul
	- 'Emerald Gaiety' (v) ♀H4	Widely available
*	- 'Emerald Green'	IFoB
	- 'Emerald 'n' Gold' (v) ♀H4	Widely available
	- 'Emerald Surprise' (v) ♀H4	EPfP SRGP
	- 'Gold Spot'	see *E. fortunei* 'Sunspot'
	- 'Gold Tip'	see *E. fortunei* Golden Prince
	- 'Golden Harlequin' (v)	EGxp EMil LRHS MAsh
§	- 'Golden Pillar' (v)	EHoe EPla WFar
§	- Golden Prince (v)	CMac EHoe EPfP EPla MBar MGos MRav MSwo SLim SRms WGor
	- 'Harlequin' (v)	CBcs CMac CSBt CWSG EBee EHoe ELan EPfP LAst LBMP LBuc LRHS LSRN MAsh MBar MGos MLHP MNHC MRav NBir NBlu NPro SAga SLim SPer SRms SWvt WFar WFoF
	- 'Kewensis'	CDoC CMac CWib EBee EPfP LRHS MBar MWhi SAPC SArc SBod SPoG WCru
	- 'Minimus'	CDul CTri EPPr EPla MGos NHol NPro WFar
*	- 'Minimus Variegatus' (v)	ECho SPlb
	- 'Perrolino'	EBee
§	- var. ***radicans***	MGan
	- - 'Variegatus' (v)	MAsh
	- 'Sheridan Gold'	CMac CTri EPla MRav
	- 'Silver Gem'	see *E. fortunei* 'Variegatus'
	- 'Silver Pillar' (v)	CPLG EHoe WFar
	- 'Silver Queen' (v)	Widely available
	- 'Silverstone'PBR (v)	EPfP LRHS NHol NPro SPoG
	- 'Sunshine' (v)	CAbP ELan EPfP LRHS MAsh MGos SLon SPoG
§	- 'Sunspot' (v)	CBcs CMac CWSG EBee ECrN ELan IFoB LBMP MBar MGos MSwo NHol SLim SRms WDin WFar WHar
	- 'Tustin' ♀H4	SLPl
§	- 'Variegatus' (v)	MBar SRms STre WDin
	- var. ***vegetus***	EPla
	frigidus	EPfP WPGP
	'Gaiety Girl' **new**	ISea
	grandiflorus	CPMA EPfP GKir LRHS NLar SCoo WFar
	- 'Red Wine'	CPMA CTho EMil EPfP LHop LRHS MAsh NLar SEND WPGP WPat
	- f. ***salicifolius***	CPMA EPfP
	hamiltonianus	CMCN EBtc EPfP SSpi WAbe
I	- 'Calocarpus'	CPMA GKir LRHS SCoo
	- 'Fiesta'	CPMA EPfP NLar
	- subsp. ***hians***	see *E. hamiltonianus* subsp. ***sieboldianus***
	- 'Indian Summer'	CPMA EPfP GKir LRHS MAsh MBri MMHG NLar SCoo SSpi WPGP WPat
	- 'Koi Boy'	CPMA GKir LRHS MAsh MGos SPoG
	- 'Miss Pinkie'	CDul CPMA EPfP GKir LRHS MAsh MGos NLar SCoo SSpi WPat
	- 'Pink Delight'	CPMA EPfP
	- 'Poort Bulten'	CPMA EPfP NLar
	- 'Popcorn'	CPMA EPfP MBri WPat
	- 'Rainbow'	CPMA EPfP MBri NLar
	- 'Red Chief'	CPMA EPfP
	- 'Red Elf'	CPMA EPfP
	- 'Rising Sun'	CPMA EPfP MBri NLar
§	- subsp. ***sieboldianus***	CDul CMen CPLG CPMA CTho EPfP GAuc LRHS MAsh MRav NPCo SLPl WFar WPat
	- - B&SWJ 10941	WCru
	- - 'Calocarpus'	EPfP
	- - 'Coral Charm'	CPMA EPfP NLar
	- - Semiexsertus Group	EPfP
*	- - var. ***yedoensis*** f. ***koehneanus***	EPfP
	- 'Snow'	CPMA EPfP MBri NLar WPat
	- 'Winter Glory'	CPMA EPfP GKir LRHS MMHG WPat
	- var. ***yedoensis***	see *E. hamiltonianus* subsp. ***sieboldianus***
	japonicus	CBcs CCVT CDoC CDul CMac ECrN EPfP NBlu SAPC SArc SBch SEND SPer WDin
	- 'Albomarginatus'	CBcs CChe CTri EPfP LRHS MMuc NBlu SEND SRms
	- 'Aureopictus'	see *E. japonicus* 'Aureus'
	- 'Aureovariegatus'	see *E. japonicus* 'Ovatus Aureus'
§	- 'Aureus' (v)	CBcs CDoC CSBt CWib EBee ECrN LAst NBlu NPri SCoo SLon SPer WDin WHar
	- 'Benkomasaki'	EPfP
	- 'Bravo'	CDoC CDul EBee ECrN EHoe EMil EPfP ERas LAst LRHS MGos MWea NLar SCoo SLim SPer SPoG SWvt WDin WFar
	- 'Chollipo' ♀H4	ELan EPfP EPla LRHS MAsh MGos
	- 'Compactus'	SArc SCoo
	- 'Duc d'Anjou' misapplied	see *E. japonicus* 'Viridivariegatus'
	- 'Duc d'Anjou' Carrière (v)	CBcs CHrt EBee EHoe ELan EPla EWTr EWes MRav SBch SEND SPoG
	- Exstase = 'Goldbolwi'PBR (v)	SPoG
	- 'Extase' (v) **new**	WCot
	- 'Francien' (v)	SPoG
	- 'Golden Maiden'	ELan EPfP LRHS MAsh SLim SLon SPoG SWvt
	- 'Golden Pillar'	see *E. fortunei* 'Golden Pillar'
	- 'Green Rocket'	EPfP LRHS SPoG
	- 'Green Spider'	SPoG
	- 'Grey Beauty'	EBee NLar
	- 'Hibarimisake'	EPfP
	- 'Kathy'PBR	ERas LRHS MGos SPoG SRGP
§	- 'Latifolius Albomarginatus'	CDul ELan EPfP MRav MSwo SBch SPer SPoG WDin
	- 'Luna'	see *E. japonicus* 'Aureus'
	- 'Macrophyllus Albus'	see *E. japonicus* 'Latifolius Albomarginatus'
	- 'Maiden's Gold'	CSBt EBee
	- 'Marieke'	see *E. japonicus* 'Ovatus Aureus'
	- 'Microphyllus'	CDoC MRav NBlu SBch STre WFar

§ - 'Microphyllus Albovariegatus' (v)	CBcs CChe CDoC CDul CMac CMea CSBt CTri CWSG ELan EPfP EPla LAst LRHS MBar MGos NHol SBch SLim SPoG SRms SWvt WDin WFar WHCG WPat
§ - 'Microphyllus Aureovariegatus' (v)	CDoC CMea ELan EPfP LRHS MGos NLar SBch SPoG WPat
- 'Microphyllus Aureus'	see *E. japonicus* 'Microphyllus Pulchellus'
§ - 'Microphyllus Pulchellus' (v)	CBcs CDoC CMac CSBt CWSG EBee ECrN EPfP EPla LHop LRHS MBar NHol SBch SPoG SWvt WDin
- 'Microphyllus Variegatus'	see *E. japonicus* 'Microphyllus Albovariegatus'
§ - 'Ovatus Aureus' (v) ♀H4	CChe CDoC CDul CPLG CSBt CTri CWSG EBee ECrN EPfP LAst LRHS MBar MGos MRav NBlu NPri SBch SLim SPer SPlb SPoG SRms SWvt WDin WFar
- 'Président Gauthier' (v)	CDoC EBee ECrN EQua MGos MWea SCoo SLim SWvt WCFE WDin
- 'Pulchellus Aureovariegatus'	see *E. japonicus* 'Microphyllus Aureovariegatus'
I - 'Pyramidatus'	EPfP
- 'Robustus'	EPfP EPla
- 'Royal Gold'	SPoG
- 'Silver King'	CMac
- 'Silver Krista' (v)	SPoG
- 'Susan'	CDoC EPla EQua MAsh SRGP
§ - 'Viridivariegatus' (v)	LRHS
kiautschovicus	EPfP GKir
- 'Berry Hill'	EPfP NLar
- 'Manhattan'	EPfP NLar
latifolius	CMCN CPMA EPfP GKir WPat
§ ***laxiflorus*** WWJ 11668 new	WCru
lucidus	CBcs CHll CPLG SSpi WFar
maackii	MMHG
macropterus	CPMA EPfP
maximowiczianus	EPfP WPat
morrisonensis	EPfP
- B&SWJ 3700	WCru
myrianthus	CPMA EPfP EWes MAsh MBlu NLar
§ ***nanus***	CWib EPfP EPla MAsh NHol NLar
- var. ***turkestanicus***	EPfP EPla LHop SLon SRms WFar
obovatus	EPfP NLar
occidentalis	EPfP
oresbius	CPMA EPfP
oxyphyllus	CMCN CPMA EPfP EWTr GKir IArd LRHS MBri NLar SCoo SSpi WCru WDin
- 'Angyo Elegant' (v)	EPfP
- 'Waasland'	CPMA EPfP
pauciflorus	EPfP
phellomanus ♀H4	CDul CEnd CTho CWSG EBee EPfP EWTr GKir LHop LRHS MBar MBlu MGos MRav NLar SCoo SPoG WDin WFar WPGP WPat
- 'Silver Surprise' (v)	CPMA EPfP NLar WPat
Pierrolino = 'Heespierrolino'[PBR]	EGxp LRHS NBlu SCoo SPoG
§ ***planipes*** ♀H4	Widely available
- 'Dart's August Flame'	CPMA EPfP
- 'Gold Ore'	EPfP
- 'Sancho'	CPMA EPfP MBri
quelpaertensis	EPfP
radicans	see *E. fortunei* var. *radicans*
'Rokojō'	CStu NWCA
rongchuensis	CPMA EPfP
rosmarinifolius	see *E. nanus*
rubescens	see *E. laxiflorus*
sachalinensis misapplied	see *E. planipes*
sacrosanctus	CPMA EPfP NLar
sanguineus	CPMA EPfP NLar SSpi
sieboldianus	WCru
var. ***sanguineus*** B&SWJ 11140	
spraguei	EPfP
tingens	CBcs CPMA EPfP GKir NLar
trapococcus	EPfP
vagans	EPfP
- L 551	EPla
velutinus	EPfP NLar
verrucosus	CPMA EPfP EPla GKir LRHS MAsh NLar
vidalii	EPfP
wilsonii	MAsh NLar
yedoensis	see *E. hamiltonianus* subsp. *sieboldianus*

Eupatoriadelphus see *Eupatorium*

Eupatorium ✿ (*Asteraceae*)

B&SWJ 9052 from Guatemala	WCru
album L.	NBid SWat WPer
altissimum	CBot SRms
aromaticum	see *Ageratina aromatica*
atrorubens	see *Bartlettina sordida*
cannabinum	CArn CWan EBWF EBee EHon ELan EMFW GBar GGar GPWP GPoy IFoB LPBA MBNS MHer MNHC MRav NBir NGHP NMir NPer SECG SGSe SPav SWat WBVN WPer WSFF
§ - f. ***albiflorum***	SPhx
- 'Album'	see *E. cannabinum* f. *albiflorum*
- f. ***cannabinum*** 'Flore Pleno' (d)	CMac CPrp CSev EBee ECha ECtt ELan ELon EPfP LHop LRHS MBel MHer MRav NEgg NGdn SAga SPhx SWat WAul WCAu WCom WCot WFar WHil WMnd WPtf WSFF WTin
- - 'Spraypaint' (v)	EPPr
capillifolium ♀H3	CAby CSpe EBee ECtt EShb EWes GBin LHop LRHS LSou MBel MCot MDKP SAga SDix SDys SHar SMrm SPhx SUsu WCot WHil WPGP WWEG
coelestinum	see *Conoclinium coelestinum*
fistulosum	NGdn
- f. ***albidum*** 'Bartered Bride'	CKno EBee EBrs ECtt EWes GCal
- - 'Joe White'	WSFF
- - 'Massive White' ♀H4	CFir EBee GCal NBir NSti SMad WSpi
- 'Berggarten'	EBee GCal
- 'Carin'	WSFF
fortunei	CArn
- 'Fine Line' (v)	CBow CKno EBee LSou MDKP MHer MLHP WCot WPGP WSFF
- white-flowered new	LFur
glaucum 'Golden Foam' new	LFur
glechonophyllum	see *Ageratina glechonophylla*
hyssopifolium	EBee
japonicum	EBee GPoy
ligustrinum	see *Ageratina ligustrina*
lindleyanum	CKno EBee
maculatum	EBee EHrv MDKP NGHP NGdn NLar STes WHil WHrl WPer
- Atropurpureum Group ♀H4	Widely available
- - 'Gateway'	CRow EBee EBrs GCal NBPC NBre SPhx WHoo WPtf WTin

- - 'Glutball'	CHVG CKno EBee EBrs ELon GCal LBMP LPla LRHS MNrw NChi SMad WWEG
- - 'Little Red'	WSFF
- - 'Orchard Dene' ♀H4	SPur
- - 'Phantom'	EBee ECtt GQue IPot MBri
- - 'Purple Bush' ♀H4	CAby CKno CSam EBee ECha ELon GCal MDKP NBre NCGa NEgg SMad SPhx SSvw WHil WSFF WWEG
- - 'Riesenschirm' ♀H4	CKno CSam EBee ECGP ECtt ELon EPPr EShb EWes GBin GCal LBMP LRHS MAvo MNFA MSCN NCGa NEgg SDix SMad SPhx SPoG SWat WCot WHrl
makinoi	WCru
var. ***oppositifolium*** B&SWJ 8449	
micranthum	see *Ageratina ligustrina*
occidentale	see *Ageratina occidentalis*
perfoliatum	CArn GPoy MNrw NBre NLar SPav
purpureum	Widely available
- 'Album'	CTri MBel SPhx
rugosum	see *Ageratina altissima*
- album	see *Ageratina altissima*
variabile 'Golders Green' (v)	EWes MDKP WHil
weinmannianum	see *Ageratina ligustrina*

Euphorbia ✿ (*Euphorbiaceae*)

'Abbey Dore'	MAvo WCot WSHC
altissima	ITim
amygdaloides	EBla ECtt GKir SWat SWvt
- 'Bob's Choice'	EWes
- 'Craigieburn'	CDes EBla EWes GCal GCra LBMP LBuc LRHS MGos MRav SUsu WCom WPGP WWEG
- 'Mark's Red'	WCot
§ - 'Purpurea'	Widely available
§ - var. ***robbiae*** ♀H4	Widely available
- - dwarf	EWes
- - 'Pom Pom'	CDes EBee ELon LSou WPGP
- - 'Redbud'	EBee EPla EWes GCal LSou SLPl
- 'Rubra'	see *E. amygdaloides* 'Purpurea'
- 'Variegata' (v)	GBuc SMad
- 'Winter Glow'	CSpe
baselicis	CBow CMea CPom CSpe EBee GAbr GKev LPio WHoo WPer
biglandulosa Desf.	see *E. rigida*
Blackbird = 'Nothowlee'[PBR]	Widely available
'Blue Haze'	CDes NWit SMeo
'Blue Lagoon'	NBhm
canariensis	EPfP
capitulata	EWes MTho
cashmeriana	NWit
- CC&McK 607	EWes
- CC&McK 724	GBin
ceratocarpa	CFwr CSpe EBee EPPr EWes GBuc GMaP LSou MAvo MBri NEgg NWit SEND SMad WClo WCot WPGP WSHC
characias	CBcs CBot CHEx CMac CWCL EBee EBla ECtt EPfP GKir LRHS MCot MLHP MRav NChi NPer NPri NVic SBch SMrm SPer SRms SWvt WBrk WCom WCot WMnd WPer WWEG
- Ballyrogan hybrids	NBhm
- 'Best Yet' **new**	WCot
- 'Black Pearl'	CBcs CCVN EBee EPfP LAst LBMP LRHS LSou MAvo MCCP MGos NBPC NCGa NEgg NSti NWit SBch SDnm SEND SPav SPer SPoG SWvt WFar
- 'Blue Wonder'	CMac CSpe EBee ECtt EHrv ELan EPfP GMaP LRHS LSou MAvo MCCP NEgg NLar NWit SAga SDnm SPav SPoG WCot WGwG WHoo WWEG
- subsp. ***characias***	CPrp CWCL EHrv GMaP MGos SPoG
- - 'Blue Hills'	ECtt GBuc
- - 'Burrow Silver' (v)	CFir EBee GMaP LDai LSRN MRav NEgg SDnm SMrm SPav SPer SPoG SWvt WFar
- - 'H.E. Bates'	NBir
- - 'Humpty Dumpty'	Widely available
- - 'Perry's Winter Blusher'	ECtt
- 'Dwarf Black Pearl' **new**	WWEG
- 'Forescate'	EBee EMil EPfP GMaP LHop LPio LRHS LSRN SBch SDnm SPav
- 'Goldbrook'	CMac EBla EHoe LBMP MBNS MRav
- 'Kestrel' (v)	WCom WCot
- 'Portuguese Velvet' ♀H4	Widely available
- Silver Swan = 'Wilcott'[PBR] (v)	CBcs CMac CSpe CWGN EBee EBrs ELan EPfP EShb EWes IFoB LAst LBMP LBuc LRHS LSRN LSou MBNS MGos MRav NPri NSti SBch SDix SPoG SWvt WCot WFar
- 'Spring Splendour'	EWes
- 'Starbright'	EBee GBin
- 'Tasmanian Tiger' (v) **new**	CSpe CWGN EWes NCGa SBch SPad
- subsp. ***wulfenii*** ♀H3-4	Widely available
- - 'Bosahan' (v)	CBcs GCra
- - dwarf	WOut
- - 'Emmer Green' (v)	CBow CSpe EBee EHrv ELon EWTr EWes GCal GMaP LLWG MBel MMHG NWit SMrm SPoG WClo WCot WFoF WWEG
- - 'Jayne's Golden Giant'	SMad
- - 'Jimmy Platt'	ERCP MTho SRms WBrE WCom WCot WGwG
§ - - 'John Tomlinson' ♀H3-4	CMoH EHrv EWes GBin LSRN MRav WCot WSpi
- - Kew form	see *E. characias* subsp. *wulfenii* 'John Tomlinson'
- - 'Lambrook Gold' ♀H3-4	CSam CWCL EBee ECtt EPPr EPfP GCra MRav MWat NLar NPer SMad WCot WFar WGwG WMnd WSpi WWEG
- - 'Lambrook Gold' seed-raised	see *E. characias* subsp. *wulfenii* Margery Fish Group
- - 'Lambrook Yellow'	GBuc GCal MWhi NWsh
§ - - Margery Fish Group	CMac EBee LBMP LRHS NBir SPer
- - 'Perry's Tangerine'	EWes NPer NWit
§ - - 'Purple and Gold'	CSpe EBee EWes GMaP LFur MAvo NCGa NLar NWit SMad SWvt WSpi WWEG
- - 'Purpurea'	see *E. characias* subsp. *wulfenii* 'Purple and Gold'
- - 'Thelma's Giant'	NWit
clavarioides var. ***truncata***	WCot
'Copton Ash'	CSpe EBee EPPr EWes MAvo NWit
corallioides	CSsd EBee ECha GCal IFro LRHS NPer NSti SPav SRms WBrE WHer WPnP
§ ***cornigera*** ♀H4	CHrt EAEE EBee ECha EPfP GBin GBuc GMac LPio LRHS MAvo MCot MRav NBid NGdn NSti NWit SWat WCru WPGP WPen
- 'Goldener Turm'	CMoH EBee GBuc LRHS LSou MAvo SMrm SPer WCot
cyparissias	CArn CBcs EBee ECha ELan LRHS MCot MLHP MRav NBir NGdn

	NMen SBch SMrm SPav SRms WBrk WEas WFar WFoF WPer WTin
- 'Baby'	WFar
- 'Betten'	see *E.* × *gayeri* 'Betten'
- 'Bushman Boy'	SMrm
- 'Clarice Howard'	see *E. cyparissias* 'Fens Ruby'
§ - 'Fens Ruby'	Widely available
- 'Orange Man'	EBee EBla EPfP EPla EWes GBin LBMP LRHS NBro NEgg NGdn NHol SWat SWvt WFar
- 'Purpurea'	see *E. cyparissias* 'Fens Ruby'
- 'Red Devil'	CBre NWit SMrm
- 'Tall Boy'	EWes SMrm
deflexa	EBee
dendroides	WCot
§ ***donii***	EBee EWes IFoB NWit SDix WCot
- HWJK 2405	WCru
- 'Amjillasa'	SAga SDix SUsu
dulcis	CBre CStu ECtt NBro NWit
- 'Chameleon'	Widely available
'Efanthia'PBR	CCVN CEnd CMil CPrp CSpe EBee EPfP EWes LHop LRHS LSou MBri NLar NPri SPoG STes SVil
enopla	EPfP
epithymoides	see *E. polychroma*
esula Baker's form	NWit
Excalibur = 'Froeup'PBR ♀H4	CMHG CWCL EBee ELan ELon GBin GBuc LHop LRHS MBNS MBri MCCP MRav NBir NEgg NHol NSti SBch WFar WSHC
flavicoma	GCal
fragifera	EBee NWit
'Garblesham Enchanter'	EPPr
§ × ***gayeri*** 'Betten'	EBee
glauca	CFir ECou NWit
'Golden Foam'	see *E. stricta*
griffithii	CHll GGal IFoB NBro SPav SWat WFar WMoo
- 'Dixter' ♀H4	Widely available
- 'Dixter Flame'	IFoB NWit
- 'Fern Cottage'	CElw CWCL EBee EHrv EWes GAbr SUsu WMnd WWEG
- 'Fireglow'	Widely available
- 'King's Caple'	EBee ELon EWes GBin LRHS MBNS SBch SPoG WCru
- 'Wickstead'	GAbr GBin MLHP NLar
'Helena'PBR (v)	CSpe EBee EPfP LHop LLHF LSRN NLar NPri SPoG SVil WClo WCot
hyberna	LLHF NMen NWit SWat
hypericifolia	CCVN CSpe EPfP LHop LSou SVil
Diamond Frost = 'Inneuphe'PBR	
ingens	NScw
jacquemontii	EBee IFoB LPio MNrw MRav NChi NWit
'Jade Dragon'	CSpe EBee SPoG WWEG
'Jessie'	MAvo NSti
jolkinii	GKev
- SDR 4307	GKev
Kalipso = 'Innkalff'PBR	CPrp EBee EPfP NLar SVil
lambii	EShb
'Lambrook Silver'	SRkn
lathyris	CArn CBre MHer MLHP NHol NLar NPer NWit SRms WEas
longifolia misapplied	see *E. cornigera*
longifolia D. Don	see *E. donii*
longifolia Lam.	see *E. mellifera*
mammillaris	WCor
- 'Variegata' (v) **new**	WCor
margalidiana	EWes
× ***martini*** ♀H3	Widely available
- 'Aperitif'PBR	CBow CWCL EBee EPfP
- 'Baby Charm'	EBee EPPr GBBs LBuc LRHS WCot
- dwarf	CFir CSpr GCal
- 'Helen Robinson'	CDes MAvo WCot
- Helena's Blush = 'Inneuphhel' (v) **new**	LRHS
- 'Kolibri'	EBee EPfP LSou SPoG
- 'Red Dwarf'	LRHS
- Rudolph = 'Waleuphrud' **new**	LRHS
- 'Tiny Tim'	EPfP EWTr LRHS LSRN MBri MWat SBch SPoG SWvt
- 'Walberton's Rudolf'	SPoG
§ ***mellifera*** ♀H3	Widely available
milii ♀H1	EBak LRHS
myrsinites ♀H4	Widely available
nereidum	EWes NWit
nicaeensis	CPom EBee GCal LRHS SEND SMrm SPhx WCot WPGP WSHC
- subsp. ***glareosa***	NWit
oblongata	EWes NWit
'Orange Grove'	NBhm SGol
palustris ♀H4	Widely available
- 'Walenburg's Glorie'	CMHG CWCL EBee EBla ECha ELan EWTr GBin LRHS MBri MNrw MRav NCGa NSti NWit SMad SWat WKif WSpi
- 'Zauberflöte'	CHrt SRms WFar
× ***paradoxa***	NWit
paralias	WCot WHer
× ***pasteurii***	CBgR CDTJ CFir CPom EBee EWes LSou MAvo NWit WPGP
- 'John Phillips'	SBch WPGP
pilosa 'Major'	see *E. polychroma* 'Major'
piscatoria	WPGP
pithyusa	CBgR CBot CPom CSpe EBee ECha ECtt ELan EPfP LHop MAvo MRav NGdn WCom
§ ***polychroma*** ♀H4	Widely available
§ - 'Candy'	CBot CWCL EBee ECha EHrv ELan EPfP MCCP MMuc WCom WCot WFar WMnd
- compact	LBuc LRHS
- 'Emerald Jade'	WPGP
- 'First Blush' (v) **new**	CWGN EBee EWes NBre
- 'Golden Fusion' **new**	LRHS WFar
§ - 'Lacy' (v)	CDoC EBee ECtt EHrv EWes GCal LAst LBMP LRHS MCCP MRav NBir NCob NGdn NWit SPoG WFar
§ - 'Major' ♀H4	CMHG CPLG SAga WCom WCot WKif
- 'Midas'	GBin MAvo MNrw NWit SMrm
- 'Purpurea'	see *E. polychroma* 'Candy'
* - 'Senior'	MGos MWat NWit
- 'Sonnengold'	EWes WSHC
- 'Variegata'	see *E. polychroma* 'Lacy'
portlandica	NWit WHer
§ × ***pseudovirgata***	NWit
pulcherrima	LRHS
'Purple Preference'	EPPr
Redwing = 'Charam'PBR ♀H4	CBcs EBee ELan EMil EPfP LBuc LRHS LSou MBri MGos MRav NLar NWit SCoo SPer SPhx SPoG SWvt
reflexa	see *E. seguieriana* subsp. *niciciana*
§ ***rigida*** ♀H4	CBot CBro CDes CSpe EBee ECGP EHrv ELan EPfP EPyc EWes GKir LPio LRHS MAvo MBel NSti SMrm SPhx SUsu WCot WFar WHoo WPGP WSHC WSpi WWEG
- 'Sardis'	NWit SUsu
robbiae	see *E. amygdaloides* var. *robbiae*
'Rosies Surprise'	LLHF MTho
rothiana GWJ 9479a	WCru

'Roundway Titan' SSpi
'Royal Velvet' CBow
sarawschanica ECha GBBs GBin GQue LPla LRHS NWit SMad SMrm SPhx
schillingii ♀H4 CSam CWCL EBee EHoe ELan EPfP GCra GMaP LHop LPio LRHS MCot MRav MSCN SDix SPer SPoG SUsu WCru WFar WGwG WHoo WPGP WSpi WTin
seguieriana ECha MAvo NLar WPer
§ - subsp. ***niciciana*** CBot CBow CMoH GBin IMou NWsh
serrulata Thuill. see *E. stricta*
sikkimensis ♀H4 CBot CBow CHrt CMHG CPLG CPom CSam CWCL EBee ECha ELan GCal ILad LPio LRHS MAvo NEgg NPer SMrm SPav SRms WCom WCru WEas WFar WHoo
- GWJ 9214 WCru
soongarica MAvo NWit
spinosa NWit SPlb
§ ***stricta*** WTin
stygiana CMil CSam CSpe CWCL EBee ELon EWes GCal LPio MAvo SAga WCot WPGP
Thalia = 'Innthal' **new** EPfP
tirucalli EShb
uralensis see *E.* × *pseudovirgata*
valdevillosocarpa MAvo WPer
'Velvet Ruby' **new** LSou NWit WCot
verrucosa NWit WFar
- Baker's form EPPr
villosa Waldst. & Kit. ex Willd. NWit
§ ***virgata*** EWes NWit SPav
× ***waldsteinii*** see *E. virgata*
wallichii misapplied see *E. donii*
wallichii Kohli see *E. cornigera*
wallichii Hook. f. CPLG EBee GCal GKir MBri NOrc SPoG WPGP
- 'Lemon and Lime' CWib LSou WFar
'Whistleberry Garnet' EBee LHop LLHF LRHS LSou MWea SDix SPoG

Euptelea (*Eupteleaceae*)

franchetii see *E. pleiosperma*
§ ***pleiosperma*** EBee NLar SSpi
polyandra EPfP MBri NLar WPGP

Eurya (*Theaceae*)

japonica WPGP
- 'Moutiers' (v) WPat
- 'Variegata' misapplied see *Cleyera japonica* 'Fortunei'

Euryops (*Asteraceae*)

abrotanifolius CCCN CTrC
§ ***acraeus*** ♀H4 CMea CSBt ECho EPfP EPot LHop LRHS MWat NLAp NMen NWCA SAga SIng WAbe WCom WFar
candollei CTrC
§ ***chrysanthemoides*** CCCN CHEx CSam EShb
- 'Sonnenschein' EBee SPet
evansii see *E. acraeus*
lateriflorus SPlb
pectinatus ♀H2 CBcs CCCN CDTJ CDoC CHEx CHrt CPLG CSam CTrC CTrG CTri EBee EPfP EShb GGal GGar IMon MNrw MRav NPri SBod SEND SGar SWvt WCFE WHer
spathaceus **new** CTrC
tenuissimus **new** CTrC
tysonii CTrC EBee GCal GEdr SPlb WCot
virgineus CCCN CPLG CTrC CTrG GGar IDee

Eustachys (*Poaceae*)

§ ***distichophylla*** EBee MAvo NWsh WCot WPrP

Eustoma (*Gentianaceae*)

§ ***grandiflorum*** LRHS MBri
russellianum see *E. grandiflorum*

Eustrephus (*Philesiaceae*)

latifolius ECou

Eutaxia (*Papilionaceae*)

obovata ECou

Euthamia (*Asteraceae*)

gymnospermoides EWes

Eutrochium see *Eupatorium*

Evolvulus (*Convolvulaceae*)

'Blue Sher' **new** CSpe

Ewartia (*Asteraceae*)

planchonii WAbe

Exacum (*Gentianaceae*)

affine ♀H1+3 MBri
- 'Rococo' MBri

Exochorda (*Rosaceae*)

giraldii var. ***wilsonii*** CMac CPLG CSam EBee EPfP GBin LHop LRHS MBNS NLar SLim SSta SWvt
× ***macrantha*** EBee LRHS
- 'Irish Pearl' CPLG
- 'The Bride' ♀H4 Widely available
racemosa EPfP NLar SPer WDin WHCG
serratifolia EPfP GAuc LRHS
- 'Snow White' CPMA EBee EWes IArd LRHS MAsh MBlu MBri NLar

F

Fabiana (*Solanaceae*)

imbricata CAbP EPfP GQui LLHF LRHS SAga SLon SPer
- 'Prostrata' EBee EPfP LRHS SSpi WAbe
- f. ***violacea*** ♀H3 CBcs CSBt CTri EBee EPfP GQui LLHF LRHS MMuc SPer WKif

Fagopyrum (*Polygonaceae*)

cymosum see *F. dibotrys*
§ ***dibotrys*** CArn EBee ECha ELan EWld LEdu WMoo
- 'Variegatum' (v) CBow

Fagus ✿ (*Fagaceae*)

§ ***crenata*** CMCN CMen WDin
- 'Mount Fuji' SBir
engleriana CMCN SBir
grandifolia CMCN ISea
- subsp. ***mexicana*** SBir
japonica SBir
- var. ***multinervis*** SBir
orientalis CMCN ECrN LRHS
- 'Iskander' MBlu
sieboldii see *F. crenata*
sylvatica ♀H4 Widely available

§	- 'Albomarginata' (v)	CMCN
	- 'Albovariegata'	see *F. sylvatica* 'Albomarginata'
	- 'Ansorgei'	CEnd CMCN MBlu NLar
	- 'Arcuata' **new**	SBir
N	- Atropurpurea Group	Widely available
	- - 'Friso'	CEnd
	- - 'Swat Magret'	SMad
	- 'Aurea Pendula'	CEnd CMCN ECrN GKir MBlu SBir
	- 'Bicolor Sartini'	MBlu
	- 'Birr Zebra'	CEnd
	- 'Black Swan'	CMCN CPMA ECrN GKir IArd ISea LRHS MAsh MBlu NEgg NLar NPCo SBir SLon SMad
	- 'Cochleata'	CMCN
	- 'Cockleshell'	CDul MBlu MBri SBir
	- 'Comptoniifolia'	see *F. sylvatica* var. *heterophylla* 'Comptoniifolia'
	- 'Cristata'	MBlu
N	- Cuprea Group	NWea
§	- 'Dawyck' ♀H4	Widely available
	- 'Dawyck Gold' ♀H4	Widely available
	- 'Dawyck Purple' ♀H4	Widely available
	- 'Eugen' **new**	SBir
	- 'Fastigiata' misapplied	see *F. sylvatica* 'Dawyck'
	- 'Felderbach'	MBlu SBir
	- 'Franken' (v)	MBlu SBir
	- 'Grandidentata'	CMCN
	- 'Greenwood'	MBlu
	- var. ***heterophylla***	CLnd CSBt CTho ECho ISea NWea
	- - 'Aspleniifolia' ♀H4	CBcs CDoC CDul CEnd CMCN CMac ECrN ELan EPfP EWTr GKir IMGH LRHS MAsh MBar MBlu MBri MGos NPCo SBir SCoo SLau SLon SPer SPoG WDin WFar WMou
§	- - 'Comptoniifolia'	SBir
	- - f. ***laciniata***	GKir MBlu
	- 'Horizontalis'	MBlu SLon
	- 'Incisa'	MBlu
	- 'Luteovariegata' (v)	CDul CEnd CMCN CPMA LRHS
	- 'Mercedes'	CDoC CMCN MBlu NPCo WPat
	- 'Miltonensis'	IArd
N	- 'Pendula' ♀H4	CBcs CDoC CDul CEnd CMCN CSBt CTho EBee ECho ECrN ELan EWTr GKir IMGH LMaj LRHS MBar MGos MSwo NEgg NPCo NWea SCrf SLau SPer SPoG WDin WHar WMou
	- 'Prince George of Crete'	CDul CMCN SBir
	- 'Purple Fountain' ♀H4	CDoC CDul CEnd CMCN CPMA EBee ELan GKir LAst LHop LRHS MAsh MBar MBlu MBri MGos NLar SBir SLau SLim SPoG WFar
	- Purple-leaved Group	see *F. sylvatica* Atropurpurea Group
	- 'Purpurea Latifolia'	EWTr LMaj
	- 'Purpurea Nana'	NPri
	- 'Purpurea Pendula'	Widely available
§	- 'Purpurea Tricolor' (v)	CDoC CDul CEnd CMCN CPMA ECrN EWTr LRHS MAsh MBlu MBri MGos NBea NWea SBir SCoo SCrf SPer WDin
	- 'Quercifolia'	MBlu
I	- 'Quercina'	SBir
	- 'Red Obelisk'	see *F. sylvatica* 'Rohan Obelisk'
	- 'Riversii' ♀H4	CBcs CDoC CDul CEnd CLnd CMCN CSBt CTho CTri CWib EBee ECrN ELan EPfP LAst LRHS MAsh MBri MGos NBlu NEgg NWea SLim SPer WDin WFar WHar
	- 'Rohan Gold'	CDul CEnd CMCN EBee MBlu
§	- 'Rohan Obelisk'	CDul CEnd CMCN EBee ELan EWTr IArd ISea MBlu MGos NLar SBir
I	- 'Rohan Pyramidalis'	CEnd
	- 'Rohan Trompenburg'	CMCN MBlu
	- 'Rohan Weeping'	MBlu SBir
	- 'Rohanii'	CAbP CBcs CDoC CDul CEnd CLnd CMCN CTri EBee ECho ECrN ELan EPfP EWTr LHop LRHS NPCo SBir SCoo SCrf SPer WDin WFar WHar
	- 'Roseomarginata'	see *F. sylvatica* 'Purpurea Tricolor'
	- 'Rotundifolia'	CDoC CDul MBlu
	- 'Spaethiana'	EWTr
	- 'Striata'	NPCo SBir
	- 'Sychrov' **new**	SBir
	- 'Tortuosa Purpurea'	CDul MBlu
	- 'Tricolor' misapplied (v)	see *F. sylvatica* 'Purpurea Tricolor'
	- 'Tricolor' ambig. (v)	SLau WFoF
	- 'Tricolor' (v)	CBcs CLnd CMac CSBt CWib EBee ELan NEgg WDin
	- 'Viridivariegata' (v)	CMCN
	- 'Zlatia'	CBcs CDoC CDul CLnd CMCN CSBt CWib ELan EPfP GKir MBar MBlu MBri MGos MSwo SBir SCoo SLau SPer WDin

Fallopia (Polygonaceae)

	aubertii	see *F. baldschuanica*
§	***baldschuanica***	Widely available
	× ***bohemica*** 'Spectabilis' (v)	CBow CRow
§	***japonica*** var. ***compacta***	CRow NLar WFar WMoo
	- - 'Fuji Snow'	see *F. japonica* var. *compacta* 'Milk Boy'
§	- - 'Milk Boy' (v)	CBow CRow EShb
	- - f. ***rosea*** hort.	CSpe WSpi
	- - 'Variegata' misapplied	see *F. japonica* var. *compacta* 'Milk Boy'
	- 'Crimson Beauty'	CRow
§	***multiflora***	CArn EOHP WWEG
	- var. ***hypoleuca***	EBee MCCP SCoo SPoG
	- - B&SWJ 120	WCru
	sachalinensis	NLar

Farfugium (Asteraceae)

§	***japonicum***	CHEx EPPr LRHS MTho
	- B&SWJ 884	WCru
	- 'Argenteum' (v)	CFir SMad WCom WCot WFar
§	- 'Aureomaculatum' (v) ♀H1	CFir CHEx EPfP LFur MCCP MTho SDnm SPav WFar
	- 'Crispatum'	CAbP CBct CBod CBow CFir CHEx EBee ECtt ELan EPPr EPfP EWll LAst LEdu LFur MCCP NSti SDnm SMad SPav SPer WCot WFar WHil WWEG
	- double-flowered (d)	WCru
	- var. ***formosanum*** B&SWJ 7125	WCru
	- var. ***giganteum***	CHEx WCot
	- 'Kagami-jishi' (v)	EPPr WCot
	- 'Kinkan' (v)	WCot
I	- 'Nanum'	CHEx
	- 'Ryuto'	EBee EPPr SMad WCot
I	- 'Tsuwa-buki'	WCot
	tussilagineum	see *F. japonicum*

Fargesia (Poaceae)

	from Jiuzhaigou, China	CEnt ETod MBri MMoz MMuc NLar WJun
	adpressa	EPla WJun
	angustissima	CDTJ CEnt ENBC EPla MMuc MWht SBig WJun WPGP
	'Baby'	STre
	confusa	CDTJ
	denudata	CEnt ENBC EPla SBig WJun
	- L 1575	CGHE MMoz MWht WPGP

- Xian 1	EPla MMoz WPGP
- Xian 2	EPla
dracocephala	CAbb CDoC CEnt CGHE EBee EPfP EPla GBin LEdu LRHS MAvo MBrN MBri MMoz MMuc MWht NGdn SBig SLPl SPoG WJun WMoo WPGP
ferax	EPla WJun WPGP
fungosa	EPla WJun WPGP
§ ***murielae*** ♀H4	Widely available
- 'Amy'	NLar NMoo
- 'Bimbo'	CEnt EBee EPfP EPla ETod GBin LAst MWht NPal NWsh STes WJun WMoo WPGP
- 'Grüne Hecke'	MWht SBig
- 'Harewood'	CWSG GBin MGos MMoz MWht NMoo SWvt WFar WPGP
- 'Joy'	GBin NLar WMoo WPnP
- 'Jumbo'	CAbb CEnt CHEx CSBt CWSG EAmu EBee ELan ENBC EPfP EPla GBin LPal LRHS MAvo MBri MGos MMoz MWht NGdn NWsh SBig SPer SPoG SRms SWvt WFar WJun
- 'Kranich'	NLar
- 'Lava'	MBri
- 'Little John'	ENBC
- 'Mae'	CDTJ MWht
- 'Novecento'	ELan
- 'Pinocchio'	MBri
- 'Simba' ♀H4	Widely available
- 'Vampire'	GCal MBri MGos SBig
- 'Willow'	EBee MBri
murieliae	LRHS
'Dana Jumbo' **new**	
* ***nepalensis***	CDTJ
§ ***nitida***	Widely available
* - from Jiuzhaigou, China	CDTJ EBee EMui EPla GBin MWht NWsh SBig WPGP
- 'Anceps'	MWht
- 'Chennevières'	EPla
- 'Eisenach'	EBee GKir MAvo MMoz WFar WMoo
- Gansu 2	CGHE GKir
- 'Great Wall'	ENBC ETod GBin MBri MWhi MWht
- 'Jiuzhaigou 1'	EPla WJun
- 'Jiuzhaigou 2'	EPla WJun
- 'Jiuzhaigou 4'	EPla
- 'Nymphenburg' ♀H4	CEnd CPMA ENBC GKir MBNS MBar MBri MMoz MWhi MWht NLar NMoo SBig WFar WMoo WPGP
- 'Wakehurst'	MWht NLar
nujiangensis	EPla
perlonga	EPla WJun
- Yunnan 95/6	MMoz WPGP
robusta	CAbb CDTJ CEnd CEnt EBee ENBC EPfP EPla ETod GCal LPal MBrN MBri MMoz MMuc MWht NGdn NLar NMoo SBig SLPl WDyG WJun
- 'Ming Yunnan'	LEdu WJun
- 'Pingwu'	CDTJ CEnt ENBC ERas ETod GBin MBri MWht NLar SBig WJun
- 'Red Sheath'	CEnt EPla ERod MMoz MWht NPal NScw WJun WPGP
- 'Wolong'	CDoC EPla GBin MMoz MWht WJun WPGP
rufa	CAbb CEnt EBee EMil ENBC EPPr EPfP EPla EShb GCal LMaj LRHS LSRN MAvo MBar MBrN MBri MCCP MMoz MMuc MWhi MWht NLar NPal SBig WJun WPGP
- variegated (v)	EPla
spathacea misapplied	see *F. murielae*
utilis	CEnt EPla ERod LEdu MAvo MMoz MMuc MWht NLar SEND WJun WPGP
yulongshanensis	EPla MWht WJun
aff. ***yulongshanensis***	EPla

Farsetia (*Brassicaceae*)

clypeata	see *Fibigia clypeata*

Fascicularia (*Bromeliaceae*)

andina	see *F. bicolor*
§ ***bicolor***	Widely available
§ - subsp. ***canaliculata***	CHEx EBee EPla IBlr LEdu LPio SBch SChr WCot WPGP
kirchhoffiana	see *F. bicolor* subsp. *canaliculata*

× *Fatshedera* (*Araliaceae*)

lizei ♀H3	CAlb CBcs CDoC CDul CHEx CMac CTri EBee EPfP EPla GQui LRHS MRav NEgg SAPC SArc SBch SDix SPer SPlb SPoG SWvt WCFE WDin
§ - 'Annemieke' (v) ♀H3	CBcs CBow CDoC CHEx EBee ELan EPfP LHop LRHS MRav NEgg SBch SMad SPer SPoG WBor
§ - 'Aurea' (v)	ELan LRHS MAsh SEND
- 'Aureopicta'	see × *F. lizei* 'Aurea'
- 'Lemon and Lime'	see × *F. lizei* 'Annemieke'
- 'Maculata'	see × *F. lizei* 'Annemieke'
- 'Variegata' (v) ♀H3	CHEx CMac EBee ELan EPfP ERas LAst LRHS MAsh MGos NEgg SBch SEND SHGN SPer SPoG SWvt WCFE WDin

Fatsia (*Araliaceae*)

§ ***japonica*** ♀H4	Widely available
- 'Annelise' (v) **new**	EGxp
- 'Golden Handshake'	CBow
- 'Moseri'	CAbP CMdw CTrC ECtt IBal LHop NGdn NLar SWvt WCot WGwG WPat
- 'Murakumo-nishiki' (v)	SPer
- 'Spider's Web' (v)	CBow LHop LSou NBhm NGdn SPad SPer SPoG WCot WGwG
- 'Variegata' (v) ♀H3	CBcs CMac EAmu EGxp EPfP LRHS MBri MGos MRav NPal SArc SLim SPer SPoG
papyrifera	see *Tetrapanax papyrifer*
polycarpa	CDTJ EAmu EBee WPGP
- B&SWJ 7144	WCru
- RWJ 10133	WCru

Faucaria (*Aizoaceae*)

tigrina ♀H1	EPfP

Fauria see *Nephrophyllidium*

Feijoa see *Acca*

Felicia (*Asteraceae*)

aethiopica	GFai
§ ***amelloides***	CHEx EShb LAst MCot SBch SEND SGar SPlb
- 'Astrid Thomas'	see *F. amelloides* 'Read's Blue'
§ - 'Read's Blue'	SDnm SGar
- 'Read's White'	SDnm
- 'Santa Anita' ♀H3	CTri ERea
§ - variegated (v)	CMoH ECtt ELon LAst MBri MCot NPer SBch SPet
§ ***amoena***	CTri SRms
- 'Variegata' (v)	CTri
capensis	see *F. amelloides*

	coelestis	see *F. amelloides*
	erigeroides	GFai
	filifolia	SPlb
	- blue-flowered	LAst
	fruticosa	CHll
	natalensis	see *F. rosulata*
	pappei	see *F. amoena*
§	***petiolata***	CMea CTri EBee NSti WCot WEas WWFP
§	***rosulata***	CPBP ECho LRHS MBrN MHer MTho NBro SFgr SRms SRot
	uliginosa	ECho EWes GEdr GGar MTho

fennel see *Foeniculum vulgare*

fenugreek see *Trigonella foenum-graecum*

Ferraria (*Iridaceae*)

§	***crispa***	ECho
	- var. ***nortieri***	WCot
	undulata	see *F. crispa*

Ferula (*Apiaceae*)

	assa-foetida	CArn LDai
	chiliantha	see *F. communis* subsp. *glauca*
§	***communis***	CArn CMea CSpe EBee ECGP ECha ELan EWTr GCal LPio NBPC NBid NLar NSti SDix SDnm SEND SMad SPav SPlb WCAu WCot WFar WJek WPGP WPtf
	- SDR 5606	GKev
	- 'Gigantea'	see *F. communis*
§	- subsp. ***glauca***	EWes SDix SGar WCot WHal WPGP
	'Giant Bronze'	see *Foeniculum vulgare* 'Giant Bronze'
	tingitana 'Cedric Morris'	ECha LPio SDix WSHC

Festuca (*Poaceae*)

	amethystina	CKno CWCL CWib EBee EHoe GFor LEdu MNrw NGdn NHol NNor SEND SPer WMoo WPer WTin WWEG
	- 'Aprilgrün'	EPPr
	arenaria	EBWF
	arundinacea	CRWN EBWF SEND
	californica	CKno EPPr
	coxii	GBin MAvo WCot
	curvula subsp. ***crassifolia***	EPla EShb NHol
	'Eisvogel'	EBee
	elegans	EPPr
	eskia	CKno EAEE EBee EHoe EHul EPPr LRHS NHol WDyG
	filiformis	EHoe
	'Fromefield Blue'	EHul
§	***gautieri***	EBee EGxp EPPr GBin GFor MBar NGdn
	- 'Pic Carlit'	EBee GBin
	gigantea	GFor
	glauca Vill.	Widely available
I	- 'Auslese'	CPLG EPPr GFor NGdn NPro
	- 'Azurit'	EAlp EBee EHoe EPPr EWes LAst NHol NWsh SPad SPoG
§	- 'Blaufuchs' ♀H4	EAEE EAlp EBee EBrs EHrv EPPr EPfP EWes GGar GKir GMaP LRHS MAvo MBlu MGos MMoz MRav NHol SBod SLim SPer SPlb SWvt WFar WWEG
§	- 'Blauglut'	EAEE EAlp EBee EHul EPPr EPfP EPla LRHS MBri MRav NHol WFar
	- Blue Fox	see *F. glauca* 'Blaufuchs'
	- Blue Glow	see *F. glauca* 'Blauglut'
	- 'Elijah Blue'	Widely available
	- 'Euchre'	LSRN
	- 'Golden Toupee'	CWSG EAlp EBee ECha ELan EPfP EWes GKir LAst LRHS MBar MBlu MGos MRav NBir NBlu NEgg NHol NPri NSti SGSe SLim SPer SPlb SWvt WDin WFar WWEG
	- 'Harz'	EBee EHoe EHul MBar SApp
*	- ***minima***	CCCN SPoG WWEG
	- 'Pallens'	see *F. longifolia*
	- Sea Urchin	see *F. glauca* 'Seeigel'
§	- 'Seeigel'	EBee EHoe EPPr GKir LRHS NHol NPro
	- Select	see *F. glauca* 'Auslese'
	- 'Seven Seas'	see *F. valesiaca* 'Silbersee'
	- 'Silberreiher'	EBee EPPr WWEG
	- 'Uchte'	CWCL EBee EPPr WPtf
	'Hogar'	EHoe EPPr
	idahoensis	EShb
§	***longifolia***	EBee EPPr
	mairei	CKno EBee ECha EHoe EPPr GFor GQue NWsh SPhx SWal
	novae-zelandiae	CWCL NNor
	ovina	CWan EBWF GFor LRHS WPer WSFF
	- var. ***gallica***	NWsh
I	- 'Kulturform'	NNor
	- 'Söhrewald'	EPPr WMoo
*	- 'Tetra Gold'	SWvt
	paniculata	CKno EHoe EPPr NWsh
	punctoria	GFor
	rubra	CRWN EBWF WSFF
	- subsp. ***rubra***	CRWN
	scoparia	see *F. gautieri*
	'Siskiyou Blue'	CKno CMea EAlp EBee EPPr
	tatrae	EBee WCot
	valesiaca var. ***glaucantha***	CWib EPPr GFor NGdn NLar WWEG
§	- 'Silbersee'	EBee EHoe EPPr LRHS MBar NHol NWsh SRms WFar WSpi
	- Silver Sea	see *F. valesiaca* 'Silbersee'
	violacea	EHoe EPPr NNor SWal
	vivipara	CPrp EBWF EGoo EHoe LEdu NBid NHol
*	'Willow Green'	SLim SPlb

Fibigia (*Brassicaceae*)

§	***clypeata***	LDai SGar
I	- 'Select'	CSpe

Ficus ✿ (*Moraceae*)

	afghanistanica	ERea
	australis misapplied	see *F. rubiginosa* 'Australis'
	benghalensis	MBri
	benjamina ♀H1	MBri SEND SRms
	- 'Exotica'	LRHS MBri
	- 'Golden King' (v)	LRHS MBri
	- 'Starlight' (v) ♀H1	LRHS MBri
	carica (F)	CCCN ETod LMaj MBri MREP SArc SLon SPad
	- 'Abicou' (F) **new**	ERea
	- 'Adam' (F)	ERea
	- 'Alma' (F)	ERea
	- 'Angélique' (F)	ERea
	- 'Archipel' (F)	ERea
	- 'Beall' (F)	ERea
	- 'Black Ischia' (F)	ERea
	- 'Black Jack' (F)	ERea
	- 'Boule d'Or' (F)	ERea
	- 'Bourjassotte Grise' (F)	ERea SDea
	- 'Brogiotto' (F)	CCCN NLar
	- 'Brown Turkey' (F) ♀H3	Widely available

	– 'Brunswick' (F)	CAgr CCCN CHll ELon EMui EPfP ERea GTwe LRHS MCoo NGHP SEND SLim SPoG WCot
	– 'Castle Kennedy' (F)	ERea GTwe
	– 'Colummaro Black Apulia' (F)	CCCN
	– 'Colummaro White Apulia' (F)	CCCN
	– 'Conandria' (F)	ERea
	– 'Dalmatie' (F)	ELan ERea LRHS MCoo
I	– 'Digitata' (F)	MBlu
	– 'Drap d'Or' (F)	ERea
	– 'Figue d'Or' (F)	ERea
	– 'Filacciano' (F)	CCCN
	– 'Goutte d'Or' (F)	ERea SDea
	– 'Green Sicilian' (F) **new**	LRHS
	– 'Grise de Saint Jean' (F)	ERea
	– 'Kadota' (F)	ERea NLar
*	– 'Laciniata' (F)	MBri SMad
	– 'Lisa' (F)	ERea
	– 'Little Yellow Wonder' (F)	ERea
	– 'LSU Purple' (F)	ERea
	– 'Malcolm's Giant' (F)	ERea
	– 'Malta' (F)	GTwe
	– 'Marseillaise' (F)	GTwe SDea
	– 'Melanzana' (F)	CCCN
	– 'Nazaret' (F) **new**	LRHS
	– 'Negro Largo' (F)	ERea
	– 'Nero' (F) **new**	ELon
	– 'Nero del Portogallo' (F) **new**	EMil
	– 'Newlyn Harbour' (F)	ELon
	– 'Noir de Provence'	see *F. carica* 'Reculver'
	– 'Noire de Carombe' (F)	ERea MCoo
	– 'Osborn's Prolific' (F)	EMil ERea MAsh SEND SWvt
	– 'Panachée' (F)	ERea
	– 'Pastilière' (F)	ERea
	– 'Peter's Honey' (F)	ERea
	– 'Petite Nigra' (F)	ERea
	– 'Pinet' (F) **new**	LRHS
	– 'Pittaluse' (F)	ERea
	– 'Porthminster' (F)	CHEx
	– 'Précoce de Dalmatie' (F)	EMil ERea MAsh NLar WPGP
	– 'Précoce Ronde de Bordeaux' (F)	ERea SEND
§	– 'Reculver' (F)	ERea
	– 'Rouge de Bordeaux' (F)	CCCN ERea MAsh SDea
	– 'Saint Johns' (F)	ERea
	– 'San Pedro Miro' (F)	EMil ERea
	– 'Sollies Pont' (F)	ERea
	– 'Sugar 12' (F)	ERea
	– 'Sultane' (F)	ERea
	– 'Tena' (F)	ERea
	– 'Texas Everbearing' (F)	ERea
	– 'Violetta' PBR (F) **new**	EMui
	– 'Violette Dauphine' (F)	EPfP ERea
	– 'Violette de Sollies' (F)	ERea
	– 'Violette Normande' (F) **new**	EMil LRHS MAsh SEND
	– 'Violette Sepor' (F)	ERea
	– 'White Genoa'	see *F. carica* 'White Marseilles'
	– 'White Ischia' (F)	ERea
§	– 'White Marseilles' (F)	CAgr CCCN CWib ECrN EMui EPfP ERea MBri MCoo NGHP SDea SPoG
	cyathistipula	MBri
	deltoidea var. ***diversifolia***	MBri
	elastica 'Robusta'	MBri
	foveolata Wallich	see *F. sarmentosa*
	lyrata ♀H1	MBri
	pubigera	CPLG
	pumila ♀H1	CHEx MBri
	– 'Minima'	CFee
	– 'Sonny' (v)	MBri
	– 'Variegata' (v)	CHEx MBri
	radicans 'Variegata'	see *F. sagittata* 'Variegata'
	retusa **new**	STre
§	***rubiginosa*** 'Australis'	MBri
§	***sagittata*** 'Variegata' (v)	MBri
§	***sarmentosa***	MBri

fig see *Ficus carica*

filbert see *Corylus maxima*

Filipendula ✿ (*Rosaceae*)

	alnifolia 'Variegata'	see *F. ulmaria* 'Variegata'
	camtschatica	CFir CRow EBee ECha ELan LEdu MCot NBid NLar NPol WFar WMoo WPGP
	– B&SWJ 10828	WCru
	– 'Rosea'	LHop MRav SMad
	digitata 'Nana'	see *F. multijuga*
	formosa B&SWJ 8707	WCru
	hexapetala	see *F. vulgaris*
	– 'Flore Pleno'	see *F. vulgaris* 'Multiplex'
	'Kahome'	CPrp CRow EBee EBrs ELon EPPr EPla EShb GBuc GGar GKir GMaP IFoB LAst LRHS NBPC NBir NGdn NLar NMir NOrc SPer SPhx SWat WFar WHoo WMoo WPnP WWEG
	kiraishiensis B&SWJ 1571	WCru
§	***multijuga***	CRow GCal GGar IFoB LRHS NHol WFar WMoo
	palmata	ECha MBri MLHP NBre SWat WMoo
	– 'Digitata Nana'	see *F. multijuga*
	– dwarf	CLAP MLHP
	– 'Elegantissima'	see *F. purpurea* 'Elegans'
	– 'Nana'	see *F. multijuga*
	– 'Rosea'	CMac NBir WCHb
	– 'Rubra'	CTri GCra MRav NGdn
	purpurea ♀H4	CKno CRow CSBt EBee ECha ELon EPfP EWTr GGar IBlr LPBA MBri SBod WCru WFar WMoo WPnP
	– f. ***albiflora***	EBee MBri NPri WMoo WOut
§	– 'Elegans'	CRow EBee ECha ELon GGar GMac LAst MLHP NBPC NBid NHol NSti SPet SWat WHlf WMoo WPnP WSpi
	– 'Nephele'	EBee GMac
	– 'Pink Dreamland'	SAga
*	– 'Plena' (d)	NLar
	'Queen of the Prairies'	see *F. rubra*
§	***rubra***	CRow IFro LAst LSRN MCot SHlg WSFF
§	– 'Venusta' ♀H4	Widely available
	– 'Venusta Magnifica'	see *F. rubra* 'Venusta'
	rufinervis B&SWJ 8611	WCru
§	***ulmaria***	CArn CBen CHby COld CRWN CWan EBWF EBee EHon ELau EMFW GBar GMaP GPoy MCot MHer MNHC NHol NLan NMir SIde SWat WMoo WPer WSFF WShi
	– 'Aurea'	CArn CMac CRow EBee EBrs ECha ECtt EHoe ELan GAbr GBar GBuc GMaP MLHP MRav NBid NGHP NPri SAga SMad SRms WEas WFar WMoo WSHC WTin WWEG
	– 'Flore Pleno' (d)	CBre CRow EBrs LAst LHop LRHS MRav NBPC NBid NBre NGdn SIde SPer SWat WCAu WCot WFar WTin
	– 'Rosea'	CDes IBlr MHer WPGP
§	– 'Variegata' (v)	Widely available
§	***vulgaris***	CArn CFee CRWN CTri CWan EBWF ECtt GBar GKir LRHS MLHP

	MNHC NBlu NBro NMir NNor SBch SWat WPer WWEG
- 'Alba'	EBee
- 'Flore Pleno'	see *F. vulgaris* 'Multiplex'
- 'Grandiflora'	CBre GKir
§ - 'Multiplex' (d)	CMac CRow EBee EBrs ECha ELan GGar GKir GMaP MBel MBri MHer MRav NBid NBir NPri NRya SRms WAul WEas WFar WHlf WMoo WTin
- 'Plena'	see *F. vulgaris* 'Multiplex'
- 'Rosea'	NBre

Firmiana (*Sterculiaceae*)

simplex	CHEx EShb WPGP

Fittonia (*Acanthaceae*)

albivenis Argyroneura Group ♀H1	EShb
§ - Verschaffeltii Group ♀H1	EShb WHil
verschaffeltii	see *F. albivenis* Verschaffeltii Group

Fitzroya (*Cupressaceae*)

cupressoides	CBcs CDoC CMac CTho GKir IDee IFFs LRHS SCoo SLim WThu

Fockea (*Asclepiadaceae*)

edulis	EShb

Foeniculum (*Apiaceae*)

vulgare	CArn CHEx CHby CPrp CWan EBWF ECha ELan ELau EPfP GBar GKir GMaP GPoy LHop MGos MHer MNHC NBlu NGHP NPri SBch SIde SPer SPhx SPlb SPoG SVic WMoo WPer
- 'Bronze'	see *F. vulgare* 'Purpureum'
- var. ***dulce***	CSev SIde
§ - 'Giant Bronze'	CChe EBee ELan SPhx WSpi
- green-flowered **new**	SEND
§ - 'Purpureum'	Widely available
- 'Smokey'	ECha MRav

Fontanesia (*Oleaceae*)

phillyreoides	CBcs

Fontinalis (*Fontinalaceae*)

sp.	LPBA
antipyretica	MSKA

Forsythia ✿ (*Oleaceae*)

'Anna Silveria' **new**	LSou
'Arnold Dwarf'	ECrN GKir NBir NLar SRms
'Beatrix Farrand' ambig.	CTri CWSG EBee MGos MWat SPer SRms
'Beatrix Farrand' K. Sax	GKir NLar SEND
'Fiesta' (v)	CPMA CWSG EBee EPfP LAst LRHS MAsh MBar MGos MRav MSwo NWea SBch SLim SPer SPoG WCom WCot WDin WFar WRHF
giraldiana	GKir MSwo SLon SRms WSpi
Gold Tide[PBR]	see *F.* Marée d'Or
'Golden Bells'	WHar
'Golden Nugget'	CMac EBee ELan EPfP LBuc LRHS MAsh MBri SCoo SLon SPoG WCFE
'Golden Times' (v)	CMac ERas EWes LAst LBuc LSRN MGos NLar NWea SCoo SPoG SWal SWvt WDin WFar
× ***intermedia***	ECrN
- 'Arnold Giant'	MBlu
- 'Casque D'Or' **new**	MAsh
- Courdijau	see *F.* × *intermedia* 'Casque D'Or'
- 'Goldrausch'	LAst MAsh MBri MGos
- 'Goldzauber'	NWea
- 'Josefa' (v)	ELan MAsh
- 'Lynwood Variety' ♀H4	Widely available
- 'Lynwood Variety' variegated (v)	CWib
- Minigold = 'Flojor'	CSBt EPfP LAst MGos MSwo MWat NBlu SRms WBVN
- Show Off = 'Mindor'[PBR]	MAsh
- 'Spectabilis'	CDul EBee EMac EPfP LBuc MBar NWea SCoo SLim WDin WFar
- 'Spectabilis Variegated' (v)	CBow MBNS NPro
- 'Spring Glory'	EBee LRHS MHer WSpi
- 'Variegata' (v)	WCom WGwG
- Week-End = 'Courtalyn'[PBR] ♀H4	CWSG EBee EPfP LBuc LRHS LSou MAsh MBri MGos NLar NPri SEND SLPl SLim SLon SPlb WDin WFar
§ Marée d'Or = 'Courtasol'[PBR] ♀H4	CWSG LRHS MAsh MBri MGos MRav NLar NWea SLon SPoG WDin
Mêlée d'Or = 'Courtaneur'	EMil LRHS MAsh SCoo SPer
Melissa = 'Courtadic'	NLar NWea
ovata 'Tetragold'	MBar NWea
'Paulina'	NLar
'Satellite' **new**	LSou
suspensa	CArn CMac CTri CWib EOHP EPfP GKir LRHS MGos NWea SPer SPlb SRms WSpi
- f. ***atrocaulis***	NWea WSpi
- var. ***fortunei***	MBri
- 'Nymans'	EPfP GKir MBri MRav NSti SEND
§ - 'Taff's Arnold' (v)	CPLG CPMA EBee
- 'Variegata'	see *F. suspensa* 'Taff's Arnold'
'Tremonia'	ECrN NEgg NLar WGwG
'Verfors Minor Gold'	MBri
viridissima	NWea
- 'Bronxensis'	CMac ECho GEdr LLHF MAsh NBir NLar WPat
- var. ***koreana*** 'Kumsom' (v)	EMil LRHS MAsh
- 'Weber's Bronx'	NLar NWea

Fortunella (*Rutaceae*)

'Fukushu' (F) ♀H1	ERea
§ ***japonica*** (F)	EPfP
§ ***margarita*** (F)	CDoC LRHS LSRN MBri

Fothergilla (*Hamamelidaceae*)

gardenii	CBcs CPMA EBee ELan EPfP MBlu MBri MGos MRav NLar SPer SSpi SWvt WDin
- Beaver Creek = 'Klmtwo'	NLar
- 'Blue Mist'	CAbP CDoC CEnd CPLG CPMA CWSG EBee ELan EPfP NLar SMad SPer SReu SSta WDin WFar WPat
- 'Harold Epstein'	NLar
- 'Suzanne'	NLar
- 'Zundert'	NLar
'Huntsman'	CCCN CDul EBee WFar
× ***intermedia*** 'Blue Shadow' **new**	CPMA ESwi LRHS LSRN MGos
- 'Windy City' **new**	CPMA
major ♀H4	CBcs CDul CEnd CPMA CWib EBee ELan EPfP LRHS LSRN MBri MGos NEgg NLar NPri SPer SPoG SReu SSpi SWvt WDin WFar WPat WSpi
- 'Bulkyard'	MBri
- Monticola Group	CDoC CEnd CPMA CSBt CWSG ELan EPfP IMGH LRHS MAsh MBar MDun MGos MMuc NPal SBch SLim SPer SSpi SSta WBrE WFar
- 'Red Licorice'	CPMA MBri NLar

- 'Seaspray'	CPMA
'Mount Airy'	CMCN CPMA EPfP LRHS SPoG SSpi

Fragaria (*Rosaceae*)

from Taiwan	WHer
alpina	see *F. vesca* 'Semperflorens'
- 'Alba'	see *F. vesca* 'Semperflorens Alba'
× ***ananassa*** (F)	LRHS
- 'Albion'PBR (F) **new**	EMui SVic
- 'Alice'PBR (F) ♀H4	CSut EMui ERea LBuc MCoo
- 'Aromel' (F) ♀H4	CAgr EPfP GTwe LRHS SDea SEND
- 'Bolero' (F)	EMui LRHS MBri
- 'Calypso'PBR (F)	CAgr CSBt EMui LBuc LRHS SDea SEND
- 'Cambridge Favourite' (F) ♀H4	CAgr CSBt CTri EMil EMui EPfP ERea GTwe LBuc LRHS MBri MCoo MGan MGos NEgg NGHP NPri SDea
- 'Cambridge Late Pine' (F)	EMui
- 'Cambridge Vigour' (F)	GTwe SDea
- 'Challenger' (F)	EMui
- 'Chelsea Pensioner' (F)	EMui
- 'Christine' (F)	CSut EMil
- 'Daisy' (F) **new**	EMui
- 'Darlisette' (F) **new**	EMui
- 'Darselect'PBR (F)	EMui
- 'Elsanta'PBR (F)	CSBt CTri EMil EMui EPfP GKir GTwe IArd LBuc LRHS MGan NEgg NPri SDea SEND SPer
- 'Elvira' (F)	EMui EPfP LRHS
* - 'Emily' (F)	CAgr GTwe
- 'Eros'PBR (F)	EMui GTwe LBuc
- 'Everest'PBR (F)	EMil LBuc
- 'Flamenco'PBR (F)	CSut EMil EMui
- 'Florence'PBR (F)	CSBt CTri EMil EMui ERea GTwe LBuc LRHS MBri SPer
- Fraise des Bois	see *F. vesca*
- 'Fruitful Summer' (F) **new**	LRHS
- 'Gariguette' (F)	EMui
- 'Hapil' (F) ♀H4	CTri EMil EMui EPfP ERea GTwe LBuc NGHP
- 'Honeoye' (F) ♀H4	CAgr CSBt EMui EPfP GTwe LBuc LRHS MBri NBlu NGHP SEND SPer
- 'Judibell' (F)	EMui
- 'Korona'PBR (F)	EMui
- 'Loran' (F)	LAst
- 'Mae'PBR (F)	EMui
- 'Malling Opal' (F)	GTwe
- 'Malling Pearl' (F)	EMil EMui GTwe
- 'Maxim' (F)	EMui
- 'Ostara' (F)	LRHS
- 'Pegasus'PBR (F) ♀H4	CSBt EMui EPfP GTwe LRHS NGHP NPri
- Pink Panda = 'Frel'PBR (F)	CBcs CTri EAEE EBee ELan LBuc LRHS MRav NEgg NHol NLar SIng SPer SPoG WCAu WEas WWFP
- pink-flowered (F)	CFee EMui
- Red Ruby = 'Samba'PBR	EAEE EBee ECGP LHop LRHS MNrw NEgg NGdn NLar SIng SPer SPoG WCAu
- 'Redgauntlet' (F)	EPfP GTwe LRHS NBlu
- 'Rhapsody' (F) ♀H4	GTwe LBuc
- 'Rosie'PBR (F)	EMui SDea
- 'Royal Sovereign' (F)	GTwe LBuc LRHS MGan
- 'Senga Sengana' (F) **new**	SVic
- 'Sonata'PBR (F)	CSut EMui
- 'Sophie'PBR (F)	EMil LRHS
- 'Symphony'PBR (F) ♀H4	CAgr CSBt EMui EPfP LBuc LRHS MBri SEND
- 'Tamella' (F)	EMui
- 'Tenira' (F)	EMui
- 'Totem' (F)	GTwe LRHS
§ - 'Variegata' (v)	CArn CMea CTri EBee EPla LDai LHop LRHS MRav SIng SPer SPoG WCom WMoo
- 'Viva Rosa' (F)	EMui LRHS
'Bowles's Double'	see *F. vesca* 'Multiplex'
chiloensis (F)	ILis LEdu SHar
- 'Chaval'	CHid ECha EGoo EHrv EPPr IMou MRav WMoo
- 'Variegata' misapplied	see *F.* × *ananassa* 'Variegata'
daltoniana	GCra
indica	see *Duchesnea indica*
'Lipstick'	EBee NLar WSpi
moschata	CAgr
nubicola	CAgr GPoy
- 'Mount Omei'	EBee
'Roman' **new**	LAst
'Variegata'	see *F.* × *ananassa* 'Variegata'
§ ***vesca*** (F)	CAgr CArn CRWN CWan EBWF EPfP GPoy MHer MNHC NBlu NGHP NMir NPri SECG SIde SMad SPlb SVic WGwG WJek WPer WSFF WShi
- 'Alexandra' (F)	CArn CBod CPrp ELau ERea GAbr NVic SIde WCHb
- 'Baron Solemacher' (F)	SBch SHDw
- 'Flore Pleno'	see *F. vesca* 'Multiplex'
- 'Fructu Albo' (F)	CAgr CArn CBre CRow CWan NLar WMoo WPer
- 'Golden Alexandra'	EAlp EBee ECha EHoe ELau ERea EWes LSou WHer
- 'Golden Surprise'	SBch SHDw
- 'Mara des Bois'PBR (F)	EMui
- 'Monophylla' (F)	CRow IGor SIde WCom WHer
§ - 'Multiplex' (d)	CRow CSev ILis MRav NChi NGHP NHol NLar WAlt WCHb WCom WHer WOut
§ - 'Muricata'	CBre CPou CRow IGor ILis LEdu WAlt WCom WHer
- 'Pineapple Crush'	WHer
- 'Plymouth Strawberry'	see *F. vesca* 'Muricata'
- 'Rügen' (F)	IGor
§ - 'Semperflorens' (F)	ILis WAlt
§ - 'Semperflorens Alba' (F)	CAgr
- 'Variegata' misapplied	see *F.* × *ananassa* 'Variegata'
* - 'Variegata' ambig. (v)	EHoe EHrv NEgg NGHP SMac WFar WHrl WPer WWEG
virginiana	CAgr
- subsp. ***glauca***	EPPr
viridis	CAgr

Francoa (*Saxifragaceae*)

appendiculata	CAbP EBla GQui MBel MDKP SGar SWal WFar WHer WMoo WPnP
- red-flowered	CDes EBee
Ballyrogan strain	IBlr
'Confetti'	CDes CKno CPLG ELan LPio LRHS MAvo MCot MNrw NCob SMrm SWal WCot WFar WPGP
'Purple Spike'	see *F. sonchifolia* Rogerson's
ramosa	CCVN CTri EHrv EWld GBuc IBlr MHav MNrw NBro SAga SDix SHGN SMrm SPav WFar WKif WMoo
* - 'Alba'	CSpe
sonchifolia	Widely available
- 'Alba'	MDKP SMrm SUsu WFar WMoo
- 'Culm View Lilac'	CCVN
- 'Doctor Tom Smith'	WCot
- 'Lynda Windsor'	MAvo
- 'Molly Anderson'	EBee LPio MAvo SUsu
§ - Rogerson's	Widely available

Frangula (*Rhamnaceae*)

§ ***alnus*** CArn CCVT CDul CLnd CRWN EMac LBuc MBlu NWea SLPl STre WDin WFar WMou WSFF
- 'Aspleniifolia' CBgR CTho EBee EPfP LRHS MBlu MBri MMuc NLar WDin WFar WPat
- 'Columnaris' EMil SLPl
- 'Minaret' MBri

Frankenia (*Frankeniaceae*)

laevis SRms
thymifolia CTri EAlp ECho GGar LRHS MHer MWat NPri SPlb WFar WTin

Franklinia (*Theaceae*)

alatamaha CBcs CPMA IMou LHyd MBlu MBri WFar

Fraxinus ✿ (*Oleaceae*)

americana CDul CMCN EPfP EWTr IFFs NEgg WDin
- 'Autumn Purple' CDul CEnd CMCN CTho EBee ECrN EPfP LRHS MAsh MBlu WMou
- 'Rosehill' CTho
angustifolia CMCN EGFP IFFs
- 'Raywood' ♀H4 Widely available
* - 'Variegata' (v) MGos
bungeana EGFP
chinensis CLnd CMCN EGFP
elonza CLnd
excelsior CBcs CCVT CDoC CDul CLnd CMac CRWN CSBt CTri CWib EBee ECrN EMac EPfP GKir IFFs LAst LBuc MAsh MBar MBri MGos NWea SBch SEND SLim STre WDin WMou
- 'Aurea Pendula' CCVT CDul CEnd CMac CWib EBee ECrN LRHS MBlu MGos NPal SPoG
- 'Crispa' MBlu MBri NLar WCom
- f. ***diversifolia*** CDul CLnd
- 'Jaspidea' ♀H4 Widely available
- 'Nana' LMaj WPat
- 'Pendula' ♀H4 CCVT CDoC CDul CEnd CLnd CMac EBee ECrN ELan LAst LMaj LRHS MAsh MBlu NEgg NPal NWea SLim SPer SPoG WDin WMou
- 'R.E. Davey' CDul CNat
- variegated (v) CMac ECrN WPat
- 'Westhof's Glorie' ♀H4 CCVT CDoC CDul CLnd EBee ECrN LMaj SBch WDin WFar
hopeiensis **new** MBlu
insularis var. ***henryana*** CDul WPGP
latifolia CLnd CMCN
mandshurica MBri
mariesii see *F. sieboldiana*
nigra 'Fallgold' CEnd
ornus ♀H4 CArn CCVT CDul CLnd CMCN CMac CTri EBee ECrN ELan EMac EPfP EWTr GKir IFFs IMGH LAst LMaj MSnd MSwo NPal NWea SEND SPer WDin WFar WMoo
- 'Arie Peters' CDul
- 'Mecsek' MBlu
- 'Obelisk' EBee LMaj LRHS MAsh MBlu NLar
- 'Rotterdam' EBee
pennsylvanica CDul CLnd
- 'Cimmaron' see *F. pennsylvanica* 'Cimmzam'
§ - 'Cimmzam' CDul
- 'Variegata' (v) CLnd EBee GKir MAsh WPat
quadrangulata EGFP WDin
richardi CDul
§ ***sieboldiana*** CDoC CDul CLnd CMCN CPMA EPfP MBlu MBri NLar SSpi WPGP WPat
velutina CDul CLnd SLPl
xanthoxyloides MBlu NEgg
- var. ***dumosa*** EBee WPGP

Freesia (*Iridaceae*)

alba Foster see *F. lactea*
'Beethoven' (d) LRHS
fucata **new** ECho
hybrids EBrs
§ ***lactea*** ECho
laxa see *Anomatheca laxa*
'Marianne' (d) LRHS
xanthospila EBrs WCot

Fremontodendron (*Sterculiaceae*)

'California Glory' ♀H3 Widely available
californicum CTri CWib EBee ELan MBri NBlu SEND SLim SPlb WDin WFar
'Pacific Sunset' CPMA EPfP LHop LSRN MGos MREP MRav NEgg SPer SPoG WFar
'Tequila Sunrise' CBcs CDoC CPMA CWGN GBin ISea LHop LLHF MBlu MGos NLar SBch SPoG

Freylinia (*Scrophulariaceae*)

cestroides see *F. lanceolata*
densiflora GFai
§ ***lanceolata*** CBcs CCCN CTrC CWib CWit EShb
tropica CHII GFai
visseri GFai

Fritillaria ✿ (*Liliaceae*)

acmopetala ♀H4 CAvo CBro CFFs CHid CMea CPom CWCL EBrs ECho EPot ERCP ERos GBuc GEdr ITim LAma LLWG LRHS MSSP MTho NMen SPhx WCot
- 'Baga Dag' **new** LRHS
- 'Brunette' EBrs ECho SPhx WWst
- subsp. ***wendelboi*** EBrs ECho EPot LAma SPhx WCot
- - 'Zwanenburg' **new** WWst
affinis CWCL ECho GBin GBuc GGar ITim LAma MPoH MSSP NMen WCot
- 'Limelight' ECho
- 'Sunray' EBrs ECho EPot GEdr ITim
§ - var. ***tristulis*** ERos NMen
- 'Vancouver Island' EBrs ECho
alburyana ECho
alfredae subsp. ***glaucoviridis*** ECho WCot WWst
arabica see *F. persica*
ariana WWst
armena EBrs ECho
- MP 8146 MPoH WWst
assyriaca EPot GBuc MWea
aurea ECho MPoH NMen WCot WWst
- 'Golden Flag' EBrs ECho EPfP EPot LLHF SPhx WHil
biflora ECho EPot GEdr MPoH
- 'Martha Roderick' EBrs ECho ERCP LAma MSSP NMen
§ ***bithynica*** EBrs ECho GEdr ITim LAma MPoH MSSP
bucharica EBee ECho EPot WWst
- 'Giant' **new** ERCP
- 'Nurek Giant' ECho WWst
camschatcensis CAvo CBro CPom CWCL EBrs ECha ECho EFEx EPfP EPot ERCP GAuc GEdr GGar GKir GMaP LAma MSSP MTho NBir NMen NWCA SPhx WAbe WCru

I	- ***alpina aurea***	GEdr
	- 'Aurea'	ECho GBuc NMen SPhx WWst
	- black-flowered	ECho GBuc
	- double-flowered (d)	CFir EBrs ECho NMen
	- f. ***flavescens***	EBrs ECho EFEx GEdr LAma
	- green-flowered	MSSP NMen
	carduchorum	see *F. minuta*
	carica	EBrs ECho EPot GEdr LRHS MSSP NMen
	- NS 2181	MPoH
	- brown-flowered	ECho
	- tall clone **new**	WWst
	caucasica	EBrs ECho GAuc NMen WWst
	chlororhabdota **new**	GAuc
	cirrhosa	EBrs ECho GEdr GKir WWst
	- brown-flowered	EBrs ECho GEdr NMen WWst
	- green-flowered	ECho GEdr NMen WWst
	citrina	see *F. bithynica*
§	***collina***	ECho NMen
	conica	NMen WCot
	crassifolia	ECho LAma
	- subsp. ***crassifolia***	WWst
§	- subsp. ***kurdica***	EBrs ECho EPot NMen WCot WWst
	- - 'Aragats' **new**	WWst
	- - 'Talish'	WWst
	davidii	ECho SCnR WWst
	davisii	EBrs ECho EPot ERCP GAuc GBuc GEdr LAma LRHS NMen WCot
	delphinensis	see *F. tubiformis*
	drenovskii	WWst
	eduardii	EBee EBrs ECho ERCP MPoH WWst
	elwesii	CHid EBrs ECho EPot ERCP GEdr ITim MPoH NMen SPhx WCot
	ferganensis	see *F. walujewii*
	fleischeriana	WWst
	frankiorum	WCot
	gentneri	WCot
	glauca	LAma MPoH MSSP
*	- 'Golden Flag'	ECho
	- 'Goldilocks'	EBrs ECho ERCP NMen
	graeca	CBro EBrs ECho EPot GBuc LLWG LRHS MTho NMen NMin WCot
	- subsp. ***ionica***	see *F. thessala*
	gussichiae	EBrs ECho NMen WWst
	hermonis subsp. ***amana***	CWCL EBrs ECho EPot ERCP GEdr GKev ITim LAma LLHF LPio MSSP NMen WCot
	- - 'Cambridge' ♀H4	WCot
	- - yellow-flowered	EPot
	- subsp. ***hermonis***	WWst
	hispanica	see *F. lusitanica*
	imperialis	ECGP GKir IHer MBri WBVN WTin
	- 'Argenteovariegata' (v)	GKir
	- 'Aureomarginata' (v)	EBee EBrs ELon LAma
	- 'Aurora'	EBee EBrs EPot ERCP GAbr GKev LAma LLWG LRHS NGHP NLar NPer NPri SMrm SPer SPhx WFar
	- 'Garland Star'	EBee EBrs LAma LRHS
	- var. ***inodora***	EBee EBrs ERCP
	- 'Lutea'	CAvo CSam EBee EBrs ELan EPfP ERCP LRHS NBPC NPri SPhx SPoG WFar
	- 'Maxima'	see *F. imperialis* 'Rubra Maxima'
	- 'Maxima Lutea' ♀H4	CBro ELan EPfP EPot GAbr LAma LLWG LRHS NLar SMrm SPer
	- 'Orange Brilliant'	EBee EBrs
	- 'Prolifera'	EBee EBrs ECho LAma NLar WHer
	- 'Rubra'	EBee EBrs ECho ERCP GKev LAma LLWG LRHS MSCN NLar NPri SMrm SPer WFar
§	- 'Rubra Maxima'	CBro EBee EBrs ELan EPfP EPot LAma LRHS SPad SPhx
	- 'Slagzwaard'	EBee EBrs
	- 'Striped Beauty' **new**	EBee LAma
	- 'Sulpherino'	EBee EBrs LAma LRHS
	- 'The Premier'	EBee EBrs ECho LAma LRHS
	- 'William Rex'	CAvo CFFs CWCL EBee EBrs EPot ERCP LAma LRHS SPhx SPoG
	- yellow-flowered	CFFs
	involucrata	EBrs ECho MPoH WCot
	ionica	see *F. thessala*
	japonica var. ***koidzumiana***	EBrs ECho EFEx GEdr WWst
	karadaghensis	see *F. crassifolia* subsp. *kurdica*
I	***karelinii***	ECho
	kotschyana	EBrs ECho GEdr MPoH NMen WCot WWst
	lanceolata	see *F. affinis* var. *tristulis*
	latakiensis	EBrs ECho EPot GEdr MPoH WCot WWst
§	***latifolia***	GAuc GEdr MPoH
	- var. ***nobilis***	see *F. latifolia*
§	***lusitanica***	MPoH MSSP NMen
	lutea Bieb.	see *F. collina*
	maximowiczii	ECho
	meleagris	Widely available
	- 'Mars'	ECho
	- var. ***unicolor***	CBro EBrs ECho GBuc LAma LRHS
	subvar. ***alba*** ♀H4	MAsh MBri MMHG MSSP NHol NLAp SPer SPhx WAul WPnP WShi
	- - - 'Aphrodite'	EPot GBuc NBir WCot
	meleagroides	EBrs WWst
§	***messanensis***	MPoH MSSP
	- subsp. ***gracilis***	ITim MSSP WCot
	michailovskyi ♀H2	CAvo CFFs CHid CTri EBrs ECho EPfP EPot ERCP EWal GBuc GEdr GGar GKev LAma LLWG LRHS MNrw MTho NHol NLAp NMen SPhx SRms WFar WHil
	minima	ECho
§	***minuta***	EBrs ECho EPot ERCP GAuc MPoH NMen NMin
	montana	EBrs ECho NMen WWst
	nigra Mill.	see *F. pyrenaica*
	obliqua	WCot
	olivieri GBK 82	WWst
§	***orientalis***	ECho MSSP WWst
	pallidiflora ♀H4	CAvo CBro CLAP CWCL EBee EBrs ECho EPot ERCP ERos GBuc ITim LAma LPio LRHS MSSP MTho NBid NBir NMen SPhx WCru WPnP
§	***persica***	EBee EBrs ECha ECho ECtt EHrv EPfP EPot ERCP LAma LHop LRHS MBri NBPC NMen NPri SPad SPer SPhx SPoG WFar WHil
	- 'Adiyaman' ♀H4	CAvo CBro EBrs ELan LLWG LRHS
	- 'Alba'	MPoH
	- 'Ivory Bells'	CAvo EBrs ECho EPot ERCP LAma LRHS WWst
	- 'Ivory Queen'	CBro
*	- 'Senkoy'	ECho MPoH WWst
	pinardii	ECho EPot NMen
	- MPR 7921	WWst
	pontica ♀H4	CBro CHid CLAP CWCL EBrs ECho EPot ERCP ERos EWal GAbr GAuc GBuc GEdr ITim LAma LPio LRHS MSSP MTho NMen SPhx WCru WPnP
	- subsp. ***substipilata***	WCot
	pudica	EBrs ECho GBuc GEdr LAma MSSP MTho NHol NMen WAbe WCot
*	- 'Fragrant'	ECho MPoH NMen
	- 'Giant'	EBrs ECho EPot
	- 'Richard Britten'	NMen
	purdyi	EBrs ECho

§ ***pyrenaica*** 🏆H4	CLAP CWCL EBrs ECho ERos GCra GEdr LPio LRHS MSSP NMen SPhx WCot WCru WTin WWst
- 'Bernard Tickner' new	MSSP
- 'Cedric Morris'	MSSP WCot
- 'Lutea'	MSSP
raddeana	CAvo EBee EBrs ECho EPot ERCP LAma LRHS SPhx WHil WWst
recurva	EBrs ECho
- NNS 00-179	WCot
regelii	WWst
rhodocanakis	EBrs ECho EPot MPoH NMen NMin WCot
- subsp. ***argolica***	ECho NMen
- - OS 864	MPoH
rixii new	GAuc
rubra major	see *F. imperialis* 'Rubra Maxima'
ruthenica	EBrs ECho ERos NMen
sewerzowii	EBrs ECho EPot ERCP GAuc MPoH WCot WWst
sibthorpiana	ECho WWst
sinica new	WCot
sororum new	GAuc
sphaciotica	see *F. messanensis*
stenanthera	EBrs ECho EPot LAma NMen WWst
stribrnyi	EBrs ECho WWst
tachengensis	see *F. yuminensis*
tenella	see *F. orientalis*
§ ***thessala***	EBrs ECho GBuc MSSP MTho NMen WCot
- Hoa 8964	WWst
thunbergii	EBee EBrs ECho EPot GEdr NMen SMrm WCot
tortifolia	NMen
§ ***tubiformis***	EBrs ECho GAuc GEdr MPoH MSSP
tuntasia	WCot
uva-vulpis	CMea EBrs ECrN ECtt EHon EPfP EPot EWal GBuc GEdr GGar GKev LAma LHop LPio LRHS MNrw MTho NBir NMen SPad SPhx WCot WCru WFar WHil
verticillata	CBro EBee EBrs ECha ECho EHrv EPot ERCP GEdr LAma LRHS MTho NMen SPhx WCru WWst
§ ***walujewii***	EPot MSSP WCot
whittallii	EBrs ECho EPot MSSP NMen
- PW 72-64B	WWst
- 'Green Light'	EBrs NMin
§ ***yuminensis***	ECho WCot

Fuchsia ✿ (*Onagraceae*)

'A.M. Larwick'	CSil EBak EKMF
'A.W. Taylor'	EBak
'A1' (d)	CTsd
'Aalt Groothuis' (d)	WPBF
'Aaltje' new	WPBF
'Aandenken Bert Pelgrims' (d)	WPBF
'Aart Verschoor' (d)	WPBF
'Abbé Farges' (d)	CDoC CLoc CSil CWVF EBak EKMF EPts SPet SVic WFuv WRou
'Abigail' ambig.	CWVF EKMF WRou
'Abigail Storey'	CSil
'Abundance'	CSil
'Acclamation' (d)	WPBF
'Achievement' 🏆H4	CDoC CLoc CSil EKMF LCla MJac SPet SVic WPBF
'Adagio' (d)	CLoc
'Adalbert Bogner' (d) new	WPBF
'Adelaide Hoodless'	WRou
'Adinda' (T)	CDoC EKMF EPts LCla MWar SLBF WRou
'Admiration'	CSil EKMF
'Adrienne' (d)	MHav
'Agnes de Ridder' (d)	WPBF
'Aiguillette'	WPBF
'Ailsa Garnett' (d)	EBak
'Aintree'	CTsd CWVF
'Airedale'	CWVF
'Aisen'	WRou
'Aladna's Sander' (d)	CWVF WPBF
'Alan Ayckbourn'	CWVF
'Alan Titchmarsh'	CDoC EKMF EPts LCla MHav MWar SLBF
'Alaska' (d)	CLoc EBak EKMF SVic
'Albertina'	SVic WFuv WRou
'Albertus Schwab'	LCla
'Alde'	CWVF
'Alderford'	SLBF WPBF
'Alf Thornley' (d)	CTsd CWVF WPBF
'Alfred Rambaud' (d)	CDoC CSil EKMF
'Ali' (d)	EKMF
'Alice Ashton' (d)	EBak EKMF
'Alice Blue Gown' (d)	CWVF
'Alice Doran'	CDoC CSil EKMF LCla
'Alice Hoffman' (d) 🏆H3-4	Widely available
'Alice Mary' (d)	EBak
'Alice Sweetapple' (d)	CWVF
'Alice Travis' (d)	EBak
'Alipat'	EBak EKMF
'Alison Ewart'	CLoc CWVF EBak EKMF MJac SPet SVic
'Alison Patricia' 🏆H3	CWVF EBak EKMF LAst MJac MWar SLBF SRGP SVic WFuv WPBF WRou
'Alison Reynolds' (d)	CWVF WPBF
'Alison Ruth Griffin' (d)	MJac
'Alison Ryle' (d)	EBak
'Alison Sweetman' 🏆H1+3	CSil CWVF EKMF MJac
'Allen Jackson'	MWar
'Allure' (d)	CWVF
Aloha = 'Sanicomf'PBR (Sunangels Series)	LAst SLBF
'Alpengluhn'	WPBF
alpestris	CDoC CSil EBak LCla LPio SVic WPBF
- Berry 64-87	EKMF
'Alton Waters' (d/v)	MWar
'Alwin' (d)	CWVF
'Alyce Larson' (d)	CTsd CWVF EBak MJac SVic
'Amanda Bridgland' (d)	EKMF
'Amanda Jones'	EKMF
'Amaranth'	WPBF
'Amazing Maisie' (d)	MWar SLBF WPBF
'Ambassador'	CTsd EBak MHav SVic
'Ambiorix'	WFuv
'Amelie Aubin'	CLoc CWVF EBak EKMF SVic
'America'	CWVF
'Americana Elegans' new	WPBF
'Amethyst Fire' (d)	CSil
'Amigo' ambig.	EBak
§ ***ampliata***	CDoC EKMF LCla
'Amy'	MJac
'Amy Jade Whitehouse' new	MWar
'Amy Lye'	CLoc CSil EBak EKMF SVic
'Amy Ruth'	CWVF
§ 'Andenken an Heinrich Henkel' (T)	CDoC CLoc CWVF EBak EKMF WRou
'André Le Nostre' (d)	CWVF EBak SVic
'Andreas Schwab'	LCla
andrei	CDoC LCla
- Berry 4637	EKMF
'Andrew'	EBak EKMF
'Andrew Carnegie' (d)	CLoc
'Andrew George'	MJac

	Name	Suppliers
	'Andrew Hadfield'	CWVF EKMF MWar SVic WRou
	'Andromeda' De Groot	CSil
	'Andy Jordens' (d)	WFuv
	'Angel Kiss' (E) **new**	CDoC
	'Angela Dawn'	WPBF WRou
	'Angela Leslie' (d)	CLoc CWVF EBak SVic
	'Angela Rippon'	CWVF MJac
	'Angelika Fuhrmann' (d)	WPBF
	'Angel's Flight' (d)	EBak
	'Anita' (d)	CCCN CLoc CWVF EKMF EPts LAst MHav MJac SLBF SVic WFuv WGor WPBF WRou
	'Anjo' (v)	CWVF SLBF
	'Ann Howard Tripp'	CDoC CLoc CWVF MBri MJac SVic WFuv WPBF WRou
	'Ann Lee' (d)	EBak
	'Ann Marie Batty'	EKMF
	'Anna Louise'	EKMF MWar
	'Anna of Longleat' (d)	CCCN CTsd CWVF EBak MJac SPet WFuv
	'Anna Silvena'	CCCN LSou MHav
	'Annabel' (d) ♀H3	CCCN CDoC CLoc CTri CTsd CWVF EBak EKMF EPts LAst LRHS MBri MJac MWar SLBF SPet SRGP SVic WFuv WPBF WRou
	'Annabelle Stubbs' (d)	SRGP
	'Anneke de Keijzer'	CDoC LCla
	'Annie Den Otter'	WPBF
	'Annie Earle'	EKMF
	'Annie Geurts' **new**	WPBF
	'Annie M.G. Schmidt'	EPts WPBF
	'Another Little Cracker' **new**	MWar WRou
	'Another Storey'	CSil
	'Anouchka de Weirdt' (d) **new**	WPBF
	'Ant and Dec' (d/v) **new**	MHav MJac
	'Anthea Day' (d)	CLoc
	'Antigone'	SLBF WPBF
	apetala	EKMF
	- DG 1044	EKMF
	'Aphrodite' (d)	CLoc CWVF EBak
	'Applause' (d)	CLoc CWVF EBak EKMF EPts SPet SVic
	'Apple Blossom'	EKMF
	aprica misapplied	see *F.* × *bacillaris*
	aprica Lundell	see *F. microphylla* subsp. *aprica*
	'Apricot Ice'	CLoc SVic
	'Arabella'	CWVF
	'Arabella Improved'	CWVF EKMF SVic
	arborea	see *F. arborescens*
§	***arborescens***	CBcs CDoC CHEx CLoc CSil CWVF EBak EKMF EShb LCla LPio SDys SVic WRou WWlt
	- B&SWJ 10475	WCru
	'Arcadia Gold' (d)	CWVF SVic
	'Arcady'	CLoc CWVF
	'Arels Arjen' **new**	WPBF
	'Arend Moerman' (d)	WPBF
	'Aretha' (Diva Series) **new**	MHav
	'Ariel' (E)	CDoC CSil SVic WCom WRou
	'Arlendon' (d)	CWVF
	'Army Nurse' (d) ♀H4	CDoC CLoc CSil CWVF EKMF EPts LRHS MAsh MBri MGos MSmi NBir NDlv SLBF SPet SVic WFuv
	'Aronst Hoeck'	WPBF
	'Art Deco' (d)	WPBF
	'Arthur Baxter'	EBak
	'Artosa' (d) **new**	WPBF
	'Ashley'	CDoC CTsd EKMF LCla
	'Ashley and Isobel'	CWVF
	'Ashtede'	SLBF
	'Atahualpa' **new**	WPBF
	'Athela'	EBak
	'Atlantic Star'	CWVF EKMF MJac WPBF
	'Atlantis' (d)	CWVF MJac
	'Atomic Glow' (d)	EBak SVic
	'Aubergine'	see *F.* 'Gerharda's Aubergine'
	'Audrey Hepburn'	CWVF
	'Augustin Thierry' (d)	EKMF
	'Aunt Juliana' (d)	EBak
	'Auntie Jinks'	CCCN CDoC CWVF EBak EKMF LAst LCla MJac SPet SVic WFuv WRou
	'Aurora Superba'	CLoc CTsd CWVF EBak EKMF MHav SLBF WRou
	'Australia Fair' (d)	CWVF EBak
§	***austromontana***	EBak
	'Autumnale' ♀H1+3	CCCN CDoC CHEx CLoc CWVF EBak EKMF EPts LAst LCla MSmi NVic SBch SLBF SMrm SPet SPoG SVic WFuv WPBF WRou
	'Avalanche' ambig. (d)	CDoC CLoc CSil EBak EKMF SLBF
	'Avocet'	CLoc EBak
	'Avon Celebration' (d)	CLoc
	'Avon Gem'	CLoc CSil
	'Avon Glow' (d)	CLoc
	'Avon Gold'	CLoc
	ayavacensis	CDoC LCla
	- Berry 3601	EKMF
	'Aylisa Rowan' (E)	EKMF
	'Azure Sky' (d)	EKMF MJac WPBF
	'Babette' (d)	EKMF
	'Baby Blue Eyes' ♀H3-4	CDoC CSil CWVF EKMF ELon LRHS MBri WFuv WRou
	'Baby Blush'	CSil
	'Baby Bright'	CWVF MWar SLBF WRou
	'Baby Chang'	LCla WPBF
	'Baby Girl'	WFuv
	'Baby Love'	WPBF
	'Baby Pink' (d)	CWVF
	'Baby Thumb' (d/v)	EPts
	'Baby van Eijk'	WPBF
	'Babyface' Tolley (d)	SVic
§	× ***bacillaris*** (E)	CChe CDoC CDul CEnt CSil EBak EWes GCal ITim MBlu SBch SEND SLBF SPoG SRms WPBF
§	- 'Cottinghamii' (E)	CDoC CSil EKMF IDee WSHC
	- 'Oosje'	see *F.* 'Oosje'
§	- 'Reflexa' (E)	CAbP CCCN CTrC GKir GQui LSou
	'Baden Powell' (E)	SVic
	'Bagworthy Water'	CLoc
	'Bahia'	WPBF
	'Baker's Tri' (T)	EBak
	'Balkonkönigin'	CLoc CWVF EBak WFuv
	'Ballerina'	CDoC
	'Ballet Girl' (d) ♀H1+3	CDoC CLoc CWVF EBak EKMF SLBF
	'Bambini'	CWVF EPts
	'Banks Peninsula'	GBin GQui
	'Barbara'	CLoc CSil CTsd CWVF EBak EKMF EPts MJac MWar SPet SVic WFuv WPBF WRou
	'Barbara Evans'	EKMF MWar SLBF
	'Barbara Norton'	CCCN
	'Barbara Pountain' (d)	CWVF
	'Barbara Reynolds' **new**	MWar
	'Barbara Windsor'	CWVF MJac
	'Barnet Belle' **new**	SLBF
	'Baron de Ketteler' (d)	CSil CTsd EKMF
	'Baroncelli' (d) **new**	WPBF
	'Barry M. Cox'	WPBF
	'Barry's Queen'	see *F.* 'Golden Border Queen'
	'Bart Comperen' (d)	WPBF
	'Bart-Els' (d) **new**	WPBF

'Bartje'	SLBF WPBF
'Bashful' (d)	CDoC CSil EPts LCla SPet SVic WPBF
'Beacon'	CDoC CLoc CSil CWVF EBak EKMF EPfP EPts LAst LBMP LRHS MBri MJac MWat NDlv SPet SPoG SRGP SVic WFuv WRou
'Beacon Rosa'	CCCN CDoC CLoc CSil CWVF EKMF EPts LAst LRHS MBri MJac NBlu NDlv SLBF SPet SPoG SVic WFuv WPBF WRou
'Beacon Superior'	CSil
'Bealings' (d)	CLoc CWVF MBri MHav SVic WFuv
'Beansweyr' (d)	WPBF
'Beau Nash'	CLoc
'Beauty of Bath' (d)	CLoc EBak
'Beauty of Cliff Hall' Monk	EKMF
'Beauty of Clyffe Hall' Lye	CSil EBak
'Beauty of Exeter' (d)	CWVF EBak EKMF
'Beauty of Meise' (d) **new**	WPBF
'Beauty of Prussia' (d)	CLoc CSil CWVF
'Beauty of Swanley'	EBak
'Beauty of Trowbridge'	CWVF LCla
'Beckey' (d)	WPBF
'Becky Jane'	CSil
'Becky Reynolds'	MWar
'Belinda Jane'	WPBF
'Bella Forbes' (d) 🏆$^{H1+3}$	CLoc CSil EBak EKMF MSmi
'Bella Rosella' (California Dreamers Series) (d)	CCCN CWVF EKMF EPts LAst MJac MSmi SCoo WFuv WPBF
'Belsay Beauty' (d)	CWVF MJac SVic
'Belvoir Beauty' (d)	CLoc
'Ben de Jong'	CDoC CTsd LCla WRou
'Ben Jammin'	CBgR CDoC CLoc CSil CWVF EKMF EPts LAst LRHS LSou MJac MWar SPoG SVic WFuv WRou
'Beninkust'	WPBF
'Benisser' **new**	MAsh
'Béranger' Lemoine, 1897 (d)	CSil EBak EKMF
'Berba's Coronation' (d)	WPBF
'Berba's Happiness' (d)	CWVF
'Bergnimf'	CTsd
'Berliner Kind' (d)	CSil CWVF EBak
'Bermuda' (d)	CWVF
'Bernadette' (d)	CWVF
'Bernie's Big-un' (d)	MJac
'Bernisser Hardy' 🏆$^{H3-4}$	CDoC CSil EKMF EPts LCla LRHS
'Bert de Jong'	WPBF
'Bertha Gadsby'	EKMF
'Beryl Shaffery'	WPBF
'Beryl's Jewel' **new**	WPBF
'Berys Elizabeth'	EKMF MWar
'Bessie Girl'	WPBF
'Bessie Kimberley' (T)	CDoC EKMF LCla WPBF
'Beth Robley' (d)	CWVF
'Betsy Huuskes'	WPBF
'Betsy Ross' (d)	EBak
'Betty Jean' (d)	MWar WPBF
Betty = 'Shabetty'^{PBR} (Shadowdancer Series)	LAst LBMP
'Beverley'	CSil CWVF EBak EKMF EPts
'Beverley Sisters' (d) **new**	MJac
'Bewitched' (d)	EBak
'Bianca' (d)	CWVF SVic WPBF
'Bicentennial' (d)	CCCN CLoc CTsd CWVF EBak EKMF EPts MJac MSmi MWar SPet SVic WFuv WPBF
'Big David' (d) **new**	WPBF
'Big Slim'	WPBF
'Bill Stevens' (d)	CTsd

'Billy'^{PBR}	CDoC SRGP
'Billy Green' (T) 🏆$^{H1+3}$	CDoC CLoc CWVF EBak EPts LCla MHer MJac MWar SLBF SPet SVic WFuv WPBF WRou
'Bishop's Bells' (d)	CWVF SVic
'Bits' (d)	CTsd
'Bittersweet' (d)	SVic
'Black Beauty' (d)	CWVF
'Black Prince'	CDoC CWVF MHav MWar SVic WFuv WPBF
'Blackmore Vale' (d)	CWVF
'Blacky' (d)	CCCN EBak LAst LSou MHav MSCN SPet SVic
I 'Blanche Regina' (d)	CWVF MJac
'Bland's New Striped'	CDoC EBak EKMF EPts SLBF
'Blauer Engel'	WPBF
'Blaze Away' (d)	LAst MBri MJac WGor
'Bliss' (d)	WPBF
'Blober' **new**	WPBF
'Blood Donor' (d)	EKMF MJac
'Blowick'	CDoC CWVF MBri MJac SPet
'Blue Beauty' (d)	CSil EBak EKMF
'Blue Boy'	WFuv WPBF
'Blue Bush'	CBgR CSil CWVF EKMF EPts MJac SVic
'Blue Butterfly' (d)	CWVF EBak SVic
'Blue Eyes' (d)	CDoC SPet
'Blue Gown' (d)	CDoC CLoc CSil CWVF EBak EKMF LRHS MGos SPet SVic WPBF WRou
'Blue Lace' (d)	CSil WFuv
'Blue Lagoon' ambig. (d)	CWVF
'Blue Lake' (d)	CWVF
'Blue Mink'	EBak
'Blue Mirage' (d)	CLoc CTsd CWVF EKMF MHav SVic WFuv
'Blue Mist' (d)	EBak
'Blue Pearl' (d)	CWVF EBak MHav
'Blue Pinwheel'	CWVF EBak
'Blue Sails'	WPBF
'Blue Satin' (d)	LAst
'Blue Sleighbells'	WPBF
'Blue Tit'	CSil LCla
'Blue Veil' (d)	CCCN CLoc CTsd CWVF EKMF MHav MJac SCoo SVic WFuv
'Blue Waves' (d)	CLoc CSBt CTsd CWVF EBak MJac SPet SVic
'Blush o' Dawn' (d)	CLoc CTsd CWVF EBak EKMF EPts SVic
'Bob Bartrum'	EKMF SLBF
'Bob Pacey'	CWVF
'Bobby Boy' (d)	EBak
'Bobby Dazzler' (d)	CWVF EKMF
'Bobby Shaftoe' (d)	EBak WPBF
'Bobby Wingrove'	EBak
'Bobby's Girl'	EPts
'Bobolink' (d)	EBak
'Bob's Best' (d)	CWVF EPts MJac
'Boerhaave'	EBak
'Bohémienne'	WPBF
boliviana Britton	see *F. sanctae-rosae*
boliviana ambig.	CTsd LPio
§ ***boliviana*** Carrière	CDoC CHEx CLoc CWVF EBak EKMF LCla WRou
§ - var. ***alba*** 🏆$^{H1+3}$	CDoC CLoc EBak EKMF EPts LCla LPio SVic WRou
- var. ***boliviana***	CRHN SVic
- f. ***puberulenta***	see *F. boliviana* Carrière
- var. ***luxurians*** 'Alba'	see *F. boliviana* Carrière var. *alba*
'Bomber Command' (d)	EKMF
'Bon Accorde'	CLoc CWVF EBak EKMF EPts SLBF SVic WFuv WRou

'Bon Bon' (d)	CTsd CWVF EBak SVic
'Bonita' (d)	CWVF SVic
'Bonnie Lass' (d)	EBak
'Bonny' (d)	CLoc
'Bonzai Overijsel' **new**	WPBF
'Bora Bora' (d)	CTsd CWVF EBak EKMF SVic
'Borde Hill' (d)	EPts SLBF
'Border Princess'	EBak
'Border Queen' 🏆H3-4	CDoC CLoc CSil CTsd CWVF EBak EKMF EPts LCla MJac MWar SPet SVic WRou
'Border Raider'	MWar
'Border Reiver'	CWVF EBak SVic
'Börnemann's Beste'	see *F.* 'Georg Börnemann'
'Boswinning'	WPBF
'Bouffant'	CLoc SVic
'Bountiful' Munkner (d)	CLoc CWVF EKMF
'Bouquet' (d)	CDoC CSil EKMF
'Bow Bells'	CDoC CLoc CWVF MJac SPet SVic WFuv
'Boy Marc' (T)	LCla WPBF
'Braamt's Glorie'	WPBF
bracelinae	CDoC CSil EKMF
'Bram Verdonk' (d) **new**	WPBF
'Brandt's 500 Club'	CLoc EBak
'Brechtje'	WPBF
'Breckland'	EBak
'Breeders' Delight'	CSil CWVF MBri WFuv
'Breeder's Dream' (d)	EBak
'Breevis Arion' (d) **new**	WPBF
'Breevis Electo' (d)	WPBF
'Breevis Evelien' (d)	WPBF
'Breevis Hector' (d) **new**	WPBF
'Breevis Homerus' (d)	WPBF
'Breevis Ilia' (d) **new**	WPBF
'Breevis Iris' (d)	WPBF
'Breevis Karna' (d)	WPBF
'Breevis Lucina' (d)	WPBF
'Breevis Minimus'	SLBF
I 'Breevis Nobilis' (d)	WPBF
'Breevis Panclione' (d)	WPBF
'Breevis Pomona' (d) **new**	WPBF
'Breevis Rubi' (d)	WPBF
'Breevis Selene' (d)	WPBF
'Breevis Varuna' (d)	WPBF
'Breevis Zagreus' (d)	WPBF
'Brenda' (d)	CLoc CWVF EBak
'Brenda White'	CDoC CLoc CWVF EBak EKMF SVic WRou
'Brentwood' (d)	EBak
brevilobis	CSil WPBF
- Berry 4445	EKMF
'Brian C. Morrison' (T)	EKMF LCla
'Brian G. Soanes'	EBak
'Brian Hilton'	MWar
'Brian Kimberley' (T)	EKMF LCla
'Bridal Pink' (d)	CTsd
'Bridal Veil' (d)	EBak
'Bridesmaid' (d)	CWVF EBak SPet SVic
'Brigadoon' (d)	EBak
'Bright Lights'	EKMF WPBF
'Brightling'	WPBF
'Brighton Belle' (T)	CDoC CWVF
'Brilliant' Bull, 1865	CDoC CLoc CSil EBak EKMF LCla
'Brilliant' ambig.	CWVF MBri MHav NDlv WFuv
'Briony Caunt'	CSil EKMF
'British Jubilee' (d)	CWVF EKMF SVic
'Brixham Orpheus'	CWVF
'Brodsworth'	CSil EKMF
'Bronze Banks Peninsula'	CDoC CSil EKMF
'Brookwood Belle' (d)	CTsd CWVF EPts LCla MJac SLBF
'Brookwood Joy' (d)	CWVF MJac

'Brutus' 🏆H4	CDoC CLoc CSil CWVF EBak EKMF EPts LRHS MBri MWat SPet SPoG SVic WFuv
'Bryan Breary' (E)	LCla
'Buddha' (d)	EBak
'Bugle Boy'	LCla MWar
'Bunny' (d)	CWVF EBak SLBF SVic
'Burning Bush'	CTsd
'Burstwick'	CSil
'Burton Brew'	MJac
'Buster' (d)	EKMF LCla
'Buttercup'	CLoc CTsd CWVF EBak MHav SVic
'C.J. Howlett'	CSil EBak EKMF
'Caballero' (d)	EBak
'Caesar' (d)	CWVF EBak
'Caitlin'	WPBF
'Caledonia'	CSil EBak EKMF
'California'	WRou
'Callaly Pink'	CWVF
'Cambridge Louie'	CWVF EBak MBri MWar SPet
campii	EKMF
campos-portoi	CDoC CSil CTsd LCla
- Berry 4435	EKMF
'Candlelight' (d)	CLoc CTsd EBak
'Candy Bells' (d)	CSBt
'Candy Stripe'	CLoc
canescens misapplied	see *F. ampliata*
canescens Benth.	EKMF
'Canny Bob'	MJac
'Canopy' (d)	CWVF
'Capri' (d)	CTsd CWVF EBak
'Cara Mia' (d)	CLoc CTsd SPet
'Caradela' (d)	CLoc EKMF MJac MWar
'Cardinal'	CLoc CTsd EKMF WPBF
'Cardinal Farges' (d)	CLoc CSil CWVF EKMF MHav SLBF SPet SVic WFuv
'Careless Whisper'	LCla SLBF WPBF
'Carioca'	EBak
'Carisbrooke Castle' (d)	EKMF
'Carl Drude' (d)	CSil CTsd SVic
'Carl Wallace' (d)	EKMF
'Carla Johnston' 🏆H1+3	CDoC CLoc CWVF EKMF EPts MBri MJac MWar SVic WFuv WPBF WRou
'Carla Knapen' (d)	WPBF
'Carleton George'	MWar
'Carlisle Bells'	WPBF
'Carmel Blue'	CCCN CDoC CLoc CTsd LAst MSCN SBch SPet SVic WFuv WGor
'Carmen' ambig.	WPBF
'Carmen' Lemoine (d)	CDoC CSil EKMF
'Carmine Bell'	CSil EKMF
'Carnea'	CSil CWib
'Carnival' (d)	CTsd
'Carnoustie' (d)	EBak
'Carol Grace' (d)	CLoc
'Carol Nash' (d)	CLoc
'Carol Roe'	EKMF
'Carole Hipkin'	EKMF
'Caroline'	CLoc CWVF EBak EKMF EPts SVic WFuv WPBF WRou
'Caroline's Joy'	CCCN LAst MHav MJac MWar SBch SCoo SPet
'Carol's Choice'	WPBF
'Caron Keating'	WPBF
'Cascade'	CCCN CDoC CLoc CWVF EKMF EPts MBri MJac SPet WFuv WPBF
'Caspar Hauser' (d)	CWVF EKMF SLBF SVic
'Catherine Bartlett'	CWVF EKMF WPBF
'Catherine Law' (d) **new**	WPBF
'Cathie MacDougall' (d)	EBak
'Cecil Glass'	CSil EKMF

'Cecile' (d)	CCCN CDoC CTsd CWVF EKMF EPts LAst MJac MSmi SRGP SVic WFuv WPBF WRou
'Celadore' (d)	CWVF SVic
'Celebration' (d)	CLoc CWVF
'Celia Smedley' ♀H3	CCCN CDoC CLoc CSil CTsd CWVF EBak EKMF EPts LCla MBri MJac MWar SLBF SPet SVic WFuv WPBF WRou
'Celine'	MWar
'Centerpiece' (d)	EBak
'Ceri'	CLoc
'Cerrig'	SVic
'Champagne Celebration'	CLoc
'Chancellor' (d)	CWVF
'Chandleri'	CWVF EKMF SLBF SVic
'Chang' ♀H1+3	CDoC CLoc CTsd CWVF EBak EKMF LCla MWar SLBF SVic WPBF
'Chantel Lavrijsen' (d) **new**	WPBF
'Chantry Park' (T)	LCla
'Charisma'	SVic
§ 'Charles de Gaulle'	WPBF
'Charles Edward' (d)	CSil EKMF
'Charles Welch'	EPts
Charlie Dimmock = 'Foncha'PBR (d)	CLoc LAst MWar WPBF
'Charlie Gardiner'	CWVF EBak
'Charlie Girl' (d)	EBak SVic
'Charm of Chelmsford'	LCla WPBF
'Charming'	CDoC CLoc CSil CWVF EBak EKMF LRHS MAsh MJac MWar SPet SVic WRou
'Chartwell'	WPBF
'Chase Delight' (v)	CDoC
'Chase Royal'	CTsd
'Chatt's Delight'	EKMF SLBF
'Checkerboard' ♀H3	CCCN CLoc CSil CTsd CWVF EBak EKMF EPts LCla MJac MSCN MWar SLBF SPet SVic WEas WFuv WPBF
'Cheeky Chantelle' (d)	SLBF WPBF
'Cheers' (d)	CWVF EKMF WFuv
'Chelsea Louise'	EPts
'Chenois Godelieve'	WPBF
'Cherry' Götz PBR	LAst WPBF
'Chessboard'	CLoc
'Chillerton Beauty' ♀H3	CLoc CSil CTri CWVF EKMF ELon EPts LRHS MJac SLBF SPer SPet SVic WMnd WPBF WRou
'China Doll' (d)	CWVF EBak SVic
'China Lantern'	CLoc CSil CTsd CWVF EBak EKMF SVic
'Chor Echo'	WPBF
'Chris'	WPBF
'Chris Bright' **new**	MWar
'Chris Nicholls' (d)	CSil EKMF
'Christa Lehmeier' **new**	WPBF
'Christel Poelmans' **new**	WPBF
'Christina Becker'	SVic
'Christine Bamford'	CDoC CSil CTsd CWVF
'Christine Rogers' **new**	CDoC
'Christmas Gem' (T)	WPBF
'Christmas Ribbons' (d)	MSmi
'Chriwito' **new**	WPBF
'Churchtown'	CWVF
cinerea	CDoC LCla
- Berry 004-86	EKMF
'Cinnabarina' (E)	CLoc
'Cinnamon' (d)	WPBF
'Cinque Port Liberty' (d)	SLBF
'Cinvenu'	LCla
'Cinvulca'	LCla
'Circe' (d)	CWVF EBak EKMF SVic
'Circus'	EBak
'Circus Spangles' (d)	CLoc EKMF LAst
'Citation'	CLoc CWVF EBak SVic
'City Lights'	SLBF
'City of Adelaide' (d)	CLoc
'City of Leicester'	CWVF MHer SPet
'Clair de Lune'	CDoC CWVF EBak MHav SVic WRou
'Claire Evans' (d)	CWVF
'Claire Oram'	CLoc
'Clare Frisby'	EKMF WPBF
'Claudia' (d)	LAst LCla MJac MWar WFuv WPBF WRou
'Cliantha' (d)	CCCN EKMF MJac WFuv WRou
'Clifford Gadsby' (d)	CTsd EBak
'Cliff's Hardy'	CSil EKMF LCla MSmi
'Cliff's Own'	SVic
'Cliff's Unique' (d)	CWVF EPts
'Clifton Beauty' (d)	CTsd CWVF MJac
'Clifton Belle' (d)	CWVF
'Clifton Charm'	CSil EKMF EPts LCla MJac SVic WPBF
'Clipper'	CSil CWVF
'Cloth of Gold'	CLoc CWVF EBak MJac SPet SVic
'Cloverdale Jewel' (d)	CDoC CTsd CWVF EBak MHav SPet SVic
'Cloverdale Joy'	EBak
'Cloverdale Pearl'	CTsd CWVF EBak EKMF EPfP SPet SPoG SVic WPBF
'Coachman' ♀H4	CLoc CWVF EBak EKMF EPts LCla MWar SLBF SPet SVic WFuv WRou
'Cobalt'	SLBF
coccinea	CDoC CSil CTsd EKMF LCla
'Codringtonii'	CSil
'Coen Bakker' (d) **new**	WPBF
× ***colensoi***	CDoC CSil ECou EKMF LCla
'Collingwood' (d)	CLoc CWVF EBak
'Colne Fantasy' (v)	EKMF
'Come Dancing' (d)	CDoC CTsd CWVF MHav SPet SVic
'Comet' Banks	CWVF
I 'Comet' Tiret (d)	CDoC CLoc EBak SPet
'Comperen Alk'	WPBF
'Comperen Groenling'	WPBF
'Comperen Havik' (d)	WPBF
'Comperen Lineola' (d)	WPBF
'Comperen Lutea' (d)	WPBF
'Conchilla' (d)	EBak
'Condor'	WPBF
'Confection' (d)	CTsd
'Connie' (d)	CSil EBak EKMF SVic WPBF
'Conspicua' ♀H3-4	CSil CWVF EBak EKMF SVic
'Constable Country' (d)	CWVF
'Constance' (d)	CDoC CLoc CSil CTsd CWVF EKMF LCla MJac NDlv SLBF SPet SVic WPBF WRou
'Constance Comer'	MJac WRou
'Constellation' ambig.	CTsd CWVF
'Constellation' Schnabel, 1957 (d)	CLoc EBak
'Consuelo' (d) **new**	WPBF
'Continental' (d)	WFuv
'Contraste' (d) **new**	SBch
'Coombe Park'	MJac
'Copycat'	CSil
'Coquet Bell'	CWVF EBak WPBF
'Coquet Dale' (d)	CWVF EBak
'Cor Spek' (d) **new**	WPBF
'Coral Baby' (E)	LCla
'Coral Rose' (d)	SVic
'Coral Seas'	EBak

	Name	Suppliers
	'Coralle' (T)	CCCN CDoC CLoc CWVF EBak EKMF EPts LBMP LCla MHer MJac MSCN MSmi SLBF SVic WFuv WRou
	'Corallina' ♀H3-4	CDoC CLoc CSil CTsd EBak EKMF ELon MHav SBch SPet SVic WFar WPnn
I	'Corallina Variegata' (v)	CSil WPBF
*	***cordata*** B&SWJ 9095	WCru
	cordifolia misapplied	see *F. splendens*
	'Core'ngrato' (d)	CLoc CWVF EBak
	coriacifolia	EKMF
	'Corneel Cornelis' (d) **new**	WPBF
	'Cornelia Smith' (T)	LCla
	'Cornwall Calls' (d)	EBak
	'Corrie Barten' (d)	WPBF
	'Corsage' (d)	CWVF SVic
	'Corsair' (d)	EBak SVic
	corymbiflora misapplied	see *F. boliviana* Carrière
	corymbiflora Ruíz & Pav.	CDoC EBak SVic
	'Cosmopolitan' (d)	EBak
	'Costa Brava'	CLoc EBak
	'Cotta Bright Star'	CDoC CWVF EKMF LCla
	'Cotta Carousel'	EKMF LCla WRou
	'Cotta Christmas Tree'	CDoC EKMF LCla SLBF
	'Cotta Fairy'	CWVF EKMF
	'Cotta Two Thousand'	EKMF
	'Cotta Vino'	EKMF SVic
	'Cottinghamii'	see *F. × bacillaris* 'Cottinghamii'
	'Cotton Candy' (d)	CLoc CWVF LCla SVic
	'Countdown Carol' (d)	EPts
	'Countess of Aberdeen'	CLoc CSil CWVF EBak EKMF SLBF WFuv
	'Countess of Maritza' (d)	CLoc CWVF
	'County Park'	CTsd ECou
	'Court Jester' (d)	CLoc EBak
	'Cover Girl' (d)	EBak EPts MJac SPet WPBF
	'Coxeen'	EBak
	'Crackerjack'	CLoc EBak
	crassistipula Berry 3553	EKMF
	'Creampuff' (d)	CDoC CTsd
	'Crescendo' (d)	CLoc CWVF
	'Crinkley Bottom' (d)	EPts MJac SLBF WFuv
	'Crinoline' (d)	EBak
	'Crosby Serendipity'	CLoc
	'Crosby Soroptimist'	CWVF MJac WRou
	'Cross Check'	CWVF MBri MJac WFuv
	'Crusader' (d)	CWVF
	'Crystal Blue'	EBak SVic
	'Crystal Stars' (d)	SVic
	'Cupid'	CSil EBak EKMF
	'Curly Q'	EBak SPet SVic
	'Curtain Call' (d)	CLoc CTsd CWVF EBak SVic
	× ***cuzco***	EKMF
	cylindracea misapplied	see *F. × bacillaris*
	cylindracea Lindl. (E)	CSil LCla WPBF
	- (m/E) BRE 43908	EKMF
	'Cymon' (d)	CWVF
	'Cymru' (d)	SVic
	'Cyndy Robyn' (d)	WPBF
	cyrtandroides	CSil
	- Berry 4628	EKMF
	'Dainty'	EBak
	'Dainty Lady' (d)	EBak
	'Daisy Bell'	CDoC CLoc CTsd CWVF EBak EKMF LCla MJac SPet SVic WRou
	'Dalton'	EBak
	'Dana Samantha'	EPts
	'Dancing Bloom'	EPts
	'Dancing Elves' (d)	WPBF
	'Dancing Flame' (d) ♀H1+3	CCCN CLoc CTsd CWVF EBak EKMF EPts LAst LBMP MBri MJac MWar SLBF SPet SVic WFuv WPBF
	'Daniel Reynolds'	MWar WPBF
	'Danielle'	WPBF WRou
	'Danielle Frijstein'	WPBF
	'Danish Pastry'	CTsd CWVF SPet
	'Danny Boy' (d)	CLoc CWVF EBak EKMF SVic WFuv WPBF
	'Danny Kaye' (d)	WPBF
	'Dark Eyes' (d) ♀H4	CCCN CLoc CSil CTsd CWVF EBak EKMF LAst MBri MJac SBch SLBF SPet SVic WFuv WPBF
	'Dark Night' (d)	CSil
	'Dark Secret' (d)	EBak
	'Dark Treasure' (d)	CDoC CTsd EKMF
	'Darreen Dawn' (d)	WPBF
	'Daryn John Woods'	CDoC LCla
	'Dave's Delight'	EKMF WPBF
	'David' ♀H3-4	CDoC CLoc CSil CWVF EKMF ELon EOHP EPts LAst LCla LSRN SLBF SPoG SRGP WFuv WGor WPBF WRou
	'David Alston' (d)	CLoc CWVF EBak
	'David Lockyer' (d)	CLoc CWVF SVic
	'David Savage' (d)	LCla
	'David Ward' (d)	NEgg WPBF
	'Dawn'	EBak
	'Dawn Carless' (d)	WPBF
	'Dawn Fantasia' (v)	CLoc EKMF EPts MHav MWar WPBF
	'Dawn Mist' (d)	WFuv
	'Dawn Redfern' (d)	CWVF
	'Dawn Sky' (d)	EBak
	'Dawn Star' (d)	CCCN CTsd CWVF MHav MJac SVic WFuv
	'Dawn Thunder' (d)	CTsd SVic
	'Day by Day'	CSil
	'Day Star'	EBak
	'De Groot's Beauty'	WPBF
	'De Groot's Black Beauty' (d)	WPBF
	'De Groot's Kattiensnor' **new**	WPBF
	'De Groot's Lady'	WPBF
	'De Groot's Moonlight'	WPBF
	'De Groot's Parade'	WPBF
	'De Groot's Regenboog'	WPBF
	'De Lemmentjes' (d) **new**	WPBF
	'De Mijnlamp' (d) **new**	WPBF
	'De Zeveraar' (d) **new**	WPBF
	'Debby' (d)	EBak
	'Deben Petite' (E)	LCla
	'Deben Rose'	CTsd
	'Deborah Jane' **new**	EKMF
	'Deborah Street' (d)	CLoc
§	***decussata*** Ruíz & Pav.	CDoC EBak
	- Berry 3049	EKMF
	'Dee Copley' (d)	EBak
	'Dee Star' (d)	SVic
	'Deep Purple' (d)	CCCN CDoC CLoc CWVF EKMF LAst MJac SCoo WFuv WPBF
	'Delilah' (d)	CWVF
	'Delta's Angelique'	WPBF
	'Delta's Bride'	SLBF
	'Delta's Dream'	CTsd CWVF WPBF
	'Delta's Drop'	SLBF SVic WPBF
	'Delta's Groom'	LCla WRou
	'Delta's Ko' (d)	SVic
	'Delta's Matador'	CCCN
	'Delta's Paljas'	WPBF
	'Delta's Parade' (d)	EPts
	'Delta's Pim'	WPBF
	'Delta's Rien'	SVic

	Name	Suppliers
	'Delta's Sara'	CDoC EKMF LAst LRHS MAsh NPri WPBF
	'Delta's Song'	WPBF WRou
	'Delta's Star' **new**	WPBF
	'Delta's Symphonie' (d)	CWVF
	'Delta's Wonder'	CSil SVic
	'Demi van Roovert'	WPBF
§	***denticulata***	CDoC CLoc CWVF EBak EKMF EPts LCla MHer SLBF SVic WPBF WRou
	'Depardieu' (d) **new**	WPBF
	dependens	EKMF
	'Derby Imp'	CWVF EKMF
	'Desperate Daniel'	EPts
	'Devonshire Dumpling' (d)	CCCN CDoC CLoc CTsd CWVF EBak EKMF EPts LAst MBri MJac MSmi MWar SLBF SPet SVic WFuv WPBF
	'Diablo' (d)	EBak
	'Diamond Celebration' (d)	EKMF MWar
	'Diamond Wedding'	SVic
	'Diana' (d)	EBak
	'Diana Princess of Wales'	CWit LAst LSou MJac SBch SVil WFuv WPBF
	'Diana Wills' (d)	CWVF
	'Diana Wright'	CDoC CSil EKMF LPla
	'Diane Brown'	CWVF EKMF WFuv WPBF
	'Diane Marie'	EKMF
	'Didgeridoo' (d) **new**	WPBF
§	'Die Schöne Wilhelmine'	SLBF SVic WFuv WPBF
	'Dijk van Tuin' (d) **new**	WPBF
	'Dilly-Dilly' (d)	CWVF
	'Dimples' (d)	CSil MBri
	'Diny Hetterscheid' (T)	WPBF
	'Dipton Dainty' (d)	CLoc EBak SVic
	'Display' 🏆H4	CCCN CDoC CDul CLoc CSil CWVF EBak EKMF EPts LAst LBMP LCla LRHS MBri MJac NPer SLBF SPet SPoG SVic WFar WFuv WPBF WRou
	'Divia' **new**	NPri
	'Doc'	CDoC CSil EPts MHav SPet SVic WFuv WPBF
	'Docteur Topinard'	CLoc EBak EKMF
	'Doctor'	see *F.* 'The Doctor'
	'Doctor Foster' 🏆H4	CDoC CLoc CSil CTri EBak EKMF EPfP SVic
	'Doctor Mason'	CWVF
	'Doctor Olson' (d)	CLoc EBak
	'Doctor Robert'	CWVF EKMF EPts MBri MJac SVic WFuv WPBF
	'Dodo'	WPBF
§	'Dollar Prinzessin' (d) 🏆H4	CCCN CDoC CLoc CSil CWVF EBak EKMF EPfP EPts LAst LCla LRHS MAsh MBri MJac MWar MWat NDlv NPer NPri SLBF SMrm SPet SPlb SVic WBVN WFar WFuv WPBF
	'Dollie Pausch'	WPBF
	'Dolly Daydream' (d)	EKMF
	'Dominique' (d)	EKMF
	'Dominyana'	CSil CTsd EBak EKMF LCla
	'Don Peralta'	EBak
	'Dopy' (d)	CDoC CSil EPts SPet SVic WFuv WPBF
	'Doreen Redfern'	CLoc CTsd CWVF MHav MJac SPet SVic WRou
	'Doreen Stroud' (d)	CWVF
	'Doretteke'	WPBF
	'Doris Deaves'	SLBF
	'Doris Joan'	SLBF WPBF
	'Dorothea Flower'	CLoc CSil CWVF EBak EKMF
	'Dorothy'	CSil EKMF LCla SLBF SPet
	'Dorothy Ann'	LCla SLBF WPBF
	'Dorothy Cheal'	CWVF
	'Dorothy Day' (d)	CLoc
	'Dorothy Hanley' (d)	CAlb CBgR CCCN CLoc CSil EKMF EPts LAst LRHS LSRN LSou MAsh MBri MJac SLBF SPet SPoG SVic WFuv WPBF WRou
	'Dorothy Oosting' (d)	WPBF
	'Dorothy Shields' (d)	CWVF MHav MJac
	'Dorrian Brogdale' (T)	LCla WPBF
	'Dorset Abigail'	CWVF
	'Dorset Delight' (d)	CWVF
	'Dot Woodage'	EKMF
	'Double Trouble'	WPBF
	'Douglas Boath' (d)	WFuv
	'Dove House'	EKMF
	'Dragon Fang'	WPBF
	'Dragon Moon' (d) **new**	WPBF
	'Drake 400' (d)	CLoc
	'Drama Girl' (d)	CWVF
	'Drame' (d)	CDoC CSil CWVF EBak EKMF LCla SPet SVic WRou
	'Drum Major' (d)	EBak
	'Du Barry' (d)	EBak
	'Duchess of Albany'	CLoc EBak
	'Duchess of Cornwall' (d)	CSil EPts
	'Duet' (d)	CTsd SVic
	'Duke of Wellington' Haag, 1956 (d)	CLoc
	'Dulcie Elizabeth' (d)	CWVF EBak MJac SPet
	'Dunrobin Bedder'	CSil WPBF
	'Dusky Beauty'	CWVF SVic WRou
	'Dusky Rose' (d)	CLoc CWVF EBak MHav MJac SVic
	'Dutch Mill'	CLoc CWVF EBak
	'Duyfken'	CTsd CWVF
	'Dying Embers'	CLoc WRou
	'Dymph Werker van Groenland' (E)	EKMF LCla MWar WPBF
	'Earre Barré'	WPBF
	'East Anglian'	CLoc EBak
	'Easter Bonnet' (d)	CLoc CWVF
	'Ebanflo'	EBak MWar
	'Ebbtide' (d)	CLoc EBak
	'Echo'	CWVF
	'Ectors Nursery'	WPBF
	'Ed Largarde' (d)	EBak EKMF
	'Eden Lady'	CDoC CLoc CTsd SPet
	'Eden Princess'	CWVF MJac
	'Eden Rock' (d)	MHav SRGP WGor
	'Edith' ambig.	EPts NDlv WRou
	'Edith' Brown (d)	CSil EKMF LCla SLBF
	'Edith Emery' (d)	SPet
	'Edna May'	CWVF
	'Edna W. Smith'	CWVF
	'Edwin J. Jones'	SLBF
	'Eileen Drew'	SLBF
	'Eileen Raffill'	EBak
	'Eileen Saunders'	CSil EBak EKMF
	'Eileen Storey'	EKMF
	'El Camino' (d)	CWVF
	'El Cid'	CLoc CSil EBak EKMF SVic
	'Elaine Ann'	EPts MJac
	'Elaine Taylor' (d)	MJac WPBF
	'Eleanor Clark'	WPBF
	'Eleanor Leytham'	CWVF EBak EKMF SVic WRou
	'Eleanor Rawlins'	CSil EBak EKMF
	'Elf'	CSil
	'Elfin Glade'	CLoc CSil CWVF EBak EKMF
	'Elfrida' (d)	CSil EKMF WPBF
	'Elfriede Ott' (T)	CLoc EBak LCla WPBF
	'Elisabeth Schnedl' (d)	WRou
	'Elizabeth' ambig.	CTsd
I	'Elizabeth' Tiret, 1970 (d)	WPBF

'Elizabeth' Whiteman, 1941 EBak EKMF
'Elizabeth Broughton' EKMF
'Elizabeth Honnorine' SVic
'Elizabeth Travis' (d) EBak
'Ellen Morgan' (d) CWVF EBak
'Ellvee' **new** MWar
'Elma' LCla WPBF
'Elsa' (d) CWVF LRHS SPet SVic
'Elsie Maude' (d) CWVF
'Elsie Mitchell' (d) CTsd CWVF SPet WRou
'Elsie Vert' (d) WPBF
'Elsstar' (d) WPBF
'Elysée' CSil EKMF
§ 'Emile de Wildeman' (d) CWVF EBak EKMF SPet WFuv
'Emile Zola' CSil
'Emily' WPBF
'Emily Austen' CWVF
'Emma Alice' (d) CWVF
'Emma Margaret' SLBF
'Emmakins' (d) EKMF
'Empress of Prussia' ♀H4 CDoC CLoc CSil CWVF EBak EKMF EPts ERas LRHS MSmi SLBF SPet SVic WMnd WPBF WRou
'Enchanted' (d) CWVF EBak MWar
encliandra CDoC EKMF WRou
subsp. ***encliandra*** (E)
* - var. ***gris*** (E) CSil
- subsp. ***microphylloides*** EKMF
(E) Berry & Brako 7592
§ - subsp. ***tetradactyla*** (E) EKMF
§ 'Enfant Prodigue' (d) CDoC CLoc CSil EKMF LPla SDix SLBF SMrm SVic WMnd
'English Rose' (d) CWVF WPBF
'Enstone' see *F. magellanica* var. *molinae* 'Enstone'
'Erecta Novelty' **new** EKMF
'Eric's Everest' (d) EKMF
'Eric's Majestic' (d) EKMF MJac
'Erik' SLBF
'Erika Köth' (T) LCla
'Ernest Rankin' CSil SVic
'Ernie'PBR EKMF LAst SLBF SRGP
'Ernie Bromley' CSil CWVF SLBF
'Ernie Wise' (d) MJac SCoo
'Eroica' SVic
'Errol' (d) CLoc
'Eruption' WPBF
'Esmerelda' MJac
'Estelle Marie' CLoc CWVF EBak EKMF MBri MWar SLBF SPet SVic WFuv
'Eternal Flame' (d) CTsd CWVF EBak EPts MBri SVic WFuv
'Ethel' ambig. WPBF
'Ethel May' (d) MJac
'Ethel Wilson' CSil
'Eureka Red' (Californian Dreamers Series) (d) CWVF
'Eurofuchsia' (d) WPBF
'Eurofuchsia 2007 Denmark' (d) **new** WPBF
'Eurydice' (d) CLoc
'Eusebia' (d) CTsd SVic
'Eva Boerg' CCCN CLoc CSil CTri CWVF EBak EKMF LAst LCla MBri SPet SVic WFuv WKif WPBF
'Evelyn Stanley' (d) CWVF
§ 'Evelyn Steele Little' EBak
'Evening Sky' (d) EBak
'Evensong' CLoc CTsd CWVF EBak SVic WFuv
'Everbeur' (d) WPBF
excorticata CBcs CDoC CPLG CSil CTsd EKMF SPlb
'Exmoor Woods' CSil
'Expo '86' (d) WFuv
'Fabian Franck' (T) CDoC LCla
'Fairy Falls' WRou
'Falklands' (d) CSil SLBF
'Falling Stars' CLoc CTsd CWVF EBak SVic
'Fan Dancer' (d) EBak
'Fancy Free' (d) MBri
'Fancy Pants' (d) CLoc CWVF EBak SVic
'Fanfare' CDoC EBak EKMF LCla SVic WPBF WRou
'Fascination' see *F.* 'Emile de Wildeman'
'Fashion' (d) EBak
'Fasna 1100' WPBF
'Favourite' EBak
'Fay's Folly' **new** LAst
'Felicity Kendal' (d) MJac SCoo
'Feltham's Pride' CWVF EKMF
'Fenman' CWVF SVic
'Ferre Peeters' (d) **new** WPBF
'Festival Lights' (E) SLBF
'Festoon' EBak
'Fey' (d) CWVF EKMF WFuv
'Ffion' EPts
'Fiery Spider' EBak SVic
'Fighter Command' EKMF
'Finn' CWVF EPts MHav
'Fiona' CDoC CLoc CWVF EBak MHav SPet SVic
'Fiorelli Flowers' (d) WPBF
'Fire Mountain' (d) CLoc SVic
'Firecracker'PBR see *F.* 'John Ridding'
'Firefly' SVic
'Firelite' (d) EBak
'Firenza' (d) CWVF
'First Kiss' (d) CWVF
'First Lady' (d) CTsd CWVF
'First Lord' CWVF
'First Success' (E) CDoC CTsd CWVF EKMF LCla SVic WRou
'Flair' (d) CLoc CWVF
'Flame' EBak
'Flamenco Dancer' (California Dreamers Series) (d) CLoc CWVF
'Flament Rose' WPBF
'Flamingo' (d) SVic
'Flash' ♀H3-4 CLoc CSil CTri CWVF EBak EKMF EPfP EPts LCla MJac SLBF SPet SPoG SVic WFuv WRou
'Flashlight' CDoC CSil CWVF EPfP EWld LAst MHav MJac WPBF
'Flashlight Amélioré' CSil
'Flat Jack o' Lancashire' (d) CSil EKMF SLBF
'Flavia' (d) EBak
'Fleur de Picardie' SLBF
'Flirtation Waltz' (d) CLoc CTsd CWVF EBak EKMF MJac SVic WFuv
'Flocon de Neige' CSil EBak
'Flogman' **new** WPBF
'Flor Izel' (d) WPBF
'Floral City' (d) CLoc EBak
'Floren Kennes' (d) **new** WPBF
'Florence Mary Abbott' WPBF
'Florence Taylor' (d) CWVF
'Florence Turner' CSil EBak EKMF
'Florencio' (d) **new** WPBF
'Florentina' (d) CLoc CWVF EBak EKMF SVic
'Florrie's Gem' (d) SLBF
'Flowerdream' (d) CWVF
'Flyaway' (d) EBak
'Fly-by-night' (d) CWVF

	Name	Suppliers
	'Flying Cloud' (d)	CLoc CSil CWVF EBak EKMF MBri SVic
	'Flying Scotsman' (d)	CCCN CDoC CLoc CTsd CWVF EBak EKMF EPts MJac SCoo SVic WFuv WRou
	'Fokkos Katrientje'	WPBF
	'Folies Bergères' (d)	EBak
	'Foline'	SVic
	'Foolke'	CSil EBak
	'Forfar's Pride' (d)	CSil
	'Forget-me-not'	CLoc CSil CWVF EBak EKMF SVic WPBF
	'Forgotten Dreams'	WPBF
	'Fort Bragg' (d)	CWVF EBak
	'Forward Look'	WPBF
	'Fountains Abbey' (d)	CWVF
	'Four Farthings' (d)	EKMF EPts
	'Foxgrove Wood' 🏆H3-4	CSil CWVF EBak EKMF EPts SLBF
	'Foxtrot' (d)	CWVF
	'Foxy Lady' (d)	CWVF EKMF WPBF
	'Frances Haskins'	CSil WRou
	'Frank Saunders'	CWVF LCla SLBF WPBF
	'Frank Unsworth' (d)	CWVF EKMF EPts MJac SPet WFuv WPBF
	'Frankie's Magnificent Seven' (d)	EPts
	'Frank-Marlyse' (d) **new**	WPBF
	'Franz von Zon'	LCla
	'Frau Hilde Rademacher' (d)	CDoC CSil CWVF EBak EKMF EPts MHav SLBF SVic WPBF
	'Frauke'	SVic
	'Fred Hansford'	CSil CWVF
	'Fred Swales' (T)	WPBF
	'Frederick Woodward' (T)	EKMF
	'Fred's First' (d)	CDoC CSil EKMF
	'Freefall'	EBak
	'Freunden Tanzer' (d) **new**	WPBF
	'Frida Cox' (d) **new**	WPBF
	'Friendly Fire' (d)	CLoc
	'Frosted Flame'	CCCN CLoc CTsd CWVF EBak EKMF LAst LCla MJac SPet
	'Frühling' (d)	CSil EBak EKMF
	'Fuchsiade'	WRou
	'Fuchsiade '88'	CLoc CSil CTsd CWVF EBak EKMF WPBF
	'Fuchsiarama '91' (T)	CWVF WRou
	'Fuji-San'	CDoC ELon EPts
	'Fuksie Foetsie' (E)	CDoC CSil EKMF
	fulgens 🏆H1+3	CDoC EKMF GCal LCla MRav WPBF WRou
*	- var. ***minuata***	EKMF
*	- 'Variegata' (T/v)	CDoC CLoc EKMF EPts LCla WRou
	'Fulpila'	EKMF LCla SLBF
	'Für Elise' (d)	EBak
	furfuracea	EKMF
	'Gala' (d)	EBak
	'Galadriel'	WPBF
	'Garden News' (d) 🏆H3-4	CCCN CDoC CLoc COlW CSil CWVF EKMF EPfP EPts LAst LCla LHop LRHS MAsh MBri MJac MSCN MSmi MWar NPer SLBF SPet SVic WFar WMnd WPBF WRou
	'Garden Week' (d)	CTsd CWVF SVic
	'Gartenbauverein Eupen' (d) **new**	WPBF
	'Gartenmeister Bonstedt' (T) 🏆H1+3	CCCN CDoC CLoc CWVF EBak EKMF LCla SPet SVic
	'Gary Rhodes' (d)	EBak MJac SBch SCoo WFuv
	'Gay Fandango' (d)	CLoc CTsd CWVF EBak SPet
	'Gay Future'	EKMF
	'Gay Parasol' (d)	CCCN CLoc LAst MJac SVic WFuv WRou

	Name	Suppliers
	'Gay Paree' (d)	EBak
	'Gay Senorita'	EBak
	'Gay Spinner' (d)	CLoc
	gehrigeri	EBak EKMF
	gehrigeri* × *nigricans	EKMF
	'Gemma Fisher' (d)	EPts
	Gene = 'Goetzgene' PBR (Shadowdancer Series)	LAst LBMP LSou MHav SCoo
	'Général Charles de Gaulle'	see *F.* 'Charles de Gaulle'
	'Général Monk' (d)	CDoC CSil CTsd CWVF EBak EKMF EPts LAst MBri SRGP SVic WPBF
	'Général Voyron'	CSil
	'General Wavell' (d)	CTsd SVic
	'Genii' 🏆H4	Widely available
	'Geoff Amos' (d)	MSmi
	'Geoff Oke'	MWar WPBF
	'Geoffrey Smith' (d)	CSil EKMF EPts
§	'Georg Börnemann' (T)	CLoc EBak EKMF WPBF
	'George Allen White'	CDoC CWVF WPBF
	'George Barr'	EKMF WPBF
	'George Johnson'	CDoC CTsd
	'George Travis' (d)	EBak
	'Gerald Drewitt'	CSil
§	'Gerharda's Aubergine'	CDoC CLoc CSil CWVF EKMF
	'Gerharda's Kiekeboe'	WPBF
	'Gerharda's Panache' **new**	WPBF
	'Gesneriana'	CDoC CLoc EBak EKMF WWlt
	'Giant Pink Enchanted' (d)	CLoc EBak
	'Gilda' (d)	CWVF MJac SVic
	'Gillian Althea' (d)	CTsd CWVF SRGP WFuv
	'Gilt Edge' (v)	CLoc
	'Gimlie'	WPBF
I	'Gina'	WPBF
	'Gina Bowman' (E)	LCla SLBF
	Ginger = 'Goetzginger' PBR (Shadowdancer Series)	LAst LBMP LSou MHav SCoo
	'Gipsy Princess' (d)	CLoc
	'Girls' Brigade'	CWVF EKMF
	'Gitana'	WPBF
	'Gladiator' (d)	EBak EKMF SVic
	'Gladys Godfrey'	EBak
	'Gladys Lorimer'	CWVF EPts LRHS
	'Gladys Miller'	CLoc
	glazioviana	CDoC CSil CTsd CWVF EKMF ERas LCla MHer SLBF SWal WGwG WRou
	'Glenby' (d)	CWVF
	'Glendale'	CWVF
	'Glitters'	CWVF EBak
§	'Globosa'	CAgr CSil EBak EKMF
	'Gloria Johnson'	EKMF
	'Glow'	CSil EBak EKMF WPBF
	'Glowing Embers'	EBak
	Glowing Lilac (d)	EPts WFuv
	'Glyn Jones' (d)	EKMF
	'Gold Brocade'	CSil SPet
	'Gold Crest'	EBak
	'Gold Leaf'	CWVF
	'Golden Anniversary' (d)	CLoc CWVF EBak EKMF MJac MSmi SVic WFuv WPBF
	'Golden Arrow' (T)	CDoC LCla SVic
§	'Golden Border Queen'	CLoc CSil EBak EKMF SPet
	'Golden Dawn'	CLoc CWVF EBak SPet SVic
	'Golden Girl'	SLBF
	'Golden Herald'	CSil SLBF
	'Golden la Campanella' (d/v)	CLoc MBri
	'Golden Lena' (d/v)	CSil CWVF
	'Golden Margaret Roe' (v)	CSil
	'Golden Marinka' (v) 🏆H3	CCCN CLoc EBak EKMF LAst LSou MBri SPet SVic WPBF
	'Golden Melody' (d)	CSil

'Golden Peppermint Stick' (d)	CTsd
'Golden Swingtime' (d)	CTsd MBri MHav MJac SPet SVic WFuv
'Golden Treasure' (v)	CLoc CSil CWVF EKMF MBri MWar
'Golden Vergeer' (v)	SLBF
'Golden Wedding'	EKMF SVic
'Goldsworth Beauty'	CSil
'Golondrina'	CSil CWVF EBak
'Goody Goody'	EBak SVic
'Goosebery Belle'	WRou
'Gordon Boy' (d)	CSil
'Gordon Thorley'	CSil EKMF
'Gordon's China Rose'	LCla
'Gota'	WPBF
'Göttingen' (T)	EBak EKMF WPBF
'Gouden Pater' (d)	WPBF
'Governor Pat Brown' (d)	EBak
'Grace Darling'	CWVF EBak
gracilis	see *F. magellanica* var. *gracilis*
'Graf Witte'	CDoC CSil CWVF EKMF SPet SVic
'Grand Duchess' (T)	WPBF
'Grand Duke' (T/d)	CWVF
'Grand Prix' (d)	CTsd SVic
'Grand Slam' (d)	CTsd SVic
'Grandad Hobbs' (d)	LCla SLBF
'Grandma Hobbs'	LCla
'Grandma Sinton' (d)	CLoc CTsd CWVF MBri
'Grandpa George' (d)	LCla
'Grandpa Jack' (d)	SLBF
'Grayrigg'	CDoC CSil CTsd EKMF EPts LCla
'Great Ouse' (d)	EPts
'Great Scott' (d)	CLoc CTsd
'Green 'n' Gold'	EBak
'Greenpeace'	CDoC CTsd EKMF SVic WPBF
'Greta' (T)	MWar WPBF
'Gretna Chase'	MBri
'Grey Lady' (d)	CSil SVic
'Grietus Luisman' (d) **new**	WPBF
'Groene Boelvaar' (d)	WPBF
'Groene Kan's Glorie'	CTsd EKMF SVic WPBF
'Groovy'	WPBF
'Grumpy'	CDoC CSil CWVF EPts MHav SPet SVic WFuv WPBF
'Grumpy Gord'	MWar
'Gruss aus dem Bodethal'	CLoc CWVF EBak EKMF EPts
'Guinevere'	CWVF EBak
'Gustave Doré' (d)	CDoC CSil EBak EKMF
'Guy Dauphine' (d)	EBak
'Guy-Ann Mannens'	WPBF
'Gwen Dodge'	SVic WPBF
'Gwendoline Clare'	WPBF
'Gypsy Girl' (d)	CWVF
'H.G. Brown'	CSil EBak EKMF
'Habanero' (d) **new**	WPBF
'Hagelander'	WPBF
'Halsall Beauty' (d)	MBri
'Halsall Belle' (d)	MBri
'Halsall Pride' (d)	MBri
'Hamadryad' (d)	WPBF
'Hampshire Blue'	CDoC CWVF SVic WFuv
'Hanna' (d)	SRGP
'Hannah Gwen' (d)	EKMF
'Hannah Louise' (d)	EPts
'Hannah Rogers'	MWar
'Hans Callaars'	LCla
'Hansi'	WPBF
'Happiness' (d)	SVic
'Happy'	CDoC CSil CTsd CWVF EPts LCla MHav SPet SVic WFuv WPBF
'Happy Anniversary'	CLoc SVic WPBF
'Happy Fellow'	CDoC CLoc CSil EBak MHav NDlv
'Happy Wedding Day' (d)	CLoc CWVF EKMF EPts LAst MJac MSmi SCoo SPet SRGP SVic WFuv
'Hapsburgh'	EBak
'Harbour Lites'	MWar SLBF WPBF WRou
'Harlow Car'	CDoC CWVF EKMF EPts
'Harlow Perfection'	CDoC EKMF
'Harmony' Niederholzer, 1946	EBak
'Harnser's Flight'	CSil
'Harriett' (d)	WPBF
'Harry Dunnett' (T)	EBak
'Harry Gray' (d)	CCCN CLoc CTsd CWVF EBak EPts LAst MBri MJac SPet SRGP SVic WFuv
'Harry Pullen'	EBak
'Harry Taylor' (d)	EPts
'Harry's Sunshine'	SLBF
'Harti's Olivia'	WPBF
hartwegii	CDoC CSil EKMF LCla MHer
'Harvey's Reward'	SLBF
'Hastings' **new**	MWar
'Hathersage' (d)	EBak
hatschbachii	CDoC CSil CTsd ELon EWes LCla MHer SDix SPoG WPnn
– Berry 4464	EKMF
– Berry 4465	EKMF
'Haute Cuisine' (d)	CLoc EKMF SVic
'Hawaiian Sunset' (d)	CLoc CWVF EPts SLBF WFuv WPBF
'Hawkshead' ♀H3-4	Widely available
'Hazel' (d)	CCCN CWVF MHav SVic
'Hazerland'	WPBF
'Heart Throb' (d)	EBak
'Heavenly Hayley' (d)	SLBF
'Hebe'	EBak
'Heemaeer'	WPBF
'Heidi Ann' (d) ♀H3	CCCN CDoC CLoc CSil CWVF EBak EKMF EPts LAst LRHS MBri MSCN SLBF SPet SVic WFuv WPBF
'Heidi Blue' (d)	SLBF
'Heidi Joy'	CSil
§ 'Heidi Weiss' (d)	CDoC CLoc CSil CWVF MBri SPet WFuv WPBF
'Heinrich Henkel'	see *F.* 'Andenken an Heinrich Henkel'
'Heirloom' (d)	EKMF
'Helen Clare' (d)	CLoc CWVF EBak
'Helen Elizabeth' (d)	EKMF
'Helen Gair' (d)	CWVF
'Helen Lang' **new**	EKMF
'Helen Nicholls' (d)	EKMF WPBF
'Helen Spence' (d)	EKMF
'Helena Rose'	EKMF
'Hellen Devine'	CWVF
'Hemsleyana'	see *F. microphylla* subsp. *hemsleyana*
'Henk Kaspers' (d)	WPBF
'Henkelly's Athena'	WPBF
'Henkelly's Consivia' **new**	WPBF
'Henkelly's Diana' **new**	WPBF
'Henkelly's Elisabeth'	WPBF
'Henkelly's Jasmine' **new**	WPBF
'Henkelly's Tim'	WPBF
'Henning Becker' ♀H3	CBgR CWVF ELon
'Henri Poincaré'	EBak EKMF
'Henrieke Dimi' (d) **new**	WPBF
'Herald' ♀H4	CDoC CSil CWVF EBak EKMF MHav SLBF SVic WFuv
'Herbé de Jacques'	see *F.* 'Mr West'
'Heri Arapaima' **new**	WPBF
'Heri Candiru' **new**	WPBF
'Heri Leng' **new**	WPBF
'Heri Mochara' (d) **new**	WPBF

'Heri Panga' (d) **new**	WPBF
'Heri Shusui' (d) **new**	WPBF
'Heri Snapper' (d) **new**	WPBF
'Heritage' (d)	CLoc CSil EBak EKMF
'Herman de Graaff' (d)	EKMF WPBF
'Hermiena'	CLoc CTsd CWVF EPts MHav MWar SLBF SVic WFuv WPBF
'Hermienne'	WRou
'Heron'	CSil EBak EKMF
'Herps Baljurk' **new**	WPBF
'Herps Bazuin'	WPBF
'Herps Bongo'	WPBF
'Herps Cornu'	WPBF
'Herps Helicopter' **new**	WPBF
'Herps Kwikstep'	WPBF
'Herps Pierement'	SLBF
'Herps Schalmei' **new**	WPBF
'Herps Trailer' **new**	WPBF
'Herps Tweespan' **new**	WPBF
'Hertogin van Brabant' (d)	WPBF
'Hessett Festival' (d)	CWVF EBak WFuv
'Heston Blue' (d)	CWVF EKMF
'Heydon'	CWVF
'Hi Jinks' (d)	EBak SVic
hidalgensis	see *F. microphylla* subsp. *hidalgensis*
'Hidcote Beauty'	CLoc CTsd CWVF EBak EKMF LCla MHav SLBF SPet SVic WPBF
'Hidden Treasure'	MWar WPBF WRou
'Highland Pipes'	EKMF LCla SVic
'Hilda May Salmon'	CWVF
'Hindu Belle'	EBak
'Hinnerike' (E)	CSil CWVF LCla SVic WPBF
'Hiroshige' (T)	LCla
'His Excellency' (d)	EBak
'Hobo' (d)	CSil
'Hobson's Choice' (d)	CWVF SLBF
'Holly's Beauty' (d)	CDoC CLoc EKMF EPts LAst LSou MWar SRGP WFuv
'Hollywood Park' (d)	EBak
'Hot Coals'	CLoc CWVF EKMF EPts MCot MJac MWar SVic WPBF WRou
'Howerd Hebden'	CDoC EKMF
'Howlett's Hardy' ♀H3-4	CDoC CLoc CSil CWVF EBak EKMF GKir MHav NLar SVic WMnd WRou
'Huckeswagen'	SLBF
'Huet's Akabar' **new**	WPBF
'Huet's Almandien' **new**	WPBF
'Huet's Amaril' **new**	WPBF
'Huet's Andalusiet' (d) **new**	WPBF
'Huet's Baraketh' **new**	WPBF
'Huet's Calamijn' (d)	WPBF
'Huet's Draviet' **new**	WPBF
'Huet's Heliotroop' (d) **new**	WPBF
'Huet's Kwarts'	WPBF
'Huet's Parelmoer' (d) **new**	WPBF
'Huet's Topaas'	WPBF
'Huet's Turkoois' **new**	WPBF
'Huet's Uvardiet' (d)	WPBF
'Hula Girl' (d)	CDoC CTsd CWVF EBak EKMF MJac MWar SPet
'Humboldt Holiday' (d)	EKMF
'Huntsman' (d)	CCCN CDoC MHav MJac WPBF
'Huygen Ireen' (d) **new**	WPBF
'Ian Brazewell' (d)	CLoc
'Ian Leedham' (d)	CTsd EBak EKMF
'Ian Storey'	CDoC CSil EKMF WPBF
'Ice Cool' (d)	MSmi
'Ice Cream Soda' (d)	EBak
'Ice Maiden' ambig. (d)	WPBF
'Iceberg'	CWVF EBak SVic
'Icecap'	CWVF EKMF MBri SVic

'Iced Champagne'	CLoc CWVF EBak MHav MJac
'Ichiban' (d)	CLoc CTsd
'Icicle' (d)	WPBF
'Ida' (d)	EBak
'Ien Van Adrichem' (d) **new**	WPBF
'Igloo Maid' (d)	CLoc CWVF EBak EKMF SPet SVic WFuv
'Ijzerwinning' (d)	WPBF
'Illusion'	WPBF
'Impala' (d)	CWVF WPBF
'Imperial Fantasy' (d)	CWVF
'Improved Hanna'	EKMF
'Impudence'	CLoc CWVF EBak SPet
'Impulse' (d)	CLoc
'Independence' (d)	SVic
'Indian Maid' (d)	CDoC CWVF EBak EKMF
inflata	EKMF
'Ingram Maid'	WPBF
'Insulinde' (T)	CDoC CFee CTsd CWVF EPts LCla MJac MWar SLBF
'Intercity'	WPBF
'Interlude' (d)	EBak
'Iolanthe' (T)	CWVF WPBF
'Irene L. Peartree' (d)	CWVF LCla
'Irene Sinton' (d)	CCCN MJac
'Iris Amer' (d)	CLoc CWVF EBak
'Irving Alexander' (d)	WPBF
'Isabel Ryan'	CSil
'Isis' Lemoine	CSil
'Isle of Mull'	CDoC CSil SPet
'Isle of Purbeck'	SVic
'Italiano' (d)	CWVF MJac SVic
'Ivy Grace'	CSil
'Jack Acland'	CWVF
'Jack Shahan' ♀H3	CCCN CDoC CLoc CSil CTsd CWVF EBak EKMF LAst LCla MBri MJac SPet SRGP WFuv WPBF
'Jack Stanway' (v)	CDoC CWVF EKMF MWar WPBF
'Jack Wilson'	CSil
'Jackie Bull' (d)	CWVF EBak
'Jackpot' (d)	EBak
'Jackqueline' (T)	CWVF
'Jacq Puts' **new**	WPBF
'Jadi Femke' **new**	WPBF
'Jamboree' (d)	EBak
'James Lye' (d)	CWVF EBak EKMF
'James Shaffery'	WPBF
'James Travis' (E/d)	CDoC CSil EBak EKMF LCla
'Jan Bremer'	SVic
'Jan Murray'	SLBF
'Jandel'	CWVF
'Jane Humber' (d)	CWVF EKMF
'Jane Lye'	EBak
'Janet Williams' (d)	CSil
'Janice Ann'	EKMF LCla MWar WPBF
'Janice Perry's Gold' (v)	CCCN CLoc MHav MJac
'Janie' (d)	EPfP LRHS MAsh
'Janske Vermeulen'	WPBF
'Jap Vantveer' (T)	LCla WPBF
'Jaspers Kameleon'	WPBF
'Jasper's Vlammetje'	WPBF
'Jaunty Jack'	SLBF
'Jean Baker'	CDoC CSil
'Jean Campbell'	EBak
'Jean de Fakteur' (d)	WPBF
'Jean Frisby'	CLoc
'Jean Smith' (d) **new**	MSmi
'Jeane'	EKMF
'Jef van der Kuylen' (d)	WPBF
'Jelle Veemen'	WPBF
'Jennie Rachael' (d)	WFuv
'Jennifer'	EBak

	'Jennifer Ann' **new**	SLBF
	'Jennifer Ann Porter'	MWar
	'Jennifer Hampson' (d)	CSil
	'Jennifer Lister' (d)	CSil EKMF
	'Jenny May'	CLoc EPts
	'Jenny Sorensen'	CWVF EKMF WFuv WPBF
	'Jess'	LCla SLBF
	'Jessica Reynolds'	MWar WPBF
	'Jessie Pearson'	CWVF
	'Jessimae'	CWVF SPet
	'Jester' Holmes (d)	CLoc CSil
	'Jet Fire' (d)	EBak
	'Jezebel'	SVic WPBF
	'Jiddles' (E)	EKMF LCla WRou
	'Jill Holloway' (T)	SLBF WPBF
	'Jill Whitworth'	CDoC WPnn
	'Jim Coleman'	CWVF SVic
	'Jim Dodge' (d)	EPts
	'Jim Hawkins'	EBak
	'Jim Muncaster'	CWVF EKMF
	'Jim Watts'	CDoC CTsd EKMF WPBF
	jimenezii	CDoC LCla WPBF
	'Jimmy Carr' (d)	EKMF
	'Jimmy Cricket' (E)	CDoC
	'Jingle Bells'	CTsd
	'Jinlye'	EKMF
	'JJ Roberts'	MWar
	'Joan Barnes' (d)	CTsd CWVF
	'Joan Cooper'	CLoc CSil CWVF EBak EKMF SLBF SVic
	'Joan Goy'	CWVF EKMF MJac SVic WFuv
	'Joan Knight'	CLoc
	'Joan Leach'	CSil
	'Joan Margaret' (d)	MJac
	'Joan Morris'	SLBF
	'Joan Pacey'	CDoC CWVF EBak EKMF
	'Joan Smith'	EBak
	'Joan Waters' (d)	CWVF
	'Joanna Lumley' (d) **new**	EPts MHav MJac
	'Jo-Anne Fisher' (d)	EPts
	'Joanne Woodward' **new**	EKMF
	'Joan's Delight'	WPBF
	'Jock Buchanan' **new**	WPBF
	'Jody Goodwin'	WPBF
	'Joe Kusber' (d)	CWVF EBak WFuv
	'Joe Nicholls' (d)	EKMF
	'Joel'	CLoc WPBF
	'Joergen Hahn'	WPBF
	'John Bartlett'	CLoc
	'John Boy' (d)	EKMF
	'John E. Caunt' ♀H3-4	CSil EKMF
	'John Green'	EKMF
	'John Grooms' (d)	CLoc SVic WFuv WRou
	'John Lockyer'	CLoc CWVF EBak
	'John Maynard Scales' (T)	CDoC CWVF LCla MJac WPBF WRou
§	'John Ridding'[PBR] (T/v)	CLoc EPts LAst LRHS LSou SPoG SVil WPBF
	'John Shead'	WPBF
	'John Suckley' (d)	EBak
	'John Wright'	CSil EKMF LCla
	'Joke's Albino'	WPBF
	'Jolanda Weeda'	WPBF
	'Jomam' ♀H3	CLoc CWVF MWar
	'Jon Oram'	CLoc CWVF
	'Jorma van Eijk' (d)	WPBF
	'Jose Tamerus' (d)	WPBF
	'Jose's Joan' (d)	CWVF SVic
	'Joy Bielby'	EKMF
	'Joy Patmore'	CLoc CTsd CWVF EBak EKMF MBri SLBF SPet WFuv WPBF
	'Joyce'	WPBF
	'Joyce Adey' (d)	CWVF
	'Joyce Sinton'	CLoc CWVF MBri WFuv
	'Joyce Wilson' (d)	EPts
	'Jubie-Lin' (d)	WPBF
	'Jubilee Quest'	EKMF MWar WPBF
	'Judith Coupland'	CWVF
	'Judith Lissenden'	EKMF
	'Juella'	EKMF
	'Jülchen'	CWVF
	'Jules Daloges' (d)	EBak EKMF
	'Julia' (d)	EKMF WPBF
	'Julie Ann Goodwin'	WPBF
	'Julie Horton' (d)	WPBF
	'Julie Marie' (d)	CWVF MJac
	'June Gardner'	CWVF EKMF
	'Jungle'	LCla SLBF
I	'Juno' Kennett	EBak
	juntasensis	EKMF
	'Jupiter Seventy'	EBak
	'Jus' For You'	MJac
	'Justin's Pride'	CDoC CSil EKMF
	'Kaboutertje'	EKMF
	'Kaleidoscope' (d)	EBak
	'Kara Faye'	EKMF
	'Kareeloven' (d) **new**	WPBF
	'Karen Isles' (E)	CDoC EKMF LCla STre WRou
	'Karen Louise' (d)	CLoc
	'Karin de Groot'	SVic WFuv
	'Karin Siegers'	CSil
	'Kate Taylor' (d)	SLBF WPBF
	'Kate Wylie'	MWar
	'Kath Kirk'	EKMF
	'Kath van Hanegem'	SLBF WPBF WRou
	'Kathleen Muncaster' (d)	EKMF
	'Kathleen Smith' (d)	EKMF
	'Kathleen van Hanegan'	CLoc EKMF MWar
	'Kathryn Maidment'	SVic
	'Kathy Louise' (d)	WPBF
	'Kathy's Prince'	EKMF
	'Kathy's Sparkler' (d)	EKMF
	'Katie Elizabeth Ann' (d)	MWar
	'Katie Reynolds' (d)	MWar
	'Katie Rogers'	EPts
	'Katie Susan'	SLBF
	'Katinka' (E)	CDoC CWVF LCla WPBF
	'Katjan'	CSil EKMF LCla SLBF WPBF
	'Katrina' (d)	CLoc EBak
	'Katrina Thompsen'	CLoc CWVF EKMF EPts MWar WFuv
	'Katy James'	EKMF MWar
	'Katy M'	WPBF
	'Keepsake' (d)	CLoc EBak
	'Kees van Eijk' (d)	WPBF
	'Keesje'	CTsd
	'Kegworth Carnival' (d)	CWVF
	'Ken Goldsmith' (T)	CWVF
	'Ken Jennings'	CWVF
	'Kenny Dalglish' (d)	CSil EKMF
	'Kenny Holmes'	CWVF
	'Kenny Walkling'	LCla SLBF
	'Kernan Robson' (d)	CLoc CWVF EBak
	'Kerry Theresa' **new**	EKMF
	'Keystone'	EBak
	'Kim de Groot' **new**	WPBF
	'Kim Nicholls'	EKMF
	'Kimberley Hadfield'	MWar
	'Kimberly' (d)	EBak WPBF
	'King of Bath' (d)	EBak
	'King of Hearts' (d)	EBak
	'King's Ransom' (d)	CLoc CTsd CWVF EBak EKMF SPet SVic
	'Kiss 'n' Tell'	CWVF MJac

'Kit Oxtoby' (d)	CCCN CDoC CWVF EKMF LCla MJac WFuv WPBF
'Kiwi' (d)	EBak
'Knockout' (d)	CWVF EKMF SVic
'Kobold'	WPBF
'Kolding Perle'	CWVF EKMF MHav SPet
'Komeet'	CDoC EKMF SBch
'Kon-Tiki' (d)	CLoc CTsd SPet
'Koog Aan de Zaan'	WPBF
'Kwintet'	CWVF EBak MJac SPet
'Kyoto'	EKMF
'La Bianca'	EBak
'La Campanella' (d) ♀H3	CCCN CDoC CLoc CWVF EBak EKMF EPts LAst MBri MJac MSCN MWar NVic SBch SPet SVic WPBF
'La Fiesta' (d)	EBak
'La France' (d)	EBak EKMF
'La Neige' ambig.	CTsd CWVF
'La Neige' Lemoine (d)	EBak EKMF
'La Porte' (d)	CLoc CWVF
'La Rosita' (d)	EBak SLBF
I 'La Traviata' Blackwell (d)	EBak
'Lace Petticoats' (d)	EBak EKMF SVic
'Lady Bacon'	CBgR ELon EPts EWes GCal SDys SLBF
'Lady Beth' (d)	SVic
'Lady Boothby'	CBgR CDoC CHEx CPLG CSil CWVF EBak EKMF EPfP EShb LAst LRHS LSou MHer MSCN NEgg SLBF SMrm SPet SPlb SPoG SVic WBor WFuv WPBF
'Lady Framlingham' (d)	EPts
'Lady Heytesbury'	EKMF
'Lady in Grey' (d)	CCCN EKMF LAst MJac SVic WPBF
'Lady Isobel Barnett'	CLoc CTsd CWVF EBak EKMF MBri MJac SPet SVic WFuv WPBF
'Lady Kathleen Spence'	CWVF EBak EKMF SPet SVic
'Lady Lupus'	EPts
'Lady Patricia Mountbatten'	CWVF EKMF SVic WRou
'Lady Ramsey'	EBak
'Lady Rebecca' (d)	CLoc
'Lady Thumb' (d) ♀H3	Widely available
'Lady's Smock'	EKMF
'Laepines' **new**	WPBF
'Laing's Hybrid'	CWVF EBak
'Lakeland Princess'	EBak
'Lakeside'	EBak
'Laleham Lass'	EKMF
'Lambada'	EKMF LAst MWar WPBF WRou
'Lancambe'	CSil
'Lancashire Lad' (d)	CTsd MWar SLBF
'Lancashire Lass'	CWVF MBri
'Lancelot'	EBak
'Land van Beveren'	MWar SLBF
'Lapshead White'	CPLG
'Lark' (T)	CWVF WPBF
'Lassie' (d)	CDoC CLoc CWVF EBak
'Last Chance' (E)	SLBF
'Laura' ambig.	CWVF SVic WFuv WRou
I 'Laura' (Dutch)	CLoc EPts LCla SLBF
I 'Laura' Martin (d)	EKMF
'Laura Biolcati-Rinaldi' (d)	WPBF
'Laura Cross' (E)	EKMF
'Laurena' **new**	WPBF
'Lavaglut'	WPBF
'Lavender Heaven' (d)	WPBF
'Lavender Kate' (d)	CLoc CWVF EBak
'Lazy Lady' (d)	CWVF EBak
'Lechlade Apache'	CDoC LCla
'Lechlade Bullet'	LCla
'Lechlade Chinaman'	CDoC SVic
'Lechlade Debutante'	CDoC LCla SLBF
'Lechlade Fire-eater' (T)	CDoC LCla
'Lechlade Gorgon'	CDoC CWVF EKMF LCla SLBF
'Lechlade Magician'	CDoC CHEx CSil CTsd EKMF EPts LCla MHav SPet SVic
'Lechlade Maiden'	CDoC CWVF LCla
'Lechlade Martianess'	LCla SVic
'Lechlade Potentate'	LCla
'Lechlade Rocket'	WPBF
'Lechlade Tinkerbell' (E)	CDoC LCla SLBF
'Lechlade Violet' (T)	CSil EKMF LCla SVic
'Leendert Beije' **new**	WPBF
lehmanii	LCla
'Len Bielby' (T)	CDoC CWVF LCla
'Lena' (d) ♀H3	CDoC CLoc CSil CTri CTsd CWVF EBak EKMF EPts MBri MJac SMrm SPer SPet SPlb SRGP SVic WPBF
'Lena Dalton' (d)	CLoc CWVF EBak EKMF SVic
'Leonhart von Fuchs'	WPBF
'Leonie Boffe' (d)	WPBF
'Leonora'	CDoC CLoc CSil CTsd CWVF EBak EKMF MBri SLBF SPet SVic WFuv WRou
'Lesley' (T)	CWVF LCla WPBF
'Leslie Drew'	SLBF
'Lett's Delight' (d)	CWVF EPts
'Letty Lye'	EBak
'Leverhulme'	see *F.* 'Leverkusen'
§ 'Leverkusen' (T)	CDoC CLoc EBak LCla MJac WRou
'Li Kai Lin'	CSil
I 'Liebesträume' Blackwell (d)	EBak
'Liebriez' (d) ♀H3-4	CSil CTsd EBak EKMF SPet SVic
'Liemers Lantaern'	CWVF
'Likalin'	CWVF
'Lilac'	CSil EBak
'Lilac Dainty' (d)	CSil
'Lilac Lustre' (d)	CLoc CWVF EBak SPet SVic
'Lilac Queen' (d)	EBak
'Lilac Tint'	WPBF
'Lilian'	EKMF
'Lilian May' **new**	EKMF
'Lillian Annetts' (d)	CCCN CDoC CWVF EKMF LAst LCla MJac MWar SLBF WFuv WPBF WRou
'Lillibet' (d)	CDoC CLoc CWVF EBak
'Lime Lite' (d)	MJac
I 'Limelight' Weston	SLBF
'Lincoln Castle'	EKMF MWar
'Linda Goulding'	CTsd CWVF EBak SVic WFuv
'Linda Grace'	EKMF MJac MWar
'Linda Mary Nutt'	MWar
'Linda Rosling' (d)	CDoC EKMF
'Lindisfarne' (d)	CLoc CWVF EBak EKMF MJac SPet WPBF
'Lindsey Victoria' (d)	SVic
'Lionel'	CSil WPBF
'Lisa' (d)	CDoC EPts SPet WPBF
'Lisa Rowe' (d)	WPBF
'Little Annie Gee'	MWar
'Little Baby'	EKMF
'Little Beauty'	CDoC CSil CWVF EKMF SVic WPBF
'Little Boy Blue'	EPts
'Little Brook Gem'	SLBF
'Little Catbells' (E)	SLBF
'Little Gene'	EBak
'Little Giant' **new**	LPla
'Little Jewel'	CTsd SPet
'Little Nan'	SLBF
'Little Ouse' (d)	CWVF
'Little Ronnie' (d)	WPBF
'Little Scamp' **new**	WRou
'Little Snow Queen'	WPBF
'Little Witch'	EKMF SLBF

	Name	Suppliers
	'Liz' (d)	CSil EBak EKMF WPBF
	Liza = 'Goetzliza'[PBR] (Shadowdancer Series)	CDoC LAst LSou
	'Lochinver' (d)	CWVF
	'Loeky'	CLoc CWVF EBak SPet SVic WPBF
	'Logan Garden'	see *F. magellanica* 'Logan Woods'
	'Lolita' (d)	CWVF EBak
	'London 2000'	LCla MJac MWar SLBF WPBF WRou
	'London Eye'	MWar
	'London in Bloom'	SLBF WPBF
	'Lonely Ballerina' (d)	CLoc CWVF
	'Long Distance' (T)	LCla WPBF
	'Long John'	WPBF
	'Long Wings'	EKMF SVic
	'Longfellow' Hoag	WPBF
	'Lonneke'	WPBF
	'Lord Byron'	CLoc EBak EKMF
	'Lord Derby'	CSil
	'Lord Jim'	CDoC LCla
	'Lord Lonsdale'	CWVF EBak EPts LCla MSCN SVic WFuv WPBF WRou
	'Lord Roberts'	CLoc CSil CWVF SLBF
	'Lorentz Schwab' **new**	WPBF
	'Lorna Fairclough'	MJac
	'Lorna Florence'	SLBF
	'Lorna Swinbank'	CLoc CWVF SVic
	'Lorraine's Delight' (d)	SVic
	'Lottie Hobby' (E) ♀H1+3	CDoC CLoc CMac CSil CTrC CTsd CWVF EKMF EPfP EPts EShb ISea LCla MLHP MSmi SIng SPet SVic WFuv WRou
	'Louise Emershaw' (d)	CWVF EBak MJac SVic
	'Louise Nicholls'	EKMF MJac MWar SLBF
	'Loulabel'	SVic
	'Lovable' (d)	EBak
	'Loveliness'	CLoc CWVF EBak EKMF SVic
	'Lovely Linda'	SLBF
	'Love's Reward' ♀H1+3	CLoc CWVF EKMF MJac MWar SLBF SVic WFuv WPBF WRou
	'Lower Raydon'	EBak
I	'Loxensis'	CDoC CWVF EBak EKMF SVic
N	***loxensis*** misapplied	see *F.* 'Loxensis', *F.* 'Speciosa'
N	***loxensis*** Kunth Berry 3233	EKMF
	- DG 1001	EKMF
	'Loxhore Herald'	CSil
	'Loxhore Lullaby' (E)	CSil LCla
	'Loxhore Mazurka' (T)	WPBF
	'Loxhore Minuet' (T)	CDoC LCla WRou
	'Loxhore Posthorn' (T)	LCla
	'Lucinda'	CWVF
	'Lucky Strike' (d)	CLoc EBak
	Lucy = 'Goetzlucy' (Shadowdancer Series)	EBak WPBF
	'Lucy Locket'	MJac
	'Lukas'	WPBF
	'Lunter's Klokje'	WPBF
	'Lunter's Trots' (d)	WPBF
	'Luscious Lisa'	WPBF
	'Lustre'	CWVF EBak SVic
	'Lut' (d)	WPBF
	'Luuk van Riet' (d)	WPBF
	lycioides misapplied	see *F.* 'Lycioides'
§	***lycioides*** Andrews	EBak EKMF
I	'Lycioides'	LCla
	'Lydia'	WPBF
	'Lye's Elegance'	CSil EKMF
	'Lye's Excelsior'	EBak EKMF
	'Lye's Own'	EBak EKMF SPet
	'Lye's Perfection'	EKMF
	'Lye's Unique' ♀H1+3	CCCN CDoC CLoc CSil CWVF EBak EKMF EPts LCla MJac MWar SLBF SPet SVic WFuv WRou

	Name	Suppliers
	'Lynette' (d)	CLoc
	'Lynn Cunningham' **new**	CDoC
	'Lynn Ellen' (d)	CDoC CTsd CWVF EBak
	'Lynne Marshall'	CSil
	'Lynne Patricia'	MWar
	'Mabel Greaves' (d)	CWVF
	'Mac Wagg'	WRou
	'Machu Picchu'	CLoc CWVF EKMF EPts LCla SVic WPBF WRou
	macrophylla	CDoC WMoo
	- BEA 922539	EKMF
	- Berry 3080	EKMF
	- Berry 80-539	EKMF
	- Berry 80-541	EKMF
	'Madame Aubin'	CSil EKMF
	'Madame Butterfly' (d)	CLoc
	'Madame Cornélissen' (d) ♀H3	CBgR CDoC CLoc CSBt CSil CTri CWVF EBak EKMF EPfP EPts GBuc LHop LRHS MAsh MBar MRav SCoo SLim SPer SPet SPoG SVic WFar WFuv WRou
	'Madame Eva Boye'	EBak
	'Madeleine Sweeney' (d)	EKMF MBri
	'Maes-y-Groes'	CSil EKMF
	'Maet Suycker'	WPBF
	'Magda Cerules' (d) **new**	WPBF
	magellanica	CDoC COld CSil CTrG CTsd CWib EKMF GGar GKir LBMP LRHS MLHP MSCN NPer NWea SPer SVic WFar WPnn
	- Dahl, S.	EKMF
	- 'Alba'	see *F. magellanica* var. *molinae*
I	- 'Alba Aureovariegata' (v)	CBgR CDoC CMac CTrC CWan EPfP SPer SVic WFar
	- 'Alba Variegata' (v)	CSil NPol
	- 'Americana Elegans'	CDoC CSil WPBF
	- 'Comber'	CSil
	- var. ***conica***	CDoC CSil EKMF
	- var. ***discolor***	CSil
	- 'Duchy of Cornwall'	CDoC
	- 'Exmoor Gold' (v)	CSil
§	- var. ***gracilis*** ♀H3	CAgr CDoC CHEx CLoc CSil CTri CWVF EKMF EPfP MLHP NBro SCoo SVic WGwG WPnn WSpi
	- - 'Aurea' ♀H3-4	CBcs CBot CDoC CMac CSil CTsd CWVF EBee EKMF ELan EPfP GGar GQui ISea LCla LRHS MHer MRav SAga SCoo SDix SLBF SPer SPet SPoG WCom WFar WRou WSpi
§	- - 'Tricolor' (v) ♀H3	CDoC CSil CTsd EKMF EPts EWes LBMP LCla LRHS SEND SLBF SRms WCFE WPnn WRou
	- - 'Variegata' (v) ♀H3	CDoC CSil EBak EKMF EPfP GGar LCla LRHS LSou MGos MRav SAga SBch SDix SIng SPet WCom WFuv WPnn WSpi
	- 'Guiding Star'	CDoC
	- 'Lady Bacon'	CDoC CSil EKMF GCal LPla
§	- 'Logan Woods'	CDoC CSil EKMF ELon EQua GBuc ISea SLBF SMrm
	- 'Longipedunculata'	CDoC CSil EKMF SLPl WPBF
	- 'Lyonesse Lady'	CDoC
	- var. ***macrostema***	CSil EKMF
§	- var. ***molinae***	Widely available
§	- - 'Enstone' (v)	CBgR EHoe EKMF ELon LAst
	- - 'Enstone Gold'	EKMF
	- - 'Golden Sharpitor' (v)	CBgR CCCN LAst MDKP MHav SBch WAbe WCom
	- - 'Mr Knight's Blush'	GBuc
§	- - 'Sharpitor' (v)	CBcs CBgR CDoC CSil EBak EHoe EKMF ELan EPfP GQue IFro LRHS MAsh MBar NBlu NPer NPri SAga

	Name	Suppliers
		SBch SCoo SVic WAbe WCom WFar WKif WMoo WPBF WRou WSHC
	- var. ***myrtifolia***	CDoC CSil CTsd EKMF
*	- var. ***prostrata***	CSil
	- var. ***pumila***	CAby CBgR CDoC CEnt CSil EWes GCal GGar GKir ITim LAst LRHS MHer MLHP SAga SCoo SHGN SIng SRot SVic WAbe
	- ***purpurea***	LRHS
	- 'Sea King'	CDoC
	- 'Sea Spray'	CDoC
	- 'Seahorse'	CDoC
§	- 'Thompsonii' ♀H3-4	CDoC CSil ECGP EKMF LPla SBch
§	- 'Versicolor' (v)	Widely available
	'Magenta Flush'	CDoC CTsd CWVF
	'Maggie Rose'	MWar SLBF
	'Magic Flute'	CLoc CWVF MJac SVic
	'Maharaja' (d)	EBak
	'Maid Marion' **new**	SLBF
	'Maik Luijten' (d) **new**	WPBF
	'Major Heaphy'	CWVF EBak EKMF MSmi WPBF
	'Making Waves' **new**	WRou
	'Malibu Mist' (d)	CWVF WPBF
	'Mama Bleuss' (d)	EBak WFuv
	'Mancunian' (d)	CTsd CWVF
I	'Mandarin' Schnabel	EBak
	'Mandi Oxtoby' (T)	LCla
	'Manfried Kleinau' (d) **new**	WPBF
	'Mantilla' (T)	CDoC CLoc CWVF EBak EKMF LCla MJac MSmi SVic
	'Maori Maid'	WPBF
	'Maori Pipes' (T)	WPBF
	'Marbled Sky'	SVic
	'Marcel Michiels' (d)	WPBF
	'Marcia'PBR (Shadowdancer Series)	LAst LSou
	'Marcus Graham' (d)	CCCN CLoc CTsd CWVF EBak EKMF MWar SCoo SVic WFuv WPBF WRou
	'Marcus Hanton' (d)	CWVF EKMF
	'Mardi Gras' (d)	CTsd EBak
	'Margaret' (d) ♀H4	CDoC CDul CLoc CSil CTri CTsd CWVF EBak EKMF EPts GKir ISea LCla MWar NDlv SEND SLBF SPet SVic WFuv
	'Margaret Bird'	LCla
	'Margaret Brown' ♀H4	CDoC CLoc CSil CTri CWVF EBak EKMF LCla LRHS SLBF SMrm SPet SRGP SVic WRou
	'Margaret Davidson' (d)	CLoc
	'Margaret Hazelwood'	EKMF
	'Margaret Jenkinson' **new**	MWar
	'Margaret Lowis'	MWar
	'Margaret Pilkington'	CTsd CWVF SVic
	'Margaret Roe'	CDoC CSil CWVF EBak EKMF MJac SPet WPBF
	'Margaret Susan'	EBak
	'Margaret Tebbit'	CCCN
	'Margarite Dawson' (d)	CSil
	'Margery Blake'	CSil EBak EKMF
	'Margrit Willimann'	WPBF
	'Maria Landy'	CWVF EKMF LCla MJac MWar WRou
	'Maria Mathilde' (d)	SLBF
	'Maria Merrills' (d)	MHav
	'Mariah' (Diva Series) **new**	MHav
	'Marie Elizabeth' (d)	WPBF
	'Marielle van Dummelen' (d)	WPBF
	'Marie-Louise Luyckx' (d)	WPBF
	'Marilyn Jane'	EKMF
	'Marilyn Olsen'	CWVF
	'Marin Belle'	EBak
	'Marin Glow' ♀H3	CLoc CWVF EBak SLBF SPet SVic WFuv
	'Marina Kelly'	WRou
	'Marinka' ♀H3	CCCN CLoc CWVF EBak EKMF EPts LAst LCla MBri MJac SLBF SPet SVic WFuv WPBF
	'Marion Hilton'	MWar
	'Mark Kirby' (d)	CWVF EBak EKMF
	'Marlea's Marlot' (d) **new**	WPBF
	'Marlea's Schouwpijpke'	WPBF
	'Marlies de Keijzer' (E)	LCla SLBF WPBF
	'Marry Perry' **new**	WRou
	'Mart'	WPBF
	'Martien A. Soeters'	WPBF
	'Martin Beije'	WPBF
	'Martina'	SLBF
	'Martin's Choice'	WPBF
	'Martin's Delight 2002' **new**	WPBF
	'Martin's Double Delicate' (d)	WPBF
	'Martin's Inspiration'	LCla MWar
	'Martin's Little Beauty'	WPBF
	'Martin's Yellow Surprise' (T)	LCla SLBF SVic
	'Martinus' (d)	WPBF
	'Marty' (d)	EBak
	'Mary' (T) ♀H1+3	CDoC CLoc CWVF EKMF EPts LCla MSmi SLBF SVic WPBF
	'Mary Jones' (d)	EKMF
	'Mary Lockyer' (d)	CLoc CTsd EBak
	'Mary Poppins'	CWVF SVic
	'Mary Reynolds' (d)	CWVF
	'Mary Shead' (d)	MWar
	'Mary Thorne'	CSil EBak EKMF
	'Mary's Beauty' (d) **new**	MSmi
	'Mary's Millennium'	CWVF
	'Masquerade' (d)	EBak SVic
	mathewsii	EKMF
	'Maud Murphy'	WPBF
	'Maureen Ward'	EKMF
	'Mauve Beauty' (d)	CSil CWVF EKMF SLBF
	'Mauve Lace' (d)	CSil
	'Mauve Wisp' (d)	SVic
	'Max Jaffa'	CSil CWVF
I	'Maxima'	EKMF EPts LCla WFuv WPBF
	'Maxima's Baby'	WPBF
	'Maxima's Girl' **new**	WPBF
	'Maybe Baby'	WPBF
	'Mayblossom' (d)	CWVF SPet
	'Mayfayre' (d)	CLoc
	'Mayfield'	CWVF
	'Mazda'	CWVF
	'Meadowlark' (d)	CTsd CWVF EBak
	'Mechtildis de Lechy'	WPBF
	'Medard's Botsaert' (d) **new**	WPBF
	'Medard's Hersinde'	WPBF
	'Medard's Koning Nobel'	WPBF
	'Medard's Krieke Putte'	WPBF
	'Medard's Reinaertsland'	WPBF
	'Medard's Tiecelijn' (d) **new**	WPBF
	'Meditation' (d)	CLoc CSil
	'Megeti'	WPBF
	'Melanie'	CDoC CTsd MHav SVic WFuv WPBF
	'Melissa Heavens'	CWVF
	'Melody'	EBak SPet SVic
	'Melody Ann' (d)	EBak
	'Melting Moments' (d)	EKMF MHav SCoo WFuv
	'Mendocino Mini' (E)	WPBF
	'Mendocino Rose'	SVic
	'Menna'	WPBF
	'Mephisto'	CSil CWVF

	Name	Suppliers
	'Mercurius'	CSil
	'Merlin'	CDoC CSil EKMF LCla
	'Merry England' (d)	WPBF
	'Merry Mary' (d)	CWVF EBak EKMF
I	'Mexicali Rose' Machado	CLoc
	'Michael' (d)	CWVF EPts
	'Michael Barker' **new**	WPBF
	'Michael Wallis' (T)	EKMF LCla SLBF WPBF
	'Michelle Wallace'	SVic
	michoacanensis misapplied	see *F. microphylla* subsp. *aprica*
	michoacanensis Sessé & Moç. (E) B&SWJ 8982	WCru
	- B&SWJ 9027	WCru
	- B&SWJ 9148	WCru
	- F&M 356	WPGP
	'Micky Goult' 🏆$^{H1+3}$	CDoC CLoc CWVF EKMF EPts LCla MJac SPet SVic WFuv WPBF WRou
	'Microchip' (E)	CSil LCla
	microphylla (E)	CBcs CBgR CBrd CDoC CElw CLoc CPLG CSil CTsd CWVF EBak ELon GCal GGar MSCN NBro NChi STre SVic WBor
	- B&SWJ 10331	WCru
§	- subsp. ***aprica*** (E)	CDoC LCla
	- - B&SWJ 9101	WCru
	- - BRE 69862	EKMF
	- 'Cornish Pixie' **new**	CDoC
§	- subsp. ***hemsleyana*** (E)	CDoC CPLG CSil EKMF LCla WOut
	- - B&SWJ 10478	WCru
§	- subsp. ***hidalgensis*** (E)	CDoC CSil EKMF LCla
	- subsp. ***microphylla*** (E)	CSil EKMF
§	- subsp. ***minimiflora***	SVic
	- subsp. ***quercetorum*** (E)	CDoC CSil EKMF LCla
	- 'Sparkle' (E/v)	WCot
	- 'Variegata' (E/v)	EWes MCCP
	'Midas'	CWVF MBri
	'Midnight' (Diva Series) **new**	MHav
	'Midnight Sun' (d)	CWVF EBak
	'Midwinter'	CWVF SVic WPBF
	'Mieke Meursing' 🏆$^{H1+3}$	CLoc CWVF EBak EKMF MJac SPet
	'Mieke Sarton'	WPBF
	'Mien Kuypers'	WPBF
	'Mien van Oirschot' (d)	WPBF
	'Miep Aalhuizen'	CDoC LCla SVic WRou
	'Mike Foxton'	EKMF
	'Mike Oxtoby' (T)	CWVF EKMF
	'Millennium'	CLoc EBak EKMF EPts MJac SCoo
	'Millie Butler'	CWVF
	'Ming'	CLoc CTsd EKMF
	'Miniature Jewels' (E)	SLBF
	minimiflora misapplied	see *F.* × *bacillaris*
	minimiflora Hemsl.	see *F. microphylla* subsp. *minimiflora*
	'Minirose'	CCCN CDoC CWVF EPts WFuv WRou
	'Minnesota' (d)	EBak
	'Mipam'	SLBF
	'Miramere' **new**	EPts
	'Mischief'	CSil SVic
	'Miss California' (d)	CDoC CLoc CWVF EBak EKMF MBri
	'Miss Debbie' (d)	WFuv
	'Miss Great Britain'	CWVF
	'Miss Lye'	CSil EKMF
	'Miss Muffett' (d)	CSil EPts
	'Miss Vallejo' (d)	CTsd EBak
	'Mission Bells'	CDoC CLoc CSil CTsd CWVF EBak EKMF EPts MHav SPet
	'Mistoque'	CTsd
	'Misty Blue' (d)	SVic
	'Misty Haze' (d)	CWVF SVic
	'Misty Pink' (d)	WPBF
	'Molenkerk' (d)	WPBF
	'Molesworth' (d)	CWVF EBak MJac SPet
	'Mollie Beaulah' (d)	EKMF
	'Money Spinner'	CLoc EBak
	'Monica Dare' (T)	WPBF
	'Monique Comperen'	WPBF
	'Monsieur Thibaut' 🏆^{H4}	CSil EKMF LRHS MGos
	'Monte Rosa' (d)	CWVF
	'Montevideo' (d)	CWVF
	'Monument' (d)	CSil
	'Mood Indigo' (d)	CTsd CWVF SVic WFuv WRou
	'Moonbeam' (d)	CLoc
	'Moonglow'	CTsd LAst MJac WFuv WPBF
	'Moonlight'	CCCN
	'Moonlight Sonata'	CLoc CWVF EBak SPet
	'Moonraker' (d)	CWVF SVic
	'More Applause' (d)	CLoc EKMF
	'Morning Light' (d)	CLoc EBak SPet SVic
	'Morning Mist'	EBak
	'Morning Star'	MBri
	'Morrells' (d)	EBak
	'Morton Martianette'	EKMF
	'Morton Splendide'	EKMF
	'Moth Blue' (d)	CWVF EBak MHav SPet
	'Mother's Day'	SVic
	'Mount Edgcumbe'	CTsd
	'Mountain Mist' (d)	CWVF EKMF SVic
	'Moyra' (d)	CWVF
	'Mr A. Huggett'	CLoc CSil CWVF EKMF EPts SLBF
	'Mr W. Rundle'	EBak SVic
§	'Mr West' (v)	EKMF LRHS LSou MCot SPet WRou
	'Mrs Churchill'	CLoc
	'Mrs John D. Fredericks'	CSil
	'Mrs Lawrence Lyon' (d)	EBak
	'Mrs Lee Belton' (E)	LCla SLBF
	'Mrs Lovell Swisher' 🏆^{H4}	CTsd CWVF EBak EKMF LCla SPet SVic WFuv
	'Mrs Marshall'	CWVF EBak SLBF SPet
	'Mrs Popple' 🏆^{H3}	Widely available
	'Mrs W. Castle'	CDoC CSil CTsd SVic
	'Mrs W.P. Wood' 🏆^{H3}	CBgR CDoC CLoc CSil CWVF EKMF ELon LRHS SVic WFuv WRou
	'Mrs W. Rundle'	CLoc CSil CTsd CWVF EBak EKMF SLBF SPet
	'Multa'	EKMF
	'Muriel' (d)	CLoc CWVF EBak EKMF
	'Murru's Pierre Marie' (d)	SLBF
	'My Dear' (d)	WPBF
	'My Delight'	CWVF
	'My Fair Lady' (d)	CLoc CWVF EBak SPet
	'My Little Cracker'	MWar WPBF
	'My Little Gem' **new**	MWar
	'My Little Star'	MWar
	'My Mum'	LCla SLBF WFuv
	'My Pat'	EKMF SLBF
	'My Reward' (d)	CWVF
	'Naaldwijk 800'	WPBF
	'Nancy Lou' (d)	CDoC CLoc CWVF LAst MJac SLBF SPet SRGP SVic WFuv WRou
	'Nanny Ed' (d)	CWVF EKMF MBri
	'Natasha Sinton' (d)	CCCN CLoc CTsd CWVF EKMF LAst MBri MJac SLBF SPet WPBF WRou
	'Native Dancer' (d)	CWVF EBak WPBF
	'Naughty Nicole' (d)	WPBF
	'Nautilus' (d)	EBak
	'Navy Blue'	CSil
	'Neapolitan' (d)	CDoC MHav SLBF
	'Nectarine'	EKMF
	'Nell Gwyn'	CLoc CWVF EBak SVic

	'Nellie Nuttall' ♀H3	CLoc CWVF EBak EKMF EPts MWar SPet SVic WFuv
	'Neon White' (Diva Series) **new**	MHav
	'Neopolitan' (E)	CLoc CSil EPts MHav SVic WPBF
	'Nettala'	CDoC SVic WPBF
	'Neue Welt'	CSil CWVF EBak EKMF
	'New Fascination' (d)	EBak
	'New Millennium'	CDoC LAst LSou
	'Niagara Falls' (d) **new**	WPBF
	'Nice 'n' Easy' (d)	MBri MJac
	'Nicki Fenwick-Raven' (E) **new**	LCla
	'Nicki's Findling'	CDoC CTsd CWVF EKMF EPts LCla MJac WFuv WRou
	'Nicky Veerman'	WPBF
	'Nicola'	EBak
	'Nicola Claire'	MHav
	'Nicola Jane' (d)	CDoC CSil CTsd CWVF EBak EKMF EPts LCla LRHS MBri MJac SHar SLBF SPet SVic WFuv WRou
	'Nicola Storey'	EKMF
	'Nicolette'	CWVF MJac
	'Nick' (d) **new**	WPBF
	'Nightingale' (d)	CLoc EBak WPBF
§	***nigricans***	CDoC EKMF
	'Nina Wills'	EBak
	'Niobe' (d)	EBak
	'Niula'	CDoC EKMF LCla
	'No Name' (d)	EBak
	'Noel van Steenberghe' (d)	WPBF
	'Nonchalance'	LCla WPBF
	'Nora' (d)	WPBF
	'Norfolk Ivor' (d)	WPBF
	'Normandy Bell'	EBak SVic
	'North Cascades' (d)	WPBF
	'Northern Dancer' (d)	EKMF
	'Northilda'	SVic
	'Northumbrian Belle'	EBak
	'Northumbrian Pipes'	LCla
	'Northway'	CLoc CWVF MJac SPet SVic
	'Norvell Gillespie' (d)	EBak
	'Novato'	CTsd EBak
	'Novella' (d)	CWVF EBak
	'Nuance'	LCla WPBF
	'Nunthorpe Gem' (d)	CDoC CSil MHav
	'O Sole Mio'	SVic
	obconica (E)	CDoC CSil EKMF LCla
	'Obcylin' (E)	CDoC EKMF LCla WRou
	'Obergärtner Koch' (T)	CDoC EKMF SLBF
	'Ocean Beach'	CDoC CTsd EPts WPBF
	'Oetnang' (d)	CTri SCoo
	'Old Somerset' (v)	CCCN CDoC CTsd LCla SVic WPBF
	'Olga Storey' **new**	CDoC
	'Olive Moon' (d)	WPBF
	'Olive Smith'	CWVF EPts LCla MJac MWar WPBF WRou
	'Olympia'	EKMF
	'Olympic Lass' (d)	EBak
	'Olympic Sunset'	SVic
	'Onward'	CSil EKMF WPBF
§	'Oosje' (E)	CDoC CSil LCla SLBF SVic WPBF WRou
	'Opalescent' (d)	CLoc CWVF SVic
	'Orange Crush'	CCCN CLoc CTsd CWVF EBak MHav MJac MWar SPet WFuv
	'Orange Crystal'	CCCN CWVF EBak EKMF MJac SVic WPBF
	'Orange Drops'	CLoc CTsd CWVF EBak EKMF EPts SVic WFuv
	'Orange Flare'	CLoc CWVF EBak MHav SLBF SVic WFuv WRou
	'Orange Heart'	LCla
	'Orange King' (d)	CLoc CWVF
	'Orange Mirage'	CLoc CTsd CWVF EBak LAst SPet SVic WFuv WPBF WRou
	'Orange Star' (E) **new**	CDoC
	'Orangeblossom'	MHav SLBF
	'Oranje van Os'	CWVF
	'Orient Express' (T)	CCCN CDoC CLoc CWVF MJac SVic WFuv WPBF
	'Oriental Flame'	EKMF
	'Oriental Sunrise'	CWVF
	'Ornamental Pearl'	CLoc CWVF EBak
	'Ortenburger Festival'	WFuv
	'Orwell' (d)	CWVF
	'Oso Sweet'	CWVF
	'Other Fellow'	CWVF EBak EKMF EPts LCla MJac SLBF SPet SVic WFuv
	'Oulton Empress' (E)	SLBF
	'Oulton Fairy' (E)	SLBF
	'Oulton Painted Lady'	WRou
	'Oulton Red Imp' (E)	LCla SLBF
	'Oulton Travellers Rest' (E)	SLBF
	'Our Boys'	WPBF
	'Our Darling'	CWVF
	'Our Debbie'	MWar
	'Our Hilary' **new**	SLBF
	'Our Nan' (d)	MJac
	'Our Pamela'	MJac
	'Our Ted' (T)	EBak EPts LCla WPBF
	'Our William'	SLBF WPBF
	'Overbecks'	see *F. magellanica* var. *molinae* 'Sharpitor'
	'Overbecks Ruby'	GBuc
	'P.J.B.' (d)	WPBF
	'Pabbe's Kirrevaalk' **new**	WPBF
	'Pabbe's Klompnoagel' **new**	WPBF
	'Pabbe's Kopstubber' (d)	WPBF
	'Pabbe's Loug' **new**	WPBF
	'Pabbe's Lutjemaid' **new**	WPBF
	'Pabbe's Premeur'	WPBF
	'Pabbe's Pronkjewail' (d) **new**	WPBF
	'Pabbe's Siepeltrien'	WPBF
	'Pabbe's Torreldöve'	WPBF
	'Pabbe's Wikwief'	WPBF
	'Pacemaker'	MGos
	'Pacific Grove' Greene	see *F.* 'Evelyn Steele Little'
	'Pacific Grove' Niederholzer (d)	EBak
	'Pacific Queen' (d)	EBak
	'Pacquesa' (d)	CDoC CTsd CWVF EBak SPet SVic
	'Padre Pio' (d)	CWVF EBak MJac
	'Pagona Fuhrmann' (d) **new**	WPBF
	'Pallas'	CSil
	pallescens	EKMF
	'Pam Plack'	CDoC CSil EKMF LCla SLBF
	'Pamela Knights' (d)	EBak
	'Pam's People'	LCla
	'Pan'	MWar WPBF
	'Pan America' (d)	EBak
	'Panache' (d)	LCla
	'Pangea' (T)	EKMF LCla WPBF
	paniculata ♀H1+3	CBot CCCN CDoC CFee CHrt CRHN CTsd CWVF EBak EKMF EPts LCla LPio MHer SLBF WCru WPBF
	'Panique'	CDoC LCla
	'Pantaloons' (d)	EBak
	'Pantomine Dame' (d)	CWVF
	'Panylla Prince'	CDoC LCla WRou
	'Papa Bleuss' (d)	CWVF EBak

'Papoose' (d)	CDoC CSil EBak EKMF LCla SEND SVic
'Papua' (d)	SLBF
'Parasol'	WPBF
'Parkstone Centenary' (d)	CWVF
'Party Frock'	CDoC CLoc CTsd CWVF EBak
'Party Time' (d)	CWVF
parviflora misapplied	see *F.* × *bacillaris*
parviflora Lindl.	see *F. lycioides* Andrews
'Pastel'	EBak
'Pat Meara'	CLoc EBak
'Pat Rogers' (d)	MWar WPBF
'Pathétique' (d)	CLoc
'Patience' (d)	CDoC CWVF EBak
'Patio King'	EBak EKMF
'Patio Princess' (d)	CCCN CLoc CWVF EPts LAst MBri WFuv WGor
'Patricia' Wood	CSil EBak EKMF MSmi
'Patricia Hodge'	MHav WRou
'Pat's Smile'	SLBF
'Patty Evans' (d)	CWVF EBak
'Patty Sue' (d)	EKMF MBri WRou
'Paul Berry' (T)	EKMF LCla WPBF
'Paul Cambon' (d)	EBak EKMF
'Paul Kennes'	EKMF WPBF
'Paul Roe' (d)	MJac
'Paul Storey'	CDoC CSil EKMF WPBF
'Paula Jane' (d)	CCCN CDoC CTsd CWVF LAst LCla LRHS MBri MJac SLBF SRGP SVic WFuv WGor WPBF WRou
'Pauline Rawlins' (d)	CLoc EBak
'Paulus'	WPBF
'Peace' (d)	EBak
'Peachy' (California Dreamers Series) (d)	CCCN CDoC CLoc EKMF LAst MJac SCoo WFuv WPBF
'Peachy Keen' (d)	EBak
'Peacock' (d)	CLoc
'Pearly Queen' (d)	WPBF
'Pee Wee Rose'	CSil EBak EKMF SVic WPBF
'Peggy Belle G' (T)	EKMF
'Peggy Burford' (T)	EKMF LCla
Peggy = 'Goetzpeg'[PBR] (Shadowdancer Series)	CDoC LAst LSou SCoo
'Peggy King'	CDoC CSil CTsd EBak EKMF SPet SVic WPBF
'Peloria' (d)	CLoc EBak
'Pennine'	MBri WFuv
'People's Princess'	MJac
'Peper Harow'	EBak
'Pepi' (d)	CLoc CWVF EBak SPet
'Peppermint Candy' (d)	CDoC CWVF EKMF MJac
'Peppermint Stick' (d)	CDoC CLoc CWVF EBak EKMF MBri MSmi SPet SVic WFuv WRou
'Perky Pink' (d)	CWVF EBak EPts SPet
'Perry Park'	CWVF EBak MBri MJac SVic
'Perry's Jumbo'	NBir NPer
perscandens	CBcs CPLG CSil EKMF LCla WGwG
'Personality' (d)	EBak
'Peter Bellerby' (d)	EKMF
'Peter Bielby' (d)	CWVF EKMF MWar
'Peter Crookes' (T)	CWVF
'Peter Grange'	EBak
'Peter James' (d)	CSil EKMF
'Peter Lemmen' (d) **new**	WPBF
'Peter Meredith' **new**	MWar
'Peter Pan'	CSil CWVF
'Peter Peeters' (d)	WPBF
petiolaris	CDoC LCla
- Berry 3142	EKMF
'Petit Four'	CWVF WPBF
'Petite' (d)	EBak
'Petra van Britsom'	SLBF
'Pfaffenhutchen' (d)	WPBF
'Phaidra'	CDoC LCla
'Pharaoh'	CLoc
'Phénoménal' (d)	CSil CWVF EBak EKMF LRHS MSmi WPBF
'Philippe'	WPBF
'Phillip Taylor'	MJac WPBF
'Phryne' (d)	CSil EBak EKMF SVic
'Phyllis' (d) ♀H4	CAgr CBgR CDoC CLoc CSil CTsd CWVF EBak EKMF ELon EPts LCla LRHS MJac SHar SLBF SPet SRGP SVic WFar WFuv WRou
'Piet G. Vergeer'	WRou
'Piet van der Sande'	CDoC LCla
'Piggelmee' **new**	WPBF
'Pinch Me' (d)	CWVF EBak MHav SPet SVic
'Pink Aurora'	CLoc
'Pink Ballet Girl' (d)	CLoc EBak SVic
'Pink Bon Accorde'	CLoc CTsd CWVF SVic WPBF
'Pink Cascade'	CTsd
'Pink Cloud'	CLoc CTsd EBak
'Pink Cornet'	LCla
'Pink Darling'	CLoc EBak
'Pink Dessert'	CTsd EBak
'Pink Domino' (d)	CSil EKMF
'Pink Fairy' (d)	EBak SPet
'Pink Fandango' (d)	CLoc
'Pink Fantasia'	CCCN CDoC CLoc CWVF EBak EKMF EPts LAst LCla MJac MWar SVic WFuv WPBF
'Pink Flamingo' (d)	CLoc EBak
'Pink Galore' (d)	CCCN CLoc CTsd CWVF EBak EKMF LAst MBri MJac SPet SVic WFuv WPBF
'Pink Goon' (d)	CDoC CSil EKMF LCla LRHS MSmi SLBF SVic
'Pink Haze'	CSil SVic
'Pink Ice' (d)	MSmi
'Pink Jade'	CWVF EBak
'Pink la Campanella'	CWVF EBak LAst MBri MWar WGor
'Pink Lace' (d)	CSil SPet
'Pink Marshmallow' (d) ♀H1+3	CCCN CDoC CLoc CWVF EBak EKMF MJac SLBF SPet SVic WFuv WPBF
'Pink Panther' (d)	EKMF SVic
'Pink Pearl' Bright (d)	CSil EBak EKMF
'Pink Poppet'	EKMF
'Pink Profusion'	EBak
'Pink Quartet' (d)	CLoc CWVF EBak MHav SPet
'Pink Rain'	CWVF EKMF MJac WFuv WPBF WRou
'Pink Slippers'	CLoc
'Pink Spangles'	CCCN CWVF MBri SVic
'Pink Surprise' (d)	CTsd
'Pink Temptation'	CLoc CWVF EBak LAst SVic
'Pinkmost' (d)	EKMF
'Pinto de Blue' (d)	EKMF MHav MSmi MWar WPBF
'Pinwheel' (d)	CLoc EBak
'Piper' (d)	CDoC CWVF
'Piper's Vale' (T)	CCCN LAst MJac SLBF
'Pippa Rolt'	EKMF
'Pirbright'	CWVF EKMF
'Pixie'	CDoC CLoc CSil CTsd CWVF EBak EKMF MHav MJac SLBF SPet SVic
'Playboy'	SVic WPBF
'Playford'	CWVF EBak
'Plenty'	CSil EBak EKMF SVic
'Plumb Bob' (d)	CWVF EKMF
'Pol Jannie' (d)	WPBF
'Pole Star'	CSil
'Pop Whitlock' (v)	CWVF EKMF MCot SPet SVic
'Poppet'	CWVF

	'Popsie Girl'	CDoC SLBF WPBF WRou
	'Port Arthur' (d)	CSil EBak
	'Postiljon'	CCCN CTsd CWVF EBak
	'Postman' **new**	CDoC
	'Powder Puff' ambig.	CWVF MBri WFuv
	'Powder Puff' Hodges (d)	CLoc SVic
I	'Powder Puff' Tabraham (d)	CSil
	'Prawn Cracker'	LAst
	'Prelude' ambig.	SVic
	'Prelude' Blackwell	CLoc CSil
I	'Prelude' Kennett (d)	EBak EKMF
	'President'	CDoC CSil EBak EKMF
	'President B.W. Rawlins'	EBak
§	'President Elliot'	CSil EKMF
	'President George Bartlett' (d)	CCCN CDoC CLoc CSil EKMF EPts LCla MJac MWar SLBF WFuv WPBF WRou
	'President Jim Muil'	SLBF WPBF
	'President Joan Morris' (d)	EKMF SLBF
	'President Leo Boullemier'	CSil CWVF EBak EKMF MJac SPet SVic WPBF
	'President Margaret Slater'	CLoc CTsd CWVF EBak LCla MHav SPet SVic WPBF
	'President Moir' (d)	SLBF WPBF
	'President Norman Hobbs'	CWVF EKMF
	'President Roosevelt' (d)	CDoC WPBF
	'President Stanley Wilson'	CWVF EBak EPts
	'President Wilf Sharp' (d)	SVic
	'Preston Guild' ♀H1+3	CDoC CLoc CSil CTsd CWVF EBak EKMF MWar NPer SDys SLBF SPet SVic WPBF WRou
	'Prickly Heat'	EKMF
	'Pride of Ipswich'	WPBF
	'Pride of Roualeyn'	WRou
	'Pride of the West'	CSil EBak EKMF
	'Pride of Windsor'	EKMF
	'Prince of Orange'	CLoc CSil CWVF EBak EKMF SVic WPBF
	'Princess Dollar'	see *F.* 'Dollar Prinzessin'
	'Princess Pamela' (d)	SLBF
	'Princessita'	CTsd CWVF EBak MHav SPet
	procumbens	CBcs CCCN CDoC CLoc CPLG CSil CTrC CWVF EBak ECou EKMF EPfP EPts EShb EWld GCal GGar IDee ITim LCla LPio MHer NWCA SLBF SWal WDyG WPBF WPtf WRou
	- 'Argentea'	see *F. procumbens* 'Wirral'
	- 'Variegata'	see *F. procumbens* 'Wirral'
§	- 'Wirral' (v)	CDoC CLoc CSil CTrC CTsd EKMF ELon EQua ITim WBor WPBF WPrP
	'Prodigy'	see *F.* 'Enfant Prodigue'
	'Profusion' ambig.	SVic
	'Prosperity' (d) ♀H3	CDoC CLoc CSil CWVF EBak EKMF EPfP EPts LCla LRHS MJac MRav NDlv SPet SVic WFuv WRou
	'Pumila'	CMac CPLG CWib EKMF ELan EPfP EPts LRHS SDix SLBF SPer SPet SVic WPBF WPat WRou
	'Purbeck Mist' (d)	CWVF EKMF
	'Purperklokje'	CSil CWVF EBak SVic WPBF
	'Purple Ann'	EKMF
	'Purple Emperor' (d)	CLoc
	'Purple Heart' (d)	CLoc EBak
	'Purple Lace'	CSil SVic
	'Purple Patch'	MBri
	'Purple Pride'	MBri
	'Purple Rain'	EKMF EPts WFuv WPBF WRou
	'Purple Splendour' (d)	CDoC CSil
	'Pussy Cat'	CLoc CWVF EBak SVic
	'Putney Pride'	EPts
	'Put's Folly'	CWVF EBak EKMF MJac SLBF SPet WFuv
	putumayensis	CSil EBak EKMF
	'Quasar' (d)	CCCN CDoC CLoc CTsd CWVF EKMF EPts LAst LCla LSou MJac SLBF SPet SVic WFuv WPBF WRou
	'Queen Elizabeth II'	EKMF
	'Queen Esther'	CTsd
	'Queen Mabs'	EBak
	'Queen Mary'	CLoc CSil EBak EKMF
	'Queen of Bath' (d)	EBak SVic
	'Queen of Derby' (d)	CSil CTsd CWVF
	'Queen of Hearts' Kennett (d)	SVic
	'Queen Victoria' Smith (d)	EKMF
	'Queen's Park' (d)	EBak
	'Query'	CSil EBak SVic
	'R.A.F.' (d)	CCCN CLoc CTsd CWVF EBak EKMF EPts MWar SLBF SPet SVic WFuv
	'Rachel Craig' (d)	MWar
	'Rachel Sinton' (d)	MBri SRGP WRou
	'Radcliffe Bedder' (d)	CSil EKMF
	'Radings Gerda' (E)	LCla SLBF
	'Radings Inge' (E)	CDoC EKMF LCla
	'Radings Karin'	CDoC EKMF
	'Radings Mapri'	WPBF
	'Radings Michelle'	CSil CWVF
	'Rahnee'	CWVF
	'Rainbow'	CWVF MSmi
	'Rakastava' (d)	WPBF
	'Ralph Oliver' (d)	WPBF
	'Ralph's Delight' (d)	CCCN CTsd CWVF EKMF WFuv
	'Ram' **new**	WPBF
	'Rambling Rose' (d)	CLoc CWVF EBak MJac
	'Rams Royal' (d)	CDoC CWVF
	'Randy Andy' **new**	EKMF
	'Raspberry' (d)	CLoc CTsd CWVF EBak SVic WFuv
	'Raspberry Punch' (d)	WFuv
	'Raspberry Ripple' (d) **new**	MWar
	'Raspberry Sweet' (d)	CWVF
	'Ratae Beauty'	CWVF
	'Ratatouille' (d)	CTsd EKMF SVic WFuv WPBF
	ravenii	CSil LCla
	'Ravensbarrow'	CSil
	'Ravenslaw'	CSil EKMF
	'Ray Redfern'	CWVF
	'Razzle Dazzle' (d)	EBak
	'Reading Show' (d)	CSil CWVF EKMF EPts
	'Rebecca Williamson' (d)	CWVF MJac WPBF
	'Rebeka Sinton'	CLoc CTsd EBak MBri
	'Red Ace' (d)	CSil WPBF
	'Red Imp' (d)	CSil
	'Red Jacket' (d)	CWVF EBak
	'Red Petticoat'	CWVF
	'Red Rain'	CWVF LCla WPBF WRou
	'Red Ribbons' (d)	EBak
	'Red Rover'	MWar WRou
	'Red Rum' (d)	SPet
	'Red Shadows' (d)	CLoc CWVF EBak
	'Red Spider'	CCCN CLoc CTsd CWVF EBak EKMF LAst MWar SCoo SPet SVic WFuv WGor WPBF
	'Red Sunlight'	WPBF
	'Red Wing'	CLoc
	'Reflexa'	see *F.* × *bacillaris* 'Reflexa'
	'Reg Gubler'	SLBF
	'Regal'	CLoc
	'Regal Robe' (d)	CDoC
	regia	CSil
	- var. ***radicans***	CSil
	- subsp. ***regia***	CDoC CSil CTsd LCla
	- - Berry 87-87	EKMF
	- subsp. ***reitzii***	CSil EQua EWes LCla

- - Berry 04-87	EKMF
- - Berry 67A-87	EKMF
- subsp. ***serrae***	CDoC CSil
- - Berry 4504	EKMF
- - Berry 49-87	EKMF
'Remember Eric'	CSil EKMF WPBF WRou
'Remember Tommy Struck' **new**	WPBF
'Remembrance' (d)	CSil EKMF EPts LCla SLBF
'Remus' (d)	SVic
'Rene Schwab'	LCla
'Requiem'	CLoc
'Reverend Doctor Brown' (d)	EBak
'Reverend Elliott'	see *F.* 'President Elliot'
'Rhapsody' ambig.	SVic
I 'Rhapsody' Blackwell (d)	CLoc
'Rhombifolia'	CSil
'Riccartonii' ♀H3	Widely available
'Richard John' (v)	SVic
'Richard John Carrington'	CSil
'Ridestar' (d)	CLoc CWVF EBak
'Rigoletto'	SVic
'Rijs 2001' (E)	CDoC EKMF MWar SLBF
'Rik Knapen' **new**	WPBF
'Ringwood Gold'	SVic
'Ringwood Market' (d)	CSil CWVF EPts MJac SCoo SPet SVic
'Riverdancer Liam' **new**	WPBF
'Robbie'	EKMF WPBF
'Robert Lutters'	SVic
'Robin Hood' (d)	CSil
'Rocket'	WPBF
'Rocket Fire' (California Dreamers Series) (d)	CWVF LAst MJac WFuv
'Roesse Auriga' (d)	WPBF
'Roesse Belinda' (d) **new**	WPBF
'Roesse Bianca' (d) **new**	WPBF
'Roesse Blacky'	CDoC EKMF WFuv WPBF
'Roesse Callisto' **new**	WPBF
'Roesse Cancer'	WPBF
'Roesse Cetus' (d)	WPBF
'Roesse Charon' **new**	WPBF
'Roesse Cressida' (d) **new**	WPBF
'Roesse Crux' (d)	WPBF
'Roesse Franklin' (d) **new**	WPBF
'Roesse Gauss' **new**	WPBF
'Roesse Hydrus' (d)	WPBF
'Roesse Indus' (d)	WPBF
'Roesse Juliet' **new**	WPBF
'Roesse Lacerta' (d)	WPBF
'Roesse Larissa' (d) **new**	WPBF
'Roesse Littrow' **new**	WPBF
'Roesse Peacock' (d)	WPBF
'Roesse Pictor' (d)	WPBF
'Roesse Piscus' (d)	WPBF
'Roesse Sextans'	WPBF
'Roger de Cooker' (T)	CLoc LCla LPio MWar WPBF
'Rohees Alioth' (d)	WPBF
'Rohees King'	WPBF
'Rohees Lava'	SLBF
'Rohees Leada' (d)	SLBF
'Rohees New Millennium' (d)	SLBF WPBF
'Rohees Nunki'	WPBF
'Rohees Tethys' (d)	SLBF
'Rolla' (d)	CWVF EBak EKMF WPBF
'Rollezenger' **new**	WPBF
'Rolt's Ruby' (d)	CSil CWVF EKMF SVic
'Roman City' (d)	CLoc SVic
'Romance' (d)	CWVF WFuv
'Romany Rose'	CLoc
'Ron Chambers Love'	MWar
'Ron Ewart'	WFuv WRou
'Ronald L. Lockerbie' (d)	CLoc CTsd CWVF EKMF SVic
'Rondo'	MJac
'Ronnie Barker' (d) **new**	MHav MJac
'Ronny Bogaert' (d) **new**	WPBF
'Ron's Ruby'	CSil EKMF
'Roos Breytenbach' (T)	CCCN CDoC EKMF LAst LCla MJac WPBF WRou
'Rooster'	EKMF
'Rosamunda'	CLoc
'Rose Aylett' (d)	EBak
'Rose Bower'	WPBF
'Rose Bradwardine' (d)	EBak
'Rose Churchill' (d)	MBri MJac
'Rose Fantasia'	CCCN CDoC CLoc CWVF EKMF EPts LAst LCla MJac MWar SLBF WFuv WPBF
'Rose Marie' (d)	CLoc
'Rose of Castile'	CDoC CLoc CSil CTsd EBak EKMF LCla MJac SVic WFuv WRou WWlt
'Rose of Castile Improved' ♀H4	CSil CWVF EBak EKMF LCla MJac SPet WPBF
'Rose of Denmark'	CCCN CLoc CSil CTsd CWVF EBak EKMF LAst MBri MJac SCoo SPet WFuv WGor WPBF
'Rose Reverie' (d)	EBak
'Rose van der Bergh'	WPBF
'Rose Winston' (d)	LAst LRHS SCoo
rosea misapplied	see *F.* 'Globosa'
rosea Ruíz & Pav.	see *F. lycioides* Andrews
'Rosebud' (d)	EBak
'Rosecroft Beauty' (d)	CSil CWVF EBak SVic
Rosella = 'Goetzrose'PBR (Shadowdancer Series)	LAst SLBF WPBF
'Roselynne' **new**	MWar
'Rosemarie Higham'	CCCN MHav MJac SCoo
'Rosemary Day'	CLoc
'Roslyn Lowe' (d)	CDoC
'Ross Lea' (d)	CSil
'Roswitha'	EKMF SLBF WPBF
'Rosy Bows'	CWVF
'Rosy Frills' (d)	CWVF MJac SVic WFuv
'Rosy Morn' (d)	CLoc EBak
'Rosy Ruffles' (d)	EKMF
'Rothbury Beauty'	CTsd
'Rough Silk'	CLoc CWVF EBak
'Roy Castle' (d)	CWVF
'Roy Walker' (d)	CLoc CWVF WFuv
'Royal Academy'	EPts WRou
'Royal and Ancient'	CWVF
'Royal Mosaic' (California Dreamers Series) (d)	CCCN CDoC CWVF MJac WFuv
'Royal Orchid'	EBak
'Royal Parade' (d)	WRou
'Royal Purple' (d)	CSil EBak EKMF MBri
'Royal Serenade' (d)	CWVF
'Royal Touch' (d)	EBak
'Royal Velvet' (d) ♀H3	CCCN CLoc CTsd CWVF EBak EKMF EPts LCla MJac MWar SLBF SPet SVic WFuv WRou
'Royal Welsh'	WRou
'Rubra Grandiflora'	CWVF EBak EKMF LCla SDys SLBF WRou
'Ruby Wedding' (d)	CWVF EKMF SLBF WPBF
'Ruddigore'	CWVF
'Ruffles' (d)	CWVF EBak
'Rufus' ♀H3-4	CDoC CLoc CSil CTsd CWVF EBak EKMF EPfP EPts LCla MJac NDlv SLBF SPet SVic WFar WFuv WRou
'Rusty' (d) **new**	WPBF
'Ruth'	CSil SVic
'Ruth Brazewell' (d)	CLoc

'Ruth King' (d)	CWVF EBak MHav
'Sabrina'	WFuv WRou
'Sailor'	EPts SVic
'Sally Bell'	CSil
'Salmon Cascade'	CTsd CWVF EBak EKMF EPts LCla MJac SLBF WFuv WRou
'Salmon Glow'	CWVF MJac SVic
'Salmon Perfection'	WPBF
'Salmon Queen'	WPBF
'Sam' (d)	WPBF
'Sam Sheppard'	SLBF
'Samantha Reynolds'	MWar
'Samba' (d)	LAst
'Samson' (d/v)	EBak
'San Diego' (d)	CTsd CWVF
'San Francisco'	EBak
'San Leandro' (d)	EBak
'San Mateo' (d)	EBak
§ ***sanctae-rosae***	CDoC CTsd EBak EKMF LCla
'Sandboy'	CWVF EBak
'Sanguinea'	CSil EKMF
'Sanrina'	CDoC EKMF
'Santa Cruz' (d)	CSil CTsd CWVF EBak EKMF MHav SLBF SVic
'Santa Lucia' (d)	CLoc EBak
'Santa Monica' (d)	EBak WPBF
'Santorini Sunset'	WPBF
'Sapphire' (d)	EBak
'Sara Helen' (d)	CLoc EBak
'Sarah Brightman' (d) **new**	MHav MJac
'Sarah Eliza' (d)	CCCN MHav MSmi SCoo WFuv
'Sarah Jane' (d)	CSil EBak SVic
'Sarah Louise'	CWVF
'Sarong' (d)	EBak
'Satellite'	CLoc CWVF EBak EKMF LAst
'Saturnus'	CBgR CSil CWVF EBak ELon LRHS MAsh SPet
'Saxondale Sue'	SVic
'Scabieuse'	CSil
scabriuscula	CDoC EKMF LCla
scandens	see *F. decussata* Ruíz & Pav.
'Scarcity'	CDoC CSil CWVF EBak EKMF SVic
'Scarlet Cascade'	EKMF
'Schiller' ambig.	EKMF WPBF
'Schlosz Bentheim'	WPBF
'Schneeball' (d)	CDoC CSil EBak EKMF SVic
'Schneewitcher'	CDoC EKMF EPts
'Schneewittchen' Hoech	CSil EKMF
'Schneewittchen' Klein	CSil EBak
'Schönbrunner Schuljubiläum' (T)	EBak
'Schone Hanaurin'	SLBF
'Schöne Wilhelmine'	see *F.* 'Die Schöne Wilhelmine'
'Scotch Heather' (d)	CWVF MSmi
'Sea Shell' (d)	CWVF EBak
'Seaforth'	EBak EKMF
'Sealand Prince'	CDoC CSil CTsd CWVF EKMF LCla SVic WPBF
'Sebastopol' (d)	CLoc EKMF
'Selma Lavrijsen'	WPBF
serratifolia Hook.	see *F. austromontana*
serratifolia Ruíz & Pav.	see *F. denticulata*
sessilifolia	EKMF
'Seventh Heaven' (d)	CCCN CLoc CTsd CWVF LAst LSou MHav MJac SCoo SVic WPBF
'Shady Blue'	CWVF
'Shangri-La' (d)	EBak
'Shania' (Diva Series) **new**	MHav
'Shanley'	CWVF SVic WPBF
'Sharon Allsop' (d)	CWVF
'Sharon Caunt' (d)	CSil EKMF
'Sharon Leslie'	WRou
'Sharonelle'	EKMF
'Sharpitor'	see *F. magellanica* var. *molinae* 'Sharpitor'
'Shauna Lindsay'	LCla
'Shawna Ree' (E)	CDoC EKMF
'Sheila Crooks' (d)	CWVF EBak MHav
'Sheila Kirby'	CWVF
'Sheila Mary' (d)	EKMF
'Sheila Steele' (d)	CWVF
'Sheila's Love'	MJac
'Sheila's Surprise' (d)	WPBF
'Shelford'	CDoC CLoc CWVF EBak EKMF EPts MJac MWar SLBF SVic WRou
'Shell Pink'	SVic
'Shelley Lyn' (d)	WPBF
'Shirley Halladay' (d)	EKMF LCla WPBF
'Shirley'[PBR] (Shadowdancer Series)	CDoC LAst LSou SCoo SLBF
'Shooting Star' (d)	EBak
'Showfire'	EBak
'Showtime' (d)	CWVF
'Shrimp Cocktail'	CLoc LRHS
'Shuna Lindsay'	WPBF
'Shy Lady' (d)	CTsd
'Siberoet' (E)	LCla SLBF
'Sierra Blue' (d)	CDoC CLoc CWVF EBak MHav
'Silver Anniversary' (d)	EKMF SVic
'Silver Dawn' (d)	EKMF MHav
'Silver Dollar'	SVic WPBF
'Silver Pink'	CSil
'Silverdale'	CDoC CSil EKMF EPts
'Simon J. Rowell'	EKMF LCla
'Simonne Bosmans' (d) **new**	WPBF
simplicicaulis	CDoC EBak EKMF LCla WPBF
'Sincerity' (d)	CLoc
'Sinton's Standard'	MBri
'Siobhan'	CWVF
'Siobhan Evans' (d)	MWar SLBF
'Sipke Arjen'	WRou
'Sir Alfred Ramsey'	CWVF EBak
'Sir David Attenborough' (d) **new**	MHav MJac
'Sir David Jason'	MJac WFuv
'Sir Ian Botham' (d) **new**	MJac
'Sir Matt Busby' (d)	CTsd EKMF EPts LAst MHav MJac MWar WPBF WRou
'Sir Steve Redgrave' (d)	MJac
'Sir Thomas Allen'	SLBF
'Siren' Baker (d)	EBak
'Sister Ann Haley'	EKMF EPts
'Sister Sister' (d)	SLBF
'Six Squadron'	EKMF
'Sjan Schilders' (d)	WPBF
'Sleedoorn' (d) **new**	WPBF
'Sleepy'	CSil CTsd EPts MHav SPet SVic WFuv WPBF
'Sleigh Bells'	CLoc CTsd CWVF EBak EKMF SPet SVic
'Small Pipes'	CWVF LCla WFuv WPBF
'Smokey Mountain' (d)	MWar SVic WFuv
'Sneezy'	CSil EPts MHav SVic WFuv WPBF
'Snow Burner' (California Dreamers Series) (d)	CCCN CDoC CLoc CWVF LAst MHav
'Snow Pearls'	WPBF
'Snow White' (d)	SVic WPBF
'Snowbird' (d)	SLBF
§ 'Snowcap' (d) ♀H3-4	CCCN CDoC CLoc CSil CTsd CWVF EBak EKMF EPts GKir LCla LRHS MAsh MBri MGos MJac MSmi MWar MWat NPer SBch SCoo SGar SLBF SPet SPoG SVic WFar WFuv WRou

'Snowdon' (d) CWVF
'Snowdrift' Colville (d) CLoc
'Snowdrift' Kennett (d) EBak
'Snowfall' CWVF
'Snowfire' (d) CLoc CWVF EKMF SCoo SVic WFuv WPBF
'Snowflake' (E) CDoC EKMF LCla SLBF WBor WRou
'Snowstorm' (d) WPBF
'So Big' (d) EKMF
'Softpink Jubelteen' WPBF
'Software' (d) WPBF
'Son of Thumb' ♀H4 CDoC CLoc CSil CTsd CWVF EKMF EPfP EPts LAst LBMP LRHS MAsh MBar MGos MJac NDlv SIng SLBF SLim SPet SVic WFar WFuv WPBF WRou
'Sonata' (d) CLoc CWVF EBak SVic
'Sophie Louise' CWVF EKMF EPts MWar WFuv WPBF WRou
'Sophie's Silver Lining' (d) MJac
'Sophie's Surprise' WPBF
'Sophisticated Lady' (d) CLoc CWVF EBak EKMF EPts SPet SVic
'Source du Loiret' EKMF
'South Gate' (d) CLoc CTsd CWVF EBak EKMF EPts LAst MBri MJac MSCN MSmi SPet SVic WPBF
'South Lakeland' CSil
'South Seas' (d) EBak SVic
'Southern Pride' SLBF
'Southlanders' EBak
'Southwell Minster' EKMF
'Space Shuttle' CLoc EKMF LCla LPio SLBF
'Sparky' (T) CLoc CWVF EPts LCla WRou
§ 'Speciosa' CDoC EBak EKMF LCla LPio WRou
'Spion Kop' (d) CCCN CDoC CTsd CWVF EBak EKMF LAst SPet WFuv WGor
§ ***splendens*** ♀H1+3 CBcs CCCN CDoC CLoc CSil EBak EKMF IDee LCla MCot MHer NPer SLBF SMrm WRou
- B&SWJ 10325 WCru
- B&SWJ 10469 WCru
- 'Karl Hartweg' CDoC
'Squadron Leader' (d) CWVF EBak EPts
'Stad Genk' (d) WPBF
'Stadt Telc' SLBF
'Stals Kevin' (T) WPBF
'Stan' WPBF
'Stanley Cash' (d) CLoc CTsd CWVF EKMF MWar SPet SVic WFuv
'Star Wars' CDoC CLoc EPts LAst MBri MJac MWar WPBF WRou
'Stardust' CDoC CWVF EBak MHav MJac
'Steeley' (d) SVic
'Steirerblut' (T) WPBF
'Stella Ann' (T) CWVF EBak EPts LCla WFuv WPBF
'Stella Marina' (d) EBak
'Stevie Doidge' (d) WPBF
'Stewart Taylor' MJac
'Storeytime' EKMF
'Straat Bali' **new** WPBF
'Straat Cumberland' **new** LCla
'Straat Fiji' LCla
'Straat Flores' **new** WPBF
'Straat Fuknoka' CDoC LCla
'Straat Futami' (e) CDoC EKMF LCla
'Straat Kobe' (T) CDoC EKMF LCla WPBF
'Straat La Plata' LCla
'Straat Magelhaen' LCla
'Straat Messina' LCla
'Straat Moji' WPBF
'Straat of Plenty' CDoC LCla SLBF
'Straat Van Diemen' LCla
'Strawberry Daiquiri' (d) WPBF
'Strawberry Delight' (d) CLoc CWVF EBak EKMF MHav MJac SPet SVic WFuv
'Strawberry Fizz' (d) MHav
'Strawberry Sundae' (d) CLoc CWVF EBak
'Strawberry Supreme' (d) CSil EKMF
'String of Pearls' CLoc CWVF EKMF MJac SLBF SPet SVic
'Stuart Joe' CWVF EKMF
* ***subparamosis*** Green 1006 EKMF
'Sue' CTsd SLBF
'Sugar Almond' (d) CWVF
'Sugar Blues' (d) EBak
'Summerdaffodil' WPBF
(Sunbeam Series) 'Sunbeam Ernie' WPBF
- 'Sunbeam Hillary' WPBF
'Sunkissed' (d) EBak
'Sunlight Path' WPBF
'Sunningdale' (T) CWVF LCla
'Sunny Jim' SVic
'Sunny Smiles' CSil CWVF EKMF SPet
'Sunray' (v) CChe CDoC CLoc COlW CWVF EBak EKMF GGar LBuc MAsh MGos MWar MWat NEgg NPri SBch SCoo SLim SMrm SPoG WPBF
'Sunset' CLoc CWVF EBak SPer
'Sunset Boulevard' (d) WPBF
'Supersport' (d) SVic
'Superstar' CWVF EPts SVic
'Susan Drew' SLBF
'Susan Ford' (d) CWVF SPet
'Susan Green' CSil CWVF EBak EKMF MJac MWar
'Susan McMaster' CLoc
'Susan Olcese' (d) CWVF EBak
'Susan Skeen' WPBF WRou
'Susan Travis' CLoc CSil CWVF EBak EKMF MAsh SVic
'Susanna D. Dijkman' WPBF
'Suzanna' WPBF
'Swanley Gem' ♀H3 CLoc CWVF EBak EKMF SLBF SPet SVic
'Swanley Pendula' CLoc MHav
'Swanley Yellow' CWVF EBak EKMF SVic
'Sweet Leilani' (d) CLoc EBak
'Sweet Sixteen' (d) CLoc
I 'Sweetheart' van Wieringen EBak
'Swingtime' (d) ♀H3 CCCN CLoc CTsd CWVF EBak EKMF EPts LAst LCla MGos MJac MWar SLBF SPet SVic WFuv WPBF
'S'Wonderful' (d) CLoc EBak
sylvatica misapplied see *F. nigricans*
sylvatica Benth. CDoC
'Sylvia Barker' CWVF LCla MWar WFuv WPBF WRou
'Sylvia Rose' (d) CWVF
'Sylvia's Choice' EBak
'Symphony' CLoc CWVF EBak
'T.C. Grootenboer Droger' **new** WPBF
'T. Heivrouwke' (d) WPBF
'T.S.J.' (E) LCla
'Taco' CDoC LCla
'Taddle' CWVF SLBF
'Taffeta Bow' (d) CLoc SVic
'Taffy' EBak
'Tam O'Shanter' (d) CTsd WFuv
'Tamara Balyasnikova' (d) **new** WPBF
'Tamerus Hop' (d) WPBF

'Tamerus Nandoe' WPBF
'Tamerus Toerako' WPBF
'Tamworth' CLoc CTsd CWVF EBak MJac SVic
'Tangerine' CLoc CWVF EBak MHav SVic WRou
'Tango' **new** LAst
'Tanja's Blue Bells' (d) WPBF
'Tantalising Tracy' (d) WPBF
'Tanya' CLoc EKMF SPet
'Tanya Bridger' (d) EBak
'Tarra Valley' LCla SVic WPBF
'Task Force' CWVF SVic
'Tausendschön' (d) CLoc
'Ted Perry' (d) CWVF
'Ted's Tribute' EKMF WPBF
'Television' (d) CTsd
'Temptation' ambig. CTsd CWVF SPet
'Temptation' Peterson CLoc EBak
'Tennessee Waltz' (d) ♀H3 CDoC CLoc CSil CTsd CWVF EBak EKMF EPts LRHS MWar SLBF SPet SVic WFuv WRou
'Tequila Sunrise' WPBF
'Tessa Jane' CSil
tetradactyla misapplied see *F.* × *bacillaris*
tetradactyla Lindl. see *F. encliandra* subsp. *tetradactyla*
'Texas Longhorn' (d) CLoc CWVF EBak EKMF MSmi SVic WPBF
'Thalia' (T) ♀H1+3 Widely available
'Thamar' CDoC CLoc CWVF EKMF EPts SVic WPBF WRou
'That's It' (d) EBak SVic WPBF
'The Aristocrat' (d) CLoc EBak
'The Boys' WPBF
§ 'The Doctor' CLoc CSil CWVF EBak
'The Jester' (d) EBak
'The Madame' (d) CTsd CWVF EBak
'The Tarns' CSil CWVF EBak EKMF SVic
'Thelma Vint' **new** CDoC WPBF
'Therese Dupois' CSil
'Théroigne de Méricourt' EBak EKMF
'Thilco' CDoC CSil EKMF
'Think Pink' CTsd
'Thistle Hill' (d) CSil EKMF
'Thomas' (d) EPts
'Thomas Berge' **new** WPBF
'Thomas Pips' WPBF
'Thompsonii' see *F. magellanica* 'Thompsonii'
'Thornley's Hardy' CSil EKMF MRav SPet SVic WPBF
'Three Cheers' CLoc EBak
'Three Counties' EBak
'Thumbelina' WPBF
'Thunderbird' (d) CLoc CWVF EBak
thymifolia (E) CWVF GCra GQui LRHS MHer SHGN WBor WKif
- subsp. ***minimiflora*** (E) CSil EKMF LCla
- subsp. ***thymifolia*** (E) CDoC CSil EKMF LCla
'Tiara' (d) EBak
'Tickled Pink' MWar WRou
'Tiffany' Reedstrom (d) EBak
tillettiana EKMF
'Tillingbourne' (d) CSil SLBF
Tilly = 'Goetztil'PBR (Shadowdancer Series) LAst
'Time After Time' WRou
'Timlin Brened' (T) CWVF EBak WPBF
'Timothy Titus' (T) LCla SLBF
'Ting-a-ling' CLoc CTsd CWVF EBak EKMF SLBF SPet SVic WFuv WPBF
'Tinker Bell' ambig. WPBF
'Tinker Bell' Hodges EBak SVic WPBF
I 'Tinker Bell' Tabraham CSil EKMF
'Tintern Abbey' CWVF
'Tiny Whisper' WPBF
'Tinytobes' **new** EKMF
'Titania' WPBF
'Tjinegara' CDoC LCla
'Toby Bridger' (d) CLoc EBak
'Toby Foreman' SLBF
'Tolling Bell' CTsd CWVF EBak EKMF SPet WPBF WRou
'Tom Goedeman' LCla
'Tom H. Oliver' (d) EBak
'Tom Knights' EBak SPet
'Tom Thorne' EBak
'Tom Thumb' ♀H3 Widely available
'Tom West' misapplied see *F.* 'Mr West'
'Tom West' Meillez (v) CDoC CHEx CLoc CMHG CSBt CSil CWVF CWib EBak EHoe EKMF EPts LAst LCla LHop MAsh MHer MJac MSCN MWar NVic SAga SBch SDix SLBF WFar WFuv WPBF
'Tom Woods' CWVF
'Tommy Struck' (d) WPBF
'Ton Ten Hove' LCla
'Tony's Treat' (d) EPts
'Toon's Tuinklokje' WPBF
'Toos' SVic
'Topaz' (d) CLoc EBak
'Topper' (d) CWVF
'Torch' (d) CLoc CWVF EBak SVic
'Torchlight' CWVF EPts LCla WFuv WRou
'Torvill and Dean' (d) CCCN CLoc CTsd CWVF EKMF EPts LAst MJac SPet WFuv WGor WRou
'Tosca' CWVF
'Town Crier' SLBF
'Tracid' (d) CLoc CSil
'Tracie Ann' (d) EKMF
'Trail Blazer' (d) CLoc CWVF EBak MJac SPet
'Trailing King' WPBF
'Trailing Queen' EBak EKMF MJac
'Transport Command' EKMF
'Trase' (d) CDoC CSil CTsd CWVF CWib EBak EKMF MHav SVic WPBF
'Traudchen Bonstedt' (T) CDoC CLoc CWVF EBak EKMF LCla SLBF SPet SVic WPBF
'Traviata' see *F.* 'La Traviata' Blackwell
'Treasure' (d) EBak
'Tresco' CSil
'Treslong' WPBF
'Tric Trac' WPBF
'Tricolor' see *F. magellanica* var. *gracilis* 'Tricolor'
'Trientje' LCla SLBF
'Trimley Bells' EBak
'Trio' (d) CLoc
triphylla (T) EBak LRHS MHer
'Tripi' EKMF
'Trish's Triumph' EPts
'Tristesse' (d) CLoc CWVF EBak
'Troika' (d) EBak EKMF
'Troon' CWVF
'Tropic Sunset' (d) CTsd MBri WPBF
'Tropicana' (d) CLoc CWVF EBak SVic WPBF
'Troubador' Waltz (d) CLoc
'Troutbeck' CSil
'Trudi Davro' CCCN LAst MJac SCoo
'Trudy' CSil CWVF EBak EKMF SVic
'Truly Treena' (d) SLBF
'Trumpeter' ambig. CDoC CWVF WFuv
'Trumpeter' Fry SVic
'Trumpeter' Reiter (T) CLoc EBak EKMF EPts LCla MJac MSmi
'Tsjiep' CDoC WPBF

'Tubular Bells' (T) EKMF LCla
'Tuonela' (d) CLoc CWVF EBak WPBF
'Turandot' WPBF
'Turkish Delight' MWar WRou
'Tutti-frutti' (d) CLoc
'T'Vöske' (d/v) WPBF
'Twinkling Stars' CWVF MJac SVic
'Twinny' CWVF EKMF EPts MWar
'Twirling Square Dancer' (d) WPBF
'Twist of Fate' (d) CSil EKMF
'Two Tiers' (d) CSil CWVF EKMF WPBF
'U.F.O.' CTsd CWVF SVic
'Ullswater' (d) CWVF EBak
'Ultramar' (d) EBak
'Uncle Charley' (d) CDoC CLoc CSil EBak EKMF MSmi SVic
'Uncle Jinks' SPet
'Uncle Steve' (d) CTsd EBak SVic
'University of Liverpool' CLoc MJac WPBF
'Upward Look' EBak EKMF
'Valda May' (d) CWVF
'Valentine' (d) EBak
'Valerie' WFuv
'Valerie Ann' (d) EBak EKMF SPet SVic
'Valiant' EBak
'Van Eijk Bello' (a) WPBF
'Van Eijk Sheltie' (d) WPBF
'Vanessa Jackson' CLoc CWVF MHav MJac SVic
'Vanity Fair' (d) CLoc EBak
'Variegated Brenda White' (v) EKMF
'Variegated Lottie Hobby' (E/v) CSil CTsd EKMF WPBF
'Variegated Pink Fantasia' (v) WFuv
'Variegated Pink Fascination' WRou
'Variegated Pixie' CSil EKMF
'Variegated Procumbens' see *F. procumbens* 'Wirral'
'Variegated Superstar' (v) MBri
'Variegated Swingtime' (v) EBak LAst
'Variegated Vivienne Thompson' (d/v) MBri
'Variegated Waveney Sunrise' (v) MBri
'Variegated White Joy' (v) EKMF
'Veenlust' CCCN EBak WPBF WRou
'Vendeta' CDoC EKMF LCla
'Venus Victrix' CSil EBak EKMF WPBF
venusta CDoC CTsd EBak EKMF LCla
'Vermeulen Rani' **new** WPBF
'Versicolor' see *F. magellanica* 'Versicolor'
'Vesuvio' EKMF
'Vicky' EKMF
'Victorian' (d) SVic
'Victory' Reiter (d) EBak
'Vielliebchen' CDoC CSil WPBF
'Vienna Waltz' (d) WFuv
'Vincent van Gogh' WPBF
'Vintage Dovercourt' LCla
'Violet Bassett-Burr' (d) CLoc EBak
'Violet Gem' (d) CLoc
'Violet Lace' (d) CSil
'Violet Rosette' (d) CTsd CWVF EBak SVic
Violetta = 'Goetzviol'PBR (Shadowdancer Series) CDoC LAst LSou SCoo SVil WPBF
'Viva Ireland' EBak
'Vivien Colville' CLoc EKMF
'Vlasberg 39' (d) **new** WPBF
'Vobeglo' CWVF
'Vogue' (d) EBak
'Voltaire' CSil EBak EKMF
'Voodoo' (d) CCCN CDoC CLoc CWVF EBak EKMF EPts LAst SCoo SLBF SVic WPBF WRou
'Vrens Louisa' **new** WPBF
vulcanica CDoC EKMF LCla WPBF
* - subsp. ***hitchcockii*** EKMF
'Vuurwerk' WPBF
'Vyvian Miller' CWVF
'W. Grootenboer' (d) **new** WPBF
'W.P. Wood' CDoC CSil
'Waanrode Bloemendorp' **new** WPBF
'Wagtails White Pixie' CSil EBak EPfP
'Waldfee' (E) CCVN CDoC CSil EKMF LCla WPBF
'Waldis Alina' WRou
'Waldis Geisha' (d) SLBF
'Waldis Junella' (d) SLBF
'Waldis Maja' WPBF
'Waldis Marion' **new** WPBF
'Waldis Ovambo' SLBF
'Waldis Simon' WPBF
'Waldis Spezi' CDoC LCla
'Waldis Speziella' SLBF
'Wally Yendell' (v) WPBF
'Walsingham' (d) CWVF EBak WPBF
'Walton Jewel' EBak
'Waltz Harp' MHav
'Walz Banjo' WPBF
'Walz Bella' LCla WFuv WPBF
'Walz Blauwkous' (d) CWVF
'Walz Cello' WPBF
'Walz Cocktail' WPBF
'Walz Dreumes' **new** WPBF
'Walz Epicurist' WPBF
'Walz Fanclub' LCla WPBF
'Walz Fluit' CCCN MJac WPBF WRou
'Walz Fonola' WPBF
'Walz Freule' CWVF EKMF MJac
'Walz Harp' CWVF SVic WPBF
'Walz Hoorn' WPBF
'Walz Jubelteen' CAlb CDoC CLoc CTsd CWVF EKMF ELon EPts LCla MJac MWar SLBF SVic WFuv WPBF WRou
'Walz Kattesnoor' WPBF
'Walz Klarinet' WPBF
'Walz Klokkenspel' WFuv
'Walz Lucifer' CWVF LCla MWar WPBF
'Walz Mandoline' (d) CWVF SVic
'Walz Orgelpijp' WPBF
'Walz Panfluit' LCla WPBF
'Walz Polka' LCla SLBF
'Walz Ratel' WPBF
'Walz Saxofoon' WPBF
'Walz Sitar' WPBF
'Walz Spinet' WPBF
'Walz Triangel' (d) EKMF SVic WPBF
'Walz Trombone' WPBF
'Walz Trompet' **new** WPBF
'Walz Tuba' WPBF
'Walz Viool' WPBF
'Walz Waterval' WPBF
'Walz Wipneus' WPBF
'Walz Xylofoon' **new** WPBF
'Wapenveld's Bloei' CDoC EKMF LCla SLBF
'War Paint' (d) CLoc CTsd EBak
'Warke' (d) WPBF
'Warton Crag' CWVF SVic
'Water Nymph' CLoc SLBF SVic WPBF
'Wattenpost' **new** SLBF
'Wave of Life' CWVF EKMF

'Waveney Gem'	CDoC CWVF EBak EKMF LCla MJac MWar SLBF SPet WFuv WPBF
'Waveney Queen'	CWVF SVic
'Waveney Sunrise'	CTsd CWVF MHav MJac MWar SPet SVic
'Waveney Unique'	CWVF
'Waveney Valley'	CWVF EBak MJac
'Waveney Waltz'	CWVF EBak
'Waxen Beauty'	WPBF
'Wedding Bells' ambig.	SVic WFuv
'Welsh Dragon' (d)	CLoc CWVF EBak EKMF
'Wendy' Catt	see *F.* 'Snowcap'
'Wendy Atkinson' (d)	EKMF
'Wendy Hebdon' **new**	EKMF
'Wendy Leedham' (d)	EKMF
'Wendy van Wanten'	WPBF
'Wendy's Beauty' (d)	CCCN CLoc EBak EPts MHav MJac WFuv WRou
'Wentworth'	CWVF SVic WPBF
'Wessex Belle' (d/v)	CWVF
'Wessex Hardy'	CSil EKMF
'Westham'	LCla
'Westminster Chimes' (d)	CLoc CWVF SPet SVic
'Wharfedale' ♀H3	CSil ELon MJac SLBF SVic
'Whickham Blue'	CWVF MWar
'Whirlaway' (d)	CLoc CWVF EBak SVic
'White Ann'	see *F.* 'Heidi Weiss'
'White Clove'	CDoC CSil MHav SVic WPBF
'White Fairy'	WPBF
'White Galore' (d)	CWVF EBak EKMF SVic
'White Général Monk' (d)	CDoC CSil MHav
'White Gold' (v)	EBak
'White Haven'	SVic
'White Heidi Ann' (d)	CSil CTsd
'White Joy'	EBak EKMF
'White King' (d)	CLoc CTsd CWVF EBak EKMF SPet SVic WFuv WRou
'White Lace'	CSil
'White Pixie' ♀H3-4	CDoC CSil EKMF EPts MHav MJac SLBF SPer SPet SVic
'White Queen' ambig.	CWVF
'White Queen' Doyle	EBak
'White Spider'	CLoc CWVF EBak SVic
'White Veil' (d)	CWVF
'Whitehill Sensation' (d) **new**	MHav
'Whiteknights Amethyst'	CDoC CSil EKMF
'Whiteknights Blush'	CChe CDoC CMdw CPLG CSil EWes GCal GGar GQui SMrm WPBF
'Whiteknights Cheeky' (T)	CWVF EBak EPts LCla SVic
'Whiteknights Green Glister'	CDoC CSil EKMF EPfP
'Whiteknights Pearl' ♀H1+3	CDoC CSil CTsd CWVF ECha EKMF EPfP EPts LCla LRHS SEND SLBF SPet SVic WFuv WPBF
'Whiteknights Ruby' (T)	LCla
'Whitney'	LAst
'Whitney' (Diva Series) **new**	MHav
'Whitton Starburst'	CDoC LCla
'Wicked Queen' (d)	CSil LRHS SVic WPBF
'Widow Twanky' (d)	CWVF WPBF
'Wiebke Becker'	EKMF
'Wigan Pier' (d)	LCla SLBF WPBF WRou
'Wight Magic' (d)	MJac WFuv
'Wild and Beautiful' (d)	CTsd CWVF EKMF SVic
'Wilf Langton'	MWar WPBF WRou
'Wilhelmina Schwab'	CDoC LCla
'Willeke Smit' (d)	WPBF
'William Caunt'	EKMF
'Willie Tamerus'	WPBF
'Willy Winky'	CSil
'Wilma van Druten'	CDoC EKMF LCla
'Wilma Versloot'	WPBF
'Wilson's Colours'	EPts
'Wilson's Joy'	MJac
'Wilson's Pearls' (d)	CWVF SLBF SPet
'Wilson's Sugar Pink'	EPts LCla MJac
'Win Oxtoby' (d)	CWVF EKMF
'Windhapper'	LCla WFuv WPBF
'Windmill'	CWVF
'Wine and Roses' (d)	EBak
'Wingrove's Mammoth' (d)	SVic
'Wings of Song' (d)	CWVF EBak
'Winston Churchill' (d) ♀H3	CCCN CLoc CTsd CWVF EBak EKMF LAst MBri MJac MWar SBch SCoo SPet SPlb SVic WFuv WPBF
'Winter Yellow'	WPBF
'Winter's Touch'	EKMF WPBF
'Witchipoo'	SLBF
'Witte Van Munster' **new**	WPBF
'Woodnook' (d)	CWVF
'Woodside' (d)	CSil SVic
'Wor Geordie' **new**	MWar
wurdackii	EKMF
'Xmas Tree'	WPBF
'Yellow Heart'	WPBF
'Ymkje'	EBak
'Yolanda Franck'	CDoC LAst WRou
'York Manor'	WRou
'Youth'	EKMF
'Yvonne Schwab'	CDoC LCla
'Zeebrook'	SVic
'Zellertal'	WPBF
'Zeta'	WPBF
'Zets Bravo'	CDoC CTsd
'Ziegfield Girl' (d)	EBak SVic
'Zifi'	SLBF
'Zulu King'	CDoC CSil SVic
'Zulu Queen'	SVic
'Zus Liebregts' (d) **new**	WPBF
'Zwarte Dit'	WPBF
'Zwarte Snor' (d)	CWVF WPBF

Fumaria (*Papaveraceae*)

lutea	see *Corydalis lutea*
officinalis	CArn

Furcraea (*Agavaceae*)

bedinghausii	see *F. parmentieri*
§ ***foetida***	CCCN SBig
§ - var. ***mediopicta*** (v)	SBig
- 'Variegata'	see *F. foetida* var. *mediopicta*
gigantea	see *F. foetida*
longaeva misapplied	see *F. parmentieri*
longaeva ambig.	CAbb CDTJ CFir CHEx CPen CTrC CTsd EAmu EBee GGar LEdu SAPC SArc SBst SChr SDix SPlb WCot WPGP
§ ***parmentieri***	CBct CCCN CHll CMdw EAmu EBee LEdu MAga WPGP
- NJM 05.081	WPGP
selloa	MAga
- var. ***marginata*** (v)	CDoC CHEx EAmu MAga

G

Gagea (*Liliaceae*)

lutea	EPot
pratensis	EPot

Gahnia (*Cyperaceae*)

sieberiana	SPlb

Gaillardia (*Asteraceae*)

aristata Pursch	EBee
– 'Granada' **new**	LRHS
– 'Maxima Aurea'	EBee EBla EPfP LAst LRHS NBre NPri NVic SPhx WCAu
'Arizona Sun'	EBee ECtt LSou MHer NPri
'Bijou'	EBee LRHS MBri NBre NVic SWvt
'Dakota Reveille' **new**	EBee
'Dwarf Goblin'	LAst NGBl SPet
§ 'Fackelschein'	EBee NBre SRms
'Fanfare'PBR	CMac EBee ECtt ELon ENor LBuc LHop LRHS LSou MGos MMHG MWea SCoo SPer SPoG
Goblin	see *G.* × *grandiflora* 'Kobold'
× ***grandiflora*** 'Amber Wheels'	COlW CSam EBee LBMP LLHF LRHS NGdn NPri SBch
– 'Bremen'	EBee WWEG
– 'Burgunder'	Widely available
– 'Dazzler' ♀H4	CMac CSBt EAEE EBee EBla ECtt ELan EPfP LAst LBMP LRHS NLar NPri NVic SMrm SPer SPoG WCAu WPer WWEG
§ – 'Kobold'	CBcs CMac COlW CSBt EBee EBla ECtt ELon EPfP GJos GKir GMaP LAst LBMP LHop LRHS MBri MWat NBre NEgg NPri SMrm SPad SPer SPlb SPoG SRms SWvt WWEG
– Monarch Group	WSpi
– 'Summer's Kiss'	EBee
– 'Tokajer'	EBee EPfP LBMP LRHS NBre NLar SMrm SPhx
'Mandarin'	SRms
'Marmalade and Butter' **new**	LRHS
* new giant hybrids	WFar
§ 'Oranges and Lemons'PBR	EBee ECtt EGxp EWll LHop LRHS LSou MBri MWea SHar SPoG SUsu
Saint ClementsPBR	see *G.* 'Oranges and Lemons'
Torchlight	see *G.* 'Fackelschein'

Galactites (*Asteraceae*)

tomentosa	CSpe EBee EHrv ELan EPfP EPyc EWTr LDai MWea NBur SBHP SDnm SGar SPav WEas
– white-flowered	EGoo NBur

Galanthus ✿ (*Amaryllidaceae*)

× ***allenii***	CBro WIvy
alpinus	CLAP ECho
– var. ***alpinus***	ECho MTho NMen
angustifolius	CBro WCot
'Annette'	ECho LAma
'Armine'	CAvo CElw
'Atkinsii' ♀H4	Widely available
'Barbara's Double' (d)	CLAP LRHS
'Benhall Beauty'	CAvo MHom WTin
'Bertram Anderson'	MAsh
'Bill Bishop' **new**	CDes ECha
'Brenda Troyle'	CBro CElw CLAP ECha EHrv ELon EPot GEdr IGor LRHS MAsh MHom NCot NMyG NPol WCot WFar WIvy WPnP
byzantinus	see *G. plicatus* subsp. *byzantinus*
caucasicus misapplied	see *G. elwesii* var. *monostictus*
caucasicus ambig.	ECho IFoB
– 'Comet'	see *G. elwesii* 'Comet'
– var. ***hiemalis*** Stern	see *G. elwesii* var. *monostictus* Hiemalis Group
– 'Mrs McNamara'	see *G. elwesii* 'Mrs McNamara'
cilicicus	EBrs WCot
'Clare Blakeway-Phillips'	CLAP
'Colesborne'	EHrv
corcyrensis spring-flowering	see *G. reginae-olgae* subsp. *vernalis*
– winter-flowering	see *G. reginae-olgae* subsp. *reginae-olgae* Winter-flowering Group
'Cordelia' (d)	CLAP IFoB LRHS MAvo
'Cowhouse Green'	EHrv
'Curly'	CDes
'Desdemona' (d)	CBro CLAP EPot LRHS WCot WIvy
'Dionysus' (d)	CBgR CBro CLAP CPLG ECha EHrv EPot ERos GEdr LRHS MHom NBir NMyG WBrk WTin
'Drummond's Giant' **new**	IFoB
§ ***elwesii*** ♀H4	CBro CTri EBrs ECho ELan EPfP EPot ERCP ERos EWTr IFoB IGor IHer ITim LAma LRHS MAsh MWat NBir NPol SRms WCot WHoo WPnP WShi
– 'Cedric's Prolific'	ECha
§ – 'Comet'	CElw ECho ELon LRHS MAsh NCot
– 'David Shackleton'	EHrv
– Edward Whittall Group	CLAP
– var. ***elwesii*** 'Magnus'	CLAP NBir
– – 'Maidwell L'	CAvo CBro EHrv MAsh
* – 'Flore Pleno' (d)	EBrs
– (Hiemalis Group) 'Barnes'	EHrv
– 'J. Haydn'	ECho IHer LAma NMyG WWst
– 'Kyre Park'	LRHS
– 'Long 'drop' **new**	IFoB
§ – var. ***monostictus*** ♀H4	CAvo EBrs ECho EHrv LRHS MAsh WBrk WFar WIvy
– – 'G. Handel'	ECho IHer LAma NMyG WWst
* – – 'Green Tips'	NPol
– – 'H. Purcell'	CElw ECho IHer LAma WWst
§ – – Hiemalis Group	CBro ECha EHrv EPot LRHS WCot WWst
– – late-flowering **new**	LRHS
– – 'Warwickshire Gemini'	CDes MAvo
§ – 'Mrs McNamara'	IFoB
– 'Sickle'	CDes
– 'Zwanenburg'	LRHS
'F63' **new**	IFoB
'Faringdon Double' (d)	EHrv
fosteri	CBro EBrs ECho EHrv SCnR
'G71' (d) **new**	IFoB
'Galatea'	CLAP ECha EHrv LRHS MAsh MHom WIvy
'Gill Gregory'	MNrw
'Ginns'	CDes CLAP
§ ***gracilis***	CAvo CBgR CBro CLAP CPLG ERos LRHS MTho NPol
– 'Highdown'	CAvo CElw CLAP MHom
– 'Vic Horton'	WThu
graecus misapplied	see *G. gracilis*
graecus Orph. ex Boiss.	see *G. elwesii*
'Grande Juge' **new**	IFoB
Greatorex double (d)	CLAP
'Greenfields'	CStu LRHS
'Heffalump' (d)	LRHS
'Hill Poë' (d)	CBro CDes CElw CLAP EPot IFoB IGor NMyG
'Hippolyta' (d)	CAvo CBro CElw CLAP ECha ECho EHrv ELon EPot GEdr LAma LRHS MAsh NMyG SMrm WCot WFar WIvy
× ***hybridus*** 'Merlin'	CElw IFoB IGor LRHS MAsh MHom NCot WCot WIvy
– 'Robin Hood'	CDes CFee CLAP EHrv ERos WFar
§ ***ikariae*** Bak.	CElw ECho EPfP EPot ERos IGor LRHS WFar WHoo
– subsp. ***ikariae*** Butt's form	NPol

	- Latifolius Group	see *G. platyphyllus*
	- subsp. ***snogerupii***	see *G. ikariae* Bak.
	'Imbolc'	CAvo
	'Jacquenetta' (d)	CBro CDes CElw CFee CLAP CStu EHrv IFoB ITim MHom WPGP WTin
	'James Backhouse'	ECha WHoo
	'John Gray'	CBro IFoB LRHS MAsh
	'Ketton'	CBro CElw LRHS MAsh NRya WIvy
	'Kingston Double' (d)	CBgR CLAP
	'Lady Beatrix Stanley' (d)	CAvo CBro CElw CLAP ECha EHrv EPot ERos GEdr LLWP LRHS MAsh MTho NMyG WFar
	lagodechianus	EBrs ECho MPhe
	latifolius Rupr.	see *G. platyphyllus*
	'Lavinia' (d)	CAvo CElw CFee CLAP WFar
	'Lerinda'	EHrv
	'Limetree'	CBgR CElw CLAP EHrv NPol
	'Little John'	EHrv WBrk
	'Longstowe' **new**	LRHS
	lutescens	see *G. nivalis* Sandersii Group
	'Lyn'	EHrv NBir
	'Magnet' ♀H4	CAvo CBgR CBro CElw CFFs CFee CLAP ECha ECho ELon EPot GEdr IGor LAma LRHS MAsh MHom NBir NMyG NPol WBrk WCot WFar WHoo WPGP WWst
	'Mighty Atom'	CDes CFee CLAP EHrv WBrk
	'Moccas'	CBgR CElw
	'Modern Art'	IFoB
	'Mrs Backhouse No 12'	EHrv
	'Mrs Thompson'	ECha EHrv LRHS WIvy
	nivalis ♀H4	Widely available
	- from Slovenia	LRHS
	- 'Anglesey Abbey'	CAvo IFoB LRHS
	- 'April Fool'	MHom
	- 'Bitton'	CBro CLAP NPol
	- 'Chedworth'	CAvo CElw WBrk
	- dwarf	GAbr
	- 'Greenish'	CDes
	- subsp. ***imperati***	CPLG
	- 'Lutescens'	see *G. nivalis* Sandersii Group
	- 'Maximus'	WShi
	- f. ***pleniflorus*** (d)	ECha GKev MAsh WAbe
	- - 'Blewbury Tart' (d)	CAvo CLAP WBrk
	- - 'Flore Pleno' (d) ♀H4	CBro CPLG CStu CTri CWCL EBrs EPfP EPla EPot ERCP IFoB LAma LHop LLWP LRHS NCot NRya SEND SMrm SPer SRms WBrk WCot WFar WHoo WPnP WShi
	- - 'Hambutt's Orchard' (d)	CFee
	- - 'Lady Elphinstone' (d)	CAvo CBgR CBro CDes CFee CLAP CRow CWCL EHrv LRHS MAsh MTho NRya WIvy
	- - 'Pusey Green Tip' (d)	CAvo CBro CElw CLAP EPot GEdr LRHS MHom NMyG WCot WPGP WTin
	- - 'Walrus' (d)	LRHS
	- Poculiformis Group	CLAP LRHS MAsh
§	- Sandersii Group	CDes IFoB
§	- Scharlockii Group	CAvo CBgR CBro CElw EBrs IGor LRHS NCot WBrk
	- 'Tiny'	MHom NBir
	- 'Tiny Tim'	EBrs ITim NRya
	- 'Virescens'	CLAP IFoB
	- 'Viridapice'	CAvo CBgR CBro CElw CPLG EBrs ECha ECho EPot ERCP GEdr IFoB LAma LRHS MAsh MWat NBir NMen NPol WFar WHoo WPGP WShi WTin
	'Nothing Special'	LRHS
	'Ophelia' (d)	CAvo CBro EPot IGor LRHS MHom WBrk WFar WHoo
	'Orion' **new**	CDes
	peshmenii	EBrs ECho EPot SCnR
	- Hoa 0201	WWst
§	***platyphyllus***	CPLG EBrs NHol
	plicatus ♀H4	CAvo CElw CFee ECho EHrv EPot GEdr LRHS MCot MHom NMen WBrk WFar WHoo WShi WTin
	- 'Augustus'	CAvo CDes CElw CFee EHrv ELon ERos IFoB LRHS MAvo MHom WBrk WFar WIvy
	- 'Baxendale's Late'	CAvo CLAP
	- 'Bolu Shades' **new**	WWst
	- 'Bowles's Large'	CElw
§	- subsp. ***byzantinus***	CBro ERos WThu
	- - 'Ron Ginns'	LRHS
	- 'Edinburgh Ketton'	EHrv
	- 'Florence Baker'	EHrv
	- large-flowered	NPol
	- late flowering **new**	WWst
	- 'Sally Pasmore'	CAvo
	- 'Sophie North'	CLAP
	- 'The Pearl'	EHrv
	- 'Three Ships'	EHrv
	- 'Trym'	CLAP WFar
	- 'Warham'	CBro EHrv EPot GEdr IFoB LRHS WPGP
	- 'Wendy's Gold'	CBro LRHS WFar
	reginae-olgae	CAvo CBro EBrs EHrv ERos MAsh WThu
	- Hoa 0165	WWst
	- subsp. ***reginae-olgae*** ♀H2-4	ECho
	- - 'Cambridge'	EBrs MAsh
§	- - Winter-flowering Group	CBro
§	- subsp. ***vernalis***	EBrs ECho IFoB
	- - 'John Marr'	LRHS
	rizehensis	CAvo CLAP EHrv GEdr
	'S.Arnott' ♀H4	CAvo CBro CElw CFFs CLAP CPLG EBrs ECha ECho ELan EPot GBuc GCal GEdr IFoB IGor LAma LRHS MAsh NBir NMen NRya NSla WBrk WCom WCot WFar WHoo WPGP WTin
	'Saint Anne's'	CDes CElw LRHS WIvy
	'Scharlockii'	see *G. nivalis* Scharlockii Group
	'Silverwells'	CElw EHrv GEdr
§	'Straffan'	CAvo CBro CElw EPot GEdr IFoB IGor LRHS MAsh MHom NMyG NPol WBrk WCot WFar
	'Sutton Courtenay'	CDes
	'The Apothecary'	EHrv
	'The O'Mahoney'	see *G.* 'Straffan'
	'Titania' (d)	CBro EHrv ELon WFar
	'Tubby Merlin'	CAvo CDes CElw CLAP WIvy
	× ***valentinei*** 'Compton Court' **new**	ITim
	'Washfield Warham'	ECha ITim LRHS MAsh
	'White Dreams' **new**	WFar
	'William Thomson'	LRHS
	'Winifrede Mathias'	CElw CLAP
	woronowii ♀H4	CBro CElw CLAP EBrs ECho ERCP GKev IFoB LAma LRHS MAsh MHom NBir NMyG WBrk WCot WFar

Galax (*Diapensiaceae*)

	aphylla	see *G. urceolata*
§	***urceolata***	IBlr

Galega (*Papilionaceae*)

	bicolor	MBel NBir NBre NChi SRms SWat WFar

'Duchess of Bedford'	EBee GBin
× ***hartlandii***	CPLG LRHS
- 'Alba' 𝕐H4	EBee EHrv ELon EWes IBlr MArl MBri MCot MRav SPhx SWat WCot WHoo WPrP WSHC
- 'Candida'	NBir
- 'Lady Wilson' 𝕐H4	CElw CPom EBee ECtt ELon EWes EWld MArl MBri MLHP WCom WCot WFoF WHoo WOut WPen
- 'Spring Light' (v)	EWes LSou
'Her Majesty'	see *G.* 'His Majesty'
§ 'His Majesty'	CKno ECtt ELon GMac IFro MArl MBri MCot MDKP MLHP MRav NBre NCob NGby SMrm WCom WCot WFar WHoo WHrl WPGP WWlt
officinalis	Widely available
- 'Alba' 𝕐H4	CBgR CPrp ECtt ELan EPfP MBrN MHer MNHC NCob SBod SMrm WCHb WFar WHer WHrl WMoo WOut WSpi
- Coconut Ice = 'Kelgal' (v)	CAbP LRHS NCob WHer
- 'Lincoln Gold'	EBee ELon
orientalis	CDes EBee ECha ECtt EPPr EWes MArl MBel MCot SMac SPhx WAbb WCot WMoo WPGP WSHC

Galeobdolon see *Lamium*

Galium (*Rubiaceae*)

aristatum	ECha MBel
boreale	EBWF
cruciata	see *Cruciata laevipes*
mollugo	CArn CRWN EBWF NSco SIde WCHb
§ ***odoratum***	Widely available
palustre	EBWF
verum	CArn CRWN EBWF EBee GJos GPoy MCoo MHer NLan NMir NMun NSco SECG SIde WCHb WFar WHer

Galtonia (*Hyacinthaceae*)

candicans 𝕐H4	Widely available
- 'Moonbeam' (d)	EBee ERCP WCot
princeps	CBro CDes CSam EBrs ECha ERos GBuc WPGP WTin
regalis	CPLG ERos GEdr WPGP
viridiflora	Widely available

Galvezia (*Scrophulariaceae*)

speciosa	WHil

Garcinia (*Clusiaceae*)

mangostana	CCCN

Gardenia (*Rubiaceae*)

augusta	see *G. jasminoides*
florida L.	see *G. jasminoides*
grandiflora	see *G. jasminoides*
§ ***jasminoides*** 𝕐H1	CBcs CCCN CDoC EBak LRHS MBri
- 'Kleim's Hardy'	CDTJ CHll CSBt CWit EBee ELan ELon EPfP EShb EWTr EWes GKir IMon LAst LRHS LSqu MAsh MBlu MDun MMHG NLar NPri SAPC SArc SPer SPoG SSta WCot WHlf
- 'Veitchiana'	EShb
thunbergia	EShb SPlb

garlic see *Allium sativum*

garlic, elephant see *Allium ampeloprasum* 'Elephant'

Garrya ✿ (*Garryaceae*)

F&M 215	WPGP
congdonii	NLar
elliptica	CBcs CDul CMac EBee ECrN EMui EPfP GGal IMon ISea LRHS LSRN MBri MGos NHol NPri NWea SBch SEND SPlb WFar WHar WPat
- (f)	MSwo SWvt
- (m)	CCVT CDoC CSBt CTri LAst LRHS MAsh MBlu MGan NBlu SLim SPoG
- 'James Roof' (m) 𝕐H4	Widely available
fremontii	NLar
× ***issaquahensis*** 'Glasnevin Wine'	CAbP CDul CPMA EBee ELan EPfP LRHS MAsh MBri MGos NLar NSti SBch SCoo SLim SPoG WFar WSpi
- 'Pat Ballard' (m)	EPfP NLar
× ***thuretii***	CBcs CDul MBri MGos NLar WDin WFar

× *Gasteraloe* (*Aloaceae*)

hybrid (***Aloe descoingsii*** × ***Gasteria brevifolia***) new	MAga

Gasteria ✿ (*Aloaceae*)

brachyphylla new	STre
carinata var. ***verrucosa***	EShb MSCN WCor
nitida var. ***nitida*** variegated (v)	WCot

× *Gaulnettya* see *Gaultheria*

Gaultheria ✿ (*Ericaceae*)

sp.	MGan MGos
adenothrix	NMen
antarctica	WThu
antipoda 'Adpressa'	WThu
cardiosepala	GEdr
- CLD 1351	GEdr
cumingiana B&SWJ 1542	WCru
cuneata 𝕐H4	ECho GEdr GKev GKir LRHS MAsh MBar SPoG WThu
- 'Pinkie'	ECho
depressa var. ***novae-zelandiae***	NHol
hispidula	ECho
hookeri	IBlr
itoana	ECho GEdr GKir MBar
'Jingle Bells'	MGos SPoG
macrostigma	WThu
- BR 67	GGar
§ ***mucronata***	CDul EPfP GKir MBar NWea SPlb WDin WFar WGwG
- (m)	CDoC CMac CSBt CTri CWSG EPfP LRHS MBar MGos NBlu NEgg NHol SPer SPoG SRms
- 'Alba' (f)	MBar MGos
- 'Bell's Seedling' (f/m) 𝕐H4	CBcs CDoC CDul CTri CWSG EPfP GKir LRHS MAsh NBir NEgg SPer SPoG
- 'Cherry Ripe' (f)	CMac
- 'Crimsonia' (f) 𝕐H4	CBcs CMac EPfP MBar SPer SRms
- 'Indian Lake'	NHol
- 'Lilacina' (f)	CBcs CMac
- 'Lilian' (f)	CSBt CWSG EBee EPfP NHol
- Mother of Pearl	see *G. mucronata* 'Parelmoer'
- 'Mulberry Wine' (f) 𝕐H4	CSBt CTri EPfP LRHS MGos NEgg NHol SPer SPoG

§ - 'Parelmoer' (f) | CSBt LAst NEgg SPer SPoG
- 'Pink Pearl' (f) ♀H4 | SRms
- pink-berried (f) | NBlu
- red-berried (f) | NBlu
- 'Rosea' (f) | MBar MGos
- 'Rosie' (f) | SBod
§ - 'Signaal' (f) | CBcs CMac EPfP LAst LRHS MGos NEgg NHol SPer
- Signal | see *G. mucronata* 'Signaal'
§ - 'Sneeuwwitje' (f) | CBcs CWSG EBee EPfP LAst LRHS NBir SPer SPoG
- Snow White | see *G. mucronata* 'Sneeuwwitje'
- 'Thymifolia' (m) | EPfP
- white-berried (f) | MMuc NBlu
- 'Wintertime' (f) ♀H4 | CMac MGos SRms
* ***mucronifolia*** dwarf | NWCA
§ ***myrsinoides*** | GKev
nummularioides | GEdr GGar NHol NLar
'Pearls' | GKir NHol WThu
procumbens ♀H4 | Widely available
prostrata | see *G. myrsinoides*
pumila | GAbr LEdu MBar NHol
- 'E.K. Balls' | NHol
pyroloides | CStu
shallon | CAgr CBcs CDul CMac CSBt EBee EPfP MBar MDun MGos SPer SRms SWvt WDin WFar
sinensis lilac-berried | WThu
tasmanica | ECou GAbr
× ***wisleyensis*** | LRHS SLon SRms SSta
- 'Glenroy Maureen' | LRHS
- 'Pink Pixie' | ECho GKir LRHS MAsh MBar NLar SSta
- 'Ruby' **new** | CMac
- 'Wisley Pearl' | CBcs EBee IBlr IDee MBar NLar SCoo SReu WFar
yunnanensis | SReu

Gaura (*Onagraceae*)

Karalee Petite Improved | see *G. lindheimeri* Lillipop Pink
lindheimeri ♀H4 | Widely available
- 'Ballerina Blush' **new** | LAst
- 'Ballerina Rose' | LAst SGar SPet
- Cherry Brandy = 'Gauchebra'PBR | EBee ECtt EPfP EWes EWll LBMP LHop LRHS NLar SPur SWvt WFar WHil
- 'Corrie's Gold' (v) | CMac CWSG EAEE EBee ECha ECtt EHoe ELan EPfP EShb LAst LRHS MGos MHer SBch SGar SPav SPer SPet SPoG WCFE WMnd WWEG
- 'Crimson Butterflies'PBR | EBee ECtt EPfP LRHS MAvo
§ - 'Heather's Delight' | LRHS MRav SHar
- 'Heaven's Harmony' | LRHS MGos
- In the Pink | see *G. lindheimeri* 'Heather's Delight'
- 'Jo Adela' (v) | ELan EPfP
- Karalee Petite = 'Gauka' | CWCL EPfP NLar SCoo SIng
- Karalee Pink | MBri
- Karalee White = 'Nugauwhite'PBR | CSpe CWCL EPfP LHop LRHS LSou MBri NLar SBch SCoo SIng SPoG
§ - Lillipop Pink = 'Redgapi' | EBee ECtt EPfP EWll LAst LHop LSou MBri NEgg NPri SBch SMrm SPoG STes SVil
- 'Madonna' (v) | CBow
- 'My Melody'PBR (v) | CSpr CWCL EBee EWll LBMP LRHS NLar SBch SPoG
- 'Passionate Blush'PBR | CMac EBee ENor LRHS LSRN LSou MGos SPoG
- 'Passionate Pink'PBR | CBcs LRHS
- 'Passionate Rainbow'PBR (v) | EBee EPfP LSou SPoG
- 'Pink Dwarf' | CMac CSpr EPfP LRHS
- short | LSou SGar
- 'Siskiyou Pink' | CBcs CKno CSBt CSpe CWCL EBee ECha ECtt EHoe ELan EPfP EShb LBMP LRHS LSRN MWat SBch SBod SGar SMad SMrm SPer SWat SWvt WCFE WFar WMnd WWEG
- 'Sunset Dreams' | SPad
- 'The Bride' | CEnt CTri EBee ECtt EPfP GCal LRHS LSRN LSou MBel MRav MWat SPav SPet SRGP STes SWal SWvt WMnd
- 'Whirling Butterflies' | CKno CSpe CWCL EBee ECrN ECtt ELan EPfP GMaP LRHS MAvo MWat SBch SBod SMad SMrm SPav SPer SWat SWvt WMnd WWEG
- 'White Dove' **new** | EPfP
- 'White Heron' | MNrw
sinuata | CAby
I 'Variegata' (v) | CWCL

Gaylussacia (*Ericaceae*)

baccata (F) | NLar

Gazania (*Asteraceae*)

'Aztec' ♀H1+3 | CCCN
'Bicton Orange' | CCCN COIW LSou MAJR SCoo
'Blackberry Ripple' | CCCN COIW GGar LAst MAJR SAga SCoo SMrm
'Blackcurrant Ice' | MCot
'Caledon Giants' **new** | SGar
'Christopher' | SCoo
'Christopher Lloyd' | CCCN COIW LAst LHop MAJR SMrm WHil
'Cookei' ♀H1+3 | WCot
'Cornish Pixie' | CCCN
Daybreak Series | MPet WFar
'Evening Sun' | LSou
Gazoo Series | LRHS
'Jamaica Ginger' **new** | SMrm
krebsiana | CCCN WHil
linearis | WClo
- 'Colorado Gold' | CFir
'Magic' | CCCN COIW MAJR NPri SCoo
Nahui = 'Suga119' (PLA Sunbathers Series) **new** | SVil
'Northbourne' ♀H1+3 | GGar
'Orange Beauty' | CHEx ELan
'Red Velvet' | CHEx SAga
§ ***rigens*** | MPet
- var. ***uniflora*** 'Variegata' (v) | CBot
- 'Variegata' (v) ♀H1+3 | CBow CCCN COIW ELan LSou
Rumi = 'Suga116' (PLA Sunbathers Series) **new** | SVil
'Silver Beauty' | CBot
splendens | see *G. rigens*
Sunset Jane = 'Sugaja'PBR | CCCN
'Talent' | SEND
Talent Series ♀H3 **new** | MPet
'Tiger Eye' | CCCN COIW LAst LSou WHil
'Torbay Silver' | CHEx
Totonaca = 'Suga212' (PLA Sunbathers Series) **new** | SVil

Geissorhiza (*Iridaceae*)

aspera | ECho
inequalis **new** | ECho
inflexa | ECho
monanthos | ECho

	radians	ECho

Gelasine (*Iridaceae*)

	azurea	see *G. coerulea*
§	***coerulea***	WSHC

Gelidocalamus (*Poaceae*)

	fangianus	see *Drepanostachyum microphyllum*

Gelsemium (*Loganiaceae*)

	rankinii	MBri
	sempervirens ♀H1-2	CArn CCCN CHll CRHN EBee EShb IDee LRHS LSRN SPoG

Genista (*Papilionaceae*)

	aetnensis ♀H4	CBcs CCVT CDul CTri ECrN ELan EPfP EWTr MDun NLar SAPC SArc SEND SMad SPer SRms WDin WPat WSpi
§	***canariensis***	CPLG CWib WBrE
	cinerea	WCFE
	decumbens	see *Cytisus decumbens*
	delphinensis	see *G. sagittalis* subsp. *delphinensis*
	'Emerald Spreader'	see *G. pilosa* 'Yellow Spreader'
	fragrans	see *G. canariensis*
	hispanica	CBcs CDul CSBt CTri EBee ECrN ELan EPfP GGal GGar MBar MGos MNHC NWea SEND SLim SPer SRms SWvt WCFE WDin WFar WHar
	humifusa	see *G. pulchella*
	lydia ♀H4	Widely available
§	***maderensis***	EWes LRHS SMrm
§	***monspessulana***	ECho
	pilosa	CTri EPot MBar NMen
	- 'Goldilocks'	EBee LRHS MMuc
	- 'Lemon Spreader'	see *G. pilosa* 'Yellow Spreader'
	- var. ***minor***	NLar NMen
	- 'Procumbens'	CMea MDKP MHer WPat
	- 'Vancouver Gold'	CBcs EBee ELan EPfP GGar GKir MGos MRav SMad SPer SPoG SRms WDin WFar WGor
§	- 'Yellow Spreader'	CBcs CMHG GEdr MSwo
§	'Porlock' ♀H3	CAlb CBcs CDoC CDul CPLG CSBt CSPN CTri CWSG CWib EBee ELon GGal LRHS MAsh MBri MRav SBch SEND WDin
§	***pulchella***	CTri
	sagittalis	CTri LRHS MMuc NBir NLar SPer WTin WWFP
§	- subsp. ***delphinensis*** ♀H4	GKir NMen
	- ***minor***	see *G. sagittalis* subsp. *delphinensis*
§	× ***spachiana*** ♀H1	CTri SPoG
	tenera 'Golden Shower'	SLPl
	tinctoria	CArn EOHP GBar GPoy ILis MHer SIde WHer
§	- 'Flore Pleno' (d) ♀H4	ECho GEdr MGos NMen NPro
	- 'Humifusa'	EPot GEdr NWCA
	- 'Plena'	see *G. tinctoria* 'Flore Pleno'
	- 'Royal Gold' ♀H4	CWSG CWib EPfP LRHS MGos MRav SPer SPlb
	villarsii	see *G. pulchella*

Gentiana ✿ (*Gentianaceae*)

	SDR 5113 **new**	GKev
	SDR 5164	GKev
§	***acaulis*** ♀H4	CMea CStu EBee ECho ELan EPfP EPot GKev GMaP ITim LHop LRHS MWat NGdn NHol NLAp NMen NRya SIng SPlb SRms WAbe WCFE WEas WFar WPat
	- f. ***alba***	LLHF NLAp WThu
	- - 'Snowstorm'	GKev
	- 'Belvedere'	GCal NMen WAbe
	- 'Coelestina'	EPot WThu
	- 'Dinarica'	see *G. dinarica*
	- 'Holzmannii'	NMen
	- 'Krumrey'	EPot GKev
I	- 'Maxima Enzian'	EPot
	- 'Rannoch'	EPot GEdr NMen
	- 'Stumpy'	EPot
	- 'Trotter's Variety'	EPot WAbe
	- 'Undulatifolia'	EPot
	affinis	LHop NLAp
	'Alex Duguid'	GEdr
	'Amethyst'	GEdr GMaP WAbe
	andrewsii	GEdr
	angulosa misapplied	see *G. verna* 'Angulosa' hort.
	angustifolia	WAbe
	- 'Iceberg' **new**	GKev
	- 'Rannoch'	GKev
	'Ann's Special'	GEdr
	arethusae **new**	GKev
	asclepiadea ♀H4	Widely available
	- var. ***alba***	CBot CLAP EBee GBee GBuc GCal GEdr GGar GKev GMaP IGor LHop MDKP MTho NBid SGSe SRms WTin
	- 'Knightshayes'	CLAP EBee GKev GKir LLHF
I	- 'Nana'	EBee GKev GKir
	- pale blue-flowered	WPGP
	- 'Phyllis'	EBee GBuc
	- 'Pink Cascade'	GEdr GKev SGSe
	- 'Pink Swallow'	CLAP GAbr GBuc GMac WWEG
	- 'Rosea'	GBuc GMaP MDKP MNrw WPGP
	- 'Whitethroat'	GKev
	atuntsiensis	EBee
	'Balmoral'PBR	GMaP
	'Barbara Lyle'	WAbe
	bavarica var. ***subacaulis***	SPlb
	bellidifolia	GKev
	× ***bernardii***	see *G.* × *stevenagensis* 'Bernardii'
	'Berrybank Dome'	CSam GEdr GMaP NHol
	'Berrybank Sky'	GEdr GMaP NCGa NHol
	'Berrybank Star'	GEdr GMaP
	bisetaea	SRms
	'Blue Heaven'	GEdr
	'Blue Sea'	LRHS
	'Blue Silk'	EWes GBuc GEdr GKev LRHS NHol SIng SPer WAbe
	brachyphylla	WAbe
	- subsp. ***favratii***	WAbe
	'Braemar'PBR	GMaP
*	***buglossoides***	WSHC
	'Cairngorm'	GEdr NDlv
	'Carmen' **new**	GEdr
	× ***caroli***	WAbe
	'Christine Jean'	SIng
	clusii	EPot NMen WAbe
	- purple-flowered	WAbe
	- subsp. ***rochelii*** **new**	GKev
	'Compact Gem'	GEdr NHol NLAp SIng WAbe
§	***cruciata***	EAlp EBee LHop MMHG MTho
§	***dahurica***	EBee ECho GEdr NGdn NHol
	'Dark Hedgehog'	GEdr
	decumbens	EBee GKev
	dendrologi	WHil
	depressa	MTho WAbe
	'Devonhall'	GEdr NHol WAbe
	'Diana'PBR	LRHS
§	***dinarica***	ECho EPot MTho NMen

	Name	Suppliers
	- 'Colonel Stitt'	GEdr WThu
	- 'Frocheneite'	EPot WThu
	divisa	GKev
	'Dumpy'	CPBP GEdr WAbe
	'Elizabeth'	GEdr
	'Ettrick'	GEdr NHol
	'Eugen's Allerbester' (d)	CCVN GEdr GKev LRHS NHol SPer WAbe
	'Eugen's Bester'	SIng
	farreri	GKev WAbe
	- 'Duguid'	GEdr NHol WAbe
	- hybrids	WAbe
	fetissowii	see *G. macrophylla* var. *fetissowii*
	gelida	GKev LLHF
	Glamis strain	GEdr
	glauca new	GKev
	'Glen Isla'	EWes
	'Glen Moy'	GEdr
	'Glendevon'	GEdr WAbe
§	***gracilipes***	ECho GKev MWat SPlb SRms
	- 'Yuatensis'	see *G. macrophylla* var. *fetissowii*
	× ***hascombensis***	see *G. septemfida* var. *lagodechiana* 'Hascombensis'
	'Henry'	GEdr WAbe
	hexaphylla	WAbe
	'Indigo'	WAbe
	Inshriach hybrids	LRHS SPer
	'Inverleith' ♀H4	EWes GEdr LRHS NHol NLAp SPlb
	'Iona'[PBR]	GMaP
	'Joan Ward'	LRHS
	'Kirriemuir'	EWes NDlv
	kochiana	see *G. acaulis*
	kurroo	LHop
	- var. ***brevidens***	see *G. dahurica*
	lagodechiana	see *G. septemfida* var. *lagodechiana*
	cf. ***lawrencei*** new	GKev
	'Little Diamond'	LRHS NBlu
	loderi	GKev
	'Lucerna'	GEdr GKev LRHS NDlv NHol NLAp
	lutea	EBee ECho GAbr GKev GPoy LRHS NBid NChi SMad SRms WAul WPer
	- SDR 3502	GKev
	× ***macaulayi*** ♀H4	SIng SRms
	- 'Elata'	NHol
	- 'Kidbrooke Seedling'	CTri EWes GEdr GKev GMaP LRHS NDlv NHol WAbe
	- 'Kingfisher'	CTri GKev LRHS NBir SIng WAbe
§	- 'Praecox'	GEdr
§	- 'Wells's Variety'	WAbe
§	***macrophylla*** var. ***fetissowii***	EBee GKev LHop LLHF
	makinoi 'Marsha'[PBR]	EBee LRHS
	- 'Royal Blue'	GCal WWEG
	'Margaret'	GEdr WAbe
	'Maryfield'	GEdr
	'Melanie'	GEdr NHol
*	***nepaulensis***	GAuc
	nipponica	GKev
§	***nubigena***	GKev
	occidentalis	EPot
	olgae	EBee LHop
	olivieri	GKev
	paradoxa	GKev LLHF NLAp WAbe WPat
	- 'Blauer Herold'	MWat
	patula new	GKev
	phlogifolia	see *G. cruciata*
	pneumonanthe	LRHS SPlb
	prolata	GKev
	przewalskii	see *G. nubigena*
	pumila subsp. ***delphinensis***	WAbe WPat
	purdomii	see *G. gracilipes*
	'Robyn Lyle'	WAbe
	'Saphir Select'	GEdr NHol
	saxosa	GGar GKev NBir
	scabra	LRHS
	- 'Zuikorindo'	EBee NLar
	'Sensation'	GEdr
	septemfida ♀H4	CEnt EAEE GAbr GEdr GKev GKir LBee LHop LRHS MBri MTho NBir NBlu NWCA SIng SPlb SRms WHoo
	- 'Alba'	GKir NBir
§	- var. ***lagodechiana*** ♀H4	EBee GKir LRHS NMen SRms WFar
§	- - 'Hascombensis'	ECho
	'Serenity'	GEdr LRHS NHol WAbe
	'Shot Silk'	CSam CTri EWes GEdr GGar GJos GKev GMaP LRHS NBir NHol SPer WAbe
	'Silken Giant'	GEdr WAbe
	'Silken Night'	WAbe
	'Silken Seas'	GEdr NHol WAbe
	'Silken Skies'	GBuc GEdr WAbe
	'Silken Surprise' new	WAbe
	sino-ornata ♀H4	CTri EBee ECho EMil GGar GKev GKir LSRN MBri MWat NLAp NMen SIng SPer SRms WAbe WFar
	- CLD 476B	GEdr
	- SDR 5127	GKev
	- 'Alba'	NHol WFar
	- 'Angel's Wings'	GEdr NHol
	- 'Bellatrix'	GEdr NHol
	- 'Brin Form'	SRms WAbe
	- 'Downfield'	GKev GMaP LRHS NHol SIng
	- 'Edith Sarah'	GEdr SRms
	- 'Mary Lyle'	GEdr WAbe
	- 'Praecox'	see *G.* × *macaulayi* 'Praecox'
	- 'Purity'	GEdr WAbe
I	- 'Trotter's Form'	EWes
	- 'Weisser Traum'	GEdr NHol
	- 'White Wings'	EWes
	'Soutra'	GEdr
	× ***stevenagensis*** ♀H4	CTri LRHS SIng
§	- 'Bernardii'	GEdr SIng WAbe
	- dark-flowered	WAbe
	stipitata subsp. ***tizuensis*** new	GKev
	straminea	EBee GKev LLHF MDKP
	'Strathmore' ♀H4	CSam CSpr CTri EWes GAbr GEdr GGar GKev GMaP LRHS NHol NLAp SIng SPer SPlb WAbe
	'Suendermannii'	GKev LLHF
	szechenyii	GKev
	- SDR 4938	GKev
	ternifolia 'Cangshan'	GEdr WAbe
	- 'Dali'	GEdr NBir NHol
	tianschanica new	LHop
	tibetica	CArn EBee EWld GAuc GEdr GPoy MWat WAul WEas WPer WTin
	trichotoma SDR 4720	GKev
	- SDR 4746	GKev
	triflora	GBuc GKev LHop WFar WPGP
	- 'Alba'	GBuc GKev
	- f. ***horomuiensis*** new	GCal
	- var. ***japonica***	GBuc WWEG
	- var. ***montana***	GKev
	- 'Royal Blue'	EBee WCot
	verna	CWCL EAEE EBee ECho EPfP EPot EWes GKev ITim LHop LRHS LSRN MTho NMen NSla SIng SPoG WAbe WFar WHoo WPat
	- 'Alba'	NLAp WAbe WPat
§	- 'Angulosa' hort. ♀H4	ITim
	- subsp. ***balcanica***	MTho NLAp SRms WPat

- subsp. ***oschtenica***	NSla WAbe
- slate blue-flowered	WPat
- subsp. ***tergestina***	ITim
villosa new	LHop
'Violette'	GEdr LRHS NDlv NHol
waltonii	ECho EWes
wellsii	see *G.* × *macaulayi* 'Wells's Variety'
wutaiensis	see *G. macrophylla* var. *fetissowii*

Geranium ✿ (*Geraniaceae*)

from Bambashata Altai Mountains	NCot
from Pamirs, Tadzhikistan	WPnP
from Sikkim	NWCA
aconitifolium misapplied	see *G. palmatum*
aconitifolium L'Hér.	see *G. rivulare*
'Alan Mayes'	CElw CMac CPrp CSev EBee EBla ECtt EPPr LRHS MAvo MWea NGdn SRGP
albanum	CElw EBee EPPr GAbr LLWP MMuc MNrw NWsh SDix SRGP WMoo
albiflorum	EPPr WMoo WPnP
anemonifolium	see *G. palmatum*
'Ann Folkard' ♀H4	Widely available
'Ann Folkard' × ***psilostemon***	LSRN
'Anne Thomson' ♀H4	Widely available
× ***antipodeum*** 'Black Ice'	GBuc WCru
- 'Chocolate Candy'PBR	EPfP LBuc LRHS MGos
§ - Crûg strain	CMoH EHrv NGdn NWCA WBrE WCru
- 'Elizabeth Wood'	LSou SMrm
- (*G. sessiliflorum* subsp. *novae-zelandiae* 'Nigricans' × *G. traversii* var. *elegans*)	SRms
- 'Kahlua'	EHrv EPfP
- 'Pink Spice'PBR	EBla ECtt LBuc LRHS MGos
- 'Sea Spray'	CMHG ECtt GCra GGar MCot NBro WMnd
- 'Stanhoe'	EBee ECtt SRot WBrk
antrorsum	ECou
argenteum	LFur
aristatum	CDes EBee EBla EPPr EWes GCal GGar MNFA MNrw MRav NBir NCot SMrm SPav SRGP STes WCru WMoo WPnP WPtf
- NS 649	NWCA
armenum	see *G. psilostemon*
'Arnoldshof'	EPPr
asphodeloides	CBre CElw CHid CSsd GAbr IFro LLWP MBNS MNFA MNrw MWhi NBid NBir NCot SPav SRGP WBrk WFar WHCG WMnd WMoo WPnP WTin
- subsp. ***asphodeloides*** 'Prince Regent'	EBee EPPr GCal WPnP
- - white-flowered	EBla EPPr SRGP STes WFar WMoo
- 'Starlight'	CMoH EBee GCal NBid
atlanticum Hook. f.	see *G. malviflorum*
'Aussie Gem'	CFwr EBee WWEG
'Baby Blue'	see *G. himalayense* 'Baby Blue'
'Benjamin Browne' new	CSev
'Bertie Crûg'	CHVG CSpe EBee EBla ECtt EHrv GAbr LAst LLHF NBir NMoo SBch SMrm SPoG SRms SRot SWat SWvt WCru WFar
'Bill Baker'	GKir
biuncinatum	IFro
'Blue Boy'	MNFA NLar
'Blue Cloud' ♀H4	CDes CElw CMea EBee EBla EPPr EPfP GCal GKir GMaP LRHS LSou MAvo MNFA NBid NBir NCob NCot SBch SMeo SMrm SRGP SSvw SUsu WHoo WMoo WPnP WSpi
'Blue Pearl'	EPPr MAvo NBir NSti SRGP SVil WMoo WPnP
§ Blue Sunrise = 'Blogold'PBR ♀H4	Widely available
'Bob's Blunder'	CMHG EBee EBla ECtt LFur LRHS LSRN MAvo MBNS NBPC NLar SMrm SWvt WCot WFar WHoo
bohemicum	EBla NCot SRGP WHer
- 'Orchid Blue'	EPfP SWvt WFar
'Brookside' ♀H4	Widely available
brutium	LAst
brycei	MNrw
'Buckland Beauty'	CDes CElw EBee SBch
'Buxton's Blue'	see *G. wallichianum* 'Buxton's Variety'
caeruleatum	EBee EBla EPPr GCal SUsu
caffrum	SRGP WOut
canariense	see *G. reuteri*
candicans misapplied	see *G. lambertii*
§ × ***cantabrigiense***	CMac CSBt ECtt EShb GAbr LRHS MHer MNrw NBid NBir NBro NPer NSti SGar SMrm SRms WAbe WBrk WCru WFar WHCG WMoo
- 'Berggarten'	CDes CElw EBee EPPr SBch SRGP WPtf
- 'Biokovo'	Widely available
- 'Cambridge'	Widely available
- 'Harz'	EPPr NCot
- 'Karmina'	CElw EBee EBla EPPr EPfP EPla GKir LRHS MWhi SBch WCom WHoo WMoo WPnP WWEG
- 'Rosalina'	NCot
- 'Show Time'	EBla
- 'St Ola'	Widely available
- 'Vorjura'	EBee EPPr NCot
- 'Westray'PBR	CHVG CHid COIW EBee EPPr EShb GAbr GBuc GQue LRHS LSou MCCP NCot NGdn SBch SMrm SPoG SRms STes SVil SWvt
cataractarum	MBel
'Chantilly'	EBee EBla ECGP ECtt EPPr GBuc GCal MAvo MNFA MNrw MWea NBir NCGa SBch WCru WMoo WPnP WPtf
christensenianum B&SWJ 8022	WCru
cinereum	EBla ECho
- 'Album'	GKir NChi
- 'Apple Blossom'	see *G.* × *lindavicum* 'Apple Blossom'
- 'Ballerina'	see *G.* (Cinereum Group) 'Ballerina'
- 'Elizabeth'	ECtt LPio
- 'Hidgate's Emily'	EBla
- 'Sateene'PBR	EBee EBla EPPr NMoo NSti SPoG SRot
- 'Souvenir de René Macé'PBR	EBee LBuc SPoG
- subsp. ***subcaulescens*** var. ***ponticum***	see *G. ponticum*
(Cinereum Group) 'Alice'PBR	EBee EBla EPPr IPot LLHF LRHS LSRN MBNS NCGa NGdn NLar NSti
§ - 'Ballerina' ♀H4	Widely available
- 'Carol'	CDes EAEE EBee EBla EPPr EWes GKir LRHS LSRN LSou MAvo MBNS MBri NLar NSti SWvt WFar
I - 'Heather'	EBla EPPr MBNS
- 'Lambrook Helen'	CPLG EBla
- 'Laurence Flatman'	CElw CHar CKno CSam EBee EBla ECtt EPfP GKir GMaP LAst LBMP

	LRHS MSCN NBPC NBid NEgg NRya SRms SRot SWat WAbe WCAu WClo WFar WHCG WHoo WMnd WPat
- 'Lizabeth'PBR **new**	EPPr NCGa
- 'Penny Lane'PBR **new**	EPPr
- 'Prima Ballerina'	EBee NLar
- 'Purple Pillow'	Widely available
- René Macé = 'Progera' **new**	LRHS
- Rothbury Gem = 'Gerfos'PBR ♀H4	CMac CWGN EBee EBla EKen LLHF LRHS MWea NChi NSti
- 'Signal'	EBee EBla GEdr NLar SBch
'Claridge Druce'	see *G.* × *oxonianum* 'Claridge Druce'
clarkei 'Kashmir Pink'	Widely available
§ - 'Kashmir White' ♀H4	Widely available
- 'Mount Stewart'	CPLG GCal WCru WPGP
- (Purple-flowered Group) 'Gulmarg'	NCot
- - 'Kashmir Purple'	Widely available
collinum	EPPr MNrw NBir NCot SRGP
'Coombland White'	CDes CSam CSpe EBee EBla ECtt EPPr LAst LFur LPio LSou MAvo MCot MNFA MNrw NBPC NCGa NGdn NLar NSti NWsh SBch SPoG SRGP SVil WCot WHoo WMoo WPnP
'Criss Canning'	EPPr
Crûg strain	see *G.* × *antipodeum* Crûg strain
'Cyril's Fancy'	EBee EBla EPPr LPio MAvo SUsu WPtf
dahuricum	WCru
dalmaticum ♀H4	Widely available
- 'Album'	CPrp CSsd EBee EBla ECho ECtt ELan EPPr EPot LRHS MRav MTho NRya SIng SRGP SRms SRot SWat WAbe WCom WCru WFar
- 'Bressingham Pink'	EPPr WPnP
- 'Bridal Bouquet'	EBee LLHF NChi NCot NMen NSla WAbe WHer
- 'Croftlea'	GKir
- 'Stades Hellrosa'	EPPr NCot
dalmaticum* × *macrorrhizum	see *G.* × *cantabrigiense*
delavayi misapplied	see *G. sinense*
'Dilys' ♀H4	CElw EBee EBla ELan EPPr LPio MAvo MCot MLHP MNrw NBir NChi NGdn SBch SRGP SUsu WCru WFar WHal WMoo WPnP
dissectum	CHll
'Distant Hills'	CDes EBee EBla EPPr MAvo SRGP SUsu WPtf
'Diva'	CSam EBee EBla EPPr EPfP LLHF LRHS MAvo MNrw SRGP WCru WPnP
'Double Jewel' (d) **new**	CWGN EBee EPfP IPot MAsh MBNS NMRc
'Dragon Heart'	EBee ECtt EPPr LSRN NLar NSti SPoG
'Dusky Crûg'	Widely available
'Dusky Gem'	SUsu
'Dusky Rose'	CLAP CMoH CPrp CSpe EBee ELan EPfP LAst MGos SRot WFar
'Edith May'	GSec
'Eleanor Fisher'	SUsu
'Elizabeth Ross'	LPio MAvo MNrw SMrm WCru WHoo
'Elke'	CElw CSev EBee EBla EPPr EPfP EWTr MAsh MAvo MNrw MWea NBid NCGa NCot NGby NGdn SBch SPer WHlf WPnP
'Ella'	CWGN
'Elworthy Dusky'	CElw
'Elworthy Eyecatcher'	CDes CElw EPPr MAvo SBch SUsu
'Elworthy Tiger'	CElw
'Emily'	SRGP
endressii ♀H4	CBre CElw CSev EBee EBla ECha ECho EHrv EPPr EPfP GAbr GKir GMaP MBNS MCot MHer NBro NPer SGar SPlb SRGP SRms SWvt WFar WMoo WWEG
- 'Album'	see *G.* 'Mary Mottram'
- 'Betty Catchpole'	EPPr
- 'Castle Drogo' ♀H4	EBee EBla EPPr MAvo SRGP
- 'Prestbury White'	see *G.* × *oxonianum* 'Prestbury Blush'
- 'Rose'	MAvo WPer
- 'Wargrave Pink'	see *G.* × *oxonianum* 'Wargrave Pink'
- white-flowered	WPtf
erianthum	GBuc GCal GMaP IMou MLHP NBre NCGa NLar SRGP STes WCru WMoo WPnP
- 'Calm Sea'	EBla GBuc SUsu WCru WMoo WPnP
- f. ***leucanthum*** 'Undine'	SUsu
- 'Neptune'	EPPr MNFA SUsu WCru WPnP
eriostemon Fischer	see *G. platyanthum*
'Eva'	EBee WCAu WPnP
'Expression'PBR	see *G.* 'Tanya Rendall'
'Farncombe Cerise Star'	EBee EPPr NCot
§ ***farreri***	CPLG EBla GBuc LHop LRHS NBir SIng WEas
'Fireworks'	LRHS
fremontii	EWld
gracile	EBee GBuc GMaP LSou MNrw NBir NBre NVic SRGP WBrk WCru WMoo WPnP
- 'Blanche'	CElw EBee EPPr SBch SMrs
- 'Blush'	CElw EBee EPPr LPla
grandiflorum	see *G. himalayense*
'Grasmere'	ECtt
guatemalense B&SWJ 10461	WCru
gymnocaulon	CMHG EBee EBla EPPr LRHS MAvo SRGP WCru WWFP
gymnocaulon* × *platypetalum	EBee NCot
'Harmony'	EBee EPPr
harveyi	CDes CElw CMea CSpe EBla EPPr EWes GCal NChi SPhx SRGP WAbe WCru WKif WPGP WPat WSpi
hayatanum	NCot WPnP
- B&SWJ 164	WCru WMoo
§ ***himalayense***	Widely available
- from Tibetan border	CPLG
- - CC 1957	EPPr
- ***alpinum***	see *G. himalayense* 'Gravetye'
§ - 'Baby Blue'	CElw CSpe EBee EBla EBrs EPPr GBuc GCal GCra IFro MAvo MNFA MNrw NCot NGdn NLar NSti SRGP SUsu WBrk WCru WMoo WPnP WPtf
- 'Birch Double'	see *G. himalayense* 'Plenum'
- 'Derrick Cook'	CElw EBee EPPr MNFA MWhi NCot SUsu
- 'Devil's Blue'	EPPr NCot SRGP WPtf
§ - 'Gravetye' ♀H4	Widely available
- 'Irish Blue'	CElw EBee EBla ECtt EPPr GBuc GCal GCra MNFA NCot NLar NPol SRGP WAbb WCAu WCru WMoo WPnP WPtf WTin

	Name	Suppliers
	- ***meeboldii***	see *G. himalayense*
	- 'Pale Irish Blue'	GCal
§	- 'Plenum' (d)	Widely available
	- 'Spiti Valley'	EBee NCot
	hispidissimum	CFee
	ibericum misapplied	see *G.* × ***magnificum***
	ibericum ambig.	MBel
	ibericum Cav.	CSBt CTri EBla NBre NLar SPav SRGP STes WFar
	- 'Blue Springs'	ECtt
	- subsp. ***ibericum***	CMac EBee EPPr
	- subsp. ***jubatum***	EBla EPPr MNFA MNrw NCot SRms WCru WPnP
	- - 'White Zigana'	EBee ECtt EPPr MAsh MWea NCot WPnP
	- subsp. ***jubatum*** × ***renardii***	SWvt
	- var. ***platypetalum*** misapplied	see *G.* × ***magnificum***
	- var. ***platypetalum*** Boissier	see *G. platypetalum* Fisch. & C.A. Mey.
§	- 'Ushguli Grijs'	EBee EBla NChi NCot NLar WPnP
	ibericum × ***libani***	CDes
	incanum	CAbP CHll EBee EShb EWes MNrw NBir SGar SRGP SRot
	- white-flowered	SRGP
	'Ivan' ♀H4	CElw CEnt CLAP CMoH EBee EBla EBrs ECtt EPPr GBuc GMac LPio LRHS MBNS MNFA NChi NCob NCot NGdn NLar SAga SRGP WCAu WCru WMoo WPnP
	'Jean Armour'	CDes CPrp EAEE EBee ECtt EPPr GBuc LRHS MAvo MWea NGdn SPoG SRGP WCru WPGP
	'Jean's Lilac'	see *G.* × *oxonianum* 'Jean's Lilac'
	'Johnson's Blue' ♀H4	Widely available
	'Jolly Bee' PBR ♀H4	Widely available
	'Jolly Pink'	EPPr WPnP
	'Joy'	EBee EBla ECtt EPPr EWTr GBuc LPio LRHS LSqH MAvo MCot MMuc MNFA MNrw MRav NBPC NBir NCGa NCot NEgg NLar NSti SBch SPoG SRGP STes WCot WCru WMoo WPnP
§	'Kanahitobanawa'	CDes EBee
	'Kashmir Blue'	CPLG EBee ECtt EPPr GMaP LRHS MAvo NCot NGdn NLar SBch SMrs SWat WFar WMoo WPnP WPtf WWEG
	'Kashmir Green'	EBee ECtt EPPr GBin LBMP MAvo MNFA MWea NCot STes WMoo WPnP
§	'Kate'	EBla WCru
	'Kate Folkard'	see *G.* 'Kate'
§	'Khan'	EBee EBla EPPr IFro IPot MAvo MNrw NCot NPro SDys SRGP SUsu WCru
	'Kirsty' **new**	EBee
	kishtvariense	EBee EBla EPPr GCal MNrw MRav NCot NSti WCru
	koraiense	CDes CPLG EBla NBre WMoo
	- B&SWJ 797	WCru
	- B&SWJ 878	EBee WCru
	koreanum ambig.	CDes CPLG EBee EBla GBuc WFar WMoo
	- B&SWJ 602	WCru
§	***kotschyi*** var. ***charlesii***	EBee EBla EPPr
	krameri	CPLG EBla IMou
	- B&SWJ 1142	EBla WCru
	'Lakwijk Star' **new**	NCot
§	***lambertii***	EBla EWes GBuc GCal MNrw NBir
	- 'Swansdown'	EBla GBuc MNrw WCru WPtf WSHC
I	***libani***	EBee ELon EPPr GBuc GKir LLWP MCot MTho NBid NChi NCot NSti WBrk WCot WCru WEas WPnP WTin
	- RCB RL B-2	WCot
	libani × ***peloponnesiacum***	CDes EBee
	'Libretto'	WCru
§	× ***lindavicum*** 'Apple Blossom'	CMea CMoH EBee EBla EBrs EPPr GBuc LRHS NMen WAbe WHCG WSpi
	- 'Lissadell'	EPot
	linearilobum subsp. ***transversale***	EPPr NCot SRot WCru WPnP
I	- - 'Laciniatum' **new**	NCot WWst
	- - 'Rose Foundling' **new**	WWst
§	'Little David'	EBee NLar SUsu
	'Little Devil'	see *G.* 'Little David'
	'Little Gem'	CMea EBee EBla EBrs EPPr LRHS MAvo NChi NLar WFar WPnP
	lucidum	WPtf
	'Luscious Linda' PBR	EBee MAvo NGdn NLar WFar WPnP
	'Lydia'	NCot SRGP
§	***macrorrhizum***	CArn CFee CSBt EBee EPfP GKev GKir IFro LEdu LRHS MBNS MCot MRav MWat MWhi NBro NCGa NCot NHol SBod SRms SWat WBrE WCAu WFar WGor WHCG WWEG
	- AL & JS 90179YU	CHid EPPr
	- 'Album' ♀H4	Widely available
	- 'Bevan's Variety' ♀H4	Widely available
	- 'Bulgaria'	EPPr
	- 'Camce'	EPPr
	- 'Czakor'	Widely available
I	- 'De Bilt'	EBee EWes
	- 'Freundorf'	EBee EPPr EWes GCal
	- 'Ingwersen's Variety' ♀H4	Widely available
	- 'Lohfelden'	CDes EBee EPPr EWes GBuc GCal SRGP WCru WPGP
	- 'Mount Olympus'	see *G. macrorrhizum* 'White-Ness'
	- 'Mytikas' ♀H4	EBee EPPr NCot
	- 'Pindus'	CBod CPrp EAEE EBee EBla EBrs ECGP EPPr GAbr LRHS MBNS NBre NCot NSti SPoG SRGP WCru WFar WPtf
	- 'Prionia'	NCot
	- 'Purpurrot' **new**	WWEG
	- 'Ridsko'	CFee EPPr GBuc GCal LPla NBro NCot SRGP WCru
	- ***roseum***	see *G. macrorrhizum*
	- 'Rotblut'	EPPr SRGP
	- 'Sandwijck'	EBee EPPr MNFA NCot
	- 'Snow Sprite'	CBod CEnt CMea EPPr EPyc LBMP MCCP NCot NPro SPoG STes WHrl
	- 'Spessart'	EBee EBla ELan EPPr EPfP GMaP LAst LBMP LRHS MBri MGos NLar NPri SBch SEND SPoG WBVN WFar WPnP WRHF WWEG
	- 'Variegatum' (v)	EBee EBla EHrv ELan GMaP MHer MNFA MTho NBPC NBir SPer SRGP SRms WCom WCot WFar WMnd WSHC WWEG WWFP
	- 'Velebit'	EBee EPPr NCot SRGP WCru
§	- 'White-Ness' ♀H4	Widely available
	- 'Witoscha' **new**	EBee LRHS
	macrostylum	EBrs WCot WCru WPer
	- MP 8103D	EBee
	- 'Leonidas'	EBee EBrs EPPr NCot WCot WPnP
	- 'Marocco' **new**	NCot
	- 'Talish'	EPPr LRHS NCot
	- 'Uln Oag Triag'	EPPr

	Name	Suppliers
	maculatum	CElw CMea CSev EBee EBrs EPfP EWTr LLWP LRHS MAvo MRav NSti SMac SRGP SWat WCru WHal WPnP
	- from Kath Dryden	EBee EPPr
	- f. ***albiflorum***	CElw CLAP EBee EBla EPPr MNFA MNrw MWhi MWte NBid NChi NLar NSti SMac SMrm SRGP STes WBrk WCru WMoo WPnP
	- 'Beth Chatto'	Widely available
	- 'Elizabeth Ann'PBR ♀H4	Widely available
	- 'Espresso'	Widely available
	- 'Shameface'	EBee EPPr SBch SDys SGar
	- 'Silver Buttons' **new**	CDes EBee
	- 'Smoky Mountain'	EBee EPPr
	- 'Spring Purple'	CElw EBee EPPr NCot NLar
	- 'Sweetwater'	EPPr
	- 'Vickie Lynn'	CLAP EBee EPPr NChi
	maderense ♀H2	CAbb CArn CBod CHEx CPrp CSpe CTsd EBee EBla ELan EShb EWes LRHS NPer SAPC SArc SBod SChr SDix SDnm SHom SMrm SPav SPhx SRGP SRkn WCom WCru WPer WPnP
	- 'Guernsey White' **new**	NCot
	- white-flowered	CSpe LDai WCot
§	× ***magnificum*** ♀H4	Widely available
	- 'Blue Blood'	CElw CLAP CSev CWGN EBee ECtt EKen EPPr IPot LRHS LSou MCot MWea NBPC NCob NCot NGdn NSti SBch SMrm SRGP WClo WCot WFar
	- 'Ernst Pagels'	NCot
	- 'Hylander'	EBee EPPr
	- 'Peter Yeo'	EBee EPPr MNFA SRGP
	- 'Rosemoor'	CElw CHid EBee EBla EHrv ELan EPPr EPfP GCal LHop LRHS NPro WCot WMnd WPtf
	- 'Vital'	EBee NCot
	magniflorum	EWes LFur MRav MSCN NBid NChi NGdn
§	***malviflorum***	CDes CMHG ECha ELan EPPr LLWP LRHS MNFA MNrw MTho NCot SBch SMeo SRms WAul WCom WCot WCru WFar WPnP
	- from Spain	EWes WSHC
	- pink-flowered	CDes EBee EPPr WCru
§	'Mary Mottram'	CElw EBee EPPr LDai LPio NBir NCot WCot WEas WPnP
	'Mavis Simpson' ♀H4	Widely available
	maximowiczii	CElw
	'Maxwelton'	NCot
	'Melinda' **new**	EBee MBri
	'Memories'PBR	EBee ECtt EPPr LRHS LSRN MBNS NCGa NSti WFar
	'Menna Bach'	CDes MAvo WCru WPnP
	'Meryl Anne'	SRGP WPtf
	microphyllum	see *G. potentilloides*
	molle	NBir
	- white-flowered	NBir
	× ***monacense***	CPrp EBee EBla ELan EPla GGar IFoB LEdu LRHS MBNS SBch SBod SRGP SWat WBrk WCru WHer WMoo WPnP WPtf
	- var. ***anglicum***	CFir EBla EBrs ECtt EPPr GMaP LRHS MRav MWhi WCAu WMoo WPnP
	- 'Anne Stevens'	EBee NCot
	- 'Claudine Dupont'	CElw CMoH EBee EPPr IFro MAvo MNFA NCot WCot
	- dark-flowered	WMoo WPtf
	- var. ***monacense***	EBla NEgg WFar
	- - 'Breckland Fever'	EBee EPPr MAvo NChi SRGP
§	- - 'Muldoon'	EBee EBla EBrs EPPr LRHS NBir SRGP STes WFar WHCG WMoo WPer WPnP
	'Monita Charm'	CMoH
	moupinense	NCot
	'Mourning Widow'	see *G. phaeum* var. *phaeum* black-flowered
	'Mrs Jean Moss'	EBee EPPr EWes
	napuligerum misapplied	see *G. farreri*
	'Natalie'	CDes EBla EPPr LRHS MAvo NChi SUsu
	nepalense	IFro SRGP SRms
	'Nicola'	CElw EBee EBla EPPr IFro MNFA NCob NHaw SBch SRGP
	'Nimbus' ♀H4	Widely available
	nodosum	Widely available
	- dark-flowered	see *G. nodosum* 'Swish Purple'
	- 'Hexham Big Eyes' **new**	EBee
	- 'Julie's Velvet'	CDes SMrs WBor WHoo WPGP WTin
	- pale-flowered	see *G. nodosum* 'Svelte Lilac'
	- 'Pascal'	EPPr
	- 'Saucy Charlie'	SBch
	- 'Silverwood'	CElw EBee EPPr MAvo SBch SUsu
	- 'Simon'	EBee LBMP
§	- 'Svelte Lilac'	CElw EAEE EBee EBla EPPr EPfP LBMP LRHS MNFA NHol SRGP SWat WCAu WCot WCru WFar WMoo WPnP
§	- 'Swish Purple'	CElw EBee EBla EPPr MAvo MNFA NLar SIng SRGP WCru WFar WMoo WPGP WPnP
	- 'Whiteleaf'	CElw CMea EBla EPPr MAvo NChi NPro SBch SRGP WCom WCru WFar WHal WMoo WPnP
	- 'Whiteleaf' seedling	CElw EBla
	'Nora Bremner'	EBee NChi SUsu
	'Nunnykirk Pink'	EWes SUsu
	'Nunwood Purple'	EBee EPPr MAvo NCot WPtf
	oreganum	CMoH
§	***orientalitibeticum***	CMHG CPLG CPrp CSev CSpe EBee EBla ECtt EPPr GAbr GGar IFro LRHS MCot MHer MTho NBid NBre NLar SMad WBrk WCot WEas WFar WHCG WMoo WPGP WPnP WWEG
	'Orion' ♀H4	Widely available
	'Orkney Blue'	EPPr WCru WPnP
	'Orkney Cherry'	EBee EPfP LAst LLHF LRHS MWea SPoG SRkn
	'Orkney Dawn'	NHaw WCru WPnP
	'Orkney Pink'	CMac EBee EBla ECtt EPPr EPfP GBuc GKir LAst LSRN MLHP NHol NSti NWCA SPer SPoG SRGP SWat WCom WFar WHoo
	'Out of the Blue'	WOut
	× ***oxonianum***	NCot WMoo
	- 'A.T. Johnson' ♀H4	Widely available
	- 'Andy's Star' **new**	NCot
	- 'Ankum's White'	EBee NCot
	- 'Anmore'	EPPr SRGP
	- 'Beholder's Eye' ♀H4	CHid CPrp EBee EBla EPPr GKir MNFA NBre SBch SRGP WPnP WPtf WWEG
	- 'Breckland Sunset'	EBee EPPr MAvo SBch SRGP WPnP
	- 'Bregover Pearl'	CBre CElw EBee EBla EPPr SRGP WMoo
	- 'Bressingham's Delight'	EBla ECtt LRHS SRGP
	- 'Buttercup'	EBee EPPr NCot SRGP
I	- 'Cally Seedling'	EBee EBla EWes GCal
	- 'Chocolate Strawberry' **new**	EBee

§	- 'Claridge Druce'	Widely available
	- 'Coronet'	EPPr GCal NCot SMrm SRGP WMoo
	- 'David Rowlinson'	EPPr
	- 'Delabroye' **new**	EBee
	- 'Diane's Treasure'	NCot NHaw
	- 'Dirk Gunst'	CElw
	- dwarf pink-flowered **new**	NCot
	- 'Elsbeth Blush'	EBla NCot
	- 'Elworthy Misty'	CElw EBee EBla EPPr MSpe NCot SBch SRGP
	- 'Frank Lawley'	CElw CPrp EBee EBla EPPr GBuc LLWP NBid SBch SMrm SRGP WBrk WMoo
§	- 'Fran's Star' (d)	EBla EGoo SRGP WBrk WCru WRHF
	- 'Frilly Gilly'	EBee EPPr
	- 'Hexham Pink'	EBee EPPr NChi SBch SRGP
	- 'Hollywood'	EBee EBla ELan EPPr EPfP GBuc LRHS MBri MTho NCot NLar NPer SRGP SRms WBrk WFar WMoo WPnP WPtf WWEG
I	- 'Jean's Lilac'	NCot
	- 'Julie Brennan'	CHVG EBee GAbr SMrs WSHC
	- 'Kate Moss'	EBla EPPr EWes NSti SRGP
	- 'Katherine Adele'	CBod EBee EBla ECtt EPPr EPfP EWes GGar IPot LPla LRHS LSou MWea NBhm NCGa NCot NLar NSti SRGP SRms WFar
§	- 'Kingston'	CElw EBee EPPr
	- 'Klaus Schult'	EPPr LPio
	- 'Königshof'	EPPr EWes NCot NLar
	- 'Kurt's Variegated'	see *G.* × *oxonianum* 'Spring Fling'
	- 'Lace Time'	CBre CElw CSev EAEE EBee EBla ECtt EPPr GBuc LBMP LRHS LSRN MNrw NCot NEgg NGdn NHol SBch SPoG SRGP SRms WCAu WMnd WMoo WPnP
	- 'Lady Moore'	EBee EBla EPPr EPla GBuc MNrw NBro NCot SRGP WMoo WPnP
	- 'Lambrook Gillian'	EBee EPPr NCot SBch SRGP WBrk WPnP WPtf
	- 'Lasting Impression'	EBee EPPr SRGP
	- 'Laura Skelton'	CElw EBee NCot NHaw
	- 'Little John'	EBee EWes
	- 'Maid Marion'	EWes
	- 'Man of Mystery'	EBee
	- 'Miriam Rundle'	CElw EBrs EPPr LRHS NCot SRGP WCru WMoo WPnP WWEG
	- 'Moorland Jenny'	CElw WMoo
	- 'Moorland Star'	WMoo
	- 'Music from Big Pink' **new**	EBee
	- 'Old Rose'	EPPr GKir SRGP WCru WPnP
	- 'Pale Walter's Gift' **new**	GCal
	- 'Pat Smallacombe'	EBla NCot WMoo
	- 'Patricia Josephine'	WCAu
	- 'Pearl Boland'	EBee EPPr SRGP
	- 'Phantom'	EBee EPPr
	- 'Phoebe Noble'	CBre CElw EBla EPPr MNrw NCob NCot SMad SRGP WMoo WPnP WPtf
	- 'Phoebe's Blush'	EBla EPPr GCal SRGP
	- 'Pink Cluster'	CLAP
	- 'Pink Lace'	LSou
§	- 'Prestbury Blush'	CBre CElw EPPr SRGP WCru
	- 'Prestbury White'	see *G.* × *oxonianum* 'Prestbury Blush'
	- 'Raspberry Ice'	EBee EBla EWes
	- 'Rebecca Moss'	CPrp CSev EAEE EBee EBla ECtt EPPr GBuc GCra GMac LRHS NCot NSti SBch SBod SRGP WCru WFar WPnP WPtf WWEG
	- 'Robin's Ginger Nut'	EBee
	- 'Rodbylund'	EBee
	- 'Rose Clair'	EAEE EBee EBla EPfP GKir LRHS MWhi NBir SBch SGar SPet SRGP SRms WBrk WCAu WCru WEas WMnd WMoo WPer WWEG
	- 'Rosemary'	SBch
	- 'Rosemary Verey'	SBch
	- 'Rosenlicht'	CHrt CSev EAEE EBee EBla ECGP EPPr LRHS MNFA MRav NGdn NLar SBod SRGP WCAu WCru WMnd WMoo WPnP WPrP WPtf
	- 'Rosewood'	SRos
	- 'Rosita'	NCot
§	- 'Spring Fling' (v)	EBee EBla ECtt EHrv EPPr LFur LPla NCot NGdn NSti SRGP WCAu WFar WSpi
	- 'Stillingfleet Keira'	EBee NCot NSti SRGP
	- 'Summer Surprise'	EBee EPPr EWes NCob NLar SBch WCru WPnP
	- 'Susan'	EBee EBla EPPr EWes
	- 'Susie White'	CElw EPPr MAvo SRGP WCru
§	- f. ***thurstonianum***	Widely available
	- - 'Armitageae'	EBee EPPr NCot SRGP
	- - 'Breckland Brownie'	CElw EBee EBla EPPr EWes MAvo SRGP
	- - 'Crûg Star'	WCru
	- - 'David McClintock'	EBee EPPr SBch SRGP WFar WMoo
	- - 'Peter Hale'	CMea
	- - 'Red Sputnik'	EBee EPPr MAvo SRGP
	- - 'Sherwood'	EBee EBla ECtt EPPr GCal GQue MBel MSpe MTho NBro NCob NEgg NVic SApp SGar SMrm SRGP WCAu WFar WMoo WPnP WPtf
	- - 'Southcombe Double' (d)	CElw CSev EAEE EBee EBla ECtt EHrv EPPr EPfP GCra LAst LRHS MBel NBPC NChi NCot SPer SPoG SRGP SRms WBrk WCru WFar WMoo WWEG
§	- - 'Southcombe Star'	EBee EBla EPPr GAbr GCal LRHS NBro NGdn SRGP WCru WFar WMoo WPer WPnP
	- - 'Sue Cox'	EPPr NCot NLar
	- 'Trevor's White'	CLAP EBee EBla EPPr EWTr LLWP MNFA SBch SRGP WCru
	- 'Wageningen' ♀H4	CBre EAEE EBee EPPr GCal GMac LPla LRHS MBri MNFA NCot NGdn SMrm SRGP SRms WBrk WCot WCru WHer WMoo WPtf
	- 'Walter's Gift'	EBee EBla ECtt EPPr EPla EShb LBMP LLWP LRHS MAvo MRav MTho MWhi NBir NBro NChi NCob NHol NPer NSti SGar SPoG WBrk WClo WCru WFar WHoo WMoo WPnP
§	- 'Wargrave Pink' ♀H4	Widely available
	- 'Waystrode'	EBla EPPr SRGP
	- 'Westacre White' **new**	EWes
	- 'Whitehaven'	EBee NCot SRGP
	- 'Winscombe'	CHrt GCal LLWP MRav MTho NCob SRGP WFar WMnd WMoo WWEG
	× ***oxonianum*** × ***sessiliflorum*** subsp. ***novae-zelandiae*** 'Nigricans'	EHrv
	'Pagoda'	MNrw SUsu
§	***palmatum*** ♀H3	Widely available
	palmatum × ***maderense***	WCru
	palustre	CElw EBee EBla EPPr MNFA MNrw NBro NHol SRGP WFar WMoo

Name	Suppliers
papuanum	WCru
'Part Purple Hero'	EBee
Patricia = 'Brempat' 𝕐[H4]	Widely available
peloponnesiacum	EAEE EBee EPPr EWes LRHS MAvo NOrc SBch WFar
- NS 660	CElw
'Perfect Storm'	CWGN EBee ECtt EPPr LLHF LSou MAsh MWea NLar
phaeum	Widely available
- 'Album'	Widely available
- 'Alec's Pink'	EBla EPPr LLWP SHar WOut
- 'All Saints'	EBee EPPr LEdu SRGP
- 'Angelina'	NCot
- 'Aureum'	see *G. phaeum* 'Golden Spring'
- 'Blauwvoet'	EBee EPPr MAvo NCot
- 'Blue Shadow'	CDes CElw EBee EBla EPPr LLWP MAvo NCot SRGP
- 'Caborn Lilac' **new**	LLWP
- 'Calligrapher'	CElw EBee EBla EPPr LLHF LPio MAvo NChi NCot SBch SMac SMrs SRGP SUsu WMoo
- 'Chocolate Chip'	EBla
- 'Conny Broe' (v)	CLAP EBee NCot
- 'Countess of Grey'	SMrs
- 'Dark Dream' **new**	NChi
- 'David Bromley'	EBla NCot WCru
- 'David Martin' **new**	NCot
- 'Enid'	EPPr NCot
- 'George Stone'	EBee EBla EPPr LLHF
- 'Golden Samobor'	CElw EBla EPPr NCot
§ - 'Golden Spring'	CElw EBee EBla EPPr MAvo NChi NCot NPro SBch SRGP
- 'Hannah Perry'	CMoH EBla EPPr LLWP WPtf
- 'Hector's Lavender'	EBee
- var. ***hungaricum***	EBee EPPr LLWP SRGP WPtf
- 'James Haunch'	EBla EPPr
- 'Klepper'	EBee EPPr GBin NCot
- 'Lady in Black' **new**	NCot
- 'Lady in Mourning' **new**	EPPr NChi
- 'Lily Lovell'	Widely available
- 'Lisa'	EBee EPPr NCot
- 'Little Boy'	EBee EBla EPPr NGdn
- var. ***lividum***	CBgR CBre CFee CPrp GMaP LLWP LRHS MAvo MRav NCot NHol NLar SRGP SRms STes WCAu WFar WPer WPnP
- - 'Joan Baker'	CBgR CBre CSam EBee EPPr GBuc LPla MAvo MNFA NChi NCot NGdn NSti SBch SPhx SRGP WCAu WCru WFar WMoo WPnP WPtf WWEG
- - 'Majus'	CElw EBee ECtt EPPr EPfP EPyc LLWP LPla LRHS SPoG WFar WMoo
- 'Maggie's Delight' (v)	SRGP
- 'Marchant's Ghost'	MAvo NGdn
- 'Margaret Hunt'	NLar
- 'Margaret Wilson' (v)	CBow CDes CFir EBee EBla ECha ECtt EPPr EShb EWes GCal LEdu LPio MAvo NBPC NCot NEgg NGdn NSti SBch SMrs SPer SPoG SRGP STes SUsu WCot WFar WPnP WPtf
- 'Mierhausen'	CElw EBee EBla EPPr EShb MAvo NCot WPtf
- 'Moorland Dylan'	EBla WMoo WOut
- 'Moortown Pink' **new**	NCot
- 'Mourning Widow'	see *G. phaeum* var. ***phaeum*** black-flowered
- 'Mrs Charles Perrin'	CBgR CElw CPrp EBee EBla EPPr MAvo STes WPtf
- 'Mrs Withey Price' **new**	EPPr
- 'Night Time'	EBee EPPr
- 'Nightshade' **new**	EBla
- 'Our Pat' 𝕐[H4]	EBee EPPr NChi NCot
- 'Pannonia'	NCot
- var. ***phaeum***	SBch WOut
§ - - black-flowered	CFwr CMoH CPLG EShb GCal GKir MCot MNFA NCob NCot SGar SRGP SRms SWat WCru WMoo
- - 'Langthorns Blue'	CElw CMoH CSev EBee EBrs ELan EPPr EWes GKir LEdu LRHS MAvo MNrw NBre NCot SRGP SWvt
- - 'Samobor'	Widely available
I - 'Ploeger de Bilt'	EPPr
- purple-flowered	MDun
- 'Rachel's Rhapsody'	CElw EBee EBla EPPr MAvo NCot
- 'Raven'	EBee EPPr MDun NCot SUsu
- red-flowered	MRav
- 'Rise Top Lilac'	EBee NCot WPGP
- 'Rose' **new**	LRHS
- 'Rose Air'	EBee EPPr MAvo NCot SRGP WMoo WPnP WPtf
- 'Rose Madder'	CBgR CElw EBee EBla EPPr EPyc GBuc GCal LEdu LLWP LPio LPla MNrw NChi NCot NMRc SMrs SRGP SUsu WCru WMoo WPnP
- 'Saturn'	EBee EPPr
- 'Séricourt'	EBee WCot
- 'Slatina'	EBla WPtf
- 'Small Grey'	EBla EPPr
- 'Springtime'[PBR]	CBod CElw EBee EPPr EPfP LLHF MBNS NBhm NChi NCot NGdn NSti SPoG
- 'Stillingfleet Ghost'	CBow CElw EBla EPPr GKir LEdu LRHS NChi NCot NPro NSti
- 'Taff's Jester' (v)	CElw EWes GCal LHop LPla NHol SApp SRGP WCot
§ - 'Variegatum' (v)	Widely available
- 'Walküre'	EBee EPPr EWes MAvo WPtf
'Philippe Vapelle'	Widely available
'Pink Delight'	CElw EBla LPio MAvo
'Pink Ghost'	CBow
'Pink Penny'	EBee EPPr EPfP IPot WPnP
'Pink Splash'	LSou WPtf
§ ***platyanthum***	EBee EPPr GGar MNrw MWhi NBre SRGP WBrk WCru WHCG WPer
- var. ***reinii***	WCru
- 'Russian Giant'	EPPr SGar
platypetalum misapplied	see *G.* × ***magnificum***
platypetalum Franch.	see *G. sinense*
§ ***platypetalum*** Fisch. & C.A. Mey.	EPPr LRHS NBid NBir NBre SRGP SRms WCru WPtf
- 'Georgia Blue'	WCru WFar WPtf
- 'Genyell'	EBee
§ ***pogonanthum***	CDes GBuc IFro NBir NChi
polyanthes	GBuc
§ ***ponticum***	NSti
§ ***potentilloides***	GCal NBir SRGP WMoo
pratense	Widely available
I - 'Alboroseum' **new**	WCot
- 'Bittersweet'	EBee EBla EPPr NCot
- Black Beauty = 'Nodbeauty'[PBR]	CBcs CChe CHVG CPar CSBt CSpe CWGN EBee ECtt EPPr EPfP EWes IMon LBuc LRHS LSou MDun MGos MWea NCGa NPri SBch SDnm SPav SPer SRkn SRot SUsu WFar
- 'Blue Lagoon' **new**	EBee EPPr EWll
* - 'Blue Skies'	LSou
- 'Cluden Sapphire'	CAbP EBla EPPr GKir MWhi NBre NGdn NHol NLar NPro WCru
- 'Else Lacey' (d)	EBee WCot
- 'Feebers Double' (d)	CFee
- 'Flore Pleno'	see *G. pratense* 'Plenum Violaceum'
I - 'Himalayanum'	NLar

Plant	Suppliers
- 'Hocus Pocus'	EBee ECtt EHrv ELan EPfP LPio LRHS MAvo MBNS MBri MWea NBhm NBid NBro NLar NMoo NSti SMrm
- 'Ilja'	EBee NCot
- 'Janet's Special'	CSev WHoo
- 'Lichtenstein'	NCot
- Midnight Reiter strain	CBcs CBct CCVN CHar CSpe CWGN EBee EPfP GGar GKir IFoB LRHS MBNS NBro NChi NGdn NLar NSti SBch SGSe SIng SMrm SRms SWat SWvt WCru WFar WPnP
- 'Mrs Kendall Clark' Υ^{H4}	Widely available
- 'New Dimension'	CBcs EBee ELan EPPr EPfP GBin LHop LRHS MGos MWea NBre NSti
- 'Okey Dokey'	EBee
- pale-flowered	EBee WPnP
- 'Picotee'	EBee NCot
- 'Plenum Album'	CBre CLAP CMea ECtt ELan EPPr EWes LLHF MCot NBPC NCob NEgg NGdn NLar SMrm SMrs SPer SPoG WGwG WPtf WWEG
- 'Plenum Caeruleum' (d)	CHar CMHG EBee ECtt EPPr GBuc GMaP MRav NBid NEgg NGdn NHol NLar STes SWat WFar WHCG WMoo WPnP WSHC
§ - 'Plenum Violaceum' (d) Υ^{H4}	Widely available
- var. ***pratense*** f. ***albiflorum***	CBot CElw CSam EPPr GCra GMaP IFro LRHS MNrw NBid NCot NOrc SBch SPoG WCom WCot WHCG WMnd WMoo WPtf
- - - 'Galactic'	EBee EPPr GKir NBir NBre NGby SPhx WCot WCru WMoo WPnP
- - - 'Plenum Album' (d)	CDes EBee EPPr NLar NSti WCot WPnP
- - - 'Silver Queen'	CBre CHar EBee EBla ECtt EPPr MNrw NBir NBre SRGP WFar WMoo WPGP
- 'Purple Heron'	CDes EBee EBla EPPr LSRN MCCP MNrw WFar
* - 'Purple-haze'	CSpr GBuc MCCP MCot NCob NLar STes WBVN WHrl WMoo WTou
- 'Rectum Album'	see *G. clarkei* 'Kashmir White'
§ - 'Rose Queen'	EBee EBla EPPr MNrw MRav NBir NHol NLar SRGP WCom WCru
- 'Roseum'	see *G. pratense* 'Rose Queen'
- 'Splish-splash'	see *G. pratense* 'Striatum'
- 'Stanton Mill'	NBid
- var. ***stewartianum***	EBee MRav
- - 'Elizabeth Yeo'	EBee EBla ECtt EPPr MWea NCot NLar WCru
- - 'Purple Silk'	EPPr
§ - 'Striatum'	Widely available
- 'Striatum' dwarf	WCru
- 'Striatum' pale-flowered	CBre
§ - Victor Reiter Junior strain	CElw CPrp CSpe EBee EHrv ELan EPPr EShb GKir GMac LHop MLHP MMHG MNFA MWhi NBPC NBir NCob NGdn SHar SPoG SRot WCru WFar WPnP WPtf
- 'Wisley Blue'	EBla EPPr SBch SRGP WHal
- 'Yorkshire Queen'	EBee EPPr NCob NGdn WCru
'Prelude'	CBre CDes CElw EBee EPPr LPio MNFA NBir NCot NPro SRGP SUsu
'Prima Donna'	EBee
procurrens	CBre CElw COIW CSev EBee EPPr EShb GAbr GCal GGar LLWP MBel NBid NChi NGdn WBor WBrk WCru WFar WMoo
§ ***psilostemon*** Υ^{H4}	Widely available
- 'Bressingham Flair'	CPrp EBee EBla ECtt EPfP GAbr GCra LHop LRHS MRav NBid NChi NGdn NHol NLar SPer SRms WCAu WCru WFar WMoo WSHC
- 'Coton Goliath'	EBee EPPr EWes MCot NBPC NCot SUsu WCot
- 'Fluorescent'	NCot
- hybrid	CElw
- 'Jason Bloom'	EBrs GKir LRHS
- 'Madelon'	CElw EBee NCot NLar
- 'Moorland Jack' **new**	WMoo
- 'Sumela'	NCot
pulchrum	CHid CSpe EBee EPPr EWld MNrw SGar SRGP WCot WPer
punctatum hort.	see *G.* × *monacense* var. *monacense* 'Muldoon'
- 'Variegatum'	see *G. phaeum* 'Variegatum'
pylzowianum	EBee GGar MRav NBid NRya SBch WFar WMoo
pyrenaicum	CRWN CSev EBWF GAbr NBre NHol NSti WTou
- f. ***albiflorum***	EBla IFro LLWP LRHS MNrw NBir SAga SRGP WBrk WPer WPnP WTou
- 'Barney Brighteye'	SRGP
- 'Bill Wallis'	Widely available
- 'Bright Eyes'	LLWP NCot
- 'Isparta'	EBee EPPr IFro NCot SBch SPhx SRGP SUsu WBrk WTou
- 'Summer Sky'	EBrs GBin NCot SMrm SPav SRGP
- 'Summer Snow'	EPyc LFur NCot NLar
'Rachel'	CBow
'Rainbow' **new**	EBee MBNS WHlf
Rambling Robin Group	CBow CSpe EBee ECre ECtt EPPr EWes LAst LFur MCCP MWhi SMad WCru
rectum	EPPr NBre NCot WCru
- 'Album'	see *G. clarkei* 'Kashmir White'
'Red Admiral'	CWGN EBee ECGP ECtt EPPr EWll GBuc GCal GGar IPot LBMP LRHS MAvo NCGa NCot NLar NSti SPoG SRGP SUsu WCAu WFar
reflexum	CPrp CSev EBla EPPr NCot WFar WPrP
refractum	CPLG
regelii	CPrp CSam EBee EPPr GAuc LEdu NCot WCru WMoo WPnP
renardii Υ^{H4}	Widely available
- 'Beldo'	EBee
- blue-flowered	see *G. renardii* 'Whiteknights'
- 'Rothbury Hills' **new**	EBee
- 'Tcschelda'	CMHG EBee EBla ECha ECtt LBMP LPio LRHS NBir SBch SBod SMrm SRms WFar WMoo WPnP
§ - 'Whiteknights'	CMoH EBee EBla GBuc NBir WCru
- 'Zetterlund'	CPrp EAEE EBee EBla ECGP EHrv EPPr EPfP GKir LPio LRHS MAvo MBel MSpe MWat NEgg NPri SBch WBrk WFar WMnd WMoo
repens B&SWJ 9089	WCru
§ ***reuteri***	CTsd IDee LDai SChr SDnm SGar SPav SRGP WCru WPnP
'Richard Nutt'	EBee NChi
richardsonii	EBee EBla EPPr EPfP MNrw NBir NCot SRGP SRms WCru
× ***riversleaianum*** 'Russell Prichard' Υ^{H4}	Widely available
§ ***rivulare***	EBla NBre WHCG WMnd WPtf
- 'Album'	CSpr EBla
robertianum	CArn EBWF EPPr LLHF MHer SECG SRms

§	- 'Album'	EBla EPPr SHar SRGP SRms WAlt
	- f. ***bernettii***	see *G. robertianum* 'Album'
	- 'Celtic White'	CBre EPPr GCal MHer NGHP SHlg SPav SRGP WAlt WOut
	- subsp. ***celticum***	WAlt
	robustum	EBee EGoo EPPr ILad MNrw MWhi NBir NBro NCot SHGN SMad SPav SRGP WCot WFar WHal WKif WPGP WSHC
	- Hannays' form	CSev CSpe WPGP
	'Rosetta' **new**	EBee EPfP MAsh
	'Rosie Crûg'	CHid SWvt
	rosthornii	WCru
	'Rothbury Red' **new**	EBee
	Rozanne = 'Gerwat'PBR ♀H4	Widely available
	rubescens	see *G. yeoi*
	rubifolium	CFir WCru
§	'Ruprecht'	LFur WWEG
	ruprechtii misapplied	see *G.* 'Ruprecht'
	ruprechtii (Grossh.) Woronow	EPPr GAuc MAvo MNrw NBre SRGP WPer WPtf
	Sabani Blue = 'Bremigo'PBR	CMac CSpe EBee EPPr EWes LHop LRHS NChi NLar NSti SPer SPoG SRkn STes WPtf
	'Salome'	Widely available
	'Sandrine'	CAby CBcs CSev CSpe CWGN EBee ECGP EPPr EPfP GAbr GBin GMac GQue LLHF MAsh MAvo MNrw MWea NBPC NBre NCGa SPoG WClo WCot WFut WHlf WPnP WPtf WRHF
	sanguineum	Widely available
	- Alan Bloom = 'Bloger'PBR	EBee EBrs LRHS SIng
	- 'Album' ♀H4	Widely available
	- 'Alpenglow'	EPPr SBch SRGP
	- 'Ankum's Pride' ♀H4	CMMP EBee EBla EPPr IPot LPio MNFA NChi NCot NGdn NSti SBch SRGP SUsu SWat WCru WFar WMoo WPnP WPtf
	- 'Apfelblüte'	EBee EPPr NCot NGby NLar SSvw WFar
	- 'Aviemore' ♀H4	EBee EPPr GBin GCal NCot SBch
	- 'Barnsley'	CElw CPrp EPPr NBro NPro WHrl
	- 'Belle of Herterton'	EPPr MAvo NBid NChi NPro SBch SUsu WCru
	- 'Bloody Graham'	EPPr MAvo NCot NHaw SBch WMoo
	- 'Candy Pink'	EPPr
	- 'Canon Miles'	EBee EPPr GGar LRHS MAsh NCot
	- 'Catforth Carnival'	EPPr
	- 'Cedric Morris'	CElw EBee EBla ECha EPPr GCra LPio LRHS MAvo MTho NBid SRGP WCru WPnP
	- 'Compactum'	EBee
§	- 'Droplet'	SRGP
	- 'Elsbeth'	CElw EBee EBla ECha ECtt EPPr EWes GBuc GCal NCot NGdn NSti SBch SPoG SRGP WCru WFar WHal WMoo WPnP WWEG
	- 'Feu d'Automne'	EBee EPPr
	- 'Fran's Star'	see *G. × oxonianum* 'Fran's Star'
	- 'Glenluce'	Widely available
	- 'Hampshire Purple'	see *G. sanguineum* 'New Hampshire Purple'
	- 'Holden'	CElw EPPr NCot SBch
	- 'Inverness'	EBee EPPr NCot
	- 'Joanna'	MAvo
	- 'John Elsley'	CPrp EAEE EBee EBla ECtt EHoe EPPr GKir LAst LLWP LRHS MNFA MSCN NBro NCot NGdn NLar SRGP SWat WMnd WPer WWEG
	- 'John Innes'	EBee EPPr NCot
	- 'Jubilee Pink'	EBla GCal WCru
	- 'Kristin Jacob'	EPPr
	- var. ***lancastrense***	see *G. sanguineum* var. *striatum*
	- 'Leeds Variety'	see *G. sanguineum* 'Rod Leeds'
§	- 'Little Bead' ♀H4	EBee EBla ECho GKir NHol
	- 'Max Frei'	Widely available
	- 'Minutum'	see *G. sanguineum* 'Droplet'
	- 'Nanum'	see *G. sanguineum* 'Little Bead'
§	- 'New Hampshire Purple'	CLAP EBee ECtt EPPr GGar LRHS LSou NBro NGdn NLar NSti SSvw
	- 'Nyewood'	EBee ECGP ECtt EPPr MAsh MBel SEND SRGP WCru
I	- 'Plenum' (d)	EPPr
	- var. ***prostratum*** (Cav.) Pers.	see *G. sanguineum* var. *striatum*
	- 'Purple Flame'	see *G. sanguineum* 'New Hampshire Purple'
§	- 'Rod Leeds'	CLAP EBee LPio MWea NPro SRGP WFar WPnP
	- 'Sandra'	SRGP
	- 'Sara'	MAvo WPnP
	- 'Shepherd's Warning' ♀H4	CMea CTri EAEE EBee EBla ECtt EPPr GCal GKir LRHS MBel NBir NLar SEND SRGP SUsu SWat WCru WFar WHoo WSpi WTin
	- 'Shooting Star'	EBee NCot
	- 'South Nutfield'	MAvo NCot SUsu
§	- var. ***striatum*** ♀H4	Widely available
	- - deep pink-flowered	CSBt MSwo SWvt
	- - 'Reginald Farrer'	GBuc WCru
	- - 'Splendens' ♀H4	CElw CEnt CSev CWib EBla ELan EPPr LBee LHop LRHS NBid NCot WCru WEas WTin
	- 'Vision Light Pink'	EBee LRHS SGar WWEG
	- 'Vision Violet'	COlW EBee EBla LRHS NHol SWvt WFar WPer
	- 'Westacre Poppet'	EPPr EWes
	saxatile	CElw EPPr
	schlechteri	EBee
	'Sea Pink'	EDAr
	'Sellindge Blue'	NCot
	sessiliflorum	ECou
I	- subsp. ***novae-zelandiae*** 'Nigricans'	EBla ECha ECho EHrv ELan EPfP GAbr GGar IPot MCot MHer NMoo NWCA SBch SRGP SWal WBrE WFar WHCG
§	- - 'Porter's Pass'	CBow CSpe CWib EBee ECho EHoe EWes GBuc MCCP MNrw NBir SBch SPlb WCom WHoo
	- - red-leaved	see *G. sessiliflorum* subsp. *novae-zelandiae* 'Porter's Pass'
	'Sheilah Hannay'	CSpe
	shikokianum	CLAP LFur MCCP NLar SGar SPer SRGP WHrl
	- var. ***kaimontanum***	EBla WCru
	- var. ***quelpaertense***	EBee EBla MAvo WPtf
	- - B&SWJ 1234	WCru
	- var. ***yoshiianum***	CElw GBuc
	- - B&SWJ 6147	WCru
	'Shocking Blue'	EBee NCGa NSti
	'Shouting Star'	see *G.* 'Kanahitobanawa'
	'Silva'	CElw CMoH EBee ECtt EPPr MAvo MNFA MRav SWat WCru
*	'Silver Shadow'	SPhx
§	***sinense***	CFir CMHG CPLG EBee EBla ECtt EPPr EPfP GCal LBMP LFur LPio

	LRHS MCot MNrw NGdn NSti SPoG SRGP STes WMnd WMoo WPer WPnP
'Sirak' ΨH4	Widely available
soboliferum	EBee EBla EBrs ELan EPPr GKir LRHS NBir NChi NDlv NWCA SRGP SUsu WCru WMoo WPtf
- Cally strain	CDes GCal
- var. ***kiusianum***	CElw MWea
- 'Starman'	EBee EPPr MBri NLar
'Southcombe Star'	see *G.* × *oxonianum* f. *thurstonianum* 'Southcombe Star'
'Southease Celestial'	SSth SUsu
'Spinners'	Widely available
stapfianum var. ***roseum***	see *G. orientalitibeticum*
'Starman' **new**	MAsh
'Stephanie'	CDes CElw EBee EPPr EPfP EWes LBMP LPio MBNS MNFA MWea NChi NCot NGdn NSti WPnP
'Storm Chaser' **new**	EBee MWea NSti
'Strawberry Frost'	EBla LLHF
subcaulescens ΨH4	Widely available
- 'Giuseppii' ΨH4	CPLG EAEE EBee EBla ECtt ELon EPPr EShb GEdr GGar GKir LRHS LSou MHer MNFA MNrw MRav NBro NCot NPri SBch SMrm SRGP SRot WBrE WFar WPnP
- 'Splendens' ΨH4	CTri EAEE EBee EBla ECtt EPPr EPfP LHop LRHS MCot MDun MHer NEgg NPri NSla SRms SWat WClo WFar WPat WPnP
'Sue Crûg'	Widely available
'Sue's Sister'	WCru
'Summer Cloud'	EBla EPPr MNFA SRGP
Summer Skies = 'Gernic'PBR (d)	Widely available
suzukii	WPtf
- B&SWJ 016	WCru
swatense	MBel
'Sweet Heidy'	EBee ECtt EKen LLHF MAsh MAvo MWea NBhm NMoo WBor
sylvaticum	CMMP CRWN EBWF EBee EBla NBid NGdn WBrk WMoo WPer WShi
- 'Afrodite'	EPPr
- f. ***albiflorum***	CBot CBre CElw EBee ELan NSti WCru
- 'Album' ΨH4	Widely available
- 'Amanda' **new**	EBee
- 'Amy Doncaster'	Widely available
- 'Angulatum'	CElw EBee EPPr MNFA NCot SBch WMoo
- 'Birch Lilac'	CElw CSam EBee EBla EPPr GBuc GCal LRHS MAvo MNFA SMrm WFar WMoo WPnP
- 'Birgit Lion'	EBee
- 'Ice Blue'	EBla EPPr GBin MNFA
- 'Immaculée'	EPPr MRav
- 'Kanzlersgrund'	CElw EPPr
- 'Lilac Eyes' **new**	EBee
- 'Lilac Time'	EBla EPPr
- 'Mayflower' ΨH4	Widely available
- 'Meran'	EPPr
- 'Nikita'	EPPr
- f. ***roseum***	EPPr GGar NBre NLar WPtf
- - 'Baker's Pink'	CElw EBee EBla EPPr MNFA MRav NBir NCot SBch SRGP WCru WFar WHCG WMoo WPnP
- 'Southcombe Beauty' **new**	EBee
- subsp. ***sylvaticum*** var. ***wanneri***	EBee EPPr SBch WCru
§ 'Tanya Rendall'PBR	CMHG EBee ECtt EPPr GBin GMac GQue LOck LRHS MBNS MBri MWea NBPC NBhm NMoo SPer WCot WFar WPnP WWFP
'Terre Franche'	EBee EPPr MAvo NGby SMrs SSvw WFar WWEG
§ ***thunbergii***	CEnt CFir CHid EBla EWes EWld LSou SRGP WMoo WPer WPnP
- dark-flowered	WSpi
- 'Jester's Jacket' (v)	CFir EKen EPPr LRHS MCCP MGos NPro SGar SRGP WFar WHrl WPtf
- pink-flowered	EPPr SRGP
- white-flowered	EPPr SRGP
thurstonianum	see *G.* × *oxonianum* f. *thurstonianum*
'Tinpenny Mauve'	WHoo WTin
'Tiny Monster'	CDes EBee EBla EPPr EWes LSou MAvo MBNS MNFA MWhi NGby NGdn NLar NMoo NSti SBch SPhx WFar
transbaicalicum	EBee EPPr GBin MNrw NHaw
traversii	CWib GGar LRHS
- var. ***elegans***	CFee CSpe CWib EAEE ECtt LRHS WEas WHCG WKif
tuberosum	CBro CElw CHid CHrt EBee EBla EBrs ECha ECho ELan EShb LRHS MRav MTho NBir NBro NCot NGdn SAga SGar SMrs SPhx WFar WPnP WSpi
- var. ***charlesii***	see *G. kotschyi* var. *charlesii*
- subsp. ***linearifolium***	WCru
'Ushguli Grijs'	see *G. ibericum* Cav. 'Ushguli Grijs'
'Vera May'	SUsu
'Verguld Saffier'PBR	see *G.* Blue Sunrise
versicolor	CElw CMac CMea CRWN CSsd EBWF EBee EBla EPfP GAbr GGar LRHS MBri MHer MNrw MTho NVic SPet SRms WBrk WCAu WFar WHCG WMoo WPnP
- 'Kingston'	see *G.* × *oxonianum* 'Kingston'
§ - 'Snow White'	CElw EBee ECtt EGoo EPPr MNrw NBre SRGP WCru WMoo WPnP
- 'The Bride'	CMea ECtt
- 'White Lady'	see *G. versicolor* 'Snow White'
'Victor Reiter'	see *G. pratense* Victor Reiter Junior strain
violareum	see *Pelargonium* 'Splendide'
viscosissimum	EBla SRGP WMnd
- var. ***incisum***	EBrs MCCP NBre
- rose pink-flowered	NBir
wallichianum	CHrt CMac CPou EBee IFro NBir NChi NSti WCot WMoo
§ - 'Buxton's Variety' ΨH4	Widely available
- 'Chadwell's Pink'	EBee
- 'Chris'	EPPr NCot SRGP SUsu
- 'Crystal Lake'	CWGN EBee EKen EPfP IPot MAsh MBNS MWea NBir WHlf
- magenta-flowered	GBuc
- pale blue-flowered	CElw
- 'Pink Buxton'	EBee EWes NLar
- pink-flowered	EBla GBuc GCal NCGa NCot WCru
- 'Rosie'	SRGP
- 'Syabru'	CMea EBla GBuc MNrw NCot NLar WFar WMoo WPnP
'Wednesday's Child'	WFar
'Welsh Guiness'	WCru
wilfordii misapplied	see *G. thunbergii*
wilfordii Maxim.	EBee
Wisley hybrid	see *G.* 'Khan'
'Wisley Jewel'	EBee
wlassovianum	Widely available

- 'Blue Star'	IPot MRav NPro SRGP WCon WFar
- 'Zellertal'	NCot
§ ***yeoi***	CSpe EPPr MNrw NBir NBro NSti SRGP WCru WOut WTou
yesoense	EBla EPPr NBir NSti SRGP WOut
- var. ***nipponicum***	NCot WCru
yoshinoi misapplied	see *G. thunbergii*
yoshinoi Makino	MWhi
yunnanense misapplied	see *G. pogonanthum*
yunnanense ambig.	CFir

Gerbera (*Asteraceae*)

Everlast Series Everlast Carmine = 'Amgerbcar'PBR **new**	LBuc LSou NBhm WHlf
- Everlast Pink = 'Amgerbpink'PBR	LBuc NBhm SHar SPoG STes WHlf
- Everlast White = 'Amgerbwhi'PBR	CSpe LBuc NBhm SHar SPoG STes WHlf

Gerrardanthus (*Cucurbitaceae*)

macrorhizus	ERea

Gesneria (*Gesneriaceae*)

cardinalis	see *Sinningia cardinalis*
* ***macrantha*** 'Compacta'	EShb

Gethyllis (*Amaryllidaceae*)

barkerae **new**	ECho
ciliaris **new**	ECho
- 'Porterville' **new**	ECho
grandiflora **new**	ECho
gregoriana **new**	ECho
linearis 'Piketburg' **new**	ECho
transkarooica 'Waboomsberg' **new**	ECho
verticillata **new**	ECho
- 'Pikenierskloof' **new**	ECho
villosa **new**	ECho

Gethyum (*Alliaceae*)

atropurpureum	WCot

Geum ✿ (*Rosaceae*)

from India **new**	GCal
'Abendsonne'	CDes CElw EBee MAvo
aleppicum	CFee NBre
alpinum	see *G. montanum*
andicola	NBre
'Beech House Apricot'	CBre CElw CLAP CSev EBee EBla EBrs ECtt EPPr GCra LRHS MAvo MNFA MNrw MRav NCGa NChi NHol NPro SApp WAbe WMoo WPnP WPrP WTin WWEG
'Bell Bank'	Widely available
'Birkhead's Creamy Lemon'	CElw MAvo
'Blazing Sunset' (d)	Widely available
N 'Borisii'	Widely available
'Borisii' × ***montanum***	LHop
'Bremner's Nectarine'	CElw MAvo NChi
bulgaricum	CElw EBee GKir MRav NBir NLar NPro NRya WPnP WPrP WTin
'Butterscotch'	EBee NCot
calthifolium	EPPr GKir MCCP MRav NBre NBro
canadense	EBee
capense	LSou NBre NPro SHGN SPlb
- JJ&JH 9401271	EBee
§ ***chiloense***	EBla LEdu
- 'Farncombe'	NCot
- 'Red Dragon'	CMac EBee LLHF LSRN NBre SGSe SPoG SWvt
'Chipchase'	GJos MAvo NCGa NChi
coccineum misapplied	see *G. chiloense*
coccineum ambig.	EBla
coccineum Sibth. & Sm. MESE 374	EBee
- 'Ann' **new**	EBee
- 'Cooky'	CElw CSam EAEE EBla EPfP EWll GJos LRHS LSou MMuc MSCN NGBl NPri SBch SPad SPoG SWal SWvt WClo WFar WHil WPer WWEG
- 'Eos'	CDes CElw EBee EBla EWes LEdu MAsh MAvo WCot
- 'Queen of Orange' **new**	LRHS
- 'Werner Arends'	CMHG EBee EBla GAbr GCal MAvo MNrw MRav NBro WCot WFar WMoo
'Coppertone'	CDes CElw CLAP CWGN EBee EBla ECtt EHrv ELan MAvo MNrw MRav NBir NBro NCGa NChi NRya SPav WAul WCom WHoo WMoo WPrP WTin
'Dingle Apricot'	CElw ECtt GAbr GBin MAvo MNrw MRav NBir WWEG
'Dolly North'	EBee EBla EPyc GAbr GKir MAvo MNrw MRav MSpe NBro NGdn WAul WCAu WHal WPrP WWEG
elatum	EBee EBla
'Farmer John Cross'	CBre CDes CElw CLAP EBee EBla ECtt GJos LPla MAvo MNrw MSpe NCGa NCob NCot NLar WHal WMoo WWEG
fauriei × ***kamtschatica***	EBee EBla
'Feuerball'	NBre NCob NGdn
'Feuermeer'	EBee EBla NLar NPro
'Fire Opal' ♀H4	CDes CElw EBee EWes MAvo MNrw NBir NBre SUsu WGwG WMoo
'Fireball'	EBee NBhm
'Flame' **new**	CElw MAvo
'Flames of Passion'PBR	CCVN CHar CWGN EBee EBla ECtt EWTr GBin GMac GQue MAvo MBNS MBri NBPC NCob NLar SRGP STes WAul WCAu WWEG
'Fresh Woods'	WPGP
'Georgenberg'	CElw CPrp CSam EBee EBla ECtt EPfP GMaP LRHS MAvo MCot MHer MNrw MRav NBir NBre NCob NGdn NHol SPer SPoG SRms SWvt WAul WCAu WFar WHoo WMoo WPrP WWEG
'Hannay's' **new**	MAvo
'Herterton Primrose'	CElw CWCL EBla ECtt GCal LLHF LLWG MAvo MSpe MWte NCGa NCob NGby SUsu WHal WHoo WWEG
'Hilltop Beacon'	WHoo WPrP
hispidum **new**	SGar
* ***hybridum luteum***	NSti
× ***intermedium***	CBre EBee EBla EPPr MAvo MNrw NGdn NLar NPro SHGN WFar WMoo WWEG
- 'Diane'	CDes GJos MAvo NBre NChi WHoo
I ***japonicum*** 'Variegatum' (v)	CBow EBee
'Karlskaer'	CElw EBee EBla ECtt EWes GBin GQue LRHS MAvo MBri MNrw MSpe NCob NGdn WCot WFar WMoo WPnP WPtf WWEG
'Kashmir'	LRHS MAvo
'Lady Stratheden' ♀H4	Widely available
'Lemon Drops'	CElw CHar CLAP COIW CPrp EBee EBla ECha ECtt EPPr GJos LHop LSRN MNrw MRav MSpe MWte

NChi NCob NGdn NPro NSti SAga SPav STes WFar WGwG WMoo WPnP WWEG
'Lionel Cox' Widely available
'Lisanne' CSam EBee NCGa NCot
macrophyllum EBee GAuc GBar
- var. ***sachalinense*** GAuc
magellanicum EBee EBla EWes NBre NLar
'Mandarin' CElw CFir EBla GAbr GCal MAvo
'Marmalade' EBee EBla ECtt ELon EWTr GAbr GJos LLWG MAvo MNrw MSpe NBre NCGa NLar NPro SAga SDys SUsu WHrl WKif WMoo WWEG
§ ***montanum*** ♀H4 CEnt EBla ECho EDAr GAuc GCra GGar GKir NBir NBro NGdn NPri NRya SPet SRms WMoo WWEG
- 'Diana' EBla MNrw NCot NLar NPro WWEG
'Moorland Sorbet' NCot WFar WMoo WPtf WWEG
'Mrs J. Bradshaw' ♀H4 Widely available
'Mrs W. Moore' CBre CDes CElw CLAP CWGN EBee EBla ECtt EShb GAbr GJos LDai MAvo MBel MHer MNrw NBir NChi NCot NLar NPro SPad SRGP WMoo WPrP WWEG
'Nordek' EAEE EBee ECtt GAbr GBuc GJos IPot LAst LRHS MAvo MRav NCob NEgg NGdn WSpi WWEG
* 'Orangeman' MNrw
parviflorum NBre NBro
'Paso Doble' CElw
pentapetalum see *Sieversia pentapetala*
- 'Flore Pleno' (d) WAbe
'Pink Frills' CDes CElw EBee EBla EWes GAbr LLWG LPla MAvo MRav MSpe NCGa NCot NLar SMrm STes WPrP WWEG
'Poco' NPro
ponticum GAuc WOut
'Present' CElw EBee EBla ECtt MAvo MSpe NBre NCGa NChi WWEG
'Primrose' GAbr GJos GQue NGdn NLar NPro
'Prince of Orange' CElw EBla GAbr IGor MAvo MNrw MRav NBre WFar WHrl
'Prinses Juliana' Widely available
pyrenaicum EBee EBla NBre
quellyon see *G. chiloense*
I 'Rearsby Hybrid' MAvo MRav SUsu
'Red Wings' EBee EBla MRav NCGa SHar SUsu
§ ***reptans*** GBin NCob
- SDR 5500 EBee GKev
× ***rhaeticum*** MNrw WMoo
rhodopeum LLHF
'Rijnstroom' EBee EBla ELan LDai MAvo MWea NBPC WPtf
rivale Widely available
- 'Album' Widely available
- 'Barbra Lawton' EBla MAvo MDKP MSpe
- 'Cream Drop' EBla LLWG NCGa NChi NGby NPro SMrm WWEG
- cream-flowered, from Tien Shan, China CFee
- 'Leonard's Double' (d) CPrp WFar WWEG
- 'Leonard's Variety' Widely available
- 'Marika' CBre CCVN CHid CRow EBee EBla LRHS NBre NCGa NCot SMrm SRGP WMoo WWEG
- 'Marmalade' EBla NBPC NChi
- 'Oxford Marmalade' CElw SApp
- 'Snowflake' NChi
'Rubin' CElw EBla ECtt EPPr EPyc GBuc MNrw NBre NBro SBch SUsu WAul WCAu
'Sigiswang' CDes CElw EBee GAbr GJos GMac MAvo MNrw MRav NBre NCob NPro SMrm WMoo WWEG
'Stacey's Sunrise' **new** NPro
I 'Starker's Magnificum' WCot
'Tangerine' EBla LSou MAvo MRav NPro
'Tinpenny Orange' CElw MAvo WTin
× ***tirolense*** EBee EBla NBre NCGa
triflorum CElw EBee EBla EHrv EShb LBMP MCCP MNrw NLar SPhx STes WFar WTin
- var. ***campanulatum*** NChi NPro WWEG
urbanum CArn EBWF GBar GJos GPWP NLan NPri NSco SECG SWat WHer WMoo
- from Patagonia EBla MAvo MDKP
'Wallace's Peach' SWal

Gevuina (*Proteaceae*)

avellana CBcs CHEx CTrG IDee WPGP

Gilia ✿ (*Polemoniaceae*)

aggregata see *Ipomopsis aggregata*
caespitosa CPBP
californica see *Leptodactylon californicum*
tricolor NPol

Gillenia (*Rosaceae*)

stipulata CLAP EBee LEdu NLar SUsu
trifoliata ♀H4 Widely available
- 'Pink Profusion' **new** EBee
- 'Pixie' WPGP

Ginkgo ✿ (*Ginkgoaceae*)

biloba ♀H4 Widely available
- B&SWJ 8753 WCru
- 'Anny's Dwarf' MAsh SCoo
- 'Autumn Gold' (m) CBcs CEnd CMCN EBee ECrN LAst MBlu MGos MPkF NLar SBig SMad SPoG WPGP
I - 'Barabits Nana' SBig
- 'Beijing Gold' **new** MBlu NLar
- 'California Sunset' **new** NLar
- 'Chi-chi' MPkF SBig
- 'Chotek' SBig
- 'Doctor Causton' (f) CAgr
- 'Doctor Causton' (m) CAgr
- 'Elmwood' **new** NLar
- 'Elsie' SBig
- 'Fairmount' (m) CMCN MBlu SBig
- 'Fastigiata' (m) CLnd CMCN EPfP MBlu MGos
- 'Gnome' **new** ESwi LSRN MGos
- 'Golden Globe' ESwi NLar
- 'Horizontalis' CLnd CMen MBlu SBig
- 'Jade Butterflies' CBcs MBlu MBri MPkF NLar SLim
- 'King of Dongting' (f) CMCN MBlu SBig
- 'Mariken' EOrn ESwi MAsh MGos MPkF NLar NPal SBch SBig SLim SPoG
- 'Mayfield' (m) SBig
- Ohazuki Group (f) CAgr SBig
- Pendula Group CEnd CMCN CTho ECrN EPfP ESwi IDee LRHS MBlu MPkF NPal SLim
- 'Princeton Sentry' (m) SBig SMad
I - 'Prostrata' CPMA
- 'Robbie's Twist' **new** MPkF NLar
- 'Saratoga' (m) CBcs CDoC CEnd CLnd CMCN CPMA CTho MBri MGos MPkF SBig SLim SMad SSpi WPGP
- 'Tit' CEnd CMCN CMen EPfP MGos NLar SBig WPGP
- 'Tremonia' CMCN EPfP MBlu MPkF NLar SBig SLim

- 'Troll'	MBlu SBig SCoo SMad
- 'Tubifolia'	CMCN CMen MBlu NLar SBig SLim SMad
- 'Umbrella'	SBig
- Variegata Group (v)	CBcs CMCN CMen CPMA ESwi MGos MPkF NLar SBig SLim SPoG

ginseng see *Panax ginseng*

Gladiolus (*Iridaceae*)

abyssinucus **new**	GCal
acuminatus	WCot
alatus	EBrs ECho LPio
- white-flowered	WCot
'Alba' (N)	CGrW
'Alexandra' (P)	WCot
'Alice' (Min)	LRHS
'Allosius' (S)	CGrW
'Amsterdam' (G)	CGrW
'Andre Viette'	LFur LLHF WCot
angustus	CGrW WCot
antakiensis	CPou
'Antica' (L)	CGrW
'Antique Lace' (L)	CGrW
'Antique Rose' (M)	WCot
'Anyu S' (L)	CGrW
'Arctic Day' (M/E)	CGrW
'Atom' (S/P)	CGrW EBee EBrs ECho WHil
atroviolaceus	WPGP
'Aubade' **new**	LRHS
Barnard hybrids	CGrW
'Beautiful Angel'	CGrW
'Beauty Bride' (L)	CGrW
'Beauty of Holland'PBR (L)	CGrW
'Belinda' (S) **new**	LRHS
'Bizar'	EPfP LRHS WCot
'Black Jack'	CSpe EPfP LRHS
'Blackbird' (S)	CGrW
'Blue Clouds' (L)	CGrW
'Blue Tropic'	CSut LRHS
'Bonfire' (G) **new**	CGrW
'Boone'	SMrm
× ***brenchleyensis*** **new**	CPen
'Brittania' (L)	CGrW
'Bronze Tiger' (M/E)	WCot
byzantinus	see *G. communis* subsp. *byzantinus*
callianthus	see *G. murielae*
cardinalis	CDes CMea CPne CPrp GCal GGar IBlr SAga SChr WBor WCot WCru WPGP
carinatus	CDes CGrW GGar WCot
carinatus* × *orchidiflorus	WCot
'Carine' (N)	LRHS
carmineus	CGrW CPen EBee ECho WCot WPGP
carneus	CGrW CPen CPou EBee EBrs ECho EPot GCal LPio SMeo WPGP
'Carquirenne' (G)	CGrW
caryophyllaceus	CPou
'Charlotte'PBR **new**	LRHS
'Charm' (N/Tub)	CAvo CBro CFFs CPrp EBee
'Charming Beauty' (Tub)	EBrs ECho LRHS WHil
'Charming Lady' (Tub)	ECho WHil
'Chartreuse Ruffles' (S)	CGrW
'Cheops'PBR	CSut
'Chocolate Smores' (E) **new**	CGrW
'Christabel' (L)	ERos
'Cindy' (B)	ECho
citrinus	see *G. trichonemifolius*
'Claudia' (N)	CGrW EBrs LRHS
'Columbine' (P)	LRHS
× ***colvillii***	CPne IBlr
- 'Albus'	EBrs LPio LRHS
- 'The Bride' ♀H3	CAvo CBro CElw CFFs CMea CPrp EBee ECho ITim LAma LDai LEdu LPio LSRN
'Comet' (N)	CAvo EBrs LPio
§ ***communis***	Widely available
subsp. ***byzantinus*** ♀H4	
'Contessa Queen'	CGrW
'Coral Dream' (L)	CGrW
'Country Knoll' (S) **new**	CGrW
crassifolius	GBuc
'Cream Perfection' (L)	CGrW
'Creamy Yellow' (S)	CGrW
'Cristabel'	WCot
§ ***dalenii***	CGrW CPou CPrp CSam EBee ECho ERos IBlr LPio WCot WPGP
- subsp. ***dalenii***	IBlr
- green-flowered	IBlr
- orange-flowered	CDes WPGP
* - f. ***rubra***	IBlr
- yellow-flowered	CDes EBee WPGP
'Dandy' (M) **new**	CGrW
'Daydreamer' (L)	CGrW
'Day's End' (S)	CGrW
'Deanna' (L)	CGrW
'Director' (L) **new**	CGrW
'Donatella' (L) **new**	CGrW
'Drama' (L)	CGrW
ecklonii	WPGP
'Elderberry Wine' (E) **new**	CGrW
'Elegance' (G)	CGrW
'Elvira' (N)	EBee EBrs ECho WPGP
'Emerald Spring' (S)	CGrW CSpe WCot
'Emily'PBR **new**	LRHS
equitans	CGrW
'Esta Bonita' (G)	CGrW
'Felicta' (L)	CGrW
ferrugineus	LPio
'Fidelio' (L)	LRHS
'Finishing Touch'PBR (L)	CGrW
flanaganii	CPBP CSpe CStu EBrs ECho GBin GCal ITim LLHF LPio LRHS SChr WCot
- JCA 261.000	EBee
'Flevo Bambino' (S)	CGrW LRHS
'Flevo Cosmic' (Min)	CGrW LPio
'Flevo Dancer' (S)	CGrW
'Flevo Eclips'PBR (G)	CGrW
'Flevo Eyes'PBR (L)	CGrW
'Flevo Jive' (S)	CGrW
'Flevo Junior' (S)	CGrW
'Flevo Party' (S)	LRHS
'Flevo Salsa' (S) **new**	CGrW
'Flevo Smile' (S)	CGrW WCot
'Flevo Souvenir'PBR (L)	CGrW
'Flevo Sunset'PBR (L)	CGrW
floribundus	EBee
fourcadei	ECho
'Frederica' (B) **new**	LRHS
'French Silk' (L)	CGrW
Glamini Series **new**	LRHS
- 'Glamini Christopher' **new**	LRHS
- 'Glamini Eva' **new**	LRHS
- 'Glamini Zoë' **new**	LRHS
'Gold Struck' (L)	CGrW
'Good Luck' (N)	CBro
gracilis	WCot

	Name	Suppliers
	grandis	see *G. liliaceus*
	'Green Star' (L)	CGrW LRHS
	'Green Woodpecker' (M)	EBee
	'Guernsey Glory' (N)	EBrs
	'Halley' (N)	CGrW ECho
	hirsutus	CGrW
	'Home Coming' (L) **new**	LRHS
	'Hunting Song' (L)	LRHS
	'Huron Dancer' (L)	CGrW
	'Huron Fox' (S)	CGrW
	'Huron Frost' (L)	CGrW
	'Huron Heaven' (L)	CGrW
	'Huron Jewel' (M)	CGrW
	'Huron Lady'	CGrW
	'Huron Meadow' (M)	CGrW
	'Huron Pleasure'	CGrW
	'Huron Silk' (L)	CGrW
	huttonii	CGrW ECho WCot
	huttonii* × *tristis	CPou
	huttonii* × *tristis var. ***concolor***	WCot
	hyalinus	WCot
	'Ice Cream'	LRHS
	illyricus	CGrW CPen CSam ECho GBuc GCal WPGP
	imbricatus	CGrW EBee EBrs ECho ERos GBuc LRHS
	'Impressive' (N)	EBrs WHil
	inflatus **new**	ECho
	'Inspector's Choice' (M) **new**	CGrW
	'Irish Blessing' (S)	CGrW
§	***italicus***	CGrW CHid CPen CSam EBee EBrs ELan GCal GKev LEdu WHil
	'Ivory Priscilla'[PBR] (L)	CGrW
	'Jayvee' (S)	CGrW
	'Jessica' (L) **new**	LRHS
	'Jester' (L)	LRHS
	'Jim S' (G)	CGrW
	kotschyanus	EBrs ECho
	'Kristin' (L)	CGrW
	'Lady Eleanor' (P)	WCot
	'Lady Lucille' (M)	CGrW
	'Laguna' **new**	LRHS
	'Las Vegas' **new**	WHil
	'Lavender Flare' (S)	CGrW
	'Lemon Zest' (M)	CGrW
§	***liliaceus***	CDes CGrW ECho WCot
	'Little Darling' (P/S)	LRHS
	'Little Rainbow' (P)	WCot
	'Little Wiggy' (P)	CGrW
	'Loulou' (G)	CGrW
	'Lowland Queen' (L)	CGrW
	maculatus	WPGP
	'Mademoiselle de Paris' **new**	LRHS
	'Magenta Queen' (L) **new**	CGrW
	'Maria K' (L)	CGrW
	'Marj S' (L)	CGrW
	'Mexico'	CSut
	'Mileesh' (L)	CGrW
	miniatus	CDes
	'Mirella' (N)	EBrs MRav WHil
	'Mon Amour'[PBR]	CSut
	montanus	CPen
	monticola	EBee
	'Morning Gold'[PBR] **new**	LRHS
	mortonius	GCal WPGP
§	***murielae*** ♀H3	Widely available
	'Murieliae'	see *G. murielae*
	'My Treasure' (L) **new**	CGrW
	natalensis	see *G. dalenii*
	'Nathalie' (N)	CGrW EBee EBrs LEdu
	'New Wave'[PBR] (L)	CGrW
	'Nova Lux' (L)	LRHS
	'Nymph' (N)	CAvo CFFs EBee EBrs EPot ITim LAma LDai LEdu LPio WHil
	'Oasis'[PBR] (G)	CGrW
	'Of Singular Beauty' (G)	CGrW
§	***oppositiflorus***	CDes CPou EBee SChr WPGP
	- subsp. ***salmoneus***	see *G. oppositiflorus*
	orchidiflorus	CGrW
	'Orlando' (L)	CGrW
	'Oscar' (G)	LRHS
	palustris	ERos
	papilio	Widely available
	- 'David Hills'	NCGa WCot WHal
§	- Purpureoauratus Group	CBro CSam EBee ERos IBlr SRms
	- 'Ruby'	CAby CMea CMil CPen CPne CPou IPot NCGa NChi SMad WHil
	- yellow-flowered	CMdw CMea SMad
	pappei	EBee WPGP
	'Parade' (G)	CGrW
	'Peach Royale' (L)	CGrW
	'Peggy' (P)	CGrW
	permeabilis	WPGP
	'Perseus' (P/Min)	LRHS
	'Perth Pearl' (M)	CGrW
	'Peter Pears' (L)	LRHS
	'Phyllis M' (L)	CGrW
	Pilbeam hybrids	CGrW
	'Pink Elegance' (L)	CGrW
	'Pink Lady' (L)	CGrW
	'Plum Tart' (L)	LRHS
	'Praha' (L)	LRHS
	primulinus	see *G. dalenii*
	'Princess Margaret Rose' (Min)	LRHS
	'Prins Claus' (N)	CBro CGrW EBrs WHil
	'Priscilla' (L)	LRHS MLHP
	punctulatus var. ***punctulatus***	ERos
	'Purple Prince' (M)	CGrW WCot
	purpureoauratus	see *G. papilio* Purpureoauratus Group
	quadrangularis	ECho
	'Raspberry Swirl' (L/E)	CGrW
	recurvus **new**	ECho
	'Rhodos' (B) **new**	LRHS
	'Robinetta' (*recurvus* hybrid) ♀H3	CBro CElw EBrs ECho EPfP GGar LAma LDai LRHS WHil
	'Rose Flame' (L) **new**	CGrW
	'Royal Spire'	CGrW
	'Ruffled Côte d'Azur' **new**	LRHS
	'Rusty Red' (P) **new**	CGrW
	'Ruth Ann'	CGrW
	'San Remo'[PBR] (L)	CGrW
	saundersii	EBee GCal WCot WPGP
	'Scarlet Lady' (P)	CGrW
	segetum	see *G. italicus*
	sericeovillosus	IBlr
	'Sharkey' (G)	CGrW
	'Shocking' **new**	LRHS
	'Show Star' (L)	CGrW
	'Show Stopper' (G)	CGrW
	'Silvana' (S)	CGrW
	'Silver Green' (L)	CGrW
	'Sirael' (L/E)	CGrW WCot
	'Sky High' (M)	CGrW
	'Smoke Stack' (L)	CGrW
	'Snow Queen' (L)	CGrW
	'Solveiga' (L/E)	CGrW
	'Sophie'[PBR]	CGrW
	'Soul' (M) **new**	CGrW
	'Sparkler' (M)	CGrW

	'Spic and Span' (L)	CSut
	splendens	CAby CDes CGrW WCot WPGP
	'Spring Green'	LRHS
	'Spring Thaw' (L/E)	CGrW
	stefaniae	CGrW
	'Stiena' (L) **new**	CGrW
	'Summer Skies' (L) **new**	CGrW
	'Sunrise' (L)	CGrW
	symonsii	EBee
	'Tan Royale' (P)	CGrW
	'Tante Ann' (M)	CGrW
	teretifolius	WPGP
	'Tineka' (M) **new**	CGrW
	'Topaz' (L)	CGrW
	'Trader Horn' (G)	LRHS
§	***trichonemifolius***	CGrW ECho WPGP
	tristis	Widely available
	- var. ***concolor***	CGrW CPrp EBee ERos LFur LPio WCot
	undulatus	CDes ECho ERos WCot WPGP
	usyiae	CGrW ECho
	vandermerwei **new**	ECho
	'Velvet Eyes' (M)	LRHS
	venustus	ECho WPGP
	'Victor Borge' (L)	LRHS
	'Video' (L)	CGrW
	'Vienna' (L)	CGrW
	'Violet Charm' (S) **new**	CGrW
	'Violetta' (M)	CGrW ECho LRHS SMrm
	virescens	WCot
	watermeyeri	CGrW WPGP
	watsonioides	CPou ERos
	watsonius	WPGP
	'White Prosperity' (L)	CSut LRHS
	'Wind Song' (L)	LRHS
	'Wine and Roses' (L)	LRHS

Glandularia see *Verbena*

Glaucidium (*Glaucidiaceae*)

	palmatum ♀H4	EBee EFEx EPot GCra GEdr GKev NSla WCru WHal WPtf
	- 'Album'	see *G. palmatum* var. *leucanthum*
§	- var. ***leucanthum***	EFEx GBin GEdr NSla

Glaucium (*Papaveraceae*)

§	***corniculatum***	CAbP CBot CSpe EBrs LRHS SEND SPav SPhx WEas
	flavum	CArn CSpe EBWF ECha EGoo ELan MHer SMad SPav
	- ***aurantiacum***	see *G. flavum* f. *fulvum*
§	- f. ***fulvum***	ECha IFro SDix SMrm WCot
	- orange-flowered	see *G. flavum* f. *fulvum*
	- red-flowered	see *G. corniculatum*
	phoenicium	see *G. corniculatum*

Glaux (*Primulaceae*)

	maritima	EBWF WPer

Glebionis (*Asteraceae*)

	coronaria	MNHC
§	***segetum*** **new**	SECG

Glechoma (*Lamiaceae*)

	hederacea	CArn EBWF GBar GPoy MHer NMir NSco WHer
	- 'Rosea'	GBar WAlt
§	- 'Variegata' (v)	MBri NBlu SPer SPet

Gleditsia (*Caesalpiniaceae*)

	aquatica	EGFP
	caspica	CArn SMad
	japonica	EPfP
	macrantha	EGFP
	sinensis	NLar
	triacanthos	CDul CWib ECrN EMac LEdu SPlb WDin
	- 'Calhoun'	CAgr
	- 'Elegantissima' (v)	SPer
	- 'Emerald Cascade'	CDul CEnd EBee MAsh MBri
	- f. ***inermis*** Spectrum = 'Speczam'	EBee LRHS MAsh
	- 'Millwood'	CAgr
	- 'Rubylace'	CBcs CEnd CLnd CMCN CMac CSBt EBee ECrN ELan EPfP EWTr LAst LSRN MAsh MBar MBlu MGos MRav MSwo SLim SPer WCot WDin WFar
	- 'Shademaster'	NLar
	- 'Skyline'	LMaj
	- 'Sunburst' ♀H4	Widely available

Globba (*Zingiberaceae*)

	marantina	EBrs ECho LRHS
	'Mount Everest'	EBrs LRHS
I	***winitii*** 'Pink Dancing Girl'	ECho

Globularia (*Globulariaceae*)

	bellidifolia	see *G. meridionalis*
	bisnagarica	CElw GKev
	cordifolia ♀H4	EBee ECho EDAr EPot GEdr GKev LRHS MTho NBir NLAp NMen SIng WCom WFar WPat
	- NS 696	NWCA
§	***meridionalis***	CElw CFee ECho EPot EWes GMaP MWat NLAp NMen SAga WHal WPat
	- 'Blue Bonnets'	GEdr
	- 'Hort's Variety'	CPBP NMen WAbe WPat
	nana	see *G. repens*
	nudicaulis	GEdr
	punctata	CSpe GMaP NChi NWCA SMrm SRms
	pygmaea	see *G. meridionalis*
§	***repens***	CPBP EPot MTho NMen SIng WAbe WPat
	trichosantha	CFee ECho LRHS SRms WFar

Gloriosa (*Colchicaceae*)

	lutea	see *G. superba* 'Lutea'
	rothschildiana	see *G. superba* 'Rothschildiana'
	superba ♀H1	EShb MBri
§	- 'Lutea'	EBrs LAma LRHS
§	- 'Rothschildiana'	CBcs CRHN CStu EBrs ECho EGxp EPfP LAma LRHS SPer SRms

Glottiphyllum (*Aizoaceae*)

	grandiflorum **new**	WHil
	nelii	CStu

Gloxinia (*Gesneriaceae*)

	sp. **new**	EABi
	nematanthodes 'Evita'	WCot
	sylvatica	CSpe EShb WDib

Glumicalyx (*Scrophulariaceae*)

	flanaganii	GKev NLAp WCom
	- HWEL 0325	NWCA
	montanus	CFee

Glyceria (*Poaceae*)

	aquatica variegata	see *G. maxima* var. *variegata*

	maxima	CRWN EBWF EMFW GFor IFoB MMuc NMir NPer SPlb
§	- var. ***variegata*** (v)	Widely available
	notata	SVic
	spectabilis 'Variegata'	see *G. maxima* var. *variegata*

Glycyrrhiza (*Papilionaceae*)

	echinata	CArn
§	***glabra***	CArn CBod CCCN CHby CWan EBtc ELau EShb GPWP GPoy MBri MHer MNHC NLar SIde WJek
	glandulifera	see *G. glabra*
	uralensis	CArn ELau GPoy MHer

Glyptostrobus (*Cupressaceae*)

	pensilis	CGHE EGFP WPGP

Gmelina (*Verbenaceae*)

	hystrix	CCCN

Gnaphalium (*Asteraceae*)

	'Fairy Gold'	see *Helichrysum thianschanicum* 'Goldkind'
	trinerve	see *Anaphalis trinervis*

Godetia see *Clarkia*

Gomphocarpus (*Asclepiadaceae*)

§	***physocarpus***	CArn CDTJ CEnt NLar SBch WCot

Gomphostigma (*Buddlejaceae*)

	virgatum	CDes CSpe EBee EPPr LFur MBel MNFA SPlb SSvw WCot WHrl WPGP WSHC
	- 'White Candy'	LBMP SHGN

Gomphrena (*Amaranthaceae*)

	globosa	CCCN

Goniolimon (*Plumbaginaceae*)

	collinum 'Sea Spray'	CSpr EDAr SMad WClo WHil
§	***incanum***	SMrm
	- 'Blue Diamond'	WCot
	speciosum new	LLHF
§	***tataricum***	NBre NLar
§	- var. ***angustifolium***	EBee NBlu SEND SRms WPer
	- 'Woodcreek'	NLar

Goniophlebium (*Polypodiaceae*)

§	***subauriculatum*** 'Knightiae'	WRic

Goodenia (*Goodeniaceae*)

	heteromera new	ECou

Goodia (*Papilionaceae*)

	lotifolia	CCCN

Goodyera (*Orchidaceae*)

	biflora	EFEx
	pubescens	EFEx
	schlechtendaliana	EFEx

gooseberry see *Ribes uva-crispa*

Gordonia (*Theaceae*)

	axillaris	CCCN

Gossypium (*Malvaceae*)

	herbaceum	CCCN

granadilla see *Passiflora quadrangularis*

granadilla, purple see *Passiflora edulis*

granadilla, sweet see *Passiflora ligularis*

granadilla, yellow see *Passiflora laurifolia*

grape see *Vitis*

grapefruit see *Citrus* × *paradisi*

Graptopetalum (*Crassulaceae*)

	bellum ♀H1	CPBP CStu
	filiferum	EWII SRot
	pachyphyllum new	MSCN
§	***paraguayense***	SEND

× *Graptoveria* (*Crassulaceae*)

	'Doctor Phillips Pink' new	STre

Gratiola (*Scrophulariaceae*)

	officinalis	CArn CWan EHon EMFW LLWG MHer MSKA

Greigia (*Bromeliaceae*)

	sphacelata new	EBee

Grevillea ✿ (*Proteaceae*)

	alpina	CPLG EBee
	- 'Olympic Flame'	CBcs CCCN CDoC CPLG CSBt CWib EBee LHop LRHS SCoo SPoG SRms WBor WFar WGrn
	banksii 'Canberra Hybrid'	see *G.* 'Canberra Gem'
	'Bonnie Prince Charlie'	CPLG
§	'Canberra Gem' ♀H3-4	Widely available
	'Clearview David'	CCCN CMac CPLG CTrC LBuc LRHS LSRN SCoo SLim
	'Cranbrook Yellow'	CDoC CPLG
	crithmifolia	SPlb
	johnsonii	CMac CTrC EShb IDee
	juniperina	CBcs CCCN CMac CPLG CTsd EBee EPfP MGos SLim
	- 'Molonglo'	CPLG
	- f. ***sulphurea***	CCCN CDoC CHII CPLG CTrC CTrG EPfP SPlb SSpi WAbe WPat WSHC
	lanigera	CPLG ECou
	- 'Mount Tamboritha'	CBcs CCCN CDoC CMac CPLG CTrC CWGN GGar IDee LRHS SBch SPoG WBrE WFar
	- prostrate	ECou MAsh NLAp WAbe WGrn WPat
	leucopteris	SPlb
	'Misty Red'	LRHS
	paniculata	SPlb
	'Pink Lady'	ECou LRHS SCoo
	'Poorinda Peter'	CPLG
	'Poorinda Rondeau'	CPLG
	'Red Dragon' (v)	LBuc LRHS
	robusta ♀H1+3	CTsd EShb SPlb SSta WCot
	- 'Red Salento' PBR new	LRHS
	'Rondeau'	CCCN EShb
	rosmarinifolia ♀H3	CAbb CDoC CHII CMac CPLG CSBt CTrC CTrG CTri CWib EBee EPfP EShb GGar IDee IMGH MWat SArc SBod SCoo SLim SLon SPer SPlb SPoG SSta WAbe WCot WFar
	- 'Desert Flame'	CPLG
	- 'Jenkinsii'	CDoC CPLG CSBt CWit EBee LAst SBch SLim
§	× ***semperflorens***	CBcs CPLG CTrC CWib EBee LRHS SCoo SPlb

'Sid Reynolds'	CPLG
'Spider Man'	LBuc LRHS
thelemanniana	ECou
- 'Silver'	CPLG
thyrsoides	GGal
tolminsis	see *G.* × *semperflorens*
victoriae	CPne CWGN GGar SCoo SSpi WCot
- subsp. ***victoriae***	CPLG
- yellow-flowered	LRHS
williamsonii	ECou LRHS SCoo WPat

Greyia (*Greyiaceae*)

sutherlandii	CTrC SGar SPlb WCot

Grindelia (*Asteraceae*)

§ ***camporum***	CWCL GBar IMou NBre NLar SPlb WPer
chiloensis	CAbb ECha SMad WCot
integrifolia	CSam
- KM CI-128-02	EBee
robusta	see *G. camporum*
squarrosa	GBar WHil
stricta	CArn

Griselinia (*Griseliniaceae*)

* ***dependens***	ISea
littoralis ♀H3	Widely available
- 'Bantry Bay' (v)	CAbP CCCN CDoC CTsd CWSG EBee EHoe ELan ERas ESwi LRHS NCGa SEND SLim SPer SWvt WFar
- 'Brodick Gold'	CPLG EQua GGar
- 'Crinkles'	CPMA SLon
- 'Dixon's Cream' (v)	CBcs CCCN CDul CMac CSBt EBee EPfP GQui IArd IFoB LRHS MDun SAga SLon SPoG
- 'Green Jewel' (v)	CBcs CCCN CPMA CTrC CWib NLar
- 'Variegata' (v) ♀H3	Widely available
lucida 'Variegata' (v)	IFoB
scandens	WSHC

guava, common see *Psidium guajava*

guava, purple or strawberry see *Psidium littorale* var. *longipes*

Gunnera (*Gunneraceae*)

chilensis	see *G. tinctoria*
cordifolia new	CPne
dentata	CPne
flavida	CSpr CStu EBee GGar NWCA WGwG
hamiltonii	CPne ECha ECou GAbr NBir NWCA WMoo
magellanica	Widely available
- 'Muñoz Gamero'	WShi
- 'Osorno'	WPGP
manicata ♀H3-4	Widely available
× ***mixta*** new	CPne
monoica	CPne GGar
perpensa	CBcs CCCN IMou WCot
prorepens	CFee ECha ECou GEdr GGar GKev IDee NBir NWCA SBch SWat WFar WMoo WWEG
scabra	see *G. tinctoria*
§ ***tinctoria*** ♀H4	CCCN CHEx CMHG CRow CTrG CWib EBee EBla ECha EHon ELan EPfP EPla GAbr GGar LBMP LHop LRHS MDun NCot SBch SDix SWat SWvt WBVN WClo WFar WPGP WPat

Guzmania (*Bromeliaceae*)

conifera new	LRHS
'Gran Prix'	MBri
'Surprise'	see × *Niduregelia* 'Surprise'
'Vulkan'	MBri

Gymnadenia (*Orchidaceae*)

conopsea	EBee ECho EFEx

Gymnocarpium (*Woodsiaceae*)

dryopteris ♀H4	CLAP EBee EBrs EFer EFtx GGar GKev GMaP LEdu MMoz NLar NWCA SGSe SRms WAbe WFib WPnP WPtf WRic WShi
- 'Plumosum' ♀H4	CBty CLAP CWCL EBee EFtx EPfP EPla ERod GBin GQui MAsh NBid NHol NLar NVic SMad WFib WHal WMoo
fedtschenkoanum	WAbe WRic
oyamense	CLAP EFer EFtx
robertianum	EBee EFer EWld

Gymnocladus (*Caesalpiniaceae*)

chinensis	CBcs EGFP
dioica	CBcs CDul CLnd CMCN EBee EBtc ELan EPfP LRHS MBlu MBri SPer SSpi WDin WPGP

Gymnospermium (*Berberidaceae*)

§ ***albertii***	EBrs ECho GKev WWst
sylvaticum new	WWst

Gynandriris (*Iridaceae*)

setifolia	ECho
sisyrinchium	CStu EBee EBrs ECho
* - ***purpurea***	ECho

Gynerium (*Poaceae*)

argenteum	see *Cortaderia selloana*

Gynostemma (*Cucurbitaceae*)

pentaphyllum	CAgr
- B&SWJ 570	WCru

Gynura (*Asteraceae*)

§ ***aurantiaca*** 'Purple Passion' ♀H1	MBri
sarmentosa misapplied	see *G. aurantiaca* 'Purple Passion'

Gypsophila (*Caryophyllaceae*)

acutifolia	EBee ELan
aretioides	ECho EPot GKev LRHS NMen
§ - 'Caucasica'	CPBP EBur ECho EPot GEdr LLHF NDlv
- 'Compacta'	see *G. aretioides* 'Caucasica'
briquetiana	EPot WPat
cephalotes new	GAuc
cerastioides	CSpe CTri ECho ECtt EDAr EPfP GAbr GGar LAst LBMP LHop LRHS MMuc MRav NDlv NLAp NMen NWCA SPlb SRms WHoo WPer WPnn
dubia	see *G. repens* 'Dubia'
fastigiata	WPer
- 'Silverstar'	EBee LRHS LSou SPoG
'Festival Pink' (Festival Series)	ECtt GBee GMac LRHS SHar SPoG WFar
gracilescens	see *G. tenuifolia*
'Jolien' (v)	CBow EBee ELan NBPC
muralis 'Garden Bride'	SWvt
- 'Gypsy Pink' (d)	SWvt

	- 'Pink Sugardot' new	SBch
	nana 'Compacta'	CPBP
	oldhamiana	MBel
	'Pacific Rose'	MRav
	pacifica	EBee MWea NBre NLar SBch WPer
	paniculata	EBee LAst MGos NBre NEgg SMrm SRms
	- 'Bristol Fairy' (d) ♀H4	CSBt CTri EBee ECha ECtt ELan EPfP GKir GMaP LRHS NOrc NPri SPoG SWvt WCAu WWEG
	- 'Compacta Plena' (d)	EBee ECtt ELan EPfP GMaP LAst LHop LRHS MLHP MRav NEgg NVic SPet SRms WPer
	- 'Fairy Perfect'	EBee IPot
	- 'Flamingo' (d)	CBcs EBee ECha IPot LHop NLar
	- 'Perfekta'	CBcs SPer
	- 'Pink Star' (d)	EBee
§	- 'Schneeflocke' (d)	EBee EPfP EShb GMaP LRHS NBre NLar SRms WPer WWEG
	- Snowflake	see *G. paniculata* 'Schneeflocke'
	repens ♀H4	ECtt GJos LBee MWat SBch SPlb SWvt WFar WPer
	- 'Dorothy Teacher'	CMea ECho ECtt LBee LRHS SIng WGor
§	- 'Dubia'	EAlp ECha ECho ECtt EDAr EPot MHer NBlu SEND SPoG SRms WPer WSHC
	- 'Fratensis'	ECho ECtt ELan LLHF NMen
	- Pink Beauty	see *G. repens* 'Rosa Schönheit'
§	- 'Rosa Schönheit'	EBee ECha EPot LRHS NLar SPer
	- 'Rosea'	CMea CPBP CTri CWib EBee ECho ECtt EDAr EPfP EShb GJos GMaP LBMP LRHS MWat NBlu NWCA SPet SPoG SRms SWvt WFar WHoo
	- 'Silver Carpet' (v)	EBee
	- white-flowered	CMea CWib EBee ECho ELan EPfP LRHS SPet SWvt WPer WRHF
§	'Rosenschleier' (d) ♀H4	CMea EBee ECha ECtt ELan EPfP IPot LAst LRHS MCot MRav NCGa NEgg SPer SRms SWvt WCAu WHoo WSHC WTin WWEG
I	'Rosenschleier Variegata' (v) new	WWEG
	'Rosy Veil'	see *G.* 'Rosenschleier'
§	***tenuifolia***	EAlp ECho EPot LBee LRHS NMen WPat
	Veil of Roses	see *G.* 'Rosenschleier'
	'White Festival'PBR (Festival Series) (d)	EBee GMac LRHS SPoG WFar

Gyptis (*Asteraceae*)

commersonii new	LHop

H

Haberlea (*Gesneriaceae*)

ferdinandi-coburgii	CLAP ECho GBuc NMen NWCA
- 'Connie Davidson'	GBuc GEdr GKev NMen
rhodopensis ♀H4	CDes CElw CFee CStu EBee ECho GEdr GGar GKev NLAp NMen NSla NWCA SIng SRms WAbe WCom WKif WPGP WTin
- 'Virginalis'	CElw CLAP CStu NMen NSla NWCA WThu

Habranthus ✿ (*Amaryllidaceae*)

	andersonii	see *H. tubispathus*
	'Argentine Pink'	EDif
	brachyandrus	CBro EDif GCal SRms WPrP
	gracilifolius	CBro CStu ERos WThu
	martinezii	CBro CPBP CStu EPot NWCA
	'Pinky' new	WHil
§	***robustus*** ♀H1	CCCN CPne EBee EBrs ECho EDif EPot EShb IHer LAma LHop LRHS WCot WHil WPGP
§	***tubispathus*** ♀H1	CBro CGHE CStu EBee ECho EDif ERos GCal ITim NWCA WCot WPrP

Hackelia (*Boraginaceae*)

floribunda	SBod

Hacquetia (*Apiaceae*)

	epipactis ♀H4	Widely available
§	- 'Thor' (v)	CBow CLAP EWes GEdr LLHF MAvo NMen WAbe WCom WCot WFar WPGP
	- 'Variegata'	see *H. epipactis* 'Thor'

Haemanthus (*Amaryllidaceae*)

albiflos ♀H1	CHEx CSpe CStu CTsd ECho LAma SRms STre WCot
amarylloides	CLak
subsp. ***amarylloides*** new	
- subsp. ***polyanthes***	CLak ECho
barkerae	CLak ECho
coccineus ♀H1	ECho
crispus	ECho
humilis	ECho
- subsp. ***hirsutus***	WCot
kalbreyeri	see *Scadoxus multiflorus* subsp. *multiflorus*
katherinae	see *Scadoxus multiflorus* subsp. *katherinae*
lanceifolius new	ECho
montanus new	ECho
natalensis	see *Scadoxus puniceus*
pauculifolius	ECho
pubescens subsp. ***leipoldtii***	CLak ECho
sanguineus	ECho

Hakea (*Proteaceae*)

§	***drupacea***	CTrC EShb
	epiglottis	CTrC ECou
	laurina	SPlb
	lissocarpha	CTrC
§	***lissosperma***	CDoC CWit ECou EPfP EPla LRHS SPlb WPGP
	microcarpa	ECou
	nodosa	CCCN CTrC
	platysperma	SPlb
§	***salicifolia***	CCCN EBee IDee SPlb
	- 'Gold Medal' (v)	CTrC
	saligna	see *H. salicifolia*
	sericea misapplied	see *H. lissosperma*
	sericea Schrad. & J.C.Wendl.	ECou
	- pink-flowered	SPlb
	suaveolens	see *H. drupacea*
	teretifolia	CTrC

Hakonechloa ✿ (*Poaceae*)

	macra	CEnt CGHE CKno CPrp CSam EBee EBrs EHoe EPPr EPla EShb GCal GKir MAvo MMoz MRav SApp SMad SPhx SPoG SWal WCot WDyG WPGP WSHC
§	- 'Alboaurea' ♀H4	CBcs CChe CFee CKno CPLG CWGN EBrs ELan EPfP EShb GFor

	GKir LAst LRHS LSRN MGos MRav NCGa NScw NWCA SAga SApp SBod SPhx STre WFar
- 'Albovariegata'	CKno CWan EPPr GCal LEdu LHop MAvo WDyG WSpi
- 'All Gold'	EBee EPPr EWes GBin SMad
- 'Aureola' ♀H4	Widely available
* - 'Mediopicta' (v)	SApp
- 'Mediovariegata' (v)	CGHE CWCL EBee EPPr EPla WPGP
- 'Naomi' (v)	EBee GBin
- 'Nicolas'	EBee GBin LSou SMrm SPoG WCot
- 'Variegata'	see *H. macra* 'Alboaurea'

Halenia (*Gentianaceae*)

elliptica	EBee
- SDR 4273	GKev

Halesia (*Styracaceae*)

§ ***carolina***	Widely available
- 'Wedding Bells'	CPMA
diptera	CBcs MBlu NEgg
- var. ***magniflora***	EPfP LRHS MBlu SSpi
monticola	CBcs CDul CMCN EBee ELan EPfP IFFs LRHS MAsh NLar SSpi
- var. ***vestita*** ♀H4	CDoC CDul CPMA CTho EPfP ERas LRHS MAsh MBlu MBri MGos MRav NLar NVic SPoG SSpi WDin WFar WGob WHCG WPGP WPat
- - f. ***rosea***	CBcs CPMA EPfP MBlu
tetraptera	see *H. carolina*

× *Halimiocistus* (*Cistaceae*)

algarvensis	see *Halimium ocymoides*
'Ice Rose' **new**	NBlu
§ 'Ingwersenii'	CBcs CDoC EBee ELan EWes LRHS MMuc SBch SPer SPoG SRms WAbe WPer
revolii misapplied	see × *H. sahucii*
§ ***sahucii*** ♀H4	CBcs CBgR CDoC CSBt CTri EBee ECha ELan EPfP LAst LBMP LRHS MAsh MBNS MMuc MRav MSwo MWat NPri SBch SDys SPer SPoG SRms SWvt WDin WFar
- Ice Dancer = 'Ebhals'PBR (v)	CDoC EBee EPfP LAst MAsh SBch SPer SWvt WClo
'Susan'	see *Halimium* 'Susan'
§ ***wintonensis*** ♀H3	CBcs CDoC EBee ELan EPfP LRHS MAsh SPer SRms WHar WSHC
§ - 'Merrist Wood Cream' ♀H3	CBcs CBgR CDoC CMac CSBt EBee ELan EPfP LAst LHop LRHS MAsh MMuc MRav MSwo NBir SBch SBod SPer SPoG SSpi SWvt WAbe WDin WFar WKif WPat WSHC

Halimium (*Cistaceae*)

§ ***calycinum***	CAbP CChe CDoC EBee ELan EPfP GKev LRHS MAsh MBri MMuc SBch SCoo SLim SPer SPoG SWvt WAbe WCFE WClo WDin
commutatum	see *H. calycinum*
formosum	see *H. lasianthum* subsp. *formosum*
N ***halimifolium*** misapplied	see *H.* × *pauanum*
§ ***lasianthum*** ♀H3	CBcs CMac CSBt CWib ELan EPfP LRHS MBri MRav SBch SLim WBrE WEas WKif
- 'Concolor'	CWib EBee LRHS MSwo NPri SWvt WDin
§ - subsp. ***formosum***	GGar SBod
- - 'Sandling'	EBee ELan EPfP LRHS MMuc SPoG SRms
- 'Hannay Silver'	WAbe
libanotis	see *H. calycinum*
§ ***ocymoides*** ♀H3	CBcs CChe CDoC CWib ELan EPfP LRHS MMHG MSwo NPri WHar WKif
§ × ***pauanum***	EBee MMuc WAbe
'Sun Spot' **new**	LRHS
§ 'Susan' ♀H3	CBgR CDoC EBee ELan EPfP ERas LHop LRHS LSou MMHG SCoo SLim SPer SPoG WAbe
§ ***umbellatum***	EBee MMuc SPer WHCG WKif
wintonense	see × *Halimiocistus wintonensis*

Halimodendron (*Papilionaceae*)

halodendron	CArn CBcs CDul EBee MBlu SPer WDin

Halleria (*Scrophulariaceae*)

lucida	CCCN

Halocarpus (*Podocarpaceae*)

§ ***bidwillii***	CDoC ECou

Haloragis (*Haloragaceae*)

erecta 'Rubra'	WCot WPer
- 'Wellington Bronze'	CBow CEnt CSpe EBee ECtt EHoe EPPr GGar LEdu LFur MBNS MCCP MLHP SBod SDys WCon WEas WHer WMoo

Hamamelis ✿ (*Hamamelidaceae*)

'Amethyst'	NLar
'Brevipetala'	CBcs GKir NHol
'Danny'	CPMA
'Doerak'	CPMA MBlu MBri
'Girard Orange'	EPfP
× ***intermedia*** 'Advent'	CPMA NLar
- 'Angelly' ♀H4	CPMA LRHS MBlu MBri MGos NLar
- 'Aphrodite' ♀H4	CPMA EMil EPfP GKir LRHS MAsh MBlu MBri MGos MRav NBhm NCGa NLar SSpi
- 'Arnold Promise' ♀H4	Widely available
- 'Aurora' ♀H4	CPMA GKir LRHS MBlu MBri NHol NLar
- 'Barmstedt Gold' ♀H4	CPMA EBee EPfP GKir LRHS LSRN MAsh MBri MGos MRav NHol NLar SPoG SReu SRms SSpi SSta
- 'Carmine Red'	CMac CPMA MGos NLar
- 'Copper Beauty'	see *H.* × *intermedia* 'Jelena'
- 'Diane' ♀H4	Widely available
§ - 'Feuerzauber'	CEnd CMac CSBt CTri LBuc LRHS MSwo NLar SBir SPer SRms WDin WPat
- Fire Cracker	see *H.* × *intermedia* 'Feuerzauber'
- 'Frederic'	CPMA LRHS MAsh
- 'Gimborn's Perfume'	NLar
- 'Gingerbread'	CPMA LRHS MAsh
- 'Glowing Embers'	CPMA LRHS
- 'Harlow Carr' **new**	LRHS
- 'Harry'	CPMA GKir LRHS MAsh MBri NLar SBir SPoG SSpi
- Hillier's clone	NHol
- 'Hiltingbury'	LRHS
§ - 'Jelena' ♀H4	Widely available
- 'John'	LRHS
- 'Limelight'	CPMA MBri
- 'Livia'	CPMA LRHS MAsh MBri SBir SPoG SSpi
- Magic Fire	see *H.* × *intermedia* 'Feuerzauber'
- 'Moonlight'	CDul CPMA NLar
- 'Nina'	LRHS MAsh NLar

- 'Orange Beauty'	CBcs EBee LRHS MBlu MGos NLar SCoo
- 'Orange Peel'	EPfP LRHS MAsh MBri NLar SPoG
- 'Pallida' ♀H4	Widely available
- 'Primavera'	CPMA CWSG NHol NLar NPCo SBch SLim
- 'Ripe Corn'	CPMA EPfP LRHS MBri SPoG
- 'Robert'	CPMA LRHS MAsh MBri SPoG
- 'Rubin'	CPMA GKir LRHS MAsh MBri NLar SSpi
- 'Rubinstar'	CPMA
- 'Ruby Glow'	CBcs CMac CWib EBee ECho EGxp LMaj LRHS LSRN MGos NLar NPCo NPri NWea SBch SCoo SLim SPer WDin
- 'Savill Starlight'	CPMA
- 'Strawberries and Cream'	CPMA
- 'Sunburst'	EBee EPfP LRHS MGos NLar
- 'Twilight'	CPMA
- 'Vesna' ♀H4	CMac CPMA EPfP LRHS MBlu NLar SPoG SSpi
- 'Westerstede'	CPMA CWSG EBee EPfP LAst LRHS LSRN MGos MRav NHol NLar NScw NWea SBch SCoo SLim WDin WHar
- 'Wiero'	CPMA
- 'Zitronenjette' **new**	CPMA
japonica	EBee WFar
- 'Pendula'	CPMA MBlu NLar
- 'Robin'	NLar
- 'Rubra'	NPCo
- 'Zuccariniana'	NLar
mollis ♀H4	Widely available
- 'Boskoop'	NLar
- 'Coombe Wood'	CPMA LRHS
- 'Goldcrest'	CPMA
- 'Jermyns Gold' ♀H4	CPMA EPfP LRHS
§ - 'Princeton Gold'	CWib
- 'Select'	see *H. mollis* 'Princeton Gold'
- 'Wisley Supreme'	CAbP CPMA ELan EPfP LRHS MAsh MBri SPoG SSpi
'Rochester'	CPMA LRHS MBri NPCo SBir
vernalis	WDin
- 'Lombarts' Weeping'	NLar
- 'Orange Glow'	LRHS
- purple	MBlu NLar
- 'Sandra' ♀H4	CBcs CMCN ELan EPfP EWTr GKir LRHS MAsh MBlu MBri MGos MRav NLar SLon SPer SPoG SReu SSpi SSta
virginiana	CAgr ECrN GPoy IDee LLHF NWea WDin
- 'Mohonk Red' **new**	CPMA

Hamelia (*Rubiaceae*)

patens	CCCN EShb

Hanabusaya (*Campanulaceae*)

§ ***asiatica***	NCGa NChi WFar

Haplocarpha (*Asteraceae*)

rueppellii	CFee NBro SRms SRot WPer

Haplopappus (*Asteraceae*)

brandegeei	see *Erigeron aureus*
coronopifolius	see *H. glutinosus*
§ ***glutinosus***	EBee ECha ECho ECtt EPot GEdr MMuc MTho NLar NWCA SEND SPlb SRms WCom
lyallii	see *Tonestus lyallii*
prunelloides	GEdr NWCA
rehderi	MWat WCon

Hardenbergia (*Papilionaceae*)

comptoniana ♀H1	CPLG EBee
- 'Rosea'	ERea
violacea ♀H1	CAbb CBcs CCCN CHll CRHN CSPN CTrC CTsd EGxp ELan ERas ERea GQui LRHS SEND SLim SPer
- f. ***alba***	CBcs ECou ERas IDee LRHS
- - 'White Crystal'	EBee ERea SPer WPGP
- dwarf	ECou
- 'Happy Wanderer'	CCCN EBee ERea LRHS SChF WPGP
- f. ***rosea***	CBcs CCCN EBee LRHS SPer

Harpephyllum (*Anacardiaceae*)

caffrum (F)	XBlo

Harrimanella see *Cassiope*

Hastingsia (*Hyacinthaceae*)

alba	GBuc

Haworthia ✿ (*Aloaceae*)

attenuata	EShb SWal
'Black Prince'	EPfP
cooperi	STre
cymbiformis	EPfP STre
fasciata	EPfP
glabrata var. ***concolor***	EPfP EShb
pumila ♀H1 **new**	SEND
radula	EPfP

hazelnut see *Corylus*

Hebe ✿ (*Scrophulariaceae*)

albicans ♀H4	CCVT CChe CMac ECou ELan EPfP GGar GKir IFFs IFoB LAst LRHS LSRN MBar MBri MGos MRav NBlu SBch SCoo SPer SPoG STre SWal WClo WFar WHCG
- 'Cobb'	ECou
- 'Cranleigh Gem'	LRHS
- prostrate	see *H. albicans* 'Snow Cover'
* - 'Snow Carpet'	CCCN LRHS
§ - 'Snow Cover'	EWes LRHS
- 'Snow Drift'	see *H. albicans* 'Snow Cover'
§ - 'Sussex Carpet'	STre
§ 'Alicia Amherst'	LRHS SPer SRms SWal WCFE
allanii	see *H. amplexicaulis* f. *hirta*
'Amanda Cook' (v)	MCCP NPer SPoG
'Amethyst'	SBch
amplexicaulis clone 4	STre
§ - f. ***hirta***	NDlv NHol
§ 'Amy'	ELon GGal LRHS NPer SPer WCom
× ***andersonii***	CDul EPfP LRHS
§ - 'Andersonii Variegata' (v)	LRHS NBur SBch SRms
- 'Argenteovariegata'	see *H.* × *andersonii* 'Andersonii Variegata'
'Andressa Paula'	CCCN LRHS
'Anita'	SPoG
anomala misapplied	see *H.* 'Imposter'
anomala (Armstr.) Cockayne	CCCN LRHS
'Aoira'	see *H. recurva* 'Aoira'
§ ***armstrongii***	ECho GGar MBar MGos WDin WPer
'Arthur'	ECou
astonii	ECho
'Autumn Glory'	CSBt CWSG ECho ELan EPfP GKir LAst LRHS MBar MGos MLHP

	Name	Suppliers
		MSwo NBir NPri SBch SBod SPer SPlb SPoG SWvt WDin
	azurea	see *H. venustula*
	'Azurens'	see *H.* 'Maori Gem'
	'Baby Blush'[PBR]	LRHS
	'Baby Marie'	CAbP CChe CSBt ECho ECou ELan EPfP LRHS LSRN MGos MSwo NMen NPer NPri SBch SCoo SPoG SRGP SRms SRot SWvt
	'Beatrice'	NDlv
	'Beverley Hills'[PBR]	CSBt LRHS NLar WHar
	'Bicolor Wand'	CCCN CTsd LRHS
	bishopiana	ECou EPfP MGos SCoo
	'Black Panther' **new**	LBuc LRHS NPri
	'Blue Clouds' ♀H3	LAst LLHF LRHS MSwo NDlv SPer WCFE
§	'Blue Gem'	LRHS MGos
	Blue Star = 'Vergeer 1'[PBR]	CBgR LRHS LSou MAsh NLar SPoG
	bollonsii	GGar
	'Boscawenii'	CTrG CTsd MGos
	'Bouquet'[PBR]	NEgg NLar
§	'Bowles's Hybrid'	CCCN ECou LEdu LRHS MRav MSwo SRms STre
	brachysiphon	CTrC CTri EPfP LRHS MGos MRav SPer WDin
	brevifolia	ECou LRHS
	'Bronzy Baby' (v)	SPoG
	buchananii	ECho GGar MBar MGos MHer MTho NDlv NPer STre WPer
§	- 'Fenwickii'	ECho WHoo
	- 'Minima'	ECho
	- 'Minor' Hort N.Z.	ECho GBin MBar NBir NDlv NWCA
*	- 'Nana'	MGos
	buxifolia misapplied	see *H. odora*
	buxifolia (Benth.) Ckn. & Allan	CMac NHol NWea WDin WHar
*	- ***patens***	LAst
§	'Caledonia' ♀H3	CCCN CSBt EPfP LBMP LRHS LSRN MBri MGos NPer SBch SCoo SPoG WCom WFar
	'Candy'	ECou
§	***canterburiensis***	ECou GGar
N	'Carl Teschner'	see *H.* 'Youngii'
	'Carnea Variegata' (v)	LRHS MGos MSCN SPer WOut
	carnosula	GGar MGos NBir SPer WHar WPer
	catarractae	see *Parahebe catarractae*
	'Celine'	GGar MGos SPoG SRGP
I	'Chalk's Buchananii'	WCom
	'Champagne'	CCCN LAst LRHS LSRN NBlu NHol SBch SCoo
	Champion = 'Champseiont'[PBR]	EKen LRHS LSou NLar SCoo WClo WRHF
	'Charming White'	CChe EQua LRHS LSRN MGos SBch SPoG
	chathamica	ECou GGar LRHS
	'Christabel'	LRHS
	ciliolata × ***odora***	GGar
	'Claymoddie Blue Seedling'	GGal
	'Clear Skies'[PBR]	ECou LRHS NEgg
	'Colwall'	ECho
	'Conwy Knight'	WAbe
*	'Coral Pink'	LRHS
	'County Park'	ECou EWes NHol NMen
	'Cranleighensis'	CTsd SBch
	'Cupins'	NWCA
	cupressoides	NDlv SEND WDin
	- 'Boughton Dome'	CTri EAlp ECho EPfP ERas GGar MGos MHer MTho NMen WAbe WCFE WHoo WPer
	'Dazzler' (v)	CAbP
	decumbens	EWes GGar MGos NHol
	'Denise'	LRHS
	'Diamond'	LRHS
	dieffenbachii	GGar
	diosmifolia	CAbP CBot CDoC ELan LRHS WAbe WFar
	divaricata	ECou
*	- 'Marlborough'	ECou
	- 'Nelson'	ECou
	× ***divergens***	NDlv
	'Dorothy Peach'	see *H.* 'Watson's Pink'
	'E.A. Bowles'	ECou
	'E.B. Anderson'	see *H.* 'Caledonia'
	'Early Blue'	NBir
	'Edington'	LRHS SPer WCFE
	'Ellie' **new**	LRHS
	elliptica	CDul ECou LRHS MGos
	- 'Anatoki'	ECou
	- 'Charleston'	ECou
	- 'Kapiti'	ECou
	- 'Variegata'	see *H.* 'Silver Queen'
	'Emerald Dome'	see *H.* 'Emerald Gem'
§	'Emerald Gem' ♀H3	CDul CStu CTri ECho EPfP GGar GKev LAst LRHS LSRN MAsh MBar MBri MGos MHer MMuc MSwo NBlu NDlv NHol NMen NWCA SBch SCoo SPer SPlb SWal WCom WPat
	'Emerald Green'	see *H.* 'Emerald Gem'
	epacridea	ECho EWes WAbe
§	'Eveline'	CSBt CTri LRHS MGos NBir SPer WKif
	evenosa	GGar NDlv
	'Eversley Seedling'	see *H.* 'Bowles's Hybrid'
	'Fairfieldii'	ERas WPat
	'First Light'[PBR]	CWSG LRHS MGos SCoo SPoG WHar
	'Fragrant Jewel'	CWib LRHS SEND
	× ***franciscana***	ECou LRHS
	- 'Blue Gem' misapplied	see *H.* × *franciscana* 'Lobelioides'
	- 'Blue Gem' ambig.	ECho ELan EPfP LRHS MRav NBir NPer SBch SPer SPlb SPoG SRms WHar
	- 'Lavender Queen'	LRHS
§	- 'Lobelioides'	GGar
	- 'Purple Tips' misapplied	see *H. speciosa* 'Variegata'
	- 'Variegata'	see *H.* 'Silver Queen'
I	- 'White Gem'	SRms
	- yellow-variegated (v)	SPer
	'Franjo'	ECou
	Garden Beauty Blue = 'Cliv'[PBR]	LBuc LRHS MGos
	Garden Beauty Pink = 'Lowink' **new**	LBuc LRHS
	Garden Beauty Purple = 'Nold'[PBR]	LBuc LRHS
	'Gauntlettii'	see *H.* 'Eveline'
	'Gibby'	LRHS
	glaucophylla 'Clarence'	ECou GGar
I	'Glaucophylla Variegata' (v)	CTri EPfP LRHS NBir SCoo SPer WKif
	'Glengarriff'	NHol
§	'Gloriosa'	CEnt
	'Gnome'	LRHS
	'Godefroyana'	see *H. pinguifolia* 'Godefroyana'
	'Goethe' **new**	SEND
	'Gold Beauty' (v)	LRHS NPri
	'Golden Nugget' **new**	LRHS
	'Goldrush'[PBR] (v)	LBuc LRHS MGos SPoG
	'Gran's Favourite'	CCCN LRHS
	'Great Orme' ♀H3	Widely available

	'Green Globe'	see *H.* 'Emerald Gem'
	'Greensleeves'	GGar LRHS
	'Grethe'	SPoG
	'Gruninard's Seedling'	GGar
	haastii	NLar
	'Hadspen Pink'	LRHS
	'Hagley Park'	EPfP LRHS WHCG
§	'Hartii'	LRHS MRav SBch
	'Heartbreaker'PBR (v)	EGxp ELan GGar LBuc LRHS MGos NPri SBch SCoo SPoG
	'Hielan Lassie'	LRHS
	'Highdownensis'	LRHS
	'Hinderwell'	NPer
	'Hinerua'	GGar NNor
	'Hobby' **new**	LRHS
	'Holywell'	SBod SWal
	hookeriana	see *Parahebe hookeriana*
	hulkeana ♀H3	CBot CTri ERas GGar LRHS LSou MHer SAga SSpi SUsu SWal WCom WEas WHCG WKif WPat WTin
§	'Imposter'	SRms
	'Inspiration'	LRHS
	insularis	ECho ECou
	'James Stirling'	see *H. ochracea* 'James Stirling'
	'Jane Holden'	LRHS
	'Janet'	SGar
	'Jean Searle'	LAst
	'Joanna'	ECou
§	'Johny Day'	LRHS
	'Joyful' **new**	LRHS
	'Judy'	LRHS
	'Karna'	SPoG
	'Katrina' (v)	SPoG
	'Kirkii'	EPfP SBch SCoo SPer SWal
	'Knightshayes'	see *H.* 'Caledonia'
	'La Séduisante'	CTri ECou GGal LRHS MLHP SEND WKif WOut
	'Lady Ann'PBR (v)	CSBt CWSG LRHS LSou MAsh NEgg NLar SPoG WHar
	'Lady Ardilaun'	see *H.* 'Amy'
	laevis	see *H. venustula*
	latifolia	see *H.* 'Blue Gem'
	'Lavender Spray'	see *H.* 'Hartii'
	'Lilac Wand'	CTsd
	'Linda'	SPoG
	'Lindsayi'	ECou LRHS
	'Lisa'	SPoG
§	'Loganioides'	GGar
	'Lopen' (v)	ECou
	'Louise'	LIMB SGar
	lyallii s	ee *Parahebe lyallii*
	lycopodioides	EWes WThu
	- 'Aurea'	see *H. armstrongii*
	'Lynash'	LRHS
	mackenii	see *H.* 'Emerald Gem'
	macrantha ♀H3	ECho EPfP GGar LRHS SPer SRms WAbe WCom
	macrocarpa	ECou LRHS
	- var. ***latisepala***	ECou LRHS
§	'Maori Gem'	GGar NBlu SBch
	'Margery Fish'	see *H.* 'Primley Gem'
	'Margret'PBR ♀H4	CSBt EPfP ERas LAst LRHS LSRN MAsh MGos MWat NPri SBch SCoo SPer SPoG SRGP
	'Marie Antoinette'	LRHS
	'Marjorie'	CCVT CDul CMac CTrC ELan EPfP LAst LRHS MGos MRav MSwo NLar NPer NWea SBch SBod SPer SPoG SRms WDin
	matthewsii	WPat
	'Mauve Queen'	LRHS
	'Mauvena'	SPer
	'McKean'	see *H.* 'Emerald Gem'
	'Megan'	ECou
	'Mercury'	ECou
	'Midnight Sky' **new**	LRHS
	'Midsummer Beauty' ♀H3	ECou EPfP ISea LAst LRHS MGos MLHP MRav NBir NPri SBch SBod SEND SMad SPer SPlb SPoG SWvt WDin WHar WOut WSFF
	'Milmont Emerald'	see *H.* 'Emerald Gem'
*	***minima*** 'Calvin'	ECho
	'Miss Fittall'	ECou
	'Misty'	CCCN
§	'Mohawk'PBR	LBuc LRHS MGos
*	'Moppets Hardy'	SPer WHar
§	'Mrs Winder' ♀H4	Widely available
	'Mystery'	ECou ELan SWal
	'Mystery Red'	MGos
	'Nantyderry'	CCCN LRHS SWal WOut
§	'Neil's Choice' ♀H4	CCCN ECou ELon STre
	'Neopolitan' **new**	LRHS
	'Nicola's Blush' ♀H4	CCVN CSBt CSam ECou EPfP EShb LAst LRHS LSRN MCot MGos MRav MWat NBir NCot NHol SBch SBod SCoo SGar SIng SPer SPoG SRGP SRms STre SWvt WBrE WFar
	ochracea	LRHS MGos
§	- 'James Stirling' ♀H4	CBcs CSBt ECho ELan EPfP LRHS LSRN MAsh MBar MBri MGos MSwo MTho NBir NBlu SBch SCoo SLim SPer SPlb SPoG SRGP STre SWvt WDin WFar
	'Oddity'	LRHS
§	***odora***	ECou EPfP GGar MGos MMuc STre WCFE
I	- 'Nana'	EPfP MBar
	- 'New Zealand Gold'	LRHS MAsh MGos MMuc NDlv NHol SCoo SWal
	- var. ***patens***	WHCG
	- 'Summer Frost'	LRHS NHol
	'Oratia Beauty' ♀H4	MGos MRav NPri SBch SEND
	'Orphan Annie'PBR (v)	CWSG LRHS MGos SPoG
	parviflora misapplied	see *H.* 'Bowles's Hybrid'
§	***parviflora*** (Vahl) Cockayne & Allan	GGar
	- 'Holdsworth'	LRHS SDys
	- 'Palmerston'	ECou
	- var. ***angustifolia***	see *H. stenophylla*
	- var. ***arborea***	see *H. parviflora* (Vahl) Cockayne & Allan
	'Pascal' ♀H4	CCCN ECou ELan EPfP LRHS LSRN MBri MGos MRav SBch SCoo SPer SPoG
	'Patti Dossett'	see *H. speciosa* 'Patti Dossett'
	pauciramosa	SRms
	'Paula'	LRHS
	'Pearl of Paradise'PBR	LRHS MGos SPoG
	perfoliata	see *Parahebe perfoliata*
	'Perry's Rubyleaf'	NPer
	'Petra's Pink'	CCCN LRHS
	'Pewter Dome' ♀H4	CMac CSBt ECou EPfP LHop LRHS MGos MRav NDlv NHol SBch SDix SPer SRms STre WBrE WCom
	'Pimeba'	WCom
	pimeleoides	ECou NHol
	- 'Glauca'	NPer
	- 'Glaucocaerulea'	ECou
	- 'Quicksilver' ♀H4	CBgR CSBt CTri ECou EDAr ELan EPfP GGar LAst LRHS LSRN MBar MGos MMuc MRav MSCN MSwo

		NBir NHol NPer SBch SCoo SPer SPoG STre SUsu SWal WAbe WHar WPat
	- 'Red Tip'	ECho
	pinguifolia	ECou SPlb
	- 'Dobson'	LRHS
§	- 'Godefroyana'	SWal
	- 'Pagei' ♀H4	Widely available
	- 'Sutherlandii'	CBcs CDoC ECho GGar IFFs LEdu LRHS MBar MGos NDlv SCoo WFar
	'Pink Elephant' (v) ♀H3	CAbP ELan EPfP LAst LBuc LRHS MAsh NPri SBch SPoG WCom
	'Pink Fantasy'	CChe LRHS MGos MRav NHol
	'Pink Goddess'	LRHS MGos SRGP
	'Pink Lady'[PBR]	SPoG
	'Pink Paradise'[PBR]	CAbP ELan EPfP LRHS LSou MGos NHol SPoG
	'Pink Payne'	see *H.* 'Eveline'
	'Pink Pearl'	see *H.* 'Gloriosa'
	'Pink Pixie'	LBuc LRHS LSou MBri MGos SCoo
	'Pink Princess' **new**	LRHS
	'Pink Wand'	CTsd
	'Porlock Purple'	see *Parahebe catarractae* 'Delight'
§	'Primley Gem'	CCCN EQua LRHS SCoo
	propinqua	MHer NMen
	- 'Minor'	NDlv
I	'Prostrata'	CSBt NDlv
	'Purple Emperor'	see *H.* 'Neil's Choice'
	'Purple Paradise'[PBR]	EPfP LSou MBri NEgg SPoG
	'Purple Picture'	ELon
	'Purple Pixie'[PBR]	see *H.* 'Mohawk'
	'Purple Princess'	LRHS
	'Purple Queen'	ELan EPfP EShb GGar LIMB LRHS SPoG WAbe
	Purple Shamrock = 'Neprock'[PBR] (v)	EPfP LBuc LRHS LSRN MBri MGos NEgg NLar NPri SBch SCoo SPer SPoG SWal WClo WHar
	'Purple Tips' misapplied	see *H. speciosa* 'Variegata'
	'Rachel'	LRHS LSRN
	rakaiensis ♀H4	Widely available
	ramosissima	GGar NDlv
	raoulii	NMen NWCA WAbe
	'Raven' **new**	LRHS
	recurva	CSam CTri EPfP LAst MGos MMuc NHol SRms SWal WBrE WCom WCot WDin
§	- 'Aoira'	ECou
	- 'Boughton Silver' ♀H3	ELan EPfP LRHS
	- 'White Torrent'	ECou
	'Red Edge' ♀H4	Widely available
	'Red Rum'	ELan LRHS
	'Red Ruth'	see *H.* 'Eveline'
	rigidula	LRHS MGos NHol
	'Ronda'	ECou
	'Rosie'[PBR]	EPfP LAst LBuc LHop LRHS LSRN NMen SCoo SPer
	'Royal Purple'	see *H.* 'Alicia Amherst'
	salicifolia	CCCN CChe CMac ECou ELan EPfP GGar LAst LRHS MDun MGos MRav NHol SBch SCoo SEND SPer SPlb SRms WFar WHCG
	- BR 30	GGar
	- 'Snow Wreath'	see *H.* 'Snow Wreath'
	'Sandra Joy'	CCCN LRHS
	'Sapphire' ♀H4	ECou EPfP LRHS MBar MGos NBlu NPri SBch SCoo WFar
	'Sarana'	CCCN ECou LRHS
	selaginoides hort.	see *H.* 'Loganioides'
	'Shiraz'	LRHS
	'Silver Dollar' (v)	CAbP CCCN CMMP CMac CSBt CSam ELan EPfP LBuc LRHS MGos MMuc NEgg SPer SPoG SWal WSpi
§	'Silver Queen' (v) ♀H2	CSBt ECou ELan EPfP LRHS MBar MGos NEgg NPer SBch SPer SPoG WHar WOut
	'Simon Délaux'	CEnt ECou LRHS SEND
§	'Snow Wreath' (v)	WCom
I	'Southlandii'	ECho LAst MWhi
	speciosa	ECho
	- 'Johny Day'	see *H.* 'Johny Day'
§	- 'Patti Dossett'	LRHS
	- 'Rangatira'	ECou
§	- 'Variegata' (v)	LRHS NPer WEas
	'Spender's Seedling' misapplied	see *H. stenophylla*
	'Spender's Seedling' ambig.	MCot MMuc
	'Spender's Seedling' Hort.	ECou EPfP LRHS MRav SEND SPoG SRms STre
	'Spring Glory'	LRHS
§	***stenophylla***	ECou EShb GGal MSCN SAPC SArc SBch SDix
	- 'White Lady'	GGar
	stricta	ECou LRHS
	- var. ***egmontiana***	ECou LRHS
	- var. ***macroura***	ECou
	subalpina	CSBt ECho ERas LRHS NHol
	'Summer Blue'	EPfP LRHS MMuc MRav
	'Super Red'	CSBt LRHS
	'Sussex Carpet'	see *H. albicans* 'Sussex Carpet'
	'Sweet Kim' (v)	CMac LBuc LRHS MGos NPri
	'Tina'	ECou
	'Tiny Tot'	MTho
	'Tom Marshall'	see *H. canterburiensis*
	topiaria ♀H4	CAbP CChe CSBt CSam ECho ECou EPfP GGar LAst LHop LRHS MAsh MBrN MMuc MRav MSwo NHol SBch SCoo SPer SPoG STre SWal WAbe WCom WCor WFar
*	- 'Doctor Favier'	LRHS
	townsonii	ECou LHop LRHS SCoo
	traversii	ECou NHol SRms
	- 'Mason River'	ECou
	- 'Woodside'	ECou
	'Tricolor'	see *H. speciosa* 'Variegata'
	'Trixie'	CCCN ECou LRHS
	'Trudi' **new**	LRHS
	'Twisty'	ELan MGos
	'Valentino'[PBR]	LRHS NEgg
	'Veitchii'	see *H.* 'Alicia Amherst'
§	***venustula***	ECou GGar IArd LRHS MGos MMuc
	- 'Patricia Davies'	ECou
	vernicosa ♀H3	CChe CDul ECho EPfP LAst LRHS MBar MGos MHer NDlv NHol SBch SCoo SPer SPlb SPoG SRot STre SWvt WAbe WCom WFar WHCG
	'Violet Wand'	LRHS
	'Vogue'	EPfP LRHS
	'Waikiki'	see *H.* 'Mrs Winder'
	'Warley Pink'	LRHS
	'Warleyensis'	see *H.* 'Mrs Winder'
§	'Watson's Pink'	SPer WKif
	'White Gem' (*brachysiphon* hybrid) ♀H4	CCCN ECou LRHS MGos NDlv NPer SPer WFar
	'White Heather'	LRHS MGos NBir SBch
	'White Paradise'[PBR]	SPoG
	'Willcoxii'	see *H. buchananii* 'Fenwickii'
	'Wingletye' ♀H3	CCCN ECho ECou EPot LRHS NDlv NNor WAbe WCom WPer
	'Winter Glow'	CCCN LRHS MGos SBch SCoo
	'Wiri Blush'	LRHS SWvt
	'Wiri Charm'	CAbP CBcs CMac CSBt EPfP GGar LAst LBMP LRHS MGos MRav

		MSwo NEgg SBch SEND SPoG SWal WBrE WClo
	'Wiri Cloud' ♀H3	CAbP CMac EPfP GGar LRHS LSou MGos MSwo SBch SWal
	'Wiri Dawn' ♀H3	CAbP ELan EPfP EWes LRHS LSou MGos SBch SWvt WHrl
	'Wiri Desire'	CCCN LRHS
	'Wiri Gem'	LRHS MRav
	'Wiri Icing Sugar'	LRHS
	'Wiri Image'	CBcs CSBt LRHS SEND SPoG
	'Wiri Joy'	LRHS SEND SPoG
	'Wiri Mist'	CTrC GGar LRHS MGos SBch SCoo SPoG WFar
	'Wiri Prince'	LRHS SPoG
	'Wiri Splash'	CTrC LRHS MGos SPoG
	'Wiri Vision'	CSBt LRHS SEND
§	'Youngii' ♀H3-4	CSBt CTri ELan EPfP GGar LAst LBMP LRHS MBar MGos MHer MRav MWat NBir NMen NPri SBch SPer SPlb SPoG SRms STre SWvt WHoo

Hebenstretia (*Scrophulariaceae*)

	dura	CPBP
	- 'Jeanie' **new**	SDys
*	***quinquinervis***	LSou

Hechtia (*Bromeliaceae*)

	F&M 188	WPGP

Hedeoma (*Lamiaceae*)

	hyssopifolia	SPhx

Hedera ✿ (*Araliaceae*)

§	***algeriensis***	CDoC SAPC SArc WFib WGwG
	- 'Bellecour' **new**	WFib
§	- 'Gloire de Marengo' (v) ♀H3	Widely available
§	- 'Gloire de Marengo' arborescent (v)	SPer
	- 'Marginomaculata' (v) ♀H3	CDoC EBee EPfP LRHS SBch SMad WFib
	- 'Montgomery'	EBee LRHS LSRN MWht SBch
	- 'Ravensholst' ♀H3	CMac MRav WFib
§	***azorica***	WFar WFib
	- 'Pico'	EBee EPfP WFib
	canariensis hort.	see *H. algeriensis*
	- var. ***azorica***	see *H. azorica*
	- 'Cantabrian'	see *H. maroccana* 'Spanish Canary'
	- 'Gloire de Marengo' arborescent (v)	see *H. algeriensis* 'Gloire de Marengo' arborescent
	- 'Variegata'	see *H. algeriensis* 'Gloire de Marengo'
	chinensis	see *H. sinensis* var. *sinensis*
	- typica	see *H. sinensis* var. *sinensis*
§	***colchica*** ♀H4	CDul EPfP SPer WCFE WDin WFar WFib
	- 'Batumi'	MBNS WFib
	- 'Dentata' ♀H4	EHoe EPla MRav MWhi NEgg WFib
	- 'Dentata Aurea'	see *H. colchica* 'Dentata Variegata'
§	- 'Dentata Variegata' (v) ♀H4	Widely available
	- 'My Heart'	see *H. colchica*
	- 'Paddy's Pride'	see *H. colchica* 'Sulphur Heart'
§	- 'Sulphur Heart' (v) ♀H4	Widely available
	- 'Variegata'	see *H. colchica* 'Dentata Variegata'
	cristata	see *H. helix* 'Parsley Crested'
§	***cypria***	EShb WFib
	'Dixie'	NLar
	helix	CArn CCVT CRWN CTri GKir LRHS MBar MGos NWea WDin WHer WSFF
	- 'Adam' (v)	CWib EBee LAst LSRN MBri MTho WFib
	- 'Amberwaves'	MBri WFib
	- 'Angularis Aurea' ♀H4	EBee EPfP MWht NBir WFib
	- 'Anita'	GBin WFib WGwG
§	- 'Anna Marie' (v)	CMac LRHS MBri SRms WFib
	- 'Anne Borch'	see *H. helix* 'Anna Marie'
	- 'Arborescens'	EBee MGos NPal WDin WSFF
	- 'Ardingly' (v)	MWhi WFib
	- 'Asterisk'	WFib
	- 'Atropurpurea'	EBee EPPr GBin MBar WDin WFib
	- 'Baby Face'	WFib
	- var. ***baltica***	EBee WFib
	- 'Barabits' Silver' (v)	EGoo EPla
	- 'Bill Archer'	GBin WFib
	- 'Bird's Foot'	see *H. helix* 'Pedata'
	- 'Blarney' **new**	WFib
	- 'Blue Moon'	WFib
	- 'Boskoop'	WFib
	- 'Bowles's Ox Heart'	WFib
	- 'Bredon'	MRav
	- 'Brimstone' (v) **new**	WFib
§	- 'Brokamp'	MWht SLPl WFib
	- 'Bruder Ingobert' (v)	WHrl
	- 'Buttercup'	Widely available
	- 'Caecilia' (v) ♀H4	EPfP EQua LRHS MSwo NLar SPer SWvt WCot WFib
N	- 'Caenwoodiana'	see *H. helix* 'Pedata'
	- 'Caenwoodiana Aurea'	WFib
	- 'Calico' (v)	WFib
	- 'California Gold' (v)	WFib
	- 'Calypso'	WFib
	- 'Carolina Crinkle'	CBgR GBin MWhi WFib
	- 'Cathedral Wall'	WFib
§	- 'Cavendishii' (v)	SRms WFib WRHF
	- 'Cavendishii Latina'	WCot
	- 'Celebrity' (v) **new**	WFib
§	- 'Ceridwen' (v) ♀H4	CRHN MBri SPlb WFib
	- 'Chalice'	WFib
	- 'Cheap Thrills' **new**	WFib
	- 'Cheeky'	WFib
	- 'Cheltenham Blizzard' (v)	CNat
	- 'Chester' (v)	LRHS MAsh WFib
	- 'Chicago'	CWib WFib
	- 'Chicago Variegated' (v)	WFib
	- 'Chrysophylla'	MSwo
	- 'Clotted Cream' (v)	CMac ELon LBMP LHop LRHS MAsh MWat WFib
	- 'Cockle Shell'	WFib
	- 'Colin'	GBin
§	- 'Congesta' ♀H4	EPla GCra MTho NBir SRms STre WFib
	- 'Conglomerata'	CBcs ELan EPla MBar NBir SRms WDin WFib
	- 'Conglomerata Erecta'	MAsh NVic SRms WCFE WFib
	- 'Courage'	WFib WGwG
	- 'Crenata'	WFib
	- 'Crispa'	MRav
	- 'Cristata'	see *H. helix* 'Parsley Crested'
	- 'Curleylocks'	see *H. helix* 'Manda's Crested'
	- 'Curley-Q'	see *H. helix* 'Dragon Claw'
	- 'Curvaceous' (v)	WCot WFib
	- 'Cyprus'	see *H. cypria*
	- 'Dainty Bess'	CWib
	- 'Danish Crown' **new**	WFib
	- 'Dead Again'	GBin WCot
§	- 'Dealbata' (v)	CMac WFib
	- 'Delft' **new**	WFib
	- 'Deltoidea'	see *H. hibernica* 'Deltoidea'
	- 'Discolor'	see *H. helix* 'Dealbata', *H. helix* 'Minor Marmorata'
§	- 'Donerailensis'	MBlu WFib

	- 'Don's Papillon'	CBgR CNat WAlt
	- 'Dovers'	WFib
§	- 'Dragon Claw'	WFib
	- 'Duckfoot' ♀H4	CBgR CDoC EDAr EShb GBin MTho MWhi WFib WOut
	- 'Egret'	WFib
	- 'Eileen' (v)	WFib
	- 'Elfenbein' (v)	WFib
	- 'Emerald Jewel'	WFib
	- 'Erecta' ♀H4	CBgR CDul ELon EPPr EPfP EPla GCal LAst MBar MBlu MGos MTho NGHP NHol SBch SHGN SPer SPlb WDin WFar WFib
	- 'Erin'	see *H. helix* 'Pin Oak'
	- 'Ester' (v)	EQua LAst SRGP WFib
§	- 'Eva' (v)	LRHS MGos WDin WFib
	- 'Fanfare'	WFib
	- 'Fantasia' (v)	EShb MBri WFib
	- 'Feenfinger'	WFib WGwG
	- 'Ferney'	WFib
	- 'Filigran'	NLar WFib WHer
	- 'Flashback' (v)	WFib
	- 'Flavescens'	WFib
	- 'Fluffy Ruffles'	WFib
I	- 'Francis Ivy'	WFib
	- 'Frizzle'	WFib
	- 'Frosty' (v)	WFib
	- 'Funny Girl'	WFib
	- 'Garland'	WFib
	- 'Gavotte'	MTho MWht WFib
	- 'Ghost'	WFib
	- 'Gilded Hawke'	WFib WGwG
	- 'Glache' (v)	WFib
	- 'Glacier' (v) ♀H4	Widely available
	- 'Glymii'	GBin WCFE WFar WFib WTin
	- 'Gold Harald'	see *H. helix* 'Goldchild'
	- 'Gold Ripple'	SEND
§	- 'Goldchild' (v) ♀H3-4	CBcs CDoC CMac CSam EBee EHoe EPfP LAst LOck LRHS MAsh MBar MGos MRav MSwo NBir NEgg NHol SAga SBch SPer SPoG SWvt WDin WFib
	- 'Goldcraft' (v)	WFib
	- 'Golden Ann'	see *H. helix* 'Ceridwen'
*	- 'Golden Arrow'	ELan LRHS MAsh
	- 'Golden Curl' (v)	CMac EPfP LRHS MAsh
	- 'Golden Ester'	see *H. helix* 'Ceridwen'
	- 'Golden Gate' (v)	LAst WFib
	- 'Golden Girl'	WFib
	- 'Golden Ingot' (v) ♀H4	ELan EQua LBMP MBar MWhi WFib WGwG
	- 'Golden Jytte' (v) **new**	WFib
	- 'Golden Kolibri'	see *H. helix* 'Midas Touch'
	- 'Golden Mathilde' (v)	GBin
	- 'Golden Pittsburgh' (v)	WFib
	- 'Golden Snow' (v)	WFib
	- 'Goldfinch'	MBri WFib
	- 'Goldfinger'	MBri WFib
	- 'Goldheart'	see *H. helix* 'Oro di Bogliasco'
	- 'Goldstern' (v)	MRav MWhi WFib
	- 'Gracilis'	see *H. hibernica* 'Gracilis'
§	- 'Green Feather'	EGoo
	- 'Green Finger'	see *H. helix* 'Très Coupé'
	- 'Green Ripple'	CBcs CTri CWib EBee ECrN GKir LRHS MAsh MBar MGos MRav MSwo MWht NBro NPri SEND SPer SPlb SRms WBor WDin WFar WFib
	- 'Greenman'	WFib WGwG
	- 'Halebob'	MBri WFib WGwG
	- 'Hamilton'	see *H. hibernica* 'Hamilton'
	- 'Harald' (v)	CTri CWib WDin WFib
	- 'Harry Wood'	see *H. helix* 'Modern Times'
*	- 'Hazel' (v)	WFib
	- 'Hedge Hog'	WFib
	- 'Heise' (v)	WFib
	- 'Heise Denmark' (v)	WFib
	- 'Helvig'	see *H. helix* 'White Knight'
	- 'Henrietta'	WFib
	- 'Hester'	WFib
	- 'Hispanica'	see *H. iberica*
	- 'Hite's Miniature'	see *H. helix* 'Merion Beauty'
	- 'Holly'	see *H. helix* 'Parsley Crested'
	- 'Hullavington'	CNat
	- 'Humpty Dumpty'	CPLG MBar
	- 'Imp'	see *H. helix* 'Brokamp'
	- 'Ingelise' (v)	WFib
	- 'Ingrid' (v)	WFib
	- 'Itsy Bitsy'	see *H. helix* 'Pin Oak'
	- 'Ivalace' ♀H4	CBcs CRHN EBee ECha ECrN EPfP MGos MSwo MWhi MWht SRms WDin WFib WTin
	- 'Jake'	MBri WFib
	- 'Jasper'	WFib
	- 'Jersey Doris' (v)	WFib
	- 'Jerusalem'	see *H. helix* 'Schäfer Three'
	- 'Jester's Gold'	EBee ELan EPfP MBri MGos SBch WDin WRHF
	- 'Jubilee' (v)	WCFE WFib
	- 'Kaleidoscope'	WFib
	- 'Kevin'	WFib
	- 'Kloster's Joy' **new**	WFib
	- 'Knülch'	WFib
	- 'Kolibri' (v)	CDoC CRHN CWan EBee EMil EPfP LAst LRHS MBar MBri MGos MWht SBch SMad WFib
§	- 'Königer's Auslese'	CDul WFib
	- 'Lalla Rookh'	MRav WFib WGwG WHrl
	- 'Lemon Swirl' (v)	WFib
	- 'Leo Swicegood'	CBgR MWhi WFib
	- 'Light Fingers'	EBee LRHS WFib WGwG WHrl
	- 'Limey'	WFib
	- 'Little Diamond' (v)	CDoC CTri EBee ELan EPfP LHop LRHS MAsh MBar MBri MWht NHol SLon SWvt WDin WFib WHrl WTin
	- 'Little Luzii' **new**	WFib
	- 'Liz'	see *H. helix* 'Eva'
	- 'Lucille'	WFib
	- 'Luzii' (v)	EBee MBar MGos WFib WGwG
	- 'Maculata'	see *H. helix* 'Minor Marmorata'
§	- 'Manda's Crested' ♀H4	CDul CSWP NLar WFib WGwG
	- 'Maple Leaf' ♀H4	GBin WFib
	- 'Maple Queen'	MBri
	- 'Marginata' (v)	SRms
	- 'Marginata Elegantissima'	see *H. helix* 'Tricolor'
	- 'Marginata Minor'	see *H. helix* 'Cavendishii'
I	- 'Marmorata' Fibrex	WFib
	- 'Masquerade' (v)	WFib WGor
	- 'Mathilde' (v)	EBee MWht WFib
	- 'Meagheri'	see *H. helix* 'Green Feather'
	- 'Melanie' ♀H4	ECha SRGP WFib WGwG
	- 'Meon'	WFib
§	- 'Merion Beauty'	WFib
§	- 'Midas Touch' (v) ♀H3-4	CWib EPfP MBri WFib
	- 'Midget'	CRow
	- 'Mini Ester' (v)	EPfP MBri
	- 'Mini Heron'	LAst MBri
	- 'Mini Pittsburgh'	LAst
	- 'Minikin' (v)	LLHF WCot WFib
	- 'Minima' misapplied	see *H. helix* 'Spetchley'
	- 'Minima' Hibberd	see *H. helix* 'Donerailensis'
	- 'Minima' M. Young	see *H. helix* 'Congesta'
§	- 'Minor Marmorata' (v) ♀H4	CWan WSHC
	- 'Mint Kolibri'	EHoe LAst MBri
	- 'Minty' (v)	MWht WFib

	– 'Misty' (v)	WFib
§	– 'Modern Times'	EBee
	– 'Mon Premier' **new**	WFib
	– 'New Ripples'	MWht
	– 'Niagara Falls'	LRHS MAsh
	– 'Nigra Aurea' (v)	WFib
	– 'Obovata'	WFib
N	– 'Oro di Bogliasco' (v)	CDul CTri EBee EPfP GKir LRHS MAsh MBar MBri MRav MSwo NBea NBlu NHol NPri NWea SBch SGar SPer SPet SPlb SPoG SRms STre SWvt WDin WFar WFib WPat
	– 'Ovata'	WFib
§	– 'Parsley Crested' ♀H4	CMac EBee EPfP EQua LRHS MAsh MBar MGos SRms WBVN WFib WGwG
	– 'Patent Leather'	WFib
N	– 'Pedata'	CDul MSwo WFib
	– 'Perkeo'	WFib
	– 'Persian Carpet'	WFib
	– 'Peter' (v)	WFib
	– 'Peter Pan'	WFib WGwG
	– 'Phantom' **new**	WFib
§	– 'Pin Oak'	WDin
	– 'Pink 'n' Curly'	WFib
	– 'Pink 'n' Very Curly'	WCot
§	– 'Pittsburgh'	MGos SBch WFib
	– 'Plattensee' **new**	EBee
	– 'Plume d'Or'	WFib
§	– f. ***poetarum***	EPla MBlu WFib
	– – 'Poetica Arborea'	ECha SDix
	– 'Poetica'	see *H. helix* f. *poetarum*
	– 'Professor Friedrich Tobler'	EBee
	– 'Raleigh Delight' (v)	WCot
	– 'Ray's Supreme'	see *H. helix* 'Pittsburgh'
	– subsp. ***rhizomatifera***	WFib
	– 'Richard John'	WFib
	– 'Ritterkreuz'	WFib WGwG
	– 'Romanze' (v)	WFib WGwG
	– 'Rotunda' **new**	WFib
	– 'Russelliana'	WFib
	– 'Sagittifolia' misapplied	see *H. helix* 'Königer's Auslese'
	– 'Sagittifolia' Hibberd	see *H. hibernica* 'Sagittifolia'
	– 'Sagittifolia' ambig.	MAsh
	– 'Sagittifolia Variegata' (v)	EBee MBri NBea WFib WRHF
	– 'Saint Agnes'	MAsh
	– 'Sally' (v)	WFib
	– 'Salt and Pepper'	see *H. helix* 'Minor Marmorata'
§	– 'Schäfer Three' (v)	CWib WFib
	– 'Seabreeze' **new**	WFib
	– 'Shadow'	WFib
	– 'Shamrock'	EPfP MWht WFib
	– 'Shannon'	WFib
	– 'Silver Butterflies' (v)	WFib
	– 'Silver Ferny'	WFib
	– 'Silver King' (v)	MRav MWht WFib WGwG
	– 'Silver Queen'	see *H. helix* 'Tricolor'
	– 'Spectre' (v)	WHer
§	– 'Spetchley' ♀H4	EPla EPot GCal MAsh MBar MRav MWhi NHol NPer SMad WCFE WCot WFib WGwG WHrl WPat WPtf WTin
	– 'Spiriusa'	WFib
	– 'Splashes' **new**	WFib
	– 'Stuttgart'	WFib
	– 'Sunrise'	WFib
	– 'Suzanne'	see *H. nepalensis* 'Suzanne'
	– 'Tanja'	WFib
	– 'Teardrop'	WFib
	– 'Telecurl'	WFib
	– 'Temptation' (v) **new**	WFib
	– 'Tenerife' (v)	WFib
	– 'Tiger Eyes'	WFib
	– 'Topazolite' (v)	WFib
§	– 'Très Coupé'	CBgR CDoC LRHS MAsh SAPC SArc SPer WDin
§	– 'Tricolor' (v)	CTri EBee EPfP LRHS MAsh MCot MGos MWht WCFE WFib
	– 'Trinity' (v)	WFib
	– 'Tripod'	WFib WGwG
	– 'Triton'	EPfP MBar WFib
	– 'Troll'	EDAr WFib WPat
	– 'Tussie Mussie' (v)	WFib
	– 'Ursula' (v)	EShb WFib
	– 'Very Merry'	EPPr WFib
*	– 'Vitifolium' **new**	WFib
	– 'White Heart'	MGos
§	– 'White Knight' (v) ♀H4	WFib
	– 'White Mein Herz' (v)	GBin WFib
	– 'White Ripple' (v) **new**	WFib
	– 'White Wonder'	WFib
	– 'William Kennedy' (v)	WFib
	– 'Williamsiana' (v)	WFib
	– 'Woeneri'	MWht WFib
	– 'Wonder'	LRHS WFib
	– 'Woodsii'	see *H. helix* 'Modern Times'
	– 'Yellow Ripple'	EBee LAst LRHS MBri WDin WFib
	– 'Zebra' (v)	WFib
	hibernica ♀H4	CCVT CDul CSBt EPfP IFFs LBuc MBar MRav MSwo MWhi NBlu NWea SBch SPer SRms WDin WFib
	– 'Anna Marie'	see *H. helix* 'Anna Marie'
	– 'Aracena'	EPla SLPl
	– 'Betty Allen'	WFib
§	– 'Deltoidea' ♀H4	EPla MWht WFib
I	– 'Digitata Crûg Gold'	WCru
	– 'Ebony' **new**	WFib
	– 'Glengariff' **new**	WFib
§	– 'Gracilis'	WFib
§	– 'Hamilton'	WFib
	– 'Harlequin' (v)	WFib
	– 'Lobata Major'	SRms
	– 'Maculata' (v)	SLPl WSHC
	– 'Palmata'	WFib
	– 'Rona'	WFib WGwG
§	– 'Sagittifolia'	CTri EBee EPfP GBin LBMP LRHS MBar SBch SPer SRms WDin
	– 'Sulphurea' (v)	MGos WFib
	– 'Tess'	EPla
	– 'Variegata' (v)	MBar MGos WFib
§	***iberica***	WFib
	maderensis	WFib
	maroccana 'Morocco'	WFib
§	– 'Spanish Canary'	WFib
	nepalensis	WFib
	– 'Marble Dragon'	see *H. sinensis* var. *sinensis* 'Marble Dragon'
§	– 'Suzanne'	MBar WFib
	pastuchovii	WFib
	– 'Lagocetti' **new**	WFib
	– from Troödos, Cyprus	see *H. cypria*
	– 'Ann Ala'	EBee EPfP GBin WFib WGwG
§	***rhombea***	WCot WFib
	– 'Eastern Dawn'	WFib
	– 'Japonica'	see *H. rhombea*
I	– f. ***pedunculata*** 'Maculata'	CWib
	– var. ***rhombea*** 'Variegata' (v)	WFib
	'Sabine' **new**	LRHS
§	***sinensis*** var. ***sinensis***	MWht WFib
§	– – 'Marble Dragon' **new**	WFib

Hedychium ✿ (*Zingiberaceae*)

B&SWJ 3110 — WPGP
B&SWJ 7155 — WPGP
CC 5611 — GKev
'Anne Bishop' — SEND WPGP
aurantiacum — CBcs CBct CHEx EAmu EBee IDee LAma LEdu LRHS NScw SBig SSwd
brevicaule B&SWJ 7171 — WCru
chrysoleucum — CCCN EShb LAma SBst
coccineum ΨH1 — CDTJ CTsd EAmu EBee EBrs ECho EPfP EShb ETod IKil LRHS MNrw SBig SSwd
- B&SWJ 5238 — WCru
- CC 3801 — WCot
- var. ***angustifolium*** — CDes CGHE CRHN EBee EPfP WPGP
- 'Disney' — CDTJ
- 'Tara' ΨH3 — CBct CDes CDoC CGHE CHEx CPLG CPne CRHN CSam EAmu EBee EPfP IBlr IDee IGor LEdu LPJP MNrw SAPC SArc SBch SBst SChr SDix SUsu WCru WPGP
coronarium — CBct CCCN CDTJ CDes CFee CTsd EAmu EBee EBrs EShb IDee IKil LEdu LRHS MWea SBig WPGP
- B&SWJ 8354 — WCru
- 'Gold Spot' — SSwd
- var. ***maximum*** — ETod
- 'Orange Spot' — EAmu
- var. ***urophyllum*** — IBlr
coronarium* × *gardnerianum — SPer SSwd
'Daniel Weeks' — EBee
densiflorum — CBct CCCN CDTJ CDes CHEx CHll CPLG CPne EAmu EBee ECha EPfP ETod IBlr LEdu MBel NScw SDix SSpi WCom WCru WPGP
- 'Assam Orange' — Widely available
- 'Sorung' — CPLG LEdu
- 'Stephen' — CAvo CBct CCCN CDTJ CDes CFir CGHE CHEx CPLG CPne CSam EAmu EBee EPfP LEdu MNrw NPal WPGP
'Devon Cream' — CCCN CPLG EAmu NPal
'Doctor Moy' (v) — CDTJ
'Double Eagle' — WPGP
'Elizabeth' — CDes EBee LEdu WPGP
ellipticum — CDTJ CHEx CRHN EAmu EBee ETod LAma LEdu LRHS MNrw SBig SSwd
'Filigree' — CDes CPLG EBee LEdu WPGP
flavescens — CBct CDTJ EAmu EBee EBrs EPfP EShb LAma LEdu LRHS MNrw SChr SSwd WCru WPGP
flavum Roxb. — EBee
forrestii misapplied — CTrC IDee
forrestii Diels — CDes CPLG EAmu EBee EShb ETod GCal IBlr LPJP MNrw MREP SAPC SArc WKif WPGP
gardnerianum ΨH1 — Widely available
- B&SWJ 7155 — WCru
'Gold Flame' — CDes CMdw EBee LEdu MNrw WPGP
gracile — EAmu LEdu WCru
greenii — CBct CDoC CHEx CPne CRHN CSam CSpe CTsd EBee EBrs ECho EPfP EShb LEdu LRHS MNrw NScw SArc SBch SBig SChr SDix SHaC SSwd WBor WCru WPGP
griffithianum — CSpe EAmu EBee EPfP IKil LRHS MNrw SBig SSwd
- white-flowered — CCCN
'Hardy Exotics 1' — CHEx
I × ***kewense*** — SSwd
'Kinkaku' — WDyG WPGP
'Luna Moth' — WPGP
luteum new — CBcs
maximum — EAmu SSwd WDyG WPGP
- B&SWJ 8261A — WCru
- HWJ 604 — WCru
- HWJ 810 — WCru
'Pink Flame' — LEdu
'Pink V' — EBee WPGP
pink-flowered — CDes SSwd
'Pradhan' — CFir
× ***raffillii*** — MNrw SBig
spicatum — CAby CDTJ CDes CFir CHEx CPLG CRHN EBee GCal GPoy IBlr LEdu LRHS MNrw SSwd WCFE
- B&SWJ 2303 — WPGP
- B&SWJ 7231 — WCru
- BWJ 8116 — WCru
- P. Bon. 57188 — WPGP
- from Salween Valley, China — CPLG
- var. ***acuminatum*** — EBee WPGP
- 'Himalayan Lipstick' new — EBee
- 'Singalila' — CDes WCru
'St Martin's' new — EBee
thyrsiforme — EAmu EBee EShb IDee LEdu SBig SSwd WCru
villosum — CDTJ EBee EBrs ECho
wardii — CHEx CPLG WPGP
yunnanense — CDes CPLG CRHN CSam EBee IBlr LEdu MNrw SBig WPGP
- B&SWJ 9717 — WCru
- BWJ 7900 — WCru

Hedysarum (*Papilionaceae*)

coronarium — CArn CSpe EHrv ELan EPfP MCot NBur SMrm WCot WKif
hedysaroides — IKil
multijugum — CBcs MBlu SPer

Heimia (*Lythraceae*)

salicifolia — CArn EOHP IDee MBlu SGar

Helenium ✿ (*Asteraceae*)

'Autumn Lollipop' — EBee IBal MBNS MCCP MSCN NLar NOrc SHGN SPav
autumnale — CSBt CSam CTri EPPr GKir LDai LSRN MLHP MNHC NChi SMrm SPet SWvt WClo WFar WGwG WMoo
- 'All Gold' — SWvt
I - 'Cupreum' — SBch
- Helena Series — LBMP LRHS SWvt
- - 'Helena Gold' — CEnt EBee NBre WPer
- - 'Helena Rote Töne' — CChe EBee LBMP MWhi WPer
'Baronin Linden' — CSam MAvo
'Baudirektor Linne' ΨH4 — CSam EBee WSpi
'Biedermeier' — CAby CBct CPrp CSam CWCL EBee EBla ECtt EShb MBel MRav MSpe NCob NEgg NGdn SPhx SPoG WHlf
bigelovii — EBrs
'Blütentisch' ΨH4 — CHVG CMHG CMea COIW CSam EBee GMaP MNFA NCGa NLar NVic SPur WHal WMnd
'Bressingham Gold' — CSam EBrs LRHS MAvo MNrw WBrk WHrl
'Bruno' — CAby CHar CWCL EBrs ELan ELon GKir LRHS MArl NGby NLar WSpi

'Butterpat' ♀H4 EBee ECtt EHrv EPfP GCra GKir GMaP GMac LBMP LRHS MRav NCGa NPri NSti SMrm WWEG
'Can Can' CSam
'Chelsey' CPrp EBee EHrv ELan EPfP IBal IPot LRHS LSRN MBel MBri NBPC NBhm NChi NLar NMoo NPri SPoG WWlt
'Chipperfield Orange' CElw CSam ECtt MArl MRav NBre NGdn NVic WOld WWEG
'Coppelia' CSam EBrs LRHS MRav NBir NGdn
Copper Spray see *H.* 'Kupfersprudel'
'Crimson Beauty' ECtt ELan MBel MRav WSpi
Dark Beauty see *H.* 'Dunkelpracht'
'Dauerbrenner' CSam MAvo MSpe
'Die Blonde' EBee NBre
'Double Trouble'[PBR] EBee EHrv EPfP IPot LLHF MAvo MBNS MSpe NBPC NPri SMrm SPoG WCot WWlt
§ 'Dunkelpracht' CElw CMHG CSam CWGN EBee ECtt EHrv EWll LAst LSRN MBel MCot NBPC NCob NEgg NGdn NLar NSti SPoG WFar WGwG WOld WWEG
'El Dorado' CSam
'Fata Morgana' EBee LLHF NBre SPoG
'Feuersiegel' ♀H4 CAby CSam EBee NBre WOld
'Fiesta' CAby CSam EBee MSpe
'Flammendes Käthchen' CAby CSam CWCL EBee EBrs IPot LRHS MAvo NBre SAga SMrm
'Flammenrad' CSam EBee SDys
'Flammenspiel' EBee ECtt LRHS MCot MNrw NGby WSpi
flexuosum EBee NBre WPer
'Gartensonne' ♀H4 CSam NBre SMrm
'Gay-go-round' CSam MSpe
Gold Fox see *H.* 'Goldfuchs'
'Gold Intoxication' see *H.* 'Goldrausch'
Golden Youth see *H.* 'Goldene Jugend'
§ 'Goldene Jugend' CElw CMea CSam ECtt ELan MRav MSpe WCot WEas WHal WWEG
§ 'Goldfuchs' CSam CWCL SDys WCot
§ 'Goldlackzwerg' EBrs GKir LRHS MAvo MBri NBre
§ 'Goldrausch' CHar CPrp CSam EBee EBla ECtt GCra LEdu LRHS MDKP MSpe MWat NBre NGdn SPhx WOld WSpi WWEG
'Goldreif' CSam
'Hartmut Reiger' CSam MSpe
'Helena' NLar WPer
hoopesii see *Hymenoxys hoopesii*
'Indianersommer' CElw CSam CWCL EBee EBla ECtt EHrv GMaP IBal LDai LRHS MBNS MDun MNFA NCGa NLar NMRc NOrc SGSe SMrm SUsu WClo WFar WHoo
'Jam Tarts' MAvo WCot
'July Sun' NBir
'Kanaria' CAby CHVG CPrp EBee EBrs EWll GQue LRHS MBel MSpe NCob NEgg NLar SMrm SMrs SPhx SPoG WMnd WOld WSpi
'Karneol' ♀H4 CSam NBre SUsu
'Kleiner Fuchs' CSam EHrv NLar
'Kokarde' CSam MSpe
'Königstiger' CPrp CSam EBee EBrs ECtt LRHS MNrw MSpe MWea NBre NCGa SMrs WFar
'Kugelsonne' EBee NBre
'Kupfersiegel' CSam
§ 'Kupfersprudel' CSam MAvo MSpe
'Kupferzwerg' CElw CSam CWCL EBee ELan IPot NBre
'Loysder Wieck' WHlf
'Luc' CSam MSpe
'Lyndley' **new** CHVG
'Mahagoni' CSam GBin
'Mahogany' see *H.* 'Goldlackzwerg'
'Mardi Gras' **new** ECtt
'Margot' CAby CSam CWCL MSpe NBre SDys SUsu
'Marion Nickig' CSam
'Meranti' CMea CSam MAvo MSpe SMrs WHlf
'Moerheim Beauty' ♀H4 Widely available
'Orange Beauty' EBee
Pipsqueak = 'Blopip' CWCL ECtt GKir LLHF LRHS MSpe NBre
'Potter's Wheel' CSam IPot MAvo MSpe SMrs
puberulum SPav
'Pumilum Magnificum' CHar CSam CWCL EBee EPfP GQue LEdu LHop LRHS SPer WFar WPGP
'Ragamuffin' CSam MSpe
'Rauchtopas' CAby CDes CSam EBee IBal IPot MAvo MSpe NCGa SDys SUsu WPGP
Red and Gold see *H.* 'Rotgold'
'Red Army' EBee EKen GMac IBal LRHS MAvo MNrw MSCN MSpe NCGa NGdn
'Red Glory' CHid EBee EHrv GMac
'Red Jewel' CWGN LLHF LPla LRHS LSou MAvo NBPC NEgg NGdn NSti SPoG SUsu WCot WRHF
'Ring of Fire' ♀H4 CSam IPot
'Riverton Beauty' CSam LLHF MSpe WCot WHoo
'Riverton Gem' CSam ECtt EHrv LLHF NBre NChi WHoo
§ 'Rotgold' ECGP ECtt LRHS LSRN NBre NChi SGar SRms WFar WMoo WPer WWEG
'Rotkäppchen' CSam
'Rubinkuppel' CAby NCGa SPhx
'Rubinzwerg' ♀H4 Widely available
§ 'Ruby Thuesday' CAby CMac EBee EHrv EPPr EPfP GMac GQue LLHF LRHS LSRN LSou MBNS NBPC NCGa NEgg NGdn NOrc NSti SBch SPoG WCot WWEG
'Ruby Tuesday' see *H.* 'Ruby Thuesday'
'Sahin's Early Flowerer' ♀H4 Widely available
'Septemberfuchs' GMac LEdu MCot NBre WWEG
'Sonnenwunder' EBee ECha LEdu MLHP NBre
'Summer Circle' ♀H4 CSam
'The Bishop' COIW CSam EBee EBla ECtt ELon EPPr EPfP GMac IBal LAst LEdu LRHS MDKP MRav MSCN MSpe NBro NPri SPer SPet SRGP SWvt WCAu WFar WMnd WMoo WWEG
'Tip Top' EBee LBMP LRHS MWat SBch WHil
'Vivace' CSam MSpe SMrs
'Wagon Wheel' EBee WCot
'Waltraut' ♀H4 Widely available
'Wesergold' ♀H4 EBee EBla GBBs LLHF LSou
'Wonnadonga' EBee
'Wyndley' Widely available
'Zimbelstern' CAby CDes CElw CMdw EBee ECha ECtt ELon LHop LRHS MCot MNFA MRav MSpe SMrm SMrs SPhx WAul WFar WPGP

Heliamphora ✿ (*Sarraceniaceae*)

minor SHmp
nutans SHmp

Helianthella (Asteraceae)

§	***quinquenervis***	EBee GBin GCal LLHF NLar
	uniflora NNS 06-272 new	WCot

Helianthemum ✿ (Cistaceae)

	SDR 5508 new	GKev
	'Albert's Brick'	LIMB
	'Albert's Gold'	LIMB
	'Alice Howarth'	LIMB WHoo
	alpestre serpyllifolium	see *H. nummularium* subsp. *glabrum*
	'Amabile Plenum' (d)	EPfP GAbr GCal GEdr LIMB
	'Amy Baring' ♀H4	CTri ECtt GAbr LIMB LRHS NHol WCom WPer
	'Annabel' (d)	ECho ECtt GAbr IGor LRHS NGby NHol WCom WPer
	apenninum	LLHF SRms
	- var. ***roseum***	ECho
	'Apricot'	CTri LIMB SPer
	'Apricot Blush'	LIMB WAbe
	'Baby Buttercup'	CMea LIMB
	'Banwy Copper'	LIMB WBVN
	'Banwy Velvet'	LIMB WBVN
	'Beech Park Red'	CTri ECho ECtt LIMB MHer SDix WAbe WFar WHoo WKif
	'Ben Afflick'	ECho LHop LIMB LRHS SPer SRms WFar
	'Ben Alder'	ECho GAbr LIMB MHer
	'Ben Attow'	LIMB
	'Ben Dearg'	CMea ECho ECtt LIMB SRms
	'Ben Fhada'	CBcs CMea COlW CPBP CTri ECho ECtt EPfP GAbr GKev GKir GMaP IMon LBee LIMB LRHS MHer NEgg SBch SPer SPoG SRms WAbe WBrE WFar WPer
	'Ben Heckla'	CSam ECho ECtt EPfP GAbr LHop LIMB LRHS WPer
	'Ben Hope'	CTri ECho ECtt EPfP LIMB NHol SPer SRGP
§	'Ben Ledi'	CBcs COlW CPBP ECho ECtt EPfP GAbr GMaP LHop LIMB MHer MSCN NChi NHol NSla SBch SPer SPoG SRms WAbe WClo WFar WPer
	'Ben Lomond'	ECho LIMB
	'Ben Macdhui'	LIMB
	'Ben More'	CBcs CMea COlW ECho ECtt EPfP GAbr GJos GMaP LHop LIMB LRHS MSCN MSwo NBir SBch SEND SIng SPer SPoG SRGP SRms WFar
	'Ben Nevis'	CTri ECho LIMB SPer SRms WFar
	'Ben Vane'	LIMB LRHS
	'Big Orange'	LIMB
	'Birch Double' (d) new	LIMB
	'Blutströpfchen'	LIMB
	'Boughton Double Primrose' (d)	CPBP ECho ELan GMaP LHop WEas WHoo WSHC WTin
	'Braungold'	LIMB
	'Brilliant'	NBir
	'Bronzeteppich'	LLHF
	'Broughty Beacon'	GAbr LIMB WGor
	'Broughty Orange'	LIMB
	'Broughty Sunset'	CSam ECtt LIMB NBir NHol WHoo
	'Bunbury'	COlW IMon LHop LIMB LRHS MBrN NBir SPoG SRms WRHF
*	'Butter and Eggs'	LIMB
	'Captivation'	GAbr LIMB
I	'Carminium Plenum'	LIMB
	'Cerise Queen' (d)	CTri EAlp ECha ECho ECtt GEdr IMon LAst LHop LIMB MMHG MSwo NCGa SDix SPer SRms WCom WHoo
	chamaecistus	see *H. nummularium*
	'Cheviot'	CMea GAbr LIMB NBir SAga WEas WHoo WPer
	'Chichester'	LIMB
	'Chocolate Blotch'	ECho GAbr GCra GEdr LHop LIMB LRHS NChi NHol SEND SRms WPer
	'Cornish Cream'	ECho EWTr GAbr LBee LIMB
	croceum	LLHF
	cupreum	GAbr
	'David'	EGoo LIMB
	'David Ritchie'	LIMB LLHF WHoo
	'Diana'	CMea LIMB SAga
	'Dompfaff'	LIMB
	'Dora'	LIMB
	double apricot-flowered (d)	GAbr LIMB
	double cream-flowered (d)	ECho
	double orange-flowered (d)	LHop
	double primrose-flowered (d)	CHVG GAbr LIMB
	double red-flowered (d)	NChi
	'Eisbar'	LIMB
	'Elfenbeinglanz'	LIMB NGby
	'Elisabeth'	EGoo
	'Ellen' (d)	CMea LIMB
	'Etna'	LIMB NHol STre
	'Everton Ruby'	see *H.* 'Ben Ledi'
	'Fairy'	ECho EPfP GAbr LIMB LLHF
	'Feuerbraund'	LIMB
§	'Fire Dragon' ♀H4	CMea ECho EPfP GAbr GEdr GMaP GQue LIMB LRHS MGos NBir NWCA SAga SEND SRms WAbe WCom
	'Fireball'	see *H.* 'Mrs C.W. Earle'
	'Firegold' (v)	LIMB WAbe WFar
	'Flame'	LIMB
	'Frau Bachtaler'	LIMB
	'Georgeham'	CMea CPBP EAlp ECho ECtt ELon EPfP GAbr LBee LHop LIMB NBir SAga SRms WEas WGor WHoo WPer
§	'Golden Queen'	ECho ECtt EPfP GAbr LIMB MSwo NCGa WFar WPer
	'Hampstead Orange'	CTri
	'Hartshorn'	LIMB
	'Hartswood Ruby' new	LRHS MBNS
	'Henfield Brilliant' ♀H4	CHVG CPBP CPLG ECho ECtt EPfP GAbr LHop LIMB LRHS MRav MSCN NBir NHol SBch SMad SPer SRms WCot WEas WHoo WPer WSHC
	'Highdown'	GAbr SRms
	'Highdown Apricot'	LHop LIMB LLHF SPoG WFar
	'Honeymoon'	ECtt EPfP GAbr GEdr LIMB NHol
	'Ilna's Master' (d)	LIMB
	'Ilona' (d/v)	LIMB
	'Jubilee' (d) ♀H4	CTri ECho ECtt ELan EPfP GAbr LHop LIMB MBNS NBir NBlu NChi NPri SPoG SRms WEas WFar WKif
I	'Jubilee Variegatum' (v)	GAbr LIMB
	'Karen's Silver'	LIMB WAbe
	'Kathleen Druce' (d)	ECho ECtt EWes GAbr LIMB NHol SAga WHoo
	'Kathleen Mary'	CMea LIMB
	'Lawrenson's Pink'	ECho ECtt GAbr GEdr LIMB LRHS SPoG SRGP WPer
	'Lemon Queen'	CWan LIMB
	'Lucy Elizabeth'	GAbr LIMB
	lunulatum	CMea ECtt GKir LIMB LLHF LRHS NLAp NMen WAbe WPat
	'Magnificum'	MWat
	'Marianne'	LIMB
	'Mette'	LIMB
§	'Mrs C.W. Earle' (d) ♀H4	COlW CTri ECho ECtt ELan EPfP GBuc GCra LIMB LRHS MBNS NEgg NHol SRms WFar WPer

	'Mrs Clay'	see *H.* 'Fire Dragon'
	'Mrs Croft'	LIMB WPer
	'Mrs Hays'	GAbr LIMB
	'Mrs Jenkinson'	LIMB
	'Mrs Lake'	GAbr LIMB
	'Mrs Moules'	LIMB SRms
	mutabile	CEnt SPlb
§	***nummularium***	EBWF GPoy MHer MNHC NMir NSco SHGN WAbe WPat WSFF
§	- subsp. ***glabrum***	GAbr NHol NLAp SIng WPat
§	- subsp. ***tomentosum***	GAbr NHol
I	'Oblongatum'	LIMB
	oelandicum	GAbr NHol NWCA SRms WAbe
	- subsp. ***alpestre***	NMen WPer
	- subsp. ***piloselloides***	WAbe
	'Old Gold'	EGoo ELon GAbr LIMB NHol SRms WAbe WPer
	'Orange Phoenix' (d)	EPfP GAbr LIMB MBNS NHol NPri SRot WFar
	'Orange Surprise'	LIMB
	'Ovum Supreme'	LIMB
	'Peach'	LIMB
	'Pershore Orange'	LIMB
	'Pink Angel' (d)	CBow LIMB MBNS WPer
	'Pink Beauty'	LIMB
	'Pink Glow'	GAbr LIMB WPer
	'Praecox'	CMea CTri CWan ECho GAbr LBee LIMB SRms WHoo WPer
	'Prima Donna'	ECGP EPfP NBir
	'Prostrate Orange'	LIMB SRms
	'Raspberry Ripple'	CBow EAlp ECho ECtt ELan EPfP EPot LIMB LRHS NGby NHol SPoG SRms WAbe WFar
	'Razzle Dazzle' (v)	CBow GKev LIMB LLHF SRms SRot WFar
	'Red Dragon'	EAlp EPot LIMB WAbe
	'Red Orient'	see *H.* 'Supreme'
	'Regenbogen' (d)	GCal LIMB SEND
§	'Rhodanthe Carneum' ♀H4	Widely available
§	'Rosakönigin'	ECho ECtt GAbr LIMB MHer WAbe
	'Rose of Leeswood' (d)	CMea CPBP CTri LBee LIMB NChi NEgg SAga SPoG SRms WClo WEas WFar WHoo WKif WRHF WSHC
	Rose Queen	see *H.* 'Rosakönigin'
	'Roxburgh Gold'	SRms
	'Rubin' (d)	LIMB
	'Rushfield's White'	LIMB
	'Ruth'	LIMB
	'Saint John's College Yellow'	CSam ECho GAbr LIMB LRHS
	'Salmon Queen'	ECho ECtt GAbr LHop LIMB LRHS SRms WPer
*	***scardicum***	CMea NLAp
	'Schnee' (d)	EGoo LIMB
	serpyllifolium	see *H. nummularium* subsp. *glabrum*
	'Shot Silk'	CPBP ECtt EWes
	'Snow Queen'	see *H.* 'The Bride'
	'Southmead'	ECho LIMB
	'Sterntaler'	GAbr GEdr LIMB LLHF SRms
	'Sudbury Gem'	CTri ECha ECho GAbr GKir LIMB LRHS
	'Sulphur Moon'	LHop LLHF LRHS
	'Sulphureum Plenum' (d)	ECtt EPfP GEdr LIMB
	'Sunbeam'	CSam ECho LIMB SRms
	'Sunburst'	LIMB
§	'Supreme'	ECho ELan EPfP EWes GEdr LIMB MAvo SRms
	'Tangerine'	ECtt GAbr LIMB NHol
§	'The Bride' ♀H4	Widely available
	'Tigrinum Plenum' (d)	EWes LIMB
	'Tomato Red'	NSla
	tomentosum	see *H. nummularium* subsp. *tomentosum*
	umbellatum	see *Halimium umbellatum*
	'Venustum Plenum' (d)	LIMB WEas
	'Victor' (d)	LIMB
	'Voltaire'	ECho ECtt EPfP LIMB LLHF NHol
	'Watergate Rose'	ECho ECtt LIMB MWat NBir
	'Welsh Flame'	LIMB WAbe WFar
	'Windmill Gold'	LIMB
	'Wisley Pink'	see *H.* 'Rhodanthe Carneum'
	'Wisley Primrose' ♀H4	Widely available
	'Wisley Rose' **new**	LRHS WCom
	'Wisley White'	CTri EAlp ECha ECho ECtt EGoo EPfP GAbr LIMB
	'Wisley Yellow'	ECtt GKir
	'Yellow Queen'	see *H.* 'Golden Queen'
I	'Zonatus'	LIMB

Helianthus (*Asteraceae*)

	RCB/Arg CC-3	WCot
	angustifolius	WFar WPer
	atrorubens	EBee LHop MRav NBro
	'Bitter Chocolate' **new**	WCot
	'Capenoch Star' ♀H4	CElw CPrp EBee EBrs ECha ECtt GBuc GMaP LEdu LPio LRHS MAvo MBel MRav NBPC NBro NLar SDix SMrm WCAu WFar WOld WWEG
	'Capenoch Supreme'	EBee EBrs ECtt LRHS
	'Carine' **new**	WCot
	decapetalus	CHar CMac MBel WHal WHil
	- 'Maximus'	SRms
	- Morning Sun	see *H.* 'Morgensonne'
	divaricatus	NBre
	× ***doronicoides***	SRms
	giganteus 'Sheila's Sunshine'	CAby CBre CElw IPot WOld
	gracilentus	NBre
	'Gullick's Variety' ♀H4	CAby CBre EBee ECtt EPfP LLWP NBro NChi STes WOld WWEG
	'Happy Days'	EBee MAvo WCot
	'Hazel's Gold'	EBee ECtt NBre
	hirsutus	EBee NBre
	× ***kellermanii***	CAby EBee NBre SAga
§	× ***laetiflorus***	EBee ELan GAbr LPio MWhi NBre NLar NOrc WPer
	- var. ***rigidus***	see *H. pauciflorus*
§	'Lemon Queen' ♀H4	Widely available
	'Limelight'	see *H.* 'Lemon Queen'
	'Loddon Gold' ♀H4	CHar EBee ECtt ELan EPfP EShb LRHS MAvo MBel MRav MSCN NBPC NBir NVic SAga SRGP WBrE WBrk WCot WFar WWEG
§	***maximiliani***	CHrt CSam EBee ELon EShb EWll LDai LEdu LPio MDKP SPav SWal WPer
	microcephalus	CSam EBee
	'Miss Mellish' ♀H4	CWan MSCN WBrk WCot WHoo
	mollis	CSam EBee NBre SPav WPer
	'Monarch' ♀H4	CMea CSam EBee ELon MBel MDKP MRav MWat NBre NCGa NVic SDix SMad SMrm WCot WMoo WOld
§	'Morgensonne'	CPrp EBee ECtt EHrv MAvo MWat WCot WFar
	× ***multiflorus*** 'Anemoniflorus Flore Pleno'	MBri
	- 'Meteor'	EBee ECtt LRHS MAvo NBre NChi WWEG
	occidentalis	CSam WPer
	orgyalis	see *H. salicifolius*

§	***pauciflorus***	EBee
	quinquenervis	see *Helianthella quinquenervis*
	rigidus misapplied	see *H.* × *laetiflorus*
	rigidus (Cass.) Desf.	see *H. pauciflorus*
§	***salicifolius***	EBee ECtt ELon EPPr EShb LEdu LHop LPio LPla LRHS MBel MBri MMuc NBPC NCGa SDix SGSe SMad SMrm WCot WFar WHil WHlf WMnd WMoo WPGP WSpi WTin
	- 'Low Down'[PBR]	EBee LRHS MCCP NMoo
	- 'Table Mountain'	EBee MBri
	scaberrimus	see *H.* × *laetiflorus*
	'Soleil d'Or'	EBee EBrs ECtt EWll IPot WHal WWEG
	strumosus	WCot
	'Triomphe de Gand'	MRav MWat WFar WOld
	tuberosus	CArn EBee EBrs GPoy SVic
	- 'Fuseau'	LEdu NHol
	- 'Garnet'	LEdu
	- 'Sugarball'	LEdu

Helichrysum (*Asteraceae*)

	from Drakensberg Mountains, South Africa	NWCA
	adenocarpum	SPlb
	aggregatum	MSCN
	alveolatum	see *H. splendidum*
	ambiguum	CStu EPfP WCom
	amorginum Ruby Cluster = 'Blorub'[PBR]	EBee LRHS LSou SPer
	angustifolium	see *H. italicum*
	- from Crete	see *H. microphyllum* (Willd.) Cambess.
	- 'Nanum'	SEND
	arenarium	ECho
§	***arwae***	CPBP EPot LRHS WAbe
	bellidioides	see *Anaphalioides bellidioides*
	bellum	NWCA
	chionophilum	EPot
	'Coco'	see *Xerochrysum bracteatum* 'Coco'
	coralloides	see *Ozothamnus coralloides*
	'County Park Silver'	see *Ozothamnus* 'County Park Silver'
	'Dargan Hill Monarch'	see *Xerochrysum bracteatum* 'Dargan Hill Monarch'
	depressum	EPot
	'Elmstead'	see *H. stoechas* 'White Barn'
	fontanesii	WHer
	frigidum	CPBP SMrm
	heldreichii NS 127	NWCA
	hookeri	see *Ozothamnus hookeri*
§	***hypoleucum***	CSpe GGar WHer
§	***italicum*** ♀H3	CArn CEnt CWan ECha GPoy MBar MHer MNHC NBlu NGHP NPri SBch SPet SPoG SRms WCom WDin WGwG WHCG
	- from Crete	GEdr NWCA
	- 'Dartington'	EBee EOHP NGHP SIde WJek
I	- 'Glaucum'	CWib
	- 'Korma'[PBR]	CAbP EBee EHoe ELan EPfP LRHS LSRN LSou MAsh NGHP NPri SIde SLon SPoG STes WJek
	- subsp. ***microphyllum***	see *H. microphyllum* (Willd.) Cambess.
	- 'Nanum'	see *H. microphyllum* (Willd.) Cambess.
§	- subsp. ***serotinum***	CBcs EBee EGoo EHoe EPfP GGar GPoy LRHS MCot MRav SBch SLim SMad SPer SRms STre SWal SWvt WDin WPer
	lanatum	see *H. thianschanicum*
	ledifolium	see *Ozothamnus ledifolius*
	marginatum misapplied	see *H. milfordiae*
§	***microphyllum*** (Willd.) Cambess.	EPot GBar MHer MNHC NBlu SIde SPer WJek
§	***milfordiae*** ♀H2-3	ECho EPot GEdr NSla SRms WAbe WPat
	orientale	EPot SPoG
	petiolare ♀H2	EBak ECtt MCot NBlu SBch SGar SPer SPoG
	- 'Aureum'	see *H. petiolare* 'Limelight'
	- 'Goring Silver' ♀H2-3	SPet SPoG
§	- 'Limelight' ♀H2	ECtt MCot NBlu NPri SBch SPer SPet SPoG
	- 'Variegatum' (v) ♀H2	ECtt LAst MCot NPri SBch SPet SPoG
	populifolium misapplied	see *H. hypoleucum*
	rosmarinifolium	see *Ozothamnus rosmarinifolius*
§	'Schwefellicht'	EBee ECha EPPr EPfP EShb LRHS MLHP MNFA SPer WCAu WEas WKif WSHC WWEG
	selago	see *Ozothamnus selago*
	serotinum	see *H. italicum* subsp. *serotinum*
	sessilioides	CPBP EPot WAbe
§	***sibthorpii***	ECho NWCA
	'Skynet'	see *Xerochrysum bracteatum* 'Skynet'
§	***splendidum*** ♀H3	EPfP LRHS NBro SLon WBrE WCom WDin WPer
	stoechas	CArn
§	- 'White Barn'	CSpe EBee WCot
	Sulphur Light	see *H.* 'Schwefellicht'
§	***thianschanicum***	EDAr EShb SRms
	- Golden Baby	see *H. thianschanicum* 'Goldkind'
§	- 'Goldkind'	EPfP NBir
	thyrsoideum	see *Ozothamnus thyrsoideus*
	trilineatum	see *H. splendidum*
	tumidum	see *Ozothamnus selago* var. *tumidus*
	virgineum	see *H. sibthorpii*
	wightii B&SWJ 9503	WCru
	woodii	see *H. arwae*

Helicodiceros (*Araceae*)

§	***muscivorus***	CHid CStu EBee WCot

Heliconia ✿ (*Heliconiaceae*)

	caribaea 'Burgundy'	see *H. caribaea* 'Purpurea'
§	- 'Purpurea'	XBlo
	'Golden Torch'	XBlo
	indica 'Spectabilis'	XBlo
	latispatha 'Orange	XBlo
*	- 'Red Gyro'	XBlo
	metallica	XBlo
	psittacorum	CCCN
	rostrata	CCCN XBlo

Helictotrichon (*Poaceae*)

	pratense	EBWF EBee EHoe
§	***sempervirens*** ♀H4	Widely available
	- var. ***pendulum***	EBee GBin MAvo
	- 'Saphirsprudel'	CKno CMdw EBee GBin LRHS WPGP

Heliophila (*Brassicaceae*)

	longifolia	CSpe

Heliopsis (*Asteraceae*)

	Golden Plume	see *H. helianthoides* var. *scabra* 'Goldgefieder'
	helianthoides	MLHP NBre
	- 'Limelight'	see *Helianthus* 'Lemon Queen'

- Loraine Sunshine = 'Helhan'PBR (v)	LLWG LRHS LSou NBPC SPoG WClo WCot
- var. ***scabra***	CMac MDKP SRot WMnd WWFP
- - 'Asahi'	EBee EBla ECtt ELan MAvo MCCP NLar NPri NVic SPoG SSvw WHoo
- - Ballerina	see *H. helianthoides* var. *scabra* 'Spitzentänzerin'
- - 'Benzinggold' 𝕐H4	LSou MRav SMrm
- - Golden Plume	see *H. helianthoides* var. *scabra* 'Goldgefieder'
§ - - 'Goldgefieder' 𝕐H4	EBee EBla EPfP NBre SMrm WFar
- - Goldgreenheart	see *H. helianthoides* var. *scabra* 'Goldgrünherz'
§ - - 'Goldgrünherz'	EBee EBrs LRHS MAvo NBre
- - 'Hohlspiegel'	EBee NBre
- - 'Incomparabilis'	EBee MRav
- - 'Karat'	EBee
- - 'Mars'	EBee
- - 'Patula'	EBee
- - 'Prairie Sunset'PBR	EBee ECtt LSou MBri MWea SPoG
§ - - 'Sommersonne'	CSBt EBee ECtt GKir MWhi NGBl NPer NPri SMrm SPer SRms WCAu WMnd WWEG
- - 'Sonnenschild'	EBee
§ - - 'Spitzentänzerin' 𝕐H4	EBee EBla MAvo NBre NGby
- - 'Summer Nights'	CMac CSam EBee EPPr GCal GMac LBMP LDai LSou MDKP MNFA NBPC SPhx
- - Summer Sun	see *H. helianthoides* var. *scabra* 'Sommersonne'
- - 'Venus'	EBee EBla EBrs ECtt LAst MAvo MBri NBhm NLar NSti NVic WCAu WFar
- 'Super Dwarf' **new**	LSou

Heliotropium ✿ (*Boraginaceae*)

§ ***amplexicaule***	SDys
anchusifolium	see *H. amplexicaule*
§ ***arborescens***	CArn EPfP EShb MAJR MCot MHom
- 'Chatsworth' 𝕐H1	CAby CCCN CSev CSpe ECre ECtt ERea EShb MAJR MHom SDnm WFar
- 'Chequerboard'	ERea MAJR
- 'Dame Alice de Hales'	ERea MAJR MHom
- 'Florence Nightingale'	MAJR
- 'Fowa'	ERea
- 'Gatton Park'	MAJR MHom SMrm
- 'Lord Roberts'	ERea MAJR MHom WWlt
- 'Marine'	ECtt SGar SPav WGor
- 'Marino 2000'	MAJR
- 'Mary Fox'	ERea MAJR MHom
- 'Mrs J.W. Lowther'	MAJR MHom
- 'Netherhall White'	ERea
- 'President Garfield'	ERea MAJR MHom WFar
- 'Princess Marina' 𝕐H1	CSpe EPfP LAst LSou MAJR NLar SDys SPav
- 'Reva'	MAJR MHom
- 'Seifel'	ERea MAJR
- 'The Queen'	ECtt ERea MAJR
- 'The Speaker'	ERea MAJR MHom
- 'White Lady'	CCCN CSpe ECtt ERea MAJR MHom NLar
- 'White Queen'	ECtt MAJR MHom
- 'Woodcote'	MAJR MHom
'Baby Blue'	NPri
peruvianum	see *H. arborescens*

Helipterum see *Syncarpha*

anthemoides	see *Rhodanthe anthemoides*

Helleborus ✿ (*Ranunculaceae*)

abruzzicus WM 0227	MPhe
abschasicus	see *H. orientalis* Lam. subsp. *abchasicus*
§ ***argutifolius*** 𝕐H4	Widely available
- from Italy	EHrv
- 'Janet Starnes' (v)	MAsh
- mottled-leaved	see *H. argutifolius* 'Pacific Frost'
§ - 'Pacific Frost' (v)	CBow CLAP EBee EBla EWes LRHS MAsh WCot WWEG
- 'Red Riding Hood' **new**	EBee
- 'Silver Lace'	CBod CBow CFir CHid CSpe CWCL EBee ELan ELon EPfP GKir LDai LRHS LSRN MBel MCCP MGos NBir NHol NLar NMyG NSti SPer SPoG WCom WPtf
atrorubens misapplied	see *H. orientalis* Lam. subsp. *abchasicus* Early Purple Group
atrorubens Waldst. & Kit.	CDes MAsh MRav WAbe WPGP
atrorubens WM 9028 from Slovenia	MPhe
- WM 9805 from Croatia	MPhe
- WM 9825 **new**	WWst
- from Croatia	EBee EBrs EPot
- from Slovenia	GBuc
- spotted form	MPhe
× ***ballardiae***	CLAP MAsh WAbe WFar
bocconei **new**	WWst
- subsp. ***bocconei***	see *H. multifidus* subsp. *bocconei*
colchicus	see *H. orientalis* subsp. *abchasicus*
corsicus	see *H. argutifolius*
- 'Marble' (v)	CSpe
croaticus	GBuc MAsh WFar
- WM 9313	MPhe
- WM 9810 from Croatia	MPhe
cyclophyllus	EBrs GBin GBuc GEdr GKir GMaP MAsh MHom MPhe SPer WFar
- Hoa 8934	WWst
- Hoa 9144	WWst
dumetorum	EBee EBrs GBuc GKir MAsh WFar
- WM 0023	WWst
- WM 9209 from Hungary	MPhe
- WM 9209 from Slovenia	MPhe
- WM 9627 from Croatia	MPhe
- WM 9832	WWst
§ × ***ericsmithii***	Widely available
- 'Bob's Best'	MBel SPoG WCot
- 'HGC Silvermoon'PBR	LRHS SPoG
- 'Winter Moonbeam' **new**	EPfP LRHS
foetidus 𝕐H4	Widely available
- 'Chedglow'	CNat WCom
- 'Gold Bullion'	CBow CSpe MAsh MAvo NHol NSti SBch WFar WPtf WWEG
- 'Green Giant'	MTho WBrE
- 'Harvington Pewter' **new**	LRHS
- 'Pewter'	CLAP
- 'Sopron'	CLAP
- sweet-scented	MHom
- Wester Flisk Group	Widely available
- 'Yorkley'	LSRN
'HGC Josef Lemper'PBR **new**	LRHS
'HGC Red Riding Hood' **new**	LRHS
N × ***hybridus***	Widely available
- 'Agnes Brook'	WFib
- 'Alys Collins'	WFib
- anemone-centred	CHid CLAP EHrv IFoB LHel LRHS MNrw NRar SPoG WFar
- 'Angela Tandy'	WFib
- 'Antique Shades'	WFar
- 'Apple Blossom'	EHrv WFar
- apricot-flowered	CLAP EHrv GBuc WFar WTin
- Ashwood Garden hybrids	CPMA EBrs EHrv EPPr EPfP LRHS MAsh MGos MRav SCoo SPoG WSpi WWEG

- Ashwood Garden hybrids, anemone-centred — CPMA MAsh
- Ashwood Garden hybrids, double-flowered (d) — LRHS MAsh
- Ballard's Group — CLAP EBee GEdr MBri MNFA MWat NCGa NRar SPer WCru WFar WMnd WPnP WSpi
- 'Black Beauty' — NEgg NPri WBVN
- black-flowered — CLAP EHrv EPPr GBuc SSth WFar WHoo WTin
- 'Blue Lady' — CBcs COlW EBee EBla EBrs EPfP GAbr GBin GEdr IFoB LRHS MBNS MGos MNFA MNrw MWat MWea NGdn NMoo SMad SPer STes WBVN WSpi
- 'Blue Metallic Lady' — COlW CSpe CWCL EBee EPfP GAbr LAst LRHS MBNS MWat NCGa NEgg NPri WSpi
- blue-grey-flowered — EHrv
- Blumen Group — MBri
- Bradfield hybrids — EHrv MCot
- Bradfield hybrids, anemone-centred — EHrv
- Bradfield Star Group — EHrv
- Caborn hybrids — LLWP
- 'Carlton Hall' — WFib
- 'Cheerful' — NBir
- 'Cherry Davis' — WFib
- 'Citron' — CLAP
- 'Clare's Purple' — GBin LSRN SCoo WBor
- 'Cosmos' — MBNS
- cream-flowered — CLAP CPMA MCCP WFar WTin
- Credale strain, double-flowered (d) new — LRHS
- dark purple-flowered — LHel SBch
- dark red-flowered new — LHel
- 'David's Star' (d) — CFir
- deep red-flowered — CLAP NHol WFar WTin
- double-flowered (d) — CLAP GBuc LHop MDun MNrw NRar WFar WHoo
- - pink-flowered new — LHel SSth
- - black-flowered (d) — CPLG IFoB MDun NRar
- - purple-flowered (d) new — LHel
- - red-flowered (d) — CPLG MDun WSpi
- - white-flowered (d) — CPLG IFoB LHel SSth
- - yellow-flowered (d) — CPLG IFoB LHel MDun
- - Double Ladies, mixed (d) new — MWat
- - 'Double Vision' (d) — EPPr WWEG
- Draco strain — NChi
- 'Elizabeth Coburn' — WFib
- Farmyard anemone-centred new — WFar
- 'Farmyard Appleblossom' new — WFar
- Farmyard apricot new — WFar
- Farmyard black new — WFar
- Farmyard cream new — WFar
- Farmyard cream, dark-eyed new — WFar
- Farmyard cream spotted new — WFar
- Farmyard dark pink new — WFar
- Farmyard double apricot (d) new — WFar
- - black (d) new — WFar
- - cream (d) new — WFar
- - cream spotted (d) new — WFar
- - pink (d) new — WFar
- - pink spotted (d) new — WFar
- - primrose (d) new — WFar
- - primrose spotted (d) new — WFar
- - red (d) new — WFar
- - slate grey (d) new — WFar
- - white (d) new — WFar
- - white spotted (d) new — WFar
- Farmyard green new — WFar
- Farmyard green spotted new — WFar
- Farmyard picotee new — WFar
- Farmyard pink new — WFar
- Farmyard pink spotted new — WFar
- Farmyard plum new — WFar
- Farmyard primrose new — WFar
- Farmyard primrose dark-eyed new — WFar
- Farmyard primrose spotted new — WFar
- Farmyard red new — WFar
- Farmyard slate grey new — WFar
- Farmyard slate spotted new — WFar
- Farmyard veined new — WFar
- Farmyard white new — WFar
- Farmyard white dark-eyed new — WFar
- Farmyard white splash new — WFar
- Farmyard white spotted new — WFar
- 'Farmyard Woodland' new — WFar
- 'Fibrex Black' — WFib
- 'Fred Whitsey' — WFib
- 'Gertrude Raithby' — WFib
- 'Gladys Burrow' — WFib
- 'Green Ripple' — WFar
- green-flowered — LHel WFar
- 'Günther Jürgl' (d) — WFar
- 'Harvington Anemone' new — LRHS
- 'Harvington Apricots' — NBir NLar
- Harvington double, lime green (d) new — LRHS
- - pink (d) — SPoG
- - purple (d) — NBir NLar SPoG
- - red (d) — GKir NBir NLar SPoG
- - white (d) — NBir NLar SPoG
- - yellow (d) — NBir NLar SPoG
- Harvington picotee — GKir LRHS MGos NBir NLar SPoG
- Harvington pink — GKir LRHS MGos MHer NLar SPoG
- Harvington pink speckled — GKir LRHS MGos NLar SPoG
- Harvington red — GKir LRHS MGos MHer NLar SPoG
- 'Harvington Shades of the Night' — GKir LRHS MGos MHer NLar SPoG WSpi
- 'Harvington Smokey Blues' new — LRHS
- Harvington speckled — LRHS MHer SPoG
- Harvington white — GKir LRHS MGos MHer NLar SPoG WSpi
- Harvington yellow — GKir LRHS MGos MHer NLar SPoG
- Harvington yellow speckled — LRHS MGos MHer NLar SPoG WSpi
- 'Hazel Key' — WFib
- 'Helen Ballard' — GKev
- 'Helena Hall' — WFib
- 'Hidcote Double' (d) — NRar
- Hillier hybrids, burgundy new — LRHS
- - clear-white new — LRHS
- - green new — LRHS
- - anemone-centred new — LRHS
- - double pink new — LRHS
- - double red new — LRHS
- - double yellow new — LRHS
- - picotee new — LRHS
- - pink and white new — LRHS
- - 'Spring Romance' new — LRHS

– – purple **new**	LRHS
– – slate **new**	LRHS
– – spotted, double yellow (d) **new**	LRHS
– – – double-pink (d) **new**	LRHS
– – – green **new**	LRHS
– – – pink **new**	LRHS
– – – white **new**	LRHS
– – yellow **new**	LRHS
– – – magenta eye **new**	LRHS
– 'Ian Raithby'	WFib WSpi
– ivory-flowered	WFar
– 'John Raithby'	WFib
– Joy hybrids	EBee MBri
– Kaye's garden hybrids	EPfP NBPC WMnd
– 'Lady Macbeth'	EWes
– Lady Series	NSum
– large, pink-flowered	WTin
– 'Le Max Creme'	EBee
– maroon-flowered	NRar WFar
– 'Mary Petit'	WFib
– 'Maureen Key'	WFib
– 'Monita Nightshades'	CMoH
– 'Mrs Betty Ranicar' (d)	CBro EPfP ERas EWes IFoB LBuc MBNS MGos NBPC NCGa NLar NSum SPoG WFar WWEG
– pale pink-flowered **new**	LHel
– 'Pamina'	EHrv IFoB
§ – Party Dress Group (d)	CHid EBla EHrv ELan ELon EPfP IFoB LRHS SPoG WFar
– Picotee Group	SSth WTin
– 'Picotee'	CLAP EGxp EHrv GBuc IFoB LHel NRar WCru WFar WHoo
– 'Picotee' double-flowered (d) **new**	LHel
– 'Pink Lady'	EBee EBrs EPfP GQue LRHS MGos MWat NEgg NGdn NPri SPer
– 'Pink Upstart' **new**	IFoB
– pink-flowered	CLAP CPMA GAbr GBuc LHel MBNS MCCP MMuc NRar SSth WAbe WFar WHoo WTin
– plum-flowered	CLAP EHrv MMuc SSth WFar WTin
– 'Pluto'	WFar
– primrose-flowered	CLAP ELan EWTr GBuc MMuc NEgg NRar SBch WAbe WFar WTin
– purple-flowered	CLAP CPMA NHol NRar SGSe SSth WBor WFar WHoo
* – 'Purpurascens'	MCCP
– 'Queen of the Night'	CLAP CPLG EPfP IBal MWhi SPad
– 'Ray Peters'	WFib
– 'Red Lady'	CBcs COIW CPLG CWCL EAEE EBee EBla EPfP GAbr GBin GQue IBal LHop LRHS MBNS MGos MWat MWea NEgg NMoo NOrc NPri SPer WHil
– 'Red Spotted' **new**	EPfP
– 'Red Upstart' **new**	IFoB
– 'Rosina Cross'	WFib
– 'Shades of Night'	EHrv LRHS
– slaty blue-flowered	CLAP EHrv GBuc IFoB LHel SSth WFar
– slaty purple-flowered	GBuc NRar WFar
– 'Smokey Blue'	EGxp EWTr LRHS WPtf
– smokey purple-flowered	ELan MMuc SBch SEND WFar WPtf
– 'Snow Queen'	EHrv
– 'Speckled Draco'	CPLG
§ – spotted	CLAP EPfP GBuc GMaP MCCP NBlu NEgg SBch WCot WCru WHoo WTin WWEG
– – cream	CLAP NBir SSth WTin
– – green	CLAP WFar WTin
– – ivory	CLAP
– – pink	CLAP GBuc LHel LRHS MBNS NBir NHol NRar SEND WFar WHoo WTin
– – pink, double (d)	SSth
– – primrose	CLAP ELan GBuc WFar WTin
– – white	EBla GBuc LHel NBir NRar SSth WFar WTin
– – white, double (d)	GBin LHel
– – yellow **new**	LHel LRHS
– 'Spotted Lady'	GBin
– Sunshine selections	GKev IBal
– 'Swirling Skirts' **new**	EBla
– 'Tricastin'	CHid SPad
– 'Tutu' **new**	EGxp
– 'Ushba'	CLAP
– 'Victoria Raithby'	WFib
– 'Washfield' **new**	LRHS
– Washfield double-flowered (d)	CSpe EWTr LAst LHop LRHS MGos SPoG SRkn WBor WHil
– – white (d) **new**	IFoB
– 'White Lady'	COIW CPLG EBee EBla GEdr GQue IFoB LRHS MBNS MGos MWat MWea NEgg NPri SPer
– 'White Lady Spotted'	CHVG COIW CWCL EBee EPfP GQue LHop LRHS NBPC NEgg NGHP SMad
– white-flowered	GKev LHel NRar SSth WCFE WFar WHoo WTin
– white-veined	MMuc WFar
– 'Winter Joy Bouquet' **new**	LRHS
– Winter Queen strain **new**	WWEG
– 'Yellow Lady'	CBcs EBee EPfP EPot GQue LHop LRHS MBNS MNFA MWat MWea NCGa NEgg NPri SMrm SPer
– yellow-flowered	CBow GMaP IFoB LHel SSth WFar WHoo WTin
– Zodiac Group	EBla GBuc LBuc
liguricus WM 0230	MPhe
lividus ♀H2-3	CAby CBro CEnt CLAP CSpe EAEE ECho EPfP EWes GKev GKir LHop LRHS MAsh MPhe NBir SWal SWat WAbe WFar
– subsp. ***corsicus***	see *H. argutifolius*
– 'Silver Edge' **new**	EPfP
'Moonshine' PBR	EKen GCai NHol NLar
multifidus	EBee GKir NBir WFar
§ – subsp. ***bocconei***	EBee EHrv MAsh MHom WFar
– – WM 9719 from Italy	MPhe
– – WM 9905 from Sicily	MPhe
– subsp. ***hercegovinus***	EHrv MDun WFar
– – WM 0020	MPhe
– – WM 0622	MPhe
– subsp. ***istriacus***	CBro GBuc MAsh WFar
– – WM 9322	MPhe
– – WM 9324	MPhe
– subsp. ***multifidus***	EHrv MAsh MHom
– – WM 9529	MPhe
– – WM 9748 from Croatia	MPhe
– – WM 9833	MPhe
niger ♀H4	Widely available
– Ashwood strain	CLAP MAsh
– Blackthorn Group	CBow CLAP EHrv LRHS
– double-flowered (d)	ELan
– Harvington hybrids	EHrv GKir LRHS MHer
– 'HGC Jacob' **new**	EBee LRHS
– 'Ivory Prince' **new**	EPfP LRHS
§ – subsp. ***macranthus***	EBee NMoo
– ***major***	see *H. niger* subsp. *macranthus*
– 'Marion' (d) **new**	IFoB
– 'Maximus'	CLAP EBee EWes WFar
– 'Potter's Wheel'	CDes CLAP CMoH CPMA EBee ELan EPfP GBuc GKir LRHS MRav NBir

- 'Praecox' CWan EBee EPPr EPfP EWes LRHS
- 'Ras Buis' NMoo
- Sunset Group WM 9113 GBuc
- 'White Christmas' LRHS
- 'White Magic' CPMA MGos MNrw

× ***nigercors*** 🏆H4 CDes CElw CEnt CMac CSam CSpe EBrs ECha ECtt EHrv GBin GBuc GEdr GKir GMaP LHop LRHS MBri MCot SPoG WAbe WCot WFar WPGP
- double-flowered (d) EHrv IBal LSou
- 'HGC Green Corsican'[PBR] LRHS
- 'Pink Beauty' LBuc

× ***nigristern*** see *H.* × *ericsmithii*

odorus EHrv EWes GMaP IFoB MAsh MPhe SPer WFar WPGP
- WM 0312 from Bosnia MPhe
- WM 9310 GBuc
- WM 9415 MPhe
- WM 9728 from Hungary MPhe

N ***orientalis*** misapplied see *H.* × *hybridus*

orientalis ambig. WCAu

orientalis Lam. CBcs CChe EPot EWTr EWes LRHS MPhe MSwo STre

§ - subsp. ***abchasicus*** (A. Braun) B. Mathew EBee GEdr MAsh SRms WFar

§ - - Early Purple Group CBre CTri GCal MRav WFar
- subsp. ***guttatus*** misapplied see *H.* × *hybridus* spotted
- subsp. ***guttatus*** (A. Braun & Sauer) B. Mathew EBee EWTr GGar NChi NHol SRkn
- subsp. ***orientalis*** from the Caucasus **new** WWst

'Pink Beauty'[PBR] EPfP LRHS MBri MGos NCGa NLar SPoG

purpurascens CSsd EBee EBrs EHrv EPPr EPfP GBuc GEdr GMaP IFoB MAsh MBNS MNFA MRav NBir SMad SPer WAbe WBrE WFar WPnP
-WM 9211 from Hungary MPhe
- WM 9412 MPhe
- WM 9922 EPot WWst
- from Hungary WCAu

'Ruby Glow' **new** EPfP

Snowdon strain LRHS WSpi

× ***sternii*** Widely available
- Aberconwy strain CLAP
- Ashwood strain MAsh
- 'Beatrice le Blanc' MAsh
- Blackthorn Group 🏆H3-4 CBcs CPMA CSpe EHrv ELon EPfP GAbr GBuc IFoB LRHS MBNS MBri MRav SBch SPoG WBrk WFar WPGP
- Blackthorn dwarf strain CLAP EBee GBuc LRHS WBor
- 'Boughton Beauty' CAvo CLAP CMea EBee EHrv ELan GBuc LHop MTho NSum WSpi
- Bulmer's blush strain WSpi
- dwarf WFar
- 'Joy's Purple' EBla LAst
- pewter-flowered CAby CSpe EBrs EDAr

thibetanus CFir CLAP CPLG EBee EBrs EFEx EHrv EPot EWes GBuc GEdr LAma MPhe WCru WWst

torquatus CBro EBee EBla EBrs EHrv MAsh MPhe MTho SPer WFar WTin
- Hoa 9115 WWst
- LD 308 from Serbia WWst
- WM 0609 from Montenegro MPhe
- WM 0617 from Serbia MPhe
- WM 9106 from Montenegro GBuc MPhe
- WM 9745 EHrv
- WM 9820 from Bosnia MPhe
- Caborn hybrids LLWP
- 'Dido' (d) CPLG WFar
- double-flowered hybrids (d) WFar
- double-flowered, from Montenegro (d) WFar
- - WM 0620 MPhe
- hybrids ECGP EHrv WFar
- Party Dress Group see *H.* × *hybridus* Party Dress Group
- semi-double-flowered (d) WFar
- Wolverton hybrids WFar

'Verboom Beauty' **new** LRHS

vesicarius EHrv EWes

viridis EBee EHrv EPfP GKir GPoy IFoB MAsh SRms WFar WTin
- WM 0444 MPhe
- subsp. ***occidentalis*** CBro EHrv MHom
- - WM 9401 MPhe
- - WM 9502 from Germany MPhe
- subsp. ***viridis*** WM 9723 from Italy MPhe

'White Beauty'[PBR] CBcs EPPr EPfP EWes LBuc LRHS MBri MGos MRav NCGa NLar SPoG

Helonias (*Melanthiaceae*)

bullata EBee GEdr

Heloniopsis (*Melanthiaceae*)

acutifolia CDes GEdr
- B&SWJ 218 WCru
- B&SWJ 6817 WCru

japonica see *H. orientalis*

§ ***kawanoi*** CDes CLAP EBee GEdr NMen WCot WCru

§ ***orientalis*** CBro CLAP ECho GBuc GCal GEdr GGar NMen SIng WCot WCru
- B&SWJ 822 from Korea WCru
- B&SWJ 956 from Korea WCru
- B&SWJ 4173 from Korea WCru
- B&SWJ 5873 from Japan WCru
- B&SWJ 6380 from Japan WCru
- from Korea EBee GEdr WCot
- var. ***breviscapa*** GEdr WCru WPGP
- variegated (v) GEdr WCru
- var. ***yakusimensis*** see *H. kawanoi*

umbellata CDes CLAP CPom EBee GEdr
- B&SWJ 1839 WCru
- B&SWJ 6836 WCru
- B&SWJ 6846 WCru
- B&SWJ 7117 WCru

Helwingia (*Helwingiaceae*)

chinensis CSam IDee MBri NLar SSpi WBor

himalaica CGHE WPGP

japonica CBot EFEx IDee NLar WFar

Helxine see *Soleirolia*

Hemerocallis ✿ (*Hemerocallidaceae*)

'Aabachee' CBgR SApp

'Absolute Treasure' **new** CFwr

'Absolute Zero' CFwr SDay SPol SRos

'Adah' SDay

'Added Dimensions' SApp

'Addie Branch Smith' EGol SDay

'Admiral' CHar

'Adoration' SPer

'Aerea' **new** EMar

'Africa' **new** EMar

'African Chant'	ELan
'Age of Miracles'	SPol
'Ah Youth'	SApp
'Ahoya'	CBgR SRos
'Alabama Jubilee' new	WNHG
'Alan'	ECtt LRHS MRav SRos
'Alan Adair'	SDay
'Alaqua'	CFir EMar LAst MBNS MNrw SApp SPer WFar
'Alec Allen'	SDay SRos
'Alejandro Pavlos' new	SApp
'Alien Encounter'	SPol
'All American Baby'	CWat EMar MBNS SPol
'All American Chief'	CAbx SDay
'All American Magic' new	SPol
'All American Plum'	EMar EPfP GBin IPot MBNS WAul WHrl
'All American Tiger'	SDay SRos
'All American Windmill'	CAbx SRos
'All Fired Up'	CFwr EMar SPol
'All the Magic' new	CFwr
'Allegiance'	WNHG
'Alma Atha' (d)	EMar
'Alpine Rhapsody'	SPol
'Alpine Snow'	SRos
altissima	CHEx EBee MNrw SMrm SPhx
'Always Afternoon'	CKel EBee EBla EMar GBuc LRHS MBNS MSpe NCGa SApp SPol SRos WAul WCAu WHrl WWEG
'Amadeus'	LRHS SApp
'Ambassador'	CBgR
'Amber Classic'	SApp
'American Original' new	SRos
'American Revolution'	CBgR CCVN CPar CSpe CWGN EBee ECtt EHrv ELon EPPr MBNS MCCP MCot MNFA NBPC NChi SApp SDnm SMad SPav SPol SRos WAul WCAu WCot WHrl WMoo WPnP WSpi WTin
'Amersham'	MNFA SApp
'Amerstone Amethyst Jewel'	SApp SRos
'Amy'	WWEG
'Andrew Christian'	SPol
'Angel Artistry'	SApp SDay
'Angel Curls'	EGol
'Angel Unawares'	SApp WTin
'Ann Blocher' new	CFwr
'Ann Kelley'	SApp SDay SRos
'Annabelle's Ghost'	CAbx
'Annie Welch'	ELon EPla MBNS NBre
'Antarctica'	SApp SPol
'Antique Rose'	CKel EMar SDay
'Anzac'	COIW ECha ECtt EHrv EMar EPla GMac LRHS MBNS NBre NGdn NHol NPri SAga SApp SPav SRos SWvt WMoo
'Apache Uprising'	SRos
'Apollodorus'	EMar
'Apple Court Chablis'	SApp SPol
'Apple Court Champagne'	SApp
'Apple Court Damson'	CAbx SApp SPol
'Apple Court Ruby'	SApp SPol
'Apple Crisp'	SApp
'Après Moi'	EBla EKen EMar MBNS NLar WBrE WCAu
'Apricot Angel'	SApp
'Apricot Beauty' (d)	CPrp ECho EMar MBNS WSpi
'Apricotta'	WCot WPnP
'Aquamarine'	SDay WCon
'Aquamarine Seedling'	SApp
'Arctic Snow'	CAbx CBgR CBro CMac EBee ELon EMar LAst LRHS MBNS MNrw NBPC NLar SDnm SPav SPoG SRos SUsu SWal WAul WCon
'Arpeggio' new	WHrl
'Arriba'	MNFA NBro
'Arthur Moore'	SDay
'Arthur Vincent'	SPol
'Artistic Gold'	WTin
'Asian Artistry' new	WNHG
'Asiatic Pheasant'	SPol
'Asterisk' new	CAbx SRos
'Aten'	CSpr SBch WAul
'Atlanta Bouquet'	SRos
'Atlanta Fringe'	SApp
'Atlanta Full House'	SDay
'August Frost'	CAbx CBgR
'August Orange'	MNFA
'Augusto Bianco'	SApp
'Autumn Red'	CBcs CBgR EBla EMar MBNS MMuc MNrw NBir SPol WCot
'Autumn Wood' new	SDay
'Ava Michelle'	SApp SDay
'Avant Garde'	SApp SPol
'Avon Crystal Rose'	WNHG
'Awakening Dream'	SRos
'Awash With Color'	SRos
'Awesome Blossom'	GBin LSou MBNS NMoo SMrm SRos WCAu
'Awesome Candy'	LSRN
'Baby Blues'	SPol
'Baby Darling'	SDay WCon
'Baby Red Eyes' new	CFwr
'Baby Talk'	CFir GBuc
'Badge of Honor'	SApp
'Baja'	MNFA WFar
'Bald Eagle'	WWEG
'Bali Hai'	COIW EMar GBee GBin LRHS MBNS MSCN WHrl WSpi
'Ballerina Girl'	SRos
'Ballerina on Ice' new	CFwr
'Bambi Doll' new	CFwr
'Bamboo Blackie'	EMar SPol
'Banana Man'	CAbx
'Banbury Cinnamon'	MBNS
'Bangkok Belle'	CWat SDay
'Banned in Boston'	MSpe
'Banzai' new	CFwr
'Barbara Mitchell'	CFwr EWTr MBNS MNrw NMoo SApp SDay SHar SRos WAul
'Barbary Corsair'	SApp SDay
'Baronet's Badge'	SPol
'Baroni'	ECha SMrm
'Bathsheba' new	SPol SRos
'Battle Hymn'	WCAu
'Bayou Bride'	SRos
'Beat the Barons'	SPol SRos
'Beautiful Edgings'	EMar SDay SPol SRos
'Beauty to Behold'	SApp SDay SRos
'Becky Lynn'	ECtt MBNS SApp
'Bedarra Island'	SDay
'Bejewelled'	EGol EPla NMoo SApp WTin
'Bela Lugosi'	Widely available
'Belconto' new	CFwr
'Bellini'	SDay SRos
'Ben Adams' new	SRos
'Ben Lee' new	SDay
'Benchmark'	EMar MNFA SApp SRos WCon
'Berlin Lemon' ♀H4	LRHS MNFA
'Berlin Maize'	SApp
'Berlin Oxblood'	WAul
'Berlin Red' ♀H4	EBla ECha EMar EPla GBee LBMP LRHS MNFA MSpe SApp WFar
'Berlin Red Velvet' ♀H4	MNFA

'Berlin Tallboy' SApp SDay
'Berlin Watermelon' MBNS
'Berlin Yellow' CAbx
'Berliner Premiere' MNFA
'Bernard Thompson' EMar SApp SRos
'Bertie Ferris' NLar SRos
'Bess Ross' CMHG MNFA
'Bess Vestale' GBuc MWat NHol
'Best Kept Secret' SPol
'Bette Davis Eyes' CBgR CWat EMar SApp SPol SRos
'Betty Benz' SRos
'Betty Jenkins' SRos
'Betty Lyn' SApp
'Betty Warren Woods' SDay SRos
'Betty Woods' (d) SDay SRos
'Beyond 2000' **new** SApp
'Bible Story' **new** CFwr
'Big Apple' EMar SApp SPol SRos
'Big Bird' CPar GMac LSRN MBNS MWea NCGa SApp WAul
'Big City Eye' MBNS SApp
'Big Golden' **new** WWEG
'Big Smile' CWCL EBee EMar IPot MAvo MBNS MNrw MWea NBPC NBro NMoo WFar
'Big Snowbird' CFwr EMar SRos
'Big Time Happy' MBNS SBch SPoG
'Bill Norris' SApp SDay SRos
'Bird Bath Pink' SPol
'Bitsy' EGol MNFA SPet WMnd WWEG
'Black Adder' **new** SDay
'Black Ambrosia' CFwr SDay
'Black Briar Bay' EMar SRos
'Black Emmanuella' CPLG EBee ECho EMar ERCP IKil LAst LDai MBNS MNrw SBch
'Black Eye' WNHG
'Black Eyed Stella' CKel MBNS WSpi
'Black Eyed Susan' MBNS
'Black Ice' **new** SPol
'Black Knight' NLar SRms
'Black Magic' CBro CHar CTri CWat EBee EBla EGol ELan EPla GBuc GMaP GMac LRHS LSRN MBel MRav NBir NEgg NGdn NHol SAga SGSe SMrs SPer SPoG WHer WHrl WMoo
'Black Moon' **new** CFwr
'Black Plush' SPol SRos
'Black Prince' CFir EBee EWll MBNS NBlu NBre NBro WAul
'Blackberry Candy' LRHS MBNS WAul WCAu
'Blackberry Sherbert' **new** CAbx
'Blackberry Sundae' **new** MSCN
'Blackthorne' **new** CFwr
'Blessing' SDay SRos
'Blonde Is Beautiful' SDay SRos
'Blue Moon' SApp
'Blue Sheen' CFir CMac CPar EBee ECtt EGol GMaP MBNS MCCP NGdn WFar WMoo WRHF WSpi
'Blueberry Candy' EBee MBNS SApp WAul WHrl
'Blueberry Cream' CWCL EPfP MBNS MMHG MNrw MWea SPad WWlt
'Blue-eyed Butterfly' **new** SPol
'Blushing Belle' CMil EBla ECGP EMar LRHS MBNS NBro NEgg SApp
'Blushing Valentine' SRos
'Bold Courtier' CBgR
'Bold Encounter' **new** CFwr
'Bold One' CMHG SPol SRos
'Bold Ruler' SPol
'Bold Tiger' EMar SDay
'Bonanza' Widely available
'Boney Maroney' SApp SRos
'Booger' SRos
'Bookmark' EMar
'Boom Town' EMar
'Border Baby' ECtt
'Born Yesterday' SApp
'Boulderbrook Serenity' SDay
'Bourbon Kings' EBee EGol EMar MBNS MSpe NBre SPav WCon WHrl
'Bowl of Roses' SApp
'Bradley Bernard' SPol
'Brand New Lover' SApp
'Brass Buckles' see *H.* 'Puddin'
'Breed Apart' SPol
'Brenda Newbold' SPol
'Bridget' ELan
'Bright Banner' WCAu
'Bright Beacon' SPol
'Bright Spangles' SApp SDay SRos WEas
'Brilliant Circle' SApp
'Bristol Fashion' SApp
'Broadway Image' **new** SRos
'Broadway Valentine' SApp SRos
'Brocaded Gown' ELan SApp SDay SRos
'Brookwood Wow' SApp
'Brunette' SApp
'Bruno Müller' MNFA SApp
'Brutus' EMar
'Bubbling Brown Sugar' SRos
'Bubbly' SApp SDay SRos
'Buc Crête de Coq' **new** EMar
'Buc Soleil Couchant' **new** EMar
'Bud Producer' SPol
'Buffy's Doll' EBee EMar MBNS MNFA SApp SRos WGob
'Bumble Bee' CWat ECtt EMar GKir LRHS MBNS NBre SApp SBch
'Burlesque' SPol
'Burning Daylight' ♀H4 CBgR EBee EBrs ECtt EHrv EMar EPfP EPla GAbr LRHS MNFA MNrw MRav MSpe MWat NBre NEgg NHol SMad SPer SRms SRos WCFE WCon WCot WFar WWHy
'Burning Embers' SApp
'Burning Inheritance' SRos
'Bus Stop' SApp SPol
'Butter Curls' SRos
'Butterfly Ballet' SRos
'Butterfly Charm' CWat
'Butterscotch' WFar
'Butterscotch Ruffles' SDay
'Buzz Bomb' CWat ECtt EHrv EMFW EMar LRHS LSRN MBNS NCob NEgg NGdn SApp SPer SPoG SRos WFar WWEG
'By Myself' **new** CFwr
'Caballero' CAbx
'Calico Spider' SRos
'California Sunshine' SApp SRos
'Camden Glory' SApp
'Camden Gold Dollar' EGol SApp SRos
'Camelot Green' **new** WNHG
'Cameron Quantz' SApp
'Campfire Embers' GBin
'Canadian Border Patrol' CWCL EMar EPfP IBal IPot LRHS MBNS MNrw MSCN MWea NLar SApp SPol SRos WCAu WFar WHrl
'Canary Feathers' SApp
'Canary Glow' CTri SMrm SRos WFar
'Canary Wings' CBgR
'Candide' SApp SDay
'Cantique' SApp SPol

'Cap and Bells' EMar
'Cape Romain Harbor' **new** CFwr
'Capernaum Cocktail' SPol
'Captain Ahab' SApp
'Captive Audience' SRos
'Cara Mia' CBgR EMar LAst MBNS NBir WFar
'Caramba' CAbx
'Carmine Monarch' SRos
'Carolicolossal' SPol
'Carolina Cranberry' ELan
'Carolina Ruffles' **new** CFwr
'Caroline Taylor' **new** WHrl
'Carolipiecrust' SApp
'Carrot' CFwr
'Cartwheels' $\mathbb{Y}^{H4}$ EBee EBla EHrv EMFW EMar EPfP EPla ERas GBuc GMaP LRHS MBNS NBro SBch SPer SRos WCAu WCon WFar WMoo WTin
'Casino Gold' SRos
'Castle Strawberry Delight' SPol
'Catherine Neal' SPol SRos
'Catherine Woodbery' Widely available
'Cathy's Sunset' CKel CSam EBee EBla ECtt EMar EPla LRHS MBNS MSpe MWat NBre NBro NEgg NGdn SMrm SRGP
'Cedar Waxwing' EGol
'Cedric Morris' EBrs
'Cee Tee' SRos
'Celebration of Angels' SApp
'Celtic Christmas' **new** CFwr SPol
'Cerulean Star' SApp
'Challenger' EMar
'Champagne Memory' SApp
'Chance Encounter' MBNS
'Charles Johnston' CBgR CKel CMMP EMar LAst MBNS MNrw SApp SRos WAul
'Charlie Pierce Memorial' EMar SPol SRos
'Chartreuse Magic' CMHG EGol EPla
'Chasing the Sun' **new** CFwr
'Cheerful Note' WNHG
'Cherry Cheeks' CEnt CFir ECtt EGol ELan EPfP LRHS MBNS MBri MRav NBPC NHol SApp SMrm SPav SRos WAul WCAu WCon WCot WFar WGob WWEG
'Cherry Eyed Pumpkin' EMar SRos
'Cherry Kiss' SRos
'Cherry Ripe' EQua
'Cherry Smoke' SApp
'Cherry Tiger' MBNS
'Cherry Valentine' CBcs EBee MBNS SApp
'Chesières Lunar Moth' ELon SApp SPol SRos
'Chester Cyclone' SDay
'Chestnut Lane' SApp SRos
'Chewonki' EMar
'Chicago Apache' CFir EMar EPfP GBuc MBNS MNFA MWea NBir NHol SApp SBch SDay SPer SPol SRos SUsu WAul WCon WSpi
'Chicago Aztec' SRos
'Chicago Blackout' CFir CWat ECtt EGol EPfP MSCN NHol SApp WCAu
'Chicago Cattleya' CFir EGol SApp WAul
'Chicago Cherry' WNHG
'Chicago Fire' EGol EPfP GKir MBNS NBPC SHar
'Chicago Heirloom' CFir EGol MBNS WAul WCAu
'Chicago Jewel' CFir EGol NSti WAul
'Chicago Knobby' EMar MBNS
'Chicago Knockout' CFir EGol ELan EPfP LPio SPer WAul WCAu
'Chicago Mist' WNHG
'Chicago Peach' IPot NBir WCAu
'Chicago Petticoats' EGol NHol SApp
'Chicago Picotee Lace' EGol NGdn SApp WCAu WWEG
'Chicago Picotee Memories' EBee MBNS WCAu
'Chicago Picotee Promise' WNHG
'Chicago Picotee Queen' SApp SMrs
'Chicago Princess' EGol
'Chicago Queen' GKir WMnd WNHG
'Chicago Rainbow' CBgR MBNS WAul
'Chicago Rosy' EGol
'Chicago Royal' ELon
'Chicago Royal Crown' ECtt EMar LRHS
'Chicago Royal Robe' CWCL CWat EBrs EGol EPla EWll LLWP LRHS MBNS MNFA NBid NCGa SMrm SWal SWat WCot WTin
'Chicago Ruby' SApp SRos WWHy
'Chicago Silver' CFir EGol IPot MBNS WCAu
'Chicago Star' SRos WNHG
'Chicago Sunrise' EBee EBla EBrs EGol EMar EPla GKir GMaP LPio LRHS MBNS MBri MRav NGdn NHol NMoo NOrc SApp SPet SRos SWvt WCot WPer WWEG
'Chicago Weathermaster' EMar
'Chief Sarcoxie' $\mathbb{Y}^{H4}$ SApp SRos
'Child of Fortune' SApp SDay
'Children's Festival' CSpe EBee ECtt EGol EMar GKir GMaP LPBA LRHS MBNS MRav MSpe NLar SApp SGSe SRos SWvt WCon WFar WMoo WPer
'China Bride' SApp SRos
'China Grove Plantation' **new** CFwr
'China Lake' EMar
'Chinese Autumn' SApp SRos
'Chinese Cloisonne' EMar SApp
'Chinese Imp' NLar
'Chocolate Candy' **new** CWGN EPfP MBNS
'Chocolate Cherry Truffle' SApp
'Chorus Line' SApp SRos WNHG
'Chorus Line Kid' **new** SPol
'Chosen Love' CFwr SApp
'Christine Lynn' WNHG
'Christmas Carol' SApp
'Christmas Is' CBgR COlW EBee EBla EGol EMar MBNS MNFA NMoo SApp SDay SDnm SMrm SPav SPhx SPol WAul WCAu WGob WWEG
'Christmas Island' MCot NBre
'Christmas Tidings' SApp
'Ciao' EMar SApp
'Ciel d'Or' GKir
'Cimarron Knight' SPol
'Circle of Beauty' SPol
citrina CBgR CHid CMac CPLG EBee IMou LRHS MCot NGdn WCot WHrl WTin
– Mahien's clone **new** CAbx
'Civil Law' SDay
'Civil Rights' SRos
'Classic Caper' WNHG
'Classic Spider' SApp
'Claudine' SApp
'Cleopatra' CPar SPol SRos WAul
'Clothed in Glory' CWCL MBNS NMoo SApp WCot
'Coburg Fright Wig' EMar
'Colonial Dame' WTin
'Colour Me Yellow' SApp
'Comanche Eyes' SApp
'Comet Flash' SPol
'Coming Up Roses' CPar SApp SRos
'Commandment' EMar
'Concord' **new** SDay
'Condilla' (d) CFwr SApp

Cultivar	Suppliers
'Conspicua'	EMar
'Contessa'	CBro EBrs SPer
'Cool It'	CEnt CKel EBee EMar GBuc IPot MBNS NBre NCGa NHol NMoo SApp WCAu WHrl
'Cool Jazz'	EMar SApp SDay SRos
'Copper Dawn'	NChi SApp
'Copper Windmill'	CAbx EMar SPol SRos
'Copperhead'	SPol
'Coral Crab'	SApp
'Coral Mist'	MBNS NBre
'Coral Sparkler'	WNHG
'Coral Spider'	ECtt EMar
'Corky' ♀H4	Widely available
'Cornwall'	EMar
'Corryton Pink'	SPol
'Corsican Bandit'	CMMP SDay
'Cosmic Hummingbird'	MSpe SApp
'Cosmopolitan'	MBNS MCot
'Country Club'	EGol MBNS NHol SApp WWEG
'Country Melody'	SDay SRos
'Court Magician'	EMar MDun MSpe SApp SRos
'Court Troubadour'	SPol
'Coyote Moon'	SRos
'Crackling Rosie'	EMar
'Cranberry Baby'	CWan EMar SRos WHoo WNHG WTin
'Cranberry Coulis'	CWat MBNS
'Crawleycrow'	EMar
'Crazy Pierre'	EMar SPol WHrl
'Cream Drop'	CPrp EBee EBla ECtt EGol EMar EPPr GMaP LFur LRHS MCot MHer MRav MSpe NBro NGdn NLar NSti SApp SDnm SPav SPer WAul WCot WMoo WTin
'Creative Art'	SRos
'Creative Edge'	SDnm SPav WAul
'Creature of the Night'	SApp
'Crimson Icon'	WTin
'Crimson Pirate'	CBgR CBre EBee ELon EMar EPPr GKev LSRN MBNS MHer MSpe NBir NHol NMoo NOrc NPro SApp SBch SMrm SPer SPlb SPoG SPol SWat WCon WHrl WTin
'Crimson Wind'	SApp
'Croesus'	NHol SRms
'Crystalline Pink'	SRos
'Cupid's Bow'	EGol
'Cupid's Gold'	SDay SRos
'Curls'	LRHS MBNS SDay
'Curly Brick Road' **new**	SRos
'Curly Cinnamon Windmill'	CAbx SRos
'Curly Ripples'	SApp
'Curly Rosy Posy'	EMar SRos
'Custard Candy'	CWCL MBNS MBri MSpe NBir NMoo SApp SBch SRos SUsu WAul WCAu
'Cynthia Mary'	ECtt EMar EQua LHop LRHS MBNS MNFA MSpe NBro SRGP WCon WFar
'Dad's Best White'	EMar WTin
'Daily Bread'	EMar
'Daily Dollar'	EBee EBla LRHS MBNS NGdn SApp
'Dainty Pink'	EGol
'Daisy MacCarthy'	LRHS
'Dallas Spider Time'	MNFA
'Dallas Star'	EMar SApp SPol
'Dan Mahony'	MBNS
'Dan Tau'	CKel
'Dance Ballerina Dance'	EBee SDay SRos
'Dancing Dwarf'	SApp WCon
'Dancing Shiva'	SApp SDay
'Dancing Summerbird'	SApp SPol SRos
'Daring Deception'	CFir CKel ECtt ELon EMar IPot LAst MBNS MBel MSpe MWea NMoo SApp WCAu WCon WFar WHrl
'Daring Dilemma'	MSpe SPol
'Daring Reflection'	SDay
'Darius'	WNHG
'Dark and Handsome' **new**	MBNS
'Dark Avenger'	CSpe MBNS
'Dark Elf'	SApp WCon
'Dark Star' **new**	SDay
'Darker Shade'	SRos
'Darkest Night'	SApp
'David Holman'	WNHG
'David Kirchhoff'	CFwr IPot SApp WAul
'Davidson Update'	WNHG
'Dazzle'	SApp
'De Colores' **new**	SRos
'Decatur Ballerina'	WNHG
'Decatur Captivation'	WNHG
'Decatur Cherry Smash' **new**	SDay
'Decatur Dictator'	WNHG
'Decatur Imp'	EGol WHrl
'Decatur Rhythm'	WNHG
'Decatur Supreme'	WNHG
'Decatur Treasure Chest'	WNHG
'Dee Dee Mac'	SApp
'Deep Fire'	SRos
'Delicate Design'	SApp SPol
'Delightsome'	SRos
'Demetrius'	CWat MNFA MWea SApp
'Desdemona'	CMil EMar
'Desert Bandit'	SApp
'Designer Gown'	SApp
'Designer Jeans'	SPol SRos
'Destined to See'	Widely available
'Devil's Footprint'	SDay SPol
'Devon Cream'	SPer
'Devonshire'	SApp SDay SRos
'Dewberry Candy'	SRos
'Diamond Dust'	CKel EBee ECtt EMar EPla GBee LRHS MBNS MSpe NLar SApp SMrm SPer SPhx WSpi WTin
'Dido'	CTri GBuc
'Dipped in Ink' **new**	SPol
'Diva Assoluta'	SApp
'Divertissment'	CBgR ELon EMar SApp SRos
'Dixie Stampede'	CAbx
'Do You Know Doris' **new**	SRos
'Doll House'	SRos
'Dominic'	CPar EBee EMar SApp SRos WMoo
'Don's Wild Heather' **new**	CAbx
'Dorethe Louise'	CBgR SDay SPol SRos
'Dorothy McDade'	COIW
'Dot Paul' **new**	ELan
'Double Action' (d)	SPol
'Double Coffee' (d)	SApp SPav SPol
'Double Corsage' (d)	SApp SPol
'Double Cream' (d)	WCot
'Double Cutie' (d)	EMar NBre NLar SDay WAul
'Double Delicious' (d)	WCot
'Double Dream' (d)	EMar GBuc WHrl
'Double Entendre'	EMar
'Double Firecracker' (d)	CBcs CCVN CWCL CWat EGxp EMar GMac IBal MBNS MDun NBro NLar NMoo SMrm
'Double Grapette' (d)	SApp
'Double Layer' **new**	CFwr
'Double Oh Seven' (d)	ELon SApp SPol
'Double Passion' (d)	MBNS
'Double Red Royal' (d)	EMar

'Double River Wye' (d)	CBgR CFir COlW CWat EBee ECtt EGol EMar GMac IPot LRHS MBNS MNrw NGdn NPri SApp SHar SPol SRos SWat WAul WCot WHoo WMnd WTin WWEG
§ 'Doubloon'	COlW GBuc NHol
'Dover Plantation' **new**	CFwr
'Dragon Dreams'	SApp SPol
'Dragon King'	SPol
'Dragon Lore'	MBNS
'Dragon's Eye'	CFwr CWat MSpe SDay SPol
'Dragon's Orb'	CKel
'Dream Baby'	NBre
'Dream Legacy'	CFwr
'Dreamy Cream'	SRos
'Dresden Doll'	SPer
'Driven Snow'	SApp
'Druid's Chant'	LRHS MSpe
'Duke of Durham'	MBNS MSpe SApp
dumortieri	CAvo CBro CSam ECha EGol EHrv ELan EPla GGar LFur LRHS MCot MNrw MRav NBid NBir NHol NSti NVic SPer WCot WHrl WTin WWEG
- B&SWJ 1283	WCru
'Dune Needlepoint'	SPol
'Dutch Beauty'	EMar EPla LRHS WFar
'Dutch Gold'	MNrw NBro
'Earl Barfield'	EMar
'Earl of Warwick'	CBgR
'Earlianna'	CAbx SPol
'Earth Angel'	SApp SPol
'Easy Ned'	EMar SDay SRos WTin
'Ed Kirchhoff'	EMar
'Ed Murray'	GBin SRos WAul WCAu
'Edgar Brown'	MBNS MSpe
'Edge Ahead'	ECtt LRHS MBNS MSpe
'Edge of Darkness'	CKel CWGN EPfP IPot MBNS MWea NBro NSti SApp SDnm SPav WAul WCAu WFar
'Edna Spalding'	CFwr EBrs LRHS SApp SRos
'Eenie Allegro'	CBgR CBro ECtt EGol IBal LRHS MBNS SPer WCon WHil WMnd
'Eenie Fanfare'	EGol LRHS MBNS NBir WAul WCon WWEG
'Eenie Weenie'	CBro CFee EBla ECtt EGol EPla ERos GKir IBal LRHS MBNS MNFA NBro NBur SAga SApp SHGN SPer SRms WPer WWEG
'Eenie Weenie Non-stop'	CMoH ECha EPPr
'Eggplant Escapade'	CAbx EMar SPol SRos
'Egyptian Ibis'	WMnd WNHG
'Egyptian Queen'	EMar SRos
'El Desperado'	Widely available
'El Glorioso'	CAbx EMar
'El Padre'	SApp
'Elaine Farrant' **new**	SDay
'Elaine Strutt'	MBNS MNFA MNrw NMoo SApp SDay SRos SWvt WSpi
'Elegant Candy'	CKel CMac EBee MBNS NCGa NMoo SApp SRos WCon WGob
'Eleonor'	EPfP EWTr MBNS SApp WFar
'Elfin Daydream' **new**	SPol
'Elizabeth Salter'	CWCL EBee IPot MBNS NLar NMoo SApp SPol SRos SUsu WCAu
'Elizabeth Yancey'	EGol
'Elsie Spalding'	GKir
'Elva White Grow'	SDay
'Embuscade'	EMar
'Emerald Enchantment'	SApp
'Emerald Lady'	SRos
'Emily Anne'	SApp
'Emily Jaye'	SApp
'Emmaus'	SApp
'Emperor Butterfly'	SApp
'Enchanting Blessing'	SRos
'English Cameo' **new**	SRos
'English Toffee'	SApp
'Enjoy' **new**	SRos
'Entransette'	SApp
'Entrapment'	MBNS
'Erin Prairie'	SApp
esculenta	SMad
'Etched Eyes'	SPol
'Eternal Blessing'	SPol SRos
'Ethel Smith'	SApp
'Etruscan Tomb'	SPol
'Etrusque'	EMar
'Evelyn Claar'	CMac
'Evelyn Lela Stout'	SApp
'Evening Bell'	SApp
'Evening Enchantment'	SRos
'Evening Glow'	SApp SRos
'Ever So Ruffled'	SRos
'Exotic Love'	SDay
'Eye of Round' **new**	CFwr
'Eye-yi-yi'	SPol
'Ezekiel'	EMar WHrl
'Fabergé'	SApp
'Fabulous Paradise'	EMar
'Fabulous Prize'	SApp SRos
'Fairest Love'	EBee EMar LDai MBNS
'Fairy Charm'	SApp SDay
'Fairy Summerbird'	SApp SRos
'Fairy Tale Pink'	MNFA SApp SDay SPol SRos
'Fairy Wings'	SPer
'Faith Nabor'	EMar SRos
'Fall Farewell'	WNHG
'Fall Guy'	SApp
'Fama'	GKir SRos
'Fan Club'	EMar GKir
'Fan Dancer'	EGol
'Fandango'	LPla SPer
'Farmer's Daughter'	SApp SRos
'Fashion Model'	SApp WPer
'Feather Down'	SPol
'Feathered Fascination'	SApp
'Feelings'	SApp
'Fellow'	CAbx
'Femme Osage'	SRos
'Ferengi Gold' **new**	CFwr
'Ferris Wheel'	CBgR SApp
'Festive Art'	SPol SRos
'Final Touch'	CBgR GMac IPot MBNS MBel MSCN MSpe MWea NBro WGob
'Finlandia'	MNFA
'Fire and Fog' **new**	CFwr MBNS
'Fire Dance'	SRos
'Fire from Heaven'	SApp
'Fire Tree'	CBgR SPol
'Firestorm'	CAbx SApp SPol
'First Formal'	SPer
'Flames of Fantasy'	SRos
'Flaming Sword'	EBee GBuc LRHS NHol WRHF
flava	see *H. lilioasphodelus*
'Fleeting Fancy'	SRos
'Flight of the Dragon'	SApp
'Flip Flop' **new**	CFwr
'Flower Pavilion'	SPol
'Floyd Cove'	SDay SRos
'Flutterbye'	SRos
'Fly Catcher'	CBgR EMar SRos
'Flyaway Home'	SPol
'Foggy London Town' **new**	CFwr
'Fol de Rol'	SRos

	Name	Suppliers
	'Fooled Me'	EBee LRHS MBNS MSpe MWea SPad SPol SRos
	'Forgotten Dreams'	CWCL MBNS MWea
	forrestii	CPLG
	'Forsyth Lemon Drop'	SDay
	'Forsyth Tangerine Ruffles'	GKir
	'Forsyth White Sentinel'	CFwr SRos
	'Forty Second Street'	CFir EBee LRHS MBNS MBel NMoo SApp WCon WFar
	'Fragrant Bouquet'	SRos
	'Fragrant Pastel Cheers'	SDay SRos
	'Frances Fay'	SPol SRos WAul
	'Frandean'	MNFA
	'Frank Gladney'	MNFA SApp SRos
	'Frans Hals'	Widely available
	'Fred Ham' **new**	SRos
	'French Doll'	SApp
	'Frilly Bliss' **new**	CFwr
	'Frosted Encore'	SApp
	'Frosty White' **new**	SDay
	'Frozen Jade'	SRos
	'Fuchsia Dream'	EMar
	'Fuchsia Fashion'	SApp
	fulva	CTri ELan NBir NBre SGar SPol SRms WBrk WHrl
N	- 'Flore Pleno' (d)	CAvo CFee CMHG CMac CStu EBee EBla ECtt EGol EHon ELan EPfP LHop LRHS MCot MHer MRav NBir NBro NGdn NSti SBch SPav SPer SRms SWat WBrk WCAu WMoo WWEG
N	- 'Green Kwanso' (d)	CBgR CPLG CSWP ECGP ECha EPla LBMP MMHG NVic SMad WAul WFar WPnP WTin
	- var. ***kwanso*** B&SWJ 6328	WCru
N	- 'Kwanso' ambig. (d)	NOrc LRHS
	- var. ***littorea***	CMac EPla
	- var. ***rosea***	SPol WCot
N	- 'Variegated Kwanso' (d/v)	CBot CBow CRow EBee EPPr GCal GCra MRav MTho NBir SBod SMad SPav SUsu WBor WCot WFar WHer WHoo WHrl
	'Fun Fling'	SPol
	'Funky Fuchsia'	SPol
	'Gadsden Goliath'	SPol
	'Gadsden Light'	CAbx SDay SPol
	'Gala Gown'	SApp
	'Garden Portrait'	CMil SRos
	'Gaucho'	MNFA
	'Gauguin'	EMar
	'Gay Music'	LRHS MBNS SPoG
	'Gay Octopus'	CAbx CBgR EMar SPol SRos
	'Gay Rapture'	SPer
	'Gemini'	SRos
	'Geneva Firetruck' **new**	CFwr
	'Gentle Country Breeze'	SApp SPol SRos
	'Gentle Rose' **new**	SDay
	'Gentle Shepherd'	Widely available
	'George Cunningham'	ECtt EGol EHrv ELan MNFA MRav NBir SMrs SPol SRos SUsu WFar
	'George David' **new**	WHrl
	'Georgetown Lovely'.	SRos
	'Georgette Belden'	EBee EBla ECGP ECtt EMar LRHS MBNS MBri MMHG MSpe MWea NHol SPol WTin
	'German Ballerina'	SPol
	'Get All Excited'	SPol
	'Giant Moon'	CBgR CMHG EBee EBrs ECtt ELan EMar EPla LRHS MBNS NCGa NHol SPer SRms WFar WHal WWlt
	'Gingerbread Man'	SApp
	'Girl Scout'	SApp SRos
	'Glacier Bay'	CBgR CWat MBNS NCGa
	'Glazed Heather Plum'	SApp
	'Gleber's Top Cream'	SApp
	'Glomunda'	SApp
	'Glory's Legacy'	SRos
	'Glowing Heart'	SApp
	'Gold Dust'	SRos
	'Gold Imperial'	NBre
	'Golden Bell'	NGdn NHol
	'Golden Change' **new**	CFwr
	'Golden Chimes' ♀H4	Widely available
	'Golden Empress'	SApp
	'Golden Ginkgo'	MBri MSpe SApp
	'Golden Orchid'	see *H.* 'Doubloon'
	'Golden Peace'	SRos
	'Golden Prize'	CBgR EPla GQue LRHS MNFA NGdn NPri SApp SRos WCot WFar
	'Golden Scroll'	SApp SDay SRos
	Golden Zebra = 'Malja'PBR (v)	CWGN ELan EPfP LBuc LRHS MBNS MGos MRav NLar NSti SDnm SPoG WCon WCot WSpi
	'Goldeneye'	SApp
	'Golliwog'	CBgR
	'Good Looking'	EGol
	'Good Morning America' **new**	SRos
	'Grace and Favour'	SDay SPol
	'Graceful Eye'	SApp SRos
	'Graceland'	EMar
	'Grain de Lumière'	EMar
	'Grand Masterpiece'	CMMP IPot NGdn SPet WAul
	'Grand Palais'	EMar SApp SRos
	'Grandma Kissed Me' **new**	SPol
	'Grape Magic'	EGol SRos WTin
	'Grape Velvet'	CHar CPar CSpe EGol MCCP MNFA NBre NMyG NSti SApp SRos WAul WCAu WMnd WWEG
	'Great Northern'	SApp
	'Green Dolphin Street'	SDay SRos
	'Green Dragon'	SDay
	'Green Drop'	WFar
	'Green Eyed Giant'	MNFA
	'Green Eyed Lady'	SDay
	'Green Flutter' ♀H4	CFwr EBee EPfP GCal LPio LPla LRHS LSRN MBNS NBir NBre NGdn NSti SApp SPhx SPol SRos WCot WSpi WWEG
	'Green Gold'	CMHG
	'Green Morning Glow'	EMar
	'Green Nautilus' **new**	SRos
	'Green Puff'	NBir
	'Green Spider'	SDay SRos
	'Green Valley'	MNFA
	'Green Widow' **new**	SDay
	'Groovy Green'	SDay
	'Grumbly'	ELan WPnP
	'Guardian Angel'	WCFE WTin
	'Gypsy Ballerina'	SApp
	'Gypsy Cranberry' **new**	SPol
	'Hail Mary'	WCon
	'Happy Hopi'	SApp
	'Happy Returns'	CBgR CHid CSBt CTri EBee EBla ECha EGol ELan EMar IBal LAst LRHS LSRN MBNS MBri MNFA NEgg NGdn SApp SRGP SRos WCFE WTin WWEG
	'Harbor Blue'	SApp SDay
	'Havana Banana'	SApp
	'Hawaiian Punch'	EGol
	'Hawaiian Purple'	EGol
	'Hawk'	SApp SPol
	'Hazel'	SRos
	'Hazel Monette'	EGol

'Heather Green'	SApp
'Heavenly Treasure'	LRHS SApp SPol SRos
'Heidi Eidelweiss'	CPLG
'Heirloom Lace'	WFar
'Helen Boehm'	EMar
'Helle Berlinerin' ♀H4	MNFA SApp SPol SRos
'Helter Skelter'	EMar
'Her Majesty's Wizard'	MAvo MBNS MHer NBro SPol
'Hercules'	NBre
'Hey There'	SRos
'High Energy'	SApp
'High Mogul'	EMar
'High Tor'	GBin GQui SPol WTin
'Highland Belle'	SApp
'Highland Lord' (d)	EPfP MBNS MWea SApp
'Highland Summerbird'	SApp
'Holiday Delight' **new**	MBNS
'Holiday Mood'	ELan SApp
'Holly Dancer'	SPol
'Homeward Bound' **new**	SDay
'Honey Jubilee'	SPol
'Honey Redhead'	SRos
'Honky Tonk Blues' **new**	CFwr
'Hope Diamond'	SDay SRos WCAu
'Hornby Castle'	CBro EBrs LRHS NHol WPer
'Hot Chocolate'PBR	CFwr
'Hot Ticket'	SApp SRos
'Hot Town'	ELan
'Hot Wheels'	EMar
'Hot Wire'	SRos
'Houdini'	EGol MSpe WCAu WMnd
'House of Orange'	SApp SPol
'Howard Goodson'	MNFA
'Howdy' **new**	CFwr
'Humdinger'	SRos
'Hymn' **new**	SDay WCon
'Hyperion'	CBgR CMac COIW CPrp CSev CTri EBee ECha ECtt EGol EPfP LAst LEdu LRHS MNFA MRav MSpe NGdn NHol SApp SMrs SPer SPoG SRos SUsu WCot WWEG
'Ice Carnival'	CKel EBee ELon EPfP GMac LAst LDai MBNS NBre NGdn NOrc SApp SPet WSpi
'Ice Castles'	CTri SApp
'Ice Cool'	SApp SRos
'Icecap'	CBgR WAul WFar WMoo WPnP
'Icy Lemon'	SRos
'Ida Duke Miles'	SDay SRos
'Ida Munson'	EGol
'Ida's Magic'	EBee SApp WFar
'If' **new**	EMar
'Imperator'	CBen EPla LPBA NHol
'Imperial Lemon'	SApp
'In Depth' (d)	EPfP MBNS NBro NLar SWal WCot WHrl
'In Search of Angels' **new**	CFwr
'In Strawberry Time'	WNHG
'Indian Chief'	WHoo
'Indian Fires' **new**	CFwr
'Indian Giver'	SPol
'Indian Paintbrush'	LRHS MBri NBir SBch SPol WCAu
'Indian Sky'	SRos
'Indigo Moon'	SApp
'Indy Envy' **new**	CFwr
'Inky Fingers'	SApp
'Inner View'	ECtt MBNS MSpe NLar SApp WMnd
'Inspired Word'	SRos
'Invicta'	SRos
'Iridescent Jewel'	SDay
'Irish Elf'	ELon GBuc SApp SHar WTin
'Iron Gate Glacier'	CSpr
'Iron Gate Maiden' **new**	WCom
'Isle of Capri'	SRos
'Isle of Dreams'	SPol
'Ivelyn Brown'	CAbx SRos
'Jake Russell'	MBNS MNFA
'Jamaican Jammin'' **new**	SPol
'James Marsh'	CBgR EPfP EWes MBNS MBri MNFA MNrw SApp SRos WAul WCAu WCot WMnd
'Jan Kay' **new**	SDay
'Janet Gordon'	SPol SRos
'Janice Brown'	CKel CWCL EMar LAst LSou MBNS MSpe NLar NMoo SApp SDay SPol SRos WCAu
'Jan's Twister'	MNrw SApp SRos
'Jason Salter'	NCGa SApp SDay WAul
'Jay Turman'	SApp
'Jazz Diva'	EMar
'Jean'	SDay
'Jean Swann'	MBNS
'Jedi Dot Pierce'	CFwr SApp SRos
'Jedi Irish Spring'	SApp
'Jedi Rose Frost'	SApp
'Jenny Wren'	EBee EBla EMar EPPr EPla ETod LRHS MBNS MSpe NBre NBro NHol SRGP WAul WWEG
'Jersey Spider'	EMar
'Jerusalem'	SDay SRos
'Jesse James'	SApp SPol
'Jessica Lilian' **new**	SRos
'Jewel Case' **new**	WNHG
'Joan Senior'	Widely available
'Jocelyn's Oddity'	SApp
'Jock Randall'	MNFA
'Jockey Club' (d)	ECtt EMar MBNS
'Joe Marinello'	SPol
'Jogolor'	CAbx
'John Allen' **new**	CFwr
'John Bierman'	SRos
'John Robert Biggs'	SApp
'Jolyene Nichole'	SApp SRos
'Journey's End'	SDay
'Jovial'	SApp SDay SRos
'Judah'	SApp SDay SRos
'Judge Roy Bean'	SPol SRos
'Jungle Beauty'	CBgR SPol
'Justin George'	SPol
'Karen's Curls' **new**	SPol SRos
'Kasia' **new**	WHrl
'Kate Carpenter'	SPol SRos
'Kathleen Salter'	SRos
'Katie Elizabeth Miller'	SDay SRos
'Kazuq'	SApp
'Kecia'	EMar MNFA
'Kelly's Girl'	SDay SPol SRos
'Kempion'	EMar
'Kent's Favorite Two'	SRos
'Kindly Light'	EMar MNFA SPol SRos
'King Haiglar'	EGol SApp SPhx SRos
'Kiowa Sunset' **new**	MSpe
N 'Kwanso Flore Pleno'	see *H. fulva* 'Green Kwanso'
N 'Kwanso Flore Pleno Variegata'	see *H. fulva* 'Variegated Kwanso'
'La Peche'	LRHS SDay
'Lacy Marionette'	EMar SApp SPol SRos
'Lady Cynthia'	CKel
'Lady Fingers'	CBgR EMar MNFA SRos
'Lady Hillary'	SApp
'Lady Inara' **new**	CFwr
'Lady Inma'	SApp
'Lady Liz'	MNFA
'Lady Mischief'	SApp

'Lady Neva' CBgR CPar SApp SRos
'Ladykin' SApp SPol SRos
'Lake Norman Spider' MNFA SApp
'Lake Norman Sunset' **new** CFwr
'Land of Cotton' EMar
'Land's End' CAbx
'Lark Song' EBrs EGol LRHS SRos WFar
'Lauren Leah' SRos
'Lavender Arrowhead' SApp
'Lavender Bonanza' CFwr
'Lavender Deal' EBee EMar LRHS MNrw WNHG
'Lavender Dusk' **new** CFwr
'Lavender Flushing' SApp
'Lavender Illusion' CSev SApp
'Lavender Memories' SDay
'Lavender Rainbow' **new** CFwr
'Lavender Silver Cords' SPol
'Lavender Spider' SApp
'Lee Reinke' **new** CAbx
'Leebea Orange Crush' EMar
'Lemon Bells' ♀H4 CWat EBee EBla ECGP ECha EMFW EMar EPfP GKev GMaP LRHS MBNS NBro NCGa NGdn SApp SDay SRos WCAu WSpi
'Lemon Dessert' SRos
'Lemon Mint' EGol SRos
'Lemon Starfish' SApp
'Lemonora' SDay
'Lenox' SDay SRos
'Leonard Bernstein' SApp SPol SRos
'Lesmona' **new** CFwr
'Licorice Candy' CFwr SRos
'Light the Way' ECha GBin
'Light Years Away' ELon MBNS NBro SMrm
'Lil Ledie' SApp
§ ***lilioasphodelus*** ♀H4 Widely available
\- 'Rowden Golden Jubilee' (v) CRow
'Lillian Frye' EGol
'Lilting Belle' SRos
'Lilting Lady' SApp SDay
'Lilting Lady Red' SApp
'Lime Frost' CAbx EMar SRos
'Limoncello' SApp
'Linda' MNFA MRav NHol SRos
'Lines of Splendor' SRos
'Lipstick Print' SRos
'Little Angel' SApp
'Little Audrey' SApp
'Little Bee' NBre
'Little Beige Magic' EGol
'Little Big Man' SDay WCon
'Little Bugger' CMoH NGby NLar WWEG
'Little Bumble Bee' CFir COlW EGol EMar LRHS MBNS SApp WWEG
'Little Business' MBNS SApp WAul
'Little Cadet' MNFA
'Little Cameo' EGol
'Little Carpet' MBNS SPer SPet
'Little Cranberry Cove' EGol
'Little Dandy' EGol
'Little Deeke' COlW SApp SDay SRos WHrl
'Little Fantastic' EGol
'Little Fat Cat' SApp
'Little Fat Dazzler' SApp SPol SRos
'Little Fellow' MBNS
'Little Fruit Cup' SApp
'Little Grapette' COlW EGol EPfP GCra GQue MBNS MNFA NLar NSti SApp SMrs SRos WAul WBrk WCAu WTin WWEG
'Little Greenie' EMar SDay
'Little Gypsy Vagabond' CWat SDay SRos
'Little Heavenly Angel' COlW SPol
'Little Lavender Princess' EGol
'Little Maggie' SApp SDay SPol
'Little Missy' CBgR COlW CWat EMar LAst MBNS NBPC NBre SPet WGob WHoo
'Little Monica' SApp
'Little Orange Slices' CFwr
'Little Pumpkin Face' EGol
'Little Rainbow' EGol WWEG
'Little Red Hen' CSam EBla ECGP EMar GBuc LRHS MBNS MSpe NBro NEgg NGdn SDay SUsu WFar
'Little Show Stopper' MBNS NBro NLar NMRc NMoo
'Little Sweet Sue' MNFA
'Little Sweet Talk' SRos
'Little Toddler' SApp SDay
'Little Violet Lace' SDay
'Little Wart' EGol SDay WHrl
'Little Wine Cup' Widely available
'Little Wine Spider' SApp
'Little Women' MBNS SDay
'Little Zinger' SDay
'Littlest Angel' SDay
'Lobo Lucy' **new** SRos
'Lochinvar' GBuc MRav SRos
'Lonesome Dove' SPol
'Long John Silver' SRos
'Long Stocking' SPol SRos
'Longfield's Beauty' MBNS NCGa
'Longfield's Glory' MBNS NBre NMoo WGob
'Longfield's Mandy' MSpe
'Longfield's Maxim' (d) MBNS
'Longfield's Pride' ECho MBNS WBor
'Longfield's Purple Edge' EBee
'Longfield's Purple Eye' NCGa NLar NMoo
'Longfield's Tropica' MBNS
'Longfield's Twins' EKen MBNS NMoo WCot
longituba B&SWJ 4576 WCru
'Look at Me' **new** ELan
'Lori Goldston' MBNS
'Love Glow' CFir
'Loving Memories' SApp
'Lowenstine' SApp
'Lucille Lennington' WNHG
'Lucretius' MNFA
'Luke Senior Junior' SApp
'Lullaby Baby' CWat EGol ELan MBNS NLar SApp SDay SPol SRos
'Luscious Honeydew' WNHG
'Lusty Lealand' EGol EMar MBNS MNFA SRos
'Luverne' SRos
'Luxury Lace' CPrp CSpe CWat EBla ECho ECtt EGol ELan EMar EPfP EPla LRHS MSpe NBir NGdn NPri SPer SPol SRos WAul WCAu WCFE WFar WMoo WPnP WTin
'Lydia Bechtold' CAbx SRos
'Lynn Hall' ECtt EGol EMil MBNS NLar WSpi
'Lyric Opera' SDay
'Mabel Fuller' CBgR MRav SPer SRos WHrl
'Macbeth' EPfP MBNS SPad
'Mae Graham' SApp
'Maggie Fynboe' SPol
'Magic Carpet Ride' EMar SPol
'Magic Lace' SRos
'Magnificent Eyes' EMar
'Magnificent Rainbow' **new** SApp SRos
'Mahogany Magic' SRos
'Make Believe Magic' **new** CFwr
'Malaysian Masquerade' SApp
'Malaysian Monarch' SRos WMnd WNHG
'Malaysian Spice' WNHG

'Maleny Tapestry' MSpe
'Mallard' CBgR CWat ECGP ECtt EGol EHrv EMar EPla LLWP LRHS MBNS MRav MSpe SApp SPer SRos SWat
'Man on Fire' **new** CWGN MBNS
'Manchurian Apricot' SRos
'Marble Faun' SApp SRos
'Margaret Perry' CFee CPrp GBin MNrw WAul
'Marietta Delight' CAbx
'Marion Caldwell' SPol
'Marion Vaughn' Υ^{H4} CSev ECtt EHrv ELan EPfP GMaP LBMP LHop LRHS MNFA NSti SBch SDix SPer SRGP SRos SSpi WCot WFar
'Mariska' SApp SDay SRos WNHG
'Mark My Word' SApp
'Marked by Lydia' **new** SPol
'Marse Connell' SRos
'Martina Verhaert' **new** CWGN MAvo
'Mary Ethel Anderson' MSpe
'Mary Todd' EGol MBNS SApp WCAu WMnd
'Mary's Gold' SDay SPol SRos
'Mask Ball' SRos
'Matt' CFwr SRos SWal
'Mauna Loa' CSBt CWGN EBee EMar GQue MBNS MNFA MNrw MWea NBre SApp WAul WCAu WCot
'May Colvin' LRHS
'May May' SApp SPol
'Meadow Mist' EGol
'Meadow Sprite' SRos
'Meadow Sweet' **new** CFwr
'Medicine Feather' **new** SRos
'Medieval Guild' SApp
'Mega Stella' SApp
'Melody Lane' EGol
'Ménage Enchanté' EMar
'Meno' EGol
'Mephistopheles' EMar
'Merlot Rouge' WAul
'Metaphor' EMar SApp SRos
'Michele Coe' CMMP EBee EBla ECtt EGol EHrv EMar EQua LPla LRHS MBNS MNFA MSpe NBre NBro NCGa NEgg NGdn SApp SPav SRGP SRos WHrl WMoo
middendorffii CAvo CMac EBee GMaP LRHS NSti SMrm WFar WHrl WSpi
– 'Major' CFee
'Midnight Dynamite' MBNS
'Midnight Magic' EMar SRos
'Mikado' CBgR CMac LRHS
'Milady Greensleeves' SPol SRos
'Milanese Mango' MSpe
'Mildred Mitchell' CFwr CWat EBee EWTr MBNS NLar NMRc SApp
'Millie Schlumpf' EMar SApp SDay SPol SRos
'Mimosa Umbrella' CAbx SPol
'Ming Lo' SDay
'Ming Porcelain' CMil SApp SDay SRos
'Mini Pearl' CBgR CMMP COlW EGol EPfP LRHS MBNS MBri SApp SRos WPer
'Mini Stella' CBro CMea ECtt IBal MBNS NBre NOrc SPet WAul WFar
miniature hybrids SRms
'Minnie Wildfire' **new** SPol
minor CBro EBrs EGol GBin GKev LRHS NGdn SRms
– B&SWJ 8841 WCru
'Miracle Maid' WNHG
'Miss Amelia' SRos
'Miss Jessie' CAbx SRos
'Missenden' Υ^{H4} MNrw SApp SRos
'Mission Moonlight' EGol
'Missouri Beauty' EBee MBNS SApp
'Missouri Memories' SRos
'Mokan Cindy' EMar
'Moment of Truth' EBee NBre
'Monica Marie' SRos
'Monita Gold Stripe' CMoH
'Mont Royal Demitasse' **new** SPol
'Moon Witch' SDay SPol SRos
'Moonbeam' SApp
'Moonlight Masquerade' CWat EBee ECtt EPfP NLar SApp
'Moonlight Mist' SApp SPol SRos
'Moonlit Caress' EBee EMar IPot MBNS NBro SApp SRos WAul WFar
'Moonlit Crystal' CSpe SApp SPol
'Moonlit Masquerade' CPar CWGN EMar GBuc GMac MBNS MBel MBri MCCP MSCN MSpe NCGa SBch SDnm SEND SPav SPer SPet SPol SRos WAul WCAu WHrl
'Moonlit Pirouette' SApp
'Moonstruck Madness' **new** CFwr
'Moontraveller' WCot
'Mormon Spider' SApp SPol SRos
'Morning Dawn' WWEG
'Morning Sun' EMar MBNS NBre NLar WCot
'Morocco' SPol
'Morocco Red' CBro CMdw CTri ELan EPla NBre WWEG
'Morrie Otte' SPol
'Mosel' SDay
'Moses' Fire' **new** EPfP EWTr MBNS
'Mount Joy' SPer
'Mountain Laurel' EBee ECGP ECtt LDai LRHS LSRN MBNS MCot MRav MSpe NEgg SApp SPol WFar
'Mountain Violet' SApp
'Mrs David Hall' CMdw
'Mrs Hugh Johnson' CSev EBee GCra LAst NHol
'Muffet's Little Friend' **new** SPol
'Mulberry Truffle Double' (d) **new** EMar
multiflora MNFA NHol
'My Belle' SRos
'My Darling Clementine' SDay SRos
'My Kind' **new** CFwr
'My Melinda' SDay
'My Sweet Rose' SRos
'Mynelle's Starfish' CPar EMar SDay SPol SRos
'Mysterious Veil' EGol
'Nairobi Dawn' SRos
nana CFir EPot GKev
'Nanuq' SApp SDay SRos
'Naomi Ruth' EGol LAst MBNS SApp WTin
'Nashville' CBro ELan WHrl
'Nashville Lights' CBgR SPol
'Natural Veil' SPol
'Navajo Princess' CBcs CWat EPfP MBNS MNrw
'Neal Berrey' SApp SDay SRos
'Nefertiti' CBgR ELon MBNS NBir NCGa SAga SPer WAul WCAu WTin
'Neon Rose' EBla MWat SRos
'Netsuke' SApp SMrm
'New Swirls' SApp
'Newberry Borrowed Time' **new** CFwr
'Neyron Rose' Υ^{H4} CHar EGol EMar EPfP EPla GBuc LAst LHop LRHS MBNS MWea NBre NEgg NGdn SRos WCAu WMoo
'Nick's Faith' **new** WHrl
'Night Beacon' CBgR CFwr CPar ECho ECtt EGol ELon EMar EWes EWll IBal MBNS

	MBel MBri MNrw MSpe NLar NMoo SApp SDay SRos WCAu WGob WHrl
'Night Raider'	CAbx EMar SApp SRos
'Night Wings'	SApp
'Nigrette'	CBen LPBA NHol
'Nile Crane'	CBgR CFwr LRHS MBNS MNrw SApp SDay SPer WAul
'Nile Plum'	SApp
'Nina Winegar'	SRos
'Nivia Guest'	SApp SDay
'Nob Hill'	CMdw EGol EPla GBin MNFA SApp SRos WHrl
'Nona's Garnet Spider'	SApp SRos
'Nordic Night'	EMar
'North Star'	SApp
'Norton Eyed Seedling'	WNHG
'Norton Orange'	MNFA SAga WCon WFar
'Nosferatu'	EMar
'Nova' ♀H4	CPrp SApp SRos
'Nuka'	EMar
'Numinous Moments'	SDay
'Ocean Rain'	EMar SApp SRos
'Octopus Hugs'	SRos
'Old Tangiers'	EMar SRos
'Old-fashioned Maiden'	EMar SRos
'Olive Bailey Langdon'	EGol MNFA SApp SRos
'Olive's Odd One'	CAbx EMar
'Olympic Showcase'	SRos
'Omomuki'	SApp SRos
'On and On'	EBee MAvo MBNS
'On Silken Thread'	SPol SRos
'On the Web'	SApp
'Oom Pah Pah'	ECha
'Open Hearth'	EMar SDay SPol SRos
'Orange Dream'	SDay
'Orange Velvet'	SApp SDay SRos
'Orangeman' hort.	EBla EPla LRHS MBNS NGdn NHol
'Orchard Sprite'	SApp
'Orchid Beauty'	ECha MLHP WMoo
'Orchid Candy'	MBNS NBir SPol WAul
'Orchid Corsage'	CAbx SApp SDay
'Oriental Ruby'	EGol MNFA SRos
'Orion Sky' **new**	CFwr
'Ostrich Plume'	SRos
'Ottis Leonard' **new**	CFwr
'Ouachita Beauty'	SPol
'Outrageous'	CAbx CFwr SApp SRos WNHG
'Over the Top' **new**	MBNS
'Paige Parker'	EGol
'Paige's Pinata'	CFwr EBee MBNS NBPC SApp SRos
'Paint Your Wagon'	SApp
'Painted Lady'	MNFA SApp
'Painted Pink'	SDay
'Painted Trillium'	CMil
'Painter Poet'	EMar
'Palace Garden Beauty'	SApp
'Palace Guard'	MNFA
'Palantir'	SApp
'Panama Hattie'	EMar
'Pandora's Box'	Widely available
'Pantaloons'	SApp
'Pantherette'	SApp SPol
'Paper Butterfly'	EMar SPol SRos
'Paradise Prince'	EGol
'Pardon Me'	CMHG CMMP ECho EGol ELan EMar GMaP LRHS MBNS MNFA NCGa NGdn NHol SApp SPol SRos SWal WAul WBor WCAu
'Pardon Me Boy'	SPol
'Parfait'	CBgR EMar SPol
'Party Queen' **new**	SDay
'Pas de Deux'	SApp
'Pastel Ballerina'	SDay SRos
'Pastel Classic'	SApp SRos
'Pastilline'	SPol
'Pat Mercer'	SApp SDay
'Patchwork Puzzle'	SRos
'Patricia'	EPfP MBNS SPoG
'Patricia Fay'	MNFA SApp SRos
'Patsy Bickers'	SApp
'Paul Weber'	SApp
'Peach Jubilee'	SPol
'Peach Petticoats'	SRos
'Peacock Maiden'	EMar SApp SPol SRos
'Pear Ornament'	SRos
'Pearl Lewis'	SDay SRos
'Peggy Jeffcoat' **new**	CFwr
'Penelope Vestey'	EBla EMar GBuc LRHS MBNS SApp SPol SRGP SRos
'Penny's Worth'	EBrs EGol MBNS NOrc WAul WCot WFar WHoo
'Perfect Pleasure'	MBNS
'Persian Ruby'	EMar SPol
'Petite Ballerina'	SDay
'Piano Man'	EMar MBNS MWea NLar NMoo WAul WGob WNHG
'Piccadilly Princess'	SRos
'Pink Attraction'	SApp
'Pink Ballerina'	EGol
'Pink Charm'	CBen CMac COIW EBee ECha ECtt EMar EPPr GMaP LPBA LRHS MBNS NBro NGdn NHol SPol SRos WCAu
'Pink Cotton Candy'	SRos
'Pink Damask' ♀H4	Widely available
'Pink Dream'	EMar EQua MBNS NBir NBre NHol SPol WCAu
'Pink Flirt'	SDay
'Pink Glow'	CMMP
'Pink Grace'	SPol
'Pink Heaven'	EGol
'Pink Lady'	MNrw MRav NBur SRms WCon
'Pink Lavender Appeal'	EGol WCAu
'Pink Monday'	WNHG
'Pink Prelude'	EBee EMar LRHS MBNS MWat NBro SMrm
'Pink Puff'	MBNS NBir NBre NLar WGob
'Pink Ruffled Love' **new**	CFwr
'Pink Salute'	SRos
'Pink Spider' **new**	SDay
'Pink Sundae'	ECha WHrl
'Pink Super Spider'	MNFA SRos
'Pink Windmill'	SDay SPol SRos
'Pinocchio'	NMoo
'Pirate Treasure'	MBNS
'Pirate's Patch'	EMar SPol SRos
'Pixie Parasol'	WMnd WNHG WSpi
'Pixie Pipestone'	SApp
'Pixie Pleasure' **new**	CFwr
'Pizza' **new**	SDay
'Platinum and Gold' **new**	CFwr
'Plum Beauty'	NLar
'Pocket Size'	SApp
'Pojo'	CFwr SDay
'Pompeian Purple'	EGol
'Pony'	CWat EGol SPol SRos
'Ponytail Pink'	EGol
'Pookie Bear'	SApp
'Porcelain Pleasure'	SDay
'Prague Spring'	EMar MNFA SPol SRos WCAu
'Prairie Belle'	CBcs CSWP MBNS NBre SApp SPol WCAu WFar
'Prairie Blossoms' **new**	CFwr

'Prairie Blue Eyes' ECha EChо ECtt EGol LFur MBNS MNFA NMoo NPri SApp SBch SPlb SPol SRos WAul WCAu WCot WHrl WMnd WWEG
'Prairie Charmer' MMuc SEND WHrl
'Prairie Moonlight' SRos
'Prairie Sunset' WCAu
'Prelude to Love' EMar
'Pretty Miss' ECtt EMar LRHS MBri
'Pretty Peggy' MNFA
'Preview Party' WNHG
'Primal Scream' SApp
'Primrose Mascotte' NBir
'Prince of Midnight' SDay
'Prince of Purple' CAbx EMar SRos
'Prince Redbird' SDay SRos
'Princess Blue Eyes' SPol
'Princess Ellen' SApp
'Princess Lilli' MBNS
'Princeton Eye Glow' SDay
'Princeton Point Lace' SApp
'Princeton Silky' SRos
'Priscilla's Rainbow' **new** EMar
'Prissy Frills' **new** SPol
'Prize Picotee Deluxe' SPol SRos
'Prize Picotee Elite' EMar SPol SRos WTin
'Protocol' SDay WCon
'Ptarmigan' **new** SDay
'Pterodactyl Eye' **new** SRos
§ 'Puddin' CWat NHol SDay WAul
'Pudgie' SApp
'Pug Yarborough' SPol
'Pumpkin Kid' SApp SPol SRos
'Puppet Lady' SApp
'Puppet Show' SDay
'Pure and Simple' CFwr SDay SPol SRos
'Pure Country' **new** CFwr
'Purple Bicolor' WHrl
'Purple Corsage' SApp
'Purple Oddity' SPol
'Purple Pinwheel' SPol
'Purple Rain' CWat LRHS MBNS MWea SApp SPol SRos SWvt
'Purple Rain Dance' SPol
'Purple Waters' EMar EPfP EWll MBNS NBre NOrc NPri SPol WAul WPnP
'Pursuit of Excellence' EMar SRos
'Pyewacket' SApp
'Pygmy Plum' SDay SRos
'Queen Lily' WNHG
'Queen of May' SApp WCot
'Queen Priscilla' CAbx
'Queens Fancy' SApp
'Queen's Gift' SApp
'Queensland' SApp
'Quick Results' SApp SRos
'Quilt Patch' SRos
'Quinn Buck' EMar
'Ra Hansen' SApp SDay SRos
'Radiant' CBcs
'Radiant Greetings' MNFA
'Radiant Moonbeam' **new** CAbx
'Rags to Riches' **new** CFwr
'Rainbow Candy' CWGN LLHF MAvo MBNS NMoo SPad
'Rainbow Drive' **new** CFwr
'Raindrop' EGol
'Rajah' CBgR CMac EMar MBNS MSpe NBro SPer WHrl
'Randall Moore' SPol
'Raspberry Candy' CBro EChо EMar EWll GCra MBNS MBel MNrw NBro NCGa NHol NOrc SApp SRos WCAu WGob WHrl
'Raspberry Pixie' EGol SPol
'Rave On' SApp
'Real Wind' CFwr EMar MNFA SApp SPol SRos
'Red Admiral' LRHS
'Red Butterfly' EMar
'Red Joy' SApp
'Red Precious' ♀^{H4} EGol EMar MNFA MNrw SApp SRos
'Red Rain' CAbx EMar
'Red Ribbons' SDay SPol SRos
'Red Ruby' ERCP
'Red Rum' CBgR EWll NBro SBch SMrm WCon WMoo WPnP
'Red Suspenders' CAbx MBNS
'Red Volunteer' EMar SPol SRos
'Reflections' **new** WCon
'Regal Giant' **new** EMar
'Regal Vision' SApp
'Regency Dandy' SApp SPol
'Renee' MNrw
'Respighi' SApp SRos
'Return Trip' SPol
'Revolute' **new** SDay
'Rhapsody in Time' EMar
'Rhode Island Red' **new** CFwr
'Ribbonette' EBee MBNS MSpe NMoo
'Right on Red' **new** CFwr
'Ringlets' LRHS MNFA
'Riptide' SApp
'Robert Coe' SRos
'Rocket City' ELan SRos
'Rodeo Sweetheart' **new** CFwr
'Roger Grounds' SApp SPol SRos
* 'Romantic Rose' EMar MBNS NLar WHrl
'Ron Rousseau' SApp
'Root Beer' SRos WTin
'Rose' **new** SDay
'Rose Emily' SApp SDay SRos
'Rose Roland' NBre
'Rosella Sheridan' SRos
'Roses in Snow' MBNS
'Rosewood Flame' SRos
'Rosewood Rainbow End' SRos
'Rosewood Snowflakes' SRos
'Roswitha' CWat SApp SPol
'Rosy Returns' MBNS MWea NLar NMoo WHoo
'Round Midnight' SPol
'Royal Braid' EPfP MBNS MNrw MSpe NCGa NLar SApp SPer WCot
'Royal Charm' SRos
'Royal Corduroy' SRos
'Royal Crown' CSev
'Royal Hunter' **new** CFwr
'Royal Occasion' SRos
'Royal Palace Prince' EMar GAbr
'Royal Prestige' SApp
'Royal Robe' CTri
'Royal Saracen' SDay
'Royal Thornbird' CBgR
'Royalty' GCra
'Ruby Sentinel' **new** SDay
'Ruby Spider' EMar SPol SRos
'Ruffled Apricot' CKel LBMP LRHS MBNS SDay SPav SRos WNHG
'Ruffled Carousel' WNHG
'Rumble Seat Romance' WNHG
'Russian Easter' SRos
'Russian Rhapsody' CKel SApp SPol SRos
'Rutilans' CFee
'Sabie' SApp

'Sabine Baur' CWat EBee IBal IPot MBNS MNrw MWea SApp WAul WFar
'Sabra Salina' SRos
'Sachsen Little Gold' **new** CFwr
'Sachsen Rustic' **new** CFwr
'Sachsen White Gigant' **new** CFwr
'Saffron Glow' SDay
* 'Sagamore' SApp
'Salmon Sheen' SDay SPer SRos
'Sammy' CAbx
'Sammy Russell' Widely available
'Sandra Walker' EGol
'Sangre de Cristo' **new** CFwr
'Santiago' SPol
'Satin Clouds' EGol
'Satin Glass' EBrs MNFA
'Satin Glow' ECha MLHP
'Scarlet Flame' ECha WMoo
'Scarlet Oak' LRHS MBri SRos
'Scarlet Orbit' EMar SApp SHar SPol SRos
'Scarlet Prince' **new** WNHG
'Scarlet Ribbons' CAbx SPol
'Scarlock' MNFA SDay
'Scatterbrain' CKel
'Schnickel Fritz' NCGa
'Schoeppinger Anfang' EBee
'School Girl' EBrs LRHS
'Scorpio' CBgR EMar SPol
'Scotland' IBal SApp
'Searcy Marsh' EGol
'Sebastian' SApp SRos
'Secret Splendor' SPol
'Segramoor' SApp
'Selma Longlegs' CAbx SRos
'Seminole Wind' SPol
'Serena Dark Horse' SRos
'Serena Sunburst' CFwr SPol SRos
'Serene Madonna' CFir GBin MWea SBch
'Serenity Morgan' EBee EPfP MBNS
'Shadowed Pink' WNHG
'Shady Lady' SDay
'Shaman' EMar SApp SPol SRos
'Sherry Lane Carr' SPol SRos
'Shimek September Morning' SPol
'Shimmering Elegance' CFwr SRos
'Shogun' MBNS
'Shotgun' SPol SRos
'Show Amber' SApp SRos
'Significant Other' SApp
'Silent Sentry' SApp
'Silken Fairy' EGol SDay
'Silken Touch' SApp SPol SRos
'Siloam Amazing Grace' SApp SDay SRos
'Siloam Baby Talk' EGol ELon EMar LAst NBir SApp SRos WAul WHoo WMoo WPnP WTin
'Siloam Bertie Ferris' MBNS
'Siloam Bo Peep' EGol SApp SRos WAul
'Siloam Brian Hanke' SRos
'Siloam Button Box' EBee EGol MBNS WAul WHrl
'Siloam Bye Lo' EGol SRos
'Siloam Cinderella' EGol SRos
'Siloam David Kirchhoff' EMar MBNS MSpe SDay SRos
'Siloam Doodlebug' CBgR CWat EGol SRos
'Siloam Double Classic' (d) EGol EMar SPol SRos
'Siloam Dream Baby' EPPr MBNS NCGa
'Siloam Edith Sholar' EGol
'Siloam Ethel Smith' EGol SApp SPol SRos
'Siloam Fairy Tale' CWat EGol
'Siloam French Doll' MBNS NLar SApp
'Siloam French Marble' SDay SRos
'Siloam Frosted Mint' SApp
'Siloam Gold Coin' SApp SDay
'Siloam Grace Stamile' CFir EMar MBNS SApp SRos WGob
'Siloam Harold Flickinger' SRos
'Siloam Helpmate' **new** WNHG
'Siloam Jim Cooper' MSpe SRos
'Siloam Joan Senior' EGol MBNS
'Siloam John Yonski' SDay
'Siloam June Bug' CBgR EGol ELan SApp WCAu
'Siloam Justine Lee' MBNS
'Siloam Kewpie Doll' EGol
'Siloam Little Angel' EGol SApp SPol
'Siloam Little Girl' CWat ECtt EGol SDay SRos
'Siloam Mama' SApp SRos
'Siloam Merle Kent' EMar MNFA SApp SDay SPol SRos
'Siloam New Toy' EGol
'Siloam Nugget' SApp
'Siloam Orchid Jewel' EGol
'Siloam Paul Watts' SApp SPol SRos
'Siloam Peewee' EGol
'Siloam Penny' SApp
* 'Siloam Pink' LAst
'Siloam Pink Glow' EGol SWat WAul
'Siloam Pink Petite' EGol
'Siloam Plum Tree' EGol SApp
'Siloam Pocket Size' EGol SApp
'Siloam Powder Pink' SApp
'Siloam Prissy' EGol SApp
'Siloam Purple Plum' EGol
'Siloam Queen's Toy' SPol
'Siloam Ra Hansen' SApp
'Siloam Red Ruby' EGol
'Siloam Red Toy' EGol
'Siloam Red Velvet' EGol
'Siloam Ribbon Candy' EGol SApp SDay WNHG
'Siloam Rose Dawn' SApp SPol SRos
'Siloam Royal Prince' EBee EGol EPfP NHol SApp
'Siloam Shocker' CAbx EGol
'Siloam Show Girl' CWGN EGol EMar MBNS NCGa SApp
'Siloam Sugar Time' EGol
'Siloam Sunburst' EMar
'Siloam Tee Tiny' EGol
'Siloam Tinker Toy' EGol
'Siloam Tiny Mite' EGol SDay WHrl
'Siloam Toddler' EGol
'Siloam Tom Thumb' CBgR EGol EMar MBNS WGob
'Siloam Ury Winniford' CBro CMac CSsd CWan ECho EGol EMar EMil MBNS MCCP MNFA NBre NLar NMoo SApp WAul WHoo WHrl WPnP WTin
'Siloam Virginia Henson' EGol NCGa SApp SRos WWEG
'Silver Ice' SApp SRos
'Silver Lance' SRos
'Silver Quasar' SRos
'Silver Trumpet' EGol WWEG
'Silver Veil' WFar
'Sinbad Sailor' EMar NLar
'Sir Blackstem' ELon GCal SApp SRos
'Sir Modred' CAbx SPol SRos
'Sirius' NHol
'Sirocco' EBee WTin
'Sixth Sense' MBNS SPad
'Slapstick' **new** SDay
'Slender Lady' SRos
'Smith Brothers' **new** SPol
'Smoky Mountain Autumn' EMar SApp SPol SRos
'Smoky Mountain Bell' SApp
'Smuggler's Gold' ECtt SApp

Name	Suppliers
'Snappy Rhythm'	MNFA
'Snowed In'	SRos
'Snowy Apparition'	EBla ECtt EMar EWTr GKir LHop LRHS MBNS MNFA MSpe MWea NHol SApp SMrm SPol
'Snowy Eyes'	CHid EGol EMar GBuc IPot MBNS NHol SApp SWat WHrl
'So Lovely'	SApp
'So Many Stars' **new**	CFwr
'Solano Bull's Eye'	MLHP
'Solid Scarlet'	CAbx SRos
'Someone Special'	SPol SRos
'Song Sparrow'	CBro GMac LRHS SApp WPer
'Sounds of Silence' **new**	SRos
'South Seas'	LRHS
'Sovereign Queen'	EGol WNHG
'Spacecoast Scrambled'	CBcs CWGN EPfP MBNS MSpe
'Spacecoast Starburst'	CBcs EMar MBNS MSpe NBro WCAu WCon WCot WFar
'Spanish Fandango'	CAbx
'Spanish Glow'	SRos
'Spanish Sketch'	SRos
'Speak of Angels'	SApp
'Spider Breeder'	CAbx SApp
'Spider Man'	CAbx MNFA SApp SDay SPol SRos WCAu
'Spider Miracle'	MNFA SDay SPol
'Spider Red' **new**	CWGN
'Spider Spirits'	EMar
'Spilled Milk'	SPol
'Spin Master'	CAbx
'Spindazzle'	CBgR SPol SRos
'Spinne in Lachs'	CAbx SRos
'Spiral Charmer'	SApp
'Spode'	SApp SDay WHrl
'Spooner'	CBgR
'Spray of Pearls' **new**	CFwr
'Spring Ballerina'	SApp
'Spring Willow Song'	SDay
'Stafford'	Widely available
'Staghorn Sumac'	EBla EMar LEdu LRHS MBNS MSpe NHol WCAu WCon
'Star of Fantasy'	EMar
'Starling'	CFir CPar EGol MNFA SApp SHGN WAul WSpi WWEG
'Starman's Quest' **new**	SPol
'Stars and Stripes'	MNFA
'Starstruck'	WNHG
'Startle'	CFir CWGN ELon EPfP MBNS MNrw SApp WCot
'Startling Creation' **new**	CFwr
'Statuesque'	WCon WFar
'Stella de Oro'	Widely available
'Stoke Poges' ♀H4	CAvo CBgR CBro EBee EBla EGoo EMFW EMar EPPr EPfP EPla LAst LBMP LHop LRHS LSRN MBNS MNFA MSpe NGdn SAga SApp SPoG SRos STes SWat
'Stoplight'	CAbx EBla ELon EMar SApp SDay SPol SRos
'Strawberry Candy'	CMMP CMac CSBt CWGN ECtt ELon EMar EWll GKir LAst LRHS LSRN MBNS MBri MSCN NCGa NGdn SApp SBch SPad SPer SPet SRos WAul WCAu WHoo WHrl WSpi WWEG
'Strawberry Fields Forever'	LRHS MBNS MSpe NLar SHar SPol SRos
'Strawberry Swirl'	MNFA
I 'Streaker' B. Brown (v)	WCot
'Street Urchin'	SPol
'Strider Spider'	SApp
'Strutter's Ball'	IPot MBNS MNFA MSCN NGdn SApp SBch SDay SPer SPol SRos SWat WAul WCAu WHoo WMnd
'Sugar Cookie'	SApp SDay SRos
'Summer Dragon'	EBee MBNS NMoo
'Summer Interlude'	WMoo
'Summer Jubilee'	SApp
'Summer Wine'	Widely available
'Sunday Gloves'	EGol SRos WNHG
'Sungold Candy'	SApp
'Super Purple'	CKel SApp
'Superlative'	SApp SRos
'Susan Weber'	SApp SPol SRos
'Suzie Wong'	MNFA SRos
'Svengali'	SDay SPol
'Sweet Hot Chocolate' **new**	MBNS
'Sweet Pea'	EGol
'Swirling Spider'	EMar
'Tahitian Waterfall' **new**	CFwr
'Taj Mahal'	ELon SApp SDay WFar
'Tall Boy'	SApp
'Tang'	CHid LFur MBNS MMuc NMoo NOrc WCAu
'Tang Porcelain' **new**	SDay
'Tango Noturno'	SApp SPol
'Tarantella'	CBgR
'Tarantula'	ELon SApp
'Tasmania'	SPer
'Techny Peach Lace'	SRos
'Techny Spider'	SRos
'Tejas'	CElw EBee NBre SPer
'Ten to Midnight'	SApp
'Tender Shepherd'	EGol
'Tennessee Flycatcher'	EMar SPol
'Tet Set' **new**	WNHG
'Tetraploid Stella de Oro'	MBri SDay
'Tetrina's Daughter' ♀H4	CBgR EPfP LRHS NHol SApp SGSe SRos WCAu
'Texas Sunlight'	WAul
'Texas Toffee'	SRos
'Thanks a Bunch'	SPol
'Theresa Hall'	WCon WFar
'Three Diamonds' **new**	SPol
'Thumbelina'	ECha WMoo
§ ***thunbergii***	CAvo ECha GCal MNrw
- 'Ovation'	MBNS
'Thundercloud'	WHrl
'Thundering Ovation'	CWGN MWea
'Thy True Love'	SApp
'Tigerling'	SRos
'Tigger'	CFwr
'Time Lord'	EMar SApp
'Time to Believe' **new**	SPol
'Timeless Fire'	SApp SRos
'Tinker Bell'	SRos
'Tiny Talisman'	SApp SDay
'Tis Midnight'	WNHG
'Tom Collins'	SRos
'Tom Wise'	SPol SRos
'Tomorrow's Song'	SApp
'Tone Poem'	WNHG
'Tonia Gay'	SApp SPol SRos
'Too Marvelous' **new**	WNHG
'Too Much Fun' **new**	CFwr
'Toothpick'	EMar SPol
'Tootsie Rose'	SPol SRos
'Top Honors'	SPol
'Torpoint'	EBla EMar GBee LRHS MBNS MRav NCob NEgg SBch WWlt
'Touched by Magic' **new**	CFwr
'Towhead'	EGol MRav

'Toyland' EGol EMar EPfP MBNS NBir NGdn NLar NPri SPol
'Trahlyta' CPar SApp SDay SPol SRos WTin
'Tremor' new CFwr
'Trog' CAbx EMar
'Tropical Heat Wave' SApp
'True Gertrude Demarest' new EMar
'True Glory' SApp
'True Grit' SApp
'Tune the Harp' new SPol
'Tuolumne Fairy Tale' SPol
'Turandot's Tiara' new SRos
'Turkish Turban' SPol
'Tuscawilla Blackout' SApp SRos
'Tuscawilla Tiger' new LRHS
'Tuscawilla Tigress' ECho EMar IKil MBNS MWea NCGa SMad SRos WAul WHrl
'Tuxedo' SApp SPol
'Twenty Third Psalm' WHal
'Twilight Secrets' new MBNS
'Twist of Lemon' SRos
'Two Faces of Love' SPol
'Two Part Harmony' new CFwr
'Umbrella Parade' CBgR
'Unchartered Waters' MBNS
'Uniquely Different' SPol
'Upper Class Peach' SRos
'Uptown Girl' SRos
'Valiant' EMar MBNS WHrl
'Valley Monster' CAbx EMar
'Vanessa Arden' SApp
'Vanilla Candy' SRos
'Varsity' CPLG EBrs EGol GMac LRHS NBir SPer SRos
'Vendetta' WNHG
'Vera Biaglow' SApp SDay SPol SRos
'Very Berry Ice' SPol
'Vespers' CAbP LRHS WFar
vespertina see *H. thunbergii*
'Vesuvian' new SDay
'Veuve Joyeuse' new EMar
'Vi Simmons' SRos
'Victoria Aden' CBro
'Victoria Elizabeth Barnes' WNHG
'Victorian Collar' SApp
'Victorian Ribbons' SPol
'Video' SApp SRos
'Vino di Notte' EMar SRos
'Vintage Bordeaux' ELan SApp WAul
'Vintage Burgundy' WNHG
'Violet Hour' SDay
'Viracocha' SApp WMnd WNHG
'Virgin's Blush' SPer
'Vision of Beauty' SApp
'Vohann' SApp SRos
'Waiting in the Wings' SRos
'Walking on Sunshine' SApp SRos
'Wally Nance' SApp
'War Paint' SDay
'Watch Tower' CBgR
'Water Witch' CWat EGol SApp SRos
'Wayside Green Imp' EGol MNrw SApp
'Weaver's Art' new CFwr
'Web Browser' SRos
'Wedding Band' SRos
'Wee Chalice' EGol
'Welchkins' WAul
'Welfo White Diamond' SApp SPol
'Wendy Glawson' SApp
'Whichford' ♀H4 CBgR CBro CMMP CSam EBee ECGP ECha ECtt EGol ELan EMar EPla GBuc LRHS MBNS MNFA MSpe NCob NEgg SPer SPhx SRos
'Whirling Fury' SApp
'Whiskey on Ice' SApp
'White Coral' EMar LRHS LSRN MBNS MNFA NBro WFar
'White Dish' EGol
'White Edged Madonna' EMar SBch WHrl
'White Lemonade' SApp
'White Pansy' SDay SRos
'White Temptation' CFir CMMP EGol EPfP MWea NCGa NGdn SApp SRos WAul WHoo WMnd WNHG
'White Tie Affair' SApp SRos
'White Zone' SRos
'Whooperee' SDay SRos
* 'Wide Eyed' EPla MNFA
'Wild about Sherry' SPol
'Wild and Wonderful' SRos
'Wild Horses' LRHS SPol
'Wild Mustang' MBNS
'Wild One' SApp
'Wildest Dreams' SRos
'Wildfire Tango' SApp
'Will Return' CFwr
'Wilson Spider' SApp SPol
'Wind Frills' EMar SApp SDay SPol
'Wind Song' SApp SRos
'Window Dressing' EGol
'Windsor Castle' SApp
'Wine Bubbles' EGol SApp
'Wine Delight' SDay
'Wineberry Candy' LHop MBNS MBel NLar SApp WAul WCAu
'Wings on High' SApp
'Winnie' EMar
'Winsome Lady' ECha ECtt EMar MBNS MSpe WHrl
'Wisest of Wizards' MBNS NCGa WHrl
'Wishing Well' WCot
'Witches Brew' CBgR
'Women's Work' SApp
'Wood Duck' SApp
'Woodland Spider' new SDay
'Woodside Velour' EMar
'Wyatt's Cameo' new EMar
'Xia Xiang' SDay SRos
'Xochimilco' new WNHG
'Yabba Dabba Doo' EMar SApp SPol SRos
'Yearning Love' SApp
'Yellow Angel' ELon SApp SPol
'Yellow Explosion' SApp SRos
'Yellow Lollipop' SApp SDay SRos
'Yellow Spider' SApp
'Yellow Submarine' MBNS
'Yesterday Memories' SRos
'You Angel You' MBNS SApp
'Yuma' WNHG
'Zagora' WCAu
'Zampa' CAbx SDay
'Zara' CAbx SPer
'Zarahemla' EMar

Hepatica ✿ (*Ranunculaceae*)

acutiloba CBgR CBro CLAP EBee EBrs ECho EPot GBuc GEdr GKir LAma MHom NBir NHol NLar NMen NSla WAbe
- blue-flowered MAsh WCru
- white-flowered GGar MAsh WCru
americana CLAP EBee EBrs ECho EHrv ELan GBuc LHop MAsh NBir NLar WCru

angulosa	see *H. transsilvanica*
henryi	EBee LAma MAsh WCru
insularis	CLAP EBee
- B&SWJ 859	WCru
maxima	EBee GEdr MAsh NSla
- B&SWJ 4344	WCru
× ***media***	WCom
- 'Ballardii'	GBuc GEdr GKir IBlr MNFA
- 'Harvington Beauty'	CLAP EHrv GBuc IBlr LRHS MAsh MHom NBir
'Miyuki' (d)	GEdr
§ ***nobilis*** ♀H4	Widely available
- var. ***asiatica***	MAsh
- - variegated (v)	EBee
- blue-flowered	ECho GBuc GEdr IFoB MAsh NSla WAbe WCru
- 'Cobalt'	CLAP ECho MAsh NSla WAbe
- 'Cremar'	MAsh
- dark blue-flowered	CLAP MAsh
- dwarf white	GKir IFoB
- var. ***japonica***	EPfP EWes GBuc LAma LHop MAsh NBir NHol
- - 'Akane'	EBee ECho GEdr
- - 'Akebono'	GEdr
- - 'Akenezora' (d)	GEdr
- - 'Aniju'	GEdr
- - 'Asahi' (d)	GEdr
- - 'Benikanzan'	EBee GEdr
- - 'Benioiran'	GEdr
- - 'Benisuzume' **new**	GEdr
- - 'Dewa' (d)	GEdr
- - 'Echigobijin'	EBee GEdr
- - 'Gosyozakuro'	GEdr
- - 'Gyousei'	EBee ECho GBuc GEdr
- - 'Harukaze' (d)	GEdr
- - 'Haruno-awayuki' (d)	GEdr
- - 'Houkan' (d) **new**	GEdr
- - 'Isaribi'	EBee ECho GEdr
- - 'Kasumino'	EBee ECho GEdr
- - 'Koshino-maboroshi'	GEdr
- - 'Kougyoku'	GEdr
- - 'Kousei' (d) **new**	GEdr
- - 'Koushirou'	GEdr
- - f. ***magna*** dark blue-flowered	EBee
- - - double, blue-flowered (d)	EBee
- - - - magenta-flowered (d)	EBee
- - - - pink-flowered (d)	EBee
- - - - white-flowered (d)	EBee
- - - 'Ensyu' **new**	GEdr
- - - 'Hohobeni'	GEdr
- - - 'Kimon'	GEdr
- - - 'Kuukai'	GEdr
- - - 'Murasaki-shikibu'	GEdr
- - - 'Seizan'	GEdr
- - - 'Shikouryuu'	GEdr
- - - 'Taeka'	GEdr
- - - 'Toki'	GEdr
- - 'Mangekyou' **new**	GEdr
- - 'Murasaki-Shikibu' (d) **new**	GEdr
- - (Nidan Group) 'Hakurin' (d)	GEdr
- - 'Odoriko' (d) **new**	GEdr
- - 'O-mwasaki'	ECho GEdr
- - 'Orihime'	GEdr
- - 'Ryokusetsu' (d) **new**	GEdr
- - 'Ryokuun'	GEdr
- - 'Ryougetsu'	EBee GEdr
- - 'Sadobeni'	EBee GEdr
- - 'Saichou'	GEdr
- - 'Sakuragari'	EBee GEdr
- - 'Sansetsu'	GEdr
- - 'Sawanemidori'	EBee GEdr
- - 'Sayaka'	EBee GEdr
- - 'Shikouden'	GEdr
- - 'Shirayuki'	GEdr
- - 'Shirin' (d) **new**	GEdr
- - 'Shiun'	GEdr
- - 'Shoujyouno-homare'	GEdr
- - 'Sougetsu'	EBee ECho GEdr
- - 'Subaru' (d)	GEdr
- - 'Suien'	GEdr
- - 'Tamahime' **new**	GEdr
- - 'Tamakujyaku' **new**	GEdr
- - 'Tamamushi'	GEdr
- - 'Tamao'	EBee GEdr
- - 'Tamasaburou'	EBee GEdr
- - 'Tensei'	GEdr
- - 'Touryoku'	GEdr
- - 'Toyama-chiyoiwai'	GEdr
- - 'Usugesyou'	GEdr
- - 'Yahikomuasaki'	EBee GEdr
- - 'Yoshinosato' (d)	GEdr
- - 'Yukishino'	EBee GEdr
- - 'Yumegokochi'	GEdr
- - 'Yuunami' (7)	EBee GEdr
- - 'Yuzuru'	GEdr
- lilac-flowered	MTho
- mottled leaf	CSsd ECho EHrv MTho
- pink-flowered	CLAP ECho EPot GKir MAsh NLar SIng WCru
* - var. ***pyrenaica***	GBuc LEdu MAsh
* - - 'Apple Blossom'	CLAP MAsh NBir WAbe
- 'Pyrenean Marbles'	CLAP GKir
- red-flowered	ECho GKir WAbe
- Rene's form	WFar
- var. ***rubra***	CLAP ECho NMen NSla
- 'Rubra Plena' (d)	GKir MAsh MAvo MHom NSla SCnR
- 'Tabby'	ECho
- violet-flowered	MAsh
- white-flowered	CLAP ECho MAsh NMen NSla SIng WAbe WCru
'Sakaya'	ECho
§ ***transsilvanica*** ♀H4	CBro CLAP CMea EBee ECho EWTr GAbr GBuc GKir LAma LHop LRHS MAsh MCot NHol NMen WAul WCru WHal WTin
- 'Ada Scott'	GEdr
- 'Blue Eyes'	EBee EBrs ECho GEdr GKev
- 'Blue Jewel'	CBgR CFir CLAP EBee EBrs ECho EPot GBBs GEdr MHom NLar NMen WPnP
- blue-flowered	IBlr MAsh
- 'Buis'	CAvo CBgR CLAP EBee EBrs ECho EPot GEdr GKev MCot MHom NLar SPhx WPnP
- 'Eisvogel'	CLAP EBrs ECho GEdr NMen
- 'Elison Spence' (d)	GEdr IBlr
- 'Lilacina'	ECho GEdr MAsh NSla
- 'Loddon Blue'	IBlr
- pink-flowered	CLAP EBrs ECho MAsh
- white-flowered	ECho MAsh
- 'Winterfreude'	EBee
triloba	see *H. nobilis*
'Wakana'	EBee GEdr
yamatutai	EBee EBrs
aff. ***yamatutai***	MAsh

Heptacodium (*Caprifoliaceae*)

jasminoides	see *H. miconioides*
§ ***miconioides***	Widely available

Heptapleurum see *Schefflera*

Heracleum (*Apiaceae*)

lehmannianum	CBct EBee NBPC WCot
maximum 'Washington Limes' (v)	EWes
sphondylium 'Hoggin' the Limelight'	WAlt

Herbertia (*Iridaceae*)

§ ***lahue***	CDes CStu EBrs ECho WPGP

Hereroa (*Aizoaceae*)

glenensis	EDAr SPlb
odorata	EShb

Hermannia (*Sterculiaceae*)

erodioides JCA 15523	CPBP
flammea	SPlb
pinnata	CPBP NMen WAbe
pulchella	NWCA WAbe
stricta	CPBP NWCA WAbe

Hermodactylus (*Iridaceae*)

§ ***tuberosus***	CAby CArn CAvo CBro CFFs CHid CPrp CSpe CTri CWCL EBee EBrs ECGP ECha ECho EPfP ERCP GKev LAma LRHS MCot NWCA SBch SMrm WCot WTin
- BS 348	WCot
- MS 76	WCot
- MS 729	WCot
- MS 731	WCot
- MS 821	WCot
- MS 964	WCot
- PB	WCot

Herniaria (*Illecebraceae*)

glabra	CArn GBar GPoy NGHP SIde

Herpolirion (*Anthericaceae*)

novae-zealandiae	ECou

Hertia see *Othonna*

Hesperaloe (*Agavaceae*)

parviflora	CTrC IDee LEdu SBig SChr WCot

Hesperantha (*Iridaceae*)

§ ***baurii***	CStu EBee EBrs ECho GBuc GGar NMen
buhrii	see *H. cucullata* 'Rubra'
coccinea	see *Schizostylis coccinea*
cucullata	EBee EBrs ECho
* - 'Rubra'	NWCA
falcata	EBee
grandiflora	ECho
huttonii	EBee ECho GKev GMac MSCN NBir
mossii	see *H. baurii*
§ ***radiata***	EBee GGar
tysonii	see *H. radiata*

Hesperis (*Brassicaceae*)

matronalis	Widely available
- ***alba***	see *H. matronalis* var. *albiflora*
§ - var. ***albiflora***	CPrp CSpe CTri EBee ELau EPfP GMaP LRHS MCot MMuc NGHP NGdn SIde SMrm SPer SSvw STes SWat WBrk WCAu WFar WMnd WMoo WPer
- - 'Alba Plena' (d)	CAbP EBee ECtt ELan ELon GBuc MCot MNrw NBir NCob WBrk WCot WFar WHer WSHC
- double-flowered (d)	NCob NGdn
- 'Frogswell Doris'	CBow
- 'Lilacina'	SWat
- 'Variegata' new	CBow

Hessea (*Amaryllidaceae*)

breviflora new	ECho
mathewsii new	ECho
pulcherrima new	ECho
speciosa new	ECho
stellaris new	ECho

Heterolepis (*Asteraceae*)

aliena	SGar

Heteromeles (*Rosaceae*)

arbutifolia	see *H. salicifolia*
§ ***salicifolia***	EShb

Heteromorpha (*Apiaceae*)

arborescens	CPLG SPlb

Heteropappus (*Asteraceae*)

altaicus	GAuc

Heteropyxis (*Myrtaceae*)

natalensis	EShb

Heterotheca (*Asteraceae*)

camporum var. ***glandulosum*** new	IMou
mariana	see *Chrysopsis mariana*
pumila	NWCA
§ ***villosa***	NBre WCot
- 'Golden Sunshine'	MWea

Heuchera ✿ (*Saxifragaceae*)

'Amber Waves'PBR	CMMP CWCL EBee ECtt EHrv ELan EPfP EWll LRHS MDun MGos NBro NGdn NHol SBch SDnm SPav SPer SPoG SRGP SWvt WBrk WFar
§ ***americana***	CEnt ECha GBar MRav NBir SWvt
- var. ***americana*** new	EBee
- Dale's strain	CChe EBee EHoe IFoB LBMP LFur LRHS MNrw NLar SPlb SPur SWvt WClo WHrl WMnd WPnP
- 'Eco-magnififolia'	CLAP
- 'Harry Hay'	CDes EBee EPPr WCot WPGP WSHC
- 'Ring of Fire'	EBee ECtt EPfP LHop MDun MGos NPri SApp SDnm SPav SPoG SWvt WClo WFar WWEG
'Amethyst Myst'	CMMP COIW ECtt EPfP LRHS LSRN MGos NLar NPri NScw SBch SDnm SMeo SMrm SPav SPer SRkn SRot WFar WGor
'Autumn Haze'PBR	LSou NHol
'Baby's Breath'	ECho
'Beaujolais' new	CBow EBee GCai MBNS MPnt
'Beauty Colour'	CWCL CWGN EBee ECtt ELan EPfP GKir GMaP LAst LHop LRHS LSRN LSou LSqH MDun MGos MRav NGdn NHol NMyG SBch SMrm SPer SPoG SWvt WClo WCot WFar WMnd WWEG
* 'Black Velvet'	EPfP NBre
'Blackbird' ♀H4	CMac EBee LBuc LFCN MBNS SApp SDnm SPav SPoG SRkn SWvt WMnd
'Blood Red'	LSou

	Name	Suppliers
	'Blood Vein'	CBow LBMP NBre NHol SHlg
	Bressingham hybrids	CWib GJos IFoB LBMP LRHS MLHP MMuc NBir NBlu NMir SBch SEND SPer SRms WFar WPer WWEG
	'Brownfinch'	SUsu
	'Brownies'	CBow MBNS
	'Burgundy Frost' 🏆H4	WCot
	'Cafe Ole'	GCai SGol WHer
	'Can-can' 🏆H4	CTri CWCL EBee ECtt EPfP GKev GKir LAst LBMP LRHS LSou MBel MDun MGos NBir NEgg NGdn NHol NPri SBch SHar SPav SRot SWvt WBrk WCFE WCot WSpi WWEG
	'Canyon Duet'	EAEE EBee LRHS MBNS NOrc
	'Canyon Pink'	NSti
	'Cappuccino'	EBee ECtt ELan EPfP LRHS LSqH MBNS MBel MRav NBro NGdn NPri SBch SDnm SPav SWvt WCFE WFar WWEG
	'Caramel' PBR	Widely available
	'Cascade Dawn'	CWCL EBee ECtt GBuc LAst LBMP LSRN LSou LSqH MBNS MRav NBir NHol NLar SBch SPav SPer SWvt WBrk WClo WFar
	'Champagne Bubbles' PBR	EBee
	'Cherries Jubilee' PBR	CAbP CFir EBee EBla GMaP LBMP LRHS LSou MBNS MBel MBri MGos NHol SPav WBrk WFar WGor
*	'Cherry Red'	LSou
	chlorantha	NBre
	'Chocolate Ruffles' PBR	Widely available
	'Chocolate Veil' 🏆H4	EBee EPfP LRHS LSRN WWEG
	'Christa' **new**	MPnt
	'Citronelle'	CBow CWCL EBee GCai MAsh MBNS MWea NMRc NMoo SMrm WCot
	'City Lights'	LSou
	'Color Dream' PBR	EBee GKir MAsh
	coral bells	see *H. sanguinea*
	'Coral Bouquet'	LAst LSou MBNS MBel SHar
	'Coral Cloud'	MRav
	Crème Brûlée = 'Tnheu041' (Dolce Series)	Widely available
	'Crème Caramel'	IFoB SHar
	'Crimson Curls'	GKir LBuc LRHS SBch SWvt
	'Crispy Curly'	NBre NBur
	cylindrica	EBee EPfP LLWP MBNS MRav NBre WPer
	- var. ***alpina***	NWCA
	- 'Greenfinch'	CWan EBee ECha ELan EPfP GMaP LBMP MLHP MNFA MRav MWhi NBir NOrc SPav SPer SWat WFar WMnd WPer
	'Dark Beauty' PBR	ECtt EWll GJos LRHS LSou MBNS NHol NLar NPri SBch SMrm SPoG WGor
	'David'	CBow
	'Dennis Davidson'	see *H.* 'Huntsman'
	Ebony and Ivory = 'E and I' PBR	Widely available
	'Eden's Aurora'	WMnd
	'Eden's Mystery'	ECtt
	elegans	LFur
	- NNS 05-372	WCot
	'Emperor's Cloak'	CEnt CSsd ECGP LEdu NBur NLar SHlg SWal SWvt WMoo
	'Emperor's Cloak' green-leaved	CEnt
	'Encore' **new**	MAsh
	'Fantasia'	CBow NHol
	'Firebird'	NBir NVic
	Firefly	see *H.* 'Leuchtkäfer'
	'Fireworks' PBR 🏆H4	CBow EBee ECtt GQue LAst LRHS LSou MBNS MBel NCob NLar NPri SHar SPer WBrk WClo WFar WGor
	'Florist's Choice'	CAbP IBal MBNS MNFA
	'Frosted Violet' PBR	see *H.* 'Frosted Violet Dream'
§	'Frosted Violet Dream' PBR	CBow CHar EBee EBrs ECtt EPfP LAst LRHS LSRN MAsh SBch WWEG
	'Georgia Peach' **new**	CBow GCai MAsh MPnt NBhm NHol SGol
	'Ginger Ale'	CWCL EBee EWes GCai LSou MAsh NBhm NHol SBch
	glauca	see *H. americana*
	'Green Ivory'	EBee MRav NSti SBch WBrk
	'Green Spice'	CWCL EBee ECtt EWll GBin LAst LHop LRHS LSou NCGa NHol NScw SBch SMrm SPav SPer SPoG SRkn SRot SWvt WClo WGor WSpi
	grossulariifolia	WPer
	'Guardian Angel'	EBee MAsh
	'Gypsy Dancer' PBR (Dancer Series)	LRHS
	'Helen Dillon' (v)	CBow EBee GMaP NBir NPri SRGP SWvt WFar WWEG
	'Hercules' PBR	ECtt EPfP
	hispida	WPer
	'Hollywood' PBR	CBow CWCL LBuc LRHS LSou NBhm WFar
§	'Huntsman'	ECha ELan GBuc MBNS MRav WFar WMnd
	'Ibis'	EBee
	'Jade Gloss' PBR	EBee LRHS SBch
	'Jubilee'	EBee
	Key Lime Pie = 'Tnheu042' PBR (Dolce Series)	CBcs CBct CBod CWCL EBee ECtt EWll GCai IFoB LAst LHop LRHS LSRN MBri MGos MWea NBro NCGa NPri NScw SBch SDnm SPoG SRot STes SVil SWvt WGor
	'Lady in Red'	NBre
§	'Leuchtkäfer'	Widely available
	Licorice = 'Tnheu044' PBR (Dolce Series)	CBod CWCL ECtt EWll GCai LRHS MBNS MBri MGos NLar NPri SBch SDnm SRot SVil WFar WGor WHoo
	'Lime Rickey' PBR (Rainbow Series)	Widely available
	'Little Tinker'	CHid LAst NBir STes WBrk
	'Magic Color'	CBow MAsh MBNS NMoo
	'Magic Wand' PBR 🏆H4	CAbP EBee ECtt ELon LRHS MBNS NEgg WCot
	'Mahogany' **new**	GCai MPnt
	'Marmalade' PBR	CMac CWCL EBee EKen ENor EPfP GCai LBuc LRHS LSRN LSou MBNS MBri MGos MLHP MMHG MWea NBhm NEgg NHol SBch SHar SPoG SRkn SUsu SWvt WFar
	'Mars'	EBee EPfP MBNS SPav WCot
	'Melting Fire' **new**	EBee MBNS
	'Mercury'	NMoo SPav WCot
	'Metallica'	NGBl NLar SWal WMoo
	micans	see *H. rubescens*
	micrantha	GCal MLHP SRms
	- var. ***diversifolia*** misapplied	see *H. villosa*
	- 'Martha's Compact'	WCot
§	- 'Ruffles'	ECha LRHS
	'Midnight Burgundy'	GCai
	'Midnight Rose'	CBow CCVN CWCL ECtt EWes GCai LAst LSou MAsh MBNS MBel NCGa NHol SBch SGol SPad SPhx SPoG STes SVil SWvt WCot WGor WHer

'Mini Mouse'	EWes
'Mint Frost'PBR	CWCL EBee EBrs ECtt ELan EPfP GAbr LAst LSou MGos MRav NGdn NHol NPri SDnm SMrm SPav SPoG SWvt WFar WWEG
'Miracle' **new**	MPnt
'Mocha'	CBow EBee GCai LRHS MBNS MNrw MWea NMoo SBch SMrm SPoG
'Molly Bush' ♀H4	EBee NMoo
'Monita Lime'	CMoH
'Montrose Ruby'	NBre
'Mother of Pearl'	ECtt
'Neptune'	EBee EPfP MBNS NMoo SPav
'Northern Fire'	MBNS
'Oakington Jewel'	EBee EBrs ELan LRHS WSpi
'Obsidian'PBR	Widely available
'Painted Lady'	GBuc
parishii NNS 93-384	NWCA
'Peach Flambé'PBR	Widely available
'Peach Pie'	NScw
'Peachy Keen'	NBhm
'Peppermint Spice' (21st Century Collection Series)	EBee LSou SGol
'Persian Carpet'	CHEx CWCL ECha ECtt EHrv GMaP MDun NBir NGdn NHol NPri SDnm SPer SWvt WFar WPtf
(Petite Series) 'Petite Marbled Burgundy'	EBee ECtt EHoe GKir LAst LLHF LRHS NGdn NLar SWvt WAul WFar WWEG
- 'Petite Pearl Fairy'	CAbP CBow EBee ECtt EHoe ELan NGdn NLar SWvt WFar WWEG
- 'Petite Pink Bouquet'	EBee ECtt EHoe MBNS NLar WWEG
'Pewter Moon'	CBcs EBee ECtt ELan EPfP GMaP LAst MGos MRav NBir SDnm SPer WFar WTin
'Pewter Veil'PBR	EBee ECtt EPfP LAst MBNS MDun NPri SPoG WFar WMnd WWEG
pilosissima	NBre
'Pinot Gris' **new**	EBee
'Pistache' **new**	CBow EBee GCai MAsh MBNS MPnt
§ 'Pluie de Feu'	CFir EBee EBrs ECtt EPPr EPfP GKir LRHS MRav SMrm WFar WSpi
'Plum Pudding'PBR	Widely available
'Prince'	EBee EBrs ELan EPfP GCai LRHS LSRN MBNS NMRc NMoo SApp SPoG SRkn SWvt WPtf
'Prince of Silver'	MBNS NMoo
pringlei	see *H. rubescens*
* × ***pruhoniciana*** Doctor Sitar's hybrids	SRms
- 'Sancyl'	SRms
pubescens	EBee
pulchella	CBow CPBP CSsd EBee LFur MHer MWat SRms
- JCA 9508	NMen
'Purple Mountain Majesty'	EBee ECtt WBrk WFar
'Purple Petticoats' ♀H4	CBcs EBee EPfP GCai LAst LRHS LSou MDun MLHP NBre NCob NDlv NGdn NHol NLar NPri SHar SMrm SRot WFar WSpi
'Quick Silver'	EBla MNFA NBir SWvt WFar
'Quilter's Joy' ♀H4	NBre
'Rachel'	CAbP CMea CWCL EBee EBrs ECtt ELan EPfP GCal GMaP IFoB LRHS LSRN MRav MWat NBir SRGP SWvt WAul WBrk WFar WTin
Rain of Fire	see *H.* 'Pluie de Feu'
'Raspberry Ice'PBR	GKir
'Raspberry Regal' ♀H4	ECtt GAbr MBNS MBel MRav NBir NSti SWvt WAul WFar
'Rave On'	CBow CCVN CWGN EBee GCai LSou MBri NCGa NEgg SMrm SRot SWvt WCot WGor WHoo
'Red Dream' **new**	WWEG
'Red Spangles'	EPfP LRHS NBir WWEG
'Regina' ♀H4	CAbP EBee ECGP ECtt EPfP LRHS LSRN LSou NBro SBch SHar SWvt WFar
richardsonii	MNrw
'Robert'	MBNS
'Rose Mirrors'PBR **new**	LRHS
Rosemary Bloom = 'Heuros'PBR	LRHS MBNS
§ ***rubescens***	CAbP ECho MTho NBro NMen WPer WThu
'Ruby Veil'	EBee
'Ruffles'	see *H. micrantha* 'Ruffles'
§ ***sanguinea***	CMac CSBt MRav NBir WPer
- 'Alba' ♀H4	EPPr LRHS
- 'Geisha's Fan'	CBow CWCL EAEE EBee LRHS LSou NBhm NEgg NHol SPer SWvt
- 'Monet' (v)	CBow EBee EPfP MLHP
- var. ***pulchra***	CPBP
- 'Ruby Bells'	EAEE EPfP LBMP LRHS MBNS NPri
- 'Sioux Falls'	EWes MBNS NBre WPnP
- 'Snow Storm' (v)	CBow CMoH ELan EPfP MGos MRav SPlb WFar WMnd
- 'Taff's Joy' (v)	CBow EWes
- 'White Cloud' (v)	EBee EWTr NBre SRms WPer
'Sashay' ♀H4	SGol
'Saturn'	LRHS MBNS NMoo SWvt
'Scarlet Flame'	EBee MDun
'Schneewittchen'	EPfP MRav
'Scintillation' ♀H4	CMoH ECtt NBre SRms
'Shamrock'	NBre
'Shenandoah Mountain' **new**	WWEG
'Silver Indiana'PBR	EBee LSRN
'Silver Light'PBR **new**	EPfP LRHS MBNS
'Silver Lode'PBR	EBee SBch
'Silver Scrolls'PBR	Widely available
'Silver Shadows'	ETod MBrN
'Silver Streak'	see × *Heucherella* 'Silver Streak'
'Snow Angel'	EBee EPfP GCai MBNS NSti WCot
'Snowfire' (v)	GCai SGol
'Southern Comfort' **new**	GCai MPnt SGol
'Sparkling Burgundy'	CWCL ECtt GCai LSou SBch SMrm SVil WGor
'Starry Night'PBR	SBch SHar
'Steel City'	EBee LRHS
'Stormy Seas'	CMHG COIW EBee EHoe ELan EPfP EPla GCra LRHS MBel MLHP MRav NBir NWsh SBch SWvt WBrk WCAu WFar
'Strawberries and Cream' (v)	EHrv WHer
'Strawberry Candy'PBR	CBow CMac CWCL EBee ELon GJos LAst LRHS LSRN LSou MMHG MWea NHol NLar SPoG SRkn WWEG
'Strawberry Swirl'	CHar EBee EBla ECtt EWTr GMaP LAst LFCN LRHS MBel MRav NBir NLar NPri NSti SBch SWvt WCAu WFar WWEG
Sugar Frosting = 'Pwheu0104'	EWll GKev LAst LRHS NCGa NScw SRot SVil SWvt WClo WFar
'Swirling Fantasy'PBR	CBow EPfP EShb GJos LRHS MAsh MBNS MBel NMoo SMrm
'Tiramisu' **new**	GCai MBNS MPnt
'Van Gogh'	MBNS
'Vanilla Spice' **new**	NHol
'Veil of Passion'	NBre

	'Velvet Night'	CBow EBee EPfP LRHS MBri NBir NBre NHol NWsh WFar WMnd WPtf WWEG
	'Venus'	CMHG CWGN EBrs ECtt ELon EPfP EShb GQue LRHS LSou MBNS MBel NGdn NMRc NSti SMrm SPer SPur WBrE WBrk WCot WHoo WWEG
§	***villosa***	ECha MRav
	- 'Autumn Bride'	EBee ECtt EWTr
	- Bressingham Bronze = 'Absi'PBR	EPla ETod LRHS SPer WFar
	- 'Chantilly'	EBee
	- var. ***macrorhiza***	EShb LBMP NBre WClo WMnd WPer WPnP
N	- 'Palace Purple'	Widely available
	- 'Palace Purple Select'	CMac CTri CWCL CWat CWib LAst MCot NEgg SWvt WFar
	- 'Royal Red'	ECha GBuc WSpi
	'White Marble'	SHar
	'White Spires'	EBrs LRHS SHar
	'Winter Red'	EAEE EBee LRHS MBNS NEgg SPur WCAu
	'Yeti'	WPnP
	'Zabeliana'	GBee

× *Heucherella* (*Saxifragaceae*)

	'Alabama Sunrise' **new**	GCai
	alba 'Bridget Bloom'	CPrp EBee EBrs ECGP ECha ELan EPfP GMaP LBMP LRHS MRav NOrc SPer SRms WCAu WFar
§	- 'Rosalie'	CBow EBee ECha GJos GKev GKir LRHS MBri MRav NBir NBro NPro SMrs SPlb WBrk WFar WMoo WSHC
	'Birthday Cake'	EBee LSou
	'Burnished Bronze'PBR	CBow CMoH EBee ECtt GCai GKev LRHS LSou MBel NBro NEgg NGdn NHol NLar NScw SDnm SHar SMrm SPav SPoG SRot SWvt WCot WFar
	'Chocolate Lace'PBR	EBee MBel SHar
	'Cinnamon Bear'	EBee
	'Dayglow Pink'PBR	CHar EBla EShb GMaP LFCN LRHS LSou MBri NBro NHol SHar SMrm SRkn SRot WFar WGor
	Gold Strike = 'Hertn041'PBR	CBow EWll GJos LAst LRHS MBNS SVil WGor
	'Heart of Darkness'PBR	EBee SBch WWEG
	'Kimono'PBR ♀H4	EBee ECtt EHrv EKen EPfP GCai GKev GMaP LAst LBMP LPla LRHS LSou MAvo MBel MSpe NBro NCGa NGdn NHol NLar NMyG NPri SHar SRot WFar WWEG
	'Ninja'PBR	see *Tiarella* 'Ninja'
	'Party Time'PBR	LSou
	'Pink Frost'	GBuc
	Pink Whispers = 'Hertn042'PBR	CBow LAst WFar
	'Quicksilver'	EBee EHrv GBuc GMaP LAst MDun NGdn NPri SWvt WCAu WFar WWEG
	'Ring of Fire'	CMac CMoH WFar
§	'Silver Streak'	CBow EBee MRav NBro SPoG SWvt WFar WMoo WWEG
	'Stoplight'PBR	Widely available
	'Sunspot'PBR (v)	EAEE EBee ECtt EKen EPfP LFCN LRHS MGos NBro NSti SGol SHar SPoG WHer
	tiarelloides ♀H4	CMac EPfP WMnd
§	'Viking Ship'PBR	CElw CMHG CMMP CPrp EAEE EBee EBla ECha ECtt GBuc LAst LBMP LRHS MBri MRav NBir NGdn NScw SHar SIng SRkn WFar

Hexastylis see *Asarum*

Hibanobambusa (*Poaceae*)

	tranquillans	CEnt CMCo EPla MBrN MMoz MMuc MWht WJun WPGP
	- 'Shiroshima' (v) ♀H4	CAbb CDTJ CDoC CEnt CGHE EAmu EBee ENBC EPla ERod LPal LRHS MAvo MBrN MBri MCCP MMoz MMuc MWhi MWht NMoo NPal NVic SApp SBig WJun WPGP

Hibbertia (*Dilleniaceae*)

	aspera	CBcs CCCN CDoC CRHN EBee ECre LRHS WFar WSHC
§	***cuneiformis***	CCCN MAsh
	procumbens	WAbe
§	***scandens*** ♀H1	CCCN CHll CRHN CTsd ECou ELan
	'Spring Sunshine' **new**	SRkn
	stricta	ECou
	tetrandra	see *H. cuneiformis*
*	***venustula***	ECou
	volubilis	see *H. scandens*

Hibiscus ✿ (*Malvaceae*)

	acetosella 'Red Shield'	CSpe
	Blue Chiffon = 'Notwoodthree' **new**	SPoG
	cannabinus	SIde
	coccineus	EShb SMad
	fallax	CHll
	hamabo	ELan
	huegelii	see *Alyogyne huegelii*
	'Kopper King'PBR	LRHS MAsh MBNS
	leopoldii	SPer SRms
	'Moesiana'	MBri
	moscheutos	CArn CFir SMad SVic
	- 'Carolina Mix' **new**	NExo
	- 'Galaxy'	EShb NExo WHil
	- Southern Belle Group	CHEx
	paramutabilis	EWes SMad
	'Pyranees Pink'	EMil SPoG
	rosa-sinensis	EBak EShb LRHS MBri
	- 'Black Dragon' **new**	LBur
	- 'Bon Temps' **new**	LBur
	- 'Bonjour' **new**	LBur
	- 'Casablanca'	MBri
	- 'C'est Bon' **new**	LBur
	- 'Fireworks' **new**	LBur
	- 'Gator Pride' **new**	LBur
	- 'Helene'	LSRN
	- 'Holiday'	MBri
	- 'Kardinal'	MBri
	- 'Königer'	MBri
	- 'Love Bite' **new**	LBur
	- 'Madrid'PBR **new**	LRHS
	- 'Magnifique' **new**	LBur
	- 'Marseille'PBR **new**	LRHS
	- 'Mon Ami' **new**	LBur
	- 'Napoli'PBR **new**	LRHS
	- 'Nightfire' **new**	LBur
	- 'Orange Delight' **new**	LBur
	- 'Patrick' **new**	LBur
	- 'Persimmon' **new**	LBur
	- 'Pride of Arcadia' **new**	LBur
	- 'Sassy Girl' **new**	LBur
	- 'Tivoli'	MBri
	- 'Très Bon' **new**	LBur
	schizopetalus ♀H1	CCCN EShb
	sinosyriacus	EPfP

- 'Autumn Surprise'	MAsh
- 'Lilac Queen'	CPLG LRHS SPoG WPGP
- 'Ruby Glow'	CPLG LRHS MGos WPGP
syriacus	MNHC WFar
- 'Admiral Dewey' (d)	EBee EGxp MGos
- 'Aphrodite'	CPMA EBee EPfP LRHS SEND
- 'Ardens' (d)	CEnd CSBt EBee ELon EMui EPfP LAst LRHS MGos NLar SPer
- Blue Bird	see *H. syriacus* 'Oiseau Bleu'
- 'Boule de Feu' (d)	EBee ELan SEND
- 'Caeruleus Plenus' (d)	MGos
- 'China Chiffon'	EBee EMil MAsh
- 'Coelestis'	EBee MGos SPer
- 'Diana' ♀H4	EBee EMil EPfP EQua LRHS LSRN MAsh MGos MRav SLon
- 'Dorothy Crane'	CEnd LRHS MGos
- 'Duc de Brabant' (d)	CSBt EBee EGxp ELon EMil EMui EPfP SPer
- 'Elegantissimus'	see *H. syriacus* 'Lady Stanley'
- 'Eleonore'	EBee EMil
- 'Hamabo' ♀H4	CDul CSBt CTri EBee EMil EPfP LAst LRHS LSRN MAsh MBri MGos MWat NLar SBch SCoo SLim SPer SPoG SWvt WDin WFar
- 'Helene'	EBee ELan EMil EQua LRHS LSRN MAsh MBlu MRav
- 'Jeanne d'Arc' (d)	EBee EMil MAsh
§ - 'Lady Stanley' (d)	CMac CSBt EBee MAsh MGan SCoo SPer
- Lavender Chiffon = 'Notwoodone'PBR ♀H4	EBee ELan EMil EPfP EWes LRHS MAsh MGos NPri SCoo SPer SPoG
- 'Lenny' ♀H4	MGos
- 'Leopoldii'	EBee EQua SBch
- 'Marina'	EBee EMui EPfP EWTr LRHS MAsh MRav SBch
- 'Meehanii' misapplied	see *H. syriacus* 'Purpureus Variegatus'
- 'Meehanii' (v) ♀H4	CEnd CSBt EMil EPfP LRHS MAsh MGos SCoo SPer SPoG
- 'Monstrosus'	EBee NLar
§ - 'Oiseau Bleu' ♀H4	Widely available
- Pastelrose = 'Minpast'PBR	MAsh
- Pink Giant = 'Flogi'	EBee ELan EPfP EQua LAst MBri MGos SPer
- 'Purpureus Plenus' (d)	EBee
§ - 'Purpureus Variegatus' (v)	CMac CSBt EBee LAst LRHS MGos SPoG
- 'Red Heart' ♀H4	CEnd CMac CPMA CSBt CTri EBee ELan EPfP LAst LRHS MAsh MBri MCCP MRav NLar SEND SPer SPoG SRms SWvt WCFE WDin
- Rosalbane = 'Minrosa'	EMil
- 'Roseus Plenus' (d)	EBee WDin
- Russian Violet = 'Floru'	CBcs CEnd EBee ELan EMil EPfP LAst LRHS MAsh MGos SEND
- 'Sanchon Yo'	EPfP
- 'Shintaeyang'	LRHS MGos
- 'Souvenir de Charles Breton'	EBee EMil MAsh
- 'Speciosus'	EBee EMui SPer
- 'Stadt Erlenbach'	EBee
- 'Totus Albus'	CMac CSBt EWTr SPoG
- 'Variegatus'	see *H. syriacus* 'Purpureus Variegatus'
- 'Violet Clair Double' (d) **new**	CMac
- White Chiffon = 'Notwoodtwo'PBR (d) ♀H4	EBee ELan EMil EPfP EWes LRHS LSRN MAsh MGos MRav SCoo SPer SPoG
- 'William R. Smith' ♀H4	CPMA EBee ELan EMil LAst LRHS MSwo SBch SEND SPer WDin
- 'Woodbridge' ♀H4	Widely available
trionum	CSpe SBch WKif
- 'Sunny Day'	ELan

hickory, shagbark see *Carya ovata*

Hieracium (*Asteraceae*)

aurantiacum	see *Pilosella aurantiaca*
brunneocroceum	see *Pilosella aurantiaca* subsp. *carpathicola*
§ ***glaucum***	WEas
§ ***lanatum***	CSpe ECho MDKP NBir WEas
maculatum	see *H. spilophaeum*
pilosella	see *Pilosella officinarum*
praecox	see *H. glaucum*
scullyi	EPPr
§ ***spilophaeum***	EHoe GGar NBid NPer WOut WPer
- 'Leopard'	CEnt CSsd SGar
umbellatum	EBWF WOut
villosum	CPBP CSpe EBee ECho EHoe GGar MDun NBro WHer
waldsteinii	MDKP
welwitschii	see *H. lanatum*

Hierochloe (*Poaceae*)

odorata	EPPr GBin GPoy MBNS

hildaberry see *Rubus* 'Hildaberry'

Himalayacalamus (*Poaceae*)

asper	CDTJ CGHE ERod WJun WPGP
cupreus **new**	WJun
* ***equatus***	EPla
§ ***falconeri***	CDTJ CEnt EPfP EPla MAsh MMoz SDix WPGP
§ - 'Damarapa'	CDTJ CEnt EPla MMoz WDyG WJun
§ ***hookerianus***	EAmu EPla IMou SBst WJun
- 'Himalaya Blue' **new**	CDTJ CTrC ETod
- 'Jim Dawe' **new**	ESwi
porcatus	CDTJ CGHE WJun WPGP

× *Hippeasprekelia* (*Amaryllidaceae*)

'Red Beauty'	EBrs WCot
'Red Star'	CCCN

Hippeastrum (*Amaryllidaceae*)

× ***acramannii***	WCot
advenum	see *Rhodophiala advena*
'Amoretta'	LRHS
'Amputo'	LAma LRHS
'Apple Blossom'	EBrs LAma LRHS MBri SGar
'Benfica'	LAma
bifidum	see *Rhodophiala bifida*
'Black Pearl'	LRHS
'Blossom Peacock' (d)	EBrs LAma
'Bogota'	LAma
'Bouquet'	LAma
'Britney'PBR	LAma
'Calimero'	EBrs
'Charisma'	EBrs LRHS
'Chico'	LAma LRHS
'Christmas Gift'	EBrs
'Clown'	EBrs
'Dancing Queen'	LAma
'Double Record' (d)	EBrs
'Elvas'	EBrs
'Emerald'	LAma LRHS
'Estella'	LAma
'Exotica'PBR **new**	LRHS
'Fairytale'	EBrs MBri
gracile 'Pamela'	CStu LAma
'Grandeur'	LAma

'Green Goddess'	LAma
'Hercules'	LRHS MBri
'Inca'	LAma
'Jewel' (d)	EBrs MBri
× ***johnsonii***	CPLG
'Jungle Star'	EBrs
'La Paz'	LAma LRHS
'Lady Jane'	LRHS MBri
'Lemon Lime'	EBrs LAma
'Lima' LAma	LRHS
'Limona' PBR **new**	LRHS
'Lovely Garden'	LAma
'Loyalty' PBR	LAma
'Ludwig Dazzler'	LRHS
'Mary Lou' (d)	EBrs
'Merengue'	EBrs LAma
'Minerva'	LRHS
'Misty'	LAma
'Mount Blanc' Goedert	LRHS
'Naughty Lady'	LAma
papilio ♀H1	EGxp IHer LAma LRHS MMHG
pardinum CDPR 3001	WPGP
'Philadelphia' (d)	EBrs LRHS
'Picotee'	EBrs LAma LRHS
'Pink Floyd'	EBrs LAma
'Pink Star'	EBrs
'Quito'	LAma
'Rebecca'	LAma
'Red Lion'	EBrs LAma LRHS
'Red Peacock' (d)	LAma LRHS
'Reggae'	LAma
'Rembrandt van Rijn'	LAma
'Rilona'	LAma
'Roma'	LRHS
'Royal Velvet'	LAma
'Ruby Meyer'	LAma LRHS
'San Antonio Rose'	CDes EBee WCot WPGP
'Santiago'	LAma
'Scarlet Baby'	LRHS
'Solomon'	EBrs
striatum	WCot
stylosum	EBrs
'Sumatra' PBR **new**	LRHS
'Sweet Surrender'	LAma
'Tango'	LAma
'Toscane' **new**	LRHS
'Toughie'	CAby CDes CMdw CSpe EBee LLHF WCot WPGP
'Unique' (d)	EBrs
'Vera'	LRHS
vittatum	EBrs
'White Christmas'	LAma
'White Dazzler'	LAma
'White Peacock' (d)	LRHS
'Yellow Goddess'	EBrs EShb

Hippocrepis (*Papilionaceae*)

§ ***comosa***	CRWN EBWF SSpi
§ ***emerus***	CBcs CBgR CCCN CMHG CPLG EBee ELan EPfP LAst LHop LRHS MBri MGos NLar STre WAbe WSHC WSpi

Hippophae (*Elaeagnaceae*)

rhamnoides ♀H4	CAlb CArn CBcs CCVT CDul CLnd CMac CRWN CSBt CSpe CTri EBee ECrN EHoe ELan EMac EPfP IFFs LBuc MBar MBlu MCoo NWea SEND SPlb WDin WFar WMou
- 'Askola' (f)	MGos
- 'Frugna' (f)	CAgr
- 'Hergo' (f)	CAgr MBri MCoo
- 'Hikal Dafo' (m)	CAgr
- 'Juliet' (f)	CAgr
- 'Leikora' (f)	CAgr ELan EPfP MBlu MCoo MGos NCGa NLar SPer
- 'Matt' (m)	MCoo
- 'Orange Energy' (f/F) **new**	CAgr MCoo
- 'Pollmix' (m)	CAgr ELan EPfP MBlu MBri MGos NCGa NLar SPer
- 'Pollmix 3' (m) **new**	MCoo
- 'Romeo' (m)	CAgr
salicifolia	CAgr
- GWJ 9221	WCru
sinensis SDR 4940 **new**	GKev

Hippuris (*Hippuridaceae*)

vulgaris	CBen CWat EHon EMFW MSKA NPer WMAq

Histiopteris (*Dennstaedtiaceae*)

incisa	WRic

Hoheria ✿ (*Malvaceae*)

§ ***angustifolia***	ECou EPfP SSpi
'Borde Hill'	CMac CPMA ECou EPfP LRHS MAsh SPur SSpi WCFE WHCG WPat
'County Park'	ECou
glabrata	CBcs ECou EPfP GGal GGar GKir NBir NPal WPGP
- 'Silver Stars'	EPfP
'Glory of Amlwch' ♀H3	CAbb CDul CPMA CSam EBee ECou EPfP LRHS SSpi WKif WPGP WSpi
'Hill House'	CHll
'Holbrook'	CSam
§ ***lyallii*** ♀H4	CBcs CCCN CDoC CPLG ECou ELan EPfP IDee LRHS LSRN SPer SSpi WDin
- 'Chalk Hills'	ECou
- 'Swale Stream'	ECou
microphylla	see *H. angustifolia*
populnea	CBcs CCCN IDee SGar
- 'Alba Variegata' (v)	CDoC CTrC ECou
- 'Moonlight'	CDoC
- 'Purple Shadow'	ECou
- 'Sunshine' (v)	CDoC SSta
- 'Variegata'	ECou
'Purple Delta'	ECou
sexstylosa	CAbb CDoC CDul CHEx CHid CMHG CSpe CTho CTri EBee ECou ELan EPfP EWTr IMGH ISea LHop LRHS MGos NEgg SEND SPer SPur SSta SWvt
- 'Pendula'	CBcs WDin
- 'Stardust' ♀H4	Widely available

Holarrhena (*Apocynaceae*)

pubescens	CCCN

Holboellia (*Lardizabalaceae*)

angustifolia	MBri NLar WCru
- subsp. ***obtusa*** DJHC 506	WCru
chapaensis HWJ 1023	WCru
coriacea	CBcs CHll CSam EBee ELan EPfP IDee MGos MRav NLar SAPC SArc SSta WBor WCru
fargesii	WCru
grandiflora B&SWJ 8223	WCru
latifolia	CAlb CCCN CHEx CMac CRHN CSam CTrG CTri EBee ELan EPfP GGal LRHS NLar SAPC SArc SEND SLPl SLim SPer SPoG WCFE WCru WFar WPGP

- HWJK 2014 WCru
- HWJK 2213 WCru

Holcus (*Poaceae*)

lanatus EBWF WSFF
mollis 'Albovariegatus' (v) CBen CWCL EBee ECha EHoe ELan EPPr EPfP GMaP LBMP LRHS MBar MWhi NBid NBro NGdn NPer NSti SPlb SRms WEas WFar WMoo WPer WTin WWEG
- 'Jackdaw's Cream' (v) EPPr
- 'White Fog' (v) CChe EBee EHul EPPr MBlu MMuc NHol SApp SEND WFar

Holmskioldia (*Verbenaceae*)

* ***lutea*** new CCCN
sanguinea CCCN EShb

Holodiscus (*Rosaceae*)

discolor CBcs CDul EBee ELan EPfP EWes GQui IDee LRHS MBlu MBri MMuc MRav NBlu SCoo SLon SMad SPer SPlb SPoG SSpi WDin WHCG
- var. ***ariifolius*** EBee EPfP LRHS
dumosus EBee NLar WPGP

Homalocladium (*Polygonaceae*)

§ ***platycladum*** EShb

Homeria (*Iridaceae*)

breyniana see *H. collina*
- var. ***aurantiaca*** see *H. flaccida*
§ ***collina*** ECho ERos
§ ***flaccida*** EBrs ECho
ochroleuca EBrs ECho

Homoglossum see *Gladiolus*

Hordeum (*Poaceae*)

chilense EBee
jubatum CBod CHrt CKno CSpe CWCL CWib EAlp EHoe EWes GKev MSCN MWat MWhi NChi NGdn NHol SApp SEND SIng SPhx SPoG SUsu
- from Ussuri NGBl

Horkeliella (*Rosaceae*)

purpurascens NNS 98-323 WCot

Horminum (*Lamiaceae*)

pyrenaicum CPrp EBee ECho GAbr LBMP LRHS MMuc SRms WFar WMoo WOut WPer WPtf WTin
- SDR 5479 GKev
- dark-flowered new GCal
- pale blue-flowered MDKP

horseradish see *Armoracia rusticana*

Hosta ✿ (*Hostaceae*)

AGSJ 302 CDes
'A Many-Splendored Thing' EMic IBal
'Abba Dabba Do' (v) CBdn EGol EMic EPGN LBuc NBPC NEgg NHol NMyG SApp
'Abba Irresistible' (v) EMic
'Abba Showtime' EMic IBal
'Abby' (v) CBdn CBgR EGol EMic EPGN IBal NMyG SApp
'Abiqua Ariel' CBdn EMic SApp
'Abiqua Blue Crinkles' CBdn EMic IBal NBir SApp
'Abiqua Blue Edger' EMic
'Abiqua Blue Madonna' EMic
'Abiqua Blushing Recluse' EMic
'Abiqua Delight' (v) new IBal
'Abiqua Drinking Gourd' CBdn EBee EGol EMic EPGN GBin IBal MHom NMyG SApp WWEG
'Abiqua Ground Cover' EGol IBal
'Abiqua Moonbeam' (v) CBdn CFir EMic EPGN IBal MSwo NGdn NMyG SApp
'Abiqua Recluse' EGol EMic SApp
'Abiqua Trumpet' CBdn EGol EMic IBal NGdn NLar NMyG SApp
'Abiqua Zodiac' CBdn
'Academy Fire' (v) EMic
aequinoctiiantha EGol
'Afternoon Delight' (v) EMic
'Aksarben' EMic
'Alan Titchmarsh' new EPGN
albomarginata see *H. sieboldii* 'Paxton's Original'
§ 'Albomarginata' (*fortunei*) (v) CBcs CBdn CMac EBee EGol EMic EQua GKir MBar MNrw NBir SGSe SPoG SWvt WBrE WCAu
'Alex Summers' EBee EMic IBal NBhm WFar
alismifolia IBal
'Allan P. McConnell' (v) CBdn EGol EMic EPGN GCra IBal MHom NMyG SPoG WHal WWEG
'Allegan Emperor' (v) IBal
'Allegan Fog' (v) CBdn EBee EGol EMic IBal
'Alligator Shoes' (v) EGol EMic IBal
'Alpine Aire' EMic
'Alpine Dream' IBal
'Alternative' new IBal
'Alvatine Taylor' (v) EGol EMic LAst
'Amanuma' EGol EMic IBal MHom
'Amazing Grace' (v) new IBal
'Amber Maiden' (v) EGol
'Amber Tiara' EMic IBal
'American Dream' (v) CBdn EBee EGol EMic EPGN GSec IBal NMyG
'American Halo' EMic IBal LRHS NBPC NLar NMRc SPoG
'American Icon' EMic IBal
'American Sweetheart' IBal SApp
'Amy Elizabeth' (v) CBdn EGol EMic IBal NMyG
'Angel Feathers' (v) EGol
'Anglo Saxon' (v) new IBal
'Ann Kulpa' (v) CBdn EMic EPGN IBal NMyG
'Anne' (v) EGol EMic IBal LSRN NMyG
'Anne Arett' (*sieboldii*) (v) EPGN
'Ansly' (v) new IBal
'Antioch' (*fortunei*) (v) CBdn EGol EMic GQue IBal MRav NBPC NMyG WFar
'Aoba Tsugaru' new IBal
'Aoki' (*fortunei*) EMic EPGN NHol
'Aphrodite' (*plantaginea*) (d) EBee EGol EHrv EMic IBal LSou MBNS MCot MHom NCob NGdn NLar NMoo SApp SMrm SPoG WCot WGwG WWEG
'Apollo' NNor
'Apple Court' SApp
'Apple Green' EMic IBal
'Apple Pie' SApp
'Aqua Velva' EGol IBal
'Arc de Triomphe' EMic IBal SApp
'Archangel' EGol
'Argentea Variegata' (*undulata*) see *H. undulata* var. *undulata*
'Aristocrat' (Tardiana Group) (v) CBdn EGol EMic EPGN IBal LRHS NMyG SApp WFar
'Asian Beauty' EGol
'Aspen Gold' (*tokudama* hybrid) EMic SApp
'Athena' (v) IBal
'Atlantis' EMic IBal

	Name	Suppliers
	'August Beauty'	CBdn EMic IBal
	'August Moon'	Widely available
	aureafolia	see *H.* 'Starker Yellow Leaf'
	'Aureoalba' (*fortunei*)	see *H.* 'Spinners'
	'Aureomaculata' (*fortunei*)	see *H. fortunei* var. *albopicta*
	'Aureomarginata' ambig. (v)	CPrp GKir SCoo
	'Aureomarginata' (*montana*) (v)	CBdn CMac EGol EHoe ELan EMic EPGN GCal GMaP IBal NCGa NEgg NGdn NHol NLar NWsh SApp SGSe SMrm WFar WTin WWEG
	'Aureomarginata' (*rohdeifolia*) (v)	EMic
§	'Aureomarginata' (*ventricosa*) (v) ♀H4	CBdn CBro ECha EGol EMic EPfP IBal MWat NGdn NVic SApp WFar WTin
	'Aureostriata' (*tardiva*)	see *H.* 'Inaho'
	'Aurora Borealis' (*sieboldiana*) (v)	EGol
	'Austin Dickinson' (v)	EGol EMic IBal LBuc LRHS NEgg
	'Avalanche'	IBal
	'Avocado'	IBal
	'Awesome' (*venusta*)	EMic
	'Azure Mediterranean' **new**	IBal
	'Azure Snow'	EGol EMic
	'Babbling Brook'	EGol
	'Baby Blue' (Tardiana Group)	EMic
	'Baby Blue Eyes'	IBal
	'Baby Bunting'	CBdn EGol EMic EPGN IBal IFoB MBNS NBro NLar NPro
	'Ballerina'	EGol IBal
	'Banana Boat' (v)	EGol EMic IBal
	'Banana Muffins' **new**	IBal
	'Banana Sundae' (v) **new**	IBal
	'Band of Gold'	IBal
	'Banyai's Dancing Girl'	EGol EMic
	'Barbara Ann' (v)	CBdn EMic EPGN IBal MBri NMyG WWEG
	'Barbara May'	IBal
	'Barbara White'	EGol IBal
	'Baue's Boat'	EMic
	'Bea's Colossus'	SApp
	'Beauty Little Blue'	EGol
	'Beauty Substance'	CBdn EGol EMic EPGN NMyG
	'Beckoning'	IBal
	'Bedford Blue'	EMic IBal
	'Bell Bottom Blues'	IBal
	bella	see *H. fortunei* var. *obscura*
	'Bennie McRae'	EGol
	'Betcher's Blue'	EGol EMic
	'Betsy King'	CMac EBee EGol EMic MRav NHol NMyG
	'Bette Davis Eyes'	EGol
	'Betty'	EGol IBal
	'Bianca'	SApp
	'Biddy's Blue'	IBal
	'Big Boy' (*montana*)	EGol GSec NNor
	'Big Chance' **new**	IBal
	'Big Daddy' (*sieboldiana* hybrid) (v)	Widely available
	'Big Mama'	EGol EMic IBal MBNS NBhm NLar
	'Big Top' **new**	IBal
	'Bigfoot'	EGol EMic
	'Biggie'	IBal SApp
	'Bill Brinka' (v)	EGol EMic
	'Bill Dress's Blue'	EMic IBal
	'Bingo' (v)	EMic
	'Birchwood Blue'	EGol
	'Birchwood Blue Beauty'	IBal NMyG
	'Birchwood Elegance'	CBdn NMyG SApp
	'Birchwood Gem'	IBal
§	'Birchwood Parky's Gold'	CBdn CMHG CMoH EBee EGol EMic EPfP GMaP IBal LBMP LRHS MBNS NCob NGdn NHol SApp SPoG
	'Birchwood Ruffled Queen'	EGol EMic IBal
	'Bitsy Gold'	EGol EMic IBal
	'Bitsy Green'	EGol
	'Bizarre'	EMic IBal
	'Black Beauty'	EGol EMic IBal
	'Black Hills'	EGol EMic IBal MBNS NMyG
	'Black Pearl' **new**	IBal
	'Blackfoot'	EGol EMic
	'Blaue Venus'	EGol IBal
	'Blauspecht'	IBal
	'Blazing Saddles'	EMic IBal MBNS
	'Blonde Elf'	EGol EMic IBal NEgg NGdn NHol NMyG SApp WWEG
	'Blue Angel' misapplied	see *H. sieboldiana* var. *elegans*
	'Blue Angel' (*sieboldiana*) ♀H4	CBdn COIW ECtt EGol EHoe ELan EMic EPGN EPfP GBBs GBin GMaP IBal LEdu LRHS MHer MHom MSwo NBPC NBid NBir NEgg NGdn NMyG NOrc NPri WAul WFar WMnd
	'Blue Arrow'	CBdn EGol EPGN IBal LPla SApp
	'Blue Baron' **new**	IBal
	'Blue Beard'	IBal
	'Blue Belle' (Tardiana Group)	CBdn EGol EMic IBal NGdn NPro WHoo WTin
	'Blue Blazes'	EMic
	'Blue Blush' (Tardiana Group)	CBdn EGol EMic GSec IBal NGdn
	'Blue Boy'	CBdn EGol EMic EWes NHol NMyG
	'Blue Cadet'	CBcs CBdn EGol EMic GEdr IBal IFoB LPBA LRHS MBar MLHP NBir NGdn NLar NMyG SApp SBod SMrm SPoG WCAu WFar WMnd WWEG
	'Blue Canoe'	EMic IBal SApp
	'Blue Chip'	CBdn EMic EPGN IBal SApp
	'Blue Clown'	IBal
	'Blue Cup' (*sieboldiana*)	CBdn EMic MRav
	'Blue Danube' (Tardiana Group)	CBdn EGol EMic IBal MHom NMyG
	'Blue Diamond' (Tardiana Group)	CBdn EGol EMic EPGN IBal WFar WWEG
	'Blue Dimples' (Tardiana Group)	CBdn EGol EMic IBal NMoo
	'Blue Edger'	CBdn EMic NBir
	'Blue Eyes'	IBal
	'Blue Flame'	EMic IBal
	'Blue Haired Lady'	IBal
	'Blue Hawaii'	IBal
	'Blue Heart' (*sieboldiana*)	EMic IBal
	'Blue Ice' (Tardiana Group)	CBdn EGol EMic EPGN IBal
	'Blue Impression'	EMic
	'Blue Jay' (Tardiana Group)	CBdn EGol EMic IBal SApp
	'Blue Lady'	CBdn EMic IBal
	'Blue Mammoth' (*sieboldiana*)	CBdn EGol EMic IBal SApp
	'Blue Maui' **new**	IBal
	'Blue Monday'	EMic
	'Blue Moon' (Tardiana Group)	CBdn CMea EGol EMic EPfP IBal MHom NGdn NHol WAul
	'Blue Mountains'	IBal LBuc
	'Blue Mouse Ears'	CBdn EBee EGol EMic EPGN GBin GQue IBal MBNS MHom NGdn NMyG
	'Blue River' (v) **new**	EMic SApp
	'Blue Seer' (*sieboldiana*)	CBdn EGol EMic IBal
	'Blue Shadows' (*tokudama*) (v)	CBdn EMic ESwi IBal SApp WFar
	'Blue Skies' (Tardiana Group)	CBdn EGol EMic IBal MHom SApp

Name	Suppliers
'Blue Sophistication'	EMic
'Blue Splendor' (Tardiana Group) **new**	IBal
'Blue Umbrellas' (*sieboldiana* hybrid)	CBdn CMoH EGol ELan EMic EPGN EPfP IBal MHom NGdn NHol NLar NMyG SMrm
'Blue Veil'	EGol
'Blue Velvet'	CBdn
'Blue Vision'	EMic EPGN SApp
'Blue Wedgwood' (Tardiana Group)	CBdn CBro CPrp EBee EGol ELan EMic GKir IBal LPBA NGdn NHol NMyG SApp SPoG WHil WWEG
'Blueberry Tart'	IBal
'Blütenwunder'	SApp
'Bob Deane' (v)	EMic
'Bob Olson' (v)	EGol EMic IBal
'Bobbie Sue' (v)	EGol IBal
'Bodacious Blue'	IBal
'Bold Edger' (v)	CBdn EGol
'Bold Intrigue' (v) **new**	IBal
'Bold Ribbons' (v)	CBdn EGol EMic GAbr IBal WTin
'Bold Ruffles' (*sieboldiana*)	EGol SApp
'Bolt out of the Blue'	EMic IBal
'Bonanza'	EMic
'Border Bandit' (v)	EGol IBal
'Border Favorite' **new**	EMic
'Borsch 1'	CBdn
§ 'Borwick Beauty' (*sieboldiana*) (v)	CBdn EGol EMic IBal NBPC NGdn NLar NMyG SApp SPer WWEG
'Bountiful'	EGol EMic
'Bouquet'	EGol
'Brandywine' **new**	IBal
'Brash and Sassy'	IBal
'Brass Ring' (v) **new**	IBal
'Brave Amherst' (v)	EMic
'Bread Crumbs'	IBal
'Brenda's Beauty' (v)	EGol EMic IBal
'Bressingham Blue'	CBdn CPrp EBee EBrs ECtt EGol EMic GQue IBal LRHS MRav NMyG SWvt WFar WMnd
'Bridal Veil'	IBal
'Bridegroom'	EGol EMic
'Bridgeville'	IBal
'Brigadier'	EGol
'Bright Glow' (Tardiana Group)	EGol EMic
'Bright Lights' (*tokudama*) (v)	CBdn EGol EMic EPGN GBBs GSec IBal NGdn NMyG WFar
'Brim Cup' (v)	CBdn EBee EGol ELon EMic EPGN IBal LAst MBNS MBri NBro NGdn NMyG NOrc SApp SBch SMrm SPer SPoG WWEG
'Brooke'	EGol EMic IBal NMyG WWEG
'Brother Ronald' (Tardiana Group)	CBdn EGol EMic IBal SApp
'Brother Stefan'	IBal SApp
'Bruce's Blue'	EGol EMic
'Bubba'	IBal
'Buckshaw Blue'	CBdn EGol EMic EPGN GSec IBal MDKP NBir NGdn NPro
'Buckwheat Honey' **new**	IBal
'Bunchoko'	IBal
'Burke's Dwarf'	IBal
'Butter Rim' (*sieboldii*) (v)	EGol
'Cadillac' (v)	CBdn EMic
'Caliban'	SApp
'Cally Atom' **new**	GCal
'Calypso' (v)	CBdn EGol EMic EPGN IBal LBuc WWEG
'Camelot' (Tardiana Group)	CBdn EGol EMic IBal LRHS NGdn
'Cameo'	EGol EMic IBal SApp
'Camouflage'	IBal
'Canadian Blue'	EMic
'Candy Hearts'	CBdn CMHG CSam EGol EMic EPGN MHom MWat WTin
capitata	EMic
- B&SWJ 588	WCru
'Captain Kirk' (v)	CBdn EBee EMic IBal NMyG
caput-avis	see *H. kikutii* var. *caput-avis*
'Carder Blue'	EMic
'Carnival' (v)	CBdn EGol EMic EPGN IBal NBPC NCGa NEgg SApp
'Carol' (*fortunei*) (v)	CBdn EGol EMic IBal NEgg NMyG NNor NWsh SApp WHal
'Carolina Blue'	IBal
'Carolina Sunshine' (v)	EMic
'Carousel' (v)	EGol EMic
'Carrie' (*sieboldii*) (v)	EGol SApp
'Cascade Mist' (v)	EMic
'Cascades' (v)	CBdn EGol EMic EPGN IBal
'Catherine'	IBal
'Cat's Eyes' (*venusta*) (v)	CBdn EGol EMic EPGN IBal SApp
'Cavalcade' (v)	EMic
'Celebration' (v)	EGol ELan EMic EPGN LRHS MDKP WHal WWEG
'Celestial'	IBal
'Center of Attention'	EBee EMic IBal NMyG SApp
'Cha Cha Cha' **new**	IBal
'Challenger'	EMic
'Change of Tradition' (*lancifolia*) (v)	CBdn EMic
'Chantilly Lace' (v)	CBdn EGol EMic IBal NMyG SApp WTin
'Chariots of Fire' (v) **new**	IBal
'Chartreuse Waves'	EGol
'Chartreuse Wiggles' (*sieboldii*)	IBal
'Cheatin' Heart'	EGol EMic IBal WWEG
'Chelsea Babe' (*fortunei*) (v)	EGol IBal
'Cherish'	EGol EMic EPGN IBal
'Cherry Berry' (v)	CBdn CMHG EGol EMic EPGN IBal LRHS MBNS NBro NCob NEgg NGdn NLar NMyG NPro SApp SBch SMrm SPoG WAul WBor WFar WWEG
'Cherub' (v)	CBdn EGol IBal
'Chesapeake Bay' **new**	EMic IBal
* 'China' (*plantaginea*)	EMic
'Chinese Sunrise' (v)	CBdn CWCL EGol EMic EPGN IBal LBuc MHom NMyG WHal
'Chiquita'	EGol
'Chodai Ginba'	IBal
§ 'Chōkō Nishiki' (*montana*) (v)	CBdn EGol EMic EPGN EQua IBal LRHS NGdn NMyG NNor SApp SBch SMad SPoG
'Choo Choo Train'	EGol EMic SApp
'Chopsticks' **new**	IBal
'Christmas Candy'[PBR]	EMic EPGN IBal NBhm NCob
'Christmas Cookies'	IBal
'Christmas Lights' (v) **new**	IBal
'Christmas Pageant' (v)	EMic IBal
'Christmas Tree' (v)	CBdn CMMP EGol EMic EPGN IBal IFoB IPot LRHS NBPC NEgg NGdn NMyG SApp WMoo WWEG
'Cinderella'	IBal
'Cinnamon Sticks'	IBal
'Citation' (v)	EGol
'City Lights'	EGol EMic NEgg
'City Slicker' (v) **new**	IBal
clausa var. ***normalis***	CBdn CMoH EGol GQui NBir NGdn NLar NMyG
'Clear Fork River Valley' **new**	IBal
'Cleopatra' (v) **new**	IBal

Name	Suppliers
'Clifford's Forest Fire'	EBee EMic EPGN IBal NMyG SPoG WFar
'Clifford's Stingray'	EMic IBal
'Climax' (v)	EMic IBal
'Cloudburst' **new**	IBal
'Cody'	EMic IBal
'Collector's Banner'	EGol
'Collector's Choice'	EGol IBal
'Color Glory'	see *H.* 'Borwick Beauty'
'Colossal'	EGol EMic
'Columbus Circle' (v)	CBdn EGol EMic
'Cookie Crumbs' (v)	CBdn EGol EMic EPGN IBal SApp
'Cool Hand Luke' (*tokudama*) (v)	EMic
'Coquette' (v)	CBdn EGol EMic NMyG
'Corkscrew'	EMic IBal SApp
'Corona' (v)	EMic
'Corryvreckan'	EMic
'Cotillion' (v)	CBdn EGol EMic SApp
'Counter Point' (v)	EMic
'Country Mouse' (v) **new**	IBal
'County Park'	CBdn EGol EMic IBal
'Cracker Crumbs' (v)	CBdn EGol EMic EPGN IBal MHom SApp
'Craig's Temptation'	CBdn NMyG
'Crater's Heart' (*venusta*) (v) **new**	IBal
'Cream Cheese' (v)	EGol IBal
'Cream Delight' (*undulata*)	see *H. undulata* var. *undulata*
'Cream Edge'	see *H.* 'Fisher Cream Edge'
'Crepe Soul' (v)	EGol IBal
'Crepe Suzette' (v)	CBdn EGol EPGN
'Crested Reef'	CBdn CMoH EGol EMic NMyG
'Crested Surf' (v)	EGol EMic EPGN IBal
'Crinoline Petticoats'	EGol
§ ***crispula*** (v) ♀H4	CBdn CBot EGol EMic EPfP MBar MCot MHom MRav NChi NCob NMyG
'Crown Jewel' (v)	EPGN IBal
'Crown Prince' (v)	CBdn EGol EMic IBal
§ 'Crowned Imperial' (*fortunei*) (v)	CBdn CWat EMic NHol
'Crumples' (*sieboldiana*)	EGol EMic
'Crusader' (v)	CBdn EGol EMic EPGN IBal LRHS NMyG SApp WFar WWEG
'Crystal Charm'	IBal
'Crystal Chimes'	IBal
'Cupboard Love'	SApp
'Cupid's Dart' (v)	EGol
'Curlew' (Tardiana Group)	CBdn EGol EMic IBal
'Curtain Call' **new**	IBal
'Cutting Edge'	IBal
'Dab a Green' **new**	IBal
'Daisy Doolittle' (v) **new**	IBal SApp
'Dance with Me'	EMic IBal
'Dancing in the Rain' (v)	EBee EMic MAvo MBNS NBro SApp SMrm WFar
'Dark Shadows'	IBal
'Dark Star' (v)	CBdn EGol EMic EPGN IBal SApp
'Dark Victory'	IBal
'Dartmoor Forest'	CBdn
'Darwin's Standard' (v)	CBdn
'Dawn'	CBdn EGol EMic GSec IBal NMyG
'Daybreak'	CBdn EGol EMic EPGN IBal LAst LRHS MBri NBro SApp
'Day's End' (v)	EGol EMic IBal
'Deane's Dream'	EMic IBal
decorata	CBdn EGol EMic MBar
'Deep Blue Sea'	CBdn EMic IBal SApp
'Deep Pockets'	IBal
'Déjà Blu' (v)	CBdn
'Delia' (v)	EPGN
'Delta Dawn'	EMic IBal LRHS
'Delta Desire'	IBal
'Deluxe Edition'	IBal
'Designer Genes'	IBal SApp
'Devon Blue' (Tardiana Group)	CBdn CBgR EGol EMic NMyG
'Devon Desire' (*montana*)	CBdn EMic
'Devon Discovery'	CBdn
'Devon Giant'	CBdn EMic SApp
'Devon Gold'	CBdn EMic
'Devon Green'	CBdn ELan EMic EPGN IBal IPot LRHS MBel MHom NBro NCGa NCob NEgg NGdn NLar NMyG NNor NPro SApp SBch SPoG WAul WFar WHal WWEG
'Devon Hills'	CBdn
'Devon Mist'	CBdn
'Devon Tor'	CBdn EMic
'Dew Drop' (v)	CBdn EGol EMic IBal NMyG SGSe WWEG
'Diamond Tiara' (v)	CBdn EGol EMic EPGN IBal LRHS NBir NGdn NMyG WWEG
'Diana Remembered'	EGol EMic EPGN GKir IBal LRHS MBNS WBor
'Dick Ward'	EMic IBal
'Dillie Perkeo'	IBal
'Dilys' **new**	EMic
'Dimple'	EMic
'Dinky Donna'	IBal
'Diva'	EMic
'Dixie Chick' (v)	EGol EMic IBal
'Dixieland Heat'	IBal
'Doctor Fu Manchu'	IBal
'Domaine de Courson'	EMic EPGN IBal WFar
'Don Stevens' (v)	EGol
'Donahue Piecrust'	CBdn EGol EMic GSec
'Dorothy'	EMic IBal
'Dorset Blue' (Tardiana Group)	CBdn EGol EMic EPGN IBal NMyG SApp SBch
'Dorset Charm' (Tardiana Group)	CBdn EGol EMic
'Dorset Flair' (Tardiana Group)	EGol EMic IBal
'Doubloons'	EGol EMic
'Dragon Tails'	EMic IBal LRHS
'Dragon Wings'	EMic IBal
'Drawn Butter'	EMic
'Dream Queen' (v)	EMic IBal
'Dream Weaver' (v)	EBee EGol EMic IBal LRHS MNrw NBro NGdn NMyG SApp SPer SPoG WFar
'Dress Blues'	CBdn CMac EBee EMic IBal
'Drummer Boy'	CBdn EGol EMic WWEG
'Duchess' (*nakaiana*) (v)	EMic IBal
'DuPage Delight' (*sieboldiana*) (v)	CBdn EGol EMic IBal NGdn NLar
'Dust Devil' (*fortunei*) (v)	EGol IBal
'Dustin' (v)	EMic
'Dylan's Dillie' (v)	EMic IBal
'Eagle's Nest' (v) **new**	IBal
'Earth Angel' (v)	CBdn EGol EMic IBal NGdn NMyG
'Ebb Tide' (*montana*) (v)	EMic IBal
'Edge of Night'	CBdn EGol EMic
'Edwin Bibby'	EMic
'El Capitan' (v)	CBdn EGol EMic EPGN IBal
'El Niño' PBR (Tardiana Group) (v)	CBdn CWGN EGol EMic IBal MHom MNrw NBro NGdn NMyG SApp WFar
§ 'Elata'	EBee EGol EMic SApp
'Elatior' (*nigrescens*)	CBdn EMic IBal LRHS
'Eldorado'	see *H.* 'Frances Williams'
'Eleanor Lachman' (v)	EGol EMic IBal

	Name	Suppliers
	'Eleanor Roosevelt'	IBal
	'Electrum Stater' (v)	CBdn EMic
	'Elegans'	see *H. sieboldiana* var. *elegans*
	'Elfin Power' (*sieboldii*) (v)	EGol
	'Elisabeth'	CBdn EMic GBin IBal LSRN NMyG
	'Elizabeth Campbell' (*fortunei*) (v)	CBdn EGol EMic IBal
	'Elkheart Lake' **new**	EMic
	'Ellen'	EMic
	'Ellerbroek' (*fortunei*) (v)	EGol EMic IBal
	'Ellie Bee' **new**	IBal
	'Elsley Runner'	EGol IBal
	'Elvis Lives'	CBdn EDAr EGol EMic EPGN GBin IBal LAst NEgg NGdn NLar NMyG NNor NPro
	'Embroidery' (v)	EMic
	'Emerald Carpet'	EGol IBal
	'Emerald Necklace' (v)	EGol
	'Emerald Ruff Cut'	IBal SApp
	'Emerald Skies'	EGol
	'Emerald Tiara' (v)	CBdn EBee EGol EMic EPGN GSec LRHS MLHP NMyG SApp SBch WTin WWEG
	'Emeralds and Rubies'	EGol EMic IBal
	'Emily Dickinson' (v)	CBdn EBee EGol EMic IBal LRHS MMuc SApp SPad WWEG
	'Encore' **new**	IBal
	'English Sunrise' (Tardiana Group) **new**	IBal
	'Enterprise'	EMic IBal SApp
	'Eric Smith' (Tardiana Group)	CBdn EGol EMic EPGN IBal MHom NMyG WFar
	'Eric's Gold'	EPGN IBal
	'Erie Magic' (v)	EGol IBal
	'Eskimo Pie' (v)	CBdn EBee EMic IBal WFar
	'Essence of Summer'	EMic EPfP IBal SApp
	'Eternal Flame'	EMic IBal
	'Eternity'	GSec
	'Evelyn McCafferty' (*tokudama* hybrid)	EGol
	'Evening Magic' (v)	EGol EMic
	'Eventide' (v)	EGol
	'Everlasting Love' (v)	EGol
	'Excitation'	CBdn EGol EMic
	'Eye Candy' (v) **new**	IBal
	'Eye Catcher'	EMic
	'Eye Declare' (v) **new**	IBal
	'Fair Maiden' (v)	EMic IBal
	'Faithful Heart' (v)	EMic IBal
	'Fall Bouquet' (*longipes* var. *hypoglauca*)	EGol
	'Fall Emerald'	EMic
	'Fallen Angel'	IBal
	'Falling Waters' (v)	EGol IBal
	'Fan Dance' (v)	EGol EMic IBal
	'Fantabulous' (v)	EMic EPGN IBal
	'Fantastic' (*sieboldiana* hybrid)	EGol
	'Fantasy Island' (v)	EMic IBal
	'Fatal Attraction'	EMic IBal
	'Feather Boa'	EGol EMic IBal NMyG WWEG
	'Fenman's Fascination'	EMic
	'Fiesta' (v)	IBal
	'Fire and Brimstone' (*sieboldiana*) (v) **new**	IBal
	'Fire and Ice' (v)	Widely available
	'Fire Island'	CBdn EGol EMic EPGN GBin IBal SApp
	'Fireworks' (v)	CBdn EBee EGol EMic EPGN GBin IBal MBNS NBro NGdn NMyG SMrm
	'First Frost' (v)	CBdn EMic IBal LRHS NGdn NMyG
	'First Mate' (v)	CBdn EMic IBal
§	'Fisher Cream Edge' (*fortunei*) (v)	EMic
	'Five O'Clock Shadow' (v)	EMic IBal
	'Five O'Clock Somewhere' (v)	IBal
	'Flame Stitch' (*ventricosa*) (v)	EGol EMic IBal
	'Flemish Sky'	EMic IBal NGdn
	'Floradora'	EGol EMic IBal NMyG
	'Flower Power'	EGol GSec
	'Fool's Gold' (*fortunei*)	EMic IBal
	'Forest Shadows'	EMic IBal
	'Formal Attire' (*sieboldiana* hybrid) (v)	CBdn EGol EMic IBal LRHS
	'Forncett Frances' (v)	EGol EMic IBal
	'Fort Knox'	EMic
	'Fortis'	see *H. undulata* var. *erromena*
	fortunei	CBdn CMMP EGol EMic NHol NNor WEas WFar
§	- var. ***albopicta*** (v) ♀H4	Widely available
	- - f. ***aurea*** ♀H4	CBdn CMHG CMac ECha EGol EHoe ELan EMic EPla LRHS MBar MRav NEgg NLar NMyG SRms WFar WHal
	- - - dwarf	EMic
§	- var. ***aureomarginata*** ♀H4	Widely available
	- var. ***gigantea***	see *H. montana*
	- var. ***hyacinthina*** ♀H4	CBdn EGol EMic EPfP IBal LRHS MBar MRav NGdn SApp WCAu WPtf
	- - variegated (v)	see *H.* 'Crowned Imperial'
§	- var. ***obscura***	CBdn EGol EMic IBal LRHS
	- var. ***rugosa***	EMic IBal
	'Foundling'	EMic
	'Fountain of Youth' (*kikutii*) **new**	IBal
	'Fourth of July'	EGol
	'Fragrant Blue'	CBdn EBee EGol EMic GBBs IBal LRHS NBro NGdn NMyG SApp SCoo SPoG
	'Fragrant Bouquet' (v)	CBdn CMHG EGol ELan EMic EPGN GAbr IBal LAst LRHS LSRN NCGa NGdn NHol NLar NMyG WPtf WWEG
	'Fragrant Dream'	CBdn EGol EMic EPfP IBal NLar
	'Fragrant Fire'	EMic IBal SApp
	'Fragrant Gold'	EGol EMic IBal
	'Fragrant King'	IBal
	'Fragrant Star'	EMic IBal SApp
	'Fragrant Surprise' (v)	IBal
	'Fran Godfrey'	EPGN IBal
	'Francee' (*fortunei*) (v) ♀H4	Widely available
§	'Frances Williams' (*sieboldiana*) (v) ♀H4	Widely available
	'Frances Williams Improved' (*sieboldiana*) (v)	EGol EPfP LAst MWat
	'Freising' (*fortunei*)	EBee
	'Fresh' (v)	EGol EMic EPGN IBal SApp
	'Friar Tuck'	EMic
	'Fried Bananas'	CBdn EBee EGol EMic EWll SApp SPoG WWEG
	'Fried Green Tomatoes'	CBdn EGol EMic GBin NLar NMyG SApp
	'Fringe Benefit' (v)	EGol EMic GAbr SApp WWEG
	'Frosted Dimples'	EMic IBal
	'Frosted Jade' (v)	CBdn EBee EGol EMic EPGN IBal NLar SApp SBch SMrm SRGP WTin
	'Frozen Margarita'	IBal
	'Frühlingsgold' (v)	IBal
	'Fujibotan' (v)	EGol EMic IBal SApp

'Fulda'	EGol EMic
'Gaiety' (v)	EGol EMic EPGN
'Gaijin' (v)	CBdn EGol EMic IBal SApp
'Gala' (*tardiflora*) (v)	CBdn
'Galaxy'	IBal
'Garden Party' (v)	IBal
'Garden Treasure'	EGol EMic
'Garnet Prince'	EGol IBal
'Gay Blade' (v)	EGol SApp
'Gay Feather' (v)	EMic IBal NMyG SApp
'Gay Search' (v)	EPGN IBal
'Geisha' (v)	CBdn EGol EPGN IBal MCCP NGdn NMyG NPro SApp WHal WWEG
'Geisha Satin Ripples' **new**	IBal
'Gemini Moon' (v)	IBal
'Gemstone' **new**	IBal
'Gene's Joy'	EMic EPGN IBal
'Ghost Spirit'	EBee IBal WFar
'Ghostmaster' (v) **new**	IBal
'Gigantea' (*sieboldiana*)	see *H.* 'Elata'
'Gilt by Association'	IBal
'Gilt Edge' (*sieboldiana*) (v)	CWat EMic NMyG WWEG
'Gin and Tonic' (v)	EMic
'Gingee'	IBal
'Ginko Craig' (v)	Widely available
'Ginrei' **new**	IBal
'Ginsu Knife' (v)	IBal
'Glass Hearts'	EMic IBal
glauca	see *H. sieboldiana* var. *elegans*
'Glitter'	EMic IBal
'Glockenspiel'	CBdn EGol
I 'Gloriosa' (*fortunei*) (v)	EGol EMic IBal LRHS WFar
'Glory'	CBdn EGol
'Goddess of Athena' (*decorata*) (v)	EGol
'Gold Drop' (*venusta* hybrid)	CBdn EGol EMic IBal NHol
'Gold Edger'	CBcs CBdn CBro CMac CPrp EGol EHoe ELan EMic EPfP ERos GEdr GMaP LRHS MRav NBir NGdn NHol NMyG NNor NSti SApp WFar WTin WWEG
'Gold Edger Surprise' (v)	EMic
'Gold Flush' (*ventricosa*)	EMic
§ 'Gold Haze' (*fortunei*)	CBdn EGol EMic EPGN IBal MHom NBir NCGa NHol NMyG WWEG
'Gold Leaf' (*fortunei*)	EGol
'Gold Regal'	CBdn EBee EGol EMic EPGN LRHS MHom NMyG WFar WMnd
'Gold Rush'	CBdn EMic GSec NMyG
'Gold Standard' (*fortunei*) (v)	Widely available
'Goldbrook' (v)	EGol EMic IBal WTin
'Goldbrook Galleon'	EGol IBal
'Goldbrook Gayle' (v)	EGol
'Goldbrook Gaynor'	EGol IBal
'Goldbrook Genie'	EGol IBal
'Goldbrook Ghost' (v)	EGol
'Goldbrook Girl'	EGol IBal
'Goldbrook Glamour' (v)	EGol IBal
'Goldbrook Glimmer' (Tardiana Group) (v)	EGol IBal
'Goldbrook Gold'	EGol IBal
'Goldbrook Grace'	EGol IBal
'Goldbrook Gratis' (v)	EGol IBal
'Goldbrook Grayling'	EGol IBal
'Goldbrook Grebe'	EGol IBal
'Goldbrook Greenheart'	IBal
'Golden Age'	see *H.* 'Gold Haze'
'Golden Anniversary'	CBdn EGol IBal NHol
'Golden Bullion' (*tokudama*)	CBdn EGol
'Golden Fascination'	EGol
'Golden Fountain'	EMic
'Golden Friendship'	EGol
'Golden Gate'	EGol EMic
'Golden Guernsey' (v)	EMic
'Golden Isle'	EGol EMic IBal
'Golden Meadows'^{PBR} (*sieboldiana*)	EMic EPGN IBal MAvo NCob SMrm
'Golden Medallion' (*tokudama*)	CBdn CMHG EGol ELan EMic IBal NEgg NGdn NHol NMyG WFar
'Golden Nakaiana'	see *H.* 'Birchwood Parky's Gold'
'Golden' (*nakaiana*)	see *H.* 'Birchwood Parky's Gold'
'Golden Oriole'	CBdn EGol EMic IBal NMyG WWEG
'Golden Prayers' (*tokudama*)	CBdn CMea ECtt EGol EHoe ELan EMic EPGN ERos IBal MRav NBir NBro NEgg NGdn NHol NLar NOrc WHal WFar WSHC
'Golden Scepter'	CBdn EGol EMic EPGN GSec IBal LRHS NHol NMyG SApp WFar
'Golden Sculpture' (*sieboldiana*)	CBdn EGol
'Golden Spades'	EMic
'Golden Spider'	EGol EMic WWEG
'Golden Sunburst' (*sieboldiana*)	CBdn CPrp EGol ELan EMic IBal NEgg NGdn NHol WFar
'Golden Tiara' (v) Υ^{H4}	Widely available
'Golden Waffles'	CMHG EMic NEgg
'Golden Years'	EMic
'Goldpfeil'	EMic
'Goldsmith'	EGol SApp
'Gone Fishin'' (v)	IBal
'Goober'	IBal
'Good as Gold'	EMic EPGN IBal NMyG
'Gorgeous George'	IBal
'Gorgon'	IBal
'Gosan Gold Midget'	EMic
'Gosan Gold Mist'	EMic
'Gosan Hildegarde'	EMic GSec
'Gosan Leather Strap'	EMic IBal
'Gosan Mina'	EMic
'Gosan' (*takahashii*)	EGol
gracillima	EMic EPGN IBal NRya
'Granary Gold' (*fortunei*)	CBdn EGol EPGN GSec
'Grand Canyon' **new**	EMic SApp
'Grand Finale'	IBal
'Grand Forks' **new**	IBal
'Grand Marquee' (v)	EMic GBin IBal SApp WFar
'Grand Master'	EGol EMic IBal MDKP SApp
'Grand Prize' (v)	EMic IBal
'Grand Slam'	EGol
'Grand Tiara' (v)	CBdn EGol EMic EPGN GSec IBal NMyG SApp
'Grand Total' **new**	IBal
'Grant Park' **new**	IBal
'Gray Cole' (*sieboldiana*)	CBdn EGol EMic IBal NMyG
'Great Arrival'	IBal
'Great Escape' (v) **new**	EMic IBal
'Great Expectations' (*sieboldiana*) (v)	Widely available
'Great Lakes Gold'	IBal
'Green Acres' (*montana*)	EMic IBal LEdu SMeo WFar
'Green Angel' (*sieboldiana*)	EGol
'Green Dwarf'	NWCA WFar
'Green Eyes' (*sieboldii*) (v)	EGol EMic IBal
'Green Fountain' (*kikutii*)	CBdn EGol EMic NMyG WWEG
'Green Gold' (*fortunei*) (v)	CBdn EMic
'Green Lama'	IBal
'Green Mouse Ears'	EMic IBal
'Green Piecrust'	CBdn EGol EMic
'Green Sheen'	EGol EMic EPGN NMyG
'Green Summer Fragrance'	CBdn
'Green Velveteen'	CBdn EGol
'Green with Envy' (v)	CBdn EGol EMic IBal SApp
'Greenwood'	EMic

'Grey Ghost'	EMic IBal
'Grey Piecrust'	EGol IBal
'Ground Cover Trompenburg'	SApp
'Ground Master' (v)	CBdn CMHG CMac EBee ECtt EGol ELan EPfP GCra GMaP IBal IFoB LPBA MRav MSwo NBro NGdn NHol NMyG NSti SPer WFar WMoo WWEG
'Ground Sulphur'	EGol EMic
'Grünherz'	IBal
'Grunspecht' (Tardiana Group) **new**	IBal
'Guacamole' (v)	CBcs CBdn CBgR ECha EGol EMic EPGN EPfP GBin IBal IPot LRHS NGdn NLar NMyG SApp WAul WTin WWEG
'Guardian Angel' (*sieboldiana*)	CBdn EGol EMic EPGN IBal
'Gum Drop'	CBdn EMic
'Gun Metal Blue'	EGol IBal
'Gypsy Rose'	EBee EMic EPGN EPfP NMyG WFar
'Hadspen Blue' (Tardiana Group)	Widely available
'Hadspen Hawk' (Tardiana Group)	EGol IBal NMyG SApp
'Hadspen Heron' (Tardiana Group)	CBdn EGol EMic IBal MHom MWat NMyG
'Hadspen Nymphaea'	EGol IBal
'Hadspen Rainbow'	CBdn IBal
'Hadspen Samphire'	EGol EMic EPGN MHom NBir NMyG
'Hadspen White' (*fortunei*)	EMic IBal
'Haku-chu-han' (*sieboldii*) (v)	CBdn EMic IBal
'Hakujima' (*sieboldii*)	EGol IBal
§ 'Halcyon' (Tardiana Group) ♀H4	Widely available
'Halo'	EGol
'Hampshire County' (v)	EMic IBal
'Hanky Panky' (v)	EBee IBal
'Happiness' (Tardiana Group)	CBdn EGol EHoe EMic MHom MRav NMyG
'Happy Camper' (v)	IBal
'Happy Hearts'	EGol EMic
'Happy Valley' (v)	IBal
'Harlequin'	SApp
'Harmony' (Tardiana Group)	CBdn EGol EMic
'Harpoon' (v) **new**	IBal
'Harriette Ward' **new**	IBal
'Harrison'	EMic
'Harry van de Laar'	CBdn EMic IBal SApp
'Harry van Trier'	EMic GBin
'Hart's Tongue'	IBal
'Harvest Dawn' **new**	IBal
'Harvest Glow'	EGol
'Harvest Moon'	EMic GKir
'Hawkeye' (v) **new**	IBal
'Hazel'	EMic IBal
'Heart Ache'	EGol
'Heart and Soul' (v)	EGol IBal SApp
'Heart Broken'	IBal
'Heart of Chan' **new**	IBal
'Heartbeat' (v) **new**	IBal
'Heartleaf'	EMic
'Heart's Content' (v)	CBdn EGol
'Heartsong' (v)	EGol EMic NMyG
'Heat Wave' (v)	CBdn EMic EPGN IBal SApp
'Heavenly Beginnings' (v)	IBal
'Heavenly Tiara' (v) **new**	IBal
'Heideturm'	EBee EGol
'Helen Doriot' (*sieboldiana*)	EGol EMic
'Helen Field Fischer' (*fortunei*)	EMic IBal
helonioides misapplied f. ***albopicta***	see *H. rohdeifolia*
'Herifu' (v)	CBdn EBee EGol EMic
'Herkules'	EMic IBal
'Hertha' (v)	EMic
'Hidden Cove' (v)	EGol EMic IBal
'High Kicker'	EGol IBal NMyG
'High Noon'	EMic
'High Society'	CBcs CBdn EMic EPfP GBin IBal MHom MNrw NGdn NMyG SApp
'High Tide' **new**	IBal
'Hi-ho Silver' (v)	EMic EPGN IBal
'Hilda Wassman' (v)	EGol EMic
'Hillbilly Blues' (v)	EMic IBal
'Hippodrome' (v)	IBal
'Hirao Elite'	IBal
'Hirao Grande'	GSec
'Hirao Majesty'	CBdn EGol
'Hirao Splendor'	EGol NMyG
'Hirao Supreme'	CBdn EGol
'Hirao Tetra'	CBdn
'His Honor' (v)	EMic IBal
'Hoarfrost'	EMic
'Holly's Honey'	EGol EMic
'Hollywood Lights' (v) **new**	EMic IBal
'Holstein'	see *H.* 'Halcyon'
'Holy Molé' (v)	IBal
'Honey Moon'	CBdn EGol
'Honeybells' ♀H4	Widely available
'Honeysong' (v)	EGol EMic EPGN NMyG
'Hoosier Dome' **new**	EMic
'Hoosier Harmony' (v)	EGol EMic
'Hoosier Homecoming'	SApp
'Hope' (v)	EGol EMic IBal SApp
'Hotspur' (v)	EGol EMic IBal SApp
'Hush Puppie'	IBal
'Hyacintha Variegata' (*fortunei*) (v)	CMHG CMac NNor
'Hydon Gleam'	EGol EMic IBal
'Hydon Sunset' (*nakaiana*)	CBdn CMHG CMMP CMea ECtt EGol EMic EPGN GCra GKir IBal NBir NHol NMyG NRya NSti NWCA SApp SGSe WHal WMnd WPtf WTin WWEG
hypoleuca	EGol EMic
'Hyuga Urajiro' (v)	EMic IBal SApp
'Ice Age Trail' (v)	IBal
'Ice Cream' (*cathayana*) (v)	EGol EMic
'Iced Lemon' (v)	CBdn EMic IBal
'Illicit Affair'	EGol EMic IBal SApp
'Ilona' (v)	EGol
'Imp' (v) **new**	EMic IBal
§ 'Inaho'	CBdn EGol EPGN LRHS
'Inca Gold'	EGol EMic IBal
'Independence' (v)	EBee EMic EPGN IBal NBro NMyG WFar
'Indigo' **new**	IBal
'Innisjade' **new**	IBal
'Inniswood' (v)	CBdn CWCL EGol EMic EPGN EPfP IBal IPot MBNS MBri NBro NGdn NLar NSti SApp SPoG WFar WMnd WWEG
'Invincible'	CBdn CBgR EGol EMic EPGN IBal LAst NBid NEgg NGdn NLar NMyG NNor SApp SPoG WPtf WTin WWEG
'Iona' (*fortunei*)	CBdn EGol EMic EPGN NMyG
'Irische See' (Tardiana Group)	EGol
'Irish Eyes' (v)	IBal
'Iron Gate Delight' (v)	CBdn

	Name	Suppliers
	'Iron Gate Glamour' (v)	EGol IBal
	'Iron Gate Special' (v)	EMic
	'Iron Gate Supreme' (v)	EMic
	'Island Charm' (v)	CBdn EGol EMic EPGN IBal MBNS NBhm NLar SApp
	'Island Forest Gem'	IBal
	'Iszat U Doc'	GSec
	'Itsy Bitsy Spider' **new**	IBal
	'Ivory Coast' (v) **new**	EPGN NMyG
	'Ivory Necklace' (v)	EMic IBal
	'Iwa Soules'	EGol EMic
	'Jack of Diamonds'	EMic IBal
	'Jade Beauty'	CBdn
	'Jade Cascade'	CBdn EGol ELan EMic NBir NEgg NHol NLar SApp WWEG
	'Jade Scepter' (*nakaiana*)	EGol EMic GSec
	'Jadette' (v)	EGol GBin
	'Janet Day' (v)	EMic SApp
	'Janet' (*fortunei*) (v)	EBee EGol EMic GMaP NGdn
	'Janet's Green Sox'	IBal
	'Japan Girl'	see *H.* 'Mount Royal'
	'Jaz' **new**	IBal
	'Jerry Landwehr' **new**	IBal
	'Jester'	SApp
	'Jewel of the Nile' (v)	EMic IBal
	'Jim Mathews'	IBal
	'Jimmy Crack Corn'	CBdn EGol EMic IBal LRHS
	'Jingle Bells' **new**	IBal
	'John Wargo'	EGol
	'Jolly Green Giant' (*sieboldiana* hybrid)	EMic
	'Joseph'	EGol EMic IBal
	'Josephine' (v)	NNor
	'Journeyman'	EBrs EGol EMic IBal LRHS
	'Journey's End' (v)	EMic IBal SApp
	'Joyce Trott' (v)	EMic IBal
	'Joyful' (v)	IBal
	'Judy Rocco'	IBal
	'Juha' (v) **new**	EMic
	'Julia' (v)	EGol EMic IBal
	'Julie Morss'	CBdn EGol EMic EPGN GMaP IBal MHom MWat NEgg NMyG SApp WWEG
	'Jumbo' (*sieboldiana*)	EMic
	'June' PBR (Tardiana Group) (v) ♀H4	Widely available
	'June Beauty' (*sieboldiana*)	MGos NWsh
	'June Fever' PBR (Tardiana Group)	EMic ESwi GBin GKir IBal NBhm NBro NLar NMoo SApp SPoG
	'June Moon' (v)	EMic
	'Jurassic Park' **new**	IBal
	'Just So' (v)	CBdn EGol EMic IBal
	'Kabitan'	see *H. sieboldii* var. *sieboldii* f. *kabitan*
	'Kabuki'	IBal
	'Kalamazoo' (v) **new**	EMic
	'Karin'	EGol EMic
	'Katherine Lewis' (Tardiana Group) (v)	CBdn ECtt EMic IBal LSRN NHol NMyG
	'Kath's Gold'	EMic
	'Katie Q' (v)	EMic IBal
	'Katsuragawa-beni' (v)	EBee IBal
	'Kelly'	EMic GSec
	'Kelsey'	EGol EMic
	'Key Lime Pie'	EMic IBal SApp
	'Ki Nakafu Otome' (*venusta*)	IBal
§	'Kifukurin Hyuga' (v)	CBdn IBal
	'Kifukurin' (*kikutii*)	see *H.* 'Kifukurin Hyuga'
	'Kifukurin Ko Mame' (*gracillima*) (v)	EMic
	'Kifukurin' (*pulchella*) (v)	EGol EMic
	'Kifukurin Ubatake' (*pulchella*) (v)	EGol EMic EPGN IBal
	kikutii	EGol EMic IMou NWCA WTin
§	- var. ***caput-avis***	EGol EMic
	- - 'Chabo-unazuki'	EBee
	- var. ***kikutii*** f. ***leuconota***	SApp
	- var. ***polyneuron***	EGol SApp
	- var. ***pruinosa***	SApp
§	- var. ***yakusimensis***	CPBP EGol EMic GBin GKir IBal SMad
	'Kinbotan' (v)	EGol EMic IBal
	'King James'	IBal
	'King of Spades' **new**	IBal
	'King Tut' **new**	EMic
	'Kingfisher' (Tardiana Group)	EGol IBal
§	'Kirishima'	CBdn EMic
	'Kitty Cat'	EMic IBal SApp
	'Kiwi Black Magic'	EGol EMic IBal
	'Kiwi Blue Baby'	EGol IBal
	'Kiwi Blue Ruffles'	IBal
	'Kiwi Blue Sky'	IBal
	'Kiwi Canoe'	IBal
	'Kiwi Cream Edge' (v)	EMic
	'Kiwi Forest'	IBal
	'Kiwi Fruit'	SApp
	'Kiwi Full Monty' (v)	EMic IBal
	'Kiwi Gold Rush'	IBal
	'Kiwi Hippo'	EGol IBal
	'Kiwi Jordan'	IBal
	'Kiwi Kaniere Gold'	IBal
	'Kiwi Leap Frog'	IBal
	'Kiwi Minnie Gold'	IBal
	'Kiwi Parasol'	IBal
	'Kiwi Skyscraper'	IBal
	'Kiwi Spearmint'	EMic IBal
	'Kiwi Splash'	IBal
	'Kiwi Sunlover'	IBal
	'Kiwi Sunshine'	IBal
	'Kiwi Treasure Trove'	IBal
	kiyosumiensis	NMyG
	'Klopping Variegated' (v)	EGol EMic
	'Knight's Journey' **new**	IBal
	'Knockout' (v)	CBdn EGol EMic IBal MBNS MNrw MRav NBPC NBro NEgg NGdn NLar NMyG NNor SApp
	'Komodo Dragon'	EMic IBal WTin
	'Kong'	IBal
	'Korean Snow'	IBal
I	'Koreana Variegated' (*undulata*)	EMic
	'Koriyama' (*sieboldiana*) (v)	CBdn EMic IBal
	'Krinkled Joy'	EMic
	'Krossa Cream Edge' (*sieboldii*) (v)	EMic IBal
	'Krossa Regal' ♀H4	Widely available
	'Krugerrand'	IBal
	'Lacy Belle' (v)	CBdn CSBt EGol EMic GSec IBal NBro NGdn NMyG NPro SBch SPoG
	'Lady Godiva'	IBal
	'Lady Guineverre'	IBal
	'Lady Helen'	EMic
	'Lady Isobel Barnett' (v)	CBdn EMic IBal NMyG SApp
	laevigata	EGol EMic SApp
	'Lake Hitchock'	EGol EMic IBal
	'Lakeside Accolade'	EGol IBal NMyG
	'Lakeside April Snow' (v)	EMic
	'Lakeside Baby Face' (v)	EMic IBal
	'Lakeside Beach Captain' (v) **new**	EMic IBal
	'Lakeside Black Satin'	CBdn EMic IBal LRHS SApp
	'Lakeside Blue Cherub'	EMic GSec IBal

'Lakeside Butter Ball' IBal SApp
'Lakeside Cha Cha' (v) CBdn EGol EMic
'Lakeside Cindy Cee' (v) IBal
'Lakeside Coal Miner' EMic IBal
'Lakeside Contender' IBal
'Lakeside Cranberry Relish' (v) **new** IBal
'Lakeside Cricket' (v) **new** IBal
'Lakeside Cupcake' (v) CBdn EMic IBal NMyG
'Lakeside Delight' EPGN
'Lakeside Dividing Line' (v) **new** IBal
'Lakeside Down Sized' (v) IBal
'Lakeside Dragonfly' (v) EMic EPfP IBal MAvo NMyG
'Lakeside Elfin Fire' EMic IBal
'Lakeside Feather Light' (v) IBal
'Lakeside Hoola Hoop' (v) **new** IBal
'Lakeside Iron Man' IBal
'Lakeside Kaleidoscope' CBdn EGol EMic IBal LBuc
'Lakeside Legal Tender' IBal
'Lakeside Lime Time' IBal
'Lakeside Little Gem' IBal
'Lakeside Little Tuft' (v) IBal
'Lakeside Lollipop' EGol EMic SApp
'Lakeside Looking Glass' CBdn EMic IBal LRHS
'Lakeside Love Affaire' EGol EMic IBal NMyG
'Lakeside Meadow Ice' (v) IBal
'Lakeside Meter Maid' (v) GSec IBal
'Lakeside Miss Muffett' (v) IBal
'Lakeside Missy Little' (v) **new** IBal
'Lakeside Neat Petite' EGol GSec IBal
'Lakeside Ninita' (v) EGol EMic EPGN GSec IBal NMyG
'Lakeside Party Dress' **new** IBal
'Lakeside Premier' CBdn EGol EMic
'Lakeside Prophecy' **new** IBal
'Lakeside Rhapsody' (v) EMic IBal
'Lakeside Ring Master' (v) IBal
'Lakeside Ripples' IBal
'Lakeside Rocky Top' (v) IBal
'Lakeside Roy El' (v) EMic IBal
'Lakeside Sapphire Pleats' EMic
'Lakeside Shadows' (v) IBal
'Lakeside Shockwave' (v) IBal
'Lakeside Shoremaster' (v) EMic IBal
'Lakeside Sir Logan' **new** IBal
'Lakeside Small Fry' (v) IBal
'Lakeside Sparkle Plenty' (v) IBal
'Lakeside Spellbinder' (v) **new** IBal
'Lakeside Spruce Goose' (v) IBal
'Lakeside Symphony' (v) EGol EMic
'Lakeside Tycoon' **new** IBal
'Lakeside Zinger' (v) EMic IBal
lancifolia ♀H4 CBdn CBro CMHG CMac EBee ECha EGol EHrv ELan EMic EWTr GMaP MRav NGdn NHol NMyG NSti SApp SBod SGSe SRms WAul WGwG WTin
'Last Dance' (v) IBal
'Lavender Doll' **new** IBal
'Lavender Lace' IBal
'Leading Lady' EMic
'Leather Sheen' EGol EMic EPGN IBal
'Leatherneck' IBal
'Lederhosen' EMic IBal
'Lee Armiger' (*tokudama* hybrid) EGol
'Lemon Delight' CBdn EGol EMic EPGN GSec IBal NMyG
'Lemon Frost' EMic IBal
'Lemon Lime' CBdn CBgR EGol EMic GBin IBal MHom MNrw NMyG NPro SIng WBrk WPat WTin WWEG
'Lemon Meringue' EMic
'Lemonade' GBin
'Leola Fraim' (v) CBdn EGol EMic IBal LRHS NMyG
'Let Me Entertain You' **new** EMic
'Leviathan' EMic
'Libby' IBal
'Liberty'[PBR] (v) CBcs CBdn CWGN EBee EGol EMic EPGN GBin IBal NBro NGdn NMyG SApp WFar
'Li'l Abner' (v) EMic IBal
* ***lilacina*** WFar
'Lily Pad' EPGN IBal
'Lime Fizz' EMic IBal SApp
'Lime Piecrust' EGol
'Lime Shag' (*sieboldii* f. *spathulata*) EGol
'Limey Lisa' EGol EMic EPGN IBal NMyG
'Linda Sue' (v) **new** IBal
'Little Aurora' (*tokudama* hybrid) EGol EMic EPGN IBal WWEG
'Little Bit' EMic
'Little Black Scape' EGol EMic EPGN GBin IBal LSRN MHom NCob NEgg NGdn NHol NLar NMyG NPro
'Little Blue' (*ventricosa*) EGol EMic
'Little Bo Beep' (v) EGol
'Little Boy' **new** IBal
'Little Caesar' (v) CBdn EGol EMic EPGN IBal MHom
'Little Doll' (v) EGol
'Little Jay' (v) **new** EMic SApp
'Little Miss Magic' IBal
'Little Razor' EGol
'Little Red Joy' **new** EMic IBal
'Little Red Rooster' CBdn EMic IBal NGdn NMyG
'Little Stiffy' EMic SApp
'Little Sunspot' (v) CBdn EGol EMic IBal
'Little Town Flirt' (v) IBal
'Little White Lines' (v) CBdn EGol EMic EPGN IBal
'Little Wonder' (v) CBdn EGol EMic EPGN IBal
'Lizard Lick' **new** IBal
'Lochness Monster' (v) EMic
'Lollapalooza' (v) **new** IBal
'London Fog' (v) **new** IBal
'Lonesome Dove' (v) IBal
longipes EGol GSec SApp
\- B&SWJ 10806 WCru
\- var. ***latifolia*** EMic
longissima CMHG WCru
'Love Pat' ♀H4 CBdn CBgR CFir EBee EGol EMic EPGN EPfP GAbr GBin IBal LAst LSRN MRav NGdn NMyG NNor SApp WCAu
'Lovely Loretta' **new** IBal
'Loyalist'[PBR] (v) CBdn EBee EMic NLar WFar WWEG
'Lucky Charm' EMic
'Lucy Vitols' (v) CBdn EGol EMic IBal
'Lullabye' **new** EMic
'Lunar Eclipse' (v) CHid EGol EMic GSec NEgg SApp WWEG
'Lunar Orbit' (v) CBdn
'Machete' **new** IBal
'Mack the Knife' IBal
'Maekawa' EGol EMic
'Magic Fire' (v) EMic EPGN EPfP GSec IBal MNrw
'Majesty' EGol IBal NGdn
'Mama Mia' (v) CWat EGol EMic EPGN EQua IBal MBNS NBro NGdn NHol SBch SPoG SRGP

'Manhattan' **new** EMic
'Maple Leaf' (*sieboldiana*) (v) EMic
'Maraschino Cherry' EGol EMic GBin IBal NEgg NMyG SApp
'Marble Rim' (v) EGol
'Mardi Gras' (v) **new** EMic SApp
'Marge' (*sieboldiana* hybrid) **new** EMic
'Margin of Error' (v) EGol EPGN NMyG
'Marginata Alba' ambig. (v) ECha LPBA
'Marginata Alba' misapplied see *H.* 'Albomarginata' (*fortunei*), *H. crispula*
'Marilyn' EGol EMic GSec
'Marilyn Monroe' EMic IBal
'Marquis' (*nakaiana* hybrid) EGol GSec
'Maruba Iwa' (*longipes* var. *latifolia*) CBdn
'Maruba' (*longipes* var. *latifolia*) EGol
'Mary Joe' EMic IBal
'Mary Marie Ann' (*fortunei*) (v) CBdn EGol EMic EPGN IBal NMyG
'Masquerade' (v) CBdn EGol EMic EPGN IBal SApp WFar WHal
'Maui Buttercups' IBal SApp
'May' IBal
'Maya' (*fortunei*) (v) **new** IBal
'Mediovariegata' (*undulata*) see *H. undulata* var. *undulata*
'Medusa' (v) EGol EMic IBal
'Memories of Dorothy' EMic IBal
'Mentor Gold' EGol EMic
'Merlin' (v) **new** IBal
'Mesa Fringe' (*montana*) CBdn EMic
'Metallic Sheen' CBdn
'Metallica' CBdn
'Mid Afternoon' **new** IBal
'Midas Touch' CBdn EGol GBin NEgg NHol NLar
'Middle Ridge' EMic
'Midnight Ride' IBal
'Midwest Gold' MHom SApp
'Midwest Magic' (v) CBdn EGol EMic IBal NLar NMyG SApp
'Mieke' (v) **new** IBal
'Mikawa-no-yuki' EGol IBal
'Miki' IBal
'Mildred Seaver' (v) CBdn EGol EMic GAbr IBal LRHS NMyG
'Millennium' EMic SApp
'Millie's Memoirs' (v) EGol IBal
'Ming Jade' GSec SApp
'Ming Treasure' (v) IBal
'Minnie Bell' (v) EGol IBal
'Minnie Klopping' EMic
minor misapplied f. ***alba*** see *H. sieboldii* var. *alba*
§ ***minor*** Maekawa CBdn EBee EGol EPGN ERos EWTr GEdr GGar ITim MTho NHol NMyG WCot WFar
– from Korea EGol IBal
– Goldbrook form EGol IBal
'Minor' (*ventricosa*) see *H. minor* Maekawa
'Mint Candy' **new** IBal
'Mint Julep' (v) EMic IBal
'Minuet' (v) IBal
'Minuteman' (*fortunei*) (v) CBdn ECtt EMic EPGN EPfP IBal IPot LAst MBNS NBPC NCGa NGdn NNor NOrc SApp SBch SPoG WClo WFar WGor WTin WWEG
'Miss Saigon' (v) EMic
'Miss Tokyo' (v) **new** EMic
'Mississippi Delta' EMic
'Mister Watson' EMic IBal SApp
'Misty Waters' (*sieboldiana*) EMic
'Moerheim' (*fortunei*) (v) CBdn EGol EMic EPGN IBal LRHS MBar NHol WHal WWEG
N ***montana*** EGol EMic NHol WBrE
– B&SWJ 4796 WCru
– B&SWJ 5585 WCru
– 'Kinkaku' EPGN
– f. ***macrophylla*** EGol IBal
'Moon Glow' (v) EGol EMic
'Moon Lily' EMic
'Moon River' (v) CBdn EGol EMic EPGN NMyG SApp
'Moon Shadow' (v) EGol
'Moon Waves' EGol
'Moonbeam' CBdn EShb
'Moonlight' (*fortunei*) (v) CBdn EBee EGol EMic EPGN GMaP GSec IBal LRHS NMyG SApp
'Moonlight Sonata' CBdn EGol EMic
'Moonstruck' (v) CBdn ECtt EGol EMic EPGN IBal
'Moorheim' **new** LRHS
'Morning Light'^PBR CBdn EBee EGol EMic EPGN EPfP IBal MBNS MBri NBhm NBro NGdn NMoo NMyG SApp SRkn WBor
'Moscow Blue' EGol EMic
'Mount Everest' CBdn EMic IBal
'Mount Fuji' (*montana*) EGol IBal
'Mount Hope' (v) EGol
'Mount Kirishima' (*sieboldii*) see *H.* 'Kirishima'
§ 'Mount Royal' (*sieboldii*) NHol
'Mount Tom' (v) EGol EMic IBal
'Mountain Fog' (v) **new** IBal
'Mountain Snow' (*montana*) (v) CBdn CWat EGol EMic NMyG SApp
'Mountain Sunrise' (*montana*) EGol
'Mourning Dove' (v) EMic IBal
'Mrs Minky' EBrs EMic EPGN LRHS
'Muffie' (v) EMic
'Munchkin' (*sieboldii*) CBdn EMic WPat
'My Child Insook' (v) EMic
'My Claire' (v) IBal
'My Friend Nancy' (v) EGol
'Myerscough Magic' CBdn
'Naegato' SApp
nakaiana EBee EMic GEdr NDlv
'Nakaimo' CBdn EMic NHol
'Nameoki' NHol
'Nana' (*ventricosa*) see *H. minor* Maekawa
'Nancy' **new** EMic IBal
§ 'Nancy Lindsay' (*fortunei*) CBdn CTri EGol EMic NGdn SApp
'Nancy Minks' CBdn EMic IBal
'Neat and Tidy' IBal
'Neat Splash' (v) CBdn CWCL NBir NHol WWEG
'New Wave' EGol EMic
'Niagara Falls' CBdn CFir EGol EMic IBal NGdn
'Nicola' EGol EMic EPGN IBal MHom NMyG
'Night before Christmas' (v) CBdn CBgR CFir CHid CMMP CWGN EBee EGol EMic EPGN EWTr IBal IPot LAst LPBA LRHS MNrw NBro NCGa NEgg NGdn NHol NMyG NNor SApp SPad SRGP WCAu WHoo WWEG
'Night Life' **new** EMic IBal
nigrescens CBdn EBee EGol EMic EPGN LRHS NMyG
– 'Cally White' GCal NCGa
'Nokogiryama' EMic
'None Lovelier' (v) IBal
'North Hills' (*fortunei*) (v) CBdn CMoH EAEE EBee EGol EMic LRHS NBir NCob NGdn NMyG SWvt WCAu WWEG

'Northern Exposure' (*sieboldiana*) (v)	CFir EGol EMic EWTr IBal MBel NGdn NMyG SApp WClo WCot
'Northern Halo' (*sieboldiana*) (v)	EGol EMic NMyG
'Northern Lights' (*sieboldiana*)	EGol
'Northern Mist' (*sieboldiana*)	EMic
'Northern Sunray' (*sieboldiana*) (v)	IBal
'Nougat' (v) **new**	IBal
'Nouzang'	IBal
'Nutty Professor' (v)	IBal
'Obscura Marginata' (*fortunei*)	see *H. fortunei* var. *aureomarginata*
'Obsession'	EGol IBal
'Ocean Isle' (v)	IBal
'Oder'	IBal
'O'Harra'	EGol EMic
'Okazuki Special'	CBdn
'Old Faithful'	CBdn EGol EMic
'Old Glory'^{PBR} (v)	EGol IBal
'Olga's Shiny Leaf'	EGol EMic
'Olive Bailey Langdon' (*sieboldiana*) (v)	CBdn EMic IBal SApp
'Olive Branch' (v)	EGol EMic IBal NMyG
'Olympic Edger'	EMic IBal
'Olympic Glacier' (v)	EMic IBal SApp
'Olympic Sunrise' (v)	CBdn EMic IBal
'On Stage'	see *H.* 'Choko Nishiki'
'On the Border' (v) **new**	IBal
'One Man's Treasure'	EBee EMic EPGN GBin IBal MBNS NMyG SApp
'Ooh La La' (v)	IBal
'Ophir'	EMic IBal
'Ops' (v)	EMic IBal
'Orange Crush' (v)	IBal SApp
'Orange Marmalade'	EMic IBal
'Orange Slices' **new**	IBal
'Oriana' (*fortunei*)	EGol EMic IBal
'Orphan Annie' (*venusta*) (v)	EMic
'Osprey' (Tardiana Group)	EGol
'Outhouse Delight' (v)	EMic
'Oxheart'	EMic
pachyscapa	EMic
'Pacific Blue Edger'	CBdn CBgR CFir CMMP EGol EMic EPGN NGdn NPri SApp WAul WWEG
'Pamela Lee' (v) **new**	IBal
'Pandora's Box' (v)	CBdn EGol EMic EPGN GBin GEdr IBal SApp SIng WCot
'Paradigm' (v)	CBdn EBee EBrs EGol EMic EPGN IBal LRHS NMyG
'Paradise Backstage' (v)	CBdn EMic
'Paradise Beach'	EMic IBal
'Paradise Expectations' (*sieboldiana*) (v)	EMic SApp
'Paradise Glory'	EMic
'Paradise Gold Line' (*ventricosa*) (v)	EMic
'Paradise Island' (v) **new**	CBdn EMic SApp
'Paradise Joyce'^{PBR}	CBdn EGol EMic EPGN IBal LRHS NLar NMyG SApp WWEG
'Paradise on Fire' (v)	CBdn EMic IBal SApp
'Paradise Passion' (v)	EMic
'Paradise Power'^{PBR}	CBdn EGol EMic
'Paradise Puppet' (*venusta*)	CBdn EMic EPGN IBal SApp
'Paradise Red Delight' (*pycnophylla*)	CBdn EMic
'Paradise Standard' (d)	CBdn EMic
'Paradise Sunset'	EGol EMic IBal
'Party Favor'	GSec
'Pastures Green'	EGol IBal
'Pastures New'	EGol EMic EQua MHom NHol NMyG SApp
'Pathfinder' (v)	EGol EMic IBal SApp
'Patricia'	EMic
'Patrician' (v)	EGol EMic EPGN IBal NMyG
'Patriot' (v)	Widely available
'Patriot's Fire' (v)	IBal
'Patriot's Green Pride' **new**	IBal
'Paul Revere' (v)	EMic IBal
'Paul's Glory' (v)	CBdn EGol EMic EPGN EQua GAbr GBin GMaP IBal LPBA LRHS MBri NBhm NBir NGdn NMyG SApp WFar WWEG
'Peace' (v)	EGol EMic EPGN IBal
'Peacock Strut'	IBal
'Peanut'	IBal
'Pearl Lake'	CBdn EBee EGol EMic EPGN GEdr IBal LRHS MHom MWat NBir NCob NEgg NGdn NHol NLar NMyG SApp SRGP WTin
'Peedee Absinth'	EMic GSec
'Peedee Elfin Bells' (*ventricosa*)	GSec
'Peedee Gold Flash' (v)	CBdn EMic NMyG
'Peedee Laughing River' (v)	EMic IBal
'Pelham Blue Tump'	EGol EMic GSec
'Peppermint Cream' (*cathayana*) **new**	IBal
'Peppermint Ice' (v)	EGol IBal
'Percy'	EMic IBal
'Peridot' (Tardiana Group)	GSec
'Permanent Wave'	EGol GSec
'Perry's True Blue'	CBdn EMic
'Peter Pan'	CBdn EGol EMic IBal
'Peter the Rock' **new**	IBal
'Pete's Dark Satellite'	EMic IBal
'Pewterware'	IBal
'Phantom'	EMic IBal SApp
'Philadelphia' **new**	IBal
'Phoenix'	EGol EMic SApp
'Photo Finish' (v)	EGol EMic
'Phyllis Campbell' (*fortunei*)	see *H.* 'Sharmon'
'Picta' (*fortunei*)	see *H. fortunei* var. *albopicta*
'Piecrust Power'	CBdn EGol
'Piedmont Gold'	CBdn EGol EMic EPGN IBal LRHS NBPC SApp
'Pilgrim' (v)	CBdn EBee EGol ELan EMic EPGN IBal LRHS NBPC NBro NMyG SApp WFar
'Pineapple Poll'	CBdn EGol EMic EPGN NMyG WTin
'Pineapple Upside Down Cake' (v)	EMic EPGN IBal LRHS NBhm NBro NLar NMyG WFar
'Pinky'	IBal
'Pinwheel' (v)	IBal
'Pistachio Cream'	EMic
'Pizzazz' (v)	CBdn EGol EMic IBal LRHS MHom NGdn NHol NLar NMyG SApp WFar WHil WWEG
plantaginea	CBdn CBgR EGol EMic IBal LEdu LPla LRHS MHom NMyG SSpi WCru WFar WKif WSpi
- var. ***grandiflora***	see *H. plantaginea* var. *japonica*
§ - var. ***japonica*** Υ^{H4}	CBot CDes ECha EHrv EMic EPGN IBal MRav SApp SGSe WCFE WFar WPGP WWEG
'Platinum Tiara' (v)	CBdn EGol EMic EPGN GSec IBal NBir NMyG
'Plug Nickel'	EMic IBal
'Polar Moon' (v)	IBal

'Pooh Bear' (v)	CBdn EGol EMic
'Popcorn'	CBdn EMic IBal SApp
'Popo'	CBdn EGol EMic EPGN IBal SApp
'Porky's Prize' (v)	EGol
'Potomac Pride'	CBdn EGol EMic EPGN NMyG SApp
'Powder Blue' (v)	IBal
'Powderpuff'	IBal
'Prairie Glow' **new**	IBal
'Prairie Sky'	IBal
'Praying Hands' (v)	CBdn EGol EMic EPGN EPfP GBin IBal IPot MBNS NMyG WWEG
'Pretty Flamingo'	EMic IBal
'Prima Donna'	EMic
'Primavera Primrose'	SApp
'Prince of Wales'	CBdn EMic IBal LRHS LSqu NMyG SApp SPoG SRkn
'Princess of Wales'	EBee
'Puck'	EGol
'Punky' (v)	IBal
'Purple and Gold'	CBdn EMic
'Purple Boots' **new**	EMic IBal
'Purple Dwarf'	CBdn EGol EMic LRHS NGdn NHol NLar WHal
'Purple Glory'	EMic
'Purple Lady Finger'	GSec WWEG
'Purple Passion'	EGol EMic
'Purple Profusion'	EGol EMic
pycnophylla	EGol
'Quarter Note' (v) **new**	IBal
'Queen Josephine' (v)	CBdn EGol EMic EPGN IBal IPot LRHS MBNS MBri MHom NCGa NGdn NMyG NPro SApp SBch SPoG SRGP WFar
'Queen of Islip' (*sieboldiana*) (v)	CBdn
'Queen of the Seas'	EMic IBal SApp
'Quill'	EMic
'Quilting Bee'	EGol EMic
'Radiant Edger' (v)	CBdn EGol EMic EPGN GCra IBal NHol SBch WWEG
'Radio Waves'	EMic IBal
'Rain Forest'	EMic IBal
'Rainbow's End' (v) **new**	EMic IBal
'Rainforest Sunrise'	EMic IBal
'Raleigh Remembrance'	EGol EMic
'Rascal' (v)	CBdn EGol EMic
'Raspberries and Cream' (v) **new**	IBal
'Raspberry Sorbet'	EGol EMic EPGN IBal
rectifolia	NHol NNor
- 'Kinbuchi Tachi' (v)	IBal
- 'Ogon Tachi' (v)	IBal
'Red Cadet' **new**	EMic IBal
'Red Dragon' **new**	IBal
'Red Hot Flash' (v)	IBal
'Red Neck Heaven' (***kikutii*** var. ***caput-avis***)	CBdn EGol GSec SApp WTin
'Red October'	CBdn CMHG EBee EBrs EGol EMic EPGN EPfP GAbr GBin IBal LRHS MBNS MBri NGdn NLar NMoo NMyG WFar WWEG
'Red Salamander'	EGol
'Red Stepper' **new**	IBal
'Regal Chameleon' **new**	IBal
'Regal Rhubarb'	EGol EMic IBal
'Regal Splendor' (v)	CBdn EGol EMFW EMic EPGN IBal LRHS MHom NBro NCGa NGdn NHol NMyG SApp WAul WCAu WMnd
'Regalia'	EMic
'Reginald Kaye'	EMic
'Remember Me'[PBR]	CBdn CWCL CWGN EDAr EGol ELan EMic EPGN IBal LRHS LSRN MBNS MCCP MDun NCob NGdn NLar NMyG NNor SApp SMrm WFar WGor
'Reptilian'	EGol EMic GSec
'Resonance' (v)	EPGN GKir NGdn NLar NPro
'Restless Sea' **new**	EMic IBal
'Reversed' (*sieboldiana*) (v)	CBdn CWat EBee EGol ELan EMic EPGN LRHS MDKP NBro NGdn NNor NWsh WHal
'Revolution'[PBR] (v)	CBdn CWGN EBee EBrs EGol EMic EPGN GKir IBal IPot LRHS LSRN MBri NBPC NBro NCob NEgg NGdn NHol NLar NMyG NOrc SApp WAul WFar WWEG
'Rhapsody' (*fortunei*) (v)	EGol EMic
'Rhapsody in Blue'	EGol
'Rhein' (*tardiana*)	EMic
'Rheingold' (v)	IBal
'Rhino' (v)	EMic
'Rhythm and Blues'	IBal
'Rich Uncle'	IBal
'Richland Gold' (*fortunei*)	CBdn EGol EMic EPGN GSec NMyG
'Richmond' (v)	EMic
'Rickrack'	IBal
'Rim Rock'	EMic
'Rippled Honey'	CBdn EGol EMic EPGN GSec IBal NCob NMyG NPro SApp
'Rippling Waves'	EGol EMic
'Riptide'	CBdn EMic
'Rise and Shine' (v) **new**	EGol
'Rising Sun'	EGol
'Risky Business' (v)	CBdn IBal
'Robert Frost' (v)	CBdn EGol EMic IBal WTin
'Robin Hood'	EMic IBal SApp
'Robusta' (*fortunei*)	see *H. sieboldiana* var. *elegans*
'Robyn's Choice' (v)	EMic
'Rock Island Line' (v)	IBal
'Rock Princess'	IBal
'Rocky Mountain High' (v)	EMic
§ ***rohdeifolia*** (v)	LRHS
- f. ***albopicta***	CBdn EGol ELan NHol
'Roller Coaster Ride'	IBal
'Ron Damant'	EPGN IBal
'Rosedale Golden Goose'	IBal
'Rosedale Knox'	IBal
'Rosedale Melody of Summer' (v)	IBal
'Rosedale Misty Magic' (v) **new**	IBal
'Rosedale Misty Pathways' (v)	EMic
'Rosedale Richie Valens'	EMic IBal
'Rosemoor'	CBdn EGol EMic IBal
'Rotunda'	EGol
'Rough Waters'	SApp
'Roxsanne'	EMic
'Royal Flush' (v)	EMic
'Royal Golden Jubilee'	EMic EPGN IBal NMyG
§ 'Royal Standard' 🏆[H4]	Widely available
'Royal Tapestry' (v)	IBal
'Royal Tiara' (*nakaiana*) (v)	EGol
'Royalty'	EGol
rupifraga	EGol EMic
'Rusty Bee' **new**	IBal
'Ryan's Big One'	EMic IBal NMyG
§ 'Sagae' (v) 🏆[H3-4]	CBdn CMoH CWat EBee EBrs EGol EMic EPGN EPfP IBal IPot LRHS MBri MHom MNrw NGdn NMyG SApp SDix SPoG WAul WFar WHoo WWEG

'Saint Elmo's Fire' (v)	CBdn CHid EGol EMic EPGN IBal LRHS NCGa SApp
'Saint Fiacre'	CBdn
'Saint Paul'	EMic IBal
'Saishu Jima' (*sieboldii* f. *spathulata*)	EMic WCru
'Saishu Yahite Site' (v)	EGol
'Salute' (Tardiana Group)	CBdn EGol EMic GSec
'Samual Blue'	EGol
'Samurai' (*sieboldiana*) (v)	CBdn EBee EGol EMic IBal IPot MRav NBir NBro NGdn NLar SApp
'Sand Pebbles' (v)	EMic
'Sandhill Crane' (v) **new**	IBal
'Sarah Kennedy' (v)	EPGN
'Satisfaction' (v)	EMic
'Savannah'	EGol IBal
'Sazanami' (*crispula*)	see *H. crispula*
'Schwan'	GBin
'Scooter' (v)	CBdn EGol EMic EPGN NMyG
'Sea Beacon' (v)	EGol EMic
'Sea Bunny'	EGol
'Sea Dream' (v)	CBdn EGol EMic LRHS NEgg NMyG
'Sea Drift'	EGol
'Sea Fire'	EGol
'Sea Frolic'	EGol
'Sea Gold Star'	CBdn EGol NMyG
'Sea Gulf Stream'	EMic IBal
'Sea Hero'	EGol
'Sea Lotus Leaf'	CBdn EGol EMic LLWP NLar NMyG
'Sea Mist' (v)	CBdn
'Sea Monster'	EGol IBal
'Sea Octopus'	EGol
'Sea Sapphire'	EGol
'Sea Sunrise'	EPGN
'Sea Thunder' (v)	CBdn EGol EMic EPGN IBal NMyG
'Sea Yellow Sunrise'	CBdn EGol EMic IBal SApp
'Second Wind' (*fortunei*) (v)	CBdn EGol EMic EPGN IBal NMyG SApp
'Secret Love'^PBR	CBdn EMic IBal
'See Saw' (*undulata*)	EGol EMic SApp
'September Sun' (v)	CBdn EGol EMic GSec IBal LRHS NMyG
'Serena' (Tardiana Group)	IBal SApp
'Serendipity'	CBdn EGol EMic MHom
'Shade Beauty' (v)	EGol
'Shade Fanfare' (v) ♀H4	CBdn CChe EBrs EGol ELan EMic EPGN EPfP IBal LAst LBMP LRHS MBNS MBri MRav NBir NGdn NLar NMyG NSti SApp SPer WFar WMnd WTin WWEG
'Shade Finale' (v) **new**	IBal
'Shade Master'	CBdn EGol EMic NHol
'Shamoa'	SApp
§ 'Sharmon' (*fortunei*) (v)	CBdn EGol EMic EPGN IBal MBNS NEgg NHol NMyG SApp SBch
'Sharp Dressed Man'	IBal
'Shazaam' **new**	IBal
'Sheila West'	CBdn EMic
'Shelleys' (v)	EGol IBal
'Sherborne Profusion' (Tardiana Group)	CBdn EMic IBal
'Sherborne Songbird' (Tardiana Group)	EGol EMic IBal
'Sherborne Swan' (Tardiana Group)	EGol EMic IBal
'Sherborne Swift' (Tardiana Group)	CBdn EGol EMic LRHS
'Shere Khan' (v)	EGol EMic
'Shining Tot'	CBdn EGol LLHF
'Shiny Penny' (v)	EGol EMic IBal
'Shirley Vaughn' (v)	EGol
'Shogun' (v)	EGol
'Showboat' (v)	CBdn EGol EMic IBal LRHS NMyG
sieboldiana	CMac CSBt ECha EGol ELan EMic EPfP GCra GMaP LLWP MMuc MRav MSwo NChi NHol SPlb SRms WFar WGwG WWEG
§ - var. ***elegans*** ♀H4	Widely available
- 'George Smith'	EMic IBal SApp
- var. ***mira***	EMic
- var. ***sieboldiana***	GAuc
sieboldii	CWat MRav
§ - var. ***alba***	EGol IBal
§ - 'Paxton's Original' (v) ♀H4	EGol EHrv MBar SGSe SRms WWEG
§ - var. ***sieboldii*** f. ***kabitan*** (v)	CBdn EGol EPGN NMyG SApp WTin WWEG
- - f. ***shiro-kabitan*** (v)	EGol EMic EPGN LRHS
- f. ***spathulata***	EMic
'Silberpfeil'	EMic
'Silk Kimono' (v)	EGol EMic
'Silver Bay' **new**	EMic
'Silver Bowl'	EGol
'Silver Crown'	see *H.* 'Albomarginata'
'Silver Lance' (v)	CBdn EGol EMic EPGN NMyG
'Silver Lining'	IBal
'Silver Shadow' (v)	CBdn CHid EMic EPGN GBin IBal NBir NCob NGdn NHol NMyG SApp WClo WPtf
'Silver Spray' (v)	EGol IBal
'Silver Threads and Gold Needles' (v) **new**	IBal
'Silverado' (v)	IBal
'Silvery Slugproof' (Tardiana Group)	CBdn LRHS MWat NMyG SApp
'Singin' the Blues' **new**	IBal
'Sitting Pretty' (v)	EGol EPGN
'Sky Dancer'	CBdn EMic IBal
'Sleeping Beauty'	CWGN EMic GQue IBal MAvo NGdn NMyG SPoG
'Slick Willie'	EGol
'Slim Polly'	CBdn
'Small Parts' **new**	EMic
'Small Sum'	IBal
'Smooth Sailing' (v) **new**	IBal
'Snow Cap' (v)	CBdn EBee EGol EMic IBal MBri NGdn NLar NMoo NMyG NNor NPro SApp WAul WWEG
'Snow Crust' (v)	CBdn EGol EMic
'Snow Flakes' (*sieboldii*)	CBdn CMac EGol EPGN EPfP EWTr MBar NBro NGdn NHol NMyG NPro SBod WFar WWEG
'Snow Mound' **new**	IBal
'Snow White' (*undulata*) (v)	EGol IBal
'Snowbound' (v)	IBal
'Snowden'	CBdn CMHG ECha EGol EMic EPGN ETod GMaP IBal LRHS MWat NBir NCob NGdn NHol NMyG SApp SSpi WCru WWEG
'Snowstorm' (*sieboldii*)	CBdn NHol
'So Sweet' (v)	CBdn COIW EBee EGol EHoe ELan EMFW EMic EPGN IBal LAst LBMP LPBA LRHS MHom MSwo NBro NGdn NHol NMyG SApp SBch SPad SPoG SRGP WSpi WWEG
'Solar Flare'	EGol
'Soldier Boy'	EMic
'Something Blue'	CBdn EMic
'Something Different' (*fortunei*) (v)	EGol EPGN
'Sophistication' (v)	EGol
'Southern Gold' **new**	EMic
'Sparkling Burgundy'	CBdn EGol IBal
'Sparky' (v)	EGol EMic IBal
'Spartan Glory' (v)	IBal

'Special Gift'	CBdn EGol EMic WWEG
'Spellbound' (v)	IBal
'Spilt Milk' (*tokudama*) (v)	CBdn EGol EMic EPGN IBal SApp SPoG WHoo
§ 'Spinners' (*fortunei*) (v)	CBdn ECha EGol EMic
'Spinning Wheel' (v)	EGol IBal
'Spring Fling'	EMic IBal
'Spritzer' (v)	CBdn EGol EMic GSec IBal NMyG SApp
'Squash Casserole'	EGol
'Squiggles' (v)	EGol
'Stained Glass'	CBcs EGol EMic EPGN IBal NGdn NMyG WFar
'Standing Ovation' (v)	EMic
'Star Kissed'	IBal
'Starburst' (v)	EGol
'Starburst' stable (v)	IBal
§ 'Starker Yellow Leaf'	EMic
'Stenantha' (*fortunei*)	EMic
'Stenantha Variegated' (*fortunei*) (v)	NHol
'Step Sister'	EMic IBal
'Stepping Out' (v)	EMic IBal
'Stetson' (v)	EGol
'Stiletto' (v)	Widely available
'Stirfry'	EGol GSec
'Stolen Kiss' (v) **new**	IBal
'Stonewall'	IBal
'Striker' (v)	EGol IBal
'Striptease' (*fortunei*) (v)	CBdn CBgR CMac EGol EMic EPGN GBin GQue IBal LRHS MBNS NGdn NHol NLar NMyG SApp WFar WHoo WWEG
'Sugar and Cream' (v)	CMMP CWat EGol EMic IBal LRHS MWat NGdn
'Sugar and Spice' (v) **new**	EMic IBal
'Sugar Babe' (v)	EMic
'Sugar Daddy'	EMic IBal
'Sugar Plum Fairy' (*gracillima*)	EGol
'Sultana' (v)	EMic IBal WWEG
'Sum and Substance' 🏆H4	Widely available
'Sum Cup-o-Joe' (v)	EMic
'Sum it Up' (v)	EMic
'Sum of All' (v)	CBdn EMic
'Summer Breeze' (v)	EGol EMic IBal
'Summer Fragrance'	CBdn ECtt EGol EMic GBin IBal LRHS NMyG
'Summer in Georgia' **new**	IBal
'Summer Joy'	EMic
'Summer Music' (v)	CBdn CWCL EGol EMic EPGN IBal MBNS MBri NMyG SApp WWEG
'Summer Serenade' (v)	CBdn EGol EMic IBal SApp
'Summer Warrior'	EMic
'Sun Catcher' **new**	EMic
'Sun Glow'	EGol EMic
'Sun Kissed' (v)	IBal
'Sun Power'	CBdn EGol EMic EPfP GBin IBal LRHS MBNS NBro NGdn NLar NMyG NSti SApp SBch SDix SMrm SPoG SRGP
'Sun Worshipper'	EMic IBal SApp
'Sundance' (*fortunei*) (v)	EGol EMic
'Sunlight Child'	IBal
'Sunny Delight'	EMic
'Sunny Disposition'	EMic
'Sunnybrook' (v) **new**	IBal
'Sunshine Glory'	EGol EMic
'Super Bowl'	EGol
'Super Nova' (v)	CBdn EGol EMic IBal SApp SPoG
'Surf and Turf' **new**	IBal
'Surprised by Joy' (v)	EGol EMic IBal SApp
'Susy'	IBal
'Sutter's Mill' **new**	IBal
'Suzuki Thumbnail'	EMic
'Sweet Blonde Babe' **new**	IBal
'Sweet Bo Beep'	EGol GSec
'Sweet Bouquet'	EMic
'Sweet Home Chicago' (v)	EGol EMic IBal
'Sweet Innocence' (v) **new**	EMic IBal
'Sweet Marjorie'	EGol
'Sweet Standard'	NMyG
'Sweet Sunshine'	EGol
'Sweet Susan'	EGol EMic GBin GSec LSRN MBNS SApp SPer SWvt
'Sweet Tater Pie'	CBdn EGol EMic
'Sweetheart'	EMic
'Sweetie' (v)	CBdn EGol EMic IBal LRHS SApp WWEG
'Sweetness' **new**	IBal
'Swirling Hearts'	EGol GSec
'Swizzle Sticks'	IBal
'T. Rex' **new**	EMic
'Tall Boy'	CBdn CSev ECha EGol EMic NBir NNor
'Tall Twister'	EMic
'Tamborine' (v)	CBdn CWat EGol EMic LRHS NMyG SApp
'Tango'	EMic IBal
Tardiana Group	CBdn EGol ELan MHom NGdn NHol
tardiflora	CBdn EGol ERos SApp WCot WPGP
tardiva	CBdn GKir
'Tattoo'[PBR] (v)	CBdn CWGN EDAr EGol EMic EPGN LSRN MBNS MNrw NLar NMoo NMyG SApp WWEG
'Tea and Crumpets' (v)	CBdn EPGN IBal
'Teaspoon'	EMic IBal SApp
'Teeny-weeny Bikini' (v)	IBal
'Templar Gold'	IBal
'Temple Bells'	EGol
'Temptation'	EMic IBal
'Tenryu'	EGol
'Tequila Sunrise'	IBal
'Tet-a-Poo' **new**	IBal
'The Shining' **new**	IBal
'The Twister'	EGol EMic IBal NMyG
'Theo's Blue'	EMic IBal
'Thomas Hogg'	see *H. undulata* var. *albomarginata*
'Three Sisters' (v) **new**	IBal
'Thumb Nail'	CBdn ECha EGol EMic IBal SApp SCnR
'Thumbelina'	IBal
'Thunderbolt'[PBR] (*sieboldiana*)	CBdn CWat EGol EMic EPGN IBal MBNS NCob NLar SApp WFar
tibae	CBdn EMic
'Tick Tock' (v)	IBal
'Tidewater'	IBal
'Tijuana Brass'	EMic
'Time Tunnel'[PBR] (*sieboldiana*) (v)	EMic IBal
'Tiny Tears'	CBdn CStu EGol IBal
'Titanic'[PBR]	IBal
'Toasted Waffles' **new**	WFar
tokudama	EGol EMic IBal MHom NBir NGdn NHol NNor NSti SApp WFar
§ - f. ***aureo-nebulosa*** (v)	CBdn EGol EMic EPGN IBal NGdn NSti WMnd
'Tokudama Blue'	SApp
tokudama f. ***flavocircinalis*** (v)	CBdn CBgR CPrp EGol EMic EPGN GMaP IBal NBPC NBro NMyG SApp WFar WHoo WMnd

Name	Suppliers
'Tom Rex'	IBal
'Tom Schmid' (v)	EGol EMic IBal
'Tom Thumb'	EMic IBal SApp
'Topaz'	EMic IBal
'Topscore'	NNor
'Torchlight' (v)	CBdn EGol EMic GSec IBal
tortifrons	EBee EMic IBal
'Tortilla Chip'	IBal
'Tot Tot'	EGol IBal
'Touch of Class'[PBR] (v)	CBdn EMic IBal NMyG WWEG
'Touchstone' (v)	CBdn GSec IBal LRHS NMyG SApp SWvt WWEG
'Toy Soldier'	CBdn EMic IBal SApp
'Trail's End'	EMic
'Tranquility' (v)	EMic
'Treasure Island'	IBal
'Tremors' **new**	EMic
'Trill'	SApp
'Trixi' (v)	IBal
'True Blue'	CBdn CBgR EBee EGol EMic IBal SApp WWEG
'Tsugaru Komachi'	EMic
'Tsugaru Komachi Kifukurin' (v)	IBal
tsushimensis	EMic
'Turning Point'	EGol
'Tutu'	EGol EPGN
'Twiggie'	EMic SApp
'Twilight' (*fortunei*) (v)	CBdn EBee EGol EKen EMFW EMic EPGN IBal LRHS MBNS NLar NMyG SApp SWvt WClo WWEG
'Twilight Time'	IBal
'Twinkle Toes'	EGol EMic
'Twist of Lemon' **new**	GBin
'Twist of Lime' (v)	CBdn EGol EMic IBal
'Ultramarine'	EMic IBal
'Ultraviolet Light'	EGol
'Unchained Melody'	IBal
undulata	NNor WFar
§ - var. ***albomarginata***	Widely available
§ - var. ***erromena*** ♀H4	CBdn EMic GMaP IBal LPBA NBid NHol
§ - var. ***undulata*** (v) ♀H4	CBdn CBot EBee EHrv ELan EMFW EPGN EPfP GMaP IBal LAst LPBA LRHS MCot MRav MSwo NBlu NEgg NGdn NMyG NVic SIng SPer SPoG WFar WWEG
- var. ***univittata*** (v) ♀H4	CBro ECha EGol EMic IBal LAst MHom MWhi NBir NPro WBrk WFar WMoo
'Unforgettable'	EMic IBal SApp
'Urajiro Hachijo' (*longipes* var. *latifolia*)	EGol IBal
'Urajiro' (*hypoleuca*)	EGol
'Urajiro' (*longipes*)	EMic
'Uzo-no-mai'	EBee
'Valentine Lace'	CBdn EBee EGol EMic
'Valley's Chute the Chute' **new**	CBdn EMic
'Valley's Vanilla Sticks' **new**	EMic
'Van Wade' (v)	CBdn EGol EMic EPGN IBal
'Vanilla Cream' (*cathayana*)	EGol EMic NMyG
'Variegata' (*gracillima*)	see *H.* 'Vera Verde'
'Variegata' (*tokudama*)	see *H. tokudama* f. *aureo-nebulosa*
'Variegata' (*undulata*)	see *H. undulata* var. *undulata*
'Variegata' (*ventricosa*)	see *H.* 'Aureomarginata' (*ventricosa*)
'Variegated' (*fluctuans*)	see *H.* 'Sagae'
'Velvet Moon' (v)	IBal
ventricosa ♀H4	CBcs CBdn CBro CMac EGol EGoo EMic EPfP EWTr GMaP LPBA MWhi NHol NMyG SGar WBrk WFar

Name	Suppliers
- var. ***aureomaculata***	CBdn EGol EMic LRHS NBir NSti WFar
- BWJ 8160 from Sichuan	WCru
I 'Venucosa'	EGol EMic LAst
'Venus' (d)	IBal MBel NGdn SMrs SPer SPoG WClo WCot
'Venus Star'	EGol EMic IBal NMyG
venusta ♀H4	CBdn CBro CDes EBee ECho EDAr EGol EMic EPGN ERos GCra GEdr IBal LRHS MHer MRav NBid NBir NMen NMyG NRya NSti SApp SMad SRot WCot WEas WSHC WTin WWEG
- B&SWJ 4389	WCru
- dwarf	CSWP GCal
- 'Porter'	EMic IBal
- 'Red Tubes'	IBal
- ***yakusimensis***	see *H. kikutii* var. *yakusimensis*
§ 'Vera Verde' (v)	CBdn EPGN GCra GQui IBal MHom NBir NMyG
'Verdi Valentine' **new**	IBal
'Verkade's No 1'	IBal
'Verna Jean' (v)	CBdn EGol EMic IBal
'Veronica Lake' (v)	CBdn EGol EMic GSec IBal LRHS NMyG WHal
'Victory'	EMic IBal
'Viette's Yellow Edge' (*fortunei*) (v)	EMic
'Vilmoriniana'	EGol EMic IBal
'Viridis Marginata'	see *H. sieboldii* var. *sieboldii* f. *kabitan*
'Wagtail' (Tardiana Group)	CBdn EGol EMic IBal
'Wahoo' (*tokudama*) (v)	EGol
'Wakey-Wakey' **new**	EGol
'War Paint'	EMic IBal
'War Party'	EMic
'Warwick Ballerina'	EGol
'Warwick Choice' (v)	CBdn
'Warwick Comet' (v)	IBal SApp
'Warwick Curtsey' (v)	EGol EMic GSec IBal
'Warwick Delight' (v)	EGol EMic IBal
'Warwick Edge' (v)	CBdn EGol IBal
'Warwick Essence'	EGol EMic
'Warwick Sheen'	IBal
'Waving Winds' (v)	EGol IBal
'Waving Wuffles'	EMic NMyG
'Wayside Blue'	EMic
'Wayside Perfection'	see *H.* 'Royal Standard'
'Website' **new**	IBal
'Weihenstephan' (*sieboldii*)	EGol EMic
'Weser'	EGol
'Wheaton Blue'	CBdn EMic IBal
'Whirligig' (v)	EMic
'Whirling Dervish' (v)	EMic IBal
'Whirlwind' (*fortunei*) (v)	CBcs CBdn CBgR EDAr EGol EMic EPGN GBin GQue IBal IPot MBri MNrw MRav NBro NEgg NGdn NMyG NNor NOrc SApp SMad SMrm WAul WMnd WWEG
'Whirlwind Tour' (v)	EGol IBal SApp
'Whiskey Sour'	EMic IBal SApp
'White Bikini' (v)	IBal
'White Christmas' (*undulata*) (v)	EGol EMic EPGN EQua IBal
'White Fairy' (*plantaginea*) (d)	CBdn EMic IBal
'White Feather' (*undulata*)	CBdn CHid IBal NBir NGdn NMyG
'White Gold'	CBdn EGol NMyG
'White Knight' **new**	IBal
'White On' (*montana*)	EMic IBal
'White Tacchi'	EMic

'White Triumphator' (*rectifolia*)	CBdn EGol EMic GBin IBal NBPC NMyG
'White Trumpets'	EMic
'White Vision'	EGol IBal
'Wide Brim' (v) 🏆H4	Widely available
'Wily Willy'	IBal
'Wind River Gold'	EGol EMic
'Windsor Gold'	see *H.* 'Nancy Lindsay'
'Winfield Blue'	CMHG EGol EMic IBal
'Winfield Gold'	CBdn EGol EMic IBal
'Winfield Mist' (v)	IBal
'Winsome' (v)	EGol EMic IBal
'Winter Snow' (v)	CBdn EMic IBal
'Wintergreen' (v)	IBal
'Wogon' (*sieboldii*)	CBdn CMMP EMic GEdr GKev GMaP NDlv NHol NMen NSti
'Wogon's Boy'	CBdn EGol EMic EPGN IBal LRHS WWEG
'Wolverine' (v)	CBdn CWit EBee ECGP ECtt EGol EHoe EMic EPGN GAbr GEdr IBal LPla LSou MBNS MHom NGdn NMyG SWvt WClo WCot WWEG
'Woolly Mammoth' (v)	IBal
'Wooly Bully' **new**	NMyG
'Woop Woop' (v) **new**	IBal
'World Cup' **new**	IBal
'Worldly Treasure' **new**	IBal
'Wrinkles and Crinkles'	EGol EMic IBal
'Wylde Green Cream'	EGol EMic IBal
'Xanadu' (v)	EMic IBal
'X-rated' (v)	IBal
'X-ray' (v)	IBal
'Yakushima-mizu' (*gracillima*)	CBdn EGol EMic IBal
* ***yakushimana***	NMen
'Yang'	IBal
'Yankee Blue'	IBal
'Yellow Boa'	EGol EMic
'Yellow Edge' (*fortunei*)	see *H. fortunei* var. *aureomarginata*
'Yellow Edge' (*sieboldiana*)	see *H.* 'Frances Williams'
'Yellow River' (v)	CBdn EGol EMic GBin IBal MBri NGdn NMyG SApp
'Yellow Splash' (v)	CBdn CMoH ECha EPGN LRHS MHom NMyG
'Yellow Splash Rim' (v)	EGol NCGa
'Yellow Splashed Edged' (v)	EMic
'Yellow Submarine'	IBal
'Yellow Waves'	CBdn
'Yesterday's Memories' (v) **new**	EMic
'Yin' (v)	EMic IBal SApp
yingeri	EGol SApp WPGP
- B&SWJ 546	WCru
'Yucca Ducka Do' (v)	EGol
'Zager Blue'	EMic
'Zager Green'	EMic
'Zager White Edge' (*fortunei*) (v)	EGol EMic IBal NMyG SApp WTin
'Zippity Do Dah' (v)	IBal
'Zitronenfalter'	EGol IBal
'Zodiac' (*fortunei*) (v)	EMic
'Zounds'	CBdn CBgR CBot CMHG EBee ECtt EGol ELan EMic EPGN EPfP EShb GKir IBal LRHS MDun MRav NHol NMyG NOrc NSti SApp SBch SPoG WBor WFar WWEG

Hottonia (*Primulaceae*)

palustris	CBen CWat EHon ELan EMFW LPBA MMuc MSKA NPer NSco SWat WPnP

Houstonia (*Rubiaceae*)

caerulea misapplied	see *H. michauxii*
caerulea L.	ECho EDAr NPri SIng
- var. ***alba***	SPer SPlb
longifolia	EWes
§ ***michauxii***	SPer
- 'Fred Mullard'	EWes
serpyllifolia	ECho

Houttuynia (*Saururaceae*)

cordata	GBar GPoy SBch SDix SWat WFar
§ - 'Boo-Boo' (v)	CMac EPfP EPla LBMP LRHS NBro SBch SMrm WFar WWEG
§ - 'Chameleon' (v)	Widely available
- 'Fantasy'	EBee
- 'Flame' (v)	CBcs CMac CWCL LRHS MAsh MBri NPri SBch SIng SMrm WWEG
- 'Flore Pleno' (d)	CBen CMac CRow CSsd EBee ECha EHon ELan EMFW EPfP EPla GBar LPBA MCCP MRav NBir NPer NVic SGar SIde SPer SPlb SPoG SRms SWat WFar WPnP WTin
- 'Joker's Gold'	CMac EBee ECtt EPPr EPfP EPla LBMP LRHS NBro NVic SMrm SPoG
- 'Pied Piper'	CDoC EBee EPla EWll SBch SPad
- 'Sunshine'	EBee
- 'Tequila Sunrise'	CHEx
- 'Terry Clarke'	see *H. cordata* 'Boo-Boo'
- 'Tricolor'	see *H. cordata* 'Chameleon'
- Variegata Group (v)	GBar LPBA NBro SIng

Hovea (*Papilionaceae*)

celsii	see *H. elliptica*
§ ***elliptica***	SPlb

Hovenia (*Rhamnaceae*)

dulcis	CAgr CBcs CMCN EPfP LEdu MBlu NLar NMun WBVN
- B&SWJ 11024	WCru

Howea (*Arecaceae*)

§ ***belmoreana*** 🏆H1	LPal
§ ***forsteriana*** 🏆H1	CCCN LPal LRHS MBri NScw XBlo

Hoya (*Asclepiadaceae*)

bella	see *H. lanceolata* subsp. *bella*
carnosa 🏆H1	CBcs CRHN EBak EOHP SEND SRms SWal WWFP
- 'Hindu Rope'	NPer
- 'Krinkle 8'	NPer
- 'Red Princess'	MBri
- 'Tricolor'	LRHS NPer
- 'Variegata' (v)	MBri
* ***compacta*** 'Tricolor'	NPer
lacunosa	CCCN
§ ***lanceolata*** subsp. ***bella*** 🏆H1	EShb LRHS SRms
linearis	LRHS

huckleberry, garden see *Solanum scabrum*

Huernia (*Asclepiadaceae*)

aspera	CFwr
campanulata	CFwr
confusa	see *H. insigniflora*
hallii	CFwr
§ ***insigniflora***	CFwr
'Kwa Sandile'	CFwr
loesneriana	CFwr
- 'Middleburgh'	CFwr

macrocarpa	CFwr
occulta	CFwr
pendula	CFwr
schneideriana	CFwr
thurettii	CFwr

Huerniopsis (*Asclepiadaceae*)

decipiens	CFwr

Humata (*Davalliaceae*)

tyermannii	CMen WFib WRic

Humea see *Calomeria*

elegans	see *Calomeria amaranthoides*

Humulus (*Cannabaceae*)

lupulus	CArn CBcs CRWN EPfP GBar GPoy ILis MNHC NGHP NMir SIde WDin WHer
- 'Aureus' ♀H4	Widely available
- 'Aureus' (f)	CRHN ELon EOHP GBar GCal GGar GKev MCCP SPoG WCot WWFP
- 'Aureus' (m)	MCCP
* - ***compactus***	GPoy
- 'Fuggle'	CAgr GPoy SDea
- 'Golden Showers' **new**	MCCP
- 'Golden Tassels' (f)	CAgr CDul EBee ELon EMui EPfP LBuc LHop LRHS MBri MGos NGHP SBch SLim SMad SPoG
- (Goldings Group) 'Cobbs'	SDea
- - 'Mathons'	CAgr SDea
- 'Hallertauer'	SDea
- 'Prima Donna'	CAgr CDul EBee EGxp EMui GBin LHop MCoo NLar SBch SCoo SIde SPoG SWvt
- 'Taff's Variegated' (v)	EWes MAvo NGHP WSHC
- 'Wye Challenger'	CAgr GPoy
- 'Wye Northdown'	CAgr SDea

Hunnemannia (*Papaveraceae*)

fumariifolia	CSpe

Huodendron (*Styracaceae*)

biaristatum	WPGP
tibeticum	WPGP

Hutchinsia see *Pritzelago*

Hyacinthella (*Hyacinthaceae*)

acutiloba	ECho ERos
dalmatica	ERos
- 'Grandiflora'	ECho WWst
glabrescens	WCot WWst
heldreichii	EBrs ECho ERos
lazuliria	ERos
leucophaea	EBrs ECho ERos WWst
lineata	WCot
millingenii	EBrs ECho ERos
pallens	EBrs ECho

Hyacinthoides (*Hyacinthaceae*)

aristidis	EBrs ECho
§ ***hispanica***	EBrs ECho LRHS NBir WHil
- 'Alba'	ECho LRHS
- 'Dainty Maid'	EBrs ECho
- 'Excelsior'	EBrs ECho
- 'Miss World'	EBrs ECho WCot
- 'Mount Everest' **new**	ECho
- 'Queen of the Pinks'	EBrs ECho WCot
- 'Rosea'	ECho LRHS
- 'White City'	EBrs ECho WCot
§ ***italica*** ♀H4	CPom ECho SIng SPhx WShi
§ ***non-scripta***	Widely available
- 'Alba'	EBrs ECho MMuc NBir
- 'Bracteata'	CNat
- 'Rosea'	EBrs ECho MMuc
- 'Wavertree'	EBrs ECho
'Stuart Williams' **new**	CAvo
§ ***vicentina***	ERos WCot
- 'Alba'	ERos

Hyacinthus ✿ (*Hyacinthaceae*)

amethystinus	see *Brimeura amethystina*
azureus	see *Muscari azureum*
comosus 'Plumosus'	see *Muscari comosum* 'Plumosum'
fastigiatus	see *Brimeura fastigiata*
multi-flowered blue	CAvo EBrs
multi-flowered pink	EBrs
multi-flowered white	CAvo EBrs
orientalis	EBrs SMeo
- 'Aiolos'	LRHS SPer
- 'Amethyst'	EWal LAma
- 'Amsterdam'	EWal
- 'Anna Liza'	LRHS MBri
- 'Anna Marie' ♀H4	CBro EBrs EWal LAma MBri
- 'Atlantic'	LRHS
- 'Ben Nevis' (d)	LAma
- 'Blue Festival'	LRHS
- 'Blue Giant'	LAma LRHS
- 'Blue Jacket' ♀H4	CBro EBrs EWal LAma LRHS MBri
- 'Blue Pearl'PBR	SMeo
- 'Blue Star'	LAma SPhx
- 'Carnegie'	CAvo CBro EBrs EPfP EWal LAma SMeo SPhx
- 'China Pink'	LRHS SPer
- 'City of Haarlem' ♀H4	CAvo CBro EBrs EPfP EWal LAma LRHS MBri SMeo
- 'Crystal Palace' (d)	LAma
- 'Delft Blue' ♀H4	CAvo CBro EBrs EPfP EWal LAma LRHS MBri SPer SPhx
- 'Fondant'	LAma LRHS
- 'General Köhler' (d)	LAma
- 'Gipsy Princess'	LAma
- 'Gipsy Queen' ♀H4	EBrs EWal LAma LRHS MBri SPer
- 'Hollyhock' (d)	EWal LAma WCot
- 'Jan Bos'	EBrs EPfP EWal LAma LRHS MBri SPer
- 'L'Innocence' ♀H4	CBro EPfP
- 'Odysseus'	LAma LRHS
- 'Ostara' ♀H4	EPfP LAma MBri
- 'Peter Stuyvesant'	EBrs LAma
- 'Pink Festival'	LRHS SPer
- 'Pink Pearl' ♀H4	EBrs EPfP LAma LRHS MBri SPhx
- 'Pink Royal' (d)	LAma
- 'Purple Sensation'PBR	EBrs SMeo SPhx
- 'Red Magic'	LAma
- 'Rosette' (d)	LAma
- 'Sky Jacket'	LRHS
- 'Splendid Cornelia'	EBrs EWal LRHS SMeo SPer
- 'White Festival'	LRHS SPer
- 'White Pearl'	LAma LRHS MBri
- 'Woodstock'	CAvo EBrs EWal LAma LRHS SMeo SPer
- 'Yellow Queen'	LRHS

Hydrangea ✿ (*Hydrangeaceae*)

BWJ 8120 from Sichuan, China	WCru
SDR 5148 **new**	GKev
angustipetala	see *H. scandens* subsp. *chinensis* f. *angustipetala* Hayata, 1911
anomala subsp. ***anomala*** B&SWJ 2411	WCru

	Name	Suppliers
	- - BWJ 8052 from China	WCru
	- - 'Winter Glow'	WCru
	- subsp. ***glabra*** B&SWJ 6804	WCru
	- - 'Crûg Coral'	WCru
§	- subsp. ***petiolaris*** ♀H4	Widely available
	- - B&SWJ 5996 from Yakushima	WCru
	- - B&SWJ 6081	WCru
	- - B&SWJ 6337	WCru
§	- - var. ***cordifolia***	EBee NLar
§	- - - 'Brookside Littleleaf'	EQua IMon NLar WFar
	- - dwarf	see *H. anomala* subsp. *petiolaris* var. *cordifolia*
	- - 'Mirranda'	LRHS NBro SGol
*	- - var. ***tiliifolia***	EBee LRHS SHyH WFar WSHC
	- - - B&SWJ 8497	WCru
	- - 'Yakushima'	WCru WPGP
*	- subsp. ***quelpartensis*** B&SWJ 8799	WCru
	- - B&SWJ 8846	WCru
	- 'Winter Surprise'	MBri
§	***arborescens***	CArn CPLG MRav WFar WPGP
	- 'Annabelle' ♀H4	Widely available
	- 'Astrid Lindgren'	MBri
	- 'Bounty' **new**	MAsh
§	- subsp. ***discolor***	WCru WPat
	- - 'Sterilis'	GGGa SHyH WPGP
	- 'Grandiflora' ♀H4	CBcs CBot CMac ELan EPfP EQua LSRN MRav NBro NEgg WDin WHCG WPGP
	- 'Hayes Starburst' **new**	LRHS SPoG WHil
	- 'Hills of Snow'	MAsh
	- 'Picadilly' **new**	NLar
	- 'Pink Pincushion' **new**	MBri NLar
	- 'Puffed Green' **new**	NLar
	- subsp. ***radiata***	CAbP LRHS MAsh MRav SPoG SSpi WFar WPGP
	- - 'Samantha' **new**	NLar
	- 'Vasterival' **new**	NLar
	- White Dome = 'Dardom'[PBR]	MBri NBro SGol WCot
	aspera	CTri MGos SHyH SLon SSpi SSta WCom WCru WKif WPGP
	- HWJCM 452	WCru
	- from Gongshan, China	CPLG WPGP
	- 'Anthony Bullivant'	IArd LRHS MAsh MBri NLar SSpi WPat
	- Kawakamii Group	CGHE CHEx CMil CPLG CSpe EBee EPla NLar SSpi WCru WPGP
	- - B&SWJ 1420	WCru
	- - B&SWJ 3456	WCru
	- - B&SWJ 3462	WCru
	- - B&SWJ 6702	WCru
	- - B&SWJ 6714	WCru
	- - B&SWJ 6827	WCru
	- - B&SWJ 7025	WCru
	- - B&SWJ 7101	WCru
	- - 'August Abundance'	WCru
	- - 'Maurice Mason' **new**	CPLG
	- - 'September Splendour'	WCru
	- 'Macrophylla' ♀H3	CWib EPfP GCal MRav NBlu NPal SMad SSpi WCru WFar WPGP WSpi
	- 'Mauvette'	CMil LRHS MAsh MBlu NBro NLar NPal SPer SSpi WCru WPGP
	- 'Peter Chappell'	CMil LRHS SSpi WPGP
§	- subsp. ***robusta***	SLPl WCru WPGP WSpi
	- 'Rocklon'	CMil MBri NLar WPGP
	- 'Rosthornii'	see *H. aspera* subsp. *robusta*
	- 'Sam MacDonald'	CPLG GKir LRHS SHyH SSpi WPGP WSpi
§	- subsp. ***sargentiana*** ♀H3	Widely available
	- - large-leaved	WCot WCru
	- 'Spinners'	MBri
	- subsp. ***strigosa***	CDul CMil CPLG EPfP LRHS SHyH SSpi WCru WPGP
	- - B&SWJ 8201	WCru
	- - HWJ 653	WCru
	- - HWJ 737	WCru
	- - from Gong Shan, China	CGHE EBee
	- 'Taiwan'	EQua
	- 'Taiwan Pink'	EPfP MBri NLar
	- 'Velvet and Lace'	LBuc LRHS NLar
§	- Villosa Group ♀H3	Widely available
	cinerea	see *H. arborescens* subsp. *discolor*
	'Cohhii'	ECre
	'Compact Red'	ERas
	glandulosa B&SWJ 4031	WCru
§	***heteromalla***	CGHE CMHG CTrG EWTr GGal GKir SLPl SSpi WPGP
	- BWJ 7657 from China	WCru
	- B&SWJ 2142 from India	WCru
	- B&SWJ 2602 from Sikkim	WCru
	- HWJCM 180	WCru
	- HWJK 2127 from Nepal	WCru
	- SF 338	ISea
	- Bretschneideri Group	EBee EPfP GQui SHyH WCru WFar
	- 'Fan Si Pan'	WCru
	- 'Snowcap'	EPfP GQui IArd LRHS NLar SHyH SLPl SSpi WPGP
*	***heterophylla***	MGos
	hirta B&SWJ 5000	WCru
	indochinensis	CPLG
	- B&SWJ 8307	WCru
	integerrima	see *H. serratifolia*
	integrifolia	GGGa NLar WPGP
	- B&SWJ 022	WCru
	- B&SWJ 6967	WCru
	involucrata	EBee EPfP LLHF LRHS MMHG SHyH WDin
	- dwarf	WCru
	- 'Hortensis' (d) ♀H3-4	CMil EPfP MGan MRav SMad SSpi WAbe WCru WKif WPGP WSHC WSpi
	- 'Mihara-kokonoe' **new**	CPMA
	- 'Plena' (d)	CLAP LRHS MBri MRav SPoG SSta WCru WFar WPGP
	- 'Sterilis'	EPfP
	- 'Viridescens'	LLHF LRHS MBri SHyH WCru WPGP WSpi
	- 'Yokudanka' (d)	GQui
	involucrata* × *aspera Kawakamii Group	GGGa WPGP
	lobbii	see *H. scandens* subsp. *chinensis*
	longipes	CPLG GQui WCru WPGP
	- var. ***fulvescens*** B&SWJ 8188 **new**	WCru
	luteovenosa	WCru WPGP
	- B&SWJ 5602	WCru
	- B&SWJ 5647	WCru
	- B&SWJ 5929	WCru
	macrophylla	CTrG GGal LRHS
	- (H) **new**	LRHS
	- 'AB Green Shadow'[PBR]	IFFs MAsh MMHG SPoG
	- 'Adria' (H)	GGGa IFFs SHyH
	- 'Aduarda'	see *H. macrophylla* 'Mousmée'
	- 'All Summer Beauty' (H)	CMil
	- Alpen Glow	see *H. macrophylla* 'Alpenglühen'
§	- 'Alpenglühen' (H)	CBcs CPLG CSBt ELan LRHS SRms WPGP
	- 'Altona' (H) ♀H3-4	CBcs EPfP GGGa IArd ISea LRHS MAsh MGos MRav NBir NPri SHyH SPer WPGP
	- 'Amethyst' (H/d)	CGHE WPGP

	- 'Ami Pasquier' (H) ♀H3-4	CDoC CMac CSBt CTri EBee ELan EPfP GGal GKir LRHS LSRN MRav MSwo NEgg SBod SCoo SGar SHyH SLim SSpi SWvt WPGP
*	- 'Aureomarginata' (v)	EPfP SHyH WCot
	- 'Aureovariegata' (L/v)	ELan
	- 'Ave Maria' (H)	EQua ERas GGGa
§	- 'Ayesha' (H)	Widely available
	- 'Bachstelze' (Teller Series) (L)	MAsh SSpi
	- 'Beauté Vendômoise' (L)	CGHE CMil LRHS NLar SSpi WPGP
	- 'Bela'[PBR] (H) **new**	LRHS
	- 'Benelux' (H)	CBcs SHyH
	- 'Bicolor'	see *H. macrophylla* 'Harlequin'
§	- 'Blauer Prinz' (H)	CSam MAsh SHyH
	- 'Blauer Zwerg' (H)	MGos
§	- 'Bläuling' (Teller Series) (L)	CDoC EPfP LSRN MGos SBch SHyH WBrE
§	- 'Blaumeise' (Teller Series) (L)	CDoC CMHG CMil CSBt EPfP EQua GGGa GKir LRHS MAsh MBri MDKP MGos MRav NBlu NCGa NEgg SCoo SHyH SLim SLon SPoG SSpi SWvt WDin WPGP WSpi
	- 'Blue Bonnet' (H)	CChe EPfP LRHS LSRN MRav SHyH SPer
	- Blue Butterfly	see *H. macrophylla* 'Bläuling'
	- Blue Prince	see *H. macrophylla* 'Blauer Prinz'
	- Blue Sky	see *H. macrophylla* 'Blaumeise'
	- Blue Tit	see *H. macrophylla* 'Blaumeise'
	- 'Blue Wave'	see *H. macrophylla* 'Mariesii Perfecta'
	- 'Bluebird' misapplied	see *H. serrata* 'Bluebird'
	- Bluebird	see *H. macrophylla* 'Bläuling'
	- Blushing Bride = 'The Bride'	MAsh
	- 'Bodensee' (H)	LRHS MBri MMuc SHyH
	- 'Bouquet Rose' (H)	CWib ECtt LBMP MMuc NBlu
	- 'Bridal Bouquet' (H)	CDoC
	- 'Brügg' (H)	LRHS MAsh SHyH WPGP
	- 'Buchfink' (Teller Series) (L)	SSpi WPGP
	- Cardinal	see *H. macrophylla* 'Kardinal' (Teller Series)
§	- 'Cardinal Red' (H)	ECre LRHS
	- 'Chaperon Rouge' (H)	LRHS
	- 'Colour Fantasy' (H)	MBrN
	- 'Cordata'	see *H. arborescens*
	- 'Dandenong' (L)	GQui
	- 'Dart's Song'	NLar
	- 'Deutschland' (H)	CTri
	- 'Doctor Jean Varnier' (L)	MAsh
	- 'Domotoi'	see *H. macrophylla* 'Setsuka-yae'
	- Dragonfly	see *H. macrophylla* 'Libelle'
*	- 'Dwaag Pink'	MRav
	- 'Eldorado' (H)	SHyH
	- Endless Summer = 'Bailmer' (H)	EBrs EMil EPfP LBuc LRHS MAsh MGos NPri
§	- 'Enziandom' (H)	CBcs CPLG CSBt GGal MAsh WPGP
	- Eternity = 'Youmetwo'[PBR] (H/d)	EMil LRHS
	- 'Etoile Violette'	EQua MAsh
	- 'Eugen Hahn' **new**	LRHS
	- 'Europa' (H) ♀H3-4	CBcs CPLG LRHS MGos SHyH
§	- 'Fasan' (Teller Series) (L)	EQua SHyH WPGP
	- Firelight	see *H. macrophylla* 'Leuchtfeuer'
	- Fireworks	see *H. macrophylla* 'Hanabi'
	- Fireworks Blue	see *H. macrophylla* 'Jōgasaki'
	- Fireworks Pink	see *H. macrophylla* 'Jōgasaki'
	- Fireworks White	see *H. macrophylla* 'Hanabi'
	- Forever and Ever = 'Early Sensation' (Forever and Ever Series) (H)	CMac LRHS MBri SPoG
	- 'Forever Pink' (H)	MAsh NLar
§	- 'Frau Fujiyo' (Lady Series) (H)	CPLG
§	- 'Frau Katsuko' (Lady Series) (H)	SPer
§	- 'Frau Mariko' (Lady Series) (H)	MRav
§	- 'Frau Taiko' (Lady Series) (H)	SPer
	- 'Frillibet' (H)	CAbP CDoC EPfP MRav WPGP
	- 'Gartenbaudirektor Kühnert' (H)	SHyH
§	- 'Générale Vicomtesse de Vibraye' (H) ♀H3-4	CDoC CEnd CMHG CTri EBee EPfP GGal GKir LRHS MAsh SDix SEND SHyH SLim SPer SSpi WBVN WPGP
	- Gentian Dome	see *H. macrophylla* 'Enziandom'
	- 'Geoffrey Chadbund'	see *H. macrophylla* 'Möwe'
	- 'Gerda Steiniger' (H)	SHyH
	- 'Gertrud Glahn' (H)	SHyH WFar
	- 'Gimpel' (Teller Series) (L)	MAsh
	- 'Glowing Embers' (H)	IArd MBNS WPGP
	- Goldrush = 'Nehyosh' (v)	CMil CWGN LRHS MAsh NEgg SBch SLim SPoG
	- 'Goliath' (H)	EPfP GGar
§	- 'Grant's Choice' (L)	EQua GGGa NBro
	- Great Star = 'Blanc Bleu' **new**	EPfP LRHS MAsh SBch
	- 'Hamburg' (H)	CEnd CTri EBee ECtt EPfP MGos SDix SHyH SLim WFar
§	- 'Hanabi' (L/d)	CDoC CLAP CMil ECre EQua GGal MBlu NLar SHyH
§	- 'Harlequin' (H)	CMac WCot WPGP
	- 'Harry's Red' (H)	MAsh
	- 'Hatsu-shime' (L)	NLar
	- 'Heinrich Seidel' (H)	CBcs CTri WMoo
	- 'Holehird Purple' **new**	MAsh
	- 'Homigo'[PBR] (Hovaria Series) (H)	SHyH
	- 'Izu-no-hana' (L/d)	CAlb CBcs CLAP CMil ELon LEdu LHop LRHS MAsh MBlu NLar SHyH SPoG SSpi SUsu WBor WPGP
	- 'James Grant'	see *H. macrophylla* 'Grant's Choice'
	- 'Jofloma'	EQua NLar
§	- 'Jōgasaki' (L/d)	CBcs CLAP CMil CPLG MAsh MBlu NLar SHyH WPGP
	- 'Joseph Banks' (H)	CBcs CTri SHyH
	- 'Kardinal'	see *H. macrophylla* 'Cardinal Red' (H)
§	- 'Kardinal' (Teller Series) (L)	ERas MAsh
	- 'King George' (H)	CBcs CDoC CDul CSBt EBee IMon LAst LBMP LRHS MBar MGos NEgg NPri SBch SHyH SLim SPer SPoG SWvt WFar WMoo
§	- 'Klaveren'	CMil GGGa MAsh NBro
	- 'Kluis Superba' (H)	CBcs CTri GGal SHyH
	- 'La France' (H)	CTri EBee LRHS MBar SBch SHyH WFar
	- 'Lady Fujiyo'	see *H. macrophylla* 'Frau Fujiyo'
	- 'Lady in Red' (L) **new**	IMon
	- Lady Katsuko	see *H. macrophylla* 'Frau Katsuko'
	- 'Lady Mariko'	see *H. macrophylla* 'Frau Mariko'
	- 'Lady Taiko Blue'	see *H. macrophylla* 'Frau Taiko'
	- 'Lady Taiko Pink'	see *H. macrophylla* 'Frau Taiko'
*	- 'Lanarth' blue-flowered	GGal
	- 'Lanarth White' (L) ♀H3-4	CBcs CDoC CPLG CSBt CTri EBee ELan EPfP GGal IMon LBMP LRHS MAsh MSwo SBod SHyH SLPl SLim SPer SRms SSpi WBor WKif WPGP
	- 'Lemon Wave' (L/v)	NLar
§	- 'Leuchtfeuer' (H)	LRHS MGos SHyH WMoo
§	- 'Libelle' (Teller Series) (L)	CBcs CDoC EPfP ISea LBMP LRHS MGos MRav NBlu NCGa NEgg SBch

		SHyH SLim SPer SPoG SSpi WKif WSpi
	- 'Lilacina'	see *H. macrophylla* 'Mariesii Lilacina'
	- 'Love You Kiss'PBR (Hovaria Series) (L)	CBcs LBuc LRHS MAsh SCoo SHyH SPoG SRGP
§	- 'Maculata' (L/v)	ELan GQui MSCN WGwG
	- 'Madame A. Riverain' (H)	SHyH
	- 'Madame Emile Mouillère' (H) ♀H3-4	Widely available
	- 'Maréchal Foch' (H)	CTri GGal NLar
	- 'Mariesii' (L)	CMHG CTri CTsd ELan GGal ISea MMuc MSwo NMun SDix SPer WGwG WKif
§	- 'Mariesii Grandiflora' (L) ♀H3-4	CAlb CTsd EPfP GGal LRHS MBar NBro SHyH SPer SRms WDin WFar WMoo WPGP
§	- 'Mariesii Lilacina' (L) ♀H3-4	EPfP SEND SLon SPer WKif WMoo WPGP
§	- 'Mariesii Perfecta' (L) ♀H3-4	Widely available
	- 'Mariesii Variegata' (L/v)	CWib
	- 'Masja' (H)	EBee IArd IMon LRHS MAsh MGos MRav MSwo NBro SHyH
	- 'Mathilde Gütges' (H)	CDoC GGal LRHS WPGP
	- 'Max Löbner' (H)	SHyH
	- 'Merveille Sanguine' (H)	CDoC CGHE CMHG CMil EMil EPfP EQua GCal GGGa GGal IArd IMon LRHS MBri MRav NCGa NLar SPoG WCot WGrn WPGP WPat
	- 'Messalina' (L)	MAsh MGos SHyH
	- 'Mirai'PBR (H)	SCoo SHyH WCot
	- 'Miss Belgium' (H)	CMac CTri EQua MAsh
§	- 'Mousmée' (L)	IArd SSpi
	- 'Mousseline' (H)	MAsh
§	- 'Möwe' (L) ♀H3-4	CBcs CDoC CEnd CMil CPLG EBee ECtt ELon EPfP GGal LHop LRHS LSRN MAsh MMuc NLar SCoo SDix SHyH SLim SPer SRms SSpi SSta WPGP WPat
	- 'Mrs W.J. Hepburn'	CSBt SHyH SPer
§	- 'Nachtigall' (Teller Series) (L)	CMil EBee GGal MAsh
	- 'Niedersachsen' (H)	CDoC CTri MRav SHyH WPGP
	- Nightingale	see *H. macrophylla* 'Nachtigall'
	- 'Nigra' (H) ♀H3-4	CBcs CChe CMil CPLG CWib EBee ELan EPfP GGGa IFoB LRHS MAsh MBri MGos MMuc MRav MSCN NBro SDix SHyH SPer WClo WFar WGrn WGwG WPGP WPat WSpi
	- 'Nikko Blue' (H)	CBcs CTsd EPfP MBar MHav NBlu
	- var. ***normalis*** (L)	CPLG
§	- 'Nymphe' (H)	SHyH
	- 'Oregon Pride' (H)	GGGa LRHS MAsh WPGP
	- 'Otaksa' (H)	NLar
	- 'Papagei' (Teller Series)	SPer
	- 'Parzifal' (H) ♀H3-4	CDul GGGa WPGP
	- 'Pax' (H)	see *H. macrophylla* 'Nymphe'
	- 'Pfau' (Teller Series) (L)	ELon MAsh
	- Pheasant	see *H. macrophylla* 'Fasan'
	- 'Pia' (H)	CBgR CDoC CMil CPLG CStu ELan GGGa LBuc LRHS MAsh MGos MRav NWCA SMad SPer SRms WBor WClo WCru WFar
	- Pigeon	see *H. macrophylla* 'Taube'
	- 'Pink Wave' (L)	LRHS NPri
	- 'Pirate's Gold' **new**	CMil MAsh WClo WHar
	- 'Prinses Beatrix' (H)	SHyH
	- 'Quadricolor' (L/v)	CAbb CMac CMil CPLG EHoe GCal GGal MRav SDix SGar SHyH SLim SPer SPlb SRms WCot WHCG WSHC
	- 'R.F. Felton' (H)	CBcs SHyH
	- 'Red Baron'	see *H. macrophylla* 'Schöne Bautznerin'
	- 'Red Red' (H)	MAsh
	- Redbreast	see *H. macrophylla* 'Rotkehlchen'
	- 'Regula' (H)	SHyH
	- 'Renate Steiniger' (H)	MGos MMuc MRav SHyH WGwG
	- 'Romance'	LBuc LRHS MAsh SPoG
	- 'Rosita' (H)	IFFs LRHS MAsh NBir WFar
§	- 'Rotkehlchen' (Teller Series) (L)	CDoC CSBt EPfP GKir LRHS NBlu NCGa NEgg SCoo SPlb SPoG SWvt WDin
	- 'Rotschwanz' (Teller Series) (L)	CMil EQua ERas LRHS MAsh SHyH SSpi WPGP
	- 'Sabrina'PBR (H)	CBcs MBri MGos SPoG
	- 'Saint Claire' (H)	CBcs SHyH
	- 'Sandra' (Dutch Ladies Series) (L)	CBcs ELon
	- 'Schneeball' (H)	MAsh MGos SHyH
§	- 'Schöne Bautznerin'	ERas LRHS NCGa SHyH WClo WMoo
	- 'Sea Foam' (L)	EBee NBlu
	- 'Selina'	CBcs LSRN MDKP MGos SPoG
	- 'Selma'PBR (Dutch Ladies Series) (L)	CBcs MBri
§	- 'Setsuka-yae' (L/d)	CMil MBri
	- 'Sheila' (Dutch Ladies Series) (L)	CBcs LSRN MBri
	- 'Sibilla' (H)	CBcs LRHS SPlb WPGP
	- Sister Therese	see *H. macrophylla* 'Soeur Thérèse'
§	- 'Soeur Thérèse' (H)	CSBt EBee EMil LRHS MAsh MGos SWvt WGwG WPGP
	- 'Soraya'PBR (Dutch Ladies Series) (L)	CBcs
	- 'Sumida-no-hanabi' (L/d)	WPGP
*	- 'Sunset' (L)	CBcs
§	- 'Taube' (Teller Series) (L)	CBcs CDoC CMHG CPLG EPfP GGal GQui MAsh NBlu NCGa SCoo SHyH SWvt
	- 'Teller Pink'	see *H. macrophylla* 'Taube'
	- 'Teller Red'	see *H. macrophylla* 'Rotkehlchen'
N	- Teller variegated	see *H. macrophylla* 'Tricolor'
N	- Teller Weiss	see *H. macrophylla* 'Libelle'
	- var. ***thunbergii***	see *H. serrata* var. ***thunbergii***
	- 'Tokyo Delight' (L) ♀H3-4	CDoC CGHE CLAP CMil CPLG CTsd EBee LRHS MAsh SHyH WPGP
	- 'Tovelit' (H)	GGGa
§	- 'Tricolor' (L/v)	CBcs CBot CDoC CDul CTri EBee ELon EMil EQua ERas LAst LRHS MGos SHyH SLon SMad SPer SPoG WFar WKif WMoo
	- 'Variegata'	see *H. macrophylla* 'Maculata'
	- 'Veitchii' (L) ♀H3-4	CBcs CBot CMHG CMil CPLG CSBt EPfP GGal LRHS MRav MSwo SDix SGar SHyH SPoG SSpi WPGP WSpi
	- 'Vicomte de Vibraye'	see *H. macrophylla* 'Générale Vicomtesse de Vibraye'
	- 'Westfalen' (H) ♀H3-4	CMac IArd SDix
I	- 'White Lace' (L)	ELan SHyH
	- 'White Mop' (H)	CWib
	- 'White Wave'	see *H. macrophylla* 'Mariesii Grandiflora'
	- 'Zaunkoenig' (L)	MAsh
	- 'Zhuni Hito'	NLar
	- 'Zorro'PBR	CBcs EPfP LRHS MAsh SCoo SPoG
	aff. ***mangshanensis*** BWJ 8120 **new**	WCru
	paniculata	CMCN WBor
	- B&SWJ 3556 from Taiwan	WCru
	- B&SWJ 5413 from Japan	WCru
	- 'Ammarin'	GQui LLHF NLar WPat
	- Angel's Blush	see *H. paniculata* 'Ruby'

- 'Big Ben'	EPfP GGGa GQui LRHS MBri NLar
- 'Brussels Lace'	CAbP EBee EPfP GKir LEdu LRHS LSRN MBri MRav SGol SHyH SLon SPoG SSpi WPat
- 'Burgundy Lace'	CBcs EQua GGGa MBlu MBri NLar
- 'Chantilly Lace' **new**	CMil LRHS
- Dart's Little Dot = 'Darlido'PBR	LLHF LSRN MAsh NLar SGol WPat
- 'Dharuma'	EBee LLHF LRHS MAsh
- 'Dolly'	GQui
- 'Everest'	CAbP EPfP LRHS MAsh SHyH SPoG
- 'Floribunda'	CGHE ELan EPfP LRHS MAsh WPGP
- 'Goliath' **new**	NLar
- 'Grandiflora' ♀H4	Widely available
- 'Great Escape'	NLar
- 'Greenspire'	LRHS MAsh MBlu MRav WFar
- 'Harry's Souvenir'	NLar
- 'Kyushu' ♀H4	Widely available
- 'Last Post' **new**	GQui
- 'Limelight'PBR	Widely available
- 'Little Lamb' **new**	SGol
- 'Mathilde' **new**	NLar
- 'Mega Pearl'	LSRN
- 'Melody' **new**	NLar
- 'Mount Aso'	GQui MAsh NBro NLar WPGP
- 'October Bride'	GQui MBri NLar WPGP
- 'Papillon'	WPat
- 'Pee Wee'	GGGa LLHF NLar
- 'Phantom'	CBcs CMil EPfP GGGa LRHS LSRN LSqu MAsh MBri MDKP MRav NCGa NLar SGol SPoG WCot WPGP WPat WSpi
- 'Pink Beauty'PBR	LSRN
- Pink Diamond = 'Interhydia' ♀H4	CAbP CBcs CDoC CSBt EBee ECrN EPfP GQui LAst LEdu LHop LRHS LSRN MAsh MGos MRav NBro NLar NPri SHyH SMad SPoG SSpi SSta WClo WCom WCot WFar WPGP WPat
- 'Pink Jewel'	CWib LLHF WPat
- Pinky-Winky = 'Dvppinky'PBR	CWGN EGxp EMil GGGa IMon LLHF LRHS MBlu MGos NLar SGol SPoG
- 'Praecox'	GQui MAsh MRav WPat
- Quickfire = 'Bulk'PBR **new**	SGol
§ - 'Ruby' **new**	CBcs NPal
- 'Silver Dollar'	EPfP GGGa LRHS LSRN MBri
- 'Tardiva'	CBcs CBot CChe CDoC CMac EBee EPfP EWTr GQui LRHS MGos MRav NBro NPri SDix SHyH SPer SRms WDin WFar WPGP WPat
- 'Tender Rose'	NLar
- 'Unique' ♀H4	CBcs CDoC CGHE CSpe EBee EPfP GQui LEdu LHop LRHS LSRN MAsh MRav NBro NCGa SBch SHyH SPer SPoG SSpi WBor WClo WDin WFar WPGP WPat
- Vanille Fraise = 'Renhy'	CAlb EPfP GGGa LRHS LSRN MAsh NCGa SGol SPoG
- 'Waterfall'	CLAP
- 'White Goliath' **new**	GQui
- 'White Lace'	CBcs NLar
- 'White Lady'	CBcs
- 'White Moth'	CBcs CWGN EQua GGGa LLHF LRHS MAsh NBro NLar SHyH WPat
petiolaris	see *H. anomala* subsp. *petiolaris*
'Preziosa' ♀H3-4	Widely available
quelpartensis	CRHN GQui WCom
- B&SWJ 4400	WCru
quercifolia ♀H3-4	Widely available
- 'Alice'	CPMA EBee EPfP EPla LRHS MAsh MBri SRGP SSpi WPGP
- 'Alison'	EPfP
I - 'Amethyst' Dirr	MBri
- 'Burgundy'	CBcs CPMA EPfP MBri NLar WPGP
- 'Flore Pleno'	see *H. quercifolia* Snowflake
- 'Harmony'	CMil CPMA EPfP IArd LRHS MBri NLar SSta WPGP WPat
- 'Lady Anne'	MRav SMad WPGP
- Little Honey = 'Brihon'	CAbP LRHS MAsh MBri SPoG
* - 'Pee Wee'	CBcs CDoC CMil CPMA EPfP LRHS MAsh NLar SHyH SLon SPoG SReu SSta WPGP WPat
- 'Sike's Dwarf'	CPMA EBee GCal LRHS MGos MPkF MRav SGol WPat WSpi
- 'Snow Giant' **new**	NLar
- Snow Queen = 'Flemygea'	CBcs CDoC CDul CKno CMac CPMA EBee ELan EPfP EWTr LRHS MAsh MGos MPkF MRav NCGa NLar SHyH SLim SPer SPoG SWvt WFar WHCG WPGP WPat WSpi
- 'Snowdrift'	CPMA
§ - Snowflake = 'Brido' (d)	CAbP CBcs CDoC CEnd CHar CMil CPMA CSPN CWGN EBee ELan EPfP GKir LRHS MAsh MGos MRav SLon SPer SPoG SSpi SSta WPGP WPat
- 'Stardust'	MMHG
- 'Tennessee Clone'	CPMA EBee MBri NLar
sargentiana	see *H. aspera* subsp. *sargentiana*
scandens B&SWJ 5448	WCru
- B&SWJ 5481	WCru
- B&SWJ 5496	WCru
- B&SWJ 5523	WCru
- B&SWJ 5602	WCru
- B&SWJ 5893	WCru
- B&SWJ 5929	WCru
- B&SWJ 6159	WCru
- B&SWJ 6317	WCru
§ - subsp. ***chinensis***	CPLG WFar
- - B&SWJ 1488	WCru
- - B&SWJ 3214	WCru
- - B&SWJ 3420	WCru
§ - - f. ***angustipetala***	WPGP
- - - B&SWJ 3454	WCru
- - - B&SWJ 3553	WCru
- - - B&SWJ 3667	WCru
- - - B&SWJ 3733	WCru
- - - B&SWJ 3814	WCru
- - - B&SWJ 6038 from Yakushima	WCru
- - - B&SWJ 6041	WCru
- - - B&SWJ 6056	WCru
- - - B&SWJ 6787	WCru
- - - B&SWJ 6802	WCru
- - - B&SWJ 7121	WCru
- - - B&SWJ 7128	WCru
- - f. ***formosana***	NLar
- - - B&SWJ 1488	WCru
- - - B&SWJ 3271	WCru
- - - B&SWJ 3410 from Taiwan	WCru
- - - B&SWJ 3423	WCru
- - - B&SWJ 3487	WCru
- - - B&SWJ 7058	EQua WCru
- - - B&SWJ 7097	WCru
- - - BWJ 8000 from Sichuan	WCru
- - f. ***macrosepala*** B&SWJ 3423	WCru
- - - B&SWJ 3476	WCru

- - f. ***obovatifolia*** B&SWJ 3487b	WCru
- - - B&SWJ 3683	WCru
- - - B&SWJ 7121	WCru
- subsp. ***liukiuensis***	WCru
- - B&SWJ 6022	WCru
- 'Splash' (v)	CMil
seemannii	Widely available
- 'Variegata' new	CBcs
Semiola = 'Inovalaur' new	MAsh SBch
serrata	CPLG CTri CWib WDin WKif
- B&SWJ 4817	WCru
- B&SWJ 6241	WCru
- 'Acuminata'	see *H. serrata* 'Bluebird'
- 'Aigaku' (L)	CLAP CPLG WPGP
- 'Aka Beni-yama'	GQui
- 'Akabe-yama' new	NBro
- Amacha Group	CGHE
- - 'Amagi-amacha' (:)	CMil GQui NBro
- - 'Ō-amacha'	CMil GQui
- 'Amagyana' (L)	CGHE CPLG WPGP
- 'Belladonna' new	GQui
- 'Belle Deckle'	see *H. serrata* 'Blue Deckle'
- 'Beni-gaku' (L)	CLAP CMil CPLG CTsd EBee EGxp GGGa LRHS MAsh NBro NLar SHyH WPGP
- 'Beni-yama' (L)	CGHE CMil GQui WPGP
- 'Blue Billow' (L)	GGGa NBro NLar
§ - 'Blue Deckle' (L)	CMHG CMac EQua GGal MAsh MRav NBro SHyH WPGP
§ - 'Bluebird' (L) ♀$^{H3-4}$	CBcs CDul EBee ELan EPfP GKir GQui LRHS MAsh MBar MBlu MGos MMuc MRav MSwo NBlu NEgg SBod SDix SHyH SLim SPer SWvt WBVN WBrE WFar WHar WMoo WSpi
- 'Diadem' (L) ♀$^{H3-4}$	CMil CPLG EPfP EQua GGGa LRHS NBro SDix WPGP
- dwarf white-flowered (L)	WCru
- 'Forget Me Not' new	GQui
- 'Fuji Waterfall'	see *H. serrata* 'Fuji-no-taki'
§ - 'Fuji-no-taki' (L/d)	CAbP CMil LLHF LSou NCGa NEgg SMad WBor WFar
- 'Golden Showers' (L)	GGGa MAsh NBro
- 'Golden Sunlight'^{PBR} (L)	CBcs CDoC GGGa GQui LRHS SWvt
- 'Graciosa' (L)	MAsh WPGP
- 'Grayswood' (L) ♀$^{H3-4}$	CBcs CEnd CEnt CMac CSBt EPfP EQua ERas GGal GKir GQui LRHS MAsh MRav NBro SDix SGar SHyH SPer SSpi WBor WKif WPGP
- 'Hakucho' (L/d)	NBro
- 'Hallasan' misapplied	see *H. serrata* 'Maiko', 'Spreading Beauty'
- 'Hallasan' ambig.	CMil
- 'Hime-benigaku' (L)	CLAP CMil MAsh
- 'Impératrice Eugénie' (L)	GQui
- 'Intermedia' (L)	CPLG NBro
- 'Isusai-jaku' (L)	GQui
- 'Kiyosumi' (L)	CDoC CEnd CGHE CLAP CMil CPLG ECre GGGa GGal GQui MAsh NBir SHyH WBor WCot WCru WPGP WSpi
- 'Klaveren'	see *H. macrophylla* 'Klaveren'
- 'Koreana' (L)	EQua GGGa MAsh
- 'Kurenai' (L)	NBro NLar
- 'Kurenai-nishiki' (L/v)	CMil
- 'Kurohime' (L)	NBro
- 'Macrosepala' (L)	MAsh SHyH
§ - 'Maiko' (L)	IArd
- 'Midora'	CPLG
- 'Midori' (L)	SHyH
- 'Mikata Yae' new	CMil
- 'Miranda' (L) ♀$^{H3-4}$	CBow CBrd CPLG CSam EPfP LRHS MAsh NBro SHyH SSpi WFar
- 'Miyama-yae-murasaki' (L/d)	CGHE CLAP CMil EQua LRHS MAsh WCom WPGP
- 'Momo Beni Yama' new	CMil
- 'Pretty Maiden'	see *H. serrata* 'Shichidanka'
- 'Professeur Iida' (L)	WPGP
§ - 'Prolifera' (L/d)	CGHE CMil WPGP
- 'Pulchella'	see *H. serrata* 'Prolifera'
- 'Ramis Pictis' (L)	EQua ERas GQui NBro NLar WPGP
- 'Rosalba' (L) ♀$^{H3-4}$	CLAP CPLG EPfP GGal NBro SPer WFar WSHC
- 'Sapphirine' (L) new	GQui
§ - 'Shichidanka' (L/d)	NBro
- 'Shichidanka-nishiki' (L/d/v)	CDoC CGHE CPLG ECre LRHS SHyH WBor
- 'Shinonome' (L/d)	CLAP CMil GQui WPGP
- 'Shirofuji' (L/d)	CLAP CMil LRHS MAsh WPGP
- 'Shiro-gaku' (L)	MAsh NBro
- 'Shirotae' (L/d)	CMil GGGa WPGP
- 'Shōjō'	CMil MAsh
§ - 'Spreading Beauty' (L)	CMil WPGP
§ - var. ***thunbergii*** (L)	CMHG GQui WFar WPGP
* - - 'Plena' (L/d)	WCru
- 'Tiara' (L) ♀$^{H3-4}$	CAbb CMil GGGa GGal LRHS LSRN MAsh NBir NBro NLar SDix SHyH SSpi WPGP
- 'Uzu-azisai'	WPGP
- 'Yae-no-amacha' (L/d)	NBro SHyH WPGP
- subsp. ***yezoensis*** new	GQui
§ ***serratifolia***	CHEx CPLG EPfP EPla SPoG SSpi SSta WCru WFar WPGP
- HCM 98056	WCru
sikokiana	CLAP
- B&SWJ 5035	WCru
- B&SWJ 5855	WCru
'Silver Slipper'	see *H. macrophylla* 'Ayesha'
tiliifolia	see *H. anomala* subsp. *petiolaris*
villosa	see *H. aspera* Villosa Group
'Water Wagtail'	ERas
xanthoneura	see *H. heteromalla*
'You and Me'	SCoo

Hydrastis (*Ranunculaceae*)

canadensis	CArn COld GBuc GPoy WCru

Hydrocharis (*Hydrocharitaceae*)

morsus-ranae	CRow EHon EMFW LPBA NPer NSco SWat WPnP

Hydrocleys (*Limnocharitaceae*)

nymphoides	XBlo

Hydrocotyle (*Apiaceae*)

asiatica	see *Centella asiatica*
sibthorpioides	CBow
- 'Crystal Confetti' (v)	EPPr EShb LLWG SIng WCHb WPer
vulgaris	CWat EBWF EMFW

Hydrophyllum (*Hydrophyllaceae*)

canadense	EBee IMou
virginianum	EBee

Hylomecon (*Papaveraceae*)

* ***hylomecoides***	EBee WCru
§ ***japonica***	CFwr CLAP EBee ECho ELan GBBs GBuc GCra GEdr GKev GKir NBir NMen NRya SHGN WAbe WCru WFar WTin

Hylotelephium see *Sedum*

Hymenanthera see *Melicytus*

Hymenocallis (*Amaryllidaceae*)

'Advance'	EBrs ECho LAma
§ ***caroliniana***	ECho
× ***festalis*** 𝕐H1	CCCN CDes ECho EPfP IHer LAma LRHS MBri SPav SPer WCot WFar
- 'Zwanenburg'	CGrW EBrs ECho WHil
harrisiana	CCCN EBrs ECho LRHS SPer WCot
§ ***longipetala***	EBrs ECho WCot
occidentalis	see *H. caroliniana*
'Sulphur Queen' 𝕐H1	CGrW EBrs ECho LRHS SPav WCot WHil

Hymenolepis (*Asteraceae*)

parviflora	see *Athanasia parviflora*

Hymenosporum (*Pittosporaceae*)

flavum	EShb

Hymenoxys (*Asteraceae*)

cooperi var. ***canescens***	CPBP
grandiflora	see *Tetraneuris grandiflora*
§ ***hoopesii***	CMHG CMac EBee EBla EGxp EHrv ELan EPfP EShb GAbr GKir GMaP LHop LRHS NBir NChi NEgg NPri SPer SRms WClo WCot WFar WMnd WPer WWEG

Hyophorbe (*Arecaceae*)

lagenicaulis	LPal
verschaffeltii	LPal

Hyoscyamus (*Solanaceae*)

albus	CSpe
aureus RCB RL -16	WCot
niger	CArn GPoy

Hypericum ✿ (*Clusiaceae*)

CC 4131	CPLG
CC 4544	CPLG
SDR 5106	GKev
SDR 5153	GKev
acmosepalum	WPGP WPat
aegypticum	CPBP ECho ECtt EPot LRHS MHer NMen NWCA WAbe WCom WFar WOld WPat WPer
androsaemum	CArn CRWN ECha ELan MHer MRav MSwo NPer NSco SIng WDin WMoo WOut
§ - 'Albury Purple'	EShb GBuc LDai MRav WCom WHrl WMoo
- 'Autumn Blaze'	CBcs EBee MGos
§ - 'Dart's Golden Penny'	SPer
- 'Excellent Flair'	EBee MGos NLar
- 'Orange Flair'	MGos
§ - f. ***variegatum*** 'Mrs Gladis Brabazon' (v)	EAro NBir NLar NScw SBod WCom WHrl
athoum	NBir WAbe WThu
atomarium	EBee WPGP
balearicum	CMea EHrv MTho WAbe WPGP
barbatum	WFar
§ ***beanii***	GAuc
bellum	EBee GCal SLon
- subsp. ***latisepalum***	SLon
calycinum	CBcs CDul CMac CTri CWan EBee ECho ECrN ELan EPfP LBuc MBar MGos MRav MWat NWea SBch SPer SPoG SWvt WCFE WDin WGwG WMoo
- 'Brigadoon' **new**	SGol
- 'Senior'	LAst
cerastioides	CMea CTri CWib LRHS SIng SMrm SRms WFar WPat WPer
coris	ECho EWes MTho MWat NMen SRms
cuneatum	see *H. pallens*
× ***cyathiflorum*** 'Gold Cup'	CMac LRHS
× ***dummeri*** 'Peter Dummer'	NLar WSpi
elatum	see *H.* × *inodorum*
elodes	CWat EMFW LLWG MSKA
empetrifolium	ECho
- 'Prostatum'	see *H. empetrifolium* subsp. *tortuosum*
§ - subsp. ***tortuosum***	ECho EWes
forrestii 𝕐H4	EPfP MMuc WFar WPGP
- B&L 12469	WPGP
- Hird 54	WPGP
N ***fragile*** misapplied	see *H. olympicum* f. *minus*
frondosum 'Buttercup'	EBee NLar
- 'Sunburst'	EPfP
N 'Gemo'	ECrN MGos
'Gold Penny'	see *H. androsaemum* 'Dart's Golden Penny'
'Golden Beacon'	CBow CSpe EBee LAst LRHS LSou NEgg NLar SMad SPoG WCot
grandiflorum	see *H. kouytchense*
henryi	MSnd
- L 753	SRms
'Hidcote' 𝕐H4	Widely available
'Hidcote Variegated' (v)	CBow LRHS MAsh MCCP SLim SPer SRms WFar
hirsutum	EBWF NMir
§ × ***inodorum***	NBir
- 'Albury Purple'	see *H. androsaemum* 'Albury Purple'
- 'Autumn Surprise' PBR	NEgg NHol WHar
- 'Dream'	NLar
- 'Elstead'	EBee ECrN ECtt ELan EPfP MBar MGos MMHG MRav MWat NBlu NHol SRms WDin WHCG WSpi
- 'Hysan'	GGar
- 'Rheingold'	LRHS MAsh
- 'Ysella'	MRav
japonicum	ECho EWes
kalmianum	EWes
kamtschaticum	ECho
§ ***kiusianum*** var. ***yakusimense***	MBar MTho
kotschyanum **new**	ITim
§ ***kouytchense*** 𝕐H4	CDul CMCN EBee ELon EPfP EQua EWes GQui LRHS MAsh MMuc MRav SPoG WCFE WHrl WPat WSpi
lancasteri	EPfP LRHS MAsh SPoG WPat
leschenaultii misapplied	see *H.* 'Rowallane'
leschenaultii Choisy	CMCN
linarioides	EBee
maclarenii	EWes WPGP
Magical Beauty = 'Kolmbeau' PBR	EBee NHol NLar
Magical Red = 'Kolmred' PBR	NLar SPoG
× ***moserianum*** 𝕐H4	CMac EBee EPfP LRHS MBar MRav NPer SLon SPer SRms WDin
- 'Daybreak' **new**	MAsh
§ - 'Tricolor' (v)	Widely available
- 'Variegatum'	see *H.* × *moserianum* 'Tricolor'

'Mrs Brabazon' see *H. androsaemum* f. *variegatum* 'Mrs Gladis Brabazon'
nummularium NBir NMen WAbe
oblongifolium CPLG WAbe WCot
olympicum ♀H4 CEnt CHrt CTri ECha ECho ELan EPfP GJos LRHS MBrN MWat SHGN SPer SRms WAbe WDin WFar
- 'Grandiflorum' see *H. olympicum* f. *uniflorum*
§ - f. ***minus*** CTri ECho ECtt NBlu SPlb SRms WCom WHrl WPer
§ - - 'Sulphureum' CBgR CBot CChe CPrp ECho EWes GMaP LRHS MLHP NBir SPer SRms WCFE
- - 'Variegatum' (v) CBow CWan EWes LBee LRHS NBir NLAp SPoG WPat
§ - f. ***uniflorum*** ECho LRHS MBar NBlu NBro NVic SEND
- - 'Citrinum' ♀H4 CMea EBee ECha ECtt EPfP LBee LRHS MRav MWat NBro NDlv NLAp SPoG WAbe WCot WEas WHoo WKif WPGP WPat
orientale EWes
§ ***pallens*** ECho NMen WAbe
patulum var. ***henryi*** Rehder & hort. see *H. pseudohenryi*
- var. ***henryi*** Veitch ex Bean see *H. beanii*
perforatum CArn CBod CHby CWan EBWF EBee EPfP GBar GPoy MHer MNHC NMir NMun SEND SIde WHer WJek WMoo WSFF
polyphyllum see *H. olympicum* f. *minus*
- 'Citrinum' see *H. olympicum* f. *minus* 'Sulphureum'
- 'Grandiflorum' see *H. olympicum* f. *uniflorum*
prolificum ECtt MMHG WCFE
§ ***pseudohenryi*** L 1029 GBuc
pseudopetiolatum var. ***yakusimense*** see *H. kiusianum* var. *yakusimense*
'Purple Smoke' EMil
quadrangulum L. see *H. tetrapterum*
reptans misapplied see *H. olympicum* f. *minus*
reptans Dyer CMea ECho EWes
§ 'Rowallane' ♀H3 CTri EPfP GCal SDix SMrm SSpi
stellatum WFar
subsessile CPLG
'Sungold' see *H. kouytchense*
§ ***tetrapterum*** CArn EBWF NSco
trichocaulon EWes WAbe
uralum HWJ 520 WCru
xylosteifolium SLon
yakusimense see *H. kiusianum* var. *yakusimense*

Hypocalymma (*Myrtaceae*)

angustifolium ECou

Hypocalyptus (*Papilionaceae*)

sophoroides SPlb

Hypochaeris (*Asteraceae*)

maculata WHer
radicata EBWF NMir

Hypocyrta see *Nematanthus*

Hypoestes (*Acanthaceae*)

aristata CPLG EShb
- white-flowered **new** WHil
§ ***phyllostachya*** (v) ♀H1 EShb MBri
- 'Bettina' (v) MBri
- 'Carmina' (v) MBri
- 'Purpuriana' (v) MBri
- 'Wit' (v) MBri
sanguinolenta misapplied see *H. phyllostachya*

Hypolepis (*Dennstaedtiaceae*)

ambigua WRic
millefolium GGar WCot
punctata EFer
rufobarbata WRic

Hypoxis (*Hypoxidaceae*)

hirsuta CPen ECho
hygrometrica CPBP EBee EBrs ECho ECou NMen WAbe WThu
krebsii ECho LLHF
obtusa LLHF
parvula CFee NMen
- var. ***albiflora*** EBrs ITim
§ - - 'Hebron Farm Biscuit' CBro ECho EWes GEdr WAbe WFar
- pink-flowered EBrs
villosa ECho

Hypoxis × *Rhodohypoxis* see × *Rhodoxis*

H. parvula × ***R. baurii*** see × *Rhodoxis hybrida*

Hypsela (*Campanulaceae*)

sp. CFee
longiflora see *H. reniformis*
§ ***reniformis*** ECho EDAr GAbr GGar LBee LLWG LRHS MRav NWCA SIng WFar
- 'Greencourt White' ECho GBuc

Hypseocharis (*Oxalidaceae*)

pimpinellifolia WCot

Hyptis (*Lamiaceae*)

emoryi CArn

Hyssopus ✿ (*Lamiaceae*)

officinalis Widely available
- f. ***albus*** CWan EBee ECha ELau EPfP GPoy MHer MNHC NGHP SBch SGar SHGN SHlg SIde SPlb WCHb WJek WPer
- subsp. ***aristatus*** CArn CBod CHrt EBee ECho ELau GCal GPoy LLWP LRHS MHer MNHC NChi SBch SIde SPoG WCHb WJek
- 'Blaue Wolke' GBin
- 'Roseus' CEnt CHrt EBee ECha ELau EPfP GPoy LLWP LRHS MHer MNHC NGHP SBch SEND SHGN SIde SPoG WCHb WJek WKif WPer WSHC

Hystrix (*Poaceae*)

patula CHrt CKno CSam EHoe EShb GFor ILad LLWP MCCP MMoz MNrw MWhi NHol SEND SPlb WPer WTin

I

Iberis (*Brassicaceae*)

aurosica 'Sweetheart' GEdr WFar
candolleana see *I. pruitii* Candolleana Group
commutata see *I. sempervirens*
'Dick Self' LRHS
gibraltarica ECho EWTr SRms WGor
- 'Betty Swainson' CHrt SPhx SUsu
§ ***pruitii*** Candolleana Group ECho WAbe WFar

	saxatilis	ECho LRHS
	semperflorens	WCFE WCom WWEG
§	***sempervirens*** ♀H4	CMea CTri CWib ECho ELan EPfP GKir IFoB LAst MHer MMuc MWat NBro NHol NOrc NVic SEND SRms SWal WBrE WCFE WClo WFar WHoo WPer
	- 'Compacta'	ECho
	- 'Elfenreigen' **new**	GCal
	- 'Golden Candy'PBR	LRHS SPoG WFar
	- 'Little Gem'	see *I. sempervirens* 'Weisser Zwerg'
	- 'Pygmaea'	ECho NMen
	- Schneeflocke	see *I. sempervirens* 'Snowflake'
	- 'Snow Cushion' **new**	WWEG
§	- 'Snowflake' ♀H4	ECho EPfP GAbr GEdr IFoB LAst MWat NBlu NPri SBch SPer SPoG SWvt WFar WRHF
§	- 'Weisser Zwerg'	CMea ECha ECho ECtt ELan LAst LBee LRHS MHer MRav MWat NMen NRya SPoG SRms WHoo

Idesia (*Flacourtiaceae*)

	polycarpa	CAbP CDul CMCN EBee EPfP IDee LHop MMuc NLar SSpi WBVN WDin WFar WPGP WPat
	- var. ***vestita*** **new**	SSpi

Ilex ✿ (*Aquifoliaceae*)

N	× ***altaclerensis***	SHHo WFar
	- 'Atkinsonii' (m)	SHHo WWHy
	- 'Balearica' (f)	SHHo
	- 'Barterberry' (f)	WWHy
	- 'Belgica' (f)	SHHo
§	- 'Belgica Aurea' (f/v) ♀H4	CBcs CDoC CPMA CSBt CTho EBee EPfP EQua ERas MBar MBri MSwo NHol NWea SHHo WFar WWHy
	- 'Camelliifolia' (f) ♀H4	CDul CMac CSBt CTho EBee ELan EPfP ERas GKir IFoB LMaj MBlu MBri MWat NEgg NLar NPCo NWea SHHo WFar WSpi WWHy
	- 'Golden King' (f/v) ♀H4	Widely available
	- 'Hendersonii' (f)	NPCo SHHo WWHy
	- 'Hodginsii' (m) ♀H4	CTri MRav SEND SHHo WFar WWHy
	- 'Howick' (f/v)	SHHo
	- 'James G. Esson' (f)	SHHo
	- 'Jermyns' (m)	SHHo
	- 'Lady Valerie' (f/v)	SHHo WWHy
	- 'Lawsoniana' (f/v) ♀H4	Widely available
	- 'Maderensis Variegata'	see *I. aquifolium* 'Maderensis Variegata'
	- 'Marnockii' (f)	SHHo WWHy
	- 'Moorei' (m)	SHHo
	- 'Mundyi' (m)	SHHo
	- 'N.F. Barnes' (f)	SHHo
	- 'Purple Shaft' (f)	EQua MRav SHHo
	- 'Ripley Gold' (f/v)	EBee LRHS MAsh NHol SHHo WWHy
	- 'Silver Sentinel'	see *I.* × *altaclerensis* 'Belgica Aurea'
	- 'W.J. Bean' (f)	SHHo WWHy
	- 'Wilsonii' (f)	EBee EPfP ERas NPCo SHHo WWHy
	aquifolium ♀H4	Widely available
	- 'Alaska' (f)	CCVT CDoC CDul CMCN ECrN LAst LBuc LRHS MAsh NBlu NHol NLar NSti SBch SHHo SWvt WFar WWHy
	- 'Amber' (f) ♀H4	CTri EQua NPCo SHHo SMad WWHy
	- 'Angustifolia' (f)	LRHS MAsh WCFE WFar WWHy
	- 'Angustifolia' (m or f)	EPfP MBar MWat SHHo SPoG WBVN WFar
	- 'Angustimarginata Aurea' (m/v)	NPCo SHHo
	- 'Argentea Longifolia' (m/v)	WWHy
§	- 'Argentea Marginata' (f/v) ♀H4	Widely available
§	- 'Argentea Marginata Pendula' (f/v)	CDoC CMac CTri ELan EPfP ERas GKir LRHS MAsh MRav NHol NLar NWea SHHo SRms WFar WPat WWHy
	- 'Argentea Pendula'	see *I. aquifolium* 'Argentea Marginata Pendula'
	- 'Argentea Variegata'	see *I. aquifolium* 'Argentea Marginata'
	- 'Atlas' (m)	CBcs CDoC LBuc WWHy
	- 'Aurea Marginata' (f/v)	CMac CTho EBee EPfP LBuc LRHS MGos NBlu NHol NPCo NWea SCoo SHHo WCFE WDin WFar WPat
	- 'Aurea Marginata Pendula' (f/v)	CDoC NHol WPat
	- 'Aurea Marginata Stricta' (f/v)	WWHy
	- 'Aurea Regina'	see *I. aquifolium* 'Golden Queen'
	- 'Aureovariegata Pendula'	see *I. aquifolium* 'Weeping Golden Milkmaid'
	- 'Aurifodina' (f)	IMGH NPCo SHHo WWHy
	- 'Bacciflava' (f)	Widely available
	- 'Bella' (f)	SHHo
	- 'Bokrijk' (f/v)	SHHo WWHy
	- 'Bowland' (f/v)	NHol
	- 'Chris Whittle'	NHol
	- 'Cookii' (f)	SHHo WWHy
	- 'Crassifolia' (f)	CWib SHHo SMad WWHy
	- 'Crispa' (m)	EBee NHol SHHo WWHy
	- 'Crispa Aurea Picta' (m/v)	SHHo WWHy
	- 'Elegantissima' (m/v)	LRHS SCoo SHHo WWHy
	- 'Fastigiata Sartori' **new**	NLar
	- 'Ferox' (m)	CDul ELan EPfP LRHS SHHo SPer SPoG WDin WWHy
	- 'Ferox Argentea' (m/v) ♀H4	Widely available
*	- 'Ferox Argentea Picta' (m/v)	WFar WWHy
	- 'Ferox Aurea' (m/v)	CDoC CPMA CSBt CWib EBee ELan ELon EPfP ERas LAst MAsh NEgg NHol NPCo SHHo WWHy
§	- 'Flavescens' (f)	CBot EBee EPfP EQua GKir MBlu NHol NPCo SHHo
	- 'Frogmore Silver' (m/v)	EQua SHHo
	- 'Gold Flash' (f/v)	EBee LRHS MBri MGos NBlu NEgg NHol NLar SHHo WClo WDin WWHy
I	- 'Golden Hedgehog'	SHHo SPoG WWHy
	- 'Golden Milkboy' (m/v)	CMac ELan EPfP GKir LRHS MGos SHHo WDin WPat WWHy
§	- 'Golden Queen' (m/v) ♀H4	CDoC CMac CWSG CWib EBee MGos NBir NHol NPCo SHHo SRms WPat WWHy
	- 'Golden Tears' (f/v)	SHHo WWHy
	- 'Golden van Tol' (f/v)	Widely available
§	- 'Green Pillar' (f)	EPfP MBar SHHo WWHy
	- 'Green Spire'	see *I. aquifolium* 'Green Pillar'
	- 'Handsworth New Silver' (f/v) ♀H4	Widely available
	- 'Harpune' (f)	MAsh SHHo WWHy
§	- 'Hascombensis'	CDoC GKir LHop MGos NHol NMen NWea WWHy
	- 'Hastata' (m)	CWib IArd MRav WWHy
	- 'Ingramii' (m/v)	SHHo WWHy
	- 'Integrifolia' (f)	WWHy
	- 'J.C. van Tol' (f) ♀H4	Widely available
	- 'Latispina' (f)	SHHo WWHy
	- 'Laurifolia Aurea' (m/v)	SHHo
	- 'Lichtenthalii' (f)	IArd NPCo SHHo
	- 'Madame Briot' (f/v) ♀H4	Widely available

§ - 'Maderensis Variegata' (f/v) SHHo
- 'Monstrosa' (m) SHHo
- moonlight holly see *I. aquifolium* 'Flavescens'
- 'Myrtifolia' (f) **new** NEgg NPCo
- - (m) ELan EPfP ERas GCal LRHS MBar MGos NBlu NEgg NLar NPCo SCoo SHHo SMad SPoG WFar WMoo WWHy
- 'Myrtifolia Aurea' (m/v) GKir NEgg SWvt WFar
- 'Myrtifolia Aurea Maculata' (m/v) 🏆^{H4} CDoC CSBt CSam EBee ELan EPfP LAst LRHS MAsh NEgg NHol NPCo NWea SHHo SMad SPer SPoG SWvt WBVN WFar WPat WWHy
- 'Ovata' (m) WWHy
- 'Ovata Aurea' (m/v) SHHo WWHy
- 'Pendula' (f) EPfP GKir MRav SHHo
- 'Pendula Mediopicta' see *I. aquifolium* 'Weeping Golden Milkmaid'
- 'Pyramidalis' (f) 🏆^{H4} CDoC CDul CMac CSBt CTri EBee ELan IFoB LRHS MAsh MBar MBri MGos NHol NLar NPCo NWea SHHo SPer SRms WDin WFar WMoo WWHy
- 'Pyramidalis Aureomarginata' (f/v) CDoC LRHS MBri MGos NLar SHHo
- 'Pyramidalis Fructu Luteo' (f) 🏆^{H4} MBar SHHo
- 'Recurva' (m) CMac SHHo WWHy
- 'Rederly' (f) WWHy
- 'Rubricaulis Aurea' (f/v) ERas NHol NLar NPCo SHHo WWHy
- 'Scotica' (f) GKir NWea SHHo WWHy
- Siberia = 'Limsi'^{PBR} (f) EBee SHHo WWHy
- 'Silver King' see *I. aquifolium* 'Silver Queen'
- 'Silver Lining' (f/v) SHHo
- 'Silver Milkboy' (f/v) ELan GKir LRHS MBlu MGos WFar WWHy
- 'Silver Milkmaid' (f/v) CDoC CWSG EBee EPfP LAst LBMP LRHS MBar NEgg NHol SHHo SLim SWvt WMoo WWHy
§ - 'Silver Queen' (m/v) 🏆^{H4} Widely available
- 'Silver Sentinel' see *I.* × *altaclerensis* 'Belgica Aurea'
- 'Silver van Tol' (f/v) CDoC ELan LAst NEgg NHol NLar NPCo NPer NWea SHHo WFar WWHy
- 'Somerset Cream' (f/v) CPMA CWib NLar WWHy
* - 'Variegata' (v) **new** LRHS
§ - 'Watereriana' (m/v) MAsh SHHo
- 'Waterer's Gold' see *I. aquifolium* 'Watereriana'
§ - 'Weeping Golden Milkmaid' (f/v) MRav SHHo WPat
× ***aquipernyi*** SHHo
- Dragon Lady = 'Meschick' (f) CAlb MBri NLar NPCo SHHo WWHy
- 'San Jose' (f) CMCN SHHo
× ***attenuata*** WFar
- 'Sunny Foster' (f/v) CDoC CMCN EBee EPfP MGos SHHo SPoG WFar
§ ***bioritsensis*** CMCN CTri GKir NWea
'Brilliant' (f) **new** NPCo
China Boy = 'Mesdob' (m) LMaj SHHo
China Girl = 'Mesog' (f) SHHo
ciliospinosa WPGP
'Clusterberry' (f) **new** NPCo
colchica CMCN SHHo
corallina CBcs LRHS
cornuta EPfP ERom LRHS SHHo WFar
- 'Anicet Delcambre' (f) SHHo
* - 'Aurea' SHHo
- 'Burfordii' (f) SHHo
§ - 'Dazzler' (f) SHHo
- 'Fine Line' (f) SHHo
- 'Ira S. Nelson' (f/v) SHHo
- 'O. Spring' (f/v) SHHo WSpi
- 'Rotunda' (f) SHHo
crenata CMCN CTri ERom GCra GKir LRHS MBar MGos NWea SHHo STrG WDin WFar
* - 'Akagi' WFar
- 'Aureovariegata' see *I. crenata* 'Variegata'
- 'Convexa' (f) 🏆^{H4} EPfP GKir IMGH MAsh MBar MRav MSwo NBlu NEgg NHol NPCo NWea WFar WGwG WPat
- 'Convexed Gold' (f/v) MBri MGos NHol SPoG
- 'Fastigiata' (f) CDoC ECrN EPfP GKir LAst LRHS MAsh MBar MBri MGos NBlu NLar SCoo SHHo SPer SPoG WFar
* - 'Glory Gem' (f) CBcs
- 'Golden Gem' (f/v) 🏆^{H4} CDoC CDul CSBt CTri EBee ELan EPfP GKir LAst LRHS MAsh MBar MGos NBlu NHol NWea SCoo SLim SPer SPoG SWvt WDin WFar WGwG WPat WWHy
- 'Helleri' (f) EPfP MBar WPat
- 'Hetzii' (f) NLar
- 'Ivory Tower' (f) NEgg NPCo
- 'Luteovariegata' see *I. crenata* 'Variegata'
- 'Mariesii' (f) CMac EBee IMGH MBlu SIng
I - 'Pyramidalis' (f) MRav NHol NWea
§ - 'Shiro-fukurin' (f/v) CMCN CMHG ELan EPfP GQue LRHS SHHo
- 'Snowflake' see *I. crenata* 'Shiro-fukurin'
- 'Stokes' (m) NHol NLar
§ - 'Variegata' (v) CMac EPfP EPla LRHS MBar
'Dazzler' see *I. cornuta* 'Dazzler'
dimorphophylla CBcs CDoC CMac SHHo SMad
- 'Somerset Pixie' (f) SHHo
dipyrena CBcs
'Doctor Kassab' (f) CMCN SHHo
'Drace' (f) SHHo
'Elegance' (f) MBlu WFar
ficoidea CMCN
aff. ***gagnepainiana*** HWJ 946 **new** WCru
glabra SHHo
'Good Taste' (f) SHHo WFar WWHy
hascombensis see *I. aquifolium* 'Hascombensis'
'Indian Chief' (f) CSam NPCo SMad WFar
insignis see *I. kingiana*
'John T. Morris' (m) SHHo
§ ***kingiana*** WFar WPGP
× ***koehneana*** CBot CDul ELan EWTr
- 'Chestnut Leaf' (f) 🏆^{H4} CCVT CDoC CLnd CMCN EBee EBtc ECrN EMil EPfP EQua EWTr GKir LRHS MRav NPCo SHHo SMad WFar WGrn WPGP WWHy
- 'Wirt L. Winn' (f) WWHy
latifolia CBcs CHEx CMCN NLar SHHo SMad WPGP
'Lydia Morris' (f) CSam SHHo WFar
'Mary Nell' (f) SHHo
maximowicziana var. ***kanehirae*** CBcs WWHy
× ***meserveae*** SHHo
- 'Blue Angel' (f) CBcs CDoC CDul CMac EBee ELan EPfP IFoB IMGH LRHS MBar MBri MRav MWat NBlu NEgg NHol NLar NPCo NWea SHHo SPoG SRms WDin WFar WMoo WPat WWHy
- Blue Maid = 'Mesid' (f) NPCo WWHy
- Blue Prince (m) CBcs CDoC CMac EBee ELan LBuc LRHS MBar MBlu NEgg NHol NLar NPri NWea SHHo SLim SPer SPoG WDin WFar WWHy

- Blue Princess = 'Conapri' (f) CBcs CMac ELan EPfP GKir LBuc LRHS MBar MBlu MRav NBlu NHol NLar NPCo NPri NSti NWea SCoo SHHo SLim SPer SPoG WDin WMoo WWHy
- Golden Girl = 'Mesgolg' (f) WWHy
- 'Goliath' (f) WWHy
myrtifolia CMac MRav NPri
'Nellie R. Stevens' (f) EBee EMil LMaj NLar NWea SCoo WWHy
opaca CMCN
paraguariensis EOHP GPoy
perado subsp. ***perado*** CBcs GKir NPCo
- subsp. ***platyphylla*** CBcs CHEx CMCN MBlu SAPC SArc SHHo WWHy
pernyi CMCN CMac CTrG CTri EPfP GKir LRHS MAsh SHHo SLon SPoG WFar WWHy
- var. ***veitchii*** see *I. bioritsensis*
rugosa WWHy
'September Gem' (f) CMCN NPCo
serrata CMac CMen
- 'Leucocarpa' CMen
suaveolens CMCN
verticillata CMCN EBee LRHS NEgg WDin WFar
- (f) EPfP NLar NWea WFar
- (m) EPfP NLar
- 'Christmas Cheer' (f) WFar
* - 'Fructu Albo' (f) MAsh
- 'Maryland Beauty' (f) CPMA
- 'Southern Gentleman' (m) CPMA
- 'Winter Gold' (f) **new** CPMA
- 'Winter Red' (f) CMCN CPMA EBee
vomitoria CMCN EBtc EShb SHHo
× ***wandoensis*** CMCN SHHo WWHy
'Washington' (f) SHHo WWHy
yunnanensis SHHo

Iliamna see *Sphaeralcea*

Illicium (*Illiciaceae*)

anisatum CBcs CMac CPLG EPfP NLar SSpi WFar WPGP WPat WSHC
floridanum CBcs CPne EPfP MBri NLar SSpi SSta WPat
- f. ***album*** EPfP
I - 'Compactum' WPGP
- 'Halley's Comet' NLar
henryi CDoC CGHE CMHG CPLG CWib EBee EPfP NLar SSpi WPGP WSHC
aff. ***henryi*** CBcs
simonsii CPLG MBlu
- BWJ 8024 WCru

Ilysanthes see *Lindernia*

Impatiens ✿ (*Balsaminaceae*)

CC 4980 CPLG
DJHC 98415 CDes WPGP
apiculata GCal WPrP
arguta CDes CFir CLAP CPLG CPom CSpe EBee EPPr EShb GCal MCCP MDKP WCot WPGP WPrP
auricoma EBak WCot
- 'Jungle Gold' EShb
auricoma × ***bicaudata*** EShb WDib
balfourii EHrv LFur
congolensis CCCN EPfP
flanaganae CFir WPGP
forrestii CLAP
aff. ***forrestii*** WPrP
gomphophylla CFir
(Harmony Series) Harmony Dark Red = 'Danhardkrd' WGor
- Harmony Orange Blaze = 'Danharoblaze' WGor
- Harmony Pink Smile WGor
- Harmony Salmon = 'Danharsal' WGor
- Harmony Violet = 'Danharvio' WGor
hawkeri see *I. schlechteri*
keilii WDib
kerriae B&SWJ 7219 WCru
kilimanjari subsp. ***kilimanjari*** CSpe GCal
kilimanjari × ***pseudoviola*** CDoC CFee CSpe
langbianensis HWJ 1054 WCru
'Linda's White' **new** GCal
macrophylla B&SWJ 10157 WCru
namchabarwensis CSpe LFur
New Guinea Group see *I. schlechteri*
niamniamensis CHll EBak EShb WCot WDib
- 'Congo Cockatoo' CDTJ CDoC CHEx CTsd EOHP ERea GCal NPer SRms
- 'Golden Cockatoo' (v) CDTJ CDoC EBak ERea EShb
noli-tangere WSFF
omeiana CCCN CDes CFir CHEx CLAP CPom CSpe EBee EPPr ESwi EWld GAbr GCal LEdu MCCP MNrw SBch SBig SUsu WBor WCot WCru WPGP WPrP WSHC
- silver-leaved CDes CHEx CLAP GCal LFur MCCP MDKP WPGP WPrP
parasitica WDib
platypetala B&SWJ 9722 WCru WPrP
pseudoviola SDix
puberula WPrP
- HWJK 2063 WCru
rothii **new** GCal
scabrida **new** CSpe
§ ***schlechteri*** **new** EBak
sodenii CDTJ CSpe EShb SBHP
stenantha CFir
sultani see *I. walleriana*
* ***sutherlandii*** CFir
tinctoria CDoC CFir CGHE CHEx CHll CPLG CSpe EBee EShb GCal GCra LFur LPio MCCP MNrw WCot WPGP WPrP WWlt
- subsp. ***elegantissima*** CFee
- subsp. ***tinctoria*** IFro
tuberosa EShb WDib
ugandensis GCal
uniflora CFir GCal MCCP
Velvetea = 'Secret Love'PBR CCCN
§ ***walleriana*** EBak MBri
- (Fiesta Series) Fiesta Appleblossom = 'Balfieplos' (d) NPri SVil
- - Fiesta Coral Bells = 'Balfiecobl' (d) NPri
- - Fiesta Olé Frost = 'Balolefro' (d) NPri
- - Fiesta Olé Peach = 'Balolepeac'PBR (d) NPri
- - Fiesta Olé Rose = 'Balolerose'PBR (d) NPri
- - Fiesta Olé Salmon = 'Balolesal' (d) NPri
- - Fiesta Olé Stardust = 'Balolestop' (d) NPri

- - Fiesta Sparkler Cherry = 'Balfiespary' (d) — NPri
- - 'Lavender Orchid'PBR (d) — NPri
- - 'Pink Ruffle'PBR (d) — SVil
- (Spellbound Series) Spellbound Dark Red = 'Imtradared' — WGor
- - Spellbound Pink = 'Imtrarepu' — WGor

Imperata (*Poaceae*)

cylindrica — CMen
- 'Red Baron' — see *I. cylindrica* 'Rubra'
§ - 'Rubra' — Widely available

Incarvillea (*Bignoniaceae*)

SDR 4804 — GKev
arguta — CBot EShb LLHF LPio SGSe
brevipes — see *I. mairei*
compacta — GKev
- ACE 1455 — EBee
- BWJ 7620 — WCru
delavayi — Widely available
- SDR 4711 — GKev
- 'Alba' — see *I. delavayi* 'Snowtop'
- 'Bees' Pink' — CSpe EBee EBrs ECho EDAr GBuc GGar GKir LRHS LSou SHGN
- 'Rose' **new** — LRHS
§ - 'Snowtop' — CBot EBee EBrs ECho ELan EPfP EPot GBuc GCal GMaP MBel MDun NBPC NBir NLar SGSe SPer SWvt WBrE WCot WFar WHil WPGP WWEG
forrestii — EBee ECho GKev LPio
grandiflora — ELan
himalayensis 'Frank Ludlow' — GBuc
- 'Nyoto Sama' — GBuc
lutea BWJ 7784 — WCru
§ ***mairei*** — CAby CTsd EBee EBrs ECho EDAr EGoo EPfP GEdr GKir LPio LRHS NLar SIng WHil WPer
- var. ***mairei*** — GBuc GKev
- - f. ***multifoliata*** — see *I. zhongdianensis*
- pink-flowered — GCal GKir
olgae — EBee EPfP LPio
sinensis 'Cheron' — CSpe
younghusbandii — GEdr
§ ***zhongdianensis*** — CPBP EBee ERos GBuc GEdr GKev MDKP NWCA
- BWJ 7692 — WCru
- BWJ 7978 — WCru

Indigofera (*Papilionaceae*)

amblyantha ♀H4 — EBee ELon EPfP LHop LRHS MAsh MBlu MBri NLar SBod SEND SPlb SPoG SSpi WCot WDin WKif WSHC WSpi
balfouriana BWJ 7851 — WCru
cassioides — WCru
decora f. ***alba*** — EPfP
dielsiana — CWGN EPfP MWea WKif WPGP
'Dosua' — SLPl
gerardiana — see *I. heterantha*
hebepetala — EPfP WPGP WSHC
§ ***heterantha*** ♀H4 — Widely available
himalayensis — WSHC
- Yu 10941 — WPGP
- 'Silk Road' — LBuc LRHS MBri
kirilowii — EPfP MBri WPGP WSHC
pendula — EPfP IDee LRHS MAsh SEND SSpi WPGP WSHC
- B&SWJ 7741 — WCru
potaninii — CMac EPfP WHer
pseudotinctoria — CCCN EMil EPfP MBri SHGN SRms
splendens — MBri
subverticillata — WPGP WSHC
tinctoria — CArn

Indocalamus (*Poaceae*)

latifolius — EPPr EPla ERod MMoz MMuc MWht NLar WJun
- 'Hopei' — EPla
longiauritus — EPla
solidus — see *Bonia solida*
§ ***tessellatus*** ♀H4 — CAbb CDoC CEnt CGHE CHEx CMCo EAmu EBee ENBC EPfP EPla ERod GKir MBri MCCP MMoz MMuc MWht NGdn NMoo SMad WDyG WFar WJun WMoo WPGP WPnP
- f. ***hamadae*** — EPla ERod MMoz MWht WJun

Inula (*Asteraceae*)

acaulis — WCot
afghanica — EBee
barbata — MBel NBre
britannica var. ***chinensis*** — NBre
crithmoides — WHer
dysenterica — see *Pulicaria dysenterica*
ensifolia — CBcs ELan EPfP GJos LEdu MBNS MBel MDKP MTho NBro SLPl WWEG
- 'Compacta' — ECho GCal
- 'Gold Star' — CMac EBee ECho GKir LRHS MBel MNFA MRav MWat NBid NBir NEgg SPet WFar WMnd WPer
glandulosa — see *I. orientalis*
'Golden Beauty' — see *Buphthalmum salicifolium* 'Golden Wonder'
helenium — CArn CHby COld CPrp CSev EBWF EBee ELau GAbr GBar GPoy ILis LEdu LPBA MBel MHer MNHC NBid NBir NGHP NMir SECG SHlg SPoG SRms WGwG WHer WMoo WPer
- 'Goliath' — MBel SHlg SMrm
hirta — EBee MBel NBre WPer
hookeri — Widely available
- GWJ 9033 — WCru
macrocephala misapplied — see *I. royleana*
macrocephala Boiss. & Kotschy ex Boiss. — MBel
magnifica — Widely available
- 'Sonnenstrahl' ♀H4 — SPhx
oculus-christi — CDes EBee EWes NBre WCot
- MESE 437 — EPPr
§ ***orientalis*** — CHrt CKno CMea EBee EPfP GJos MBri MNFA NBre NGBl SGSe SHlg SMad SPad SPoG WBrE WFar WMnd WPGP WPer WPtf WWEG
racemosa — EPPr EPla EWes GCal IBlr MNrw NBid NChi SMrm SPlb SRms WFar
- 'Sonnenspeer' — EBee GMac NBre NLar SLPl SMad WPer WPtf
rhizocephala — ECho MDKP WPer
§ ***royleana*** — CEnt GBuc GCal MDKP MNrw MRav NBre WPtf
salicina — EBee
verbascifolia — ECho

Iochroma (*Solanaceae*)

§ ***australe*** — CHll CSpe SGar SPad WCom
§ - 'Andean Snow' — CHll CPLG EShb

§ - 'Bill Evans' CPLG EShb
cyaneum CCCN CDoC CHll CTri
- purple-flowered CHll
gesnerioides 'Coccineum' CCCN CDoC CHll
§ ***grandiflorum*** CCCN CDoC CHEx CHll CSev SGar
warscewiczii see *I. grandiflorum*

Iostephane (*Asteraceae*)

§ ***heterophylla*** MMuc

Ipheion ✿ (*Alliaceae*)

'Alberto Castillo' Widely available
dialystemon CStu EBee EBrs ECho EPot LPio SIng WAbe WHil
hirtellum EBrs
'Jessie' CMea EBee EBrs ECho ELon EPot ERCP GBuc LAma LHop LLHF LRHS NHol NMin SPhx WCot WHil WHoo
'Rolf Fiedler' ♀H2-3 Widely available
sellowianum MAsh SCnR SUsu WCot
sessile ECho
§ ***uniflorum*** CBro CSpe CStu CTri EBee EBrs ECha ECho LAma LEdu MNrw MRav NMen NWCA SBch SGSe SIng SMrm SPer SRms WAbb WAul WCot WFar WPer WPnP WTin
- 'Album' CBro CPom CPrp EBee EBrs ECha ECho ELon EPPr EPot ERCP ERos EWes LEdu LPio LRHS MAsh MRav MTho SIng SPhx WCot WHal WHil
- 'Charlotte Bishop' Widely available
- 'Froyle Mill' ♀H4 Widely available
- 'Wisley Blue' ♀H4 Widely available
yellow-flowered CDes

Ipomoea (*Convolvulaceae*)

sp. LSou
acuminata see *I. indica*
alba CCCN EShb
batatas 'Blackie' EShb LPio WFar
- 'Margarita' EShb
- 'Pink Frost' (v) EShb
- 'Sweet Caroline Light Green'PBR **new** SVil
- 'Sweet Caroline Purple'PBR **new** SVil
carnea CCCN
coccinea var. ***hederifolia*** see *I. hederifolia*
hederacea LSou
§ ***hederifolia*** CCCN
× ***imperialis*** 'Sunrise Serenade' CCCN
§ ***indica*** ♀H1 CCCN CHEx CHll CRHN EPfP EShb MREP
learii see *I. indica*
§ ***lobata*** CSpe LBMP LSou SBch SGar
'Milky Way' CCCN
muellerii CCCN
× ***multifida*** CSpe
purpurea 'Kniola's Purple-black' CSpe SBch
quamoclit CSpe
versicolor see *I. lobata*

Ipomopsis (*Polemoniaceae*)

§ ***aggregata*** NPol
congesta LLHF
subsp. ***montana*** **new**
longiflora **new** LFur
rubra NPol

Iresine (*Amaranthaceae*)

herbstii EBak ERea EShb
- 'Aureoreticulata' EShb
- 'Brilliantissima' CBow
'Shiny Rose Purple' LBuc

Iris ✿ (*Iridaceae*)

CLD 1399 NHol
AC 4413 from Tibet GAuc
AC 4450 from Tibet GAuc
AC 4471 from Tibet GAuc
AC 4490 from Tibet GAuc
AC 4623 from Tibet GAuc
AC 4674 from Tibet GAuc
'Abbey Road' (TB) WCAu WViv
'Ablaze' (MDB) **new** WViv
'Abracadabra' (SDB) SMrm
'Acadian Miss' (La) WCAu
'Ace' (MTB) ESgI
'Acoma' (TB) WCAu WViv
'Action Front' (TB) EAEE EBee EBla EHrv EIri ESgI ETod IPot LFCN LHop LRHS MSpe NGdn SBch SDnm WWEG
'Actress' (TB) CWGN EAEE EBla ECGP ETod IPot LBuc LFCN LRHS LSRN SPet
acutiloba subsp. ***lineolata*** WWst
'Adobe Rose' (TB) ESgI WViv
'Adrienne Taylor' (SDB) ♀H4 WCAu
'African Queen' ERCP
'After Dark' CKel
'After the Storm' (TB) ECho
'Afternoon Delight' (TB) CWCL ESgI WCAu WViv
'Agatha Christie' (IB) WCAu
'Aggressively Forward' (TB) WCAu
'Agnes James' (CH) ♀H3 CBro
'Aicho-no-kagayaki' (SpH) CBow WCot
'Airy Fancy' (Spuria) ESgI
'Alabaster Unicorn' (TB) ESgI
'Albatross' (TB) SMrm
albicans ♀H4 CMea EBrs ECho EPot LEdu WCAu WWst
albomarginata ECho WWst
'Alcazar' (TB) ESgI LSRN NMoo SWat WMnd WWEG
'Aldo Ratti' (TB) ESgI
'Alerte Rose' **new** WViv
'Alexia' (TB) ♀H4 CKel
'Alice Harding' (TB) ESgI
'Alida' (Reticulata) ECho ERCP
'Alien Mist' (TB) WCAu
'Alizes' (TB) ♀H4 ESgI WCAu WViv
'All Night Long' (TB) CIri
'Allegiance' (TB) WCAu
'Alpine Journey' (TB) ESgI
'Alpine Lake' (MDB) WCAu
'Alsterquelle' (SDB) WTin
'Altruist' (TB) WCAu
'Amadora' (TB) CKel EIri ESgI
'Amas' (TB) WCAu
'Ambassadeur' (TB) EBee
'Amber Queen' (DB) EBee EBla ECtt ELan ERos NBir NGdn NMen SPer SPet
'Ambersand' (IB) **new** SIri
'Ambroisie' (TB) ♀H4 ESgI ETod WViv
'American Patriot' (IB) CKel WCAu
'America's Cup' (TB) WCAu
'Amethyst Flame' (TB) ECho ESgI NBre SRms WCAu
'Amherst Blue' (IB) SIri
'Amherst Bluebeard' (SDB) SIri
'Amherst Caper' (SDB) WCAu

Name	Suppliers
'Amherst Jester' (BB)	SIri WAul
'Amherst Moon' (SDB)	SIri WCAu
'Amherst Mustard' (SDB)	SIri
'Amherst Purple Ribbon' (SDB)	SIri WCAu
'Amherst Sweetheart' (SDB)	SIri WCAu
'Amigo' (TB)	ESgI
'Amiguita' (CH)	CFir EBee WCom
'Amphora' (SDB)	CBro ERos GBuc
'Ancient Echoes' (TB)	ESgI
'Andalou' (TB) Ψ^{H4}	CWCL ESgI SCoo WViv
'Angel Unawares' (TB)	WCAu
'Angelic' (SDB)	WCAu
'Angel's Tears'	see *I. histrioides* 'Angel's Tears'
'Angel's Touch' (TB)	ESgI
anglica	see *I. latifolia*
'Anna Belle Babson' (TB)	ESgI
'Annabel Jane' (TB)	CKel COIW CWan WCAu
'Anne Elizabeth' (SDB)	CBro ERos
'Annikins' (IB) Ψ^{H4}	CKel
'Anniversary Celebration' (TB)	CKel
'Announcement' (TB)	CIri
'Antarctique' (IB)	CBgR ESgI
'Antigone' (TB)	ESgI
'Anything Goes' (TB)	WAul
aphylla	WCAu
- subsp. ***fieberi***	WCot
'Apollo' (Dut)	CAvo EBrs
'Apparent Secret' (TB)	WAul
'Appledore' (SDB)	CBro ERos
'Appointer' (SpH)	CRow GBin
'Apricorange' (TB) Ψ^{H4}	CKel
'Apricot Blaze' (TB)	ESgI
'Apricot Drops' (MTB) Ψ^{H4}	ESgI WAul WCAu
'Apricot Frosty' (BB)	ESgI
'Apricot Silk' (IB)	CWGN SBch SEND SMrm WWEG
'Apricot Topping' (BB) **new**	WAul
'Arab Chief' (TB)	CKel
'Arabi Pasha' (TB)	ESgI WCAu
* 'Arabic Night' (IB)	WCAu
'Arc de Triomphe' (TB)	ESgI
'Archie Owen' (Spuria)	WCAu
'Arctic Express' (TB)	ESgI
'Arctic Fancy' (IB) Ψ^{H4}	CKel
'Arctic Snow' (TB)	WCAu
'Arctic Sunrise' (TB)	ESgI
'Arctic Wine' (IB)	WCAu
arenaria	see *I. humilis*
'Argument' (J)	WWst
'Argus Pheasant' (SDB)	ESgI WCAu
'Armageddon' (TB)	ESgI
'Arnold Sunrise' (CH) Ψ^{H3}	GAbr
'Around Midnight' (TB)	LRHS
'Art Deco' (TB)	SIri WViv
'Art School Angel' (TB)	CIri
'Artful' (SDB)	WCAu
'As de Coeur' (TB)	ESgI
'Ascension Crown' (TB)	ESgI
'Ask Alma' (IB)	ESgI WAul WCAu WViv
'Astrid Cayeux' (TB)	ESgI WViv
'Astro Flash' (TB)	ESgI
* 'Atlantique' (TB)	CKel
'Attention Please' (TB)	CKel ELan SMrm WWEG
attica	CBro CPBP ECho ERos LLHF NRya WAbe WThu
- J&JA 583.900	NWCA
- lemon-flowered	CPBP WThu
§ ***aucheri*** Ψ^{H2}	EBrs ECho EPot GKev NMin WWst
- indigo flowered **new**	WWst
- 'Leylek Ice' **new**	GAuc
- 'Leylek Lilac' **new**	WWst
- 'Snow Princess' **new**	WWst
- 'Snow White' **new**	GAuc
- 'Turkish Ice' **new**	WWst
'Aunt Corley' (TB)	CIri
'Aunt Josephine' (TB)	ESgI
'Aunt Martha' (BB)	LRHS WCAu
'Aurean' (IB)	CKel
'Aurelie' (TB) **new**	SIri
'Austrian Sky' (SDB)	CMac EBee EBla ECtt LFCN LHop SPet SPhx STes WAul WCAu WCot
'Autumn Circus' (TB)	WAul WCAu WViv
'Autumn Echo' (TB)	ESgI SPet
'Autumn Encore' (TB)	COIW WBor
'Autumn Leaves' (TB)	ESgI WCAu
'Autumn Maple' (SDB)	ESgI
'Autumn Tryst' (TB)	ESgI WCAu
'Avalon Sunset' (TB)	EIri ESgI WViv
'Avanelle' (IB)	NBre
'Awesome Blossom' (TB)	ESgI
'Az Ap' (IB)	CHid EBee ELon WCAu
'Aztec Sun' (TB)	SIri WViv
babadagica **new**	LRHS
'Babbling Brook' (TB)	ESgI
'Baboon Bottom' (BB)	CIri WCAu
'Baby Bengal' (BB)	WCAu
'Baby Blessed' (SDB)	CBro SRGP WCAu
'Baby Prince' (SDB)	ESgI
'Baccarat' (TB)	WCAu
'Back in Black' (TB)	CKel
'Baie Rose' (IB)	CBgR
'Bajazzo' (La)	WCAu
bakeriana	EBrs ECho IHer NMin
'Bal Masqué' (TB)	ESgI WViv
baldschuanica	WWst
'Ballerina' (TB)	NBir
'Ballyhoo' (TB)	WCAu
'Banbury Beauty' (CH) Ψ^{H3}	CLAP MAvo
'Banbury Gem' (CH)	CSam
'Banbury Melody' (CH)	CFee MAvo
'Banbury Ruffles' (SDB)	ESgI NMen WAul WCAu
'Bandera Waltz' (TB)	WCAu
'Bang' (TB)	CKel
'Bangles' (MTB) Ψ^{H4}	CIri ESgI WCAu
'Bar de Nuit' (TB)	ESgI
'Barbara's Kiss' (Spuria)	CIri
barbatula BWJ 7663	WCru
'Baria' (SDB)	GEdr
'Barletta' (TB)	WCAu
'Baroque Prelude' (TB)	CKel
'Batik' (BB)	WCAu WCot WViv
'Batsford' (SDB)	CBro
'Baubles and Beads' (MTB)	ESgI
'Bayberry Candle' (TB)	ESgI MWea WAul WCAu
'Be Happy' (SDB)	WViv
'Be My Baby' (BB)	WCAu
'Bedtime Story' (IB)	EBee SSvw SWat WCot WViv WWEG
'Bee Wings' (MDB)	WViv
'Bee's Knees' (SDB) Ψ^{H4}	SIri
'Before the Storm' (TB)	CKel ELon ESgI WCAu
'Beguine' (TB)	ESgI
'Being Busy' (SDB)	ESgI
'Bel Azur' (IB)	CBgR ESgI WViv
'Bel Esprit' (TB)	ESgI
'Belvi Queen' (TB)	MNrw
'Ben a Factor' (MTB)	ESgI
'Benton Caramel' **new**	EMal
'Benton Cordelia' (TB)	EMal ESgI
'Benton Daphne' **new**	EMal
'Benton Dierdre' (TB)	ELon SRms
'Benton Evora' (TB)	EMal

	'Benton Nigel' (TB)	EMal WCAu
	'Benton Sheila' (TB)	CFee ECha
	'Berkeley Gold' (TB)	CSBt EBee EBla ECtt ELan EPfP EShb EWes GKir LRHS MSpe NOrc NVic SBch SCoo SPer SWat WCAu WWEG
	'Berlin Tiger' (SpH) 𝕐H4	CAbx CRow EPPr EPfP GBin NBhm SApp WCAu
	'Bermuda Triangle' (BB)	CIri
	'Best Bet' (TB)	ESgI WCAu
	'Bethany Claire' (TB)	ESgI
	'Betty Cooper' (Spuria)	ESgI WAul WCAu
	'Betty Simon' (TB)	CKel CWCL ESgI ETod WViv
	'Beverly Sills' (TB)	CWGN ESgI LSou MRav MSpe SRGP WAul WCAu WViv
	'Bewilderbeast' (TB)	WCAu
	'Bianco' (TB)	WCAu WWEG
	'Bibury' (SDB) 𝕐H4	WCAu
	'Big Dipper' (TB)	ECtt ESgI WViv
	'Big Melt' (TB)	CKel
	'Big Money' (CH) 𝕐H3	GBuc
	'Big Squeeze' (TB)	WViv
	biglumis	see *I. lactea*
	biliottii	CBro
	'Billie the Brownie' (MTB)	ESgI
	'Bishop's Robe' (TB)	SSvw
N	'Black Beauty' (Dut)	EPfP LRHS
	'Black Beauty' (TB)	SPer
	'Black Dragon' (TB)	CHid SHar SPad
	'Black Gamecock' (La)	CFir CWCL ELan EPPr LPBA MBNS MNrw NBro NMoo NOrc SMrm WCAu WMAq
	'Black Hills' (TB)	EBee WCAu
	'Black Ink' (TB)	COIW
	'Black Knight' (TB)	EWll MRav NGdn SPoG
	'Black Night' (IB)	MWea SRGP WBor WWEG
	'Black Sergeant' (TB) 𝕐H4	CKel
	'Black Stallion' (MDB)	ESgI
	'Black Suited' (TB)	CIri
	'Black Swan' (TB)	CMac EBla ECha ECtt ELan EPfP ESgI EShb GCal LAst LFCN LPio LRHS LSRN MAvo NBre NGdn SBch SDnm SPer SPoG STes WAul WCAu WEas
	'Black Taffeta' (TB)	CKel
	'Black Tie Affair' (TB)	ESgI WCAu WViv
	'Blackalicious' (TB)	CIri
	'Blackbeard' (BB) 𝕐H4	CKel WCAu
	'Blackcurrant' (IB)	WAul
	'Blackout' (TB)	ESgI SIri
	'Blast' (IB)	CKel WViv
	'Blatant' (TB)	ESgI WCAu
	'Blazing Light' (TB)	ESgI
	'Blazing Sunrise' (TB)	ESgI
	'Blenheim Royal' (TB)	ESgI WCAu WPen WViv
	'Blessed Assurance' (IB)	GKir
	'Blitzen' (IB)	WCAu
	bloudowii	ITim
	'Blue Ballerina' (CH) 𝕐H3	GBuc
	'Blue Beret' (MDB) **new**	WViv
	'Blue Bossa' (CH) 𝕐H4	WAul
	'Blue Crusader' (TB)	WCAu WViv
	'Blue Denim' (SDB)	ECho ECtt EPfP GCal MBNS MRav NBir NBro NMoo WCAu WCot WHoo WTin WWEG
	'Blue Eyed Blond' (IB)	MWea WCAu
	'Blue Eyed Brunette' (TB)	ESgI WCAu
	'Blue Fin' (TB)	WCAu
	'Blue Flirt' (IB) **new**	WAul
	'Blue Hendred' (SDB)	NBir WCAu
	'Blue Horizon' (TB)	ERos
	'Blue Lamp' (TB)	CKel
	'Blue Line' (SDB) 𝕐H4	CDes NBre
	'Blue Luster' (TB) 𝕐H4	ESgI
	'Blue Meadow Fly' (Sino-Sib)	EBee SMrm
*	'Blue Mystery'	WWst
	'Blue Note Blues' (TB)	WCAu
	'Blue Pigmy' (SDB)	CPBP CWat EBla ECtt ERos MBNS NGdn NMen SBch SPer SPet
	'Blue Pools' (SDB)	LRHS MBri NBir WTin
	'Blue Reflection' (TB)	CMac ESgI
	'Blue Rhythm' (TB)	CKel EAEE EBla ELan ELon EPfP GMaP LRHS MRav NBre NMoo SBch SCoo SPer SPhx SSvw WAul WCAu WMnd WWEG
	'Blue Sapphire' (TB)	ESgI WCAu
	'Blue Shimmer' (TB)	CSBt CWGN EAEE EBee EBla ECha ELan EPfP ESgI ETod LFCN LRHS LSRN MAvo NGdn SBch SPer SPet SPoG SWat WCAu
	'Blue Staccato' (TB)	CKel ESgI WCAu
	'Blue Suede Shoes' (TB)	ESgI LSRN WViv
	'Blue Velvet' (TB)	WMoo
	'Blue Warlsind' (J)	WWst
	'Bluebird Wine' (TB)	WCAu
	'Bob Nichol' (TB) 𝕐H4	CKel
	'Bodacious' (TB)	ESgI
	'Bohemia Sekt' (TB)	CKel
	'Bohemian' (TB)	CWCL ESgI WViv
	'Boisterous' (BB)	WCAu
	'Bold Gold' (TB)	WViv
	'Bold Look' (TB)	ESgI
	'Bold Pretender' (La)	ELan EPfP MBNS
	'Bold Print' (IB)	CWan EAEE EBee EBla ELon LAst LRHS LSRN SBch SPoG WAul WCAu WWEG WWlt
	'Bollinger'	see *I.* 'Hornpipe'
	'Bonbon Acidulé' (TB) **new**	WViv
	'Bonnie Davenport' (TB)	CIri
	'Bonny' (MDB)	CBro
	'Bonus Bucks' (TB)	CKel
	'Boo' (SDB)	CKel WAul WCAu
	'Bourgeois' (SDB)	CIri
	'Bouzy Bouzy' (TB)	ESgI
	bracteata	CPBP GBuc WPer
	- JCA 13427	CLAP
	- NNS 04-223	WCot
	- NNS 05-384	WCot
	'Braggadocio' (TB)	CWCL WCAu WViv
	'Braithwaite' (TB)	CKel CWGN EAEE EBee EBla ELan ESgI IPot LRHS MSpe NBre SBch SPer SPur SRms SWat WAul WCAu
	'Brannigan' (SDB)	CBro LRHS MBri NBir WPen
	'Brasero' (TB)	CWCL ECtt WViv
	'Brash' (SDB)	WViv
	'Brasilia' (TB)	NBir NBre
	'Brass Tacks' (SDB)	WCAu
	'Brassie' (SDB)	CBro ERos GKir MBNS NBro NMoo SHGN WWEG
	'Brave New World' (TB) 𝕐H4	CIri
	'Brazilian Holiday' (TB)	WAul
	'Breakers' (TB) 𝕐H4	CKel ESgI SBch WCAu
	'Breezy Blue' (SDB)	WCAu
§	'Bride' (DB)	NBlu WMnd
	'Bride's Halo' (TB)	LSRN WCAu WViv
*	'Brigantino' (BB)	ESgI
	'Bright Button' (SDB)	CBgR CKel ESgI
	'Bright Chic' (SDB)	ESgI
	'Bright Child' (SDB)	WCAu
	'Bright Fire' (TB)	EIri SIri WViv

'Bright Spring' (DB) new WViv
'Bright Vision' (SDB) ESgI
'Bright White' (MDB) CBro CKel ECho ERos LRHS NMen SMrm
N 'Bright Yellow' (DB) MRav
'Brighteyes' (IB) SRms
'Brindisi' (TB) ESgI WCAu
'Brise de Mer' (TB) ESgI
'Broad Shoulders' (TB) WAul
'Broadleigh Angela' (CH) CBro GKir
'Broadleigh Ann' (CH) CBro
'Broadleigh Carolyn' (CH) ♀H3 CBro
'Broadleigh Charlotte' (CH) CBro
N 'Broadleigh Clare' (CH) CBro
'Broadleigh Dorothy' (CH) CBro GGar
'Broadleigh Elizabeth' (CH) CBro
'Broadleigh Emily' (CH) CBro
'Broadleigh Jean' (CH) CBro
'Broadleigh Joan' (CH) CBro
'Broadleigh Joyce' (CH) CBro
'Broadleigh Lavinia' (CH) CBro MAvo MRav NHol
'Broadleigh Mitre' (CH) CBro CElw GMac
'Broadleigh Nancy' (CH) CBro MAvo
'Broadleigh Peacock' (CH) CBro CElw EShb MAvo
'Broadleigh Penny' (CH) CBro
'Broadleigh Rose' (CH) CBro CElw EHrv EPyc GBuc GKir MAvo MBrN MRav MWte NHol SApp SMrm SWal WSHC
'Broadleigh Sybil' (CH) CBro GKir
'Broadleigh Victoria' (CH) CBro GBuc
'Broadway Baby' (IB) ESgI WAul WViv
'Bromyard' (SDB) ♀H4 CBro WCAu
'Bronzaire' (IB) ♀H4 CKel EIri ESgI WCAu WGwG
'Bronze Beauty' (Dut) LAma SBch
'Bronze Beauty' van Tubergen (*hoogiana* hybrid) EPfP LRHS MWat NBir
'Bronzed Aussie' (TB) CIri
'Bronzed Violet' (TB) CKel
N 'Brown Chocolate' (TB) WCAu
'Brown Lasso' (BB) ♀H4 WCAu
N 'Brummit's Mauve' (TB) WCAu
'Bruno' (TB) LSRN
'Brussels' (TB) ESgI
bucharica misapplied see *I. orchioides* Carrière
bucharica ambig. CAvo CMea EBla EBrs ECho IFro IHer MWat NCGa SIng SMrm WBor WHil WWst
§ ***bucharica*** Foster ♀H3-4 CBgR CBro CSam EBee EBrs ECho EPfP EPot GKev LAma LRHS WCAu
- 'Baldschuan Yellow' (J) new WWst
- bicoloured new LRHS
- 'Princess' EBrs ECho WWst
N - 'Sanglok' WWst
- 'Top Gold' EBrs ECho WWst
bucharica × ***orchioides*** ECho WWst
'Buckwheat' (TB) SIri WViv
'Buddy Boy' (SDB) WCAu
'Bugsy' (MDB) ESgI
'Buisson de Roses' (TB) ESgI WViv
bulleyana ECho EWTr GAuc GKev NWCA SRms WAbe WCot
- ACE 2296 EBee GBuc
- BWJ 7912 WCru
- CLD 495 NHol
- black-flowered CPLG EBee GKev GKir
- - SDR 1792 GKev
- - SDR 2714 GKev
'Bumblebee Deelite' (MTB) ♀H4 CKel WCAu
bungei GAuc
'Burgundy Party' (TB) ESgI
'Burka' (TB) ESgI
'Burnt Toffee' (TB) ESgI WAul WViv
'Burst' (TB) new CKel
'Butter Pecan' (IB) WCAu
'Buttercup Bower' (TB) WCAu
'Buttermere' (TB) SRms
'Butterpat' (IB) ESgI
'Butterscotch Carpet' (SDB) WCAu
'Butterscotch Kiss' (TB) EAEE EBee EBla ELan LDai LHop LRHS MRav MSpe MWea NBir SDnm SPer
'Bye Bye Blues' (TB) ESgI
'Cabaret Royale' (TB) ESgI WCAu
'Cable Car' (TB) CKel CWCL ECtt ESgI WViv
'Caliente' (TB) COIW CWGN EKen EPfP ESgI EWll MCot MRav MWhi SPet WBor WCAu
'California Dreamin'' (TB) new CIri
'California Gold' (TB) WWEG
'California Style' (IB) ESgI
§ Californian hybrids CAby CElw CPBP EPot GCra MCot NBir WBor WCFE WCot
'Calm Stream' (TB) ♀H4 CKel
'Cambridge Blue' see *I.* 'Monspur Cambridge Blue'
'Camelot Rose' (TB) WCAu
'Cameo Queen' (SDB) ♀H4 new CIri
'Cameo Wine' (TB) CPMA ECtt EPPr ESgI WViv
'Cameroun' (TB) ESgI
'Campbellii' see *I. lutescens* 'Campbellii'
canadensis see *I. hookeri*
'Canadian Streaker' (TB/v) WCot
'Candy Clouds' (TB) WCAu
'Candylane' (MTB) CKel
'Cannington Apricot' (IB) new CBgR CKel
'Cannington Bluebird' (TB) WCAu
'Cannington Ochre' (SDB) CBro
'Cannington Skies' (IB) CKel
'Cantab' (Reticulata) CAvo CBro CFFs EBrs ECho EPot ERCP GBin GKev LAma LRHS SPhx
capnoides WWst
capnoides × ***orchioides*** (J) WWst
'Capricious' (TB) ESgI
'Captain Gallant' (TB) WCAu
'Captain Indigo' (IB) CKel ESgI
'Caption' (TB) ESgI
'Caramba' (TB) WCAu
'Carenza' (BB) CKel
'Caribbean Dream' (TB) WViv
'Carilla' (SDB) ERos
'Carnaby' (TB) EAEE EBla ESgI EShb LRHS MBri MRav MSpe MWea SBch STes WCAu WViv WWEG
'Carnival Song' (TB) WCAu
'Carnival Time' (TB) CMac CWGN EAEE EBee EBla ECGP ECtt EShb IPot LBuc LDai LFCN LRHS MSpe MWea SBch SPer STes WAul
'Carnton' (TB) WEas
'Carolyn Rose' (MTB) ♀H4 NBre
* 'Caronte' (IB) ESgI
'Carriwitched' (IB) CKel
'Cascade Sprite' (SDB) SRms
'Cat's Eye' (SDB) CIri WViv
caucasica CMac
'Cayenne Capers' (TB) ESgI

N	'Cedric Morris'	EWes MWat WEas
	'Cee Jay' (IB) Υ^{H4}	WViv
	'Celebration Song' (TB)	CWCL ESgI SIri WAul WCAu WViv
	'Celestial Glory' (TB)	WCAu
	'Celtic Glory' (TB)	WAul
	'Cerdagne' (TB)	ESgI
	chamaeiris	see *I. lutescens*
	'Champagne Elegance' (TB)	ECtt EIri ESgI NBir WAul WCAu WViv
	'Champagne Encore' (IB)	ESgI
	'Champagne Frost' (TB)	WCAu
	'Champagne Music' (TB)	WCAu
	'Champagne Waltz' (TB)	CWCL WViv
	'Chance Beauty' (SpH) Υ^{H4}	WCAu WViv
	'Change of Pace' (TB)	ESgI WCAu WViv
	'Chanted' (SDB)	EPPr ESgI WCAu WViv
	'Chantilly' (TB)	CMil EAEE EBee EBla ECGP ELan EPfP LPio LRHS MRav NBir NGdn SDnm SPer SPoG SWat WFoF
	'Chapeau' (TB)	ESgI WCAu
	'Chapel Bells' (TB)	CKel
	'Charlotte Maria' (TB)	CKel
	'Chartreuse Ruffles' (TB)	ECtt
	'Char-true' (Spuria)	WCAu
	'Chasing Rainbows' (TB)	WCAu
	'Chaste White' (TB)	ESgI
	'Cher' (TB) **new**	LSRN
	'Cherished' (TB)	EBee GBin WWEG
	'Cherokee Lace' (Spuria)	WTin
	'Cherry Blossom Special' (TB)	CIri
	'Cherry Garden' (SDB)	Widely available
	'Cherry Smoke' (TB)	WCAu
	'Cherub Tears' (SDB)	WCAu
	'Cherub's Smile' (TB)	ESgI
	'Chevalier de Malte' (TB)	ESgI WViv
	'Chickee' (MTB) Υ^{H4}	CKel
	'Chicken Little' (MDB)	CBro EBee NMoo
	'Chief Moses' (TB)	WCAu
I	'Chieftain' (SDB)	MRav
	'China Dragon' (TB)	SWat
	'China Nights' (TB)	ESgI
	'China Seas' (TB)	NBre
	'Chinese Treasure' (TB)	WAul
	'Chinook Winds' (TB)	ESgI
	'Chivalry' (TB)	ESgI WTin
	'Chocolate Marmalade' (TB)	ECtt WViv
	'Chocolate Vanilla' (TB)	ESgI WCAu
	'Chorus Girl' (TB)	CKel
	'Christmas Angel' (TB)	WCAu
	chrysographes Υ^{H4}	Widely available
I	- 'Black Beauty'	CFir ECho EPfP
	- 'Black Gold' **new**	ITim
I	- 'Black Knight'	CBot CMdw CPLG EDAr ELon EPfP GBuc GCal GCra GGar LHop MDun MHer NCGa NChi NLar SHGN SMad SWat WBor WGwG WMnd
	- black-flowered	Widely available
*	- 'Ellenbank Nightshade'	CBgR GMac
N	- 'Inshriach'	GBuc IMou LEdu WAbe
N	- 'Kew Black'	ECho EShb LEdu NBir NHol NWCA WHer WHil WWEG
	- 'Mandarin Purple'	CBgR GBuc GCal LRHS MBri SMrm SPer SWat WMoo
	- red-flowered	ECho
	- 'Rob'	ECho
§	- 'Rubella'	CRow ECho GCra NCot WFar WPrP
*	- 'Rubens'	GCal
	- 'Rubra'	see *I. chrysographes* 'Rubella'
N	- 'Tsiri'	NWCA
	- yellow-flowered	GKir LRHS WFar
	chrysographes* × *forrestii	GBin GKir NBir
	chrysophylla	GBuc
	- JCA 13233	CLAP
	- NNS 04.225	CPBP
	- NNS 05-387	WCot
	'Chubby Cheeks' (SDB)	CKel WCAu
	'Chuckwagon' (TB)	ESgI
	'Church Stoke' (SDB)	WCAu
N	'Cider Haze' (TB)	CKel
	'Ciel et Mer' (TB) **new**	WViv
	'Cimarron Rose' (SDB)	ESgI WCAu WViv
	'Cimarron Strip' (TB) **new**	EPfP WWEG
	'Cinnabar Red' (Spuria)	WAul
	'Cinnamon Apples' (MDB)	ESgI
	'Cinnamon Roll' (Spuria)	WCAu
	'City Lights' (TB)	WCAu
	'Claire Doodle' (MTB)	ESgI
	'Clairette' (Reticulata)	ECho LAma LRHS NMin
	'Clara Garland' (IB) Υ^{H4}	CKel WCAu
	'Clarence' (TB)	CKel ESgI WCAu
	clarkei	CPrp GKir WCon WCot WFar
	- B&SWJ 2122	WCru
	- CC 2751	NWCA WWst
	- CC 5493	GKev
	- SDR 3819	GKev
	'Classic Hues' (TB)	ESgI
	'Classic Look' (TB)	ESgI WViv
	'Clay's Caper' (SDB)	NBre
N	'Cleo' (TB)	CKel NBir
	'Cleo Murrell' (TB)	ESgI
	'Cliffs of Dover' (TB)	CKel EIri EKen ESgI GCal MCot SGar SRms
N	'Climbing Gold'	ECho
	'Cloud Mistress' (IB)	ESgI WViv
	'Cloud Pinnacle' (IB)	CKel
	'Cloudcap' (TB)	SRms
	'Clyde Redmond' (La) Υ^{H4}	WAul WMAq
	'Coalignition' (TB)	WCAu
	'Codicil' (TB)	EIri ESgI WCAu WViv
	'Colette Thurillet' (TB)	ESgI WCAu WViv
	collettii	EBee EBrs ECho WWst
	'Colonial Gold' (TB)	WCAu
	'Colorific' (La)	EPPr EPfP NBro NMoo WBor
	'Combo' (SDB)	CKel
	'Coming Up Roses' (TB)	WCAu
	'Compact Buddy' (MDB)	ESgI
	'Con Fuoco' (TB)	ESgI
	'Concertina' (IB)	CIri
	'Condottiere' (TB)	WViv
	'Confetti' (TB)	MBri
	confusa Υ^{H3}	CAbP CHEx CSev EShb EWld IFro LEdu SAPC SArc SBig SEND SGSe SGar SMad WBrk WFar WWst
N	- 'Martyn Rix'	CBct CDes CFwr CGHE CHEx CHid CLAP CPen CPou EBee ELon EPfP GCal IGor LFur MAvo MLHP SChr SGSe WCot WFar WGwG WHil WMnd WPGP WPer
	'Congo Bongo' (BB)	WAul
	'Conjuration' (TB)	ESgI WCAu WViv
	'Connect the Dots' (MTB)	WCAu
	'Constant Wattez' (IB)	CKel EBee ESgI NLar
	'Copatonic' (TB)	ESgI WCAu
	'Copper Classic' (TB)	ESgI WCAu WViv
	'Cops' (SDB)	ESgI
	'Coquetterie' (TB)	ESgI WViv

	'Coral Point' (TB)	WCAu
	'Coral Strand' (TB)	WCAu
	'Cordoba' (TB)	WCAu
	'Corps de Ballet' (TB)	CIri
	'Côte d'Or' (TB)	WViv
	'Count Dracula' (TB) **new**	CIri
	'Countess Zeppelin' (Spuria)	ESgI
	'County Town Red' (TB)	SIri
	'Court Magician' (SDB)	SIri
	'Cowboy in Black' (TB)	CIri
	'Cozy Calico' (TB)	ESgI WCAu
	'Crackles' (TB)	CKel
	'Crackling Caldera' (TB)	CIri
	'Cranapple' (BB) ♀H4	WAul WCAu
	'Cranberry Crush' (TB)	WCAu
	'Cranberry Sauce' (TB)	CIri
	'Cranbrook' (IB) ♀H4 **new**	SIri
	'Cream and Peaches' (SDB)	SIri WViv
	'Cream Beauty' (Dut)	EBrs LAma LRHS
	'Cream Pixie' (SDB)	WCAu
	'Cream Soda' (TB) ♀H4	CKel
	'Crème d'Or' (TB)	ESgI
	'Crème Glacée' (TB)	ESgI WViv
	cretensis	see *I. unguicularis* subsp. *cretensis*
	'Crimson Snow' **new**	LRHS
	'Crinoline' (TB)	CKel
	'Crispette' (TB)	WCAu
	cristata ♀H4	CPBP GBuc NLar SIng SRms
	- 'Alba'	ERos GCal WAbe
	cristata* × *lacustris	EPot NMen
	croatica	ESgI
	crocea ♀H4	GBin
	'Croftway Lemon' (TB)	COIW ELon
	'Cross Current' (TB)	WCAu
	'Crowned Heads' (TB)	CKel ESgI WAul WCAu WViv
	'Crownette' (SDB)	CKel
	'Crushed Velvet' (TB)	WCAu
	'Crystal Glitters' (TB)	ESgI WViv
	cuniculiformis	ECho GAuc
	- ACE 2224	GBuc
	'Cup Cake' (MDB)	ESgI
	'Cup Race' (TB)	WCAu
	'Cupid's Cup' (SDB)	ESgI
	'Curio' (MDB)	WViv
	'Curlew' (IB)	WCAu
	'Cutie' (IB)	ESgI WAul WCAu WViv WWEG
	'Cyanea' (DB)	ECho
	cycloglossa	CPBP EBrs ECho EPot LRHS WCot WWst
	'Dance Away' (TB)	ESgI WCAu WViv
	'Dancer's Veil' (TB)	CHar CKel ECtt ELon ESgI IPot LRHS MRav NBre NVic SPer WCAu
	'Dancing Lilacs' (MTB)	ESgI
	'Dandy' (TB)	ESgI
	'Dandy Candy' (TB)	CIri
	danfordiae	CAvo CBcs CBro CFFs EBrs ECho EPfP EPot GKev LAma LRHS NHol SGar SPet WFar WGwG
	'Danger' (TB)	ESgI
	'Dappled Pony' (MTB)	SMrm
	'Dardanus' (AB)	CMea EBrs ECho EPot ERCP LRHS WCot
	'Dark Crystal' (SDB)	ESgI
	'Dark Rosaleen' (TB) ♀H4	NBre
	'Dark Spark' (SDB)	WCAu
	'Dark Vader' (SDB)	ESgI WCAu WViv
	darwasica	GAuc WWst
	'Dash Away' (SDB)	ESgI SIri WViv
	'Daughter of Stars' (TB)	ESgI
	'Dauntless' (TB)	ESgI
	'David Guest' (IB)	CKel
	'Dawn of Fall' (TB)	ESgI
	'Dawning' (TB) ♀H4	CIri ESgI WViv
	'Dazzle Me' (SDB)	WCAu
	'Dazzling Gold' (TB)	ESgI WCAu WViv
	'Death by Chocolate' (SDB)	CIri ESgI
§	***decora***	NWCA
	'Deep Black' (TB)	CKel CPar CWGN EAEE EBla EHrv ELan EPfP IPot LAst LFCN LRHS LSRN MBNS MCot MRav MWat NOrc SBch SDnm SPer SPhx SPoG SWat WAul WCAu WCot
	'Deep Caress' (TB)	ESgI
	'Deep Pacific' (TB)	LRHS MBri WCAu
	'Deep Space' (TB)	WCAu
	'Deft Touch' (TB)	CKel WCAu
	delavayi ♀H4	EBee ECho EWes GAuc GBin GMaP IBlr MBel NLAp WPrP WRHF
	- SDR 50	GKev
N	- 'Didcot'	LRHS
	'Delicate Lady' (IB) ♀H4	CKel
	'Delirium' (IB)	WAul WViv
	'Delta Blues' (TB)	WViv
	'Delta Butterfly' (La)	WMAq
	'Demelza' (TB)	CKel
	'Demon' (SDB)	CKel
	'Denys Humphry' (TB)	CKel WCAu
	'Deputé Nomblot' (TB)	ESgI
	'Derwentwater' (TB)	SRms WCAu
	'Desert Dream' (AB)	GGar
I	'Desert Dream' (Sino-Sib)	GAbr
	'Desert Echo' (TB)	COIW SPet
	'Desert Orange' (SDB)	WViv
	'Desert Song' (TB)	CKel WCAu
	'Destination' (Spuria) ♀H4	CIri
	'Devil David' (TB)	CIri
	'Devil May Care' (IB)	CIri
	'Devilish Nature' (SDB)	CIri
	'Devil's Spoon' (TB) **new**	CIri
	'Devonshire Cream' (TB)	CIri
	'Diabolique' (TB)	CIri WViv
	'Diligence' (SDB) ♀H4	CKel
	'Disco Jewel' (MTB)	ESgI
	'Distant Roads' (TB)	WCAu
	'Ditto' (MDB)	WViv
	'Diversion' (TB)	ESgI
	'Divine' (TB)	CKel
	'Dixie Darling' (TB)	ESgI
	'Dixie Pixie' (SDB)	WCAu WTin
	'Dolce Acqua' (TB)	CIri
	dolichosiphon	GAuc
	aff. ***dolichosiphon***	GAuc
	'Dolly Madison' (TB)	ESgI
	'Don Juan' (TB)	ESgI
	'Donegal' (IB)	WViv
	'Don't Touch' (TB)	CIri
	'Doodads' (TB)	CIri ESgI WCAu
	'Doozey' (MDB)	ESgI
	'Double Espoir' (TB)	ESgI WViv
	'Double Lament' (SDB)	CBro ERos
	'Doublemint' (TB)	CIri
	douglasiana ♀H4	CAby CPen ECho GCal GKev NWCA WFar WTin WWEG
	'Dovedale' (TB) ♀H4	WCAu
	'Dover Beach' (TB)	SGar
	'Draco' (TB)	ESgI
	'Dragone' (TB)	CIri
	'Drake Carne' (TB)	CKel
	'Drama Queen' (TB)	CIri
	'Dream Indigo' (IB)	CKel WCAu
	'Dream Lover' (TB)	ESgI
	'Dreamsicle' (TB)	SIri WViv

'Dresden Candleglow' (IB) WCAu
'Dualtone' (TB) CKel
'Dude Ranch' (TB) CIri
'Dunlin' (MDB) CBro ERos NBir NMen
'Dural White Butterfly' (La) CHid CSpe LAst
'Dusky Challenger' (TB) CKel ESgI SCoo WAul WCAu WViv
'Dusky Evening' (TB) ESgI
'Dutch Chocolate' (TB) ESgI ETod WCAu WViv
'Dwight Enys' (TB) ♀H4 CKel
'Dynamite' (TB) WAul
'Eagle's Flight' (TB) CKel
'Earl of Essex' (TB) WCAu
'Early Frost' (IB) CKel EPPr WAul WViv
'Early Light' (TB) ♀H4 ESgI WCAu
'East Indies' (TB) WCAu
'Easter Tide' (La) WCAu
'Eastertime' (TB) ECtt ESgI WViv
'Echo de France' (TB) ESgI
'Ecstatic Echo' (TB) ESgI WViv
'Ecstatic Night' (TB) WCAu
'Edge of Winter' (TB) CKel SIri
'Edith Wolford' (TB) CWCL EBee ECtt ESgI EWll GBin MWea SRGP WBor WCAu WWEG
N 'Ed's Blue' (DB) ELan
'Edward' (Reticulata) CBro EBrs ECho EPfP EPot LAma LRHS MWat SMrm WCAu
'Edward of Windsor' (TB) CMil ELan GMaP LPio NLar SDnm SRGP WCAu WMnd
'Eileen Louise' (TB) ♀H4 WCAu
'El Torito' (SDB) ♀H4 **new** CIri
'Eleanor Clare' (IB) ♀H4 CKel
'Eleanor Hill' (Spuria) WAul
'Eleanor's Pride' (TB) CKel ESgI WCAu
'Electrique' (TB) WCAu
'Elegans' (TB) **new** MCot
'Elegant Lass' (BB) ♀H4 **new** CIri
elegantissima see *I. iberica* subsp. *elegantissima*
'Elizabeth Arden' (TB) CKel
'Elizabeth of England' (TB) COIW EWll SPet SRGP WWEG
'Elizabeth Poldark' (TB) ESgI WCAu
'Ella' (IB) **new** CSpr
* 'Ellenbank Damselfly' CBgR GMac
* 'Ellenbank Sapphire' GMac
'Elsa Sass' (TB) ESgI
N 'Elvinhall' CBro
'Empress of India' (TB) EBee SEND
'Encircle' (CH) GBuc
'Encre Bleue' (IB) CBgR ESgI WViv
'Endless Love' (TB) **new** EIri
'English Charm' (TB) ESgI WAul WCAu WViv
'English Cottage' (TB) COIW EBee GCal LSRN MWat NLar SMrm WCAu WWEG
'Ennerdale' (TB) SRms
'Ennoble' (TB) CIri ESgI
'Enriched' (MTB) ♀H4 **new** CIri SIri
§ ***ensata*** ♀H4 CBcs CBro CHEx COIW CWat ELan EMFW EPfP EWTr GKev GKir IFro LPBA LRHS MNrw NBro NCob NGdn NLar SPlb SRms SWat WCAu WCFE WClo WFar WPer
N - 'Activity' CRow NBro NGby SHar WFar WPrP WWEG
- 'Alba' ECha
- 'Aldridge Prelude' WAul
- 'Aoigata' CPrp
- 'Apollo' CBen CRow
- 'Artist' NBro
- 'Asian Warrior' CElw
- 'August Emperor' CBgR EKen LAst NBhm SMrm
- 'Azuma-kagami' CBgR CFir EBee EKen ELan EPfP MNrw WCon
- 'Barr Purple East' ♀H4 CHid CRow
- 'Beni-tsubaki' ESgI WAul
I - 'Blue King' NBro SMrm SPet
I - 'Blue Peter' CBen CRow
- 'Blue Pompon' NMoo WViv
- 'Blue Prince' CBen
N - 'Blush' NBro
- 'Butterflies in Flight' CRow
- 'Caprician Butterfly' ♀H4 CMHG EPfP ESgI GBin MBri NBhm NMoo WAul WCAu
N - 'Carnival Prince' CFir NBro SBod WFar WMoo WPnP
- 'Cascade Crest' WAul
- 'Cascade Spice' WAul
- 'Center of Interest' LRHS MSCN NCGa
- 'Charm' LRHS
* - 'Chico Geisho' ESgI WAul
- 'Chitose-no-tomo' CRow
- 'Chiyodajō' CKel
- 'Crepe Paper' WFar
N - 'Cry of Rejoice' EBee ECho ECtt EWll NBhm NBre NBro SWat WAul WCAu WFar
- 'Crystal Halo' NMoo SMrm
- 'Dace' EBee GAbr GBin
- 'Dancing Waves' CRow
I - 'Darling' CPen CPrp CRow EBee ECho EPfP EWTr MBri NBro NLar SRGP SWat WAul WCAu WCon WFar WMoo WWEG
- 'Diomedes' ESgI
- 'Dramatic Moment' GBuc WFar WWEG
I - 'Dresden China' CRow
- 'Eden's Artist' LRHS
N - 'Eden's Blue Pearl' CHid EBee GBin IPot
N - 'Eden's Blush' EBee MLHP WAul
N - 'Eden's Charm' ELan EPfP GBin LPBA NHol SPet
N - 'Eden's Delight' NHol
N - 'Eden's Harmony' EBee WAul
N - 'Eden's Paintbrush' EBee ELan EPfP SPer
N - 'Eden's Picasso' CFir EBee ELan EPfP IPot
N - 'Eden's Purple Glory' CHid GBin WCot WTin
N - 'Eden's Starship' CFir EBee
- 'Electric Rays' WAul
I - 'Emotion' CMac EBee NBro NGby WAul WFar WPnP
- 'Epimetheus' **new** WViv
- 'Exstase' **new** WViv
- 'Flashing Koi' ESgI
I - 'Fortune' EHrv LAst WAul
- 'Freckled Geisha' CElw
- 'Frilled Enchantment' ♀H4 WAul
* - 'Galathea' CPrp EBee
- 'Geisha Gown' SWal WViv
N - 'Gipsy' EBee WAul
- 'Gold Bound' NMoo
N - 'Gracieuse' CBgR CPen EBee ELan EPfP GBin LRHS MBri MSCN NBro NLar SUsu SWat WAul WFar WMoo WPnP WPrP WWEG
- 'Gusto' CMHG CPen EBee EPfP IPot LDai NBhm NBro NMoo SMrm WBor
- 'Haru-no-umi' CKel
- 'Hegira' WAul
- 'Hercule' CHid CPLG CRow GAbr NBir
- Higo white SPer
* - 'Himatsuri' CMHG
N - 'Hokkaido' CBen CRow ESgI
- 'Hue and Cry' ♀H4 ESgI WAul
- hybrids EHon ESgI

	- 'Iapetus'	ESgI
*	- 'Innocence'	CKel EHrv EWll MSpe NBre NGby NLar SMrm SWat WAul WFar WMoo
	- 'Iso-no-nami'	EBee EWll NBro WAul WPrP
*	- 'Jacob's Coat'	NCot
	- 'Jitsugetsu'	CFir CMHG NMoo
N	- 'Jodlesong'	EBee WFar
	- 'Kalamazoo'	WFar
	- 'Katy Mendez' ♀H4	WAul
	- 'Kiyo-tsura'	CKel
*	- 'Kiyo-zuru'	EPfP
N	- 'Kogesho'	EBee EPfP GBuc LHop NBro NLar NMoo WAul
N	- 'Koh Dom'	SPer
	- 'Kongo San'	WFar
	- 'Kuma-funjin'	CRow
	- 'Kumo-no-obi'	CMHG EBee EBla GBuc NBro SPoG SWat WAul WCAu
*	- 'Kunshikoku'	NLar
N	- 'Laced'	SPer
	- 'Lady in Waiting'	GBin NLar SWal
	- 'Landscape at Dawn'	CRow
N	- 'Laughing Lion'	CPen EBee EBla ECtt GKir NBro WAul WFar WMoo WWEG
	- 'L'Idéal'	CPen
	- 'Light at Dawn'	CEnt CMHG CPen EPfP LDai NBPC NBhm NBro WAul WBor WFar WMoo
N	- 'Lilac Blotch'	SPer
I	- 'Loyalty'	EBla ECho EWTr SRGP WFar
	- 'Mancunian' ♀H4	CKel
I	- 'Mandarin'	CBen CRow
	- 'Midnight Stars'	WAul
	- 'Midnight Whisper'	WAul
	- 'Midsummer Reverie'	CRow WViv
	- 'Mist Falls'	ESgI
N	- 'Momozomo'	LLHF NBhm NBro NLar
§	- 'Moonlight Waves'	CHid CMHG CRow EBla ELan EMFW EPPr EPfP EShb GAbr GBuc GCra GGar GMaP GMac LRHS NBro NGdn NHol SMrm SPoG SWat WAul WCAu WFar
	- 'Murasame' ♀H4	CMHG WAul
	- 'Ocean Mist'	CHid CMHG CPen EBee NBro NMoo WViv
	- 'Oku-banri'	CHEx CPrp EShb
	- 'Oriental Eyes'	EBee GBin NGdn NLar NMoo WAul WCAu
	- pale mauve-flowered	NBir SPer
	- 'Pastel Princess'	WAul
§	- 'Peacock'	EBee
	- 'Pin Stripe'	MBri NLar NMoo SMrm SUsu SWat WAul WMoo
	- 'Pink Frost'	CBgR CRow EBee ELan EPPr EPfP EWll GCal LBMP LRHS NBro NHol WAul WFar WTin
	- 'Pleasant Earlybird'	WAul
	- 'Pleasant Journey'	ECtt EHrv
	- 'Prairie Frost'	EBee EPfP NLar
	- 'Prairie Noble'	EBee NBro NLar
N	- 'Purple Glory'	ELan
	- purple-flowered	SPer
	- 'Ranpo'	CRow
I	- 'Red Dawn'	CBen
	- 'Reign of Glory'	WAul
I	- 'Reveille'	NBro SWat WAul WPtf
§	- 'Rose Queen' ♀H4	Widely available
	- 'Rose Tower'	CMHG
	- 'Rowden Amir'	CRow
	- 'Rowden Autocrat'	CRow
	- 'Rowden Begum'	CRow
	- 'Rowden Caliph'	CRow
	- 'Rowden Consul'	CRow
	- 'Rowden Dauphin'	CRow
	- 'Rowden Dictator'	CRow
	- 'Rowden Emperor'	CRow
	- 'Rowden King'	CRow
	- 'Rowden Knave'	CRow
	- 'Rowden Knight'	CRow
	- 'Rowden Mikado'	CRow
	- 'Rowden Naib'	CRow
	- 'Rowden Nuncio'	CRow
	- 'Rowden Pasha'	CRow
	- 'Rowden Prince'	CRow
	- 'Rowden Queen'	CRow
	- 'Rowden Shah'	CRow
	- 'Rowden Sultana'	CRow
I	- 'Royal Banner'	EBee MBri NBro SMrm WAul WCon WFar
	- 'Royal Crown'	ECho
	- 'Royal Pageant'	CMHG EBee NBPC NBro
I	- 'Ruby King'	WAul
	- 'Ruffled Dimity'	EWTr GMac IPot NBPC
	- 'Sapphire Star'	CKel
	- 'Sea of Amethyst'	ESgI
	- 'Sennyo-no-hora'	CPrp
I	- 'Sensation'	CMHG CPen CWCL ECho ECtt EWTr EWll GBin SMrm SWat WAul WCAu WPrP WWEG
	- 'Shiro-nihonkai'	EBee NMoo
I	- 'Snowflake'	LRHS
	- 'Snowy Hills'	WAul
	- 'Sorcerer's Triumph'	EBee GBin GGar WFar WViv
	- 'Southern Son' ♀H4	ESgI
	- var. ***spontanea***	SPet SWat WAbe
	- - B&SWJ 1103	WCru
	- - B&SWJ 8699	WCru
	- 'Springtime Melody'	WAul
I	- 'Star'	CBen
	- 'Summer Snowflake' **new**	WViv
	- 'Summer Storm' ♀H4	CKel SPer
	- 'Taga-sode'	WViv
	- 'The Great Mogul' ♀H4	CKel CRow
	- 'Tropic Showers' **new**	WViv
	- 'Umi-kaze'	NLar
	- 'Variegata' (v) ♀H4	Widely available
N	- 'Velvety Queen'	CPrp WAul
	- 'Waka-murasaki'	EBee MSpe NBro
I	- 'White Ladies'	CSBt EWll SWat WWEG
I	- 'White Pearl'	CRow
	- white-flowered	WFar
	- 'Wine Ruffles'	LBuc LSRN MBri SIri SMrm
	- 'Worley Pink'	WViv
	- 'Yako-no-tama'	CRow WMoo
	- 'Yamato Hime'	CMHG EPfP NLar NMoo
N	- 'Yedo-yeman'	WFar
	- 'Yezo-nishiki'	GBin NBro SBod
N	- 'Yu Nagi'	SPer
	'Entice' (TB)	CIri
	'Epicenter' (TB)	WCAu
	'Eramosa Skies' (SDB)	WCAu
	'Erect' (IB)	CKel
	'Esoteric' (SDB)	ESgI
	'Etched Apricot' (TB)	WCAu
	'Eternal Bliss' (TB)	WViv
	'Evening Episode' **new**	WViv
	'Evening Pond' (MTB)	CKel
	'Evening Shade' (J)	WWst
	'Ever After' (TB)	ECtt ESgI WViv
	'Evergreen Hideaway' (TB)	CIri
	'Everything Plus' (TB)	ESgI WCAu
	'Exclusivity' (TB)	ESgI
	'Exotic Gem' (TB)	WCAu

	Name	Suppliers
	'Exotic Isle' (TB)	ECtt ESgI WViv
	'Extra' (MDB)	LLHF WViv
	'Eye Magic' (IB) 🏆H4	CKel
	'Eye of Tiger' (Dut)	LAma SBch
	'Eye Shadow' (SDB)	WCAu
	'Eyebright' (SDB) 🏆H4	CBro WCAu
	'Fade to Black' (TB)	CIri
	'Faenelia Hicks' (La)	WMAq
	'Falcon's Crest' (Spuria) 🏆H4	CIri
	'Fall Fiesta' (TB)	ESgI WViv
	'Fancy Woman' (TB)	WAul WCAu
	'Fanfaron' (TB)	ESgI
	'Faraway Places' (TB)	WCAu
	'Fashion Holiday' (IB) new	SIri
	'Fashion Lady' (MDB)	CBro ECho
	'Fashion Statement' (TB)	WViv
	'Fast Forward' (IB)	WAul
	'Fatal Attraction' (TB)	WCAu
	'Feature Attraction' (TB)	CIri WCAu WViv
	'Feminine Charm' (TB)	MRav WCAu
	fernaldii	GAuc
	'Festive Skirt' (TB)	CKel WCAu
	'Feu du Ciel' (TB) 🏆H4	ESgI WViv
	'Fierce Fire' (IB) 🏆H4	CKel
	'Fiesta Time' (TB)	CWCL ECtt WViv
	filifolia var. ***latifolia***	NMin
	'Film Festival' (TB)	ESgI
	'Finalist' (TB)	WAul WViv
N	'Fire and Flame' (TB)	NBir
	'Firebeard' (TB)	CIri WAul
	'Firebug' (IB)	ESgI WViv
	'Firecracker' (TB)	MRav WCAu
	'First Interstate' (TB)	CWCL ESgI WCAu WViv
	'First Movement' (TB)	ESgI
	'First Romance' (SDB)	LSRN SIri WViv
	'First Violet' (TB)	WCAu
	'Flambé' (IB)	WAul
	'Flaming Victory' (TB)	ESgI
	'Flareup' (TB)	WCAu
	flavescens	ESgI WCAu
	'Flavours' (BB)	WCAu
	'Fleece As White' (BB)	CIri
	'Fleur Collette Louise' (La)	CIri
	'Flight of Fantasy' (La)	CKel
	'Flight to Mars' (TB)	CIri
	'Flirting' (SDB)	WViv
	'Flirting Again' (SDB) 🏆H4 new	SIri
	'Floating World' (CH) 🏆H4	SIri
§	'Florentina' (IB/TB) 🏆H4	CArn CBro CHby COIW ECGP EGoo EOHP ESgI EWll GCal GPoy ILis MHer MNHC MRav NBid NBir SEND SIde WAul WCAu
	'Flumadiddle' (IB)	CBro CKel
	'Flushed Delight' (TB)	CIri
	foetidissima 🏆H4	Widely available
	- 'Aurea'	GQue WCot
	- ***chinensis***	see *I. foetidissima* var. *citrina*
§	- var. ***citrina***	CBre CFir CRow CSsd ECGP EPla GAbr GCal GCra GKir IBlr NBid SChr SUsu WCot WEas WWEG
	- 'Fructu Albo'	GBin GKev GQue NSti WCot
	- var. ***lutescens***	CHid EPPr IBlr
N	- 'Moonshy Seedling'	CSWP
	- 'Variegata' (v) 🏆H4	CElw CHar CRow ECtt EHrv EPfP GBar MCCP MSCN NBir NCob NPer WBor WCAu WWEG
	- yellow-seeded	GCal GKev WTin
	'Fogbound' (TB)	CIri
	'Foggy Dew' (TB)	ECGP EShb LRHS MWea SPoG
	'Fondation Van Gogh' (TB)	ESgI
	'Foolish Fancy' (TB)	SIri
	'Forest Light' (SDB)	CBro ESgI
	'Forever Blue' (SDB)	WViv
*	'Forever Trevor' (CH)	SPhx
	'Forever Yours' (TB)	WAul
	'Forge Fire' (TB)	ESgI
	formosana	ECho
	- B&SWJ 3076	WCru
	forrestii 🏆H4	CHVG CHid ECho EPfP EWTr GAbr GAuc GCal GCra GKev GKir ITim LPBA LRHS MBri MHer NBPC NBir NBro NCob NGdn SBch SPhx SRot WAbe WPtf
	'Fort Apache' (TB)	ESgI EWes
	'Fortune Teller' (TB)	CKel
	fosteriana	GKev NWCA
	'Fourfold Blue' (SpH)	GBin
	'Foxy Lady' (TB)	ESgI
	'Frank Elder' (Reticulata)	EBrs ECho EPot ERos LAma LLHF LRHS MRav MTho NMen WCAu
	'Frans Hals' (Dut)	EBrs GKev MMHG MNrw WCot
	'Freedom Flight' (TB)	CIri
	'French Can Can' (TB) new	SIri
	'French Rose' (TB)	CKel
	'Fresh Image' (TB)	WCAu
	'Fresh Start' (SDB)	WAul
	'Fresno Calypso' (TB)	ESgI WCAu
	'Frimousee' (TB)	ESgI
	'Fringe Benefits' (TB)	ESgI WCAu
	'Frison-roche' (TB)	CWCL ESgI WViv
	'Frisounette' (TB)	ESgI
	'Fritillary Flight' (IB) 🏆H4	CKel
	'Frivolité' (TB)	ESgI
	'Frontier Lady' (TB)	CIri
	'Frontier Marshall' (TB)	NMoo
	'Frost and Flame' (TB)	EAEE EBla ECtt ELan EWll LBMP LBuc LFCN LRHS MBri MRav NGdn NLar SBch SPer SPoG SWat WAul WWEG
	'Frosted Angel' (SDB)	CBro
	'Frosted Biscuit' (TB) 🏆H4	CKel
	'Frosted Fantasy' (TB)	CIri
	'Frosted Velvet' (MTB)	WAul WCAu
	'Frosty Jewels' (TB)	ESgI
	'Fruit Cocktail' (IB) new	CKel
	'Full Impact' (TB)	CIri
	fulva 🏆H3	CBgR CDes CPrp CRow EBee GCal NBir NBro NSti WBor WCot WTin
	- 'Marvell Gold' (La)	CRow
	× ***fulvala*** 🏆H4	CAby CDes CFir EBee EPPr EWes GBin NBir NSti
	- 'Violacea'	EBee WCot
	'Fumo Negli Occhi' (TB)	ESgI
	'Furnaceman' (SDB)	CBro ERos MBri
	'Fuzzy' (MDB)	ERos
	'Gai Luron' (TB) new	WWEG
	'Gala Gown' (TB)	WCAu
	'Gallant Moment' (TB)	ECtt SIri WViv
	'Galleon Gold' (SDB)	CKel
	'Galway' (IB)	SIri WViv
	'Gay Parasol' (TB)	WViv
N	'Gelbe Mantel' (Sino-Sib)	CBot CHid CLAP EBee NBir NBro NGdn NHol NSti WFar WPrP
	'Gemstar' (SDB)	WCAu WViv
	'Gemstone Walls' (TB)	ESgI
	'Gentius' (TB)	WMnd
	'Gentle' (SDB)	WCAu
	'Gentle Grace' (SDB)	ESgI
	'George' (Reticulata) 🏆H4	CAvo CBro CFFs CPrp ECho EPfP EPot ERCP ERos GAbr GKev LRHS NHol NMin SPhx WBrk WHoo
	'George Smith' (TB)	ESgI
	'Gerald Darby'	see *I.* × *robusta* 'Gerald Darby'

'Gérard Brière' (TB) new — WViv
germanica ♀H4 — EGoo MGos WCAu
- var. ***florentina*** — see *I.* 'Florentina'
N - 'Mel Jope' — NBir
- 'Nepalensis' — EGoo
N - 'The King' — WCAu
'Ghost Train' (TB) — CIri WViv
'Gibson Girl' (TB) — WCAu
'Gingerbread Castle' (TB) — WCAu
'Gingerbread Man' (SDB) — CBro CMea EHrv ERos ESgI MBrN MWea NMen SMrm SWal WCAu WHoo
'Glacier' (TB) — ECho
'Glad Rags' (TB) — ESgI
'Glam' (IB) — WCAu
'Glowing Smile' (TB) — WAul
'Gnus Flash' (TB) — WCAu
'Go Between' (TB) — WCAu
'Godfrey Owen' (TB) — CKel WCAu
'Godsend' (TB) — CIri CKel WCAu
'Going My Way' (TB) — ESgI LSou SIri WCAu WViv WWEG
'Gold Country' (TB) — ESgI
'Gold Galore' (TB) — WViv
'Gold of Autumn' (TB) — CKel SMrm
'Goldberry' (IB) — WCAu
'Golden Alien' (TB) — CIri
'Golden Alps' (TB) — SRms WCAu
'Golden Child' (SDB) — ESgI
'Golden Encore' (TB) — CKel WCAu
'Golden Fair' (SDB) — NBir
'Golden Forest' (TB) — EAEE LRHS MWea SPoG WCAu
'Golden Immortal' (TB) — WViv
'Golden Panther' (TB) — CIri
'Golden Planet' (TB) — CKel
'Golden Violet' (SDB) — ESgI
'Goldkist' (TB) — CIri
goniocarpa — EBee WAbe
- var. ***grossa*** — EBee
'Good Looking' (TB) — ESgI WCAu
'Good Show' (TB) — WAul WCAu WViv
'Good Vibrations' (TB) — SIri WViv
'Goodbye Heart' (TB) — ESgI LSRN WViv
'Gordon' (Reticulata) — CAvo EBrs ECho EPfP EPot ERCP GKev LAma LRHS MWat SMrm WRHF
gormanii — see *I. tenax*
'Gosh' (SDB) — CBgR CKel
'Gossip' (SDB) — CBro ESgI
gracilipes — GKev WAbe
gracilipes* × *lacustris — GAuc GEdr WAbe
graeberiana — EBrs ECho EPot WWst
- white fall — WWst
- yellow fall — EBee EBrs ECho LRHS WWst
graminea ♀H4 — CAvo CBro CHid CMac CPrp CRow EBee ECha ECho EHrv ELan EPPr EPfP ERos IFro LLWP LRHS NBir NCot NMen NSti NWCA SPer WAul WCAu WCom WCot
- var. ***pseudocyperus*** — CRow GCal NMRc SDys
graminifolia — see *I. kerneriana*
'Granada Gold' (TB) — SRms
'Grape Jelly' (TB) — WCAu WViv
'Grapelet' (MDB) — ERos WCAu WViv
'Grapeshot' (TB) — CIri
'Great Gatsby' (TB) — CKel
'Great Lakes' (TB) — ESgI
'Grecian Skies' (TB) — ESgI
'Green Ice' (TB) — CKel MRav
'Green Prophecy' (TB) — CKel
'Green Spot' (SDB) ♀H4 — CBgR CBro CKel CWGN EBee EBla ECtt EHrv ELan EPfP GBuc GEdr MRav MSpe NBir NCob NHol NLar NMen NWCA SPer SPhx WAul WCAu WCFE WWEG
'Green Streak' (TB) — CIri
'Grenade' (TB) new — WViv
'Gringo' (TB) — WCAu
'Guatemala' (TB) — CIri
'Gudrun' (TB) — ESgI
'Gwyneth Evans' (BB) ♀H4 — CKel
'Gypsy Beauty' (Dut) — EBrs EPfP LAma LRHS SBch WCot
'Gypsy Jewels' (TB) — CKel ESgI
'Gypsy Romance' (TB) ♀H4 — EIri ESgI SIri WCAu WViv
'Habit' (TB) — WAul WCAu
'Hafnium' (SDB) — CKel
halophila — see *I. spuria* subsp. *halophila*
'Handshake' (TB) ♀H4 — CIri WViv
'Happenstance' (TB) — ESgI WViv
'Happy Birthday' (TB) — ESgI
N 'Happy Border' (BB) — WCAu
'Happy Mood' (IB) ♀H4 — NBre WCAu
'Harbor Blue' (TB) — CKel MWat SWat WCAu WWEG
* 'Hareknoll' — NWCA
'Harlow Gold' (IB) — ESgI
'Harmony' (Reticulata) — CAvo CBro CFFs EBrs ECho EPfP EPot GAbr GKev LAma LRHS MBri NHol SMrm SPhx
'Harriette Halloway' (TB) — CSam EBee EBla EShb ETod GMaP LPio LRHS LSRN NLar SPet SRGP WCot
hartwegii — ECho
- NNS 05-394 — WCot
- subsp. ***hartwegii*** — GAuc
- subsp. ***pinetorum*** — EPot GAuc
'Harvest King' (TB) — ECtt ESgI WViv
'Harvest of Memories' (TB) — ESgI WWEG
'Haut les Voiles' (TB) — CWCL WViv
'Haute Couture' (TB) — WCAu WViv
'Haviland' (TB) — SIri WViv
'Hazelnut Delight' (TB) — CIri
'Headcorn' (MTB) ♀H4 — SIri WAul
'Headlines' (TB) — WCAu
'Heather Carpet' (SDB) — WCAu
'Heather Sky' (TB) — CIri
'Heavenly Days' (TB) — WCAu
'Helen Boehm' (TB) — ESgI WViv
'Helen Collingwood' (TB) — ESgI
'Helen Dawn' (TB) new — CIri
'Helen McGregor' (TB) — CKel ESgI
'Helen Proctor' (IB) — ESgI WCAu
'Helen Traubel' (TB) — WCAu
'Helge' (IB) — COIW ECho NBre SWat
'Hellcat' (IB) — WAul WCAu WViv
'Hello Darkness' (TB) ♀H4 — CIri ESgI WCAu WCot WViv
'Hercules' (Reticulata) — ECho ERCP LRHS NMin
'Heure Bleue' (TB) — WViv
hexagona new — GAuc
'Hey There' (MDB) — ESgI WViv
'High Barbaree' (TB) — WCAu
'High Blue Sky' (TB) — WCAu
'High Command' (TB) — CKel
'High Ho Silver' — ESgI
'High Roller' (TB) ♀H4 — CIri
'Highline Amethyst' (Spuria) — WAul
'Highline Halo' (Spuria) — WCAu
'Hindu Magic' (TB) — WCAu
hippolyti — WWst
'Hissy-Fit' (IB) — CKel
histrio — ECho GAuc
- subsp. ***aintabensis*** — EBrs ECho EPot LAma
histrioides — ECho GAuc WAbe
§ - 'Angel's Tears' (Reticulata) — EBrs ECho ERCP ERos NMen NMin WWst
- 'Halkis' (Reticulata) — EPot ERCP LAma NMin

	- 'Lady Beatrix Stanley'	CBro EBrs ECho EPot ERCP GBin LRHS NHol NMen NMin
N	- 'Major'	CDes ECho LAma NMin SPhx WWst
N	- 'Michael Tears'	ECho WWst
	- var. ***sophenensis***	EBrs ECho
	'Hocus Pocus' (SDB)	EPPr WAul WViv
	'Holden Clough' (SpH) ♀H4	Widely available
	× ***hollandica*** hort.	EBrs LRHS NBir
	'Holy Fire' (TB)	CIri
	'Holy Night' (TB)	CKel
	'Honey Behold' (SDB)	CKel
	'Honey Glazed' (IB)	ESgI WAul WCAu WViv
	'Honeyplic' (IB) ♀H4	SIri WAul WCAu
	'Honington' (SDB)	WCAu
	'Honky Tonk Blues' (TB)	CKel ESgI LSRN WAul WViv
	'Honky Tonk Hussy' (BB)	CKel
	'Honorabile' (MTB)	WCAu
	hoogiana ♀H3	EBrs ECho EPot GKev LRHS WWst
	- 'Blue Mount' **new**	LRHS
	- deep purple-flowered **new**	LRHS
	- 'Purpurea'	EBrs ECho WWst
	'Hook' (TB)	WAul
§	***hookeri***	CPBP CSam ELan EWTr GAuc GBBs GBin GEdr GMac IGor LEdu NBPC SGSe SMrm WAbe WCot
§	'Hornpipe' (TB)	WCAu
	'Hot Fudge' (IB)	EPPr
	'Hot Gossip' (TB)	WCAu
	'Hot Jazz' (SDB)	WCAu
	'Hot Spice' (IB)	WCAu
	'Hot to Trot' (TB)	ESgI
	'Howard Weed' (TB)	EBee SPad
	'Huckleberry Fudge' (TB)	WAul
	'Hugh Miller' (TB)	WCAu
	'Hula Doll' (MDB)	NMen
	'Hula Moon' (TB)	ESgI
§	***humilis***	GKev
	hyrcana	EBrs ECho
	'I Repeat' (TB)	ESgI
	'I Seek You' (TB)	ESgI
	iberica	ECho GAuc
§	- subsp. ***elegantissima***	EBrs ECho WWst
	- subsp. ***iberica***	WWst
§	- subsp. ***lycotis***	WWst
	'Ice Dancer' (TB) ♀H4	CKel
	'Ice Wings' (BB)	WCAu
	'Iced Tea' (TB) ♀H4	CIri
	'Ida' (Reticulata)	ECho LAma
	'Ila Crawford' (Spuria) ♀H4	WCAu
	illyrica	see *I. pallida*
	imbricata	GKev
	'Imbue' (SDB)	ESgI WViv
	'Immortal Hour' (TB)	WCAu
	'Immortality' (TB)	CKel CWGN EKen ESgI EWll WCAu WWEG
	'Imperator' (Dut)	ECho
	'Imperial Bronze' (Spuria)	SMrm WAul WCAu
	'Impetuous' (BB) ♀H4	CKel
	'Imprimis' (TB)	ESgI WCAu
	'In a Flash' (IB)	WCAu
	'In Limbo' (IB)	CKel
	'In Reverse' (TB)	CKel WViv
	'In Town' (TB)	ESgI
	'Incentive' (TB)	ECtt
*	'Incoscente' (TB)	ESgI
	'Indeed' (IB)	CBgR
	'Indian Chief' (TB)	CWCL ESgI GBin MRav SPur WCAu WWEG
	'Indian Idyll' (IB)	CKel
	'Indian Pow Wow' (SDB)	CSev
N	'Indiana Sunset' (TB)	CKel
	'Indigo Flight' (IB)	CKel
	'Indigo Princess' (TB)	CKel WViv
	'Indiscreet' (TB)	WCAu WViv
	'Infernal Fire' (TB)	CIri
	'Inferno' (TB)	WViv
	'Infinite Grace' (TB)	ESgI
	'Innocent Devil' (TB)	CIri
	'Innocent Heart' (IB) ♀H4	WCAu
	'Innocent Pink' (TB)	ESgI
	innominata	ECha ECho GAbr GAuc GGar GKev IBlr LHop LRHS NBir NBro NMen SRms SWal WWEG
	- JCA 13225	CLAP
	- NNS 01-407	WCot
	- apricot-flowered	CPrp IBlr
	- Ballyrogan hybrids	IBlr
	- 'Bronze'	MMuc
	- yellow-flowered	NMen NRya
	'Interpol' (TB)	ESgI WCAu
	'Intrepid' (TB)	CWCL WViv
	'Invicta Blackguard' (IB) **new**	SIri
	'Invicta Daybreak' (IB) **new**	SIri
	'Invitation' (TB)	ESgI
	'Irisades' (TB) **new**	WViv
	'Irish Doll' (MDB)	WCAu
	'Irish Moss' (SDB)	WAul WViv
	'Irish Tune' (TB)	ESgI
	'Island Sunset' (TB)	ESgI SIri WViv
	'Isoline' (TB)	ESgI
	'J.S. Dijt' (Reticulata)	CAvo CBro CFFs EBrs ECho EPfP EPot ERCP LAma LRHS MBri MGos SPhx
	'Jabal' (SDB)	SIri WViv
	'Jane Phillips' (TB) ♀H4	Widely available
	'Jane Taylor' (SDB)	CBro
	'Janet Lane' (BB)	CKel
	'Jangles' (IB)	WCAu
	'Janice Chesnik' (Spuria)	ESgI
	'Janine Louise' (TB) ♀H4	CKel
	japonica ♀H3	CHEx ECho EHrv EPfP NPer WAul WOut
	- B&SWJ 8921	WCru
	- 'Aphrodite' (v)	WTin
	- 'Bourne Graceful'	CAby WCAu
	- 'Ledger'	CAby CHll CKel CMac CPrp CSpe ECha EHrv ELan EPfP IGor MRav SEND SGSe SHom SMad WPGP
	- f. ***pallescens***	SGSe
N	- 'Rudolph Spring'	CPen GCal
I	- 'Snowflake'	CAvo
§	- 'Variegata' (v) ♀H3	CAvo CBgR CBot CBow CBro CHEx CKel CPrp CSpe ECha EHrv ELan ELon ESwi GGar LRHS NBro NPer SAPC SAga SArc SBch SMad WAul WEas WHil WPGP
	'Jasper Gem' (MDB)	ERos NBir
	'Jay Kenneth' (IB)	CBgR
	'Jazz Festival' (TB)	SIri WCAu WViv
	'Jazzamatazz' (SDB)	ESgI WCAu WViv
	'Jazzed Up' (TB)	WCAu WViv
	'Jean Cayeux' (TB)	ESgI
	'Jean Guymer' (TB)	ESgI NBir WCAu
	'Jeanne Price' (TB)	LSRN SCoo WCAu WViv
	'Jennie Grace' (SDB)	SIri
	'Jeremy Brian' (SDB) ♀H4	WCAu
	'Jersey Lilli' (SDB)	WCAu
	'Jesse Lee' (SDB)	CKel
	'Jesse's Song' (TB)	ESgI WCAu
N	'Jeunesse' (TB)	ESgI
	'Jewel Baby' (SDB)	CBro CKel

'Jeweler's Art' (SDB) WCAu
'Jiansada' (SDB) CBro
'Jigsaw' (TB) ESgI
'Jitterbug' (TB) EHrv WCAu
'Joanna' (TB) LSRN NLar WWEG
'Joanna Taylor' (MDB) ERos NMen WCAu
'John' (IB) CKel LSRN WAul
'Joli Coeur' (TB) ESgI WViv
'Joy Boy' (SDB) ESgI
'Joyce' (Reticulata) CBro EBrs ECho EPot GKev LAma LRHS MBri SGar SMrm SPhx
'Joyce Terry' (TB) CWan ESgI SPad
'Joyful' (SDB) ESgI WViv
'Jubilant Spirit' (Spuria) EBee EWes
'Jubilé Rainier III' (TB) WViv
'Jubilee Gem' (TB) CKel
'Jud Paynter' (TB) CKel
'Juicy Fruit' (TB) WCAu
'Julia Vennor' (TB) CKel
'Juliet' (TB) ESgI
'June Prom' (IB) EAEE LRHS SRGP WCAu
'June Rose' (IB) WAul
'Jungle Fires' (TB) WCAu
'Jungle Shadows' (BB) MRav NBir WCAu
'Jungle Warrior' (SDB) CKel
'Jurassic Park' (TB) ESgI WAul WCAu
'Juris Prudence' (TB) ESgI
'Jus d'Orange' (TB) **new** WViv
'Just Dance' (IB) ESgI
'Just Jennifer' (BB) WCAu
kaempferi see *I. ensata*
'Kangchenjunga' (TB) ESgI
'Karen' (TB) LSRN WViv
kashmiriana CBcs
'Katharine Hodgkin' (Reticulata) ♀H4 Widely available
'Katie-Koo' (IB) ♀H4 CKel
'Katy Petts' (SDB) ESgI WCAu
'Kayleigh-Jayne Louise' (TB) CKel
'Keeping up Appearances' (TB) WAul WCAu
'Kelway Renaissance' (TB) CKel
kemaonensis GAuc
'Ken's Choice' (TB) ♀H4 CKel
'Kent Compote' (IB) **new** SIri
'Kent Pride' (TB) CSBt CWGN EAEE EBee EBla ECha ECtt EPfP ESgI EShb ETod IPot LRHS MCot MRav MSpe MWat SBch SGar SMrm SPer SPoG SWat WAul WCAu WTin
'Kentucky Bluegrass' (SDB) WCAu
'Kentucky Derby' (TB) WViv
§ ***kerneriana*** ♀H4 ERos GBuc LRHS MBel NBir WPen
'Kevin's Theme' (TB) WCAu
'Kildonan' (TB) WCAu
'Kilt Lilt' (TB) WCAu
'Kirkstone' (TB) WCAu
kirkwoodii WWst
'Kiss of Summer' (TB) ♀H4 ESgI
'Kissing Circle' (TB) ESgI SBch
'Kiwi Slices' (SDB) ESgI
klattii see *I. spuria* subsp. *musulmanica*
'Knick Knack' (MDB) CBro CMea CPBP EAEE EBee EBla ECho ELan ERos ETod GAbr LBee LRHS MRav MSpe NMen SBch SDnm SMrs SPhx SPoG
kolpakowskiana WWst
'Kona Nights' (BB) ESgI
koreana GAuc
korolkowii ECho EPot WWst
N 'La Belle Aube' (TB) ESgI
'La Nina Rosa' (BB) WCAu
'La Senda' (Spuria) WCAu WCot
'La Vie en Rose' (TB) ESgI WViv
'Lace Legacy' (TB) ECtt WViv
'Laced Cotton' (TB) ESgI WCAu
'Laced Lemonade' (SDB) LRHS MBri
§ ***lactea*** ♀H4 GAuc NWCA
- var. ***lactea*** **new** GAuc
lacustris ♀H4 CBro NMen NWCA WAbe
'Lacy Snowflake' (TB) COIW LHop SPet
'Lady Essex' (TB) WCAu
'Lady Friend' (TB) ESgI WCAu WViv
'Lady Gale' (IB) CKel
'Lady Ilse' (TB) WCAu
'Lady in Red' (SDB) ESgI
'Lady Marilyn' (TB) **new** CIri
'Lady Mohr' (AB) CKel WCAu
'Lady of Fatima' (TB) ESgI
laevigata ♀H4 CRow CWat ECha ECho EHon ELan EMFW EPfP GAuc ITim LPBA MRav NBro NPer SEND SGar SPer SWat WCAu WFar WMAq WMoo WPnP WShi
- var. ***alba*** CBen CRow ECha ECho EHon ELan EPfP EWTr GAuc LPBA MMuc MRav SWat WAbe WFar WMoo
- 'Albopurpurea' SGSe
- 'Atropurpurea' CRow
- blue-flowered **new** MMuc
- 'Colchesterensis' CRow EMFW ITim LPBA NGdn NPer SWat WMAq
I - 'Dorothy' LPBA NGdn
N - 'Dorothy Robinson' LRHS SWat
- 'Elegant' see *I. laevigata* 'Weymouth Elegant'
* - 'Elgar' WMAq
- 'Liam Johns' CRow
- 'Midnight' see *I. laevigata* 'Weymouth Midnight'
- 'Mottled Beauty' CRow
- 'Rashomon' CRow
- 'Regal' CWat
- 'Richard Greaney' CRow
- 'Rose Queen' see *I. ensata* 'Rose Queen'
- 'Rowden Seaspray' CRow
- 'Rowden Starlight' CRow
I - 'Snowdrift' CBen CRow CWat EHon EMFW LPBA LRHS NBir NGdn NPer SPer SWat WCAu WFar WMAq WPnP
- 'Variegata' (v) ♀H4 CBen CBow CRow CWat EAEE ECha ECho EHoe EHon EMFW EPfP EPla LLWG LPBA NBro NGdn NPer SPer SWat WMAq WMoo WPnP WTin
- 'Violet Garth' CRow
- 'Weymouth' see *I. laevigata* 'Weymouth Blue'
§ - 'Weymouth Blue' CBen CRow
§ - 'Weymouth Elegant' CRow
§ - 'Weymouth Midnight' CBen CMil CRow LPBA SWat
N 'Langport Chapter' (IB) CBgR CKel ESgI
N 'Langport Chief' (IB) CKel
N 'Langport Claret' (IB) CBgR CKel ESgI
N 'Langport Curlew' (IB) CBgR CKel ESgI
N 'Langport Duchess' (IB) ESgI WTin
N 'Langport Fairy' (IB) CBgR CKel ESgI
N 'Langport Finch' (IB) NBir
N 'Langport Flame' (IB) CBgR CKel CMac ESgI WTin
N 'Langport Haze' (IB) ESgI
N 'Langport Hope' (IB) CKel ESgI
N 'Langport Jane' (IB) CKel
N 'Langport Lady' (IB) CKel
N 'Langport Lord' (IB) ESgI
'Langport Minstrel' (IB) CKel ESgI
N 'Langport Pearl' (IB) CKel

	Plant	Suppliers
	'Langport Phoenix' (IB)	CKel
N	'Langport Pinnacle' (IB)	CKel
N	'Langport Robe' (IB)	ESgI
N	'Langport Smoke' (IB)	CKel
	'Langport Snow' (IB)	CKel
N	'Langport Song' (IB)	CKel ESgI
N	'Langport Star' (IB)	CKel ESgI
	'Langport Storm' (IB)	CKel CMil EAEE EBee EBla ESgI MRav MSpe WAul WTin
N	'Langport Sun' (IB)	CBgR CKel ESgI SMrm
N	'Langport Swift' (IB)	CKel
	'Langport Sylvia' (IB)	CBgR CKel
N	'Langport Tartan' (IB)	CKel
N	'Langport Violet' (IB)	CBgR CKel ESgI
	'Langport Vista' (IB)	CKel
	'Langport Warrior' (IB)	CKel
	'Langport Wren' (IB) ♀H4	CBgR CBro CKel ECGP EPfP ESgI EShb GBuc GCal IPot LRHS MBri NBir SMrm SPhx WAul WEas WPen WTin WWEG
	'Lark Rise' (TB) ♀H4	CKel
	'Larry Gaulter' (TB)	WCAu
	'Las Vegas' (TB)	WCAu
§	***latifolia*** ♀H4	ECho IHer WShi
	- 'Duchess of York'	ECho
	- 'Isabella'	EBee EBrs ECho
	- 'King of the Blues'	EBrs ECho GKev
	- 'Mansfield'	EBee EBrs ECho GKev
	- 'Montblanc'	EBee EBrs ECho
	- 'Queen of the Blues' (Eng)	ECho
	- wild-collected **new**	GCal
	'Latin Lady' (TB)	ESgI
	'Latin Lark' (TB)	ESgI
	'Latin Rock' (TB)	WCAu
	'Lavender Park' (TB)	ESgI
	'Lavender Royal' (CH)	CPrp
	lazica ♀H4	CAbP CBct CBro CMac CPen CPrp CRow CSpe EAEE EBee EPPr EPfP EPot ESgI EWTr GGar GKev IBlr LEdu LFCN LRHS MRav NBir NCGa NSti NWsh SIng WAbe WPGP WSpi
	- 'Joy Bishop'	CBct WCot
*	- 'Richard Nutt'	ELon WCot
N	- 'Turkish Blue'	CPrp GBin IBlr
	'Leda's Lover' (TB)	ESgI
	'Legato' (TB)	ESgI
	'Lemon Beauty' (TB)	LHop
	'Lemon Brocade' (TB)	ESgI MBri WCAu WViv
	'Lemon Dilemma' (Spuria)	CIri
	'Lemon Fever' (TB)	ESgI
	'Lemon Flare' (SDB)	EIri MRav SRms WCAu
	'Lemon Ice' (TB)	EAEE EBee EBla LBuc LFCN LRHS SMrm SPer
	'Lemon Lyric' (TB)	ESgI
	'Lemon Mist' (TB)	ESgI
*	'Lemon Peel' (IB)	CKel
	'Lemon Pop' (IB)	WCAu
	'Lemon Puff' (MDB)	CBro WCAu
	'Lemon Tree' (TB)	WCAu
N	'Lena' (SDB)	CBro
	'Lenna M' (SDB)	CKel ECho
	'Lenora Pearl' (BB)	ESgI WCAu
	'Lent A. Williamson' (TB)	GMaP WWEG
	'Lenten Prayer' (TB)	CIri WViv
	'Leprechaun's Delight' (SDB)	CKel
	'Leprechaun's Purse' (SDB)	WCAu WViv
	leptorhiza (J)	WWst
	'Let's Elope' (IB)	ESgI WCAu
	'Licorice Fantasy' (TB)	ESgI
	'Light Cavalry' (IB)	ESgI
	'Light Laughter' (IB)	WCAu
	'Lightning Streak' (TB)	WViv
	'Lilli-white' (SDB)	CKel CWat EBee EBla EHrv ELan GEdr MBNS MRav SBch SPhx SPoG WCAu WWEG
	'Lima Colada' (SDB)	NBre SMrm
	'Limbo' (SpH)	CRow
	'Lime Fizz' (TB)	ESgI
	'Limelight' (TB)	SRms
	'Lingering Love' (TB)	WCAu
N	'Little Amoena'	ERos NMen
	'Little Black Belt' (SDB)	SIri
	'Little Blackfoot' (SDB)	ESgI WCAu WHoo
	'Little Blue-eyes' (SDB)	ESgI
	'Little Bluets' (SDB)	ESgI
	'Little Dandy' (SDB)	WCAu
	'Little Dream' (SDB)	WCAu
	'Little Episode' (SDB)	ESgI WCAu
	'Little John' (TB)	WCAu
	'Little Paul' (MTB)	ESgI
	'Little Rosy Wings' (SDB)	CBro CPBP ERos
	'Little Sapphire' (SDB)	GEdr
	'Little Shadow' (IB)	MRav SRms WWEG
	'Little Sheba' (AB)	WCAu
	'Little Showoff' (SDB)	ESgI WAul
	'Little Tilgates' (CH) ♀H3	WCot
	'Live Jazz' (SDB)	WCAu
	'Living Legacy' (TB)	WAul
	'Llanthony' (SDB)	WCAu
	'Local Color' (TB)	ESgI WAul WViv
	'Lodore' (TB)	SRms WCAu
	'Logo' (IB)	WCAu
	'Lollipop' (SDB)	ESgI SIri WViv
	longipetala	EWes NBir
	'Lookingglass Eyes' (Spuria)	CIri
	'Loop the Loop' (TB)	CMac EBee EPfP EWll LAst MWea NBre SCoo SPoG SWat WViv
	'Loose Valley' (MTB) ♀H4	SIri WCAu
	'Lord Warden' (TB)	CMac CSam EAEE EBla ECtt LDai LFCN LRHS MCot SPet SPur WAul WCAu
	'Loreley' (TB)	ESgI
	'Lorenzaccio de Médicis' (TB)	ESgI
	'Lorilee' (TB)	ESgI
	'Lothario' (TB)	WCAu WFoF
	'Loud Music' (TB)	WCAu
	'Louis d'Or' (TB) ♀H4	WViv
	'Louvois' (TB)	ESgI
	'Love for Leila' (Spuria) ♀H4	CIri
	'Love the Sun' (TB)	ESgI
	'Lovely Again' (TB)	MRav WCAu
	'Lovely Leilani' (TB)	ESgI
	'Lovely Light' (TB)	MBri
	'Lover's Charm' (TB)	WCAu
	'Love's Tune' (IB)	EAEE EBla LRHS SRGP SWat
	'Low Ho Silver' (IB)	WCAu
	'Loyalist' (TB)	SIri WViv
	'Lucky Charm' (MTB)	CMea
	'Lucky Devil' (Spuria) ♀H4	CIri
	'Lucy's Gift' (MTB) ♀H4	WAul
	'Lugano' (TB)	ESgI
	'Luli-Ann' (SDB) ♀H4	CKel
	'Lullaby of Spring' (TB)	CKel WCAu
	'Lumalite' (SDB)	WAul
	'Lumière d'Automne' (TB)	ESgI
	'Luminosity' (TB)	ESgI
	'Luna di Miele' (BB)	ESgI
	'Lunar Frost' (IB)	SIri WViv
§	***lutescens*** ♀H4	EBrs ECho EPot ERos GCra GEdr NSla WAbe
§	- 'Campbellii'	ERos NMen
§	- 'Nancy Lindsay'	WCAu
	lycotis	see *I. iberica* subsp. *lycotis*

	Name	Suppliers
	'Lyrique' (BB)	CKel WAul
	'Ma Mie' (IB)	ESgI WViv
	maackii from Ussuri River	GAuc
	'Madame Maurice Lassailly' (TB)	ESgI
	'Madeira Belle' (TB)	ESgI WCAu
	'Magharee' (TB)	ESgI
	'Magic Man' (TB)	EBee
	magnifica ♀H3-4	EBrs ECho ELon WWst
N	- 'Agalik'	EBrs ECho GAuc LRHS
	- 'Alba'	EBrs ECho WWst
	'Mahogany Mix' (Dut) **new**	LAma
	'Maisie Lowe' (TB)	ESgI
	'Making Eyes' (SDB)	ESgI WCAu
	'Mallow Dramatic' (TB)	WCAu WViv
I	'Mandarin' (TB)	ESgI WViv
	'Mandarin Purple' (Sino-Sib)	CDes EBee GGar NGdn NHol WPrP
	mandshurica	CPBP GKev LFur
	'Mango Entree' (TB)	CIri
	'Maple Treat' (TB)	WViv
	'Mara' (IB)	CKel
	'Marcel Turbat' (TB)	ESgI WViv
	'Marche Turque' (TB)	ESgI
	'Marco Polo' (TB)	ESgI
	'Margarita' (TB)	WCAu
	'Margrave' (TB)	SIri WCAu WViv
	'Marguérite' (Reticulata/v)	EBrs ECho EPPr ERCP
	'Marhaba' (MDB)	ERos
	'Marilyn Holloway' (Spuria)	WCAu
	'Mariposa Skies' (TB)	ESgI
	'Marmalade Skies' (BB)	WCAu
	'Martyn Rix'	see *I. confusa* 'Martyn Rix'
	'Mary Constance' (IB) ♀H4	CKel
	'Mary Frances' (TB)	ESgI LSRN WCAu WViv
	'Mary McIlroy' (SDB) ♀H4	CBro CKel WTin
	'Mary Randall' (TB)	WCAu
	'Maslon' (MTB)	ESgI
	'Master Touch' (TB)	ELon
	'Mastery' (TB)	CIri
	'Matinata' (TB)	CKel
	'Maui Moonlight' (IB) ♀H4	CKel ESgI WAul
	'Maui Surf' (BB) ♀H4	WAul
	'Mauna Loa Fire' (TB)	CIri
	'Mauvelous' (TB)	CIri
	'May Melody' (TB)	LRHS WCAu
	'Maya Mint' (MDB)	LLHF
	'Meadow Court' (SDB)	CBro CKel ERos NBro WCAu WWEG
	'Media Luz' (Spuria)	WCAu
	'Medway Valley' (MTB) ♀H4	SIri WAul WCAu
	'Meg's Mantle' (TB) ♀H4	CKel
	'Melbreak' (TB)	WCAu
	mellita	see *I. suaveolens*
	'Melon Honey' (SDB)	CKel ELon WCAu
	'Memphis Delight' (TB)	WCAu
	'Men in Black' (TB)	WCAu
	'Menton' (SDB)	CKel
	'Mer du Sud' (TB) ♀H4	EIri ESgI WViv
*	'Merebrook Blue Lagoon' (La)	WMAq
	'Merebrook Jemma J' (La)	WMAq
*	'Merebrook Lemon Maid' (La)	WMAq
N	'Merebrook Malvern Shadow' (La)	WMAq
N	'Merebrook Purpla' (La)	WMAq
*	'Merebrook Rusty Red' (La)	WMAq
*	'Merebrook Snowflake' (La)	WMAq
N	'Merebrook Sunnyside Up' (La)	WMAq
	'Merit' (MTB)	WCAu
	'Merry Dance' (SDB) **new**	CKel
	'Mesmerizer' (TB)	CIri ESgI WCAu WViv
	'Metaphor' (TB)	WCAu
	'Mezza Cartuccia' (IB)	ESgI
	'Michael Paul' (SDB) ♀H4	ESgI
*	'Michael's Angel'	WWst
	'Midnight Caller' (TB)	ESgI
	'Midnight Mango'	see *I.* 'Midnight Web'
	'Midnight Oil' (TB)	WAul WCAu WViv
§	'Midnight Web' (IB) ♀H4	CKel
	'Midsummer Night's Dream' (IB) **new**	WAul
	milesii ♀H4	CPLG CPou EWld GBuc IGor NBir WPer
	- CC 4590	CHid
	'Millennium Falcon' (TB)	CIri WAul
	'Millennium Sunrise' (TB)	WCAu
	'Ming' (IB)	WCAu
	'Mini Big Horn' (IB)	CIri
	'Mini-Agnes' (SDB)	CBro
	'Miss Carla' (IB)	NBre
	'Miss Nellie' (BB)	CKel
	'Mission Sunset' (TB)	EHrv WCAu
	'Missouri Orange' (Spuria) ♀H4	CIri
	missouriensis ♀H4	CMac EBee IGor NBid
	'Mister Matthew' (TB) ♀H4	CKel
	'Mister Roberts' (SDB)	ESgI
	'Mistigri' (IB)	CBgR WAul WViv
	'Mme Chéreau' (TB)	ESgI WCAu
	'Mme Louis Aureau' (TB)	ESgI
	monnieri	GAuc NLar
	'Monsieur-Monsieur' (TB)	ESgI
	Monspur Group	WCot
§	'Monspur Cambridge Blue' (Spuria) ♀H4	WCAu
	'Monty's Sweet Blue' (TB)	CIri
	'Moon Journey' (TB)	SIri WAul WViv
	'Moon Sparkle' (IB)	CKel
	'Moonbeam' (TB)	CKel
	'Moonlight' (TB)	WCot
	'Moonlight Waves'	see *I. ensata* 'Moonlight Waves'
	'Moonlit Waves' (TB)	CKel
	'Morning Show' (IB)	CWGN EBee
	'Morning Sky' (J) **new**	WWst
	'Morning's Blush' (SDB) ♀H4	CIri
	'Morwenna' (TB) ♀H4	CKel WCAu
	'Mote Park' (MTB)	SIri
	'Mother Earth' (TB)	ESgI WAul
	'Mountain Majesty' (TB)	ESgI
	'Mrs Horace Darwin' (TB)	CFir SWat WMnd
	'Mrs Nate Rudolph' (SDB)	EBee MBri
	'Mrs Tait' (Spuria)	NChi
	'Mukaddam' (TB) **new**	CIri
	'Mulberry Rose' (TB)	CFee NChi
	'Mulled Wine' (TB)	ESgI
	'Murmuring Morn' (TB)	WCAu
	'My Honeycomb' (TB)	WCAu
	'My Kayla' (SDB)	ESgI
N	'My Seedling' (MDB)	CBro ERos NMen
	'Myra' (SDB)	ESgI
	'Mystic Beauty' (Dut)	LAma SBch
	'Naivasha' (TB)	CKel
	'Nancy' (TB)	SApp
	'Nancy Hardy' (MDB)	CBro ERos NMen
	'Nancy Lindsay'	see *I. lutescens* 'Nancy Lindsay'
	'Nanny' (SDB)	SIri
	'Naples' (TB)	ESgI WViv
	narbutii (J)	WWst
	narbutii	WWst
	× ***maracandica*** **new**	
	narcissiflora	EBee

	'Nashborough' (TB)	WCAu
	'Natascha' (Reticulata)	EBrs ECho EPot LAma LRHS NHol SMrm SPhx
	'Natchez Trace' (TB)	MWea
	'Navajo Jewel' (TB)	ESgI WCAu
	'Near Myth' (SDB)	WCAu
	'Nectar' (IB)	ESgI WAul
	'Needlecraft' (TB)	NBre
	'Needlepoint' (TB)	ESgI
	'Neige de Mai' (TB)	ESgI WViv
	nepalensis	see *I. decora*
	nertschinskia	see *I. sanguinea*
N	'New Argument' (J)	WWst
	'New Centurion' (TB)	WCAu WViv
	'New Day Dawning' (TB)	CIri
	'New Idea' (MTB)	ESgI WCAu
	'New Leaf' (TB)	WCAu
	'New Snow' (TB)	WCAu
	'Nibelungen' (TB)	ELon EPfP MWea NBre WFar
	'Nice 'n' Nifty' (IB)	WTin
	'Nicola Jane' (TB) ♀H4	CKel
	nicolai	ECho WWst
	'Nigerian Raspberry' (TB)	WCAu
	'Night Edition' (TB)	ESgI
	'Night Game' (TB)	WCAu WViv
	'Night Owl' (TB)	CKel COlW ELan ELon ESgI LAst LHop MCot SBch SPet
	'Night Ruler' (TB)	ESgI WCAu WViv
	'Night Shift' (IB)	NBre WViv
	'Nightfall' (TB)	EBee
	'Nights of Gladness' (TB)	ESgI
	'Nineveh' (AB)	WCAu
*	'Noces Blanches' (IB)	ESgI
	'Noon Siesta' (TB)	ESgI
	'Nora Eileen' (TB) ♀H4	CKel
	'Nordica' (TB)	ESgI WViv
	'North Downs' (BB) new	SIri
	'Northern Jewel' (IB)	SIri WViv
	'Northwest Pride' (TB)	WCAu WViv
	'Nut Ruffles' (SDB)	WAul
	'Obsidian' (TB)	CIri
	'Ocean Depths' (TB)	ESgI
	'Ocelot' (TB)	ESgI
	'Ochraurea' (Spuria)	NGdn NSti
	'Ochre Doll' (SDB)	CKel
	ochroleuca	see *I. orientalis* Mill.
	'O'Cool' (IB)	CKel
	odaesanensis	EBee
	'Oh So Cool' (MTB)	ESgI
N	'Oiseau Lyre' (TB)	ESgI
	'Oktoberfest' (TB)	ESgI
	'Ola Kalá' (TB)	EAEE EBla ECGP ESgI EWll GMaP LRHS NBre NLar SPer SPet SPoG WCAu WWEG
	'Old Black Magic' (TB)	ESgI
	'Olympiad' (TB)	ESgI
	'Olympic Challenge' (TB)	ESgI MRav WCAu
	'Olympic Torch' (TB)	ESgI WCAu
	'Ominous Stranger' (TB)	ESgI WCAu
	'One Desire' (TB)	WCAu
	'Open Sky' (SDB)	SIri WViv
	'Orageux' (IB)	CBgR CWCL ESgI WAul WViv
	'Orange Caper' (SDB)	EAEE EBla ECtt EGoo ESgI GBuc GEdr LRHS MAvo MRav NGdn NLar SBch SMrm WCAu
	'Orange Harvest' (TB)	LRHS
	'Orange Order' (TB)	WCAu
N	'Orange Plaza'	ECho NMen
	'Orange Pop' (BB)	WAul
	'Orange Tiger' (SDB)	WCAu WViv
	'Orchardist' (TB)	CKel
	'Orchidarium' (TB)	CKel
	'Orchidea Selvaggia' (TB)	ESgI
	orchioides misapplied	see *I. bucharica* Foster
§	***orchioides*** Carrière	ECho ELan ERos MLHP
	– deep yellow-flowered new	WWst
	– dwarf new	WWst
N	– 'Urungachsai'	EPot WWst
	'Oregold' (SDB)	WCAu
	'Oregon Skies' (TB)	ESgI ETod WViv
	'Oreo' (TB)	CIri
N	'Oriental Argument' (J)	WWst
	'Oriental Baby' (IB)	CKel WAul
	'Oriental Beauty' (TB)	EWll
	'Oriental Beauty' (Dut)	CAvo EBrs GKev LAma LRHS SBch WCot WFar
	'Oriental Glory' (TB)	WCAu
	'Oriental Touch' (SpH)	CRow
	orientalis Thunb.	see *I. sanguinea*
	orientalis ambig.	CAvo ELan EPyc
§	***orientalis*** Mill. ♀H4	CBot EPPr EWTr GCal IFro SGar WCAu WDyG
	– 'Alba'	see *I. sanguinea* 'Alba'
	'Orinoco Flow' (BB) ♀H4	CHar CKel ESgI WCAu
	'Orion' new	LRHS
	'Orloff' (TB)	ESgI
	'Oro Antico' (TB)	CIri
	'Osage Buff' (TB)	CKel
	'Osay Canuc' (TB)	CIri
	'Ostrogoth' (TB)	CIri
N	'Oulo' (TB)	ESgI
	'Our House' (TB)	ESgI
	'Out Yonder' (TB)	WCAu
	'Ovation' (TB)	ESgI
	'Over Easy' (SDB)	CKel
	'Overjoyed' (TB)	WCAu
	'Overnight Sensation' (TB)	WViv
	'O'What' (SDB)	ESgI
	'Owyhee Desert' (TB)	WCAu
	'Oxford Tweeds' (SDB)	ESgI
	'Ozone Alert' (TB)	CIri
	Pacific Coast hybrids	see *I.* Californian hybrids
	'Pacific Gambler' (TB)	SMrm
	'Pacific Mist' (TB)	WCAu WViv
	'Pacific Panorama' (TB)	ESgI
	'Pagan Dance' (TB)	WCAu
	'Pagan Princess' (TB)	WCAu
	'Paint It Black' (TB)	ETod WViv
	'Pale Primrose' (TB)	WCAu
	'Pale Shades' (IB) ♀H4	CBro CKel ERos
	'Palissandro' (TB)	ESgI
§	***pallida***	CCVT EBee EGoo ESgI GMaP MCCP MRav MWat WCAu WMnd
§	– 'Argentea Variegata' (TB/v)	CBcs CSBt CWCL CWGN EBee EBrs ECha ECho EHoe EHrv EPfP EShb GMaP LAst LFur LRHS MBrN MBri MCot MRav NBir NSti SBch SPer SPhx SPoG WAul WCot WWEG
	– 'Aurea'	see *I. pallida* 'Variegata' hort.
	– 'Aurea Variegata'	see *I. pallida* 'Variegata' hort.
	– var. ***dalmatica***	see *I. pallida* subsp. *pallida*
§	– subsp. ***pallida*** ♀H4	CBot CKel CWan EAEE ECha ELan GCal LRHS MBri SDix SPer
	– 'Variegata' misapplied	see *I. pallida* 'Argentea Variegata'
§	– 'Variegata' Hort. (v) ♀H4	Widely available
	'Palm Springs' (IB) new	NMin
	'Palomino' (TB)	WCAu
	'Paltec' (IB)	CPou EBee
	'Pane e Vino' (TB)	ESgI
	'Pansy Top' (SDB)	SIri
	'Paradise' (TB)	CKel
	paradoxa	EBrs ECho WWst

	Name	Suppliers
	'Paricutin' (SDB)	CBro
	'Parisien' (TB)	CWCL EIri WViv
	'Party Dress' (TB)	CMac CSBt CWGN EBee EBla ELan EPfP LRHS MBNS MRav MSpe NBir NGdn NLar SBch SPer SPoG SRms SWat WCFE WCot
	'Passport' (BB)	ECho
	'Pastel Charm' (SDB)	SMrm WMnd
	'Patches' (TB)	ESgI
	'Patina' (TB)	ECtt EIri ESgI ETod WAul WCAu WViv
	'Patterdale' (TB)	NBir NBre NVic WCAu
	'Paul Black' (TB)	CIri
	'Pauline' (Reticulata)	CAvo CBro EBrs ECho EPfP EPot ERCP GKev LAma LRHS MWat SMrm
	'Peaceful Waters' (TB)	ECtt WViv
	'Peacetime' (TB)	WCAu
	'Peach Eyes' (SDB)	CBro CKel ERos
	'Peach Float' (TB)	WCAu
	'Peach Picotee' (TB)	ESgI WViv
	'Peach Spot' (TB)	WCAu
	'Peaches ala Mode' (BB)	WCAu
	'Peacock'	see *I. ensata* 'Peacock'
	'Peacock Pavane' (CH) ♀H4	SIri
	'Pearls of Autumn' (TB)	WCAu
	'Pearly Dawn' (TB)	EBee EBla ECha ECtt LRHS MCot MSpe SPer SRGP SSvw SWat WAul WCot WWEG
	'Peau de Pêche' new	WViv
	'Pêche Melba' (TB)	ESgI
	'Pegaletta' (La)	EPPr NBro
	'Peggy Chambers' (IB) ♀H4	SMrm
	'Pele' (SDB)	ESgI WCAu
	'Penny Pinch' (TB)	WWEG
	'Pepita' (SDB)	ELon SIri WViv
	'Perfect Interlude' (TB)	ECtt EIri WViv
	'Perfume Shop' (IB)	CKel
	'Persian Berry' (TB)	WCAu
	'Persian Wood' (IB)	WAul
	'Petit Tigre' (IB)	CBgR WViv
	'Petite Monet' (MTB)	ESgI
	'Pharaoh's Daughter' (IB)	SIri WAul
	'Phil Keen' (TB) ♀H4	CKel
N	'Picadee'	EBla EPfP GBuc MWea
	'Piero Bargellini' (TB)	ESgI
	'Pigmy Gold' (IB)	EBee ERos
	'Pinewood Sunshine' (CH)	SUsu
	'Pink Attraction' (TB)	ESgI
	'Pink Bubbles' (BB)	WAul
	'Pink Charm' (TB)	CWGN EAEE EBla EPfP IPot LBuc LRHS SBch SMrm SPet SPlb WAul
	'Pink Confetti' (TB)	ESgI WViv
	'Pink Fawn' (SDB)	ESgI
	'Pink Formal' (TB)	ESgI
	'Pink Horizon' (TB)	EPfP
	'Pink Kitten' (IB)	WCAu WGwG
N	'Pink Lavender' (TB)	ELon
	'Pink Parchment' (BB) ♀H4	CKel
	'Pink Pele' (IB)	ESgI WAul
	'Pink Pussycat' (TB)	LRHS MBri
	'Pink Reprise' (BB)	WAul
	'Pink Swan' (TB)	ESgI WViv
	'Pink Taffeta' (TB)	ESgI
	'Pinnacle' (TB)	CKel ESgI GCal SWat WCAu
	'Pipes of Pan' (TB)	ESgI WCAu
	'Pirate's Patch' (SDB)	ESgI
	'Pirate's Quest' (TB)	ESgI WViv
	'Piroska' (TB) ♀H4	ESgI SGar WViv
*	'Piu Blue' (TB)	ESgI
	'Pixie' (Reticulata) ♀H4	EBrs ECho ELan EPot LRHS
	'Pixie' (DB)	GKev
	'Pixie Flirt' (MDB)	ERos
	planifolia	ECho
*	- f. ***alba***	EBrs ECho
	'Pledge Allegiance' (TB)	ECtt ESgI WCAu WViv
	plicata	WCAu
	'Plickadee' (SDB)	CBro
	'Pluie d'Or' (TB)	ESgI
	'Plum Lucky' (SDB)	SIri WViv
	'Plum Wine' (SDB)	CKel
	'Poco Taco' (SDB)	WAul
	'Poem of Ecstasy' (TB)	WCAu
	'Poetess' (TB)	WCAu
	'Pogo' (SDB)	CMac CWGN EBla ECtt ELan EPfP EPot ETod GBuc GMaP LRHS MMHG MRav NBir NWCA SBch SPet SRms
	'Pond Lily' (TB)	ESgI WCAu
	'Pookanilly' (IB)	ESgI WViv
	'Portfolio' (TB)	ESgI
	potaninii new	GAuc
	'Powder Blue Cadillac' (TB)	CKel
	'Power Point' (TB)	CIri
	'Precious Heather' (TB) ♀H4	CKel
	'Presby's Crown Jewel' (TB)	CIri
	'Presence' (TB)	SIri WViv
	'Prestige Item' (TB)	WAul
	'Pretender' (TB)	WCAu
	'Pretty Please' (TB)	ESgI
	'Prince Indigo' (TB)	MRav
	'Prince of Burgundy' (IB) ♀H4	WCAu
	'Princess Beatrice' (TB)	WCAu
	'Princess Bride' (BB) ♀H4 new	CIri
	'Princess Sabra' (TB) ♀H4	CKel
	'Princesse Caroline de Monaco' (TB)	CWCL ESgI
	prismatica	EBee GKev
	- ***alba***	IGor
	- 'Quartz' new	ITim
	'Prodigy' (MDB)	WViv
	'Professor Blaauw' (Dut) ♀H4	CAvo EBrs EPfP LRHS
	'Progressive Attitude' (TB)	WCAu
	'Protocol' (IB)	CKel WViv
	'Prototype' (TB)	CIri
	'Proud Tradition' (TB)	SIri WCAu WViv
	'Provençal' (TB)	CKel CWCL ECtt ESgI ETod WAul WCAu WViv
	'Proverb' (Spuria)	WCAu
	'Prudy' (BB) ♀H4	CKel
	'Prunelle' (TB) new	CBgR
	pseudacorus ♀H4	Widely available
	- B&SWJ 5018 from Japan	WCru
	- from Korea	CRow
	- 'Alba'	CPrp CRow EBee GBin GCal LAst LRHS MRav NGdn SWat
	- var. ***bastardii***	CBgR CRow CWat EBee ECha ELon EMFW EPfP ESgI IGor LPBA NPer SLon SMrm SPer SWat WBrk WFar WMoo WPnP WTin WViv
	- 'Beuron'	CRow
	- cream-flowered	NBir SWat WAul
N	- 'Crème de la Crème'	GBin
	- 'Esk'	GBin GCal
N	- 'Flore Pleno' (d)	CBgR CBot CPrp CRow EBee EBrs ECho EMFW EPPr ESgI GCra LPBA MSKA NLar NPer WBrk WCot WFar WPnP WWEG

	Name	Suppliers
N	– 'Golden Daggers'	CRow
I	– 'Golden Fleece'	SPer
	– 'Golden Queen'	CRow IGor
	– 'Ilgengold'	CRow
N	– 'Ivory'	CRow
*	– ***nana***	CRow
	– 'Roccapina'	GBin
	– 'Roy Davidson' 🏆^{H4}	CBgR CPrp CRow EMFW ESgI GBin GCal IBlr LPBA WFar WHil WPtf WTin WViv
N	– 'Sulphur Queen'	CBgR WCot
	– 'Sun Cascade'	CRow
N	– 'Tiger Brother'	SIri WBrk
	– 'Tiggah'	CRow
N	– 'Turnipseed'	ESgI WTin
	– 'Variegata' (v) 🏆^{H4}	Widely available
	– white-flowered, from Lake Michigan	WTin
*	***pseudocapnoides*** (J)	GKev WWst
	pseudopumila	ERos
	'Puddy Tat' (SDB)	CIri
	'Pulse Rate' (SDB)	CBro
	pumila	CPBP LRHS MCot MWat NHol NMen NWCA
	– 'Alba' (DB)	CPBP
	– ***atroviolacea***	CBgR CKel ESgI SMrm WMnd
	– blue-flowered	SWal
*	– 'Caerulea'	GAuc
N	– 'Gelber Mantel'	NBir
N	– 'Lavendel Plicata'	EBee NBro NGdn
	– 'Violacea' (DB)	LRHS SRms
	– yellow-flowered	GAbr SWal
	'Pumpin' Iron' (SDB) 🏆^{H4}	CKel ESgI
	'Punch' (BB)	WAul
	'Punchline' (TB)	CWCL ECtt WViv
	'Punk' (MDB)	CIri
	'Puppet Baby' (MDB)	WViv
	purdyi	GBuc
	'Pure As Gold' (TB)	CWCL ESgI WViv
	'Purple Gem' (Reticulata)	EBrs ECho EPfP EPot LAma LRHS MCot
	'Purple People Eater' (TB)	CIri
	'Purple Sensation' (Dut)	ECho
	'Quaker Lady' (TB)	ESgI SIri WCAu
	'Quark' (SDB)	CBro CKel
	'Quechee' (TB)	CWCL EBee EBla ECGP EPfP ESgI ETod GMaP IPot LBuc LDai LRHS LSRN MBNS MCot MRav MSpe MWat NLar STes SWat WAul WSpi
	'Queen in Calico' (TB)	ESgI WCAu WViv
	'Queen of May' (TB)	ESgI
	'Queen's Circle' (TB) 🏆^{H4}	CIri
	'Queen's Ivory' (SDB)	SMrs WCAu
	'Queen's Prize' (SDB)	SIri WViv
	'Rabbit's Foot' (SDB)	LSRN WViv
	'Radiant Apogee' (TB)	ECtt EIri ESgI WViv
	'Radiant Burst' (IB) **new**	SIri
	'Rain Dance' (SDB) 🏆^{H4}	ESgI WCAu
	'Rainbow Rim' (SDB)	ESgI
	'Rajah' (TB)	CSam EBee EBla EHrv ELan EPfP ESgI EShb GMaP LFCN LPio LRHS LSRN MCot MLHP MMHG MRav NOrc SBch SPer SPoG SPur STes WMnd
	'Rameses' (TB)	ESgI
	'Rancho Rose' (TB)	CKel
	'Rapture in Blue' (TB)	WAul WViv
	'Rare Edition' (IB)	CKel ESgI LRHS NBre WAul WCAu WViv
	'Rare Quality' (TB)	WAul WViv
	'Rare Treat' (TB)	WCAu
	'Raspberry Acres' (IB)	MRav WCAu
	'Raspberry Blush' (IB) 🏆^{H4}	CKel CPar EAEE EBla EIri EPfP LBMP LHop LRHS MAvo MCot MRav NBre SPur STes SWat WAul WCAu
	'Raspberry Fudge' (TB)	WCAu
	'Raven Hill' (TB)	WCAu
	'Razoo' (SDB)	CKel
	'Real Coquette' (SDB)	SIri WViv
	'Realm' (TB)	ESgI
	'Rebecca Perret' (TB)	WViv
	'Red at Night' (TB)	WAul
	'Red Atlast' (MDB)	ESgI
	'Red Canyon Glow' (TB)	CIri
	'Red Flash' (TB)	ESgI
	'Red Hawk' (TB)	WViv
	'Red Heart' (SDB)	ESgI GEdr MRav STes WTin WWEG
	'Red Oak' (Spuria)	ESgI WCAu
	'Red Orchid' (IB)	ELan NBlu NBre WCAu WWEG
	'Red Revival' (TB)	MRav WCAu
N	'Red Rum' (TB)	CKel
	'Red Tornado' (TB)	ESgI
	'Red Zinger' (IB)	ESgI LAst WAul WViv
	'Redwood Supreme' (Spuria)	WAul
	'Reg Wall' (TB) 🏆^{H4}	CIri
	'Regal Surprise' (SpH) 🏆^{H4}	CBgR CRow WAul
	'Regards' (SDB)	CBro
§	***reichenbachii***	CPBP CSsd EPot ERos LBee LLHF NWCA WHil WThu
	'Reminiscence' (MTB)	ESgI
	'Renown' (TB)	ESgI
	'Repartee' (TB)	ESgI
	reticulata 🏆^{H4}	CBcs CBro EBrs ECho ELan EPfP LRHS SBch SPer SPet WCAu WGwG
	– 'Spring Time'	EBrs ECho ERCP LAma LRHS NHol
N	– 'Violet Queen'	EBrs ECho
	'Return to Bayberry' (TB)	CIri
	'Rime Frost' (TB)	WCAu
	'Ringer' (SDB)	ESgI WViv
	'Ringo' (TB)	CKel ESgI LSRN MRav WCAu
	'Rip City' (TB)	ESgI WViv
	'Ripple Chip' (SDB)	WTin
	'Rippling Waters' (TB)	ESgI
	'Rising Moon' (TB)	SIri WViv
	'Ritz' (SDB)	WWEG
	'Rive Gauche' (TB)	ESgI
	'River Avon' (TB) 🏆^{H4}	CKel WCAu
	'Rivulets of Pink' (Spuria)	CIri
	'Robe d'Eté' (TB)	CWCL WViv
	'Robin Goodfellow' (MTB) 🏆^{H4} **new**	CIri
§	× ***robusta*** 'Dark Aura' 🏆^{H4}	WCot WTin WViv
§	– 'Gerald Darby' 🏆^{H4}	Widely available
	– 'Mountain Brook'	CRow LLWG
	– 'Nutfield Blue'	WTin
	– 'Purple Fan'	LLWG
	'Rockabye' (SDB)	WAul
§	'Rocket' (TB)	CMil EBla GMaP LBuc LRHS MRav NBir NBre SPer WAul
	'Rocket Master' (TB)	ESgI
	'Role Model' (TB)	WCAu
	'Roman Rhythm' (TB)	WCAu
	'Romance' (TB)	WViv
	'Romantic Evening' (TB)	EIri ESgI WCAu WViv
	'Romantic Mood' (TB)	CKel WViv
	'Romney Marsh' (IB) **new**	SIri
	'Rondo' (TB)	ECtt
	'Rosalie Figge' (TB)	ESgI WCAu WViv
	'Rosé' (TB)	LSRN WViv
	'Rose Queen'	see *I. ensata* 'Rose Queen'
	'Rose Violet' (TB)	WCAu
	'Rosemary's Dream' (MTB)	ESgI NBre

	Name	Suppliers
	rosenbachiana	EBrs ECho WWst
	- 'Deep Purple' **new**	WWst
N	- 'Harangon'	ECho WWst
I	- 'Sina'	WWst
N	- 'Varzob'	WWst
	'Roseplic' (TB)	ESgI WViv
	'Rosette Wine' (TB)	ESgI WCAu
	'Rosy Wings' (TB)	ESgI
	'Roulette' (TB)	LRHS MBri
N	'Roy Elliott'	NMen
	'Royal Blue' (Reticulata) **new**	GAbr
	'Royal Courtship' (TB)	ESgI
	'Royal Crusader' (TB)	CMdw WCAu
	'Royal Elegance' (TB)	SIri WViv
	'Royal Intrigue' (TB)	SIri WViv
	'Royal Magician' (SDB)	WTin
	'Royal Satin' (TB)	CHid SPad
	'Royal Tapestry' (TB)	NBre
	'Royal Yellow' (Dut)	LRHS
	'Royalist' (TB)	CKel
	'Rubacuori' (TB)	ESgI
	'Ruban Bleu' (TB)	ESgI WViv
	'Rubistar' (TB)	ESgI
	'Ruby Chimes' (IB)	ESgI WCAu
	'Ruby Contrast' (TB)	WCAu
	'Ruby Eruption'	WViv
	rudskyi	see *I. variegata*
	'Ruée vers l'Or' (TB)	ESgI
	'Ruffled Canary' (Spuria)	WCAu
	'Ruffled Revel' (SDB)	GKir
	'Russet Crown' (TB)	CKel
	'Rustic Cedar' (TB)	ESgI WCAu WViv
	'Rustic Royalty' (TB)	WViv
	'Rustler' (TB)	ESgI WAul WCAu
	'Rusty Beauty' (Dut)	LAma SBch
	'Rusty Magnificence' (TB)	WViv
	'Ruth Black' (TB)	WCAu
	ruthenica	CPBP ECho ERos GBin NMen
	- var. ***nana***	CPLG EBee GKev
	'Ryan James' (TB)	CKel
	'Sable' (TB)	CSam EAEE EBee EBla EHrv ELan EPfP ESgI ETod GMaP LBuc LRHS LSRN MCot MRav MSpe MWat NGdn NOrc SCoo SEND SPer WAul WCAu WWEG
	'Sable Night' (TB)	CHar CKel ESgI
	'Sager Cedric' (TB)	WCAu
	'Saint Crispin' (TB)	EAEE EPfP GBee GCra GMaP LRHS MRav SBch SPer SPet SPoG
	'Sally Jane' (TB)	WCAu
	'Salonique' (TB)	NBre NLar WCAu
	'Saltwood' (SDB)	CBro NBre SIri
	'Sam Carne' (TB)	WCAu
	'San Leandro' (TB)	MBri
	'Sand Princess' (MTB)	SIri
	'Sandro' (TB) **new**	WViv
	'Sandstone Sentinel' (BB)	CIri
	'Sandy Caper' (IB)	WCAu WTin
	'Sangone' (IB)	ESgI
§	***sanguinea*** ♀H4	LEdu WBVN
§	- 'Alba'	IBlr
	- 'Nana Alba'	GBin IBlr
§	- 'Snow Queen'	Widely available
	'Santana' (TB)	ECtt
	'Sapphire Beauty' (Dut)	EPfP EWll LRHS
	'Sapphire Gem' (SDB)	CKel ESgI LSRN WAul WCAu WViv
	'Sapphire Hills' (TB)	WCAu WViv
	'Sapphire Jewel' (SDB)	EPPr
	'Sarah Taylor' (SDB) ♀H4	CBro WCAu
	'Sarajaavo' (AB)	CKel
	sari	EBrs ECho WWst
	'Sass with Class' (SDB)	CKel WTin
	'Satin Gown' (TB)	LRHS WCAu
	'Saturday Night Live' (TB)	ESgI
	schachtii	CPBP
	- J&JA 596.802	NWCA
	'Scribe' (MDB)	CBro NBir WCAu
	'Sea Double' (TB)	WWEG
	'Sea Fret' (SDB)	CBro
	'Sea Monster' (SDB)	EPPr SIri
	'Sea Wisp' (La)	EPPr NBro
	'Season Ticket' (IB)	ESgI WViv
	'Second Wind' (TB)	ECtt
	'Secret Melody' (TB)	WViv
	'Secret Rites' (TB)	CIri
	'Secret Service' **new**	LRHS
	'Self Evident' (MDB)	LLHF
	'Semola' (SDB)	ESgI
	'Senlac' (TB)	NLar WMnd
	'Señor Frog' (SDB)	ESgI
	serbica	see *I. reichenbachii*
	'Serene Moment' (TB)	SIri WViv
	'Serenity Prayer' (SDB)	WCAu WViv
	setosa ♀H4	CBro CMac CWCL EAlp EBee ECho EKen EMFW EPfP ERos GAuc GCra GKev GMaP IGor LEdu LPBA LRHS MHer MNrw NDlv NLAp SBch WSpi
	- ***alba***	GBuc NLar SIng
	- var. ***arctica***	EBee EPot GBuc LEdu LRHS MHer NMen NWCA WHoo WPer
	- 'Baby Blue' **new**	LRHS WHlf
	- subsp. ***canadensis***	see *I. hookeri*
	- 'Kosho-en'	MBri
	- var. ***nana***	see *I. hookeri*
	'Severn Side' (TB) ♀H4	CKel
	'Shakespeare's Sonnet' (SDB)	ESgI
	'Shameless' (IB)	NBre
	'Shampoo' (IB)	CKel SIri SMrm WCAu
	'Shaun Emerson' (TB) **new**	CIri
	'Sheer Class' (SDB) **new**	WViv
	'Sheila Ann Germaney' (Reticulata)	EBrs ECho EPot ERCP LLHF NHol NMen NMin WWst
	'Shelford Giant' (Spuria) ♀H4	NEgg
	'Shepherd's Delight' (TB)	WCAu
	'Sherbet Lemon' (IB) ♀H4	CKel WCAu
	'Shindig' (SDB)	WCAu
	'Shirley Chandler' (IB) ♀H4 **new**	SIri
	'Shocking Blue'	WWst
	'Short Distance' (IB)	SIri WViv
	shrevei	see *I. virginica* var. *shrevei*
	'Shurton Brook' (TB) **new**	CKel
	'Shurton Inn' (TB)	CKel WCAu
	sibirica ♀H4	CAvo CMHG COIW CWat EDAr EHon ESgI GAbr GBBs GKir LAma LAst LLWP MHer MLHP NChi NCob NVic SIng SPlb WBrE WBrk WClo WEas WFar WHer WHoo WMoo WShi
	- 'Ann Dasch'	EBee
	- 'Annemarie Troeger' ♀H4	EBee NBre SMrm
	- 'Anniversary'	CLAP EBee SMrm
	- 'Atlantic Crossing'	SIri WAul
	- 'Atoll'	WViv
	- 'Baby Sister'	CMHG CSsd EBee EBla GAbr GBin GBuc GGar GKir GMac LRHS MBri NBre NBro SRGP SWat WAul WViv
	- 'Berlin Purple Wine'	CAbx WViv
	- 'Berlin Ruffles' ♀H4	EWes GBin WViv
	- 'Berlin Sky'	ESgI EWes

	- 'Berlinger Overture'	GBin
	- 'Bickley Cape'	EBee GKir
	- 'Blaue Milchstrasse' ♀H4	GBin
	- 'Blaumacher'	GBuc WViv
	- 'Blue Burgee'	ECha
I	- 'Blue Butterfly'	ELan EPfP MSCN NGdn
N	- 'Blue Emperor'	EBee
	- 'Blue King'	CHid CKel EBee EBla ELan EPfP GMaP MDun MRav NBro NGdn NMoo SMrm SPer SPoG WMnd WMoo WWEG
	- 'Blue Mere'	MCot
	- 'Blue Moon'	EWll GBin MSCN WFar
	- 'Blue Pennant'	EBee GBin
	- 'Blue Reverie'	CAbx CPen EPPr ESgI WViv
N	- 'Blue Sceptre'	IBlr
	- 'Blue Seraph'	GBin
	- 'Blueberry Fair'	CIri
	- 'Bournemouth Ball Gown'	SIri
	- 'Bracknell'	WBor
	- 'Bridal Jig'	EBee
	- 'Butter and Sugar' ♀H4	Widely available
	- 'Caesar'	CRow SDys SRms
	- 'Caesar's Brother'	CBgR CHid EAEE EBee ECGP ELan EPfP IBlr LRHS MNFA NBro SMrm SPer SPet SWal SWat WCAu WWEG
	- 'Camberley'	LRHS
	- 'Cambridge' ♀H4	CPrp EAEE EBee EBla ECGP EIri GBin MNFA NBre SWat WCAu WFar WWlt
	- 'Chandler's Choice'	EWes
	- 'Chartreuse Bounty'	EBee EWes GAbr GBin GQue LAst MBel MBri NBPC NLar NMoo NSti WPtf WViv
N	- 'Chateuse Belle'	WBrE
	- 'Circle Round'	CSpe EPPr MWte
	- 'Cleedownton' ♀H4	CAbx
	- 'Cleve Dodge'	ESgI SIri WViv
	- 'Clouded Moon'	see *I. sibirica* 'Forncett Moon'
	- 'Coquet Waters'	NBid
	- 'Coronation Anthem'	WAul WViv
	- 'Dance Ballerina Dance'	CHid CRow CWCL EBee EPfP EWTr GGar GMac GQue NBPC NCGa NMoo SBch SMrm SPoG SPur WFar WPtf
	- 'Dancing Nanou'	NBre SBch SWat
	- 'Dark Circle'	EBee
	- 'Dark Desire'	MRav
	- 'Dear Delight'	EPPr LLHF WFar
	- 'Dear Dianne'	CHid CKel ECha NBre
	- 'Double Standards'	CIri
	- 'Dreaming Orange'	WViv
	- 'Dreaming Spires' ♀H4	ESgI SIri WCot
	- 'Dreaming Yellow' ♀H4	CBre CFee CSam EAEE EBee ECha EHon EPfP EShb GBin GGar GMac LHop LLWG LRHS MMuc MNFA MRav NBro NGdn SApp SBch SMrm SPer SVic WCAu WMoo
	- 'Dunkler Wein'	EWes
	- 'Ego'	CHid ECha EWTr GAbr GBin GMac NBro SGSe SWat WMoo WPen WPrP WViv
	- 'Ellesmere'	NGdn
	- 'Emma Ripeka'	WAul
	- 'Emperor'	CRow CWat NBre NBur NSti SWat
	- 'Eric the Red'	IBlr NBur
	- 'Ever Again'	CAbx
	- 'Ewen'	CBgR CHVG CHid CLAP CPou CRow EBee GBin GBuc GKir GMaP IBlr MNrw NGdn SGSe SMrm SWat WCot WFar WPrP WWEG WWlt
	- 'Exuberant Encore' ♀H4	WCAu
	- 'Flight of Butterflies'	Widely available
§	- 'Forncett Moon'	CBgR
	- 'Fourfold Lavender'	EBee EWes WAul
	- 'Fourfold White'	ESgI MWte
	- 'Gatineau'	CLAP EBee GBuc
N	- 'Gerbel Mantel'	EWll GBin GMac SPet WFar
	- 'Golden Edge' **new**	CAbx
	- 'Goldkind' **new**	CAbx
	- grey-flowered	SApp
	- 'Gull's Wing'	EBee LHop
	- 'Harpswell Hallelujah'	EBee
	- 'Harpswell Happiness' ♀H4	CHVG CLAP CPrp EBee EPfP EPyc GBin GCra SWat WAul WCon WMoo WViv
	- 'Harpswell Haze'	ECha WMoo WViv
	- 'Heavenly Blue'	MWat SPer
	- 'Helen Astor'	CHVG CLAP CMea CPrp CRow CTri EBee EShb MRav SApp SWat
N	- 'Himmel von Komi'	GBin
	- 'Hoar Edge'	CAbx
	- 'Hohe Warte' ♀H4	GBin
	- 'Hubbard'	CEnt CPen EShb GBin MNrw NBro NCGa NHol
	- 'Illini Charm'	CHid CPen EWll NBro SSvw WFar WMoo
	- 'Jac-y-do'	EWes
	- 'Jewelled Crown'	CPen WFar
	- 'Kabluey'	CIri
	- 'Kent Arrival'	SIri WAul
	- 'Lady Vanessa'	CPou EBee EPPr GAbr GBin GMac MBNS MRav NBro NMoo NSti SBch SMrm WAul
§	- 'Lake Niklas'	ELon GBin NCGa
	- 'Langthorns Pink'	CMdw ELan MRav
	- 'Laurenbuhl'	CAbx CPLG
	- 'Lavendelwein' ♀H4	GBin
	- 'Lavender Bounty'	CHid EBee EBla NBre NBro SPet WCAu WViv
	- 'Limeheart'	CPou CSev ELan LLHF LRHS
	- 'Little Blue'	EBee LRHS
N	- 'Little Twinkle Star'	CHid EBee GBin NPro WFar
	- 'Mad Magenta'	WCAu
	- 'Marilyn Holmes'	EBee WCot
	- 'Marshmallow Frosting'	WFar
§	- 'Melton Red Flare'	CMHG CPen EAEE EBee EBla EHon ELan EPPr EShb GBin LRHS MSpe SBch SDys SMrm SPoG WCAu WFar
	- 'Memphis Memory'	ELan GBin GCra GMac MAvo MSCN NGdn SPer WHoo
I	- 'Mint Fresh'	WViv
	- 'Moon Silk'	EBee EPyc GBin GBuc GGar LLHF WCot WFar
	- 'Mountain Lake'	CPen CSam EAEE EPPr EShb GBin LRHS MSpe SVic SWat WCAu WCot WFar WSpi
	- 'Mrs Rowe'	CDes CFee CPou CRow EBee EBla EIri EPPr GBuc LLWP MRav MWat SWat WCAu WFar WPtf
	- 'Navy Brass'	NBre WViv
	- 'Night Breeze'	SIri WViv
	- 'Niklas Sea'	see *I. sibirica* 'Lake Niklas'
	- 'Nottingham Lace'	EBee LLHF SWat
	- 'Oban' ♀H4	CHVG ESgI GBuc GMac
	- 'Orville Fay'	CBgR GMac WCot WFar
	- 'Ottawa'	CPou CRow ECGP ELan LRHS MBNS SWat WFar
	- 'Outset'	EBee SSvw WWEG
I	- 'Pageant'	WCot
I	- 'Painted Desert'	EBee GKir
	- 'Papillon'	CHVG CTri EAEE EBee EBla ECtt ELan EPPr EWTr GAbr GGar LHop

LPio LRHS MWat NBir NBro NCob NGdn NHol NSti SApp SMrm SPer STes SWat WBor WFar WPer WPnP
N - 'Pearl Queen' MCot WFar
- 'Peg Edwards' EBee
- 'Percheron' ESgI SIri WViv
- 'Perfect Vision' ♀H4 MBri
- 'Perry's Blue' Widely available
I - 'Perry's Favourite' CFee CRow
- 'Perry's Pigmy' GBuc
- 'Persimmon' misapplied see *I. sibirica* 'Tycoon'
- 'Persimmon' ambig. CFir CHid EAEE EBee EBla ECtt EMFW GCra LRHS MWat NMoo SVic SWat WFar WMoo
- 'Pink Haze' CRow EBee EPfP ESgI GBin MBel MMuc NBro NMoo NPri NSti SMrm WAul WViv
- 'Pirate Prince' NPer
- Plant World hybrids MDKP
- 'Plissee' ♀H4 GBin
- 'Polly Dodge' LRHS
- 'Pounsley Purple' CPou
- 'Primrose Cream' WCot
- 'Prussian Blue' ♀H4 CAbx GBin
- 'Purple Mere' WFar
N - 'Red Flag' NHol
- 'Reddy Maid' CHVG WCAu
- 'Redflare' see *I. sibirica* 'Melton Red Flare'
N - 'Regality' CWCL GBin MHer MMuc NBro SHGN
- 'Regency Belle' ♀H4 SIri
- 'Regency Buck' MAvo MSCN
- 'Rikugi-sakura' EBla GBin LLHF NBPC NBhm NBro WCot
- 'Roanoke's Choice' CElw EBee EWes GBin LRHS MBNS NCGa WBor WFar
- 'Roaring Jelly' EWes WCAu WCot WViv
- 'Roger Perry' CFee
- 'Rosselline' ♀H4 CAbx
- 'Royal Blue' ECha GBuc SWat
- 'Ruby Wine' CPen LEdu
- 'Ruffled Velvet' ♀H4 Widely available
- 'Ruffles Plus' WCot
- 'Savoir Faire' ECha
- 'Sea Horse' GBuc
- 'Sea Shadows' ESgI NBir WCAu
- 'Shaker's Prayer' ♀H4 EWes GAbr WAul
- 'Shall We Dance' ♀H4 EWes WAul
- 'Shirley Pope' ♀H4 COIW EBee EWes GAbr GBin GKir LRHS MBri MWte NCGa NMoo NSti SMeo WAul WCot WFar WMoo WWEG
- 'Shirley's Choice' GKir SIri WViv
- 'Showdown' EBee ECtt GKir GMaP NHol SAga SWat WCAu WFar
- 'Shrawley' WCAu
- 'Silver Edge' ♀H4 Widely available
- 'Simple Gifts' ♀H4 CIri
- 'Sky Wings' CRow ECha GKir MArl WMoo
- 'Snow Queen' see *I. sanguinea* 'Snow Queen'
- 'Snowcrest' CBre
* - 'Snowflake' CSsd
- 'Soft Blue' ♀H4 CAbx EBee NBre
N - 'Southcombe White' CRow GBin GBuc NGdn SIri WWEG
- 'Sparkling Rosé' Widely available
- 'Splashdown' (Sino-Sib) SWat
- 'Star Cluster' WFar
- 'Steve' CHVG CPar EBee EWes GMac LPio NBro SWat WAul
- 'Steve Varner' WFar WViv
- 'Strawberry Fair' CIri
- 'Summer Sky' CAbx CBre CIri MSCN NCGa SWat WAul WCAu WCot WPrP WTin
- 'Super Ego' WTin WViv
- 'Superact' CAbx
- 'Sutton Valence' SIri WAul
- 'Sweet Surrender' **new** CAbx
- 'Tal-y-Bont' WFar
- 'Tanz Nochmal' GBin
- 'Teal Velvet' CAbx ECha WCAu WFar WViv
- 'Temper Tantrum' CEnt CKel CPrp MBNS
- 'Tropic Night' Widely available
§ - 'Tycoon' EAEE EBee EShb GBin GBuc GKir IBlr LRHS NHol SMrm SPer SVic
- 'Über den Wolken' NCot
- 'Valda' EBee
- 'Velvet Night' ECtt WBrE
- 'Vi Luihn' CAbx CBcs ECha WMoo
- 'Viel Creme' ♀H4 GBin
N - 'Violet Skies' EBee GBin
- 'Visual Treat' SIri
- 'Walter' EBee
- 'Wealden Butterfly' ♀H4 SIri WAul
- 'Wealden Mystery' WAul
- 'Wealden Skies' SIri WAul
- 'Weisse Etagen' CAbx
- 'Welcome Return' CElw CHVG EBee GBin GQue IPot MBNS MMuc NBro NMoo NPri SUsu SWat WFar WMoo
N - 'Welfenfürstin' GBin
- 'Welfengold' **new** CAbx
- 'Welfenprinz' ♀H4 CAbx
I - 'White Queen' EBla ESgI SWat WBrE
- 'White Swirl' ♀H4 Widely available
- 'White Triangles' SIri
- 'Wisley White' GMac NBre
- 'Zakopane' ♀H4 EWes
- 'Zweites Hundert' GMac NBre WFar
'Sibirica Alba' CMac ECha EPfP EShb GAbr GBBs LLWP SIng SWat WBrk WCFE WFar
'Sibirica Baxteri' CFee
N 'Sibtosa Princess' (SpH) WViv
sichuanensis CPLG EBee
sieboldii see *I. sanguinea*
'Sierra Blue' (TB) ESgI
'Sierra Grande' (TB) WCAu WViv
'Sierra Nevada' (Spuria) SMrm
sikkimensis NWCA
'Silent Strings' (IB) LRHS MBri
'Silicon Prairie' (TB) ESgI
'Silkirim' (TB) CKel
'Silver Shower' (TB) **new** WViv
'Silverado' (TB) CKel ECtt ESgI WCAu WViv
'Silvery Beauty' (Dut) EWll LAma LRHS NBir SBch
'Simmer' (BB) WAul
sindjarensis see *I. aucheri*
'Sindpers' (Juno) ♀H3 WWst
'Sinister Desire' (IB) WCAu WViv
sintenisii ♀H4 CBro CHid CPBP EBrs ECho NWCA WTin WWst
'Sir Michael' (TB) ESgI GBBs
'Siva Siva' (TB) MRav WCAu
'Six Pack' (TB) **new** CIri
'Sixtine C' (TB) SIri WViv
'Skating Party' (TB) CKel ESgI WViv
'Skiers' Delight' (TB) NBre WCAu
'Skyfire' (TB) CWCL ESgI MWea SBch WViv WWEG
'Skylark's Song' (TB) **new** EIri
'Skyline' (J) WWst
'Slap Bang' (SDB) ESgI
'Sleepy Time' (MDB) WViv
'Slovak Prince' (TB) CIri

'Small Sky' (SDB) CBro
'Smart Aleck' (TB) ECtt WViv
N 'Smart Girl' (TB) CKel EIri
'Smart Move' (TB) CWCL WViv
'Smokey Dream' (TB) CKel
'Smokey Salmon' (TB) CKel
'Sneezy' (TB) WCAu
'Snow and Wind' (TB) **new** WAul
'Snow Plum' (IB) SIri WViv
'Snow Season' (SDB) WViv
'Snow Tracery' (TB) EAEE LRHS MBri
'Snow Troll' (SDB) WCAu
'Snowbrook' (TB) WCAu
'Snowcone' (IB) ESgI
'Snowdrift' (TB) **new** MSKA
'Snowdrift' (*laevigata*) see *I. laevigata* 'Snowdrift'
'Snowmound' (TB) CKel ESgI WCAu
'Snowy Owl' (TB) ♀H4 CKel WCAu
'Soaring Kite' (TB) WCAu
'Social Event' (TB) ESgI WCAu
'Soft Caress' (TB) WCAu
'Solar Fire' (TB) CIri
'Solid Mahogany' (TB) MRav WCAu
'Somerset Blue' (TB) ♀H4 CKel WCAu
N 'Somerset Vale' (TB) SMrm
'Somerton Brocade' (SDB) CKel
'Somerton Dance' (SDB) CBgR CKel
'Son of Sun' (Spuria) CIri
'Song of Norway' (TB) ECtt EIri EPPr ESgI WCAu WViv
'Sopra il Vulcano' (BB) ESgI
'Sostenique' (TB) ESgI WCAu
'Southern Clipper' (SDB) LRHS MBri
'Space Cowboy' (TB) CIri
'Space Mist' (TB) CKel
'Sparkplug' (SDB) ESgI
'Sparks Fly' (SDB) WCAu
'Spartan' (TB) CKel
'Special Feature' (TB) CIri WViv
'Speck So' (MTB) ESgI
'Spellbreaker' (TB) ESgI WViv
'Spice Lord' (TB) WCAu
'Spiced Custard' (TB) CKel EIri ESgI
'Spiced Tiger' (TB) WCAu
'Spinning Wheel' (TB) SIri
'Splashacata' (TB) WViv
'Spot of Tea' (MDB) ESgI
'Spreckles' (TB) ESgI
'Spring Festival' (TB) WCAu
'Spun Gold' (TB) ESgI
spuria CMac CPou
– subsp. ***carthaliniae*** WPer
§ – subsp. ***halophila*** GAuc WCAu
§ – subsp. ***musulmanica*** LRHS
– subsp. ***ochroleuca*** see *I. orientalis* Mill.
– subsp. ***spuria*** GBuc
× ***squalens*** WCAu
'St Louis Blues' (TB) ESgI
'Stairway to Heaven' (TB) ESgI WAul WCAu
'Stapleford' (SDB) CBro
'Staplehurst' (MTB) ♀H4 SIri WAul
'Star Prince' (SDB) ESgI
'Star Shine' (TB) CKel ESgI WCAu
'Starcrest' (TB) ESgI WAul WViv
'Stardate' (SDB) CKel
'Starring' (TB) CIri WAul
'Starship' (TB) ESgI
'Starship Enterprise' (TB) CIri
'Starwoman' (IB) WAul
'Staten Island' (TB) ESgI SEND SRms WCAu WTin
'Status Seeker' (TB) WCAu
'Stella Polaris' (TB) CWan ELon
'Stellar Lights' (TB) EIri WCAu
'Stepping Out' (TB) ♀H4 CMac CPar CWGN EAEE EBee EBla EPfP ESgI EWll GBin IPot LBMP LDai LRHS MCot MSpe MWea NBre SBch WAul WBor WCAu
'Stinger' (SDB) ♀H4 CIri
'Stingray' (TB) CIri ESgI
'Stitch in Time' (TB) EIri WCAu WViv
'Stockholm' (SDB) CKel
stolonifera EBrs ECho WWst
– 'Vera' LRHS
– 'Zwanenburg Beauty' EBrs ECho
'Stormy Circle' (SDB) WCAu
'Strawberry Love' (IB) ♀H4 CKel
'Strictly Jazz' (TB) WCAu
'Striking' (TB) WViv
'Study In Black' (TB) WCAu
stylosa see *I. unguicularis*
§ ***suaveolens*** CBro CPou NMen WIvy
* – var. ***flavescens*** WWst
– 'Rubromarginata' ERos
* – var. ***violacea*** ECho GCal NMen NWCA WWst
subbiflora WCot
subbiflora × ***timofejewii*** WCot
subdichotoma EBee
'Sugar' (IB) WCAu
'Sultan's Palace' (TB) CWCL ECho ESgI EWll NBPC WBor WSpi WViv WWEG
'Sumatra' (TB) ESgI
'Summer's Smile' (TB) ESgI
'Sun Ada Beach' (TB) **new** CIri
'Sun Doll' (SDB) ♀H4 CKel
'Sundown Red' (IB) NBir
'Sunny and Warm' (TB) CKel
'Sunny Dawn' (IB) ♀H4 CKel WViv
'Sunset Colors' (Spuria) ♀H4 CIri
'Sunshine Boy' (IB) CKel
'Superstition' (TB) ♀H4 EIri ELan EPPr ESgI GBin MRav MWhi SMrm SSvw WCAu WCot WViv WWEG
'Supreme Sultan' (TB) ESgI ETod WAul WCAu WViv
'Susan Bliss' (TB) CKel EBee ELan EPfP ESgI GBBs GMaP NBre WCAu
'Susan Gillespie' (IB) ♀H4 CKel
'Suspicion' (TB) CIri WViv
svetlanae WWst
'Swain' (TB) ESgI
'Swaledale' (TB) WCAu
'Swazi Princess' (TB) CKel ESgI WCAu
'Sweet Kate' (SDB) ♀H4 WCAu
'Sweet Lena' (TB) ESgI
'Sweet Musette' (TB) WCAu WViv
'Sweeter than Wine' (TB) ESgI MRav WCAu WViv
'Swingtown' (TB) WCAu
'Sybil' (TB) GBin GCra
'Sylvia Murray' (TB) WCAu
'Symphony' (Dut) ECho NBir
'Syncopation' (TB) CKel ESgI WCAu WViv
'Tall Chief' (TB) WCAu
N 'Tanex' ECho
'Tangerine Sky' (TB) WCAu WViv
'Tangfu' (IB) ESgI
'Tango Bond' (BB) **new** CIri
'Tango Music' (SpH) ♀H4 GBin
'Tantara' (SDB) WTin
'Tanzanian Tangerine' (TB) WCAu
'Tarheel Elf' (SDB) ESgI WTin
'Tarn Hows' (TB) ESgI SRms WCAu
'Tchin Tchin' (IB) WAul WViv
tectorum CMdw CSWP CSsd ERos GAuc GBin GKev NWCA
– BWJ 8191 WCru
– 'Alba' CPBP ERos WThu

	- 'Variegata' misapplied	see *I. japonica* 'Variegata'
	- 'Variegata' (v)	EBee NSti SGSe SPoG
	'Tell Fibs' (SDB)	CBro CKel
	'Temple Gold' (TB)	CKel NPer
	'Temple Meads' (IB)	ESgI WCAu
	'Templecloud' (IB) ♀H4	CBgR CHar CKel
	'Tempting Fate' (TB)	WAul WViv
§	***tenax***	CLAP CPBP ECho GAuc GBuc GEdr GKir NWCA SMrm
	- NNS 04-240	WCot
	'Tender Years' (IB)	WAul
	'Tennison Ridge' (TB)	WCAu
	tenuissima	GBuc
	- subsp. ***tenuissima***	CPBP GAuc NMen
	'Terre de Feu' (TB)	ESgI WViv
	'Thaïs' (TB)	ESgI
	'That's Red' (MTB)	WCAu
	'The Black Douglas' (TB)	EMal
	'The Bride'	see *I.* 'Bride'
	'The Citadel' (TB)	ELon
	'The Red Douglas' (TB)	ESgI
	'The Rocket'	see *I.* 'Rocket'
	'Theatre' (TB)	ESgI
	'Third Charm' (SDB)	CBro
	'Third World' (SDB)	CBro
	thompsonii NNS 05-416	WCot
	'Thornbird' (TB) ♀H4	ECtt EIri ESgI WCAu WViv
	'Three Cherries' (MDB)	CBro ECho WViv
	'Thriller' (TB)	ESgI WCAu
	'Throb' (TB)	WViv
	thunbergii	see *I. sanguinea*
	'Thunder Echo' (TB)	ESgI WViv
	'Thundering Hills' (TB)	CKel
	'Tickety Boo' (SDB)	CIri
	'Tickle Me' (MDB)	WCAu
	'Tide's In' (TB)	ECtt ESgI WViv
	'Tiffany' (TB)	WTin
	'Tiger Butter' (TB)	ESgI
	'Tiger Honey' (TB)	WCAu WViv
*	'Tiger's Eye'	EPfP
	tigridia	CPLG EBee
	'Tiki Bird' (Sino-Sib)	CIri
	'Tillamook' (TB)	WCAu
	'Time Piece' (TB)	CKel
	tingitana var. ***fontanesii***	EBee WPGP
	'Tinkerbell' (SDB)	CPBP ECGP GMaP LRHS MAvo NBir NGdn SPet
	'Tintinara' (TB) ♀H4	CKel
	'Titan's Glory' (TB) ♀H4	ESgI MRav WAul WCAu WCot WViv
	'To the Point' (TB)	WCAu
	'Toasted Watermelon' (TB)	WCAu
	'Tol-long'	see *I.* 'Tollong'
§	'Tollong' ♀H4	IKil
	'Tom Johnson' (TB) ♀H4	CIri WCAu
	'Tom Tit' (TB)	WCAu
	'Tomingo' (SDB)	WCAu
	'Tomorrow's Child' (TB)	ESgI WViv
	'Toots' (SDB)	WTin
	'Top Flight' (TB)	ELan SRms
N	'Topolino' (TB)	CKel SAga
	'Topsy Turvy' (MTB)	NBre
	'Torchlight' (TB)	SEND
	'Total Eclipse' (TB)	SRms
	'Totally Cool'	LSRN WViv
	'Toucan Tango' (TB)	CIri
	'Touch of Mahogany' (TB)	WCAu
	'Tracy Tyrene' (TB)	ESgI WViv
	'Trade Secret' (TB) **new**	CIri
	'Trails West' (TB)	ESgI WViv
	'Trapel' (TB)	ESgI
	'Treccia d'Oro' (TB)	ESgI
	'Trencavel' (TB)	ESgI
	'Trenwith' (TB)	CKel
	'Trillion' (TB)	CIri
	'Triple Whammy' (TB)	ESgI
	'Triplet'	WAul
	'Triplicate' (SDB)	SMrm
N	'Trout River' **new**	ITim
	'True Navy' (SDB)	WCAu WViv
	tubergeniana (J)	WWst
	tuberosa	see *Hermodactylus tuberosus*
	'Tumultueux' (TB)	ESgI WViv
	'Tut's Gold' (TB)	ECtt ESgI WCAu WViv
*	'Twin'	WWst
	typhifolia	GAuc
	'Tyrian Dream' (IB)	WCAu
	'Ultimate' (SDB) **new**	CIri
§	***unguicularis*** ♀H4	Widely available
	- from Lady Gibson **new**	GEdr
	- 'Abington Purple'	CBro CPMA CPen EIri WCot
	- 'Alba'	CAvo CBct ECho
N	- 'Bob Thompson'	CAvo CBro
	- subsp. ***carica*** J&JA 600.416	NWCA
§	- subsp. ***cretensis***	CAby ECho GKev NMen SHGN WAbe WCot WHil
	- - Hoa 017	WWst
N	- 'Diana Clare'	WCot
N	- 'Marondera'	CAvo WSHC
	- 'Mary Barnard' ♀H4	CAvo CBct CBro CFee CHar CPMA CPen CPou CSam ECGP ECha ECho EHrv GEdr IBlr NBir NMen WAbe WCot WHil WMnd
N	- 'Oxford Dwarf'	CBro EBee ECho
N	- 'Palette'	ELan
§	- 'Walter Butt'	CAvo CBro EBee ECGP ECho NBir SMad WFar
	uromovii	GBuc MArl
	'Ursula Warleggan' (TB)	CKel
	'Vague à l'Ame' (TB)	ESgI WViv
	'Valimar' (TB)	WCAu
	'Vamp' (IB)	CKel EPPr SIri WAul WViv
	'Vandal Spirit' (TB)	ESgI
	'Vanity' (TB) ♀H4	ESgI WCAu WViv
	'Vanity's Child' (TB)	WCAu
§	***variegata*** ♀H4	EGoo EShb WCAu WCot
	- var. ***reginae***	WCAu
	'Vegas Heat' (BB)	CIri
	'Verdissant' (IB)	CBgR WViv
	'Verity Blamey' (TB)	CKel
	verna	ERos NHol
	versicolor ♀H4	CArn CBen CRow CWat EBee EHon EMFW EPPr GKir GMaP IBlr LPBA LRHS MGos MMuc MNHC MNrw NWCA SPlb SRms SWat WBrk WFar WMAq WPnP WShi WSpi WTin WViv
	- 'Between the Lines'	CRow WViv
	- 'Candystriper'	WViv
	- 'China West Lake'	CRow
	- 'Claret Cup'	CPou WWEG
	- 'Dottie's Double'	CRow
	- 'Georgia Bay'	CRow
	- 'Kermesina'	CRow CWat EBee ECha EHon ELan EMFW ESgI GBuc GGar IBlr LPBA MBri MGos NPer NSti SRms SWat WBrk WFar WMAq WMoo WPnP
	- 'Mysterious Monique'	CMdw CRow CWat
	- 'Party Line'	SIri
	- var. ***rosea***	CRow
	- 'Rowden Allegro'	CRow
	- 'Rowden Aria'	CRow
	- 'Rowden Cadenza'	CRow
	- 'Rowden Calypso'	CRow
	- 'Rowden Cantata'	CRow

	- 'Rowden Concerto'	CRow
	- 'Rowden Harmony'	CRow
	- 'Rowden Lullaby'	CRow
	- 'Rowden Lyric'	CRow
	- 'Rowden Mazurka'	CRow
	- 'Rowden Melody'	CRow
	- 'Rowden Nocturne'	CRow
	- 'Rowden Pastorale'	CRow
	- 'Rowden Prelude'	CRow
	- 'Rowden Refrain'	CRow
	- 'Rowden Rondo'	CRow
	- 'Rowden Sonata'	CRow
	- 'Rowden Symphony'	CRow
	- 'Rowden Waltz'	CRow
	- 'Silvington'	CRow
	- 'Whodunit'	CRow
	'Vert Galant' (TB)	ESgI
	'Via Domitia' (TB)	ESgI
	'Vibrant' (TB)	ESgI WCAu
	'Vibrations' (TB)	ESgI
	vicaria	EBrs ECho WWst
	- RM 8269	WWst
	- 'Hodji-obi-Garm'	LRHS WWst
	- 'Prominence' **new**	WWst
I	- 'Sina'	WWst
	'Victoria Falls' (TB)	ESgI WCAu
	'Vinho Verde' (IB) ♀H4	CKel
	'Vino Rosso' (SDB)	ESgI
	'Vintage Press' (IB)	WCAu
	'Vintage Year' (Spuria)	WCAu
	violacea	see *I. spuria* subsp. *musulmanica*
	'Violet Beauty' (Reticulata)	ECho ERCP LAma LRHS NHol SMeo SPhx
	'Violet Classic' (TB)	WCAu
	'Violet Harmony' (TB)	ESgI
	'Violet Icing' (TB) ♀H4	CKel
	'Violet Rings' (TB)	WCAu WViv
	'Violet Tiara' **new**	LHop
	'Viper' (IB)	CIri
	virginica 'De Luxe'	see *I.* × *robusta* 'Dark Aura'
	- 'Pink Butterfly'	NMoo
	- 'Pond Crown Point'	CRow
	- 'Pond Lilac Dream'	CRow
N	- 'Purple Fan'	CRow
§	- var. ***shrevei***	CRow WCAu WViv
	'Visual Arts' (TB)	WViv
	'Vitafire' (TB)	ECtt WViv
	'Vitality' (IB)	ESgI
	'Vitrail' (IB)	CBgR WViv
	'Vive la France' (TB)	ESgI WViv
	'Vizier' (TB)	WCAu
	'Voilà' (IB)	ESgI
	'Volts' (SDB)	CKel
	'Voluminous' (TB)	CIri
	'Volute' (TB)	ESgI WViv
I	'Vonnies Wedding Iris' **new**	ELon
	'Wabash' (TB)	ELan ESgI EWll WBor WCAu WTin
	'Walker Ferguson' (Spuria)	WCAu
	'Walter Butt'	see *I. unguicularis* 'Walter Butt'
	'War Chief' (TB)	ESgI MRav WCAu
	'War Sails' (TB)	SIri WCAu WViv
	'Warl-sind' (J)	WWst
	'Warranty' (TB)	CIri WCAu
	'Warrior King' (TB)	WCAu
	wattii	CPLG EBee GCal WCot
	'Way to Go' (TB)	CIri
	'Wealden Canary' (Spuria)	WAul
	'Wealden Elegance' (Spuria)	WAul
	'Wealden Sunshine' (Spuria)	WAul
	'Wedding Candles' (TB)	WCAu
	'Wedding Vow' (TB)	CKel EIri
	'Wedgwood' (Dut)	NBre
	'Welch's Reward' (MTB) ♀H4	CKel ESgI
	'Well Suited' (SDB)	WViv
	'Westar' (SDB) ♀H4	CBgR CKel EIri
	'Westwell' (SDB)	WCAu
	'What's My Line' (TB)	CIri
	'Wheels' (SDB)	WTin
	'Whispering Spirits' (TB)	CIri
	'White City' (TB)	EAEE EBla ECGP EPfP ESgI GMaP LPio LRHS MCot MRav MWat NPer SBch SCoo SDnm SPer SRms SWat WAul WCAu WMnd
	'White Excelsior' (Dut)	ECho
	'White Knight' (TB)	EBee ELan EPfP NBre WMnd WWEG
	'White Reprise' (TB)	ESgI
	'White Wine' (MTB)	WCAu
	'Whole Cloth' (TB)	ESgI
N	'Wild Echo' (TB)	CKel
	'Wild Jasmine' (TB)	ECtt WCAu WViv
	'Wild Ruby' (SDB)	CKel
	'Wild West' (TB)	CKel
	'Wild Wings' (TB) **new**	NCGa SBch STes WWEG
	willmottiana 'Alba'	EBrs ECho WWst
	wilsonii ♀H4	EBee GAuc GBuc GKev GKir WBVN
	'Windjammer Seas' **new**	WAul
	'Winemaster' (TB)	ECtt SIri
	'Wings of Peace' (TB) **new**	CIri
	winogradowii ♀H4	CAvo CBro EBrs ECho EPot ERos LAma LLHF LRHS NHol NMen NMin WAbe WWst
	'Winter Crystal' (TB) ♀H4	CKel
	'Winter Olympics' (TB)	CMil EAEE EBee ESgI EShb LBuc LRHS MRav MSpe
	'Wishful Thinking' (TB)	SIri WViv
	'Wisteria Sachet' (IB)	WCAu
	'Witching' (TB)	WCAu
	'Wizard of Id' (SDB)	WTin
	'Wondrous' (TB)	CIri ESgI
	'Worlds Beyond' (TB)	WCAu
	'Wyckhill' (SDB)	WCAu
	'Xillia' (IB)	CKel
	xiphioides	see *I. latifolia*
	xiphium	EBrs ECho
	'Yaquina Blue' (TB)	ESgI WCAu WViv
	'Yellow and White' **new**	GAbr
	'Yes' (TB)	CPMA ESgI WCAu WViv
	'Young Blood' (IB)	WCAu
	'Yo-yo' (SDB)	EPPr GEdr STes
	'Yvonne Pelletier' (TB)	WCAu
	'Zantha' (TB)	ESgI WCAu
	zenaidae	WWst
	'Zero' (SDB) ♀H4	CKel WViv
	'Zinc Pink' (BB)	WCAu
	'Zing Me' (IB)	WViv
	'Zipper' (MDB)	ESgI WCAu

Isatis (*Brassicaceae*)

	tinctoria	CArn CBod CHby COld CRWN CSev EBWF EOHP GJos GPoy ILis LRHS MHer MNHC SECG SHlg SIde SPav WCHb WJek
	- var. ***indigotica***	CArn

Ischyrolepis (*Restionaceae*)

§	***subverticillata***	CHEx CTrC MAvo

Ismene see *Hymenocallis*

Isodon (*Lamiaceae*)

	calycinus	SPlb

effusus B&SWJ 11027 **new**	WCru
longitubus	EBee WCot
- 'Momokaze'	EBee LFur
trichocarpus	EBee
umbrosus f. ***kameba*** **new**	EBee

Isolepis (*Cyperaceae*)

§ ***cernua***	CMil CWat EAlp EMFW EPfP LRHS MBri MSKA NOak SBch SCoo SHDw WFar WMAq

Isoloma see *Kohleria*

Isomeris see *Cleome*

Isoplexis (*Scrophulariaceae*)

canariensis	CAbb CBcs CBot CCCN CDTJ CHEx CHll CHrt CRHN CSpe EBee ECre EWll IDee SEND SGar SPlb WCFE WWlt
isabelliana	CCCN CDTJ EShb LDai SDix
sceptrum	CAbb CBot CCCN CDTJ CHEx CHll CHrt CPLG CRHN EBee ECre SAPC SArc WPGP
- pink-flowered	WPGP

Isopogon (*Proteaceae*)

anemonifolius	SPlb
anethifolius	SPlb

Isopyrum (*Ranunculaceae*)

biternatum	GBuc NLar
nipponicum	CDes CLAP EBee WCru WPGP
stoloniferum **new**	WCru
thalictroides	EPot LLHF WAbe

Isotoma (*Campanulaceae*)

sp.	LAst SWvt
§ ***axillaris***	CSpe IDee NPer NPri SCoo SPer SPet SPoG
- 'Fairy Carpet'	SRms
'Fairy Footsteps' **new**	EPfP
fluviatilis	NLar

Itea (*Escalloniaceae*)

chinensis	WPGP
ilicifolia ♀H3	Widely available
* - 'Rubrifolia'	LRHS MAsh SLon SPoG
japonica 'Beppu'	MGos SLPl SSpi
virginica	CAbP CBcs CMCN EBee ELan LRHS MBlu MRav SLon SPer WBVN WFar
§ - 'Henry's Garnet'	CAbP CDoC CEnd CMCN CMHG CMac CPMA CSBt CWSG EBee ECrN EPfP LAst LEdu LRHS MAsh MBlu MBri MGos NCGa NLar SLim SPoG SRGP SSpi SWvt WDin WGwG
- Little Henry = 'Sprich'PBR	CBgR CMac CSBt EBee ELan ELon IMon LAst LRHS NLar NPri
- 'Long Spire'	CPMA IArd IDee WDin
- 'Merlot'	CPMA LRHS MBlu MGos NLar
- 'Sarah Eve'	CMCN CPMA EBee NLar SRGP
- 'Saturnalia'	NLar WDin
- 'Shirley's Compact'	NLar
- Swarthmore form	see *I. virginica* 'Henry's Garnet'
yunnanensis	CPLG SSpi

Ixia (*Iridaceae*)

'Blue Bird'	CFir EBrs ECho LAma WHil
'Castor'	CAvo CPne CPrp EBrs ECho WHil
curta **new**	ECho
dubia	ECho
flexuosa	ECho WCot
'Giant'	EBrs ECho WHil
'Hogarth'	CPrp ECho LAma WHil
'Holland Glory'	ECho
hybrids	EBrs SMrm
latifolia var. ***latifolia*** **new**	ECho
lutea	ECho
'Mabel'	CAvo EBrs ECho WCot WHil
maculata	ECho
'Marquette'	ECho
metelerkampiae **new**	ECho
monadelpha	ECho
orientalis **new**	ECho
paniculata	ECho
'Panorama'	CPne ECho WHil
polystachya	ECho
- var. ***longistylis*** **new**	ECho
- var. ***lutea*** **new**	ECho
purpureorosea 'Saldanha'	ECho
rapunculoides	ECho
var. ***rigida*** **new**	
- var. ***subpendula*** **new**	ECho
'Rose Emperor'	CPrp ECho LAma
'Spotlight'	ECho WHil
thomasiae	WCot
trifolia **new**	ECho
'Venus'	CFir CPne EBrs ECho LAma WHil
versicolor **new**	ECho
viridiflora	CBow CPne ECho EDif WCot
'Vulcan'	CPrp ECho
'Yellow Emperor'	CAvo CPne EBrs ECho WHil

Ixiolirion (*Ixioliriaceae*)

montanum	CHid CMea ECho
pallasii	see *I. tataricum*
§ ***tataricum***	CPrp EBrs ECho LAma MBri MCot SBch
- Ledebourii Group	CAvo CFFs EBee

J

Jaborosa (*Solanaceae*)

integrifolia	CDes CFir CPLG CStu EBee ELan LFur LRHS SSvw WAul WCom WCon WCot WPGP

Jacaranda (*Bignoniaceae*)

acutifolia misapplied	see *J. mimosifolia*
§ ***mimosifolia***	CBcs CCCN CHll ELan ERea EShb GQui MBri MREP SPlb

Jacobinia see *Justicia*

Jamesia (*Hydrangeaceae*)

americana	MBri NLar

Jasione (*Campanulaceae*)

§ ***heldreichii***	GAbr NBir SRms
jankae	see *J. heldreichii*
§ ***laevis***	ECho GAbr MSCN NBlu SRms WGwG WWFP
§ - 'Blaulicht'	CMHG CWib EBee ECha EPfP GGar LRHS MBNS MMuc MNFA NBPC NEgg NLar SBch SMrm SPhx SPlb WMoo
- Blue Light	see *J. laevis* 'Blaulicht'
montana	EBWF ECho WFar WPnn WRHF WSFF
perennis	see *J. laevis*

Jasminum (Oleaceae)

CC 4728	CPLG
affine	see *J. officinale* f. *affine*
angulare ♀H1	CPLG CRHN ERea EShb
azoricum ♀H1	CCCN CDoC CRHN ELan EPfP ERea EShb NPal
beesianum	Widely available
bignoniaceum	WSHC
blinii	see *J. polyanthum*
dispermum	CRHN
farreri	see *J. humile* f. *farreri*
floridum	EWes NScw
fruticans	ELon EPfP EPla LRHS NScw
giraldii hort.	see *J. humile* f. *farreri*
grandiflorum misapplied	see *J. officinale* f. *affine*
grandiflorum L. 'De Grasse' ♀H1	CRHN ERea EShb
humile	CEnt CPLG EQua GAuc MGos MHer WFar WKif
§ - f. ***farreri***	MBri
- var. ***glabrum***	see *J. humile* f. *wallichianum*
§ - 'Revolutum' ♀H4	Widely available
§ - f. ***wallichianum*** B&SWJ 2559	WCru
§ ***laurifolium*** f. ***nitidum***	ERea EShb
§ ***mesnyi*** ♀H2-3	CEnt CMac CPLG CRHN CSBt CTri CWib EBak EBee ELan EPfP ERas ERea IGor LRHS MAsh MRav SAga SBch SPer STre WSHC
multipartitum	EShb
- bushy	CSpe
nitidum	see *J. laurifolium* f. *nitidum*
§ ***nudiflorum*** ♀H4	Widely available
- 'Argenteum'	see *J. nudiflorum* 'Mystique'
- 'Aureum'	EBee ELan EPfP EPla LBMP LRHS MAsh MBNS MRav NHol NSti SLim SPer SPoG WCot WPat
* - 'Compactum'	MAsh
§ - 'Mystique' (v)	ELan LRHS LSou MAsh NLar SLon SPer SPoG WClo WCot WPat
odoratissimum	ERea EShb
officinale ♀H4	Widely available
§ - f. ***affine***	CBcs CRHN CSPN CSam CTri CWSG CWib EBee ELan ELon EPfP LAst LRHS MAsh MGan MRav NHol SCoo SDix SLim SRms WCru WFar
§ - 'Argenteovariegatum' (v) ♀H4	Widely available
- 'Aureovariegatum'	see *J. officinale* 'Aureum'
§ - 'Aureum' (v)	Widely available
- 'Clotted Cream'	CBcs CCCN CDul CSBt CWGN EBee EPfP EShb EWTr LAst LBuc LRHS LSRN MAsh MBri MGos MWea NHol NLar NPri SBch SCoo SLim SPer SPoG WCot WPat
- 'Crûg's Collection'	WCru
- 'Devon Cream' PBR	SBch
- Fiona Sunrise = 'Frojas' PBR	Widely available
- 'Grandiflorum'	see *J. officinale* f. *affine*
- 'Inverleith' ♀H4	CDoC CWSG EBee ELan EPfP IArd LAst LBMP LHop LRHS MAsh MBNS MBri MCCP MRav SBch SCoo SLim SMad SPad SPer SPoG WFar WSHC
- 'Variegatum'	see *J. officinale* 'Argenteovariegatum'
parkeri	CBcs CBgR CFee CMea CTri EBee ECho ELon EPfP EPot GEdr GKev GMaP LHop LRHS MBNS NLar NMen WFar WPat
§ ***polyanthum*** ♀H1-2	CArn CBcs CPLG CRHN CSBt CTri EBak EBee ELan EPfP ERea ERom EShb LAst LOck LRHS MBri NEgg NPal SBch SEND SLim SPer SRms
- dark red-leaved	WPGP
primulinum	see *J. mesnyi*
reevesii hort.	see *J. humile* 'Revolutum'
sambac ♀H1	CDoC CHll CRHN EAmu ELan EPfP EShb
- 'Bangkok Peony' (d)	ERea
- 'Grand Duke of Tuscany' (d)	ERea
- 'Maid of Orleans' (d) ♀H1	ERea
sieboldianum	see *J. nudiflorum*
× ***stephanense***	Widely available

Jatropha (Euphorbiaceae)

integerrima	CCCN

Jeffersonia (Berberidaceae)

diphylla	CArn CBro CLAP EBee EBrs ECho EHrv EPPr GAbr GBuc GGar GKir LAma LEdu LRHS MNFA MTho NBir NMen NMyG SIng SMad WAbe WCru WFar WPnP
dubia	CBro CFir CLAP EBee ECho EPot ERas EWes GBuc GEdr LEdu LRHS NBir NMen NSla WAbe WCom
- 'Alba'	EHrv

jostaberry see *Ribes* × *culverwellii*

Jovellana (Scrophulariaceae)

punctata	CCCN CDoC CPLG EBee
repens	CFir EBee
sinclairii	CHll CPLG EBee ECou LLHF SMrm SUsu
violacea ♀H3	CAbP CAbb CBcs CCCN CDoC CEnt CMac CPLG CTrC CTsd CWib EPfP GCal GGar IDee IMou ITim LRHS SAPC SArc SUsu WCru WPGP WSHC WWlt

Jovibarba ✿ (Crassulaceae)

§ ***allionii***	CMea CTri CWil EDAr EPot LAst LBMP LBee LRHS MAsh MHer MOne MSCN NHol NPri SIng WAbe WCom WFar WHal WHoo WIvy WPer WTin
- 'Oki'	CWil MOne
allionii × ***hirta***	CWil MOne NHol NMen SDys SFgr
§ ***arenaria***	CWil GAbr NMen SIng
- from Passo Monte Crocecar Nico	CWil
'Emerald Spring'	CWil NMen SFgr
§ ***heuffelii***	ECho NHol NMen WIvy WPer
- 'Aga'	NHol WIvy
- 'Aiolos'	NHol
- 'Alemene'	NHol
- 'Almkroon'	NHol
- 'Angel Wings'	CWil LBee LRHS NHol NMen WHoo
§ - 'Apache'	CWil
- 'Aquarius'	CWil WIvy
- 'Artemis'	NHol
- 'Aurora'	NHol
- 'Be Mine'	CWil
- 'Beacon Hill'	CWil WIvy
- 'Belcore'	CWil WIvy
- 'Benjamin'	CWil NHol
- 'Bermuda'	WIvy
- 'Bermuda Sunset'	NHol
- 'Big Red'	NHol
- 'Blaze'	CWil

	– 'Brandaris'	NHol SDys
	– 'Brocade'	MSCN NHol WIvy
	– 'Bronze Ingot'	CWil WCot
	– 'Bronze King'	WIvy
	– 'Bulgarien'	CWil
	– 'Cakor'	NHol
§	– 'Cherry Glow'	CWil NHol
	– 'Chocoleto'	WTin
	– 'Cleopatra'	NHol
	– 'Copper King'	CWil WIvy
	– 'Dunbar Red'	NHol
	– 'Fandango'	CWil MHom WIvy
	– 'Gento'	NHol
	– 'Geronimo'	NHol
	– 'Giuseppi Spiny'	MHom NHol WIvy WTin
	– var. ***glabra***	LBee LRHS WHoo
	– – from Anabakanak	CWil MHom NHol WTin
	– – from Anthoborio	CWil NMen WIvy WTin
	– – from Backovo	NHol
	– – from Galicica	NHol
	– – from Haila, Montenegro/Kosovo	CWil NHol NMen SFgr WIvy
	– – from Jakupica, Macedonia	CWil WIvy
	– – from Ljuboten	CWil NHol NMen WTin
	– – from Osljak	CWil
	– – from Pasina Glava	CWil
	– – from Rhodope	CWil MHom NHol
	– – from Treska Gorge, Macedonia	CWil NMen WTin
	– – from Vitse, Greece	WIvy
§	– – 'Cameo'	NHol WIvy
	– 'Gold Rand'	NHol
	– 'Grand Slam'	CWil
	– 'Green Land'	CWil
	– 'Greenstone'	CMea CWil MHom NHol NMen WIvy WTin
	– 'Harmony'	CWil NHol
	– 'Henry Correvon'	CWil
	– 'Hot Lips'	CWil
	– 'Hystyle'	WIvy
	– 'Ikaros'	NHol
	– 'Inferno'	MHom NHol
	– 'Iole'	WIvy
	– 'Ithaca'	NHol
	– 'Iuno'	CWil NHol
	– 'Jade'	CWil NMen WIvy
	– 'Kapo'	WIvy
	– var. ***kopaonikensis***	CWil LBee LRHS MHom NMen
	– 'Mary Ann'	MHom WIvy
	– 'Miller's Violet'	CWil WIvy WTin
	– 'Mink'	CWil
	– 'Minuta'	CWil NHol NMen WIvy WTin
	– 'Mystique'	CMea CWil LBee LRHS NMen WIvy
	– 'Nannette'	CWil
	– 'Nobel'	NHol
	– 'Opele'	NHol
	– 'Orion'	CWil NHol NMen
	– 'Pink Skies'	CWil WIvy
	– 'Prisma'	CWil WIvy WTin
	– 'Purple Haze'	WIvy
	– 'Red Rose'	CWil WIvy
	– 'Serenade'	CWil
	– 'Springael's Choice'	CWil
	– 'Sundancer'	WIvy
	– 'Sungold'	NHol
	– 'Suntan'	CWil NHol WIvy
	– 'Sylvan Memory'	CWil
	– 'Tan'	CWil NHol WTin
	– 'Torrid Zone'	WIvy WTin
	– 'Tuxedo'	CWil
	– 'Vesta'	CWil
	– 'Violet'	SDys WIvy
§	***hirta***	CWil EDAr MOne NHol NMen SFgr STre WPer
	– from Wintergraben	SIng SPlb
§	– subsp. ***borealis***	CWil MOne NDlv NHol
	– subsp. ***glabrescens***	EPot LRHS SIng
	– – from Belianske Tatry	CWil MOne
	– – from Smeryouka	CWil SIng
I	– 'Glauca' **new**	SFgr
	– 'Hedgehog' **new**	SFgr
	– 'Lowe's 66'	MOne
	– var. ***neilreichii***	LRHS MHom SIng
	– 'Preissiana'	LBee LRHS MOne NDlv NHol NMen SFgr WIvy WTin
	– 'Rax' **new**	SFgr
§	***sobolifera***	CHEx CWil EDAr MOne NHol NMen SFgr SIng SPlb WAbe WHal WIvy WPer
	– 'August Cream'	CWil LBee LRHS
	– 'Bronze Globe' **new**	SFgr
	– 'Green Globe'	CWil LRHS SDys WTin
	– 'Miss Lorraine'	CWil SFgr

Juanulloa (*Solanaceae*)

	aurantiaca	see *J. mexicana*
§	***mexicana***	ERea

Jubaea (*Arecaceae*)

§	***chilensis***	CBrP CPHo EAmu IDee LPJP LPal MREP SBig SChr
	spectabilis	see *J. chilensis*

Juglans ✿ (*Juglandaceae*)

§	***ailanthifolia***	CMCN ECrN EGFP IDee
	– var. ***cordiformis*** 'Brock' (F)	CAgr
	– – 'Campbell Cw1' (F)	CAgr
	– – 'Campbell Cw3' (F)	CAgr
	– – 'Fodermaier' seedling	CAgr
	– – 'Rhodes' (F)	CAgr
	ailanthifolia × ***cinerea***	see *J.* × *bixbyi*
§	× ***bixbyi***	CAgr
	cinerea (F)	CMCN LMaj
	– 'Beckwith' (F)	CAgr
	– 'Booth' seedlings (F)	CAgr
	– 'Craxezy' (F)	CAgr
	– 'Kenworthy' seedling	CAgr
	– 'Myjoy' (F)	CAgr
	hindsii	CMCN EBtc
	mandshurica (F) B&SWJ 6778	WCru
	– BWJ 8097 from China	WCru
	– RWJ 9905 from Taiwan	WCru
*	– subsp. ***sieboldiana*** B&SWJ 11026	WCru
	microcarpa	CMCN
	neotropica **new**	EGFP
	nigra (F) ♀H4	Widely available
	– 'Bicentennial' (F)	CAgr
	– 'Emma Kay' (F)	CAgr
	– 'Laciniata'	CDul ERea MBlu MBri WPat
	– 'Thomas' (F)	CAgr
	– 'Weschke' (F)	CAgr
	regia (F) ♀H4	Widely available
	– 'Axel' (F)	CAgr
	– 'Broadview' (F)	CAgr CDoC CDul CEnd CTho ELan EMui ERea GTwe LAst LRHS MBlu MBri MCoo MGos NEgg SCoo SDea SKee SPoG SVic
	– 'Buccaneer' (F)	CAgr CTho ECrN GTwe LRHS SDea SKee
	– 'Chandler' (F) **new**	CAgr
	– 'Corne du Périgord' (F)	CAgr

- 'Ferjean' (F) CAgr
- 'Fernette'PBR (F) CAgr MCoo
- 'Fernor'PBR (F) CAgr MCoo
- 'Franquette' (F) CAgr CDoC ECrN EMil GTwe LRHS MCoo WDin
- 'Hansen' (F) CAgr
- 'Hartley' (F) CAgr
- 'Jupiter' (F) new CAgr
- 'Laciniata' WPat
- 'Lara' (F) CAgr GTwe MCoo
- 'Majestic' (F) EMui
- 'Mayette' (F) CAgr ECrN EMil WDin
- 'Meylannaise' (F) CAgr
- number 16 (F) CAgr
- 'Parisienne' (F) CAgr EMil
- 'Plovdivski' (F) CAgr
- 'Proslavski' (F) CAgr CDul
- 'Purpurea' CMCN MBlu MBri
- 'Rita' (F) CAgr LBuc
- 'Ronde de Montignac' (F) CAgr
- 'Rubis' EMui
- 'Saturn' (F) CAgr
- 'Soleze' (F) CAgr
- 'Sorrento' (F) CCCN

sieboldiana see *J. ailanthifolia*

jujube see *Ziziphus jujuba*

Juncus (*Juncaceae*)

acutiflorus EBWF NSco
acutus EBWF GFor
articulatus EBWF
* ***balticus*** 'Spiralis' ECho
bulbosus CNat CRWN EBWF
conglomeratus EBWF
'Curly Gold Strike' (v) ELon LRHS MSKA SBch
§ ***decipiens*** 'Curly-wurly' CFee CKno CMea CMil CSpe EBee EHoe EPfP EPla EWes GFor GGar LHop LPBA LRHS NOak SWal SWat WHal WPGP WPnP
- 'Spiralis' see *J. decipiens* 'Curly-wurly'
I - 'Spiralis Nana' NWCA
effusus CHEx CRWN CWat EBWF EHon EMFW GFor LPBA MSKA NPer NSco NSti SBch SWat WMAq
- 'Carman's Japanese' CKno
- 'Gold Strike' (v) CWCL
§ - f. ***spiralis*** CBen CFee CRow CSpe CWat EHoe EHon ELan EMFW EPfP GFor GKev LPBA LRHS NBir NHol NOak NWsh SBch SBod SLim SPer SPlb WFar WHal WMAq WMoo WPGP WPnP
§ - - 'Unicorn'PBR EBee EPPr LBMP LRHS SApp SBch SPoG WWEG
- - 'Yellow Line'PBR (v) EBee LRHS WWEG
ensifolius CKno CRow CWat EBee EHoe EMFW EWes LPBA MAvo MMHG MSKA NHol NNor NOak NPer WWEG
filiformis 'Spiralis' EAlp EBee GAbr GKev LRHS SApp WWEG
gerardii EBWF
inflexus CBen CRWN CWat EBWF EHon GFor MSKA NHol NSco SWat
- 'Afro' EAlp EBee ELan EPfP LRHS MCCP NBro NOak SPlb WHal WWEG
pallidus EBee EPPr NBid NNor
patens 'Carman's Gray' CFee CKno CWCL EBee EBrs EPPr EPla GCal GQue LRHS MAvo MCCP MMoz NGdn NHol NNor NOak NWsh SApp WMoo WWEG
- 'Elk Blue' CKno WWEG
'Silver Spears' MCCP
squarrosus EBWF
'Unicorn'PBR see *J. effusus* f. *spiralis* 'Unicorn'
xiphioides EHoe EPla NHol

Junellia (*Verbenaceae*)

azorelloides F&W 9344 WAbe
odonnellii WAbe
wilczekii WFar
- F&W 7770 NWCA

Juniperus ✿ (*Cupressaceae*)

chinensis CMac CMen SEND
- 'Aurea' ♀H4 CBcs CMac EHul EOrn LRHS MBar MGos
§ - 'Blaauw' ♀H4 CDoC CMac CMen ECho EHul EOrn MBar MGos SCoo STre WEve WFar
- 'Blue Alps' CDoC ECho EHul EOrn GKir IFFs LRHS MBar MGos MMuc NEgg NHol NLar SCoo SEND SLim WDin WEve WFar
- 'Blue Point' MBar MGos
- 'Densa Spartan' see *J. chinensis* 'Spartan'
- 'Echiniformis' CKen EOrn
- 'Expansa Aureospicata' (v) CDoC CKen ECho EHul EOrn EPfP MBar MGos SEND SLim SPoG SRms
§ - 'Expansa Variegata' (v) CDoC CWib ECho EHul EOrn EPfP GKir MAsh MBar MGos SCoo SRms WDin WFar WMoo
- 'Ferngold' CDoC MGos
- 'Globosa Cinerea' MBar
- 'Itoigawa' new CMen
- 'Japonica' EOrn MBar
- 'Japonica Variegata' (v) EPla
§ - 'Kaizuka' ♀H4 ECho EHul EOrn GKir LBee MBar NLar SCoo SLim SMad STre
- 'Kaizuka Variegata' see *J. chinensis* 'Variegated Kaizuka'
- 'Kuriwao Gold' see *J.* × *pfitzeriana* 'Kuriwao Gold'
- 'Obelisk' ♀H4 CDoC EHul MBar MGos WClo
- 'Oblonga' CDoC EHul MBar STre
§ - 'Parsonsii' MBar STre WCFE
- 'Plumosa' MBar
- 'Plumosa Albovariegata' (v) EOrn MBar
- 'Plumosa Aurea' ♀H4 EHul EOrn MBar WDin WFar
- 'Plumosa Aureovariegata' (v) CKen EOrn MBar
- 'Pyramidalis' ♀H4 CDoC ECho EHul EPfP GKir SCoo SRms WDin WFar
- 'Pyramidalis Variegata' see *J. chinensis* 'Variegata'
- 'Robust Green' ECho EOrn GKir LRHS MBar NLar SCoo
- 'San José' CDoC CMen EHul EOrn MAsh MBar SCoo SLim WDin
§ - var. ***sargentii*** CMen STre
- 'Shimpaku' CKen CMen EOrn MBar NLar
§ - 'Spartan' EHul
- 'Stricta' CSBt EHul LBee LRHS MAsh MBar MGos NBlu SLim WDin
- 'Stricta Variegata' see *J. chinensis* 'Variegata'
- 'Sulphur Spray' see *J.* × *pfitzeriana* 'Sulphur Spray'
- 'Torulosa' see *J. chinensis* 'Kaizuka'
§ - 'Variegata' (v) MBar
§ - 'Variegated Kaizuka' (v) ECho EHul EOrn MBar WFar
communis CArn CDul CRWN CTrG EHul GKir GPoy MHer MNHC NWea SIde
- (f) SIde
- 'Arnold' CDoC MBar MGos
- 'Arnold Sentinel' CKen
- 'Atholl' CKen
I - 'Aureopicta' (v) MBar
- 'Barton' MBar MGos NHol NLar

	- 'Berkshire'	CKen NHol WThu
	- 'Brien'	CDoC CKen
	- 'Brynhyfryd Gold'	CKen
§	- var. ***communis***	MBar
	- 'Compressa' ♀H4	Widely available
§	- 'Constance Franklin' (v)	ECho EHul MBar STre
	- 'Corielagan'	CKen MBar NLar
	- 'Cracovia'	CKen
	- var. ***depressa***	GPoy MBar
	- 'Depressa Aurea'	CKen CSBt ECho EHul EPla GKir IFFs LBee MBar MGos WFar
	- 'Depressed Star'	ECho EHul MBar
	- 'Derrynane'	EHul
	- 'Effusa'	CKen
	- 'Gelb'	see *J. communis* 'Schneverdingen Goldmachangel'
	- 'Gold Ball'	LBee
	- 'Gold Cone'	CKen CSli ECho EHul EPfP EPla GKir LBee LRHS MAsh MBar MGos NHol SLim SPoG WDin WFar
	- 'Golden Showers'	see *J. communis* 'Schneverdingen Goldmachangel'
	- 'Goldenrod'	MGos
	- 'Green Carpet' ♀H4	CDoC CKen CMen ECho EHul EOrn EPfP EPla GKir IFFs LBuc LRHS MAsh MBar NEgg NHol SCoo SLim SPoG WCFE WDin
	- 'Haverbeck'	CKen
	- var. ***hemispherica***	see *J. communis* var. *communis*
	- 'Hibernica' ♀H4	CDoC CDul CSBt CTri ECho ECrN EHul EOrn EPfP GKir LAst LRHS MBar MGos NWea SBch SLPl SLim SPer SPoG WBrE WDin WEve
	- 'Hibernica Variegata'	see *J. communis* 'Constance Franklin'
	- 'Hornibrookii' ♀H4	EHul EOrn MBar MGos NWea SBod SRms STre WDin
	- 'Horstmann'	MBar NLar SCoo
I	- 'Horstmann's Pendula'	CDoC
	- 'Kenwith Castle'	CKen
	- 'Prostrata'	WFar
	- 'Pyramidalis'	SPlb
	- 'Repanda' ♀H4	CBcs CDoC CMac CSBt CWib ECho EHul EPfP GGar GKir IFFs LAst MBar MGos SCoo SLim SPer SPoG SRms WBVN WDin WEve WFar
§	- 'Schneverdingen Goldmachangel'	MBri MGos NHol NLar SLim SPoG
	- 'Sentinel'	CDoC ECho EHul EPfP GKir LRHS MBar NHol SLim WCFE WDin WEve
	- 'Sieben Steinhauser'	CKen
	- 'Silver Mist'	CKen
	- 'Spotty Spreader' (v)	GKir SLim SPoG
	- Suecica Group	EHul MBar NLar NWea SLPl
	- - 'Suecica Aurea'	EHul EOrn
	- 'Wallis'	NHol
	- 'Zeal'	CKen
	conferta	see *J. rigida* subsp. *conferta*
	- var. ***maritima***	see *J. taxifolia*
	davurica	EHul
	- 'Expansa'	see *J. chinensis* 'Parsonsii'
	- 'Expansa Albopicta'	see *J. chinensis* 'Expansa Variegata'
	- 'Expansa Variegata'	see *J. chinensis* 'Expansa Variegata'
	deppeana 'Silver Spire'	MBar
	excelsa subsp. ***polycarpos***	CMen
	'Fitz Kukuri Gold' **new**	MMuc
	foetidissima	CMen
	× ***gracilis*** 'Blaauw'	see *J. chinensis* 'Blaauw'
	'Grey Owl' ♀H4	ECho EHul ELan EPfP MBar NWea SCoo SLim SRms STre WDin WFar
	horizontalis	GKir NWea WEve
§	- 'Andorra Compact'	ECho MBar NLar SCoo
	- 'Bar Harbor'	CKen CMac EHul GKir MBar MGos NWea WEve
§	- 'Blue Chip'	ECho EHul ELan EPfP GKir LBee LRHS MBar MGos NBir SCoo SLim SPer SPoG WDin
	- 'Blue Moon'	see *J. horizontalis* 'Blue Chip'
	- 'Blue Pygmy'	CKen
	- 'Blue Rug'	see *J. horizontalis* 'Wiltonii'
	- 'Douglasii'	CKen EHul MBar
	- 'Emerald Spreader'	CKen ECho EHul ELan GKir MBar
	- 'Glacier'	CKen
	- Glauca Group	EHul GKir MBar MGos NWea SPoG WDin
	- 'Glomerata'	CKen MBar
	- 'Golden Carpet'	ECho ELan EOrn EPfP GKir LBuc MGos NLar SPoG WEve
	- 'Golden Spreader'	CDoC
	- 'Grey Pearl'	CKen EHul
	- 'Hughes'	ECho EHul LBee MBar MGos NWea SBod
	- Icee Blue = 'Monber'	CKen NLar SLim SPoG
	- 'Jade River'	EHul GKir MGos SLim SPoG
	- 'Limeglow'	CKen ECho MAsh MGos NEgg NLar SCoo SLim SPoG
	- 'Mother Lode'	CKen
	- 'Neumann'	CKen EOrn
	- 'Plumosa Compacta'	see *J. horizontalis* 'Andorra Compact'
	- 'Prince of Wales'	EHul GKir IFFs MAsh MGos NLar SCoo SLim SPoG WCor WEve
	- var. ***saxatalis*** E.Murray	see *J. communis* var. *communis*
	- 'Turquoise Spreader'	CSBt ECho EHul GKir MBar SCoo
	- 'Variegata' (v)	MBar
	- 'Venusta'	see *J. virginiana* 'Venusta'
	- 'Villa Marie'	CKen
	- 'Webber'	MBar
§	- 'Wiltonii' ♀H4	CDul EHul EOrn MGos
	- 'Winter Blue'	LBee LRHS SLim SPer
	- 'Youngstown'	ECho EPla GKir IFFs MBar MGos SBod WFar
	- 'Yukon Belle'	CKen
N	× ***media***	see *J.* × *pfitzeriana*
§	× ***pfitzeriana***	CDul WEve
	- 'Armstrongii'	EHul
	- 'Blaauw'	see *J. chinensis* 'Blaauw'
	- 'Blue and Gold' (v)	CKen ECho EHul MBar
	- 'Blue Cloud'	see *J. virginiana* 'Blue Cloud'
§	- 'Carbery Gold'	CBcs CDoC CDul CMac CSBt ECho EHul EPla GKir LBee LRHS MAsh MBar MGos NHol SCoo SLim SPoG WEve WFar
	- 'Daub's Frosted' **new**	SLim
	- 'Gold Coast'	CDoC CKen CSBt ECho EHul EPfP LBee LRHS MAsh MBar MBri MGos NHol NLar SLim SPer WDin WEve
	- Gold Sovereign = 'Blound' PBR	GKir LBee MAsh MGos NHol
*	- 'Golden Joy'	LRHS SCoo SLim SPoG
	- 'Golden Saucer'	MBar MBri SCoo
	- 'Goldkissen'	MGos NLar
	- 'King of Spring' **new**	SLim
§	- 'Kuriwao Gold'	CMac EHul GKir MBar MGos NHol NLar SCoo SEND STre WFar
	- 'Milky Way' (v)	SCoo
	- 'Mint Julep'	CSBt ECho EHul GKir LRHS MBar MGos NBlu SCoo SLim SPer WDin WEve WFar WMoo
	- 'Mordigan Gold'	WEve
	- 'Old Gold' ♀H4	CKen ECho EHul EPfP LBee MBar MGos NBlu NEgg NHol

		NWea SBch SCoo SLim SPer SPlb SPoG SRms WDin WEve WFar
	- 'Old Gold Carbery'	see *J.* × *pfitzeriana* 'Carbery Gold'
	- 'Pfitzeriana'	see *J.* × *pfitzeriana* 'Wilhelm Pfitzer'
	- 'Pfitzeriana Aurea'	ECho EHul EPfP GKir MBar MGos NBlu NWea WDin WEve WFar
	- 'Pfitzeriana Compacta' 𝕐H4	EHul MBar SCoo
	- 'Pfitzeriana Glauca'	EHul MBar SCoo
	- 'Richeson'	MBar
	- 'Silver Cascade'	EHul
§	- 'Sulphur Spray' 𝕐H4	CSBt CWib ECho EHul EOrn EPla GKir LAst LRHS MAsh MBar MGos MMuc NHol SEND SLim SPer SRms WBVN WCFE WDin WEve WFar WMoo
§	- 'Wilhelm Pfitzer'	EHul EPfP MBar NWea
§	***pingii*** 'Glassell'	CDoC ECho GKir MBar NLar
§	- 'Pygmaea'	ECho EOrn MBar
§	- var. ***wilsonii***	CDoC CKen ECho EOrn GGar MBar
	procumbens 'Bonin Isles'	LRHS SLim SPoG
	- 'Nana' 𝕐H4	CDoC CKen CMac CSBt ECho EHul EOrn EPfP LAst LBee LRHS MAsh MBar MGos NEgg NHol SCoo SLim SPoG WCFE WDin WEve WFar
	recurva	CDoC GKir
	- 'Castlewellan'	CDoC EOrn MGos NLar
	- var. ***coxii***	CDoC CMac ECho EHul EOrn GGGa GKir MBar MGos NHol SRms WCFE
§	- 'Densa'	CDoC CKen ECho EHul EOrn MBar NHol
	- 'Embley Park'	EHul MBar
	- 'Nana'	see *J. recurva* 'Densa'
	rigida	CMen EHul GKir MBar NLar
§	- subsp. ***conferta***	CMac GKir IFFs LBee LRHS MBar SEND SLim SPoG STre WEve
	- - 'All Gold' **new**	SLim
*	- - 'Blue Ice'	CKen EOrn LRHS WFar
	- - 'Blue Pacific'	ECho EHul GKir MBar NLar WFar
	- - 'Blue Tosho'	ECho GKir LRHS NLar SLim SPoG
	- - 'Emerald Sea'	EHul
	- - 'Schlager'	SLim
	- - 'Silver Mist'	CKen
	sabina	NWea
§	- 'Blaue Donau'	ECho EHul MBar WEve
	- Blue Danube	see *J. sabina* 'Blaue Donau'
	- 'Broadmoor'	EHul
	- 'Buffalo'	EHul
	- Cupressifolia Group	MBar
	- 'Hicksii'	MBar
	- 'Knap Hill'	see *J.* × *pfitzeriana* 'Wilhelm Pfitzer'
	- 'Mountaineer'	see *J. scopulorum* 'Mountaineer'
	- 'Rockery Gem'	EHul EOrn LRHS SLim SPoG WGor
	- 'Skandia'	CKen
	- 'Tamariscifolia'	CBcs CWib ECrN EHul LBee LRHS MAsh MBar MGos NBlu NWea SEND SLim SPer SPoG WCFE WDin WEve WFar
	- 'Tripartita'	see *J. virginiana* 'Tripartita'
	- 'Variegata' (v)	ECho EHul MBar
	sargentii	see *J. chinensis* var. *sargentii*
	scopulorum	CKen MBar
	- 'Blue Arrow'	CDoC CDul CKen CSBt CWib ECho ECrN ELan EPfP GKir LAst LBee LRHS MAsh MBar MBri MGos NEgg NHol NPCo SCoo SLim SPer WBor WDin WEve WFar
	- 'Blue Banff'	CKen
	- 'Blue Heaven'	EHul MBar SRms
	- 'Blue Pyramid'	EHul
	- 'Boothman'	EHul
	- 'Moonglow'	EHul MBar
§	- 'Mountaineer'	EHul
	- 'Mrs Marriage'	CKen
	- 'Repens'	MBar MGos
	- 'Silver Star' (v)	EHul MBar MGos
	- 'Skyrocket'	Widely available
	- 'Springbank'	EHul MBar WCFE
	- 'Tabletop'	MBar
	- 'Wichita Blue'	EHul EPfP WEve
§	***squamata***	WBVN
	- 'Blue Carpet' 𝕐H4	Widely available
	- 'Blue Spider'	CKen LRHS MBar SCoo SLim
	- 'Blue Star' 𝕐H4	Widely available
	- 'Blue Star Variegated'	see *J. squamata* 'Golden Flame'
	- 'Blue Swede'	see *J. squamata* 'Hunnetorp'
	- 'Chinese Silver'	EHul LRHS MBar SLim
	- 'Dream Joy'	CKen LRHS NHol SCoo SLim SPoG
	- var. ***fargesii***	see *J. squamata*
	- 'Filborna'	CKen LBee MBar SLim
	- 'Glassell'	see *J. pingii* 'Glassell'
§	- 'Golden Flame' (v)	CKen
	- 'Holger' 𝕐H4	CDoC CDul CMac CSBt ECho EHul EPfP EPla GKir LAst LBee LRHS MAsh MBar MGos NBlu SCoo SLim SPoG WEve
§	- 'Hunnetorp'	MBar MGos NHol WEve
	- 'Loderi'	see *J. pingii* var. *wilsonii*
	- 'Meyeri'	CBcs ECho EHul GKev GKir IFFs MBar NWea SCoo STre WDin WFar
	- 'Pygmaea'	see *J. pingii* 'Pygmaea'
	- 'Wilsonii'	see *J. pingii* var. *wilsonii*
§	***taxifolia***	CDoC EOrn LBee
§	***virginiana*** 'Blue Cloud'	EHul MBar SLim WEve WGor
	- 'Burkii'	EHul
	- 'Frosty Morn'	CKen EHul MBar WFar
	- 'Glauca'	CSWP EHul NWea
	- 'Golden Spring'	CKen
	- 'Helle'	see *J. chinensis* 'Spartan'
	- 'Hetzii'	ECho EHul MBar NLar NWea WDin WFar
	- 'Hillii'	MBar
	- 'Hillspire'	EHul
	- 'Nana Compacta'	MBar
	- Silver Spreader = 'Mona'	CKen EHul SCoo
	- 'Staver'	EHul
	- 'Sulphur Spray'	see *J.* × *pfitzeriana* 'Sulphur Spray'
§	- 'Tripartita'	MBar
§	- 'Venusta'	CKen

Jussiaea see *Ludwigia*

Justicia (*Acanthaceae*)

	sp.	LSou
	aconitiflora	WHil
	aurea	ERea EShb WHil
§	***brandegeeana*** 𝕐H1	CCCN EShb LRHS MBri
	- 'Lutea'	see *J. brandegeeana* 'Yellow Queen'
	- variegated (v)	EShb
§	- 'Yellow Queen'	EShb
	campylostemon **new**	WHil
§	***carnea***	CHII CSev EBak ERea EShb MBri SMad WHil
	- 'Alba' **new**	CCCN EShb
	guttata	see *J. brandegeeana*
	'Nørgaard's Favourite'	MBri
	'Penrhosiensis'	ERea EShb
	petioloris	WHil
	subsp. ***bowiei*** **new**	
	pohliana	see *J. carnea*
	rizzinii 𝕐H1	CCCN CHII CSev ERea EShb SMad

scheidweileri **new** EShb NExo
spicigera ERea EShb
suberecta see *Dicliptera sericea*

K

Kadsura (*Schisandraceae*)

sp. CMac
japonica CBcs EShb IDee WPGP
- B&SWJ 1027 WCru
- B&SWJ 4463 from Korea WCru
- B&SWJ 11109 from Japan WCru
- 'Fukurin' (v) IArd NLar
- 'Variegata' (v) CBcs CCCN EPfP EShb LRHS SEND WSHC
- white fruit CBcs EPfP
verrucosa HWJ 664 WCru

Kaempferia (*Zingiberaceae*)

rotunda CCCN LAma

Kalanchoe (*Crassulaceae*)

beharensis ♀H1 CAbb CCCN CDTJ EShb MBri SBig
- 'Fang' CDTJ
- 'Rusty' CDTJ CSpe
blossfeldiana LRHS
daigremontiana EShb SRms STre WCor
§ ***delagoensis*** CCCN EShb LRHS STre
fedtschenkoi EShb STre
humilis **new** EShb
laciniata EShb
laetivirens **new** EShb
marmorata ♀H1 EShb
orgyalis EShb
'Partridge' LRHS STre WCot
pinnata EShb
porphyrocalyx EOHP
pubescens EShb
pumila ♀H1 EShb SBch SPet STre WEas
rhombopilosa EShb
sexangularis EShb
'Tessa' ♀H1 MBri SRms STre WCot
thyrsiflora EShb STre
- 'Bronze Sculpture' CHVG CSpe EWll
- 'Desert Flame' LRHS
tomentosa ♀H1 EShb WCom WCot WEas
tubiflora see *K. delagoensis*
'Wendy' ♀H1 LRHS

Kalimeris (*Asteraceae*)

§ ***incisa*** EBee MMuc MRav WBor WMoo WTin
- 'Alba' EBee ECha LHop NLar SSvw WFar
- 'Blue Star' EBee ECha EMil EWll LHop LRHS MWea NLar WFar WPtf
- 'Charlotte' CSam EBee EWes NBre NGby
- 'Madiva' EBee ECha LHop
* - 'Variegata' (v) NBre
integrifolia WTin
intricifolia NBre
§ ***mongolica*** CDes EBee ECha GAuc NBre WFar WPer WSHC
§ ***pinnatifida*** EBee EPPr WCot
- 'Hortensis' ECtt NBPC
§ ***yomena*** 'Shogun' (v) CEnt CMoH EBee ECha EHoe ELan EMil EPPr EPfP GBuc LRHS NBir NPri SAga SMrm SPer WCom WFar WSHC WWEG
- 'Variegata' see *K. yomena* 'Shogun'

Kalmia ✿ (*Ericaceae*)

angustifolia ♀H4 MBar SRms WDin WFar
- f. ***rubra*** ♀H4 CBcs CDoC CDul EBee ELan EPfP LRHS MAsh MGos NDlv NLar NPri SBch SPer SPoG SReu SRot WBrE WFar WPat WSpi
latifolia ♀H4 CBcs CEnd CTrG EBee ELan EMil EPfP IMon LSou MBar MGos MMuc NPri NWea SPer SSpi SSta SWvt WDin WFar WSpi
- 'Alpine Pink' SRot WSpi
- 'Bigboy' **new** GGGa
- 'Carousel' ECho EPfP GGGa MGos NDlv NLar WFar WGob
- 'Elf' CEnd ECho LRHS MAsh MGos MLea MPkF NLar SLim WFar
- 'Freckles' ♀H4 ECho ELan EPfP GGGa LRHS MAsh NDlv NPCo SPoG WFar
- 'Fresca' ECho NPCo WGob
- 'Galaxy' GGGa
- 'Keepsake' GGGa
- 'Little Linda' ♀H4 ECho GGGa LRHS NDlv
- 'Madeline' **new** GGGa
- 'Minuet' CBcs CDoC CDul CEnd CWSG EBee ECho EPfP GGGa GKev ISea LRHS MAsh MGos MLea MMuc MPkF NDlv NPCo SLim SPoG SSpi SWvt WBrE WFar
- 'Mitternacht' **new** GGGa
- f. ***myrtifolia*** ECho MLea WFar WGob
- 'Nancy' WFar
- 'Olympic Fire' ♀H4 CEnd EBee EPfP GGGa MGos MPkF MRav NHol NLar SLim
- 'Ostbo Red' CBcs CDoC CDul CMac EBee ECho EPfP ISea LRHS MAsh MGos MLea MPkF NDlv NPCo SPer SPoG SReu SSpi SSta SWvt WFar
- 'Peppermint' EBee GGGa SLim
- 'Pink Charm' ♀H4 ECho
- 'Pink Frost' ECho NLar NPCo WFar
- 'Pinwheel' CEnd MPkF NLar SLim
- 'Quinnipiac' MPkF
- 'Raspberry Glow' GGGa
- 'Richard Jaynes' ECho MLea WFar
- 'Sarah' ECho LRHS MAsh NPCo SSpi
- 'Snowdrift' ECho GKev LRHS MAsh NDlv NLar WFar
polifolia CBcs EBee ECho GKev MBar NLAp NMen SPer WPat WThu
- var. ***compacta*** WSHC
- f. ***leucantha*** NLAp NMen WPat WThu

Kalmia × *Rhododendron* (*Ericaceae*)

***K. latifolia* × *R. williamsianum*,** 'Everlasting' see *Rhododendron* 'Everlasting'

× *Kalmiothamnus* (*Ericaceae*)

ornithomma 'Cosdon' WAbe WThu
- 'Haytor' WAbe

Kalopanax (*Araliaceae*)

pictus see *K. septemlobus*
§ ***septemlobus*** CBcs CDul ELan EPfP GBin NLar WBVN
- subsp. ***lutchuensis*** B&SWJ 5947 WCru
- f. ***maximowiczii*** CDoC EPfP MBlu NLar

Keiskea (*Lamiaceae*)

japonica EBee

Kelseya (*Rosaceae*)

uniflora	WAbe

Kennedia (*Papilionaceae*)

coccinea	CCCN WSHC
nigricans	CBcs CCCN ERea EShb
prostrata	SPlb
rubicunda	CCCN CRHN ERea

Kentia (*Arecaceae*)

belmoreana	see *Howea belmoreana*
forsteriana	see *Howea forsteriana*

Kentranthus see *Centranthus*

Kerria (*Rosaceae*)

japonica misapplied single	see *K. japonica* 'Simplex'
japonica (d)	see *K. japonica* 'Pleniflora'
- 'Albescens'	CBot WFar
- 'Golden Guinea' ♀H4	CPLG CWSG EBee ECtt ELan EPfP GGal IFro LRHS MAsh MGos MNrw MRav MSwo SBch SCoo SPer SRms SWal SWvt WDin WFar
§ - 'Picta' (v)	CDul CWib EBee ECrN ELan EPfP LAst LRHS MBar MGos MRav MSwo SBch SGar SLim SLon SPer SPoG SRms WDin WFar WSHC
§ - 'Pleniflora' (d) ♀H4	Widely available
§ - 'Simplex'	CMac CPLG CSBt GGal NWea WDin WFar
- 'Variegata'	see *K. japonica* 'Picta'

Khadia (*Aizoaceae*)

acutipetala	CCCN LRHS

Kirengeshoma (*Hydrangeaceae*)

palmata ♀H4	Widely available
- Koreana Group	CFir CLAP CPLG CSpe EBee EHrv ELan EPPr EPfP GBuc GCal IPot LAst LRHS MDun MRav NBPC NBid NBir NHol SMad SPer WCot WCru WFar WGwG WHil WPnP WWEG

Kitagawia (*Apiaceae*)

§ ***litoralis***	EBee

Kitaibela (*Malvaceae*)

vitifolia	CPLG CSpe EBee EDAr ELan GCal NBid SDnm SEND SGSe SGar SPav SPlb WKif WPer

Kitchingia see *Kalanchoe*

kiwi fruit see *Actinidia deliciosa*

Kleinia (*Asteraceae*)

articulata	see *Senecio articulatus*
grantii	EShb
repens	see *Senecio serpens*
senecioides	WEas
stapeliiformis ♀H1	EShb

Knautia (*Dipsacaceae*)

§ ***arvensis***	CArn CHll CMac CRWN EBWF EPfP MHer MNHC NLan NLar NMir NPri NSco SECG SEND SGSe SPer WFar WHer WMoo WSFF
- 'Rachael'	CElw
dipsacifolia	SHar
* 'Gracelema'	SEND
§ ***macedonica***	Widely available
- 'Crimson Cushion'	CSpe ECtt GAbr LSou MBNS NPri SMrm SPav WCot WFar
- 'Mars Midget'	CHll CSam EBee EGoo ELan EPfP EShb ETod GQue LAst LBMP LRHS LSRN LSou MGos NBPC NLar SAga SHGN SPoG SUsu SWvt WFar WHoo WSHC WWEG
- Melton pastels	COlW EBee EGoo EPfP EShb GJos LBMP LLWG LRHS LSRN LSou MCot MGos NBPC NCob NPer SPav SPet SRot SWat SWvt WClo WFar WWEG
- pink-flowered	CSam WCom
- 'Red Knight'	EPfP LRHS MCot MSCN SGSe
- red-flowered	CWib NCob
- short	ECtt EHrv LLWG NCob SPad STes
- tall, pale-flowered	SPhx
sarajevensis	EBee MAvo SUsu
§ ***tatarica***	NBre

Knightia (*Proteaceae*)

excelsa	CBcs CWit

Kniphofia ✿ (*Asphodelaceae*)

'Ada'	CMdw EBla EBrs EWTr EWes LRHS MBel SGSe SMrm
albescens	CAbb SGar
'Alcazar'	CBcs CDes CElw EBee EBla ECrN ECtt EPfP LPio LSRN MBri MHer NPri SBch SGSe SPer SPoG SWvt WBrE WCot WFar WMnd WPGP WSpi
'Amber'	NBre
'Ample Dwarf' **new**	WCot
'Amsterdam'	MWat SHar
angustifolia	SPlb
'Apricot'	EPla LRHS
'Apricot Souffle'	SGSe SMrm WCot WPGP
'Atlanta'	SBch SGSe
'Barton Fever'	WCot
baurii	MSpe
'Beauty of Wexford'	EBla
'Bees' Flame'	EBee
'Bees' Jubilee' **new**	WHoo
'Bees' Lemon'	Widely available
'Bees' Sunset' ♀H4	CAby CAvo CDes EBee GBuc GCra LPla MNrw SGSe SMrm SUsu WCot WPGP WPrP WSpi WWEG
'Bees' Yellow' **new**	WCAu
* ***bicolor***	EBee ECtt MSpe NSti WPrP
'Bitter Chocolate' **new**	WCot
'Bob's Choice' **new**	WCot
'Border Ballet'	EDAr LBMP LHop LRHS MNHC NBir NBre NBro NLar SWat WFar
brachystachya	CPou ELon GAbr GBin GCal GGar SPlb WCot
'Bressingham Comet'	EBla EBrs ECtt GKir LRHS MAvo MBri MRav NBir SRms WPGP
'Bressingham Gleam'	EBrs LRHS WCot
Bressingham hybrids	GKir IFoB
Bressingham Sunbeam = 'Bresun'	EBee EBla EBrs LRHS NBir SMrm WCot WWEG
'Bressingham Yellow' **new**	EBee
Bridgemere hybrids	WFar
'Brimstone' ♀H4	Widely available
bruceae	CPou
buchananii	CDes
'Buttercup' ♀H4	CAvo LSRN WSHC WSpi WTin
'C.M. Prichard' misapplied	see *K. rooperi*
'C.M. Prichard' Prichard	EBee WCot
'Candlelight'	CDes CMdw COlW EBee ECtt LPio NBre SDys SGSe SUsu WPGP

'Candlemass'	EBee LPio SBch
caulescens 🏆H3-4	Widely available
- 'Coral Breakers'	EBee ECGP ECtt GBin LRHS NEgg SBch SDix SPer WCot
- early-flowering **new**	LRHS
- from John May	CKno ECtt LRHS NLar SPoG WCot
- short	ECha
'Chichi' **new**	WCot
citrina	CFir EBee EDAr EPfP GCra LAst LRHS MBrN NBre NChi NLar NPri WCot WHil
'Cobra'	EBla EBrs GBin LRHS MRav NBhm NLar SBch SUsu WCot WHil
'Comet'	ECtt
'Coral Flame' **new**	LRHS
'Coral Sceptre' **new**	WCot
'Corallina'	EBee WFar
'Dingaan'	CAbb CPou CSam EBee ECtt EPPr GBin GMac GQue LFur MAvo MNrw NBir NEgg NPri SAga SDnm SPav WBrk WCot WFar
'Dorset Sentry'	CAbP CAbb CMdw EBee EBla ECtt ELon GAbr GBuc GCal LAst LPio LRHS MBel MCot MNrw MSpe NBir NCGa NEgg NLar NOrc SAga SBch SGSe WCAu WCot WFar WWEG
'Dropmore Apricot'	SPav
'Drummore Apricot'	CMHG EAEE EBee ECha ELan GBuc GCal GKir LAst LRHS LSRN LSou MBel MRav MSpe NBir NEgg NSti SAga SDnm WCot WFar WPGP WPrP WPtf
I 'Earliest of All'	EBee GMac
'Early Buttercup'	EBee MRav SBch WCot WFar
ensifolia	CPou ECtt NGdn SRms WMnd
'Ernest Mitchell'	EBee MRav WCot
Express hybrids	NBre NLar
'Fairyland'	ECGP LRHS NGBl WBrk WFar WTin
fibrosa	CFir
'Fiery Fred'	EBla EBrs ELan LRHS MRav NBre SBch SGSe SMrm WCot
'First Sunrise' PBR	EBee EWll
'Flamenco'	CChe CFwr COlW CWan EBee EDAr EWll GKir LRHS NBre NGdn NWsh SBch SMac SPet WRHF WWEG
'Flaming Torch'	ECha
foliosa	GCal SMrm
'Frances Victoria'	WCot
galpinii misapplied	see *K. triangularis* subsp. *triangularis*
galpinii ambig.	WCAu WWEG
galpinii Baker 🏆H4	CBot EBee MAvo MRav NBre SRms
'Gilt Bronze'	EBee LFur WCot
'Gladness'	ECtt LFur MRav NBir NBre NSti SGSe WCot WPrP WWEG
'Goldelse'	NBir WCot
'Goldfinch'	CMdw CSam MRav SGSe SUsu
gracilis	LEdu
'Green and Cream'	MNrw
'Green Goddess' **new**	SGSe
'Green Jade'	CBct CFir CMdw CRow CSpe EBee EBla ECha ECtt ELan EPfP EWTr GBBs LPio LRHS MMuc MRav MWte NBir NLar NSti SEND SGSe SGar SPer WCAu WCot WFar WTin WWEG
'Green Lemon'	NBre
'H.E. Beale'	GCal SMrm WCot
'Hen and Chickens'	WCot
hirsuta	CFir CSam EBee EShb GBin LPio LRHS SPad WCot WSHC
- JCA 3.461.900	WCot
- 'Traffic Lights'	EWll LRHS NBhm
'Hollard's Gold'	WCot
'Ice Queen'	CAvo CFir CPar CSev EBee ECha ECtt ELon EPPr LAst LPio MAvo MMuc MRav NCGa NChi NGdn SBch SEND SGSe SMad SSvw SWvt WBrE WCAu WCot WTin WWEG
ichopensis	CDes GBuc WPGP
'Incandesce' **new**	WCot
'Ingénue'	WCot
'Innocence'	EBla EBrs LRHS NBre SMrm
'Jane Henry'	CDes EBee MAvo WPGP
'Jenny Bloom'	Widely available
'John Benary'	CHar CMac CPou EBee EBla ECtt GAbr GBBs GMaP IGor IKil LLWG LPio LRHS LSou MAvo MBel MSpe NBir NEgg NGdn SBch SMrm SPer SPoG WCot WFar WKif WTin WWEG
'Johnathan'	WCot
laxiflora	CPou EBee WPGP
'Lemon Ice'	EBee WCot
'Light of the World'	see *K. triangularis* subsp. *triangularis* 'Light of the World'
linearifolia	CPou CTrC GCra GGar MAvo MBel MNrw SGSe SGar SPlb WCot
'Little Elf'	SDys WSHC
'Little Maid'	Widely available
littoralis	SGSe
'Lord Roberts'	ECha GCal LPio MRav SBch SDix SGSe SMad SPav WCot
'Luna'	SMrm WCot
macowanii	see *K. triangularis* subsp. *triangularis*
'Maid of Orleans'	CRow WCot
'Mermaiden'	CMHG CRow CSam EBee ECtt LAst LSou MAvo MNrw NCob WCot WFar
'Minister Verschuur'	EBee EBla EBrs GQue LRHS MBri NBre WCAu WFar WMnd WSpi
'Modesta'	WPGP
'Moonstone' **new**	WCot
'Mount Etna'	EBee SMrm WCot WPGP
multiflora	ECtt WCot
'Nancy's Red'	Widely available
nelsonii Mast.	see *K. triangularis* subsp. *triangularis*
'New England' **new**	EBee
'Nobilis'	see *K. uvaria* 'Nobilis'
northiae 🏆H4	Widely available
- JCA 3.462.600	WCot
'November Glory'	WCot WPnP
'Old Court Seedling'	EBee GGal SGSe WCot
'Orange Torch'	CPou
'Painted Lady'	CAbP CAvo CSam CTri EBee ECGP ECtt EPfP GAbr GMaP GMac MBri MNFA MRav MSpe NPri WBrk WCot WPrP WRHF
pauciflora	CBro ERos SDys WCot WPrP
'Percy's Pride'	Widely available
'Pfitzeri'	SRms
× ***praecox***	MAvo SGSe SGar WCFE WCot
'Primulina' Bloom	CPou EBrs LRHS
'Prince Igor' misapplied	see *K. uvaria* 'Nobilis'
'Prince Igor' Prichard	EBee GAbr LRHS MLHP MRav MWea NBir SGSe SMad WCot WHrl
pumila	LLHF
'Raging Inferno' **new**	WCot
'Ranelagh Gardens'	SArc
'Rich Echoes'	EBee WCot
ritualis	EDAr LSou NLar WPGP

§	***rooperi*** ♀H4	Widely available
	- 'Cally Giant'	GCal
	- 'Cally Torch'	GCal
I	- 'Torchlight'	CAbb CPne
	'Royal Castle'	CFwr LRHS MHav MRav NBir NOrc WFar WWEG
	'Royal Standard' ♀H4	CBcs CMac EBee EBla ELan EPfP EShb LAst LRHS LSRN MCot MNrw MRav NLar SBch SPer SPoG SRms SWvt WCot WFar WMnd WSpi WWEG
	rufa	CPou MSpe SMrm SUsu
	- CD&R 1032	SGar
	'Safranvogel'	EBee LRHS MAvo SGSe SMad WCot
	'Samuel's Sensation' ♀H4	CFir EBla EBrs ELan LFur LRHS MRav NLar SGSe SMrm SRGP WWEG
	sarmentosa	EBee MAvo MSpe SGSe SGar SPlb WCot WPGP
	'September Sunshine'	MRav
	'Sherbet Lemon'	CHid EBee ECtt EPPr GQue LFur MBel MNrw SMrm STes WBrk WCot
	'Shining Sceptre'	CSam EBee EBrs ECha ECtt LPla LRHS MRav MWat MWte NLar SBch SGSe SGar SMad SMrm SSvw SWvt WAul WEas WWEG
	'Springtime'	WCot
	'Star of Baden Baden'	MMuc NBir SEND SMad WCot WWEG
	'Strawberries and Cream'	CAvo CBcs CFir CMoH COIW CPen CWCL EBee EBla ECha EPfP GQue LAst LPio SAga SBch SMrm SPer WCot
	stricta	WCot
	'Sunbeam'	NBir
	'Sunningdale Yellow' ♀H4	CDes CMdw COIW EBee EBla ECha EHrv EPfP GMaP MLHP MWat MWte SMrm SRms WCot WEas WHoo WPGP WWEG
	'Tawny King'	Widely available
	'Tetbury Torch'PBR	EAEE EBee EBla ECtt LHop LRHS MBNS MSpe NCGa SGSe SMrm WAul WClo WWEG
	thomsonii	GCal MAvo
	- var. ***snowdenii*** misapplied	see *K. thomsonii* var. *thomsonii*
	- var. ***snowdenii*** ambig.	SMad WPGP
§	- var. ***thomsonii***	CBot CDes CEnt CFir ECGP LPio SUsu WCot WHal WWlt
	'Timothy'	Widely available
	'Toffee Nosed' ♀H4	Widely available
	'Torchbearer'	NBre WCot WFar
	'Torchlight' **new**	SGSe
	triangularis	CPrp EPfP EShb LRHS MBNS WFar
§	- subsp. ***triangularis***	CBro CMac COIW EBee EPfP GBuc GCal LAst LRHS LSRN MRav SMrm SRms SWat WBrE WCot
§	- - 'Light of the World'	CBcs CDes CHar CMac CSpe EBee ECtt EHrv GAbr LAst LPio LSou NBPC NBir NLar SGSe SMrm SPav SRms SUsu SWvt WBrk WCot WFar WGwG
	'Tubergeniana'	WCot
	'Tuckii'	SRms
	typhoides	NBir
	tysonii	SPlb
	uvaria	CPou CTrC EBrs LRHS NBir NVic SPer SRms WCot WMnd WPnP
	- 'Grandiflora'	MWhi SBch WFar WSpi
§	- 'Nobilis' ♀H4	Widely available
	'Vanilla'	CFir EBee LAst LRHS LSRN MAvo MRav NGdn NLar SBch SGSe SMrm WAul WCAu WWEG
	'Vesta'	LRHS
	'Victoria'	LRHS SGSe
	'Vincent Lepage'	EBee NBhm NLar
	'Wol's Red Seedling'	CAby CAvo CBct CEnt CFir CSam EBee EBla ECtt ELon GAbr LSou MAvo NBPC NCGa NEgg SBch SPoG SUsu WCot WGwG WRHF WWlt
	'Wrexham Buttercup'	CMac CSam EBee EBla ECrN ECtt ELan EPfP GAbr GMaP GMac GQue IPot LSRN MAvo MBel MCot MNFA MRav SBch SGSe SMrm SUsu WCot WHal WPrP WSpi WWEG
	'Yellow Fire' **new**	EBee
	'Yellowhammer'	CSam EBee MMuc NBre SEND WFar WPrP
	'Zululandii'	WCot WHil

Knowltonia (*Ranunculaceae*)

	filia	CPLG

Koeleria (*Poaceae*)

	cristata	see *K. macrantha*
	glauca	Widely available
§	***macrantha***	GFor NBre NLar
	vallesiana	EBee EHoe

Koelreuteria (*Sapindaceae*)

	bipinnata	CMCN LEdu
	paniculata ♀H4	Widely available
	- 'Coral Sun'PBR	CGHE MBlu MBri NLar WPGP WPat
	- 'Fastigiata'	CMCN EBee EPfP LRHS MBlu MBri SCoo SSpi WHar
	- 'Rosseels'	MGos NLar
	- 'September'	MBlu MBri

Kohleria (*Gesneriaceae*)

	'Clytie'	MBri
	'Cybele'	EABi WDib
	'Dark Velvet'	WDib
	eriantha ♀H1	CDoC EShb MBri WDib
	hirsuta	WDib
	'Jester' ♀H1	EABi WDib
	'Marquis de Sade'	EABi
	'Red Ryder'	EABi
	'Ruby Red'	WDib
	'Strawberry Fields' ♀H1	MBri
§	'Sunrise'PBR	LRHS WDib
	'Sunshine'PBR	see *K.* 'Sunrise'
	warscewiczii ♀H1	EABi WDib

Kolkwitzia (*Caprifoliaceae*)

	amabilis	CPLG CSBt CTri ECGP ELan EPfP GKir GQue MGan MGos MMuc NWea SPlb SRms WCFE WClo WDin WHar WMoo WRHF
	- 'Maradco'	CMac CPMA EBee EPfP MRav NLar NPro SCoo SSta WPat WSpi
	- 'Pink Cloud' ♀H4	Widely available

kumquat see *Fortunella*

Kunzea (*Myrtaceae*)

	ambigua	EBee ECou SPlb
	- pink-flowered	ECou
	- prostrate	ECou
	baxteri	ECou
	ericifolia	SPlb
§	***ericoides***	CTsd ECou GGar
	- 'Auckland'	ECou
	- 'Bemm'	ECou
	parvifolia	ECou
	pomifera	ECou

L

Lablab (*Papilionaceae*)

§	***purpureus***	LSou
	- 'Ruby Moon'	CSpe

+ *Laburnocytisus* (*Papilionaceae*)

	'Adamii'	CDul CLnd CMac CPMA EBee ECrN ELan EMil EPfP LAst LSRN MBlu MGos MRav NLar SMHT SMad SPer

Laburnum ✿ (*Papilionaceae*)

	alpinum	EPfP GGar NWea SPlb
	- 'Pendulum'	CDoC CDul CLnd EBee ELan EMil EPfP GKir LRHS LSRN MAsh MBar MBri MGos MRav NEgg SCrf SLim SPer SPoG
§	***anagyroides***	CDul CWib ECrN EMac GKir ISea LMaj MMuc NMun NWea SEND SRms WBVN WDin
	- var. ***alschingeri***	MGos
	- 'Aureum'	GKir
	vulgare	see *L. anagyroides*
I	× ***watereri*** 'Fastigata'	ECrN
	- 'Vossii' ♀H4	Widely available

Lachenalia (*Hyacinthaceae*)

	algoensis	ECho
§	***aloides***	CBow CGrW CStu EBrs ECho MBri NMen
	- var. ***aurea*** ♀H1	EBrs ECho SBch WCot
I	- var. ***luteola***	ECho
	- 'Nelsonii'	ECho WCot
	- 'Pearsonii'	CBgR EBrs ECho
	- var. ***quadricolor*** ♀H1	CBgR CGrW EBrs ECho IHer WCot
	attenuata	ECho
	barkeriana new	ECho
	bolusii new	ECho
§	***bulbifera*** ♀H1	CBgR EBrs ECho MBri
	- 'George' ♀H1	ECho
	capensis new	ECho
	contaminata ♀H1	CBgR EBrs ECho WCot
	doleritica new	ECho
	elegans	EBrs ECho
	fistulosa new	ECho
	framesii	ECho
	'Fransie'PBR	EBrs ECho
	gillettii	EBrs ECho
	glaucophylla new	ECho
	hirta	EBrs ECho
	juncifolia	EBrs ECho
	lactosa new	ECho
	latimerae	ECho
	'Lemon Ripple'	WCot
	liliiflora	CGrW EBrs ECho
	longibracteata new	ECho
	mathewsii	ECho
	maximilianii	EBrs
	mediana	CBgR EBrs ECho
	montana	EBrs ECho
	multifolia new	ECho
	mutabilis	EBrs ECho WCot
	'Namakwa' (African Beauty Series)	EBrs ECho
	namaquensis	EBrs ECho
	namibiensis	EBrs ECho
	nardoubergensis new	ECho
	neilii	ECho
	nervosa new	ECho
	'Nova'	EBrs
	obscura	ECho
	orchioides var. ***glaucina***	ECho WCot
	orthopetala	EBrs ECho WCot
	pallida	EBrs ECho
	pendula	see *L. bulbifera*
	polyphylla new	ECho
	pusilla	ECho
	pustulata ♀H1	EBrs ECho WCot
	- blue-flowered	CGrW EBrs ECho
	- yellow-flowered	EBrs ECho
	reflexa	EBrs ECho WCot
	'Robijn'	CGrW EBrs ECho SBch WCot
	'Rolina'	EBrs ECho
	'Romaud'	EBrs ECho WCot
	'Romelia'PBR	EBrs ECho WCot
	'Ronina' (African Beauty Series)	EBrs ECho WCot
	'Rosabeth'	EBrs WCot
	rosea	ECho
	rubida	CBgR EBrs ECho WCot
	'Rupert' (African Beauty Series)	CGrW EBrs ECho SBch WCot
	splendida	ECho
	stayneri new	CLak
	thomasiae	EBrs ECho
	trichophylla new	ECho
	tricolor	see *L. aloides*
	unicolor	ECho WCot
	unifolia	EBrs ECho
	violacea	EBrs ECho WCot
	- var. ***glauca*** new	ECho
	viridiflora ♀H1	ECho SBch WCot
	xerophila new	ECho
	zebrina new	ECho
	zeyheri	ECho WCot

Lactuca (*Asteraceae*)

	alpina	see *Cicerbita alpina*
	lessertiana	EBee
	perennis	CSpe CWan EBee EHoe EPPr LRHS MTho NLar WCot WHer WHrl
	tenerrima	WCot
	virosa	CArn

Lagarosiphon (*Hydrocharitaceae*)

§	***major***	CBen EHon EMFW EPfP MSKA WMAq WPnP

Lagarostrobos (*Podocarpaceae*)

§	***franklinii***	CDoC CTrG STre
	- 'Fota' (f)	WThu
	- 'Picton Castle' (m)	WThu

Lagerstroemia (*Lythraceae*)

	indica ♀H1	CCCN CMen EGxp EPfP ERom EShb LRHS SHGN SPlb WSHC
	- 'Berlingot Menthe' new	IFFs SEND
	- Little Chief hybrids	EShb
	- 'Red Imperator'	SEND
	- 'Rosea'	CBcs SEND

Lagunaria (*Malvaceae*)

	patersonii	CHll WPGP

Lagurus (*Poaceae*)

	ovatus ♀H3	CHrt CKno CWCL EGoo EHoe GJos NGBl SBch SEND

Lamiastrum see *Lamium*

Lamium ✿ (*Lamiaceae*)

album	CArn EBWF NMir
- 'Friday' (v)	CBow NBir WHer WWEG
armenum	LFur
flexuosum	EPPr
§ ***galeobdolon***	CArn CTri CWib EBWF MHer NSco SRms WAlt WHer
- 'Dark Angel'	WAlt
- 'Hermann's Pride'	EBee ECtt EHoe EPfP GKir GMaP LBMP LRHS MAvo MNFA NBir NBlu NCob NMir SAga SMad SMrm SPer SRms SWvt WAul WFar WHoo WMoo WWEG
- 'Kirkcudbright Dwarf'	EBee EWes GBin NBre
§ - subsp. ***montanum*** 'Florentinum' (v)	CMac CSBt CWan EBee ECha EPfP GKir MMuc MRav WCAu WFar WPer WWEG
§ - 'Silberteppich'	ECha ELan MRav MTho
- Silver Carpet	see *L. galeobdolon* 'Silberteppich'
- 'Variegatum'	see *L. galeobdolon* subsp. *montanum* 'Florentinum'
garganicum	WSpi
- subsp. ***garganicum***	CPom EWes LPla WPer
luteum	see *L. galeobdolon*
maculatum	CArn EGoo EPot NChi SEND SRms WClo WFar
- 'Album'	EBee ELan EPfP LBMP LRHS SHar SPer SRms WCFE
- 'Anne Greenaway' (v)	CBow EBee EWes SPet WWEG
§ - 'Aureum'	CArn ECha EGoo EHoe ELan MTho SMrm SPet SWvt WFar WPer
- 'Beacon Silver'	Widely available
- 'Beedham's White'	EBee NBir
- 'Brightstone Pearl'	EGoo EWes MAvo
- 'Cannon's Gold'	EBee ECtt ELan EPPr EWes SWvt WWEG
- 'Chequers' ambig.	CMac EBee LBMP LRHS NBPC NBre SPer
- 'Elaine Franks'	CSam
- 'Elisabeth de Haas' (v)	CBow EWes NBre WWEG
- 'Forncett Lustre'	EBee EWes
- 'Forncett White Lustre'	NBre
- 'Gold Leaf'	see *L. maculatum* 'Aureum'
- Golden Anniversary = 'Dellam'[PBR] (v)	ELan LAst LSRN NBro SPoG SWvt WFar
- 'Golden Nuggets'	see *L. maculatum* 'Aureum'
- 'Ickwell Beauty' (v)	EBee WWEG
- 'James Boyd Parselle'	CBow CSam NBre WHal
- 'Margery Fish'	SRms
- 'Orchid Frost' **new**	CHid EWll
- Pink Chablis = 'Checkin' **new**	SVil
- 'Pink Nancy'	CBot CSpe EGoo GKir SWvt WCFE
- 'Pink Pearls'	CSBt LRHS NBre SHar SPet WFar WMoo WWEG
- 'Pink Pewter'	COIW EBee ECGP ECha ECtt EHoe ELan EPfP EShb GGar GMaP IFFs LBMP LRHS SPer SPlb SPoG SUsu WBrE WWEG
- 'Red Nancy'	EBee GCal SWvt
§ - 'Roseum'	CWib EBee ELan EPfP GGar GMaP LBMP LRHS MRav MWat NChi SGar SPer WCAu WPer
- 'Shell Pink'	see *L. maculatum* 'Roseum'
- 'Silver Shield'	EWes
- 'Sterling Silver'	CSam EBee GQue NBre WPer
- 'White Nancy' ♀H4	Widely available
- 'Wootton Pink'	GBuc MBri MHer NBir NLar SSvw SWvt WEas
orvala	Widely available
- 'Album'	CBod CBot CDes CLAP CPrp EBee EHrv ELan EPPr LEdu LRHS NBir NChi NLar SGar SHar SMrm WHer WPGP WPtf WTin
- pink-flowered	CLAP CSpe
- 'Silva'	CCVN CDes CLAP CSam EBee EPPr GBin IMou LEdu LRHS NBre SPoG WCot WSHC
sandrasicum	CPBP

Lampranthus (*Aizoaceae*)

sp.	EDAr WClo
aberdeenensis	see *Delosperma aberdeenense*
aurantiacus	CBcs CHEx SPet
aureus	WCor
'Bagdad'	CHEx
blandus	CBcs CCCN
'Blousey Pink'	CHEx
§ ***brownii***	CBcs CCCN EAlp ECho ELan ELon SEND SPet SPlb WPnn
coccineus	SPet
deltoides	see *Oscularia deltoides*
edulis	see *Carpobrotus edulis*
glaucus	SEND
multiradiatus	SEND
oscularis	see *Oscularia deltoides*
roseus	CCCN CHEx EAlp LRHS SPet SPoG WClo WCor
spectabilis	CBcs CCCN CTri ELon SAPC SArc SPet WBrE WCor
- 'Tresco Apricot'	CCCN
- 'Tresco Brilliant'	CCCN CHEx CStu SPet WCom
- 'Tresco Fire'	CCCN CDoC ELon LRHS
- 'Tresco Orange'	CCCN LRHS WPnn
- 'Tresco Peach'	CCCN CStu WCor
- 'Tresco Red'	CCCN ELon SEND WPnn
- white-flowered	CStu
'Sugar Pink'	CHEx

Lamprothyrsus (*Poaceae*)

hieronymi	EPPr
- RCB RA K2-2	WCot

Lantana (*Verbenaceae*)

'Aloha' (v)	LSou
camara	CArn ELan EPfP EShb MBri SRms WFar
- 'Kolibri'	LAst
- orange-flowered	CCCN
- pink-flowered	CCCN EShb
- red-flowered	CCCN
- 'Sonja'	LAst
- variegated (v)	EShb
- white-flowered	CCCN EShb
- yellow-flowered	EShb NPri
'Goldsome'	LAst
§ ***montevidensis***	EShb LAst
- RCB/Arg AA-1	WCot
* - ***alba***	EShb
sellowiana	see *L. montevidensis*

Lapageria ✿ (*Philesiaceae*)

rosea ♀H3	CBcs CCCN CPLG CPne CRHN CTsd EBee EPfP EShb GQui MDun NLar SChF WFar WPGP
- var. ***albiflora***	CRHN
- 'Avalanche' **new**	CBcs
- 'Flesh Pink'	CPLG CRHN
- 'Pink Panther' **new**	CBcs
- 'Tierra del Fuego' **new**	CBcs
- 'Torres del Paine' **new**	CBcs

Lapeirousia (*Iridaceae*)

cruenta	see *Anomatheca laxa*
divaricata	ECho
laxa	see *Anomatheca laxa*
oreogena	CStu

Lapiedra (*Amaryllidaceae*)

martinezii	ECho

Lapsana (*Asteraceae*)

communis 'Inky'	CNat WAlt

Lardizabala (*Lardizabalaceae*)

biternata	see *L. funaria*
§ ***funaria***	CTrG

Larix ✿ (*Pinaceae*)

decidua ♀H4	CBcs CCVT CDoC CDul CMen CRWN CSBt ECrN ELan EMac EPfP EWTr GKir MBar MGos MMuc NBlu NEgg NWea SPer SPlb WDin WEve WFar WMou
- 'Autumn Gold Weeping'	NHol
- 'Corley'	CKen ECho MBlu NLar SLim
- 'Croxby Broom'	CKen SLim
§ - var. ***decidua***	WFar
- 'Globus'	LRHS NHol NLar SLim
- 'Grott' new	NLar
- 'Horstmann Recurved'	ECho GKir LRHS NLar SCoo SLim SPoG
- 'Kornik' new	NLar
- 'Krejci'	MAsh NLar SLim
- 'Little Bogle'	CKen MAsh NHol NLar
- 'Oberförster Karsten'	CKen ECho NLar
- 'Pendula'	CBcs ECho WFar
- 'Puli'	CEnd ECho GKir LRHS MAsh MBlu MGos NHol NLar SCoo SLim SPer SPoG WFar
- 'Schwarzenburg' new	NLar
× ***eurolepis***	see *L.* × *marschlinsii*
europaea Lam. & DC.	see *L. decidua* var. *decidua*
europaea Middend.	see *L. sibirica*
gmelinii var. ***olgensis***	NLar
- var. ***principis-rupprechtii***	GKir
- 'Tharandt'	CKen ECho SLim
griffithii	GKir
§ ***kaempferi*** ♀H4	CCVT CDoC CDul CLnd CMen CTri ECrN ELan EMac EPfP GKir LBuc LMaj LRHS MAsh MBar NBlu NWea SCoo SLim SPer STre WDin WEve WFar WMou
- 'Bambino'	CKen
- 'Bingman'	CKen
- 'Blue Ball'	CKen NLar SLim WEve
- 'Blue Dwarf'	CKen GKir LRHS MBar MGos SCoo SLim SPoG WEve WFar
- 'Blue Haze'	CKen
- 'Blue Rabbit'	CKen CTho
- 'Blue Rabbit Weeping'	GKir LRHS MGos SCoo SLim WDin
- 'Cruwys Morchard'	CKen
- 'Cupido'	NHol SLim
- 'Diane'	CEnd CKen ECho EPfP LRHS MAsh MBar MBlu MGos NHol NLar SLim SPoG WFar
- 'Elizabeth Rehder'	CKen ECho
- 'Grant Haddow'	CKen
- 'Grey Green Dwarf'	NHol
- 'Grey Pearl'	CKen ECho EMil NLar WFar
- 'Hanna's Broom'	SLim
- 'Hobbit'	CKen
* - 'Jakobsen's Pyramid'	CDoC CMen LRHS MAsh NHol SCoo SLim SPoG WEve WFar
- 'Nana'	CKen ECho NLar SLim WFar
I - 'Nana Prostrata'	CKen
- 'Pendula'	CDul CEnd ECho ECrN EPfP MAsh MBar MBlu MGos NHol NLar SPer SPoG
- 'Peve Tunnis'	NLar
- 'Pulii'	ECho GKir
- 'Stiff Weeping'	CTri GKir LRHS MAsh MBlu NLar NPCo SCoo SLim
- 'Swallow Falls'	CKen
- 'Varley'	CKen
- 'Walter Pimven'	NLar
- 'Wehlen'	CKen
- 'Wolterdingen'	CKen ECho MBlu NLar SLim
- 'Yanus Olieslagers'	CKen
laricina 'Arethusa Bog'	CKen ECho NLar SLim
- 'Bear Swamp'	CKen SLim WFar
- 'Bingman'	CKen
- 'Hartwig Pine'	CKen ECho
- 'Newport Beauty'	CKen ECho
leptolepis	see *L. kaempferi*
§ × ***marschlinsii***	GBin GKir NWea WMou
- 'Domino'	CKen ECho SLim
- 'Gail'	CKen
- 'Julie'	CKen
russica	see *L. sibirica*
§ ***sibirica***	MBar
sukaczevii	see *L. sibirica*
'Varied Directions'	SCoo SLim

Larrea (*Zygophyllaceae*)

tridentata	CArn

Laserpitium (*Apiaceae*)

siler	CArn EBee NLar SPlb WSHC WSpi

Lasiagrostis see *Stipa*

Lasiospermum (*Asteraceae*)

bipinnatum	SPlb

Lastreopsis (*Dryopteridaceae*)

glabella	WRic
hispida	WRic
microsora	WRic

Latania (*Arecaceae*)

loddigesii	EAmu LPal
verschaffeltii	LPal

Lathyrus ✿ (*Papilionaceae*)

§ ***articulatus***	WCHb
§ ***aureus***	Widely available
- 'Cally Variegated' (v) new	GCal
azureus misapplied	see *L. sativus*
chilensis	CFir CSpe CSsd EBee LSou
chloranthus	SPav
cirrhosus	CDes EBee MPet WPGP
clymenum articulatus	see *L. articulatus*
cyaneus misapplied	see *L. vernus*
cyaneus (Steven) K.Koch	SAga
davidii	EBee EWes GCal LLHF WSHC
filiformis	WSHC
fremontii hort.	see *L. laxiflorus*
§ ***gmelinii***	EBee NLar
grandiflorus	CSev EBee NLar SSvw SWat WCom WCot
heterophyllus	CSpe EBee LRHS MNrw SGSe
incurvus	MPet
inermis	see *L. laxiflorus*

	japonicus	EBWF
	'Lamorna's Love'	WViv
	latifolius Υ^{H4}	CArn CRHN CRWN EBee EPfP GBar LAst MWat MWhi NBlu NPer SDnm SGar SPoG SRms SVic SWal WBrk WEas WFar WHer WPer
§	- 'Albus' Υ^{H4}	CBot EBee ELan SGSe SPav SRms WCom WEas
	- 'Blushing Bride'	SPav
	- deep pink-flowered	MHer NLar NSti
	- pale pink-flowered	NSti
	- Pink Pearl	see *L. latifolius* 'Rosa Perle'
	- 'Red Pearl'	ECtt ELan EPfP GAbr LRHS MBri MCot NPri SEND SPav SPer SPlb SPoG SSvw WPer
§	- 'Rosa Perle' Υ^{H4}	CBcs CTri EBee ECha ECtt EShb EWTr LBMP LHop LRHS MBri MCot MLHP MNHC MRav NBir NLar NPer NPri SGSe SPav SPer SSvw WCAu WHil WMoo WWEG
	- Weisse Perle	see *L. latifolius* 'White Pearl'
	- 'White Pearl' misapplied	see *L. latifolius* 'Albus'
§	- 'White Pearl' Υ^{H4}	ECha EPfP EShb GAbr GBuc GCal GKir LBMP LRHS MBri MCot MHer MNHC MRav MWat NBir NLar NPer NPri NSti SMad SMrm SPer SPoG SSvw WCAu WFar WPer
§	***laxiflorus***	CDes EBee MCCP MNrw MTho NChi SSvw WPGP
	linifolius	CDes NLar WPGP
	luteus (L.) Peterm.	see *L. gmelinii*
	maritimus	NLar
	montanus	GPoy
	nervosus	CSpe EBee EWes MTho SMrm SRms WCom
	neurolobus	CDes CPom
	niger	CSpe EBee GBuc LHop LRHS LSou MCot MHer MMHG NLar WFar WWEG
	odoratus	LRHS NBlu SVic
	- 'Black Prince'	CSpe
	- 'Cupani'	CHrt
	- 'Dancing Queen'	MPet
	- 'Lightening'	MPet
	- 'Mammoth Mixed' **new**	MPet
	- 'Matucana'	CSpe MWat SBch
	- Winter Elegance Series **new**	MPet
	palustris	EBee NLar
	polyphyllus	EBee MPet NSti
	pratensis	EBWF NMir NSco WSFF
	pubescens	CRHN EBee MPet
	roseus	GCal WSHC WViv
	rotundifolius Υ^{H4}	MNrw MTho SSvw WCom WFar WHoo
	- 'Tillyperone'	EPPr
§	***sativus***	CHid CSpe ECho ELan SBch WCHb
	- var. ***azureus***	see *L. sativus*
	sylvestris	CMac EBWF EBee MNrw NLar SBch SMrs WBrk
	tingitanus	CRHN WCHb
	- 'Roseus'	CRHN
	transsilvanicus	CPom LRHS
	tuberosus	EBee MNrw WCot
	'Tubro'	EBee SHar
	venetus	CPom CSsd EBee GCal MNrw MWea WSHC
§	***vernus*** Υ^{H4}	Widely available
	- 'Alboroseus' Υ^{H4}	Widely available
	- var. ***albus***	CDes CLAP ECho GMaP WPGP
	- ***aurantiacus***	see *L. aureus*
	- 'Caeruleus'	CLAP ECGP MNFA WHoo WPGP
*	- 'Cyaneus'	SAga SWat WCom
I	- 'Filifolius'	CSpe
	- 'Flaccidus'	CAby SMeo WCom WCot WTin
*	- 'Gracilis'	WViv
	- purple-flowered **new**	LRHS
	- 'Rainbow'	CLAP ELon LRHS NWCA SMrm WFar WHil WWEG
	- 'Rosenelfe'	CBot CDes CMea EBee GBuc MCot MDKP NPri SBod SMrm WCot WHal WPGP
	- f. ***roseus***	EBee ECha LRHS MRav NBir NCGa SRms
	- 'Spring Beauty'	CLAP
	- 'Spring Delight'	GKir LRHS
	- 'Spring Melody'	MRav WCot WPat

Laurelia (*Monimiaceae*)

§	***sempervirens***	CBcs CTrC EBee IDee WPGP
	serrata	see *L. sempervirens*

Laureliopsis (*Monimiaceae*)

	philippiana	EBee IDee

Laurentia see *Isotoma*

Laurus (*Lauraceae*)

§	***azorica***	CBcs
	canariensis	see *L. azorica*
	nobilis Υ^{H4}	Widely available
	- f. ***angustifolia***	CMac CSWP CTsd EOHP EPla GGal GQui MBlu MHer MRav NGHP NLar SAPC SArc SPoG WCHb WPGP
	- 'Aurea' Υ^{H4}	CBcs CDul CMac EBee ELan EPfP GQui LHop LRHS MBlu MGos NEgg SBch SLim SLon SPer SPoG SWvt WCHb WDin WFar WJek WMoo WPat
	- clipped pyramid	GKir MGos NBlu
	- 'Crispa'	MRav

Lavandula ✿ (*Lamiaceae*)

	'After Midnight'	see *L.* 'Avonview'
	'Alba'	see *L. angustifolia* 'Alba', *L.* × *intermedia* 'Alba'
	'Alba' ambig.	CSev CWib MHrb SIde SPer SWat WEas WPer
	'Alexandra'^{PBR} **new**	LRHS
	× ***allardii*** (Gaston Allard Group) 'African Pride'	GBar
§	***angustifolia***	CArn CCVT CWCL CWib EBee ELau EPfP EWTr GKir GPoy LBuc LRHS MBar MBri MGos MHer MREP MWat NPer NPri SAll SBch SLim SPlb SVic SWal WClo WFar WHil
	- 'Alba' misapplied	see *L. angustifolia* 'Blue Mountain White'
§	- 'Alba'	CChe EAro EBee EPfP GPoy LBuc LSRN MHer MRav MSwo NGHP NMen SLon SPlb WDin WFar
	- 'Alba Nana'	see *L. angustifolia* 'Nana Alba'
	- 'Arctic Snow'	CBcs CChe CEnt EAEE ENor LRHS LSRN MAvo MHrb MSwo MWat NBPC NGHP NGdn NLLv NPri SDnm SDow SIoW SPoG WLav
	- 'Ashdown Forest'	CWan GBar LRHS LSou MAsh MHer MHrb MLHP MNHC NGHP NPri SBch SDow SIde SIoW WHoo WJek WLav WRHF WSpi
	- 'Beechwood Blue' Υ^{H4}	MHrb SDow WLav
	- 'Betty's Blue'	SDow
	- Blue Cushion	EPfP LRHS LSRN MAsh SDow WFar
	= 'Lavandula Schola'^{PBR}	WLav

- 'Blue Ice' CWSG ENor LRHS LSou MGos NBPC NGHP SDow WLav
- 'Blue Mountain' GBar MHrb
§ - 'Blue Mountain White' NLLv SDow WLav
- 'Blue Rider' EWTr LRHS NGHP SWal
- 'Blue River'PBR WFar
- Blue Scent = 'Syngablusc' LRHS
- 'Bowles Grey' see *L. angustifolia* 'Bowles's Early'
- 'Bowles Variety' see *L. angustifolia* 'Bowles's Early'
§ - 'Bowles's Early' GBar NGHP SAga WFar
- 'Cedar Blue' CSev CWan EAro EGoo ELau EPfP GBar MHer NBur NGHP SBch SDow SHDw SIde SIoW WFar WLav WRHF
- 'Coconut Ice'PBR CWCL CWSG NLLv SIoW SPoG WLav WSpi
- 'Compacta' MHrb SDow WLav
- 'Crystal Lights'PBR SIoW
- 'Dwarf Blue' EPfP LSRN MBrN WFar
- 'Eastgrove Dome' WEas
- 'Elizabeth' **new** ENor NGHP SDow SPoG WLav
- 'Folgate' CArn CWCL EBee ECtt ELau EPfP GBar LSou MHer MHrb MNHC NBur NGHP SAll SDow SIde SIoW WFar WHoo WLav WMnd
- 'Fring A' MHrb SDow
- 'Garden Beauty' (v) **new** LRHS NPri
- 'Granny's Bouquet' LSRN LSou SBch SIoW WSpi
§ - 'Hidcote' ♀H4 Widely available
- 'Hidcote Pink' CEnt CWCL CWib EPfP GBar LSRN LSou MHer MNHC MRav NGHP SDow SPer SWat WFar WMnd WPer
- 'Hidcote Superior' LBMP
- 'Imperial Gem' ♀H4 Widely available
- 'Jean Davis' see *L. angustifolia* 'Rosea'
- 'Lady' CWSG NPer SBch SHDw SWal WPer
- 'Lady Ann' CWCL MHrb NLLv SDow SIoW WLav
- 'Lavenite Petite'PBR ENor EPfP LLHF LRHS LSRN MAsh MHrb NBPC NGHP NLLv NLar SDow SIoW SPoG SVil WLav
- Little Lady = 'Batlad' EBee ECtt ENor EPfP LAst LRHS LSRN MAsh MHrb MSwo MWat NBPC NGHP NLLv NLar NPri SAll SIoW WLav
- Little Lottie = 'Clarmo' ♀H4 CWCL CWSG EBee EPfP GBar LSRN MHer SCoo SDow SIde SWvt WLav WRHF
- 'Loddon Blue' ♀H4 CEnt EBee ENor EPfP GBar LRHS MHrb NGHP SDow SIde SIoW WHoo WLav
§ - 'Loddon Pink' ♀H4 CWan EBee ELan ENor EPfP GBar GMaP LAst LRHS MAsh MLHP MNHC MRav NGHP NPri WEas WFar WLav WPGP
- 'Maillette' MHrb NGHP SDow SIde SIoW SPet WLav
- 'Melissa Lilac' CBcs ENor LRHS LSRN LSou MAsh MGos MHer MHrb SDow SIoW SPoG SRkn WLav WWlt
- 'Miss Donnington' see *L. angustifolia* 'Bowles's Early'
- 'Miss Katherine'PBR ♀H4 CWCL EBee ECtt ELan ENor EPfP LHop LRHS LSRN MAsh MHrb NBPC NGHP NLar SDow SIoW SPer SPoG WLav
- Miss Muffet = 'Scholmis' ♀H4 CWCL LLHF SDow WLav
- 'Munstead' Widely available
§ - 'Nana Alba' ♀H4 CArn CMea CWan EBee ECha ELan EPfP GBar GPoy LAst LRHS MAsh MBar MHer MHrb MNHC MWat NGHP SDow SPoG SWvt WEas WHoo
- 'No 9' SDow
- 'Pacific Blue' **new** LRHS
- 'Peter Pan' CWCL ECtt LSRN MAvo MHer MHrb NGHP NGdn SBch SDow SIoW WLav
- 'Princess Blue' CSBt CWCL EAro EBee ELan ENor GBar LRHS MAsh NPri SAga SDow SIde SIoW WFar WLav WPer
- 'Rêve de Jean-Claude' WLav
§ - 'Rosea' Widely available
- 'Royal Purple' CBcs EBee ENor EWes GBar LSou MHrb NGHP SDow SIde SIoW SWvt WLav
- 'Royal Velvet' SDow
- 'Saint Jean' MHrb SDow
- 'Silver Mist' GGar
- 'Thumbelina Leigh' **new** ENor SDow
- 'Twickel Purple' CHrt CWCL CWSG EBee EPfP GKir LAst LHop LRHS LSRN MAsh MNHC MRav NGHP NPri SBch SDow SIde SPer SWat SWvt WFar WLav
- 'Walberton's Silver Edge' see *L.* × ***intermedia*** Walberton's Silver Edge
- 'Wendy Carlile' ♀H4 ENor EPfP SIoW SPoG WLav
- 'White Horse' NGHP

'Aphrodite' LRHS
aristibracteata MHer WLav
§ 'Avonview' CBcs CWCL GBar MHer NGHP SDow WHoo WLav
'Badsey Starlite' WLav
'Ballerina' CWCL MHrb SDow
§ 'Bee Brilliant'PBR LRHS NGHP SPoG WLav
§ 'Bee Cool'PBR MHer MHrb NGHP NLLv SPoG WLav
§ 'Bee Happy' CWCL NBir NGHP NLLv SHGN SPoG WLav
§ 'Bee Pretty' LRHS NGHP
'Blue Star' EBee EPfP GBar LBMP LRHS NGHP SAll WFar WGwG
'Bowers Beauty' LRHS
buchii var. ***buchii*** SDow WLav
- var. ***gracilis*** CSpe
Butterfly Garden = 'Avenue'PBR CWSG SIoW
canariensis MHer MHrb SDow SPet WCHb WLav
× ***chaytoriae*** 'Gorgeous' SDow
- 'Richard Gray' ♀H3-4 CArn EBee GBar LHop LSRN MHer MHrb MNHC NGHP SDnm SDow SSvw WAbe WLav WMnd
§ - 'Sawyers' ♀H4 Widely available
- 'Silver Sands' ENor LRHS LSRN LSou SBch SPoG
× ***christiana*** CArn GBar LRHS MHrb NGHP SBch SDow SHDw WJek WKif WLav
'Cornard Blue' see *L.* × *chaytoriae* 'Sawyers'
dentata CEnt CSev EAro EBee EShb GBar GCal MNHC MRav NGHP SGar SMrm
§ - var. ***candicans*** CSev EBee GBar MHer MHrb MNHC NLLv SAga SBch SDow WCHb WLav
- var. ***dentata*** 'Dusky Maiden' CWCL MHrb SDow WLav
- - 'Linda Ligon' (v) CBow GBar NGHP WGwG WHer WLav
- - 'Monet' NGHP
- - 'Ploughman's Blue' CWCL GBar WGwG WLav
- - f. ***rosea*** SDow WLav
- - 'Royal Crown' ♀H2-3 GBar MHer WFar WLav

	- - 'Serenity'	ENor
	- - 'Silver Queen'	WLav
	- silver-leaved	see *L. dentata* var. *candicans*
	'Devonshire Compact'	CSBt CWCL LRHS LSou MHer NGHP WJek
	'Devonshire Compact White' **new**	CWCL
	'Fathead'	CBcs CWCL EBee ECtt ELan EPfP GBar LAst LRHS LSRN LSou MAsh MHer MHrb MNHC NBir NEgg NGHP NPri SCoo SDow SIoW SLim SPet SPoG WBrE WJek
	'Fathead Light Blue' **new**	LRHS
	× ***ginginsii*** 'Goodwin Creek Grey'	CSpe MHer MHrb NLLv SDow WGwG WLav WOut
	'Hazel'	LRHS
	'Helmsdale' PBR	Widely available
	heterophylla misapplied	see *L.* × *heterophylla* Viv. Gaston Allard Group
§	***heterophylla*** Viv. Gaston Allard Group	CHrt CSev EBee GBar NGHP NLLv WLav
	'Hidcote Blue'	see *L. angustifolia* 'Hidcote'
§	× ***intermedia***	WFar
	- 'Abrialii'	CHrt GBar MHrb NLLv SDow WLav
§	- 'Alba' ♀H4	CArn CBot CMea EPfP GBar MHer MNHC SAga SDow
*	- 'Alexis'	WLav
	- 'Arabian Night'	see *L.* × *intermedia* 'Impress Purple', 'Sussex'
	- 'Chaix'	GBar
§	- Dutch Group	CArn CSBt CWan CWib EBee EPfP GBar MAsh MBar MRav MSwo SBch SCoo SDow SLim SPer SPoG SWat WFar WPer
	- 'Edelweiss'	CWan EAro EBee EPfP LRHS LSou MHrb MRav NBur NEgg NGHP NLLv SAll SDow WClo WLav
	- 'Fragrant Memories'	EBee EPfP GBar LRHS MHrb NGHP SAga SDow SIde WLav WRHF
	- Goldburg = 'Burgoldeen' (v)	CBow EPfP MCCP MGos MRav MWat NLLv SPav SPoG WLav
	- 'Grappenhall' misapplied	see *L.* × *intermedia* 'Pale Pretender'
	- 'Grey Hedge'	CWan NGHP SAga WLav WRHF
	- 'Gros Bleu'	MHrb SDow WLav
	- 'Grosso'	CArn CBcs CEnt CSev CTri EAro EBee ELan EPfP GBar GMaP LSou MHer MHrb MLHP MNHC NGHP SAll SBch SCoo SDow SIoW SPer SSvw SWvt WDin WFar WJek
	- 'Hidcote Giant' ♀H4	CArn EPfP GBar MHrb NPer SAga SDow WKif WLav
§	- 'Impress Purple'	GBar MHrb MNHC NLLv SDow WLav
	- 'Lullingstone Castle'	CBod EAro GBar NGHP SAga SDow SIoW WGwG WJek WLav
	- 'Old English' misapplied	see *L.* × *intermedia* 'Seal'
	- 'Old English'	GBar MHrb SDow WCom
	- Old English Group	CArn CBod ELau MNHC NGHP WHoo WJek WLav
§	- 'Pale Pretender'	CArn CSBt CSam CTri EBee GBar GKir LRHS LSou MHer MSwo NGHP SPer SWal WFar WMnd WPer WPnn
§	- 'Seal'	CArn CPrp EAro ELau GBar GMaP MHrb MNHC NGHP SAga SDow SPoG WFar WHCG WMnd WPer WRHF
	- 'Sumian'	WLav
§	- 'Sussex' ♀H4	GBar LRHS MHrb NGHP SDow WLav
	- 'Twickel Purple'	CArn CWSG CWib ECtt EWes LSRN NGHP SWat WJek WMnd
§	- Walberton's Silver Edge = 'Walvera' (v)	CBow CSBt ENor EShb LBuc LRHS MGos MHer MWat NEgg SBch SCoo SDow SIde SIoW SPoG
	'Jamboree' **new**	WLav
	'Jean Davis'	see *L. angustifolia* 'Rosea'
	lanata ♀H3	CBot ECha GPoy MHer MHrb NWCA WLav
§	***latifolia***	CArn NHol
I	'Lavender Lace'	CWSG LSRN NGHP SCoo
	'Loddon Pink'	see *L. angustifolia* 'Loddon Pink'
	'Madrid'	NBlu
	'Madrid Blue'	see *L.* 'Bee Happy'
	'Madrid Pink'	see *L.* 'Bee Pretty'
	'Madrid Purple' PBR	see *L.* 'Bee Brilliant'
	'Madrid White' PBR	see *L.* 'Bee Cool'
	'Marshwood' PBR	CTri EBee EPfP SCoo SDow SIde SIoW SLim
	'Mediterranean White' **new**	CHEx
	minutolii	MHrb SDow
	multifida	LDai MHer NLLv WCHb WLav
	- 'Blue Wonder'	IFro
	officinalis	see *L. angustifolia*
	'Passionné'	CWSG EBee LRHS LSou NGHP WClo WLav
§	***pedunculata*** subsp. ***pedunculata*** ♀H3-4	Widely available
	- - 'James Compton'	CWib ECha LRHS MAsh NBir
	- - 'Wine'	CBcs CHEx WLav
	- subsp. ***sampaiana*** 'Purple Emperor'	CWSG LRHS SPoG WLav
	- - 'Roman Candles'	WLav
	pinnata	CSev EPfP EShb GBar MHer MHrb MNHC SDow SPoG WCHb
	'Pippa White'	NLLv
	'Pretty Polly'	CBcs ENor LRHS LSou NBPC NGHP NLLv SDow SIoW SRkn WLav
	'Pukehou'	EPfP GBar LRHS MHrb NLLv SCoo SDow SIoW WLav
	'Regal Splendour' PBR	CSBt CWCL EBrs ECtt ELan ENor EPfP LRHS LSRN LSou MAsh MGos MHer MHrb NGHP NLLv NPri SCoo SDow SIoW SLim SPoG WLav
	'Rocky Road'	ENor LRHS LSRN MAsh MGos MHrb NBPC NGHP NLLv NPri SDow SIoW SPav SRkn WLav
	'Rosea'	see *L. angustifolia* 'Rosea'
	rotundifolia	MHer SDow
	'Roxlea Park'	CChe CWCL WLav
	'Russian Anna'	LSRN
	'Saint Brelade'	CWCL EPfP GBar LRHS NLLv SDow WLav
	'Silver Edge'	see *L.* × *intermedia* Walberton's Silver Edge
	'Somerset Mist'	WLav
N	***spica***	see *L. angustifolia*, *L.* × *intermedia*, *L. latifolia*
	- 'Hidcote Purple'	see *L. angustifolia* 'Hidcote'
	stoechas ♀H3-4	Widely available
	- var. ***albiflora***	see *L. stoechas* subsp. *stoechas* f. *leucantha*
	- 'Anouk' PBR	LRHS SPoG
	- 'Antibles' (Provençal Series) **new**	SVil
	- 'Arles' (Provençal Series) **new**	SVil
	- 'Avignon' (Provençal Series) **new**	SVil
	- (Barcelona Series) 'Barcelona Pink'	CWCL
	- - 'Barcelona Rose'	CWCL
	- - 'Barcelona White'	CWCL

- 'Blueberries and Cream'	ENor LRHS LSou NGHP
- 'Blueberry Ruffles' (Ruffles Series)	ENor SIoW
- 'Boysenberry Ruffles' (Ruffles Series)	ENor LRHS SIoW
- 'Fragrant Butterfly'	LSou
- 'Lace'	LRHS LSRN SPoG WLav
- Lilac Wings = 'Prolil'PBR	ENor EPfP LLHF LRHS LSRN NGHP SPoG WLav
- (Little Bee Series) Little Bee Lilac = 'Florvendula Lilac'	LRHS
- - Little Bee Rose = 'Florevendula Rose'	LRHS
- subsp. ***luisieri*** 'Tickled Pink'PBR	CWCL ECtt ELan NGHP SDnm SPav
- 'Madrid Rose'	NLLv
- 'Mulberry Ruffles' (Ruffles Series)	ENor SIoW
- 'Papillon'	see *L. pedunculata* subsp. *pedunculata*
- 'Peachberry Ruffles' (Ruffles Series)	ENor SIoW
- subsp. ***pedunculata***	see *L. pedunculata* subsp. *pedunculata*
- 'Purley'	CWan
- 'Raspberry Ruffles' (Ruffles Series)	ENor SIoW
§ - subsp. ***stoechas*** f. ***leucantha***	CArn CBot CSev CWCL CWan CWib ECha EPfP GBar LRHS MNHC MSwo MWat SBch SDow WAbe WCHb WClo WFar
- - - 'Snowman'	CBcs CChe CSBt EBee EGxp ENor EPfP LAst LRHS MHer MHrb MWat NBPC NGHP SBch SCoo SIoW SLim SPer SPoG SWvt WDin WFar
- - 'Liberty'	CWCL LSou NGHP NLLv SDow WLav
- - 'Provençal'	LRHS
- - 'Purple Wings'	ENor EPfP LRHS LSou SRkn
- - f. ***rosea*** 'Kew Red'	CBcs CMea CTri CWCL CWan EAro EBee ENor GGar LRHS LSRN MHer MHrb MNHC NBPC NGHP SDnm SDow SIoW SPav SPet SPoG SWvt WGwG WHil WLav
- 'Sugarberry Ruffles' (Ruffles Series)	ENor SIoW
- 'Tapestry'	CWan
- 'Victory'	LRHS SPoG
- 'With Love' **new**	LRHS
'Sugar Plum'	SHGN WLav
'Tiara'	CSBt ENor EPfP LRHS LSRN MHrb NBPC NGHP NLLv NPri SCoo SDow SIoW SLim WLav
'Van Gogh'	SDow
vera misapplied	see *L. × intermedia* Dutch Group
vera DC.	see *L. angustifolia*
viridis	CArn CChe CSev ELan ELau ELon EPfP GBar MHer MNHC NGHP NLLv NPer SDow WAbe WCHb WJek WLav
'Whero Iti'	MHrb SDow
'Willow Vale' ♀H3-4	CMea CTri CWCL EBee ENor EPfP GBar LRHS LSRN MAsh MHer MHrb MLHP NLLv SAga SDow SIoW SPav SWvt WJek WPGP
'Willowbridge Calico'PBR	LRHS LSou SIoW WClo WLav

Lavatera (*Malvaceae*)

arborea	SChr WHer
- 'Rosea'	see *L. × clementii* 'Rosea'
- 'Variegata' (v)	CBow CSsd ELan NPer NSti SBod SDix SEND SGar WCHb WCom WCot WEas WTou
bicolor	see *L. maritima*
cachemiriana	CBod EQua GBuc IDee NBir NBur NPer WPer
Chamallow = 'Inovera'PBR	EBee EPfP LBuc LRHS LSRN LSou NPri SPoG
× ***clementii*** 'Barnsley'	Widely available
- 'Barnsley Baby'	LBuc LRHS MAsh NLar NPer NPri SPer
- 'Blushing Bride'	CDoC CWCL EBee ELon EPfP LBMP LRHS LSRN MBri MGos NLar NPri SBch SBod SPer SPoG
- 'Bredon Springs' ♀H3-4	CDoC CDul CSBt CWCL CWSG EBee ECha ECtt EMil EPfP LHop LRHS LSRN MAsh MSwo NHol NScw SBod SEND SLim SPer SWvt WFar WHar
- 'Burgundy Wine' ♀H3-4	Widely available
- 'Candy Floss' ♀H3-4	CAlb CWCL EBee EPfP LRHS MAsh MBar MBri MGos NBir NLar NPer WDin
- 'Kew Rose'	CDoC CTri EBee EPfP LRHS MSwo NPer SLim SRms
- 'Lavender Lady'	ECtt GKir LHop NPer
- 'Lisanne'	LRHS MAsh MHer MSwo MWhi NHol NPri SEND
- 'Mary Hope'	EPfP LRHS MAsh
- Memories = 'Stelav'	CHid CMac EBee EPfP GBin LRHS LSRN NLar SLim
- 'Pavlova'	CDoC CPLG LRHS
- 'Poynton Lady' (v)	LHop
§ - 'Rosea' ♀H3-4	CBcs CDul CMac CWSG EBee ECtt EPfP GGar GKir LAst LRHS LSRN MAsh MBar MGos NBir NBlu NEgg NHol NPri SBch SBod SLon SPer SPoG SWvt WBVN WDin WFar
- 'Shorty'	WFar
§ - 'Wembdon Variegated' (v)	NPer
'Dorothy'	MCot
'Grey Beauty'	LHop MAsh
§ ***maritima*** ♀H2-3	CBot CDoC CHrt CMHG CMac CPLG CRHN EBee ECtt ELan EPfP IFoB LHop LRHS MCot SBch SEND SMrm SPer SPoG SUsu SWvt WCFE WCom WFar WHCG WKif WSHC
- 'Princesse de Lignes'	LRHS MGos
oblongifolia	CBot
N ***olbia***	CTri SPlb SRms
- 'Eye Catcher'	EBee LRHS MSwo NLar SMrm SPer SPoG SWal
- 'Lilac Lady'	EBee ECha ELan EPfP LRHS LSou MAsh MCCP MGos MWte NLar SLim SMrm SPer WFar WKif WSHC
§ - 'Pink Frills'	CBot EBee LRHS MBar MGos MNrw NPri SMrm SWvt WSHC WWlt
'Peppermint Ice'	see *L. thuringiaca* 'Ice Cool'
'Pink Frills'	see *L. olbia* 'Pink Frills'
'Rosea'	see *L. × clementii* 'Rosea'
'Sweet Dreams'PBR	LRHS NLar
tauricensis	NLar
N ***thuringiaca***	GCal NNor WFar
§ - 'Ice Cool'	CBot ECha ECtt ERas GCal LAst LRHS MGos MHer SWvt WCot WFar WKif
- Red Rum = 'Rigrum'PBR	CMac EBee GBin LAst LBuc LLHF LRHS LSRN MAsh MBri NEgg NHol NLar NPri SLim SPoG SWvt WFar WHar
'Variegata'	see *L. × clementii* 'Wembdon Variegated'
'White Angel'PBR	LRHS NLar
'White Satin'PBR	LHop

Lecanthus (*Urticaceae*)

peduncularis	CHEx

Ledebouria (*Hyacinthaceae*)

adlamii	see *L. cooperi*
concolor misapplied	see *L. socialis*
§ ***cooperi***	CDes CStu EBee ECho ELan ITim LEdu LHop NCGa SIng SUsu WBor WPGP WPrP
§ ***socialis***	CBgR CSWP CSpe CStu EBrs ECho ERos EShb MCot SBHP SBch SPet STre
violacea	see *L. socialis*

× *Ledodendron* (*Ericaceae*)

§ 'Arctic Tern' ♀H4	CDoC CSBt CTri ECho GGar GQui LMil LRHS MBar MGos MLea NHol NWCA SPer

Ledum (*Ericaceae*)

glandulosum SIN 1828	GLin
§ ***groenlandicum***	GGar MBar MLea SPer WDin WFar WSHC
- 'Compactum'	EBee NLar SPoG WFar
- 'Helma' **new**	NLar
- 'Lenie'	NLar
palustre	COld GGGa GPoy NLar WThu

Legousia (*Campanulaceae*)

pentagonica 'Midnight Stars'	CSpe

Leiophyllum (*Ericaceae*)

buxifolium ♀H4	EPfP WThu
- var. ***hugeri***	GBin GGar GKev NLar
- 'Maryfield'	WAbe

Lembotropis see *Cytisus*

Lemna (*Lemnaceae*)

gibba	NPer
minor	CWat EMFW LPBA MSKA NPer SWat
polyrhiza	see *Spirodela polyrhiza*
trisulca	CWat EHon EMFW LPBA MSKA NPer SWat

lemon see *Citrus limon*

lemon balm see *Melissa officinalis*

lemon grass see *Cymbopogon citratus*

lemon verbena see *Aloysia triphylla*

Leonotis (*Lamiaceae*)

leonitis	see *L. ocymifolia*
leonurus	CBcs CCCN CDTJ CHEx CHll CTrC EBee EPfP EShb EWes LRHS SMad SPoG
- var. ***albiflora***	CCCN EShb
nepetifolia	CCCN SDnm SPav
var. ***nepetifolia*** 'Staircase'	
§ ***ocymifolia***	CCCN CPLG LSou SMrm WPGP
- var. ***ocymifolia***	SPlb
- var. ***raineriana***	CHll

Leontice (*Berberidaceae*)

albertii	see *Gymnospermium albertii*

Leontochir (*Amaryllidaceae*)

ovallei	CCCN

Leontodon (*Asteraceae*)

autumnalis	EBWF NMir
hispidus	EBWF NMir
§ ***rigens***	EBee EDAr GBuc MLHP MMuc MNrw NBid NBir SBHP SDix SMad WFar WMoo WPrP
- 'Girandole'	see *L. rigens*

Leontopodium (*Asteraceae*)

SDR 5119	GKev
alpinum	CArn CTri CWib ECho EPfP EPot GAbr GEdr GKir LRHS NBlu NPri NWCA SPlb SPoG SRms WPer
- 'Mignon'	CMea ECho EWes GEdr GKev SIng WAbe WClo WFar WHoo
- subsp. ***nivale***	WPat
brachyactis **new**	GKev
coreanum	EBee GKev
himalayanum	EPot
kamtschaticum	ECho
nanum	GKev
§ ***ochroleucum*** var. ***campestre***	MDKP NLar WPer
palibinianum	see *L. ochroleucum* var. *campestre*
souliei	GKev
stracheyi **new**	GKev

Leonurus (*Lamiaceae*)

artemisia	see *L. japonicus*
cardiaca	CArn CWan EBWF EGoo GBar GPWP GPoy MHer SECG SIde
§ ***japonicus***	CArn MMuc
macranthus	EFEx
- var. ***alba***	EFEx
sibiricus misapplied	see *L. japonicus*
sibiricus L.	GCal SPav WPer
turkestanicus	EBee

Leopoldia (*Hyacinthaceae*)

comosa	see *Muscari comosum*
spreitzenhoferi	see *Muscari spreitzenhoferi*
tenuiflora	see *Muscari tenuiflorum*

Lepechinia (*Lamiaceae*)

bella	SDys SUsu
chamaedryoides	CHll CPLG CSpe
floribunda	CSev
hastata	CMdw CPom MSpe MWea SBHP SUsu
salviae	CDTJ CDoC CSpe IMou WBor WWlt

Lepidium (*Brassicaceae*)

campestre	CArn
latifolium	CArn

Lepidothamnus (*Podocarpaceae*)

§ ***laxifolius***	WThu

Lepidozamia (*Zamiaceae*)

hopei	LPal
peroffskyana	CBrP LPal

Leptecophylla (*Epacridaceae*)

§ ***juniperina***	ECou
- 'Nana'	WThu
§ - subsp. ***parvifolia***	ECou

Leptinella (*Asteraceae*)

§ ***albida***	CStu
§ ***atrata***	ECho
- subsp. ***luteola***	EBee ECho GEdr
'County Park'	ECho ECou EDAr
dendyi	ECho ECou EWes MHer NLAp NMen NSla
dioica	CTrC GBin
filicula	ECou
hispida	see *Cotula hispida* (DC.) Harv.
§ ***minor***	ECou EDAr WMoo
pectinata var. ***sericea***	see *L. albida*
- subsp. ***villosa*** CC 475	NWCA
§ ***potentillina***	CTri EBee ECha ECho EHoe GEdr MBNS NLar NRya SRms WMoo WPer WPtf
§ ***pyrethrifolia***	EBee ECho EDAr GGar NMen
- 'Macabe'	ECou
§ ***rotundata***	ECou
§ ***serrulata***	ECho MBar
§ ***squalida***	ECha ECho EDAr GBin MBar MWat NRya STre WMoo
§ - 'Platt's Black'	CPBP CStu EBee ECha ECho EDAr EHoe EShb EWes GAbr GEdr GGar GKir LEdu LRHS NLAp NRya NWCA SBch SIng SPet WFar WHoo WMoo WPat WPer WPrP WPtf WWFP
traillii	GGar

Leptocarpus (*Restionaceae*)

similis	ECou
- BR 70	GGar

Leptocodon (*Campanulaceae*)

gracilis	EWld IGor
- HWJK 2155	WCru

Leptodactylon (*Polemoniaceae*)

§ ***californicum***	CPBP
- subsp. ***leptotrichomum***	CPBP

Leptopteris (*Osmundaceae*)

hymenophylloides	WRic
superba	WRic

Leptospermum (*Myrtaceae*)

'Centaurus'	CTrC CWSG MNHC NVic WFar
citratum	see *L. petersonii*
'Confetti'	ECou
'Copper Sheen'	CTrC
'County Park Blush'	ECou
cunninghamii	see *L. myrtifolium*
'Electric Red' (Galaxy Series)	CTrC CWSG LRHS SLim
ericoides	see *Kunzea ericoides*
flavescens misapplied	see *L. glaucescens*
flavescens Sm.	see *L. polygalifolium*
§ ***glaucescens***	CMHG ECou GGar
§ ***grandiflorum***	CTrC CTrG ELan EPfP GGar ISea SSpi WSHC
grandifolium	ECou
'Havering Hardy'	ECou
humifusum	see *L. rupestre*
juniperinum	CTrC SPlb
'Karo Pearl Star'	CBcs
'Karo Spectrobay'PBR	CBcs
laevigatum 'Yarrum'	ECou
§ ***lanigerum***	CBcs CMHG CPLG CTrC CTri EBee ECou EPfP GGar SHGN SPoG
- 'Cunninghamii'	see *L. myrtifolium*
- 'Wellington'	ECou
liversidgei	CChe ECou
minutifolium	ECou
morrisonii	ECou
§ ***myrtifolium***	CTrC CTri EBee ECou EPla EWes GGar SPer WPat
- 'Newnes Forest'	ECou
myrtifolium × ***scoparium***	ECou
nitidum	CTrC ECou SPlb
- 'Cradle'	ECou
obovatum	CMHG
§ ***petersonii***	CArn ECou EOHP EShb MHer
- 'Chlorinda'	ECou
phylicoides	see *Kunzea ericoides*
'Pink Surprise'	ECou
§ ***polygalifolium***	CTrC ECou SPlb SRms
prostratum	see *L. rupestre*
pubescens	see *L. lanigerum*
'Red Cascade'	SWvt
rodwayanum	see *L. grandiflorum*
rotundifolium	CTrC ECou
§ ***rupestre*** ♀H4	CDoC CTrC CTri ECou EPot GGar MBar SPlb SRms WFar WSHC
rupestre × ***scoparium***	ECou
scoparium	CArn CTsd ECou ERom GPWP MNHC SPlb WDin
- 'Adrianne'	ELan EPfP LRHS MRav
- 'Album'	CTrC
- 'Appleblossom'	CTrC
- 'Autumn Glory'	CWSG ISea SLim
- 'Avocet'	ECou
- 'Big Red'	MMuc
- 'Blossom' (d)	CBcs CMac CTrC ECou
- 'Boscawenii'	CBcs
- 'Burgundy Queen' (d)	CBcs CMac CSBt CTrC ECou MDun
- 'Chapmanii'	CMHG CTrG GGar
- 'Coral Candy'	EBee MMuc
- 'County Park Pink'	ECou
- 'County Park Red'	ECou
- 'Crimson Glory' (d)	CAlb CSBt
- 'Dove Lake'	WAbe
- 'Elizabeth Jane'	GGar
- 'Essex'	ECou
- 'Fantasia'	ECou
- 'Fred's Red'	NLAp WPat
- 'Gaiety Girl' (d)	CSBt
- var. ***incanum***	CTrC ECou
'Keatleyi' ♀H3	
- - 'Wairere'	ECou
- 'Jubilee' (d)	CBcs CMac ISea
- 'Kerry'	CAbP LRHS
- 'Lambethii' **new**	MAsh
- 'Leonard Wilson' (d)	CTri ECou
- 'Lyndon'	ECou
- 'Martini'	CDoC CMac CSBt CTrC CTrG EPfP LRHS MMuc WGwG
- 'McLean'	ECou
- 'Moko' **new**	ECou
- (Nanum Group) 'Huia'	CBcs
- - 'Kea'	CBcs ECou MHer MMuc MRav
- - 'Kiwi' ♀H3	CAbP CBcs CCCN CDoC CDul CSBt CTrC CWSG EBee ECou ELan EPfP EWes GQui LRHS MAsh MDun SLim SPad WFar
- - 'Nanum'	ECou NMen
- - 'Pipit'	EWes WAbe
- - 'Tui'	CSBt CTrC ECou
- 'Nichollsii' ♀H3	CTrC CTri GQui WSHC
- 'Nichollsii Nanum' ♀H2-3	ITim NLAp SIng SRms WPat WThu
- 'Pink Cascade'	CBcs CMac CTrC CTri CWib GGar SEND SLim
- 'Pink Damask'	SWvt

- 'Pink Falls' ECou
- 'Pink Frills' **new** ECou
- 'Pink Queen' **new** LRHS
- 'Pink Splash' ECou
- 'Pom Pom' LRHS
- var. ***prostratum*** hort. see *L. rupestre*
- 'Red Damask' (d) ♀H3 CBcs CChe CDoC CDul CMac CPLG CTrC CWSG CWib EBee EHoe ELan EPfP GGal GKev GQui IMon LRHS LSRN MDun MRav NPCo SPad SPlb SPoG SRms SWvt WBrE WFar WSHC
- 'Red Falls' CPLG CTrC ECou
- 'Redpoll' ECou
- 'Roseum' MRav
- 'Rosy Morn' ISea
* - 'Ruby Wedding' ELan EPfP LRHS MAsh SPoG
- var. ***scoparium*** GGar
- 'Snow Drift' **new** GKev
- 'Snow Flurry' CBcs CTrC EBee LRHS MMuc SLim SPoG
- 'Snow White' **new** LRHS
- 'Wingletye' ECou
- 'Winter Cheer' (d) CBcs LRHS
- 'Wiri Joan' (d) CBcs
- 'Wiri Linda' CBcs CMac
- 'Zeehan' ECou

sericeum ECou
'Silver Sheen' ♀H3 CEnd ECou ELan EPfP LRHS MAsh NLar SPoG WPGP
'Snow Column' ECou
sphaerocarpum ECou
squarrosum CTrC
turbinatum ECou
- 'Thunder Cloud' ECou
'Wellington Dwarf' ECou

Leschenaultia (*Goodeniaceae*)

biloba ECou
- 'Sky Blue' ECou
formosa red-flowered ECou
- yellow-flowered ECou
pink-flowered ECou

Lespedeza (*Papilionaceae*)

bicolor CAgr ELon LRHS NPal SEND WDin WFar WHCG WSHC
buergeri EPfP MMHG NLar WSHC
japonica SPlb
thunbergii ♀H4 CBcs CBgR CSpe CWib CWit EBee ELan ELon EPfP IDee LHop LRHS MAsh MBlu MBri MGos SEND SLon SPer SPoG SSpi SSta WDin WFar WHCG WPGP WPtf WSHC
- 'Albiflora' CAbP EBee EPfP MWea SPoG WPGP WSHC
- 'Avalanche' NLar
- 'Edo-shibori' **new** MBri
- 'Summer Beauty' CBcs EBee EPfP LRHS MGos
- 'White Fountain' LRHS MBri
tiliifolia see *Desmodium elegans*

Lesquerella (*Brassicaceae*)

rubicundula **new** EDAr

Leucadendron (*Proteaceae*)

argenteum CBcs CCCN CHEx CTrC SPlb
daphnoides SPlb
eucalyptifolium CTrC SPlb
galpinii CTrC
'Inca Gold' CBcs CTrC
laureolum CCCN
'Maui Sunset' CTrC
'Mrs Stanley' CTrC
'Safari Sunset' CBcs CCCN CDoC CTrC LRHS SBig
'Safari Sunshine' CTrC
salignum CBcs CCCN
- 'Early Yellow' CTrC
- 'Fireglow' CDoC CTrC
strobilinum CDoC CTrC

Leucanthemella (*Asteraceae*)

§ ***serotina*** ♀H4 Widely available
- 'Herbststern' CFir NLar

Leucanthemopsis (*Asteraceae*)

§ ***alpina*** ECho
hosmariensis see *Rhodanthemum hosmariense*

Leucanthemum ✿ (*Asteraceae*)

'Angel' **new** NPri SVil
atlanticum see *Rhodanthemum atlanticum*
catananche see *Rhodanthemum catananche*
graminifolium EPfP LRHS WPer
hosmariense see *Rhodanthemum hosmariense*
mawii see *Rhodanthemum gayanum*
maximum misapplied see *L.* × *superbum*
§ ***maximum*** (Ramond) DC. NBro NPer WSpi
- ***uliginosum*** see *Leucanthemella serotina*
nipponicum see *Nipponanthemum nipponicum*
§ × ***superbum*** CMac MHer MLHP NVic NWsh WFar
- 'Aglaia' (d) ♀H4 Widely available
- 'Alaska' CAni CPLG CWCL EBee EBla EPfP GKir LAst LEdu LHop LRHS MCot NGdn SBch SPer SPur SWal SWvt WFar WPer WWEG
- 'Amelia' NBre SRGP
- 'Anita Allen' (d) CAni CElw CFee EBee EBla MAvo NBre WCot WFar WPer WWEG
- 'Anna Camilla' CAni
- 'Antwerp Star' NBre NLar
- 'Banwell' CAni
- 'Barbara Bush' (v/d) ECtt ELan LSou NBir NCob SPoG SRGP SWvt
§ - 'Beauté Nivelloise' CAni CBgR CCVN CPrp CWCL EBee EBla ECtt EPfP MAvo MDKP MMuc NBPC NBre NCGa SWat WFar WPer WPrP WPtf WSpi WWEG
- 'Becky' CMdw CWan EBee ECha ELon EPfP EWes LLHF LRHS LSou MAvo NBre NPro SPoG SRGP SSvw WWEG
- 'Bishopstone' CAni CSam EBee ELan LEdu MAvo NBre WEas WPer WWEG
- 'Brightside' **new** EBee
- Broadway Lights = 'Leumayel'PBR **new** EGxp LRHS MAvo
- 'Christine Hagemann' CAni CPrp EBee EWes MAvo MDKP MRav NCGa WWEG
- 'Cobham Gold' (d) CAni CPrp CWCL NBre NOrc SUsu SWal
- 'Coconut Ice' WPer WWEG
- 'Colwall' CAni WWEG
- 'Crazy Daisy' CAni CMMP CTri CWib LRHS MBNS NBre NCob NLar NPri SWal WHrl WRHF WSpi WWEG
- 'Devon Mist' CAni
- 'Dipsy Daisy' WPer
- 'Droitwich Beauty' CAni CBgR LLHF MAvo WCFE WHil WHoo WWEG
- 'Duchess of Abercorn' CAni CSam
- 'Dwarf Snow Lady' NBre

- 'Easton Lady'	CAni CBgR
- 'Eclipse'	CAni MAvo
- 'Edgebrook Giant'	CAni MAvo
- 'Edward VII'	CAni
- 'Eisstern'	CDes EBee LEdu MAvo WWEG
- 'Elworthy Sparkler'	CElw MAvo WWEG
- 'Esther Read' (d)	Widely available
- 'Etoile d'Anvers'	EBee
§ - 'Everest'	CAni CSam EBee NBre SRms WWEG
- 'Exhibition'	NBre WWEG
- 'Fiona Coghill' (d)	CAni CElw EAEE EBee EBla ECtt EPfP LBMP LRHS MAvo MDKP MHer MSpe NCGa NEgg NGdn NVic SPoG WCot WHoo WWEG
- 'Firnglanz'	CAni GBin MAvo WWEG
- 'Goldrausch'PBR	CCVN CWGN EBee ECtt ELon LBMP LHop LLHF LRHS LSou MDKP MMHG NBPC NEgg NPri SMrm SPer SPoG WCot WHlf WHoo WRHF WWEG
- 'Gruppenstolz'	CAni EBee GBin
- 'H. Seibert'	CAni CBgR CElw CEnt CPrp EBla MAvo WWEG
- 'Harry'	CAni
- 'Highland White Dream'PBR	LRHS WFar
- 'Horace Read' (d)	CAni CBgR CElw ELan NBir SAga SBch WEas WPer WSpi WWEG
- 'Jennifer Read'	CAni CBgR MAvo WCot WWEG
§ - 'John Murray' (d)	CAni EBee EShb EWes LSou MAvo MDKP NBir SMrm WAbb WCot WWEG
- 'Little Miss Muffet'	CBgR CWGN EAEE EBee EBla ECtt EPPr GGar LAst LBMP LLHF LRHS MBNS NCGa NCob NPro WWEG
- 'Little Princess'	see *L.* × *superbum* 'Silberprinzesschen'
- 'Majestic'	CAni
- 'Manhattan'	CAni CBgR CMdw EBee EBla EBrs EWes GBin NBre
- 'Margaretchen'	CAni CDes MAvo WWEG
- 'Marion Bilsland'	CAni MDKP NCGa NChi
- 'Marion Collyer'	CAni
- 'Mayfield Giant'	CAni CTri WPer
- 'Mount Everest'	see *L.* × *superbum* 'Everest'
- 'Octopus'	CAni MAvo WWEG
- 'Old Court'	see *L.* × *superbum* 'Beauté Nivelloise'
- 'Phyllis Smith'	Widely available
- 'Polaris'	EBee EShb LRHS MBNS NBre WMoo WSpi
- 'Rags and Tatters'	CAni EBee ECtt EWes MAvo WWEG
- 'Rijnsburg Glory'	WPer
- 'Schneehurken'	CAni CMac EBee EBla LLHF LSou MAvo SPoG STes SUsu WWEG
- 'Shaggy'	see *L.* × *superbum* 'Beauté Nivelloise'
§ - 'Silberprinzesschen'	CAni COIW EBee EBla EPfP GKir LRHS NEgg NPri SPlb SRms WFar WMoo WPer WWEG
- 'Silver Spoon'	EPfP WPer
- 'Snow Lady'	EBee EShb NEgg NPer NPri SBch SRms WFar
- 'Snowcap'	CMac EBee EBla EBrs ECha EPfP LRHS MBNS MBri MRav NEgg NGdn SPer SWvt WCAu WTin
- 'Snowdrift'	CAni CBgR CMMP EGoo LRHS MAvo NBre SBch WCot WPer
§ - 'Sonnenschein'	Widely available
- 'Starburst' (d)	SPhx SRms
- 'Stina'	EBee
- 'Summer Snowball'	see *L.* × *superbum* 'John Murray'
- 'Sunny Killin'	CAni WTin
- 'Sunny Side Up'PBR	EBee ECtt GMac MBri NBPC NLar
- Sunshine	see *L.* × *superbum* 'Sonnenschein'
- 'T.E. Killin' (d) ♀H4	CElw CKno CPrp CSam EBee EBla EBrs ECha ECtt EPfP GMaP LBMP LRHS MBri MRav SPoG WCAu WCot WFar WSpi WWEG
- 'White Iceberg' (d)	CAni WPer
- 'White Knight'	EBee LRHS MBNS NBre NPri
- 'Wirral Pride'	CAni CBgR CCVN CHar EBee ELon MAvo WBrk WMnd WWEG
- 'Wirral Supreme' (d) ♀H4	Widely available
'Tizi-n-Test'	see *Rhodanthemum catananche* 'Tizi-n-Test'
§ ***vulgare***	CArn CMac CRWN EBWF EPfP GBar LEdu MHer MNHC NLan NMir NSco SBch SECG SIde WBrk WHer WJek WMoo WShi
- 'Avondale' (v)	NGdn
- 'Filigran'	EBee EShb LRHS SIde
§ - 'Maikönigin'	EBee WHrl
- May Queen	see *L. vulgare* 'Maikönigin'
- 'Sunny'	CBre EBla EWes WAlt
'White Knight'	MBri MCCP

Leucocoryne (*Alliaceae*)

alliacea	ECho
'Andes'	CCCN EBrs ECho
'Caravelle'	EBrs ECho
hybrids	CGrW EBrs ECho
ixioides	ECho
* - ***alba***	EBrs ECho
purpurea ♀H1	CGrW EBrs ECho

Leucogenes (*Asteraceae*)

grandiceps	GKev NSla WAbe
leontopodium	GGar GKev NSla WAbe
tarahaoa	WAbe

Leucojum ✿ (*Amaryllidaceae*)

aestivum	CBcs CBgR CFee CMac CTri EBee EBrs ECGP ECho EPfP GCal LAma LHop LRHS MCot MDun NEgg NHol SMrm SPad SPer SRms WBor WCot WEas WFar WShi WWlt
- 'Gravetye Giant' ♀H4	Widely available
autumnale	see *Acis autumnalis*
longifolium	see *Acis longifolia*
roseum	see *Acis rosea*
tingitanum	see *Acis tingitana*
trichophyllum	see *Acis trichophylla*
valentinum	see *Acis valentina*
vernum ♀H4	Widely available
- var. ***carpathicum***	CLAP EBrs ECha ECho EHrv GEdr MRav NMen WAbe
- var. ***vagneri***	CLAP EBee ECha EHrv GEdr LRHS NPol WSHC WTin

Leucophysalis (*Solanaceae*)

sinense BWJ 8093	WCru

Leucopogon (*Epacridaceae*)

§ ***colensoi***	MBri NHol NLar WPat WThu
§ ***fasciculatus***	ECou
§ ***fraseri***	ECou GEdr WThu
§ ***parviflorus***	ECou

× *Leucoraoulia* (*Asteraceae*)

sp.	EPot
§ ***loganii***	NWCA WAbe

Leucosceptrum (*Lamiaceae*)

canum	CPLG CTrG
- GWJ 9424	WCru
japonicum	EBee
- B&SWJ 10981	WCru
- 'Golden Angel'	EBee
stellipilum	EBee
- var. ***formosanum***	EWld
- - B&SWJ 1804	WCru
- - RWJ 9907	WCru
- var. ***tosaense*** B&SWJ 8892	WCru

Leucospermum (*Proteaceae*)

'Scarlet Ribbon'	CCCN

Leucothoe (*Ericaceae*)

axillaris 'Curly Red'[PBR]	CBcs CWSG EBee ELan EMil EPfP LBuc LRHS MAsh MCCP MGos MMHG NLar SBch SPoG SWvt
- 'Scarletta'	see *L.* Scarletta
Carinella = 'Zebekot'	EMil MBri MGos NLar SBch SPoG
davisiae	EPfP
§ ***fontanesiana*** Υ^{H4}	CMCN CMac EPfP GGal GKir LRHS
- SDR 2249	GKev
- 'Nana'	LRHS
- 'Rainbow' (v)	Widely available
- 'Rollissonii' Υ^{H4}	MBar MRav SRms
keiskei	EPfP LRHS
- 'Royal Ruby'	CAlb CWSG EBee EPfP LRHS LSou MGos NEgg NLar SLim SPoG WDin WFar WMoo
Lovita = 'Zebonard'	EBee EPfP LRHS MBri MGos MRav NLar SCoo
populifolia	see *Agarista populifolia*
racemosa	NLar
Red Lips = 'Lipsbolwi'[PBR]	CDoC EBee ELan EPfP MGos NLar NScw
§ Scarletta = 'Zeblid'	Widely available
walteri	see *L. fontanesiana*

Leuzea (*Asteraceae*)

centaureoides	see *Stemmacantha centaureoides*
conifera	MAsh

Levisticum (*Apiaceae*)

officinale	CArn CBod CHby CHrt CPrp CSev ELau EPfP GAbr GBar GGar GPoy LEdu MBar MHer MNHC NBid NGHP NPri SBch SDix SECG SEND SIde SPlb SVic SWat WHer WPer

Lewisia ✿ (*Portulacaceae*)

'Archangel'	NRya
Ashwood Carousel hybrids	ECho LRHS MAsh
'Ashwood Pearl'	MAsh
'Ben Chace'	MAsh
Birch strain	CBcs ECho ELan
brachycalyx Υ^{H2}	ECho EWes LLHF LRHS MAsh MTho WPer
- pink	MAsh
brachycalyx × ***nevadensis*** 'Rosea' **new**	GKev
cantelovii	MAsh
columbiana	MAsh NWCA WPer
- 'Alba'	MAsh WCom
- subsp. ***columbiana***	GKev
- 'Rosea'	NLAp NSla WGor
- subsp. ***rupicola***	GKev LLHF NDlv
- subsp. ***wallowensis***	MAsh NMen
congdonii	MAsh
'Constant Comment'	NBhm
cotyledon Υ^{H4}	CWCL ECho GKev GKir LLHF LRHS MNrw WBrE WFar
- J&JA 12959	NWCA
- f. ***alba***	GKev LHop MAsh
- 'Ashwood Ruby'	MAsh
- Ashwood strain	ECho EPfP EWes LBee LRHS LSou MAsh SRms WGor
- 'Bright Eyes' **new**	GKev
- Crags hybrids	SRms
- 'Fransi'	NLar
- var. ***howellii***	LLHF MAsh SRms WGor
- hybrid	ECho EPot GGar ITim LHop SIng SPoG WCom WGor
- 'John's Special'	MAsh
- magenta-flowered	ECho MAsh WGor
§ - 'Regenbogen' mixed	EAlp NBlu WGor WPer
- 'Snowstorm'	LLHF
- Sunset Group Υ^{H4}	ECho LAst MHer NLar NWCA SBch SRms WClo WPer WRHF
- violet-flowered	GKev
- 'White Splendour'	SIng
'George Henley'	ECho EPfP EWes LLHF MAsh NMen NRya SIng WAbe WCom WGor
leeana	GKev MAsh
'Little Peach'	CPBP EDAr GAbr GGar GKev SIng WGor WPer
'Little Plum'	CMea CPBP ECho EDAr EPfP GGar GKev LRHS MDKP MSCN NDlv NLar NRya NSla NWCA SIng WGor WPer
§ ***longipetala***	ECho NDlv
§ ***nevadensis***	ECho EDAr EPot ERos GEdr GGar ITim LRHS MAsh MNrw MTho NMen NRya NWCA SRms WHoo WPer
- ***bernardina***	see *L. nevadensis*
- 'Rosea'	EPot MAsh NWCA
oppositifolia	EDAr MAsh
'Phyllellia'	MAsh
'Pinkie'	CPBP LLHF MAsh NMen
pygmaea	CWCL ECho EWes GEdr GGar ITim LAst LRHS MAsh MHer MWat NBir NLAp NMen NRya WPer
- subsp. ***longipetala***	see *L. longipetala*
Rainbow mixture	see *L. cotyledon* 'Regenbogen' mixed
'Rawreth'	LLHF WAbe
rediviva	ECho EWes GEdr LLHF MAsh WAbe
- NNS 03.369	CPBP
sierrae	EDAr WPer
'Trevosia'	MAsh SIng
tweedyi Υ^{H2}	EPfP LHop LRHS MAsh NWCA SIng WCom WGor
- 'Alba'	GKir MAsh NWCA
- 'Elliott's Variety'	MAsh NWCA WGor
- 'Rosea'	LHop LRHS MAsh NWCA SIng WGor

Leycesteria (*Caprifoliaceae*)

crocothyrsos	CAbP CArn CBcs CHid CWib EBee ELan EPfP GQui LAst MDKP SMad
formosa Υ^{H4}	Widely available
- brown-stemmed	IFoB
- Golden Lanterns = 'Notbruce'[PBR]	CDoC CSBt EBee ELan EMil EPfP EPla EQua LBuc LRHS LSRN MAsh MBri MGos MMHG NEgg NHol NLar SBch SCoo SPoG WBor WFar
- 'Golden Pheasant' (v)	CPMA EHoe ERas MDun NExo
- 'Purple Rain'	CAlb EBee EMil EQua EWes LBuc LRHS MAsh NLar SBch

'Gold Leaf' new — CBow MDKP
'Smouldering Embers' — WGrn

Leymus (*Poaceae*)

from Falkland Islands — EPPr
§ ***arenarius*** — Widely available
condensatus — CKno
'Canyon Prince'
hispidus — see *Elymus hispidus*
'Niveus' — EHul
§ ***racemosus*** — CHrt

Lhotzkya see *Calytrix*

Liatris (*Asteraceae*)

sp. — CBro
aspera — EBee NBre WPer
cylindracea — EBee
elegans — EBee NBre NLar SPlb WPer
ligulistylis — EBee NBPC NBre NLar WPer
microcephala new — EBee
mucronata — EBee
punctata — EBee NBre
pycnostachya — CRWN EBee GCal NLar SRms WPer
scariosa 'Alba' — NLar SMrm WPer
- 'Gracious' — EWII
§ ***spicata*** — Widely available
- 'Alba' — CMac CSBt CSpe EBee ECha ECtt ELan EPfP EShb IMon LAma LAst LEdu LSRN MNFA MNrw NBPC NGdn SPer SPlb WBrE WCAu WPer
- ***callilepis*** — see *L. spicata*
- 'Floristan Violett' — CBro EBee EHrv EPfP GMaP LBMP LRHS MHer NEgg NPri SCoo SPlb SPoG SUsu SWvt WFar WGwG WMnd WMoo WPer WWEG
- 'Floristan Weiss' — CArn CBro EBee EHrv EPPr EPfP GBuc GKir GMaP LBMP LRHS MHer MRav MWhi NBPC NCGa NPri SPoG SWvt WClo WFar WGwG WMnd WMoo WPer WWEG
- Goblin — see *L. spicata* 'Kobold'
§ - 'Kobold' — Widely available

Libertia ✿ (*Iridaceae*)

sp. — WPGP
HCM 98.089 — CDes EBee
'Amazing Grace' — CDes EBee GCal IBlr SBch SUsu WPGP
'Ballyrogan Blue' — CDes
Ballyrogan hybrid — IBlr
* ***breunioides*** — CDes CPLG
caerulescens — CBgR CCCN CCVN CFir CPLG EBee ECho EPla ERos EShb GGar IFoB IGor LPio LRHS NBid NBir NCGa NLar SGar SMad SMrm WCot WFar WHer WKif WMoo WPGP
chilensis — see *L. formosa*
elegans — CPLG GBuc IBlr
§ ***formosa*** — Widely available
- brown-stemmed — IBlr IFoB
grandiflora ♀H4 — Widely available
- stoloniferous — GGar
ixioides — CBcs CBgR CHid CKno EBee EBrs ECha ECho ECou EShb IBlr IFFs LEdu MAvo MCot NGdn NSti SBch SBod WCFE WFoF WPGP WRHF WSpi
- dark-leaved — MAvo
- 'Goldfinger' (v) — CBgR CTrC CWit EBee IMon LHop LRHS LSou MMHG NHol NOak SBch SGSe SHar SPoG SRkn WClo WCot WGrn WHer
- hybrid — SDix
- 'Tricolor' — CPen EBee ECho GAbr GBuc GGar IBlr LDai SIng WMoo WPat
'Nelson Dwarf' — ECho GCal
paniculata — CPLG WSHC
peregrinans — Widely available
- from East Cape — IBlr
- 'Gold Leaf' — CBcs CBgR CBow CCCN CElw CPrp CTri CTsd EHrv GKir IBlr IFFs LAst LRHS MRav NOak SMad SUsu WCot WFar WHoo WViv
- 'Gold Stripe' — EPPr
* ***procera*** — CDes CSpe EBee IBlr LEdu LRHS WPGP WSHC
pulchella — EBee IBlr
- from Tasmania — ECho
sessiliflora — CElw CFee CPLG EBee ECho IBlr NBir WFar WPGP
- RB 94073 — SMad
Shackleton hybrid — IBlr WFar
'Taupo Blaze' — CWGN EBee IFFs LRHS LSRN LSou NCGa NHol SBch SHar SPad SPoG SUsu
'Taupo Sunset'PBR — CBgR CCCN CMil EBee ELon ETod EWes GBin LSou MBNS NBir NOak SBch WClo WCot

Libocedrus (*Cupressaceae*)

chilensis — see *Austrocedrus chilensis*
decurrens — see *Calocedrus decurrens*

Libonia see *Justicia*

Licuala (*Arecaceae*)

grandis — MBri
spinosa — LPal

Ligularia ✿ (*Asteraceae*)

BWJ 7686 from China — WCru
amplexicaulis — EWld
- CC 5244 — GKev
- GWJ 9404 — WCru
'Britt Marie Crawford'PBR — Widely available
calthifolia — CRow LRHS
- B&SWJ 2977 — WCru
'Cheju Charmer' — ELon LEdu WCru WWEG
clivorum — see *L. dentata*
§ ***dentata*** — CRow EBee ECtt GAuc GGal LBMP MMuc NBro NLar SBch SBod SRms SWat WBVN WFar
- 'Dark Beauty' — CBcs COIW EWII MMuc MWhi NBre WMnd
- dark-leaved new — WWEG
- 'Desdemona' ♀H4 — Widely available
- 'Orange Princess' — NPer WPer
- 'Orange Queen' — NBre WFar
- 'Othello' — Widely available
- 'Sommergold' — EBee ECha
- 'Twilight' new — ECtt MBNS
§ ***fischeri*** — CBct LEdu NBre SGSe WPer
- B&SWJ 1158 — WFar
- B&SWJ 2570 — WCru
- B&SWJ 4478 — WCru
- B&SWJ 5540 — WCru
- B&SWJ 5841 — WCru
glabrescens — CRow
§ 'Gregynog Gold' ♀H4 — CBct CRow EBee EBrs ECha ECtt EMFW EPfP GAbr GKir GMaP LRHS MRav MWhi NBro NCGa NCob

		NGdn NOrc SDnm SPav SPer WCru WFar WWEG WWlt
	× ***hessei***	EBee GMaP LRHS MMuc NLar SWat WFar
	hodgsonii	CKno CRow EBee EBla EPPr GKir LEdu LRHS WPer WWEG
	- B&SWJ 10855	WCru
	intermedia	WFar
	- B&SWJ 606a	WCru
	japonica	CHar CLAP CRow EBee ECha GCra LEdu LMaj LRHS MWhi NLar WFar
	- B&SWJ 2883	WCru
	- 'Rising Sun'	CLAP WCru
	aff. ***kaialpina*** B&SWJ 5806	WCru
	'Laternchen'[PBR]	EBee IBal LRHS MBri NMoo
	'Little Rocket'[PBR]	EBee ECtt EKen GBin LRHS MAsh MBNS MBri MSCN NBro
	macrophylla	CRow WFar
	mortonii GWJ 9419	WCru
	- HWJK 2214	WCru
	'Osiris Fantaisie'	EBee ECtt GBin LLHF NMyG SMad SUsu WCot WRHF WWEG
	× ***palmatiloba***	see *L.* × *yoshizoeana* 'Palmatiloba'
§	***przewalskii*** ΨH4	Widely available
	- 'Light Fingered'	NBre
	sachalinensis	EBee
	sibirica	CSam NLar WFar WMoo WPer WWEG
	- B&SWJ 5806	WCru
	- var. ***speciosa***	see *L. fischeri*
	smithii	see *Senecio smithii*
	speciosa	see *L. fischeri*
	stenocephala	EBee GKir LRHS MCot NBro NLar SWat WFar
	- B&SWJ 283	WCru
	- BWJ 7964 from China	WCru
	'Sungold'	CBct CSam EBee EBla EBrs ECtt GBin GKir LRHS NCGa NGdn
	tangutica	see *Sinacalia tangutica*
	'The Rocket' ΨH4	Widely available
	tussilaginea	see *Farfugium japonicum*
	- 'Aureo-maculata'	see *Farfugium japonicum* 'Aureomaculatum'
	veitchiana	CBct CRow EBee EBla EBrs EMFW EPfP GAbr GCal GGar LAst LEdu LRHS NCob SDnm SPav SWat WFar
	vorobievii	CHar EBee GCal NLar
	'Weihenstephan'	GCal GKir
	wilsoniana	CBct CHEx CRow EBee ECtt LLWG MBel MMuc MRav NBre NMun SDnm SPav SWat WCAu WFar
§	× ***yoshizoeana*** 'Palmatiloba'	CFir CHEx EBee EBla ELan ELon EPla GCal GKir LEdu MRav SDnm SPav SPhx SWat WCot WFar WWEG
	'Zepter'	CMHG EBee EBla ECtt GBuc GCal GQue LRHS MBNS NEgg NLar SMrm WFar WWEG

Ligusticum (*Apiaceae*)

	daucoides new	WPrP
	lucidum	CMCN EBee EPfP EWTr SEND SPhx SUsu WPGP
	porteri	CArn
§	***scoticum***	CArn CElw EOHP EWTr EWes GBar GKir GPoy ILis MCot MDKP MHer NBPC NLar NSti SGSe SPav SPhx WFar WHrl WJek WOut WPtf
	striatum B&SWJ 7259	WCru
	'Summer Delight' new	ITim

Ligustrum ✿ (*Oleaceae*)

	chenaultii	see *L. compactum*
§	***compactum***	MBri NLar
§	***delavayanum***	EBee EBtc EPfP EQua ERom LRHS MBar MGos SAPC SArc STrG WFar WSpi
	ibota	EBtc NLar
	ionandrum	see *L. delavayanum*
	japonicum	CHEx ECrN SEND SPer WDin WFar
I	- 'Aureum'	MGos
	- 'Coriaceum'	see *L. japonicum* 'Rotundifolium'
*	- 'Coriaceum Aureum'	EMil LRHS
	- 'Macrophyllum'	EPfP LRHS MAsh
§	- 'Rotundifolium'	CAbP CBcs CDoC CDul CFee CHEx CMac CPLG EBee ELan EMil EPfP EPla LRHS MAsh MGos MRav SBod SCoo SMad SPer SPoG WCFE WClo WFar
	- 'Silver Star' (v)	CPMA EBee MGos NLar SEND SLon
§	- 'Texanum'	CAlb EWes LRHS NLar
	- 'Variegatum' (v)	LMaj
	lucidum ΨH4	CDoC CDul CSBt CTri ECrN ELan LAst MBar MGos MRav MSwo NLar SAPC SArc SBch SPer SWvt WDin WFar
	- 'Excelsum Superbum' (v) ΨH4	CAbP CBcs CDul CLnd CPMA ELan EPfP LAst LHop LRHS MBar MGos NBlu SSpi WCot
	- 'Golden Wax'	CAbP CPMA MRav
	- 'Tricolor' (v)	CPMA ELan EPfP LRHS MAsh NLar SPer SPoG SSpi SWvt WDin WFar
	obtusifolium 'Darts Perfecta'	SLPl
	- var. ***regelianum***	EBee
	ovalifolium	Widely available
§	- 'Argenteum' (v)	CBcs CCVT CDoC CDul CTri CWib EBee ECrN EHoe GKir IFFs LBuc LRHS MAsh MBar MWat NBlu NEgg NHol NPri SBch SLim SPer SPoG SWvt WDin WFar
	- 'Aureomarginatum'	see *L. ovalifolium* 'Aureum'
§	- 'Aureum' (v) ΨH4	Widely available
	- 'Lemon and Lime' (v)	EHoe EMil MAsh MGos SCoo SWvt
	- 'Variegatum'	see *L. ovalifolium* 'Argenteum'
	quihoui ΨH4	CTri ECre ELan EPfP IDee LRHS MBri MMuc MWea SDix SLon SMad SPer SPoG SSpi WFar WHCG WPat
	sempervirens	EPfP IArd IDee NLar SLon
	sinense	CMCN EPfP GLin IFFs MRav WFar
	- 'Multiflorum'	CWib WFar
	- 'Pendulum'	EPla
	- var. ***stauntonii***	MBri NLar
	- 'Variegatum' (v)	CBgR CPMA EBee EPla EWes LHop MMuc MRav SPer
	- 'Wimbei'	EPla WFar
	strongylophyllum	CDoC WFar
	texanum	see *L. japonicum* 'Texanum'
	tschonoskii	NLar
	undulatum 'Lemon Lime and Clippers'	CSBt EBee LRHS MWea NLar SLim
	'Vicaryi'	CPMA ELan EPfP EPla EQua ERas EWTr IArd LRHS MBar MGos NHol NPro SEND SPer WFar
	vulgare	CBcs CCVT CDul CMac CRWN CTri CWan EBWF ECrN EMac EPfP LAst LBuc MSwo NWea SEND SWvt WDin WMou WSFF
	- 'Atrovirens'	EMac
	- 'Aureovariegatum' (v)	CNat
	- 'Lodense'	EBtc MBar
	walkeri new	GAuc

Lilium ✿ (*Liliaceae*)

	'Acapulco' (VII-/d)	EBrs LAma NGdn SPet

African Queen Group (VI-/a) 🏆H4	EBrs GBuc LAma LRHS SCoo SPer
- 'African Queen' (VIb-c/a)	CBro EBrs LRHS MCri SMrm WCot
albanicum	see *L. pyrenaicum* subsp. *carniolicum* var. *albanicum*
'Algarve' (VIIIa-b/c)	MBri
'Altari' (VIIIa-b/b)	LRHS
amabile (IX)	GAuc
- 'Luteum' (IX)	GAuc
amoenum (IX)	EPot
'Apeldoorn' (Ic/a)	MCri NNor
'Aphrodite' (I)	EBrs
'Apollo' (Ia) 🏆H4	CBro EBrs GBuc GKev LAma
'Arena' (VIIa/b)	EPfP SCoo SPer WFar
'Ariadne' (Ic)	CDes
* Asiatic hybrids (VI/VII)	LAma NGdn SGar
auratum (IX)	EBee EBrs ECho EFEx EPfP GAuc GBuc LRHS
- 'Gold Band'	see *L. auratum* var. *platyphyllum*
§ - var. ***platyphyllum*** (IXb/c)	GAuc GBuc MCri SBch
- - B&SWJ 4824	WCru
- Red Band Group (IX-/b)	WFar
- var. ***rubrovittatum*** (IX) **new**	WWst
- var. ***virginale*** (IX)	GAuc
'Avignon' (Ia/b)	MCri
'Bach' (VIIIa-b/b)	MBri
bakerianum (IX)	LAma
- var. ***aureum***	GAuc
- var. ***delavayi*** (IX)	GAuc LAma
- var. ***rubrum***	LAma
'Barbaresco' (VIIa-b/b)	SCoo SPer
'Barcelona' (Ia)	LRHS NNor
Bellingham Group (IVc/d)	CLAP GBuc GEdr
'Bergamo' (VIIb/b)	EPfP SCoo WFar
'Bianco Uno'	LRHS
'Black Beauty' (VIIIb-c/d)	CAvo CBro CFFs CLAP EBrs EPfP ERCP GBuc LAma LRHS MCri NNor
'Black Dragon' (VIa)	MCri
'Black Tie' (Ia/b)	MCri
bolanderi (IX)	GAuc
'Boogie Woogie' (VIIIa-b/b)	LRHS
bosniacum **new**	GAuc
'Brasilia' (Ia-b/b)	LRHS
'Bright Pixie'	NBlu
'Bright Star' (VIb-c/c)	LAma MCri
brownii (IX)	EBee EBrs ECho GAuc LAma MCri WWst
bulbiferum	ECho GAuc GBuc
- var. ***croceum*** (IX)	ECho GAuc
'Butter Pixie'[PBR] (Ia/b)	LAma LRHS WGor
callosum	GAuc
§ ***canadense*** (IX)	CDes GAuc GBuc LAma WCru
- var. ***coccineum*** (IX)	GBuc
- var. ***flavum***	see *L. canadense*
candidum (IX) 🏆H4	CArn CAvo CBcs CBro CFFs CTri EBee EBrs ECha ECho EHrv ELan EPfP EPot ERCP GAuc IHer LAma LAst LRHS MAvo MCri MHer NGHP SEND SPer WBrE WCot WSpi
- var. ***cernuum*** **new**	GAuc
'Cappuccino' **new**	LRHS
carniolicum	see *L. pyrenaicum* subsp. *carniolicum*
'Casa Blanca' (VIIb/b-c) 🏆H4	CAvo CBro CFFs EBrs EPfP GBuc GKev LAma LRHS MCri NBir SCoo SPer WFar
'Casa Rosa'	see *L.* 'Rote Horn'
'Centrefold' (Ia-b/b)	GBuc LRHS NNor
cernuum (IX)	EBee EBrs ECho GAuc LAma LRHS MCri SPer
* - 'Album'	EBee EBrs ECho GAuc LRHS SPer
chalcedonicum (IX)	GAuc
'Chinook' (Ia/b-c)	NNor
Citronella Group (Ic/d)	CAvo CFFs EBrs ECho LAma LRHS MCri NNor WFar
Cobra = 'Zantricob'[PBR] (VIIa/b)	LRHS
'Color Parade' (VIIb/b)	LRHS
columbianum (IX)	EBrs ECho GAuc GBuc GEdr NMen WHal
- B&SWJ 9564	WCru
- NNS 96-134	EBee
- dwarf (IX)	EBrs ECho GAuc NMen
'Con Amore' (VIIb/b)	LRHS SCoo SPer WFar
'Conca d'Or'[PBR] (VIIIb/b)	SMrm WWst
concolor (IX)	GAuc
- var. ***pulchellum*** (IX) **new**	GAuc
- var. ***stictum***	GAuc
'Connecticut King' (Ia/b)	EPfP LAma MCri
'Corina' (Ia/b)	GBuc NNor SGar
'Costa del Sol' (Ia/b)	EBrs
'Côte d'Azur' (Ia/b-c)	CBro GKev LAma NBlu NNor SBch SRms WGor
'Coulance' (VII-/d)	EBrs
'Crimson Pixie' (Ia/b)	CBro ECho LRHS NGdn NPri SPet
× ***dalhansonii*** (IX)	GAuc SPhx WCot
- Backhouse hybrids (IIc/d)	CAvo
§ - 'Marhan' (IIc/d)	ECho GAuc
- 'Mrs R.O. Backhouse' (IIc/d)	EBrs ECho GEdr
§ ***dauricum*** (IX)	GAuc
- f. ***rebunense***	EBee
- var. ***yunnanense*** **new**	GAuc
davidii (IX)	CPLG EBee EBrs ECho GAuc GEdr LAma MCri WCru
§ - var. ***willmottiae*** (IX)	EBee GAuc WCot
'Denia' (Ib/-)	LRHS
'Devine' (IX) **new**	LAma
'Diabora' (Ia/b)	GBuc
distichum	GAuc
- B&SWJ 794	WCru
'Dizzy' (VIIa-b/b-c)	MCri
'Dot Com' (Ia/c) **new**	LRHS
duchartrei (IX)	CDes CPLG EBee EBrs ECho GAuc GBuc GEdr LAma LRHS NSla SMac WAbe WCru
- from Gansu, China **new**	GAuc
'Early Bird' (IIc/c-d) **new**	LRHS
'Ed' (VIIb/b-c)	LAma NNor
'Eileen North' (Ic/-)	GBuc
'Electric' (Ia/b-c)	NNor
'Elodie'[PBR] (1a/b)	CAvo CFFs ECho LRHS
'Enchantment' (Ia/b)	LAma NNor
euxanthum (IX)	GAuc
'Evelina' (VIIb/b)	EBrs
'Everest' (VII-/c)	NNor
'Fancy Joy'	MBri
'Fangio' (VIIIa/b)	LRHS
fargesii (IX)	GAuc GEdr
'Fata Morgana' (Ia/b) 🏆H4	EBrs EPfP LRHS SCoo
'Feuerzauber' (Ia-b/b)	SPer
'Fire King' (Ib/d)	EPfP LAma LRHS MCri SCoo WFar
formosanum (IX)	EBrs ECho GAuc LFur LRHS MCri MMuc NChi WCot
- RWJ 10005	WCru
- var. ***pricei*** (IX)	CWCL EBee EBrs ECho EDAr ELan EPot GAuc GEdr GGar LRHS MHer NMen NWCA SIng WPer
- 'White Swan' (IX)	GBuc
'Fresco' (VII)	ECho
'Garden Party' (VIIb/b) 🏆H4	EBrs LRHS LSou WFar
'Gerrit Zalm'[PBR] **new**	LRHS
'Gibraltar' (Ia/b)	MCri

'Glossy Wings' (VIIIa-b/b)	GBuc NNor
'Golden Joy' (Ia/-)	MBri
'Golden Melody' (Ia/b-c)	MCri
Golden Splendor Group (VIb-c/a) ♀H4	EBrs LAma LRHS MCri SCoo SMeo SPer
'Golden Stargazer' (VIIa-b/b)	CSut LRHS
'Gran Cru' (Ia/-) ♀H4	EBrs EWll LRHS MCri NNor
'Gran Paradiso' (Ia/b)	MCri SRms
Green Magic Group (VI-/a)	NNor
'Halloween' (I a/-) **new**	LRHS
hansonii (IX)	EBee EBrs ECho GAuc GEdr LAma MCri
- B&SWJ 4756 from Aomori, Japan **new**	WCru
- B&SWJ 8506	WCru
'Heloma' (Ib/-)	EBrs
henrici (IX) **new**	GAuc
henryi (IX) ♀H4	CAvo CFFs CSWP EBee EBrs ECho EPfP GAuc IHer LAma LRHS MCri SMeo WCot WCru
- var. ***citrinum***	ECho GAuc
'Hit Parade' (VII)	LAma
× ***hollandicum***	MCri
'Honey Bee' (I) **new**	LRHS
'Hotlips' (VIIb/b-d)	EPfP LRHS SPer
humboldtii (IX)	GAuc
- subsp. ***ocellatum*** **new**	GAuc
'Ibarra' (Ia/b)	MCri
Inzell = 'Holebaba' (Ia/-)	EBrs
'Ivory Pixie' (Ia/b)	SPet
'Jacqueline'	EBrs GKev
japonicum (IX)	EBee EFEx WWst
- 'Albomarginatum' (IX)	GEdr WWst
'Journey's End' (VIId)	GBuc LAma NNor
§ 'Joy' (VIIa-b/b) ♀H4	LAma LRHS MCri NNor
§ ***kelleyanum*** (IX)	GAuc GBuc
- NNS 98-373	WCot
kelloggii (IX)	ECho GAuc WCot
kesselringianum	EBrs GAuc
× ***kewense*** 'White Henryi' (VIb-c/c)	EBee
'King Pete' (Ib/b-c) ♀H4	CAvo EBrs
'Lady Alice' (VI-/d)	EBrs LRHS
§ ***lancifolium*** (IX)	CArn CHid EPot GBin LRHS WBVN WBrk WFar
- B&SWJ 539	WCru
* - ***album***	WBor
- Farrer's form	LFur WCot
- var. ***flaviflorum*** (IX)	EBrs GAuc GBuc MCri
- 'Flore Pleno' (IX/d)	CSWP EBee EBrs EPPr GAuc GBuc GCal GGar GKir LHop LRHS MHer MMHG NBir WBrk WCot WCru WFar WHil WTin
* - var. ***forrestii*** (IX)	GAuc MCri
- Forrest's form (IX)	CPMA LRHS
- var. ***fortunei*** (IX)	GAuc GCal SDix
- - B&SWJ 4352	WCru
- var. ***splendens*** (IX) ♀H4	CBro EBee EBrs ECGP ECho EPfP GAuc GKev LAma LRHS MCri NBid NNor
* - ***viridulum***	GAuc
'Landini'PBR (Ia/b)	LRHS
lankongense (IX)	CDes EBee GAuc GEdr LAma MCri
'Latvia' (Ia/b)	ECho
'Le Rêve'	see *L.* 'Joy'
ledebourii (IX)	GAuc
leichtlinii	EBee EBrs ECho EPot GAuc IHer MCri
- B&SWJ 4519	WCru
- 'Iwashimiza' (IX)	MCri
- var. ***maximowiczii*** **new**	GAuc
'Lemon Pixie'PBR (Ia/b)	LAma NPri
'Lennox' ♀H4 **new**	LRHS
'Leslie Woodriff' (VIIIb-c/d)	WWst
leucanthum (IX)	EBee GAuc LAma
- var. ***centifolium*** (IX)	GAuc MCri WCru
lijiangense	GAuc GEdr MCri
'Little John'	LRHS MBri
Lollypop = 'Holebibi' (Ia/b)	EBrs ECho EPfP GBuc LRHS MBri NNor SCoo SPet
longiflorum (IX) ♀H2-3	EBee EBrs ECho GAuc LAma MCri SCoo
- B&SWJ 11376	WCru
- 'Memories'	MBri
§ - 'White American' (Vb/a)	CBro CSWP EBrs ECho EPfP SPer
- 'White Heaven'PBR (Vb/a)	EPfP WGor
lophophorum (IX)	EBee EPot GAuc LAma WWst
- var. ***linearifolium***	GAuc
'Lovely Girl' (VII-/b)	CSut EBrs LRHS
'Luxor' (Ib)	EBrs EWll LRHS MCri NBir SPer
mackliniae (IX)	CLAP CWCL EBee EBrs ECho GAuc GBuc GCal GCra GEdr GGGa GMac ITim NBir NMen NWCA WAbe WHal
- deep pink-flowered	GGGa
- robust habit	GBuc GGar WWst
× ***maculatum*** **new**	GAuc
- var. ***davuricum***	see *L. dauricum*
'Magento' (Ia-b/b)	LRHS
'Marco Polo' (Ia/-)	SCoo WFar
'Marhan'	see *L.* × *dalhansonii* 'Marhan'
'Marrakech'PBR **new**	LRHS
martagon (IX) ♀H4	Widely available
- var. ***albiflorum*** (IX) **new**	GAuc
- var. ***album*** (IX) ♀H4	CAvo CBro CFFs CLAP CSWP EBee EBrs ECha ECho EHrv ELan EPfP EPot GAuc GBuc GEdr GMaP LAma LRHS MTho NBir NChi SRms WAbe WCom WCot WPtf WShi
- var. ***cattaniae*** (IX)	EPot GAuc MCri WCot
- var. ***daugava***	WWst
- var. ***pilosiusculum*** (IX)	EBee GAuc
- 'Plenum' (IX/d)	WCot
- var. ***sanguineo purpureum*** (IX) **new**	GAuc
'Maxwill' (Ic/d)	EBrs
medeoloides (IX)	EBee EBrs ECho EFEx GAuc GBuc LRHS NMen WWst
'Mediterrannee' (VIIb/d)	LRHS
'Menton' (Ia/c)	MCri
michiganense (IX)	CSWP GAuc GBuc
'Milano' (Ia/b)	MCri
'Miss Lucy'PBR (VIIa-b/b-c)	CHid CSut LRHS
'Miss Rio' (VII)	LRHS SCoo
'Mona Lisa' (VIIb/b-c)	EBrs EPfP IMon LAma LSou MBri NGdn NNor WBVN WFar WGor
§ ***monadelphum*** (IX)	EBee EBrs ECho EPot GAuc GBuc GCra LAma NLar WCot
'Monte Negro' (Ia/b)	CAvo CFFs EBrs ECho LRHS NGdn
'Montreal' (VIIa-b/b)	LRHS
'Montreux' (Ia/b-c)	LAma
'Muscadet'PBR (VIIa-b/b)	CSut EBrs EPfP LRHS NGdn
§ ***nanum*** (IX)	EBee EBrs ECho GAuc GBuc GEdr GGGa LAma LRHS NMen WCru WHal WWst
- AGS/ES	WWst
- EMAK 670	EBee WWst
- from Bhutan (IX)	EBee EBrs ECho GAuc GBuc GGar NMen WCru
- var. ***flavidum*** (IX)	EBee EBrs ECho GEdr NMen WWst
- - hybrids	WWst
nepalense (IX)	CBcs CBro CFir CHid CPLG CSWP EBee EBla EBrs ECho EPot ERCP GAuc GEdr GGar GKir GMac IHer

	LAma LRHS MCot MCri MDun NCob WCot WCru WFar WPnP
- B&SWJ 2985	WCru
- CC 3663	WCot
'Nerone' new	CHid
'Netty's Pride' (Ia/b-c) new	CHid LRHS
'New Wave' (I) new	NBlu
nobilissimum (IX)	EFEx
'Nove Cento' (Ia/b) ♀[H4]	LRHS MCri
Odeon Group (VI-/a)	MCri
'Olivia' (Ia/-)	EBrs ECho LAma MCri NNor
Olympic Group (VI-/a)	MCri
'Orange Pixie' (Ia/b)	EPfP LRHS MCri NBlu SCoo SPad SPet WGor
'Orange Triumph' (Ia/-)	EPfP NNor
oriental hybrids	EBrs
* Oriental Superb Group	NGdn
§ ***oxypetalum*** (IX)	ECho GAuc GBuc GGGa WWst
- var. ***insigne*** (IX)	EBee EBrs ECho GAuc GBin GBuc GEdr GGGa GGar LRHS NMen NSla WAbe WCru WHal WWst
papilliferum	EBrs ECho LAma
pardalinum (IX) ♀[H4]	CBro CWCL EBee EBrs ECho ELan ERCP GAuc GKev IFro LFur LRHS MCot WCot WCru WHal WPnP
- var. ***giganteum*** (IX)	CLAP EPfP MCri MNrw SPer WTin
- subsp. ***pardalinum*** (IX) NNS 00-488	WWst
- - NNS 02=228	WWst
- subsp. ***shastense*** (IX)	NMen WWst
- - NNS 00-490	WCot
- - NNS 98-374	WWst
- subsp. ***shastense*** × ***vollmeri***	WWst
× ***parkmanii*** Imperial Silver Group (VIIb/c)	LAma
parryi (IX)	EBee ECho GAuc GBuc WHal WWst
- NNS 03-384	WWst
parvum (IX)	EBee ECho GAuc GBuc
- 'Halliday' new	GAuc
'Peach Pixie' (Ia/b)	NBir NNor NPri SCoo
pensylvanicum	GAuc
philadelphicum (IX)	GAuc
- var. ***andinum*** new	GAuc
philippinense (IX)	CDes EBee MCri WPGP
'Pink Heart' new	LRHS
Pink Perfection Group (VIb/a) ♀[H4]	CAvo CBro CFFs EBrs EPfP ERCP LAma LRHS MCri NNor SBch SCoo SPer WFar
'Pink Pixie'[PBR] (Ia/b)	SGar
'Pink Tiger' (Ib/c)	CAvo CFFs EBrs GKev MCri NNor WGor
'Pink Twinkle'	EBrs
poilanei HWJ 681 new	WCru
pomponium (IX)	EBee GAuc GCal
primulinum var. ***burmanicum***	GAuc
- var. ***ochraceum***	GAuc LAma WCru WWst
§ ***pumilum*** (IX) ♀[H4]	EBee EBrs ECho ERCP GAuc GBuc GKev LAma LRHS MCri MTho SBch WAul
'Purple Prince' (VIIIa-b/a-b) new	LRHS
pyrenaicum (IX)	CAby EBrs ECho GAuc GGar GKir IBlr IFro MCri WCot WPGP WShi
§ - subsp. ***carniolicum*** (IX)	ECho GAuc MCri WCot
§ - - var. ***albanicum*** (IX)	EBee GAuc GBuc
- subsp. ***pyrenaicum*** var. ***rubrum*** (IX)	GEdr
'Quinta'[PBR]	ECho
'Red Carpet' (Ia/b)	EBrs MCri NBir NNor NPri SPad WGor

'Red Dutch' (Ia-b/c)	ERCP
'Red Hot' (VIIIc-d/b) new	LRHS
'Red Rum'	MBri
'Red Star'	LRHS
'Red Twinkle'	EBrs LRHS
regale (IX) ♀[H4]	CArn CAvo CBro CFFs CFir CMea CSam EBee EBrs ECha EHrv ELan EPfP ERCP GAuc GGar IHer LAma LEdu LRHS MCot MCri NNor SPer WBVN WBor WBrE WCot WFar
- 'Album' (IX)	CAvo CSWP EBee EBrs GAuc GBuc LAma LRHS MCri NNor SBch SCoo SGar WCot WFar
§ - 'Royal Gold' (IXb/a))	GAuc MCri
'Reinesse' (Ia/b)	LRHS MBri NPri
'Rialto'[PBR] new	LRHS
'Robina' new	WCot
'Rodolfa'[PBR]	LRHS LSou
'Roma' (Ia/b)	EWll LAma NBir
'Rosefire' (Ia/b)	NNor
'Rosita' (Ia/b-c)	MCri WFar
rosthornii	CPLG GAuc GBuc GEdr WCot WCru WWst
'Rote Horn' (VIIIb/a)	MCri
'Royal Gold'	see *L. regale* 'Royal Gold'
rubellum (IX)	EFEx GAuc GBuc WWst
rubescens (IX) new	GAuc
'Ruud' (VIIb/b-c)	EPfP LAma
sachalinense	CStu GAuc
- RBS 0235	EPPr
'Salmon Twinkle' (Ib-c/c)	EBrs WFar
'Sam' (VIIb/c) ♀[H4]	EPfP GBuc LAma
sargentiae (IX)	EBrs GAuc GBuc GGGa MCri NMen WCot
- Cox 7099	EBee WWst
'Satisfaction' (VIIIa-b/-) new	LRHS
'Scheherazade' new	LRHS
'Sea Treasure' (VIIIa-b/-) new	LRHS
sempervivoideum (IX)	EBrs ECho GAuc LAma
shastense	see *L. kelleyanum*
'Siberia'[PBR] (VIIa-b/b)	EBrs
'Silly Girl' (Ia/-)	MCri NNor
§ 'Snow Crystal' (Ia/b)	EPfP
'Sorbonne' (VII)	LRHS
souliei (IX)	GAuc
'Souvenir'[PBR]	LRHS NGdn
'Space Star' (VIIa-b-c) new	LRHS
speciosum (IX)	GAuc NSla
- B&SWJ 4847	WCru
- var. ***album*** (IX)	EBee EBrs ECho EPfP GAuc GBuc LEdu LRHS MCri NBir NNor SBch
- var. ***gloriosoides*** (IX)	EBrs EPot GAuc LAma
- var. ***roseum*** (IX)	GBuc NNor
- var. ***rubrum*** (IX)	EBee EBrs ECha ECho EPfP GAuc GBuc LAma LRHS MCri NBir NLar SPer
§ - - 'Uchida' (IXb-c/d)	CPLG EPfP GAuc MCri NNor
Sphinx = 'Holecaca' (Ia/c-d)	WCot
'Staccato' (Ia/c)	MCri
'Star Gazer' (VIIa/c)	CBro CSut EBrs ELan LAma LRHS MCri MHav NBlu NNor NPri SCoo SPer WFar WGor
'Starburst Sensation' (VIIIb/a) new	LRHS
'Starfighter' (VIIa-b/c)	EBrs EPfP MCri SPet
'Sterling Star' (Ia/b)	EPfP MCri NNor
Stones = 'Holebobo' (Ia/b)	LRHS NNor
'Sulphur King'	WCot
sulphureum	GAuc LAma MCri WWst
'Sun Ray' (Ia/b)	MCri
superbum (IX)	EBee ECho GAuc GBuc GEdr LAma WCot WCru WPGP

'Sweet Kiss' (Ia) MBri
'Sweet Lord' EBrs
'Sweet Surrender' (Ib-c/c-d) EBrs LRHS MCri NNor
szovitsianum see *L. monadelphum*
taliense (IX) ECho GAuc GBuc GEdr LAma MCri WCru WWst
tenuifolium see *L. pumilum*
tigrinum see *L. lancifolium*
'Time Out'PBR (VIIa-b/b-c) EPfP
'Tom Pouce' (VIIa/b) EPfP
'Touch' (VIIb/-) LRHS MCri
Triumphator = 'Zanlophator'PBR (VIIIb/a-b) EPfP LRHS MCri
tsingtauense (IX) GAuc
- B&SWJ 519 WCru
- B&SWJ 4263 WCru
'Uchida Kanoka' see *L. speciosum* 'Uchida'
'Umbria' (Ia/b) LRHS
'Vermeer' (Ia-b/b-c) EBrs EWll LRHS WFar
'Victory Joy' MBri
'Vivaldi' **new** LRHS
vollmeri (IX) GAuc NMen WCru WWst
- JCA 1.500.901 WWst
wallichianum (IX) EBee EBrs ECho EPot GAuc GBuc LAma LRHS
wardii (IX) CPLG
washingtonianum (IX) GAuc
- var. ***purpurascens*** (IX) GAuc
'White American' see *L. longiflorum* 'White American'
'White Dwarf' (Ia/b) EBrs
'White Mountain' (VIIc) SPer
'White Paradise' (V) SCoo
White Pixie see *L.* 'Snow Crystal'
'White Twinkle' (Ia-b/b) CAvo EBrs
wigginsii (IX) GAuc GEdr MCri
- NNS 00-493 WWst
willmottiae see *L. davidii* var. *willmottiae*
wilsonii GAuc
'Woodriff's Memory' (VIIa-b/b) EBrs
xanthellum var. ***luteum*** CDes
Yellow Blaze Group (Ia/b) EPfP
'Yellow Star' (Ib/b-c) EBrs NNor

lime see *Citrus aurantiifolia*

lime, djeruk see *Citrus amblycarpa*

lime, Philippine see × *Citrofortunella microcarpa*

Limnanthes (*Limnanthaceae*)

douglasii ♀H4 CArn CHrt EPfP SECG SIde SIng

Limonium (*Plumbaginaceae*)

bellidifolium CMea ECha EDAr MWat WAbe WHoo WPer WTin
- 'Dazzling Blue' WHrl
binervosum EBWF
'Blauer Diamant' EBee NBre
chilwellii ECGP LRHS NCGa
cosyrense CMea MHer NMen WAbe WPer
dumosum see *Goniolimon tataricum* var. *angustifolium*
gmelinii MBel SPlb WClo WPer
* - subsp. ***hungaricum*** NLar
gougetianum LLHF WPer
latifolium see *L. platyphyllum*
minutum WHoo
paradoxum WAbe
perezii EShb WPer
§ ***platyphyllum*** Widely available
- 'Robert Butler' GCal GKir LRHS
- 'Violetta' CPrp EBee ECGP ECha ELan EPfP GCal GKir LAst LRHS MBri MRav NCGa NOrc SPer WHoo
speciosum see *Goniolimon incanum*
tataricum see *Goniolimon tataricum*
vulgare WHer

Linanthastrum see *Linanthus*

Linanthus (*Polemoniaceae*)

sp. **new** NPol

Linaria (*Scrophulariaceae*)

aeruginea CSpe
- subsp. ***nevadensis*** 'Gemstones' SBch
alpina CSpe ECho ECtt GGar LFur MTho NRya SRms WEas
anticaria 'Antique Silver' EBee ECha GBuc LSou MRav SBch WPGP WPtf WWEG
Blue Lace = 'Yalin' LSou
cymbalaria see *Cymbalaria muralis*
§ ***dalmatica*** CEnt EBee ECha ELan EPPr GGar IFro MWea NBid NBro SBch WCFE WCot WKif WMoo WPer WWEG
dalmatica × ***purpurea*** WCot
× ***dominii*** 'Carnforth' LSou NBre NBro SBch SMrm WCot WWEG
- 'Yuppie Surprise' CHid EBee NBir SWvt WPGP WSpi
genistifolia MDKP
- subsp. ***dalmatica*** see *L. dalmatica*
hepaticifolia see *Cymbalaria hepaticifolia*
* ***lobata alba*** ECho SPlb
nevadensis 'Grenada Sol' MWea
origanifolia see *Chaenorhinum origanifolium*
pallida see *Cymbalaria pallida*
pilosa see *Cymbalaria pilosa*
purpurea CBgR COIW CTri EBWF EBee EHoe EHrv ELan EPfP IFoB LBMP LRHS MHer MMuc MNHC NBPC NBro NPer NPri NVic SECG SPhx SRms WCAu WClo WCot WMoo WPer
- 'Alba' see *L. purpurea* 'Springside White'
- 'Canon Went' Widely available
- pink-flowered CSpe
- 'Radcliffe Innocence' see *L. purpurea* 'Springside White'
§ - 'Springside White' CBgR CElw EBee ECha ECtt GBuc LBMP LRHS MBri NBir NPri SBch SPhx WAul WCot WPer
- 'Thurgarton Beauty' MDKP
repens CPom MNrw WCot WHer
reticulata 'Red Velvet' CSpe
× ***sepium*** WCot
'Toni Aldiss' SPhx
triornithophora CEnt CFir CSpe EBee ECha GBuc IGor LBMP LRHS MMuc MNFA MSpe MWea WKif WMoo
- 'Pink Budgies' LSou
- purple-flowered ELan WMoo
- 'Rosea' **new** MSpe
tristis CEnt
vulgaris CArn EBWF LDai MDKP MHer MNHC NMir NSco SECG WHer WJek
- 'Peloria' MDKP WCom
'Winifrid's Delight' EPfP NBre

Lindelofia (*Boraginaceae*)

anchusoides misapplied	see *L. longiflora*
anchusoides (Lindl.) Lehm.	EPPr NBid
§ ***longiflora***	EBee GBuc GCal GCra SMrm

Lindera (*Lauraceae*)

benzoin	CAgr CBcs CMac EPfP GKir ISea LRHS MBri NLar SSpi WDin
communis	WPGP
erythrocarpa	CBcs EPfP NLar SSpi
- B&SWJ 6271	WCru
- B&SWJ 8730	WCru
megaphylla	CBcs CHEx
obtusiloba 🏆H4	CAbP EPfP SSpi WPat
- B&SWJ 8723	WCru
praecox	EPfP WPGP
- B&SWJ 10802	WCru
reflexa	CGHE EPfP NLar WPGP
sericea	SSpi
- B&SWJ 11141	WCru
strychnifolia	EPfP
triloba B&SWJ 5570	WCru
umbellata var. ***membranacea*** B&SWJ 6227	WCru

Lindernia (*Scrophulariaceae*)

grandiflora	CSpe EBee LLWG SIng

Linnaea (*Caprifoliaceae*)

borealis	CStu ILis WAbe
- subsp. ***americana***	NWCA

Linum ✿ (*Linaceae*)

africanum	EShb
arboreum 🏆H4	CMea LLHF WAbe WPat
- NS 529	NWCA
campanulatum	WThu
- 'Sulphur'	LRHS
capitatum	CMea NSla WAbe
flavum	CTri EPfP GKev GKir
- 'Compactum'	CMea EBee ECho GGar LLHF SPad SRms WCot
'Gemmell's Hybrid' 🏆H4	ECho EWes MDKP NBir NMen WAbe WPat
monogynum	ECou
§ - var. ***diffusum***	ECou
- 'Nelson'	see *L. monogynum* var. *diffusum*
narbonense	CMdw CSam ECGP LBMP LDai LFur NLar SBch SRms
- 'Heavenly Blue'	GKir
§ ***perenne***	CArn CRWN CTri EBee ECha ELan EPfP GKir GMaP LFur LRHS MHer MNHC NBro NMun SIde SPer SRms WCAu WPer WWEG
- 'Album'	EBee ECha ELan EPfP NLar SPer WPer
- subsp. ***alpinum***	CMea
- - 'Alice Blue'	LRHS
- subsp. ***biokovoensis*** **new**	EBee GKev
§ - 'Blau Saphir'	EBee GQue LRHS MWat NLar SRms WRHF WWEG
- Blue Sapphire	see *L. perenne* 'Blau Saphir'
- 'Diamant'	EBee LRHS
- 'Himmelszelt'	LBMP NLar SMrm
- subsp. ***lewisii***	NBir
- 'Nanum Diamond'	NLar
- 'Nanum Sapphire'	see *L. perenne* 'Blau Saphir'
sibiricum	see *L. perenne*
suffruticosum	WPat
subsp. ***salsoloides*** 'Nanum'	
- - 'Prostratum'	GBuc
uninerve	WAbe
usitatissimum	CRWN MHer SIde

Lippia (*Verbenaceae*)

sp.	SWvt
canescens	see *Phyla nodiflora* var. *canescens*
chamaedrifolia	see *Verbena peruviana*
citriodora	see *Aloysia triphylla*
dulcis	CArn EOHP
nodiflora	see *Phyla nodiflora*
repens	see *Phyla nodiflora*

Liquidambar ✿ (*Hamamelidaceae*)

acalycina	CDul CLnd CPMA EBee ELan EMil EPfP GKir LRHS MGos MRav NLar SBir SCoo SPoG SSpi SSta WPGP WPat
- 'Burgundy Flush'	CPMA NLar
- 'Spinners' **new**	SSpi
formosana	CDul CEnd CMCN CMac EBee EPfP IArd MGos MSnd NPCo SBir SSpi SSta WPGP
- B&SWJ 6855	WCru
- Monticola Group	CPMA EPfP SBir SSta
orientalis	CMCN CPMA EPfP LLHF NPCo SBir SSta
styraciflua	Widely available
- 'Andrew Hewson'	CAbP CLnd CPMA EMil LRHS MAsh NLar SBir SCoo SSta
- 'Anja'	CPMA MBlu SBir SSta
- 'Anneke'	CPMA SBir SSta
- 'Aurea'	see *L. styraciflua* 'Variegata' Overeynder
- 'Aurea Variegata'	see *L. styraciflua* 'Variegata' Overeynder
- 'Aurora'	CPMA SBir SLim
- 'Brodsman' **new**	NLar
- 'Burgundy'	CPMA CTho LLHF LRHS MBlu NHol SBir SSta WPGP WPat
- 'Elstead Mill'	CAbP
- 'Festeri'	CEnd SBir SSta WPat
- 'Festival'	CPMA MBlu SSta
- 'Frosty' (v)	CPMA
- 'Globe'	see *L. styraciflua* 'Gum Ball'
- 'Golden Treasure' (v)	CBcs CDul CMCN CPMA LRHS MAsh MBri MGos NLar SMad SPoG WPat
§ - 'Gum Ball'	CEnd CLnd CMCN CPMA EBee EPfP ERom EWes LLHF MBri MGos NLar NPCo SBir SCoo SSta WPat
- Happidaze = 'Hapdell'	CEnd CPMA NLar WPat
- 'Jennifer Carol'	CPMA NLar
- 'Kia'	CAbP CEnd CPMA LLHF NLar SBir WPat
- 'Kirsten'	CPMA
- 'Lane Roberts' 🏆H4	CDoC CDul CLnd CMCN CMac CSBt CTho EBee EMil EPfP GKir IArd LHop MBlu MGos MWat NLar SBir SCoo SMad SReu SSta WDin WPGP WPat
- 'Manon' (v)	CDoC CEnd CPMA EMil NBhm SBir SPoG
- 'Midwest Sunset'	MBlu WPGP WPat
- 'Moonbeam' (v)	CDul CEnd CPMA EBee NLar SBir SLim SSta WPat
- 'Moraine'	CPMA SBir
- 'Naree'	CPMA NLar SBir
- 'Oconee'	CEnd EPfP WPat

- 'Paarl' (v) CPMA
- 'Palo Alto' CEnd CPMA LLHF LRHS MBlu NHol SBir SCoo SSta WPGP WPat
- 'Parasol' CAbP CEnd CPMA NLar NPCo SBir SSta
- 'Pendula' CLnd CPMA MBlu SBir SSta
- 'Penwood' CPMA NLar SSta
- 'Rotundiloba' CMCN CPMA EMil EPfP LLHF SBir SSta WPat
- 'Schock's Gold' CPMA
- 'Silver King' (v) CDul CLnd CMCN CMac CPMA EBee ECrN EMil LRHS MBri MGos NLar NPCo SCoo SLim SPoG SSta WFoF WPat
- 'Slender Silhouette' CAbP EBee EPfP LLHF LRHS MAsh MBlu SBir SGol SPoG SSpi WMou
- 'Stared' CEnd CLnd CPMA EBee EMil LRHS MBlu MBri NLar SBir SCoo SPoG WPGP WPat
- 'Thea' CAbP CPMA EMil EPfP LRHS MAsh MBlu SBir SSta
§ - 'Variegata' Overeynder (v) CBcs CBot CDul CLnd CMac CPMA EBee ELan EMil EPfP LRHS MAsh MGos SLim SPoG SSta WDin WPat
- 'White Star' (v) CPMA
- 'Worplesdon' ♀H4 Widely available

Liriodendron ✿ (*Magnoliaceae*)

'Chapel Hill' MBlu
chinense CBcs CDul CGHE CLnd CMCN CTho EPfP MBlu WFar WPGP WPat
chinense* × *tulipifera new WPGP
'Doc Deforce's Delight' MBlu MBri
tulipifera ♀H4 Widely available
- 'Ardis' CMCN NLar
- 'Aureomarginatum' (v) ♀H4 Widely available
- 'Fastigiatum' CDoC CDul CEnd CLnd CMCN CMac CTho EBee ECrN ELan EPfP IMGH LRHS MAsh MBlu MBri MGos SPoG SSta WPat
- 'Glen Gold' CEnd CMCN MBlu MGos NLar
- 'Mediopictum' (v) CTho
- 'Purgatory' MBlu
- 'Roodhaan' NLar

Liriope ✿ (*Convallariaceae*)

HWJ 590 from Vietnam WPGP
from Vietnam WPGP
'Big Blue' see *L. muscari* 'Big Blue'
§ ***exiliflora*** CEnd CLAP NLar WWEG
- 'Ariaka-janshige' (v) WWEG
- Silvery Sunproof misapplied see *L. muscari* 'Variegata', *L. spicata* 'Gin-ryu'
§ ***gigantea*** CLAP MBNS SWat
graminifolia misapplied see *L. muscari*
hyacinthifolia see *Reineckea carnea*
kansuensis ERos
koreana EBee EPPr GCal
- B&SWJ 8821 WCru
'Majestic' CBct CHar CLAP EBee WFar WHoo
minor new CMac
§ ***muscari*** ♀H4 Widely available
- B&SWJ 561 WCru
- 'Alba' see *L. muscari* 'Monroe White'
§ - 'Big Blue' CBct CBgR CKno CLAP CMac CPLG EBee ELon EPPr EPfP EShb LEdu LHop LRHS LSRN MRav MSwo NLar SBch SUsu SWvt WCFE WMoo WPnP WWEG
- 'Christmas Tree' CLAP EPPr WHoo WMoo
- 'Evergreen Giant' see *L. gigantea*
- 'Gold-banded' (v) CLAP EBee EMil EPfP LRHS NSti SMad SPer WCot WFar WSpi
- 'Goldfinger' CPLG EBee EPla WPGP
- 'Ingwersen' CBgR EBee EBrs ECho ELon EPPr EPfP LRHS NMRc SMeo WGrn WHoo WPnP
- 'John Burch' (v) CBct CBgR CLAP EBee ELon EShb LRHS MBNS MCCP NLar SMad WGrn WSpi WWEG
- 'Majestic' misapplied see *L. exiliflora*
- 'Moneymaker' EBee EPPr
§ - 'Monroe White' CBct CBgR CLAP CMac CPLG EBee EBla ECha ECho EHrv ELon EPfP EShb EWTr GKir LAst LEdu LRHS MRav NLar SBod SMac SPet WAul WFar WSpi WWEG
- 'Okina' (v) EBee ELon WCot
- 'Paul Aden' EPfP WPGP
- 'Pee Dee Ingot' NLar
- 'Royal Purple' CBct CHar CLAP EBee EPPr EPfP GQue LRHS NBPC NGdn NLar SBch WClo WCot WGrn
- 'Silver Ribbon' CLAP CMoH EBee EBla EMil EPfP EShb LAst LBMP LRHS LSRN MBNS NSti WOut WPGP WWEG
- 'Silvery Midget' (v) SUsu
- 'Superba' WCot
§ - 'Variegata' (v) Widely available
- variegated, white-flowered (v) CBcs CDes CFir ECho
- 'Webster Wideleaf' EBee WHoo
'New Wonder' EHrv LEdu
platyphylla see *L. muscari*
'Samantha' EBee ECha
spicata CBro EBee ECho ERos SWat WWEG
- 'Alba' ECho MRav MTho SIng WTin
§ - 'Gin-ryu' (v) CBct CHar CLAP CPLG EBee ECho ECtt EPPr EWes LEdu LRHS LSRN MAvo MCCP MRav SLPl SMad SPer WCot WPGP
- 'Silver Dragon' see *L. spicata* 'Gin-ryu'
- 'Small Green' EBee WWEG

Lisianthius (*Gentianaceae*)

russelianus see *Eustoma grandiflorum*

Listera (*Orchidaceae*)

ovata WHer

Litchi (*Sapindaceae*)

chinensis CCCN

Lithocarpus ✿ (*Fagaceae*)

edulis CGHE CHEx CPLG EBee SArc WPGP

Lithodora (*Boraginaceae*)

§ ***diffusa*** ECho MWat SRot
- 'Alba' CTri ECho EPfP LRHS MGos NBlu SPer SPoG WCom WFar
- 'Baby Barbara' GKev NLAp
- 'Cambridge Blue' ECho SPer
- 'Compacta' CWCL ECho EWes NLAp NWCA WAbe WPat
§ - 'Grace Ward' ♀H4 ECho EPfP MMuc NLAp WAbe WFar WPat
§ - 'Heavenly Blue' ♀H4 Widely available
- 'Inverleith' ECho EWes LLHF LRHS
- 'Pete's Favourite' WAbe WPat
- 'Picos' CMea CPBP ECho GGar GKev NLAp NMen WAbe WCom WFar WPat WThu

- 'Star'PBR CMHG EPfP GGar GKev GKir LRHS MAvo NHol NLar SCoo SIng SPer SPoG SRot
fruticosa CArn
hispidula CWCL
× **intermedia** see *Moltkia* × *intermedia*
§ **oleifolia** ♀H4 CWCL ECho EPot LRHS MWat NBir NMen
rosmarinifolia CMoH CSpe CWCL WCFE
zahnii ECho EPot LLHF WFar WPat
- 'Azureness' CPBP WAbe

Lithophragma (*Saxifragaceae*)

heterophyllum EBee
parviflorum CAby EWes MTho NLar NWCA

Lithospermum (*Boraginaceae*)

diffusum see *Lithodora diffusa*
doerfleri see *Moltkia doerfleri*
'Grace Ward' see *Lithodora diffusa* 'Grace Ward'
'Heavenly Blue' see *Lithodora diffusa* 'Heavenly Blue'
officinale CArn EBWF GBar GPoy NMir
oleifolium see *Lithodora oleifolia*
purpureocaeruleum see *Buglossoides purpurocaerulea*

Litsea (*Lauraceae*)

glauca see *Neolitsea sericea*

Littonia (*Colchicaceae*)

modesta CRHN EBrs ECho

Livistona (*Arecaceae*)

australis EAmu LPal
chinensis ♀H1 CBrP CPHo EAmu LPJP LPal MREP SBig
decora CPHo CTrC EAmu LPal
mariae EAmu LPal
saribus EAmu

Lloydia (*Liliaceae*)

serotina GAuc

Loasa (*Loasaceae*)

triphylla var. **volcanica** EWes GCra WSHC

Lobelia (*Campanulaceae*)

B&SWJ 8220 from Vietnam WCru
aberdarica new CHEx
angulata see *Pratia angulata*
bequaertii new GCal
bridgesii CBow CDTJ CPLG EBee EWes EWld EWll GCal GGar GKev LLHF WMoo WPGP
§ **cardinalis** ♀H3 CArn CBen CHEx CMac CRWN EBla EHon EMFW EPfP GAbr GKir GMaP LPBA LRHS NPer SMrm SPer SPet SPlb SRms SWat SWvt WFar WMAq
- 'Bee's Flame' CFir CPrp CWGN EBee EPla GBuc GGar LBMP LRHS MBel MCot MRav MSpe NBre NEgg SAga SUsu SWat
§ - 'Elmfeuer' CMHG EBee EHoe ELon EPfP EShb LAst MBNS MWat NGby NLar NPri SBch SMrm SPlb SWvt WFar
- 'Eulalia Berridge' CAby CSam EBee ECtt GBuc LRHS SMrm WFar WSHC
- subsp. **graminea** var. **multiflora** CFir
- 'Illumination' GBuc
§ - 'Queen Victoria' ♀H3 Widely available
N - 'Russian Princess' misapplied EGxp SWvt WWEG WWlt
chinensis LLWG
'Cinnabar Deep Red' see *L.* × *speciosa* 'Fan Tiefrot'
'Cinnabar Rose' see *L.* × *speciosa* 'Fan Zinnoberrosa'
Compliment Blue see *L.* × *speciosa* 'Kompliment Blau'
Compliment Deep Red see *L.* × *speciosa* 'Kompliment Tiefrot'
Compliment Purple see *L.* × *speciosa* 'Kompliment Purpur'
Compliment Scarlet see *L.* × *speciosa* 'Kompliment Scharlach'
'Diva Blue' **new** LRHS
dortmanna GAuc
erinus Anabel Blue Mystery **new** SVil
- Big Blue = 'Weslobigblue'PBR LAst
- Blue Star = 'Wesstar'PBR LAst
- 'Kathleen Mallard' (d) CCCN ECtt SWvt
- 'Pink Star' LAst
- 'Purple Star' **new** LSou SVil
- 'Richardii' see *L. richardsonii*
- 'Sailor Star' LAst
excelsa CSpe EShb GGar NCGa SGar SPav WFar WSHC
- B&SWJ 9513 WCru
Fan Deep Red see *L.* × *speciosa* 'Fan Tiefrot'
'Fan Deep Rose' see *L.* × *speciosa* 'Fan Orchidrosa'
'Fan Salmon' see *L.* × *speciosa* 'Fan Lachs'
'Flamingo' see *L.* × *speciosa* 'Pink Flamingo'
'Forncett Merry' NBre
fulgens see *L. cardinalis*
- Saint Elmo's Fire see *L. cardinalis* 'Elmfeuer'
× **gerardii** see *L.* × *speciosa*
gibberoa CDTJ CHEx
'Gladys Lindley' EBee
grandidentata F&M 133 WPGP
'Hadspen Purple'PBR see *L.* × *speciosa* 'Hadspen Purple'
inflata CArn EOHP GPoy WCHb
kalmii WPer
- 'Blue Shadow' EBla LAst LRHS
'La Fresco' EBee
laxiflora CHid CHll LRHS MTho SAga SHom SPet
- B&SWJ 9064 WCru
- var. **angustifolia** CAby CDTJ CHEx CPrp CSam ECtt EPfP EShb EWld GCal MSpe SDnm SHGN SMrm SPav SPoG SRms SUsu WBor WCot WPrP WWlt
linnaeoides SPlb
'Lipstick' WWEG WWlt
longifolia from Chile CFee
pedunculata see *Pratia pedunculata*
'Pink Passion' **new** LRHS
polyphylla ECtt MSCN
'Queen Victoria' see *L. cardinalis* 'Queen Victoria'
regalis WCHb
§ **richardsonii** ♀H1+3 ECtt LHop NBlu SWvt
roughii GKev
'Royal Velvet' **new** CSpr IPot LRHS
seguinii B&SWJ 7065 WCru
sessilifolia CPLG EBee GBuc LPBA MSKA WPer
I - 'Nana' **new** GKev
siphilitica Widely available
- 'Alba' CEnt CSam EBee EBla EPfP GCal LPBA LRHS SPav SPoG SRms SWat SWvt WBor WCAu WCHb WFar WHoo WHrl WMnd WMoo WPer
- blue-flowered CSpe SGSe SWat SWvt
- 'Rosea' MNrw
'Sonia' SWat

§ × ***speciosa***	CEnt IKil MHer NBre SMrm SVic SWat WBor WFar WMoo WSHC
- 'Butterfly Blue'	EBee EWTr LFur WWEG
- 'Butterfly Rose'	SRot WCHb
- 'Cherry Ripe'	CPrp GCra LLHF NHol WCHb WEas
- 'Cranberry Crush'PBR	SHar
- 'Dark Crusader'	CPrp CWGN EBee ECGP ECtt ELan LAst LBMP LRHS MCot MSCN NHol SAga SMrm SWat WCHb WMnd
- dark-leaved	CMHG EBee
- deep pink	SMrm
- (Fan Series) 'Fan Blau'	EPfP NBir WHil WWEG
- - 'Fan Burgundy'	CEnt CWCL EWll LRHS SPet WHil WWEG
§ - - 'Fan Lachs'	EPfP SBch SPet WHil
§ - - 'Fan Orchidrosa' ♀H3-4	EPfP LRHS NBir NGdn SGSe SPet SRot WHil WWEG
- - 'Fan Scharlach' ♀H3-4	EBee EHon EPfP LRHS MAvo MGos NBir NLar SGar SHar SRot SWvt WDyG WHil WShi WWEG
§ - - 'Fan Tiefrot' ♀H3-4	CBen CChe EPfP MSCN MWea SAga SHar SMrm SPet SRms SWat SWvt WCHb WPer
§ - - 'Fan Zinnoberrosa' ♀H3-4	CEnt CFir CMMP EHon SRms SRot SWvt WCHb WMoo WPer
- 'Grape Knee-high'	EBee EPfP GCra LLHF LSRN MAsh SPoG SWat
§ - 'Hadspen Purple'PBR	CSpe CWGN EBee ELan ELon EPfP LRHS LSRN MBri MCCP MCot MWea NCGa NCob NHol NSti SGSe SHar SPoG SWat SWvt WWlt
- 'Kimbridge Beet'	CMac SGSe
- Kompliment Series	WWEG
§ - - 'Kompliment Blau'	CFir CWat SPet SWvt WPer
* - - 'Kompliment Pale Pink'	EShb
§ - - 'Kompliment Purpur'	MNrw SPet SWvt
§ - - 'Kompliment Scharlach' ♀H3-4	CSWP EBee EPfP LHop MNrw NHol NPer SPad SPer SPet SWvt WCHb WFar WMnd WPer WWEG
§ - - 'Kompliment Tiefrot'	CWat EWll MMuc MNrw SPet SWvt WPer
- 'Monet Moment'	CBow EBee EBla EWes GCal WSpi
- 'Pauline'	ECtt
- 'Pink Elephant' ♀H4	CBow CChe CSWP CWCL EBee GCra LRHS MDKP NBre SHar SMrs WFar WWEG
§ - 'Pink Flamingo'	CBen CMMP EBee EBla EBrs SPer SWat WCHb WFar WMoo WSHC WShi
- 'Purple Towers'	NBre
- 'Rosenkavalier'	EBee ECtt NGby WFar
- 'Rosy Pink' **new**	SMrm
- 'Ruby Slippers'	CBcs CWCL EBee EBrs ECtt ELan EPfP IPot LAst LRHS LSRN SHGN SMrs SWat WFar
N - 'Russian Princess' purple-flowered	Widely available
- 'Sparkle deVine'	WFar
- 'Tania'	Widely available
§ - 'Vedrariensis'	CMac CPrp CSam CSpe CWCL CWib EBee EBla ELan EPfP EShb GGar LPBA LRHS MCot MSCN NGdn SGar SMeo SPer SPoG SRms STes SWvt WEas WFar WHil WHoo WMnd WWEG
- 'Wildwood Splendor'	WFar
- 'Will Scarlet'	LRHS
'Star Sky' **new**	LSou SVil
treadwellii	see *Pratia angulata* 'Treadwellii'
tupa	Widely available
- JCA 12527	WCot
- Archibald's form	CPLG GCra
- dark orange-flowered	SGSe SMrm
urens	WPGP
valida	SGar SWvt WFar
vedrariensis	see *L.* × *speciosa* 'Vedrariensis'
villosa **new**	SGSe
'Waterfall Light Lavender' **new**	SVil
White Star = 'Weslowei'PBR	LAst

Loeselia (*Polemoniaceae*)

mexicana	CHII

loganberry see *Rubus* × *loganobaccus*

Lomandra (*Lomandraceae*)

confertifolia	ECou
- 'Wingarra'	MAvo
filiformis Savanna Blue = 'Lfm500'	EPPr NOak
hystrix	SPlb
longifolia	ECou GCal LEdu SPlb
- 'Kulnura'	ECou
- 'Orford'	ECou
- Tanika = 'Lm300'PBR	EPPr GBin LRHS NOak SHDw SUsu WBor

Lomaria see *Blechnum*

Lomatia (*Proteaceae*)

dentata	LRHS
ferruginea	CBcs CTrG EBee EPfP GBin GGal IDee SAPC SArc WCru
fraseri	EPfP LRHS SSpi
longifolia	see *L. myricoides*
§ ***myricoides***	CBcs CCCN CDoC CTrG CTsd ELan EPfP MBri NLar SAPC SArc SLon SPer SSpi WPGP
silaifolia	EPfP
tinctoria	CBcs CDoC EPfP NLar SAPC SArc SSpi

Lomatium (*Apiaceae*)

dissectum	NBhm
foeniculaceum	WCot
subsp. ***fimbriatum*** NNS 06-349 **new**	-
grayi	SPhx

Lomatogonium (*Gentianaceae*)

perenne **new**	GKev

Lonicera ✿ (*Caprifoliaceae*)

B&SWJ 2654 from Sikkim	WCru
F&M 207	WPGP
KR 291	ELon
§ ***acuminata***	EBee LRHS WGwG WPnP
- B&SWJ 3480	WCru
alberti	EBee MBNS MMuc WGwG
alseuosmoides	EBee IArd LRHS SAga SEND SLon SPoG WCru WPGP WSHC
× ***americana*** misapplied	see *L.* × *italica* Tausch
§ × ***americana*** (Miller) K. Koch	CBcs CRHN EPfP LRHS MAsh MGos MRav MSwo MWhi NWea SGar SLim WBor WGwG WMoo
§ × ***brownii*** 'Dropmore Scarlet'	Widely available
- 'Fuchsioides' misapplied	see *L.* × *brownii* 'Dropmore Scarlet'
- 'Fuchsioides' K. Koch	WSHC
caerulea	MRav STre
- var. ***altaica***	LEdu
- var. ***edulis***	CAgr LEdu MCoo
- subsp. ***kamtschatica***	CAgr NLar

§	***caprifolium*** ♀H4	CDoC CRHN EBee ELan EPfP LFol LRHS MAsh MBar NBea SPer
	- 'Anna Fletcher'	CRHN CSPN LSRN NHaw WCFE
	- f. ***pauciflora***	see *L.* × *italica* Tausch
	chaetocarpa	MRav WSHC
	chamissoi	NLar
	'Clavey's Dwarf'	see *L.* × *xylosteoides* 'Clavey's Dwarf'
	'Copper Beauty'PBR	LBuc LSRN LSou
	crassifolia	MBri WCot
	deflexicalyx	EPfP NLar
	'Early Cream'	see *L. caprifolium*
	elisae	CAbP EBee EPfP ERea MGos NLar SSpi WPat WSHC
	etrusca	LAst MRav
	- 'Donald Waterer' ♀H4	CRHN EBee EPfP LSRN NLar WFar WGor
	- 'Michael Rosse'	EBee ELan IArd LRHS MBNS SRms
	- 'Superba' ♀H4	CRHN EBee ECtt ELan EPfP LRHS NLar SEND SLim SPer SPoG WFar WSHC
	flexuosa	see *L. japonica* var. *repens*
	fragrantissima	Widely available
	giraldii misapplied	see *L. acuminata*
	giraldii Rehder	CBot EBee EPfP MAsh MRav SLim
	glabrata	SCoo SLim
	- B&SWJ 2150	WCru
	glehnii new	GAuc
	'Golden Trumpet'	CWGN EBee LRHS LSRN
	grata	see *L.* × *americana* (Miller) K. Koch
	× ***heckrottii***	CDoC CRHN CSBt EBee ECtt MBar MGan MGos NBea NLar NSti WDin
	- 'Gold Flame' ambig.	LSRN
	- 'Gold Flame' hort.	CDul CMac EBee ELan EPfP GKir LAst LBuc LRHS MBar MBri MGos MRav NBea NHol SBch SLim SPer SRms WDin WFar WMoo WSHC
§	***henryi***	Widely available
	- B&SWJ 8109	WCru
	- Sich 1489	WPGP
	- 'Copper Beauty'	CFir EBee EQua LAst LHop LRHS LSRN MAsh MGos MRav NCGa NLar SLon SPoG WDin WPGP
	- var. ***subcoriacea***	see *L. henryi*
	hildebrandiana	CCCN CHll CPLG CRHN ERea EShb LRHS WPGP
	'Hill House'	CHll
	'Honey Baby'PBR	EBee EPfP LLHF MAsh MBlu MBri NHol WPat
	implexa	WSHC
	insularis	see *L. morrowii*
	involucrata	CFee CMCN CMHG CPLG CPMA CWib GQui LHop MBNS MBar MBlu NChi NHol SPer WCFE WDin WFar
	- var. ***ledebourii***	CBgR EBee ELan EPfP GKir LAst LLHF LRHS MRav SDys SMrm
	× ***italica*** ambig.	LFol NPer SEND
§	× ***italica*** Tausch ♀H4	CRHN CSam CTri CWSG ECtt LFol LRHS MBNS MSwo NEgg NPer NSti SCoo SLim SPer WClo WDin WFar WPnn
§	- Harlequin = 'Sherlite'PBR (v)	CBot CMac CSPN EBee EGxp EHoe EPfP LAst LRHS LSRN MGos NBea NSti SGar SLim SPer SPlb SWvt
	japonica	CMen
§	- 'Aureoreticulata' (v)	CDul CMac CWib EBee ECrN EHoe ELan EPfP LRHS LSRN MBar MBri MGos MRav MWhi NPer SGar SPer SPet SRms STre WDin WEas WFar
	- 'Cream Cascade'	COlW EBee LAst LRHS MGos MSwo NLar SCoo
	- 'Dart's Acumen'	CRHN
	- 'Dart's World'	CAlb EBee MBri NBlu WFar
	- 'Halliana' ♀H4	Widely available
	- 'Hall's Prolific'	Widely available
	- Honeydew = 'Hinlon'	SPoG
§	- 'Horwood Gem' (v)	EBee ECtt LFol LRHS LSRN MGos NLar SCoo SPoG WFar
	- 'Maskerade'	LLHF NBro
	- 'Mint Crisp'PBR (v)	CBow CSBt CWGN EBee ECrN ELan EPfP LAst LRHS LSRN LSou MBri MGos NLar SBch SPad SPer SPoG SWvt WDin WFar
	- 'Peter Adams'	see *L. japonica* 'Horwood Gem'
§	- var. ***repens*** ♀H4	Widely available
	- 'Variegata'	see *L. japonica* 'Aureoreticulata'
	korolkowii	CBgR CBot CPMA CSam EBee EPfP MBNS MWte NBir SEND SLon SPoG WCFE WGrn WHCG WSHC
	- 'Blue Velvet'	CAgr MCoo NLar
	- var. ***zabelii*** misapplied	see *L. tatarica* 'Zabelii'
	- var. ***zabelii*** (Rehder) Rehder	ELan
	lanceolata BWJ 7935	WCru
	'Le Vasterival' new	MAsh
	'Little Honey'	MMHG MRav
	maackii	CHll CMCN CPMA EBee EPfP MBri MRav NLar WCFE WHCG
	- f. ***podocarpa***	SPoG
*	***macgregorii***	CMCN
	'Mandarin'	CDoC CWSG EBee ELan GKir LBuc LRHS MBlu MGos MRav NCGa NLar SCoo SLim SWvt WSHC WSpi
	maximowiczii var. ***sachalinensis***	NLar
§	***morrowii***	CMCN GAuc
	myrtillus	GAuc NLar
	nitida	CBcs CCVT CDul CMac CMen CSBt CTri ECrN EMac EPfP NWea SBch SPer STre SWal WDin WFar WHar
	- 'Baggesen's Gold' ♀H4	Widely available
	- 'Cumbrian Calypso' (v)	NPro
	- 'Eden Spring'	NPro
	- Edmée Gold = 'Briloni'PBR	EBee EPfP LRHS MAsh
	- 'Elegant'	LBuc STre WDin
	- 'Ernest Wilson'	MBar
	- 'Fertilis'	SPer
	- 'Lemon Beauty' (v)	CDoC CMac CSBt EBee EHoe EPfP EShb EWTr GAbr LAst LHop LRHS LSRN MBNS MBar MGos MNHC NBir NEgg NHol NPri NScw SBch SLPl SPer SWvt WDin WFar WHar WMoo
	- 'Lemon Queen'	CWib ELan MSwo
	- 'Lemon Spreader'	CBcs
§	- 'Maigrün'	CAlb CBcs CDul EBee EPfP MBri MSwo NPro SBch SPer SWvt WDin WFar
	- Maygreen	see *L. nitida* 'Maigrün'
	- 'Red Tips'	EBee EHoe EMil EPfP EPla LRHS MGos NHol SCoo WDin WFar WMoo
	- 'Silver Beauty' (v)	CDul CMac CWib EBee ECrN EHoe EPfP LAst LHop MAsh MBar MGos MLHP MRav MSwo NBlu NEgg NHol SAga SBch SGar SPer SPlb SRms SWvt WDin WFar WMoo
*	- 'Silver Cloud'	NHol
	- 'Twiggy' (v)	CDoC CElw EDAr EHoe EMil LBuc LRHS MAsh NEgg NHol NLar NPro WGrn
	periclymenum	CArn CDul CRWN CTri EBWF GKir GPoy MDun MHer MLHP MRav

NLar NMir NSco NWea SPlb WDin WHCG WPnn WSFF
- 'Belgica' misapplied — see *L.* × *italica* Tausch
- 'Belgica' — Widely available
- 'Florida' — see *L. periclymenum* 'Serotina'
- 'Graham Thomas' 🏆H4 — Widely available
- 'Harlequin' PBR — see *L.* × *italica* Harlequin
- 'Heaven Scent' — EBee LBuc LSRN MGos MNHC NLar WFar WGwG WPnn
- 'Honeybush' — CDoC CPMA CSPN CWGN LRHS MAsh MBri NHol NPri SLim WMoo
- 'La Gasnérie' — SLim WPnn
- 'Munster' — EBee WPnn WSHC
- 'Purple Queen' — CChe
- 'Red Gables' — CWan EBee ELon LSRN MBNS MGos NLar SCoo SEND SLim WClo WCot WGor WKif WPat WPnn
- 'Scentsation' PBR — CMac EBee EPfP LAst LBuc LRHS MAsh MBri SCoo SLon SPoG
N - 'Serotina' 🏆H4 — Widely available
- 'Serpentine' — EBee
* - ***sulphurea*** — WFar
- 'Sweet Sue' — CRHN CSPN EBee ECtt ELan ELon EPfP EWTr LAst LBuc LFol LOck LRHS LSRN MAsh MBNS MBri MGos MLHP MSwo NEgg NHol NSti SCoo SPoG SWvt WFar WMoo WPnP
- 'Winchester' — EBee
- yellow — NEgg

pileata — Widely available
- 'Moss Green' — CDoC EBee NBlu
- 'Pilot' — SLPl
- 'Silver Lining' (v) — EPla SAga
- 'Stockholm' — SLPl

× ***purpusii*** — CBgR CDoC CMac CRHN CTri CWSG CWib EBee ECrN EPfP EWTr GKir IFFs LSRN MBNS MGos MLHP MWat NBea SBch SPer SPoG SRms WCFE WFar WHCG WSHC
- 'Spring Romance' — CMac
- 'Winter Beauty' 🏆H4 — Widely available

ramosissima — NLar
saccata — CPMA EPfP
sempervirens 🏆H4 — CBot CRHN CSBt EPfP MBNS MRav WFar WSHC
- 'Cedar Lane' — LRHS
- 'Dropmore Scarlet' — see *L.* × *brownii* 'Dropmore Scarlet'
- 'Leo' — CSPN CWGN
N - f. ***sulphurea*** — EBee EPfP NBea WSHC
- - 'John Clayton' — LRHS

setifera — CBot
- 'Daphnis' — EPfP WBVN

similis var. ***delavayi*** 🏆H4 — CBot CChe CRHN CSPN CWGN EBee ECrN ELan EPfP LRHS MAsh MBri MNHC MRav NBea NEgg NSti SBch SDix SEND SLPl SPoG WCot WFar WGwG WPGP WSHC

'Simonet' — EBee
splendida — CBot WSHC
'Spring Bouquet' — LRHS
standishii — CTri EBee MGos WDin WFar WHCG
- 'Budapest' — CBcs MAsh MBlu MBri MGos WPat
stenantha — NLar
'Stone Green' — MGos
subaequalis Og 93.329 — WPGP
Sweet Isabel = 'Genbel' **new** — LRHS NCGa
syringantha — CArn CRHN CSam EBee ELan EPfP EWTr GGar GKir LAst LEdu MAsh MBri MGos MRav MWhi NBea NEgg NHol NPro SLPl SPer WCFE WClo WDin WFar WHCG WSHC
- 'Grandiflora' — GQui SLon

tatarica — CMCN CWib EBee MRav WFar WHCG
- 'Alba' — CPMA
- 'Arnold Red' — CBcs EBee ELan EPfP MBlu NLar WDin
- 'Hack's Red' — CWib EBee EPfP GQui LHop LRHS LSou MRav SAga SCoo SPer SPoG SWvt WCot WDin WFar WHCG
- 'Rosea' — WCot
§ - 'Zabelii' — EPfP

× ***tellmanniana*** — Widely available
- 'Joan Sayers' — LSRN SCoo SLim WCFE

thibetica — SPer WFar
tianschanica — GAuc
tragophylla 🏆H4 — CDoC CSBt EBee ELan EPfP LRHS LSRN MAsh MBNS MBri MRav SCoo SLim SMad SPer SPoG SSpi SWvt WDin WSHC
- 'Maurice Foster' — EBee ELan MBNS
- 'Pharaoh's Trumpet' — EPfP LRHS MAsh MBri SLon SPoG SSta

webbiana — ELan
× ***xylosteoides*** — WFar
§ - 'Clavey's Dwarf' — EBee NHol SLPl
xylosteum — CArn EBee NLar WFar

Lopezia (*Onagraceae*)

racemosa — CSpe

Lophomyrtus (*Myrtaceae*)

§ ***bullata*** — CAbP CDTJ CTrC CTsd EBee ECou GQui SPer WCHb WFar
- 'Matai Bay' — CBcs CTrC EBee

§ × ***ralphii*** — MHer WCHb
- 'Gloriosa' (v) — CDoC CTrC
- 'Kathryn' — CBcs CDoC EBee EMil EPfP IDee LRHS NLar SPoG SRGP SSpi
- 'Little Star' (v) — CBcs CDoC CTrC EBee LRHS MAsh SPoG WCot WPat
- Logan's form **new** — EMil LRHS
- 'Multicolor' (v) — CBcs CTrC EBee IDee LRHS
- 'Pixie' — CAbP CBcs CDoC CTrC GGar LRHS MAsh SPoG WPat
- 'Red Dragon' — CBcs CTrC CTsd EBee IDee LSou MAsh WFar WPat
- 'Red Pixie' — CDoC
- 'Red Wing' — LRHS
§ - 'Traversii' (v) — MGos SPoG
- 'Tricolor' (v) — WFar
- 'Variegata' (v) — MHer
- 'Wild Cherry' — CBcs CTrC GGar

Lophosoria (*Dicksoniaceae*)

quadripinnata — CBty CDTJ CFir EBee SBig WPGP WRic

Lophospermum (*Scrophulariaceae*)

§ ***erubescens*** 🏆H2-3 — CBot CRHN SBch SGar
'Magic Dragon' — LSou
§ 'Red Dragon' — EShb SBch SGar
§ ***scandens*** — CCCN CRHN ELan

loquat see *Eriobotrya japonica*

Loropetalum (*Hamamelidaceae*)

chinense — CWib GAbr IMou
- 'China Pink' — CBcs
- 'Ming Dynasty' — CAbP MAsh MGos MREP SSta
- f. ***rubrum*** — CMen CPLG CWib

- - 'Blush'	CPMA SBch
- - 'Burgundy'	CTrC
- - 'Daybreak's Flame'	CBcs CPMA CPen CWit EGxp LRHS SSta WGob
- - 'Fire Dance'	CAbP CBgR CCCN CDoC CHII CPMA CPen CTrC EBee EGxp EPfP IDee LRHS MGos SBch SEND SPoG SSpi SWvt WBrE WFar WGwG WPat
- - 'Pipa's Red'	CPen
- 'Snowdance'	CAbP
- 'Tang Dynasty'	CPen CTrC LRHS MGos MMuc SSta

Lotus (*Papilionaceae*)

berthelotii	CCCN CDTJ CHEx CSpe ECtt ELan EOHP MCot SBch SPet SPoG WCor
- deep red-flowered ♀H1+3	SWvt
berthelotii* × *maculatus ♀H1+3	CCCN MSCN
corniculatus	CArn EBWF LRHS MCoo MHer MNHC NLan NMir NSco SECG SIde WAbe WSFF
- 'Plenus' (d)	EPot MTho NLar WPer
* 'Fire Vine'	EShb LAst NPri
'Gold Flash'	CHEx LAst
hirsutus ♀H3-4	Widely available
- 'Brimstone' (v)	CWib EBee ECtt EGoo LHop LRHS MAvo SPer SPoG SWvt
- Little Boy Blue = 'Lisbob'PBR	CSBt EBee LRHS LSou LSqu MAsh SBch SPoG
- 'Lois'	EBee EPfP LHop LRHS MDKP WPGP
maculatus	EOHP SPet
maritimus	SRot
pedunculatus	see *L. uliginosus*
pentaphyllus	NLar
'Red Flash'	LAst
tetragonolobus	SRot
§ ***uliginosus***	EBWF MCoo NMir NSco SECG WSFF

lovage see *Levisticum officinale*

Loxostigma (*Gesneriaceae*)

kurzii GWJ 9342 **new**	WCru

Ludwigia (*Onagraceae*)

uruguayensis	LPBA

Luetkea (*Rosaceae*)

pectinata	NRya WAbe

Luma (*Myrtaceae*)

§ ***apiculata*** ♀H3	Widely available
§ - 'Glanleam Gold' (v) ♀H3	Widely available
- 'Penlee' **new**	WJek
- 'Saint Hilary' (v)	LRHS WJek
- 'Variegata' (v)	CMHG CTri ISea NHol SAga SLim
§ ***chequen***	CBcs CFee EBee GGar IDee LEdu MHer NLar WBrE WCHb WFar WJek WMoo

Lunaria (*Brassicaceae*)

§ ***annua***	MNHC NPri SIde SWat WHer WSFF
- var. ***albiflora*** ♀H4	EWTr NBir SEND SWat WCot
I - - 'Alba Variegata' (v)	CSpe MAvo MNFA WBrk WTin
- 'Chedglow'	CNat
- 'Corfu Blue'	CSpe
- 'Ken Aslet'	NHol
- 'Munstead Purple'	CSpe
- 'Variegata' (v)	MTho NBir SWat WCom WEas WHer
- violet-flowered	NBir
biennis	see *L. annua*
rediviva	CDes CSpe EBee ECGP ECha EPPr EPla GAbr GCal GCra GGar IBlr IFro LPio LRHS NBid NChi NPer NSti SMeo SUsu WCot WEas WFar WHer WPGP
- 'Partway White'	CMil WCot

Lunathyrium (*Woodsiaceae*)

pycnosorum	WRic

Lupinus ✿ (*Papilionaceae*)

B&SWJ 10309 from Guatemala	WCru
'African Sunset'	CWCL
'Alan Titchmarsh'	EBee
albus	CArn
'Animal'	CWCL
'Approaching Storm'	SMrm
arboreus ♀H4	Widely available
- ***albus***	CSpe CWib GCal SHGN
- 'Barton-on-Sea'	ELon LRHS
- 'Blue Boy'	ELan ELon LSRN
- blue-flowered	CHar CWCL CWib GGar MCot MLHP MWat NBPC NLar NPri SBch SMad SMrm SPlb SPoG SWvt WBrE WFar WKif
- 'Mauve Queen'	SHGN
- mixed	CArn
- prostrate	MDKP MMHG
- 'Snow Queen'	LRHS NBur SPer SPoG
- 'Sulphur Yellow'	SHGN SWvt
- white-flowered	CAby CWCL GGar
- yellow and blue-flowered	NBir SRkn
- yellow-flowered	GGar MLHP WWEG
arboreus* × *variicolor	CHid
arcticus	CSpe EDif
argenteus var. ***depressus***	see *L. argenteus* var. *utahensis*
§ - var. ***utahensis***	EBee LFur
'Aston Villa'	CWCL
'Avalon'	CWCL
Band of Nobles Series ♀H4	ECtt WFar
'Barley Mow' **new**	CWCL
'Bishop's Tipple'	CWCL EWes
'Blossom'	CWCL EBee LSRN
'Blue Moon'	CWCL
'Blue Streak'	CWCL
bogotensis B&SWJ 10761	WCru
'Brimstone'	CWCL
'Bruiser'	CWCL
'Bubblegum'	CWCL
'Camelot Blue' **new**	EPfP
'Carmen'	CWCL
'Cashmere Cream'	CWCL
'Chameleon'	CWCL
chamissonis	CHid CHII CSpe CWCL EBee EHrv EWes LHop LRHS MTho SMrm SPer SPoG WCom WFar
'Chandelier' (Band of Nobles Series)	CBcs CSBt CTri EBee ECtt ELan EPfP GKir LRHS MBri MCot MNHC MWat NBir NGBl NMir NPri SBch SMrm SPad SPer SPoG SWal SWvt WBVN WCAu WClo WFar WMnd
costaricensis B&SWJ 10487	WCru
'Desert Sun'	CWCL
Dwarf Gallery hybrids	GKir
'Dwarf Lulu'	see *L.* 'Lulu'
Gallery Series	CSBt SCoo SGar SPlb WFar
- 'Gallery Blue'	ECtt EPfP GKir LRHS LSRN NDlv NLar NNor NPri NVic SCoo SMrm SPoG WClo WFar

- 'Gallery Pink'	EPfP GKir LRHS NDlv NLar NPri NVic SCoo SPoG WFar
- 'Gallery Red'	ECtt EPfP GKir LRHS NBlu NDlv NLar NPri NVic SCoo SMrm SPoG WClo WFar
- 'Gallery Rose'	GKir LSRN SPoG
- 'Gallery White'	EPfP GKir LRHS NDlv NLar NPri NVic SCoo SMrm SPoG WClo WFar
- 'Gallery Yellow'	ECtt EPfP LRHS NDlv NLar NPri NVic SCoo SMrm SPoG WClo
'Gladiator'	CWCL
'Imperial Robe'	CWCL
'Ink Pot' **new**	CWCL
'Inspiration' **new**	CWCL
'Le Gentilhomme' (Band of Nobles Series)	MCot
'Lindy Lou' **new**	CWCL
§ 'Lulu'	ECtt EPfP LAst LRHS SBch SPer SPoG STes SWvt WFar WMoo
'Manhattan Lights'	CWCL EBee
'Masterpiece'	CWCL EBee LRHS MWea WHlf
Minarette Group	CTri ECtt SPet SPoG SRms WClo WFar
'Mrs Perkins'	SMrm
'My Castle' (Band of Nobles Series)	Widely available
'Neptune'	CWCL
'Noble Maiden' (Band of Nobles Series)	CBcs CSBt CTri EBee ECtt ELan EPfP EWTr GKir LRHS LSRN MBri MCot MNHC MWat NGBl NMir NPri SBch SMrm SPad SPer SPoG SWal SWvt WCAu WFar WMnd WMoo
nootkatensis	EBee GKir LDai WWEG
'Pauly'	CWCL
'Pen and Ink'	CWCL
perennis	EBee
'Persian Slipper'	CWCL EBee
'Plummy Blue'	EDif MWea
'Pluto'	CWCL
'Polar Princess'	CWCL EWes GBin LRHS SUsu SWat
polyphyllus	MWhi
propinquus	CEnt SPhx
'Queen of Hearts'	EBee
'Red Arrow'	CWCL
'Red Rum'	CWCL EBee
'Redhead'	CWCL
'Rooster'	CWCL
'Rote Flamme'	CPrp EWTr EWes SMrm
Russell hybrids	CSBt EPfP LAst LHop MHer MLHP MWat NBlu SEND SPet SPlb SRms SVic SWvt WBor WFar
'Saffron'	CWCL EBee LSRN
'Saint Andrew' **new**	CWCL
'Salmon Star'	CWCL
'Sand Pink'	EWes
'Snowgoose'	CWCL
'Sparky'	CWCL
'Sunlight' **new**	LRHS
'Tequila Flame'	CWCL
'Terracotta'	CWCL
texensis	CSpe CWCL
- 'Almo Fire'	CWCL
'The Chatelaine' (Band of Nobles Series)	Widely available
'The Governor' (Band of Nobles Series)	CBcs CSBt CTri EBee ECtt ELan EPfP GKir LRHS LSRN MBri MNHC MWat NGBl NMir NPri SBch SMrm SPad SPer SPoG SWal SWvt WBVN WBor WCAu WClo WFar WMnd WMoo
'The Page' (Band of Nobles Series)	CBcs EBee ELan EPfP GKir LRHS LSRN MBri MCot MNHC MWat NMir NPri SBch SMrm SPer SPoG SWal SWvt WBVN WCFE WFar WMnd WMoo
'Thunder' **new**	CWCL
'Thundercloud'	SMrm
'Towering Inferno'	CWCL
'Tutti Frutti'	LAst LBMP SHGN
variicolor	CArn CHid CSpe CSsd LDai SGar SMad

Luzula (*Juncaceae*)

alpinopilosa	EPPr GFor MMHG
× ***borreri***	EPPr
- 'Botany Bay' (v)	ECtt EPPr EPla GBin NHol WMoo WWEG
campestris	EBWF
forsteri	EBWF IMou
lactea	EPPr
lutea	GFor
luzuloides	GFor GQui NLar WPer WPtf
- 'Schneehäschen'	EBee GBin GCal NWsh WPrP
maxima	see *L. sylvatica*
multiflora	EBWF
nivalis	GAbr GKir
nivea	Widely available
- 'Lucius'	SGar
- 'Schattenkind'	EBee
pilosa	EBWF EPla GCal NNor
- 'Igel'	EBee GBin SLPl
rufa	ECou
§ ***sylvatica***	CHEx CRWN CRow CSWP EBWF ELan EPPr EPfP EPla GKir LEdu LRHS MBel MMoz MMuc MRav NBro NMir NOrc SBch WDin WFar WHer WPGP WShi WWEG
- 'A. Rutherford'	see *L. sylvatica* 'Taggart's Cream'
- 'Aurea'	Widely available
- 'Aureomarginata'	see *L. sylvatica* 'Marginata'
I - 'Auslese'	EPPr EPfP GFor NLar NNor WMoo
- 'Barcode' (v)	CNat
- 'Bromel'	SGSe
- 'Hohe Tatra'	CBcs CElw CPrp EBee ECtt EHoe EPPr EPfP EWes GBin GMaP LEdu MBNS MCCP MWhi NBro NGdn NHol NOak NVic NWsh SBch SPoG WBor WFar WPGP WPnP WWEG
§ - 'Marginata' (v)	Widely available
* - f. ***nova***	ELon EPPr
- 'Onderbos'	EBee
§ - 'Taggart's Cream' (v)	CElw EBrs EHoe EPla GGar LRHS MBNS NBid NHol SApp WDyG WGrn WMoo WPrP WWEG
- 'Tauernpass'	EBee EHoe EPPr EPla GCal NHol
- 'Wäldler'	EPPr MBNS NHol
- 'Waulkmill Bay'	SLPl
ulophylla	CFir ECou EDAr GBin GFor NLar NWCA

Luzuriaga (*Philesiaceae*)

polyphylla HCM 98202 **new**	WCru
radicans	CCCN CFee ERos IBlr WCru WSHC
- RH 0602	WCru

Lychnis (*Caryophyllaceae*)

alpina	CMac EBee ECho EDAr EPfP GKir GMaP LRHS MSCN NBlu NNor NVic SGar WFar WPer
- 'Alba'	GKev GKir NBir

- 'Rosea' NBir
- var. ***serpentinicola*** LFur
- 'Snow Flurry' EDAr NLar
§ × ***arkwrightii*** EBee ECha ELan LRHS NBre NNor SRot WFar
- 'Orange Zwerg' CWCL LAst LBMP NBre SMrm SPoG WHal
- 'Vesuvius' CBcs CMac EAEE EBee EPfP GKir LAst LRHS MNrw MWat NBir NBlu NNor SMrm SPad SPav SPer SPoG SRms STes WMnd WPer WWEG WWlt
chalcedonica ♀H4 Widely available
- var. ***albiflora*** EBee LAst LRHS NBro SPer WBrk WCAu WFar WMoo WPer
- - 'Snow White' ECtt SGSe
- 'Carnea' EBrs EShb LRHS MBNS NBre SMrm SPhx WBrk WPer WWEG
- 'Dusky Pink' LSou
- 'Dusky Salmon' MDKP NBPC NDlv
- 'Flore Pleno' (d) EBee ELan EShb GCal MBel MBri NLar SMrm WCot WFar
- 'Morgenrot' MCCP NBPC NNor
- 'Pinkie' ELan NLar SBod SGSe
- 'Rauhreif' EBee EShb NBre SPhx
- 'Rosea' EPfP LRHS NBir WFar WHrl WMoo WPer
* - 'Salmonea' ECtt NBir SRms WCAu
cognata CDes EBee EWld GMac LFur MDKP
- B&SWJ 4234 WCru
§ ***coronaria*** ♀H4 Widely available
- 'Abbotswood Rose' see *L.* × *walkeri* 'Abbotswood Rose'
- 'Alba' ♀H4 Widely available
- 'Angel's Blush' MDKP NBir SPav SPer SRkn
- Atrosanguinea Group CBre EBee GMaP IBlr LRHS MRav NCot NEgg NPri SMrm SPer WClo
- 'Cerise' MArl MCot MDKP NBir
- 'Dancing Ladies' WMnd
- Gardeners' World = 'Blych' (d) CBcs CSpe EBee ECtt ELon EWes LOck LRHS LSou MBNS MBel NBPC NGdn NSti SPer SPhx SSvw SUsu WClo WCot WFar
- 'Hutchinson's Cream' (v) NPro WCHb
- Oculata Group CMHG CSpe EAEE EBee ECtt EGoo EPfP LEdu MCot MTho NPri SMrm SPav SPlb SWal WCom WFar WKif WMoo WTin WWEG
coronata EBee
§ - var. ***sieboldii*** MWea NBre
dioica see *Silene dioica*
flos-cuculi CArn CBen CEnt CHrt CPom CRWN EBWF ECho EHon EHrv EMFW EPfP GKir LEdu LPBA MHer MMuc NLan NMir NPri SECG SWal WHer WMAq WMoo WPnP WSFF
- var. ***albiflora*** CBre EMFW GBar LFur LPBA MSKA NBro NLar SSvw WCHb WHer WMnd WMoo WOut
- Jenny = 'Lychjen'PBR (d) CBre CWGN EBee EBrs ELan GQue LAst LOck LRHS MBNS NBPC SBch SPoG SRkn STes SUsu WCot WPnP
- 'Little Robin' ECho EDAr LLWG NHol
- 'Nana' CBre CSpe ECho EDAr GAbr IFro LFur MMuc MSKA NLar SBch WPer
- 'White Robin' CBod CBre CEnt EBee EPPr EWTr GMac GQue IKil LBMP LRHS MBNS MNFA NPri SMrm SPoG WAul WClo WFar WPtf
flos-jovis ♀H4 ECha EPfP GJos LRHS NBir NLar SBch SGSe SRms WMoo WPer
- 'Hort's Variety' EBrs GKir LRHS MRav NBir
- 'Minor' see *L. flos-jovis* 'Nana'
§ - 'Nana' LRHS MSCN NWCA
- 'Peggy' EBee EGoo EShb NBre NLar SPoG
fulgens NBre
gracillima EBee
× ***haageana*** EBee LFur LRHS NBre NLar NWCA SRms WSpi
'Hill Grounds' CDes EBee WCot
kiusiana new EBee
lagascae see *Petrocoptis pyrenaica* subsp. *glaucifolia*
miqueliana LFur NBre SPhx WGwG WMoo
'Molten Lava' CFir EBee ECho LAst LRHS MRav NBlu NBre NLar SGSe SGar WPer WWEG
'Rollie's Favorite' EBee ECtt WBor
* ***sikkimensis*** EBee NBre
'Terry's Pink' EBee WFar
§ ***viscaria*** CArn CHrt EBWF ECha GCra GJos LDai NNor SBch SECG SGar SWal WFar WMoo WTin
- 'Alba' EBee ECha NBre NBro NNor
- ***alpina*** see *L. viscaria*
§ - subsp. ***atropurpurea*** ECtt EShb EWes LSou NBre SBHP SRms SSvw WHrl WOut WPtf
- 'Feuer' CKno EBee EWes GJos MBNS NLar NVic WMoo
- 'Firebird' EWes GKir MBNS MWhi NBre NBur
- 'Plena' (d) MDun SRkn
- 'Schnee' CSpr LRHS MBNS NEgg
- 'Splendens' EPfP IMon LRHS MNFA SPad SPet
- 'Splendens Plena' (d) ♀H4 EBee GMac MArl NBre NBro SUsu WFar
§ × ***walkeri*** 'Abbotswood Rose' ♀H4 IBlr
wilfordii SHar
§ ***yunnanensis*** EBee GKev NBid SGSe SIng SPav SPhx WPtf WWlt
- ***alba*** see *L. yunnanensis*

Lycianthes (*Solanaceae*)

aff. ***quichensis*** B&SWJ 10395 new WCru
rantonnetii see *Solanum rantonnetii*

Lycium (*Solanaceae*)

barbarum EBee EWes LRHS SEND SMad SVic
chinense CArn CMen NLar

Lycopodium (*Lycopodiaceae*)

clavatum GPoy

Lycopsis see *Anchusa*

Lycopus (*Lamiaceae*)

americanus CArn EBee
europaeus CArn EBWF ELau GBar GPoy MHer WGwG WHer
virginicus COld SDys

Lycoris (*Amaryllidaceae*)

albiflora EBrs ECho WCot
aurea EBee EBrs ECho
incarnata ECho
radiata CCCN EBee EBrs ECho GBin
sanguinea EBrs ECho
sprengeri EBee EBrs ECho
squamigera EBrs ECho
straminea WCot

Lygodium (*Schizaeaceae*)

japonicum NBid WFib WRic

Lyonia (*Ericaceae*)

ligustrina	NLar

Lyonothamnus (*Rosaceae*)

floribundus	CCCN CDoC CGHE CPLG EBee
subsp. ***aspleniifolius***	NLar SAPC SArc SGar SSpi WFar WPGP

Lysichiton (*Araceae*)

sp.	GGal
americanus ♀H4	Widely available
americanus × ***camtschatcensis***	ECha SSpi
camtschatcensis ♀H4	Widely available

Lysimachia ✿ (*Primulaceae*)

B&SWJ 8632 from Korea	WCru
§ ***atropurpurea***	CHar CSpe EAro EBee ELan EPfP GJos LAst LBMP LHop MCot SBch SMad SMrm SPer SPlb WMnd WSpi WWEG
- 'Beaujolais'	CBod ECGP EShb GJos GQue LAst LRHS LSRN MBNS NBPC NPri SPav SRkn WBor WCom WWlt
- 'Geronimo'	CSpe
barystachys	GMac LPla MRav SHar SMac WFar WOut WWEG
Candela = 'Innlyscand' **new**	SPoG
candida	EBee WCot
ciliata	CMHG CMac EBee ECha EHoe ELan GMaP MNrw NBir NGdn SWat WBor WCAu WCot WFar WMnd WPer
§ - 'Firecracker' ♀H4	Widely available
- 'Purpurea'	see *L. ciliata* 'Firecracker'
clethroides ♀H4	Widely available
- 'Geisha' (v)	CBow EBee ECtt EHoe EWes GQue LLHF SMrm SPoG WCot
- 'Lady Jane'	NBur SRms
§ ***congestiflora***	NPer SPet
- HWJ 846	WCru
- 'Golden Falls'	LAst
- 'Outback Sunset' PBR (v)	ECtt LAst NBlu
ephemerum	Widely available
fortunei	EBee MWat
henryi	EBee EPPr
japonica var. ***minutissima***	CFee CStu
lichiangensis	EBee GKev GKir IMou MBNS NBir SGar WMoo WPer
lyssii	see *L. congestiflora*
'Midnight Sun' **new**	LSou
minoricensis	CArn CEls EHrv ELan LFur MBNS SWat WPer WSpi
nemorum	EBWF WPer
- 'Little Sun'	WAlt
- 'Pale Star'	CBre CDes EBee WAlt
nummularia	COIW CSBt CTri CWat EBWF ECtt EHon EPfP GPoy LPBA MBar MMuc NBir SWat WBrk
- 'Aurea' ♀H4	Widely available
paridiformis	WCot
- var. ***stenophylla***	EBee EPPr WCot WPGP
- - DJHC 704	CDes
punctata misapplied	see *L. verticillaris*
punctata L.	CRow CSBt EBee ECha EHon EPfP GKir GMaP LRHS MHer MRav NBPC NBlu NBro NHol NMir NPer SGar SPer SPlb SRms SWat WBrk WCAu WFar WMAq WMoo WPer WPnP
§ - 'Alexander' (v)	Widely available
- 'Gaulthier Brousse'	MAvo WCot WWEG
- Golden Alexander = 'Walgoldalex' PBR (v)	CBct EBee MBNS MBri NHol NLar SBch SPer SPoG WFar WWEG
- 'Golden Glory' (v)	MAvo WCot
- 'Hometown Hero'	EBee
- 'Ivy Maclean' (v)	EBee LSou SWvt WCot WWEG
- 'Sunspot'	EBee NBre
- 'Variegata'	see *L. punctata* 'Alexander'
- ***verticillata***	see *L. verticillaris*
'Purpurea'	see *L. atropurpurea*
pyramidalis	WPtf WWEG
quadrifolia	EBee
serpyllifolia	ECtt
Snow Candles = 'L9902' PBR	CCVN COIW EBee LHop LSou SPoG
taliensis BWJ 7797	WCru
thyrsiflora	CBen EBee EHon EMFW GAuc NPer SWat WHer WMAq
§ ***verticillaris***	CTri WCot
vulgaris	CArn CRWN GBar LPBA MSKA NSco SIde WFar WMoo WPer
- subsp. ***davurica***	WCot
yunnanensis	CDes EBee GKev LFur SGar WPer

Lysionotus (*Gesneriaceae*)

gamosepalus B&SWJ 7241	WCru
aff. ***kwangsiensis*** HWJ 643	WCru
'Lavender Lady'	CSpe SEND
pauciflorus	CDes CStu WAbe WSHC
- B&SWJ 189	WCru
- B&SWJ 303	WCru
- B&SWJ 335	WCru
serratus	MWea
- HWJK 2426	WCru

Lythrum (*Lythraceae*)

anceps	NBre NLar SPhx
salicaria	CArn CBen CKno CRWN CWat EBWF EBee EHon EMFW GJos LBMP LPBA MCot MHer MLHP NBro NLan SECG SPlb SRms SWat WBrk WFar WHer WMoo WPnP WSFF WShi
- 'Blush' ♀H4	Widely available
§ - 'Feuerkerze' ♀H4	CKno CMea CPrp CRow EAEE EBee ECtt ELan EPfP GKir LAst LBMP LHop LRHS MBri MCot MRav MSpe NBir NCob NEgg NHol NSti NVic SAga SPer WFar WHil WPer WWEG
- Firecandle	see *L. salicaria* 'Feuerkerze'
- 'Happy'	NHol SMrm
- 'Lady Sackville'	EBee ECtt EMFW EPPr GBuc GMaP LRHS MCot SMrm SPoG WCAu
- 'Little Robert'	LRHS NPri
- 'Morden Pink'	CChe EBee MBri MDKP NCob SPhx WFar WPtf WSHC
- 'Prichard's Variety'	CAby CKno EBee WPGP
- 'Robert'	Widely available
- 'Robin'	LLHF LRHS MAsh MCot
- 'Rose'	ELan NBir SWvt
- 'Stichflamme'	NCob SMrm
- 'Swirl'	EBee ECtt LLWG MDKP NBre SHar SMrm WFar
- 'The Beacon'	CMHG EBee EMFW MDKP SGSe SRms
- 'Zigeunerblut'	CElw CKno CMHG EBee MAvo MDKP MRav MWte NLar SMrm SPhx SWat WHil
virgatum	CMHG SPhx SUsu WMoo WOut WSHC

- 'Dropmore Purple'	CHar CSam EBee ECtt EPPr EPfP LAst LBMP LHop LRHS MBri MCot MDKP MRav MSpe NCob NEgg SAga SPhx WCAu WFar WHil WPnP WPtf
- 'Rose Queen'	ECha ECtt GKir MDKP MRav WFar WPer
- 'Rosy Gem'	CMMP EBee ECtt EPfP GMaP LAst LRHS MNHC MWat MWhi NBPC NBid NBro SGSe SRGP SRms SWal SWvt WFar WPer WWEG
- 'The Rocket'	CAby CMMP CSam CTri EBee EPfP LAst LRHS MRav NBro NCob SPer SWvt WWlt

Lytocaryum (*Arecaceae*)

§ ***weddellianum*** ♀H1	LPal MBri

M

Maackia (*Papilionaceae*)

amurensis	CBcs CDul ELan EPfP GKir IArd IDee IMGH LRHS MBri MWea SPur WSHC
- var. ***buergeri***	CDul EBee
chinensis	CBcs IArd MBlu MBri NLar

Macbridea (*Lamiaceae*)

caroliniana	WPGP

mace, English see *Achillea ageratum*

Macfadyena (*Bignoniaceae*)

§ ***unguis-cati***	CCCN CRHN EShb

Machaeranthera (*Asteraceae*)

bigelovii	NBre NWCA

Machaerina (*Cyperaceae*)

rubiginosa 'Variegata' (v)	CKno
sinclairii new	ECou

Machilus see *Persea*

Mackaya (*Acanthaceae*)

§ ***bella*** ♀H1	CHII ERea EShb

Macleania (*Ericaceae*)

ericae	WCot

Macleaya (*Papaveraceae*)

cordata misapplied	see *M.* × *kewensis*
§ ***cordata*** (Willd.) R. Br. ♀H4	CArn COIW EBee ELan EPfP LHop LRHS MBri MSCN MWhi NBPC NBir NOrc NPri NWsh SBch SPer SPhx SPlb SPoG SRms WCAu WCot WFar WMnd WMoo
- 'Celadon Ruffles'	GBin
§ × ***kewensis***	CWan SMrm WHoo WPGP WWEG
- 'Flamingo' ♀H4	CPrp EBee ECha ECtt GBuc GQue LAst LBMP LRHS MBNS MNFA NGdn SWvt WWEG
§ ***microcarpa***	SGar SWat
- 'Kelway's Coral Plume' ♀H4	Widely available
- 'Spetchley Ruby'	EBee GBin MRav SPhx SUsu WCom WCot WPGP WWEG
'Plum Tassel'	EBee WCot

Maclura (*Moraceae*)

pomifera	CArn CBcs EBee MBri NLar SPlb WDin WFar WPGP
- 'Pretty Woman'	NLar

Macrodiervilla see *Weigela*

Macropiper (*Piperaceae*)

§ ***excelsum***	CHEx ECou

Macrozamia (*Zamiaceae*)

communis	CBrP LPal
diplomera	CBrP
dyeri	see *M. riedlei*
glaucophylla	CBrP
johnsonii	CBrP
lucida	CBrP
miquelii	CBrP
moorei	CBrP ETod LPal
mountperiensis	CBrP
§ ***riedlei***	CBrP LPal

Maddenia (*Rosaceae*)

hypoleuca	NLar

Madia (*Asteraceae*)

elegans	NBur

Maesa (*Myrsinaceae*)

japonica	CPLG
montana	CPLG

Magnolia ✿ (*Magnoliaceae*)

acuminata	CBcs CDul CLnd CMCN EPfP IDee IMGH LMaj NBhm NLar WDin
- 'Golden Glow'	CBcs
* - 'Kinju'	CEnd NLar
- 'Koban Dori'	CBcs CPMA CTho ECho LRHS
- large yellow-flowered	CBcs NLar
- 'Moegi Dori' new	NLar
§ - var. ***subcordata***	EBee NLar
- - 'Miss Honeybee'	CBcs
'Advance'	CBcs CPMA
'Albatross'	CBcs CDoC CEnd CTho LRHS SSpi WPGP
'Amber' new	CPMA
'Ambrosia'	CBcs CPMA
amoena 'Multiogeca'	CBcs CWib EGxp
'Anilou' new	CPMA
'Ann' ♀H4	CBcs CPLG CSdC MGos NLar SSpi
'Anticipation'	CEnd CPMA CSdC
'Apollo'	CBcs CDoC CPMA GGGa SSpi WPat
'Asian Artistry'	CPMA MBri
'Athene'	CBcs CDoC CPMA WPat
'Atlas'	CBcs CDoC CEnd CPMA CTho GGGa LMil LRHS SSpi WPGP
'Banana Split'	CPMA
'Betty' ♀H4	CBcs CDoC CDul CMac CSdC EBee EWTr IDee LRHS LSRN MGos NLar NMun NScw SLim SSta WDin WFar
'Big Dude'	CBcs CEnd CPMA IArd LSRN
biondii	CBcs CSdC IDee LRHS LSRN NLar WPGP
'Black Beauty'	CBcs CPMA
'Black Tulip'	ELan EPfP GGGa LBuc LRHS MGos NPri SCoo SSpi
'Blushing Belle' new	CPMA
'Brenda' new	CPMA
× ***brooklynensis***	NPal
- 'Evamaria'	CBcs CTho LRHS
- 'Hattie Carthan'	CBcs CPMA NLar WPGP

Plant	Suppliers
- 'Woodsman'	CBcs NLar
- 'Yellow Bird'	CBcs CDoC CEnd CMCN CPMA CTho EBee EPfP LRHS LSRN MBlu MBri MGos NCGa NEgg NHol NLar NPal SSpi WDin
'Butterbowl'	CBcs CPMA
'Butterflies'	CBcs CDoC CEnd CMHG CMac CPMA CTho EBee ELan EMil EPfP GGGa GKir ISea LHyd LRHS LSRN MBlu MDun MGos NLar SLim SSpi SSta WBVN WFar WGob WPGP WSpi
'Caerhays Belle'	CBcs CPMA ECho MBri NLar SSpi
'Caerhays New Purple'	CLnd ECho
'Caerhays Surprise'	CBcs CPMA NHim SSpi
campbellii	CBcs CMCN ELan EPfP ISea LRHS SSpi WFar
- Alba Group	CBcs CEnd MGos WFar WPGP
- - 'Sir Harold Hillier'	CPMA
- 'Betty Jessel'	CBcs CPMA
- 'Darjeeling'	CBcs CDoC ECho LRHS
- 'Lamellan Pink'	CTho LRHS
- 'Lamellan White'	CTho LRHS
- subsp. ***mollicomata***	CEnd CHEx EPfP ISea NHim WFar
- - 'Lanarth'	CBcs CEnd LRHS
- - 'Maharanee'	CBcs
- - 'Peter Borlase'	CBcs CDoC
- - 'Werrington' **new**	CBcs
- (Raffillii Group)	CAbP CBcs CDoC CDul CLnd EBee
'Charles Raffill'	ELan EPfP LRHS MBri MGos SLim WDin WHCr WPGP
- - 'Kew's Surprise'	CDoC CPMA SSpi
- 'Sidbury'	CBcs MBri
'Candy Cane'	CBcs CPMA WPGP
'Carlos'	CBcs CPMA
cathcartii HWJ 874	WCru
'Cecil Nice'	CBcs CCVT CDoC
Chameleon	see *M.* 'Chang Hua'
§ 'Chang Hua'	CPMA NLar
'Charles Coates'	CPMA CSdC EPfP MDun NLar WPGP
'China Dream' **new**	EGxp
China Town = 'Jing Ning'	CBcs CPMA MDun
'Chinese Magic' **new**	EGxp
'Columbus'	CPMA CSdC SSpi WPGP
'Coral Lake'	CPMA MBri MDun
cordata	see *M. acuminata* var. *subcordata*
'Cotton Rose' **new**	EGxp
'Cup Cake'	CPMA
cylindrica misapplied	see *M.* 'Pegasus'
cylindrica ambig.	CBcs
cylindrica E.H.Wilson	CMCN EPfP IArd IDee SSpi
- 'Bjuv' **new**	CPMA
'Daphne'	CBcs CPMA NLar
'Darrell Dean'	CPMA LRHS WPGP
'David Clulow'	CBcs CPMA ECho SSpi
dawsoniana	CBcs EBee EPfP IMGH NLar WSpi
- 'Chyverton Red'	CBcs
'Daybreak'	CBcs CPMA MBri NPal SSpi
delavayi	CBcs CBrP CHEx CMCN EPfP SAPC SArc WPGP
§ ***denudata*** ♀$^{H3-4}$	CBcs CMCN CTho CWib EGxp EMil EPfP ISea LMaj LRHS MGos NLar SSpi WDin WFar
- 'Double Diamond' **new**	CPMA
- 'Dubbel'	CBcs MDun
- 'Forrest's Pink'	CBcs LRHS
- Fragrant Cloud = 'Dan Xin'	CBcs CPMA CWib EGxp MBri MDun NLar
- 'Gere'	CBcs CPMA
- 'Ghost Ship' **new**	CPMA
- Yellow River = 'Fei Huang'	CBcs CEnd CPMA CWib EBee EGxp LSou MBri MDun NLar NPal SPoG
'Early Rose' **new**	CPMA
'Eleanor May' **new**	CPMA
'Elegance' **new**	CPMA
'Elisa Odenwald'	CPMA
'Elizabeth' ♀^{H4}	CBcs CDoC CDul CMCN CPMA CTho EBee ECho ELan EPfP LAst LMil LRHS LSRN MAsh MBlu MDun MGos NLar NPal SPer SPoG SSpi SSta SWvt WPGP
'Eskimo'	CPMA SSpi
'Felicity' **new**	CPMA
'Felix Jury'	ELan EPfP LRHS SSpi
'Fireglow'	CBcs CPMA CTho LRHS
'Flamingo'	CPMA
'Frank Gladney'	CPMA CTho LRHS
'Frank's Masterpiece'	CPMA
fraseri	CBcs
'Full Eclipse'	WPGP
'Galaxy' ♀^{H4}	CBcs CDoC CDul CEnd CMac CPMA CSdC EBee ECho EPfP EWTr GGGa IArd IMGH ISea LMil LRHS MBar MBri MGos NBhm SLim SSpi SSta WBrE WDin WGob WPGP
'George Henry Kern'	CBcs CDoC CDul EBee EMil ERas IArd IDee LRHS MBri MGos NEgg NLar NMun NPCo SLdr SSpi SSta WCFE WClo WDin WFar WGob WPat
globosa	CBcs CPLG EBee WFar WGob WPGP
- AC 5294	CSdC
'Gold Crown'	CBcs CPMA SSpi
'Gold Star'	CBcs CDoC CEnd CPMA CSdC CTho EMil EPfP GGGa LRHS MBri MGos NCGa NLar NPal SSpi
'Golden Endeavour'	CBcs CPMA
'Golden Gift'	CPMA SSpi
'Golden Pond'	CBcs CPMA
'Golden Sun'	CBcs CPMA NLar
'Goldenship' **new**	EGxp
'Goldfinch' **new**	CBcs
grandiflora	CMCN CWib EGxp EPfP ESwi GKir LAst LEdu LRHS LSRN MGos MRav NEgg NLar SAPC SBch WDin WFar
- 'Blanchard'	CBcs CPMA
- 'Bracken's Brown Beauty'	MBri
- 'Charles Dickens'	CPMA
- 'Edith Bogue'	CDul CPMA CWit ECho EQua LRHS MGos NEgg NLar NPCo SLdr WBVN WGob
- 'Exmouth' ♀$^{H3-4}$	Widely available
- 'Ferruginea'	CBcs CPMA EBee MGos
- 'François Treyve'	ECrN EMil EPfP EQua LRHS SBch SPoG
- 'Galissonnière'	CBcs CWib ECrN EPfP ERom IDee LMaj LRHS MGos NBlu NHim SBch SLim SSpi SWvt WDin WFar WPGP
I - 'Galissonnière Nana'	LMaj LRHS
- 'Goliath'	CBcs CDul CEnd CHEx ELan EPfP LRHS SLdr SPer SSpi WPGP
- 'Harold Poole'	CBcs CPMA
- 'Kay Paris'	SSpi
- 'Little Gem'	CBcs CDoC CPMA ELan EPfP MGos SSpi
- 'Mainstreet'	CBcs CPMA
- 'Monlia'	CBcs CPMA
- 'Nannetensis'	CPMA EQua
- 'Overton'	CBcs CPMA
- 'Russet'	CPMA

- 'Saint Mary'	CBcs CPMA
- 'Samuel Sommer'	CPMA SArc SSpi
- 'Symmes Select'	CBcs CPMA
- 'Victoria' ♀H3-4	CBcs CDoC CDul CPMA CTho ELan ELon EPfP IDee ISea LHyd LMil LRHS LSRN MAsh MBlu MGos MWat NLar SLim SPoG SReu SSpi SSta WFar WGob WPGP
'Green Bee'	CBcs
'Green Mist'	CBcs CPMA
'Heaven Scent' ♀H4	Widely available
'Helen Fogg'	CPMA WPGP
heptapeta	see *M. denudata*
'Honey Liz'	SSpi
§ 'Hong Yur'	CEnd CPMA NPal
'Hot Flash'	CBcs CPMA
'Hot Lips'	CPMA
hypoleuca	see *M. obovata* Thunb.
'Ian's Red'	CBcs CPMA
'Iolanthe'	CBcs CEnd CGHE CMCN CPMA CSdC CTho ECho ELan GGGa LRHS MAsh MGos NBhm NHol NLar SPer SSpi SSta WFar WPGP
'Iufer' **new**	CPMA
'J.C. Williams'	CBcs CDoC CPMA CTho LRHS
'Jane' ♀H4	CDoC CMac CPMA CSdC ELan EPfP LMil LRHS MAsh MBri MGos MRav SPer
'Jersey Belle'	CPMA
'Joe McDaniel'	CPMA CSdC LRHS SSpi
'Judy'	NLar
× ***kewensis*** hort. ex Pearce 'Wada's Memory'	see *M. salicifolia* 'Wada's Memory'
kobus	CBcs CDul CLnd CMCN CSBt CTho CTsd EBee EMil EPfP IFFs IMGH LMaj LRHS NLar NMoo SLdr SPoG WDin WFar WGob
- var. ***borealis***	CPMA
- 'Esveld Select'	MBri SSpi
- 'Janaki Ammal'	CPMA
§ - 'Norman Gould'	CDoC CPMA EPfP MBri NLar NScw SSta WDin
'Lamellan Surprise'	LRHS
'Laura Saylor' **new**	CPMA
'Leda'	CPMA
'Legacy'	CBcs CPMA NLar
'Legend'	EPfP
§ ***liliiflora***	CBcs MBar NHim
- 'Holland Red' **new**	CBcs
§ - 'Nigra' ♀H4	Widely available
- 'Oldfield'	WPGP
* 'Limelight'	CBcs CPMA CSdC
× ***loebneri***	CBcs NEgg
- 'Ballerina'	CBcs CDoC EMil NLar
- 'Donna'	CBcs CPMA EPfP LRHS MGos NLar SSpi
- 'Encore' **new**	CPMA
- 'Leonard Messel' ♀H4	Widely available
- 'Lesley Jane' **new**	CPMA
- 'Merrill' ♀H4	Widely available
- 'Neil McEacharn'	CPMA
- 'Pink Cloud'	CPMA
- 'Raspberry Fun'	CPMA
- 'Snowdrift'	CPMA NLar SSta
- 'Star Bright'	CPMA
- 'Wildcat'	CBcs CPMA NLar
- 'Willow Wood'	CPMA
'Lois'	CBcs CPMA EPfP GGGa LSRN SSpi
'Lombardy Rose'	MBri NLar
lotungensis	CBcs NLar
'Lotus'	CPMA
'Lucy Carlson' **new**	CPMA
macrophylla	CBcs CBrP CMCN CMac EPfP IDee LRHS MBlu SAPC SArc WPGP
- subsp. ***ashei***	CPMA
× ***virginiana***	
'Mag's Pirouette' **new**	CBcs
'Manchu Fan'	CBcs CPMA CSdC ECho EMil IArd LRHS LSRN NHim NLar SSpi
'Margaret Helen'	CBcs CPMA ECho
'Marj Gossler'	CPMA
'Mark Jury'	CBcs
'Maryland'	CPMA CWib EQua
'Maxine Merrill'	CPMA IDee SSpi
'May to Frost'	CBcs CPMA
'Milky Way' ♀H4	CBcs CDoC CGHE CPMA CTho LRHS MGos SSpi WPGP
'Nimbus'	SSpi
nitida	CBcs
obovata Diels	see *M. officinalis*
§ ***obovata*** Thunb. ♀H4	CAlb CBcs CMCN CPMA CTho EPfP GAuc IDee IFFs MGos NLar SSpi SSta WDin WPGP
§ ***officinalis***	CBcs EPfP NLar WBVN WFar
- var. ***biloba***	CGHE EPfP NLar SSpi WPGP
'Olivia'	CBcs CPMA
'Peachy'	CBcs NLar
§ 'Pegasus'	CEnd GGGa NHim SSpi WDin
'Peppermint Stick'	CBcs CSdC ECho GGGa MGos NHim SSta
'Peter Smithers'	CPMA CTho LRHS WFar
'Phelan Bright'	CPMA CSdC
'Phillip Tregunna'	CBcs CTho
'Phil's Masterpiece' **new**	CPMA
'Pickard's Stardust'	EPfP LRHS
'Pickard's Sundew'	see *M.* 'Sundew'
'Piet van Veen' **new**	CPMA
'Pink Cecile Nice'	CBcs
'Pink Delight' **new**	CPMA
'Pink Goblet'	LRHS
'Pinkie' ♀H4	CPMA EMil EPfP LSRN MGos NEgg NLar SSpi SSta WGob
'Pirouette'	CPMA GGGa LLHF LRHS SSpi
'Porcelain Dove'	CPMA SSpi
'Pretty Lee' **new**	EGxp
'Princess Margaret'	CBcs CDoC CPMA ECho
× ***proctoriana***	CAbP CDoC CGHE CSdC EBee EPfP LMil LRHS NLar WPGP
- Gloster form	NLar
- 'Robert's Dream'	CPMA
- 'Slavin's No 44' **new**	CPMA
'Purple Globe' **new**	CPMA
'Purple Platter'	CBcs
'Purple Sensation'	CBcs CPMA
quinquepeta	see *M. liliiflora*
'Randy'	EPfP MGos
'Raspberry Ice'	CBcs CDoC CMHG CMac CSam CSdC CTho EBee EPfP ISea LMil LRHS MAsh NHim NLar SLim WFar WGob
'Red as Red'	CDoC
'Red Lion'	CPMA
'Ricki'	CBcs CSdC EMil EPfP LSRN MBlu MGos MHav NHim NLar NMun WFar
rostrata	CGHE EBee ELan WPGP
'Rouged Alabaster'	CBcs CDoC
'Royal Crown'	CBcs CDoC CSdC EMil EQua IDee LRHS MRav NBhm NEgg NLar NPCo SLdr SLim
'Ruby'	CBcs CPMA ECho MGos WPat
'Ruth'	CBcs
salicifolia ♀H3-4	CBcs CMCN EPfP GGal SSpi SSta WSpi

- var. ***concolor*** CPMA
- 'Jermyns' CPMA
- upright WPGP
- 'Van Veen' **new** CPMA
§ - 'Wada's Memory' 𝕐H4 CAlb CDoC CMCN CMHG CPMA CTho ELan EMil EPfP EWTr GGGa GKir IFFs LMil LRHS MAsh MBri NLar SLdr SPoG SSpi SSta WDin WFar WGob
- 'Windsor Beauty' NHim
sargentiana var. ***robusta*** CBcs CEnd CLnd CMCN EBee ELan EPfP LMil LRHS MGos SPer SSpi SSta WDin WFar
- var. ***robusta*** 'Trengwainton Glory' SSpi
'Satisfaction' CDul CPMA LRHS NCGa NLar NPal
'Sayonara' 𝕐H4 CBcs CPMA CSdC ECho EPfP LRHS MBri SSpi WDin WPGP WPat
'Schmetterling' see *M.* × *soulangeana* 'Pickard's Schmetterling'
'Serene' CBcs CEnd CPMA ECho EPfP LRHS MGos SSpi SSta WPat
'Shirazz' CBcs CPMA
sieboldii Widely available
- B&SWJ 4127 WCru
- from Korea, hardy GGGa
- 'Colossus' CPMA SSpi
- 'Genesis' CPMA
- 'Genesis' × ***tripetala*** **new** CPMA
- 'Michiko Renge' CPMA NLar
- 'Min Pyong-gal' **new** CPMA
- 'Pride of Norway' CBcs CPMA
- subsp. ***sinensis*** CBcs CDoC CLnd CMCN CPMA CTho ELan EPfP GCra GGGa IMGH MBlu MDun SSpi WDin WPGP
'Sir Harold Hillier' CBcs WPGP
'Snow Goose' **new** CPMA
'Solar Flair' CBcs
× ***soulangeana*** Widely available
- 'Alba Superba' CBcs CDoC CSBt CTri EPfP MBlu MGos MRav NMun SLim SPer WFar WSpi
- 'Alexandrina' CBcs EPfP NLar
- 'Amabilis' SBch
- 'André Leroy' EMil
- 'Brozzonii' 𝕐H3-4 CBcs CDoC EPfP ERas GGGa GKir LRHS MBri MGos NEgg NLar NPCo SLdr SSpi WBVN
- 'Burgundy' CBcs CBot CDoC MGos NPCo SLdr WFar
- 'Lennei' 𝕐H3-4 CBcs CDoC CDul CMCN CMac CSBt EBee EPfP IMGH LRHS MAsh MBri MGos MSwo NBea NHol SLim SPer SRms WFar
- 'Lennei Alba' 𝕐H3-4 CBcs CDoC CMCN CMac CSdC SPer SSpi WFar WGob WSpi
- 'Nigra' see *M. liliiflora* 'Nigra'
- 'Pickard's Ruby' MDun SLim
§ - 'Pickard's Schmetterling' CDoC CSdC LMil LRHS MAsh
- 'Pickard's Snow Queen' CBcs
- 'Pickard's Sundew' see *M.* 'Sundew'
- 'Picture' CBcs CDoC CMac CTri NLar WDin WGob
- Red Lucky see *M.* 'Hong Yur'
- 'Rosea' LMaj
- 'Rubra' misapplied see *M.* × *soulangeana* 'Rustica Rubra'
§ - 'Rustica Rubra' 𝕐H3-4 Widely available
- 'San José' LMil LRHS MAsh MBri NLar WFar
- 'Speciosa' NMun
- 'Superba' CMac NMun
- 'Verbanica' CAlb CCVT IFFs LMil LRHS MAsh SPoG

'Spectrum' CBcs CDoC CEnd CPMA CSdC EMil GGGa LRHS MBri MGos NLar SLdr SSpi WPGP
sprengeri CWib
- 'Copeland Court' CBcs GGGa
- var. ***diva*** CBcs CEnd NLar SSpi WPGP
- - 'Burncoose' CBcs CDoC
- - 'Claret Cup' GGGa
- - 'Diva' GGal WPGP
- - 'Eric Savill' CPMA LRHS SSpi SSta WPGP
- - 'Lanhydrock' SSpi WPGP
- - 'Westonbirt' WPGP
- 'Marwood Spring' CMHG
'Spring Rite' **new** CPMA
'Star Wars' 𝕐H4 CBcs CDoC CEnd CPMA CSdC CTho ECho ELan EMil EPfP GGGa LMil LRHS MAsh MBri MDun MGos NLar SPoG SSpi SSta WPGP WPat
'Stardust' **new** SSpi
'Stellar Acclaim' CPMA
stellata 𝕐H4 Widely available
- 'Centennial' CBcs CDoC CPMA CTho GGGa MBri NLar WFar
- 'Chrysanthemumiflora' CPMA EGxp
- 'Dawn' CPMA
- 'Jane Platt' CBcs CPMA ELan EWes GGGa LMil LRHS MBri MGos SPoG SSpi
- f. ***keiskei*** CBcs CEnd CPMA LRHS NHol NLar
- 'Kikuzaki' **new** CPMA
- 'King Rose' CBcs CDoC CPMA CTsd EPfP ISea LAst MSnd SLdr
- 'Massey' CPMA LRHS
- 'Norman Gould' see *M. kobus* 'Norman Gould'
- 'Rosea' CMCN CPMA CTho ELan ELon GKev ISea LMil MDun MGos MRav MSwo NEgg NLar SBch WDin
I - 'Rosea Massey' GBin WFar
- 'Royal Star' Widely available
- 'Scented Silver' CPMA CSdC
- 'Shi-banchi Rosea' **new** CPMA
- 'Two Stones' **new** LRHS
- 'Waterlily' 𝕐H4 CBcs CMCN CPMA CTho ELan ELon EMil EPfP GKir IMGH LAst LRHS LSRN NLar NPCo SLdr SLim SPer SPoG SSpi SSta WDin WFar WGob WPGP
- 'Wisley Stardust' LRHS SSpi
'Summer Solstice' CBcs CPMA
'Sun Ray' **new** CBcs CPMA
'Sunburst' CBcs CPMA
'Sundance' CBcs CPMA MBri MGos NLar
§ 'Sundew' CDoC CMac CTsd EBee EPfP EQua IArd LMil LRHS MGos NLar NPCo WBVN
'Sunsation' CBcs CPMA SSpi
'Sunspire' CBcs NLar SSpi
'Suntown' **new** CPMA
'Susan' 𝕐H4 Widely available
'Susanna van Veen' CBcs WPGP
'Swedish Star' **new** CPMA
'Sweet Valentine' CBcs CPMA
'Sweetheart' **new** CPMA
'Theodora' CBcs NLar
× ***thompsoniana*** CBcs CMCN EPfP IDee
'Thousand Butterflies' CBcs CPMA
'Tina Durio' CBcs
'Todd Gresham' CPMA WPGP
'Trewidden Belle' CEnd
tripetala CBcs CMCN CPLG CTri EBee ELan EPfP IMGH MDun NLar SSpi SSta WDin WPGP
'Ultimate Yellow' CBcs NLar

× ***veitchii***	CBcs CDul EPfP
- 'Peter Veitch'	CTho
virginiana	CBcs CMCN CPMA EPfP ISea LRHS SBig SSpi WBVN WDin WPGP
- 'Henry Hicks'	SSpi
- 'Moonglow'	CPMA
- 'Pink Halo' **new**	CPMA
- 'Satellite'	CPMA
'Vulcan'	CBcs CEnd CPMA CTho ELan LRHS MBri MDun NHol SSpi
× ***watsonii***	see *M.* × *wieseneri*
§ × ***wieseneri***	CBcs CGHE CMCN CPMA EBee ELan EPfP ERea GKir LRHS MBlu NLar SPer SSpi WFar WPGP
- 'Aashild Kalleberg'	CBcs SSpi
wilsonii ♀H4	Widely available
- 'Gwen Baker'	CEnd
'Yellow Fever'	CBcs CMCN CPMA CTho ECho LRHS MDun
'Yellow Lantern'	CAbP CBcs CDoC CEnd CPMA CSdC EBee EPfP LMil LRHS LSRN MAsh MBlu NBea NLar NPal SPoG SSpi SSta
'Yellow Sea' **new**	CBcs
zenii	CBcs
- 'Pink Parchment'	CBcs CPMA

× *Mahoberberis* (*Berberidaceae*)

aquisargentii	ECrN EMil EPfP LRHS MMuc MRav NHol SEND SPoG WFar
'Dart's Desire'	NLar
'Dart's Treasure'	EPla
'Magic'	MGos NLar
miethkeana	EBee LRHS MBar SRms WDin

Mahonia ✿ (*Berberidaceae*)

F&M 178	WPGP
F&M 193	WPGP
§ ***aquifolium***	CBcs CDul CMac CTrG EBee ECrN EMac GKir MBar MGan MGos MMuc MRav NBlu NWea SPer SPlb SReu WDin
- 'Apollo' ♀H4	CMac CSBt CWib EBee ECrN ELan EPfP GKir LAst LHop LRHS LSRN MAsh MBar MBri MGos MRav MWat NEgg NPri SCoo SPer SPoG WDin
- 'Atropurpurea'	CMac CSBt ELan EPfP EPla GKir LRHS MAsh NLar SPer WDin
- 'Cosmo Crawl'	LRHS MGos
- 'Euro'	NLar
- 'Fascicularis'	see *M.* × *wagneri* 'Pinnacle'
- 'Green Ripple'	CPMA EPfP MGos NLar
- 'Orange Flame'	CPMA EPfP NLar
- 'Smaragd'	CDoC CMac ELan EPfP LRHS LSRN MAsh MBlu MGos MRav SLPl WHCG
- 'Versicolor'	EPla MBlu
bealei	see *M. japonica* Bealei Group
bodinieri	NLar
'Bokrafoot'PBR	EPfP MAsh MBri SPoG
'Chochoco' **new**	WPGP
confusa	CDoC CGHE EPla LLHF LRHS NLar SMad SSpi WFar WPGP
eutriphylla	see *M. trifolia*
fortunei	EBee EPla MBlu NLar WSHC
- 'Winter Prince'	NLar
gracilipes	CGHE EBee EPfP EPla GCal MBlu MDun NLar SLon WPGP
gracilis	WPGP
japonica ♀H4	Widely available
§ - Bealei Group	CBcs CDul CSBt EBee ELan EPfP EPla GKir LAst LRHS MAsh MBar MGos MRav MSwo NBlu NHol NPer NScw NWea SBch SCoo SLim SPoG SWvt WBor WClo WDin WFar WGwG
- 'Gold Dust'	CMac EBee NWea
- 'Hiemalis'	see *M. japonica* 'Hivernant'
§ - 'Hivernant'	EBee EPfP MGos NEgg NWea
lanceolata **new**	WPGP
leschenaultii B&SWJ 9535	WCru
lomariifolia ♀H3	CBcs CBot CHEx EPfP EWes GCal LRHS SAPC SArc SBch SPer SSpi SSta WSpi
× ***media*** 'Buckland' ♀H4	CAlb CBcs CDul CMac CSBt CSam CTrC CWSG EBee EPfP ERas LAst MRav NCGa NEgg SDix SPer SRms WPat
- 'Charity'	Widely available
- 'Faith'	EPla
- 'Lionel Fortescue' ♀H4	CAlb CBcs CEnd CMac CSBt CSam CTrC EBee ELan EPfP ISea LHop LRHS MAsh MGos MRav NEgg NPri SBch SDix SMad SPer SPoG SSpi WBVN WClo
- 'Underway' ♀H4	CSam EPfP LRHS
- 'Winter Sun' ♀H4	Widely available
nervosa	CBcs CMac EPfP MBlu NEgg NLar WCru WDin
- B&SWJ 9562	WCru
nitens **new**	CBcs
nitida **new**	WPGP
oiwakensis B&SWJ 371	WCru
- B&SWJ 3660	WCru
pallida	SMad WPGP
pinnata misapplied	see *M.* × *wagneri* 'Pinnacle'
pinnata ambig.	EPfP EPla MBar
pumila	WCru
repens	EPla GCal NLar
- 'Rotundifolia'	EPla
× ***savilliana***	EPla WPGP
- 'Commissioner'	CWib
Sioux = 'Bokrasio'PBR **new**	MAsh
§ ***trifolia***	GCal
trifoliolata var. ***glauca***	CEnd CPMA NLar
× ***wagneri*** 'Fireflame'	GCal WSpi
- 'Hastings Elegant'	CPMA NLar
- 'Moseri'	NLar SSpi WCot WPat
§ - 'Pinnacle' ♀H4	ELan EPfP EPla LRHS MAsh MGos WDin
- 'Sunset'	CPMA MBlu NLar
- 'Undulata'	EPfP LRHS MBlu NLar SPer SRms WHCG

Maianthemum (*Convallariaceae*)

amoenum B&SWJ 10390 **new**	WCru
atropurpureum	WCru
bicolor	CDes SWat
bifolium	CBct CDes CHid EBee EBrs ECho GBuc GCra LEdu MAvo MNrw MTho NBro NMen SRms WCru WPGP WPnP WTin WWEG
- from Yakushima	CStu
§ - subsp. ***kamtschaticum***	CBct CLAP CPom EBee ECha EHrv NLar NRya SMac WCot WTin
- - B&SWJ 4360	WCru WPrP
- - CD&R 2300	WCru
* - - var. ***minimum***	GCal GEdr
canadense	CBct EBee EBrs ECho EPot GCal GGar GKir MNrw NBid NMen WCru WPnP
* ***chasmanthum***	EBee EPPr LRHS
comaltepecense B&SWJ 10215	WCru

dilatatum see *M. bifolium* subsp. *kamtschaticum*
flexuosum B&SWJ 9069 WCru
- B&SWJ 9255 WCru
aff. ***flexuosum*** B&SWJ 9026 **new** WCru
- B&SWJ 9055 WCru
formosanum EBee EPPr WCot
- B&SWJ 349 WCru
forrestii WCru
fuscum GBin WCru
- var. ***cordatum*** WCru
henryi CBct EBee ECho GEdr WCru
japonicum EBee ECho WHil
- B&SWJ 1179 WCru
- B&SWJ 4714 WCru
oleraceum CBct EBee ECho GBin GEdr LEdu WCot WFar
- B&SWJ 2148 WCru
paniculatum B&SWJ 9137 WCru
pendant B&SWJ 10305 from Guatemala **new** WCru
racemosum ♀H4 Widely available
- subsp. ***amplexicaule*** GBin GCal WPrP
- - 'Emily Moody' CBct CPou EPla SMad WPGP
- dwarf ECho
salvinii B&SWJ 9000 WCru
- B&SWJ 9019 WCru
- B&SWJ 9086 WCru
aff. ***salvinii*** B&SWJ 9088 **new** WCru
stellatum CAvo CBct CRow EBee EBrs ECha ECho EPPr EPfP EPla EPot GAuc GBBs GEdr LEdu LHop MBel NChi NMyG WCru WFar WHil WPnP WTin
szechuanicum EBee GEdr WCru
tatsienense CBct ECho WCru WFar
trifolium ECho

Maihuenia (*Cactaceae*)

poeppigii CStu SIng SPlb

Maireana (*Chenopodiaceae*)

georgei SPlb

Malacothamnus (*Malvaceae*)

fremontii MDKP

Malope (*Malvaceae*)

trifida 'Vulcan' **new** WHil

Malus ✿ (*Rosaceae*)

§ 'Adirondack' CDoC CWSG EMui EPfP GKir LRHS MAsh MBlu MBri MGos MMuc MWat NLar SCoo SLim SPoG WJas
'Admiration' see *M.* 'Adirondack'
× ***adstringens*** 'Almey' ECrN
- 'Hopa' CDul
- 'Simcoe' CLnd CTho EBee LLHF
'Aldenhamensis' see *M.* × *purpurea* 'Aldenhamensis'
× ***arnoldiana*** LMaj
× ***atrosanguinea*** 'Gorgeous' CCAT CDul CLnd CTho CWSG EBee ECrN GKir GTwe LRHS MAsh MGos MSwo NLar SCoo SKee SLim SPer SPoG WDin WJas
baccata CDul CMCN CTho GTwe NWea SCoo SEND SPlb SSpi
- 'Dolgo' CCAT CDoC CTho SKee
- 'Lady Northcliffe' CLnd CTho SFam
- var. ***mandshurica*** CTho
- 'Street Parade' LMaj
aff. ***baccata*** NWea
- MF 96038 SSpi
§ ***bhutanica*** CDul CLnd EPfP GKir SCrf
brevipes CLnd CTho GKir LRHS MBri NLar SCoo SPoG
- 'Wedding Bouquet' MAsh MWat
'Butterball' CDul CLnd CTho EBee ECrN EMil EMui EPfP GKir LAst LMaj NWea SCoo SLim SPer SPoG WDin WHar WJas
'Candymint Sargent' CLnd
'Cave Hill' CLnd
* 'Cheal's Weeping' CMac ECrN LAst NBea NEgg
Coccinella = 'Courtarou' MAsh MMuc WDin
'Comtessa de Paris' GKir LRHS MAsh
'Coralburst' LRHS MAsh MBri
coronaria CDul CLnd EBee EPfP SMHT SPer
var. ***dasycalyx*** 'Charlottae' (d) SPur
- 'Elk River' LRHS MAsh SCoo
'Crimson Brilliant' CLnd
'Crittenden' CLnd EBee ECrN LRHS MAsh MRav SLim SMHT
* 'Directeur Moerlands' CCVT CDoC ECrN EMil EPfP GKir IArd MGos SBch SPur WDin WJas
domestica (F) ECrN WMou
- 'Acklam Russet' (D) SKee
- 'Acme' (D) ECrN MCoo SDea
- 'Adams's Pearmain' (D) CCAT CTho ECrN EMui ERea GBut GKir GTwe LRHS MAsh MCoo SDea SFam SKee
- 'Admiral' (D) ECrN
- 'Akane' (D) SDea
§ - 'Alexander' (C) SKee
- 'Alfriston' (C) CAgr SKee
§ - 'Alkmene' (D) ♀H4 CAgr ECrN SDea SKee
- 'All Doer' (D/C/Cider) CTho LBuc
- 'Allen's Everlasting' (D) GTwe SDea SKee
- 'Allington Pippin' (D) CSBt CTho CTri ECrN IFFs LRHS SDea SKee
- Ambassy = 'Dalil'PBR (D) SLon
- 'American Mother' see *M. domestica* 'Mother'
- 'Ananas Reinette' (D) ECrN
- 'Anna Boelens' (D) SDea
- 'Annie Elizabeth' (C) CAgr CCAT CTho CWib ECrN GKir GTwe IFFs LAst LRHS MCoo MGan SDea SFam SKee SVic WBVN WJas
- 'Anniversary' (D) SDea
- 'Apache' **new** CSut
- 'Api Noir' (D) SKee
- 'Api Rose' (D) WJas
- 'Ard Cairn Russet' (D) ECrN IFFs SDea SKee WGwG
- 'Aromatic Russet' (D) SKee
- 'Arthur Turner' (C) ♀H4 CCAT CCVT CDoC CTri ECrN EMui GBut GKir GTwe IFFs LAst LBuc MAsh MWat SCrf SDea SFam SKee WJas
- 'Ashmead's Kernel' (D) ♀H4 CAgr CCAT CDul CSBt CTho CTri CWib ECrN EMui EPfP ERea GKir GTwe IFFs LBuc LRHS MAsh MBri MCoo MRav MWat NWea SCrf SDea SFam SKee SVic WHar WJas
- 'Ashton Bitter' (Cider) CCAT CTho GTwe
- 'Ashton Brown Jersey' (Cider) CCAT
- 'Autumn Pearmain' (D) SDea SKee
- 'Baker's Delicious' (D) CCAT ECrN GKir SDea SKee
- 'Ball's Bittersweet' (Cider) CCAT CTho
- 'Ballyfatten' (C) IFFs
- 'Ballyvaughan Seedling' (D) IFFs
- 'Balsam' see *M. domestica* 'Green Balsam'
- 'Banana Pippin' CEnd
- 'Banns' (D) ECrN

Cultivar	Suppliers
- 'Bardsey' (D)	CAgr EMui ERea LBuc LRHS WGwG
- 'Bardsley Island' **new**	WDol
- 'Barnack Beauty' (D)	CTho SKee
- 'Barnack Orange' (D)	SKee
- 'Baumann's Reinette' (D)	SKee
- 'Baxter's Pearmain' (D)	ECrN SDea SKee
- 'Beauty of Bath' (D)	CAgr CCAT CCVT CDoC CDul CTho CTri CWib ECrN EMui GBut GKir GTwe IFFs LAst LBuc SDea SFam SKee SPer WHar WJas
- 'Beauty of Hants' (D)	ECrN
- 'Beauty of Kent' (C)	SDea SKee
- 'Beauty of Moray' (C)	GBut GKir GQui SKee
- 'Bedwyn Beauty' (C)	CTho
- 'Beeley Pippin' (D)	GTwe SDea SKee
- 'Bell Apple' (Cider/C)	CCAT CTho
- 'Belle de Boskoop' (C/D) 𝕐H4	CAgr CCAT GTwe MCoo SDea SKee WGwG
- 'Belvoir Seedling' (D/C)	SKee
- 'Bembridge Beauty' (F)	SDea
- 'Benenden Early' (D) **new**	SKee
- 'Ben's Red' (D)	CAgr CCAT CEnd CTho SKee
- 'Bess Pool' (D)	SDea SFam
- 'Bewley Down Pippin'	see *M. domestica* 'Crimson King' (Cider/C)
- 'Bickington Grey' (Cider)	CTho
- 'Billy Down Pippin' (F)	CTho
- 'Bismarck' (C)	CCAT ECrN SKee
- 'Black Dabinett' (Cider)	CCAT CEnd CTho
- 'Black Tom Putt' (C/D)	CTho
- 'Blenheim Orange' (C/D) 𝕐H4	Widely available
- 'Bloody Butcher' (C)	IFFs
- 'Bloody Ploughman' (D)	ECrN EMui GBut GKir GTwe LRHS SKee WHar
- 'Blue Pearmain' (D)	SDea
- 'Blue Sweet' (Cider)	CTho
- Bolero = 'Tuscan'PBR (D/Ball)	ECrN MCoo SDea SKee
- 'Bountiful' (C)	CAgr CCAT CCVT CDoC CSBt CTri CWib ECrN EMui GKir GTwe LBuc LRHS MAsh MBri SDea SKee WBVN WHar
- 'Braddick Nonpareil' (D)	SKee
- 'Braeburn' (D)	CAgr CCAT CDul CSut ECrN EMui ERea LAst LBuc LRHS MNHC SCrf SDea SFam SKee WHar WJas
- 'Braintree Seedling' (D)	ECrN
- 'Bramley's Seedling' (C) 𝕐H4	Widely available
- 'Bramley's Seedling' clone 20	CDoC CMac EMui LRHS MBri NLar SCoo SDea SPoG WHar
- 'Bread Fruit' (C/D)	CEnd CTho
- 'Breakwell's Seedling' (Cider)	CCAT CTho WDol
- 'Breitling' (D)	SKee
- 'Bridgwater Pippin' (C)	CCAT CTho SKee
- 'Broad-eyed Pippin' (C)	SKee
- 'Broadholm Beauty'	EMui LRHS MAsh
- 'Brookes's' (D)	WHar
- 'Broom Apple' (Cider) **new**	WDol
- 'Brown Crofton' (D)	IFFs
- 'Brown Snout' (Cider)	CCAT CTho SKee
- 'Brownlees Russet' (D)	CAgr CCAT CTho CTri GTwe MCoo NEgg NWea SDea SFam SKee WGwG
- 'Brown's Apple' (Cider)	CAgr CCAT GTwe LRHS
- 'Broxwood Foxwhelp' (Cider)	CCAT
- 'Burn's Seedling' (D)	CTho
- 'Burr Knot' (C)	ECrN
- 'Burrowhill Early' (Cider)	CTho
- 'Bushey Grove' (C)	SDea SKee
- 'Buttery Do'	CTho
- 'Cadbury'	CCAT
- 'Calville Blanc d'Hiver' (D)	SKee
- 'Cambusnethan Pippin' (D)	GBut GQui SKee
- 'Camelot' (Cider/C)	CCAT LBuc
- 'Cap of Liberty' (Cider)	CCAT
- 'Captain Broad' (D/Cider)	CCAT CEnd CTho
- 'Captain Kidd' (D)	EMui
- 'Captain Smith' (F)	CEnd
- 'Carlisle Codlin' (C)	GKir GTwe NWea SDea
- 'Caroline' (D)	ECrN
- 'Catherine' (C)	ECrN
- 'Catshead' (C)	CAgr CCAT ECrN GKir GQui SDea SKee
- 'Cellini' (C/D)	SDea SKee
- 'Channel Beauty' (D) **new**	WDol
- 'Charles Ross' (C/D) 𝕐H4	Widely available
- 'Charlotte'PBR (C/Ball)	MGos SDea SKee
- 'Chaxhill Red' (Cider/D)	CCAT CTho
- 'Cheddar Cross' (D)	CAgr CTri ECrN
- 'Chelmsford Wonder' (C)	ECrN SKee
- 'Chisel Jersey' (Cider)	CAgr CCAT CTri
- 'Chivers Delight' (D)	CAgr CCAT CSBt ECrN EMui ERea GKir GTwe LRHS MCoo SDea SKee WJas
- 'Chorister Boy' (D)	CTho
- 'Christmas Pearmain' (D)	CTho ECrN GTwe SDea SFam SKee
- 'Cider Lady's Finger' (Cider)	CCAT
- 'Cissy' (D)	WDol WGwG
- 'Claygate Pearmain' (D) 𝕐H4	CCAT CTho CTri ECrN GTwe LRHS MCoo SDea SFam SKee SVic WBVN
- 'Clopton Red' (D)	ECrN
- 'Clydeside'	GKir GQui
- 'Coat Jersey' (Cider)	CCAT
- 'Cobra' **new**	EMui LBuc
- 'Cockle Pippin' (D)	CAgr CTho LRHS SDea
- 'Coeur de Boeuf' (C/D)	SKee
- 'Coleman's Seedling' (Cider)	CTho
- 'Collogett Pippin' (C/Cider)	CCAT CEnd CTho
- 'Colonel Vaughan' (C/D)	SKee
- 'Cornish Aromatic' (D)	CAgr CCAT CTho GTwe IFFs LRHS SCrf SDea SFam SKee WGwG
- 'Cornish Gilliflower' (D)	CAgr CCAT CTho ECrN EMui LRHS MCoo SDea SFam SKee WBVN
- 'Cornish Honeypin' (D)	CEnd CTho
- 'Cornish Longstem' (D)	CAgr CEnd CTho
- 'Cornish Mother' (D)	CEnd CTho
- 'Cornish Pine' (D)	CEnd CTho SDea
- 'Coronation' (D)	SDea
- 'Corse Hill' (D)	CCAT CTho
- 'Costard' (C)	GTwe SKee
- 'Cottenham Seedling' (C)	ECrN SKee
- 'Coul Blush' (D)	GBut SKee
- 'Court of Wick' (D)	CAgr CCAT CTho ECrN GKir SKee SVic
- 'Court Pendu Plat' (D)	CAgr CCAT CTho GKir LBuc MWat NWea SDea SFam SKee WHar WJas
- 'Court Royal' (Cider)	CCAT
- 'Cow Apple' (C)	CCAT
- 'Cox Cymraeg' (D)	WGwG
- 'Cox's Orange Pippin' (D)	CBcs CCAT CCVT CDul CMac CSBt CTri CWib ECrN EMui ERea GTwe IFFs LAst LRHS LSRN MAsh MGos MWat NPri SCrf SDea SFam SKee SPer WJas
- 'Cox's Pomona' (C/D)	SDea SKee
- 'Cox's Rouge de Flandres' (D)	SKee

	Cultivar	Suppliers
	- 'Cox's Selfing' (D)	CDoC CTri CWSG CWib EMui EPfP GKir GTwe LBuc LRHS MAsh MBri MGan MGos MNHC SCrf SDea SKee SPoG WHar WJas
	- 'Craigflower Classic'	GKir
	- 'Crawley Beauty' (C)	CAgr CCAT GTwe SDea SFam SKee
	- 'Crimson Beauty of Bath' (D)	CAgr
	- 'Crimson Bramley' (C)	CCAT LAst
	- 'Crimson Cox' (D)	SDea
§	- 'Crimson King' (Cider/C)	CAgr CCAT
	- 'Crimson King' (D)	CAgr
	- 'Crimson Queening' (D)	SKee
	- 'Crimson Victoria' (Cider)	CTho
	- Crispin	see *M. domestica* 'Mutsu'
§	- 'Crowngold' (D)	EMui GTwe LRHS
	- 'Cutler Grieve' (D)	SDea
	- Cybèle = 'Delrouval'	LRHS
	- 'Dabinett' (Cider)	CAgr CCAT CTho CTri EMui GTwe LBuc LRHS SCrf SDea SKee
	- 'D'Arcy Spice' (D)	CAgr CCAT ECrN EMui EPfP ERea LRHS MCoo MWat SDea SFam SKee WGwG
	- 'Dawn' (D)	SKee
	- 'Deacon's Blushing Beauty' (C/D)	SDea
	- 'Deacon's Millennium'	SDea
	- 'Decio' (D)	SKee
	- Delbarestivale = 'Delcorf' (red) (D) ♀H4 **new**	LRHS
	- 'Devon Crimson Queen' (D)	CTho SDea
	- 'Devonshire Buckland' (C)	CEnd CTho
	- 'Devonshire Quarrenden' (D)	CAgr CCAT CDul CEnd CTho ECrN GBut GKir LRHS SDea SFam SKee SVic WJas
	- 'Diamond' (D)	WGwG
	- 'Discovery' (D) ♀H4	Widely available
	- 'Doctor Harvey' (C)	ECrN ERea SFam
	- 'Doctor Kidd's Orange Red'	see *M. domestica* 'Kidd's Orange Red'
	- 'Don's Delight' (C)	CTho
	- 'Dove' (Cider)	CCAT
	- 'Dredge's Fame' (D)	CTho
	- 'Duchess's Favourite' (D)	SKee
	- 'Dufflin' (Cider)	CCAT CTho
	- 'Duke of Cornwall' (C)	CTho
	- 'Duke of Devonshire' (D)	CTho CTri SDea SFam SKee
N	- 'Dumeller's Seedling'	see *M. domestica* 'Dummellor's Seedling'
§	- 'Dummellor's Seedling' (C) ♀H4	CCAT SDea SKee
	- 'Dunkerton Late Sweet' (Cider)	CCAT CTho EMil LBuc
	- 'Dunn's Seedling' (D)	SDea
§	- 'Dutch Mignonne' (D)	ECrN SKee
	- 'Dymock Red' (Cider)	CCAT LBuc
	- 'Early Blenheim' (D/C)	CCAT CEnd CTho
	- 'Early Bower' (D)	CEnd
	- 'Early Julyan' (C)	GBut GKir GQui SKee
	- 'Early Victoria'	see *M. domestica* 'Emneth Early'
	- Early Windsor	see *M. domestica* 'Alkmene'
	- 'Early Worcester'	see *M. domestica* 'Tydeman's Early Worcester'
	- 'East Lothian Pippin' (C)	GQui
	- 'Easter Orange' (D)	GTwe SKee
	- 'Ecklinville' (C)	SDea
	- 'Eden' **new**	LBuc
	- 'Edith Hopwood' (D)	ECrN
	- 'Edward VII' (C) ♀H4	CCAT CDoC GKir GTwe SCrf SDea SFam SKee
	- 'Egremont Russet' (D) ♀H4	Widely available
	- 'Ellis' Bitter' (Cider)	CCAT CTho GTwe SKee SVic
	- 'Ellison's Orange' (D) ♀H4	CAgr CCAT CDul CMac CSBt CTri CWib ECrN EMui EPfP ERea GBut GKir GTwe IFFs LAst LBuc LRHS MAsh MWat NWea SDea SFam SKee SVic WHar WJas
	- 'Elstar' (D) ♀H4	CWib ECrN EMui GKir GTwe IFFs LAst LRHS SDea SKee
	- 'Elton Beauty' (D)	SDea SKee
§	- 'Emneth Early' (C) ♀H4	CAgr ECrN EMui ERea GKir GTwe IFFs SDea SFam SKee WJas
	- 'Emperor Alexander'	see *M. domestica* 'Alexander'
	- 'Empire' (D)	LAst SKee
	- 'Encore' (C)	SDea
	- 'Endsleigh Beauty' (D)	CEnd
	- 'English Codlin' (C)	CCAT CTho CTri
	- 'Epicure'	see *M. domestica* 'Laxton's Epicure'
	- 'Ernie's Russet' (D)	SDea
	- 'Eros' (D)	ECrN
	- 'Essex Pippin' (D)	ECrN
	- 'Evening Gold' (C)	SDea
	- 'Eve's Delight' (D)	SDea
	- 'Excelsior' (C)	ECrN
	- 'Exeter Cross' (D)	CCAT ECrN SDea SFam
	- 'Fair Maid of Devon' (Cider)	CAgr CCAT CEnd CTho
	- 'Fairfield' (D)	CTho
	- 'Falstaff'[PBR] (D) ♀H4	CAgr CCAT CCVT CDoC ECrN EMui EPfP GKir GTwe MGos SCoo SDea SKee WBVN WJas
	- 'Farmer's Glory' (D)	CAgr CTho
	- 'Fiesta'[PBR] (D) ♀H4	Widely available
	- 'Fillbarrel' (Cider)	CCAT
	- 'Firmgold' (D)	SDea
	- 'Flame' (D)	ECrN
	- 'Flamenco'[PBR]	see *M. domestica* 'Obelisk'
§	- 'Flower of Kent' (C)	CCAT SCrf SDea SKee
	- 'Forfar'	see *M. domestica* 'Dutch Mignonne'
	- 'Forge' (D)	CAgr SDea SKee
	- 'Fortune'	see *M. domestica* 'Laxton's Fortune'
	- 'Foulden Pearmain' (D)	ECrN
	- 'Foxwhelp' (Cider)	LBuc
	- 'Francis' (D)	ECrN
	- 'Frederick' (Cider)	CCAT CTho WDol
	- 'French Crab' (C)	SDea
	- 'Freyberg' (D)	SKee
	- 'Fuji' (D)	SDea SKee
	- 'Gala' (D)	CMac CSBt EMui GTwe LAst SCoo SCrf SDea SFam SKee WHar
	- 'Galloway Pippin' (C)	GKir GQui GTwe SKee
	- 'Garnet' (D)	ECrN
	- 'Gascoyne's Scarlet' (D)	CCAT GKir SDea SFam SKee WJas
	- 'Gavin' (D)	CAgr GBut SDea SKee
	- 'Genesis II' (D/C)	SDea
	- 'Genet Moyle' (C/Cider)	CCAT CTri
	- 'George Carpenter' (D)	SDea
	- 'George Cave' (D)	CDul CTho ECrN GBut GTwe IFFs LRHS MAsh MCoo SDea SFam SKee WJas
	- 'George Neal' (C) ♀H4	CAgr SDea SFam
	- 'Gibbon's Russet' (D)	IFFs
	- 'Gilliflower of Gloucester' (D)	CTho
	- 'Gin' (Cider)	CCAT
	- 'Gladstone' (D)	CAgr CTho SKee
	- 'Glansevin' **new**	WDol
§	- 'Glass Apple' (C/D)	CCAT CEnd CTho
	- 'Gloria Mundi' (C)	SDea SKee
	- 'Gloster '69' (D)	SDea
	- 'Gloucester Royal' (D)	CTho
	- 'Gloucester Underleaf'	CTho

	Cultivar	Suppliers
	- 'Golden Ball'	CTho
	- 'Golden Bittersweet' (D)	CAgr CTho
	- 'Golden Delicious' (D) ♀H4	CDul CSBt CWib ECrN EMui EPfP LAst NBlu SCrf SDea SKee SVic WHar
	- 'Golden Glow' (C)	SDea
	- 'Golden Harvey' (D)	CAgr CCAT
	- 'Golden Jubilee'	CEnd
	- 'Golden Knob' (D)	CCAT CTho SKee
	- 'Golden Noble' (C) ♀H4	CAgr CCAT CDoC CTho CTri ECrN ERea GKir GTwe IFFs LRHS MCoo SDea SFam SKee
	- 'Golden Nugget' (D)	CAgr SKee
	- 'Golden Pippin' (C)	CAgr CCAT GBut SKee
	- 'Golden Reinette' (D)	GTwe SKee
	- 'Golden Russet' (D)	CAgr ECrN GTwe SDea SKee
	- 'Golden Spire' (C)	GBut IFFs MCoo SDea SKee
	- 'Gooseberry' (C)	LSRN
	- 'Goring' (Cider)	CTho
	- 'Grand Sultan' (D)	CCAT
	- 'Granny Smith' (D)	CBcs CDul CLnd CWib ECrN GTwe LAst LRHS SCrf SDea SKee SPer SVic WHar
	- 'Gravenstein' (D)	CCAT GKir GQui SDea SFam SKee
§	- 'Green Balsam' (C)	CTri
	- 'Green Kilpandy Pippin' (C)	GQui
	- 'Green Roland'	ECrN ERea
	- 'Greensleeves'PBR (D) ♀H4	CAgr CCAT CDoC CDul CMac CSBt CTri CWSG CWib ECrN EMui EPfP GKir GTwe LAst LRHS MAsh MGos SDea SKee WBVN WHar WJas
	- 'Greenup's Pippin' (D)	GBut
	- 'Grenadier' (C) ♀H4	CAgr CCAT CDoC CSBt CTri ECrN EMui GBut GKir GTwe IFFs LRHS MGos SDea SKee SVic WJas
	- 'Hagloe Crab' **new**	LBuc
	- 'Halstow Natural' (Cider)	CAgr CTho
	- 'Hambledon Deux Ans' (C)	SDea
	- 'Hangy Down' (Cider)	CCAT CTho
	- Harmonie = 'Delorina' **new**	LRHS
§	- 'Harry Master's Jersey' (Cider)	CAgr CCAT CTho CTri SDea SKee
	- 'Harvester' (D)	CTho
	- 'Harvey' (C)	SDea
	- 'Hawthornden' (C)	GBut GQui GTwe LRHS SKee
	- 'Herefordshire Redstreak' **new**	LBuc
	- 'Herefordshire Russet'PBR	CDul EMui LBuc LRHS MAsh MBri MCoo SKee WJas
	- 'Herring's Pippin' (D)	GTwe SDea SKee
	- 'High View Pippin' (D)	SKee
	- 'Hoary Morning' (C)	CCAT CTho ECrN SDea SKee
	- 'Hocking's Green' (C/D)	CAgr CCAT CEnd CTho
	- 'Holland Pippin' (C)	SKee
	- 'Hollow Core' (C)	CAgr CTho
	- 'Holstein' (D)	CTho SDea SKee
	- 'Honey Pippin' (D)	ECrN
	- 'Hood's Supreme' (D)	GBut
	- 'Horneburger Pfannkuchen' (C)	SKee
	- 'Horsford Prolific' (D)	ECrN ERea
	- 'Horsham Russet' (D)	ERea
	- 'Howgate Wonder' (C)	CAgr CCAT CCVT CDoC CDul CSBt CWib ECrN EMui ERea GBut GKir GTwe IFFs LAst LBuc LRHS MAsh SCrf SDea SFam SKee SPer SVic WBVN WHar WJas
	- 'Hubbard's Pearmain' (D)	ECrN SKee
	- 'Hunter's Majestic' (D/C)	ECrN
	- 'Hunt's Duke of Gloucester' (D)	CTho SKee
	- 'Idared' (D) ♀H4	CCAT CWib ECrN GKir IFFs SDea SKee SVic
	- 'Improved Dove' (Cider)	CCAT
	- 'Improved Keswick' (C/D)	CEnd CTho
	- 'Improved Lambrook Pippin' (Cider)	CCAT CTho CTri
	- 'Improved Redstreak' (Cider)	CTho
	- 'Ingrid Marie' (D)	SDea SKee
	- 'Irish Peach' (D)	CAgr CCAT ECrN GBut GKir GTwe IFFs LRHS MCoo SDea SFam SKee WHar
	- 'Isaac Newton's Tree'	see *M. domestica* 'Flower of Kent'
	- 'Isle of Wight Pippin' (D)	SDea
	- 'Isle of Wight Russet' (D)	SDea
	- 'Jackson's'	see *M. domestica* 'Crimson King' (Cider/C)
	- 'James Grieve' (D) ♀H4	Widely available
	- 'Jerseymac' (D)	SDea
	- 'Jester' (D)	ECrN GTwe SDea SKee
	- 'Joaneting' (D) **new**	CAgr
	- 'Joeby Crab' **new**	WDol
	- 'John Standish' (D)	CAgr CCAT CTri ERea GTwe SCrf SDea
	- 'John Toucher's'	see *M. domestica* 'Crimson King' (Cider/C)
	- 'Johnny Andrews' (Cider)	CAgr CCAT CTho
	- 'Johnny Voun' (D)	CEnd CTho
	- 'Jonagold' (D) ♀H4	CTri CWib ECrN EMil EMui GTwe LAst LRHS MAsh SCrf SDea SFam SKee SPer SVic WJas
	- 'Jonagold Crowngold'	see *M. domestica* 'Crowngold'
§	- 'Jonagored'PBR (D)	SDea SKee
	- 'Jonared' (D)	GTwe
	- 'Jonathan' (D)	CMac SDea SKee
	- 'Jordan's Weeping' (C)	ERea SDea
	- 'Josephine' (D)	SDea
	- 'Joybells' (D)	GKir
	- 'Jubilee'	see *M. domestica* 'Royal Jubilee'
	- 'Jumbo'	LBuc LRHS MAsh MBri MCoo SKee WJas
	- 'Jupiter'PBR (D) ♀H4	CAgr CCAT CSBt CTri CWib ECrN GKir GTwe LAst LRHS MAsh SDea SKee WJas
	- 'Kapai Red Jonathan' (D)	SDea
	- 'Karmijn de Sonnaville' (D)	SDea
§	- 'Katja' (D)	CAgr CCAT CCVT CDoC CMac CTri CWib ECrN EMui ERea GBut GKir GTwe IFFs LAst LBuc LRHS MAsh NEgg NLar SCoo SDea SKee SPer WBVN WHar WJas
	- Katy	see *M. domestica* 'Katja'
	- 'Kenneth' (D) **new**	WDol
	- 'Kent' (D)	ECrN EMui GTwe LRHS MCoo NLar SCrf SDea SKee
	- 'Kentish Fillbasket' (C)	SKee
	- 'Kentish Pippin' (C/Cider/D)	SKee
	- 'Kerry Pippin' (D)	IFFs SKee
	- 'Keswick Codlin' (C)	CTho ECrN GKir GTwe LRHS MCoo NEgg NLar NWea SDea SKee WJas
§	- 'Kidd's Orange Red' (D) ♀H4	CAgr CCAT CMac CTri ECrN EMui GQui GTwe LAst LBuc LRHS MWat SCrf SDea SFam SKee WBVN
	- 'Kilkenny Pearmain' (D)	IFFs
	- 'Kill Boy'	CTho
	- 'Killerton Sharp' (Cider)	CTho
	- 'Killerton Sweet' (Cider)	CTho
	- 'King Byerd' (C/D)	CCAT CEnd CTho
	- 'King Luscious' (D)	SDea

§	Cultivar	Suppliers
§	- 'King of the Pippins' (D) ♀H4	CCAT CTho CTri ECrN GBut GTwe LRHS MCoo SCrf SDea SFam SKee SVic
	- 'King Russet' (D) ♀H4	SDea
	- 'King's Acre Pippin' (D)	CCAT SDea SFam
	- 'Kingston Bitter' (Cider)	CTho
	- 'Kingston Black' (Cider/C)	CCAT CEnd CTho CTri ECrN GTwe LBuc LRHS SDea SKee
	- 'Kirton Fair' (D)	CTho
	- 'Knobby Russet' (D)	SKee
	- 'Lady Henniker' (D)	CCAT CTho ECrN GTwe SDea SKee
	- 'Lady of the Wemyss' (C)	GKir GQui SKee
	- 'Lady Sudeley' (D)	CTho GBut SDea SKee
	- 'Lady's Finger' (C/D)	CEnd GKir
	- 'Lady's Finger of Lancaster' (C/D)	SKee
	- 'Lady's Finger of Offaly' (D)	SDea
	- 'Lake's Kernel' (D)	CTho
	- 'Lamb Abbey Pearmain' (D)	SKee
	- 'Landsberger Reinette' (D)	SKee
	- 'Lane's Prince Albert' (C) ♀H4	CAgr CCAT CSBt ECrN EMui GBut GKir GTwe MGos MRav MWat NWea SCoo SCrf SDea SFam SKee SVic WHar WJas
	- 'Langley Pippin' (D)	SDea
§	- 'Langworthy' (Cider)	CCAT CTho
	- 'Lass o' Gowrie' (C)	GBut GKir GQui SKee
§	- 'Laxton's Epicure' (D) ♀H4	CAgr CDul ECrN GBut GTwe LAst SDea SFam SKee
§	- 'Laxton's Fortune' (D) ♀H4	CCAT CMac CSBt CTri CWib ECrN EMui GBut GKir GTwe LAst SCrf SDea SFam SKee WHar WJas
	- 'Laxton's Pearmain' (D)	MCoo
	- 'Laxton's Royalty' (D)	SDea
§	- 'Laxton's Superb' (D)	CBcs CCAT CCVT CDoC CDul CMac CSBt CTri CWib ECrN EMui GKir GTwe IFFs LAst LBuc LHop LRHS MCoo MGan NPri NWea SCrf SDea SKee SPer SVic WHar WJas
	- 'Leathercoat Russet' (D)	CAgr CCAT SKee
	- 'Lemon Pippin' (C)	CCAT ECrN SDea SKee
	- 'Lemon Pippin of Gloucestershire' (D)	CTho
	- 'Liberty' (D)	GBut SDea
	- 'Limberland' (C)	CTho
	- 'Limelight' (D)	EMui ERea LBuc LRHS MAsh MBri MCoo NLar SCoo SKee
	- 'Link Wonder'	CEnd
	- 'Lodi' (C)	SDea
	- 'London Pearmain' (D)	ECrN
	- 'London Pippin' (C)	CAgr CTho
	- 'Longkeeper' (D)	CAgr CEnd CTho
	- 'Longney Russet' **new**	LBuc
	- 'Longstart' **new**	GBut
	- 'Longstem' (Cider)	CTho
	- 'Lord Burghley' (D)	SDea SKee
	- 'Lord Derby' (C)	CAgr CCAT CDul CMac CTho CWib ECrN EMui GBut GKir GTwe LAst LRHS MBri SCrf SDea SFam SKee SVic
	- 'Lord Grosvenor' (C)	SKee
	- 'Lord Hindlip' (D)	SDea SFam
	- 'Lord Lambourne' (D) ♀H4	CAgr CCAT CCVT CDoC CDul CMac CSBt CTri CWib ECrN EMui EPfP GKir GTwe IFFs LAst LRHS MAsh MCoo MGos MWat SCrf SDea SFam SKee SPer WBVN WHar WJas
	- 'Lord of the Isles' (F)	CAgr CCAT
	- 'Lord Stradbroke' (C)	ECrN
	- 'Lord Suffield' (C)	CTri ECrN SKee
	- 'Lough Tree of Wexford' (D)	IFFs
	- 'Lucombe's Pine' (D)	CAgr CEnd CTho ECrN SVic WGwG
	- 'Lucombe's Seedling' (D)	CTho
	- 'Lynn's Pippin' (D)	ECrN
	- 'Mabbott's Pearmain' (D)	SDea
	- 'Machen' **new**	WDol
	- 'Maclean's Favourite' (D)	ECrN
	- 'Madresfield Court' (D)	SDea
	- 'Maggie Sinclair' (D)	GBut GQui
	- 'Maid of Kent'	CCAT
	- 'Major' (Cider)	CCAT
	- 'Maldon Wonder' (D)	ECrN
	- 'Malling Kent' (D)	EMui ERea SDea SFam
	- 'Manaccan Primrose' (C/D)	CEnd
	- 'Manks Codlin' (C)	GBut
	- 'Marged Nicolas' (D) **new**	WDol
	- 'Margil' (D)	CCAT SDea SFam SKee
	- 'Marriage-maker' (D)	SKee
	- 'Maxton' (D)	ECrN
	- 'May Queen' (D)	SDea SFam
	- 'Maypole' PBR (D/Ball)	MGos SDea WJas
	- 'McIntosh' (D)	SKee
	- 'Melba' (D)	SKee
	- 'Melon' (D)	SDea
	- 'Melrose' (D)	ECrN SVic
	- 'Merchant Apple' (D)	CCAT CTho CTri
	- 'Mère de Ménage' (C)	GBut SFam
	- 'Meridian' PBR (D)	CAgr CDoC ECrN EMil EMui LRHS SDea
	- 'Merton Knave' (D)	SDea SFam
	- 'Merton Russet' (D)	SDea
	- 'Merton Worcester' (D)	ECrN SDea SKee
	- 'Michaelmas Red' (D)	GTwe NEgg SKee
	- 'Michelin' (Cider)	CAgr CCAT CTri GTwe SDea SKee
	- 'Miller's Seedling' (D)	SKee
	- 'Millicent Barnes' (D)	SDea
	- 'Mollie's Delicious' (D)	SKee
	- 'Monarch' (C)	CAgr CCAT CTri ECrN GBut GTwe SDea SFam SKee
	- 'Monidel' PBR	ECrN
	- 'Monmouthshire Green' (D) **new**	WDol
	- 'Montfort' (D)	ECrN
	- 'Morgan's Sweet' (C/Cider)	CCAT CEnd CTho CTri SDea SKee WDol
	- 'Moss's Seedling' (D)	SDea
§	- 'Mother' (D) ♀H4	CAgr CCAT CDoC CTri ECrN GTwe LRHS SCrf SDea SKee
§	- 'Mutsu' (D)	CCAT CTri ECrN SCrf SDea SKee
	- 'Nant Gwrtheyrn' (D)	WGwG
	- 'Nettlestone Pippin' (D)	SDea
	- 'Newton Wonder' (D/C) ♀H4	CAgr CCAT CCVT CDoC CDul CSBt CTho CTri CWib ECrN EMui GTwe IFFs LAst LRHS MAsh MCoo SCrf SDea SFam SKee WJas
	- 'Newtown Pippin' (D)	SDea
	- 'Nine Square' (D)	CCAT CTho
	- 'Nittany Red' (D)	SDea
	- 'No Pip' (C)	CTho
	- 'Nolan Pippin' (D)	ECrN
	- 'Nonpareil' (D)	SKee
	- 'Norfolk Beauty' (C)	ECrN ERea SKee
	- 'Norfolk Beefing' (C)	ECrN ERea SDea SFam SKee
	- 'Norfolk Royal' (D)	CDoC ECrN ERea GTwe SDea SKee
	- 'Norfolk Royal Russet' (D)	ECrN ERea GBut GKir LRHS WBVN
	- 'Norfolk Summer Broadend' (C)	SKee
	- 'Norfolk Winter Coleman' (C)	ERea SKee
	- 'Northcott Superb' (D)	CTho
	- 'Northern Greening' (C)	SKee
§	- 'Northwood' (Cider)	CCAT CTho

- 'Nutmeg Pippin' (D) CCAT ECrN SDea
- Nuvar Freckles (D) SKee
- Nuvar Gold (D) SKee
- Nuvar Golden Elf SKee
- Nuvar Golden Hills (D) SKee
- Nuvar Home Farm (D) SKee
- Nuvar Long Harvest (D) SKee
- Nuvar Melody (D) SKee
- Nuvar Red Gloss (D) SKee
- 'Oaken Pin' (C) CCAT CTho
§ - 'Obelisk'PBR (D) LRHS MCoo NPri SDea SKee
- 'Old Pearmain' (D) SDea
- 'Old Somerset Russet' (D) CCAT CTho
- 'Opal'PBR (D) ECrN
- 'Opalescent' (D) SKee
- 'Orkney Apple' (F) SKee
- 'Orleans Reinette' (D) CAgr CCAT CTho CTri CWib ECrN GBut GTwe IFFs LBuc LRHS MAsh MWat NEgg SCrf SDea SFam SKee WJas
- 'Oslin' (D) GKir SKee
- 'Otava'PBR SKee
- 'Owen Thomas' (D) CTri
- 'Paignton Marigold' (Cider) CTho
- 'Palmer's Rosey' (D) SKee
- 'Park Farm Pippin'PBR GKir
- 'Pascoe's Pippin' (D/C) CTho
- 'Payhembury' (C/Cider) CAgr CTho CTri
- 'Peacemaker' (D) SKee
- 'Pear Apple' (D) CAgr CEnd CTho
- 'Pearl' (D) ECrN SDea
- 'Peasgood's Nonsuch' (C) ♀H4 CAgr CCAT CDoC ECrN ERea GBut GKir GTwe IFFs LRHS MAsh NEgg SCrf SDea SFam SKee SLon
- 'Peck's Pleasant' (D) SKee
- 'Pen Caled' **new** WDol
- 'Pendragon' (D) CTho
- 'Penhallow Pippin' (D) CTho
- 'Perthyre' (Cider) **new** WDol
- 'Peter Lock' (C/D) CAgr CCAT CEnd CTho NWea
- 'Peter's Pippin' (D) SDea
- 'Peter's Seedling' (D) SDea
- 'Pethyre' (Cider) CCAT
- 'Pickering's Seedling' (D) SKee
- 'Pig Aderyn' (C) WDol WGwG
- 'Pig y Glomen' (C) WGwG
- 'Pig Yr Wydd' **new** WDol
- 'Pig's Nose Pippin' (D) CEnd
- 'Pig's Nose Pippin' Type III (D) CAgr CTho
- 'Pig's Snout' (Cider/C/D) CCAT CEnd CTho
- 'Pine Apple Russet' CAgr
- 'Pinova'PBR (D) CAgr SKee
- 'Pitmaston Pine Apple' (D) CCAT CTho CTri ECrN EMui ERea GBut LAst LRHS MAsh MCoo MWat SCrf SDea SFam SKee
- 'Pixie' (D) ♀H4 CCAT CWib EMui GTwe LRHS MWat SDea SFam SKee WJas
- 'Plum Vite' (D) CAgr CTho CTri
- 'Plympton Pippin' (C) CEnd CTho CTri
- Polka = 'Trajan'PBR (D/Ball) MGos SDea SKee
- 'Polly' (C/D) CEnd
- 'Polly Whitehair' (C/D) CCAT CTho SDea
- 'Poltimore Seedling' CTho
- 'Pomeroy of Somerset' (D) CCAT CTho CTri
- 'Ponsford' (C) CAgr CCAT CTho
- 'Port Allen Russet' (C/D) GKir GQui
- 'Port Wine' see *M. domestica* 'Harry Master's Jersey'
- 'Porter's Perfection' (Cider) CCAT
- 'Prenglas' **new** WDol
- 'Prince Charles' (D) **new** SKee
- 'Princesse' ECrN EMui GKir LRHS SDea SKee
- 'Profit' CTho
- 'Puckrupp Pippin' (D) LBuc
- 'Quarry Apple' (C) CTho
- 'Queen' (C) CAgr CTho ECrN SKee
- 'Queen Cox' (D) CTri ECrN EMui MAsh SDea SKee SLon
- 'Queen Cox' self-fertile CSut CWib EMui LRHS LSRN SDea
- 'Queens' (D) CTho
- 'Quench' (D/Cider) CTho
- 'Radford Beauty' MCoo
- 'Rajka' (D) SKee
- 'Red Alkmene' (D) MBri
- 'Red Belle de Boskoop' (D) CAgr
- 'Red Blenheim' (C/D) SKee
- 'Red Bramley' (C) CWib GKir
- 'Red Charles Ross' (C/D) SDea
- 'Red Delicious' (D) SCrf SKee
- 'Red Devil' (D) CAgr CMac CTri CWSG ECrN EMui GBut GKir GTwe LAst LRHS MAsh MBri MNHC NLar SCoo SDea SKee WHar WJas
- 'Red Ellison' (D) CCAT CTho CTri ERea GTwe SDea
- 'Red Elstar' (D) SCrf
- 'Red Falstaff'PBR (D) CAgr CCAT CCVT CDoC CDul CMac ECrN EMui ERea GKir LBuc LRHS MAsh MBri MCoo NLar SKee SPoG WBVN WHar
- 'Red Fuji' (D) SDea
- 'Red George Cave' **new** MAsh
- 'Red James Grieve' GKir
- 'Red Jersey' (Cider) CCAT
- 'Red Joaneting' (D) SKee
- 'Red Jonagold'PBR see *M. domestica* 'Jonagored'
- 'Red Jonathan' (D) SDea
- 'Red Miller's Seedling' (D) ECrN SCrf SDea
- 'Red Rattler' (D) CTho
- 'Red Roller' (D) CTho
- 'Red Ruby' (F) CTho
- 'Red Victoria' (C) GTwe
- 'Red Windsor' CMac EMui GBut GKir LBuc LRHS MAsh NLar SCoo SKee SPoG WHar WJas
- 'Redcoat Grieve' (D) GKir SDea
- 'Redsleeves' (D) CAgr ECrN GTwe SDea SKee
- 'Redstrake' (Cider) CCAT
- Regali = 'Delkistar' **new** LRHS
- 'Reine des Reinettes' see *M. domestica* 'King of the Pippins'
- 'Reinette Descardre' (D) SVic
- 'Reinette d'Obry' (Cider) CCAT
- 'Reinette du Canada' (D) SKee
- 'Reinette Rouge Etoilée' (D) SDea
- 'Reverend Greeves' (C) SDea
- 'Reverend McCormick' CTho
- 'Reverend W. Wilks' (C) CAgr CDoC CSBt CTri ECrN EMui GKir LAst LRHS MAsh SCrf SDea SFam SKee WJas
- 'Ribston Pippin' (D) ♀H4 CCAT CCVT CMac CTho CTri CWib ECrN GBut GTwe LRHS MCoo MWat SCrf SDea SFam SKee WJas
- 'Rival' (D) CAgr SDea
- 'Robert Blatchford' (C) ECrN
- 'Rome Beauty' (D) SDea
- 'Rosemary Russet' (D) ♀H4 CAgr CCAT CTho GBut GKir GTwe LRHS MCoo SCrf SDea SFam SKee
- 'Ross Nonpareil' (D) CAgr GTwe IFFs SDea SKee
- 'Rosy Blenheim' (D) ECrN

	Cultivar	Suppliers
	– 'Roter Ananas' (D)	SKee
	– 'Rough Pippin' (D)	CCAT CEnd
	– 'Roundway Magnum Bonum' (D)	CAgr CTho SDea
	– 'Royal Gala' (D) ♀H4	ECrN EMui LAst LBuc SDea SLon
§	– 'Royal Jubilee' (C)	CCAT
	– 'Royal Russet' (C)	CEnd ECrN SDea
	– 'Royal Somerset' (C/Cider)	CCAT CTho CTri
	– 'Rubinette' (D)	ECrN MGos SDea
	– 'Rubinola'PBR	SKee
	– 'Saint Ailred'	SKee
	– 'Saint Cecilia' (D)	SDea WDol WGwG
§	– 'Saint Edmund's Pippin' (D) ♀H4	CTho ECrN ERea GTwe LRHS MCoo SCrf SDea SFam SKee WGwG
	– 'Saint Edmund's Russet'	see *M. domestica* 'Saint Edmund's Pippin'
	– 'Sam Young' (D)	CAgr SKee
	– 'Sandlands' (D)	SDea
	– 'Sandringham' (C)	ECrN ERea
	– 'Sanspareil' (D)	CAgr SKee
	– 'Saturn' (D)	CAgr CTri EMui ERea GBut GTwe LRHS SDea SKee
	– 'Saw Pits' (F)	CAgr CEnd
	– 'Scarlet Crofton' (D)	IFFs
	– 'Scarlet Nonpareil' (D)	SDea
	– 'Scotch Bridget' (C)	GBut GKir LRHS NBid SCoo SKee
	– 'Scotch Dumpling' (C)	GBut GKir GTwe LRHS MCoo
	– 'Scrumptious'PBR (D)	CAgr CDoC CDul CMac EPfP GKir LBuc LRHS MAsh MBri NLar NPri NWea SCoo SKee SPer SPoG WHar WJas
	– 'Seabrook's Red' (D)	ECrN
	– 'Seaton House' (C)	GKir
	– 'Sercombe's Natural' (Cider)	CTho
	– 'Severn Bank' (C)	CCAT CTho
	– 'Sheep's Nose' (C)	CCAT CTho SDea
	– 'Shenandoah' (C)	SKee
	– 'Sidney Strake' (C)	CAgr CEnd
	– 'Sir Isaac Newton's'	see *M. domestica* 'Flower of Kent'
	– 'Sir John Thornycroft' (D)	SDea
	– 'Sisson's Worksop Newtown' (D)	SKee
	– 'Slack Ma Girdle' (Cider)	CCAT CTho
	– 'Smart's Prince Arthur' (C)	SDea
	– 'Snell's Glass Apple'	see *M. domestica* 'Glass Apple'
	– 'Somerset Lasting' (C)	CCAT CTri
	– 'Somerset Redstreak' (Cider)	CCAT CTho CTri GTwe
	– 'Sops in Wine' (C/Cider)	CCAT CTho SVic
	– 'Sour Bay' (Cider)	CAgr CTho
	– 'Sour Natural'	see *M. domestica* 'Langworthy'
	– 'Spartan' (D)	CCAT CCVT CDoC CMac CSBt CTri CWib ECrN EMui GKir GTwe LAst LRHS MGan MGos NPri SCrf SDea SFam SKee SPer SVic WHar WJas
	– 'Spencer' (D)	CTri ECrN SKee
	– 'Spotted Dick' (Cider)	CTho
	– 'Spout Apple' **new**	LBuc
	– 'Stable Jersey' (Cider)	CCAT
	– 'Stamford Pippin' (D)	SDea
	– 'Stanway Seedling' (C)	ECrN
	– 'Star of Devon' (D)	CCAT CEnd SDea
	– 'Stark' (D)	SDea
	– 'Starking' (D)	ECrN
	– 'Stark's Earliest' (D)	SVic
	– 'Stembridge Cluster' (Cider)	CCAT
	– 'Stembridge Jersey' (Cider)	CCAT
	– 'Steyne Seedling' (D)	SDea
	– 'Stirling Castle' (C)	CAgr GBut GKir GQui SKee WGwG

	Cultivar	Suppliers
	– 'Stobo Castle' (C)	GBut GKir GQui SKee
	– 'Stockbearer' (C)	CTho
	– 'Stoke Red' (Cider)	CCAT CTho
	– 'Strawberry Pippin' (D)	CTho
	– 'Striped Beefing' (C)	ECrN ERea
	– 'Sturmer Pippin' (D)	CCAT CSBt CTri ECrN GTwe IFFs MWat SCrf SDea SFam SKee
*	– 'Sugar Apple'	CTho
	– 'Sugar Bush' (C/D)	CTho
	– 'Sugar Loaf'	see *M. domestica* 'Sugar Apple'
	– 'Summer Golden Pippin' (D)	SKee
	– 'Summer Stubbard' (D)	CCAT
	– 'Summerred' (D)	ECrN EMil
	– 'Sunburn' (D)	ECrN
	– 'Sunnydale' (D/C)	SDea
	– 'Sunrise'PBR (D)	EMui SKee
	– 'Sunset' (D) ♀H4	Widely available
	– 'Suntan' (D) ♀H4	CCAT CMac CWib ECrN GTwe IFFs LAst MAsh SDea SKee
	– 'Superb'	see *M. domestica* 'Laxton's Superb'
	– 'Surprise' (D)	GTwe
	– 'Sweet Alford' (Cider)	CCAT CTho ECrN
	– 'Sweet Bay' (Cider)	CAgr CTho
	– 'Sweet Caroline' (D)	ECrN
	– 'Sweet Cleave' (Cider)	CTho
	– 'Sweet Coppin' (Cider)	CCAT CTho CTri
	– 'Sweet Society' (D)	EMui LBuc LRHS MAsh MCoo SKee WHar WJas
	– 'Tale Sweet' (Cider)	CCAT CTho
	– 'Tamar Beauty' (F)	CEnd
	– 'Tan Harvey' (Cider)	CCAT CEnd CTho
	– 'Taunton Cross' (D)	CAgr
	– 'Taunton Fair Maid' (Cider)	CCAT CTho
	– 'Taylor's' (Cider)	CCAT SDea
	– 'Ten Commandments' (D/Cider)	CCAT SDea
	– 'Tewkesbury Baron' (D)	CTho
	– 'The Rattler' (F)	CEnd
	– 'Thomas Rivers' (C)	SDea
	– 'Thorle Pippin' (D)	GBut SKee
	– 'Tidicombe Seedling' (D)	CTho
	– 'Tinyrwydd' **new**	WDol
	– 'Tom Putt' (C)	CAgr CCAT CCVT CTho CTri CWib ECrN GTwe LBuc MAsh SDea SKee WJas
	– 'Tommy Knight' (D)	CAgr CCAT CEnd CTho
	– 'Topaz'PBR (D)	SKee
	– 'Totnes Apple' (D)	CTho
	– 'Tower of Glamis' (C)	GKir GQui GTwe SKee
	– Town Farm Number 59 (Cider)	CTho
	– 'Transparent Codlin' **new**	LBuc
	– 'Tregonna King' (C/D)	CCAT CEnd CTho
	– 'Tremlett's Bitter' (Cider)	CAgr CCAT CTho SDea SVic
	– 'Trwyn Mochyn' (C)	WGwG
	– 'Twenty Ounce' (C)	SKee
	– 'Twyn y Sherriff' (Cider) **new**	WDol
§	– 'Tydeman's Early Worcester' (D)	CAgr CLnd CWib ECrN GTwe SDea SKee SVic
	– 'Tydeman's Late Orange' (D)	CMac ECrN EMil EMui ERea GTwe LAst LRHS MCoo SDea SFam SKee
	– 'Uncle John's Cooker' (C)	IFFs
	– 'Underleaf' (D)	SKee
	– 'Upton Pyne' (D)	CCAT CTho SDea
	– 'Vallis Apple' (Cider)	CCAT CTho
	– 'Veitch's Perfection' (C/D)	CTho
	– 'Venus Pippin' (C/D)	CEnd
	– 'Vicar of Beighton' (D)	ECrN ERea
	– 'Vicary's Late Keeper'	CTho

- 'Vickey's Delight' (D)	SDea
- 'Vileberie' (Cider)	CCAT
- 'Violette' (C) **new**	SKee
- 'Vista-bella' (D)	ECrN SDea SKee
- 'Wagener' (D)	ECrN SDea SKee
- 'Waltham Abbey Seedling' (C)	ECrN
- Waltz = 'Telamon'[PBR] (D/Ball)	MGos SDea SKee
- 'Warner's King' (C) ♀H4	CCAT CTho CTri LRHS SCrf SDea SKee
- 'Warrior'	CTho
- 'Wealthy' (D)	SDea
- 'Wellington' (C)	see *M. domestica* 'Dummellor's Seedling'
- 'Wellington' (Cider)	CAgr CTho
- 'Welsh Russet' (D)	SDea
- 'Wern' **new**	WDol
- 'West View Seedling' (D)	ECrN
- 'Wheeler's Russet' (D)	GBut LBuc
- 'White Alphington' (Cider)	CTho
- 'White Close Pippin' (Cider)	CTho
- 'White Jersey' (Cider)	CCAT
- 'White Joaneting' (D)	CCAT GBut SKee
- 'White Melrose' (C)	GBut GKir GTwe IFFs LRHS MCoo SDea
- 'White Transparent' (C/D)	SDea SKee
- 'Whitpot Sweet' (F)	CEnd
- 'Wick White Styre' (Cider)	CTho
- 'William Crump' (D)	CCAT CTho ECrN MAsh SDea SFam SKee
- 'Winston' (D) ♀H4	CAgr CCAT CMac CSBt CTri ECrN GTwe LRHS MAsh MCoo NWea SCrf SDea SFam SKee SVic
- 'Winter Banana' (D)	ECrN LRHS SDea SKee SVic
- 'Winter Gem' (D)	CAgr CCAT CDoC CDul ECrN EMil EMui LBuc MGos SDea SKee WHar WJas
- 'Winter Lawrence'	CTho
- 'Winter Lemon' (C/D)	GQui
- 'Winter Majetin' (C)	ECrN ERea
- 'Winter Peach' (D/C)	CAgr CEnd CTho ECrN
- 'Winter Pearmain' (D)	SKee
- 'Winter Quarrenden' (D)	SDea
- 'Winter Queening' (D/C)	SDea
- 'Winter Stubbard' (C)	CTho
- 'Woodbine'	see *M. domestica* 'Northwood'
- 'Woodford' (C)	ECrN
- 'Woolbrook Pippin' (D)	CAgr CCAT CEnd CTho
- 'Woolbrook Russet' (C)	CCAT CEnd CTho ECrN
- 'Worcester Pearmain' (D) ♀H4	Widely available
- 'Wormsley Pippin' (D)	ECrN
- 'Wyatt's Seedling'	see *M. domestica* 'Langworthy'
- 'Wyken Pippin' (D)	CCAT ECrN GTwe SDea SFam SKee
- 'Yarlington Mill' (Cider)	CAgr CCAT CTho CTri SDea SKee SVic
- 'Yellow Ingestrie' (D)	MAsh SFam SKee WHar WJas
- 'Yellow Styre' (Cider)	CTho
- 'Zabergäu Renette' (D)	SKee
'Donald Wyman'	CLnd NLar SCoo
'Echtermeyer'	see *M.* × *gloriosa* 'Oekonomierat Echtermeyer'
'Evelyn'	GKir
§ 'Evereste' ♀H4	Widely available
florentina	CLnd CTho EBee EPfP LLHF LRHS SLon SSpi
- 'Rosemoor'	EBee
floribunda ♀H4	Widely available
'Fontana'	MGos
'Gardener's Gold'	CEnd CTho
§ × ***gloriosa*** 'Oekonomierat Echtermeyer'	CCAT GKir SDea WDin WJas
'Golden Gem'	CCAT EBee EMil EPfP GTwe LRHS SLim SPer
'Golden Hornet'	see *M.* × *zumi* 'Golden Hornet'
'Harry Baker'	EBee EMui ERea LRHS MAsh MBlu MBri NLar SCoo SLim SPoG WJas
'Hillieri'	see *M.* × *scheideckeri* 'Hillieri'
hupehensis ♀H4	CCAT CDul CEnd CLnd CMCN CSBt CTho CTri EBee ECrN EPfP GKir LHop MBlu MGos MRav SCrf SFam SPer WMou WPGP WPat
'Hyde Hall Spire'	LRHS MAsh MGos SCoo SPoG
'John Downie' (C) ♀H4	Widely available
'Kaido'	see *M.* × *micromalus*
kansuensis	CLnd EPfP
'Laura'	CWSG ECrN EMui EPfP GKir LRHS MAsh MGos NLar SCoo SKee SPoG WJas
'Lisa'	CLnd
'Louisa'	LRHS NWea
× ***magdeburgensis***	CCVT CDul CLnd CSBt
'Mandarin'	GKir
'Marshal Ōyama'	CTho
'Mary Potter'	CLnd CTho
§ × ***micromalus***	CBcs
× ***moerlandsii***	CLnd
- 'Liset'	CDul CEnd CLnd CSBt CWib EBee ECrN LRHS MBri MRav NEgg SCoo SFam SMHT SPer WFar
§ - 'Profusion'	CBcs CDul CLnd CMac CTri CWSG EBee ECrN ELan EWTr LAst LRHS MAsh MGos MRav MSwo NPri NWea SBch SCrf SPer WBVN WDin WFar WJas
- 'Profusion Improved'	CCAT CEnd CSBt CWSG GKir MWat NLar SCoo SKee WHar
'Mokum'	LMaj
'Molten Lava'	CLnd
niedzwetzkyana	see *M. pumila* 'Niedzwetzkyana'
Nuvar Carnival	SKee
Nuvar Dusty Red	SKee
Nuvar Marble	SKee
Nuvar Red Lantern	SKee
orthocarpa	CLnd
Perpetu	see *M.* 'Evereste'
'Pink Glow'	CLnd CSBt EMui LRHS MAsh MBlu NLar SBch SCoo SLim SPer SPoG WHar
'Pink Mushroom'	EMil LRHS NLar SCoo
'Pink Perfection'	CDoC CEnd ECrN GKir LRHS
Pom'Zaï = 'Courtabri'	CDoC
'Pond Red'	CLnd
'Prairie Fire'	CDul GKir LRHS MAsh MBri SCoo SLim SPoG
prattii	CTho EPfP
'Princeton Cardinal'	CLnd GKir LRHS MAsh SCoo SLim SPoG
'Professor Sprenger'	see *M.* × *zumi* 'Professor Sprenger'
'Profusion'	see *M.* × *moerlandsii* 'Profusion'
prunifolia **new**	MBlu
- 'Pendula'	MGan
pumila 'Cowichan'	CLnd ECrN GKir
- 'Dartmouth'	CCAT CDul CLnd CSBt CSam CTri ECrN NEgg NPCo SFam
- 'Montreal Beauty'	CLnd GKir MAsh SCoo WJas
§ - 'Niedzwetzkyana'	CLnd
§ × ***purpurea*** 'Aldenhamensis'	CLnd SDea WDin WSpi
- 'Eleyi'	CDul CLnd ECrN LAst NWea WDin
- 'Lemoinei'	CLnd ECrN EWTr

Name	Suppliers
- 'Neville Copeman'	CCVT CDoC CDul CLnd EBee ECrN EWTr LRHS MGos SBch SMHT SPur WJas
- 'Pendula'	see *M.* × *gloriosa* 'Oekonomierat Echtermeyer'
'R.J. Fulcher'	CLnd CTho
'Ralph Shay'	CLnd
'Red Ace'	CDul
'Red Barron'	CLnd
'Red Glow'	CLnd EBee ECrN MAsh MMuc WJas
'Red Jade'	see *M.* × *scheideckeri* 'Red Jade'
'Red Obelisk'	LRHS MBri SCoo SPoG
'Red Peacock'	CLnd
'Robinson'	CLnd
§ × ***robusta***	CLnd CTri GTwe LRHS LSRN NWea SBch SCrf SLon SMHT
- 'Red Sentinel' ♀H4	Widely available
- 'Red Siberian'	ECrN SDea SPer
- 'Yellow Siberian'	CLnd
rockii	GAuc
'Royal Beauty' ♀H4	CDoC CDul CWib EBee EPfP GKir GTwe LAst LRHS MAsh MBri MGos MSwo SBch SCoo SCrf SMHT SPer WDin WHar
'Royalty'	CBcs CCAT CDul CLnd CMac CSBt CWSG EBee ECrN ELan EMui GKir GTwe LAst LBuc LRHS MGos MRav MSwo MWat NBea NEgg NScw SBch SCrf SPer SPoG WDin WHar WJas
'Rudolph'	CCAT CCVT CDul CLnd EBee ECrN EWTr GKir LBuc LMaj MAsh MGos SCoo SLim SPer WJas
'Ruth Ann'	CLnd
sargentii	CDul CLnd CTho ECrN EWTr LAst LRHS MGos NWea SFam SMHT SPer
- 'Tina'	CLnd MAsh SPoG
'Satin Cloud'	CLnd
§ × ***scheideckeri*** 'Hillieri'	CDul CLnd ECrN SFam
§ - 'Red Jade'	CCAT CDul CMCN CTri CWib EBee ECrN ELan EPfP GKir GTwe LAst LRHS MBar MGos MRav MSwo MWat NEgg NPri NWea SBch SCrf SPer WDin WFar WJas
Siberian crab	see *M.* × *robusta*
sieboldii	see *M. toringo*
- 'Wooster'	CLnd
'Silver Drift'	CLnd LRHS SCoo
'Snowcloud'	CCAT CDul CLnd EBee ECrN LRHS MAsh SLim SPer
spectabilis	CLnd
'Street Parade'	CLnd SCoo
'Striped Beauty'	CLnd CTho
× ***sublobata***	CLnd
'Sun Rival'	CCAT CCVT CDoC CDul CEnd CLnd CSBt CWSG EMui EPfP GKir GTwe LRHS MAsh MBri MGos SBch SCoo SLim SPoG WHar WJas
sylvestris	CArn CCVT CDul CLnd CRWN CTri ECrN EMac EPfP GKir LBuc MMuc MRav NWea WDin WMou
§ ***toringo***	CCAT CLnd CTho ECrN EPfP LMaj MBlu MBri WSHC
I - var. ***arborescens***	CLnd CTho
- 'Browers'	LMaj
- 'Scarlett'	IArd LRHS MBri NLar SCoo SLim SPoG WJas
- 'Wintergold' **new**	EWTr
toringoides	see *M. bhutanica*
- 'Mandarin'	GKir MBri NLar SCoo
transitoria ♀H4	CCAT CDoC CDul CEnd CLnd CTho EBee ELan EMil EPfP GKir LRHS MBlu MBri NWea SCoo SPoG SSpi WPGP
- 'Thornhayes Tansy'	CAbP CTho LRHS SPoG WSpi
trilobata	CCAT CLnd CTho EBee EMil EPfP LMaj LRHS MBlu MBri MGos SCoo SEND SPoG
- 'Guardsman'	GKir LRHS MBri NLar SCoo SPoG SSpi
tschonoskii ♀H4	Widely available
'Van Eseltine'	CCAT CDul CSBt CWSG CWib EBee ECrN EPfP GKir GTwe MAsh MMuc MWat NBea SFam SPoG WHar WJas WPat
'Veitch's Scarlet'	CDul CLnd CSBt GKir GTwe NEgg NPCo SFam
Weeping Candied Apple = 'Weepcanzam'	CLnd
'White Star'	CCVT CDoC CDul CLnd CSBt CWSG ECrN SBch SCoo SLim SPoG
'Winter Gold'	CDoC CDul CLnd LMaj MMuc SCrf SEND SPoG
'Wisley Crab'	CLnd EMil GKir GTwe SDea SFam
yunnanensis	EPfP GAuc GKir
- var. ***veitchii***	CTho
× ***zumi*** var. ***calocarpa***	CTho
§ - 'Golden Hornet' ♀H4	Widely available
§ - 'Professor Sprenger'	CLnd CSam EPfP LMaj LRHS SCoo SPer

Malva (*Malvaceae*)

Name	Suppliers
alcea var. ***fastigiata***	CMac ECGP EShb NBro NBur SPer SRms WFar WPer
bicolor	see *Lavatera maritima*
moschata	CArn CBcs CPrp CRWN CSev EBWF EBee ECtt ELan EPfP GJos GPoy MHer MNHC NBPC NMir SIde SPer SPlb SWat WCom WGwG WHer WMoo
- f. ***alba*** ♀H4	Widely available
- 'Pink Perfection'	EShb LRHS
- 'Romney Marsh'	see *Althaea officinalis* 'Romney Marsh'
- ***rosea***	EPfP GMaP NBlu NEgg NPer SBch SPoG SWvt
- 'White Perfection' **new**	LRHS
pusilla	CCCN
'Sweet Sixteen'	EBee ECtt MBNS NLar
sylvestris	CArn EBWF MNHC NBro NSco SMad SWat WFar WHer WJek WMoo
- 'Bardsey Blue'	WGwG
- 'Blue Fountain' PBR	EBee MBNS NCGa
- 'Brave Heart'	EShb GJos NBur NLar SHGN SPav SWvt
- Marina = 'Dema' PBR	EBee ELan NLar WFar
- subsp. ***mauritiana***	NPer SMad WMoo
- - 'Bibor Fehlo'	CSpe MWhi NBur
- 'Mystic Merlin'	EBee SPav
- 'Perry's Blue'	NPer
- 'Primley Blue'	CBot EBee ECtt ELan EPfP GMaP MRav MTho NBPC NPer SMad SPer WCom WFar WSpi
- 'Zebrina'	EBee EPfP LDai NBur NPer SHGN SWvt WFar WMoo

Malvastrum (*Malvaceae*)

Name	Suppliers
× ***hypomadarum***	see *Anisodontea* × *hypomadara* (Sprague) D.M. Bates

lateritium	CMea CPrp CRHN CSev CSpe CTri EBee ELan EPfP LAst LHop MAvo MTho NBir NSti SMad SMrm SPet SPhx SRms SUsu SWal WEas WHal WHoo WMoo WPGP WPer WSHC

Malvaviscus (*Malvaceae*)

arboreus	CHll

mandarin see *Citrus reticulata*

mandarin, Cleopatra see *Citrus reshni*

Mandevilla (*Apocynaceae*)

§ × ***amabilis***	CCCN
- 'Alice du Pont' ♀H1	CCCN CSpe ELan ERea EShb LRHS
× ***amoena***	see *M.* × *amabilis*
boliviensis ♀H1	CCCN CRHN ELan LRHS
§ ***laxa*** ♀H2	CBot CCCN CHEx CHll CRHN CSpe EBee ELan ERea EShb IDee LRHS SAga WCot WHrl WPGP WSHC
- 'Snowbird' new	ERea
sanderi	CCCN ERea EShb MBri
- 'Rosea'	ERea NScw
- white-flowered new	CSpe
splendens ♀H1	CCCN CHll EPfP
suaveolens	see *M. laxa*
'Sundaville Red' new	LRHS

Mandragora (*Solanaceae*)

autumnalis	CFwr CWan GCal NLar SMad WCot
caulescens	EBee WSpi
§ ***officinarum***	CArn CEls EBee GCal GPoy MHer NGHP WCot

Manettia (*Rubiaceae*)

inflata	see *M. luteorubra*
§ ***luteorubra***	CCCN ELan WCot

Manfreda see *Agave*

Mangifera (*Anacardiaceae*)

indica (F)	CCCN

Manglietia (*Magnoliaceae*)

chevalieri HWJ 533	WCru
conifera	WPGP
insignis	CBcs CHEx IMou SSpi WPGP
yuyuanensis	CBcs

mango see *Mangifera indica*

Manihot (*Euphorbiaceae*)

grahamii new	WCot

Maranta (*Marantaceae*)

leuconeura	EShb XBlo
var. ***erythroneura*** ♀H1	
- var. ***kerchoveana*** ♀H1	EShb MBri XBlo

Marattia (*Marattiaceae*)

salicina	WRic

Margyricarpus (*Rosaceae*)

§ ***pinnatus***	CFee GEdr GGar MMHG NWCA WPer
setosus	see *M. pinnatus*

Mariscus see *Cyperus*

marjoram, pot see *Origanum onites*

marjoram, sweet see *Origanum majorana*

marjoram, wild, or oregano see *Origanum vulgare*

Marrubium (*Lamiaceae*)

sp.	SEND
§ ***bourgaei*** var. ***bourgaei*** 'All Hallow's Green'	CFee EBee ECha ECtt EGoo GBuc GKir LHop LRHS MRav NEgg SPoG WOut
candidissimum	see *M. incanum*
cylleneum	EBee
* - 'Velvetissimum'	WCHb
§ ***incanum***	EGoo
libanoticum	WPer
pestalloziae	EBee
supinum	CArn
vulgare	CArn CPrp GBar GPoy MHer MNHC SIde WCHb WHer WPer
- 'Green Pompon'	NLar

Marshallia (*Asteraceae*)

grandiflora	CDes EBee SUsu
mohrii	EBee
trinerva	ELon SUsu

Marsilea (*Marsileaceae*)

quadrifolia	MSKA
- variegated (v)	LLWG

Marsippospermum (*Juncaceae*)

gracile	ECou

Mascarena see *Hyophorbe*

Massonia (*Hyacinthaceae*)

depressa	CStu ECho
echinata	CStu ECho WCot
aff. ***echinata***	CStu ECho
jasminiflora	ECho WCot
pustulata	CStu WCot
pygmaea	ECho
subsp. ***pygmaea*** new	
- subsp. ***kamiesbergensis*** new	ECho

Mathiasella (*Apiaceae*)

bupleuroides	CHid LSou
- 'Green Dream'	CAbP CAvo CBcs CBod CBre CSpe EBee ECGP ECtt ELon GAbr GBin IPot LFur LOck LRHS MAvo NCGa NSti SDix SMrm SUsu WClo WCot

Matricaria (*Asteraceae*)

chamomilla	see *M. recutita*
parthenium	see *Tanacetum parthenium*
§ ***recutita***	CArn GPoy MNHC

Matteuccia (*Woodsiaceae*)

orientalis	CBty CDTJ CLAP EBee EFer EPfP ERod GCal GGar GMaP MAsh NGby NLar NMyG NOrc WFar WMoo WRic
pensylvanica	CLAP EBee WRic
struthiopteris ♀H4	Widely available
* - 'Depauperata'	CLAP
- 'Jumbo'	CBty CCCN CLAP EBee LRHS

Matthiola (*Brassicaceae*)

fruticulosa 'Alba'	CDes WPGP
- subsp. ***perennis***	NSti SEND WHal

	incana	EBee LRHS MArl NLar WCFE WFar WKif WPer WRHF
	- alba	ECha ELan GBBs LSou NCGa SMad SPav WCot WPtf WSpi
	sinuata	GGar
	white-flowered perennial	CArn CSev CSpe ECGP MAvo MLHP NPer SEND SMeo WCom WEas

Maurandella (*Scrophulariaceae*)

§	***antirrhiniflora***	EWld

Maurandya (*Scrophulariaceae*)

§	***barclayana***	CBot CDTJ CHII CSpe MBri SGar
	- alba	CBot CSpe
	'Bridal Bouquet'	CCCN LSou
	erubescens	see *Lophospermum erubescens*
	lophantha	see *Lophospermum scandens*
	lophospermum	see *Lophospermum scandens*
	'Red Dragon'	see *Lophospermum* 'Red Dragon'

Maytenus (*Celastraceae*)

	boaria	CMCN EBee EPfP GBin GGal IArd IDee IFFs LEdu MBri NLar SAPC SArc SEND WPGP
	disticha (Hook.f.) Urb.	LEdu
	magellanica	WFar

Mazus (*Scrophulariaceae*)

	miquelii	EBee ECho
	novae-zeelandiae new	CTrC
	radicans	ECho
	reptans	EBee ECho EDAr EPfP EPot GEdr LRHS MSKA NPer NWCA
	- B&SWJ	GEdr
	- 'Albus'	EBee ECho EPfP GEdr GGar LLWG SPlb
	- 'Blue'	LLWG
	surculosus	ECho

Mecardonia (*Scrophulariaceae*)

	'Goldflake'	CCCN LSou
	'Sundona Early Yellow'	LAst

Meconopsis ✿ (*Papaveraceae*)

	SDR 4853	GKev
	baileyi	see *M. betonicifolia*
	Ballyrogan form	GEdr
	× ***beamishii***	GBuc GKev
§	***betonicifolia*** ♀H4	Widely available
	- var. ***alba***	EBee ELan GBuc GCra GGGa GKev GKir LRHS NCob NGdn NLar NSum SRms
	- 'Glacier Blue'	GCra
	- 'Hensol Violet'	CSpr EPot GBuc GCal GCra GGGa GKev ITim MBri NSum
	cambrica	CHrt CMac CPLG CTri EBWF EBee EHrv ELan EPfP GGar GJos NCot NHol NPri SGar SIng WBrk WCom WFar WHer WPnP
	- 'Anne Greenaway' (d)	WCot
	- var. ***aurantiaca***	SBch WCom WFar
	- ***flore-pleno*** (d)	GBuc MTho WCot WFar
	- - orange-flowered (d)	MSnd NBir WCot
§	- 'Frances Perry'	GBuc GCal WCom WCot WFar
	- 'Muriel Brown' (d)	GCal
	- 'Rubra'	see *M. cambrica* 'Frances Perry'
	chelidoniifolia	GCra GKir IGor NBid WCru WFar
	× ***cookei***	GMac
	- 'Old Rose'	GGGa GMaP
	delavayi	GGGa GKev
N	(Fertile Blue Group) 'Blue Ice'	see *M.* (Fertile Blue Group) 'Lingholm'
N	- 'Kingsbarns'	GGGa
N	- 'Lingholm'	Widely available
§	George Sherriff Group	GBuc GCal GCra GEdr NBir
	- 'Ascreavie'	GMaP
	- 'Branklyn' ambig.	CGHE WFar WPGP
	- 'Dalemain'	GMaP
	- 'Huntfield'	GMaP
	- 'Jimmy Bayne'	GBuc GEdr GGGa GKir GMaP
	- 'Spring Hill'	GBuc
	grandis misapplied	see *M.* George Sherriff Group
	grandis ambig.	CHar EBee GEdr GKev GLin ITim MNrw SRms WFar WSpi
	- Balruddery form	GGGa
	- GS 600	see *M.* George Sherriff Group
	horridula	GGGa MTho
	- Rudis Group	EBee GKev
	- - SDR 4568	GKev
	- - SDR 5014	GKev
	(Infertile Blue Group) 'Bobby Masterton'	GBuc GCra
	- 'Crarae'	GGGa
	- 'Crewdson Hybrid'	GBuc GMaP
	- 'Dawyck'	see *M.* (Infertile Blue Group) 'Slieve Donard'
	- 'Mrs Jebb'	GBuc GCra GMaP
§	- 'Slieve Donard' ♀H4	GBuc GCal GCra GKev GMaP ITim LRHS
	integrifolia	EPot GGGa WFar
N	***napaulensis*** misapplied	CSam EBee GCra GEdr GGGa GGar GKev GKir ITim LHop LRHS MDun NHol WCAu WMoo
	- pink-flowered	EBee LRHS NGdn WFar WPGP
	- red-flowered	CBcs GBuc ITim MDun
	nudicaulis	see *Papaver nudicaule*
	'Ormswell' ambig.	GBuc
	paniculata	GAbr GGGa MDun
	- from Bhutan	GCra
	- from Ghunsa, Nepal	CLAP
	- ginger foliage	CSpr MDun
	pseudointegrifolia	GCra GGGa
	punicea	GGGa GKev
	quintuplinervia ♀H4	CLAP GCra GGGa IGor NBir NSla WHal
	- SDR 6161	GKev
	- 'Kaye's Compact'	GBuc
	regia misapplied	WMoo
	× ***sheldonii*** misapplied (fertile)	see *M.* Fertile Blue Group
	× ***sheldonii*** misapplied (sterile)	see *M.* Infertile Blue Group
	× ***sheldonii*** ambig.	CBcs CBow CHar CWCL EBee GAbr GBuc GKir ITim LRHS MBri MCot MDun NBPC NBir NPer SRms WCru WFar
	simplicifolia	GGGa
	superba	GBuc GGGa
	villosa	GBuc GCra GGGa GKev WCru WFar
	wallichii misapplied	see *M. wallichii* Hook.
§	***wallichii*** Hook.	GGGa
	'Willie Duncan'	GKir GMaP ITim

Medicago (*Papilionaceae*)

	arborea	CArn SEND SPlb
	lupulina	EBWF
	sativa	NLar WHer WSFF

Medinilla (*Melastomataceae*)

	magnifica ♀H1	CCCN LRHS MBri

medlar see *Mespilus germanica*

Meehania (*Lamiaceae*)

cordata	CLAP EBee
fargesii	CDes CLAP
urticifolia	EPPr GCal WSHC
- B&SWJ 1210	WCru
- 'Japanblau' new	IMou
- 'Wandering Minstrel' (v)	CDes CLAP EBee WCot

Melaleuca (*Myrtaceae*)

acuminata	SPlb
alternifolia	CArn CCCN CTsd ECou EOHP GPWP GPoy LAst MHer SPlb WHer
armillaris	CBgR CCCN CDoC CStu IDee SEND SGar SPlb
blaeriifolia	ECou
bracteata	ECou
cuticularis	SPlb
decussata	ECou SPlb
§ ***diosmatifolia***	CPLG
ericifolia	CTri CTsd GLin SPlb
erubescens	see *M. diosmatifolia*
fulgens	SPlb
gibbosa	CPLG EBee ECou IDee LRHS LSou SEND WSHC
hypericifolia	CPLG CTrC ECou SPlb
incana	EBee
lateritia	ECou
linariifolia	CCCN ECou SPlb
nesophila	CTsd ECou EShb SPlb
pentagona	ECou
var. ***subulifolia***	
pulchella	ECou
pungens	SPlb
pustulata	ECou EShb
squamea	EBee GGar SPlb WBrE
squarrosa	CPLG CTrC ECou SPlb
thymifolia	ECou LRHS SPlb
viridiflora	GQui
wilsonii	ECou

Melandrium see *Vaccaria*

rubrum	see *Silene dioica*

Melanoselinum (*Apiaceae*)

§ ***decipiens***	CAbb CArn CHEx CHrt CSpe EWes GGar IMou LEdu WPGP

Melasphaerula (*Iridaceae*)

graminea	see *M. ramosa*
§ ***ramosa***	CBre CStu ECho ERos WPrP

Melastoma (*Melastomataceae*)

sp. new	CCCN

Melia (*Meliaceae*)

§ ***azedarach***	CArn CBcs CCCN EBee EShb GPoy WPGP
- B&SWJ 7039	WCru
- var. ***japonica***	see *M. azedarach*

Melianthus (*Melianthaceae*)

comosus	CDTJ EBee EShb EWes LPio NLar SCoo SPlb WCot WGwG
major ♀H3	Widely available
minor	CFir CHid LPio
villosus	CBod CBow CFir EBee EWes LPio LRHS MCCP SGar SPlb WOut

Melica (*Poaceae*)

altissima 'Alba'	EHoe MLHP
- 'Atropurpurea'	COIW CWCL EBee ECha EHoe EHul EPPr GFor LEdu LHop LLWP LRHS MCot MMoz MNrw MWat MWhi NBid SBod SPlb WFar WFoF WMnd WMoo WPer WWEG
ciliata	EBee EHoe GFor MMoz MWhi NLar SSvw WMnd WWEG
- subsp. ***taurica***	EPPr MAvo
macra	EHoe EPPr SApp
nutans	CWCL EHoe EPPr EPla EShb GFor NLar NWsh SBch SMrm
penicillaris	EPPr WPer
persica	EPPr
transsilvanica	EPPr GFor
- 'Red Spire'	CWib EShb MBNS MWhi SBch SHDw SMad SMrm WMoo
uniflora	GFor IMou NOak
- f. ***albida***	ECha EGoo EHoe EPPr MAvo SLPl WCot
- 'Variegata' (v)	CBre ECha EHoe ELon EPPr EPla EShb MBri MMoz NGdn WCot WMoo WTin WWEG

Melicope (*Rutaceae*)

ternata	ECou

Melicytus (*Violaceae*)

alpinus	ECou
angustifolius	ECou
crassifolius	ECou EPla WFar
obovatus	ECou NLar
ramiflorus	CHEx ECou

Melilotus (*Papilionaceae*)

officinalis	CArn GPoy NSco SIde WHer
- subsp. ***albus***	CArn

Melinis (*Poaceae*)

sp.	CSpe
nerviglumis	CKno LEdu LHop MAvo
§ - 'Savannah'	CSpe CWib
roseus	EHul

Meliosma (*Meliosmaceae*)

cuneifolia	CBcs NLar
dilleniifolia subsp. ***tenuis***	CBcs CPLG
parviflora B&SWJ 8408	WCru

Melissa ✿ (*Lamiaceae*)

officinalis	CArn CHrt CTri CWan ELau GJos GKir GMaP GPoy MBar MBri MHer MNHC NBir NBlu SBch SECG SIde SPlb SVic WPer
- 'All Gold'	CArn CBre CSev ECha EGoo EHoe ELan ELau EOHP GBar MNHC NBid NBlu NVic SPer SPoG WMoo
§ - 'Aurea' (v)	Widely available
* - 'Compacta'	GPoy MHer
- 'Gold Leaf' new	WPtf
- 'Lime Balm'	EOHP
- 'Quedlinburger Niederliegende'	CArn
N - 'Variegata' misapplied	see *M. officinalis* 'Aurea'

Melittis (*Lamiaceae*)

melissophyllum	CArn CFir CLAP CPom CSev CSpe EBee EWTr GAbr IMou LEdu LPio LRHS LSou MAvo MRav MWea

		NChi NMen NSti SMrm SRms SSvw SUsu WAbb WCAu
	- subsp. ***albida***	EBee LPio
	- pink-flowered	SUsu WCom
	- 'Royal Velvet Distinction'PBR	EBee MRav

Melliodendron (*Styracaceae*)

xylocarpum	IArd IDee

Menispermum (*Menispermaceae*)

canadense	CTri GPoy
davuricum	NLar

Menstruocalamus (*Poaceae*)

sichuanensis	WPGP

Mentha ✿ (*Lamiaceae*)

	angustifolia Corb.	see *M.* × *villosa*
	angustifolia Host	see *M. arvensis*
	angustifolia ambig.	SIde
	aquatica	CArn CBen CRow CWat EBWF EHon EMFW EPfP GPWP GPoy LPBA MHer MNHC NMir NPer NSco SIde SPlb SVic SWal SWat WHer WMAq WMoo WPnP WSFF
§	- var. ***crispa***	SIde
	- krause minze	see *M. aquatica* var. *crispa*
§	***arvensis***	CArn ELau MHer NSco SIde WJek
	- 'Banana'	MHer MNHC NGHP SIde
	- var. ***piperascens***	MHer SIde
§	- - 'Sayakaze'	CArn ELau
	asiatica	ELau MHer SIde WHer
	'Berries and Cream' new	WJek
	Bowles's mint	see *M.* × *villosa* var. *alopecuroides* Bowles's mint
*	***brevifolia***	SIde WHer
	cervina	CArn CBen CWat EHon EMFW LPBA MHer NLar SIde SWat WJek
*	- ***alba***	LPBA MHer NLar WMAq
I	'Chocolate Peppermint'	NBir WHer
	citrata	see *M.* × *piperita* f. *citrata*
	'Clarissa's Millennium'	SIde
	cordifolia	see *M.* × *villosa*
	corsica	see *M. requienii*
	crispa L. (1753)	see *M. spicata* var. *crispa*
	crispa L. (1763)	see *M. aquatica* var. *crispa*
	crispa ambig. × (× ***piperita)***	CArn GBar
	'Dionysus'	SIde
	'Eau de Cologne'	see *M.* × *piperita* f. *citrata*
	eucalyptus mint	ELau GBar GPWP MHer NGHP WGwG
	gattefossei	CArn
	× ***gentilis***	see *M.* × *gracilis*
§	× ***gracilis***	CArn CHby ELau GBar NGHP NPri SIde
	- 'Aurea'	see *M.* × *gracilis* 'Variegata'
§	- 'Variegata' (v)	CHrt CSev CWan ECha ELau GGar GPoy ILis MBar MCot MHer MNHC NPri NVic SPlb SWal WFar WHer WPer
	haplocalyx	CArn ELau SIde
*	'Hillary's Sweet Lemon'	ELau MHer SIde
	'Julia's Sweet Citrus'	MHer SIde
*	***lacerata***	SIde
	lavender mint	ELau GBar GPWP GPoy MHer MNHC NGHP WJek
§	***longifolia***	CWan ELau GBar MMuc SBch SIde SPlb WEas WHer WJek WPer
	- Buddleia Mint Group	CArn EBee ELau GGar GPWP MHer MRav NGHP SIde
	- - variegated (v) new	GPWP
	- subsp. ***schimperi***	MHer SIde WJek
	- silver-leaved	CArn ELau MHer MNHC NBlu NLar
*	- 'Variegata' (v)	ELau GBar WJek
	Nile Valley mint	CArn CPrp ELau SHDw SIde WCHb
	× ***piperita***	CArn CHby CHrt CSev CWan ECha EHoe ELau GAuc GBar GGar GJos GPoy ILis LHop MBri MCot MHer MNHC NGHP NPri NVic SPlb WPer
	- 'Black Mitcham'	CArn GBar
	- black peppermint	CHby CPrp EPfP GKir GPWP MMuc MNHC NBir NBlu NGHP NHol NLar SBch SWal WGwG
§	- f. ***citrata***	CArn CHby COIW CTri ECha ELau GBar GGar GJos GMaP GPWP GPoy MBar MBri MHer MMuc MNHC MRav NBir NGHP SBch SHDw SIde SPlb STre SVic WGwG WPer
*	- - 'Basil'	CHrt CWan ELau GBar GPWP MHer MNHC MRav NBlu NGHP NHol SBch SHDw SIde WGwG WJek
	- - 'Chocolate'	CArn CWan ELau EOHP EPfP GBar GGar GJos GPWP ILis MHer MNHC NGHP NPri SBch SHDw SIde WGwG WJek WPer
	- - 'Grapefruit'	CPrp CWan GBar LFol LSou MNHC NGHP SWal WGwG WJek
	- - 'Lemon'	CWan ELau GBar GGar GKir GPWP GPoy MBri MHer MNHC NGHP SBch SHDw SIde WCHb WGwG WJek WPer
	- - 'Lime'	CHrt CWan GBar GPWP ILis LSou MHer NGHP NPri SBch SHDw SIde SPlb WCHb WGwG WJek
	- - 'Orange'	GBar MHer MNHC NGHP WDyG
	- - 'Reverchonii'	SIde
	- - 'Swiss Ricola'	MHer SIde
	- 'Logee's' (v)	GBar NGHP NHol NPri SIde WCHb WHer
	- f. ***officinalis***	ELau SIde
	- var. ***ouweneellii*** Belgian mint	SIde
	- 'Reine Rouge'	SIde
	- 'Swiss'	NGHP NLar
I	- Swiss mint	CArn GPWP WGwG
*	- white-flowered	CArn GBar MHer WGwG
	pulegium	CArn CHby COIW CRWN CSev CTri CWan EBWF ELau EMFW GBar GPWP GPoy MHer MNHC NPri SIde SPlb SRms SVic WCHb WHer WJek WPer
	- 'Upright'	CArn CBod GBar GPoy MHer SBch SHDw SIde WCHb WJek WPer
§	***requienii***	Widely available
	rotundifolia misapplied	see *M. suaveolens*
	rotundifolia (L.) Hudson	see *M.* × *villosa*
	rubra var. ***raripila***	see *M.* × *smithiana*
	'Sayakaze'	see *M. arvensis* var. *piperascens* 'Sayakaze'
§	× ***smithiana***	CArn CWan ELau GBar GPWP GPoy MHer MNHC MRav NBir NGHP NPri WHer WPer
	- 'Capel Ulo' (v)	ELau WHer
§	***spicata***	CArn CHby CHrt COIW CPrp CSev CTri CWan GBar GJos GKir GPoy ILis LFol MBar MBri MCot MHer MNHC NBlu NGHP NHol NPri SPlb SRms SWal WClo WHer WJek WPer
	- Algerian fruity	SIde
*	- 'Brundall'	ELau ILis SIde
*	- var. ***crispa***	CArn CPrp CWan ECha ELau GBar GGar GPWP LEdu LHop MHer

	MMuc MNHC NGHP NHol NPri SBch SIde SPlb WCHb WCot WPer
- - 'Moroccan'	CArn CPrp CSev ELau EOHP GAbr GBar GGar GJos GPWP GPoy LEdu MHer MNHC NGHP NPri NVic SBch SEND SHDw SIde STre WCHB WClo WJek
- 'Guernsey'	SBch SHDw SIde
- 'Mexican'	CArn
- 'Newbourne'	ELau SIde
- 'Pharaoh'	CArn
- 'Russian'	NGHP NHol SIde
- 'Small Dole' (v)	SBch SHDw
- 'Spanish'	GPWP
- 'Spanish Furry'	MHer SIde
- 'Spanish Pointed'	ELau SIde
- 'Tashkent'	CArn CHby ELau EOHP GKir LEdu MHer MNHC NGHP SBch SHDw SIde WCHb WGwG WJek
* - 'Variegata' (v)	SBch SHDw WGwG
§ ***suaveolens***	CArn CHby CWan ELau GBar GJos GMaP GPWP GPoy ILis MBri MHer MNHC NBlu NGHP NPri SBch SIde SPlb SVic SWal WPer WSFF
* - 'Grapefruit'	GPWP NGHP NPri
- 'Jokka'	EBee
* - 'Mobillei'	SIde WJek
* - 'Pineapple'	GKir WGwG
- subsp. ***timija***	ELau SIde WJek
- 'Variegata' (v)	Widely available
sylvestris L.	see *M. longifolia*
§ × ***villosa***	CArn SIde
§ - var. ***alopecuroides*** Bowles's mint	CBre CHrt CPrp ELau GBar GGar GPWP GPoy ILis MHer MNHC NBir NGHP SBch SIde STre SWat WGwG WHer WJek
viridis	see *M. spicata*

Mentzelia (*Loasaceae*)

decapetala	CSpe

Menyanthes (*Menyanthaceae*)

trifoliata	CBen CRow CWat EHon EMFW GBar GPoy LLWG LPBA MCCP MMuc MSKA NPer NSco NVic WBVN WFar WHal WMAq

Menziesia (*Ericaceae*)

alba	see *Daboecia cantabrica* f. *alba*
ciliicalyx 'Honshu Blue' **new**	GGGa
- ***lasiophylla***	see *M. ciliicalyx* var. *purpurea*
- var. ***multiflora***	EPfP
- 'Plum Drops' **new**	GGGa
§ - var. ***purpurea***	GGGa
- 'Slieve Donard' **new**	CMac
'Spring Morning'	WAbe
'Ulva'	GGGa

Mercurialis (*Euphorbiaceae*)

perennis	EBWF GPoy NSco WHer WShi

Merendera (*Colchicaceae*)

attica	EBrs ECho
eichleri	see *M. trigyna*
filifolia	ECho
§ ***montana***	CPBP EBrs ECho ERos WIvy WThu
pyrenaica	see *M. montana*
raddeana	see *M. trigyna*
robusta **new**	WWst
sobolifera	CStu WCot
§ ***trigyna***	EBrs ECho
- bright pink-flowered **new**	WWst
- white-flowered clone **new**	WWst

Mertensia (*Boraginaceae*)

ciliata	CMdw CPom GKir SWat
lanceolata **new**	EBee
- var. ***nivalis***	LFur
maritima	CSpe EBee EWll GEdr GKev GMaP GPoy WCom WWEG
- subsp. ***asiatica***	see *M. simplicissima*
primuloides	GAuc
pterocarpa	see *M. sibirica*
pulmonarioides	see *M. virginica*
§ ***sibirica***	CLAP CSpe EBee GKir NLar SPlb WCom
§ ***simplicissima***	CBot CMea EBee ECho GBee GKir LRHS NBir SMrm SPlb WFar
§ ***virginica*** ♀H4	CArn CBot CBro CLAP CWCL EBee EBrs ECho ECtt ELan EPfP EPot EWTr GKir LAma LRHS NBid NBir NLar NPri NWCA SPoG SRms WCAu WCru WFar

Merwilla (*Hyacinthaceae*)

§ ***plumbea***	WCot WHil

Merxmuellera see *Rytidosperma*

Meryta (*Araliaceae*)

sinclairii	CBcs CWit

Mesembryanthemum (*Aizoaceae*)

'Basutoland'	see *Delosperma nubigenum*
brownii	see *Lampranthus brownii*

Mespilus (*Rosaceae*)

germanica (F)	CBcs CDul CLnd CMCN CTri EBee ECrN ELan IDee LMaj MWat NEgg NLar NScw SDnm SLon WDin WFar WMou WPat
- 'Bredase Reus' (F)	SKee
- 'Dutch' (F)	ERea SDea SFam SKee
- 'Iranian' (F)	SKee
- 'Large Russian' (F)	CAgr ERea
- 'Macrocarpa' (F)	SKee
- 'Monstrous' (F)	SDea
- 'Nespoli del Giappone' (F)	WSpi
- 'Nottingham' (F)	Widely available
- 'Royal' (F)	CAgr ERea MBri MCoo SCoo SKee
- 'Westerveld' (F)	SKee

Metapanax (*Araliaceae*)

davidii	SLon
delavayii	SBig

Metaplexis (*Asclepiadaceae*)

japonica B&SWJ 8459	WCru

Metarungia (*Acanthaceae*)

longistrobus	GFai

Metasequoia ✿ (*Cupressaceae*)

glyptostroboides ♀H4	Widely available
- 'Emerald Feathers'	ECho
- 'Fastigiata'	see *M. glyptostroboides* 'National'
- 'Gold Rush'	Widely available
- 'Golden Dawn' **new**	NLar SLim
- 'Green Mantle'	ECho EHul
- 'Little Giant' **new**	MBlu
- 'Matthaei Broom'	LRHS NLar SLim SPoG

- 'McCracken's White' new	NLar SLim
- 'Miss Grace'	MAsh NLar SLim
§ - 'National'	ECho MBlu
- 'Sheridan Spire'	CEnd MBlu WPGP
- 'Spring Cream'	ECho NLar
- 'Waasland'	LRHS MBlu SLim
- 'White Spot' (v)	ECho MBlu NPCo SLim WEve

Metrosideros (*Myrtaceae*)

carminea	CCCN CTrC CTsd
§ ***excelsa***	CHEx CHll CTrC CTrG CTsd EBak ECou
- 'Aurea'	ECou
- 'Fire Mountain'	CTrC
- 'Maori Princess' new	CWit
- 'Parnell'	CBcs CCCN
- 'Spring Fire'	CBcs CCCN CTrC
- 'Vibrance'	CTrC
kermadecensis	ECou
- 'Radiant' (v)	CBcs
- 'Red and Gold'	CBcs CDoC CTrC
- 'Twisty' (v)	CBcs
- 'Variegata' (v)	CBcs CDoC CTrC ECou SMrm
lucida	see *M. umbellata*
'Pink Lady'	CTrC
robusta	CBcs CCCN CHEx MREP
- ***aureovariegata***	CCCN EShb
× ***subtomentosa*** 'Mistral'	ECou
tomentosa	see *M. excelsa*
§ ***umbellata***	CBcs CCCN CHEx CTrC CTsd EBee ECou EShb GGal GGar
villosa 'Tahiti'	CBcs

Meum (*Apiaceae*)

athamanticum	CArn CSev CSpe EBee EBrs EDAr EHrv GCal GPoy LPla MAvo MCot MRav MTho NSti SGar WFar WHil WPer WPrP WTin

Michauxia (*Campanulaceae*)

campanuloides	EBee GKev
laevigata	WCot
tchihatchewii	CCCN CDTJ CSpe EBee GKev MWea NGBl

Michelia (*Magnoliaceae*)

champaca	CCCN ERea
chapensis	CBcs SSpi
- HWJ 621	WCru
compressa	CCCN EPfP ERea
doltsopa	CBcs CCCN CGHE CHEx EBee EPfP SSpi SSta WPGP
- 'Silver Cloud'	CBcs CDoC
figo	CAbb CBcs CCCN CDoC EPfP ERea LRHS SSpi SSta WPGP
- var. ***crassipes***	CBcs SSpi
- var. ***figo***	SSpi
foveolata	CBcs SSpi
- var. ***cinerascens***	CWib WPGP
macclurei	CBcs SSpi WPGP
maudiae	CDoC CGHE CMCN CPLG EPfP ISea NLar SSpi WPGP
odora	CWib
sinensis	see *M. wilsonii*
§ ***wilsonii***	CWib
yunnanensis	CBcs CCCN MBri SSpi WPGP

Microbiota (*Cupressaceae*)

decussata ♀H4	CBcs CDoC CKen CMac CSBt ECho EHul EPla GKir IFFs LAst LBee LRHS MBar MGos MWat NHol NWea SLim SPoG WCFE WEve WFar
- 'Gold Spot'	SLim SPoG
- 'Jakobsen'	CDoC CKen
- 'Trompenburg'	CKen

Microcachrys (*Podocarpaceae*)

tetragona	CDoC ECho ECou EHul EOrn EPla SCoo SIng WThu

Microcoelum see *Lytocaryum*

weddellianum	see *Lytocaryum weddellianum*

Microlaena see *Ehrharta*

Microlepia (*Dennstaedtiaceae*)

speluncae	EShb
strigosa	CBty CCCN CLAP EBee LLHF LRHS WRic

Micromeria (*Lamiaceae*)

corsica	see *Acinos corsicus*
croatica	NMen
fruticosa	CArn
graeca	CArn
rupestris	see *M. thymifolia*
§ ***thymifolia***	NMen SPlb
viminea	see *Satureja viminea*

Microseris (*Asteraceae*)

ringens hort.	see *Leontodon rigens*

Microsorum (*Polypodiaceae*)

diversifolium	see *Phymatosorus diversifolius*

Microtropis (*Celastraceae*)

petelotii HWJ 719	WCru

Mikania (*Asteraceae*)

araucana	LSou

Milium (*Poaceae*)

effusum	COld GKir
- 'Aureum' ♀H4	Widely available
- var. ***esthonicum***	EBee EPPr
- 'Yaffle' (v)	CBre CFir CKno EBee ECha EPPr EPla EShb GKir LEdu LRHS MWat SGar SPoG SSvw SUsu WCot WGrn

Millettia (*Papilionaceae*)

japonica 'Hime Fuji'	NLar
murasaki-natsu-fuji	see *M. reticulata*
§ ***reticulata***	CPLG

Millingtonia (*Bignoniaceae*)

hortensis	WHil

Mimosa (*Mimosaceae*)

pudica	CCCN CDTJ WTou

Mimulus (*Scrophulariaceae*)

'A.T. Johnson'	NVic
'Andean Nymph'	see *M. naiandinus*
§ ***aurantiacus*** ♀H2-3	CBot CElw CFee CMac CSpe CTri EBak EBee ECtt LHop MAsh NBir NPer SBch SDnm SGar SMrm SPlb SPoG SUsu WCom
§ - var. ***puniceus***	CBot CSpe CTri EDif LAst LHop LSou MAsh SAga SBHP SHom SMrm SRkn WCom
- 'Pure Gold'	EDif
- 'Rosea' new	CFee
- 'Tangerine'	EDif
× ***bartonianus***	see *M.* × *harrisonii*

	bifidus 'Tapestry'	CSpe SAga
	- 'Trish'	CSpe SAga
	- 'Verity Buff'	EDif MAsh
§	- 'Verity Purple'	EDif
	- 'Wine'	see *M. bifidus* 'Verity Purple'
	'Bonfire' **new**	WWEG
	× ***burnetii***	ECho LPBA SRms
	cardinalis 🏆H3	CEnt EBee ELan EPfP LPBA MNrw MSKA MTho NBir SMrm SPer WFar WMoo WPer WWEG
	- 'Dark Throat'	SGar
	- 'Red Dragon'	CSpr SBHP WHrl
	cupreus 'Minor'	ECho
	- 'Whitecroft Scarlet' 🏆H4	ECho ECtt ELan EPfP LSou SRms WPer
	'Eleanor'	ECtt LSou SAga SGar SHom SMrm SUsu
	'Firedragon'	GKir
	glutinosus	see *M. aurantiacus*
	- ***atrosanguineus***	see *M. aurantiacus* var. *puniceus*
	- ***luteus***	see *M. aurantiacus*
§	***guttatus***	EMFW NPer NSco SRms WMoo WPer WPnP WWEG
§	- 'Richard Bish' (v)	CBow MCCP
§	× ***harrisonii***	EBee EPfP EWes LSou SAga
	'Highland Orange'	ECho EPfP GKir NBlu SPlb SPoG WGor WPer
	'Highland Pink'	ECho EPfP SPlb SPoG WGor WPer
	'Highland Pink Rose'	WFar
	'Highland Red' 🏆H4	ECho ECtt EPfP GGar GKir LPBA LRHS NBlu SPlb SPoG SRms WFar WPer
	'Highland Yellow'	ECho ECtt GKir LPBA NBlu SPlb SPoG WFar WPer
	hose-in-hose (d)	NPer
	'Inca Sunset'	EWes
	langsdorffii	see *M. guttatus*
	lewisii 🏆H3	CHll MTho SPav SRms
	longiflorus	CBot
	- 'Santa Barbara'	MWte
	luteus	CBen CWat EHon EPfP LPBA NHol NPer SPlb WBrk WFar WMAq WRHF
§	- 'Gaby' (v)	LPBA
	- 'Variegatus' misapplied	see *M. guttatus* 'Richard Bish'
	- 'Variegatus'	see *M. luteus* 'Gaby'
	- 'Variegatus' ambig. (v)	NPer
	'Malibu Orange'	EPfP
	minimus	ECho
	moschatus	EBee
§	***naiandinus*** 🏆H3	CEnt CMMP LFur SPlb SRms
	'Orange Glow'	EPfP WHal
	orange hose-in-hose (d)	NBir
	'Orkney Lemon'	NSti
	'Popacatapetl'	CHll EDif LHop LSou MAsh SAga SBHP SMrm WCom
	'Prairie Caramel'	EDif
	'Prairie Cerise'	EDif
	'Prairie Citron'	EDif
	'Prairie Coral'	EDif
	'Prairie Lilac Frost'	EDif
	'Prairie Peach'	EDif
	'Prairie Sunshine'	EDif
	primuloides	ECho EWes LLWG SIng SPlb
	'Puck'	ECho ECtt GKir LRHS SPoG
	'Quetzalcoatl'	LSou SAga
	ringens	CBen CWat EBee EDif EHon EMFW EPfP LFur LPBA MSKA NBir NPer SPlb SRms WFar WMAq WMoo WPer WWEG
	'Threave Variegated' (v)	EBee GBuc MRav NBir WFar
	tilingii	ECho
	'Wine Red'	see *M. bifidus* 'Verity Purple'
	'Wisley Red'	ECho SRms
	'Yellow Velvet'	ECho

Mina see *Ipomoea*

mint, apple see *Mentha suaveolens*

mint, Bowles see *M.* × *villosa* var. *alopecuroides*

mint, curly see *M. spicata* var. *crispa*

mint, eau-de-Cologne see *M.* × *piperita* f. *citrata*

mint, ginger see *M.* × *gracilis*

mint, horse or long-leaved see *M. longifolia*

mint, pennyroyal see *M. pulegium*

mint (peppermint) see *M.* × *piperita*

mint, round-leaved see *M. suaveolens*

mint (spearmint) see *M. spicata*

Minuartia (*Caryophyllaceae*)

	capillacea	ECho
	caucasica	see *M. circassica*
§	***circassica***	NWCA WPer
	juniperina	GKir
	laricifolia	GKir
	parnassica	see *M. stellata*
§	***stellata***	EPot NDlv NMen SIng
	- NS 758	NWCA
§	***verna***	EAlp ECho EDAr NMen
	- subsp. ***caespitosa***	CTri ECho
	- - 'Aurea'	see *Sagina subulata* var. *glabrata* 'Aurea'

Mirabilis (*Nyctaginaceae*)

	jalapa	CArn CPLG EBrs EPfP EShb LAma LEdu LRHS SBod SEND SPad SRms WHil WTou
	- 'Buttermilk'	CCCN LRHS
	- red-flowered	SGSe WTou
	- white-flowered	CSpe WTou
	- yellow-flowered **new**	WTou
	longiflora **new**	WHil

Miscanthus ✿ (*Poaceae*)

	capensis	SPlb
	chejuensis B&SWJ 8803	WCru
	'Dronning Ingrid' **new**	EBee
	flavidus B&SWJ 6749	WCru
	floridulus misapplied	see *M.* × *giganteus*
	floridulus ambig.	EBee MMuc NLar NOak SPlb WFar WPrP
	floridulus (Labill.) Warb. ex K. Schum. & Lauterb. HWJ 522	WCru
§	× ***giganteus***	CHar CKno EAlp EBee EHoe ELon EPPr GAbr GCal GQue LRHS MAvo MCCP MMoz MMuc MWat NBea NOak NVic NWsh SApp SDix SEND SGSe SMad SVic WCot WFar WSpi
	- 'Gilt Edge' (v)	CBow CKno EPPr MAvo NWsh SApp
	- 'Gotemba' (v)	EBee ELon EPPr EWes NWsh SApp
	'Golden Bar'	EBrs EPla GBuc

	Name	Suppliers
	'Gotemba Gold'	SApp
	'Mount Washington'	SApp
	nepalensis	CElw CEnt CHrt CKno CPLG CWCL EAlp ECha ECre EHoe EPGN ERas EWes LEdu LRHS MAvo MNrw MWte NWsh SDix SGSe SMrm SUsu WHoo WTin
	- 'Shikola'	WCru
	oligostachyus	IMou NGdn SMrm
§	- 'Afrika'	CHar CKno CPen EBee LHop LRHS
I	- 'Nanus Variegatus' (v)	CDes CKno CRow EBee EHoe EWes LEdu MAvo MMoz WCot WPGP WWEG
	- variegated (v) **new**	LRHS
	'Pos'	SApp
§	'Purpurascens'	CKno CWCL ECha EHoe EHrv EHul EPla EShb LRHS LSRN MAvo MBrN MMoz MMuc MWhi NOak NWsh SApp SGSe SWal WMoo WSpi WTin
	sacchariflorus misapplied	see *M.* × *giganteus*
	sacchariflorus ambig.	CAbb CBcs CDul CHEx CKno CRow EBee ECha EHrv ELan EPfP EPla EShb LPBA LRHS MBrN SBch SPer WFar WMoo WSpi
	sacchariflorus (Maxim.) Hack.	MMuc MWhi WWEG
	- 'Robustus'	CHVG
	sinensis	CEnt CHEx CHrt CTri EBla GFor LEdu MMoz NGBl NLar NOak SVic WDin WMoo
	- from Yakushima	GKir SGSe
	- 'Adagio'	CHar CKno CPen EAEE EBee EBrs EHoe EPPr GBin GQue LEdu LRHS MWhi SBch SHDw WCot WPrP
	- 'Afrika'	see *M. oligostachyus* 'Afrika'
	- 'Andante'	CKno
	- 'Arabesque'	EPPr ERas LRHS MMoz NLar SApp WWEG
	- 'Augustfeder'	CHar CPen EBee EPPr LEdu LRHS WWEG
	- 'Autumn Light'	CKno CPen EBrs EPPr LRHS
	- 'Ballerina'	CHar CPen
	- 'Blütenwunder'	CHar CKno CPen EBee EPfP
	- 'China'	Widely available
	- var. ***condensatus***	LSou
	- - 'Cabaret' (v)	Widely available
	- - 'Central Park'	see *M. sinensis* var. *condensatus* 'Cosmo Revert'
§	- - 'Cosmo Revert'	CPen EBee LEdu MMoz NWsh WDyG WSpi
	- - 'Cosmopolitan' (v) ♀H4	Widely available
	- - 'Emerald Giant'	see *M. sinensis* var. *condensatus* 'Cosmo Revert'
	- 'David'	CPen EAEE EBee EPPr LEdu LRHS MAvo MBNS
	- 'Dixieland' (v)	CHar CKno EHoe ELan EPPr IFoB IMou LEdu LRHS MMoz NWsh SApp WWEG
	- 'Emmanuel Lepage'	CHar CKno CPen EBee EPPr
	- 'Etincelle'	CKno
	- 'Federriese'	LRHS
	- 'Ferner Osten'	Widely available
	- 'Flamingo' ♀H4	Widely available
	- 'Flammenmeer'	CHar CPen
	- 'Gaa'	SApp
	- 'Gearmella'	EPPr GKir LEdu LRHS NWsh
	- 'Gewitterwolke' ♀H4	CHar CKno EWes
	- 'Ghana' ♀H4	CHar CKno CPen ELon ILad IMou LHop MAvo
	- 'Giraffe'	CDTJ CDes CHar CKno CPen EBee EWes LEdu LRHS WPGP WWEG
	- 'Gnome'	CKno CPen EAEE EBee EPPr IMou LRHS MMHG WWEG
	- 'Gold Bar' (v)	CBow CChe CElw CKno CMea CWGN EBee ECha ECtt ELon EPPr LEdu LLWG LRHS LSRN LSou MBNS NCGa NMoo SMad SPer SPoG SUsu WClo WCot WGwG WMoo WWEG
	- 'Goldfeder' (v)	CPen EHoe LRHS
	- 'Goliath'	CHar CPen EAEE EBee EHoe ELan ELon EPPr ERas GQue IPot LBMP LEdu LRHS MBNS WFar WPnP WPrP WWEG
	- 'Gracillimus'	Widely available
	- 'Gracillimus Nanus'	CKno
	- 'Graziella'	CEnd CHar CKno CSam CWCL CWib EBee EBla EBrs EHoe EHrv EPPr EPfP EPla LEdu LRHS MBri MMoz MWhi NGdn NOak NOrc SLPl SMeo SPer SRms WBor WClo WPGP WPrP
	- 'Grosse Fontäne' ♀H4	CWCL EBee EBla EHoe ELan EPPr EPla GKir LEdu LSRN NWsh SGSe SMad WAul WCot WMoo WWEG
	- 'Haiku'	CHar CPen EPPr LEdu SPhx WPrP
	- 'Helga Reich'	EBee SApp
	- 'Hercules'	CPen EPPr MAvo MMoz SApp
	- 'Hermann Müssel'	CHar CKno CPen EAlp EBee EPPr EWes GBin IMou LEdu LPla SPhx WPrP
	- 'Hinjo' (v)	CDes CElw CHar CKno CSpe EBee ECGP ECha ECtt EPPr GBin GCal GQue LBMP LEdu LRHS LSou NGdn NWsh SApp SPoG WCot WFar WPGP WPrP WWEG
I	- 'Jubilaris' (v)	EPPr EWes
	- 'Juli'	CSsd EBrs ERas LRHS WPrP WSpi
	- 'Kaskade' ♀H4	CHar CKno CWCL EBee EBrs EHoe EPPr IPot LEdu LRHS MAvo MMoz MMuc MWhi SApp SMeo WFar WMoo WWEG
	- 'Kirk Alexander' (v)	MAvo SApp
	- 'Kleine Fontäne' ♀H4	Widely available
	- 'Kleine Silberspinne' ♀H4	Widely available
	- 'Krater'	CHar CKno EBee EBrs EHoe EPPr LEdu LRHS MBrN SGSe SMeo SWat
	- 'Kupferberg'	CHar
§	- 'Little Kitten'	CDes CHar CKno CPen CSpe EBee EPPr EPla LEdu LPla MBar NWsh SGSe SMad WMoo WPGP
	- 'Little Zebra' (v)	CKno EBee EPPr EPfP EShb LHop LRHS LSRN MGos NOak NWsh SRms
	- 'Malepartus'	Widely available
	- 'Morning Light' (v) ♀H4	Widely available
	- new hybrids	EHul NScw
	- 'Nippon'	CBow CDes CElw CHrt CKno CPrp CWCL EAEE EBee EBla EHoe EPPr EPla GKir LEdu LRHS MCCP MMoz NGdn NOrc NWsh SDys SMrm SPer WPGP WSpi WWEG
	- 'Nishidake'	CHar CPen EBee EPPr
	- 'November Sunset'	EBrs EPPr ERas EWes IPot LRHS MMoz
	- 'Overdam'	GKir
	- 'Poseidon'	EPPr MAvo NChi SDys SMad
	- 'Positano'	CKno EPPr LRHS MMoz WPGP
	- 'Professor Richard Hansen'	CHar CKno CPen GBin WPrP
	- 'Pünktchen' (v)	CHar CKno CPen CWCL EAEE EBee ECha EHoe EPPr EPla GBin LEdu

	LRHS MAvo NOak SApp SBch SHDw SMad SPad SPhx SRms WFar WMoo WPnP WTin WWEG
- var. ***purpurascens*** misapplied	see *M.* 'Purpurascens'
- 'Red Chief' new	EPPr
- 'Rigoletto' (v)	EPPr SApp
- 'Roland'	CHar CKno CPen EBee GBin LRHS SAga SPhx
- 'Roterpfeil'	CHar CPen SMeo
- 'Rotfeder'	EPPr GKir
- 'Rotfuchs'	CHar CPen EBee LPla MGos SAga WFar
- 'Rotsilber'	CHar CKno CPrp CSam CSpe CWCL CWib EAlp EBee EBrs ECha EHoe EPPr EPla GFor GMaP IArd LEdu LRHS MAvo MRav MWhi NCGa NWsh WFar WHoo WMoo WPnP WPrP WWEG
I - 'Russianus'	NWsh
- 'Samurai'	CEnt CHar EPPr GMaP GQue MAvo SMrm
- 'Sarabande'	CHar CKno EBee EHoe EHul ELan EPPr IPot LRHS NWsh SApp SMrm WFar WGwG WMoo
- 'Septemberrot' ♀H4	CHVG CHar CKno CPrp CWCL EBee LEdu MMuc SPoG
§ - 'Silberfeder' ♀H4	Widely available
- 'Silberpfeil' (v)	EHoe NWsh
- 'Silberspinne'	CMdw EBla EPla ERas LEdu LRHS MCCP MWat NGdn SAga SApp SMeo SPlb WAul WDin
- 'Silberturm'	CHar CKno EBee LRHS
- Silver Feather	see *M. sinensis* 'Silberfeder'
- 'Silver Stripe' new	EPPr
- 'Sioux'	CEnt CHar CKno EBee EBrs EHoe EPPr EPfP EPla EShb GBin LEdu LRHS MBNS MMoz MWhi SPer WTin WWEG
- 'Sirene'	CHar EAEE EBee EBrs EHoe EPPr EPla GQue LRHS MBNS MBlu WFar WPrP
- 'Spätgrün'	CHar
- 'Strictus' (v) ♀H4	Widely available
- 'Tiger Cub' (v)	CWCL EBee MAvo SApp SGSe
- 'Undine' ♀H4	CHar CKno CMea CPrp CSam EAEE EBee EBla EBrs ECha EHoe EHrv ELan EPPr EPla LEdu LRHS MBel MMoz MSnd NWsh WMoo WPrP
- 'Variegatus' (v)	Widely available
- 'Vorläufer'	CHar CKno CPen EBrs EHoe EPPr NWsh SAga
- 'Wetterfahne'	CHar LEdu LRHS
§ - 'Yaku-jima'	CHar CSam EBee ECha EPPr LHop MWhi SPoG
- 'Yakushima Dwarf'	Widely available
- 'Zebrinus' (v) ♀H4	Widely available
- 'Zwergelefant'	CHar LRHS MMoz
I 'Spartina'	SApp
tinctorius 'Nanus Variegatus' misapplied	see *M. oligostachyus* 'Nanus Variegatus'
transmorrisonensis	CDes CHar CKno EBee EHoe ELan EPPr GFor LRHS MAvo MMoz NNor NOak SApp SWal WCot WTin WWEG
- B&SWJ 3697	WCru
yakushimensis	see *M. sinensis* 'Little Kitten', *M. sinensis* 'Yaku-jima'

Mitchella (*Rubiaceae*)

repens	CBcs EBee GBin WCru
undulata B&SWJ 10928	WCru

* - f. ***quelpartensis*** B&SWJ 4402	WCru

Mitella (*Saxifragaceae*)

breweri	CFir CHid CSam ECha GCal GGar MRav NHol SBch SMac SRms WEas WFar WMoo WPnP WTin
caulescens	ECha NBro NHol WMoo WPrP
diphylla	EPPr
formosana	EPPr
- B&SWJ 125	WCru
japonica B&SWJ 4971	WCru
kiusiana	CLAP
- B&SWJ 5888	WCru
makinoi	CLAP EBee
- B&SWJ 4992	WCru
ovalis	EBee EPPr
pauciflora B&SWJ 6361	WCru
pentandra	WMoo
stylosa	LLHF
- B&SWJ 5669	WCru
yoshinagae	GEdr WMoo
- B&SWJ 4893	CHid WCru WPrP WPtf

Mitraria (*Gesneriaceae*)

coccinea	CBcs CCCN CEnt CMac CStu CTrG CTsd CWib ECho ELan LBMP LSou MBlu MDun SArc SBod SLon SPer SSpi
- Clark's form	CSam CTrC GGar LAst MDun NLar WBor
- 'Lake Caburgua'	CBgR CSpe ELon EWld GCal GGal GGar IArd IDee MDun NSti
- 'Lake Puyehue'	CBcs CCCN CDoC CFee EBee EMil EPfP ERea GQui LHop LRHS MAsh MGos SWvt WAbe WCru WFar WGwG WPGP WSHC

Moehringia (*Caryophyllaceae*)

muscosa	WCot

Molinia (*Poaceae*)

altissima	see *M. caerulea* subsp. ***arundinacea***
caerulea	CRWN CWib EBWF EHul EPPr GFor GKir LAst MBlu NChi NGBl
§ - subsp. ***arundinacea***	CKno CWCL ECha EPPr GFor LRHS MMuc NLar SApp SLPl WPer
- - 'Bergfreund'	CKno CSam EBee EHoe EPPr MAvo NWsh SApp SBod SPhx SUsu WDyG WMoo WTin
- - 'Cordoba'	CKno EBee EPPr SPhx
- - 'Fontäne'	CPen CSam EBee EHoe EPPr GCal GQue LEdu LPla LRHS NNor NWsh SApp SGSe SPhx
- - 'Karl Foerster'	Widely available
- - 'Poul Petersen'	CKno EPPr SPhx
- - 'Skyracer'	CChe CKno COIW CPrp CSam EBee EBla EHoe EPPr GCal GQue LRHS MAvo MMoz MWhi NVic NWsh SMad SPhx SPoG WCot WFar WGrn WMoo WWEG
- - 'Staefa'	EHoe
- - 'Transparent'	Widely available
- - 'Windsaule'	CKno EBee EPPr SPhx
- - 'Windspiel'	CKno CRow CSam EAEE EBee ECha EHoe EMil EPPr LEdu LPio LRHS MAvo NWsh SApp SPhx SPoG SWal WCot WMoo WPGP WTin
- - 'Zuneigung'	CKno CSam EBrs EPPr LPla LRHS MAvo SApp SPhx

	- subsp. ***caerulea***	CHar
	- - 'Carmarthen' (v)	EBee EHoe EPPr MAvo SApp WHal WPnP WPrP WWEG
	- - 'Claerwen' (v)	ECha EPPr GBuc GCal SPhx WMoo
	- - 'Coneyhill Gold' (v)	EPPr
	- - 'Dauerstrahl'	CKno EBee EPPr GBin GCal GQue LPla MAvo NHol
	- - 'Edith Dudszus'	CKno CWCL EAEE EBee ECha EHoe EPPr GQue LEdu LPio LPla LRHS MAvo MBrN MBri MMoz MNFA NGdn NHol NOrc NWsh SApp SPer WGrn WMoo WPGP WWEG
	- - 'Heidebraut'	EAEE EBee EBla EHoe EHul EPPr GBin GQue LRHS MBri MRav NBro NOrc SApp SPhx WFar WMoo WPnP WWEG
	- - 'Moorflamme'	CKno CSam EHoe EPPr MAvo SPhx
	- - 'Moorhexe'	Widely available
	- - 'Strahlenquelle'	CKno CSam EBee ELan EPPr GCal GQue LPla LRHS MAvo MMoz NBro NHol SPhx WPGP WWEG
	- - 'Variegata' (v) 𝕐H4	Widely available
	litoralis	see *M. caerulea* subsp. *arundinacea*

Molospermum (*Apiaceae*)

	peloponnesiacum	CSpe EBee ELon GCal IMou LEdu LPio NChi NLar SAga SPhx WCru WSHC

Moltkia (*Boraginaceae*)

§	***doerfleri***	NBir NChi
§	× ***intermedia*** 𝕐H4	CMea SAga WAbe WCom WFar WPat
	petraea	LLHF MWat WFar

Moluccella (*Lamiaceae*)

	laevis 'Pixie Bells'	CSpe

Monachosorum (*Adiantaceae*)

	henryi	WRic

Monadenium (*Euphorbiaceae*)

	lugardiae	MBri
	'Variegatum' (v)	MBri

Monarda (*Lamiaceae*)

	'Adam'	EBee GCal LRHS LSRN NBre WSHC
	'Amethyst'	ECtt EWes SIde
	'Aquarius'	CAby EBee EPPr LRHS MSpe NCob NGHP NHol NPro WCAu WCHb WWlt
	austromontana	see *M. citriodora* subsp. *austromontana*
	'Baby Spice'	EBee NCob
§	'Balance'	CPrp CWCL EAro EBee ECtt EPfP GCal MCot MRav MSpe NBro NCob NGHP NGdn NHol SAga SMeo WCHb WFar WPGP WSHC WWEG WWlt
	'Beauty of Cobham' 𝕐H4	CHar CPrp EBee ECha ELan EPfP GKir GMaP LAst LEdu LRHS MBri MCot MHer NGHP NHol NLar SMad SPer WBor WCHb WWEG WWlt
	'Blaukranz'	NBre
§	'Blaustrumpf'	CElw EBee ECtt GBBs LRHS NCob NLar SPer
	Blue Stocking	see *M.* 'Blaustrumpf'
	Bowman	see *M.* 'Sagittarius'
	bradburyana	EShb LLHF NBre NLar WCHb
	'Cambridge Scarlet' 𝕐H4	Widely available
	'Capricorn'	GBuc NBre WCHb WWEG
	'Cherokee'	NCob WCHb WCon WFar
	'Chippawa' **new**	LRHS
	citriodora	CArn ECtt GPoy LRHS NSti SIde SRms SWat
§	- subsp. ***austromontana***	EAro NBir SBch SGar SIde SVic WFar WPer
	- - 'Bee's Favourite'	SPad
	'Comanche'	EBee EHrv EWes NCob WCHb WFar
	'Croftway Pink' 𝕐H4	Widely available
I	'Dark Ponticum'	LRHS NCob
	didyma	CArn CHar CWan EPfP GKir NBro NGHP SBch SWat WBrE WJek
	- 'Coral Reef'	EBrs LRHS
	- 'Duddiscombe'	CPrp CSam CWCL
	- 'Goldmelise'	NBre NGHP WMoo
	- 'Pink Lace' [PBR] **new**	MBri
	'Earl Grey'	GAbr WRHF
	'Elsie's Lavender'	CAby EBee GBuc LPla NLar SAga WCHb WWEG
	'Elworthy' **new**	CElw
§	'Feuerschopf'	EBee
	'Fireball' [PBR]	CHVG CWCL EBee ECtt LLHF NBPC NCob NLar NPri SBch SPoG
	Firecrown	see *M.* 'Feuerschopf'
§	'Fishes'	CHVG EAEE EBee ECtt EHrv ELan EPPr EWes LRHS MCot MRav MSpe NCob NGHP NGdn NHol NLar STes WCHb WFar WSHC WWEG WWlt
	fistulosa	CArn CPrp CWan GPoy MNHC WJek WMoo WPer
	'Gardenview Scarlet' 𝕐H4	CPrp CSam CWCL EBee EBrs ECtt EWes GCal GCra GKir GQue LRHS MBri MCot MDKP MWat NGHP NGby NHol NLar SMrm SPoG SWal WCHb WPer WRHF WWlt
	Gemini	see *M.* 'Twins'
	'Gewitterwolke'	CSam EBee IPot SDys
	'Hartswood Wine'	SMad SMrm
	'Heidelerche'	EBee EPPr LRHS
	'Jacob Cline'	CCVN EBee EPPr GBin IPot NBre NCGa NCob SMrm STes WPtf WWEG
	'Kardinal'	EBee GBin
	'Lambada'	SPav
	Libra	see *M.* 'Balance'
	'Lilac Queen'	NCob
	'Loddon Crown'	CHar COIW CPrp EBee ECtt GQue LRHS MBri MDKP NCob NGHP NHol NLar SBch SIde WCAu WCHb WSHC WWEG
	'Mahogany'	CPrp EBee ELan GMaP LRHS MRav NCob NGHP SMad SPer WCHb WSHC WSpi
	'Marshall's Delight' 𝕐H4	CPrp EBee ECtt ELon EWes LRHS LSou MRav NCob NGHP NLar SGar SMrm WFar
	'Melissa'	EBee LSRN NBre
	menthifolia	CArn EAro EBee GCal GPWP LSou MCot SMrm
	'Mohawk'	CAby CPrp CWCL EAEE EBee ECtt EHrv EPPr LRHS MWat NChi NCob NHol NOrc SPer WCAu WCHb WWEG
	'Mrs Perry'	EWes NGHP
	'Neon'	SPhx
	'Night Rider'	EWes
	'On Parade'	EAEE EBee ECtt EWll LRHS MMHG NCob NHol
	'Ou Charm'	CWCL EBee EWes LRHS MMHG NLar SMrm WCHb WFar

'Panorama'	EAro ECtt NLar SPet SPlb WMoo WPer
'Panorama Red Shades' (Panorama Series)	CWib EAro EWTr MNHC SPet WClo
'Pawnee'	LRHS WCHb
Petite Delight = 'Acpetdel'	CBcs EBee ECtt EHoe ELan EPfP LHop MBel NCob NGHP NHol NLar SMad WFar
'Petite Pink Supreme'	EBee EPfP
'Pink Supreme'PBR	EPfP GAbr GQue MBri NCob NGHP NLar NPri SBch
'Pink Tourmaline'	EBee NGby NHol SMad SMrm WCHb WWEG
Pisces	see *M.* 'Fishes'
'Poyntzfield Pink'	GPoy
Prairie Night	see *M.* 'Prärienacht'
§ 'Prärienacht'	CHar CPrp CSBt CSam EBee ECha ELan EPfP MBel MHer NBPC NBro NGHP NGdn NHol NVic SPer SPlb SRms STes SWvt WCHb WCom WEas WFar WPer WSHC WWEG
punctata	CArn CBod EAro EBee ELan ELon LBMP MCot NGdn SDnm SGSe SMrm SPav SWat WCHb WFar
'Raspberry Wine'	ECtt
'Ruby Glow'	CAby CWCL EBee EHrv IPot LRHS MArl MMHG NGdn NHol SAga SMad SMrm SPhx WCHb
§ 'Sagittarius'	EAEE EBee MMHG MSpe NCGa NChi NCob NGdn NHol SPur WCHb
'Sahin's Mildew-free'	WCHb
'Saxon Purple'	NLar
§ 'Schneewittchen'	CPrp CWCL EAro EBee ECha ECtt EHrv ELan EPfP LRHS MHer MRav NBro NGHP NGdn NHol NSti SIde SMrm SPer SWvt WCAu WFar WWEG
'Scorpion'	CWCL EAro EBee ECtt EHrv ELan EPPr GGar LEdu LRHS MCot MRav NBPC NBir NCob NEgg NGdn NHol NOrc NPro SMrm SWvt WCAu WCHb WPGP WSHC
'Shelley'	ECha
'Sioux'	EHrv EWes GBuc WCHb WFar
'Snow Maiden'	see *M.* 'Schneewittchen'
'Snow Queen'	CSam EAro EBee ECtt EPPr LRHS MSpe MWat NCob NHol NLar NPro SHar SPur STes
Snow White	see *M.* 'Schneewittchen'
'Squaw' ♀H4	Widely available
'Talud' ♀H4	EBee
§ 'Twins'	CMil CWCL EBee EPPr LSRN NGHP NHol SWvt WCHb WSHC WWEG
'Velvet Queen'	LSou
'Vintage Wine'	CAby CWCL ECtt NCob WCHb WCon WFar
'Violacea'	NHol WCHb
'Violet Queen' ♀H4	EAEE EAro EBee EBrs ECtt EWes GQue LRHS NBre NCob NPro SCoo SMrm WCAu WFar WHil

Monardella (*Lamiaceae*)

macrantha	CPBP
- subsp. ***hallii***	CPBP
nana subsp. ***arida***	CPBP
- subsp. ***tenuiflora***	CPBP
odoratissima	CArn

Monochoria (*Pontederiaceae*)

§ ***hastata***	LLWG MSKA

Monstera (*Araceae*)

deliciosa (F) ♀H1	MBri SRms XBlo
- 'Variegata' (v) ♀H1	MBri SRms

Montbretia see *Crocosmia, Tritonia*

× ***crocosmiiflora***	see *Crocosmia* × *crocosmiiflora*
pottsii	see *Crocosmia pottsii*

Montia (*Portulacaceae*)

australasica	see *Neopaxia australasica*
perfoliata	see *Claytonia perfoliata*
sibirica	see *Claytonia sibirica*

Moraea (*Iridaceae*)

alticola	CPne EBee EBrs ECho GGar WCot WPGP
§ ***aristata***	CDes WCot
§ ***bellendenii***	ECho WCot
bipartita	WCot
calcicola new	ECho
ciliata new	ECho WCot
comptonii	CPBP
elegans	CPBP
gigandra	ECho WCot
glaucopsis	see *M. aristata*
huttonii	CCCN CFir CPBP CSpe EDif EPPr GBBs GKev LPio SGSe WBVN WCot WPrP WSHC
iridioides	see *Dietes iridioides*
loubseri	EBee
lurida	WCot
marlothii new	ECho
papilionacea	WCot
pavonia var. ***lutea***	see *M. bellendenii*
polystachya	CGrW EBrs ECho
robusta	GCal
serpentina new	ECho
setifolia new	ECho
spathacea	see *M. spathulata*
§ ***spathulata***	CBro CPLG ECho ERos GCal LEdu WCot WPrP
tricolor	CPBP ECho WCot
tulbaghensis	EBee WCot
vegeta	CPBP ECho ERea GAbr WCot
villosa	ECho WCot

Moricandia (*Brassicaceae*)

arvensis	WCot
moricandioides	CSpe

Morina (*Morinaceae*)

* ***afghanica***	GAbr
alba	GCra NChi
longifolia	Widely available
persica	EWes EWld GBuc LPio NLar WHoo
polyphylla	EBee GPoy
* ***spinosa*** new	GKev

Morinda (*Rubiaceae*)

umbellata WWJ 11688 new	WCru

Morisia (*Brassicaceae*)

hypogaea	see *M. monanthos*
§ ***monanthos***	GMaP MBar NBlu NWCA SRot WFar
- 'Fred Hemingway'	ECho ITim LRHS NDlv NMen NSla SIng WAbe WThu

Morus ✿ (*Moraceae*)

alba	CAgr CAlb CArn CBcs CCVT CDul CLnd CMCN CTho CWib ECrN

	ELan EPfP ERea GTwe IFFs LBuc LHop LMaj MGos SMrm WDin WFar
- 'Black Tabor'	CAgr
- 'Chaparral' new	EBee
- 'Fastigiata' new	LRHS
- 'Issai' new	LRHS
- 'Laciniata'	EBee
- 'Macrophylla'	CMCN NLar
- 'Nana' new	NLar
- 'Pendula'	CDoC CDul CEnd CLnd CMac CTho CTri ECrN ELan EMil ERea GTwe LAst LRHS MAsh MBlu MBri NLar SBch SCoo SLim SPer SPoG WDin
- 'Platanifolia'	LMaj MBlu
- var. ***tatarica***	CAgr LEdu NLar
§ ***bombycis***	CAlb IFFs
'Capsrum' (F)	CAgr
'Carmen' (F)	CAgr
'Illinois Everbearing' (F)	CAgr ECrN ERea
'Italian' (F)	CAgr
'Ivory' (F)	CAgr
kagayamae	see *M. bombycis*
latifolia 'Spirata'	EMil NLar
nigra (F) ♀H4	Widely available
§ - 'Chelsea' (F)	CDul CEnd CTho CTri ECrN EMui EPfP ERea GTwe LRHS MBri MGan MGos NWea SCoo SKee SPer SPoG WHar WPGP
- 'Jerusalem' (F)	CTho LRHS
- 'King James'	see *M. nigra* 'Chelsea'
- 'Large Black' (F)	EMui
- 'Wellington' (F)	CAgr CEnd
rubra	CAgr NLar
- 'Nana'	MBri NLar

Mosla (*Lamiaceae*)

dianthera	EBee EWld GCal MAvo MNrw WSHC

Muehlenbeckia (*Polygonaceae*)

astonii	CPen EBee ECou LRHS
australis	ECou
axillaris misapplied	see *M. complexa*
§ ***axillaris*** Walp.	CBcs CTri ECou GGar SBig
- 'Mount Cook' (f)	ECou
- 'Ohau' (m)	ECou
§ ***complexa***	CBcs CDoC CHEx CHll CTrC CTri CWib EBee ECou EPfP EPla EShb LRHS MCCP NSti SAPC SArc SEND SLim SLon SPer SWvt WCFE WPGP WSHC
- (f)	ECou
- 'Nana'	see *M. axillaris* Walp.
- 'Spotlight'PBR (v) new	EShb
- var. ***trilobata***	CHEx CPen CTrC EBee EPla GCal SSta WDyG
- 'Ward' (m)	ECou
ephedroides	ECou
- 'Clarence Pass'	ECou
* - var. ***muricatula***	ECou
gunnii	ECou
platyclados	see *Homalocladium platycladum*

Muhlenbergia (*Poaceae*)

capillaris	CKno IMou SBch SHDw
dumosa	CKno IMou
japonica 'Cream Delight' (v)	EHoe EPPr LEdu SBch SHDw
lindheimeri	WCot
mexicana	EBee GFor LEdu
rigens	CKno SApp

Mukdenia (*Saxifragaceae*)

acanthifolia	CDes CLAP WCru
rossii	CDes CLAP EBee ELon EPla GCal IFro ITim LEdu NBid NLar NMyG SGSe SMac SMad WCom WCot WCru WPGP WPrP WThu WTin
- 'Crimson Fans'	see *M. rossii* 'Karasuba'
- dwarf	CDes CLAP GCal
§ - 'Karasuba'	CLAP EBee GEdr NBhm NMyG SGol
- 'Ōgon'	CLAP
- 'Shishiba'	GEdr
- variegated (v)	WWEG

mulberry see *Morus*

Murraya (*Rutaceae*)

exotica	see *M. paniculata*
koenigii	EOHP GPoy
§ ***paniculata***	EShb GPoy

Musa ✿ (*Musaceae*)

from Yunnan, China	see *M. itinerans* 'Yunnan'
§ ***acuminata***	MBri
§ - 'Dwarf Cavendish' (AAA Group) (F) ♀H1	CAbb EAmu ELan EPfP EShb LRHS NLar NScw SPer SPlb XBlo
- 'Grand Nain'	EAmu
× ***acuminata*** 'Zebrina'	
- 'Williams' (AAA Group) (F)	EAmu
- 'Zebrina' ♀H1+3	CDTJ EAmu EShb XBlo
balbisiana	EAmu SBst
basjoo ♀H3-4	Widely available
I - 'Rubra'	CCCN EAmu ESwi LRHS NScw
cavendishii	see *M. acuminata* 'Dwarf Cavendish'
§ ***coccinea*** ♀H1	XBlo
'Darjeeling Giant' new	NExo
ensete	see *Ensete ventricosum*
'Helen'	EAmu ETod LPJP WCot
hookeri	see *M. sikkimensis*
* ***iterans glaucum***	CDTJ
itinerans new	NExo WCot
§ - 'Yunnan'	EAmu
lasiocarpa	CBct CDTJ CDoC CHEx CHll CMHG CWit EAmu EShb ETod LRHS MBri NPal NScw SBch SBig SBst SPlb WCot WGwG
mannii	EAmu
nana misapplied	see *M. acuminata* 'Dwarf Cavendish'
nana Lour.	see *M. acuminata*
ornata ♀H1	CCCN XBlo
× ***paradisiaca*** 'Ney Poovan' (AB Group) (F)	CCCN EAmu
- 'Orinoco' (ABB Group) (F)	EAmu
- 'Rajapuri' (AAB Group) (F)	EAmu
siamensis 'Thai Gold' new	EAmu
§ ***sikkimensis***	CDTJ CDoC EAmu ELan ETod EWes LPJP NExo SBig SBst SChr WFar XBlo
- 'Red Tiger'	CCCN CDTJ CDoC EAmu
'Tandarra Red'	CAbb CDoC CWit LSou
'Tropicana'	XBlo
uranoscopus misapplied	see *M. coccinea*
velutina ♀H1+3	CCCN CDoC EAmu NExo SBig SBst

Muscari ✿ (*Hyacinthaceae*)

PF	NWCA
'Aleyna'	ECho NMin
ambrosiacum	see *M. muscarimi*
anatolicum	EBrs ECho

armeniacum 🏆H4	CBro CHid CTri EBrs ECho EGoo EPfP ERos LRHS MBri MCot SRms WCot WFar WShi
- 'Argaei Album'	EBrs ECho EPot GAuc LAma
- 'Atlantic'	EBrs ECho ERCP LRHS
- 'Blue Pearl'	EBrs ECho GKev LRHS
- 'Blue Spike' (d)	CBro EBla EBrs ECho EPfP ERCP LAma LRHS MBri NBir NEgg SPer WCot WFar WGwG
- 'Cantab'	EBrs ECho GKev
- 'Christmas Pearl' 🏆H4	EBrs ECho GKev SPhx WCot
- 'Côte d'Azur' **new**	LRHS
- 'Dark Eyes'	CStu EBrs ECho EPfP LRHS SMrm SPer WFar WHil
- 'Early Giant'	ECho
- 'Fantasy Creation'	EBla EBrs ECho EPot LRHS WBrk
- 'Gul' **new**	WCot
- 'Heavenly Blue'	ECho
- 'New Creation'	ECho
- 'Peppermint'	ECho ERCP LRHS NMin SPhx WCot
- 'Saffier' 🏆H4	EBrs ECho LAma SPhx WCot
- 'Valerie Finnis'	Widely available
* ***auchadra***	ERos
aucheri 🏆H4	ECho ERos LAma NRya
* - var. ***bicolor***	WCot
- 'Blue Magic'	CBro EBrs ECho EPot
- 'Ocean Magic'	ECho ERCP
§ - 'Tubergenianum'	EBrs ECho
- 'White Magic'	CAvo ECho ERCP WCot
§ ***azureum*** 🏆H4	CAvo CBgR CBro CFFs EBrs ECho ELan EPfP ERos GMaP LAma LEdu LRHS NMen NWCA SPhx WCot
- 'Album'	CBgR CSsd EBla EBrs ECho EGoo ERos LAma LRHS SPhx WBrk WCot
'Baby's Breath'	see *M.* 'Jenny Robinson'
'Big Smile' **new**	WCot
'Blue Dream'	EBrs ECho
'Blue Eyes'	EBrs ECho WCot
'Blue Star'	CHid EBrs ECho LRHS
botryoides	EBrs ECho ERos LAma LEdu
- 'Album'	CAvo CBro CFFs CTri EBla EBrs ECho EPfP LAma LRHS MBri NChi SMrm SPer SRms WBor WCot WShi
caucasicum	ECho ERos WCot
chalusicum	see *M. pseudomuscari*
commutatum	WWst
Hoa 0130 **new**	
§ ***comosum***	CArn CBgR CBro EBrs ECho EPfP LEdu LRHS MWea NEgg SMrm WCot
* - 'Album'	ECho
- 'Monstrosum'	see *M. comosum* 'Plumosum'
- 'Pinard'	EBrs ECho ERos WWst
§ - 'Plumosum'	CAvo CFFs EBla EBrs ECho EPfP EPot LAma LEdu LRHS MBri SBch WAul WCot WHil
'Cupido' **new**	ECho
dionysicum	EBrs ECho
- HOA 8965	EBee WCot WWst
discolor **new**	WWst
grandifolium	ECho ERos
- JCA 689.450	WCot
- var. ***populeum***	ERos
inconstrictum	ECho WWst
'Ivor's Pink' **new**	WCot
§ 'Jenny Robinson' 🏆H4	CMil EBla ECho EHrv IFoB SCnR SMad WCot
latifolium 🏆H4	CBgR CBro EBla EBrs ECho EPfP EPot ERCP GAuc GGar LAma LRHS MBel MWat NChi NEgg SBch SGSe SMrm SPer SPhx WBor WClo WCot WTin
* - 'Blue Angels'	NBir
§ ***macrocarpum***	CAvo CBro CStu EBee EBrs ECha ECho EPot ERos GAuc LAma WAbe WCot
- 'Golden Fragrance'PBR	CBgR CHid CMil CPom EBrs ECho EPot ERCP IFoB LRHS MCot MNrw MWea WCot WHil
mirum	ECho
moschatum	see *M. muscarimi*
'Mount Hood'	EBla EBrs ECho ERCP MWea
§ ***muscarimi***	CAvo CBro CStu EBrs ECho ERCP IFoB LAma LEdu NWCA WCot
- var. ***flavum***	see *M. macrocarpum*
§ ***neglectum***	CMea CSsd EBrs ECho ERos ITim LAma SEND WCot WShi WWst
pallens	EBrs ECho ERos LRHS NMin NWCA WCot
paradoxum	see *Bellevalia paradoxa*
parviflorum	EBrs ECho ERos WWst
§ ***pseudomuscari*** 🏆H4	EBrs ECho ERos WCot
racemosum	see *M. neglectum*
'Sky Blue'	EBrs ECho LRHS WCot
'Sky Magic' **new**	LRHS
§ ***spreitzenhoferi***	EBrs ECho ERos
- Hoa 0119	WWst
- Hoa 0120	WWst
'Superstar'	EBrs ECho LEdu WCot
§ ***tenuiflorum***	ECho WCot
tubergenianum	see *M. aucheri* 'Tubergenianum'
weissii	ERos
'White Beauty'	ECho

Muscarimia (*Hyacinthaceae*)

ambrosiacum	see *Muscari muscarimi*
macrocarpum	see *Muscari macrocarpum*

Musella see *Musa*

Mussaenda (*Rubiaceae*)

'Tropic Snow'	CCCN

Musschia (*Campanulaceae*)

wollastonii	ECre

Mutisia (*Asteraceae*)

'Glendoick'	GGGa
latifolia	GKev
retusa	see *M. spinosa* var. *pulchella*
§ ***spinosa*** var. ***pulchella***	GGal

Myoporum (*Myoporaceae*)

debile	see *Eremophila debilis*
laetum	CHEx CPLG CTrC

Myosotidium (*Boraginaceae*)

§ ***hortensia***	Widely available
nobile	see *M. hortensia*

Myosotis (*Boraginaceae*)

§ ***alpestris***	EBee
- 'Ruth Fischer'	NBir NMen
* ***aquatica***	NSco
arvensis	SECG
australis	CSpr NWCA
capitata	ECou EWTr
colensoi	ECou NMen NWCA
explanata	NMen
macrantha	GBin
My Oh My = 'Myomark' **new**	LSou
palustris	see *M. scorpioides*
pulvinaris	ECou WAbe
rakiura	EPPr SBch

	rupicola	see *M. alpestris*
§	***scorpioides***	CBen CRow CWat EBWF EHon EMFW EPfP LPBA MSKA NMir SCoo SPer SPlb SRms SWat WBrk WMAq WMoo WPnP
	- 'Alba'	LPBA MSKA SPer
	- 'Ice Pearl'	CBen ECha
	- Maytime = 'Blaqua' (v)	NBir SPer
	- 'Mermaid'	CBen CRow CWat ECha EHon EMFW EPfP LLWG LPBA SBch SDix SWat WPer WPnP
	- 'Pinkie'	CWat EMFW LPBA SWat
	- 'Snowflakes'	CWat EMFW SWat
	- variegated (v)	MSKA
	sylvatica	CRWN EBWF NMir
	- 'Ultramarine' ♀H4	GJos
	- 'Victoria Blue' (Victoria Series) **new**	NBlu
	'Unforgettable' (v)	CBow NBro NCob

Myrceugenia (*Myrtaceae*)

	ovata	CTrG
	planipes	CTrG

Myrica (*Myricaceae*)

	californica	LEdu NLar
	cerifera	CArn MBri NLar
	gale	CAgr CRWN EMil GPoy GQue MBri MCoo MGos NLar SWat WDin WFar WSpi
	pensylvanica	GAuc LEdu MBri NLar

Myricaria (*Tamaricaceae*)

	germanica	NLar

Myriophyllum (*Haloragaceae*)

	propinquum	EMFW
*	'Red Stem'	LPBA
	spicatum	EHon EMFW NSco WMAq
	verticillatum	CWat EHon SCoo

Myrrhidendron (*Apiaceae*)

	glaucescens B&SWJ 10699	WCru

Myrrhis (*Apiaceae*)

	odorata	Widely available
	- 'Forncett Chevron'	GCal LEdu

Myrsine (*Myrsinaceae*)

	africana	CWib EBee IDee
	aquilonia	ECou
	divaricata	CTrC ECou
	nummularia	WThu

Myrteola (*Myrtaceae*)

§	***nummularia***	ISea NMen WThu

Myrtus (*Myrtaceae*)

	apiculata	see *Luma apiculata*
	bullata	see *Lophomyrtus bullata*
	chequen	see *Luma chequen*
	communis ♀H3	Widely available
	- 'Flore Pleno' (d)	ELau EOHP
	- 'Jenny Reitenbach'	see *M. communis* subsp. *tarentina*
	- 'Microphylla'	see *M. communis* subsp. *tarentina*
	- 'Nana'	see *M. communis* subsp. *tarentina*
	- 'Pyewood Park' **new**	WJek
§	- subsp. ***tarentina*** ♀H3	CBcs CBgR CDoC CDul CEnt CMac CSBt CWib EBee ELau EPfP EShb GBar LEdu LHop LRHS MBlu MHer MNHC MRav NGHP SBch SPer SPoG STre SWvt WBrE WDin WFar WPGP
	- - 'Compacta'	LRHS NLar
	- - 'Microphylla Variegata' (v)	CBcs GBar GQui MHer MNHC NGHP SBch SPer STre WJek
I	- - 'Variegata'	EOHP EPfP EPla
	- 'Tricolor'	see *M. communis* 'Variegata'
§	- 'Variegata' (v)	CArn CBot CMCN CMac CSBt CTri CWib EBee ELan ELau EPfP GBar LEdu LHop LRHS MAsh MHer MSwo SAga SBch SPer SPoG STre WBVN WBrE WCFE WClo WFar WMoo WSHC
	dulcis	see *Austromyrtus dulcis*
	'Glanleam Gold'	see *Luma apiculata* 'Glanleam Gold'
	lechleriana	see *Amomyrtus luma*
	luma	see *Luma apiculata*
	nummularia	see *Myrteola nummularia*
*	***paraguayensis***	CTrC
	× ***ralphii***	see *Lophomyrtus* × *ralphii*
	'Traversii'	see *Lophomyrtus* × *ralphii* 'Traversii'
	ugni	see *Ugni molinae*
*	***variegata*** 'Penlee' (v)	CTrG

N

Nananthus (*Aizoaceae*)

	vittatus	WAbe

Nandina (*Berberidaceae*)

	domestica ♀H3	Widely available
	- B&SWJ 4923	WCru
	- B&SWJ 11113	WCru
	- 'Fire Power' ♀H3	Widely available
	- 'Gulf Stream'	CBcs
	- 'Harbor Dwarf'	CEnd EBee WFar
	- var. ***leucocarpa***	NLar
	- 'Nana'	see *N. domestica* 'Pygmaea'
	- 'Nana Purpurea'	GCal
	- 'Orhime'	NLar
§	- 'Pygmaea'	CMen WDin
	- 'Richmond'	CAlb CBcs CEnd EBee ELan EPfP IFFs LAst LRHS MAsh MGos NLar NVic SBod SLim SPer SPoG SRkn SWvt WCFE WFar WPat
	- 'Wood's Dwarf'	LRHS MGos

Nannorrhops (*Arecaceae*)

	ritchiana	LPal

Napaea (*Malvaceae*)

	dioica	WCot

Narcissus ✿ (*Amaryllidaceae*)

	'Abalone' (2)	EWal
	'Abba' (4) ♀H4	CQua LRHS
	'Aberfoyle' (2) ♀H4	NMin
	'Abstract' (11a)	CQua
	'Accent' (2) ♀H4	CQua
	'Accomplice' (3)	IRhd
	'Achduart' (3)	CQua EWal
	'Achentoul' (4)	CQua
	'Achnasheen' (3)	CQua NMin
	'Acropolis' (4)	CQua EBrs EPfP EWal
	'Actaea' (9) ♀H4	CBro CQua EBrs ECho LRHS MBri
	'Acumen' (2)	CQua
	'Admiration' (8)	CQua
	'Advocat' (3)	CQua
	'African Sunset' (3)	IRhd

Name	Suppliers
'Agnes Mace' (2)	IRhd
'Ahwahnee' (2)	CQua IRhd
'Ainley' (2)	CQua
'Aintree' (3)	CQua
'Aircastle' (3)	CQua EWal
'Akepa' (5)	CQua
'Albatross' (3)	CQua
I ***albidus***	ERos
subsp. ***occidentalis*** (13)	
'Albus Plenus Odoratus'	see *N. poeticus* 'Plenus' ambig.
'Alpine Winter' (1)	IRhd
'Alston' (2)	IRhd
'Alto' (2)	IRhd
'Altruist' (3)	CQua ERCP EWal
'Altun Ha' (2)	CQua EWal IRhd
'Amazing Grace' (2)	IRhd
'Amber Castle' (2)	CQua
'Ambergate' (2)	CQua EBrs EWal LAma
'Amberglow' (2)	EWal
'American Heritage' (1)	CQua IRhd
'American Robin' (6)	CQua
'American Shores' (1)	CQua IRhd
'Amor' (3)	EWal
'Amstel' (4)	CQua
'Andalusia' (6)	ERos
'Angel' (3)	CQua NMin
'Angel Eyes' (a)	EBrs
'Angel Face' (3)	CQua IRhd
'Angelito' (3) ♀H4	IRhd
Angel's tears	see *N. triandrus* subsp. *triandrus* var. *triandrus*
'Angel's Wings' (2)	CQua
'Angkor' (4)	CQua
'An-gof' (7)	CQua
'Ann Sonia' (4) **new**	IRhd
'Anna Panna' (3) **new**	IRhd
'Apotheose' (4)	CQua EWal LRHS
'Applins' (2)	IRhd
'Apricot' (1)	CBro
'Apricot Blush' (2)	CQua
'April Love' (1)	CQua
'April Snow' (2)	CBro CQua
'April Tears' (5) ♀H4	NMin
'Aranjuez' (2)	CQua
'Arcady' (2)	EWal
'Arctic Gem' (3)	CQua
'Arctic Gold' (1) ♀H4	CQua LAma
'Ardress' (2)	CQua
'Argosy' (1)	CQua
'Arid Plains' (3)	IRhd
'Arish Mell' (5)	CQua
'Arkle' (1) ♀H4	CQua EWal
'Arleston' (2)	IRhd
'Armidale' (3)	IRhd
'Armoury' (4)	CQua
'Arndilly' (2)	CQua
'Arpege' (2)	CQua
'Arran Isle' (2)	IRhd
'Arthurian' (1)	IRhd
'Articol' (11a)	CQua
'Arwenack' (11a)	CQua
'Ashmore' (2)	CQua IRhd
'Ashton Wold' (2)	CQua
'Asila' (2)	IRhd
'Assertion' (2)	IRhd
§ ***assoanus*** (13)	CBro CQua EBrs ECho EPot ERos LAma MSSP NMen NMin WWst
'Astropink' (11a)	CQua
§ ***asturiensis*** (13) ♀H3-4	CSam ECho MNrw NMin
- 'Navarre' (I)	WCot
asturiensis × ***cyclamineus***	NMen
'Atricilla' (11a)	IRhd
'Attrus' (2)	EWal
'Auchrannie' (2)	IRhd
'Audubon' (2)	CQua EWal
'Auntie Eileen' (2)	CQua
'Auspicious' (2)	IRhd
'Autumn Gold' (7)	EBrs
'Avalanche' (8) ♀H3	CQua EBrs EWal LRHS NMin
'Avalanche of Gold' (8)	CQua
'Avalon' (2)	CQua EWal
'Azocor' (1)	IRhd
'Baby Boomer' (7) **new**	NMin
'Baby Moon' (7)	CQua EBrs EPfP EPot GEdr GKev LAma LEdu LRHS LSou MBri NHol NMin
'Badanloch' (3)	CQua
'Badbury Rings' (3) ♀H4	CQua
'Bala' (4)	CQua
'Balalaika' (2)	CQua
'Baldock' (4)	CQua
'Ballinamallard' (3)	IRhd
'Ballydorn' (9)	IRhd
'Ballygarvey' (1)	CQua EWal
'Ballygowan' (3)	IRhd
'Ballyrobert' (1)	CQua
'Baltic Shore' (3)	IRhd
'Balvenie' (2)	CQua
'Bambi' (1)	ERos
'Bandesara' (3)	CQua IRhd
'Bandit' (2)	CQua
'Bandleader' (2)	EWal
'Banker' (2)	CQua
'Banstead Village' (2)	CQua
'Bantam' (2) ♀H4	CBro CQua ERos EWal NMin
'Barbary Gold' (2)	CQua
'Barleythorpe' (1)	EWal
'Barlow' (6)	CQua
'Barnesgold' (1)	IRhd
'Barnham' (1)	CQua
'Barnsdale Wood' (2)	CQua
'Barnum' (1) ♀H4	IRhd
'Barrett Browning' (3)	EBla EBrs LRHS
'Barrii' (3)	CQua
'Bartley' (6)	CQua EWal
'Bath's Flame' (3)	CQua IHer WShi
'Bear Springs' (4)	IRhd
'Beautiful Dream' (3)	CQua
'Bebop' (7)	CBro
'Bedruthan' (2)	CQua
'Beefeater' (2)	EWal
'Beersheba' (1)	CQua EBrs
'Beige Beauty' (3)	EWal
'Belbroughton' (2)	CQua
'Belcanto' (11a)	CQua
'Belfast Lough' (1)	IRhd
'Bell Rock' (1)	CQua
'Bell Song' (7)	CAvo CBro CFFs CQua EBrs EPfP ERCP ERos EWal LRHS LSou NHol
'Belzone' (2)	CQua
'Ben Aligin' (1)	CQua
'Ben Hee' (2) ♀H4	CQua
'Berceuse' (2)	CQua IRhd
'Bere Ferrers' (4)	CQua
'Bergerac' (11a)	CQua
'Berlin' (2)	ERos EWal
'Bernardino' (2)	CQua
'Beryl' (6)	CBro CQua EBrs ECho ERos EWal LRHS NMin
'Best Seller' (1)	SPer
'Bethal' (3)	CQua
'Betsy MacDonald' (6)	CQua
'Biffo' (4)	CQua

* 'Big Cycla' (6) **new** ECho
'Bikini Beach' (2) IRhd
'Bilbo' (6) CBro CQua
'Binkie' (2) CBro CQua EWal LRHS
'Birchwood' (3) CQua
'Birdsong' (3) CQua
'Birma' (3) EWal LAma
'Bishops Light' (2) CQua
'Blair Athol' (2) CQua
'Blarney' (3) CQua EWal
'Blessing' (2) EWal
'Blisland' (9) CQua
'Blossom' (4) CQua
'Blushing Lady' (7) EBrs
'Blushing Maiden' (4) CQua
'Bob Spotts' (2) CQua
'Bobbysoxer' (7) CBro CQua ERos MTho
'Bobolink' (2) CQua
'Bodelva' (2) CQua
'Bodwannick' (2) CQua EWal
'Bold Prospect' (1) CQua
'Bolton' (7) CBro
'Bon Viveur' (11a) IRhd
'Border Beauty' (2) ♀^{H4} LRHS
'Bosbigal' (11a) CQua
'Boscastle' (7) CQua
'Boscoppa' (11a) CQua
'Boslowick' (11a) ♀^{H4} CQua
'Bosmeor' (2) CQua
'Bossa Nova' (3) CQua
'Bossiney' (11a) CQua
'Bosvale' (11a) CQua
'Bosvigo' (11a) CQua
'Bouzouki' (2) IRhd
'Bowles's Early Sulphur' (1) CRow
'Boyne Bridge' (1) IRhd
'Brackenhurst' (2) **new** EWal
'Brandaris' (11a) CQua
'Bravoure' (1) ♀^{H4} CQua EWal
'Brentswood' (8) CQua
'Bridal Crown' (4) ♀^{H4} EBrs EPfP EWal LAma LRHS SPer
'Bright Flame' (2) CQua
'Bright Spot' (8) CQua
'Brindaleena' (2) IRhd
'Brindle Pink' (2) IRhd
'Broadland' (2) CQua
'Broadway Star' (11b) EBrs EWal LAma
'Brodick' (3) CQua IRhd
'Bronzewing' (1) IRhd
'Brookdale' (1) CQua
'Brooke Ager' (2) ♀^{H4} IRhd
'Broomhill' (2) ♀^{H4} CQua
broussonetii (13) EBrs ECho
'Bryanston' (2) ♀^{H4} CQua
'Budock Bells' (5) CQua
'Budock Water' (2) CQua
'Buffawn' (7) EWal
'Bugle Major' (2) CQua
bulbocodium (13) ♀$^{H3-4}$ CBro CStu EBrs ITim LBee LEdu LRHS NWCA SBch SMrm SPer SRms
- from Atlas Mountains, Morocco MSSP
§ - subsp. ***bulbocodium*** (13) CBro LPio
§ - - var. ***citrinus*** (13) LPio SSpi
- - var. ***conspicuus*** (13) CArn CBro CHar CPMA CQua EBrs ECho EPfP EPot ERCP ERos GEdr LAma LRHS MSSP NMen NMin NRya SBch SGar WCot
* - - ***filifolius*** (13) CBro
§ - - var. ***graellsii*** (13) NSla
- - var. ***nivalis*** (13) EBrs ECho ERos WWst
- - var. ***pallidus*** (13) ERos GEdr
§ - - var. ***tenuifolius*** (13) EPot NMen
- var. ***filifolius*** **new** MSSP
§ - Golden Bells Group (10) CAvo CBro CHid CMea CQua CSam CSsd CWCL EBrs ECho EPot EWal GKev GKir GMaP LRHS MBri NHol
- var. ***mesatlanticus*** see *N. romieuxii* subsp. *romieuxii* var. *mesatlanticus*
- subsp. ***praecox*** (13) ECho LRHS WCot
- - var. ***paucinervis*** (13) EBrs ECho
- subsp. ***tananicus*** see *N. cantabricus* subsp. *tananicus*
I - subsp. ***viriditubus*** (13) ERos
- subsp. ***vulgaris*** see *N. bulbocodium* subsp. *bulbocodium*
bulbocodium* × *romieuxii WCot
'Bullseye' (3) EWal
'Bunchie' (5) CQua
'Bunclody' (2) CQua
'Bunting' (7) ♀^{H4} CQua
'Burning Bush' (3) IRhd
'Burntollet' (1) CQua
'Burravoe' (1) CQua
'Busselton' (3) IRhd
'Buster' (2) EWal
'Butterscotch' (2) CQua
'By George!' (2) EBrs
'By Jove' (1) EWal
'C.J. Backhouse' (2) CQua
'Cabernet' (2) IRhd
'Cacatua' (11a) IRhd
'Cadgwith' (2) CQua
'Cairntoul' (3) CQua
'Calabar' (2) EWal
'Calamansack' (2) CQua
calcicola (13) ERos
I - 'Idol' EPot NMin
'California Rose' (4) CQua IRhd
'Camelford' (2) EWal
'Camelot' (2) ♀^{H4} CQua EPfP EWal SPer
'Cameo Angel' (2) CQua
'Cameo King' (2) CQua
'Camoro' (10) MSSP NMen
'Campernelli Plenus' see *N.* × *odorus* 'Double Campernelle'
'Campion' (9) CQua IRhd
'Canaliculatus' (8) CArn CBro CQua EBrs ECho EPfP ERos LAma LRHS MBri SPer WGwG
canaliculatus Gussone see *N. tazetta* subsp. *lacticolor*
'Canary' (7) CQua
'Canarybird' (8) CQua LRHS WShi
'Canasta' (11a) CQua
'Candida' (4) EWal
'Canisp' (2) CQua
'Cantabile' (9) ♀^{H4} CQua
cantabricus (13) EBrs ECho WWst
- subsp. ***cantabricus*** (13) ERos LPio NMin NRya
- - var. ***foliosus*** (13) ♀^{H2} EBrs ECho EPot NMen SCnR WCot
- - var. ***petunioides*** (13) ECho
- subsp. ***monophyllus*** (13) **new** WWst
§ - subsp. ***tananicus*** (13) ECho EPot
cantabricus* × *romieuxii (13) LPio
'Canticle' (9) IRhd
'Capax Plenus' see *N.* 'Eystettensis'
'Cape Cornwall' (2) CQua
'Cape Helles' (3) IRhd
'Cape Point' (2) IRhd
'Capisco' (3) CQua
'Caramba' (2) CQua
'Carbineer' (2) CQua

'Carclew' (6)	CQua
'Cardiff' (2)	CQua
'Cardinham' (3)	CQua
'Cargreen' (9)	CQua
'Carib Gipsy' (2) Υ^{H4}	CQua EWal IRhd
'Caribbean Snow' (2)	CQua
'Carlton' (2) Υ^{H4}	CQua EBrs EPfP LAma LRHS
'Carnearny' (3)	CQua
'Carnkeeran' (2)	CQua
'Carnkief' (2)	CQua
'Carnyorth' (11a)	CQua
'Caro Nome' (2)	EWal
'Carole Lombard' (3)	CQua
'Carrara' (3)	EWal
'Carwinion' (2)	CQua
'Cassata' (11a)	EBrs EPfP EWal LAma NBir
'Castanets' (8)	IRhd
'Casterbridge' (2)	CQua IRhd
'Catalyst' (2)	IRhd
'Catistock' (2)	CQua
'Causeway Sunset' (2)	IRhd
'Causeway Sunshine' (1) **new**	IRhd
'Cavalryman' (3)	IRhd
'Caye Chapel' (3)	CQua
'Cazique' (6)	CQua
× ***cazorlanus*** (13)	MSSP
'Ceasefire' (2)	IRhd
'Cedar Hills' (3)	CQua
'Cedric Morris' (1)	CLAP ECha EHrv GBuc
'Celestial Fire' (2)	CQua
'Celtic Gold' (2)	CQua
'Centannées' (11b)	EBrs
'Centrefold' (3)	CQua
'Ceylon' (2) Υ^{H4}	EWal
'Cha-cha' (6)	CBro CQua
'Changing Colors' (11a)	EWal
'Chanson' (1) Υ^{H4}	IRhd
'Chanterelle' (11a)	EBla EWal LAma
'Chantilly' (2)	CQua
'Chapman's Peak' (2)	IRhd
'Charity May' (6) Υ^{H4}	CQua
'Charleston' (2)	CQua
'Charter' (2) Υ^{H4}	EWal
'Chasseur' (2)	IRhd
'Chaste' (1)	CQua IRhd
'Chat' (7)	CQua
'Cheer Leader' (3)	CQua
'Cheerfulness' (4) Υ^{H4}	CAvo CFFs CMea CQua EBrs EWal LAma LRHS MBri
'Cheesewring' (3)	CQua
'Cheetah' (1)	CQua IRhd
'Chelsea Girl' (2)	CQua
'Cheltenham' (2)	CQua
'Chenoweth' (2)	CQua
'Chérie' (7)	CQua
'Cherish' (2)	CQua
'Cherry Glow' (3)	IRhd
'Cherrygardens' (2)	CQua IRhd
'Chesapeake Bay' (1)	CQua
'Chesterton' (9) Υ^{H4}	CQua
'Chickadee' (6)	CBro CQua
'Chickerell' (3)	CQua
'Chief Inspector' (1)	IRhd
'Chiloquin' (1)	CQua
'China Doll' (2)	CQua
'Chinchilla' (2)	CQua IRhd
'Chingah' (1)	IRhd
'Chinita' (8)	CBro CQua EWal LRHS
'Chipper' (5)	CBro NMin
'Chit Chat' (7) Υ^{H4}	CBro CQua EBrs EPot ERos LRHS NMin
'Chiva' **new**	CBro LRHS
'Chivalry' (1)	EWal
'Chobe River' (1)	IRhd
'Chorus Line' (8)	IRhd
'Chromacolor' (2) Υ^{H4} **new**	LRHS
'Churston Ferrers' (4)	CQua
'Chy Noweth' (2)	CQua
'Chysauster' (2)	CQua
'Cisticola' (3)	IRhd
citrinus	see *N. bulbocodium* subsp. *bulbocodium* var. *citrinus*
'Citron' (3)	CQua
'Citronita' (3)	CQua
'Clare' (7)	CBro CQua IRhd NMin
'Claverley' (2)	CQua
'Clearbrook' (2)	CQua
'Clockface' (3)	EWal
'Cloud Nine' (2)	CBro
'Clouded Yellow' (2)	CQua IRhd
'Clouds Rest' (2)	IRhd
'Codlins and Cream'	see *N.* 'Sulphur Phoenix'
'Coldbrook' (2)	CQua
'Colin's Joy' (2)	CQua
'Coliseum' (2)	IRhd
'Colleen Bawn'	CAvo CQua EBrs NMin
'Colley Gate' (3)	CQua
'Colliford' (2)	CQua EWal
'Colorama' (11a)	CQua
'Colourful' (2)	IRhd
'Columbus' (2)	CQua
'Colville' (9)	CQua
'Comal' (1)	CQua
'Compressus'	see *N.* × *intermedius* 'Compressus'
'Compton Court' (3)	IRhd
concolor	see *N. triandrus* subsp. *triandrus* var. *concolor*
'Conestoga' (2)	CQua IRhd
'Congress' (11a)	CQua EWal
'Conowingo' (11a)	CQua
'Conspicuus' ambig.	CQua LAma
'Content' (1)	CQua
'Cool Autumn' (2)	CQua
'Cool Crystal' (3)	CQua
'Cool Evening' (11a)	CQua IRhd
'Cool Pink' (2)	CQua
'Cool Shades' (2)	CQua
'Coolmaghery' (2)	IRhd
'Coombe Creek' (6)	CQua
'Copper Nob' (2)	IRhd
'Copper Rings' (3)	CQua
'Copperfield' (2)	CQua
'Coquille' (2)	EWal
'Cora Ann' (7)	CBro
'Coral Fair' (2)	CQua
'Corbiere' (1)	CQua IRhd
'Corbridge' (2)	EWal
cordubensis (13)	CBro EBrs ECho GEdr
'Cornet' (6)	CQua
'Cornish Chuckles' (12) Υ^{H4}	CBgR CBro CQua
'Cornish Sun' (2)	CQua
'Cornish Vanguard' (2) Υ^{H4}	CQua
'Cornsilk' (11a)	CQua
'Coroboree'	IRhd
'Corofin' (3)	CQua
'Coromandel' (2)	IRhd
'Corozal' (3)	CQua
'Cosmic Dance' (3)	IRhd
'Cotinga' (6)	CQua EBrs EWal NMin
'Countdown' (2)	CQua
'Coverack Glory' (2)	CQua

Name	Suppliers
'Crackington' (4) 🏆H4	CQua IRhd
'Cragford' (8)	EWal
'Craig Stiel' (2)	CQua
'Craigywarren' (2)	EWal
'Creag Dubh' (2)	CQua
'Creed' (6)	CQua
'Crenver' (3)	CQua
'Crevenagh' (2)	IRhd
'Crewenna' (1)	CQua
'Crill' (7)	CQua
'Crimson Chalice' (3)	CQua IRhd
'Crinoline' (2)	EWal
'Cristobal' (1)	CQua EWal NMin
'Crock of Gold' (1)	CQua EWal
'Croesus' (2)	CQua
'Crofty' (6)	CQua
'Croila' (2)	CQua
'Crowndale' (4)	CQua IRhd
'Crugmeer' (11a)	CQua
'Cryptic' (1)	CQua IRhd
'Crystal Star' (2)	CQua
cuatrecasasii (13)	ERos
- var. ***segimonensis*** (13)	LPio
'Cudden Point' (2)	CQua
'Cul Beag' (3)	CQua
'Culmination' (2)	CQua
'Cultured Pearl' (2)	CQua
'Curlew' (7)	CQua EBrs
'Curly' (2)	EBrs
cyclamineus (13) 🏆H4	CBro CDes CStu MAsh MSSP NMen SCnR SRms
'Cyclope' (1)	CQua
cypri (8)	CQua
'Cyros' (1)	CQua
'Dailmanach' (2)	CQua IRhd
'Dailmystic' (2)	IRhd
'Dalcharn' (2) **new**	NMin
'Dallas' (3)	CQua
'Dambuster' (4)	IRhd
'Damson' (2)	CQua
'Dan du Plessis' (8)	CQua
'Dancing Queen' (2)	IRhd
'Dardanelles' (2)	IRhd
'Dateline' (3)	CQua
'David Alexander' (1)	CQua
'David Mills' (2)	CQua
'Dawn Call' (2)	IRhd
'Dawn Mist' (2)	EWal
'Dawn of Spring' **new**	LRHS
'Dawn Run' (2)	IRhd
'Dawn Sky' (2)	CQua
'Daydream' (2) 🏆H3	CQua EBrs EWal
'Daymark' (8)	CQua
'Dayton Lake' (2)	CQua
'Debutante' (2)	CQua
'December Bride' (11a)	CQua
'Decision' (2)	IRhd
'Defence Corps' (1)	IRhd
'Delia' (6)	IRhd
'Dell Chapel' (3)	CQua
'Delnashaugh' (4)	CQua EBrs LAma NHol
'Delos' (3)	CQua
'Delphin Hill' (4)	IRhd
'Delta Flight' (6)	IRhd
'Demand' (2)	CQua
'Demeanour'	IRhd
'Demmo' (2)	CQua
'Dena' (3)	IRhd
'Denali' (1)	IRhd
'Derryboy' (3)	IRhd
'Descant' (1)	IRhd
'Desdemona' (2) 🏆H4	CQua EWal
'Desert Bells' (7)	CQua
'Desert Orchid' (2)	CQua
'Dewy Dell' (3)	IRhd
'Dick Wilden' (4)	EBla EBrs
'Dickcissel' (7) 🏆H4	CQua EBrs ERos
'Dignitary' (2) **new**	IRhd
'Dimity' (3)	CQua
'Dimple' (9)	CQua
'Dinkie' (3)	CBro
'Diversity' (11a)	IRhd
'Doctor Alex Fleming' (2)	EWal
'Doctor Hugh' (3) 🏆H4	CQua EWal IRhd NMin
'Doctor Jazz' (2)	CQua
'Doll Baby' (7) **new**	NMin
'Dolly Mollinger' (11b)	EBla EBrs
'Doombar' (1)	CQua
'Dora Allum' (2)	CQua
'Dorchester' (4)	CQua IRhd
'Double Fashion' (4)	EBrs EWal
double pheasant eye	see *N. poeticus* 'Plenus' ambig.
double Roman	see *N.* 'Romanus'
'Double Smiles' (4) **new**	LRHS
'Double White' (4)	CQua
'Doubleday' (4)	CQua IRhd
'Doublet' (4)	CQua
'Doubtful' (3)	CQua
'Dove Wings' (6) 🏆H4	CQua EWal
'Dover Cliffs' (2)	CQua
'Downlands' (3)	CQua
'Downpatrick' (1)	CQua
'Dragon Run' (2)	CQua
'Drama Queen' (11a)	IRhd
'Dream Castle' (3)	EWal
'Dream Catcher' (2)	IRhd
'Drumlin' (1) 🏆H4	IRhd
dubius (13)	CBro EBrs ECho EPot
'Duet' (4)	EWal
'Duiker' (6)	IRhd
'Dulcimer' (9)	CQua
'Dunadry Inn' (4)	IRhd
'Dunkeld' (2)	CQua
'Dunkery' (4)	CQua IRhd
'Dunley Hall' (3)	CQua IRhd
'Dunmurry' (1)	CQua
'Dunskey' (3)	CQua
'Dupli Kate' (4)	IRhd
'Dusky Lad' (2)	IRhd
'Dusky Maiden' (2)	IRhd
'Dutch Delight' (2)	IRhd
'Dutch Master' (1) 🏆H4	CQua EBrs EWal LAma LRHS SPer
'Dynamite' (2)	EWal
'Early Bride' (2)	CQua
'Early Flame' (2) **new**	LRHS
'Early Splendour' (8)	CQua
'Earthlight' (3)	CQua
'Easter Bonnet' (2)	EBla
'Easter Moon' (2)	CQua
'Eastern Dawn' (2)	CQua EWal
'Eastern Promise' (2)	CQua
'Eaton Song' (12) 🏆H4	CBro CQua
'Eddy Canzony' (2)	CQua
'Edenderry' (1)	IRhd
'Edgbaston' (2)	CQua
'Edge Grove' (2)	CQua
'Editor' (2) **new**	IRhd
'Edna Earl' (3)	EWal
'Edward Buxton' (3)	CQua LRHS
'Egard' (11a)	CQua EWal LRHS
'Egmont King' (2)	CQua
'Eland' (7)	CQua
'Elburton' (2)	CQua
'Electrus' (11a)	IRhd

Name	Suppliers
elegans (13)	CAvo EBrs ECho
'Elf' (2)	CBro CQua
'Elfin Gold' (6)	CQua IRhd
'Elizabeth Ann' (6)	CQua
'Elka' (1)	CAvo CBgR CBro CMea CQua NMin
'Ella D' (2)	CQua
'Ellen' (2)	LRHS
'Elphin' (4)	CQua
'Elrond' (2)	CQua
'Elven Lady' (2)	CQua
'Elvira' (8)	CQua
'Elysian Fields' (2)	EWal
'Emcys' (6)	NMin
'Emerald Pink' (3)	CQua
'Emily' (2)	CQua NMin
'Eminent' (3)	CQua EWal
'Emperor' (1)	CQua
'Emperor's Waltz' (6)	CQua IRhd
'Empress of Ireland' (1) 🏆H4	CQua EBrs EWal IHer IRhd
'English Caye' (1)	CQua
'Ensemble' (4)	CQua
'Enterprise' (4)	CQua
'Entrancement' (1)	EWal
'Epona' (3)	CQua
'Erlicheer' (4)	CQua EBrs LRHS
'Escapee' (2)	IRhd
'Estrella' (3)	CQua
'Ethereal Beauty' (2)	IRhd
'Ethos' (1)	IRhd
'Etincelante' (11a)	EBrs NMin
'Euryalus' (1)	CQua
'Eve Robertson' (2)	CQua
'Evendine' (2)	EWal
'Evening' (2)	CQua
'Evesham' (3)	IRhd
'Exemplar' (1)	EWal
'Exotic Beauty' (4)	EBrs EWal
'Eyeglass' (3)	IRhd
'Eyelet' (3)	IRhd
'Eype' (4)	IRhd
'Eyrie' (3)	IRhd
§ 'Eystettensis' (4)	CBro ECha ERos IBlr
'Fair Head' (9)	CQua
'Fair Prospect' (2)	CQua
'Fair William' (2)	CQua
'Fairgreen' (3)	CQua
'Fairlawns' (3)	CQua
'Fairmile' (3)	CQua
'Fairy Chimes' (5)	CBro CQua
'Fairy Footsteps' (3)	CQua IRhd
'Fairy Island' (3)	CQua
'Fairy Spell' (3)	IRhd
'Fairy Tale' (3)	CQua
'Falconet' (8) 🏆H4	CBro CQua EBrs EPfP ERos EWal LRHS SPer
'Falmouth Bay' (3)	CQua
'Falstaff' (2)	CQua
'Fanline' (11a)	CQua
'Far Country' (2)	CQua
I 'Fashion' (11b)	CQua
'Fashion Model' (2)	IRhd
'Fastidious' (2)	CQua
'Favourite' (2)	EWal
'February Gold' (6) 🏆H4	CAvo CBro CFFs EBrs EPfP EPot ERCP ERos EWal LAma LRHS MBri NBir SGar SPer SPhx SRms WShi
'February Silver' (6)	CBro EBrs EPot ERCP EWal LAma
'Feeling Lucky' (2) 🏆H4	EWal
'Felindre' (9)	CQua EWal
'Feline Queen' (1)	IRhd
'Feock' (3)	CQua
fernandesii (13)	CBro EBrs ECho ERos GEdr NMin SCnR WCot WThu
'Ferndown' (3)	CQua IRhd
'Ferral' (4) **new**	IRhd
'Festivity' (2)	EWal
'Ffion Hague' (11a) **new**	EWal LRHS
'ffitch's Folly' (2)	CQua
'Filly' (2)	EWal
'Filoli' (1)	CQua IRhd
'Finchcocks' (2)	CQua
'Fine Gold' (1)	CQua
'Fine Romance' (2)	CQua
'Finland' (2)	CQua
'Fiona Linford' (3) **new**	IRhd
'Fiona MacKillop' (2)	IRhd
'Fire Tail' (3)	CQua IHer WShi
'First Born' (6)	CQua
'First Formal' (3)	CQua
'Flambards Village' (4)	CQua LRHS
'Flirt' (6)	CQua
'Florida Manor' (3)	IRhd
'Flower Drift' (4)	EPfP
'Flower Record' (2)	LAma LRHS
'Flycatcher' (7)	CQua
'Flying Colours' (4)	IRhd
'Flying High' (3)	CQua
'Flying Saucer' (2)	EWal
'Foff's Way' (1)	CQua
'Foray' (2)	EWal
'Foresight' (1)	CQua
'Forge Mill' (2)	CQua
'Fort Knox' (1)	EWal
'Fortescue' (4) **new**	IRhd
'Fortissimo' (2)	EBrs
'Fortune' (2)	CQua EWal LAma LRHS MBri
'Fossie' (4)	CQua
'Foundling' (6) 🏆H4	CBro CQua EWal
'Foxhunter' (2)	CQua
'Fragrant Breeze' (2)	EBrs EWal
'Fragrant Rose' (2)	CQua EBrs EWal IRhd
'Francolin' (1)	IRhd
'Frank' (9)	IRhd
'Freedom Rings' (2)	CQua
'Freedom Stars' (11a) 🏆H4	IRhd
'Fresco' (11a)	IRhd
'Fresh Lime' (1)	CQua
'Fresno' (3)	IRhd
'Frigid' (3)	CQua
'Frogmore' (6)	CQua
'Front Royal' (2)	CQua
'Frosted Pink' (2)	IRhd
'Frostkist' (6)	CBro CQua
'Frosty Morn' (5) **new**	NMin
'Frou-frou' (4)	CQua
'Frozen Jade' (1)	CQua
'Fruit Cup' (7)	CQua EPfP LRHS
'Fuco' (1) **new**	NMin
'Full House'	EWal
'Fulwell' (4)	CQua
'Furbelow' (4)	CQua
'Furnace Creek' (2)	IRhd
'Fynbos' (3)	IRhd
gaditanus (13)	CBro ERos
'Galilee' (3)	EBrs
'Gamebird' (1)	IRhd
'Garden News' (3)	IRhd
'Garden Princess' (6)	CBro EBrs LRHS
'Garden Treasure' (2)	IRhd
'Gatecrasher' (1) **new**	IRhd
'Gay Cavalier' (4)	CQua
'Gay Kybo' (4) 🏆H4	CQua EWal NMin

'Gay Song' (4)	CQua
'Gay Time' (4)	EWal
gayi (13)	CQua WShi
'Geevor' (4)	CQua
'Gellymill' (2)	CQua
'Gemini Girl' (2)	CQua
'George Leak' (2)	CQua
'Georgie Girl' (6)	CQua
'Geranium' (8) $\mathbb{Y}^{H4}$	CBro CQua EBrs EPfP EWal LAma SPer
'Gettysburg' (2)	CQua
'Gigantic Star' (2)	EWal
'Gillan' (11a)	CQua
'Gin and Lime' (1) $\mathbb{Y}^{H4}$	CQua
'Gipsy Moon' (2)	CQua
'Gipsy Queen' (1)	CBgR CQua NMin
'Gironde' (11)	CQua
'Glacier' (1)	CQua
'Glen Cassley' (3)	CQua
'Glen Clova' (2)	CQua EWal
'Glendermott' (2)	CQua
'Glenside' (2)	CQua
'Glissando' (2)	CQua
'Gloriosus' (8)	CQua
'Glover's Reef' (1)	CQua
'Glowing Pheonix' (4)	CQua
'Glowing Red' (4)	CQua
'Goff's Caye' (2)	CQua IRhd
'Golant' (2)	CQua
'Gold Bond' (2)	CQua IRhd
'Gold Charm' (2)	CQua
'Gold Convention' (2) $\mathbb{Y}^{H4}$	CQua IRhd
'Gold Ingot' (2) $\mathbb{Y}^{H4}$	IRhd
'Gold Medal' (1)	EWal
'Gold Medallion' (1)	CQua
'Gold Top' (2)	CQua
'Golden Amber' (2)	CQua
'Golden Aura' (2) $\mathbb{Y}^{H4}$	CQua EWal
'Golden Bear' (4)	CQua
'Golden Bells'	see *N. bulbocodium* Golden Bells Group
'Golden Cheer' (2)	CQua
'Golden Cycle' (6)	CQua
'Golden Dawn' (8) $\mathbb{Y}^{H3}$	CQua EBrs EPfP LRHS
'Golden Ducat' (4)	CQua EWal LAma LRHS MBri NBir
'Golden Flute' (2)	IRhd
'Golden Gamble' (11a)	IRhd
'Golden Goal' (2) **new**	IRhd
'Golden Halo' (2)	CQua
'Golden Harvest' (1)	CQua EBrs LAma
'Golden Incense' (7)	CQua
'Golden Jewel' (2) $\mathbb{Y}^{H4}$	CQua
'Golden Joy' (2)	CQua
'Golden Lion' (1)	CQua EPfP SPer
'Golden Marvel' (1)	CQua
'Golden Orbit' (4)	CQua
'Golden Phoenix' (4)	CQua
'Golden Quince' (12)	CQua
'Golden Rain' (4)	CQua
'Golden Rapture' (1) $\mathbb{Y}^{H4}$	CQua
'Golden Riot' (1)	EWal
'Golden Sceptre' (7)	CBro
'Golden Sheen' (2)	CQua
'Golden Splash' (11a)	IRhd
'Golden Spur' (1)	CQua LAma
'Golden Torch' (2)	CQua
'Golden Vale' (1) $\mathbb{Y}^{H4}$	CQua
'Goldfinger' (1) $\mathbb{Y}^{H4}$	CQua IRhd NMin
'Goldhanger' (2)	CQua
'Goldsithney' (2)	CBro
'Golitha Falls' (2)	CQua
'Golly' (4)	EWal

'Good Fella' (2)	CQua
'Good Measure' (2)	CQua EWal
'Goonbell' (2)	CQua
'Gorran' (3)	CQua
'Gossamer' (3)	EWal
'Gossmoor' (4)	CQua
'Gouache' (2)	EWal
graellsii	see *N. bulbocodium* subsp. *bulbocodium* var. *graellsii*
'Grand Monarque'	see *N. tazetta* subsp. *lacticolor* 'Grand Monarque'
'Grand Opening' (4)	IRhd
'Grand Primo Citronière' (8)	CQua
'Grand Prospect' (2)	CQua
'Grand Soleil d'Or' (8)	CQua EBrs LAma LRHS NHol
'Great Expectations' (2)	CQua
'Greatwood' (1)	CQua
'Greek Surprise' (4) **new**	IRhd
'Green Gold' (2)	EWal
'Green Howard' (3)	EBrs ECho
'Green Lodge' (9)	IRhd
'Greenlet' (6)	CQua
'Greenodd' (3)	CQua
'Greenpark' (9)	IRhd
'Greenstar' (4)	EWal
'Grenoble' (2)	CQua
'Gresham' (4)	CQua IRhd
'Gribben Head' (4)	CQua
'Groundkeeper' (3)	IRhd
'Gulliver' (3)	CQua
'Gunwalloe' (11a)	CQua
'Guy Wilson' (2)	CQua
'Gwennap' (1)	CQua
'Gwinear' (2)	CQua
'Hacienda' (1)	CQua
'Half Moon Caye' (2)	CQua
'Halley's Comet' (3)	CQua IRhd
'Halloon' (3)	CQua
'Halvose' (8)	CBro
'Halzephron' (2)	CQua
'Hambledon' (2) $\mathbb{Y}^{H4}$	CQua EWal
'Hammoon' (3)	EWal
'Hampton Court' (2)	CQua
'Happy Dreams' (2)	IRhd
'Happy Fellow' (2)	CQua
'Happy Valley' (2)	IRhd
'Harbour View' (2)	IRhd
'Harmony Bells' (5)	CQua
'Harp Music' (2)	IRhd
'Harpers Ferry' (1)	CQua
'Hartlebury' (3)	CQua
'Hawangi' (3)	IRhd
'Hawera' (5) $\mathbb{Y}^{H4}$	CAvo CBro CFFs CHid CMea CQua EBrs EPfP EPot ERCP EWal LAma LEdu LRHS LSou MBri SPer WHal
'Heamoor' (4) $\mathbb{Y}^{H4}$	CQua
'Heart's Desire' (4)	EWal
hedraeanthus (13)	EBrs ECho EPot
'Helford Dawn' (2)	CQua
'Helford Sunset' (2)	CQua
'Helios' (2)	CQua
hellenicus	see *N. poeticus* var. *hellenicus*
henriquesii	see *N. jonquilla* var. *henriquesii*
'Henry Irving' (1)	CQua
'Hero' (1)	CQua EWal
'Hesla' (7)	CBro
'Heslington' (3)	CQua
'Hexameter' (9)	CQua
'Hexworthy' (3)	CQua
'Hibernian' (4)	IRhd
'Hicks Mill' (1)	CQua

'High Note' (7)	EWal
'High Society' (2) ♀H4	CQua EWal
'Highfield Beauty' (8) ♀H4	CQua EWal
'Highgrove' (1)	CQua
'Highlite' (2)	CQua
'Hilda's Pink' (2)	CQua
'Hill Head' (9)	IRhd
'Hillstar' (7) ♀H4	CQua EBrs LRHS
hispanicus (13)	EBrs ECho
'Hocus Pocus' (3)	IRhd
'Holiday Fashion' (2)	EWal
'Hollypark' (3)	IRhd
'Holme Fen' (2)	CQua
'Home Fires' (2)	CQua
'Homestead' (2) ♀H4	IRhd
'Honey Pink' (2)	CQua
'Honeybird' (1)	CQua EWal
'Honeyorange' (2)	IRhd
'Honolulu' (4)	EWal
'Hoopoe' (8) ♀H4	CBro CQua EBrs LRHS
'Hope' (4)	EWal
'Horace' (9)	CQua
'Horn of Plenty' (5)	CBgR CBro CQua EBrs
'Hornpipe' (1)	IRhd
'Hors d'Oeuvre' (8)	CBro
'Hospodar' (2)	CQua
'Hot Affair' (2) **new**	IRhd
'Hot Gossip' (2)	CQua
'Hotspur' (2)	CQua
'Hugh Town' (8)	CAvo CQua
'Hullabaloo' (2)	IRhd
humilis misapplied	see *N. pseudonarcissus* subsp. *pseudonarcissus* var. *humilis*
'Hunting Caye' (2)	CQua
'Huntley Down' (1)	CQua
'Ice Chimes' (5)	CQua
'Ice Dancer' (2)	CQua
'Ice Diamond' (4)	CQua
'Ice Follies' (2) ♀H4	CQua EBrs EWal LAma MBri NBir SPer
'Ice King' (4)	EBla EBrs EWal LRHS NBir
'Ice Wings' (5) ♀H4	CAvo CBro CFFs CQua EBrs EPot ERos EWal NMin WPtf WShi
'Idless' (1)	CQua
'Immaculate' (2)	CQua
'Inara' (4)	CQua
'Inbal' [PBR] (8)	EBrs
'Inca' (6)	CQua
'Inchbonnie' (2)	CQua
'Independence Day' (4)	CQua
'Indian Maid' (7) ♀H4	CQua IRhd
'Indora' (4)	CQua
'Inner Glow' (2)	IRhd
'Innisidgen' (8)	CQua
'Inny River' (1)	IRhd
'Interim' (2)	CQua
× ***intermedius*** (13)	CBro CQua ERos WAbe WCot
§ - 'Compressus' (8)	CQua
'Intrigue' (7) ♀H4	CQua EWal IRhd LRHS SPer
'Invercassley' (3)	CQua
'Ipi Tombi' (2)	EBrs ERos
'Ireland's Eye' (9)	CQua
'Irene Copeland' (4)	CQua EWal
'Irish Fire' (2)	CQua
'Irish Light' (2)	CQua
'Irish Linen' (3)	CQua
'Irish Luck' (1)	CQua
'Irish Minstrel' (2) ♀H4	CQua
'Irish Wedding' (2)	CQua
'Isambard' (4)	CQua
'Islander' (4)	CQua
'Ita' (2)	IRhd
'It's True' (1)	EWal
'Itzim' (6) ♀H4	CAvo CBro CFFs CQua EBrs ECho ERos LRHS
jacetanus (13)	MSSP NMin
'Jack Snipe' (6) ♀H4	CAvo CBro CFFs CHid CQua EBrs ECho EPfP EPot ERos EWal LAma LRHS MBri WShi
'Jack the Lad' (4)	EWal
'Jack Wood' (11a)	CQua
'Jackadee' (2)	IRhd
'Jake' (3)	IRhd
'Jamage' (8)	CQua
'Jamaica Inn' (4)	CQua
'Jamboree' (2)	CQua
'Jamestown' (3)	IRhd
'Janelle' (2)	CQua
'Jantje' (11a)	CQua
'Jauno' (1)	IRhd
'Javelin' (2)	IRhd
'Jeanine' (2)	CQua
'Jeanne Bicknell' (4)	CQua
'Jedna' (2)	CQua
'Jenny' (6) ♀H4	CBro CMea CQua EBla EBrs ECho EPot ERCP ERos EWal LAma MCot NBir WShi
'Jersey Carlton' (2)	CQua
'Jersey Roundabout' (4)	CQua
'Jersey Sun' **new**	LRHS
'Jersey Torch' (4)	CQua
'Jetfire' (6) ♀H4	CQua EBrs ECho EPfP EPot ERCP ERos EWal LAma LRHS LSou NHol SPer WShi
'Jezebel' (3)	CBro
'Jimmy Noone' (1)	CQua
'Jim's Gold' (2)	CQua
'Jodi' (11b)	IRhd
'Jodi's Sister' (11a)	IRhd
'Johanna' (5)	CBro
'John Daniel' (4)	CQua
'John Lanyon' (3)	CQua
'John's Delight' (3)	CQua
× ***johnstonii***	CAvo EBrs ECho NMin
§ 'Jolity' (2)	EWal
jonquilla (13) ♀H4	CAvo CBro CQua EBrs EPot ERos LAma LEdu NMin WShi
§ - var. ***henriquesii*** (13)	CQua EBrs ECho NMin SCnR
jonquilla × ***cordubensis*** **new**	NMin
'Joppa' (7)	CQua
'Joy'	see *N.* 'Jolity'
'Joy Bishop'	see *N. romieuxii* 'Joy Bishop'
'Joybell' (6)	CQua
'Juanita' (2)	EPfP LRHS
'Jubilation' (2)	EWal
'Jules Verne' (2)	CQua
'Julia Jane'	see *N. romieuxii* 'Julia Jane'
'Jumblie' (12) ♀H4	CBro CQua EBrs EPfP EPot ERos EWal GGar LAma LRHS MBri SPer
juncifolius Req. ex Lag.	see *N. assoanus*
'June Lake' (2)	CQua IRhd
'Junior Miss' (12) **new**	NMin
'Kabani' (9)	CQua
'Kalimna' (1)	CQua
'Kamau' (9)	IRhd
'Kamms' (1)	CQua
'Kamura' (2)	CQua
'Kanchenjunga' (1)	CQua
'Kathy's Clown' (6)	CQua
'Katie Heath' (5)	EBrs ECho ERCP LRHS
'Katrina Rea' (6)	CQua
'Kaydee' (6) ♀H4	CQua IRhd LRHS NMin SPhx
'Kazuko' (3)	EWal

'Kea' (6) CQua
'Keats' (4) CBro CQua NMin
'Kebaya' (2) CQua
'Kehelland' (4) CBro
'Kelly Bray' (1) CQua
'Kenellis' (10) CBro CQua EBrs EPot GEdr
'Kernow' (2) CQua
'Kidling' (7) CQua EBrs ECho NMin
'Kildrum' (3) EWal
'Killara' (8) CQua
'Killearnan' (9) CQua
'Killigrew' (2) CQua
'Killivose' (3) CQua
'Kiltonga' (2) IRhd
'Kilworth' (2) CQua EWal
'Kimmeridge' (3) CQua
'King Alfred' (1) CQua EPfP GKir SPer
'King Size' (11a) CQua LRHS
'Kinglet' (7) CQua
'King's Grove' (1) ♀H4 CQua EWal
'Kings Pipe' (2) CQua
'Kingscourt' (1) ♀H4 CQua
'Kingsleigh' (1) IRhd
'Kissproof' (2) EBla EBrs EWal
'Kit Hill' (7) CQua
'Kitten' (6) CQua
'Kitty' (6) CBro ERos
'Kiwi Magic' (4) CQua IRhd
'Kiwi Solstice' (4) CQua
'Kiwi Sunset' (4) CQua
'Klamath' (2) EWal
'Knocklayde' (3) CQua
'Knowing Look' (3) IRhd
'Kokopelli' (7) ♀H4 CBro CQua EBrs LRHS NMin
'Korora Bay' (1) IRhd
'Krakatoa' (2) EWal
'La Riante' (3) CQua
'Ladies' Choice' (7) IRhd
'Ladies' Favorite' (7) IRhd
'Lady Ann' (2) IRhd
'Lady Be Good' (2) CQua
'Lady Diana' (2) CQua
'Lady Eve' (11a) IRhd
'Lady Margaret Boscawen' (2) CQua
'Lady Serena' (9) CQua
'Lake Tahoe' (2) IRhd
'Lalique' (3) CQua
'Lamanva' (2) CQua
'Lamlash' (2) IRhd
'Lanarth' (7) CBro
'Lancaster' (3) CQua EWal
'Landmark' (2) EWal
'Langarth' (11a) CQua
'Lapwing' (5) CBro ERos EWal IRhd
'Larkelly' (6) CBro ERos
'Larkhill' (2) CQua
'Larkwhistle' (6) ♀H4 EBrs ERos LAma LRHS
'Las Vegas' (1) EBrs LRHS
'Last Word' (3) EWal
'Latchley' (2) CQua
'Lauren' (3) IRhd
'Lavender Lass' (6) CQua
'Lavender Mist' (2) CQua
'Lazy River' (1) CQua
'Leading Light' (2) CQua
'Lee Moor' (1) CQua
'Lemon Beauty' (11b) CQua EBla
'Lemon Cloud' (1) EWal
'Lemon Drops' (5) CMea CQua EBrs ECho EPot ERCP EROs LRHS SPhx
'Lemon Grey' (3) IRhd
'Lemon Silk' (6) CBro CMea CQua EBrs ECho LPio NMin SPhx
'Lemon Snow' (2) IRhd
'Lemonade' (3) CQua
'Lennymore' (2) CQua IRhd
'Leonaine' (2) EWal
'Lewis George' (1) CQua
'Libby' (2) IRhd
'Liberty Bells' (5) CBro CQua EBrs ECho LAma MBri
'Lichfield' (3) EWal
'Liebeslied' (3) CQua
'Life' (7) CQua
'Lighthouse' (3) CQua
'Lighthouse Reef' (1) CQua IRhd
'Lilac Charm' (6) CQua IRhd
'Lilac Hue' (6) CBro
'Lilac Mist' (2) CQua
'Lilliput' ambig. CQua
'Limbo' (2) CQua EWal IRhd
'Limehurst' (2) CQua
'Limerick' (3) EWal
'Limpopo' (3) IRhd
'Lindsay Joy' (2) CQua
'Lintie' (7) CBro CQua EBrs ERos
'Lisbarnett' (3) IRhd
'Lisnamulligan' (3) IRhd
'Lisnaruddy' (3) IRhd
'Little Beauty' (1) ♀H4 CBgR CBro CQua EBrs ECho EPot ERos LAma LRHS NMin
'Little Dancer' (1) CBro CQua
'Little Dorr' (4) IRhd
'Little Gem' (1) ♀H4 CBgR CBro CQua EBrs EPfP LAma LRHS
'Little Jewel' (3) CQua
'Little Karoo' (3) IRhd
'Little Rosie' (2) IRhd
'Little Rusky' (7) CBro CQua NMin
'Little Sentry' (7) CBro CQua
'Little Soldier' (10) CQua NMin
'Little Spell' (1) CQua EBrs
'Little Witch' (6) CBro CQua EBrs ECho EPot ERos LAma WShi
'Littlefield' (7) CQua
'Liverpool Festival' (2) CQua
'Lizard Light' (2) EWal
'Lobularis' see *N. pseudonarcissus* 'Lobularis'
lobularis misapplied see *N. nanus*
lobularis Schultes see *N. obvallaris*
'Loch Alsh' (3) CQua IRhd
'Loch Assynt' (3) CQua
'Loch Brora' (2) CQua
'Loch Coire' (3) CQua
'Loch Fada' (2) CQua
'Loch Hope' (2) CQua
'Loch Leven' (2) CQua
'Loch Lundie' (2) CQua
'Loch Maberry' (2) CQua
'Loch Naver' (2) CQua
'Loch Owskeich' (2) ♀H4 CQua
'Loch Stac' (2) CQua
'Logan Rock' (7) CQua
'Longitude' (1) **new** IRhd
'Lordship' (1) CQua
'Lorikeet' (1) CQua
'Lothario' (2) LAma MBri
'Lough Gowna' (1) IRhd
'Lovable' (3) EWal
'Loveny' (2) CQua
'Lubaantun' (1) CQua
'Lucifer' (2) CQua
'Lucky Chance' (11a) IRhd
'Lundy Light' (2) CQua

'Lurgain' (1) EWal
'Lynher' (2) CQua
'Lyrebird' (3) CQua
'Lyric' (9) CQua
'Lysander' (2) CQua
× ***macleayi*** (13) CQua NMin
'Madam Speaker' (4) CQua
'Madison' (4) EWal
'Magician' (2) IRhd
'Magna Carta' (2) CQua
'Magnet' (1) LAma
'Magnificence' (1) CQua
'Mai's Family' (6) CQua
'Majestic Star' (1) CQua
'Mallee' (11a) ♀H4 IRhd
'Malpas' (3) CQua
'Malvern City' (1) CQua LRHS
'Mamma Mia' (4) IRhd
'Manaccan' (1) CQua
'Manchu' (2) EWal
'Mangaweka' (6) CQua
'Manly' (4) ♀H4 CQua EWal LRHS
'Manon Lescaut' (2) EWal
'Mantle' (2) CQua
'Maraval' (1) EWal
'March Sunshine' (6) EWal
'Maria Pia' (11a) IRhd
'Marieke' (1) EBrs LAma
'Marilyn Anne' (2) CQua
'Marjorie Hine' (2) CQua
'Marjorie Treveal' (4) CQua
'Marlborough' (2) CQua
'Marlborough Freya' (2) CQua
'Marshfire' (2) CQua
'Martha Washington' (8) CBro CQua
'Martinette' (8) CQua EBrs EWal MBri
'Martinsville' (8) CQua
marvieri see *N. rupicola* subsp. *marvieri*
'Mary Bohannon' (2) EWal
'Mary Copeland' (4) CQua EWal
'Mary Kate' (2) CQua IRhd
'Mary Lou' (6) IRhd
'Mary Veronica' (3) CQua
'Marzo' (7) CQua IRhd
'Matador' (8) CQua IRhd
'Mawla' (1) CQua
'Max' (11a) CQua
'Maximus' ambig. CQua
'Maya Dynasty' (2) CQua
'Mazzard' (4) CQua
'Media Girl' (2) IRhd
× ***medioluteus*** (13) CBro CQua NMin
'Medusa' (8) CBro
'Melancholy' (1) CQua
'Melbury' (2) CQua
'Meldrum' (1) CQua
'Memento' (1) CQua
'Menabilly' (4) CQua
'M n-an-Tol' (2) CQua
'Menehay' (11a) ♀H4 CQua
'Merlin' (3) ♀H4 CQua LAma NMin
'Merry Bells' (5) CQua
'Merrymeet' (4) CQua
'Mersing' (3) CQua
'Merthan' (9) CQua
'Midas Touch' (1) CQua
'Midget' CBro CMea CQua ECho EPot ERos LAma
'Mike Pollock' (8) CQua
'Milan' (9) CQua EWal
'Millennium Sunrise' (2) CQua
'Millennium Sunset' (2) CQua

'Millgreen' (1) EWal LRHS
'Milly's Magic' (2) CQua
'Minicycla' (6) CBro EBrs ECho MSSP
minimus misapplied see *N. asturiensis*
'Minnow' (8) ♀H3 CAvo CBro CFFs CHid CMea CQua EBrs ECho EPfP ERCP ERos EWal GKev LAma LRHS MBri NBir SPer
minor (13) ♀H4 CBro CQua EBrs ECha ECho EPot LAma LRHS NMin WCot WShi
- 'Douglasbank' (1) CBro ITim
- var. ***pumilus*** 'Plenus' see *N.* 'Rip van Winkle'
- Ulster form IBlr MSSP
'Mint Julep' (3) ♀H4 EBrs SPhx
'Minute Waltz' (6) CQua
'Mirar' (2) **new** EWal
'Miss Klein' NMin
'Miss Muffitt' (1) CAvo CBgR CFFs CQua
'Mission Bells' (5) ♀H4 CQua IRhd
'Mission Impossible' (11a) CQua
'Misty Glen' (2) ♀H4 CQua
'Misty Moon' (3) CQua
'Mite' (6) ♀H4 CBro CMea CQua EPot ERos LAma NMin
'Mithrel' (11a) CQua
'Mitylene' (2) CQua
'Mitzy' NMin
'Modern Art' (2) EBrs EWal
'Modulation' (2) **new** LRHS
'Mona Lisa' (2) EWal
'Mondragon' (11a) CQua EBrs LRHS
'Mongleath' (2) CQua
'Monks Wood' (1) CQua
'Monksilver' (3) CQua
'Montclair' (2) CQua
'Montego' (3) CQua
'Moon Dream' (1) CQua
'Moon Ranger' (3) CQua IRhd
'Moon Shadow' (3) CQua
'Moon Valley' (2) IRhd
'Moonshot' (1) EWal
'Moonstruck' (1) CQua
'Morab' (1) CQua
'Moralee' (4) IRhd
'Morvah Lady' (5) CQua
'Morval' (2) CQua
moschatus (13) ♀H4 CBro CQua EBrs ECho EPot LAma LRHS NMin WShi
- 'Cernuus Plenus' (4) CQua
'Motmot' CQua
'Mount Fuji' (2) CQua
'Mount Hood' (1) ♀H4 EBrs EPfP EWal LAma LRHS NBir SPer SPhx
'Mount Rainier' (1) CQua
'Mountjoy' (7) EWal
'Movie Star' (2) IRhd
'Mowser' (7) CQua
'Mr Julian' (6) CQua
'Mrs Langtry' (3) CQua WShi
'Mrs R.O. Backhouse' (2) CQua EBla WShi
'Mulatto' (1) EWal
'Mullion' (3) CQua
'Mulroy Bay' (1) CQua IRhd
'Murlough' (9) CQua
'Muscadet' (2) CQua
'My Lady' (2) EWal
'My My' (2) EWal
'My Story' (4) **new** LRHS
'My Sunshine' (2) CQua
'Mystic' (3) CQua
'Naivasha' (2) IRhd
'Namraj' (2) CQua
'Nancegollan' (7) CBro CQua

	'Nangiles' (4)	CQua
	'Nanpee' (7)	CQua
	'Nansidwell' (2)	CQua
	'Nanstallon' (1)	CQua
§	***nanus***	CWCL
	- 'Midget' (1)	EBrs ECho
	'Narrative' (2) **new**	IRhd
	'Nederburg' (1)	IRhd
	'Nelly' ambig.	CQua
	'Nether Barr' (2)	IRhd
	nevadensis (13)	EPot ERos
	'New Hope' (3)	CQua
	'New Life' (3)	CQua
	'New Penny' (3)	CQua IRhd
	'New Song' (2)	EWal
	'New Star' (2)	EWal
	'New World' (2)	EWal
	'New-Baby' (7)	CQua EBrs EPfP LRHS NMin
	'Newcastle' (1)	CQua EWal
	'Newcomer' (3)	CQua
	'Night Music' (4)	CQua IRhd
	'Nightcap' (1)	CQua
	'Nirvana' (7)	CBro
	'Niveth' (5)	CQua
§	***nobilis*** (13)	EPot
	- var. ***leonensis*** (13)	ECho
	- var. ***nobilis*** (13)	NMin
	'Nonchalant' (3)	CQua IRhd
	'Norma Jean' (2)	CQua
	'Nor-nor' (2)	CBro ERos
	'North Rim' (2)	CQua
	'Northern Sceptre' (2)	IRhd
	'Noss Mayo' (6)	CBro CQua
	'Notre Dame' (2) ♀H4	CQua IRhd
	'Nuage' (2)	EWal
	'Numen Rose' (2)	IRhd
	Nylon Group (10)	CBro EBrs ECho EPot GEdr LPio
	- yellow-flowered (10)	ECho EPot
	'Oadby' (1)	CQua
	'Obdam' (4)	EBla EBrs EWal LRHS
	'Obelisk' (11a)	CQua
	obesus (13)	EBrs ECho ERos MSSP WCot
	- 'Diamond Ring' (10) **new**	EPot LAma NMin
	'Obsession' (2)	CQua
§	***obvallaris*** (13) ♀H4	CAvo CBro CFFs CQua EBrs ECho EPfP EPot ERCP ERos IHer LRHS SGar SPer SPhx WHer WPtf WShi
	'Ocarino' (4)	CQua
	'Occasionally' (1) **new**	LRHS
	'Ocean Blue' (2)	IRhd
	'Odd Job'	CQua
	× ***odorus*** (13)	EBrs IHer LRHS WShi
§	- 'Double Campernelle' (4)	CQua ECho WShi
	'Oecumene' (11a)	CQua
	old pheasant's eye	see *N. poeticus* var. *recurvus*
	'Orange Queen' (3)	EBrs LRHS
	'Orange Walk' (3)	CQua IRhd
	'Orangery' (11a)	EBla EBrs LAma
	'Oratorio' (2)	EWal
	'Orbital Pink' (3) **new**	IRhd
	'Orchard Place' (3)	CQua
	'Oregon Pioneer' (2)	IRhd
	'Oregon Snow' (2) ♀H4 **new**	LRHS
	'Orkney' (2)	CQua
	'Ormeau' (2) ♀H4	CQua
	'Oryx' (7) ♀H4	CQua
	'Osmington' (2)	CQua
	'Ouma' (1)	CQua
	'Outline' (2)	IRhd
	'Ouzel' (6)	CQua
	'Oykel' (3)	CQua
	'Oz' (12)	CQua ERos NMin
	pachybolbus	EBrs ECho NMin
	'Pacific Coast' (8) ♀H4	CQua ECho EPfP LAma LRHS NMin
	'Pacific Mist' (11a)	CQua
	'Pacific Rim' (2)	CQua IRhd
	'Painted Desert' (3)	CQua
	'Palace Pink' (2)	IRhd
	'Pale Sunlight' (2)	CQua
	pallidiflorus (13)	ECha
	'Palmares' (11a)	CQua EWal LEdu
	'Pamela Hubble' (2)	CQua
	'Pampaluna' (11a)	CQua
	'Panache' (1)	CQua EWal
	'Pandemonium' (3) **new**	IRhd
	'Panorama Pink' (3)	IRhd
	'Paolo Veronese' (2)	EWal
	'Paper White'	see *N. papyraceus*
	'Paper White Grandiflorus' (8)	CQua EPfP MBri SPer
	'Paper White Zeva' **new**	LRHS
	'Papillon Blanc' (11b)	EBrs EWal
	'Papua' (4) ♀H4	CQua
§	***papyraceus*** (13)	CQua CStu ECho EWal LAma LRHS
	- subsp. ***panizzianus***	CQua
	- subsp. ***polyanthus*** from Morocco	WCot
	'Paradigm' (4)	IRhd
	'Paramour' (4)	IRhd
	'Parcpat' (7)	CBro
	'Paricutin' (2)	EWal
	'Parisienne' (11a)	EBla
	'Park Springs' (3)	CQua NMin
	'Parkdene' (2)	CQua
	'Party Time' (2)	IRhd
	'Passionale' (2) ♀H4	CQua EWal LAma NBir
	'Pastiche' (2)	CQua
	'Pastorale' (2)	EWal
	'Patabundy' (2)	CQua EWal
	'Pathos' (3)	IRhd
	'Patois' (9)	CQua IRhd
	'Patrick Hacket' (1)	CQua
	'Pay Day' (1)	CQua
	'Peach Prince' (4)	CQua
	'Peaches and Cream' (2) **new**	LRHS
	'Pearl Wedding' (3)	CQua
	'Pearlshell' (11a)	CQua
	'Peeping Tom' (6) ♀H4	CBro EBrs ECho ERCP ERos EWal LAma LRHS SRms
	'Peggy's Gift' (3)	IRhd
	'Pemboa'	CQua
	'Pencrebar' (4)	CAvo CBro CHid CQua EBrs EPot ERos LAma NMin WShi
	'Pend Oreille' (3)	CQua
	'Pengarth' (2)	CQua
	'Penjerrick' (9)	CQua
	'Penkivel' (2) ♀H4	CQua
	'Pennance Mill' (2)	CQua
	'Pennine Way' (1)	CQua
	'Pennyfield' (2)	CQua
	'Penpol' (7)	CBro CQua
	'Penril' (6)	CBgR CQua ERos
	'Penstraze' (7)	CQua
	'Pentewan' (2)	CQua LRHS
	'Pentille' (1)	CQua
	'Pentire' (11a)	CQua
	'Penvale'	CQua
	'Penvose' (2)	EWal
	'Peppercorn' (6)	CQua
	'Pequenita' (7)	CBro
	'Percuil' (6)	CQua
	'Perdredda' (3)	CQua

'Perimeter' (3)	CQua EWal
'Peripheral Pink' (2)	CQua
'Perlax' (11a)	CQua
'Personable' (2)	CQua
'Pet Finch' (7)	EWal
'Petanca' (5)	IRhd
'Petillant' (3)	EBrs
'Petit Four' (4)	EBla EBrs LAma
'Petrel' (5)	CBro CQua EBrs EPot LRHS SPhx
'Phalarope' (6)	CQua
'Phantom' (11a)	CQua
'Phil's Gift' (1)	CQua
'Phinda' (2)	IRhd
'Phoenician' (2)	CQua
'Picatou' (3) **new**	IRhd
'Picoblanco' (2)	CBro CQua NMin
'Pigeon' (2)	CQua
'Pinafore' (2)	EWal
'Pincambo' (2)	IRhd
'Pineapple Prince' (2) ♀H4	CQua
'Pink Angel' (7)	CQua EBrs
'Pink Champagne' (4)	CQua EBrs
'Pink Charm' (2)	EBrs EWal
'Pink Evening' (2)	CQua
'Pink Formal' (11a)	CQua
'Pink Gilt' (2)	IRhd
'Pink Glacier' (11a)	CQua
'Pink Holly' (11a)	CQua
'Pink Ice' (2)	CQua
'Pink Monarch' (2)	EWal
'Pink Pageant' (4)	CQua EWal IRhd
'Pink Paradise' (4)	CQua EBrs IRhd
'Pink Perry' (2)	IRhd
'Pink Sapphire' (2)	CQua
'Pink Silk' (1)	CQua IRhd
'Pink Smiles' (2)	SPer
'Pink Surprise' (2)	CQua
'Pink Tango' (11a)	CQua
'Pipe Major' (2)	CQua EPfP EWal LRHS SPer
'Pipers Barn' (7)	CQua
'Piper's End' (3)	CQua
'Piper's Gold' (1)	CQua
'Pipestone' (2)	CQua
'Pipit' (7) ♀H4	CAvo CBro CFFs CMea CQua EBrs ECho EPfP ERos EWal LAma LEdu MBri MNrw NBir SPer WShi
'Piraeus' (4)	IRhd
'Pismo Beach' (2)	CQua
'Pistachio' (1)	EBrs
'Pitchroy' (2)	CQua
'Pitt's Diamond' (3)	CQua
'Pixie's Sister' (7) ♀H4	CQua NMin
'Pledge' (1) **new**	NMin
poeticus (13)	CAvo WHer
§ - var. ***hellenicus*** (13)	CBro CQua EWal
- old pheasant's eye	see *N. poeticus* var. *recurvus*
- var. ***physaloides*** (13)	CQua EBrs ECho SPhx
§ - 'Plenus' ambig. (4)	CBro CQua EBrs EPot ERCP GKir GQui WShi
- 'Praecox' (3)	CBro
§ - var. ***recurvus*** (13) ♀H4	CArn CBro CFFs CMea CQua EBrs ECho EPfP EPot ERCP EWal IHer LAma LRHS NBir SPhx WShi
'Poet's Way' (9)	CQua
'Pol Crocan' (2)	CQua IRhd
'Pol Dornie' (2)	CQua
'Pol Voulin' (2)	CQua IRhd
'Polar Ice' (3)	EBrs LAma
'Polglase' (8)	CBro
'Polgooth' (2)	CQua
'Polly's Pearl' (8)	CQua
'Polnesk' (7)	CBro
'Polruan'	CQua
'Poltreen'	CQua
'Polwheveral' (2)	CQua
'Pooka' (3)	IRhd
'Poppy's Choice' (4)	CQua
'Pops Legacy' (1)	CQua IRhd
'Porthchapel' (7)	CQua
'Portloe Bay' (3)	CQua
'Portrush' (3)	CQua EWal
'Potential' (1)	CQua
'Powerstock' (2)	IRhd
'Prairie Fire' (3)	CQua EWal IRhd
'Pratincole' (3) **new**	IRhd
'Preamble' (1)	CQua
I 'Precocious' (2) ♀H4	CQua LRHS
'Premiere' (2)	CQua
'Presidential Pink' (2)	CQua
'Pretty Baby' (3)	CQua
'Pride of Cornwall' (8)	CBro
'Primrose Beauty' (4)	CQua
'Princeps' (1)	CQua
'Princess Zaide' (3)	CQua
'Princeton' (3)	CQua
'Prism' (2)	CQua
'Problem Child' (2)	IRhd
'Probus' (1)	CQua
'Professor Einstein' (2)	EBrs EPfP
'Prologue' (1)	CQua
'Prophet' (1)	EWal
'Prototype' (6)	IRhd
'Proud Fellow' (1)	IRhd
'Proverbial Pink' (2)	IRhd
'Prussia Cove' (2)	CQua
pseudonarcissus (13) ♀H4	CBro CQua CRow EBrs LAma SPhx WHer WPtf WShi
- subsp. ***eugeniae*** (13)	EPot WCot
§ - 'Lobularis'	CArn CAvo CBro CFFs CQua EBrs ECho EPot ERos MBri SPer SPhx
- subsp. ***nobilis***	see *N. nobilis*
§ - subsp. ***pseudonarcissus*** var. ***humilis*** (13)	EBrs ECho
'Pueblo' (7)	EBrs ERos LRHS WShi
'Pulsar' (2)	IRhd
pumilus (13)	EBrs ECho EPot ERos NMin WShi
'Punchline' (7) ♀H4	CQua NMin
'Puppet' (5)	CQua
'Puppy' (6)	EWal
'Purbeck' (3) ♀H4	CQua EWal IRhd
'Quail' (7) ♀H4	CQua EBrs EPfP ERos EWal LAma LRHS LSou MBri SPer
'Quasar' (2) ♀H4	CQua
Queen Anne's double daffodil	see *N.* 'Eystettensis'
'Queen Juliana' (1)	CQua
'Queen Mum' (1)	CQua EWal
'Queen's Guard' (1)	IRhd
'Quick Step' (7)	CQua
'Quiet Hero' (3)	IRhd
'Quiet Man' (1)	IRhd
'Quiet Waters' (1)	CQua
'Quince' (12)	CQua EWal LRHS LSou
'Radiant Gem' (8)	CQua
'Radiation' (2)	EWal
radiiflorus var. ***poetarum*** (13)	CBro CQua
'Radjel' (4)	CQua
'Rainbow' (2) ♀H4	CQua EWal
'Rame Head' (1)	CQua
'Rameses' (2)	CQua
'Ransom' (4) **new**	IRhd
'Rapture' (6) ♀H4	CBro CQua EBrs IRhd NMin
'Rashee' (1)	CQua
'Raspberry Ring' (2)	CQua

	Name	Suppliers
	'Rathowen Gold' (1)	CQua
	'Raoul Wallenberg' (2)	EWal
	'Ravenhill' (3)	CQua
	'Rebekah' (4)	CQua
	'Recital' (2)	CQua
	'Red Coat' (2)	CQua
	'Red Devon' (2) 🏆^{H4}	CBgR CQua
	'Red Era' (3)	CQua
	'Red Reed' (1)	IRhd
	'Red Socks' (6)	CQua
	'Redhill' (2)	EWal
	'Redstart' (3)	EWal
	'Refrain' (2)	CQua
	'Regal Bliss' (2)	CQua
	'Reggae' (6) 🏆^{H4}	CBro CQua EBrs ERCP LRHS
	'Rembrandt' (1)	CQua
	'Rendezvous Caye' (2)	CQua
	'Replete' (4)	CQua EBla EBrs LRHS
	'Reprieve' (3)	CQua
	requienii	see *N. assoanus*
	'Resistasol' (1) **new**	IRhd
	'Reverse Image' (11a)	CQua
	'Ribald' (2)	IRhd
	'Ridgecrest' (3)	IRhd
	'Riding Mill' (3)	EWal
	rifanus	see *N. romieuxii* subsp. *romieuxii* var. *rifanus*
	'Rijnveld's Early Sensation' (1) 🏆^{H4}	CAvo CBro CFFs CMea CQua EBrs ECha ERos EWal
	'Rikki' (7)	CBro CQua ERos NMin
	'Rima' (1)	CQua
	'Rimmon' (3)	CQua
	'Ring Fence' (3)	IRhd
	'Ringhaddy' (3)	IRhd
	'Ringing Bells' (5)	CQua
	'Ringleader' (2)	CQua EWal
	'Ringmaster' (2)	CQua
	'Ringmer' (3)	CQua
	'Rio Bravo' (2)	IRhd
	'Rio Gusto' (2)	IRhd
	'Rio Lobo' (2)	IRhd
	'Rio Rondo' (2)	IRhd
	'Rio Rouge' (2)	IRhd
§	'Rip van Winkle' (4)	CAvo CBro CQua CSWP CWCL EBla EBrs EPfP EPot ERCP ERos IHer LAma LRHS MBri NHol WHal WShi
	'Rippling Waters' (5) 🏆^{H4}	CBro CQua EBrs EPot ERos LAma
	'Ristin' (1)	CQua
	'Rival' (6)	CQua
	'River Dance' (2)	IRhd
	'River Queen' (2)	CQua IRhd
	'Rockall' (3)	CQua
	'Rockery White' (1)	NMin
	'Rococo' (2)	EWal
	'Roger' (6)	CBro CQua
	'Romance' (2) 🏆^{H4}	EBrs EWal LAma
§	'Romanus' (4)	CQua
	romieuxii (13) 🏆$^{H2-3}$	CBro CDes CPBP EPot ERos ITim LPio LRHS MSSP SBch SChr SCnR WCot
	- JCA	WWst
	- JCA 805	EPot WWst
	- SB&L 237	WCot
	- SF 370	WCot
	- subsp. ***albidus*** (13)	ECho EPot WCot
	- - SF 110	WCot
§	- - var. ***zaianicus*** (13)	EBrs ECho SPhx
	- - - SB&L 82	MSSP WCot
*	- - - f. ***lutescens*** (13)	GEdr
	- 'Atlas Gold'	EPot GEdr SCnR
§	- 'Joy Bishop' (10)	EPot ERos GEdr NMen SCnR
§	- 'Julia Jane' (10)	EBrs ECho EPot ERos GEdr LPio NMin SCnR SPhx WCot
	- subsp. ***romieuxii*** (13)	EBrs
§	- - var. ***mesatlanticus*** (13)	ECho ERos
§	- - var. ***rifanus*** (13)	EBrs ECho SPhx
	- - - B 8929	WCot
	- 'Treble Chance' (10)	EPot GEdr
	'Rosado' (11a)	EWal
	'Rosannor Gold' (11a)	CQua
	'Roscarrick' (6)	CQua
	'Rose of May' (4)	CQua WShi
	'Rose of Tralee' (2)	CQua
	'Rose Royale' (2)	CQua
	'Rosedown' (5)	CBro
	'Rosemerryn' (2)	CQua
	'Rosemoor Gold' 🏆^{H4}	CBro CQua EWal
	'Rosevine' (3)	CQua
	'Roseworthy' (2)	EBla ERos
	'Rosy Trumpet' (1)	CBro
	'Rosy Wonder' (2)	EWal
	'Roxton' (4)	IRhd
	'Royal Armour' (1)	LRHS
	'Royal Ballet' (2)	CQua
	'Royal Connection' (8)	CQua
	'Royal Marine' (2)	CQua
	'Royal Orange' (2)	EWal
	'Royal Princess' (3)	CQua LRHS
	'Royal Regiment' (2)	CQua
	'Rubh Mor' (2)	CQua
	'Ruby Rose' (4)	IRhd
	'Ruby Tail' (2)	EWal
	'Ruby Wedding' (2)	IRhd
	'Rubythroat' (2)	CQua
	'Ruddy Rascal' (2)	IRhd
	'Rugulosus' (7) 🏆^{H4}	CBro CQua EBrs ECho ERos
*	'Rugulosus Flore Pleno' (d)	EBrs ECho LRHS
	'Rumpus' (3) **new**	IRhd
	rupicola (13)	CBro CQua EBrs ECho EPot ERos MSSP NMen NMin NSla NWCA SCnR
§	- subsp. ***marvieri*** (13) 🏆^{H2}	EPot ERos
§	- subsp. ***watieri*** (13)	CBro CQua ECho EPot ERos ITim LLHF NMin
	'Rustom Pasha' (2)	CQua
	'Rytha' (2)	CQua
	'Saberwing' (5)	CQua
	'Sabine Hay' (3)	CQua EWal
	'Sabrosa' (7)	CBro NMin
	'Sacajawea' (2)	EWal
	'Sacre Coeur' (2) **new**	IRhd
	'Sagana' (9)	CQua
	'Sagitta' (1) 🏆^{H4} **new**	EWal
	'Sailboat' (7) 🏆^{H4}	EBrs LRHS NMin
	'Saint Agnes' (8)	CQua
	'Saint Budock' (1)	CQua
	'Saint Day' (5)	CQua
	'Saint Dilpe' (2)	CQua
	'Saint Keverne' (2) 🏆^{H4}	CQua EPfP EWal LRHS
	'Saint Keyne' (8)	CQua
	'Saint Patrick's Day' (2)	CQua EBla EWal LAma SPer
	'Saint Peter' (4)	CQua
	'Saint Petroc' (9)	CQua
	'Saint Piran' (7)	CQua
	'Salakee' (2)	CQua
	'Salcey Forest' (1)	CQua
	'Salmon Trout' (2)	CQua
	'Salome' (2) 🏆^{H4}	CQua EBla EBrs EPfP EWal LAma LRHS NBir
	'Salute' (2)	CQua
	'Samantha' (4)	CQua
	'Samaria' (3)	CBro
	'Samba' (5)	ERos

'Samite' (1)	EWal
'Sancerre' (11a)	CQua
'Sandycove' (2)	CQua
'Santa Claus' (4)	CQua
'Sarah' (2)	EWal
'Sargeant's Caye' (1)	CQua
'Satchmo' (1)	CQua
'Sateen' (2)	EWal
'Satellite' (6)	EWal
'Satin Pink' (2)	EWal
'Satsuma' (1)	CQua
'Saturn' (3)	CQua
'Savoir Faire' (2)	IRhd
scaberulus (13)	ECho EPot ERos
'Scarlet Chord' (2)	CQua
'Scarlet Elegance' (2)	CQua
'Scarlet Gem' (8)	EWal NHol
'Scarlett O'Hara' (2)	CQua
'Scented Breeze' (2)	IRhd
'Scilly Spring' (8)	CAvo
'Scilly White' (8)	CQua
'Scorrier' (2)	CQua
'Scrumpy' (2)	CQua
'Sea Dream' (3)	CQua EWal
'Sea Gift' (7)	CBro
'Sea Green' (9)	CQua
'Sea Legend' (2)	CQua
'Sea Princess' (3)	CQua
'Sea Shanty' (2)	IRhd
'Seagull' (3)	CAvo CQua ECho LAma WShi
'Sealing Wax' (2)	CQua EWal
'Segovia' (3) Υ^{H4}	CBro CMea CQua EBla EBrs EPot ERos LAma LRHS NHol NMin SCnR SPer SPhx
'Sempre Avanti' (2)	LAma MBri
'Seraglio' (3)	CQua
'Serena Beach' (4)	IRhd
'Serena Lodge' (4) Υ^{H4}	CQua IRhd
serotinus (13)	EBrs ECho EPot WCot
- MK 6374	WWst
'Sextant' (6)	CQua
'Shangani' (2)	IRhd
'She' (2)	EWal
'Sheelagh Rowan' (2)	CQua IRhd
'Sheer Joy' (6)	IRhd
'Sheleg' (8)	EBrs
'Shepherd's Hey' (7)	CQua EPfP
'Sherborne' (4) Υ^{H4}	CQua
'Sherpa' (1)	IRhd
'Sheviock' (2)	CQua
'Shindig' (2)	IRhd
'Shining Light' (2)	CQua
'Shortcake' (2)	CQua
'Shrimp Boat' (11a)	IRhd
'Sidhe' (5)	CQua
'Sidley' (3)	CQua IRhd
'Signorina' (2)	IRhd
'Silent Valley' (1) Υ^{H4}	CQua NMin
'Silk Cut' (2)	CQua
'Silkwood' (3)	CQua
'Silver Bells' (5)	CQua
'Silver Chimes' (8)	CAvo CBro CQua EBrs ECho EPfP ERos EWal LAma LEdu LRHS NBir
'Silver Convention' (1)	CQua
'Silver Crystal' (3)	IRhd
'Silver Kiwi' (2)	CQua
'Silver Minx' (1)	CQua
'Silver Plate' (11a)	CQua
'Silver Shell' (11a)	CQua
'Silver Standard' (2)	CQua EWal
'Silver Surf' (2)	CQua IRhd
'Silversmith' (2)	CQua
'Silverthorne' (3)	CQua
'Silverwood' (3)	CQua IRhd
'Singing Pub' (3)	IRhd
'Sinopel' (3)	EBrs LAma
'Sir Samuel' (2)	CQua
'Sir Watkin' (2)	CQua
'Sir Winston Churchill' (4) Υ^{H4}	CQua EPfP EWal LAma LRHS SPer
'Skerry' (2)	CQua
'Skilliwidden' (2) Υ^{H4}	CQua
'Skookum' (3)	CQua
'Skywalker' (2)	IRhd
'Slieveboy' (1)	CQua
'Slipstream' (6)	IRhd
'Small Fry' (1)	CQua
'Small Talk' (1)	CQua NMin
'Smiling Maestro' (2)	CQua
'Smiling Twin' (11a)	EBrs
'Smokey Bear' (4)	CQua
'Smooth Sails' (3)	CQua
'Snipe' (6)	CQua NMin
'Snoopie' (6)	CQua
'Snow Bunting' (7)	CBro
'Snowcrest' (3)	CQua
'Snowshill' (2)	CQua
'Soft Focus' (2)	IRhd
'Solar System' (3)	IRhd
'Solar Tan' (3)	CQua
'Soldier Brave' (2)	EWal
'Soleil d'Or' (8)	EWal
'Solera' (2)	IRhd
'Solferique' (2)	CQua
'Soloist' (2)	IRhd
'Sonata' (9)	CQua
'Songket' (2)	CQua
'Soprano' (2)	CQua IRhd
'Sorbet' (11b)	EWal
'Sorcerer' (3)	CQua
'South Street' (2)	CQua
'Spaniards Inn' (4)	CQua
'Sparkling Tarts' (8)	CQua
'Sparnon' (11a)	CQua
'Sparrow' (6)	CQua
'Special Envoy' (2) Υ^{H4}	CQua
'Speenogue' (1)	IRhd
'Spellbinder' (1) Υ^{H4}	CQua EWal MBri
'Spin Doctor' (3)	IRhd
'Spindletop' (3) Υ^{H4}	IRhd
'Spirit of Rame' (3)	CQua
'Split Image' (2)	IRhd
'Split Vote' (11a)	IRhd
'Sportsman' (2)	CQua
'Spring Dawn' (2)	EPfP EWal LRHS LSou SPer
'Spring Joy'	ERos
'Spring Morn' (2)	IRhd
'Spun Honey' (4)	CQua
'Stadium' (2)	LAma
'Stainless' (2)	EBrs SPhx
'Stann Creek' (1)	CQua
'Stanway' (3)	CQua IRhd
'Star Glow' (2)	CQua
'Star Quality' (3)	IRhd
'Starfire' (7)	CQua
'State Express' (2)	CQua
'Statue' (2)	EWal
'Steenbok' (3)	IRhd
'Stella' (2)	WShi
'Stella Glow' (3)	IRhd
'Stenalees' (6)	CQua
'Step Forward' (7)	ERos
'Stilton' (9)	CQua
'Stinger' (2)	CQua

	Name	Suppliers
	'Stint' (5) ♀H4	CBro CQua
	'Stocken' (7)	CBro CPBP CQua ERos MSSP NMin
	'Stoke Charity' (2)	CQua
	'Stoke Doyle' (2)	CQua
	'Stormy Weather' (1)	CQua
	'Stratosphere' (7) ♀H4	CQua NMin
	'Strines' (2)	CQua EWal NMin
	'Stromboli' (2)	EWal
	'Suave' (3)	CQua
	'Subtle Shades' (2)	IRhd
	'Sugar and Spice' (3)	CQua
	'Sugar Bird' (2)	IRhd
	'Sugar Cups' (8)	CQua
	'Sugar Loaf' (4)	CQua
	'Sugarbush' (7)	CBro EBrs
	'Suisgill' (4)	CQua
§	'Sulphur Phoenix' (4)	CQua WShi
	'Summer Solstice' (3)	IRhd
	'Sun Disc' (7) ♀H4	CBro CMea CQua EBrs ECho EPot ERos EWal LAma LSou MBri NMin SPer
	'Sunday Chimes' (5)	CQua
	'Sundial' (7)	CBro CQua EBrs ECho EPot ERos EWal LAma LRHS NMin
	'Sunrise' (3)	CQua
	'Sunstroke' (2)	CQua
	'Suntory' (3)	CQua
	'Suntrap' (2)	IRhd
	'Surfside' (6) ♀H4	CQua EBrs ERos LRHS
	'Surprise Packet' (2)	IRhd
	'Surrey' (2)	CQua
	'Suzie Dee' (6)	IRhd
	'Suzie's Sister' (6)	IRhd
	'Suzy' (7) ♀H4	CBro EWal
	'Swaledale' (2)	CQua
	'Swallow' (6)	CBgR CQua LAma
	'Swallow Wing' (6)	IRhd
	'Swanpool' (3)	CQua
	'Swansdown' (4)	EWal
	'Swanvale' (1)	CQua
	'Swedish Fjord' (2)	CQua
	'Sweet Blanche' (7)	CQua
	'Sweet Charity' (2)	EWal
	'Sweet Harmony' (2)	EBrs
	'Sweet Lorraine' (2)	CQua
	'Sweet Pepper' (7)	CBro
	'Sweet Sue' (3)	CQua
	'Sweetness' (7) ♀H4	CAvo CBro CFFs CQua EBrs EWal LAma SPer WPtf WShi
	'Swing Wing' (6)	CQua
	'Sydling' (5)	CQua
I	'Sylph' (1)	CQua
	'Taffeta' (10)	CBro ECho
	'Tahiti' (4) ♀H4	CQua EBrs EPfP EWal LAma
	'Talgarth' (2)	CQua
	'Tamar Fire' (4) ♀H4	CQua
	'Tamar Lad' (2)	CQua
	'Tamar Lass' (3)	CQua
	'Tamar Snow' (2)	CQua
	'Tamara' (2)	CQua SPer
	'Tangent' (2)	CQua
	'Tarlatan' (10)	CBro ERos
	'Tasgem' (4)	CQua
	'Taslass' (4)	CQua
	'Tater-Du' (5)	CQua
	tazetta (13)	EBrs ECho
§	- subsp. ***lacticolor*** (13)	CBgR CQua EBrs ERCP LAma LRHS
§	- - 'Grand Monarque' (8)	CBro CQua
*	- var. ***odoratus***	CQua
	'Teal' (1)	CQua
	'Tedstone' (1)	EWal
	'Tehidy' (3)	CQua

	Name	Suppliers
§	'Telamonius Plenus' (4)	CAvo CBro CQua IGor WCot WShi
	'Temba' (1)	IRhd
	'Temple Cloud' (4)	IRhd
	tenuifolius	see *N. bulbocodium* subsp. *bulbocodium* var. *tenuifolius*
	'Terracotta' (2)	CQua IRhd
	'Terrapin' (3)	IRhd
	'Testament' (2)	EWal
	'Tête-à-tête' (12) ♀H4	CAvo CBro CFFs CHar CQua CWCL EBrs EPfP EPot ERCP ERos EWal GKir LAma LRHS LSou MBri MNHC SPer WClo WHal
	'Thalia' (5)	CAvo CBro CFFs CMea CQua EBrs EPfP ERCP ERos EWal LAma LEdu LRHS MBri MCot NBir NHol SPer SPhx WShi
	'The Alliance' (6) ♀H4	CBro CQua
	'The Grange' (1)	CQua
	'The Knave' (6)	CQua
	'Thistin' (1)	IRhd
	'Thoresby' (3)	CQua
	'Thoughtful' (5)	CBro CQua EWal
	'Tibet' (2)	CQua EWal
	'Tideford' (2)	CQua
	'Tidy Tippet' (2)	IRhd
	'Tiercel' (1)	CQua
	'Tiffany Jade' (3)	CQua
	'Tiger Moth' (6)	CQua
	'Timolin' (3)	CQua
	'Tinderbox' (2)	IRhd
	'Tiritomba' (11a)	CQua
	'Tittle-tattle' (7)	CQua EWal
	'Toby' (2)	CBro ERos
	'Toby the First' (6)	CAvo CQua EBrs
	'Tommora Gold' (2)	CQua
	'Tommy White' (2)	CQua EWal
	'Top Hit' (11a)	CQua
	'Topolino' (1) ♀H4	CAvo CBro CFFs CQua EBrs EPot LAma LRHS SGar
	'Toretta' (3) **new**	IRhd
	'Torianne' (2) ♀H4	CQua
	'Torridon' (2)	CQua
	'Toto' (12) ♀H4	CBro CQua LRHS MBri
	'Tracey' (6) ♀H4	CQua EBrs LAma SPhx
	'Tranquil Morn' (3)	EWal
	'Treasure Hunt' (2)	IRhd
	'Trebah' (2) ♀H4	CQua EWal
	'Treble Two' (7)	CQua
	'Trecara' (3)	CQua
	'Trefusis' (1)	CQua
	'Trehane' (6)	CQua
	'Trelawney Gold' (2)	CQua
	'Tremough Dale' (11a)	CQua
	'Trena' (6) ♀H4	CBro CQua EBrs ERCP EWal NMin
	'Trendy Trail' (3) **new**	IRhd
	'Tresamble' (5)	CBro CQua EBrs EWal LAma
	'Trevaunance' (6)	CQua
	'Treverva' (6)	CQua
	'Treviddo' (2)	CQua
	'Trevithian' (7) ♀H4	CBro CHid CQua EBla EBrs EWal LAma SPhx
	'Trewarvas' (2)	CQua
	'Trewirgie' (6)	CBro CQua
	'Trewoon' (4)	CQua
	triandrus var. ***albus***	see *N. triandrus* subsp. *triandrus* var. *triandrus*
§	- subsp. ***triandrus*** var. ***concolor*** (13)	CBro EBrs ECho
§	- - var. ***triandrus*** (13)	CQua EBrs ECho
	'Tricollet' (11a)	EBrs EWal NHol
	'Trident' (3)	CQua
	'Trielfin' (5)	IRhd

'Trilune' (11a)	EWal
'Tripartite' (11a) ♀H4	CQua EBrs EWal NMin
'Triple Crown' (3) ♀H4	CQua IRhd
'Tristram' (2)	CQua
'Tropic Isle' (4)	CQua
'Tropical Heat' (2)	IRhd
'Trousseau' (1)	CQua EWal
'Troutbeck' (3)	CQua
'Tru' (3)	CQua
'Trueblood' (3)	IRhd
'Trumpet Warrior' (1) ♀H4	CQua IRhd
'Tryst' (2)	CQua
'Tudor Minstrel' (2)	CQua EWal
'Tuesday's Child' (5) ♀H4	CQua ERos EWal
'Tullybeg' (3)	EWal
'Tullynagee' (3)	IRhd
'Turncoat' (6)	CQua
'Tutankhamun' (2)	CQua
'Tweeny' (2)	CQua
'Twink' (4)	CQua
'Tyee' (2)	CQua
'Tyrian Rose' (2)	CQua IRhd
'Tyrone Gold' (1) ♀H4	CQua IRhd
'Tyrree' (1)	IRhd
'Tywara' (1)	CQua
'Ufo' (3)	EWal
'Ulster Bank' (3)	CQua
'Ulster Bride' (4)	CQua
'Uncle Duncan' (1)	CQua IRhd
'Unique' (4) ♀H4	CQua EBla EWal LAma
'Unsurpassable' (1)	CQua LAma
'Upalong' (12)	CQua
'Upshot' (3)	CQua
'Urchin' (2)	IRhd
'Utiku' (6)	CQua
'Val d'Incles' (3)	CQua IRhd
'Valdrome' (11a)	CQua EBla
'Valinor' (2)	CQua
'Van Sion'	see *N.* 'Telamonius Plenus'
'Vanellus' (11a) ♀H4	IRhd
'Veneration' (1)	CQua
'Verdin' (7)	CQua
'Verger' (3)	LAma MBri
'Vernal Prince' (3) ♀H4	CQua
'Verona' (3) ♀H4	CQua LRHS NMin
'Verran Rose' (2)	IRhd
'Vers Libre' (9)	CQua
'Vice-President' (2) ♀H4	CQua
'Vickie Linn' (6)	IRhd
'Victoria' (1)	CQua
'Victorious' (2)	CQua
'Victory' (2)	EWal
'Vigil' (1) ♀H4	CQua EWal
'Viking' (1) ♀H4	CQua
'Violetta' (2)	CQua EWal
'Virginia Waters' (3)	CQua
'Vivarino' (2)	EWal
'Volcanic Rim' (3)	IRhd
'Vulcan' (2) ♀H4	CQua EWal
'W.P. Milner' (1)	CAvo CBgR CBro CQua EBla EBrs EPfP EPot ERCP IHer LAma NMin SMrm WShi
'Wadavers' (2)	CQua
'Waif' (6)	CQua
'Waldon Pond' (3)	CQua
'Waldorf Astoria' (4)	CQua IRhd
'Walton' (7)	CQua
'War Dance' (3)	IRhd
'Warbler' (6)	CQua LAma NMin
'Warm Day' (2)	IRhd
'Warmington' (3)	CQua
'Watamu' (3)	IRhd
'Waterperry' (7)	CBro EBrs LAma
'Watership Down' (2)	CQua
'Watersmeet' (4)	CQua
watieri	see *N. rupicola* subsp. *watieri*
'Wavelength' (3)	IRhd
'Waxwing' (5)	CQua
'Wayward Lad' (3)	IRhd
'Wee Bee' (1)	CQua
'Weena' (2)	CQua EWal
'Welcome' (2)	CQua
'West Post' (3)	IRhd
'Westward' (4)	CQua EWal
'Whang-hi' (6)	CQua ERos
'Wheal Bush' (4)	CQua
'Wheal Coates' (7) ♀H4	CBgR CQua EWal
'Wheal Honey' (1)	CQua
'Wheal Jane' (2)	CQua
'Wheal Kitty' (7)	CQua ERos
'Wheal Rose' (4)	CQua
'Wheatear' (6)	CQua IRhd NMin SPhx
'Whetstone' (1)	CQua
'Whisky Galore' (2)	CQua
'Whisky Mac' (2)	CQua
'Whisper' (5)	EWal
'Whitbourne' (3)	EWal
'White Emperor' (1)	CQua
'White Empress' (1)	CQua
'White Lady' (3)	CAvo CQua IHer LAma WShi
'White Lion' (4) ♀H4	CQua EWal LAma LRHS NHol
'White Majesty' (1)	CQua
'White Marvel' (4)	CQua EBrs EWal
'White Medal' (4)	EBrs
'White Nile' (2)	CQua
'White Prince' (1)	CQua
'White Star' (1)	CQua
'White Tie' (3)	CQua
'Wicklow Hills' (3)	CQua
'Widgeon' (2)	CQua EWal
'Wild Honey' (2)	CQua
'Will Scarlett' (2)	CQua
'Williamsburg' (2) **new**	NMin
willkommii (13)	CBro CQua EBrs ECho ERos MSSP NMin
'Winchester' (2)	EWal
'Wind Song' (2)	CQua
'Windjammer' (1)	EWal
'Winged Victory' (6)	CQua
'Winholm Jenni' (3)	CQua
'Winifred van Graven' (3)	CQua
'Winter Waltz' (6)	CQua
'Witch Doctor' (3)	IRhd
'Witch Hunt' (4)	IRhd
'Woodcock' (6)	CBro CQua
'Woodgreen' (2)	EWal
'Woodland Prince' (3)	CQua
'Woodland Star' (3)	CQua
'Woodley Vale' (2)	CQua
'Woolsthorpe' (2)	CQua
'Worcester' (2)	EWal
'Xit' (3)	CAvo CBro CQua EBrs NMin SPhx
'Xunantunich' (2)	CQua IRhd
'Yellow Belles' (5)	IRhd
'Yellow Cheerfulness' (4) ♀H4	EBrs EPfP EWal LAma LRHS MBri SPhx
'Yellow Minnow' (8)	CQua
'Yellow River' (1)	LAma
'Yellow Wings' (6)	EBrs ECho
'Yellow Xit' (3)	CQua NMin
'Yes Please' (2)	EWal
'Yoley's Pond' (2)	CQua
'York Minster' (1)	CQua IRhd NMin
'Young American' (1)	CQua

'Young Blood' (2) CQua IRhd
'Young Idea' (7) EWal
'Yum-Yum' (3) IRhd
zaianicus see *N. romieuxii* subsp. *albidus* var. *zaianicus*
'Zekiah' (1) CQua
'Zion Canyon' (2) CQua
'Ziva' (8) CAvo CFFs EBrs ERCP NHol
'Zwynner' (2) IRhd

Nardostachys (*Valerianaceae*)

grandiflora GPoy

Nardus (*Poaceae*)

stricta CRWN EBWF

Narthecium (*Melanthiaceae*)

asiaticum new EBee

Nassella (*Poaceae*)

formicarum (Delile) Barkworth EBee
tenuissima see *Stipa tenuissima*
trichotoma CHrt CKno CMea EBee EHoe EPPr LDai MCCP SLim WHal WPGP

Nasturtium (*Brassicaceae*)

'Banana Split' CCCN
officinale EMFW MSKA SVic SWat

Natal plum see *Carissa macrocarpa*

Nauplius (*Asteraceae*)

sericeus CSpe

Nautilocalyx (*Gesneriaceae*)

pemphidius WDib

nectarine see *Prunus persica* var. *nectarina*

Nectaroscordum (*Alliaceae*)

sp. WFoF
bivalve ERos
koelzii EBee
§ ***siculum*** CArn CAvo CBre CBro CFFs CMea CMil CTri CWCL EBee EBrs ECho ELan GCra GKev LLWP LRHS MCot NBPC NBir NChi SGar SMrm SPad SPer SPhx WBor WFar WHoo WRHF
§ - subsp. ***bulgaricum*** EBee EBrs ECha EPfP EPot ERos IBlr ITim LRHS MDun MNrw NGHP SPhx WAbb WBrE WCot WTin
tripedale CMea EBee ECho WWst

Neillia (*Rosaceae*)

affinis CDul EBee ECrN EPfP LAst LLHF LRHS MBri NBid NLar NPro SCoo SWvt WBVN WDin WHCG
longiracemosa see *N. thibetica*
sinensis CMac
§ ***thibetica*** Widely available
thyrsiflora var. ***tunkinensis*** HWJ 505 WCru

Nelumbo (*Nelumbonaceae*)

nucifera XBlo

Nematanthus (*Gesneriaceae*)

'Apres' WDib
'Black Magic' WDib
'Christmas Holly' WDib
'Freckles' WDib
§ ***gregarius*** ♀H1 EBak WDib
§ - 'Golden West' (v) WDib
- 'Variegatus' see *N. gregarius* 'Golden West'
'Lemon and Lime' WDib
radicans see *N. gregarius*
'Tropicana' ♀H1 WDib

Nemesia (*Scrophulariaceae*)

Amelie = 'Fleurame'PBR EPfP GKir SPer SPoG
(Aromatica Series) LAst LSou
Aromatica Royal = 'Balaroyal'PBR
- Aromatica Compact White = 'Balarcomwit'PBR NPri
- Aromatica True Blue = 'Balartublue'PBR NPri
Berries and Cream EPfP LBuc LSou NPri SPoG SVil
= 'Fleurbac' WGor
'Blue Button' LSou
§ Bluebird = 'Hubbird'PBR CHll
§ ***caerulea*** ECtt WPer
N - 'Joan Wilder' (clonal) ECtt
§ ***denticulata*** ♀H3-4 CHar CPrp ECtt EPfP GBee LHop LRHS MAvo NEgg SAga SCoo SHGN SPer SPoG SRms WBrE WFar WFoF WHlf
- 'Celebration'PBR LRHS
- 'Confetti' see *N. denticulata*
- 'Maggie' LBuc LRHS
foetens see *N. caerulea*
'Fragrant Cloud' CChe ELan EPfP LSou MNrw
'Fragrant Gem' LSRN SHGN
fruticans misapplied see *N. caerulea*
Golden Eye = 'Yateye'PBR EPfP LAst LRHS LSRN LSou SBch SMrm SVil
'Innocence' ♀H3 CPrp EBee MArl SCoo
(Karoo Series) Karoo Blue = 'Innkablue'PBR LSou SCoo
- Karoo Soft Blue = 'Innkarsofb' new SVil
- Karoo White = 'Innkarwhi'PBR LSou
(Maritana Series) Blue Lagoon = 'Pengoon'PBR LAst LSRN MAvo SBch SCoo WGor
- Candy Girl = 'Pencand'PBR SCoo
- Honey Girl = 'Penhon'PBR LSRN SBch SCoo WGor
- Maritana Sky Lagoon = 'Pensky' SCoo
- Sugar Girl = 'Pensug'PBR EPfP LHop LSRN
Melanie = 'Fleuron' ♀H3 EPfP
Nemesis Cherry = 'Wesneche' new LSou
Nemesis Orange = 'Wesneo' new LSou NPri
Nemesis Yellow new LSou MAvo NPri
'Orchard Blue' EBee EPfP
'Pippa Manby' ECtt
Pure Lagoon = 'Penpur' LAst LHop SBch SVil
Rosanna Girl = 'Penros' new LAst MAvo
'Rose Wings' EPfP
'Sugar Plum'PBR EPfP LBuc LRHS SPoG
(Sunsatia Series) Sunsatia Blackberry = 'Inuppink'PBR LHop SCoo
- Sunsatia Cranberry = 'Intraired'PBR SCoo
- Sunsatia Lemon = 'Intraigold'PBR SCoo
- Sunsatia Mango = 'Inupyel'PBR LHop

- Sunsatia Peach ='Inupcream'PBR SCoo SVil
- Sunsatia Saffron ='Inupsaf'PBR SMrm
sylvatica CSpe
'Utopia Painted Face' (Utopia Series) ENor
Vanilla Mist = 'Grega'PBR EPfP LRHS LSou SPoG
'White Wings' EPfP
'Wisley Vanilla' LRHS SPoG

Nemophila (*Hydrophyllaceae*)

maculata new WTou
menziesii WTou
- 'Penny Black' CSpe

Neodypsis (*Arecaceae*)

decaryi see *Dypsis decaryi*

Neolepisorus (*Polypodiaceae*)

lancifolius new CPLG

Neolitsea (*Lauraceae*)

glauca see *N. sericea*
§ ***sericea*** SSpi WSHC

Neomarica ✿ (*Iridaceae*)

caerulea CDes EBee WCot

Neopanax (*Araliaceae*)

§ ***arboreus*** CAbb CBcs CDoC CHEx CTrC EBee ECou LEdu SBig
colensoi CTrC
§ ***laetus*** CAbb CBcs CDoC CHEx CTrC ECou LEdu SAPC SArc SBig

Neopaxia (*Portulacaceae*)

§ ***australasica*** ECou EDAr
- bronze-leaved see *N. australasica* 'Ohau'
- 'Lyndon' ECou
§ - 'Ohau' ECou EDAr

Neoregelia (*Bromeliaceae*)

carolinae MBri
§ - (Meyendorffii Group) 'Flandria' (v) LRHS MBri
- - 'Meyendorffii' MBri XBlo
- f. ***tricolor*** (v) ♀H1 MBri
Claret Group MBri
'Hojo Rojo' XBlo
'Marconfos' XBlo

Neoshirakia (*Euphorbiaceae*)

japonica MBri WPGP
- B&SWJ 8744 WCru

Neotinea (*Orchidaceae*)

ustulata new ECho

Neottianthe (*Orchidaceae*)

cucullata EFEx

Nepenthes (*Nepenthaceae*)

alata CSWC NChu
alata* × *ventricosa SHmp
ampullaria CSWC
aristolochioides new SHmp
bongso SHmp
× ***coccinea*** MBri
densiflora SHmp
diatas SHmp
ephippiata new SHmp
fusca CSWC SHmp
fusca* × *maxima SHmp
glabrata new SHmp
izumiae SHmp
khasiana SHmp
lowii SHmp
macfarlanei SHmp
maxima* × *mixta SHmp
mikei new SHmp
muluensis* × *lowii new SHmp
rajah SHmp
ramispina new SHmp
'Rebecca Soper' SHmp
sanguinea SHmp
sibuyanensis SHmp
singalana new SHmp
spectabilis SHmp
stenophylla SHmp
tobaica SHmp
truncata highland form SHmp

Nepeta ✿ (*Lamiaceae*)

RCB AM -3 WCot
RCB/TQ -H-6 WCot
from Ethiopia new GCal
'Blue Beauty' see *N. sibirica* 'Souvenir d'André Chaudron'
bucharica GBuc
* ***buddlejifolium*** NBre NLar
* - 'Gold Splash' NBre
camphorata NBre SIde SMrm
cataria CArn CPrp CTri CWan EBWF ELau GBar GJos GPoy MHer MNHC NBro NGHP NPri SBch SECG SHlg SIde SVic WMoo WPer
§ - 'Citriodora' CArn CBot CHar EAro EBee ELan GBar GPWP GPoy MHer NGHP SHlg SIde SUsu WCHb WClo WTou
citriodora Dum. see *N. cataria* 'Citriodora'
clarkei EAro EBee EPPr IFro LEdu MDKP MMHG MMuc MNFA SBch SBod SIde SWat WFar WMoo WPer WSpi
'Dropmore' EBee
§ × ***faassenii*** ♀H4 Widely available
- 'Alba' COIW EBee ECtt EPfP GBar LAst NBre NGHP NLar SBch SHGN WFar WWEG
- 'Blauknirps' NBre
- 'Kit Cat' CSpe EBee LHop LSRN NGby WFar
- 'Select' WPtf
glechoma 'Variegata' see *Glechoma hederacea* 'Variegata'
govaniana Widely available
grandiflora NBre SIde WFar WHer WOut
- 'Blue Danube' LHop SIde
- 'Bramdean' CElw CMea EBee ECtt EPfP EWes LRHS MBri MCot SAga SBch SPhx WWEG
- 'Dawn to Dusk' Widely available
- 'Pool Bank' EBee ECtt EWes GCal LPla MAvo NBre NGby SGar SIde SMrm
- 'Wild Cat' EBee EPfP MAvo MBri SPur WFar
hederacea 'Variegata' see *Glechoma hederacea* 'Variegata'
italica SIde
kubanica IMou LPla
lanceolata see *N. nepetella*
latifolia NBre SIde
- 'Super Cat' EBee
'Lilac Cloud' NBir
* ***longipes*** hort. CPrp CSam EBee EPfP LAst LEdu LHop LRHS MBel MBri MCot MNFA

	MRav NCGa NGdn NSti SMrm SPer SPoG SWat WAul WCAu WClo WCom WFar WHal WMnd WOut WPer WWEG
macrantha	see *N. sibirica*
melissifolia	SBch WCHb WPer
mussinii misapplied	see *N.* × *faassenii*
mussinii Spreng.	see *N. racemosa*
§ ***nepetella***	NBir NChi WFar WPer
nervosa	CKno CSpe EBee ECha ELan EPfP GKir LAst LRHS MBri MCot MHer MNHC NBPC NBro NPri NSti SBch SPer WClo WFar WMnd WSHC WSpi WWEG
- 'Blue Carpet'	CSpe NEgg
- 'Blue Moon'	EAEE EBee EPfP GJos LRHS NBid SMrm WFar
- 'Forncett Select'	CSam MRav NBre SDys SMrm
- 'Pink Cat'	EBee GKir MDKP SPhx WHil WWEG
§ ***nuda***	CSam EAro EBee ECha ECtt MDKP SIde WFar
- 'Accent'	GBin
- subsp. ***albiflora***	ECha
* - 'Anne's Choice'	EBee GBin MNFA SIde
* - 'Grandiflora'	NBre NLar WMoo
- 'Isis'	EBee
- 'Purple Cat'	EPfP GBin LLHF LSou SIde WFar WOut
- 'Snow Cat'	EBee GBin LSou MDKP SIde SPhx
pannonica	see *N. nuda*
parnassica	CElw EBee ECtt GKev LRHS MWhi NBPC NLar SBod SIde SMad SMrm SPav SPoG WFar WHrl WMnd WMoo
phyllochlamys	CBot CPBP
Pink Candy **new**	EWll
'Porzellan'	EBee LPla SMrm
§ ***prattii***	CSpe NLar NPro SBod SIde WSpi WWEG
§ ***racemosa*** ♀H4	CArn CBot CHby CMac CSev CWan ELau EPfP EWTr GBBs GBar GJos GKir LRHS MCot MNHC MRav MSCN SGar SIde WClo WMoo
- ***alba***	WFar
- 'Blue Ice'	GBuc SIde
- 'Grog'	EBee SIde WSpi
- 'Leporello' (v)	EPPr
- 'Little Titch'	CBod CPrp EAEE EBee ECtt EPfP EShb GCra LRHS LSRN MCot NLar NVic SAga SIde SMrm SPoG SWat WFar WSpi WWEG
- 'Snowflake'	CBcs CMea EAEE EBee ELan ELon EPfP EShb GMaP LRHS MCot MHer NBir SAga SIde SMrm SPer SPoG SWvt WCAu WClo WCom WFar
- 'Superba'	GBuc NBre WFar
- 'Walker's Low'	Widely available
* 'Rae Crug'	ECtt EWes
reichenbachiana	see *N. racemosa*
§ ***sibirica***	COlW EBee ECha ELan EPfP GMac LEdu MHer MMuc MRav MSCN NBid NBro NPri SBch SRkn WCom WCot WFar WHal WPer WPtf
§ - 'Souvenir d'André Chaudron'	Widely available
sintenisii	NBre
'Six Hills Giant'	Widely available
stewartiana	EAro GBuc LDai LLHF MRav NLar WMoo
- ACE 1611	GBuc
- BWJ 7999	WCru
subsessilis	Widely available
- 'Blue Dreams' **new**	ELon WHil WHrl
- 'Candy Cat'	EBee EHrv EPfP MBNS MBri MDKP NBPC NBre SBHP
- 'Cool Cat'	EBee ECGP EPfP LSRN MDKP NBre NLar NPro SIde SPhx WFar
- 'Laufen' **new**	EBee
- Nimbus = 'Yanim'PBR	CCVN EBee LRHS SPoG SRkn
- 'Pink Dreams' **new**	ELon EPfP GJos LRHS WHil
- pink-flowered	ECha LBMP LRHS MBel SMrm WWEG
- 'Sweet Dreams'	CHar CKno EAEE EBee ECtt EPfP LBMP LEdu LHop LRHS MBri MCot MDKP MRav NCGa NGby NLar NPro NSti SHar SPhx WCom WFar WMnd
- 'Washfield'	IPot LHop SAga
tenuifolia	CArn
transcaucasica 'Blue Infinity'	NBre NLar WMnd WMoo WWEG
troodii	MDKP SIde
tuberosa	CBod CSpe EBee ECha EKen GBuc ITim LRHS MAvo MCot MHer MRav SBch SIde SPav STes WCot WHoo WMnd WMoo
'Veluws Blauwtje'	EBee
'Veluwse Wakel' **new**	IMou
yunnanensis	CDes CMdw EBee EPPr LEdu LPla SMrm WHil WOut

Nephrolepis (*Oleandraceae*)

cordifolia	MBri WRic
duffii	EShb WRic
exaltata ♀H2	LRHS
- 'Bostoniensis'	MBri
- 'Smithii'	MBri
- 'Smithii Linda'	MBri
- 'Teddy Junior'	MBri
falcata	EShb WRic
pendula	WRic

Nephrophyllidium (*Menyanthaceae*)

crista-galli	IBlr

Nerine ✿ (*Amaryllidaceae*)

Smee 275 **new**	CDes
'Afterglow'	ECho LAma LRHS SGar WCot
'Albivetta'	CBgR CFwr EBee EBrs ECho EPot LPio WCot
angustifolia	CPen
'Aries'	WCot
'Audrey'	WCot
'Aurora'	ECho WCot
'Baghdad'	ECho WCot
'Belladonna'	WCot
'Berlioz'	WCot
'Blanchefleur'	WCot
bowdenii ♀H3-4	Widely available
- 'Alba'	CBgR CBro EBee ECho ELan EPot ERCP GAbr LPio LRHS SCoo WCot
- 'Chris Sanders' **new**	WCot
- 'Codora'	CBgR CCCN CFwr CPen EBee ECho LHop LRHS LSou SPer
- 'E.B. Anderson'	EBee WCot
- Irish clone	WCot
- 'Manina'	CMdw
- 'Marjorie'	EMal
- 'Mark Fenwick'	CBcs CBro CDes EBee ECha ECho ERas WCot WOld
- 'Marnie Rogerson'	CBro CPne EBee WCot
§ - 'Mollie Cowie' (v)	CMdw EBee GCal IBlr LPio LRHS NCGa WCot WCru WHil WSHC

– 'Ostara'	CBgR CFwr EBee LRHS WCot
– pale pink, striped darker	CDes
– 'Pink Triumph'	CAbP CBcs CBgR EBee EBla EBrs ECho EShb GBuc GQui IBlr LAma LHop LRHS NHol SChr SPer WCot WHoo
– 'Porlock'	EBee
– 'Quinton Wells'	SCnR SPhx
– 'Rowie' **new**	CBgR EBee EPot
– 'Ted Allen's Early'	EBla
– 'Variegata'	see *N. bowdenii* 'Mollie Cowie'
– 'Wellsii'	CDes CMil EBee WCot
'Canasta'	WCot
'Catkin'	ECho WCot
'Cordoba' **new**	CWGN
'Corletta'	WCot
corusca 'Major'	see *N. sarniensis* var. *corusca*
crispa	see *N. undulata*
'Doris Vos' **new**	WCot
'Eve'	WCot
'Exbury Red' **new**	WCot
filamentosa misapplied	see *N. filifolia*
filamentosa ambig.	CBro CLak EBrs ECho
§ ***filifolia***	CPBP CPen CSpe ECho EPot ERos ITim MNrw MTho WAbe WCot WHil
flexuosa	CPne ECho MRav
– 'Alba'	CBgR CBro CDes CPen EBee EBrs ECha ECho EWTr EWll LRHS MRav WAbe WCot
– pink-flowered	ECho
'Fucine'	CDes EBee WCot
'Gloaming'	WCot
gracilis **new**	ECho
'Hera'	CBro SPhx
* ***hirsuta***	EBrs ECho
humilis	EBee EBrs ECho
– Breachiae Group	CStu SBch
huttoniae **new**	CLak ECho
'Isabel' **new**	EPot
'Janet'	WCot
'Jenny Wren'	WCot
'Joan'	WCot
'Kashmir'	CDes WCot
'Killarney' **new**	WCot
'King Leopold'	WCot
'King of the Belgians'	ECho LAma WCot
'Kinn McIntosh'	WCot
'Kodora'	EBee EBrs ECho
krigei	CPen ECho
'Lady Cynthia Colville'	WCot
'Lady Eleanor Keane'	WCot
'Lady Havelock Allen'	CDes CMil WCot
laticoma	ECho
'Leila Hughes'	WCot
'Lyndhurst Salmon'	WCot
'Mansellii'	CBro IHer WCot
'Maria'	CBgR WCot
masoniorum	CBro CStu ECho ERos MTho NMen SBch WCot WThu
'Miss Cator'	WCot
'Miss Frances Clarke' **new**	WCot
'Mrs Cooper'	WCot
'Mrs Dent Brocklehurst'	WCot
'Nikita'	CBgR CFwr CPen EBee EBrs ECho EPot LRHS
'November Cheer'	ECho
peersii	WCot
'Plymouth'	SChr
pudica	SBch
– pink-flowered	EBee WCot
pusilla **new**	CLak
'Red Pimpernel'	ECho LAma
rehmannii	EBrs
'Rushmere Star'	CBgR CDes EBee SChr WCot
'Ruth' **new**	WCot
sarniensis ♀H2-3	CBro CFwr CPne CPrp EBee EBrs ECha ECho EPot GKev IHer LRHS WCot
* – 'Alba'	LPio WCot
§ – var. ***corusca***	CStu LAma
– – 'Major'	EBrs ECho SChr WCot
– var. ***curvifolia*** f. ***fothergillii***	ECho WCot
– late, dull red-flowered	CDes
'Snowflake'	WCot
'Stephanie'	CBgR CBro CCCN CFwr CWGN EBee EBrs ECho EShb LAma LHop LRHS LSou SPer WCot WFar WHoo
'Timoshenko' **new**	WCot
§ ***undulata***	CBgR CBro CCCN CPne CSut EBee EBrs ECha ECho EPot ERos LAma LSou SPer WCot
* – 'Alba'	ECho
'Variegata' (v) **new**	CWGN
'Vicky'	WCot
'Virgo'	CMdw ECho LAma
'White Swan'	ECho
'Wolsey'	ECho
'Zeal Giant' ♀H3-4	CAvo CBro CFFs CPne ECho GCal WCot
'Zeal Grilse'	CDes CPne
'Zeal Silver Stripe'	CFir

Nerium ✿ (*Apocynaceae*)

oleander	CAbb CArn CBcs CEls CHll CTri EBak ELan EShb LRHS NLar SArc SChr SEND SPad SPer SPlb SPoG SRms SWal
– 'Album'	CEls CTri
– 'Album Plenum' (d)	CEls
– 'Alsace'	CEls
– 'Altini'	CEls
– 'Angiolo Pucci'	CEls
– 'Bousquet d'Orb'	CEls
§ – 'Carneum Plenum' (d)	CEls
– 'Cavalaire' (d)	CEls
– 'Cornouailles'	CEls
– 'Docteur Golfin'	CEls
– 'Emile Sahut'	CEls
– 'Emilie'	CEls
– 'Flavescens Plenum' (d)	CEls EShb
– 'Géant des Batailles' (d)	CEls
– 'Hardy Red'	CEls
– 'Hawaii'	CEls
– 'J.R.'	CEls
– 'Jannoch'	CEls
– 'Louis Pouget' (d)	CEls
– 'Madame Allen' (d)	CEls EShb
– 'Maresciallo Graziani'	CEls
– 'Margaritha'	CEls
– 'Marie Gambetta'	CEls
– 'Mont Blanc' (d)	CEls
– 'Mrs Roeding'	see *N. oleander* 'Carneum Plenum'
– 'Nana Rosso'	CEls
– 'Oasis' (d)	CEls
– subsp. ***oleander***	CEls
– 'Papa Gambetta'	CEls
– 'Petite Pink'	CEls MREP
– 'Petite Red'	CEls MREP
– 'Petite Salmon'	CEls
– 'Professeur Granel' (d)	CEls
– 'Provence' (d)	CEls
– 'Rosario' (d)	EShb

- 'Rose des Borrels' (d) CEls
- 'Rosée du Ventoux' (d) CEls
- 'Roseum' CEls
- 'Roseum Plenum' (d) CEls CRHN
- 'Rosita' CEls
- salmon-flowered LRHS SEND
- 'Sealy Pink' CEls
- white-flowered new SEND
§ - 'Soeur Agnès' CEls
- 'Soleil Levant' CEls
- 'Souvenir d'Emma Schneider' CEls
- 'Souvenir des Iles Canaries' CEls
- 'Splendens Giganteum' (d) CEls EShb
- 'Splendens Giganteum Variegatum' (d/v) CEls
- 'Tito Poggi' CEls
- 'Vanilla Cream' MWea
- 'Variegatum' (v) ♀H1+3 CBot CHll EShb LRHS
- 'Variegatum Plenum' (d/v) CBow WCot
- 'Villa Romaine' CEls
- 'Ville de Carpentras' (d) CEls

Nertera (*Rubiaceae*)

balfouriana ECou
depressa LRHS
granadensis EShb MBri

Neviusia (*Rosaceae*)

alabamensis CBcs NLar

Nicandra (*Solanaceae*)

physalodes CArn CHby GBee ILis NBir NVic
- 'Splash of Cream' (v) CCCN
- 'Violacea' CSpe SHlg SRms SWvt WTou

Nicotiana (*Solanaceae*)

alata CSpe WSFF
- 'Grandiflora' SHlg
glauca CDTJ CHll CSpe EShb EWTr LDai LFur SDnm SPav WHil
'Hopleys' CSpe
knightiana CDTJ CSpe EBee
langsdorffii ♀H3 CSpe EBee LPio SDnm SPav
'Lime Green' ♀H3 CSpe
mutabilis CHll CSpe EBee LDai MWea SBch SPhx
suaveolens CBre CSpe
sylvestris ♀H3 CDTJ CSpe CWSG EBee ELan EPfP SBch SDnm SEND SHlg SPav SWvt
tabacum CArn SPav
- var. ***macrophylla*** CDTJ
'Tinkerbell' CSpe

Nidularium (*Bromeliaceae*)

flandria see *Neoregelia carolinae* (Meyendorffii Group) 'Flandria'
innocentii XBlo

× *Niduregelia* (*Bromeliaceae*)

§ 'Surprise' MBri

Nierembergia (*Solanaceae*)

caerulea see *N. linariifolia*
frutescens see *N. scoparia*
hippomanica see *N. linariifolia*
§ ***linariifolia*** ♀H1 CAbP EBee EHrv
§ ***repens*** CStu ECho EDAr NLar
rivularis see *N. repens*
§ ***scoparia*** CSpr

Nigella (*Ranunculaceae*)

papillosa 'African Bride' CSpe
- 'Midnight' CSpe

Nigritella see *Gymnadenia*

Nipponanthemum (*Asteraceae*)

§ ***nipponicum*** CAby CDes CWan EBee ECho GCal LAst LPio MNrw NSti SRms WBrk WCot
* - ***roseum*** LPio

Noccaea see *Thlaspi*

Nolina (*Dracaenaceae*)

F&M 333 new WPGP
bigelovii CBrP WPGP
lindheimeriana EBee
longifolia EAmu
microcarpa WCot
nelsonii EAmu WPGP
parryi WCot
- subsp. ***wolfii*** new WPGP
parviflora NJM 05.010 WPGP
texana CTrC NWCA

Nomocharis (*Liliaceae*)

aperta CPLG CWCL EBee EBrs ECho EHrv GBuc GCra GEdr GGar GKir GLin LAma LRHS WCru
- ACE 2271 WWst
- CLD 229 GBuc WWst
- CLD 482 GEdr
- CLD 524 WWst
- KGB 777 GEdr
farreri EBee EBrs ECho
× ***finlayorum*** EBee EBrs ECho GBuc GEdr WWst
mairei see *N. pardanthina*
meleagrina EBee EBrs ECho GAuc GBuc GEdr LAma WAbe WWst
nana see *Lilium nanum*
oxypetala see *Lilium oxypetalum*
§ ***pardanthina*** GAuc GBuc GGGa GGar GMac LRHS WAbe
- CLD 1490 EHrv WWst
- f. ***punctulata*** GBuc GGGa LRHS WCru WWst
saluenensis EBrs ECho GGGa WAbe WWst

Nonea (*Boraginaceae*)

lutea LSou NOrc NSti WCHb WHal

Nothochelone see *Penstemon*

Nothofagus ✿ (*Fagaceae*)

§ × ***alpina*** CBcs CDul CMCN GBin GKir IFFs LRHS NWea WDin
antarctica CBcs CCVT CDul CLnd CMCN CTho EBee ECrN ELan EPfP EWTr GKir IFFs LRHS MBar MBlu MBri MGos NPal NWea STre WDin WSHC
betuloides CBcs CMCN GBin IFFs WPGP
cunninghamii CDul GKir IArd IFFs
dombeyi CBcs CDoC CDul CLnd CMCN CTho EBee EPfP GBin GKir IArd IFFs LHyd LRHS MBlu NWea SAPC SArc SSpi STre WPGP WSpi
fusca CBcs CDoC MGos
glauca CBcs CDul IFFs
menziesii CBcs CDul CTrC IFFs
nitida CBcs GBin IArd IDee IFFs WPGP

obliqua	CDoC CDul CLnd CMCN ISea NWea STre WDin
procera misapplied	see *N.* × *alpina*
pumilio	CBcs GBin
solanderi	GGar

Notholaena see *Cheilanthes*

Notholirion (*Liliaceae*)

bulbuliferum	EBee EBrs ECho EPot GAuc GBuc GCra LRHS WAbe
- Cox 5074	WWst
campanulatum	EBee EBrs ECho GAuc WWst
macrophyllum	EBee EBrs ECho GAuc GBuc WWst
thomsonianum	EBee EBrs ECho WWst

Nothoscordum (*Alliaceae*)

sp.	GCal
gracile	CFir WPrP
montevidense new	WWst
neriniflorum	see *Caloscordum neriniflorum*
ostenii new	SCnR
strictum	EBee ECho

Nuphar (*Nymphaeaceae*)

advenum	LPBA
japonica	CRow NLar
var. ***variegata*** (v)	
lutea	CRow EHon EMFW LPBA MMuc NSco SCoo SWat
- subsp. ***advena***	EMFW

Nuxia (*Buddlejaceae*)

congesta	EShb
floribunda	EShb

Nylandtia (*Polygalaceae*)

spinosa	SPlb

Nymphaea ✿ (*Nymphaeaceae*)

alba (H)	CBen CRWN CRow CWat EHon EMFW EPfP LPBA MSKA NBir NSco SCoo SVic SWat WMAq WPnP
'Alba Plenissima' (H)	WPnP
'Albatros' misapplied	see *N.* 'Hermine'
§ 'Albatros' Latour-Marliac (H)	CWat LPBA MSKA NPer SWat WPnP
'Albatross'	see *N.* 'Albatros' Latour-Marliac, *N.* 'Hermine'
* 'Albida'	WMAq XBlo
'Almost Black' (H)	CBen MSKA
'Amabilis' (H)	CBen CRow EMFW LPBA MSKA SWat WMAq
'American Star' (H)	CBen CWat EMFW SWat WMAq
'Andreana' (H)	CBen CWat LLWG LPBA MSKA SWat
'Arc-en-ciel' (H)	CBen LPBA SCoo SWat WMAq
'Arethusa' (H)	LPBA
'Atropurpurea' (H)	CBen LLWG LPBA MSKA NPer SWat WMAq
'Attraction' (H)	CBen CRow EHon EMFW EPfP LPBA MSKA NPer SCoo SVic SWat WMAq XBlo
'Aurora' (H)	CBen EMFW LPBA SVic SWat WMAq WPnP
'Barbara Davies' (H)	LLWG
'Barbara Dobbins' (H)	CBen LLWG LPBA MSKA
'Bateau' (H)	LLWG
'Berit Strawn' (H)	LLWG
'Bernice Ikins' (H)	MSKA
'Berthold' (H)	CBen
'Brakeleyi Rosea' (H)	CBen LPBA MSKA WMAq
'Burgundy Princess' (H)	CWat LLWG MSKA NPer
candida (H)	CBen EHon EMFW MSKA NPer WMAq
'Candidissima' (H)	SWat
§ ***capensis*** (T/D)	XBlo
'Carolina Sunset' (H)	LLWG
'Caroliniana Nivea' (H)	CBen EHon EMFW
'Caroliniana Perfecta' (H)	CBen LPBA MSKA SWat
'Celebration' (H)	LLWG MSKA
'Charlene Strawn' (H)	CWat EMFW LLWG LPBA WMAq
'Charles de Meurville' (H)	CBen CRow EMFW LPBA MSKA NPer SVic WMAq WPnP
'Château le Rouge' (H)	LLWG
'Clyde Ikins' (H)	MSKA
'Colonel A.J. Welch' (H)	CBen EHon EMFW LPBA MSKA NPer SCoo SWat WMAq
'Colorado' (H)	CBen LLWG MSKA NPer
colorata	see *N. capensis*
'Colossea' (H)	CBen CWat EMFW LPBA MSKA NPer WPnP
'Comanche' (H)	CBen EMFW MSKA NPer WMAq
'Conqueror' (H)	CBen EMFW IArd LPBA MSKA NPer SCoo SVic SWat
'Dallas' (H)	EMFW
§ 'Darwin' (H)	CBen CWat LPBA MSKA NPer SWat WMAq WPnP
× ***daubenyana*** (T/D)	ECho
'David' (H)	CBen LLWG
'Denver' (H)	LLWG MSKA
'Ellisiana' (H)	CBen EMFW LLWG LPBA MSKA NPer SWat
'Escarboucle' (H) $\mathbb{Y}^{H4}$	CBen CRow CWat EHon EMFW LPBA MSKA NLar NPer SCoo SVic SWat WMAq WPnP XBlo
'Esmeralda' (H)	SWat
§ 'Fabiola' (H)	CBen CRow EHon EMFW EPfP LPBA MSKA NPer SCoo WMAq
'Fiesta'	MSKA
'Fire Crest' (H)	CBen EMFW LPBA MSKA NPer SCoo SVic SWat WMAq
'Fireball' (H)	MSKA
'Fritz Junge' (H)	CBen
'Froebelii' (H)	CBen CRow CWat EHon EMFW LPBA MSKA NPer SWat WMAq WPnP
'Fulva' (H)	LLWG
'Galatée' (H)	CBen MSKA
'Geisha Girl'	MSKA
'Georgia Peach' (H)	LLWG MSKA
'Gladstoniana' (H) $\mathbb{Y}^{H4}$	CBen CRow EHon EMFW LPBA MSKA NPer SCoo SWat WMAq
'Gloire du Temple-sur-Lot' (H)	CBen EHon EMFW NPer SWat WMAq
'Gloriosa' (H)	CBen LPBA NPer SCoo SWat WPnP
'Gold Medal' (H)	CBen LLWG MSKA
'Gonnère' (H) $\mathbb{Y}^{H4}$	CBen CRow CWat EHon EMFW EPfP LPBA MSKA NPer SWat WMAq WPnP
'Graziella' (H)	CBen LPBA MSKA WMAq WPnP
'Gypsy' (H)	LLWG
'Hal Miller' (H)	LLWG
'Hassell' (H)	LLWG
'Helen Fowler' (H)	EMFW SWat WMAq
× ***helvola***	see *N.* 'Pygmaea Helvola'
§ 'Hermine' (H)	CBen MSKA NPer SWat WMAq
'Highlight'	LLWG
'Hollandia' misapplied	see *N.* 'Darwin'
'Hollandia' Koster (H)	SWat
'Indiana' (H)	CBen EMFW LPBA MSKA NPer WMAq
'Inner Light'	LLWG MSKA

	Name	Suppliers
	'James Brydon' (H) $\mathbb{Y}^{H4}$	CBen CHid CRow CWat EHon EMFW EPfP LPBA MSKA NLar NPer SCoo SVic SWat WMAq WPnP
	'Jean de Lamarsalle' (H)	LLWG
	'Jerusalem Dawn'	MSKA
§	'Joanne Pring' (H)	SWat
	'Joey Tomocik' (H)	CBen CWat EMFW LLWG LPBA MSKA SCoo WMAq WPnP
	'King of the Blues' (T/D)	MSKA
	'Lactea' (H)	CBen LLWG
	'Laydekeri Fulgens' (H)	CBen EMFW LPBA MSKA SWat WMAq
	'Laydekeri Lilacea' (H)	CBen CRow LPBA SWat WMAq
	'Laydekeri Purpurata' (H)	CBen LPBA SWat
	'Laydekeri Rosea' misapplied	see *N.* 'Laydekeri Rosea Prolifera'
§	'Laydekeri Rosea Prolifera' (H)	CBen EMFW LPBA
	'Lemon Chiffon' (H)	CBen MSKA
	'Lemon Mist'	LLWG MSKA
	'Lily Pons' (H)	CBen MSKA
	'Limelight'	SWat
	'Liou' (H)	CBen LLWG MSKA
	'Little Sue' (H)	LLWG MSKA
	'Livingstone' (H)	LLWG
	'Luciana'	see *N.* 'Odorata Luciana'
	'Lucida' (H)	CBen EMFW LPBA MSKA SWat WMAq
	'Madame Wilfon Gonnère' (H)	CBen CWat EHon EMFW LPBA MSKA NPer SVic SWat WMAq
	'Marliacea Albida' (H)	CBen CWat EHon EMFW LPBA MSKA NPer SWat WMAq WPnP XBlo
	'Marliacea Carnea' (H)	CBen CRow EHon EMFW EPfP LPBA MSKA NPer SCoo SWat WMAq
§	'Marliacea Chromatella' (H) $\mathbb{Y}^{H4}$	CBen CHid CRow CWat EHon EMFW EPfP LPBA MSKA NLar SCoo SVic SWat WMAq WPnP XBlo
	'Marliacea Rosea' (H)	CBen MSKA SWat WMAq XBlo
	'Marliacea Rubra Punctata' (H)	LPBA
	'Mary' (H)	LLWG
	'Masaniello' (H)	CBen CRow EHon EPfP LPBA MSKA SWat WMAq
	'Maurice Laydeker' (H)	CBen LLWG
	'Maxima'	see *N.* 'Odorata Maxima'
	'Mayla'	CBen LLWG LPBA MSKA NPer
§	'Météor' (H)	CBen CWat MSKA WMAq
	mexicana	MSKA
	'Millennium Pink'	MSKA
	'Moorei' (H)	CBen LPBA MSKA SWat WMAq
	'Mrs Richmond' misapplied	see *N.* 'Fabiola'
	'Mrs Richmond' Latour-Marliac (H)	SWat XBlo
	'Neptune' (H)	LLWG
	'Newchapel Beauty'	WMAq
	'Newton' (H)	CBen LLWG MSKA SWat WMAq
	'Nigel' (H)	CBen EMFW LLWG MSKA SWat
	'Norma Gedye' (H)	CBen CWat LPBA MSKA SWat WMAq
	'Odalisque' (H)	CBen EMFW
§	***odorata*** (H)	CBen CRow EHon EMFW LPBA MSKA SCoo WMAq
§	- var. ***minor*** (H)	CBen CRow LPBA MSKA SWat WMAq
	- 'Pumila'	see *N. odorata* var. *minor*
	- subsp. ***tuberosa*** (H)	CBen LPBA
	'Odorata Alba'	see *N. odorata*
§	'Odorata Luciana' (H)	EMFW
§	'Odorata Maxima' (H)	WMAq
	'Odorata Sulphurea' (H)	CBen EHon SWat WPnP
§	'Odorata Sulphurea Grandiflora' (H)	CBen CRow LPBA MSKA SCoo SWat XBlo
§	'Odorata Turicensis' (H)	LPBA MSKA
	'Odorata William B. Shaw'	see *N.* 'W.B. Shaw'
	'Pam Bennett' (H)	CBen LLWG
	'Panama Pacific' (T/D)	XBlo
	'Patio Joe'	LLWG MSKA
	'Paul Hariot' (H)	CWat EHon EMFW LPBA MSKA NPer SWat WMAq WPnP
	'Peace Lily'	LLWG MSKA
	'Peach Glow'	LLWG MSKA
	'Peaches and Cream' (H)	MSKA
	Pearl of the Pool (H)	SWat
	'Perry's Baby Red' (H)	CBen CWat EMFW LLWG MSKA NPer SCoo WMAq
	'Perry's Crinkled Pink' (H)	CBen
	'Perry's Double White' (H)	MSKA NPer WPnP
	'Perry's Double Yellow'	MSKA WPnP
	'Perry's Dwarf Red' (H)	MSKA
	'Perry's Fire Opal' (H)	MSKA NPer
	'Perry's Orange Sunset'	MSKA
	'Perry's Pink' (H)	SWat WMAq
	'Perry's Red Beauty' (H)	CBen
	'Perry's Red Bicolor' (H)	LLWG
	'Perry's Red Glow' (H)	MSKA
	'Perry's Red Wonder' (H)	CBen
	'Perry's Viviparous Pink' (H)	CBen
	'Perry's White Star' (H)	LLWG
	'Perry's Yellow Sensation'	see *N.* 'Yellow Sensation'
	'Peter Slocum' (H)	SWat
	'Phoebus' (H)	CBen SWat
	'Picciola' (H)	LLWG
	'Pink Domino'	MSKA
	'Pink Grapefruit' (H)	XBlo
	'Pink Opal' (H)	CBen CWat EMFW LPBA
	'Pink Peony' (H)	MSKA
	'Pink Pumpkin' (H)	LLWG
	'Pink Sensation' (H)	CBen EMFW LLWG MSKA NPer SWat WMAq
	'Pink Sparkle' (H)	LLWG
	'Pink Sunrise' (H)	MSKA
	'Pöstlingberg' (H)	LLWG LPBA
	'Princess Elizabeth' (H)	CBen EHon LLWG LPBA
	'Pygmaea Alba'	see *N. tetragona*
§	'Pygmaea Helvola' (H) $\mathbb{Y}^{H4}$	CBen CHid CRow CWat EHon EMFW LPBA MSKA NLar NPer SCoo SVic SWat WMAq WPnP
	'Pygmaea Rubis' (H)	CRow EHon LPBA SWat WMAq
	'Pygmaea Rubra' (H)	CBen CWat EMFW MSKA NLar NPer SCoo SVic WMAq WPnP
	'Ray Davies' (H)	CBen EMFW LLWG
	'Red Paradise' (H)	MSKA
	'Red Spider' (H)	CWat EMFW LPBA MSKA NPer SVic
	'Rembrandt' misapplied	see *N.* 'Météor'
	'Rembrandt' Koster (H)	LPBA
	'René Gérard' (H)	CBen CWat EHon EMFW LPBA MSKA NPer SWat WMAq WPnP
	'Rosanna Supreme' (H)	LLWG SWat
	'Rose Arey' (H)	CBen EHon EMFW LPBA MSKA NPer SCoo SVic SWat WMAq
	'Rose Magnolia' (H)	CWat SWat
	'Rosea' (H)	LPBA
	'Rosennymphe' (H)	CBen LPBA MSKA NPer SWat WMAq WPnP
	'Rosy Morn' (H)	CBen LLWG MSKA
	'Seignouretti' (H)	EMFW
	'Shady Lady'	MSKA
	'Sioux' (H)	CBen EHon EMFW LPBA MSKA NPer SVic WMAq XBlo
	'Sirius' (H)	CBen EMFW LLWG LPBA MSKA SWat

'Snow Princess'	EMFW LPBA WPnP
'Solfatare' (H)	LLWG
'Somptuosa' (H)	EPfP
'Splendida' (H)	WMAq
'Starbright'	LLWG
'Starburst' (H)	MSKA
'Steven Strawn' (H)	LLWG
'Sultan' (H)	MSKA
'Sunny Pink'	LLWG MSKA
'Sunrise'	see *N.* 'Odorata Sulphurea Grandiflora'
§ ***tetragona*** (H)	CBen CRow EHon LPBA NPer WMAq
- 'Alba'	see *N. tetragona*
- 'Johann Pring'	see *N.* 'Joanne Pring'
'Texas Dawn' (H)	CBen CWat EMFW LLWG MSKA WMAq
'Thomas O'Brian'	LLWG
'Tuberosa Flavescens'	see *N.* 'Marliacea Chromatella'
'Tuberosa Richardsonii' (H)	CBen EHon EMFW MSKA NPer WPnP
'Turicensis'	see *N.* 'Odorata Turicensis'
'Vésuve' (H)	EMFW LLWG MSKA SWat
'Virginalis' (H)	EMFW LLWG LPBA MSKA NPer SWat WMAq
'Virginia' (H)	LLWG
§ 'W.B. Shaw' (H)	CBen EHon EMFW LPBA MSKA NPer SWat WMAq
'Walter Pagels' (H)	CBen EMFW LLWG WMAq
'Weymouth Red' (H)	CBen
'White Sultan' (H)	CWat LLWG MSKA
'William Doogue' (H)	MSKA
'William Falconer' (H)	CBen CWat EMFW LPBA MSKA NPer SWat
'Wow' (H)	MSKA
'Yellow Queen' (H)	MSKA
§ 'Yellow Sensation' (H)	CBen
'Yul Ling' (H)	LLWG MSKA SWat
'Zeus'	MSKA

Nymphoides (*Menyanthaceae*)

indica **new**	XBlo
peltata	CBen CWat EMFW EPfP MSKA NLar NPer NSco SCoo SVic WMAq WPnP
§ - 'Bennettii'	EHon LPBA

Nyssa ✿ (*Cornaceae*)

aquatica	CBcs CTho LRHS SBir SSta
sinensis ♀H4	CAbP CBcs CDoC CDul CMCN CTho ELan EPfP GKir IDee LRHS MBlu SBir SPer SReu SSpi SSta
- 'Jim Russell' **new**	SSta
- Nymans form	EPfP LRHS SBir
sylvatica ♀H4	Widely available
- 'Autumn Cascades'	EBee EPfP MBlu NLar SSta WPGP
- 'Haymen's Red'	see *N. sylvatica* Red Rage
- 'Isobel Grace'	LRHS MAsh MBri SBir SSpi
- 'Jermyns Flame'	CAbP EPfP LRHS MBri SBir SSpi SSta
- 'Miss Scarlet' (f)	NLar SSta
§ - Red Rage = 'Haymanred'	LRHS SSpi
- 'Red Red Wine'	CGHE EPfP NLar SBir SSta WPGP
- 'Sheffield Park'	CAbP EPfP LRHS MAsh SBir SLim SSpi
- 'Wildfire' **new**	LRHS SSpi
- 'Windsor'	EPfP LRHS SBir SSpi
- 'Wisley Bonfire' (m)	CAbP CGHE ECrN EPfP LRHS MBri NLar SBir SPoG SSpi SSta WPGP
ursina **new**	CBcs

O

Oakesiella see *Uvularia*

Ochagavia (*Bromeliaceae*)

sp.	CMac NPal SAPC SArc
carnea	WGwG
- RCB RA S-2	LSou
elegans	WPGP
* ***rosea***	CHEx

Ochna (*Ochnaceae*)

serrulata	CCCN

Ocimum (*Lamiaceae*)

'African Blue'	CArn CBod ELau EOHP GPoy LSou MHer NBlu NGHP NPri SPoG SVil
§ ***americanum***	NGHP
- 'Meng Luk'	see *O. americanum*
basilicum	CArn CSev ELau GPoy NBlu NPri SBch SIde SWat WPer
- 'Anise'	see *O. basilicum* 'Horapha'
- 'Ararat'	NGHP
- ***camphorata***	see *O. kilimandscharicum*
- 'Cinnamon'	ELau MNHC NGHP SBch SHDw WJek
- 'Cuban'	GPoy
- 'Genovese'	ELau MHer MNHC NGHP NVic
- 'Glycyrrhiza'	see *O. basilicum* 'Horapha'
- 'Green Globe'	MNHC NGHP
- 'Green Ruffles'	ELau EPfP MNHC WJek
- 'Holy'	see *O. tenuiflorum*
§ - 'Horapha'	CArn MHer MNHC NGHP SIde WJek
* - 'Horapha Nanum'	NGHP WJek
- 'Magic White' **new**	NGHP
- 'Mrs Burns'	NGHP
- 'Napolitano'	CBod NGHP SIde SWat WJek
- var. ***purpurascens***	CArn CSev NBlu SIde
- - 'Dark Opal'	CBod MNHC NGHP SBch SHDw WJek
- - 'Purple Ruffles'	EPfP MNHC SIde SMrm SWat WJek
- - 'Red Rubin'	MHer MNHC WJek
- var. ***purpurascens*** × ***kilimandscharicum***	CSpe GPoy
- 'Sweet Genovase'	SVic
- 'Thai'	see *O. basilicum* 'Horapha'
canum	see *O. americanum*
× ***citriodorum***	CArn MNHC NGHP SBch SHDw SIde WJek
- 'Lime'	MNHC NGHP
- 'Pesto Perpetuo' **new**	NGHP
- 'Siam Queen'	MHer NGHP WJek
'Cypriot'	GPoy
§ ***kilimandscharicum***	GPoy
minimum	CArn CBod CSev ELau MHer MNHC NGHP SBch SIde WJek WPer
sanctum	see *O. tenuiflorum*
'Spice'	NGHP
§ ***tenuiflorum***	CArn GPoy MNHC NGHP SBch SHDw SIde WJek

Odontonema (*Acanthaceae*)

schomburgkianum	CCCN
tubaeforme	CCCN

Oemleria (*Rosaceae*)

cerasiformis	CBcs CMac CPMA EBtc EPfP EPla NLar SSpi WCot WEas WHCG WSHC

Oenanthe (Apiaceae)

	aquatica 'Variegata' (v)	EMFW
	crocata	EBWF
*	***javanica*** 'Atropurpurea'	EHoe
	- 'Flamingo' (v)	CWat ELan EPfP GCal GGar LEdu LPBA NBro WFar WMAq WSHC
	lachenalii	EBWF
	pimpinelloides	EBee

Oenothera ✿ (Onagraceae)

	from South America	MTho
§	***acaulis***	CBot CSpe CSpr EBee MNrw SBch SGar SPhx
	- ***alba***	MDKP WCot
	'Apricot Delight'	EBee EHoe GJos LRHS NBur SMad STes WMnd WMoo
§	***biennis***	CArn COld CSev CWan EBWF ELan GAbr GPoy MHer NBro NGHP SBch SGar SIde SPhx WBrk WEas WFar WHer WJek WPer WSFF
	'Blood Orange' **new**	CBow MDKP SMrm
	caespitosa	NWCA
	subsp. ***caespitosa*** NNS 93-505	
*	***campylocalyx***	LDai
	childsii	see *O. speciosa*
	cinaeus	see *O. fruticosa* subsp. *glauca*
	'Cold Crick'	EBee ELon
	'Colin Porter'	CSsd EBur LFur MDKP NBur NWCA WHrl WMoo WPer
	'Copper Canyon'	SGSe STes
	'Crown Imperial'	CChe CMac EBee LEdu LRHS LSou MCCP NHol SHar SLon SPoG
	Crown of Gold = 'Lishal' PBR	ELan LLHF LRHS
§	***elata*** subsp. ***hookeri***	EWes NBre WPer
	erythrosepala	see *O. glazioviana*
	'Finlay's Fancy'	WCru
§	***fruticosa***	NLar SPlb
	- 'African Sun' PBR	EBee EWes SBod SRot
	- 'Camel' (v)	EBee LDai LRHS MDKP NPro SMrm WHrl WWEG
	- Fireworks	see *O. fruticosa* 'Fyrverkeri'
§	- 'Fyrverkeri' ♀H4	CBcs CMac CMea CPrp EBee ECtt ELan EShb GKir LAst LEdu LHop LRHS MRav MWat NBlu NGdn NHol NVic SBod SMrm SPer SWvt WAul WBVN WCAu WMnd WWEG
§	- subsp. ***glauca*** ♀H4	CElw CEnt CHrt EBee EPfP LRHS MDKP MNrw MWhi SBch SRms WPer
	- - 'Erica Robin' (v)	CBct CMea CPrp EBee ECtt EHoe GBuc LAst LHop LRHS LSou MRav NEgg NGdn SAga SMad SMrm SPoG SRot SWvt WCot WHoo WPGP WWEG
	- - 'Frühlingsgold' (v)	CBct CMac EBee ECtt EShb SPoG
	- - 'Longest Day'	MArl MBrN
	- - Solstice	see *O. fruticosa* subsp. *glauca* 'Sonnenwende'
§	- - 'Sonnenwende'	CBre CElw CEnt EBee EBrs LRHS MAvo NGby NLar NPro SPad WMoo WWEG
	- - 'Sunspot' (v)	GBuc
	- Highlight	see *O. fruticosa* 'Hoheslicht'
§	- 'Hoheslicht'	EBee
	- 'Lady Brookeborough'	MRav
	- 'Michelle Ploeger'	NBre NCGa SUsu
	- 'Silberblatt' (v)	CBow LSou
	- 'W. Cuthbertson'	EBee
	- 'Yellow River'	CElw EBee
	- 'Youngii'	CWan EPfP LEdu MBel MCCP WPer WWEG
	glabra Miller	see *O. biennis*
	glabra misapplied	ECha NSti SIng
§	***glazioviana***	CWan MNHC NBir SVic WPer
	hookeri	see *O. elata* subsp. *hookeri*
	kunthiana	CEnt ECho MDKP MHer NWCA WMnd WMoo WPer
	- 'Glowing Magenta'	SHGN SPoG
	lamarckiana	see *O. glazioviana*
	'Lemon Sunset'	CCVN CSsd LRHS LSou MBNS NBur NGHP WMoo
	linearis	see *O. fruticosa*
§	***macrocarpa*** ♀H4	Widely available
	- subsp. ***fremontii*** 'Silver Wings'	ECtt SMrm
	- subsp. ***incana***	CMea CSpe LRHS NBre
	- 'Yellow Queen' **new**	GJos
*	***minima***	MDKP
	missouriensis	see *O. macrocarpa*
	muricata	NBre
	oakesiana	SPhx
	odorata misapplied	see *O. stricta*
	odorata Hook. & Arn.	see *O. biennis*
	odorata Jacquin	CArn
	- cream-flowered	CSpe
	organensis	CDes EBee MBel WPGP
	pallida 'Innocence'	CBot NBre
	'Penelope Hobhouse'	CBct GBuc
§	***perennis***	CEnt CMea EBee NBre NPro SRms WBVN WEas WPer
	pilosella 'Mella Yella' **new**	EBee
	pumila	see *O. perennis*
	rosea	CMea GKev NBur
	'Rosie Baby' **new**	GJos
	'Silky Orchid'	ELon
§	***speciosa***	CMHG EBee LBMP NBre SEND SPer WFar WPer
*	- 'Alba'	EBee EWes
	- 'Ballerina'	LHop
	- var. ***childsii***	see *O. speciosa*
	- 'Pink Petticoats'	ECha NPer SWat
	- 'Rosea'	CBot ECho LEdu LRHS SPlb SWat WPer
	- 'Siskiyou'	CHrt CSpe EAEE EBee ECtt EPfP EShb GBuc GKir LBMP LEdu LRHS LSou SCoo SGar SIng SMad SMrm SPer SRot SUsu
	- Twilight = 'Turner01' PBR (v)	LRHS SHar
	- 'Woodside White'	ELon SMrm
§	***stricta***	CHar CHrt CMea ECGP EGoo GCal LRHS WBrk WPer
*	- 'Moonlight'	SGar
	- 'Sulphurea'	CHar CMHG CMea CMil ECGP EGoo ELan EWld GCal IFro MNFA NPer SBch SGar SMrm SPhx SUsu WAbb WCAu WCom WCot WPer
	'Summer Sun'	EAEE EBee ECGP LRHS NBre
	taraxacifolia	see *O. acaulis*
	tetragona	see *O. fruticosa* subsp. *glauca*
	- var. ***fraseri***	see *O. fruticosa* subsp. *glauca*
	versicolor	WCFE
	- 'Sunset Boulevard'	CPom CSam CSpe EBee EGoo GBuc LDai LRHS MBNS NGHP SBod SGar SPer WFar WMoo

Olea (Oleaceae)

europaea (F)	Widely available
- subsp. ***africana***	CTrC WPGP
- 'Aglandau' (F)	CAgr
- 'Arbequina' (F)	SBig
- 'Bouteillan' (F)	CAgr
- 'Cailletier' (F)	CAgr

- 'Chelsea Physic Garden' (F) CDoC WPGP
§ - 'Cipressino' (F) ERea ESwi SBch SBig
- 'El Greco' (F) CBcs
- 'Fastigiata' new SBch
- 'Frantoio' (F) CAgr ERea SBch SBig
- 'Hojiblanca' (F) new SBig
- 'Leccino' (F) new SBig
- 'Manzanillo' (F) ERea
- 'Maurino' (F) new SBig
- 'Pendolino' (F) new SBig
- 'Picual' (F) SBig
- 'Pyramidalis' see *O. europaea* 'Cipressino'
* - 'Sativa' (F) EMui

Olearia ✿ (*Asteraceae*)

albida misapplied see *O.* 'Talbot de Malahide'
albida Hook. f. GGar
- var. ***angulata*** CTrC CTsd
algida ECou GGar
arborescens GGar
argophylla CPLG ECou GGar
avicenniifolia CBcs CMac ECou GGar
bullata new ECou
canescens CPne
× ***capillaris*** CDoC ECou GGar
chathamica GGar IDee IFFs
§ ***cheesemanii*** CBcs CDoC CMHG CPLG CTrC EBee GGal GGar LRHS NLar
coriacea ECou GGar
'County Park' ECou
erubescens CDoC CPLG
floribunda GGar
frostii GGar IDee
furfuracea ECou
glandulosa ECou GGar
gunniana see *O. phlogopappa*
× ***haastii*** Widely available
- 'McKenzie' ECou
'Havering Blush' new ECou
hectorii ECou
§ 'Henry Travers' CBcs CCCN CDoC CPLG EPfP GGar GQui IDee LRHS NMun
ilicifolia CDoC EBee EPfP GGar IFFs LRHS WCor
§ ***ilicifolia*** × ***moschata*** GGar LRHS WKif
insignis see *Pachystegia insignis*
ledifolia GGar
lepidophylla ECou
- 'Silver Knight' EBee
- silver-leaved ECou
lirata ECou GGar
macrodonta ♀H3 Widely available
- 'Intermedia' GGar
- 'Major' CCCN GGal GGar
- 'Minor' CBcs CCCN CDoC CMac CTrC ELan EPfP GBin GGar GQui SPlb SPoG WSpi
minor LRHS
× ***mollis*** misapplied see *O. ilicifolia* × *O. moschata*
× ***mollis*** (Kirk) Cockayne EBee GQui LRHS
- 'Zennorensis' ♀H3 CBcs CCCN CDoC EPfP GGar IArd IDee IFFs WDin WEas WPGP
moschata GGar NLar
moschata × ***nummularifolia*** var. ***cymbifolia*** GGar
myrsinoides CPLG
nummularifolia CBcs CCCN CDoC CHll CTrC CTri EBee ECou EPfP EPla GGar GKir ISea LRHS SBch SPer SPoG STre SWvt WCor WDin WFar WKif
- var. ***cymbifolia*** ECou
- hybrids ECou
- 'Little Lou' ECou
odorata CPLG ECou ISea NLar WFar WHCG
oleifolia see *O.* 'Waikariensis'
paniculata CBcs CDoC CMHG CTrC CTri CTsd EBee EPfP GGar IFFs ISea LRHS
§ ***phlogopappa*** CHrt CTri ECou GGar WBrE
- 'Comber's Blue' CBcs CCCN EPfP GGal GGar GKir LRHS LSRN SCoo SPer
§ - 'Comber's Pink' CBcs CCCN CDoC CPLG CWan EBee ELon EPfP GGar GKir LRHS LSRN MAsh NPer SAga SCoo WEas WGrn WSHC
- pink-flowered CTrG
- 'Rosea' see *O. phlogopappa* 'Comber's Pink'
- 'Sawtooth' GGar
- Splendens Group WFar
I - var. ***subrepanda*** (DC.) J.H. Willis CTrC GGal GGar LEdu WAbe
- 'Tournaig Titch' GGar
ramulosa CCCN CDoC CPLG
- 'Blue Stars' ECou GGar LRHS
- var. ***ramulosa*** ECou
rani misapplied see *O. cheesemanii*
rani Druce IFFs ISea
* ***rossii*** CTrC
× ***scilloniensis*** misapplied see *O. stellulata* DC.
× ***scilloniensis*** ambig. CBcs IFFs SPoG WFar WKif
× ***scilloniensis*** Dorrien-Smith ♀H3 CCCN CTsd GGar MRav
- 'Compacta' CBcs
- 'Master Michael' CBot CCCN CDoC EBee ELon EPfP ERas LRHS NPri SBod SPer SPoG WAbe WEas WGrn WKif WSHC
semidentata misapplied see *O.* 'Henry Travers'
solandri CCCN CDoC CMac CTsd CWit EBee ECou GGar LRHS SDix SEND SPer STre
- 'Aurea' CBcs GQui
'Stardust' new CTrC CWit
stellulata misapplied see *O. phlogopappa*
§ ***stellulata*** DC. CBot CPLG CSBt CTrG CWSG CWib ECou EPfP GGal LRHS SCoo SDix SGar SPer WDin WEas WFar
- 'Michael's Pride' CPLG
- var. ***rugosa*** ECou
§ 'Talbot de Malahide' GGar
traversii CAlb CBcs CCCN CDoC CHrt CMHG CSBt CTrC CTsd EBee GGal GGar IFFs LRHS SBch SEND WHer
- 'Tweedledum' (v) CAlb CBow CCCN CDoC CTrC CWib EBee ECou GGar IMon WCom
- 'Variegata' (v) CBcs CTsd
virgata CCCN CHEx ECou GBin GGar GQui IMon LEdu MCot WCot
- var. ***laxiflora*** CTrC WHer
- var. ***lineata*** CDoC CPLG ECou GGar NLar SEND WDin WSHC
- - 'Dartonii' CBcs CDoC EBee ECou EPfP GGar LRHS SLPl
§ 'Waikariensis' CBot CMHG CMac CPLG CTrC ECou GGar IDee LRHS MSCN SEND SLon WCFE WDin

Oligoneuron see *Solidago*

Oligostachyum (*Poaceae*)

lubricum see *Semiarundinaria lubrica*
oedogonatum WPGP

olive see *Olea europaea*

Olsynium (*Iridaceae*)

§ ***douglasii*** ♀H4	CBro EBee EPot LLHF NMen NRya SIng WAbe WCot
- 'Album'	EBee ELon GAbr GBin GEdr NMen NRya NSla SIng WHal
- dwarf	GEdr
- var. ***inflatum***	EWes
§ ***filifolium***	NWCA
§ ***junceum***	MDKP WPGP
- JCA 12289	MTho
scirpoideum	LLHF
trinerve B&SWJ 10459	WCru

Omphalodes ✿ (*Boraginaceae*)

cappadocica ♀H4	CElw CEnt EBee EPot EShb IFoB LBMP LEdu LRHS MAvo NBro NCob NPer NSum NWCA SRms SWat WBrk WFar WKif WPat
- 'Anthea Bloom'	GBuc NEgg
- 'Blueberries and Cream' (v)	CBow WCot
- 'Cherry Ingram' ♀H4	Widely available
- 'Lilac Mist'	CLAP EBee EPot LLWP MRav NCob SBch SRms SSvw SWat SWvt WGwG WTin WWEG
- 'Parisian Skies'	CLAP
- 'Starry Eyes'	Widely available
§ ***linifolia*** ♀H4	CMea CSpe MCot NMen SBch
- ***alba***	see *O. linifolia*
luciliae	CLAP EBee GKev WThu
- var. ***cilicica***	WFar
nitida	CSpe EWld GGar IMou NRya
verna	Widely available
- 'Alba'	Widely available
- 'Elfenauge'	CMil NBir NCGa NRya SMrm SSvw WCot WWEG
- ***grandiflora***	WCot

Omphalogramma (*Primulaceae*)

delavayi SDR 5167	GKev

Oncostema see *Scilla*

onion see *Allium cepa*

Onixotis (*Colchicaceae*)

triquetra	WCot

Onobrychis (*Papilionaceae*)

viciifolia	EBWF EBee

Onoclea (*Woodsiaceae*)

sensibilis ♀H4	Widely available
- copper-leaved	CHEx CRow WPGP

Ononis (*Papilionaceae*)

repens	CArn EBWF NMir
rotundifolia	CPom
spinosa	EBWF EBee MHer SMrm WFar WPer WSpi

Onopordum (*Asteraceae*)

acanthium	CArn CBct EBee EBrs ECha ELan EPfP GAbr GBar GKir GMaP LRHS MHer MSpe MWat NBid NEgg NVic SBch SIde WCAu WCHb WCot WFar WHer WMnd WSpi
arabicum	see *O. nervosum*
bracteatum	WPer
§ ***nervosum*** ♀H4	CSpe EBee NBur SRms
turcicum	EBee

Onosma (*Boraginaceae*)

alborosea	CMdw CSev EBee ECha EGoo GCal GCra SAga SEND WEas WKif WPGP WPat WSHC
nana	WAbe
taurica ♀H4	CMdw

Onychium (*Adiantaceae*)

contiguum	WAbe
japonicum	EFer EFtx GQui SMad SRms WAbe
lucidum	WCot

Ophiopogon ✿ (*Convallariaceae*)

ACE 2362 **new**	NMen
BWJ 8244 from Vietnam	WCru
from India	GCal
'Black Dragon'	see *O. planiscapus* 'Nigrescens'
bodinieri	CBct ECho ERos EShb EWes LEdu SMac
- B&L 12505	CLAP EBee EPPr EPla
caulescens B&SWJ 8230	WCru
- B&SWJ 11813	WCru
aff. ***caulescens*** HWJ 590	WCru
chingii	EBee EPPr GCal LEdu SCnR
formosanus	CPrp GBin
- B&SWJ 3659	EBee WCru
'Gin-ryu'	see *Liriope spicata* 'Gin-ryu'
graminifolius	see *Liriope muscari*
intermedius	CBct CStu EBee EPPr ERos GGar NLar SGar WAbe WCot WPGP
- GWJ 9387	WCru
§ - 'Argenteomarginatus'	ECho ERos EWes WPGP
- 'Variegatus'	see *O. intermedius* 'Argenteomarginatus'
'Irish Mist' (v) **new**	NPro
§ ***jaburan***	EBee ECho EShb LBMP LEdu NHol STre WMoo
- 'Variegatus'	see *O. jaburan* 'Vittatus'
§ - 'Vittatus' (v)	CMHG ECho EHoe ELan EPfP EShb EWes LEdu MAvo MBNS MCCP MGos SAga WCot WFar WSpi
japonicus	CBro CMac ECho EPPr EPfP EPla EShb LEdu
- B&SWJ 1871	WCru
- 'Albus'	CLAP ECho NHol
- 'Compactus'	CDoC EBee WPGP
- 'Kigimafukiduma'	CMoH CPen EBee GGar LRHS MRav SPad WCot WSpi
- 'Kyoto'	EPPr NLAp
- 'Minor'	CBct CEnd CKno EBee EPPr EPfP EPla NLar WPGP WWEG
- 'Nanus Variegatus' (v)	CDes EBee NChi
- 'Nippon'	CPrp EBee ECho EHoe EPPr GGar LAst LRHS NGdn
- 'Tama-ryu'	WPat
* - 'Tama-ryu Number Two'	ECho EPPr
* - 'Variegatus' (v)	CDTJ CKno CPrp ECho LEdu SLPl
longifolius 'Takashi-shimomura' (v)	WCot
parviflorus GWJ 9387	WCru
- HWJK 2093	WCru
planiscapus	CEnd CFee CKno CMHG CPLG CSWP CSam CSev EBee ECho EPPr EPla EShb GAbr MTho MWat NBro SPad STre WMoo
* - 'Albovariegatus'	WFar
- 'Green Dragon'	ELan LRHS
- 'Kansu'	SBch
- ***leucanthus***	EPPr WCot

- 'Little Tabby' (v) CBow CDes CLAP EBee ECho EPla MDKP MMoz MWhi NPro WAbe WCot WDyG WHal WPGP WTin WWEG
* - ***minimus*** ECho ERos
§ - 'Nigrescens' ♀H4 Widely available
- 'Silver Ribbon' ECho MDKP SGar
scaber B&SWJ 1842 WCru
'Spring Gold' CMil EShb

Ophrys (*Orchidaceae*)

apifera CFir NLAp WHer
- subsp. ***trollii*** NLAp
apifera × ***holoserica*** NLAp
apifera × ***scolopax*** NLAp
araneola NLAp
bombyliflora NLAp
fuciflora NLAp
heldreichii NLAp
holoserica NLAp
speculum NLAp
sphegodes NLAp

Oplismenus (*Poaceae*)

undulatifolius EBee

Opopanax (*Apiaceae*)

chironium LEdu

Opuntia (*Cactaceae*)

compressa see *O. humifusa*
§ ***humifusa*** CDTJ EAmu EGxp ETod SChr SMad
microdasys SWal
- var. ***albospina*** SWal
§ ***polyacantha*** SChr SPlb
rhodantha see *O. polyacantha*

orange, sour or Seville see *Citrus aurantium*

orange, sweet see *Citrus sinensis*

Orbea (*Asclepiadaceae*)

caudata CFwr
§ ***variegata*** ♀H1 CFwr EShb STre
verrucosa CFwr

Orchis (*Orchidaceae*)

anthropophora EFEx
elata see *Dactylorhiza elata*
foliosa see *Dactylorhiza foliosa*
fuchsii see *Dactylorhiza fuchsii*
laxiflora see *Anacamptis laxiflora*
maculata see *Dactylorhiza maculata*
maderensis see *Dactylorhiza foliosa*
majalis see *Dactylorhiza majalis*
§ ***mascula*** ECho NLAp WCot WHer
militaris GAuc NLAp WHer
morio see *Anacamptis morio*
purpurea NLAp
simia NLAp

oregano see *Origanum vulgare*

Oreomyrrhis (*Apiaceae*)

argentea GKev NMen

Oreopteris (*Thelypteridaceae*)

§ ***limbosperma*** SRms WRic

Oreorchis (*Orchidaceae*)

patens WWst

Oresitrophe (*Saxifragaceae*)

rupifraga WCru

Origanum ✿ (*Lamiaceae*)

acutidens WCHb
amanum ♀H2-3 CPBP EBee ECho EWes MDKP NBir NMen WAbe WCom WPat
- var. ***album*** EBee ECho LLHF NSla WAbe
× ***applii*** ELau
'Barbara Tingey' CMea CPBP CWCL EBee ECho ELan EWes ITim LBee LRHS MNrw MTho NWCA SPhx WAbe WCFE
'Bristol Cross' ECha GBar MHer NGby
'Buckland' CPrp CWCL EBee ECho ECtt EPot MHer NMen NWCA SPhx WAbe WCom WSHC
caespitosum see *O. vulgare* 'Nanum'
§ ***calcaratum*** EBee ECho LLHF MTho WAbe WPat
'Carols Delight' NGby
creticum see *O. vulgare* subsp. *hirtum*
dictamnus CArn CEls CMea CStu EBee ECho GPoy LLHF LRHS NWCA SBch SHDw WJek
'Dingle Fairy' CMMP CWCL EBee ECho EDAr EPot EWes GBar MHer MNrw MTho NBir NWCA SBch SIde SIng SRot WGwG WMoo
'Emma Stanley' WAbe
'Erntedank' EBee
'Frank Tingey' EBee ECho LLHF
'Gold Splash' EPfP GBar SIde WMoo
heracleoticum L. see *O. vulgare* subsp. *hirtum*
'Hot and Spicy' GBar NPri
§ × ***hybridinum*** WCom
'Ingolstadt' SPhx
'Kent Beauty' Widely available
'Kent Beauty Variegated' (v) ECho
laevigatum ♀H3 CArn CMHG ECho ELan EPfP EPot GBee MHer NBro NMir NPer NWCA SGar SIde SUsu WCom WKif WMoo WPer WSHC
- 'Herrenhausen' ♀H4 Widely available
- 'Hopleys' Widely available
- 'Purple Charm' EBee EDAr MNHC NBre SIde WSpi
- 'Springwood' NWCA
majorana CArn CSev ELan ELau LRHS MHer MNHC SIde SWal SWat WJek WPer
I - 'Aureum' SWal
- Pagoda Bells = 'Lizbell'PBR CWCL LHop SIde WHoo
microphyllum CFee EDAr GBar MTho NMen SIng SMeo
minutiflorum EBee ECho LLHF
'Norton Gold' CBre EBee ECha ECtt EPot GBar GBuc LRHS MHer NBre NHol NPer SIde
'Nymphenburg' CFee CSam EBee LSou MHer NCob SIde WHer WSpi
onites CArn CHby CWan ELau GBar ILis LBuc MHer MNHC NBlu SBch SIde SPlb WBrk WGwG WJek WPer
pulchellum see *O.* × *hybridinum*
'Purple Cloud' NBir
'Rosenkuppel' CMea CStu EBee ECha ECtt ELan EPot GCal LAst LHop LRHS MHer MLHP MRav NGHP SMeo SPer SPhx SPlb WMoo WPnn WSpi WWEG
'Rotkugel' CAby CHVG CMHG LRHS SMrm WWEG
rotundifolium ♀H4 CMea EBee ECho ELan EPot LLHF MDKP MHer NBir SBch WAbe WCom

- hybrid	MDKP
scabrum	CArn
- subsp. ***pulchrum***	CStu
- - 'Newleaze'	SBch WHoo
syriacum	CArn
'Tinpenny Pink'	WTin
tournefortii	see *O. calcaratum*
villosum	see *Thymus villosus*
virens	CArn GBar ILis MCCP
vulgare	Widely available
- from Israel	ELau
- 'Acorn Bank'	CArn CBod CPrp EBee EGoo ELau EShb EWes GBar GGar MNHC NHol NLar SAga SIde SPoG WCHb WGwG WHer WJek
- var. ***album***	CElw WAlt
- 'Aureum' ♀H4	Widely available
- 'Aureum Crispum'	CPrp CWan ECha EGoo ELau GAbr GBar GPoy ILis NBid NBlu NGHP SBch SIde SWat WJek
- 'Compactum'	CArn CMea CPrp CSev EBee ECha EGoo ELau GBar GCal GGar GPoy ILis LEdu LRHS MHer MNHC NCob NGHP SIde SPlb SWat WCHb WGwG WHoo WMoo WPer WTin
- 'Corinne Tremaine' (v)	NBir WHer
- 'Country Cream' (v)	Widely available
- ***formosanum*** B&SWJ 3180	WCru
§ - 'Gold Tip' (v)	CEnt CMea CSev EBee ELau GBar ILis LBuc MCot MHer MNHC NGHP SBch SIde SPlb SWat WCHb WFar WHer WWEG
- 'Golden Shine'	CMMP EHoe EWes NGHP SIde
§ - subsp. ***hirtum***	CArn CHby GPoy SPlb WJek WPer
- - 'Greek'	CBod CEnt CPrp CWan ELau MHer MNHC NGHP SBch SEND WGwG
§ - 'Nanum'	ECho GBar WJek
- 'Nyamba'	GPoy
- 'Polyphant' (v)	CSev GBar LSou NBir WBrE WCHb WJek
- subsp. ***prismaticum***	GBar
- 'Thumble's Variety'	CElw CMea CPrp EAEE EBee ECha EGoo EHoe EPfP EPot GBar GCal LHop LRHS MBri MHer MRav NCob NGHP NHol SIde SSvw SWat WEas WMnd WMoo WSpi WWEG
- 'Tomintoul'	GPoy
- 'Variegatum'	see *O. vulgare* 'Gold Tip'
- 'White Charm'	EBee NHol SIde
'Z'Attar'	MHer SIde

Orixa (*Rutaceae*)

japonica	CBot CPLG EPfP GAuc MBri NLar WFar WPGP
- 'Variegata' (v)	EPfP LLHF NLar SPoG

Orlaya (*Apiaceae*)

grandiflora	CAby CBre CFir CSpe ILad LBMP LPio SBch SUsu WCot WFar WHal

Ornithogalum (*Hyacinthaceae*)

algeriense new	ECho
arabicum	CBro CFir CHid CMea EBrs ECho LAma LRHS MBri WCot
arcuatum	WCot
arianum	EBee EBrs ECho SPhx
balansae	see *O. oligophyllum*
caudatum	see *O. longibracteatum*
chionophilum	EBee EBrs ECho
comosum	ECho
cuspidatum	EBrs
dubium ♀H1	CBro CStu EBrs ECho LRHS MWea WCot
exscapum	ECho
fimbriatum	EBee EBrs ECho
hispidum new	ECho
lanceolatum	ECho WCot
§ ***longibracteatum***	CHEx CStu EBee ECho GAuc SChr WGwG WPrP
maculatum new	ECho
magnum	CAvo CBro CFFs CMea CSsd EBee EBrs ECho ERCP GAuc LRHS MNrw SPad SPhx WHil
- 'Saguramo'	EBrs ECho
montanum	ECho
'Mount Everest'	ECho ERCP
'Mount Fuji'	EBrs ECho
nanum	see *O. sigmoideum*
narbonense	EBee EBrs ECho GAuc GBuc LRHS MMHG SPhx WCot
nutans ♀H4	CAvo CBro CFFs CHid CPrp CStu EBee EBrs ECho EPfP EPot GCal GKev LAma LRHS MCot MNrw NBir NMen NWCA SMrm SPhx WAul WCot WFar
§ ***oligophyllum***	CStu EBee EBrs ECho EPfP EPot ERCP MMHG MNrw NWCA WCot
§ ***orthophyllum***	EBrs
ponticum	ECho ERos
pyramidale	CDes EBee EBrs ECho EPot GAuc GMac LRHS MNrw SPhx
pyrenaicum	CAvo CStu ECha ERos WCot WShi
reverchonii	CDes EBee EBrs ECho ERos WCot
saundersiae	CHid EBee EBrs ECho LRHS
schmalhausenii	WWst
sibthorpii	see *O. sigmoideum*
§ ***sigmoideum***	CStu EBee EBrs ECho
sintenisii	EBee EBrs ECho LRHS
sphaerocarpum	WCot
tenuifolium	see *O. orthophyllum*
- subsp. ***aridum***	ECho WWst
thyrsoides ♀H1	CCCN EBrs ECho EPfP ERCP LAma LRHS
ulophyllum	EBee EBrs ECho
umbellatum	CAvo CBro CFFs CTri EBrs ECho EPfP GAbr GPoy LAma LHop LRHS MBri MCot MNrw NMen SECG SPer SRms WBVN WFar WHil WPer WShi
unifolium	ECho

Orontium (*Araceae*)

aquaticum	CBen CWat EHon EMFW LLWG LPBA MSKA NLar NPer SWat WMAq WPnP

Orostachys (*Crassulaceae*)

erubescens new	EBee
furusei	WCot WFar
- 'Grey Cloud'	EBee
§ ***spinosa***	EWes LRHS NMen NWCA WFar

Orthrosanthus (*Iridaceae*)

chimboracensis	CDes CFir EWld MDKP MGos MWea NLar WFar WPGP WPer
- JCA 13743	CPou
laxus	CBgR CFir CHid EBee ECou EPau ERos GBuc GMac LLHF SHom SMad WMoo WPrP WWEG
multiflorus	CBro CDes CSpe EBee WPGP
polystachyus	CAby CCVN CSpe CTsd CWCL ERos EWld MAvo MWea SGSe SMrm SSvw SUsu WSHC

Orychophragmus (*Brassicaceae*)

	violaceus	CCCN WHil

Oryzopsis (*Poaceae*)

	hymenoides	LDai
	lessoniana	see *Anemanthele lessoniana*
	miliacea	CKno CSpe EBee ECha EHoe EPPr GFor LDai NWsh SUsu WCot WPGP WWEG
	paradoxa	EPPr

Oscularia (*Aizoaceae*)

§	***deltoides*** ♀H1-2	CCCN CHEx NWCA WCor WEas

Osmanthus (*Oleaceae*)

	armatus	CAbP CBcs CMac CTri EBee EPfP NLar WFar
§	× ***burkwoodii*** ♀H4	Widely available
§	***decorus***	CBcs CMac CTri EBee ELan EPfP EWTr GKir MGos MRav MWea NLar NWea SPer WDin WFar WSpi
	delavayi ♀H4	Widely available
	- 'Latifolius'	CPMA EPfP LRHS MAsh SLon SPer SPoG WFar
	- 'Pearly Gates'	LRHS
	forrestii	see *O. yunnanensis*
	× ***fortunei***	CPLG EPfP LLHF LRHS MGos SEND SLPl WFar
	fragrans	EBee EShb IFFs MBri SLon
	- 'Latifolius'	CBcs
	- f. ***thunbergii***	CBcs
§	***heterophyllus***	CBcs CDul CMac EBee EPfP MBar MRav NLar SPer SReu SRms SSta WDin WFar
§	- all gold	CAbP CDoC LAst SPer
	- 'Argenteomarginatus'	see *O. heterophyllus* 'Variegatus'
§	- 'Aureomarginatus' (v)	CBcs CDoC CMHG CSBt CTsd EBee EHoe EPfP NWea SLon SPer
	- 'Aureus' misapplied	see *O. heterophyllus* all gold
	- 'Aureus' Rehder	see *O. heterophyllus* 'Aureomarginatus'
§	- 'Goshiki' (v)	Widely available
N	- 'Gulftide' ♀H4	CDul EBee ECrN EPfP IFFs LRHS MGos NLar SCoo WFar
	- 'Kembu' (v)	NLar
	- 'Myrtifolius'	CMac NLar
	- 'Ogon'	MBar
	- 'Purple Shaft'	CAbP ELan EPfP LRHS MAsh
	- 'Purpureus'	CAbP CBcs CBot CDoC CDul CMHG CMac CSam CWib EBee ECrN EHoe EPfP MBri MGos MSwo NHol SCoo SEND SLim SLon SPer SSpi WDin
	- 'Rotundifolius'	CBcs CMac EBee NLar
	- Tricolor	see *O. heterophyllus* 'Goshiki'
§	- 'Variegatus' (v) ♀H4	Widely available
	ilicifolius	see *O. heterophyllus*
	rigidus	NLar
	serrulatus	CBot NLar WPGP
	suavis	GKir LRHS NLar
§	***yunnanensis***	EBee EPfP LRHS MBlu MBri NLar SAPC SArc WFar WPGP

× *Osmarea* see *Osmanthus*

Osmaronia see *Oemleria*

Osmitopsis (*Asteraceae*)

	asteriscoides	GFai

Osmorhiza (*Apiaceae*)

	aristata B&SWJ 1607	WCru

Osmunda ✿ (*Osmundaceae*)

	sp.	CCCN
	cinnamomea ♀H4	CBty CCCN CFwr CLAP CWCL EBee EWes GBin GCal LRHS MAsh NMyG SGSe WPGP WRic
	claytoniana ♀H4	CLAP CMil EBee EFer GBin GLin LRHS MAsh NHol NLar NMyG WCru WPnP WRic
	japonica	CLAP GBin
	regalis ♀H4	Widely available
	- from southern USA	CLAP
	- 'Cristata' ♀H4	CFwr CLAP EBee ELan GBin LRHS MBri MRav NBid NLar NMyG WFib WPGP WRic
	- 'Purpurascens'	Widely available
	- var. ***spectabilis***	CCCN CLAP LRHS WRic
	- 'Undulata'	NHol WFib

Osteomeles (*Rosaceae*)

	subrotunda	MBri

Osteospermum (*Asteraceae*)

	'African Queen'	see *O.* 'Nairobi Purple'
	'Almach'PBR (Springstar Series)	LSou MBNS
	'Arctur'PBR	LAst
	'Arusha'PBR (Cape Daisy Series)	LSou
	'Astra Purple Spoon' **new**	WGor
	Banana Symphony = 'Sekiin47' (Symphony Series)	CCCN CWCL LSou MBNS SMrm SPoG
	barberae misapplied	see *O. jucundum* (Phillips) Norlindh
	'Blue Streak'	CCCN
	'Brickell's Hybrid'	see *O.* 'Chris Brickell'
	'Buttermilk' ♀H1+3	CCCN CTsd ELan WCor WWlt
	'Cannington John'	GCra LSRN
	'Cannington Roy'	CBcs CCCN COIW CSam EBee ECtt ELan EPfP GAbr LRHS LSRN
	'Castor'	LAst
	caulescens misapplied	see *O.* 'White Pim'
§	'Chris Brickell'	GCal
	compact white-flowered **new**	CHEx
	ecklonis	CBcs CCCN CDTJ CHll CTri GGar ISea NBro NGdn WPer
	- var. ***prostratum***	see *O.* 'White Pim'
	'Edna Bond'	WEas
	'Gemma'PBR (Springstar Series)	MBNS
	'Giles Gilbey' (v)	CCCN MBNS NBur
	'Gold Sparkler' (v)	SMrm
	'Gweek Variegated' (v)	CCCN
	'Helen Dimond'	LBuc LRHS
	'Hopleys' ♀H3-4	MHer SEND
	'Iced Gem' **new**	LBuc
	'Irish'	EPot GBuc IGor LSou SMrm
§	***jucundum*** (Phillips) Norlindh ♀H3-4	CChe CEnt CMea CTri CWCL ECha EPfP LRHS LSRN MLHP MRav NBir NChi NGdn NHol NPer SEND SMrm SPlb SRms WBVN WBrk
	- 'Blackthorn Seedling' ♀H3-4	CMea CWGN GBuc GGar MWte NGdn SAga
	- var. ***compactum***	CHEx CPBP ELan ELon EPfP EShb GCal GGar LFur LRHS MBri NPer SPer SPoG SPur WAbe WCom WHoo WPat
	- 'Killerton Pink'	WPer

- 'Langtrees' ♀H3-4 SMrm
- 'White Moon' **new** GGar
Kalanga Rosy = 'Aksinto'PBR (Cape Daisy Series) LRHS
'Keia'PBR (Springstar Series) CCCN LSou SMrm
'La Mortola' GCal
§ 'Lady Leitrim' ♀H3-4 CCCN CHEx CHrt CWGN ECha ELan EPfP EShb GCra GGar GKev LHop LRHS LSRN NPer SAga SPer SSvw WFar
'Lemon Symphony'PBR (Symphony Series) CBcs
Melon Symphony = 'Seipepan'PBR (Symphony Series) **new** LAst
Milk Symphony = 'Seiremi' (Symphony Series) CCCN CWCL MBNS
'Mirach' (Springstar Series) CWCL LSou MBNS
§ 'Nairobi Purple' CBcs CCCN CFee CHEx COIW ELan LSou MBri NBur NPri SMrm WCor
Nasinga Cream = 'Aknam'PBR (Cape Daisy Series) CCCN
Nasinga Purple = 'Aksullo' (Cape Daisy Series) EPfP
oppositifolium CCCN
Orange Symphony = 'Seimora'PBR (Symphony Series) CBcs CCCN CWCL LAst LSou MBNS SMrm SPoG
'Pale Face' see *O.* 'Lady Leitrim'
Peach Symphony = 'Seitope'PBR (Symphony Series) CWCL
'Peggyi' see *O.* 'Nairobi Purple'
I 'Pink Superbum' CHEx
'Pink Whirls' ♀H1+3 CCCN
'Pollux'PBR (Springstar Series) MBNS
'Port Wine' see *O.* 'Nairobi Purple'
'Seaside'PBR (Side Series) EPfP
'Silver Sparkler' (v) ♀H1+3 CCCN CDTJ ELan EShb MBNS MHer NBur WBrE
'Snow Pixie' **new** CHVG NPri
Sonja = 'Sunny Sonja'PBR EPfP
'Sparkler' CCCN CHEx
Springstar Series CBcs
'Stardust'PBR EPfP LBuc LRHS NPer SCoo SPoG
'Sunny Amanda'PBR LRHS LSou SRGP
'Sunny Amelia' LAst SRGP
'Sunny Cecil'PBR SRGP
'Sunny Dark Florence' **new** LSou
'Sunny Dark Martha'PBR EPfP LAst
'Sunny Davina'PBR **new** LSou WGor
'Sunny Flora'PBR SRGP
'Sunny Martha'PBR LAst
'Sunny Mary'PBR LAst LRHS LSou SRGP
'Sunny Nathalie' LAst SRGP
'Sunny Philip'PBR SRGP
'Sunny Plum Serena'PBR SRGP
'Sunny Serena'PBR LAst LSou SRGP WGor
'Sunny Sheila' **new** LSou WGor
'Sunny Stephanie'PBR LAst SRGP
'Sunny Zara'PBR SRGP
* 'Superbum' CHEx
I 'Superbum' × 'Lady Leitrim' CHEx
'Tambero'PBR (Cape Daisy Series) **new** LRHS
'Tauranga' see *O.* 'Whirlygig'
'Tresco Peggy' see *O.* 'Nairobi Purple'
'Tresco Pink' CCCN
'Tresco Purple' see *O.* 'Nairobi Purple'
'Uranus' SRGP
'Vega' LAst
Warembo Arwen = 'Sakcadwar'PBR (Cape Daisy Series) LRHS LSou
'Weetwood' ♀H3-4 CCCN CWGN ECtt EPot EShb GCal LRHS MBNS MHer MLHP SAga SPer WEas WFar
§ 'Whirlygig' ♀H1+3 CCCN CSpr LRHS
§ 'White Pim' ♀H3-4 CDTJ CHll ELan ELon GBuc LRHS NPer SDix SMrm SPer SPhx SUsu
'Wine Purple' see *O.* 'Nairobi Purple'
'Wisley Pink' EPyc NEgg
'Zaurak'PBR (Springstar Series) CCCN CWCL LAst LSou MBNS WGor
'Zulu' (Cape Daisy Series) CCCN

Ostrowskia (*Campanulaceae*)

magnifica MTho WCom WWst

Ostrya (*Corylaceae*)

carpinifolia CBcs CDul CLnd CMCN CTho CWib EBee ECrN EMil EPfP EWTr GKir IFFs MBar MBlu MBri MMuc NLar NWea
japonica CDul NLar
virginiana EPfP IArd MBri

Othonna (*Asteraceae*)

cheirifolia CBot CCCN CMea EGoo EHoe ELan EWes NBir SEND WBrk WEas WPer WSHC WWEG

Othonnopsis see *Othonna*

Ourisia (*Scrophulariaceae*)

× ***bitternensis*** 'Cliftonville Lemon' **new** WAbe
- 'Cliftonville Roset' WAbe
caespitosa EBee GGar GKev NMen
- var. ***gracilis*** NMen
coccinea EBee GAbr GBuc GCra GEdr GGar GKev GKir GMac NBir NMen NWCA WAbe
crosbyi GEdr GGar LRHS
glandulosa **new** GKev
'Loch Ewe' CPLG GAbr GBuc GEdr GGar GKir MDun WCru WPGP
macrophylla EBee GBuc GGar IGor LLHF
microphylla WAbe
- f. ***alba*** WAbe
polyantha F&W 8487 CPBP WAbe
- 'Cliftonville Scarlet' CPBP EPot WAbe WFar
'Snowflake' ♀H4 GAbr GEdr MDun NBir NMen WAbe

Oxalis (*Oxalidaceae*)

sp. NMen
acetosella CRWN EBWF MHer NSco WHer WShi
- var. ***rosea*** WAlt
- var. ***subpurpurascens*** MMHG WCot
adenophylla ♀H4 CBro CElw CMea CPLG CTri EBrs ECho EPfP EPot GAbr GGar GKev GKir GMaP ITim LAma LHop LRHS MBar NBlu NEgg NHol NMen NWCA SPoG WBrE WFar WHoo WPer
- dark MTho

	Name	Suppliers
	adenophylla* × *enneaphylla	see *O.* 'Matthew Forrest'
	anomala	EBrs ECho ERos WCot
	arenaria F&W 10584 new	WCot
§	***articulata***	CArn GBuc LRHS MTho NPer SEND WCot WSHC
	- 'Alba'	SEND WCot
	- 'Aureoreticulata'	MTho
I	- f. ***crassipes*** 'Alba' new	WCot
	- 'Festival'	WCot
§	- subsp. ***rubra***	EBee EBrs WBrE
	'Beatrice Anderson'	LRHS MTho
	'Black Velvet' (Xalis Series)	MBNS SMrm
	bowiei	CPBP CStu EBee EBrs ECho EPot
	- 'Amarantha'	EBee EBrs ECho
	'Bowles's White'	MTho
	brasiliensis	CPBP CStu ECho EPot MTho NMen
	'Burgundy Wine' (Xalis Series)	MBNS
	compacta F&W 8011	CPBP
	conorrhiza	WAbe
	corniculata* var. *atropurpurea	MTho
	deppei	see *O. tetraphylla*
§	***depressa***	CStu CTri EBee EBrs ECho EPot EWes GEdr LLHF MTho NBir NLAp NMen NRya NSla SIng SRms WBrE WFar
	- 'Irish Mist'	CStu EBee EBrs ECho WHil
	eckloniana	ECho
	- var. ***sonderi***	EBee EBrs ECho WCot
	enneaphylla ♀H4	CElw ECho EPot GGar LRHS MTho NMen NRya SBch WCom WFar
	- F&W 2715	CPBP
	- 'Alba'	CMea CPBP ECho ERos GBuc GEdr GGar NMen NSla NWCA WCom WIvy
	- subsp. ***ibari***	EBrs ECho EPot ERos GEdr NMen
	- 'Lady Elizabeth'	CPBP
	- 'Minutifolia'	ERos LLHF MTho NMen NRya WCom
	- 'Rosea'	CBgR EBrs ECho EPot ERos GKev MTho NRya NSla
	- 'Ruth Tweedie'	NSla
	- 'Sheffield Swan'	ECho EPot GEdr LLHF NMen NSla
	- 'Ute' new	EPot
	falcatula	WCot
	'Fanny'	CStu EBee EBrs ECho
	flava	CGrW ECho
	floribunda misapplied	see *O. articulata*
	fourcadei	ECho WCot
	gigantea	CSpe
	glabra	CPBP WAbe
	griffithii new	WWst
	- double-flowered (d) new	WWst
	'Gwen McBride'	CPBP NMen
	hedysaroides	CCCN GCal
	'Hemswell Knight'	NMen
	hirta	CPBP EPot MTho
	- 'Gothenburg'	CPBP EBee ECho ERos MTho NMen SIng
	imbricata	CPBP EBee ECho EPot LLHF
	inops	see *O. depressa*
	'Ione Hecker' ♀H4	CBgR CPBP EBrs ECho EPot ERos GEdr GGar GKev ITim LRHS MTho NLAp NMen NRya NSla WCom WIvy
*	***karroica***	CPBP EBee EBrs ECho NMen WCot
§	***laciniata***	ECho ERos ITim MTho NMen NSla WCom
	lactea double-flowered	see *O. magellanica* 'Nelson'
	lasiandra	CCCN EBee EBrs ECho ERos
	loricata	EBrs ECho NMen
	magellanica	CRow CSpe CTri ECho EDAr GGar IMou LBee LRHS MTho NPro SIng SPlb WFar WMoo WPer
	- 'Flore Pleno'	see *O. magellanica* 'Nelson'
§	- 'Nelson' (d)	CRow CSpe CStu EBee ECho EDAr EWes GBuc GCal GGar GMac LBee LRHS MTho NBir NPer SIng WMoo WPer WPnP WPrP WPtf
	massoniana	CPBP EBee EBrs ECho NMen SIng WAbe
§	'Matthew Forrest'	NDlv NMen WCot
§	***megalorrhiza***	CHEx SChr
§	***melanosticta***	CBro CPBP CStu EBee EBrs ECho EPot LLHF SIng
	monophylla	EBee EBrs ECho
	namaquana	EBee ECho WCot
	obtriangulata	EBrs ECho
	obtusa	CBgR CStu EBee EBrs ECho MTho NMen SCnR WCom WCot
	- apricot-flowered	WCot
	oregana	CBgR CDes CHid CMac CRow EBee ECho ELon GBuc GGar NChi WCot WCru WPGP WPrP WSHC
	- f. ***smalliana***	EWes IMou WCru
	palmifrons	CPBP CStu ECho EPot LLHF MTho
	perdicaria	CBro CPBP EBee EBrs ECho ERos EWes LRHS MTho WAbe WFar
	pes-caprae	CGrW
	polyphylla	EBee EBrs ECho
	- var. ***heptaphylla***	SIng
	- var. ***pentaphylla***	CPBP EPot
§	***ptychoclada***	CSpe
§	***purpurea***	EBrs ECho MWea WAbe
	- 'Ken Aslet'	see *O. melanosticta*
	regnellii	see *O. triangularis* subsp. *papilionacea*
	rosea misapplied	see *O. articulata* subsp. *rubra*
	semiloba	EBee EBrs ECho GCal NCGa WCot
	speciosa	see *O. purpurea*
	spiralis* subsp. *vulcanicola	CCCN CStu LSou SDix WDyG
	- - 'Burgundy'	LAst NPri
	- - 'Zinfandel' new	SVil
	squamata	LLHF NLAp WPat
	squamosoradicosa	see *O. laciniata*
	stipularis	ECho LLHF
	succulenta misapplied	see *O. ptychoclada*
	stellulata Barnéoud	see *O. megalorrhiza*
	stellulata ambig.	CHll
	'Sunny'	EBrs ECho
	'Sunset Velvet'	LAst WBor WCot
	'Superstar'	NMen
§	***tetraphylla***	CMMP CPLG EBee EBrs ECho LAma LRHS MTho NPer
*	- ***alba***	ECho
	- 'Iron Cross'	CHEx CStu EBee EBrs ECho EPot LAma NBir SWal WBVN WHil WPer
	'Tina'	CPBP
	triangularis	CCCN CHEx CPLG ECho EOHP LAma MAvo NBir NPer WBrE WFar
	- 'Birgit'	EBee ECho
	- 'Cupido'	EBee ECho GGar WPer
	- 'Mijke'	EBee EBrs ECho
§	- subsp. ***papilionacea*** ♀H1	EBee EBrs ECho LAma LRHS MMHG
	- - 'Atropurpurea'	CSpe EBee ECGP LHop WBVN
*	- - ***rosea***	EBee
	- subsp. ***triangularis***	EBee EBrs ECho LDai NCGa
	truncatula	SIng
	tuberosa	CStu GGar GPoy ILis LEdu
	'Ute'	CPBP GEdr NMen NSla

	valdiviensis	MDKP NBur WTou
	versicolor ♀H1	CPBP CStu EBee EBrs ECho EPot ERos MTho NBir NMen SCnR WAbe WCom WCot
	- 'Clove Ball'	WPtf
I	'Waverley Hybrid' new	NMen
	zeekoevleyensis	WCot

Oxycoccus see *Vaccinium*

Oxydendrum ✿ (*Ericaceae*)

	arboreum	CAbP CBcs CDoC CDul CEnd CMCN EBee EPfP IDee IFFs IMGH LRHS MBri MMuc NLar SCoo SPer SSpi SSta WDin WFar WPGP
	- 'Chameleon'	LRHS SPoG SSta

Oxylobium (*Papilionaceae*)

	ellipticum	GGar

Oxypetalum (*Asclepiadaceae*)

	caeruleum	see *Tweedia caerulea*
	solanoides	CSpe EBee

Oxyria (*Polygonaceae*)

	digyna	GGar

Oxytropis (*Papilionaceae*)

	lambertii	LFur
	purpurea	LLHF
	shokanbetsuensis	LLHF

Ozothamnus (*Asteraceae*)

	antennaria	WSHC
§	***coralloides*** ♀H2-3	ECou EPot NDlv SIng WAbe
§	'County Park Silver'	EWes ITim MDKP NDlv NLAp NWCA WPat
§	***hookeri***	CBcs CDoC EBee ECou GGar LRHS MBrN MRav SPer WJek WPat
§	***ledifolius*** ♀H4	CBcs CDoC EBee ELan EPfP ERas GGar LRHS MBri NBir SLon SPer WDin WHCG WPat
§	***rosmarinifolius***	CBcs CDoC CTrG CTsd ELan EPfP GGar LRHS MSwo SBch SPer WDin WEas WFar WHCG
	- 'Kiandra'	ECou
	- 'Silver Jubilee' ♀H3	CBcs CDoC CEnd CEnt CSBt CTrG EBee ELan EPfP GCal GGar IMon LRHS MAsh MBri MGos MRav MSwo NSti SAga SLim SLon SPer SPlb SPoG SRkn WDin
	scutellifolius	ECou
	secundiflorus	GGar
§	***selago***	CStu ECou NDlv WCot WThu
§	- var. ***tumidus***	ITim SIng WThu
	'Sussex Silver'	CDoC GGar
	'Threave Seedling'	CDoC EBee ELan GBin LRHS SPer
§	***thyrsoideus***	WFar

P

Pachyphragma (*Brassicaceae*)

§	***macrophyllum***	CPom CSev EBee ECGP ECha EHrv ELan GBuc GCal IBlr IMou LRHS MNFA NLar NMRc NSti WCot WCru WMoo WPGP WSHC

Pachyphytum (*Crassulaceae*)

	oviferum	SChr SEND

Pachypodium (*Apocynaceae*)

	geayi ♀H1	EAmu
	lamerei ♀H1	EAmu

Pachysandra (*Buxaceae*)

	axillaris	CLAP EBee GCal
	- BWJ 8032	WCru
	- 'Crûg's Cover'	WCru
	procumbens	CLAP EBee EHrv EPla LHop NLar WCot WCru
	- 'Angola' (v)	WCot
	stylosa	EPla MRav NLar SMad
	terminalis	Widely available
	- 'Green Carpet' ♀H4	CBcs CDoC CPLG CSBt CSam CWib EAEE EBee EGol ELan EPfP GKir GMaP LAst LBMP LHop LRHS LSRN MBar MBri MGos MSwo NBlu NEgg NPri NPro SBch SPer SPoG SWvt
	- 'Green Sheen'	EBee ECha EPPr LRHS MGos WCon WFar
	- 'Variegata' (v) ♀H4	Widely available

Pachystachys (*Acanthaceae*)

	lutea ♀H1	CCCN EShb

Pachystegia (*Asteraceae*)

§	***insignis***	GGar IDee
	- Daizea = 'Hardec' new	EBee

Pachystima see *Paxistima*

Paederia (*Rubiaceae*)

	scandens	WSHC

Paederota (*Scrophulariaceae*)

	lutea	NWCA

Paeonia ✿ (*Paeoniaceae*)

	'Age of Gold' (S)	WCAu
	albiflora	see *P. lactiflora*
	'Alice Roberts'	LRHS
	'Alley Cat'	WAul
	'America'	GBin WCAu
	'Angelo Cobb Freeborn'	WCAu
	'Anna Marie' (S) new	GBin
	anomala	CFir EBee GEdr MHom MPhe NLar NSla WCot
§	- var. ***anomala***	GBin
	- var. ***intermedia***	EBee EBrs GCal
	'Argosy'	WCAu
	arietina	see *P. mascula* subsp. *arietina*
	'Athena'	GBin
	'Auten's Red'	WCAu
	'Avant Garde'	LRHS
	banatica	see *P. officinalis* subsp. *banatica*
	'Banquet' (S)	GBin WCAu
§	'Bartzella' (d)	GBin
	beresowskii	EBee EBrs
	'Black Monarch'	WCAu
	'Black Panther' (S)	GBin WCAu
	'Black Pirate' (S)	CKel WCAu
	'Blaze'	GMaP LRHS WCAu
	Blue and Purple Giant	see *P. suffruticosa* 'Zi Lan Kui'
	'Border Charm'	GBin
	'Bravura' new	GBin
	'Bridal Icing'	LRHS WCAu
	'Bride's Dream'	GBin
	'Brocaded Gown' (S) new	GBin
	broteroi	EBee EBrs

Name	Suppliers
'Buckeye Belle' (d)	CKel EBee EPfP GBin LFur LPio LRHS LSRN MHom MNrw MRav MWea SWat WAul WCAu WWEG
'Burma Midnight'	GBin
'Burma Ruby'	GBin WCAu
californica	WCot
'Callie's Memory'	GBin
cambessedesii ♀H2-3	CBro CSpe EBee EBrs EPPr EPot GKev LHop LRHS MTho NBir NMen NSla NWCA SSpi SUsu WCot WKif
'Canary Brilliant'PBR	GBin
'Cardinal's Robe'	GBin
'Carina'	GBin
'Carol'	WCAu
caucasica	see *P. mascula* subsp. *mascula*
'Chalice'	GBin
× ***chamaeleon***	EBee EBrs
'Cheddar Royal'	GBin LRHS
'Cherry Ruffles'	GBin WCAu
'Chinese Dragon' (S)	CKel WCAu
'Chocolate Soldier'	GBin
'Claire de Lune'	GBin MBri SHar WCAu
'Claudia'	WCAu
clusii	LRHS
'Cora Louise' **new**	GBin
'Coral Charm'	GBin WCot
'Coral Fay'	GBin WCAu
'Coral 'n' Gold'	WCAu
'Coral Sunset'	GBin NCGa SMrm SPoG
'Coral Supreme'	GBin
corallina	see *P. mascula* subsp. *mascula*
coriacea	EBee
- var. ***atlantica***	CBro
'Court Jester' **new**	GBin
Crimson Red	see *P. suffruticosa* 'Hu Hong'
'Crusader'	WCAu
'Cytherea'	MHom WCAu
'Dancing Butterflies'	see *P. lactiflora* 'Zi Yu Nu'
daurica	see *P. mascula* subsp. *triternata*
'Dawn Glow'	WCAu
decomposita	MPhe
decora	see *P. peregrina*
'Defender'	WCAu
delavayi (S) ♀H4	Widely available
- BWJ 7775	WCru
- SDR 4259	GKev
- SDR 4327	GKev
- from China (S)	MPhe
- var. ***angustiloba*** f. ***alba*** (S)	CPLG EBrs
§ - - f. ***angustiloba*** (S)	GKev MBri SSpi WCot
- - - 'Coffee Cream' (S)	CKel
§ - - f. ***trollioides*** (S)	CPLG EBrs WCAu
- var. ***atropurpurea***	see *P. delavayi* var. *delavayi* f. *delavayi*
§ - var. ***delavayi*** f. ***delavayi*** (S)	WAbe
§ - - f. ***lutea*** (S)	CDul CMea CSpe EBee EPfP GAbr GAuc GKev IFro LEdu LFur LRHS MAsh MGos NBir NEgg SAga SLon SPhx SPoG SRms STre SUsu WAul WBrE WFar WHar WHoo WTin
- var. ***lutea***	see *P. delavayi* var. *delavayi* f. *lutea*
- 'Mrs Colville' (S)	GBin GCal
- 'Mrs Sarson' (S)	CHid CSpe ELan EWTr EWes EWll GBin LFur NCGa NHol SWat
- Potaninii Group	see *P. delavayi* var. *angustiloba* f. *angustiloba*
- Trollioides Group	see *P. delavayi* var. *angustiloba* f. *trollioides*
- 'Yellow Queen' (S) **new**	GKev
delavayi × ***delavayi*** var. ***delavayi*** f. ***lutea***	ELan MMuc
delavayi × ***suffruticosa***	LSRN
'Diana Parks' **new**	GBin
Drizzling Rain Cloud	see *P. suffruticosa* 'Shiguregumo'
'Early Bird'	LRHS
'Early Glow'	GBin
'Early Scout'	GBin MHom NCGa WAul WCAu WCot
'Early Windflower'	WCAu
'Eastgrove Ruby Lace'	WEas
'Eden's Perfume'	GBin LRHS NLar WCot
'Elizabeth Foster'	WCAu
'Ellen Cowley'	GBin WCAu
emodi	CAvo EBrs LPio WCot
'Etched Salmon' **new**	GBin
'Ezra Pound' (S) **new**	GBin
'F. Koppius'	CKel
'Fairy Princess'	GBin MBri WAul WCAu
'Firelight'	GBin WCAu
'First Arrival' **new**	GBin
'First Dutch Yellow'	see *P.* 'Garden Treasure'
'Flame'	EBee EBrs EWTr GBin GKir MHom MNrw MWea WAul WCAu WCot
'Fuchsia Cuddles'	GBin
§ Gansu Group (S)	CKel EBrs MHom MPhe
- 'Bai Bi Fen Xia' (S)	MPhe
- 'Bai Bi Lan Xia' (S)	MPhe
- 'Bing Shan Xue Lian' (S)	MPhe
- 'Cheng Xin' (S)	MPhe
- 'Fen He' (S)	MPhe
- 'Fen Jin Yu Zhu' (S)	MPhe
- 'Feng Xian' (S)	MPhe
- 'He Hua Deng' (S)	MPhe
- 'He Ping Lian' (S)	MPhe
- 'Hei Feng Die' (S)	MPhe
- 'Hei Tian E' (S)	MPhe
- 'Hei Xuan Feng' (S)	MPhe
- 'Hong Lian' (S)	MPhe
- 'Hong Xia Ying Xue' (S)	MPhe
- 'Huang He' (S)	MPhe
- 'Hui He' (S)	MPhe
- 'Jiao Rong' (S) **new**	MPhe
- 'Jin Cheng Ming Yue' (S) **new**	MPhe
- 'Ju Hua Fen' (S)	MPhe
- 'Lan Hai Yiu Bo' (S)	MPhe
- 'Lan He' (S)	MPhe
- 'Lan Tian Meng' (S)	MPhe
- 'Li Xiang' (S)	MPhe
- 'Lian Chun' (S)	MPhe
- 'Long Yuan Hong' (S) **new**	MPhe
- 'Mo Hai Yin Bo' (S)	MPhe
- 'Mo Hai Yin Zhou' (S)	MPhe
- 'Shu Sheng Peng Mo' (S)	MPhe
- 'Tao Hua Nu' (S)	MPhe
- 'Tie Mian Wu Si' (S)	MPhe
- 'Xiang Lu Zi Yan' (S) **new**	MPhe
- 'Xiong Mao' (S) **new**	MPhe
- 'Xue Hai Bing Xin' (S)	MPhe
- 'Xue Lian' (S)	MPhe
- 'Ye Guang Bei' (S)	MPhe
- 'Yu Ban Xiu Qiu' (S)	MPhe
- 'Yu Guan Lan Dai' (S) **new**	MPhe
- 'Yu Lu Lian Dan' (S)	MPhe
- 'Yu Rong Dan Xin' (S) **new**	MPhe
- 'Zi Die Ying Feng' (S)	MPhe
- 'Zi Hai Yin Bo' (S) **new**	MPhe
- 'Zong Ban Bai' (S)	MPhe
Gansu Mudan Group	see *P.* Gansu Group
§ 'Garden Treasure'	GBin WHlf
'Gaugin' (S)	WCAu

'Gold Standard'	GBin LRHS WAul
'Golden Bowl'	CKel
'Golden Dream'	see *P.* 'Bartzella'
'Golden Glow'	WCAu
'Golden Isles'	CKel
'Golden Thunder'	CKel
'Golden Wings' **new**	GBin
'Grace Root' **new**	GBin
Green Dragon Lying on a Chinese Inkstone	see *P. suffruticosa* 'Qing Long Wo Mo Chi'
'Hesperus' (S)	WCAu
'Hillary' **new**	GBin
'Ho-gioku'	GBin
'Honor'	WCAu
'Horizon'	GBin
humilis	see *P. officinalis* subsp. *microcarpa*
'Illini Belle'	GBin
'Illini Warrior'	WAul WCAu
intermedia **new**	WCot
'Isani Gidui'	see *P. lactiflora* 'Isami-jishi'
'Jack Frost'	LRHS
'Japensha-ikku' **new**	MBri
japonica misapplied	see *P. lactiflora*
japonica ambig.	GEdr
japonica (Makino) Miyabe & Takeda	EBee
'Jean E. Bockstoce'	WCAu
'Joseph Rock'	see *P. rockii*
'Joyce Ellen'	GBin WCAu
'Julia Rose'	GBin
'Kamikaze'	CKel
kavachensis	EBee EBrs GBin GCal
'Kinkaku'	see *P.* × *lemoinei* 'Souvenir de Maxime Cornu'
'Kinko'	see *P.* × *lemoinei* 'Alice Harding'
'Kinshi'	see *P.* × *lemoinei* 'Chromatella'
'Kintei'	see *P.* × *lemoinei* 'L'Espérance'
'Koikagura'	CKel
'Kokamon'	CKel
'Kun Shan Ye Guang'	CKel
§ ***lactiflora***	EBee EHrv GCal GKev LFur MPhe MRav WWst
- 'A.F.W. Hayward'	CKel
- 'Abalone Pearl'	GBin
- 'Adolphe Rousseau'	CBcs EBee NBlu WCAu
* - 'Afterglow'	CKel
- 'Agida'	GBin LRHS MRav
- 'Agnes Mary Kelway'	CKel
- 'Akalu' **new**	EBee
- 'Albert Crousse'	CBcs CKel GBin MRav NBir NBlu SWat WCAu
- 'Alexander Fleming'	EBee LRHS MBNS MWea NBir SMrm SWat WBrE WCAu
- 'Algae Adamson'	CKel
- 'Alice Harding'	GBin LRHS WCAu
- 'Amibilis'	WCAu
- 'Amo-no-sode'	WCAu
- 'Angel Cheeks'	GBin WCAu
- 'Anna Pavlova'	CKel MRav
- 'Antwerpen'	MBri WCAu
- 'Arabian Prince'	CKel
- 'Argentine'	WCAu
- 'Asa Gray'	CKel
- 'Auguste Dessert'	CKel GBin MWea WCAu WCot
§ - 'Augustin d'Hour'	CKel EBee
- 'Aureole'	CKel MRav
- 'Avalanche'	EBee EPfP GBin NBPC NLar
- 'Ballerina'	CKel MRav
- 'Barbara'	CKel WCAu
- 'Baroness Schröder'	EBee ELan GBin
- 'Barrington Belle'	EPfP GBin MBri WAul
- 'Barrymore'	CKel
- 'Beacon'	CKel
- 'Beatrice Kelway'	CKel
- 'Belle Center'	GBin WCAu
- 'Best Man'	NGdn WCAu
- 'Bethcar'	CKel
- 'Better Times'	WCAu
- 'Bev'	GBin
- 'Big Ben'	GBin NCGa WCAu
- 'Blaze of Beauty'	CKel
- 'Bluebird'	CKel
- 'Blush Queen'	ELan WCAu
- 'Border Gem'	MRav
- 'Bouchela'	EBee
- 'Boule de Neige'	EWll
- 'Bower of Roses'	CKel
- 'Bowl of Beauty' $\mathbb{Y}^{H4}$	Widely available
- 'Bowl of Cream'	EBee GBin SMrm SWat SWvt WCAu
- 'Bracken'	CKel
- 'Break o' Day'	WCAu
- 'Bridal Gown'	GBin WCAu
- 'Bridal Veil'	CKel
- 'Bridesmaid'	CKel MRav
- 'British Beauty'	CKel
- 'Bunker Hill'	CKel EBee GBin SPer SWvt WCAu
- 'Butter Bowl'	GBin MBri WCAu
- 'Canarie'	MBri
- 'Candeur'	CKel EBee
- 'Cang Long'	CKel
- 'Captivation'	CKel
- 'Carnival'	CKel
- 'Caroline Allain'	CKel
- 'Carrara'	GBin
- 'Cascade'	CKel
- 'Catherine Fontijn'	CKel GBin SHar WCAu
- 'Charles' White'	EBee EPfP GBin LRHS NBPC WCAu
- 'Charm'	GBin LRHS WCAu
- 'Cheddar Charm'	GBin MBri WAul WCAu
- 'Cheddar Gold' $\mathbb{Y}^{H4}$	GKir LRHS MBri
- 'Cheddar Supreme'	GBin
- 'Cherry Hill'	WCAu
- 'Chestine Gowdy'	CKel
- 'Chief Wapello'	GBin
- 'Chippewa' **new**	GBin
- 'Chun Xiao'	CKel
- 'Circus Circus'	GBin
- 'Claire Dubois'	CKel GBin WCAu
- 'Cornelia Shaylor'	WCAu
- 'Couronne d'Or'	GBin WCAu
- 'Crimson Glory'	CKel
- 'Crinkles Linens'	GBin
- 'Dandy Dan'	WCAu
- 'Dawn Crest'	CKel EBee
- 'Dayspring'	CKel
- 'Daystar'	MRav
- 'Decorative'	CKel
- 'Delachei'	CKel
- 'Denise'	MRav
- 'Dinner Plate'	GBin LRHS MBri SPer WCAu WCot
- 'Do Tell'	GBin NGdn NLar SPer WCAu
- 'Docteur H. Barnsby'	CKel
- 'Doctor Alexander Fleming'	CKel NCGa SWat SWvt WHoo
- 'Dominion'	CKel
- 'Don Juan'	CKel
- 'Doreen'	CFir EBee GBin MBri SHar WCAu
- 'Doris Cooper'	WCAu
- 'Dorothy Welsh'	CKel
- 'Dragon'	CKel
- 'Dresden'	WCAu
- 'Duchesse de Nemours' $\mathbb{Y}^{H4}$	Widely available
- 'Duchesse d'Orléans'	WCAu
- 'Edouard Doriat'	WCAu

Cultivar	Suppliers
- 'Edulis Superba'	CKel EBee ELan GBin LRHS MBNS MRav NMoo NPer SHar SPer WCAu
- 'Elizabeth Stone'	CKel
- 'Ella Christine Kelway'	CKel
- 'Elsa Sass'	WCAu
- 'Emma Klehm'	GBin WCAu
- 'Emperor of India'	CKel
- 'Enchantment'	CKel
- 'English Princess'	CKel
- 'Ethereal'	CKel
- 'Evelyn Tibbets'	GBin
- 'Evening Glow'	CKel
- 'Evening World'	CKel
- 'Fairy's Petticoat'	WCAu
- 'Fashion Show'	CKel
- 'Félix Crousse' ♀H4	CBcs CKel CMac CTri ELan EPfP GMaP IMon LAst LRHS LSRN MBNS MRav MSCN NBir NWsh SPer SRms SWat WCAu
- 'Felix Supreme'	GBin
- 'Fen Chi Jin Yu'	CKel
- 'Festiva Maxima' ♀H4	CKel CSBt CTri CWCL EBee ELan EPfP GBin GKir LRHS NBir NEgg NLar SBch SMrm SPer SRms SRot SWat SWvt WAul WCAu WHoo WWEG
- 'Florence Ellis'	GBin
- 'Florence Nicholls' **new**	GBin
- 'France'	CKel
- 'Fuji-no-mine'	GBin
- 'Garden Lace'	GBin
- 'Gardenia'	EBee EBrs EPfP GBin
- 'Gay Paree'	GBin NCGa SPer WCAu
- 'Gayborder June'	CKel WCAu
- 'Gene Wild'	GBin WCAu
- 'Général Joffre'	MRav
- 'Général MacMahon'	see *P. lactiflora* 'Augustin d'Hour'
- 'General Wolfe'	CKel
- 'Germaine Bigot'	CKel GBin MRav WCAu
- 'Gertrude'	GBin
- 'Gilbert Barthelot'	WCAu
- 'Gladys McArthur'	GBin
- 'Gleam of Light'	CKel MBri
- 'Globe of Light'	GBin
- 'Gloriana'	WCAu
- 'Glory Hallelujah'	WCAu
- 'Glowing Candles'	WCAu
- 'Go-Daigo'	GBin
- 'Golden Fleece'	WCAu
- 'Goldmine' **new**	GBin
- 'Great Sport'	MRav
- 'Green Lotus'	WAul
- 'Guidon'	WCAu
- 'Gypsy Girl'	CKel
- 'Hakodate'	CKel
- 'Heartbeat'	CKel
- 'Helen Hayes'	GBin WCAu
- 'Henri Potin'	GBin
- 'Henry Bockstoce'	GBin
- 'Her Grace'	CKel
- 'Herbert Oliver'	CKel
- 'Hermione'	CKel GBin
- 'Hiawatha'	WCAu
- 'Hit Parade'	WCAu
- 'Honey Gold'	ELan GBin GKir LPio SPoG WAul WCAu
- 'Huang Jin Lun'	CKel
- 'Hyperion'	CKel
- 'Immaculée'	EBee EPfP GBin LPio LRHS MBri NCGa SPoG WSpi
- 'Inspecteur Lavergne'	CKel EBee LAst LRHS MBri MWea SPer STes WAul WCAu WCot WWEG
- 'Instituteur Doriat'	CKel GBin MBri WCAu
§ - 'Isami-jishi'	GBin
- 'Jacorma'	CFir GBin WHoo
- 'Jacques Doriat'	CKel
- 'Jadwigha'	EBee
- 'James Kelway'	GBin
- 'James Pillow'	WCAu
- 'Jan van Leeuwen'	EBee EPfP GBin WCAu WCot WSpi
- 'Jappensha-Ikhu'	GBin
- 'Jeanne d'Arc'	CKel
- 'Jin Chi Yu'	CKel
- 'John Howard Wigell'	WCAu
- 'Joy of Life'	CKel
- 'Judith Eileen' **new**	GBin
- 'June Morning'	CKel
- 'June Rose'	WCAu
- 'Kakoden'	GBin
- 'Kansas'	EBee ELan EPfP GBin GKir LRHS MBri NBir NGdn NMoo SMrm SPoG WCAu WCot WFar
- 'Karen Gray'	GBin WCAu
- 'Karl Rosenfield'	CKel CSBt EBee ELon EPfP GKir LAst LRHS LSRN MRav NEgg SBch SPer SPoG SRms STes SWvt WFar WHoo WWEG
- 'Kathleen Mavoureen'	CKel
- 'Kelway's Betty'	CKel
- 'Kelway's Brilliant'	CKel
- 'Kelway's Circe'	CKel
- 'Kelway's Daystar'	CKel
- 'Kelway's Exquisite'	CKel
- 'Kelway's Glorious'	CSam EBee EPfP GBin GKir LBMP LFur LPio LRHS MBNS MRav NLar SPoG WCAu
- 'Kelway's Lovely'	CKel GBin
- 'Kelway's Lovely Lady'	CKel
- 'Kelway's Majestic'	CKel MRav
- 'Kelway's Scented Rose'	CKel
- 'Kelway's Supreme'	CKel SWat
- 'King of England'	GBin
- 'Knighthood'	CKel
- 'Kocho-jishi'	CKel
- 'Königswinter'	GBin
§ - 'Koningin Wilhelmina'	GBin MNrw
- 'Krinkled White'	EBee EWTr GBin LRHS MHom MRav NLar SHar SUsu WAul WCAu WCot WWEG
- 'La Belle Hélène'	CKel
- 'La France'	GBin
- 'La Lorraine'	CKel
- 'Lady Alexandra Duff' ♀H4	CKel EBee EPfP GBin GKir MRav MWea NBir NGdn SCoo SMrm SRms SWvt WCAu WWEG
- 'Lady Kate'	WCAu
- 'Lady Ley'	CKel
- 'Lady Mayoress'	CKel
- 'Lady Orchid'	EPfP MSCN NGdn WCAu
- 'Lady Romilly' **new**	MRav
- 'Lancaster Imp'	GBin WAul
- 'Langport Triumph'	CKel
- 'Laura Dessert' ♀H4	EBee EPfP GBin GKir MBri MWea SPer WCAu
- 'Le Cygne'	GBin
- 'Le Jour'	LRHS MBri
- 'L'Eclatante'	CKel EBee GBin
- 'Legion of Honor'	CKel WCAu
- 'Lemon Ice'	CKel
- 'Lemon Queen'	GBin
- 'L'Etincelante'	GBin
- 'Lights Out'	GBin
- 'Lillian Wild'	EBee GBin WCAu
- 'Little Medicineman'	EBee GBin NBhm WBor

- 'Lois Kelsey' WCAu
- 'Longfellow' CKel GBin
- 'Lora Dexheimer' WCAu
- 'Lord Calvin' WCAu
- 'Lord Kitchener' CKel GBin
- 'Lorna Doone' CKel
- 'Lotus Queen' GBin LRHS SHar WCAu
- 'Louis Barthelot' WCAu
- 'Louis Joliet' ELan
- 'Louis van Houtte' NEgg SBch
- 'Lowell Thomas' WCAu
- 'Lyric' CKel
- 'Madame Calot' SRms WCAu
- 'Madame Claude Tain' MBri
- 'Madame de Verneville' WCAu
- 'Madame Ducel' CKel WCAu
- 'Madame Emile Debatène' CWCL EBee MBNS NMoo NOrc WBor WCAu
- 'Madame Gaudichau' MAvo WCot
- 'Madame Jules Dessert' EBee WCAu
- 'Madelon' CKel WCAu
- 'Maestro' GBin
- 'Magic Orb' CKel
- 'Margaret Truman' CKel WCAu
- 'Marguérite Gerard' WCAu
- 'Marie Crousse' WCAu
- 'Marie Lemoine' CKel EBee GBin WCAu WCot
- 'Marietta Sisson' WCAu
- 'Mary Brand' WCAu
- 'Mary Elizabeth' **new** GBin
- 'Masterpiece' CKel MRav
- 'May Treat' GBin
- 'Merry Mayshine' GBin WCAu
- 'Midnight Sun' MBri WCAu
- 'Minnie Shaylor' WCAu
- 'Mischief' MRav WCAu
- 'Miss America' EPfP GBin LRHS MBri WCAu
- 'Miss Eckhart' CKel EBee GBin WCAu
- 'Miss Mary' EPfP LAst SHar
- 'Missie's Blush' **new** GBin
- 'Mister Ed' GBin WCAu
- 'Mistral' CKel MBri
- 'Mo Zi Ling' WCAu
- 'Monsieur Jules Elie' ♀H4 CKel EBee EPfP GBin LAst LPio MBri MHom NBPC NGdn SBch SPer WAul WCAu WHlf WHoo WWEG
- 'Monsieur Martin Cahuzac' CFir EBee GBin WCAu
- 'Moon of Nippon' EBee
- 'Moon River' EPfP GBin
- 'Moonglow' WCAu
- 'Mother's Choice' GBin LSRN NGdn WCAu WCot
- 'Mr G.F. Hemerik' CKel EBee GBin MBri WCAu WCot
- 'Mr Thim' WCAu
- 'Mrs Edward Harding' WCAu
- 'Mrs F.J. Hemerik' WCAu
- 'Mrs Franklin D. Roosevelt' GBin WCAu
- 'Mrs J.V. Edlund' GBin WCAu
- 'Mrs Livingston Farrand' WCAu
- 'My Pal Rudy' GBin WCAu
- 'Myrtle Gentry' GBin
- 'Nancy Nicholls' WCAu
- 'Nancy Nora' NGdn
- 'Neomy Demay' GBin
- 'Nice Gal' WCAu
- 'Nick Shaylor' GBin WCAu
- 'Nippon Beauty' EBee GBin
- 'Norma Volz' **new** GBin
- 'Orlando Roberts' **new** GBin
- 'Ornament' CKel
- 'Orpen' CKel
- 'Paola' CKel
- 'Paul Bunyan' GBin
- 'Paul M. Wild' NCGa NLar WCAu
- 'Peche' EBee
* - 'Pecher' CWCL LPio NMoo NPer WSpi
- 'Peter Brand' EWTr GBin NBPC NLar SPoG
- 'Philippe Rivoire' WCAu
- 'Philomèle' WCAu
- 'Pico' WCAu
- 'Pillow Talk' EBee GBin SPer WCAu
- 'Pink Cameo' EBee NLar WCAu WCot
- 'Pink Giant' WCAu
- 'Pink Lemonade' WCAu
- 'Pink Parfait' GBin LRHS SPer WCAu WCot
- 'Pink Princess' GBin LRHS MBri WCAu
- 'Plainsman' **new** GBin
- 'Polar King' WCAu
- 'Port Royale' CKel
- 'President Franklin' SPer SWat WCAu
- 'Président Poincaré' CKel MRav SWat
- 'President Taft' see *P. lactiflora* 'Reine Hortense'
- 'Primevère' EBee EPfP EWll GBin GKir LAst LPio MWea NBir NLar NMoo SHar SMrm SPer SPoG WCAu WWEG
- 'Qi Hua Lu Shuang' CKel
- 'Qing Wen' CKel
- 'Queen of Sheba' WCAu
- 'Queen Victoria' GBin
- 'Queen Wilhelmina' see *P. lactiflora* 'Koningin Wilhelmina'
- 'Raoul Dessert' WCAu
- 'Raspberry Sundae' ELan GBin LRHS MAvo MRav NLar SMrm STes WCAu WCot
- 'Ray Payton' GBin LRHS
- 'Red Dwarf' CKel
- 'Red Emperor' WCAu
- 'Red Rover' CKel
- 'Red Sarah Bernhardt' ELan SMrm WWEG
§ - 'Reine Hortense' CKel GBin MRav WCAu WWEG
- 'Renato' GBin LRHS
- 'Richard Carvel' WCAu
- 'Ruth Cobb' WCAu
- 'Sante Fe' EPfP WCAu
- 'Sarah Bernhardt' ♀H4 Widely available
- 'Scarlet O'Hara' CMac GBin LRHS NGdn SHar SPer WCAu
- 'Schaffe' GBin
- 'Sea Shell' EPfP GBin LRHS NLar SHar
- 'Shawnee Chief' GBin WCAu
- 'Shen Tao Hua' CKel
- 'Shimmering Velvet' CKel SAga
- 'Shi-pen Kue' EBee
- 'Shirley Temple' CKel CWCL EBee ELan GBin GKir GMaP LFur LRHS MBNS MRav NBir NGdn SBch SPoG WCAu WWEG
- 'Silver Flare' CKel
- 'Soft Salmon Joy' GBin
- 'Solange' CKel EBee GBin LPio NCGa NLar STes WCAu
- 'Sorbet' EBee EPfP GKir LPio MBNS NBPC NBir NLar NMoo NPer SBch STes WBor WCAu WWEG
- 'Spellbinder' GBin
- 'Starlight' STes WCAu
- 'Strephon' CKel
- 'Sweet Melody' GBin WCAu
- 'Sweet Sixteen' WCAu
- 'Sword Dance' EBee EWll GBin SPoG WSpi
- 'Taff' EBee WBor
- 'Tamate-boko' WCAu
- 'The Mighty Mo' GBin
- 'The Nymph' NBir WWEG

- 'Thérèse'	WCAu
- 'Tom Eckhardt'	EKen GBin SPer
- 'Top Brass'	CBot EBee GBin MRav NLar WCAu WWEG
- 'Topeka Garnet'	GBin
- 'Toro-no-maki'	WCAu
- 'Translucient'	CKel
- 'Victoire de la Marne'	EBee LRHS
- 'Violet Dawson'	GBin
- 'Vivid Rose' **new**	GBin
- 'Vogue'	EBee GBin LRHS MRav NCGa SWvt WCAu
- 'Walter Faxon'	GBin
- 'West Elkton'	GBin
- 'Westerner'	GBin WCAu
- 'White Ivory'	MBri WCAu
- 'White Rose of Sharon'	CKel
- 'White Wings'	CBcs CKel CMac CTri EBee ELan EPfP GBin GKir LFur LPio LRHS MAvo MWea NBPC SWat SWvt WAul WCAu WCot
- 'Whitleyi Major' ♀H4	GKir MPhe
- 'Wiesbaden'	WCAu
- 'Wilbur Wright'	GBin WCAu
- 'Wine Red'	GBin
- 'Wladyslawa'	EBee EBrs GBin WCot
- 'Xue Feng'	CKel
- 'Yan Fei Chu Yu'	CKel
- 'Yan Zi Dian Yu'	CKel
- 'Zhong Sheng Feng'	GBin
- 'Zhu Sha Dian Yu'	CKel
§ - 'Zi Yu Nu'	EBee GKir LRHS LSRN WCAu
- 'Zuzu'	GBin WAul WCAu
× ***lagodechiana***	EBrs
'Late Windflower'	EBrs GCra LPio MHom
'Leda' (S) **new**	GBin
× ***lemoinei*** (S)	GBin WHal
§ - 'Alice Harding' (S)	CKel SPer WCAu
§ - 'Chromatella' (S)	CKel LAma
- 'High Noon' (S)	CKel MPhe NBPC SWat WCAu
§ - 'L'Espérance' (S)	LAma WCAu
- 'Marchioness' (S)	CKel WCAu
§ - 'Souvenir de Maxime Cornu' (S)	CKel EMui EPfP LAma LRHS MGos WCAu
'Lilith' (S) **new**	GBin
lithophila	see *P. tenuifolia* subsp. *lithophila*
'Little Joe'	LRHS
lobata 'Fire King'	see *P. peregrina*
'Lois Arleen'	WCAu
ludlowii (S) ♀H4	Widely available
lutea	see *P. delavayi* var. *delavayi* f. *lutea*
macrophylla	MPhe
'Magenta Gem'	WAul
'Mai Fleuri'	WCAu
mairei	CFir MPhe WCot
mascula	CBro EBee EPfP LFur LHop LLHF NBir NLar WCot WWEG WWst
§ - subsp. ***arietina***	MWat WCot WEas
- - 'Northern Glory'	LRHS WCAu
- from Sicily	MPhe
- subsp. ***hellenica***	EBrs
- - from Sicily	MPhe
§ - subsp. ***mascula***	EBee EBrs GBin GKev WCot
- - from Georgia	MPhe WPGP
§ - subsp. ***russoi***	EBrs GBin WCot WThu
- - from Sardinia	MPhe
- - 'Reverchoni'	EBee EBrs
§ - subsp. ***triternata***	CWit EBee EBrs GBin LFur LRHS MPhe NLar WBor WCot
- - RS 125/80	WWst
- - from Crimea	WPGP
'Mikuhino Akebono'	CKel
mlokosewitschii ♀H4	Widely available
- 'Fedora'	EBrs
- hybrids	GKev
- 'Pearl Rose'	GBin
mollis	see *P. officinalis* subsp. *villosa*
'Montezuma'	LRHS WCAu
'Moonrise'	WCAu
'Murad of Hershey Bar' (S) **new**	GBin
'My Love'	GBin
'Nymphe'	CKel EBee EPfP GKir LPio MRav WAul WCAu
obovata ♀H4	CFir EBrs GAuc GKir LFur MPhe WCot
- var. ***alba*** ♀H4	CPLG EBrs GBin GEdr GKev NDlv WAbe WEas WThu
- 'Grandiflora'	GKir LRHS
- var. ***willmottiae***	CPLG MPhe
officinalis	EBee GAuc GCra GKev GPoy NWsh WCot
- WM 9821 from Slovenia	MPhe
- from NW Croatia **new**	WWst
- 'Alba Plena'	CPou GKir GMaP LRHS MRav NEgg SWvt WCAu WWEG
- 'Anemoniflora Rosea' ♀H4	EBee EPfP GBin GKir LRHS MBri SWvt WCAu
§ - subsp. ***banatica***	EBee EBrs EPPr GKev MHom MPhe WCAu WCot
- 'China Rose'	GBin WCAu
- subsp. ***humilis***	see *P. officinalis* subsp. *microcarpa*
- 'Lize van Veen'	GBin WCAu
§ - subsp. ***microcarpa***	EBee
- 'Mutabilis Plena'	EBee IBlr WCAu
- 'Rosea Plena' ♀H4	CKel CMac EBee ECtt EPfP GBin GKir GMaP LAst LRHS MRav NEgg SPer SWat SWvt WCAu WFar WWEG
- 'Rosea Superba Plena'	WCAu
- 'Rubra Plena' ♀H4	CPou CTri CWCL EBee EBrs ECtt EPfP GAbr GBin GCra GKir GMaP LAst LHop LRHS MBri MHom MRav NEgg NGdn SMrm SPer SRms SWat SWvt WAul WCAu WCot WFar
§ - subsp. ***villosa***	CKel EBee EBrs ELan GAbr GBin LRHS SEND WCAu WFar
'Old Faithful' **new**	GBin
'Oriental Gold'	CKel
ostii (S)	CKel EPfP MPhe
§ - 'Feng Dan Bai' (S)	CKel EBee GBin MPhe WCAu WSpi
'Paladin'	GBin
papaveracea	see *P. suffruticosa*
paradoxa	see *P. officinalis* subsp. *microcarpa*
'Paula Fay'	EBee EPfP GBin MBri MRav NLar WCAu
'Peachy Rose'	GBin
§ ***peregrina***	CAby CBro EBee EBrs ECho GBin GEdr LRHS MPhe NLar NSla SSpi WAbe WCAu WCom WCot
- 'Fire King'	GBin
§ - 'Otto Froebel' ♀H4	GBin GCra NLar WCAu WCot WSpi
- 'Sunshine'	see *P. peregrina* 'Otto Froebel'
'Pink Hawaiian Coral'	GBin SPoG WCot
'Postilion'	GBin WCAu
potaninii	see *P. delavayi* var. *angustiloba* f. *angustiloba*
'Prairie Charm'	GBin
'Prairie Moon'	GBin NLar
'Red Charm'	EBrs GBin LPio LRHS MBNS MBri NCGa WCAu WCot WSpi
'Red Glory'	GBin
'Red Magic'	EBee MBri NBPC NLar SMrm WFar WSpi
'Red Red Rose'	WCAu

	'Renown' (S)	CKel
	'Requiem'	GBin WCAu
	'Robert W.Auten'	WCAu
§	***rockii*** (S)	CBcs CKel CSpe EBee EPfP GAuc LRHS MPhe NLar WCot WSpi
	- hybrid	see *P.* Gansu Group
	- subsp. ***linyanshanii*** (S)	MPhe
	aff. ***rockii*** (S) **new**	GAuc
	'Roman Gold'	CKel
	romanica	see *P. peregrina*
	'Rose Garland'	GBin WCAu
	'Roselette'	GBin WCAu
	Rouge Red	see *P. suffruticosa* 'Zhi Hong'
	'Roy Pehrson's Best Yellow'	GBin
	ruprechtiana	EBrs WCot WWst
	russoi	see *P. mascula* subsp. *russoi*
	'Scarlet Heaven' **new**	GBin
	'Shaggy Dog'	LRHS
	Shandong Red Lotus	see *P. suffruticosa* 'Lu He Hong'
	'Shimano-fuji'	CKel
	'Showanohokori'	CKel
	'Silver Dawn'	GBin
	sinensis	see *P. lactiflora*
	sinjianensis	see *P. anomala* var. *anomala*
	× ***smouthii***	MBri
	'Soshi'	GBin
	'Spring Carnival' (S) **new**	GBin
	'Stardust'	WCAu
	steveniana	EBee EBrs GBin MHom MPhe NLar WCot
§	***suffruticosa*** (S)	CWib ELan GBin LRHS MGos NBlu SSpi
	- 'Akashigata' (S)	CKel
	- 'Alice Palmer' (S)	CKel
	- 'Bai Yu' (S)	CBcs
	- 'Bai Yulan' (S)	LLHF
	- Best-shaped Red	see *P. suffruticosa* 'Zhuan Yuan Hong'
	- Bird of Rimpo	see *P. suffruticosa* 'Rimpo'
	- Black Dragon Brocade	see *P. suffruticosa* 'Kokuryū-nishiki'
	- Brocade of the Naniwa	see *P. suffruticosa* 'Naniwa-nishiki'
	- 'Cardinal Vaughan' (S)	CKel
	- Charming Age	see *P. suffruticosa* 'Howki'
	- 'Dou Lu' (S)	CBcs CKel
	- Double Cherry	see *P. suffruticosa* 'Yae-zakura'
	- 'Duchess of Kent' (S)	CKel
	- 'Duchess of Marlborough' (S)	CKel
	- 'Er Qiao' (S)	CBcs CKel
	- Eternal Camellias	see *P. suffruticosa* 'Yachiyo-tsubaki'
	- 'Fen Qiao' (S)	CBcs
	- Flight of Cranes	see *P. suffruticosa* 'Renkaku'
	- Floral Rivalry	see *P. suffruticosa* 'Hana-kisoi'
	- 'Frost on Peach Blossom' (S) **new**	LRHS
	- 'Fuji Zome Goromo' (S)	CKel
*	- 'Glory of Huish' (S)	CKel
	- 'Godaishu' (S)	CKel LAma SPer
§	- 'Hakuo-jisi' (S/d)	CKel EPfP LRHS WCAu
§	- 'Hana-daijin' (S)	LAma SPer WCAu
§	- 'Hana-kisoi' (S)	CKel GBin LAma WCAu
	- 'Haru-no-akebono' (S)	CKel
§	- 'Higurashi' (S)	EPfP LRHS
§	- 'Howki' (S)	WCAu
§	- 'Hu Hong' (S)	WCAu WSpi
§	- 'Huang Hua Kui' (S)	CKel
	- 'Hu's Family Red' (S) **new**	LRHS
	- Jewel in the Lotus	see *P. suffruticosa* 'Tama-fuyo'
	- Jewelled Screen	see *P. suffruticosa* 'Tama-sudare'
	- 'Jia Ge Jin Zi' (S)	CKel
	- 'Jitsugetsu-nishiki' (S)	CKel
	- 'Joseph Rock'	see *P. rockii*
	- Kamada Brocade	see *P. suffruticosa* 'Kamada-nishiki'
§	- 'Kamada-fuji' (S)	CKel WCAu
§	- 'Kamada-nishiki' (S)	CKel
§	- 'Kaow' (S)	CKel WCAu
	- King of Flowers	see *P. suffruticosa* 'Kaow'
	- King of White Lions	see *P. suffruticosa* 'Hakuo-jisi'
	- 'Kinkaku'	see *P.* × *lemoinei* 'Souvenir de Maxime Cornu'
	- 'Kinshi'	see *P.* × *lemoinei* 'Alice Harding'
	- 'Kokucho' (S)	CKel
§	- 'Kokuryū-nishiki' (S)	CKel GBin LAma LRHS SPer SPoG
	- 'Koshi-no-yuki' (S)	CKel
§	- 'Lu He Hong' (S)	WCAu
	- Magnificent Flower	see *P. suffruticosa* 'Hana-daijin'
	- 'Montrose' (S)	CKel
*	- 'Mrs Shirley Fry' (S)	CKel
	- 'Mrs William Kelway' (S)	CKel
	- 'Muramatsu-zakura' (S)	LRHS
§	- 'Naniwa-nishiki' (S)	CKel
	- 'Nigata Akashigata' (S)	CKel
	- Pride of Taisho	see *P. suffruticosa* 'Taisho-no-hokori'
§	- 'Qing Long Wo Mo Chi' (S)	CKel WCAu
	- 'Reine Elisabeth' (S)	CKel
§	- 'Renkaku' (S)	CKel SPer WCAu
§	- 'Rimpo' (S)	CKel EPfP GBin LAma LRHS SPer
	- subsp. ***rockii***	see *P. rockii*
	- 'Rou Fu Rong' (S)	WCAu WSpi
	- 'Sheng Hei Zi' (S)	CBcs
§	- 'Shiguregumo' (S)	CKel
	- 'Shimadaigin' (S)	CKel
	- 'Shimane-chojuraku' (S)	CKel GBin
	- 'Shimane-hakugan' (S)	CKel
	- 'Shimane-seidai' (S)	CKel
	- 'Shimanishiki' (S)	CKel
	- 'Shin Shima Kagayaki' (S)	CKel
	- 'Shintoyen' (S)	CKel
	- 'Sumi-no-ichi' (S)	CKel
	- 'Superb' (S)	CKel
§	- 'Taisho-no-hokori' (S)	CKel WCAu
§	- 'Taiyo' (S)	CKel EPfP LAma LRHS SPer
§	- 'Tama-fuyo' (S)	CKel
§	- 'Tama-sudare' (S)	CKel WCAu
	- The Sun	see *P. suffruticosa* 'Taiyo'
	- Twilight	see *P. suffruticosa* 'Higurashi'
	- Wisteria at Kamada	see *P. suffruticosa* 'Kamada-fuji'
	- 'Wu Jin Yao Hui' (S)	CBcs WCAu
	- 'Wu Long Peng Sheng' (S)	CKel GBin WCAu WSpi
	- 'Xiao Tao Hong' (S)	CBcs
	- 'Xue Ta' (S)	CKel LRHS
§	- 'Yachiyo-tsubaki' (S)	CKel LAma LRHS WCAu
§	- 'Yae-zakura' (S)	LAma WCAu
	- 'Yan Long Zi Zhu Pan' (S)	CKel
	- 'Yao's Family Yellow' (S) **new**	LRHS
	- 'Yin Hong Qiao Dui' (S)	CKel
	- 'Yoshinogawa' (S)	CKel EPfP LRHS
	- 'Zha Sha Lei' (S)	GBin
	- 'Zhao Fen' (S)	LRHS NBPC NPer
§	- 'Zhi Hong' (S)	CKel
	- 'Zhu Sha Lei' (S)	CKel WSpi
*	- 'Zhuan Yuan Hong' (S)	WSpi
	- 'Zi Er Qiao' (S)	CKel
§	- 'Zi Lan Kui' (S)	CKel
	'Sunshine'	see *P. peregrina* 'Otto Froebel'
	'Taiheko'	CKel
	'Ten' i'	CKel
	tenuifolia	CBot CSpe CWit EBee ELon EPPr GAuc GBin GCal GKir LFur LPio LRHS MAvo MDun MHom MWea NMen NSla SEND SMad SUsu WBor WCAu WCot WSpi

	- subsp. ***carthalinica***	MPhe
§	- subsp. ***lithophila***	EBee MHom MPhe WWst
	- 'Plena'	EBrs EPot GEdr LFur MHom NBhm NLar WWst
	- 'Rosea'	EBrs
	'Thunderbolt' (S)	WCAu
	'Tieganzi' new	GKev
	tomentosa	CMil MHom MPhe
	turcica	GBin
	'Vanilla Twist'	WAul
	veitchii	EBee EBrs EPfP GAbr GAuc GCal GEdr GKev GKir GMaP LPio MHom MTho NBid NDlv NLar NMen SSpi WCAu WSpi
	- from China	MPhe
	- 'Alba'	LPio SPhx
	- pale-flowered	GCal
	- var. ***woodwardii***	CMil EBee EBrs ECho ERos GBin GCra GGar GKev GKir LPio MTho NSla NWCA SSpi WCAu WCot WHoo WWst
I	- - 'Alba'	EBrs
	'Vesuvian'	CKel WCAu
	'Viking Full Moon'	GBin
	'Walter Mains'	WCAu
	White Phoenix	see *P. ostii* 'Feng Dan Bai'
	'Wine Angel'	GBin
	wittmanniana	CBot EBee EBrs GBin GCal NLar WCAu WCot
	'Xiang Yu' new	LRHS
§	'Yao Huang' (S)	CBcs WCAu
	Yao's Yellow	see *P.* 'Yao Huang'
	'Yellow Crown'	GBin MAsh NCGa SHar WCAu
	'Yellow Dream'	GBin WCAu WCot
	'Yellow Emperor'	GBin WCot
	Yellow Flower of Summer	see *P. suffruticosa* 'Huang Hua Kui'
	'Yellow Gem'	GBin

Paesia (*Dennstaedtiaceae*)

scaberula	CDes CLAP NBir SSpi WAbe

Paliurus (*Rhamnaceae*)

spina-christi	CArn CBcs IDee NLar SLon SMad

Pallenis (*Asteraceae*)

§	***maritima***	CCCN NWCA

Pamianthe (*Amaryllidaceae*)

peruviana	ERea

Panax (*Araliaceae*)

ginseng	EBee GKev GPoy
japonicus	EBee GPoy WCru
- BWJ 7932	WCru
quinquefolius	MMuc

Pancratium (*Amaryllidaceae*)

maritimum	CArn EBee EBrs ECho LRHS

Pandanus (*Pandanaceae*)

utilis	EAmu LPal

Pandorea (*Bignoniaceae*)

	jasminoides	CHll CRHN CTri CTsd EBak EBee EPfP EShb LRHS
	- 'Alba'	EShb
§	- 'Charisma' (v)	CBcs CBow CHll EAmu EBee EPfP ERea EShb LSou SEND SPer SPoG
	- 'Lady Di'	ERea
	- 'Rosea'	SMrm
	- 'Rosea Superba' ♀H1	CBcs CHEx CRHN EBee ERea SBod SPer
	- 'Variegata'	see *P. jasminoides* 'Charisma'
	lindleyana	see *Clytostoma calystegioides*
	pandorana	CRHN EBee ERea IDee LRHS SLim
	- 'Golden Showers'	CBcs CCCN CRHN ERea EShb MRav SEND SLim
	- 'Ruby Heart'	ERea

Panicum (*Poaceae*)

	amarum 'Dewey Blue'	CKno EPPr
	bulbosum	CKno EHoe EPPr EPla
	clandestinum	EBee EHoe EPPr EWes GFor IMou MCCP MWhi
	miliaceum	LRHS
	- 'Purple Majesty'	CWib
	- 'Violaceum'	CKno CSpe LRHS
	'Squaw'	EBla LRHS NOrc SGSe
	virgatum	CRWN CTri GFor LRHS SHGN SMrm WMnd WPer WWEG
	- 'Blue Tower'	CKno ELon EPPr LRHS MAvo SApp SGSe
	- 'Cloud Nine'	CKno CMea CPen EBee EPPr LRHS MAvo MSnd NLar SApp SGSe SPhx SUsu WHal WRHF
	- 'Dallas Blues'	CDes CKno CPen CPrp CSpe EAEE EBee EBla ECha EHoe EPPr EWes LEdu LHop LRHS MAvo MRav NOak NWsh SApp SBch SHDw SMeo SPer WFar WMoo
	- 'Farbende Auslese'	EBee
	- 'Hänse Herms'	CKno EBee EHoe EPPr LPio MAvo MWhi SApp SBch SPhx WFar WTin WWEG
	- 'Heavy Metal'	Widely available
	- 'Heiliger Hain'	CHar EBee LHop MWea
I	- 'Kupferhirse'	CKno EBee EPPr
	- 'Northwind'	CKno CPen EBee EPPr MAvo SApp SPhx WFar
	- 'Pathfinder'	SApp SGSe
	- 'Prairie Sky'	CKno CWCL EAEE EBee EHoe ELon EPPr GBin LEdu LPio LRHS MAvo MBri NLar SApp SDix SGSe SMeo SUsu WFar WPGP WTin
	- 'Purple Haze' new	LRHS
	- 'Red Cloud'	CKno
	- 'Red Metal'	IPot
	- 'Rehbraun'	EBee EBrs EHoe EPPr EPfP LEdu LHop LPio LRHS NGdn NMRc NOak NWsh SAga SApp SPhx SWal WCAu WFar WTin WWEG
	- 'Rotstrahlbusch'	CKno CPrp CWib EBee EBla EHoe EPPr LRHS MAvo MBri MWhi NBea NOrc SBod SPer SWal WCot WMnd WMoo WPGP WWEG
	- 'Rubrum'	CKno EBee ECha EHoe ELan EPPr EPfP LRHS MAvo MRav MWat SApp SBch SDix STes WMoo
	- 'Shenandoah'	Widely available
	- 'Squaw'	CHar CKno CPrp CWCL CWib EAEE EAlp EBee EBrs EHoe EPPr IPot LPio LRHS MBri MSpe NOak NWsh SApp SGSe SMad SWal WCot WDyG WFar WPnP WTin WWEG
	- 'Strictum'	CSpe EBee EHoe EHul EMil EPPr EWes GQue LEdu LPla LRHS NLar SApp SMeo SPhx SUsu WMoo
I	- 'Strictum Compactum'	LRHS
	- 'Warrior'	Widely available

Papaver ✿ (*Papaveraceae*)

alboroseum	LRHS MPoH
'Alpha Centauri' (SPS)	LLHF SWat WHoo
alpinum L.	CSpe ECho GJos LRHS NBlu SIng SPet SRms SWat WFar

	- 'Flore Pleno' (d)	NBir
	amurense	LEdu NLar SWat
	anomalum album	CSam CSpe
	apokrinomenon	ELan MPoH
	atlanticum	EBee LDai NBro SPlb
	- 'Flore Pleno' (d)	CSpe IFro MCCP NBro WFar WTou
	'Aurora' (SPS)	SWat
	'Beyond Red' (SPS)	SWat
	bracteatum	see *P. orientale* var. *bracteatum*
	'Bright Star' (SPS)	SWat
	burseri	SRot
	'Cathay' (SPS)	SWat
	commutatum ♀H4	CSpe ELan LEdu MPoH SWat
	corona-sancti-stephani	SWat
	'Eccentric Silk' (SPS)	SWat
	fauriei	GKev MPoH
§	'Fire Ball' (d)	ECha GCal IGor LHop NBid NBro NLar SWat WMnd WRHF WWEG
	glaucum	MPoH
	'Heartbeat'PBR (SPS)	SWat
	heldreichii	see *P. pilosum* subsp. *spicatum*
	hybridum 'Flore Pleno' (d)	LRHS NSti SWat
	'Jacinth' (SPS)	CDes LLHF SWat WCot WHoo
	lateritium	CHid CPou SRms
	- 'Nanum Flore Pleno'	see *P.* 'Fire Ball'
	'Lauffeuer'	ELon SWat
	'Matador' ♀H4	WBor
	'Medallion' (SPS)	CDes LLHF SSvw SWat WHoo
§	***miyabeanum***	CSpe ECho ELan LRHS WFar WPer
	- ***album***	ECho
	- ***tatewakii***	see *P. miyabeanum*
	nanum 'Flore Pleno'	see *P.* 'Fire Ball'
§	***nudicaule***	ELan GKir LRHS
	- 'Aurora Borealis'	CSpe
	- Champagne Bubbles Group	SWat WFar
	- - 'Champagne Bubbles Orange' new	NPri
	- - 'Champagne Bubbles Pink' new	LRHS NPri
	- - 'Champagne Bubbles White' new	LRHS NPri
	- - 'Champagne Bubbles Yellow' new	NPri
	- Garden Gnome Group	see *P. nudicaule* Gartenzwerg Group
§	- Gartenzwerg Group ♀H4	COIW CSpe EPfP LRHS MBri MHav NBlu SPet SPlb WFar WGor WWEG
	- Hazy Days Group new	GJos
	- 'Matador'	GGar
	- 'Pacino'	EWll LRHS SPet SPoG SRms WFar WWEG
	- 'Summer Breeze Orange' ♀H4	NPri
	- 'Summer Breeze Yellow'	LRHS NPri
	- Wonderland Series	EHrv SPet
	olchonense new	MPoH
N	***orientale***	CBcs EPfP LAst LRHS NBlu NNor SRms SWal SWat WBrE WFar WPer
	- 'Abu Hassan'	SWat
	- 'Aglaja' ♀H4	CElw EBee ECtt GAbr GBBs GBin LAst LPio NEgg NGdn NSti SAga SMrm SMrs SUsu SWat WClo WCot WHoo
	- 'Aladin'	NBre SWat
	- 'Ali Baba'	GCra LRHS NBre SWat
	- 'Alison'	SWat
	- 'Allegro'	CMea CSBt EAEE EBee ECtt GAbr GKir GMaP LAst LRHS MBNS MBri MHer NGdn NPri NVic SBch SPer SPlb SVic SWat SWvt WWEG
	- 'Allegro Vivace' new	LRHS
	- 'Arwide'	CMil SWat
	- 'Aslahan'	ECha ELon MRav NBre SWat
	- 'Atrosanguineum'	SWat
	- 'Avebury Crimson'	MWat SWat
	- 'Baby Kiss'PBR	EBee ECtt SWat
	- 'Ballkleid'	ECha ELon SWat
	- 'Beauty Queen'	EAEE EBee ECha GMac LPio LRHS MRav NGdn SDix SWat
	- 'Bergermeister Rot'	SWat
	- 'Big Jim'	SWat
	- 'Black and White' ♀H4	CDes CSpe EBee ECha EHrv ELan EPfP GMaP LRHS MRav NBPC NEgg SApp SMrm SWat WCAu WWEG
	- 'Blackberry Queen'	SWat
	- 'Blickfang'	SWat
	- 'Blue Moon'	WHal
	- 'Bolero'	EBee ECtt NCGa NLar
	- 'Bonfire'	EHrv LSou NCob
	- 'Bonfire Red'	EBee SWat WCAu
§	- var. ***bracteatum*** ♀H4	NBir NBur SWat WMoo
	- 'Brilliant'	EBee GJos LRHS MWat NBre NBur NGdn NLar SHlg SWat WFar WMoo
	- 'Brooklyn'	EBee ECtt IPot LPio LSRN MAvo NBre SMrs SWat
	- 'Burning Heart'	EBee ECtt SPer
	- 'Carmen'PBR	MNrw MSCN NBPC NCGa NLar
*	- 'Carneum'	NBre NLar SPoG
	- 'Carnival'	CMil EBee NBre NLar SWat
	- 'Casino' new	NGdn
	- 'Castagnette'	NLar
	- 'Catherina'	NBre SWat
	- 'Cedar Hill'	EAEE EBee ECGP ECtt EWes GCal GMac MRav NBre SMrm SWat
	- 'Cedric Morris' ♀H4	ECha ELan EPPr LPio MRav SMrm SWat WCot WHoo WMnd
	- 'Central Park'	EBee WFar
I	- 'Charming' pink-flowered	EAEE EBee ECtt LRHS NGdn SAga SMrm SWat
	- 'Checkers'	CTri LRHS MHav MLHP SEND WRHF
	- 'China Boy'	EBee LRHS SWat WHrl
	- 'Choir Boy'	CEnt CSpr ECtt ELon LRHS NBur NLar SGar STes SWat WMoo
	- 'Clochard'	CElw EBee SWat
	- 'Coral Reef'	EBee GBBs LRHS MHer MLHP NBur SAga SMeo SWat WHer WMoo WRHF
	- 'Corrina'	EBee NBre SWat
	- 'Curlilocks'	CPar EAEE EBee ECtt ELan ELon EPfP LRHS MRav MWat SBch SMrs SPer SPoG SRms SWat SWvt WCot WHoo WWEG
	- 'Derwisch'	ELon SWat
*	- 'Diana'	SAga SWat
	- 'Domino'	GMac STes
	- 'Double Pleasure'	EBee ECtt MSCN NBre NLar NMoo SMrm SWat WHrl
	- double red shades (d)	NGdn
	- 'Doubloon' (d)	EBee LRHS NBre NGdn SWat
	- 'Dwarf Allegro'	WMnd
	- 'Dwarf Allegro Vivace' new	LRHS
	- 'Effendi' ♀H4	EBee IPot MAvo SUsu SWat
	- 'Elam Pink'	SWat
	- 'Erste Zuneigung'	ECha ELon SWat
	- 'Eskimo Pie'	SWat
	- 'Fancy Feathers'PBR	EBee ECtt IPot LAst NBPC NBhm NGdn SWat
	- 'Fatima'	CDes CMil NBre SWat WHrl
	- 'Feuerriese'	SWat
	- 'Feuerzwerg'	SWat
	- 'Fiesta'	ELon GKir NBre SWat
	- 'Flamenco'	CBcs ECtt ELon NGdn SWat

– 'Flamingo'	EBee ELon MSCN SWat
– 'Flore Pleno' (d)	NGdn
– 'Forncett Summer'	CPar EAEE EBee ECtt ELon GMac LPio LRHS MRav NBre NGby NGdn SMrs SPer STes SWat WHoo WHrl WWEG
– 'Frosty' (v)	SHar
– 'Fruit Punch'	GJos
– 'Garden Glory'	EAEE EBee ECtt ELon GCra GMac LRHS LSRN NBre SMrs SWat WCAu
– 'Glowing Embers'	CSpe LRHS SWat
– 'Glowing Rose'	ELon MDKP NBre SWat
– Goliath Group	EAEE ECha ELan ELon LRHS MRav NBro NVic SDix SRms SWat WFar WMnd WWEG
– – 'Beauty of Livermere'	Widely available
– 'Graue Witwe'	EBee ELon SApp SWat WHrl WTin
– 'Halima'	NBre SWat
– 'Harlem' (New York Series)	CElw CSpe CWCL EBee EPfP IPot MAvo MWea NGdn NLar SMrm SMrs SWat WCAu WHrl
– 'Harvest Moon' (d)	CMac EBee ECtt LRHS NPer SMrm SPhx SWat WHal WWEG
– 'Heidi'	SWat
– 'Hewitt's Old Rose'	NBre
– 'Hula Hula'	ECha ELon SWat
– 'Indian Chief'	CWCL EPfP GMac IPot LPio NBPC NMoo NPer NPri SMrm WFar WWEG
– 'Joanne'	NLar
– 'John III' ♀H4	EBee LPio LPla SPhx SWat
– 'John Metcalf'	EBee ECtt EPPr LPio LRHS MAvo MBel NBre NSti SMrs SWat WCot WSpi
– 'Juliane'	EBee ECha ECtt ELon GMac NSti SWat WCot WTin
– 'Karine' ♀H4	CDes CElw CSam CSpe EBee ECha ELan EPfP GBBs GMaP GMac LPio LRHS MWte NPri SPhx SWat WCAu WHoo WPtf WTin
– 'Khedive' (d) ♀H4	EBee SWat
– 'King George'	SWat
– 'King Kong'	IPot NBPC
– 'Kleine Tänzerin'	CMil CSam ELon GMac LRHS MAvo MBel MMuc MRav MSpe NBre NGdn NPri NSti SAga SMrm SMrs SWat WCAu WCot
– 'Kollebloem'	NBre SWat
– 'Lady Frederick Moore'	GMac LPio LRHS MBel NBre SWat WWEG
– 'Lady Roscoe'	NBre SWat
– 'Ladybird'	EPfP LRHS NBre
– 'Lambada'	SWat
– 'Lauren's Lilac'	CMdw EBee ELon LBMP LPio LRHS MCot MSpe NBre SAga SMeo SMrs SPhx SPoG SWat WAul
– 'Leuchtfeuer' ♀H4	CDes EBee ECha NBre SWat
– 'Lighthouse' ♀H4	EBee SWat
– 'Lilac Girl'	CMac CSpe EBee ECha ECtt ELon EWll GMaP LPio NLar SApp STes SWat WCot WHrl
– 'Louvre'	EBee ECtt EHrv MAvo NLar SMrs WCot WFar
– 'Maiden's Blush'	ECtt NBre NGby NSti SWat
– 'Mandarin'PBR	EBee NBhm NMoo
– 'Manhattan'	CElw CSam CSpe EBee ECtt EPfP EWes GMac IPot LSou MAvo MBel MNrw NCob NEgg NGdn NLar NPri NSti SMrs SPer SPhx SSvw STes SWat WCAu WCot WHrl
– 'Marcus Perry'	EAEE EBee ECtt EWes GMaP LRHS MSpe NEgg SBch SPoG SWat WCAu WFar
– 'Mary Finnan'	EAEE EBee LRHS NBre SWat
– 'Master Richard'	SWat
– 'May Queen' (d)	EWes IBlr LRHS MRav NBre NBro NSti SWat WCot WHrl WPnn
– 'May Sadler'	EBee NBre SWat
– 'Midnight'	ELon NBre SWat
– 'Miss Piggy'PBR	EBee IPot LLHF NGdn SPer STes
– 'Mrs H.G. Stobart'	SWat
– 'Mrs Marrow's Plum'	see *P. orientale* 'Patty's Plum'
– 'Mrs Perry'	CMMP CMac CMea CSBt CSam EBee ECtt ELan EPfP GMaP IFro LRHS MDun MWat NGdn NPer NPri SPer SRGP SRms SRot SWat WBrk WCAu WFar WMnd WTin
– 'Nanum Flore Pleno'	see *P.* 'Fire Ball'
– 'Noema'	SWat
– 'Orange Glow'	NBre NMoo SWat WMoo
– 'Orangeade Maison'	LRHS NBre SWat
– 'Oriana'	NBre SWat
– 'Oriental'	SWat
– 'Pale Face'	SWat
– 'Papillon'PBR	EBee GKir WFar WPtf
§ – 'Patty's Plum'	Widely available
– 'Perry's White'	Widely available
– 'Peter Pan'	ELon MBel NBre SWat
– 'Petticoat'	ECtt ELan NBre SWat
– 'Picotée'	CBcs EBee EBrs ECtt EHrv ELan EPfP GBBs LPio LRHS MRav MSpe NBPC NCGa NCob NEgg NGdn NMoo NPri SPer SPhx SWat SWvt WBrE WCAu WFar WMoo WWEG
– 'Pink Lassie'	NBre SWat
– 'Pink Panda'	SWat
– 'Pink Pearl'PBR **new**	WBor
– 'Pink Ruffles'PBR	EBee SWat
– 'Pinnacle'	CDes EBee ELon NGdn NPri SWat WFar
– 'Pizzicato'	CEnt CMea CWib EHrv GBBs LBMP LRHS MBri MNHC NPer SBch SGar SPet SWal SWat WClo WFar WMoo WRHF WWEG
– 'Place Pigalle'	CSpe EBee EHrv EPfP LSou MAsh MAvo MWea NBPC NEgg NGdn NPri SPer SPhx SPoG WClo WCot
– 'Polka'	SWat
– 'Prince of Orange'	SWat WHlf WWEG
– Princess Victoria Louise	see *P. orientale* 'Prinzessin Victoria Louise'
– 'Prinz Eugen'	CMil EBee GMaP LRHS NBre SWat WCAu
§ – 'Prinzessin Victoria Louise'	CSWP EBee EGoo EPfP EShb EWTr GMaP ILad LAst LRHS MBel MBri NGdn SPoG SWat WBrk WFar WPer WRHF WWEG
– 'Prospero'	NBre
– 'Queen Alexandra'	EHrv LBMP LRHS NGdn NLar WWEG
– 'Raspberry Queen'	CDes CFir CMea EBee ECtt ELan ELon GMaP GMac MArl MBel MRav MWat NBPC NPri NSti SApp SMrm SPhx STes SWat WCot WFar WHal WHoo WMnd WTin WWEG
– 'Raspberry Ruffles'	NBre SPhx SWat
– 'Rembrandt'	EHrv LRHS MDKP NBre NMoo SMrm SWat WPer
– 'Rose Queen'	NBre WCot
– 'Rosenpokal'	EAEE EBee NGdn SWat
– 'Roter Zwerg'	ECha ELon SWat
– 'Royal Chocolate Distinction'	CElw CSpe CWCL EBee ECtt ELon EPfP EWTr MAvo MWea NBPC NLar NMoo NPri NSti SMrs SWat WCAu

- 'Royal Wedding' CTri EAEE EBee EShb GKir LAst LBMP LHop LRHS LSRN MBri MCot MHer MWhi NEgg NGdn NLar NPri SBch SPer SPoG SWat WFar WHrl WMoo WSpi WWEG
- 'Ruffled Patty' MAsh WHlf
* - 'Saffron' CElw SWat
- 'Salmon Glow' (d) GKir SSvw SWat WFar WPer WWEG
- 'Salome' GKir SWat
- 'Scarlet King' CMac EAEE ECGP LRHS NOrc SWat
- scarlet-flowered NCot
- 'Scarlett O'Hara'PBR (d) ECtt EPfP LLHF NPri SWat WBor WFar
- 'Showgirl' EBee ELon MBel NBre SWat
* - 'Silberosa' SWat
- 'Sindbad' ECtt ELon GMac MAvo MRav NEgg SWat
- 'Snow Goose' CMil ELon LPla NBre SAga SPhx SWat WCot WHoo
- 'Soho' (New York Series) **new** NGdn
- 'Spätzünder' NBre SWat
- 'Springtime' ELon EWes GMac LAst MRav NGdn NLar SWat WCAu WTin
- 'Staten Island' EBee ECtt MNrw
- Stormtorch see *P. orientale* 'Sturmfackel'
§ - 'Sturmfackel' NBre SWat
- 'Suleika' NBre SWat
- 'Sultana' ECha ELon GMac MWat SMrs SWat WCAu
- 'The Promise' NBre SWat
- 'Tiffany' CBow CMil CSpe EBee ECtt ELon GAbr GMac LFur LPio LSRN LSou MCot NCGa NEgg NGdn NLar SMrm SPer SSvw STes SWat WCot WWEG
- 'Trinity' SWat
- 'Türkenlouis' CMHG CSpe EBee ECGP ECtt ELon EPfP GCra GKir GMaP GMac LAst LRHS LSRN MRav MSpe NBPC SMrm SPad SPer STes SWat WCAu WCot WFar WHoo WTin WWEG
- 'Turkish Delight' EBee ECtt ELon EPfP GCra GKir GMaP GMac LRHS LSRN MAvo MBel MMuc MRav MWat NBir NPri SBch SPhx SPoG STes SWat SWvt WFar WMnd WWEG
- 'Tutu' SWat
- 'Victoria Dreyfuss' SWat
- 'Viola' SWat
- 'Violetta' SWat
- 'Walking Fire' MNrw
- 'Water Babies' SWat
- 'Watermelon' EBrs ECtt GBBs GKir IPot LRHS MAvo NBPC NPri SMeo SMrm SPer STes SWat WBor WCAu WFar WHoo
- 'White Karine' GMac
- 'White King' GMac NBre
- 'Wild Salmon' NBre
- 'Wisley Beacon' ELon SWat
- 'Wunderkind' EBee ECtt GKir SWat WCAu

'Party Fun' CSpe
paucifoliatum CDes NBre SDix
pilosum SGSe SRms SWat WTin
§ - subsp. ***spicatum*** CFir CMea CSev CSpe ECGP ECha LBMP LHop LSou NBir STes SUsu WClo WCot WFar WMoo
rhaeticum GKev NBre
'Rhapsody in Red' (SPS) SWat
rhoeas CArn EBWF GJos GPoy WJek
- Angels' Choir Group (d) SWat
- Mother of Pearl Group CSpe MCot SWat
- 'Ruffled White' **new** WHlf

rupifragum CArn CEnt CHrt CSsd ECha LEdu MSCN NPol SGar WCot WEas WFar WPer WPnn
- 'Double Tangerine Gem' see *P. rupifragum* 'Flore Pleno'
§ - 'Flore Pleno' (d) CSpe ELon LRHS LSou MBri NBre NChi WBrk WFar WHrl WMoo
- 'Tangerine Dream' MCCP SPet

'Serena' (SPS) SWat
'Shasta' (SPS) LLHF SSvw SWat WCot WHoo
somniferum CArn GPoy SWat
- 'Chedglow' (v) MPoH
- 'Danish Flag' **new** MPoH
- 'Hen and Chickens' **new** MPoH
I - (Laciniatum Group) 'Poppy Jo' **new** MPoH
- - 'Swansdown' (d) CSpe MPoH
- - 'Venus' **new** MPoH
- Paeoniiflorum Group (d) CWCL SWat
- - 'Black Beauty' (d) CSpe MPoH SWat
- - 'Black Paeony' (d) CWCL
- - 'Flemish Antique' (d) MPoH
- - 'Oase' (d) **new** MPoH
- - 'Pink Dawn' (d) **new** MPoH
- - 'Pink Paeony' (d) **new** MPoH
- - 'Plum Pudding' (d) **new** MPoH
- - 'Soft Silk' (d) **new** MPoH
- 'Persian White' **new** MPoH
- 'Pink Chiffon' SWat WEas
- 'Queen's Poppy' **new** MPoH
- 'Seriously Scarlet' **new** MPoH
- single white-flowered CSpe
- 'Victoria Cross' **new** MPoH
- 'White Cloud' (d) CWCL GJos MPoH SWat

'Tequila Sunrise' (SPS) CDes SWat
'The Cardinal' NBre
'The Falklands' (SPS) **new** SWat
triniifolium CSpe
- RCB AM -10 WCot

'Vesuvius' (SPS) SWat
'Viva' (SPS) SWat

papaya (paw paw) see *Carica papaya*

Parabenzoin see *Lindera*

Parachampionella see *Strobilanthes*

Paradisea (*Anthericaceae*)

liliastrum ♀H4 CHid EBee ECho EPPr ERos EWld GCal GKir IGor LRHS NBid NChi SRms
- 'Major' ECho GKev SPhx

lusitanica CAvo CDes CHid CMHG CPom CPrp CSam CSpe EBee ECho ERos GCal GMac IBlr IFro LEdu LRHS MCot SGSe SWal WHoo WPGP WThu WTin

Parahebe (*Scrophulariaceae*)

'Betty' GGar
× ***bidwillii*** GJos MHer NDlv NWCA SRms SRot
- 'Kea' CFee ECou ECtt MDKP SRot WPer

canescens ECou
§ ***catarractae*** CHar CMHG CPLG CTri CWib EBee ECho ECou EPfP GCra GGar MLHP MNrw MRav MSCN MWat NBir NBro SUsu WBrE WCom WFar WKif WMnd WPer
- from Chatham Island EWes
- 'Baby Blue' CAbP EPfP LRHS
- blue-flowered CDoC CHar GKir SPer

- 'County Park' ECou
- 'Cuckoo' ECou NHol
§ - 'Delight' ♀H3 CPLG ECho ECou EWes GCal GGar GMaP GQue LHop LRHS MHer NHol NPer SDix SRot WFar
- subsp. ***diffusa*** ECho ECou ERas LRHS NPer NVic NWCA WCom
- - 'Annie' ECou NHol
- subsp. ***martinii*** ECou
- 'Miss Willmott' ECho NPri SBch SPer SPlb WBVN WPer
- 'Porlock' GKev SRot
- 'Porlock Purple' see *P. catarractae* 'Delight'
- 'Rosea' CEnt ECho WFar
- white-flowered CBot CSpe ECho MLHP WPer
§ ***formosa*** WHCG
- 'Aspley White' ECou
- erect GGar
'Gillian' SWal WPer
'Greencourt' see *P. catarractae* 'Delight'
§ ***hookeriana*** GGar
§ - var. ***olsenii*** ECou GGar
'Jean' GGar
'Joy' ECou EWes
'Julia' GGar
linifolia CTri
§ ***lyallii*** CBot EBee ECho ECou EPfP GJos GKir GMaP LAst MBar MHer MMuc MRav MSwo MWat NBlu NDlv NHol NPol NWCA SPlb SRms WCom WKif
- 'Baby Pink' EPfP LRHS
- 'Clarence' ECou
- 'Glacier' ECou
- 'Julie-Anne' ♀H3 CAbP ECou EPfP GCal GMaP LRHS
- 'Rosea' CTri WPer
- 'Summer Snow' ECou
'Mervyn' CTri ECho MDKP NDlv WPer
olsenii see *P. hookeriana* var. *olsenii*
§ ***perfoliata*** ♀H3-4 CBot CMac CMea CPLG CSpe EBee ECho EGoo ELan EPPr EPfP GCal GCra GGar LEdu LHop LRHS MAsh MRav NChi SBod SPer SRms WCFE WCom WPat WPer WWFP
- dark blue-flowered GBuc SMad
- 'Pringle' CAbP EPfP LRHS
'Snow Clouds' GKev LHop LRHS SBch SRot WFar
'Snowcap' CDoC EPfP LAst LRHS MRav SPlb

Parajubaea (*Arecaceae*)

cocoides LPal
sunkha **new** NExo
torallyi NExo
var. ***microcarpa*** **new**
- var. ***torallyi*** **new** EAmu NExo

Parakmeria see *Magnolia*

Paraquilegia (*Ranunculaceae*)

adoxoides see *Semiaquilegia adoxoides*
§ ***anemonoides*** CPLG WAbe
grandiflora see *P. anemonoides*

Parasenecio (*Asteraceae*)

aff. ***yatabei*** WCru
B&SWJ 11117 **new**

Paraserianthes (*Mimosaceae*)

distachya see *P. lophantha*
§ ***lophantha*** ♀H1 CDTJ CHEx CPLG CRHN CSpr CWit EBak ELon EShb IDee SArc

Parasyringa see *Ligustrum*

× *Pardancanda* (*Iridaceae*)

norrisii CPen EBee EWes
- 'Dazzler' MBel SBch

Pardanthopsis (*Iridaceae*)

dichotoma EWes

Parietaria (*Urticaceae*)

judaica GPoy WHer WSFF

Paris ✿ (*Trilliaceae*)

Chen Yi 8 WCot
chinensis WCru
- B&SWJ 265 from Taiwan WCru
cronquistii CLAP EBee
delavayi EBee WCru
fargesii EBee GAuc LAma WCru
- var. ***brevipetalata*** WCru
- var. ***petiolata*** WCru
forrestii WCru
incompleta CLAP GCal WCru
japonica LAma WCru WWst
lancifolia B&SWJ 3044 from Taiwan WCru
luquanensis EBee
mairei WCru
marmorata EBrs WCru
polyphylla ♀H4 CArn CBct CBro CFir CLAP EBee EBrs ECho GAuc GEdr LAma MNrw WAbe WCot WCru WFar WPnP WSHC WShi WSpi WWst
- B&SWJ 2125 WCru
- Forrest 5945 GCal
- HWJCM 475 WCru
- var. ***alba*** CFir
- var. ***stenophylla*** CFir CLAP EBee LAma WCru WWst
quadrifolia CFir CLAP EBee ECho GGar GPoy NMen SPhx SSpi WCru WHer WPGP WPnP WShi WTin
tetraphylla WCru
thibetica CFir CLAP EBee WCru
- var. ***apetala*** WCru
verticillata CLAP EBee GAuc LAma WCru WWst
- 'Ryokutei' (d) **new** WCru

Parnassia (*Parnassiaceae*)

SDR 5128 **new** GKev

Parochetus (*Papilionaceae*)

§ ***africanus*** ♀H2 CHid ELon
communis misapplied see *P. africanus*
communis ambig. CBcs CFee CFir CPLG MSCN NPer
communis Buch.-Ham. ex D.Don B&SWJ 7215 from the Golden Triangle WCru
- from Himalaya GCra
* - 'Blue Gem' CCCN CSpe
- dark-flowered GBuc GGar

Paronychia (*Illecebraceae*)

argentea WPat WPer
§ ***capitata*** CTri LRHS SRms WPer
kapela SMad SPlb WPer
- 'Binsted Gold' (v) CBow WPer
§ - subsp. ***serpyllifolia*** GBin NRya
nivea see *P. capitata*
serpyllifolia see *P. kapela* subsp. *serpyllifolia*

Parrotia (*Hamamelidaceae*)

persica ♀H4	Widely available
- 'Biltmore'	CPMA
- 'Burgundy'	CPMA NLar
- 'Felicie'	CPMA EPfP NLar
- 'Globosa'	NLar
- 'Jodrell Bank'	CPMA MBlu MBri NLar
§ - 'Lamplighter' (v)	CPMA
- 'Pendula'	CMCN CPMA EPfP LRHS
- 'Summer Bronze' **new**	LRHS MAsh
- 'Vanessa'	CBcs CDoC CMCN CPMA EWes LRHS MAsh MBlu MBri MGos NLar SLPl SPur WDin WFar WMou WPat
- 'Variegata'	see *P. persica* 'Lamplighter'

Parrotiopsis (*Hamamelidaceae*)

jacquemontiana	CBcs CPMA MBlu NLar SSpi

Parrya (*Brassicaceae*)

menziesii	see *Phoenicaulis cheiranthoides*

parsley see *Petroselinum crispum*

Parsonsia (*Apocynaceae*)

capsularis	ECou
heterophylla	ECou

Parthenium (*Asteraceae*)

integrifolium	CArn GKir GPoy IMou
* ***virginicum***	SPhx

Parthenocissus (*Vitaceae*)

§ ***henryana*** ♀H4	Widely available
himalayana	CBcs
- 'Purpurea'	see *P. himalayana* var. *rubrifolia*
§ - var. ***rubrifolia***	CWCL EBee ELan LRHS MAsh MRav NLar SLim SLon SPoG WCru WFar WGrn
inserta ambig.	CTsd NLar
laetevirens	NLar
§ ***quinquefolia*** ♀H4	Widely available
- var. ***engelmannii***	CBcs EBee LAst LBuc MGos NBlu SBch SPer WCFE
- 'Guy's Garnet'	WCru
- Star Showers = 'Monham' (v)	EBee EPfP LRHS MGos WCot
semicordata B&SWJ 6551	WCru
striata	see *Cissus striata*
thomsonii	see *Cayratia thomsonii*
§ ***tricuspidata*** ♀H4	CCVT CWib EBee ECtt EHoe EPfP GKir LAst MGos SPer SReu WDin WFar
- 'Beverley Brook'	EBee ERas LBuc LOck LRHS MBri NLar SBod SPer SRms WFar
- 'Crûg Compact'	CGHE WCru
- 'Fenway Park'	EBee LRHS MGos MRav NLar
- 'Green Spring'	CBcs EBee ERas IArd MGos NLar
- 'Lowii'	EBee EPfP ERas LBuc LRHS MAsh MBlu MGos MRav NLar SLon
- 'Minutifolia'	EBee SPer
- 'Purpurea'	EBee MGos
- 'Robusta'	CHEx EBee EPfP SBch
§ - 'Veitchii'	Widely available

Pasithea (*Anthericaceae*)

caerulea	WCot

Paspalum (*Poaceae*)

glaucifolium	CElw LEdu
quadrifarium	CHrt CKno CMHG EHoe EPPr LDai WCot WPrP
- RCB/Arg RA-5-5	EBee

Passerina (*Thymelaeaceae*)

montana	NWCA

Passiflora ✿ (*Passifloraceae*)

RCB/Arg R-7	WCot
actinia	CRHN LRHS
'Adularia'	CCCN LRHS
alata (F) ♀H1	CCCN EGxp
× ***alatocaerulea***	see *P.* × *belotii*
'Alexia' **new**	NExo
'Allardii'	CCCN EShb LRHS
§ 'Amethyst' ♀H1	CCCN CRHN CSBt CSPN EAmu EBee LHop LRHS LSRN MAsh MRav NExo SPad SPoG WFar WPGP WPat
amethystina misapplied	see *P.* 'Amethyst'
§ ***amethystina*** Mikan	CBcs ECre ERea LRHS
'Anastasia'	CCCN LRHS
'Andy'	CCCN
'Angelo Blu'	CCCN
antioquiensis misapplied	see *P.* × *exoniensis*
antioquiensis ambig.	CBcs CDoC CTsd EShb LRHS
antioquiensis ambig. × ***exoniensis*** 'Hill House'	CHll
antioquiensis ambig. × ***mixta***	CTrC
antioquiensis Karst ♀H2	CHll CRHN EBee EWTr GGal ISea
× ***atropurpurea***	CCCN
§ ***aurantia***	CTsd LRHS
banksii	see *P. aurantia*
§ × ***belotii***	CCCN CRHN EAmu EBee EQua EShb SPad
- 'Impératrice Eugénie'	see *P.* × *belotii*
'Blue Bird'	CCCN
'Blue Moon'	CCCN
'Byron Beauty'	CCCN
§ ***caerulea*** ♀H3	Widely available
- RCB/Arg R-7	WCot
- 'Clear Sky' PBR	LRHS
- 'Constance Elliott'	Widely available
- ***rubra***	CSBt MGos WFar
× ***caeruleoracemosa***	see *P.* × *violacea*
× ***caponii***	CCCN
chinensis	see *P. caerulea*
citrifolia	CCCN EGxp
citrina	EShb LRHS SLim
× ***colvillii***	CHll
'Coordination'	CCCN
§ ***coriacea***	LRHS
'Crimson Trees'	CCCN
× ***decaisneana*** (F)	CCCN
'Eden'	CCCN EAmu EBee LRHS MBri NLar SCoo SLim SPoG SRkn
edulis (F)	CAgr CBcs CCCN LRHS SVic
- 'Crackerjack' (F)	ERea
'Empress Eugenie'	see *P.* × *belotii*
§ × ***exoniensis*** ♀H1	CBot CHll CRHN ECre LRHS
'Fairylights'	CCCN
'Flying V'	CCCN CRHN
gibertii	EShb
hahnii	EAmu
incarnata (F)	CAgr CArn SPlb
'Incense' (F) ♀H1	CCCN SPlb WFar
'Jelly Joker'	CCCN
* ***jureia*** × ***amethystina*** 'Santa Teresa' **new**	EShb
× ***kewensis***	CCCN
'Lady Margaret'	EGxp LRHS
§ ***ligularis*** (F)	CBcs
'Lilac Lady'	see *P.* × *violacea* 'Tresederi'

lowei	see *P. ligularis*
maliformis (F)	CHll
manicata (F)	LRHS
'Maria'	CCCN
'Mary Jane'	CCCN
'Mavis Mastics'	see *P.* × *violacea* 'Tresederi'
mayana	see *P. caerulea*
membranacea (F)	NExo
'Mini Lamb'	CRHN
mixta (F)	CCCN LRHS
mollissima misapplied	see *P. tarminiana*
mollissima ambig. (F)	CAgr CBcs CCCN CHll CTsd EShb LRHS SPlb
mollissima (Kunth) L.H. Bailey (F) ♀H1 new	CRHN
morifolia	EShb
mucronata	NExo
murucuja	CCCN
naviculata RCB/Arg P-12	WCot
'New Incense'	LRHS
obtusifolia	see *P. coriacea*
onychina	see *P. amethystina* Mikan
'Peter Lawerence'	CCCN
'Pink Festival' new	NExo
pinnatistipula (F)	NExo
× ***piresiae***	CCCN LRHS
'Pura Vida'	LRHS
'Purple Haze'	CCCN CRHN CWib EBee EPfP LRHS MAsh NEgg
quadrangularis (F) ♀H1	CCCN CHll CWSG ERea IDee LRHS
quinquangularis	CBcs
racemosa ♀H2	CTsd EBee ERea LAst LRHS MNHC NExo
rovirosae	LRHS
rubra	CCCN EBee SLim
sexocellata	see *P. coriacea*
'Smythiana'	EShb
'Star of Bristol' ♀H2	EBee SLim
'Star of Surbiton'	CDoC CRHN LRHS
subpeltata	LRHS
'Sunburst'	CCCN CHEx LRHS
§ ***tarminiana*** (F)	CRHN
tetrandra	CPLG ECou
× ***tresederi***	see *P.* × *violacea* 'Tresederi'
trifasciata	CCCN EShb
triloba	NExo
tulae	LRHS
umbilicata	WCru
§ × ***violacea*** ♀H1	CBcs CRHN ERea LHop LRHS NExo SGar WFar
- 'Eynsford Gem'	CCCN CDoC EAmu
- 'Lilac Lady'	see *P.* × *violacea* 'Tresederi'
§ - 'Tresederi'	CTsd WFar
- 'Victoria'	CDoC CSBt LRHS SLim
vitifolia 'Scarlet Flame' (F)	LRHS
'White Lightning'	LBuc LOck LRHS LSqu MAsh SBch SLim SPoG SWvt

passion fruit see *Passiflora*

passion fruit, banana see *Passiflora mollissima*

Pastinaca (*Apiaceae*)

sativa	EBWF

Patersonia (*Iridaceae*)

occidentalis	SPlb

Patrinia (*Valerianaceae*)

gibbosa	GEdr LRHS MBel MLHP SGSe WBrE WFar WMoo WPat WPnP
- B&SWJ 874	WCru
scabiosifolia	CDes CHll CKno CSpe EBee ECha ECtt GAbr GBuc GCal LRHS MBel MNFA NBir NCGa NLar NPri SGSe SPhx SPoG SUsu WAul WFar WHoo WMoo WPGP
- B&SWJ 8740	WCru
- 'Nagoya'	MNrw
triloba	ECho GBuc GCal GEdr GKir LRHS LSou SMac SUsu WBVN WFar WMoo WPnP
* - 'Minor'	ECho
- var. ***palmata***	EBee WDyG WFar WMoo WPnP
villosa	CPLG GCal IMou LRHS NGdn NLar SSvw

Paulownia (*Scrophulariaceae*)

catalpifolia	EGFP LLHF MBri NLar
elongata	CBcs EGFP LLHF NLar WBVN
fortunei	CBcs LRHS MAsh MBlu SEND SPlb WBVN WPat
- Fast Blue = 'Minfast'	CPLG EBee EMil EPfP ESwi LHop LLHF LRHS LSRN MAsh SBch SLon SPoG WHar WPGP
kawakamii	WPGP
- B&SWJ 6784	WCru
taiwaniana B&SWJ 7134	WCru
tomentosa ♀H3	Widely available
- 'Coreana'	CHll
- - B&SWJ 8503	WCru

Pavonia (*Malvaceae*)

× ***gledhillii***	ERea EShb
missionum	CSpe
multiflora ambig. new	CCCN
praemorsa	CBot
strictiflora new	CCCN
* ***volubilis***	CCCN

paw paw (false banana) see *Asimina triloba*

paw paw (papaya) see *Carica papaya*

Paxistima (*Celastraceae*)

canbyi	WPat WThu

peach see *Prunus persica*

pear see *Pyrus communis*

pear, Asian see *Pyrus pyrifolia*

pecan see *Carya illinoinensis*

Pedicularis (*Scrophulariaceae*)

SDR 4250	GKev
SDR 4523	GKev
SDR 4810	GKev
axillaris	EBee
longiflora	GKev
var. ***tubiformis*** SDR 4606	
superba SDR 4248	GKev

Peganum (*Zygophyllaceae*)

harmala	CArn

Pelargonium ✿ (*Geraniaceae*)

'A.M. Mayne' (Z/d)	WFib
'Abba' (Z/d)	WFib
'Abbie Hillier' (R)	LDea
'Abel Carrière' (I/d)	SKen SPet

	Name	Suppliers
	abrotanifolium (Sc)	CRHN LFur LPio MBPg MHer SSea WFib WGwG WPen
	'Abundance' (Sc)	CSev LDea
	acetosum	LPio MHer
*	- 'Variegatum' (v)	LPio
	'Acushla by Brian' (Sc)	MBPg
	'Ada Green' (R)	LDea WFib
	'Ada Sutterby' (Dw/d)	SKen
	'Adam's Quilt' (Z/C)	SKen WEas
	'Adele' (Min/d)	ESul
	'Ade's Elf' (Z/St)	NFir SSea
	'Aerosol' (Min)	ESul
	'Ailsa' (Min/d)	ESul SKen
	'Ainsdale Beauty' (Z)	SSea WFib
	'Ainsdale Duke' (Z) **new**	NFir
	'Ainsdale Eyeful' (Z)	WFib
	'Akela' (Min)	ESul
	'Alan West' (Z/St)	SSea
	Alba = 'Fisalb' (Z/d)	SKen
	'Alberta' (Z)	SKen
	alchemilloides	CRHN LPio
	'Alcyone' (Dw/d)	ESul SKen WFib
	'Alde' (Min)	NFir SKen SSea WFib
	'Aldenham' (Z)	WFib
	'Aldham' (Min)	ESul WFib
	'Aldwyck' (R)	ESul LDea WFib
	'Alex' (Z)	SKen
	'Alex Kitson' (Z)	WFib
	'Alex Mary' (R)	ESul
	'Algenon' (Min/d)	ESul WFib
I	'Alice' (Min)	WFib
	'Alice Greenfield' (Z)	NFir SSea
	'Alison' (Dw)	ESul
	'All My Love' (R)	LDea
	'Alma' (Dw/C)	ESul
	alpinum **new**	CDes
	'Altair' (Min/d)	ESul
	'Amari' (R)	WFib
	'Amazon' (R)	ESul
	'Ambrose' (Min/d)	ESul WFib
	Amelit = 'Pacameli'^{PBR} (I/d)	LAst NPri WGor
	'American Prince of Orange' (Sc)	MBPg
	'Amethyst' (R)	ESul LDea NBur SCoo SPet WFib
§	Amethyst = 'Fisdel'^{PBR} (I/d) 🏆$^{H1+3}$	ECtt LDea SKen
	'Amour' (R)	ESul
I	'Amy' (Dw)	WFib
	'Andrew Salvidge' (R)	LDea
	'Androcles' (A)	LDea
	'Angela' (R)	ESul LDea
	'Angela Read' (Dw)	ESul
	'Angela Thorogood' (R)	ESul
	'Angela Woodberry' (Z)	WFib
	Angeleyes Series (A)	SSea
	- Angeleyes Bicolor = 'Pacbicolor'^{PBR} (A)	LAst NPri
	- Angeleyes Burgundy = 'Pacburg'^{PBR} (A)	LAst SSea
	- Angeleyes Orange (A)	LSou
	- Angeleyes Randy (A)	LAst SSea
	- Angeleyes Velvet Duet (A)	LAst
	'Angelique' (Dw/d)	ESul NFir WFib
	'Anglia' (Dw)	ESul
	'Ann Field' (Dw/d)	ESul
	'Ann Hoystead' (R) 🏆$^{H1+3}$	ESul NFir WFib
	'Ann Redington' (R)	ESul
	'Anna' (Dw)	ESul
	'Anna Scheen' (Min)	ESul
	'Anne' (I/d)	WFib
	'Annsbrook Aquarius' (St)	ESul NFir
	'Annsbrook Beauty' (A/C)	ESul NFir WFib
	'Annsbrook Capricorn' (St/d)	ESul
	'Annsbrook Fruit Sundae' (A)	LDea
	'Annsbrook Jupitor' (Z/St)	ESul NFir
	'Annsbrook Mars' (St/C)	ESul
	'Annsbrook Peaches' (Min)	ESul
	'Annsbrook Pluto' (Z/St)	ESul
	'Annsbrook Venus' (Z/St)	ESul
	'Anthony Ayton' (R)	ESul
	Anthony = 'Pacan'^{PBR} (Z/d)	LAst LSou
	'Antoine Crozy' (ZxI/d)	WFib
	'Antoinette' (Min)	ESul
	'Antonnia Scammell' (St/d)	ESul
	'Apache' (Z/d) 🏆$^{H1+3}$	WFib
	'Aphrodite' (Z)	ECtt
	'Apollo' (R)	ESul
	appendiculatum	LPio
	'Apple Betty' (Sc)	MBPg WFib
	'Apple Blossom Rosebud' (Z/d) 🏆$^{H1+3}$	CStu ECtt EShb ESul LAst MBri MCot NEgg SKen SSea WBrk WFib
	'Appledram' (R)	LDea
	'Apri Parmer' (Min)	ESul
	'Apricot' (Z/St)	ESul LAst SKen WGor
	'Apricot Queen' (I/d)	LDea
	'Apricot Star'	SAga
	'April Hamilton' (I)	LDea WFib
	'April Showers' (A)	LDea WFib
	'Aquarell' (R)	ESul
	'Arctic Frost'	WFib
§	'Arctic Star' (Z/St)	CSpe ESul MCot NFir SKen SSea WBrk WFib
	'Ardens'	CSev CSpe EBee ESul LFur LHop LOck LPio LRHS LSou MCot MHer NCob NFir SMrm SSea SUsu SWvt WCot WFib WGwG
	'Ardwick Cinnamon' (Sc)	ESul LDea MBPg NFir WFib
	aridum	LPio WCot
	(Aristo Series) Aristo Apricot = 'Regapri' (R)	LAst NBlu WGor
	- Aristo Beauty = 'Regbeauty'^{PBR} (R)	LSou
	- Aristo Clara Schumann (R)	LAst
	- Aristo Lavender = 'Reglav'^{PBR} (R)	WGor
	- Aristo Schoko = 'Regschoko' (R)	LAst WGor
	- Aristo Velvet (R)	LSou
	- Aristo Violet = 'Regvio'^{PBR} (R)	LAst
	'Arizona' (Min/d)	SKen
	'Arnside Fringed Aztec' (R)	LDea WFib
	'Aroma' (Sc)	MBPg
	'Arthington Slam' (R)	LDea
	'Ashby' (U/Sc)	CWCL MBPg MHer NFir SBch SSea
	'Ashfield Jubilee' (Z/C)	NFir SKen
	'Ashfield Monarch' (Z/d) 🏆$^{H1+3}$	NFir
	'Ashfield Serenade' (Z) 🏆$^{H1+3}$	SKen WFib
	'Ashley Stephenson' (R)	WFib
	'Askham Fringed Aztec' (R) 🏆$^{H1+3}$	ESul LDea WFib
	'Askham Slam' (R)	LDea
	asperum Ehr. ex Willd.	see *P.* 'Graveolens'
	'Athabasca' (Min)	ESul
	'Atlantic Burgundy'	CWCL

	Name	Suppliers
§	'Atomic Snowflake' (Sc/v)	CArn CFee ESul LDea MBPg MCot MHer MNHC SDnm SIde SKen SPet SSea WFib
	'Atrium' (U)	WFib
	'Attar of Roses' (Sc) ΨH1+3	CArn CRHN ERea ESul GBar LDea MBPg MCot MHer NFir NPri SBch SDnm SIde SKen SSea WBrk WFib WGwG
	'Attraction' (Z/Ca/d)	SSea
	'Aubusson' (R)	ESul
	'Audrey Clifton' (I/d)	SKen
	'Auntie Billie' (A)	LDea
	'Aurelia' (A)	LDea
	'Aurora' (Z/d)	LAst LSou SKen
	australe	CRHN LPio MCot SBch SChr WFib
	'Australian Bute' (R)	ESul
	'Australian Mystery' (R/Dec)	CSpe ESul LPio NFir SAga WFib
	'Autumn Colours' (Min)	ESul
	'Autumn Haze' (R)	ESul
	'Aztec' (R) ΨH1+3	ESul LDea NBur NFir SSea WFib
	'Baby Bird's Egg' (Min)	ESul WFib
	'Baby Brocade' (Min/d)	ESul WFib
	'Baby Harry' (Dw/v)	WFib
	'Baby Helen' (Min)	ESul
	'Baby James' (Min)	ESul
	'Baby Snooks' (A)	ESul LDea
	'Babylon' (R)	ESul
	'Badley' (Dw)	ESul
	Balcon Imperial	see *P.* 'Roi des Balcons Impérial'
	'Balcon Lilas'	see *P.* 'Roi des Balcons Lilas'
	'Balcon Rose'	see *P.* 'Hederinum'
	'Balcon Rouge'	see *P.* 'Roi des Balcons Impérial'
	'Balcon Royale'	see *P.* 'Roi des Balcons Impérial'
I	'Ballerina' (Min)	WFib
	'Ballerina' (R)	see *P.* 'Carisbrooke'
	'Bandit' (Min)	ESul
	'Bantam' (Min/d)	ESul WFib
	'Barbara Houghton' (Dw/d)	WFib
§	'Barbe Bleu' (I/d)	ECtt LDea NFir SKen SSea WFib
	'Barcelona' (R)	ESul
	'Barham' (Min/d)	ESul
	'Barking' (Min/z)	ESul NFir
	'Barnston Dale' (Dw/d)	ESul NFir
	'Bath Beauty' (Dw)	CSpe SKen WEas
	'Baylham' (Min)	ESul
	'Beacon Hill' (Min)	ESul
	'Beatrice Cottington' (I/d)	SKen WFib
	'Beau Geste' (R)	ESul
	Beau Jangles Tom (I) **new**	NPri
	'Beauty of Diane' (I/d)	LDea
	'Beauty of Eastbourne' misapplied	see *P.* 'Eastbourne Beauty', *P.* 'Lachskönigin'
	'Beauty of El Segundo' (Z/d)	SKen
	'Beckwith's Pink' (Z)	SKen
	'Beidermeier' (R)	ESul
	'Belinda Adams' (Min/d) ΨH1+3	NFir
	Belladonna = 'Fisopa' (I/d)	ECtt SCoo
	'Belle Ville Red Star' **new**	LSou
	'Belle Ville White' **new**	LSou
	'Belvedere' (R)	ESul
	'Bembridge' (Z/St/d)	SSea WFib
	'Ben Franklin' (Z/d/v) ΨH1+3	ESul NFir SSea
	'Ben Matt' (R)	WFib
	'Ben Nevis' (Dw/d)	ESul
	'Ben Picton' (Z/d)	WFib
	'Bentley' (Dw)	ESul
	'Berkswell Blush' (A)	LDea
	'Berkswell Calypso' (A)	LDea
	'Berkswell Carnival' (A)	LDea
	'Berkswell Champagne' (A)	LDea

Name	Suppliers
'Berkswell Charm' (A)	LDea
'Berkswell Dainty' (A)	LDea
'Berkswell Debonair' (A)	LDea
'Berkswell Gaiety' (A)	LDea
'Berkswell Jester' (A)	LDea
'Berkswell Lace' (A)	LDea
'Berkswell Pixie' (A)	LDea
'Berkswell Rosette' (A)	LDea
'Berkswell Sparkler' (A)	LDea
'Berkswell Windmill' (A)	LDea
'Berliner Balkon' (I)	SKen
Bernardo = 'Guiber'PBR (I/d)	LAst
'Bernice Ladroot'	LDea
'Beromünster' (Dec)	ESul LDea MHer NFir SAga WFib
'Bert Pearce' (R)	ESul LDea WFib
'Beryl Read' (Dw)	CWCL ESul
'Beryl Reid' (R)	ESul LDea WFib
'Berylette' (Min/d)	ESul SKen
'Bess' (Z/d)	ESul SKen
'Bette Shellard' (Z/d/v)	NFir
'Betty Merry' (R)	LDea
'Betty Read' (Dw)	ESul
'Betty West' (Min/d)	ESul
betulinum	LPio SSea WFib
'Betwixt' (Z/v)	SKen
'Bianca' (Min/d)	ESul
'Big Apple' (Sc)	MBPg
'Bildeston' (Dw/C)	ESul WFib
'Bill West' (I)	SSea WFib
'Billie Read' (Dw/d)	ESul
'Bingo' (Min)	ESul
'Bird Dancer' (Dw/St) ΨH1+3	ESul MHer MNHC NFir SBch SKen SSea SWal WBrk
(Birdbush Series) 'Birdbush Andy Pandy' (Sc)	MBPg
- 'Birdbush Beautiful' (Sc) **new**	MBPg
- 'Birdbush Belinda' (Sc) **new**	MBPg
- 'Birdbush Bella' (Sc)	MBPg
- 'Birdbush Billy' (Sc)	MBPg
- 'Birdbush Blanco' (Sc) **new**	MBPg
- 'Birdbush Blush' (Sc)	MBPg
- 'Birdbush Bobby' (Sc)	MBPg
- 'Birdbush Bold and Beautiful' (Sc)	MBPg
- 'Birdbush Bountiful' (Sc) **new**	MBPg
- 'Birdbush Bramley' (Sc)	MBPg
- 'Birdbush Brawdy' (Sc) **new**	MBPg
- 'Birdbush Brilliant' (Sc) **new**	MBPg
- 'Birdbush Chloe' (St)	MBPg
- 'Birdbush Claire Louise' (Sc)	MBPg
- 'Birdbush Dawndew' (Sc)	MBPg
- 'Birdbush Eleanor' (Z)	MBPg WFib
- 'Birdbush Julie Anne' (Sc)	MBPg
- 'Birdbush Kay Lye' (Sc)	MBPg
- 'Birdbush Lemonside' (Sc)	MBPg
- 'Birdbush Limey' (Sc) **new**	MBPg
- 'Birdbush Linda Creasey' (Sc)	MBPg
- 'Birdbush Marion Louise' (Sc) **new**	MBPg
- 'Birdbush Matty'	MBPg
- 'Birdbush Miriam' (Sc)	MBPg
- 'Birdbush Nutty' (Sc)	MBPg

- 'Birdbush Pink and Perky' (U) MBPg
- 'Birdbush Pinky' (Sc) **new** MBPg
- 'Birdbush Sweetness' (Sc) MBPg
- 'Birdbush Tiny Tot' (Sc) **new** MBPg
- 'Birdbush Too Too O' (Sc) MBPg
- 'Birdbush Velvet' (Sc) MBPg
- 'Birdbush Victoria' (Sc) MBPg

'Birthday Girl' (R) WFib
'Bitter Lemon' (Sc) ERea ESul MBPg
'Black Butterfly' see *P.* 'Brown's Butterfly'
'Black Knight' (R) CSpe EShb
'Black Knight' Lea (Dw/d/C) ESul NFir
'Black Night' (A) ESul
'Black Prince' (R/Dec) NFir WFib
'Black Top' (R) ESul
'Black Velvet' (R) ESul LDea MCot
'Black Vesuvius' see *P.* 'Red Black Vesuvius'
'Blackcurrant Yhu' (Dec) NFir
'Blackdown Delight' (Z) NFir
'Blackdown Sensation' (Dw/Z) NFir
'Blakesdorf' (Dw) ESul
Blanca = 'Penwei'PBR (Dark Line Series) (Z/d) LAst
Blanche Roche = 'Guitoblanc' (I/d) LAst LSou NPri SCoo
§ 'Blandfordianum' (Sc) LDea LPio MHer
'Blandfordianum Roseum' (Sc) LDea
'Blaze Away' SSea
'Blazonry' (Z/v) SKen WFib
'Blendworth' (R) LDea
'Blooming Gem' (Min/I/d) LDea
'Blue Beard' see *P.* 'Barbe Bleu'
'Blue Orchid' (R) ESul
'Blue Peter' (I/d) SKen
Blue Sybil = 'Pacblusy'PBR (I/d) LAst LSou NPri
Blue Wonder = 'Pacbla'PBR (Z/d) LAst WGor
Blue-Blizzard = 'Fisrain'PBR (I) SCoo
'Blush Petit Pierre' (Min) ESul
'Blushing Bride' (I/d) LDea SKen
'Blushing Emma' (Dw/d) ESul
'Blushing Sophie' **new** LAst
'Bob Hall' (St) ESul
'Bob Newing' (Min/St) ESul WFib
'Bobberstone' (Z/St) WFib
'Bold Appleblossom' (Z) SSea WFib
'Bold Carmine' (Z/d) NFir
'Bold Carousel' (Z/d) WFib
'Bold Dawn' (Z) NFir
'Bold Flame' (Z/d) WFib
'Bold Limelight' (Z/d) WFib
'Bold Melody' (Z) SSea
'Bold Pixie' (Dw/d) WFib
'Bold Sunrise' (Z/d) NFir
'Bold Sunset' (Z/d) NFir WFib
'Bold White' (Z) NFir
'Bolero' (U) ♀H1+3 NFir SSea WFib
'Bon Bon' (Min/St) WFib
'Bonito' (I/d) SSea
'Bonnie Austin' (St) ESul
'Bonny' (Min/St) ESul
'Bosham' (R) ESul LDea WFib
'Both's Snowflake' (Sc/v) GBar GGar MBPg
bowkeri WFib

'Brackenwood' (Dw/d) ♀H1+3 ESul NFir
'Bramford' (Dw) ESul
'Braque' (R) LDea
Bravo = 'Fisbravo'PBR (Z/d) WFib
'Break o' Day' (R) LDea
'Bredon' (R) ♀H1+3 ESul
'Brenda' (Min/d) ESul WFib
'Brenda Hyatt' (Dw/d) ESul WFib
'Brettenham' (Min) ESul
'Brian West' (Min/St/C) ESul WFib
'Briarlyn Beauty' (A) LDea MBPg
'Briarlyn Moonglow' (A) ESul LDea SSea
'Bridesmaid' (Dw/d) ESul NFir SKen
'Bright Eyes' ambig. (Dw) WFib
'Brightstone' (Z/d) WFib
'Brightwell' (Min/d) ESul
'Brilliant' (Dec) WFib
'Brilliantine' (Sc) CSev ESul MBPg MHer WFib
'Bristol' (Z/v) SSea
'Britannia' (R) LDea
'Brixworth Pearl' (Z) WFib
'Brockbury Scarlet' (Ca) WFib
'Bronze Corinne' (Z/C/d) SKen SPet
'Bronze Velvet' (R) LDea
'Brook's Purple' see *P.* 'Royal Purple'
'Brookside Betty' (Dw/C/d) ESul
'Brookside Bolero' (Z) ESul
'Brookside Candy' (Dw/d) ESul
'Brookside Champagne' (Min/d) ESul
'Brookside Fiesta' (Min/d) ESul
'Brookside Flamenco' (Dw/d) ESul WFib
'Brookside Free Spirit' (Min/D) ESul
'Brookside Melody' (Min/D) ESul
'Brookside Polka' (Dw/D) ESul
'Brookside Primrose' (Min/C/d) ESul NFir SKen WFib
'Brookside Rosita' (Min) ESul
'Brookside Serenade' (Dw) ESul WFib
'Brookside Spitfire' (Dw/d) ESul
'Brookside Tango' (Min/D) ESul
§ 'Brown's Butterfly' (R) ECtt EShb ESul LDea LPio NFir WFib
'Brunswick' (Sc) ESul LDea MHer WFib
'Bucklesham' (Dw) ESul
'Bullfinch' (R) ESul
'Bumblebee' (Dw) ESul
'Burgenlandmädel' (Z/d) SKen
'Burns Country' (Dw) NFir
'Burstall' (Min/d) ESul
'Bushfire' (R) ♀H1+3 ESul LDea WFib
'Butley' (Min) ESul
'Butterfly' (Min/v) ECtt
'Butterfly Brian West' (Min/St) **new** WFib
Butterfly = 'Fisam'PBR (I) NFir SCoo
'Button 'n' Bows' (I/d) WFib
caffrum LPio
'Cal' see *P.* 'Salmon Irene'
Calais = 'Paclai'PBR LAst
'Caledonia' (Z) SKen
'California Brilliant' (U) MHer
'Calignon' (Z/St) SSea WFib
'Camphor Rose' (Sc) ESul GPWP LDea MBPg MHer NFir SSea
'Can-can' (I/d) WFib
'Candy' (Min/d) ESul
'Candy Kisses' (D) ESul
Candy Rose = 'Pacdy'PBR LAst
canescens see *P.* 'Blandfordianum'

'Capel' (Dw/d) ESul
capitatum LPio MBPg MHer MNHC WFib
'Capri' (Sc) MBPg WFib
'Capricorn' (Min/d) ESul
'Captain Starlight' (A) CRHN ESul LDea MBPg MHer NFir SSea WFib
'Caravan' (A) LDea
'Cardinal' see *P.* 'Kardinal'
'Cardington' (St/Dw) ESul
'Carefree' (U) LPio NFir WFib
§ 'Carisbrooke' (R) ♀H1+3 ESul LDea WFib
'Carl Gaffney' LDea
'Carmel' (Z) WFib
'Carnival' (R) see *P.* 'Marie Vogel'
'Carol' (R) ESul
'Carol Gibbons' (Z/d) NFir WFib
'Carol Helyar' (Z/d) WFib
'Caroline' (Dec) ESul
'Caroline Plumridge' (Dw) ESul
'Caroline Schmidt' (Z/d/v) LAst MCot NFir SKen SSea WBrk WFib
'Carolyn' (Dw) ESul
'Carolyn Dean' (St) **new** NFir
'Carolyn Hardy' (Z/d) WFib
Cascade Lilac see *P.* 'Roi des Balcons Lilas'
Cascade Pink see *P.* 'Hederinum'
'Catford Belle' (A) ♀H1+3 ESul LDea
'Cathay' (Z/St) ESul NFir
'Cathy' (R) NFir
caucalifolium subsp. ***caucalifolium*** LPio
- subsp. ***convolvulifolium*** LPio WFib
'Cayucas' (I/d) SKen
'Celebration' (Z/d) ESul
'Cerise' (I/d) SSea
'Cézanne' (R) ESul LDea MCot WFib
'Chantilly Claret' (R) LDea
'Chantilly Lace' (R) ESul LDea
'Charity' (Sc) ♀H1+3 EOHP ESul LDea MBPg MCot MHer NFir SSea WBrk WFib
'Charlie Boy' (R) LDea
'Charlotte Amy' (R) LDea
'Charlotte Bidwell' (Min) ESul
'Charlotte Bronte' (Dw/v) WFib
'Charm' (Min) ESul
'Charmay Adonis' NFir
'Charmay Alf' (A) LDea
'Charmay Aria' (A) LDea
'Charmay Bagatelle' (A) LDea
'Charmay Electra' (A) LDea
'Charmay Marjorie' (A) LDea
'Charmay Snowflake' (Sc/v) ESul MBPg
'Chattisham' (Dw/C) ESul NFir
'Chelmondiston' (Min/d) ESul
'Chelsea Gem' (Z/d/v) ♀H1+3 SKen WFib
'Chelsea Morning' (Z/d) WFib
'Chelsworth' (Min/d) ESul
'Chelvey' (R) LDea
'Cherie' (R) ESul LDea
'Cherie Bidwell' (Dw/d/v) ESul
'Cherie Maid' (Z/v) SSea
'Cherry' (Min) LAst WFib
'Cherry Baby' (Dec) NFir
'Cherry Cocktail' (Z/d/v) NFir
'Cherry Hazel Ruffled' (R) ESul LDea
'Cherry Orchard' (R) ESul LDea NBur SSea WFib
'Cherry Sundae' (Z/d/v) ESul
'Cheryldene' (R) LDea
'Chew Magna' (R) WFib
'Chi-Chi' (Min) ESul
'Chieko' (Min/d) WFib
'Chime' (Min/d) ESul
'China Doll' (Dw/d) WFib
'Chinz' (R) NFir
§ 'Chocolate Peppermint' (Sc) CRHN CSev EAro ESul LDea MBPg MHer MNHC NBur NFir SIde SKen SSea SWal WBrk WFib
'Chocolate Tomentosum' see *P.* 'Chocolate Peppermint'
'Chrissie' (R) ESul WFib
'Christina Beere' (R) LDea
'Christopher Ley' (Z) SKen
'Chusan' (R) SSea
'Cindy' (Dw/d) ESul WFib
'Citriodorum' (Sc) ♀H1+3 LDea MBPg MCot MHer WFib
'Citronella' (Sc) CRHN LDea MBPg MHer SSea WFib
citronellum (Sc) LPio MBPg
'City of Bath' CWCL
'Clara Read' (Dw) ESul
'Claret Rock Unique' (U) LDea MBPg SKen SSea WFib
'Clarissa' (Min) ESul
'Clatterbridge' (Dw/d) ESul NFir
'Claude Read' (Dw) ESul
'Claudette' (Min) ESul
'Claudius' (Min) ESul
'Claydon' (Dw/d) ESul NFir
'Claydon Firebird' (R) ESul
'Clorinda' (U/Sc) CRHN EShb ESul GBar MBPg MCot MHer MNHC NBur SIde SKen SSea SWal WFib
'Clovelly Rose' CWCL
'Clown' (R) ESul
'Coconut Ice' (Dw) ESul
Coco-Rico (I) SKen
'Coddenham' (Dw/d) ESul WFib
§ 'Colonel Baden-Powell' (I/d) LDea WFib
'Colwell' (Min/d) WFib
'Concolor Lace' see *P.* 'Shottesham Pet'
'Confetti' (R) ESul
'Contrast' (Z/C/v) CWCL MBri NBlu NEgg SCoo SKen SPoG SSea WFib
'Cook's Peachblossom' WFib
'Copdock' (Min/d) ESul
'Copthorne' (U/Sc) ♀H1+3 CRHN ESul LDea MBPg MHer SKen SSea WFib
'Coral Frills' (Min/d) ESul
cordifolium CRHN WFib
- var. ***rubrocinctum*** NFir
coriandrifolium see *P. myrrhifolium* var. *coriandrifolium*
'Cornell' (I/d) ECtt WFib
cortusifolium MHer
'Corvina' (R) WFib
'Cottenham Beauty' (A) ESul LDea NFir
'Cottenham Belle' (A) ESul
'Cottenham Bliss' (A) ESul
'Cottenham Charm' (A) ESul LDea
'Cottenham Cheer' (A) ESul
'Cottenham Cynthia Haird' (A) ESul
'Cottenham Delight' (A) ESul LDea NFir
'Cottenham Gem' (A) ESul
'Cottenham Glamour' (A) ESul NFir
'Cottenham Harmony' (A) ESul LDea
'Cottenham Jubilee' (A) ESul LDea MHer
'Cottenham Mervyn Haird' (A) ESul
'Cottenham Star' (A) ESul
'Cottenham Surprise' (A) ESul LDea NFir
'Cottenham Treasure' (A) ESul LDea
'Cottenham Wonder' (A) ESul
'Cotton Candy' (Min/d) ESul
'Cottontail' (Min) ESul WFib

	cotyledonis	WFib
	'Countess Mariza'	see *P.* 'Gräfin Mariza'
	'Countess of Scarborough'	see *P.* 'Lady Scarborough'
	'Country Girl' (R)	SPet
	'Cover Girl' (Z/d)	WFib
	'Cowes' (St/Min/d)	ESul
	'Cramdon Red' (Dw)	SKen WFib
	'Cransley Blends' (R)	ESul LDea
	'Cransley Star' (A)	LDea WFib
	'Cream 'n' Green' (R/v)	NFir
	'Creamery' (d)	WFib
	'Creamy Nutmeg' (Sc/v)	CArn EShb ESul GBar LDea MHer NFir SSea
	'Creeting St Mary' (Min)	ESul
	'Creeting St Peter' (Min)	ESul
	'Crescendo' (I/d)	ECtt
	'Crimson Fire' (Z/d)	MBri
	'Crimson Unique' (U) 🏆H1+3	CSpe MCot MHer SKen SSea WFib
§	***crispum*** (Sc)	GBar GPoy LDea MBPg NEgg
§	- 'Golden Well Sweep' (Sc/v)	MBPg WFib
	- 'Major' (Sc)	ESul SKen WFib
	- 'Minor' (Sc)	MHer
	- 'Peach Cream' (Sc/v)	ESul MBPg WFib
	- 'Prince Rupert' (Sc)	MBPg
	- 'Variegatum' (Sc/v) 🏆H1+3	CRHN GBar GGar GPoy LDea MBPg MHer NFir SIde SPet SSea WCom WFib
	crithmifolium	MHer
	'Crocketta' (I/d/v)	NFir SKen
	'Crocodile' (I/C/d)	ECtt ERea EShb LDea MHer NFir SKen SSea SWal WBrk WFib
	'Crowfield' (Min/d)	ESul WFib
	'Crowfoot Rose' (Sc)	EAro GBar
	'Crown Jewels' (R)	LDea
	'Crystal Palace Gem' (Z/v)	SKen SSea WFib
	'Crystal West' (Min/St)	ESul
	cucullatum	ESul LPio SSea WFib
	- 'Flore Plenum'	MHer WFib
	'Culpho' (Min/C/d)	ESul
	'Cupid' (Min/Dw/d)	WFib
	'Cyril Read' (Dw)	ESul
§	'Czar' (Z/C)	SCoo
	'Dainty Lassie' (Dw/v)	ESul
	'Dainty Maid' (Sc)	ESul GGar MBPg NFir SAga SSea
	'Dale Queen' (Z)	WFib
	'Dallimore' (Dw)	ESul
	'Danielle Marie' (A)	LDea
	'Danton' (Z/d)	WFib
I	'Daphne' (Dec)	SKen
	'Dark Ascot' (Dec)	ESul
	'Dark Red Irene' (Z/d)	SKen WFib
	'Dark Secret' (R)	CSpe ESul LDea WFib
	'Dark Venus' (R)	ESul LDea WFib
	Dark-Red-Blizzard = 'Fisblizdark' (I)	CWCL
	'Darmsden' (A) 🏆H1+3	ESul LDea NFir SSea
	'David John' (Dw/d)	ESul
	'David Mitchell' (Min/Ca/d)	ESul
	'Davina' (Min/d)	ESul WFib
	'Dawn Star' (Z/St)	ESul NFir
	'Deacon Arlon' (Dw/d)	ESul SKen
	'Deacon Avalon' (Dw/d)	WFib
	'Deacon Barbecue' (Z/d)	ESul SKen WFib
	'Deacon Birthday' (Z/d)	ESul WFib
	'Deacon Bonanza' (Z/d)	ESul SSea WFib
	'Deacon Clarion' (Z/d)	ESul SKen WFib
	'Deacon Constancy' (Z/d)	ESul
	'Deacon Coral Reef' (Z/d)	ESul WFib
	'Deacon Finale' (Z/d)	ESul
	'Deacon Fireball' (Z/d)	ESul SKen WFib
	'Deacon Flamingo' (Z/d)	ESul
	'Deacon Gala' (Z/d)	ESul WFib
	'Deacon Golden Bonanza' (Z/C/d)	ESul WFib
	'Deacon Golden Gala' (Z/C/d)	ESul SKen
	'Deacon Golden Lilac Mist' (Z/C/d)	ESul WFib
	'Deacon Jubilant' (Z/d)	ESul SKen
	'Deacon Lilac Mist' (Z/d)	ESul SKen SSea WFib
	'Deacon Mandarin' (Z/d)	ESul SKen WFib
	'Deacon Minuet' (Z/d)	ESul NFir SKen WFib
	'Deacon Moonlight' (Z/d)	ESul
	'Deacon Peacock' (Z/C/d)	ESul WFib
	'Deacon Picotee' (Z/d)	ESul SKen SSea WFib
	'Deacon Regalia' (Z/d)	ESul SKen WFib
	'Deacon Romance' (Z/d)	ESul SKen SSea
§	'Deacon Summertime' (Z/d)	ESul WFib
	'Deacon Sunburst' (Z/d)	ESul SKen
	'Deacon Suntan' (Z/d)	ESul SKen
	'Deacon Trousseau' (Z/d)	ESul WFib
	'Dean's Delight' (Sc)	LDea MBPg
	'Debbie' (A)	LDea
	'Debbie Parmer' (Dw/d)	ESul
	'Debbie Thrower' (Dw)	ESul
	'Deborah Miliken' (Z/d)	ESul NFir WFib
	'Decora Lavender'	see *P.* 'Decora Lilas'
§	'Decora Lilas' (I)	ECtt LAst NPri SKen SPet
	'Decora Mauve'	see *P.* 'Decora Lilas'
	'Decora Pink'	see *P.* 'Decora Rouge'
	'Decora Red'	see *P.* 'Decora Rouge'
§	'Decora Rose' (I)	ECtt NPri SPet
§	'Decora Rouge' (I)	ECtt LAst SKen SPet
	'Decora Scarlet' (I) **new**	SKen
	'Deerwood Darling' (Min/v/d)	WFib
	'Deerwood Lavender Lad' (Sc)	ESul LDea MBPg MHer SSea WFib
	'Deerwood Lavender Lass'	ESul LDea LPio MBPg MHer
	'Deerwood Pink Puff' (St/d)	WFib
	'Delightful' (R)	WFib
	'Delilah' (R)	LDea
	'Delli' (R)	NFir NPer WFib
	'Delta' (Min/d)	ESul
	'Denebola' (Min/d)	ESul
	'Dennis Hunt' (Z/C)	NFir
	denticulatum	GBar MHer SKen SSea
§	- 'Filicifolium' (Sc)	CRHN EShb ESul LDea LPio MBPg MHer SSea WFib
	'Diana Hull'	MBPg
	'Diana Palmer' (Z/d)	SKen
	'Diane' (Min/d)	ESul
	'Diane Louise' (d)	SSea
	'Dibbinsdale' (Z)	ESul NFir
	dichondrifolium (Sc)	CSev LPio MBPg MHer NFir SSea WFib
	dichondrifolium* × *reniforme (Sc)	ESul NFir
	'Didi' (Min)	SKen
	'Dinky' (Min/d)	ESul
	'Display' ambig. (Dw/v)	WFib
	'Distinction' (Z)	ERea MHer NFir SKen SPoG SSea WFib
	'Doctor A. Chipault' (I/d)	LDea
	'Dollar Bute' (R)	ESul
	'Dollar Princess' (Z/C)	SKen
	'Dolly Read' (Dw)	ESul
	'Dolly Varden' (Z/v) 🏆H1+3	ESul LDea NFir SKen SSea WFib
	'Don's Carosel' (Z/v)	SSea

'Don's Helen Bainbridge' (Z/C)	NFir
'Don's Mona Noble' (Z/C)	NFir SKen SSea
'Don's Richard A. Costain' (Z/C)	NFir
'Don's Silva Perle' (Dw/v)	SKen
'Don's Southport' (Z/v)	NFir
'Don's Swanland Girl' (Min)	Sul
'Don's Wensleydale' (Dw/C)	ESul
'Dorcas Brigham Lime' (Sc)	CSpe EAro
'Dorcus Bingham' (Sc)	GBar MBPg
'Doris Frith' (R)	LDea
'Doris Hancock' (R)	WFib
'Doris Shaw' (R)	ESul
'Dorothy May' (A)	LDea
'Double Bird's Egg' (Z/d)	SKen
'Double Grace Wells' (Min/d)	ESul
'Double Lilac White' (I/d)	SKen
'Double Orange' (Z/d)	SKen
'Double Pink' (R/d)	WFib
'Dovedale' (Dw/C)	ESul WFib
'Dovepoint' (Dw/2) **new**	NFir
'Downlands' (Z/d)	SWal WFib
'Dresden China' (R)	ESul LDea
'Dresden Pippa Rosa' (Z)	SKen
'Dresden White' (Dw)	WFib
Dresdner Apricot = 'Pacbriap'PBR (I/d)	NPri
'Drummer Boy' (Z)	SKen
'Dryden' (Z)	SKen
'Dubonnet' (R)	LDea SSea
'Duchess of Devonshire' (U)	WFib
'Duke of Edinburgh'	see *P.* 'Hederinum Variegatum'
'Dulcie' (Min)	ESul
'Dunkery Beacon' (R)	ESul WFib
'Dusty Rose' (Min)	ESul
'E. Dabner' (Z/d)	SKen WFib
'Earl of Chester' (Min/d) ♀H1+3	WFib
'Earliana' (Dec)	ESul LDea
'Earlsfour' (R)	LDea
'East Sussex' (Dw/C)	ESul
§ 'Eastbourne Beauty' (I/d)	SKen
'Easter Promise' (R)	ESul
echinatum	CSpe LPio MHer SSea
- 'Album'	LPio SSea WFib
'Eclipse' (Dw/d)	SKen
'Eclipse' (I/d)	SKen
'Eden Gem' (Min/d)	WFib
'Edith Stern' (Dw/d)	ESul
'Edmond Lachenal' (Z/d)	WFib
'Edward Humphris' (Z)	SKen
'Edwards Michael' (A)	LDea
'Eileen' (Min/d)	ESul
'Eileen Nancy' (Z)	NFir
'Eileen Postle' (R) ♀H1+3	WFib
'Eileen Stanley' (R)	LDea
'Elaine' (R)	LDea
'Elaine Thompson' (R)	LDea
Elbe Silver = 'Pensil' (I)	LAst NFir SCoo
'Electra' (Z/d)	SKen
elegans	ERea
'Elizabeth Angus' (Z)	SKen WFib
'Elizabeth Read' (Dw)	ESul
'Ella Martin' (St)	ESul
'Elmfield' (St/Min/d)	ESul
'Elmsett' (Dw/C/d)	ESul NFir SSea WFib
'Elna' (Min)	ESul
elongatum	SSea
'Els' (Dw/St)	ESul SKen WBrk
'Elsi' (I × Z/d/v)	WFib
'Elsie Gillam' (St)	ESul WFib
'Elsie Hickman' (R)	ESul LDea NBur
'Elsie Portas' (Z/C/d)	ESul SKen
'Embassy' (Min)	ESul WFib
'Emerald' (I)	SKen
Emilia = 'Pactina'PBR	LAst WGor
'Emma Game' (Z/St)	WFib
'Emma Hössle'	see *P.* 'Frau Emma Hössle'
'Emma Jane Read' (Dw/d)	ESul NFir WFib
'Emma Louise' (Z)	SKen
'Emmy Sensation' (R)	LDea
'Emperor Nicholas' (Z/d)	SKen
'Empress' (Z)	SKen
'Ena' (Min)	ESul
'Enchantress' (I)	SKen
endlicherianum	LPio WCot WWFP
'Endsleigh' (Sc)	MBPg SBch
'Enid Brackley' (R)	ESul
'Erwarton' (Min/d)	ESul NFir
'Escapade' (Min/d)	ESul
'Eskay Gold' (A)	WFib
'Eskay Jewel' (A)	WFib
'Eskay Sugar Candy' (A)	WFib
'Eskay Verglo' (A)	WFib
Evening Glow = 'Bergpalais'PBR	LAst
'Evka'PBR (I/v)	CWCL LAst NPri SCoo SSea
exstipulatum	EShb SSea WEas
'Fabian Gane' (St)	SSea
'Fabiola' **new**	LAst
'Fair Dinkum' (Z/v)	ESul
'Fair Ellen' (Sc)	ESul LDea MBPg MHer WFib
'Fairlee' (DwI)	WFib
'Fairy Lights' (Dw/St)	ESul NFir
'Fairy Orchid' (A)	ESul LDea WFib
'Fairy Queen'	LDea MHer
'Falkenham' (Min)	ESul
'Falkland Brother' (Z/C/v)	WFib
'Falkland Hero' (Z/v)	NFir
'Fallen Angel' (Z/St) **new**	WFar
'Fandango' (Z/St)	ESul NFir WFib
'Fanny Eden' (R)	CWCL WFib
'Fantasia' white-flowered (Dw/d) ♀H1+3	ESul WFib
'Fareham' (R) ♀H1+3	LDea WFib
'Feneela' (Dw/d)	ESul
'Fenland' (R)	ESul
'Fenton Farm' (Dw/C)	ESul NFir
'Festal' (Min/d)	ESul
'Feuerriese' (Z)	SKen
'Fiat' (Z/d)	SKen
'Fiat Queen' (Z/d)	SKen WFib
'Fiat Supreme' (Z/d)	SKen
'Fiery Sunrise' (R)	ESul LDea
'Fiesta' (I/d)	LDea
'Fifth Avenue' (R)	CSpe ESul LPio WFib
'Filicifolium'	see *P. denticulatum* 'Filicifolium'
'Fir Trees Audrey B' (St)	NFir
'Fir Trees Celebration' (Sc)	NFir
'Fir Trees Eileen' (St)	NFir SMrm
'Fir Trees Ele' (A/v)	NFir
'Fir Trees Fantail' (Min)	NFir
'Fir Trees Flamingo' (Dw)	NFir
'Fir Trees Jack' (Z/Dw)	NFir
'Fir Trees John Grainger' (Z/v)	NFir
'Fir Trees Mark' (R/Dec/v)	NFir
'Fir Trees Nan' (R/Dec)	NFir

Name	Suppliers
'Fir Trees Ruby Wedding' (C)	NFir
'Fir Trees Silver Wedding' (Z/C/d)	NFir
'Fir Trees Sparkler' (Min/C)	NFir
'Fire Dancer' (R)	ESul
'Fire Dragon' (Z/St/d)	SKen SSea
'Firefly' (Min/d)	ESul
'Firestone' (Dw)	ESul
'Fireworks' (Dw)	SWal
(Fireworks Series) Fireworks Cherry = 'Fiwocherry'^{PBR} (Z)	LAst SBch
- Fireworks Cherry-white = 'Fiwocher'^{PBR} (Z)	LAst SSea
- Fireworks Light Pink = 'Fiwopink'^{PBR} (Z/St)	LAst SBch
- Fireworks Red-white = 'Fiworewhi'^{PBR} (Z)	SBch
- Fireworks White = 'Fiwowit'^{PBR} (Z)	SBch
'First Blush' (R)	WFib
'First Love' (Z)	NFir
'Flakey' (I/d/v) 🏆$^{H1+3}$	ESul LDea NFir SKen
'Flaming Katy' (Min)	ESul NFir
'Flarepath' (Z/C/v)	NFir
'Flash' (Min)	ESul
'Flecks' (Min/St)	ESul
'Fleur-de-lys' (A)	LDea
'Fleurette' (Min/d)	ESul SKen
'Fleurisse' (Z)	WFib
'Flirt' (Min)	WFib
'Floral Cascade' (Fr/d)	SSea
'Florence Hunt' (R) **new**	NFir
'Floria Moore' (Dec)	ESul NBur NFir SAga SSea
'Flower Basket' (R/d)	ESul LDea
(Flower Fairy Series) Flower Fairy Berry = 'Sweberry'	WGor
- Flower Fairy Rose = 'Swero' (Z) **new**	LSou
- Flower Fairy White Splash = 'Swewhi' (Z) **new**	LSou
'Flower of Spring' (Z/v) 🏆$^{H1+3}$	SKen SSea
'Flowton' (Dw/d)	ESul
'Foxhall' (Dw)	ESul
Foxy = 'Pacfox'^{PBR} (Z)	LSou
fragrans	EAro
Fragrans Group (Sc)	CRHN CSev ESul GBar GPoy MBPg MCot MHer SDnm SKen SPet SSea WFib WGwG
§ - 'Fragrans Variegatum' (Sc/v)	CSev ESul MBPg NFir SKen SWal WBrk WFib
- 'Snowy Nutmeg'	see *P.* (Fragrans Group) 'Fragrans Variegatum'
'Fraiche Beauté' (Z/d)	WFib
'Francis Gibbon' (Z/d)	WFib
'Francis James' (Z)	WFib
'Francis Kelly' (R)	ESul
'Francis Parrett' (Min/d) 🏆$^{H1+3}$	ESul SKen WFib
'Francis Read' (Dw/d)	ESul
'Frank Headley' (Z/v) 🏆$^{H1+3}$	ERea EShb ESul LAst MCot NPer NVic SAga SCoo SDnm SIde SKen SMrm SSea SWal WFib
§ 'Frau Emma Hössle' (Dw/d)	ESul WFib
'Freak of Nature' (Z/v)	ESul MHer NFir SKen SSea WFib
'Frensham' (Sc)	ESul LDea MBPg MHer SSea WFib
'Freshfields Suki' (Dw)	NFir
'Freshwater' (St/C)	ESul SSea WFib
'Freston' (Dw)	ESul
'Friary Wood' (Z/C/d)	ESul NFir WFib
'Friesdorf' (Dw/Fr)	ESul MCot MHer NFir SKen WBrk WFib
'Frills' (Min/d)	ESul
'Fringed Angel' (A)	CFee
'Fringed Apple' (Sc)	LDea MBPg NBur
'Fringed Aztec' (R) 🏆$^{H1+3}$	CWCL ESul LDea NFir SPet WFib
'Fringed Jer'Ray' (A)	LDea
'Fringed Rouletta' (I)	LDea
'Frosty' misapplied	see *P.* 'Variegated Kleine Liebling'
'Frosty Petit Pierre'	see *P.* 'Variegated Kleine Liebling'
'Frühlingszauber Lila' (R)	ESul
'Fruity' (Sc)	MBPg
fruticosum	EShb LPio WFib
'Fuji' (R)	NFir
fulgidum	CSpe EShb ESul LPio WFib
'Funny Girl' (R)	ESul
'Fynn' (Dw)	ESul
'Gabriel' (A)	ESul LDea
'Galilee' (I/d) 🏆$^{H1+3}$	LDea SKen
Galleria Sunrise = 'Sunrise' (R)	ESul LDea SKen
'Galway Star' (Sc/v) 🏆$^{H1+3}$	MBPg MHer WBrk WFib
'Garland' (Dw/d)	ESul
'Garnet' (Z/d)	ESul
'Garnet Rosebud' (Min/d)	ESul NFir WFib
'Gartendirektor Herman' (Dec)	ESul NBur NFir SSea WFib
'Gatwig'	LSou WGor
'Gaudy' (Z)	WFib
'Gay Baby' (DwI)	ESul LDea
'Gay Baby Supreme' (DwI)	ESul
'Gemini' (Z/St/d)	CWCL NFir SSea WFib
'Gemma' (R)	ESul NFir
'Gemma Jewel' (R) 🏆$^{H1+3}$	ESul
'Gemma Rose' (R)	LDea
I 'Gemstone' (Min)	ESul
'Gemstone' (Sc) 🏆$^{H1+3}$	LDea MBPg MHer WBrk
'Genie' (Z/d)	SKen WFib
'Gentle Georgia' (R)	WFib
'Geofbar' (R)	ESul
'Geoff May' (Min)	ESul
'Georgia' (R)	WFib
'Georgia Mai Read'	ERea
'Georgia Peach' (R)	ESul WFib
'Georgie' (R)	LDea
'Georgina Blythe' (R) 🏆$^{H1+3}$	WFib
'Gerald Portas' (Dw/C)	ESul
'Gerald Wells' (Min)	ESul
'Geraldine' (Min)	ESul
'Gesa'	LAst
'Gess Portas' (Z/v)	ESul
'Giant Butterfly' (R)	ESul
'Giant Oak' (Sc)	ESul MBPg
gibbosum	LPio MHer SSea WFib
'Gilbert West' (Z)	SKen
'Gilda' (R/v)	LDea
'Gill' (Min/Ca)	ESul
'Ginger Frost' (Sc/v)	WFib
'Ginger Rogers' (Z)	NFir
'Glacier Claret' (Z)	WFib
'Glacier Crimson' (Z)	SKen
'Glacis'^{PBR} (Quality Series) (Z/d)	LAst LSou
'Gladys Evelyn' (Z/d)	WFib
'Gladys Stevens' (Min/d)	ESul
'Gladys Weller' (Z/d)	WFib
glaucum	see *P. lanceolatum*
'Glen Sheree' (R)	ESul

	Name	Suppliers
	'Gloria Pearce' (R)	ESul LDea
	'Glowing Embers' (R)	ESul LDea SSea
§	***glutinosum***	WFib
	'Goblin' (Min/d)	ESul SKen WFib
	'Godshill' (R)	LDea
	Golden Angel[PBR]	see *P.* 'Sarah Don'
	'Golden Baby' (Dw/I/C)	ESul LDea NFir WFib
	'Golden Brilliantissimum' (Z/v)	ESul SSea WFib
	'Golden Butterfly' (Z/C)	ESul
	'Golden Chalice' (Min/v)	ESul NFir WFib
	'Golden Clorinda' (U/Sc/C)	CRHN LDea MBPg NFir SSea
	'Golden Crest' (Z/C)	SKen
	'Golden Ears' (Dw/St/C)	ESul NFir NPer WFib
	'Golden Edinburgh' (I/v)	WFib
	'Golden Everaarts' (Dw/C)	ESul
	'Golden Fleece' (Dw/C/d)	ESul
	'Golden Gates' (Z/C)	ESul SKen
	'Golden Harry Hieover' (Z/C) ♀H1+3	ESul MBri SSea
	'Golden Lilac Gem' (I/d)	WFib
	'Golden Lilac Mist'	SKen
	'Golden Petit Pierre' (Min/C)	ESul SSea
	'Golden Princess' (Min/C)	WFib
	'Golden Roc' (Min/C)	ESul
	'Golden Square' (Dw/St)	WFib
	'Golden Staphs' (Z/St/C)	ESul MHer NFir SSea WFib
	'Golden Stardust' (Z/St)	ESul
	'Golden Wedding' (Z/d/v)	NFir
	'Golden Well Sweep'	see *P. crispum* 'Golden Well Sweep'
	'Goldilocks' (A)	ESul
	'Gooseberry Leaf'	see *P. grossularioides*
	'Gordano Midnight' (R)	LDea
	'Gordon Quale' (Z/d)	WFib
	'Gosbeck' (A)	SSea WFib
	'Gothenburg' (R)	ESul
	'Gottweig' (Z)	ESul
	'Grace' (A)	LDea
	'Grace Thomas' (Sc) ♀H1+3	LDea MBPg MHer WFib
	'Grace Wells' (Min)	ESul WFib
§	'Gräfin Mariza' (Z/d)	SKen
	'Grand Duchess' (R)	LDea
	'Grand Slam' (R)	CWCL ESul LDea NFir WFib
	'Grandad Mac' (Dw/St)	ESul NFir SSea
	grandiflorum	LPio MHer WFib
	'Grandma Fischer'	see *P.* 'Grossmutter Fischer'
	'Grandma Ross' (R)	ESul
	'Grandma Thompson' (R)	ESul
	'Granny Hewitt' (Min/d)	ESul
	graveolens *sensu* J.J.A. van der Walt	LDea LPio SBch WFib
§	'Graveolens' (Sc)	ESul GBar GPoy MBPg MHer SSea WBrk WFib
	'Great Bricett' (Dw/d)	ESul
	'Green Ears' (Z/St)	ESul
	'Green Eyes' (I/d)	MHer SKen
	'Green Goddess' (I/d)	LDea SKen
	'Green Gold Petit Pierre' (Min)	ESul
	'Green Silver Galaxy' (St)	ESul
	'Green Woodpecker' (R)	LDea SSea
§	'Greengold Kleine Liebling' (Min/C/v)	ESul SKen
	'Greengold Petit Pierre'	see *P.* 'Greengold Kleine Liebling'
	'Greetings' (Min/v)	ESul MBri SSea WFib
	'Grey Lady Plymouth' (Sc/v)	ESul LDea MBPg MCot MHer WFib
	'Grey Sprite' (Min/v)	ESul WFib
§	'Grossmutter Fischer' (R)	LDea
§	***grossularioides***	EOHP MBPg MHer
	- 'Coconut'	MBPg
	'Grozser Garten' (Dw)	ESul
	'Grozser Garten Weiss' (Dw)	ESul
	'Guardsman' (Dw)	ESul
	'Guernsey Flair' (Z)	LAst LSou NFir
	'Gustav Emich' (Z/d)	SKen
	'Gwen' (Min/v)	NFir
	'H. Rigler' (Z)	SKen
	'Hadleigh' (Min)	ESul
	'Halo' (R)	ESul
§	'Hannaford Star' (Z/St)	WFib
	'Hannah West' (Z/C)	SSea
	'Hansen's Pinkie' (R)	LDea
	'Hansen's Wild Spice' (Sc)	GBar LPio MBPg
	'Happy Appleblossom' (Z/v/d)	NFir SKen
	(Happy Face Series) Happy Face Amethyst = 'Penrad'[PBR] (I)	LAst NPri
	- Happy Face Mex = 'Pacvet'[PBR] (I)	LAst LSou NPri
	- Happy Face Scarlet = 'Penhap'[PBR] (I)	LAst
	- Happy Face Velvet Red = 'Pachafvel'[PBR] (I)	LAst NPri
	- Happy Face White = 'Pacfali' (I)	LAst NPri
	'Happy Thought' (Z/v) ♀H1+3	ESul MBri MCot NFir NVic SCoo SKen SSea WFib
	'Happy Valley' (R)	ESul
	'Harbour Lights' (R)	ESul LDea WFib
	'Harewood Slam' (R)	ESul LDea WFib
	'Harkstead' (Dw)	ESul
	'Harlequin' (Dw)	ESul
	'Harlequin Mahogany' (I/d)	LDea SKen
§	'Harlequin Miss Liver Bird' (I)	SKen
	'Harlequin Picotee' (I/d)	LDea SKen
	'Harlequin Pretty Girl' (I x Z/d)	WFib
	'Harlequin Rosie O'Day' (I)	LDea SKen WFib
	'Harlequin Ted Day' (I/d)	LDea
	'Harriet Le Hair' (Z)	SKen
	'Harvard' (I/d)	WFib
	'Havenstreet' (Dw/St)	ESul
	havlasae	ECou
	'Hazel' (R)	MSCN WFib
	'Hazel Anson' (R)	LDea
	'Hazel Barolo' (R)	LDea
	'Hazel Birkby' (R)	LDea
	'Hazel Burtoff' (R)	ESul LDea
	'Hazel Butterfly' (R)	NBur
	'Hazel Candy' (R)	ESul
	'Hazel Carey' (R)	LDea
	'Hazel Cerise' (R)	LDea
	'Hazel Cherry' (R)	CWCL ESul LDea SSea WFib
	'Hazel Chick' (R)	ESul
	'Hazel Choice' (R)	ESul LDea NFir
	'Hazel Claret' (R)	SSea
	'Hazel Glory' (R)	LDea
	'Hazel Gowland' (R)	LDea
	'Hazel Gypsy' (R)	ESul LDea NFir
	'Hazel Harmony' (R)	ESul LDea
	'Hazel Henderson' (R)	LDea
	'Hazel Herald' (R)	ESul LDea
	'Hazel Orchid' (R)	ESul
	'Hazel Perfection' (R)	NFir
	'Hazel Ripple' (R)	ESul
	'Hazel Rose' (R)	LDea NBur
	'Hazel Satin' (R)	LDea
	'Hazel Star' (R)	ESul WFib
	'Hazel Stardust' (R)	ESul LDea NFir

'Hazel Wright' (R) LDea SSea
§ 'Hederinum' (I) LSou SKen
§ 'Hederinum Variegatum' (I/v) MCot SPet SSea WFib
'Heidi' (Min/d) ESul
'Helen Christine' (Z/St) ESul NFir WFib
'Helena' (I/d) LDea
'Hemingstone' (A) LDea
'Hemley' (Sc) LDea
'Henhurst Gleam' (Dw/d) ESul
'Henley' (Min/d) ESul
'Henry Weller' (A) ESul MBPg NFir WFib
'Hermione' (Z/d) WFib
'High Fidelity' (R) ESul
'High Tor' (Dw/C/d) SKen
'Highfields Appleblossom' (Z) SKen
'Highfields Attracta' (Z/d) SKen WFib
'Highfields Candy Floss' (Z/d) NFir
'Highfields Choice' (Z) SKen
'Highfields Comet' (Z) SKen
'Highfields Contessa' (Z/d) SKen WFib
'Highfields Delight' (Z) WFib
'Highfields Fancy' (Z/d) NFir SKen
'Highfields Festival' (Z/d) NFir SKen WFib
'Highfields Joy' (Z/d) SKen
'Highfields Melody' (Z/d) WFib
'Highfields Paramount' (Z) SKen
'Highfields Pride' (Z) SKen WFib
'Highfields Prima Donna' (Z/d) SKen
'Highfields Promise' (Z) SKen
'Highfields Snowdrift' (Z) SKen
'Highfields Sugar Candy' (Z/d) SKen WFib
'Highfields Symphony' (Z) WFib
'Hilbre Island' (Z/C/d) NFir
'Hildegard' (Z/d) SKen
'Hills of Snow' (Z/v) MBri MHer SKen SSea WFib
'Hillscheider Amethyst'^{PBR} see *P.* Amethyst = 'Fisdel'
'Hindoo' (R × U) CSpe NFir SAga SSea WFib
'Hindoo Rose' (U) NFir
'Hintlesham' (Min) ESul
hirtum LPio
hispidum LPio MHer SSea
'Hitcham' (Min/d) ESul WFib
'Holbrook' (Dw/C/d) ESul NFir WFib
'Hollywood Star' (Z) EBrs
'Honeywood Lindy' (R) ESul LDea
'Honeywood Lindy Variegated' (R/V) ESul
'Honeywood Margaret' (R) ESul
'Honeywood Suzanne' (Min/Fr) ESul NFir SKen
'Honne Frühling' (Z) SKen
'Honneas' (Dw) ESul
'Honnestolz' (Dw) ESul SKen
'Hope Valley' (Dw/C/d) 🏆$^{H1+3}$ ESul NFir SKen
'Horace Parsons' (R) ESul WFib
'Horace Read' (Dw) ESul
'Horning Ferry' (Dw) ESul
'House and Garden' (R) NFir
'Hula' (U × R) MHer
'Hulda Conn' (Z/Ca/d) WFib
'Hulverstone' (Dw/St) ESul
'Hunter's Moon' (Z/C) NFir
'Hurdy-gurdy' (Z/d/v) ESul
'Ian Read' (Min/d) ESul
'Ibiza' (Dw/C) ESul
'Icing Sugar' (I/d) ESul LDea WFib
'Immaculatum' (Z) WFib
'Imperial'^{PBR} (R) LAst
'Imperial Butterfly' (A/Sc) CRHN ESul GGar LDea NFir SKen WFib
'Inca' (R) ESul
'Inspiration' (R) ESul
ionidiflorum CSpe EShb LPio MBPg MCot MHer MNHC SAga
'Ipswich Town' (Dw/d) ESul
'Irene' (Z/d) 🏆$^{H1+3}$ SKen WFib
'Irene Collet' (R) LDea
'Irene Picardy' (Z/d) SKen
'Irene Toyon' (Z) 🏆$^{H1+3}$ SKen WFib
'Isidel' (I/d) 🏆$^{H1+3}$ SKen WFib
'Islington Peppermint' (Sc) LPio MBPg SBch WFib
'Isobel Eden' (Sc) LDea MBPg
'Italian Gem' (I) SKen
'Ivalo' (Z/d) WFib
'Ivory Snow' (Z/d/v) ESul NFir SKen SSea WFib
'Jack of Hearts' (I × Z/d) WFib
'Jack Simmons' (Z/d/Dw) ESul
'Jack Wood' (Z/d) NFir WFib
§ 'Jackie' (I/d) EShb MBri SKen WFib
'Jackie Gall' see *P.* 'Jackie'
'Jackie Totlis' (Z/St) **new** WFib
'Jackpot Wild Rose' (Z/d) WFib
'Jacqueline' (Z/d) SKen
'Jacqui Caws' (Dw) ESul
'Jake Brougham' (St) ESul
'Jane Biggin' (Dw/C/d) ESul SKen
'Janet Dean' (R) LDea
'Janet Hofman' (Z/d) WFib
'Janet Kerrigan' (Min/d) ESul WFib
'Jasmin' (R) ESul LDea
'Jaunty' (Min/d) ESul
'Jayne' (Min/d) ESul
'Jayne Eyre' (Min/d) ESul WFib
'Jazzy' (Min/St) ESul
'Jean Bart' (I) SSea
'Jean Caws' (Z/St) WFib
'Jean Oberle' (Z/d) SKen
'Jeanetta' (R) LDea
'Jeanie Hunt' (Z/C/d) NFir
'Jeanne' (Z) WFib
§ 'Jeanne d'Arc' (I/d) SKen WFib
'Jenifer Read' (Dw) ESul
'Jennifer' (Min) ESul
'Jennifer Strange' (R) ESul
'Jericho' (Z/St/v) ESul
'Jer'Ray' (A) ESul LDea NFir SSea WFib
'Jessel's Unique' (U) LDea MHer SPet SSea
'Jewel'^{PBR} (R) ESul
'Jimbar' (R) ESul
'Jinny Reeves' (R) LDea
'Jip's Freda Burgess' (Z/C/d) NFir
'Jip's Nippy' (Dw) NFir
'Jip's Rosy Glow' (Min/d) ESul NFir
'Jip's Twink' (Iv/v) NFir
'Joan Cashmere' (Z/d) ESul
'Joan Fontaine' (Z) WFib
'Joan Hayward' (Min) ESul
'Joan Morf' (R) ESul LDea NFir SSea WFib
'Joan of Arc' see *P.* 'Jeanne d'Arc'
'Joan Sharman' (Min) ESul
'Joanna Pearce' (R) LDea
'John Thorp' (R) LDea
'John's Pride' (Dw) MBri NFir SSea
'Joseph Haydn' (R) ESul LDea
'Joseph Paul' (R) SSea
'Joseph Wheeler' (A) ESul LDea

	'Joy' (R) 🏆H1+3	ESul LDea LSou NFir SKen WFib
	'Joy' (I)	SPet
I	'Joy' (Z/d)	LAst SKen SSea
	'Joy Lucille' (Sc)	ESul LDea MBPg
	'Joyful' (Min)	ESul
	'Jubilant' (R)	ESul
	'Judy Read' (Dw)	ESul
	'Julia' (R) 🏆H1+3	LDea
	'Juliana' (R)	LAst LDea
	'Julie Bannister' (R)	ESul
	'Julie Smith' (R)	ESul LDea WFib
	'June Filbey' (R)	LDea
	'Jungle Night' (R)	ESul
	'Juniper' (Sc)	MBPg
	'Jupiter' (Min/d)	SKen
	'Jupiter' (R)	ESul
	'Just Bella' (d)	NFir
	'Just Beth' (Z/C/d)	NFir
	'Just Joss' (Dw/d)	NFir
	'Just Rita' (A)	SSea
	'Just William' (Min/C/d)	ESul WFib
	'Kamahl' (R)	ESul WFib
§	'Kardinal' (Z/d)	SPet
	'Karl Hagele' (Z/d)	SKen WFib
	'Karl Offenstein' (R)	ESul
	'Karmin Ball'	WFib
	karrooense Knuth	MHer
	'Karrooense'	see *P. quercifolium*
	'Kathleen' (Min)	ESul
	'Kathleen Gamble' (Z)	SKen WFib
	'Kathryn' (Min)	ESul
	'Kathryn Portas' (Z/v)	ESul SKen
	'Kathy Kirby' (R)	ESul
	'Katie' (R)	LDea
	'Katie Hillier' (R)	LDea
	'Katrine'	CWCL LAst NPri WGor
	'Kayleigh Aitken' (R)	CWCL
	'Kayleigh West' (Min)	ESul SSea
	'Keepsake' (Min/d)	ESul WFib
	'Keith Vernon' (Z)	NFir
	'Kelly Brougham' (St/dw)	ESul
	'Ken Lea' (Z/v)	ESul
	'Ken Salmon' (Dw/d)	ESul
	'Kenny's Double' (Z/d)	WFib
	'Kensington' (A)	LDea
	'Kerensa' (Min/d)	ESul SKen WFib
	'Kershy' (Min)	ESul
	'Kesgrave' (Min/d)	ESul WFib
	'Kettlebaston' (A) 🏆H1+3	LDea WFib
	'Kewense' (Z)	EShb
	'Kimono' (R)	ESul NBur NFir
	'Kinder Gaisha' (R)	NFir
	'King Edmund' (R)	ESul LDea NFir
	'King of Balcon'	see *P.* 'Hederinum'
	'King of Denmark' (Z/d)	WFib
	'King Solomon' (R)	LDea WFib
	'Kirton' (Min/d)	ESul
§	'Kleine Liebling' (Min)	ESul WFib
	'Knaves Bonfire' (R)	ESul
	'Krista' (Min/d)	ESul WFib
	'Kyoto' (R)	NFir
	'Kyra' (Min/d)	ESul WFib
	'L.E. Wharton' (Z)	SKen
	'La France' (I/d) 🏆H1+3	LDea MCot WFib
	'La Paloma' (R)	ESul WFib
	'Laced Mini Rose Cascade' (I)	NFir
	Laced Red Mini Cascade = 'Achspen' (I)	NFir SKen
	Lachsball (Z/d)	SKen
§	'Lachskönigin' (I/d)	SPet WFib
	'Lady Ilchester' (Z/d)	SKen WFib
	'Lady Love Song' (R)	ESul NFir WFib
	'Lady Mary' (Sc)	ESul MBPg MHer
	'Lady Mavis Pilkington' (Z/d)	WFib
	'Lady Plymouth' (Sc/v) 🏆H1+3	CRHN CSpe CWan EPfP ERea EShb ESul GBar GGar LDea LPio MBPg MCot MHer MNHC MSCN NEgg NFir SBch SKen SPet SSea SWal WFib
§	'Lady Scarborough' (Sc)	ESul GBar LDea LPio MBPg MHer WFib
	'Lady Woods' (Z)	SSea
	laevigatum	MHer
	'Lakeland' (I)	ESul SKen SSea
	'Lakis' (R)	LDea
	'Lamorna' (R)	ESul LDea
	'Lancastrian' (Z/d)	WFib
§	***lanceolatum***	LFur LPio MHer
	'Langley' (R)	ESul LDea
	'Lanham Lane' (I)	LDea
	'Lanham Royal' (Dw/d)	ESul
	'Lara Aladin' (A)	LDea
	'Lara Ballerina'	NFir SBch
	'Lara Candy Dancer' (Sc) 🏆H1+3	CRHN ESul LDea MBPg SBch WFib
	'Lara Jester' (Sc)	MHer WFib
	'Lara Maid' (A) 🏆H1+3	WFib
	'Lara Nomad' (Sc)	LDea MBPg
	'Lara Starshine' (Sc) 🏆H1+3	EAro ESul LPio MHer NFir SSea WFib
	'Lara Waltz' (R/d)	WFib
	'Lark' (Min/d)	ESul
	'Larkfield' (Z/v)	SSea
N	'Lass o' Gowrie' (Z/v)	ESul NFir SKen
	'Lateripes' (I)	SKen
	'Latte Coffee' (R)	ESul
	'Laura Parmer' (Dw/St)	ESul
	'Laura Wheeler' (A)	ESul LDea
	'Laurel Hayward' (R)	WFib
	'Lauren Alexandra' (Z/d)	WFib
	Lauretta = 'Pacamla'[PBR] (Quality Series) (Z/d)	LAst
	Lavenda = 'Penlava'[PBR] (Dark Line Series) (Z/d)	LAst
	'Lavender Grand Slam' (R) 🏆H1+3	ESul LDea NFir
	'Lavender Harewood Slam' (R)	ESul LDea
	'Lavender Mini Cascade'[PBR]	see *P.* Lilac Mini Cascade
	'Lavender Sensation' (R)	WFib
	'Lavender Wings' (I)	LDea
	'Lawrenceanum'	ESul LPio WFib
	'Layham' (Dw/d)	ESul
	'L'Élégante' (I/v) 🏆H1+3	LDea MHer SKen SSea SWal WEas WFib
	'Lemon Air' (Sc)	ESul MBPg
	'Lemon Crisp'	see *P. crispum*
	'Lemon Fancy' (Sc)	LDea MBPg MCot MHer NFir WFib
	'Lemon Kiss' (Sc)	MBPg
	'Lemon Meringue' (Sc)	MBPg
	'Lemon Toby' (Sc)	MBPg
	'Len Chandler' (Min)	ESul NFir
	'Lenore' (Min/d)	ESul
	'Leo' (Min)	ESul
	'Leonie Holbrow' (Min)	ESul
	'Lesley Judd' (R)	ESul
	'Leywood Bonanza'	CWCL
	Lila Compakt-Cascade	see *P.* 'Decora Lilas'
	Lilac Cascade	see *P.* 'Roi des Balcons Lilas'
	'Lilac Domino'	see *P.* 'Telston's Prima'
	'Lilac Elaine' (R)	LDea

'Lilac Gem' (Min/I/d) LDea MCot
'Lilac Gemma' (R) ESul
'Lilac Jewel' (R) ESul
'Lilac Joy' (R) ESul SSea
§ Lilac Mini Cascade = 'Lilamica'PBR (I) ESul LAst LDea NFir
'Lili Marlene' (I) SKen SPet
'Lilian' (Min) ESul
'Lilian Pottinger' (Sc) CArn CRHN ESul GBar LDea MBPg MHer NFir SKen SSea
'Lilian Woodberry' (Z) WFib
Lilly = 'Paclill'PBR **new** NPri
'Limoneum' (Sc) CSev LDea MBPg MHer NBur
'Linda' (R) ESul
'Lindsey' (Min) ESul
'Lindy Portas' (I/d) SKen
'Lipstick' (St) WFib
'Lisa' (Min/C) ESul WFib
'Lisa Jo' (St/v/Dw/d) WFib
'Little Alice' (Dw/d) ♀H1+3 ESul NFir WFib
'Little Blakenham' (A) ESul LDea SSea
'Little Fi-fine' (Dw/C) ESul
'Little Gem' (Sc) LDea MBPg SSea WFib
'Little Jim' (Min/d) NFir
'Little Jip' (Z/d/v) NFir WFib
'Little Lisa' (Dw) ESul
'Little Margaret' (Min/v) ESul
'Little Primular' (Min) ESul
'Little Rascal' (A) LDea
'Little Spikey' (St/Min/d) ESul WFib
'Lively Lady' (Dw/C) ESul
'Liverbird' see *P.* 'Harlequin Miss Liver Bird'
'Lizzie Hillier' (R) LDea
lobatum LPio
longicaule LPio MBPg
longifolium LPio
'Lord Baden-Powell' see *P.* 'Colonel Baden-Powell'
'Lord Bute' (R) ♀H1+3 CSpe ECtt ERea EShb ESul LAst LDea MCot MHer MSCN NFir NPer SBch SDnm SGar SIde SKen SPet SSea SUsu WEas WFib WPen
'Lord Constantine' (R) LDea
'Lord de Ramsey' see *P.* 'Tip Top Duet'
'Lord Roberts' (Z) WFib
Lorena = 'Pacdala'PBR (Dark Line Series) (Z/d) LAst WGor
'Loretta' (Dw) ESul
'Lorna' (Dw/d) ESul
'Lorraine' (Dw) ESul
Lotus = 'Floscala' (Z/d) LAst
'Lotusland' (Dw/St/C) LSou NFir WFib
'Louise' (Min) ESul
I 'Louise' (R) ESul NFir
'Louise Waddington' (Min/St) ESul
'Love Song' (R/v) ESul LDea NFir SSea WFib
'Love Story' (Z/v) ESul
'Loveliness' (Z) WFib
* 'Loverly' (Min/d) ESul
'Lovesdown' (Dw/St) ESul
'Lowood' (R) ESul
'Lucie Caws' (St/d) ESul
'Lucilla' (Min) ESul NFir
'Lucinda' (Min) ESul
'Lucy' (Min) ESul
'Lucy Gunnett' (Z/d/v) ESul NFir
'Lucy Jane' (R) ESul LDea
luridum WCot
'Lustre' (R) ESul
'Lyewood Bonanza' (R) ESul LDea WFib
'Lynne Valerie' (A) LDea
'Lyric' (Min/d) ESul WFib

'Mabel Grey' (Sc) ♀H1+3 CRHN CSev CSpe EShb ESul LPio MBPg MHer MNHC NBur NFir NPer SBch SIde SKen SSea WFib
§ 'Madame Auguste Nonin' (U/Sc) ESul MHer NFir SKen SSea WFib
'Madame Butterfly' (Z/d/v) ESul NFir SKen
'Madame Crousse' (I/d) ♀H1+3 WFib
'Madame Fournier' (Dw/C) ESul
'Madame Hibbault' (Z) SKen
'Madame Layal' (A) MHer NFir SBch WFib
'Madame Margot' see *P.* 'Hederinum Variegatum'
'Madame Salleron' (Min/v) ♀H1+3 LDea LSou SKen SWal
'Madame Thibaut' (R) LDea
'Madge Taylor' (R) NFir
'Magaluf' (I/C/d) SSea
'Magda' (Z/d) ESul
magenteum ESul
'Magic Lantern' (Z/C) NFir
'Magic Moments' (R) ESul
'Magnum' (R) WFib
'Maid of Honour' (Min) ESul
'Mairi' (A) LDea WFib
'Majesta' (Z/d) SKen
'Majorca' (Dw/C) ESul
'Maloya' (Z) SKen
'Mamie' (Z/d) SKen
'Mandarin' (R) ESul
'Mangles' Variegated' (Z/v) WFib
'Mantilla' (Min) ESul
'Manx Maid' (A) ESul LDea NFir
'Maple Leaf' (Sc) MBPg
'Marble Sunset' see *P.* 'Wood's Surprise'
'Marchioness of Bute' (R/Dec) LDea NFir SSea WFib
'Maréchal MacMahon' (Z/C) SKen SSea
'Margaret Harris' (A) ESul
'Margaret Parmenter' (I/C) ESul
'Margaret Pearce' (R) LDea
'Margaret Salvidge' (R) LDea
'Margaret Soley' (R) ♀H1+3 LDea WFib
'Margaret Waite' (R) ESul WFib
'Margery Stimpson' (Min/d) ESul WFib
'Maria Wilkes' (Z/d) WFib
'Marie Rober' (R) ESul
'Marie Rudlin' (R) SSea
'Marie Thomas' (Sc) LDea MBPg SBch SSea
§ 'Marie Vogel' (R) ESul
Marimba = 'Fisrimba'PBR SCoo
'Marion' (Min) ESul
'Mariquita' (R) ESul WFib
'Marja' (R) LDea
'Mark' (Dw/d) WFib
'Marmalade' (Min/d) ESul WFib
'Marquis of Bute' (R/v) ESul NFir
'Martha Parmer' (Min) ESul
'Martin Parrett' (Min/d) WFib
'Martin's Splendour' (Min) ESul
'Martlesham' (Dw) ESul
'Mary' (R) ESul
'Mary Caws' (Dw/Z/d) ESul
'Mary Ellen Tanner' (Min/d) ESul
'Mary Harrison' (Z/d) WFib
'Mary Read' (Min) ESul
'Mary Webster' (Min) ESul
'Masquerade' (R) ESul SPet
'Masquerade' (Min) ESul
'Master Paul' (Z/v) ESul
'Masterpiece' (Z/C/d) SKen
'Maureen' (Min) ESul NFir

	Name	Suppliers
	'Mauve Beauty' (I/d)	SKen WFib
	'Maxime Kovalevski' (Z)	WFib
	'Maxine' (Z/C)	NFir
	'May Day' (R)	LDea WFib
	'May Magic' (R)	ESul NFir WFib
	'Mayfield County Girl' (R)	ESul
	'Meadowside Dark and Dainty' (St)	NFir SKen WFib
	'Meadowside Harvest' (Z/St/C)	NFir WFib
	'Meadowside Julie Colley' (Dw)	NFir
	'Meadowside Midnight' (St/C)	MHer WFib
	'Medallion' (Z/C)	SSea
	'Meditation' (Min)	ESul
	'Medley' (Min/d)	WFib
	'Megan Hannah' (Dw/c/d)	NFir
	'Meike' (R)	ESul
	'Melanie' (R)	ESul LDea
	'Melanie' (Min)	ESul
	'Melanie Day' (St) **new**	NFir
*	'Melissa' (Min)	ESul
	'Melissa' (R)	ESul
	'Melody'[PBR] (Tempo Series) (Z/d)	LAst
	Melosilver = 'Penber' (Tempo Series) (Z/d/v)	SPoG
	'Memento' (Min/d)	ESul WFib
	'Mendip' (R)	WFib
	'Mendip Anne' (R)	NFir
	'Mendip Barbie' (R)	NFir
	'Mendip Blanche' (R)	NFir
	'Mendip Candy Floss' (R)	ESul
	'Mendip Lorraine' (R)	ESul
	'Mendip Louise' (R)	NFir
	'Mendip Sarah' (R)	NFir
	'Menorca' (Dw/C/d)	ESul WFib
	'Meon Maid' (R)	ESul LDea WFib
	'Mere Casino' (Z)	WFib
	'Mere Greeting' (Z/d)	WFib
	'Mere Seville' (Z)	WFib
	'Mere Sunglow' (R)	LDea
	'Merle Seville' (Z/d)	SKen
	'Mexically Rose' (R)	ESul
	'Mexican Beauty' (I)	WFib
	'Mexicana'	see *P.* 'Rouletta'
	'Mexicanerin'	see *P.* 'Rouletta'
	'Michael' (A)	ESul LDea MHer NFir
	'Michelle' (Min/C)	LDea
	'Michelle West' (Min)	ESul WFib
	'Midas Touch' (Dw/C/d)	ESul
	'Mikado' (R)	ESul
	'Milden' (Dw/Z/C)	ESul NFir
	'Millbern Clover' (Min/d)	ESul
	'Millbern Sharna' (Min/d)	ESul
	'Millfield Gem' (I/d)	SKen WFib
	'Mimi' (Dw/C/d)	ESul
	'Mina Lorenzen' (R)	ESul
	'Mini-Czech' (Min/St)	ESul WBrk
	'Minnie' (Z/d/St)	WBrk
	'Minstrel Boy' (R)	CSpe ESul LDea SSea WFib
	'Minuet' (Z/d)	SSea
	'Minx' (Min/d)	WFib
	'Miranda' (Dw)	ESul
	'Miranda Deep Salmon'	WGor
	'Miss Australia' (R/v)	LDea MBPg
	'Miss Burdett Coutts' (Z/v)	ESul MHer SKen WFib
	'Miss Liverbird' (I/d)	WBrk
	'Miss McKinsey' (Z/St/d)	NFir
	'Miss Muffett' (Min/d)	WFib
§	'Miss Stapleton'	LPio MHer WFib

	Name	Suppliers
	'Miss Wackles' (Min/d)	ESul
	'Misterioso' (R)	WFib
	'Misty Morning' (R)	WFib
	'Modesty' (Z/d)	SKen WFib
	'Mohawk' (R)	ESul LDea NFir WFib
	'Mole'	see *P.* 'The Mole'
	mollicomum	WCot
	'Mollie' (R)	CSpe
	'Mona Lisa'[PBR]	ESul
	'Monarch' (Dw/v)	ESul
	'Monica Bennett' (Dw)	ESul SKen
	'Monkwood Charm' (R)	ESul
	'Monkwood Rhapsody' (R)	ESul
	'Monkwood Rose' (A)	LDea NFir
	'Monkwood Sprite' (R)	ESul LDea
	'Monsal Dale' (Dw/C/d)	ESul SKen
	'Monsieur Ninon' misapplied	see *P.* 'Madame Auguste Nonin'
§	'Monsieur Ninon' (U)	CRHN WFib
	'Mont Blanc' (Z/v)	ESul WFib
	'Montague Garabaldi Smith' (R)	WFib
	'Moon Maiden' (A)	CSpe ESul LDea WFib
	'Moor' (Min/d)	ESul
	'Moppet' (Min/d)	ESul
	'Morello'[PBR] (R)	ESul
	'More's Victory' (U/Sc)	SSea
	'Morning Cloud' (Min/d)	ESul
	'Morse' (Z)	SKen
	'Morval' (Dw/C/d) ♀H1+3	ESul SKen WFib
	'Morwenna' (R)	ESul LDea LPio MHer NFir SKen WFib
	'Mosaic Gay Baby' (I/v/d)	WFib
	'Mountie' (Dw)	ESul
	'Mozart' (R)	ESul
	'Mr Everaarts' (Dw/d)	ESul
	'Mr Henry Cox' (Z/v) ♀H1+3	ESul MHer NFir SKen WFib
	'Mr Wren' (Z)	SKen SSea WFib
	'Mrs A.M. Mayne' (Z)	SKen
	'Mrs Cannell' (Z)	WFib
	'Mrs Dumbrill' (A)	ESul LDea
	'Mrs Farren' (Z/v)	MCot SKen
	'Mrs G.H. Smith' (A)	ESul LDea MBPg NFir SSea WFib
	'Mrs G. Morf' (R)	SSea
	'Mrs Innes Rogers' (R)	ESul
	'Mrs J.C. Mappin' (Z/v) ♀H1+3	SKen
	'Mrs Kingsbury' (U)	WFib
	'Mrs Langtry' (R)	LDea
	'Mrs Lawrence' (Z/d)	SKen
	'Mrs Martin' (I/d)	WFib
	'Mrs McKenzie' (Z/St)	WFib
	'Mrs Morf' (R)	LDea
	'Mrs Parker' (Z/d/v)	ESul NFir SKen WFib
	'Mrs Pat' (Dw/St/C)	NFir SSea
	'Mrs Pollock' (Z/v)	LAst LSou MCot NEgg NVic SCoo SKen SSea WBrk WFib
	'Mrs Quilter' (Z/C) ♀H1+3	MBri MHer NVic SKen SSea WBrk WFib
	'Mrs Salter Bevis' (Z/Ca/d)	ESul WFib
	'Mrs Strang' (Z/d/v)	SKen SSea
	'Mrs Taylor' (Sc)	MBPg
	'Mrs W.A.R. Clifton' (I/d)	LDea WFib
	multicaule	LPio
	– subsp. ***multicaule***	EShb
	mutans	WFib
§	'Mutzel' (I/v)	NFir
	'My Chance' (Dec)	NFir SSea WFib
	'My Choice' (R)	LDea
	myrrhifolium	LPio
§	– var. ***coriandrifolium***	CDes LPio MHer NFir WFib

	'Mystery' (U) ♀H1+3	CWCL LPio NFir SSea WFib
	'Nacton' (Min)	ESul
	'Nancy Grey' (Min)	ESul
	'Nancy Mac' (St)	ESul
	'Narina' (I)	SCoo
	'Natalie' (Dw)	ESul
	'Naughton' (Min)	ESul
	Nealit 2 = 'Pennea' PBR (I/d) **new**	NPri
	'Needham Market' (A)	ESul LDea WFib
	'Neene' (Dw)	ESul
	'Neil Clemenson' (Sc)	WFib
	'Neil Jameson' (Z/v)	SKen
	'Nell Smith' (Z/d)	WFib
	'Nellie' (R)	ESul LDea SSea
	'Nellie Green' (R)	LDea
	'Nellie Nuttall' (Z)	WFib
	'Nervosum' (Sc)	ESul MBPg
	'Nervous Mabel' (Sc) ♀H1+3	ESul LDea LPio MHer WBrk WFib
	'Nettlecombe' (Min/St)	ESul
	'Nettlestead' (Dw/d)	ESul
	'Nettlestone' (Dw/d)	ESul
	'Nettlestone Star' (Min/St)	ESul
	'New Day' (A)	LDea
	'New Life' (Z)	ESul NFir
	'Newbridge' (St/Min/d)	ESul
	'Newtown' (Min/St)	ESul
	'Nicola Buck' (R)	LDea NFir
	'Nicor Star' (Min)	ESul WFib
	'Nikki' (A)	LDea
	'Nimrod' (R)	LDea
	'Noche' (R)	ESul LDea SKen
	'Noel' (Z/Ca/d)	WFib
	'Noele Gordon' (Z/d)	WFib
	'Noir' (R)	SSea
	'Nono' (I)	WFib
	'Notting Hill Beauty' (Z)	SKen
	oblongatum	LPio NFir
	'Occold Embers' (Dw/C)	ESul NFir
	'Occold Lagoon' (Dw/d)	ESul
	'Occold Orange Tip' (Min/d)	ESul
	'Occold Profusion' (Dw/d)	ESul NFir
	'Occold Shield' (Dw/C/d)	ESul LAst NEgg NFir SDnm WBrk WFib
	'Occold Tangerine' (Z)	WFib
	'Occold Volcano' (Dw/C/d)	WFib
	odoratissimum (Sc)	ESul GBar GPoy LDea MBPg MHer NFir SKen SSea WFib
	'Odyssey' (Min)	WFib
	'Offton' (Dw)	ESul
	'Old Orchard' (A)	LDea
	'Old Rose' (Z/d)	WFib
	'Old Spice' (Sc/v)	ESul GBar LDea MBPg NFir SWal WFib
	'Oldbury Duet' (A/v)	ESul LDea MBPg MHer NFir SSea
	'Olga Shipstone' (Sc)	MBPg
	'Oliver Welfare' (Dw/C)	ESul
	'Olivia' (R)	WFib
	'Onalee' (Dw)	ESul WFib
	'Opera House' (R)	WFib
	'Orange Fizz' (Sc)	ESul MHer NFir SDnm WBrk
	'Orange Fizz' (Z/d)	LDea
	'Orange Imp' (Dw/d)	ESul
	'Orange Parfait' (R)	WFib
I	'Orange Princeanum' (Sc)	MBPg
	'Orange Ricard' (Z/d)	SKen
	'Orange Ruffy' (Min)	ESul
	'Orange Splash' (Z)	SKen
	'Orangeade' (Dw/d)	SKen WFib
	'Orchid Clorinda' (Sc)	MBPg WFib
	'Orchid Paloma' (Dw/d)	ESul SKen
	'Oregon Hostess' (Dw)	ESul
	'Oriental Delight' (R)	ESul
	'Orion' (Min/d)	ESul SKen SSea WFib
	'Orsett' (Sc) ♀H1+3	LDea
	'Osna' (Z)	SKen
	'Otto's Red' (R)	NFir
	'Our Gynette' (Dec)	NFir SSea
	'Overchurch' (Dw)	NFir
	'Oyster' (Dw)	ESul
	PAC cultivars	see under selling name
	'Paddie' (Min)	ESul
	'Pagoda' (Z/St/d)	ESul MHer SKen WFib
	'Paisley Red' (Z/d)	NFir WFib
	'Palais' (Z/d)	SKen
	'Pam Craigie' (R)	LDea
	'Pamela' (R)	ESul
	'Pamela Vaughan' (Z/St)	WFib
	'Pampered Lady' (A)	LDea NFir
	panduriforme	LPio WFib
	papilionaceum	CHEx CRHN LPio MCot MHer SSea WEas WFib
	'Parisienne' (R)	ESul LDea WFib
	'Parmenter Pink' (Min)	ESul
	'Party Dress' (Z/d)	SKen WFib
	'Pascal' (Z)	SKen
	'Pat Hannam' (St)	WFib
	'Paton's Unique' (U/Sc) ♀H1+3	CRHN EShb MBPg MCot MHer NFir SPet SSea WFib
	'Patricia Andrea' (T)	ESul NFir NPer WFib
	'Patricia O'Reilly' (R)	LDea
	'Patricia Read' (Min)	ESul
	'Patsy 'Q'' (Z/C)	SKen
	'Paul Crampel' (Z)	MHer SSea WFib
	'Paul Gotz' (Z)	SKen
	'Paul West' (Min/d)	CFee ESul
	'Pauline' (Min/d)	ESul SSea
	'Pauline Harris' (R)	LDea
	'Pax' (R)	LDea
	'Peace' (Min/C)	ESul WFib
	'Peace Palace' (Dw)	ESul
	'Peach Princess' (R)	ESul NFir
	'Peaches and Cream' (R)	MBPg
	'Peacock'	LDea
	'Peggy Clare' (Dw/St)	ESul
	'Peggy Sue' (R)	ESul LDea
	'Peggy West' (Min/C/d)	SSea
	PELFI cultivars	see under selling name
	peltatum	LPio WFib
	'Penny' (Z/d)	SKen WFib
	'Penny Dixon' (R)	NFir
	'Penny Lane' (Z)	WFib
	'Penny Serenade' (Dw/C)	ESul SKen
	'Pensby' (Dw)	ESul NFir
	'Peppermint Lace' (Sc)	CSev MBPg
	'Peppermint Scented Rose' (Sc)	MBPg MSCN
	'Peppermint Star' (Z/St)	ESul SSea
	'Perchance' (R)	SSea
	'Percy Hunt' (R) **new**	NFir
	'Perfect' (Z)	SKen WFib
	Perlenkette Orange = 'Orangepen' PBR (Quality Series) (Z/d)	LAst
	Perlenkette Sabine (Quality Series) (Z/d)	LAst
	'Pershore Princess'	WBrk
	'Persian King' (R)	LDea
	'Persian Ruler' (Min)	ESul
	'Persimmon' (Z/St)	WFib
	'Petals' (Z/v)	SKen
	'Peter Beard' (Dw/d)	ESul
	'Peter Godwin' (R)	ESul LDea WFib

'Peter Read' (Dw/d) ESul
'Peter's Choice' (R) ESul LDea SSea WFib
'Peter's Luck' (Sc) ♀H1+3 ESul MBPg
'Petit Pierre' see *P.* 'Kleine Liebling'
'Petite Blanche' (Dw/d) SSea WFib
'Philomel' (I/d) SPet
'Phlox New Life' (Z) ESul
'Phyllis' (Z) LDea MCot
'Phyllis' (U/v) ESul MBPg MHer NFir SAga SSea
'Phyllis Brooks' (R) ESul
'Phyllis Read' (Min) ESul
'Phyllis Richardson' (R/d) ESul LDea
'Phyllis Variegated' (v) MSCN
'Picotee' SSea
'Pin Mill' (Min/d) ESul
'Pink Aura' (Min/St) ESul SSea
'Pink Aurore' (U) WFib
'Pink Blush' (Min/St) ESul
'Pink Bonanza' (R) ESul LDea NFir WFib
'Pink Bouquet' (R) ESul
'Pink Capitatum' see *P.* 'Pink Capricorn'
§ 'Pink Capricorn' (Sc) CHVG CRHN ESul MBPg MHer SBch SDnm WFib
'Pink Carnation' (I/d) LDea SKen
'Pink Cascade' see *P.* 'Hederinum'
'Pink Champagne' (Sc) CRHN ESul MCot MHer
'Pink Countess Mariza' (Z) SKen
'Pink Dolly Varden' (Z/v) SSea WFib
'Pink Flamingo' (R) LDea
'Pink Fondant' (Min/d) ESul WFib
'Pink Gay Baby' see *P.* 'Sugar Baby'
'Pink Golden Ears' (Dw/St/C) ESul SKen
'Pink Golden Harry Hieover' (Z/C) ESul
'Pink Happy Thought' (Z/v) SDnm SSea SWal WFib
'Pink Ice' (Min/d) ESul NFir
'Pink Margaret Pearce' (R) ESul
'Pink Mini Cascade' see *P.* 'Rosa Mini-cascade'
'Pink Needles' (Min/St) ESul WFib
'Pink Paradox' (Sc) LDea
'Pink Rambler' (Z/d) SKen WFib
'Pink Raspail' (Z/d) SSea
'Pink Rosebud' (Z/d) SSea WFib
'Pink Snow' (Min/d) ESul
'Pink Sparkler' (Dw/St/C) ESul
'Pink Splash' (Min/d) ESul
'Pink Tiny Tim' (Min) ESul
'Pippa' (Min/Dw) ESul
'Pixie' (Min) ESul
'Playmate' (Min/St) ESul WFib
'Plum Rambler' (Z/d) EShb SKen SSea WFib
'Poetesse' (A) LDea
'Polestar' (Min/St) ESul
'Polka' (U) ESul MBPg MHer NFir SSea WFib
'Pompeii' (R) ESul LDea NFir WFib
'Poquita' (Sc) MBPg
'Porchfield' (Min/St) ESul
'Portsmouth' (R) ESul
'Potpourri' (Min) SKen
'Potter Heigham' (Dw) ESul
'Powder Puff' (Dw/d) WFib
'Praeludium Scarlet' WGor
'Presto' (Dw/St) ESul
'Preston Park' (Z/C) SKen WFib
'Pretty Girl' (I) LDea MCot
'Pretty Petticoat' (Z/d) WFib
'Pretty Polly' (Sc) LDea WFib
'Pride of Exmouth' CStu
'Prim' (Dw/St/d) ESul WFib
'Prince Consort' (R) LDea
'Prince of Orange' (Sc) CArn CRHN CSev ESul GBar GPoy LDea MBPg MCot MHer NFir SBch SIde SPet SSea SWal WFib
'Princeanum' (Sc) ♀H1+3 MBPg MHer WFib
'Princess Alexandra' (Z/d/v) ESul NFir
'Princess Josephine' (R) LDea MCot WFib
'Princess of Balcon' see *P.* 'Roi des Balcons Lilas'
'Princess of Orange' (Sc/v) NFir
'Princess of Wales' (R) ESul LDea SSea WFib
'Princess Virginia' (R/v) ESul LDea WFib
'Priory Salmon' (St/d) EShb ESul
'Priory Star' (St/Min/d) ESul WFib
'Prosperity' (Sc) LDea MBPg
pseudoglutinosum WFib
'Purple Ball' see *P.* Purpurball
'Purple Emperor' (R) ESul LDea WFib
'Purple Flare' (St) ESul
'Purple Heart' (Dw/St/C) ESul NFir
'Purple Rambler' (Z/d) ESul
'Purple Rogue' (R) WFib
'Purple Unique' (U/Sc) EShb ESul LDea MCot MHer NFir SSea WFib
§ Purpurball (Z/d) SKen
Purpurball 2 = 'Penbalu'PBR (Quality Series) (Z/d) LAst
'Pygmalion' (Z/d/v) SSea WFib
'Quakeress' (R) ESul
'Quakermaid' (Min) ESul
'Quantock' (R) ESul WFib
'Quantock Angelique' (A) NFir
'Quantock Beauty' (A) ESul LDea
'Quantock Blonde' (A) CWCL LDea
'Quantock Candy' (A) NFir
'Quantock Clare' (A) **new** NFir
'Quantock Classic' (A) NFir
'Quantock Cobwebs' (A) NFir
'Quantock Darren' (A) NFir
'Quantock Jayne' (A) ESul
'Quantock Kendy' (A) CWCL ESul LDea NFir
'Quantock Kirsty' (A) LDea NFir
'Quantock Louise' (A) NFir
'Quantock Marjorie' (A) CWCL ESul LDea MBPg NFir
'Quantock Matty' (A) ESul LDea NFir
'Quantock May' (A) LDea NFir
'Quantock Medoc' (A) ESul LDea
'Quantock Millennium' (A) CWCL ESul LDea
'Quantock Mr Nunn' (A) NFir
'Quantock Philip' (A) ESul
'Quantock Rory' (A) LDea
'Quantock Rose' (A) CWCL ESul LDea
'Quantock Sapphire' (A) LDea
'Quantock Sarah' (A) ESul
'Quantock Shirley' (A) ESul LDea
'Quantock Star' (A) CWCL LDea NFir
'Quantock Star Gazer' (A/Sc) NFir
'Quantock Ultimate' (A) ESul NFir
'Quantock Variegated Matthew' (A/v) NFir
'Quantock Victoria' (A) ESul
'Queen of Denmark' (Z/d) SKen WFib
'Queen of Hearts' (I × Z/d) WFib
'Queen of Sheba' (R) LDea
'Queen of the Lemons' EAro
N ***quercifolium*** (Sc) CRHN CSev GPoy LPio MBPg MHer NFir SKen WFib
- variegated (v) MBPg MHer SKen
quinquelobatum CSpe LPio
'R.A. Turner' (Z/d) WFib
'Rachel' (Min) ESul
radens (Sc) EPfP LPio WFib
'Rads Star' (Z/St) ESul NFir SSea WFib

Name	Suppliers
'Radula' (Sc) ♀H1+3	CSev ESul GBar LDea MBPg MHer MNHC SBch SSea WFib
'Radula Roseum' (Sc)	MBPg SSea WFib
'Ragamuffin' (Dw/d)	ESul
'Rager's Pink' (Dw/d)	ESul
'Rager's Star' (Dw)	ESul
'Rager's Veri-Star' (Min/C)	ESul
'Rakastani' (Z)	SKen
'Raphael' (A)	LDea
'Raspberry Parfait' (R)	LDea
'Raspberry Ripple' (A)	ESul LDea NFir WFib
'Raspberry Surprise' (R)	ESul SSea
'Raspberry Yhu' (R)	ESul
'Ray Bidwell' (Min)	ESul NFir WFib
'Raydon' (Min)	ESul
'Reba'	ESul
'Rebecca' (Min/d)	ESul WFib
'Red Admiral' (Min/d/v)	ESul SKen
§ 'Red Black Vesuvius' (Min/C)	ESul SKen SSea WFib
'Red Cactus' (St)	NFir
'Red Capri' (Sc)	MBPg
'Red Cascade' (I) ♀H1+3	WFib
'Red Glitter' (Dw/St)	ESul
'Red Ice' (Min/d)	ESul NFir
'Red Magic Lantern' (Z/C)	SKen
'Red Pandora' (z)	NFir WFib
'Red Rambler' (Z/d)	ESul SKen WBrk WFib
'Red Robin' (R)	WCot
'Red Silver Cascade'	see *P.* 'Mutzel'
'Red Spider' (Dw/Ca)	EShb ESul WFib
'Red Starstorm' (Dw/St)	ESul
'Red Startel' (Z/St/d)	SKen WFib
'Red Susan Pearce' (R)	ESul WFib
Red Sybil = 'Pensyb' PBR (I/d)	LAst NPri
'Red Witch' (Dw/St/d)	ESul SSea WBrk WFib
Red-Blizzard = 'Fizzard' PBR (I)	MCot SCoo
§ Red-Mini-Cascade = 'Rotemica' (I)	ESul LAst LDea SKen WFib
'Redondo' (Dw/d)	ESul WFib
'Reflections' (Z/d)	WFib
'Reg 'Q'' (Z/C)	NFir
'Regina' (Z/d)	SKen WFib
'Rembrandt' (R)	LDea WFib
'Renate Parsley'	CDes EShb ESul LPio MBPg MHer NFir SSea WFib
'Rene Roué' (Dw/d/v)	ESul NFir
reniforme	GBar LPio MBPg MHer SSea SUsu SWal WFib
'Retah's Crystal' (Z/v)	ESul
'Rhian Harris' (A)	LDea
Rhodonit = 'Paccherry' PBR (I/d)	LAst LSou
'Richard Gibbs' (Sc)	GGar LDea MBPg MHer
'Richard Key' (Z/d/C)	WFib
'Ricky Cheerful' (A)	LDea
Ricky = 'Pacric' **new**	LAst
'Ricky Promise' (A)	LDea
'Ricky Ruby' (A)	LDea
'Rietje van der Lee' (A)	ESul WFib
'Rigel' (Min/d)	ESul NFir SKen
'Rigi' (I/d)	MBri SKen
'Rigoletto' (I)	LDea SSea
'Rimey' (St)	NFir SSea
'Rimfire' (R)	CWCL ESul LDea MHer NFir WFib
'Rimfire Dark' (R)	ESul
'Rio Grande' (I/d)	LDea MHer NFir SKen SPet WFib
'Rising Sun'	NFir
'Rita Scheen' (A/v)	ESul LDea SSea
'Ritchie' (R)	ESul
'Robbie Hare' (R)	ESul
'Robe' PBR (Quality Series) (Z/d)	LAst
'Rober's Lemon Rose' (Sc)	CRHN ESul GBar LDea MBPg MCot MHer SIde SKen SSea WBrk
'Rober's Salmon Coral' (Dw/d)	ESul
'Robert Fish' (Z/C)	ESul SCoo
'Robert McElwain' (Z/d)	WFib
'Robin' (Sc)	LDea MBPg
'Robin' (R)	LDea SSea
'Robin's Unique' (U)	NFir WFib
'Robyn Hannah' (St/d)	NFir
rodneyanum	CDes
'Rogue' (R)	WFib
'Roi des Balcons'	see *P.* 'Hederinum'
'Roi des Balcons Des Rameaux' (I) **new**	SKen
§ 'Roi des Balcons Impérial' (I) ♀H1+3	SKen
§ 'Roi des Balcons Lilas' (I) ♀H1+3	WFib
'Roi des Balcons Mauve' (I) **new**	SKen
'Roi des Balcons Rose'	see *P.* 'Hederinum'
'Roller's Echo' (A)	ESul LDea WFib
'Roller's Pathfinder' (I/d/v)	LDea
'Roller's Pioneer' (I/v)	LDea SAga SKen SSea
'Roller's Satinique' (U) ♀H1+3	LPio MHer SSea
'Roller's Shadow' (A)	ESul LDea
'Rollisson's Unique' (U)	MHer NBur SSea WFib
'Romeo' (R)	CSpe
Romy (I)	LDea
'Rookley' (St/d)	ESul
§ 'Rosa Mini-cascade' (I)	ESul LAst NFir SKen
'Rosaleen' (Min)	ESul
'Rosalie' (R)	ESul
'Rose Bengal' (A)	CRHN ESul LDea WFib
'Rose Jewel' (R)	ESul
'Rose of Amsterdam' (Min/d)	ESul WFib
'Rose Paton's Unique' (U/Sc)	LDea SMrm
'Rose Silver Cascade' (I)	LDea MCot
'Rose Startel' (Z/St)	SKen
'Rosebud Supreme' (Z/d)	ESul WFib
'Rosette' (Dw/d)	SKen
'Rosina Read' (Dw/d)	ESul
'Rosmaroy' (R)	ESul LDea SSea WFib
'Rospen' (Z/d)	SKen
'Rosy Dawn' (Min/d)	WFib
'Rosy Morn' (R)	NFir
'Rote Mini-cascade'	see *P.* Red-Mini-Cascade
§ 'Rouletta' (I/d)	ECtt LAst LDea SKen WFib
'Rousillon' (R)	LDea
'Royal Ascot' (R)	ESul LDea NFir SMrm SPet SSea
'Royal Black Rose' **new**	LAst WGor
'Royal Carpet' (Min/d)	ESul
'Royal Celebration' (R)	ESul
'Royal Court' (R)	LDea
'Royal Decree' (R)	LDea
'Royal Hussar' (R)	ESul
'Royal Knight' (R)	ESul
'Royal Magic' (R)	ESul LDea
'Royal Majesty' (R)	ESul
'Royal Norfolk' (Min/d)	ESul NFir SKen
'Royal Oak' (Sc) ♀H1+3	CRHN CSev EAro ESul GBar LDea MBPg MCot MHer MNHC NBur SBch SGar SPet SSea WFib
'Royal Opera' (R)	LDea
'Royal Pride' (R)	LDea

'Royal Prince' (R) ESul
'Royal Princess' (R) ♀H1+3 LDea
§ 'Royal Purple' (Z/d) SKen WFib
'Royal Sovereign' (Z/C/d) LDea
'Royal Star' (R) LDea
'Royal Surprise' (R) ESul LDea NFir
'Royal Wedding' (R) ESul
'Royal Winner' (R) LDea
'Ruben' (d) LAst LSou
'Rubin' (Z/d) **new** NCot
'Rubin Improved' (Z/d) SKen
'Ruby' (Min/d) ESul WFib
'Ruby Orchid' (A) LDea
'Ruby Wedding' (Z) ESul
'Ruffled Velvet' (R) SSea
'Rushmere' (Dw/d) ESul WFib
'Rusty' (Dw/C/d) ESul
'Saint Elmo's Fire' (St/Min/d) SSea WFib
'Saint Helen's Favourite' (Min) ESul SSea
Saint Malo = 'Guisaint'PBR (I) NFir
'Sally Munro' (R) LDea
'Sally Read' (Dw/d) ESul
'Salmon Beauty' (Dw/d) WFib
'Salmon Black Vesuvius' (Min/C) ESul
§ 'Salmon Irene' (Z/d) WFib
Salmon Princess = 'Pacsalpri' LAst LSou
'Salmon Queen' see *P.* 'Lachskönigin'
salmoneum SSea
'Saltford' (R) ESul
'Samantha' (R) ESul WFib
'Samantha Stamp' (Dw/d/C) WFib
Samelia = 'Pensam'PBR (Dark Line Series) (Z/d) LAst
'Sammi Caws' (St) ESul
'Sancho Panza' (Dec) ♀H1+3 CSpe ESul LDea MHer SKen SSea WFib
'Sandford' (Dw/St) ESul
'Sandown' (Dw/d) ESul
'Sandra Lorraine' (I/d) WFib
'Sanguineum' CSpe
'Santa Maria' (Z/d) SKen
'Santa Marie' (R) LDea
'Santa Paula' (I/d) ECtt LDea SKen
§ 'Sarah Don'PBR (A/v) LAst WFib
'Sarah Hunt' (Min/d) NFir
'Sarah Jane' (Sc) MBPg
'Sassa'PBR (Quality Series) (Z/d) LAst LSou
Satellite (Z/St) SSea
'Satsuki' (R) ESul LDea NFir
'Scarborough Fair' (A) **new** NFir
'Scarlet Gem' (Z/St) WBrk WFib
'Scarlet Pet' (U) CFee CRHN ESul MBPg NFir SMrm
'Scarlet Pimpernel' (Z/C/d) ESul
'Scarlet Rambler' (Z/d) EShb SMrm SSea WFib
'Scarlet Unique' (U) CRHN LDea SKen SSea WFib
schizopetalum WFib
§ 'Schneekönigin' (I/d) ECtt LDea SKen
'Schottii' LPio NFir WFib
'Scottow Star' (Z/C) WFib
'Seale Star' (Dw/St/C) SSea
'Seaview Silver' (Min/St) WFib
'Seaview Sparkler' (Z/St) WFib
'Secret Love' (Sc) LDea MBPg
'Seeley's Pansy' (A) LDea MHer WFib
'Sefton' (R) ♀H1+3 ESul LDea WFib
'Selena' (Min) LDea
'Semer' (Min) ESul SKen
* 'Serre de la Madone' (Sc) WEas
'Shalfleet' (Min/St) ESul
'Shalimar' (St) NFir
'Shanks' (Z) NFir
'Shannon' SBch WFib
'Sharon' (Min/d) ESul
'Sheila' (Dw) ESul
'Shelley' (Dw) ESul SKen
'Shirley Ash' (A) LDea WFib
'Shirley Gillam' (Z/St/v) ESul
Shocking Pink = 'Pensho'PBR (Quality Series) (Z/d) LAst
Shocking Violet = 'Pacshovi'PBR (Quality Series) (Z/d) LAst LSou
'Shogan' (R) NFir
'Shorwell' (Dw/C/d) ESul
§ 'Shottesham Pet' (Sc) ESul MBPg MHer
'Shrubland Pet' (U/Sc) LPio SKen SSea
'Shrubland Rose' (Sc) LPio SSea
'Sid' (R) LDea
sidoides CSpe EBee ESul LPio MBPg MCot MHer MWea NFir SBch SPhx SSea WCom WCot WEas WFib WGwG
\- black-flowered CSpe LFur
\- 'Sloe Gin Fizz' CSpe LFur LPio
Sidonia = 'Pensid'PBR (Dark Line Series) (Z/d) LAst WGor
'Sienna' (R) ESul LDea NBur NFir
'Sil Claudio'PBR (Z) LAst
'Sil Falko' (I) **new** WGor
'Sil Frauke'PBR (Z) LAst
'Sil Friesia'PBR (Z) LAst
'Sil Gesa'PBR (Z) LAst
'Sil Hero'PBR (Z) WGor
'Sil Okka' **new** LAst
'Sil Pia'PBR (I) LAst LSou WGor
'Sil Raiko'PBR LAst
'Sil Renko'PBR (Z) LAst
'Sil Rumika'PBR LAst
'Sil Sören' LAst
'Sil Tedo'PBR (Z) WGor
'Sil Tomke'PBR (I) LAst LSou
'Sil Wittje' **new** LAst
'Silver Anne' (R/v) ESul NFir
'Silver Dawn' (Min/St) ESul
'Silver Delight' (v/d) WFib
'Silver Dusk' (Min/St) ESul
'Silver Glitter' (Dw/St) ESul
'Silver Kewense' (Dw/v) ESul NFir WFib
'Silver Leaf Rose' (Sc) MBPg
'Silver Rimfire' (R) ESul
'Silver Snow' (Min/St/d) ESul WFib
'Silver Wings' (Z/v) ESul NFir SSea
'Simon Read' (Dw) ESul
'Sir Colin' (Z) SSea
'Skelly's Pride' (Z) SKen WFib
'Skies of Italy' (Z/C/d) MBri SKen SSea WFib
'Small Fortune' (Min/d) ESul SKen
'Smuggler' (R) LDea
'Snape' (Min) ESul
'Sneezy' (Min) ESul NFir
'Snow Cap' (MinI) NFir
'Snow Flurry' (Sc) WBrk
Snow Queen see *P.* 'Schneekönigin'
'Snow White' (Min) ESul
'Snowbaby' (Min/d) ESul
'Snowberry' (R) ESul
'Snowbright' (St/d) ESul

	'Snowdrift' (I/d)	SSea WFib
	'Snowflake' (Min)	see *P.* 'Atomic Snowflake'
	'Snowstorm' (Z)	SKen WFib
	'Snowy Baby' (Min/d)	WFib
	'Sofie'	see *P.* 'Decora Rose'
	'Solent Waves' (R)	ESul LDea
	'Solferino' (A)	ESul LDea
	Solidor (I/d) ♀H1+3	LDea NFir
	'Somersham' (Min)	ESul WFib
	'Something Special' (Z/d)	NFir WFib
	'Sonata' (Dw/d)	ESul
	'Sophie' (R)	ESul
	Sophie Casade	see *P.* 'Decora Rose'
	'Sophie Caws' (St)	ESul
	'Sophie Dumaresque' (Z/v)	MBri NFir SKen SSea WFib
	'Sorcery' (Dw/C)	ESul SKen
	'Sound Appeal' (A)	ESul LDea
	'South American Bronze' (R) ♀H1+3	ESul LDea WFib
	'South American Pink' (R)	ESul
	'Southern Belle' (A)	LDea SSea
	'Southern Belle' (Z/d)	WFib
	'Southern Charm' (Z/v)	NFir
	'Southern Cherub' (A)	LDea
	'Southern Damsel' (R)	ESul
	'Southern Fairy' (A)	ESul
	'Southern Festival' (Dw)	ESul
	'Southern Flamenco' (R)	ESul
	'Southern Frills' (A)	ESul
	'Southern Galaxy' (Min/St)	ESul
	'Southern Gem' (Min/d)	ESul
	'Southern Michaela' (A)	ESul
	'Southern Peach' (Min/d)	ESul
	'Southern Posy' (Dw)	ESul
	'Southern Purity' (Min)	ESul
	'Southern Rosina' (Dw)	ESul
	'Southern Siewigy' (Dec)	ESul
	'Southern Starlight' (A)	ESul
	'Souvenir' (R)	ESul LDea SSea
	'Spanish Angel' (A) ♀H1+3	CWCL ESul LDea NFir SSea WFib
	'Spanish Banks' (Z/St/v)	ESul
	'Spellbound' (R)	WFib
	'Spital Dam' (Dw/d)	ESul NFir
	'Spitfire' (Z/Ca/d/v)	ESul WFib
	'Spithead Cherry' (R)	LDea
§	'Splendide'	CRHN CSpe EBee EShb ESul LPio MBPg MHer MSCN NFir SSea SWvt WCom WCot WEas WFib
	'Splendide' white-flowered	LPio MBPg
	'Spotlite Hotline' (I)	LDea
	'Spotlite Winner' (I)	LDea
	'Spot-on-bonanza' (R)	ESul LDea NFir SSea WFib
	'Spring Bride' (R)	LDea
	'Spring Park' (A)	ESul MHer SSea WFib
I	'Springfield Alba' (R)	ESul
	'Springfield Black' (R)	ESul LDea MCot SSea
	'Springfield Joy' (R)	ESul
	'Springfield Pearl' (R)	ESul LDea
	'Springfield Purple' (R)	ESul
	'Springfield Unique' (R)	ESul LDea
	'Springtime' (Z/d)	SKen WFib
I	'Springtime' (R)	ESul
	'Sproughton' (Dw)	ESul
	'Stacey' (R)	ESul LDea
	'Stadt Bern' (Z/C)	LAst MBri NFir SKen SWal
	'Stan Shaw' (R)	LDea
	'Stanley Park' (St)	SSea
	'Staplegrove Fancy' (Z)	SKen
	× ***stapletoniae***	see *P.* 'Miss Stapleton'
	'Star Flair' (St/Min/d)	ESul
	'Star Flecks' (St)	NFir
	'Star of Persia' (Z/Ca/d)	WFib
	'Star Storm' (St/d)	ESul
	'Starlet' (Ca)	WFib
	'Starlight' (R)	WFib
	'Starlight Magic' (A) ♀H1+3	ESul LDea
	'Starry Eyes' (Dw)	ESul
	'Startel Salmon' (Z/St)	MHer
	'Stella Read' (Dw/d)	ESul
	'Stellar Arctic Star'	see *P.* 'Arctic Star'
	'Stellar Hannaford Star'	see *P.* 'Hannaford Star'
	'Stephen Read' (Min)	ESul
	'Stewart Meehan' (R)	LDea
	'Stolen Kisses' (Min/D)	ESul
	'Strawberries and Cream' (Z/St)	NFir
	'Strawberry Fayre' (Dw/St)	WFib
	'Strawberry Sundae' (R)	ESul LDea WFib
	'Stringer's Delight' (Dw/v)	ESul
	'Stringer's Souvenir' (Dw/d/v)	SSea
	'Stuart Mark' (R)	LDea
	'Stutton' (Min)	ESul
	'Suffolk Agate' (R)	ESul
	'Suffolk Amethyst' (A)	ESul
	'Suffolk Coral' (R)	ESul
	'Suffolk Emerald' (A)	ESul
	'Suffolk Garnet' (Dec)	ESul
	'Suffolk Jade' (Min)	ESul
	'Suffolk Jet' (Min)	ESul
	'Suffolk Salmon' (R) **new**	ESul
§	'Sugar Baby' (DwI)	ECtt ESul LAst LDea MBri MCot SKen WFib
	'Summer Cloud' (Z/d)	WFib
	'Summertime' (Z/d)	see *P.* 'Deacon Summertime'
	'Sun Rocket' (Dw/d)	WFib
	'Sundridge Moonlight' (Z/C)	WFib
	'Sundridge Surprise' (Z)	WFib
	'Sunraysia' (Z/St)	WFib
	'Sunridge Moonlight' (Dw)	NFir
	'Sunset Snow' (R)	ESul NFir WFib
	'Sunspot' (Min/C)	NFir
	'Sunspot Kleine Liebling' (Min)	SSea WFib
	'Sunspot Petit Pierre' (Min/v)	WFib
	'Sunstar' (Min/d)	ESul WFib
	'Super Rose' (I)	SKen SPet
	'Supernova' (Z/St/d)	ESul SKen WFib
	'Surcouf' (I)	WFib
	'Surfin' Crimson' **new**	SVil
	'Surfing Purple' **new**	LSou SVil
	'Surfing Red' **new**	LSou SVil
	'Susan Hillier' (R)	LDea
	'Susan Payne' (Dw/d)	ESul MHer
	'Susan Pearce' (R)	ESul LDea
	'Susan Read' (Dw)	ESul
	'Susie 'Q'' (Z/C)	SKen SSea
	'Sussex Delight' (Min)	SPet
	'Sussex Gem' (Min/d)	ESul SKen WFib
	'Sussex Lace'	see *P.* 'White Mesh'
	'Swanland Lace' (I/d/v)	WFib
	'Swedish Angel' (A)	ESul LDea NFir SSea WFib
	'Sweet Lady Mary' (Sc)	LDea MBPg
	'Sweet Mimosa' (Sc) ♀H1+3	CRHN ESul GBar MCot MHer NEgg NFir SDnm SKen SSea SWal WBrk WFib
	'Sweet Miriam' (Sc)	GBar LDea MBPg
	'Sweet Sixteen'	WFib
	'Sweet Sue' (Min)	ESul
	'Swilland' (A)	LDea WFib

'Sybil Bradshaw' (R)	LDea
'Sybil Holmes' (I/d)	ECtt LAst MBri SKen SPet SSea WFib
'Sylbar' (R)	ESul
'Sylvia' (R)	ESul
'Sylvia Gale' (R)	ESul
'Sylvia Marie' (d)	NFir SKen
'Taffety' (Min)	ESul WFib
'Tamie' (Dw/d)	ESul NFir
'Tammy' (Dw/d)	ESul
'Tangerine' (Min/Ca/d)	ESul SSea WFib
'Tangerine Elf' (St)	WFib
'Tanzy' (Min)	ESul
'Tapriz' (R)	ESul
'Tara Caws' (Z)	ESul
'Taspo' (R)	ESul
'Tattingstone' (Min)	ESul
'Tattoo' (Min)	ESul
'Tazi' (Dw)	ESul
'Ted Dutton' (R)	ESul
'Telstar' (Min/d)	ESul SKen
§ 'Telston's Prima' (R)	ESul LDea
'Tenderly' (Dw/d)	ESul
'Tenerife Magic' (MinI/d)	ESul
tetragonum	CRHN EShb MBPg MHer SSea WFib
'The Axe' (A)	LDea
'The Barle' (A) 🏆H1+3	LDea WFib
'The Boar' (Fr) 🏆H1+3	EShb LDea SRms WFib
'The Bray' (A)	LDea
'The Creedy' (A)	LDea
'The Culm' (A)	ESul LDea WFib
'The Czar'	see *P.* 'Czar'
'The Dart' (A)	LDea
'The Heddon' (A)	LDea
'The Joker' (I/d)	WFib
'The Kenn-Lad' (A)	LDea
'The Lowman' (A)	LDea
'The Lyn' (A)	ESul LDea
§ 'The Mole' (A)	ESul LDea MHer SKen WFib
'The Okement' (A)	LDea
'The Otter' (A)	ESul LDea
'The Tamar' (A)	CFee LDea
'The Tone' (A) 🏆H1+3	LDea
'The Yar' (Z/St)	WFib
'Thomas' (Sc)	MBPg
'Thomas Earle' (Z)	WFib
'Thomas Gerald' (Dw/C)	ESul SKen
'Tilly' (Min)	NFir
'Tim' (Min)	ESul
'Timothy Clifford' (Min/d)	ESul
'Tinkerbell' (A)	LDea
§ 'Tip Top Duet' (A) 🏆H1+3	ESul LDea MHer NFir SKen SSea WFib
'Tirley Garth' (A)	WFib
'Tomcat'PBR (I/d)	NPri SSea
tomentosum (Sc) 🏆H1+3	CArn CHEx CRHN CSev CSpe EAro EShb ESul GBar GPoy LDea LPio MBPg MCot MHer MNHC NFir SBch SKen SSea WFib
- 'Chocolate'	see *P.* 'Chocolate Peppermint'
'Tomgirl' (A)	NPri
Tomgirl = 'Pactomgi'PBR (I×Z/d)	LAst SSea
'Tommay's Delight' (R)	LDea
'Tony' (Min)	ESul
'Topan' (R)	ESul
'Topcliffe' (Dw/St)	ESul
'Topscore' (Z/d)	SKen WFib
'Tornado' (R)	CWCL ESul NFir WFib
'Torrento' (Sc)	ESul GBar LDea MBPg MHer WFib
'Tortoiseshell' (R)	WFib

(Toscana Series) 'Toscana Cato' **new**	NBlu
- 'Toscana Okka' **new**	LSou
'Tracy' (Min/d)	ESul NFir
transvaalense	LPio NFir
'Treasure Chest' (Z)	SKen
'Treasure Trove' (Z/v)	NFir
tricolor misapplied	see *P.* 'Splendide'
tricolor Curt.	NFir
tricuspidatum	CSpe LPio WCot
trifidum	LPio MBPg SSea WFib
'Trimley' (Dw/d)	ESul
'Trinket' (Min/d)	WFib
'Triomphe de Nancy' (Z/d)	WFib
triste	LFur LPio SSea SUsu WCot WFib
'Trixie' (R)	LDea
'Trudie' (Dw/Fr)	ESul MHer SKen WBrk WFib
'Trulls Hatch' (Z/d)	SKen
'Tu Tone' (Dw/d)	ESul
'Tuddenham' (Min/d)	ESul
'Tuesday's Child' (Dw/C)	ESul SKen
'Tunias Perfecta' (R)	ESul
'Turkish Coffee' (R)	CWCL ESul NFir WFib
'Turkish Delight' (Dw/C)	ESul NFir SSea WFib
'Turtle's Surprise' (Z/d/v)	SKen
'Tuyo' (R)	WFib
'Tweedle-Dum' (Dw)	ESul
'Tweenaway' (Dw)	ESul
'Twinkle' (Min/d)	ESul WFib
'Two Dees' (Dw/d)	NFir
'Ullswater' (Dw/C)	ESul
'Unique Aurore' (U)	MHer SKen
'Unique Mons Ninon'	see *P.* 'Monsieur Ninon'
'Urban White' (Dec)	CSpe WFib
urbanum	EShb
'Urchin' (Min/St)	ESul NFir WFib
'Ursula Key' (Z/c)	SKen WFib
'Ursula's Choice' (A)	WFib
'Val Merrick' (Dw/St)	WFib
'Valencia' (R)	ESul
'Valentina' (Min/d)	ESul
'Valentine' (Z/C)	ESul WFib
'Vancouver Centennial' (Dw/St/C) 🏆H1+3	ESul GKir LAst MBri MCot MHer NEgg NFir SCoo SDnm SKen SPoG SSea WFib
'Vandersea'	EAro
'Variegated Attar of Roses' (Sc/v)	MBPg
'Variegated Clorinda' (Sc/v)	WFib
'Variegated Fragrans'	see *P.* (Fragrans Group) 'Fragrans Variegatum'
'Variegated Giroflée' (I/v)	SSea
'Variegated Joy Lucille' (Sc/v)	MBPg
§ 'Variegated Kleine Liebling' (Min/v)	ESul SSea WFib
'Variegated Madame Layal' (A/v) 🏆H1+3	WFib
'Variegated Petit Pierre' (Min/v)	WFib
'Vasco da Gama' (Dw/d)	ESul
'Vectis Dream' (St)	ESul
'Vectis Fanfare' (St/d)	ESul
'Vectis Finery' (St/d)	ESul NFir
'Vectis Glitter' (Z/St)	ESul NFir SSea WBrk WFib
'Vectis Pink' (Dw/St)	SSea WFib
'Vectis Purple' (Z/d)	WFib
'Vectis Sparkler' (Dw/St)	ESul NFir
'Vectis Spider' (Dw/St)	ESul NFir
'Vectis Starbright' (Dw/St)	WFib
'Vectis Volcano' (Z/St)	WFib
'Velvet Duet' (A) 🏆H1+3	LDea NFir SKen SSea

'Venus' (Min/d) ESul
'Vera Dillon' (Z) SKen
'Vera Vernon' (Z/v) SSea
'Verdale' (A) GGar LDea WFib
'Verity Palace' (R) ESul LDea WFib
'Verona' (Z/C) MBri SKen SSea
'Verona Contreras' (A) CWCL ESul LDea NFir WFib
'Veronica' (Z/d) SKen
'Vic Claws' (Dw/St) NFir
'Vicki Town' (R) WFib
'Vicky Claire' (R) CSpe ESul LDea NFir SKen WFib
Vicky = 'Pacvicky'PBR (I) LAst LSou NPri
'Vickybar' (R) ESul
Victor = 'Pacvi'PBR (Quality Series) (Z/d) LAst LSou
'Victoria' (Z/d) LAst SKen
'Victoria Regina' (R) ESul LDea
'Viking' (Min/d) SKen
'Village Hill Oak' (Sc) ESul LDea MBPg
'Ville de Paris' see *P.* 'Hederinum'
'Vina' (Dw/C/d) SKen WFib
'Vincent Gerris' (A) ESul LDea
Vinco = 'Guivin'PBR (I/d) LAst WGor
violareum misapplied see *P.* 'Splendide'
'Violet Lambton' (Z/v) WFib
I 'Violetta' (R) LDea WFib
'Virginia' (R) LDea SPet
'Viscossisimum' (Sc) MHer SKen
viscosum see *P. glutinosum*
'Vivat Regina' (Z/d) WFib
'Voo Doo' (Dec) ESul
'Voodoo' (U) ♀H1+3 CSpe EShb LAst LPio LSou MBPg MHer NFir SPet SSea WBrk WCot WFib
'Wallace Fairman' (R) LDea
'Wallis Friesdorf' (Dw/C/d) ESul
'Wantirna' (Z/v) ECtt MHer NFir SSea
'Warrenorth Coral' (Z/C/d) WFib
'Warrion' (Z/d) SSea
'Washbrook' (Min/d) ESul NFir
'Watersmeet' (R) LDea SSea
'Wattisham' (Dec) LDea
'Waveney' (Min) ESul
'Wayward Angel' (A) ♀H1+3 ESul LDea SSea WFib
'Wedding Royale' (Dw/d) WFib
'Welcome' (Z/d) WFib
'Welling' (Sc) ESul GBar LDea MBPg MHer NFir
'Wendy Anne' SKen
'Wendy Jane' (Dw/d) WFib
'Wendy Read' (Dw/d) ESul WFib
'Wendy-O' (R) LDea
'Wensum' (Min/d) ESul
'Westdale Appleblossom' (Z/d/C) ESul SSea WBrk WFib
'Westerfield' (Min) ESul
'Westside' (Z/d) WFib
'Westwood' (Z/St) WFib
'Wherstead' (Min) ESul
'Whisper' (R) WFib
'White Bird's Egg' (Z) WFib
'White Boar' (Fr) EShb WFib
'White Bonanza' (R) ESul WFib
'White Charm' (R) ESul LDea
'White Chiffon' (R) ESul NBur
'White Christmas' (Min/St) ESul
'White Duet' (A) LDea
'White Eggshell' (Min) ESul WFib
'White Feather' (Z/St) MHer
'White Glory' (R) ♀H1+3 ESul NFir
'White Lively Lady' (Dw/C) ESul
§ 'White Mesh' (I/v) ECtt MBri SKen
'White Prince of Orange' (Sc) MBPg
'White Roc' (Min/d) ESul
'White Unique' (U) CSpe LDea MHer SBch SPet SSea WFib
'White Velvet Duet' (A) ESul
White-Blizzard = 'Fisbliz'PBR SCoo
'Wickham Lad' (R) LDea
Wico = 'Guimongol'PBR (I/d) CWCL LAst WGor
'Wild Spice' (Sc) LDea
'Wilf Vernon' (Min/d) ESul
'Wilhelm Kolle' (Z) WFib
'Wilhelm Langath' SCoo SDnm
'Willa' (Dec) WFib
'Winnie Read' (Dw/d) ESul
'Wirral Target' (Z/d/v) ESul
'Wispy' (Dw/St/C) ESul
'Witnesham' (Min/d) ESul
'Wolverton' (Z) WFib
§ 'Wood's Surprise' (Min/I/d/v) ESul LDea SKen SWal
'Wooton's Unique' CSev CSpe
'Wychwood' (A/Sc) LDea
'Wyck Beacon' (I/d) SKen
'Yale' (I/d) ♀H1+3 LDea MBri SKen WFib
'Yhu' (R) ESul LDea NBur NFir SMrm WFib
'Yolanda' (Dw/C) ESul
'York Minster' (Dw/v) SKen
'Yvonne' (Z) WFib
'Zama' (R) NFir
'Zena' (Dw) ESul
'Zinc' (Z/d) WFib
'Zoe' (A) LDea
zonale SSea WFib
'Zulu King' (R) WFib
'Zulu Warrior' (R) WFib

Peliosanthes (*Convallariaceae*)

arisanensis B&SWJ 3639 **new** WCru
monticola B&SWJ 5183 WCru

Pellaea (*Adiantaceae*)

andromedifolia WRic
atropurpurea CLAP WFib
§ ***calomelanos*** WRic
falcata CLAP EShb LRHS MBri SEND WRic
hastata see *P. calomelanos*
rotundifolia ♀H2 CBty CLAP EBee EShb LLHF LRHS MBri STre WRic
viridis WPGP WRic
– var. ***macrophylla*** WRic

Pellionia see *Elatostema*

Peltandra (*Araceae*)

alba see *P. sagittifolia*
§ ***sagittifolia*** CRow
undulata see *P. virginica*
§ ***virginica*** CRow EBee EMFW LPBA NPer SWat
– 'Snow Splash' (v) CRow

Peltaria (*Brassicaceae*)

alliacea CSpe LEdu SAga

Peltiphyllum see *Darmera*

Peltoboykinia (*Saxifragaceae*)

§ ***tellimoides*** CLAP EBee GCal GEdr GKev GKir LFur NBir SMac WBVN WFar WMoo

	watanabei	CAby CDes CLAP EBee GEdr IMou LEdu LFur NLar SMac WCot WCru WMoo WPGP

Pennantia (*Icacinaceae*)

	baylisiana	ECou
	corymbosa	ECou
	- 'Akoroa'	ECou
	- 'Woodside'	ECou

Pennellianthus see *Penstemon*

Pennisetum ✿ (*Poaceae*)

§	***alopecuroides***	CEnd CHar CPrp CWCL EBee EHoe EHrv EPfP GFor GKir GMaP LRHS MAvo MBel MBrN NGdn SApp SLim SPer SPlb SWat SWvt WDin WFar
	- Autumn Wizard	see *P. alopecuroides* 'Herbstzauber'
	- 'Black Beauty'	CSpe IFro
	- 'Cassian's Choice'	CKno CSam EBee EHoe ELon SMrm
	- 'Caudatum'	CKno CPen EBee SApp
	- f. ***erythrochaetum***	EBee
	- - 'Ferris'	EBee WCru
	- 'Foxtrot'	IPot
	- 'Gelbstiel'	EBee EPPr
	- 'Hameln'	Widely available
§	- 'Herbstzauber'	CFir CKno CMdw CPen CPrp CSam EBee EHoe EPfP LEdu LHop
	- 'Little Bunny'	CKno CPen CSpe CWib EBee EBrs EHoe ELan EPPr EPfP EQua GCal LRHS NGdn SApp SBod SMrm SWvt WDin WFar WWEG
	- 'Little Honey' (v)	CKno EBee MAvo MBNS NLar
	- 'Magic'	CPen ELon EPPr MAvo MDKP WWEG
	- 'Moudry'	CKno CPLG CPen CSam EAlp EBee EHoe ELon EPPr EPfP LBMP LRHS MAvo NSti SBch SHDw
	- 'National Arboretum'	EBee EHoe EPPr LEdu SApp SMad
	- 'Red Head' **new**	LSou MAvo MBel NBPC SMrm WCot
	- f. ***viridescens***	CKno COIW EBee ECha EHoe ELan EPPr EPfP EShb GFor LEdu LRHS MBel MMoz MNFA MRav MWhi NWsh SApp SMrm SWal WPer WWEG
	- 'Weserbergland'	CKno CSam EBee EHoe SApp WWEG
	- 'Woodside'	CKno CSam CWCL EBee EHoe EPPr EQua LEdu LRHS MBNS SApp SMad
	compressum	see *P. alopecuroides*
	'Fairy Tails' **new**	CKno
	flaccidum	CSam EBee EHul EPPr
	glaucum 'Purple Baron'	SBch WWEG
	- 'Purple Majesty'	CKno CSpe CWCL LRHS MNrw NBlu NGBl NPri SBch SCoo SMad SMrm SUsu WWEG
	incomptum	EHoe LRHS WHal
	- purple-flowered	EBee MMoz
	longistylum misapplied	see *P. villosum*
	macrostachyum 'Burgundy Giant'	MGos
	macrourum	CElw CEnt CGHE CHar CHrt CKno CSam CSpe CWCL EBee ECha EHoe EPau GCal LEdu LHop MAvo MSCN MWhi NWsh SMad SMrm SUsu SWal WGwG WHrl WPGP
	massaicum	SIng
	- 'Red Bunny Tails' **new**	LRHS
	- 'Red Buttons'	see *P. thunbergii* 'Red Buttons'
	orientale ♀H3	Widely available
	- 'Karley Rose'[PBR]	CHid CKno CPen EAlp EBee EHoe EHrv EWes IPot LEdu LHop MAvo MWhi SBch SPhx SSvw SUsu WGrn WWEG
I	- 'Robustum'	CDes EPPr SApp
	- 'Shenandoah'	SApp
*	- 'Shogun'	CKno CPen EBee EPPr MAvo WCot
	- 'Tall Tails'	CHar CHrt CKno CPen EBee ECGP ECha EHoe EPPr EWes IPot LEdu LRHS MAvo MWhi NBPC NSti SMad WWEG
	'Paul's Giant'	CKno SApp
	purpureum	LEdu
	rueppellii	see *P. setaceum*
§	***setaceum*** ♀H3	CKno CWib EShb MNrw SBch SHDw SIde WKif
	- 'Eaton Canyon'	CKno EBee
	- 'Emelia Mae'	SBch SHDw
	- 'Rubrum' ♀H4	CAbb CBcs CKno CPLG CSpe CWCL EAlp EBee EShb LAst LHop LRHS LSRN MGos NPri SBch SCoo SDix SGar SHDw SMad SMrm SPad SPoG SRkn SRot SUsu SWvt
§	***thunbergii*** 'Red Buttons'	CKno CPen EAlp EBee ECha EPPr IPot LEdu MAvo MDKP SBch SHDw SUsu WGrn
§	***villosum*** ♀H3	Widely available

pennyroyal see *Mentha pulegium*

Penstemon ✿ (*Scrophulariaceae*)

	P&C 150	CFee
	PC&H 148	EAro
	RCB/MO A-7	WCot
	'Abberley'	MBNS WPer
	'Abbey Dore'	SLon
	'Abbotsmerry'	ECtt EPfP LRHS MBNS MCot SAga SGar SLon
	'Agnes Laing'	LPen MBNS SLon SPlb
	albertinus	see *P. humilis*
§	'Alice Hindley' ♀H3	Widely available
	alpinus	EAro
§	'Andenken an Friedrich Hahn' ♀H4	Widely available
§	***angustifolius***	MNrw NPol SRms
	- NNS 99-102	EBee
	- var. ***caudatus***	LFur
	'Apple Blossom' misapplied	see *P.* 'Thorn'
	'Apple Blossom' ♀H3-4	Widely available
	aridus	LFur
	arizonicus	see *P. whippleanus*
	'Ashton'	LPen MBNS SAga SLon SUsu
	attenuatus	EBee
	'Audrey Cooper'	CChe MBNS SLon
	'Axe Valley Jessica'	SAga
	'Axe Valley Pixie'	CEnt SAga
	azureus	CFir EBee
	- subsp. ***angustissimus***	GKev
	- subsp. ***azureus***	NLAp
	'Baby Lips'	LLHF
	'Barbara Barker'	see *P.* 'Beech Park'
§	***barbatus***	CArn CBot CEnt CFee EHrv ELan EPfP LRHS SPer SRms WFar
	- 'Cambridge Mixed'	LAst LRHS
	- subsp. ***coccineus***	EAro EBee LPen MBNS NChi NLar
	- 'Iron Maiden'	LRHS NBPC SGSe SHGN
	- 'Jingle Bells'	EAEE EPfP LPen NBPC SAll SMrm SPav
	- 'Navigator'	LRHS
	- orange-flowered	SPlb
	- 'Peter Catt'	LSou MDKP
	- Pinacolada Series **new**	LRHS

	- var. ***praecox***	CBot EPfP MBNS WPer
	- - f. ***nanus***	LRHS SRms
	- - - 'Rondo'	LRHS NBlu NLar NWCA WBrE
	barrettiae	LLHF
	'Beckford'	CPrp EBee EPfP EShb LLHF MBNS WCFE
§	'Beech Park' ♀H3	EBee ECtt EWes IGor LPen LRHS MBNS NBir SAga WHCG
§	***berryi***	EPot
	'Bisham Seedling'	see *P.* 'White Bedder'
	'Blackbird'	Widely available
	'Blue Spring' misapplied	see *P. heterophyllus* 'Blue Spring'
	'Blueberry Fudge' (Ice Cream Series)	WHlf
	'Bodnant'	LLHF LSou MBNS SAga WHoo WPer WWEG
	bradburii	see *P. grandiflorus*
	'Bredon'	ECtt MBNS SAga WBrk
	bridgesii	see *P. rostriflorus*
	'Bubblegum' (Ice Cream Series)	WHlf
	'Burford Purple'	see *P.* 'Burgundy'
	'Burford Seedling'	see *P.* 'Burgundy'
	'Burford White'	see *P.* 'White Bedder'
§	'Burgundy'	CHrt CMac CSam CWCL EBee ECtt GMaP IMon LLWP LPen MCot NBir NPer NPri SAga SBch SGar SMrm SPer SRms WFar WHCG WPer
	caeruleus	see *P. angustifolius*
	caespitosus subsp. ***desertipicti*** new	LFur
	californicus	LFur WAbe WFar
	calycosus	EBee
§	***campanulatus***	CEnt EAro EBee ECtt EPfP EWes GEdr MBel MHer NDlv NMen SAga SRms WFar WPer
	- PC&H 147	CFee
	- PC&H 148	SGar
	- 'Aztec Gem' new	LRHS
	- ***pulchellus***	see *P. campanulatus*
	- ***roseus*** misapplied	see *P. kunthii*
	'Candy Pink'	see *P.* 'Old Candy Pink'
	cardwellii	EWes ITim SRms
	cardwellii × ***davidsonii***	WAbe
	'Carolyn Orr' (v)	CBow EBee ECtt
	caryi	LFur
	'Castle Forbes'	EPyc GMac LPen MBNS SAga SRms WHCG WPer
	'Catherine de la Mare'	see *P. heterophyllus* 'Catherine de la Mare'
*	'Centra'	MBNS
	'Charles Rudd'	CAby CWCL EBee ECtt ELon LLWP LPen LRHS LSRN MBNS MBel SAga SPav SRGP SRms SWal SWvt WCot WHCG
§	'Cherry' ♀H3	GBee GMac LPen LRHS MBNS MHer NBur SAga SGar SHar SMrm SPlb WHCG WPer WWEG
	'Cherry Ripe' misapplied	see *P.* 'Cherry'
§	'Chester Scarlet' ♀H3	CWCL ECtt GMac LPen LRHS MBNS MNrw MRav SDix SGar SLon WHCG WPer
	'Choirboy' new	EWes
	cinicola	LLHF
	'Claret'	SAga
	clutei	GKev
	cobaea	EBee GKev LRHS WPer
	'Comberton'	ECtt MBNS SAga
	confertus	CEnt CTri CWGN EAro EBee ECho EPot LPen MBNS NChi NLAp NMen NWCA SGar SRms WGwG WPer
	- NNS 94-95	NWCA
	'Connie's Pink' ♀H3	ECtt LPen MBNS NBur SGar SLon SRms WHCG WWEG
	'Cottage Garden Red'	see *P.* 'Windsor Red'
§	'Countess of Dalkeith'	CBcs CHVG EBee ECtt ELan EWes LLWP LPen LRHS MBel MNrw MRav SGar SMrm SPer SPlb SRms SUsu SWvt WCot WFar WHCG
	crandallii	CPBP GKev
§	- subsp. ***taosensis***	MRav NWCA SMrm
	cyaneus	EBee GKev
	davidsonii	ECho EWes NLAp NMen SRms WAbe WFar WPat
	- var. ***davidsonii***	GKev
	- var. ***menziesii*** ♀H4	MDun SRms
	- - 'Microphyllus'	LLHF WAbe
	- var. ***praeteritus***	CPBP MDKP
	'Dazzler'	CMMP CWCL LPen MBNS SAga SMrm SWal SWvt WPer
	'Devonshire Cream'	CWCL ECtt LPen LRHS MBNS SAga WHCG
	diffusus	see *P. serrulatus*
	digitalis	CRWN GCal LPen LRHS MBNS NWCA SHar WFar WHCG WKif WPer
§	- 'Husker Red'	Widely available
	- 'Joke' new	IPot
	- 'Mystica' new	EWll
	- 'Purpureus'	see *P. digitalis* 'Husker Red'
	- 'Ruby Tuesday'	EBee EWes SUsu WPGP
	- white-flowered	SPhx SRms SWal
	discolor pale lavender-flowered	NBir WFar
§	'Drinkstone Red'	ECtt EGoo EPfP LPen LRHS MBNS NChi SAga SDix WHCG WPer
	'Drinkwater Red'	see *P.* 'Drinkstone Red'
	eatonii	LFur NBPC
	'Edithae'	LPen MWte SRms
	'Ellenbank Amethyst' new	GMac
	'Ellenbank Cardinal' new	GMac
	'Ellwood Red Phoenix'	LRHS MBNS
	'Elmley'	EBee EPfP MBNS WCot
	Etna = 'Yatna'	EAEE ECtt EPfP GKev GKir LBMP LHop LRHS MAvo MBNS NEgg SAga SAll SBch SGar SMrm SPad SRms WBor WClo WHlf
	euglaucus	EBee LLHF
§	'Evelyn' ♀H4	CMac CTri ECha ECtt ELan ELon EPfP GKir LAst LRHS MBNS MCot MHer MRav NBir NEgg SBch SPer SPet SPlb SPoG SRGP SRms SWvt WFar WHCG WKif WPtf WSHC WWEG
	'Evelyn' × 'Papal Purple'	LPen
	'Fanny's Blush'	CWGN SAga
	'Firebird'	see *P.* 'Schoenholzeri'
	'Flame'	LPen LRHS MBNS NBur SAga SLon WHCG WPer WWEG
	'Flamingo'	CPrp CWCL EBee ECtt EPfP EWes LAst LPen LRHS LSRN MBNS NBir NPri SAga SBch SGar SMrm SPet SPoG SRms STes SWvt WCFE WFar WHoo WWEG
	fruticosus	EBee NWCA WAbe WFar
§	- var. ***scouleri*** ♀H4	MAsh NLAp SRms
	- - f. ***albus*** ♀H4	CSpe WAbe
	- - 'Amethyst'	WAbe
	- - f. ***ruber***	NWCA
	- var. ***serratus*** 'Holly'	NMen
	Fujiyama = 'Yayama'[PBR]	CWCL ECtt EPfP GKir LHop LRHS MAvo NScw SAll SBch SMrm SPad SRms WFar WHlf
	'Garden Red'	see *P.* 'Windsor Red'

Plant	Suppliers
'Garnet'	see *P.* 'Andenken an Friedrich Hahn'
gentianoides B&SWJ 10271	WCru
'Geoff Hamilton'	CElw CWGN EBee ECtt EPfP LPen LSRN MBNS SAga
'George Elrick'	LPen
§ 'George Home' ♀H3	CWCL ECtt ELon EWes LPen LRHS MBNS NBur SMrm SRms WBVN WHCG
'Ghent Purple'	CFee
'Gilchrist'	ECtt LRHS SLon SPhx
glaber	CEnt CMac CMea EAro EBee GBee GMac LHop LLWP LPen LRHS LSRN SPlb WKif WPer
- 'Roundway Snowflake'	CWGN SAga SHar SPhx
- white-flowered	SGar
'Gloire des Quatre Rues'	MBNS
gormanii	EAro SGar
gracilis	WPer
§ ***grandiflorus***	EAro EBee EShb GMac
- 'Prairie Snow'	EBee
'Great Witley'	WPer
grinnellii	WFar
hallii	EWes LRHS
harbourii	CPBP
hartwegii ♀H3-4	EPyc LPen WHCG WPer
- 'Albus'	LHop LPen LRHS SGar WHCG
- 'Picotee Red' **new**	LRHS
- 'Tubular Bells Rose'	LRHS NGBl SPet
'Helenetti'	SDys
heterodoxus	SGar
- NNS 93-564	NWCA
§ ***heterophyllus***	CMea LPen LRHS MBel MNrw MSCN NBir NGBl NGdn SGar SPet SRkn SRms WEas WHCG WPer
- 'Blue Eye'	MBrN
- 'Blue Fountain'	CHar LPen
- 'Blue Gem'	CElw CTri GKir LRHS SIng
§ - 'Blue Spring'	CBot EBee ECtt EPfP LPen LRHS MRav NBir NLar SAga SPoG WAbe WWEG
§ - 'Catherine de la Mare' ♀H4	EBee ELan GKir LHop LPen LRHS LSRN MAvo MHer MWat NBir SAga SBch SPer SRGP SWal SWvt WEas WFar WGwG WKif WSpi WWEG
- 'Electric Blue'	MCCP
- 'Heavenly Blue'	Widely available
- 'Jeanette'	CMea WCot
- 'Les Holmes'	SAga
- subsp. ***purdyi***	EPyc
- 'Roehrslev'	LPen
- 'True Blue'	see *P. heterophyllus*
- 'Züriblau'	EBee GAbr LPen SGSe SPlb
§ 'Hewell Pink Bedder' ♀H3	CHar EAEE EBee ECtt EPfP LPen LRHS MBNS SGar SMad SMrm SRms SWvt WFar WHCG WHil WHoo WMnd WPer
'Hewitt's Pink'	CBcs ECtt SLon
'Hidcote Pink' ♀H3-4	Widely available
'Hidcote Purple'	CElw SAga SHar WHoo
* 'Hidcote White'	LIMB MHer SAga SWvt WWEG
'Hillview Pink'	SLon
'Hillview Red'	MBNS
§ ***hirsutus***	CEnt SGSe SGar WFar WPer
- f. ***albiflorus***	CEnt
- var. ***minimus***	LFur
- var. ***pygmaeus***	CMea EBee ECho EShb LRHS MHer NBlu NMen NWCA SGar SPlb SRms WHoo WPer
* - - f. ***albus***	NWCA SHGN WHoo WPer
'Hopleys Variegated' (v)	CBow CWGN LRHS MBNS NBir SAga SPav SWvt

Plant	Suppliers
§ ***humilis***	SRms
- 'Pulchellus'	NWCA
idahoensis	CPBP
isophyllus ♀H3-4	EPfP LPen LRHS SAga SEND WFar WHCG WPer WPtf
'James Bowden'	MBNS
jamesii	EBee
Jean Grace = 'Penbow'	CHar LRHS NPri WHlf
'Jessica'	CWGN SAga WCFE
'Jingle Bells'	LRHS
'John Booth'	MBNS
'John Nash' misapplied	see *P.* 'Alice Hindley'
'John Nash'	ECtt MHer SAga SRkn SRms
'John Spedan Lewis'	SLon
'Joy'	ECtt EPyc LPen MBNS MBel SAga WPer
'Juicy Grape' (Ice Cream Series)	WHlf
'June'	see *P.* 'Pennington Gem'
'Kate Gilchrist'	LRHS SLon
Kilimanjaro = 'Yajaro'	EPfP LRHS SAll SBch SMrm SRms WHil WRHF
'King George V'	Widely available
'Knight's Purple'	ECtt LPen MBNS WHCG
'Knightwick'	LPen MBNS WPer
§ ***kunthii***	CAby EAro EBee GEdr LLWP LPen MAsh MDKP NBur SAga WPer
- upright	SGar
'Lady Hamilton'	MBNS
§ ***laetus*** subsp. ***roezlii***	ECho EPot GGar LHop LRHS MAsh MDun NDlv NLAp NSla SRms
§ 'Le Phare'	LPen LRHS MBNS WHCG WPer
leonensis	EAro LFur
'Lilac and Burgundy'	EBee LPen LRHS MBNS SMrm SRms SWal SWvt WFar WWEG
'Lilac Frost'	EBee ECtt LLHF LRHS MWhi
'Lilliput'	ENor EPfP LHop LIMB LRHS MBNS NPri SBch SIng SMrm SPet SPoG
linarioides	LPen NLAp SAga WPat
'Little Witley'	LPen WHCG WPer
'Lord Home'	see *P.* 'George Home'
'Lucinda Gilchrist'	SLon
lyallii	EAro EHrv ELan GKev LPen LSou MBrN MCCP SRms WPer
'Lynette'	LPen LRHS MBNS SPlb WHCG WPer
'Macpenny's Pink'	EBee ECtt EPyc GBee LPen MBNS SAga
'Madame Golding'	CWCL GMac LPen LRHS MBNS SGar SPlb WHCG WPer
'Malvern Springs'	MBNS
'Margery Fish' ♀H3	CElw EBee ECtt EPyc EWes LPen LRHS WPer WWEG
'Marilyn Ross'	ECtt MBNS SLon
'Martley' **new**	WPer
'Maurice Gibbs' ♀H3	CBcs CMMP CWCL EAEE ECtt EPfP EPyc EWes LPen LRHS LSRN MBNS MBel NBPC SAga SGar SPav SRGP SRms SWal WBrE WHCG WMnd WWEG
'Melting Candy' (Ice Cream Series)	WHlf
mensarum	GMac
Mexicali hybrids	LPen MBel WFoF
× ***mexicanus*** 'Sunburst Ruby'	LRHS SBch
'Midnight'	CSam ECtt ELan EPfP LLWP LPen LRHS MBNS MRav SAga SEND SGar STes SWvt WCot WHCG WMnd WPer
'Mint Pink'	SAga
'Modesty'	EPfP LPen LRHS MBNS NBur SAga SRms WHCG WPer

	'Mother of Pearl'	Widely available
*	***moylii*** **new**	LFur
	'Mrs Miller'	ECtt LPen MBNS NBur
	'Mrs Morse'	see *P.* 'Chester Scarlet'
	'Mrs Oliver' **new**	EWes
	multiflorus	LPen
§	'Myddelton Gem'	LPen LRHS MWat SRms WCot WFoF WHCG
	'Myddelton Red'	see *P.* 'Myddelton Gem'
	neotericus	NWCA
	newberryi ♀H4	MDKP SAga WKif
	- subsp. ***berryi***	see *P. berryi*
	- f. ***humilior***	EPot
§	- subsp. ***sonomensis***	GEdr WAbe WFar
*	'Newbury Gem'	EBee LSRN MBNS MBel SRGP SWvt WFar
	'Oaklea Red'	ECtt EPyc
§	'Old Candy Pink'	CFee LPen MBNS SWvt WPer
	'Osprey' ♀H3	Widely available
	ovatus	CFir CSpe EBee ELan EWTr LPen NBre NDlv SGar SPhx SRms
	'Overbury'	EBee ECtt LPen MBNS NChi SAga SRms
	pallidus	EBee
	palmeri	EAro LEdu LFur WHil
	'Papal Purple'	CChe CMea LLWP LPen LRHS MAsh MBNS MHer NBir NChi SAga SLon SRms WFar WHCG
	'Patio Bells Pink'	LPen MBel MLHP SBch SWal
	'Patio Bells Shell'	SLon WHlf
	'Patio Wine'	SLon
	paysoniorum	GKev
	'Peace'	LPen LRHS MBNS MRav SLon WHCG
	'Pearl'	EPyc
§	'Pennington Gem' ♀H3	CWCL ELan GMac GQue LHop LLWP LPen LRHS MHer MNrw MSCN NBir SGSe SPer SRms SWvt WHCG WPer WWEG WWlt
	'Pensax' **new**	WPer
	'Pensham Amelia Jane'	CCVN CWGN ECtt EPfP LHop LRHS LSRN LSou MAsh MAvo MBNS MSCN MWea SAga SAll SPer SRGP SRkn SWal WClo WHlf
	'Pensham Arctic Fox'	EBee ECtt LHop MWea SAga SLon
	'Pensham Arctic Sunset'	ECtt SAga SLon WHrl
	'Pensham Avonbelle'	MBNS SRms
	'Pensham Bilberry Ice'	ECtt EPyc MBNS MBel SPav WMnd
	'Pensham Blackberry Ice'	CFir CWGN ECtt EPfP EPyc LRHS LSou MBNS MBri MWea SPav SRms WHil WMnd
	'Pensham Blueberry Ice'	CWGN EBee ECtt EPyc LRHS LSou MBNS MBel MBri SAga SPav WFar WMnd WWlt
	'Pensham Bow Bells'	SAga
	'Pensham Capricorn Moon'	ECtt SAga SLon SRGP
	'Pensham Cassis Royale'	MBel
	'Pensham Charlotte Loise' **new**	ECtt
	'Pensham Claret'	WFar
	'Pensham Czar'	CCVN ECtt EPfP LHop LRHS LSou MAsh MAvo MBNS MWea SAga SAll SLon SPer SRkn SRms WClo WHlf
	'Pensham Dorothy Wilson'	EBee EPyc SMrm SRGP
	'Pensham Edith Biggs'	CHVG CWCL EBee ECtt EPfP SHGN SMrm WFar WMoo
	'Pensham Eleanor Young'	ECtt LSou MBNS MWea SAll SRGP SUsu SWal WClo WHlf
	'Pensham Freshwater Pearl'	CElw SAga SRms WHoo
	'Pensham Great Expectations'	EBee SAga
	'Pensham Jessica Mai' **new**	ECtt LSou SPer
	'Pensham Just Jayne'	CElw CWGN EBee ECtt EPyc LSRN MBNS MBel SAll SLon SPer SRGP SRms WMnd WSpi
	'Pensham Kay Burton'	CElw EPfP EPyc SMrm SRGP WMnd
	'Pensham Laura'	CCVN CWGN EBee ECtt EPfP LHop LRHS LSRN MAsh MBNS MBri MWea SAga SAll SPer SRGP SRkn WClo WHlf
	'Pensham Loganberry Ice'	LSou MBNS MBri NBlu SLon
	'Pensham Marjorie Lewis'	CElw WMnd
	'Pensham Miss Wilson'	SAga SRms
	'Pensham Petticoat'	EBee SUsu WWlt
	'Pensham Plum Jerkum'	CWGN ECtt EPyc LHop LRHS LSou MBNS MBri MWea SAga SAll SPer SWal WClo WMnd WMoo
	'Pensham Raspberry Ice'	CElw MBNS MBel MBri SAga SPav WMnd
	'Pensham Son of Raven'	SAga
	'Pensham Tayberry Ice'	ECtt EPyc MBNS NBlu SAga SGar WMnd
	'Pensham Tiger Belle Coral'	EBee NChi SAga
	'Pensham Tiger Belle Rose'	SAga
	'Pensham Victoria Plum'	CElw LRHS MHer SHar WHoo
	'Pensham Wedding Bells'	EBee SRms WFar
	'Pensham Wedding Day'	LSRN LSou MBNS MBri SAga SAll SPer SRGP WHlf
	perfoliatus	EBee
	'Pershore Carnival'	NPro SAga SRms
	'Pershore Fanfare'	LPen SAga WHrl
	'Pershore Pink Necklace'	CWCL ECtt LPen LRHS SAga SRms SWvt WCot WHCG WWEG
	'Phare'	see *P.* 'Le Phare'
	'Phoenix' **new**	LRHS
	'Phyllis'	see *P.* 'Evelyn'
	pinifolius ♀H4	CEnt CMea CTri ECho ECtt EDAr EPot GAbr GKir GMaP LHop LRHS NLAp SGar SPoG SRms WFar WHoo WPat
	- 'Mersea Yellow'	CMea EBee ECho ECtt EDAr EPfP EPot GAbr GEdr GKir LFur LHop LRHS NDlv NLAp NWCA SPlb SPoG WFar WPat WPer
	- 'Wisley Flame' ♀H4	EAlp ECho EPfP EPot EWes GEdr GKir LRHS MBNS MHer MWat NRya NWCA
	'Pink Bedder'	see *P.* 'Hewell Pink Bedder', 'Sutton's Pink Bedder'
	'Pink Endurance'	LPen MBNS SRkn WHCG WHal WPer
	'Port Wine' ♀H3	CElw CMea CSam CTri CWCL EPfP GMaP LPen LRHS LSRN MBel MCot MWat NBPC NBir NChi SPer SPoG SRms SWal WBrE WCot WGwG WHCG WMnd WPer WWEG
	'Powis Castle'	ECtt EWes SAga WPer WWlt
	'Prairie Dusk'	LPen
	'Prairie Fire'	EBee LPen WHil
*	'Prairie Pride'	LPen
	'Pretty Petticoat'	IPot
	'Primrose Thomas'	SAga
	'Priory Purple'	MBNS WHCG WHrl WPer
	procerus	ECho MBel SRms WPer
§	- var. ***formosus***	GEdr NMen WAbe WFar
	- - NNS 01-345	NWCA
	- var. ***procerus***	LFur
§	- 'Roy Davidson' ♀H4	CMea EPot LBee LHop LRHS NLAp NMen WAbe WFar
	- var. ***tolmiei***	CElw EPot GCal GEdr GKev LRHS NMen WPat
	pubescens	see *P. hirsutus*
	pulchellus Greene	see *P. procerus* var. *formosus*
	pulchellus Lindl.	see *P. campanulatus*

	pumilus	SRms
	'Purple and White'	see *P.* 'Countess of Dalkeith'
	'Purple Bedder'	CHar CHrt COIW EBee EPfP LPen LRHS LSRN MBel MLHP MWat NBir SBch SMrm SPav SPoG SRkn SRms SWal SWvt WCFE WFar WGor WHCG
	'Purple Passion'	CElw EBee EBrs EHrv EPfP EWes LPen LRHS
	'Purple Pixie'	WCot
	'Purpureus Albus'	see *P.* 'Countess of Dalkeith'
	purpusii	EPot LLHF
§	***putus***	SGSe
	'Rajah'	LPen
	'Raven' ♀H3	Widely available
	'Razzle Dazzle'	LPen LRHS MBNS SMrm SPlb SRms WCot WPer
	'Red Emperor'	ECtt LPen LRHS SPlb WHCG WPer WWEG
	'Red Knight'	CWCL GCra LPen LRHS MBNS
	'Rich Purple'	EPyc LRHS MBNS SPlb
	'Rich Ruby'	CWCL CWGN EBee EBrs ECtt EHrv ELan EPfP EWes LHop LLWP LPen LRHS MCot NBir NCGa SAga SPlb SRGP SWvt WCot WHCG WPer WWEG
	richardsonii	SRms WPer
	'Ridgeway Red'	MBNS WCFE
	roezlii Regel	see *P. laetus* subsp. *roezlii*
	'Ron Sidwell'	SGar SLon
§	***rostriflorus*** NNS 03-094	NWCA
	'Rosy Blush'	LPen LRHS MBNS SAga SPlb WHCG
	'Roundhay'	CFee
	'Roy Davidson'	see *P. procerus* 'Roy Davidson'
	'Royal White'	see *P.* 'White Bedder'
	'Rubicundus' ♀H3	CWCL CWGN EBee ECtt EHrv ELan EPfP IMon LPen LRHS LSRN MBNS MWte SAga SBch SMrm SWvt WCot WFar WHCG WHil WMnd
	'Ruby' misapplied	see *P.* 'Schoenholzeri'
	'Ruby Field'	EPyc GBee MSCN WCFE WHCG WRHF
	'Ruby Gem'	LPen LRHS
	rupicola ♀H4	LHop LRHS NSla
	- 'Albus'	LLHF NSla
	- 'Conwy Lilac'	WAbe
	- 'Conwy Rose'	WAbe
	'Russian River'	EAEE EBee ECtt EPPr EPfP EPyc EWes LPen LRHS LSRN MBNS SGar SPlb WHCG WPer
	rydbergii	LFur NLAp
*	Saskatoon hybrids	EBee
	- rose-flowered	SLon
	Scarlet Queen	see *P.* 'Scharlachkönigin'
§	'Scharlachkönigin'	ECtt LRHS
§	'Schoenholzeri' ♀H4	Widely available
	scouleri	see *P. fruticosus* var. *scouleri*
	secundiflorus	LFur
§	***serrulatus***	EPot EWes SGar WKif
	'Shell Pink'	LPen MAvo NChi WPer
*	'Sherbourne Blue'	GBuc SAga SLon WCot WPer
	'Shock Wave'	MCCP
*	'Shrawley'	WPer
	'Sissinghurst Pink'	see *P.* 'Evelyn'
	'Six Hills'	SRms WAbe WPat
	'Skyline'	EAro EPfP
	smallii	CDes CEnt CMHG EAro EBee EPPr EShb EWes LPen LRHS LSRN MCCP NBPC NGdn NWCA SAll SGar SPhx SRkn WPGP WPer
	'Snow Storm'	see *P.* 'White Bedder'
	'Snowflake'	see *P.* 'White Bedder'
	sonomensis	see *P. newberryi* subsp. *sonomensis*
	'Sour Grapes' misapplied	see *P.* 'Stapleford Gem'
	'Sour Grapes' ambig.	CMea MCot WWEG
§	'Sour Grapes' M. Fish ♀H3-4	Widely available
	'Southcombe Pink'	LPen MBel WHCG
	'Southgate Gem'	CWCL GBee LPen LRHS MBNS MNrw MWat SRms SWvt WHCG
	'Souvenir d'Adrian Regnier'	EBee LPen MBNS SGar
	'Souvenir d'André Torres' misapplied	see *P.* 'Chester Scarlet'
	'Souvenir d'André Torres'	LLWP LPen
	speciosus subsp. ***kennedyi***	CPBP
§	'Stapleford Gem' ♀H3	Widely available
	'Strawberries and Cream' (Ice Cream Series)	WHlf
	'Strawberry and Blackberry Fancy' **new**	LRHS
	'Strawberry Fizz'	LRHS
	strictus	EAro EBee EGoo EPPr EShb GKev LPen LRHS MBNS MBel MCCP SGar SPoG SRms WPer
	- 'Bandera'	WFar
	Stromboli = 'Yaboli'	LRHS
§	'Sutton's Pink Bedder'	LRHS MBNS SPlb
	'Sylvia Buss'	LPen
	tall pink-flowered	see *P.* 'Welsh Dawn'
N	'Taoensis'	EWes MBNS SGar
	taosensis	see *P. crandallii* subsp. *taosensis*
	teucrioides	NLAp NWCA
	- JCA 1717050	CPBP
	'The Juggler'	CChe EBee ECtt EPfP LPen LRHS MBNS MBel SPav SUsu WFar WMnd
§	'Thorn'	CSpe CWGN EBee ECtt ELan EShb LPen LRHS MNrw MWat NBir SAga SEND SPer SPhx SRms SWal SWvt WHCG WWEG
	'Threave Pink'	CPrp CWCL ECtt LLWP LRHS MBNS MRav SEND SMrm SPer SWvt WCot
	'Thundercloud'	ECtt SAga
	'Torquay Gem'	EBee GBuc LLHF LPen MBNS WCot WHCG WPer
	'True Sour Grapes'	see *P.* 'Sour Grapes' M. Fish
	'Tubular Bells Red'	LRHS NGBl
	utahensis	CBot GBee SAga WPer
	venustus	GBuc MNrw SRms
	Vesuvius = 'Yasius'	EAEE ECtt EPfP EPyc GKir LRHS NEgg SBch SMrm SPad SRms SWal WFar WHlf
	virens	CPBP LFur WPer
	virgatus 'Blue Buckle'	EBee EShb IPot MAvo NBir NLar SAll SPlb WFar
	- subsp. ***putus***	see *P. putus*
	watsonii	EBee ELan SRms
§	'Welsh Dawn'	CEnt LPen MBNS
§	***whippleanus***	EAro MWea WAbb
§	'White Bedder' ♀H3	Widely available
	'Whitethroat' Sidwell	LPen LRHS MBNS SAga SLon WHCG
I	'Whitethroat' purple-flowered	SMrm WPer
	wilcoxii	EBee
	'Willy's Purple'	ECtt MBNS
§	'Windsor Red'	CTri EBee ECtt EPfP LPen LRHS MBNS MSCN NBPC SBch SGar SPoG SRms SWal SWvt WGor WHCG WRHF
	wislizeni	SRms
	'Woodpecker'	CAby ECtt MBNS SAga SGar SRms SUsu SWal

Pentachondra (*Epacridaceae*)

pumila	IBlr

Pentaglottis (*Boraginaceae*)

§ ***sempervirens***	CArn EPfP MHer

Pentagramma (*Adiantaceae*)

triangularis	WRic

Pentapanax see *Aralia*

Pentapterygium see *Agapetes*

Pentas (*Rubiaceae*)

lanceolata	CCCN ELan EShb MBri
- 'New Look Pink' (New Look Series)	LRHS

Penthorum (*Penthoraceae*)

sedoides	WPer

Peperomia (*Piperaceae*)

§ ***argyreia*** ♀H1	MBri
caperata	LRHS MBri
obtusifolia 'Jamaica'	MBri
- (Magnoliifolia Group) 'Golden Gate' (v)	MBri
- - 'Greengold'	MBri
- - 'USA' ♀H1	MBri
- 'Tricolor' (v)	MBri
- 'Variegata' (v) **new**	LRHS
orba 'Pixie'	MBri
I - 'Pixie Variegata' (v)	MBri
puteolata **new**	LRHS
rotundifolia	EShb
sandersii	see *P. argyreia*
scandens ♀H1	MBri
- 'Variegata' (v)	MBri

pepino see *Solanum muricatum*

peppermint see *Mentha* × *piperita*

Perezia (*Asteraceae*)

linearis	GBuc
recurvata	NWCA

Pericallis (*Asteraceae*)

§ ***lanata*** (L'Hér.) B. Nord.	CHll EShb
- Kew form	CSpe SAga SMrm
multiflora	SAga
Senetti Series	LRHS MGos NBlu NPer NPri
- 'Senetti Blue Bi-color' **new**	LAst
- 'Senetti Magenta Bi-color' **new**	LAst

Perilla (*Lamiaceae*)

§ ***frutescens*** var. ***crispa*** ♀H2	CArn CSpe
- var. ***japonica***	GPoy
- var. ***nankinensis***	see *P. frutescens* var. *crispa*
- var. ***purpurascens***	CArn LRHS WJek
- 'Shizo Green'	CSpe

Periploca (*Asclepiadaceae*)

graeca	CArn CBcs CMac CRHN EBee SLon WSHC
purpurea	WSHC
- B&SWJ 7235	WCru
sepium	CPLG

Peristrophe (*Acanthaceae*)

speciosa	ECre

Pernettya see *Gaultheria*

mucronata	see *Gaultheria mucronata*

Perovskia (*Lamiaceae*)

abrotanoides	LRHS
atriplicifolia	CArn CBcs CBot CDul CMea ELan LRHS MHer MNHC NSti WHCG WMnd WPer
- 'Little Spire'PBR	CAbP CBow CHar CMac CSpe EMil EPfP EWes GBin GCra GQue LRHS LSRN MAsh NLar SPer SPoG WSHC
'Blue Haze'	EBrs GCal LRHS
'Blue Spire' ♀H4	Widely available
'Filigran'	EBee EGoo GBuc LBMP LRHS MAsh SMad SPoG WFar WPat WSpi
'Hybrida'	CAlb EMil LRHS SBch
'Longin'	LRHS
scrophulariifolia	WCom

Persea (*Lauraceae*)

americana	CCCN
indica	CCCN WPGP
lingue	CBcs EBee IDee
thunbergii	CBcs CHEx WPGP

Persicaria (*Polygonaceae*)

B&SWJ 11268 from Sumatra **new**	WCru
SDR 4566	GKev
§ ***affinis***	CBcs CBen CSBt EBee GAbr MBar MTho MWhi NBro NSti NVic SWat WBrE WBrk WCFE WClo WFar WMoo
- 'Darjeeling Red' ♀H4	CBcs CRow CTri EBee EBla ELan EMFW EPfP GBBs GGar GKev GKir GMaP LBMP LRHS LSRN MBri MRav NBir NBlu NChi NEgg NGdn NPri SWat SWvt WFar WHer WPnP WWEG
- 'Dimity'	see *P. affinis* 'Superba'
- 'Donald Lowndes' ♀H4	CMac COIW CTri EBee EHoe ELan EPfP GBBs GGar GKir GMaP LAst LPBA LRHS LSRN MHer MNrw MRav SPer SPoG SRGP SRms SWat SWvt WFar WMoo WSpi WWEG
- 'Kabouter'	EBee GBin
§ - 'Superba' ♀H4	Widely available
alata	see *P. nepalensis*
alpina	CRow SBch
amphibia	CRow MSKA NSco SWat
§ ***amplexicaulis***	CBre CHVG CKno COld CPrp CRow CSpe EBee ELan EWes GKir GMaP LRHS MBel MCot MHer MMuc NOrc SEND WBor WClo WCom WFar WGwG WMoo WTin
- 'Alba'	CElw CHar CKno CRow EBee ECha ELon EPPr EPla GBuc GCal LBMP LRHS MBel MCot MRav SPhx SWat WBor WCAu WCom WFar WMnd WMoo WPnP WTin WWEG
- 'Arun Gem'	see *P. amplexicaulis* var. *pendula*
- 'Atrosanguinea'	CKno CMac CRow CTri EBee ECha ELan EMFW EPla GGar LRHS MNFA MRav MSpe NBir NVic SPer SRms SWat SWvt WCAu WFar WOld WWEG
- 'Baron'	CRow
- 'Betty Brandt'	EBee

- 'Blackfield'PBR new EBee WCot
- 'Blush Clent' WHoo WTin
- 'Border Beauty' EBee
- 'Clent Charm' NChi WWEG
- 'Cottesbrooke Gold' CRow ECtt MAvo
- 'Dikke Floskes' CRow
- 'Fat Domino'PBR new EBee
- 'Firedance' CKno EPPr IPot SMrm SPhx SWat WCot
- 'Firetail' ♀H4 Widely available
- 'High Society' EBee
- 'Inverleith' CBre CDes CHar CKno CRow EBee ECha ECtt EPPr EPla EWll GGar GQue LRHS MAvo WCot WMoo WPGP WPnP

I - 'Jo and Guido's Form' EBee SUsu WCAu WFar

* - var. ***pendula*** CRow EBee LRHS NBir WFar WMoo
- - HWJK 2255 WCru
- 'Pink Elephant' new EBee
- 'Pink Lady' CRow NLar
- 'Rosea' CElw CKno CRow CSam EBee ECha ELan EPPr EPla GMaP GQue MCot MMuc MRav NBro NChi NSti SDys SMeo SMrm SPhx SWat WCAu WCom WDyG WFar WMoo WPGP WSpi WWEG
- 'Rosy Clent' EBee
- 'Rowden Gem' CRow WMoo
- 'Rowden Jewel' CRow
- 'Rowden Rose Quartz' CRow
- 'Summer Dance' EBee EPPr NBre NLar
- Taurus = 'Blotau' CElw CKno EBee EBrs ECha EPPr LRHS MBel MBri NLar NSti WFar WPGP WPnP WTin

§ ***bistorta*** CArn CRow EBWF ELau GBar GPWP GPoy MHer MMuc MWhi NBir NGHP NSco SRms SWat WDyG
- subsp. ***carnea*** CRow EBee EBla ECha GGar LLWG LPla LRHS MBNS MMuc NBir WFar WMoo
- 'Hohe Tatra' CDes CRow LRHS WFar WMoo
- 'Superba' ♀H4 Widely available

campanulata CElw CRow EBee ECha ECtt EHoe GAbr GBuc GGar GMaP IFro MCot MRav NBro NEgg SPer WCom WFar WMoo WOld WRHF
- Alba Group CElw EBee GCal GGar MCot NBro WHer WMoo
- var. ***lichiangense*** GBin
- 'Madame Jigard' CRow GBin
- 'Rosenrot' CBre CKno CRow GBuc LRHS NBir NHol NLar SWat WFar WOld WWEG
- 'Southcombe White' CRow EPla LRHS WPer WWEG

§ ***capitata*** CRow LLWG SIng SRms WMoo
- 'Pink Bubbles' ECtt EHoe SPet SWvt

conspicua EBee NBre

* ***elata*** CSpr GBuc LRHS NBur

emodi CRow NBre

hydropiper 'Fastigiata' CArn

* ***macrophylla*** CRow LDai LRHS WFar

I - 'Cally Strain' GCal

microcephala CRow EWes
- 'Red Dragon'PBR Widely available
- var. ***wallichii*** CRow

* ***milletii*** CRow EBrs GBuc LRHS MTho NLar WCru WFar WWEG

§ ***mollis*** CRow EBee LRHS WDyG WPGP

* ***nakaii*** EBee

§ ***nepalensis*** CPLG CRow EBee EPPr EShb IMou

§ ***odorata*** CArn ELau EOHP GPWP GPoy ILis MHer MNHC NGHP NPri SBch SHDw SIde WJek

orientalis WCot

* ***polymorpha*** CBct CDes CKno CRow CSpe EBee ECha EHrv ELan EPPr EWTr GMaP LEdu LRHS MCot MRav NCGa SDix SMad SMrm SPhx SWat WCot WFar WMoo WPnP WSpi WTin

polystachya see *P. wallichii*

'Red Baron' EPPr

§ ***runcinata*** CRow EBee GGar NBir NCob NLar WFar WHer WMoo WPer WPtf
- Needham's form CRow NBid

scoparia see *Polygonum scoparium*

sphaerostachya Meisn. see *P. macrophylla*

tenuicaulis CBre CEnt CRow CSpe ECho EHrv EPla GGar LRHS SBch WCru WFar WMoo

§ ***tinctoria*** EOHP WSFF

§ ***vacciniifolia*** ♀H4 Widely available
- 'Ron McBeath' CRow

§ ***virginiana*** CRow ECtt GCal LRHS WMoo
- 'Batwings' LRHS SGSe
- Compton's form CRow EBee ECha EPPr EPfP GCal LDai LHop LPla LRHS NCob NGby WAul WCot
- 'Filiformis' CWit EBee ECtt GBin GQue LPla SBch SWvt WCot WDyG WPtf WWEG
- 'Lance Corporal' CMac CRow EBee EPPr EPla NBre NCob NLar SMrm WMnd WMoo
- 'Moorland Moss' WMoo
- Variegata Group CBot CRow ECha EPla EShb LRHS MBNS WMoo WOld
- - 'Painter's Palette' (v) Widely available
- white-flowered EPPr NCob

vivipara CRow NLar

§ ***wallichii*** CRow NBre NLar SDix SWat WCot WMoo WPtf

§ ***weyrichii*** EBee GCal NBir NBro NLar WFar WMoo

persimmon see *Diospyros virginiana*

persimmon, Japanese see *Diospyros kaki*

Petalostemon see *Dalea*

Petamenes see *Gladiolus*

Petasites (*Asteraceae*)

albus EBee GPoy MHer NLar

formosanus LEdu

fragrans EBee ELan MHer NLar SWat WFar

§ ***frigidus*** var. ***palmatus*** CRow LEdu NLar WPGP
- - JLS 86317CLOR SMad
- - 'Golden Palms' CBow EHrv

hybridus EBee EMFW LEdu MSKA NSco SWat WMAq WSFF

japonicus CBcs GPoy IDee
- var. ***giganteus*** CArn CHEx CMac CRow ECha ELan EPPr EPfP LEdu NVic SGSe SWat WMoo

§ - - 'Nishiki-buki' (v) CHEx CMac CRow EBee EPPr EPla EWld MSKA NBir NEgg NSti SGSe SMad WBor WCHb WCom WFar WPGP
- - 'Variegatus' see *P. japonicus* var. *giganteus* 'Nishiki-buki'
- f. ***purpureus*** CDes EPPr EWes SGSe WPGP

palmatus see *P. frigidus* var. *palmatus*

paradoxus	CDes CLAP EPPr EWes LEdu MBel SMad WCot

Petrea (*Verbenaceae*)

volubilis	CCCN CHll EShb

Petrocallis (*Brassicaceae*)

lagascae	see *P. pyrenaica*
§ ***pyrenaica***	WAbe
- ***alba***	WAbe

Petrocoptis (*Caryophyllaceae*)

pyrenaica	EBur SRms
§ - subsp. ***glaucifolia***	NBir NLar SIng

Petrocosmea (*Gesneriaceae*)

begoniifolia	WAbe
grandiflora	WAbe
iodioides	WAbe
kerrii	CDes WAbe
- 'Crème de Crûg'	WCru
aff. martinii 'Crûg's Capricious'	WCru
minor	CPBP WAbe
rosettifolia	WAbe
sericea	WAbe

Petrophytum (*Rosaceae*)

caespitosum	EPot LBMP WAbe
cinerascens	WAbe
§ ***hendersonii***	NHol SIng WPat

Petrorhagia (*Caryophyllaceae*)

'Pink Starlets'	LHop
saxifraga ♀H4	CSpe EBur ECho EDAr EShb LBMP LRHS NPri SRms SWal WMoo WPer WPnn WPtf
- 'Rosette'	MTho

Petroselinum (*Apiaceae*)

§ ***crispum***	CArn CSev GPoy ILis MBar MNHC NBlu NGHP SBch SIde SPoG SWal WPer
- 'Bravour' ♀H4	ELau MHer
- 'Champion Moss Curled'	SVic
- 'Darki'	CSev NGHP NPri
- French	CArn ELau MHer MNHC NBlu NPri NVic SPoG WJek
- 'Hank' (v)	CNat
- 'Italian'	see *P. crispum* var. *neapolitanum*
§ - var. ***neapolitanum***	ELau SBch SIde SPoG SVic
- 'Super Moss Curled'	NVic SWal
§ - var. ***tuberosum***	MHer MNHC SIde SVic
- variegated (v)	CNat
hortense	see *P. crispum*
tuberosum	see *P. crispum* var. *tuberosum*

Petteria (*Papilionaceae*)

ramentacea	EBtc MBri NLar

Petunia (*Solanaceae*)

'Bavarian Belle'	LAst
Candyfloss = 'Kercan'PBR (Tumbelina Series)	LSou NPri
Cherry Ripple (Tumbelina Series)	LAst NPri
(Conchita Series) Conchita Azur **new**	SVil
- Conchita Blueberry Frost = 'Conblue'PBR ♀H3	Pri
- Conchita Doble Dark Blue = 'Condost 169'PBR (d)	LAst
- Conchita Doble Lavender = 'Condost 177'PBR (d)	SVil
- Conchita Doble Pink = 'Condopink'PBR (d)	SVil
'Empaurea'	LAst NPri
Million Bells Series	see *Calibrachoa* Million Bells Series
patagonica	WAbe
Petini Pink Vein (Petini Series)	NPri SVil
* 'Purple Surprise'	LAst
(Supertunia Series) Supertunia Bordeaux = 'Lanbor'PBR **new**	SVil
- Supertunia Raspberry Blast = 'Temari' **new**	SVil
- Supertunia Royal Magenta = 'Kakegawa S36'PBR	SVil
- Supertunia Vista Bubblegum = 'Ustuni6001' **new**	SVil
(Surfinia Series) Surfinia Amethyst	LAst
- Surfinia Baby Pinkmorn = 'Sunbapimo'PBR	LSou
- Surfinia Blue = 'Sunblu'	LAst LSou NPri WGor
- Surfinia Blue Topaz = 'Sunsurfbupa' **new**	LAst
- Surfinia Blue Vein = 'Sunsolos'PBR	LAst LSou WGor
- Surfinia Burgundy	LAst LSou NPri WGor
- Surfinia Crazy Pink = 'Sunrovein'PBR	LAst NPri
- Surfinia Double Lilac (d)	LAst
- Surfinia Double Red Celebration (d)	LAst NPri
- Surfinia Giant Purple = 'Sunlapur'PBR	LAst
- Surfinia Hot Pink = 'Marrose'PBR	LAst LSou WGor
- Surfinia Hot Red = 'Sunhore'PBR	NPri
- Surfinia Lime = 'Keiyeul'PBR	LAst LSou NPri WGor
- Surfinia Pastel 2000 = 'Sunpapi'PBR	LAst WGor
- Surfinia Pink Ice = 'Hakice'PBR (v)	LAst NPri WGor
- Surfinia Pink Vein = 'Suntosol'PBR ♀H3	LAst WGor
- Surfinia Purple = 'Shihi Brilliant' ♀H3	LAst LSou NPri WGor
- Surfinia Red = 'Keirekul'PBR	LAst NPri WGor
- Surfinia Rose Vein = 'Sunrove'PBR	LAst WGor
- Surfinia Sky Blue = 'Keilavbu'PBR ♀H3	LAst LSou NPri WGor
- Surfinia Soft Pink	WGor
- Surfinia Sweet Pink **new**	LSou
- Surfinia Vanilla = 'Sunvanilla'PBR	LSou
- Surfinia Velvet	LAst
- Surfinia Victorian Yellow = 'Sunpatiki'PBR	LAst LSou NPri WGor
- Surfinia White = 'Kesupite'	LAst

(Tiny Tunia Series) Tiny Tunia Double Blue Vein new — LAst
- Tiny Tunia Pink 'Mp7' new — LAst
- Tiny Tunia Red 'Mp101' new — LAst
(Tumbelina Series) Julia = 'Kerjul'PBR — LAst
- Katrina — LAst
- Melissa (d) new — LAst LSou
- Priscilla = 'Kerpril'PBR — LAst LSou NPri
- Rosella Improved = 'Kerrosim'PBR — LAst
- Tumbelina Rosy Ripple (d) new — LAst NPri
- Victoria = 'Kervic'PBR — LAst LSou
(Veranda Series) Veranda Rose Vein = 'Kerverrovein' new — SVil
- Veranda Salmon = 'Kerversalm' new — SVil
- Veranda White = 'Kerverwhite' new — SVil
(Viva Series) 'Viva Dark Purple Vein' new — LAst
- 'Viva Forest Fire' new — LAst

Peucedanum (*Apiaceae*)

* ***aromaticum*** new — IMou
japonicum — CSpe
- B&SWJ 8816B — WCru
litorale — see *Kitagawia litoralis*
ostruthium — GPoy
- 'Daphnis' (v) — CDes CElw CSpe EBee EPPr LEdu LPla NChi NLar NMRc NPro WCot WHrl
palustre — EBWF
praeruptorum — CArn
siamicum B&SWJ 6487 — WCru
thodei — SPlb
verticillare — CArn CSam CSpe EBee EBrs GQue IMou LRHS MBel MCot MNFA NChi NLar SDix SMad SMrm SPhx WSHC WWEG

Peumus (*Monimiaceae*)

boldus — EBee IDee

Phacelia (*Hydrophyllaceae*)

bolanderi — LDai
sericea — LFur
- subsp. ***ciliosa*** — LFur

Phaedranassa (*Amaryllidaceae*)

BKBlount 2623 — WCot
carmiolii — WCot
cinerea — EBrs ECho WCot
dubia — ECho WCot
* ***montana*** — ECho
tunguraguae — EBrs ECho
viridiflora — EBrs ECho WCot

Phaedranthus see *Distictis*

Phaenocoma (*Asteraceae*)

prolifera — SPlb

Phaenosperma (*Poaceae*)

globosa — CHrt CSam CSpe EHoe EPPr EWes LEdu MAvo NWsh SUsu WBor WPGP WPrP

Phagnalon (*Asteraceae*)

saxatile (L.) Cass. RCB RL -21 — WCot

Phaiophleps see *Olsynium*

nigricans — see *Sisyrinchium striatum*

Phalaris (*Poaceae*)

'Arctic Sun' new — CKno
arundinacea — EMFW GFor MBNS MMuc SPlb SVic SWat WTin
- cream-flowered new — WWEG
- 'Elegantissima' — see *P. arundinacea* var. *picta* 'Picta'
- var. ***picta*** — CBen CDul CHEx CTri CWCL CWib EMFW MMuc MSKA NBid NBir NBur NPer SApp SPoG WDin WFar
- - 'Aureovariegata' (v) — CBcs CSWP MRav NGdn NPer SWat WMoo
- - 'Feesey' (v) — Widely available
- - 'Luteopicta' (v) — EBee EGoo EHoe EPPr EPfP MMuc WTin
- - 'Luteovariegata' (v) — EShb NGdn
§ - - 'Picta' (v) ♀H4 — COIW EBee ELan EPfP EPla GFor GKir LPBA LRHS MBar SPer SWat WMoo
- - 'Streamlined' (v) — EPPr EPla NWsh SLPl WFar
- - 'Tricolor' (v) — CPen EBee EHoe EPla MBar

Phalocallis (*Iridaceae*)

§ ***coelestis*** — EDif WHil

Phanerophlebia (*Dryopteridaceae*)

caryotidea — see *Cyrtomium caryotideum*
falcata — see *Cyrtomium falcatum*
fortunei — see *Cyrtomium fortunei*

Pharbitis see *Ipomoea*

Phaseolus (*Papilionaceae*)

caracalla — see *Vigna caracalla*
vulgaris 'Yin Yang' — LSou

Phedimus see *Sedum*

Phegopteris (*Thelypteridaceae*)

§ ***connectilis*** — EBee EFer EFtx SRms WAbe WRic
decursive-pinnata — CLAP EFtx EMil LRHS MAsh NHol NLar WAbe WFib WRic WSpi

Phellodendron (*Rutaceae*)

amurense — CBcs CCCN CDul CMCN EBee ELan EPfP EWTr GAuc IFFs LEdu NLar NMun SEND WBor WDin WPGP
- B&SWJ 11000 — WCru
- var. ***sachalinense*** — CBcs EGFP LRHS
chinense — EGFP
japonicum — EGFP
- B&SWJ 11175 — WCru
lavalleei — EPfP

Phenakospermum (*Strelitziaceae*)

guianense — XBlo

Pherosphaera (*Podocarpaceae*)

fitzgeraldii — CKen
hookeriana — ECou

Philadelphus ✿ (*Hydrangeaceae*)

F&M 152 — WPGP
SDR 4946 — GKev

'Albâtre' (d)	EBee MBri
argyrocalyx	GKir
'Avalanche'	CMHG CPLG EBee GKir NLar NPro SPer SRms WDin WFar WHCG
'Beauclerk' ΨH4	CDoC CDul CSBt CTri EBee ECrN EPfP GGal GKir GQui LRHS MBri MGos MRav NBro NCGa NEgg NHol SPer SReu SRms SWvt WDin WHCG WKif
'Belle Etoile' ΨH4	Widely available
'Bicolore'	EBee EWTr MAsh NLar WSpi
'Boule d'Argent' (d)	CMHG
'Bouquet Blanc'	EBee GKir GQui MRav NLar SRms WPat
brachybotrys	EPfP MRav WHCG
'Buckley's Quill' (d)	EBee ECrN EPfP EQua EWes LRHS MAsh MRav SWvt
'Burfordensis'	EBee EPfP LAst MRav WPGP
'Burkwoodii'	LRHS
aff. ***calvescens***	MRav
- BWJ 8005	WCru
caucasicus	WPGP
coronarius	CBcs CDul CTri EPfP GKir LBuc MLHP MWhi NWea SEND SPer WDin
- 'Aureus' ΨH4	Widely available
- 'Bowles's Variety'	see *P. coronarius* 'Variegatus'
§ - 'Variegatus' (v) ΨH4	CDul CMHG CPMA CWib EBee ELan EPfP GKir LAst LHop LRHS MAsh MGos MRav MSwo NBir NSti SLim SPer SPoG WCFE WCot WDin WFar WHCG WMoo WPat WSHC
'Coupe d'Argent'	MRav
'Dame Blanche' (d)	GKir LRHS MAsh MRav
delavayi	CGHE EPfP GGal GKir SChF WHCG WPGP
- var. ***calvescens***	see *P. purpurascens*
- var. ***melanocalyx***	GCra GKir MRav WPGP
- 'Nymans' **new**	CPLG
'Enchantement' (d)	MRav SDix
'Erectus'	CSBt CWib EBee EPfP LEdu LRHS MGos MRav SPer SPoG WDin WHCG WPat
'Etoile Rose'	GKir
'Frosty Morn' (d)	CBcs EBee GKir LRHS MBri MGos MRav NBro NCGa SPer
hirsutus	GKir
incanus	GKir
- B&SWJ 8616	WCru
§ 'Innocence' (v)	CBot CMac CPLG CWSG ECrN EHoe ELan EPfP LAst LBMP LRHS MAsh MBri MGos MRav MSwo NPri NPro SAga SBch SPer SPoG SReu WCot WFar WHCG
'Innocence Variegatus'	see *P.* 'Innocence'
§ ***insignis***	MRav
× ***lemoinei***	CDul CTri ELon LBMP MGos MWat WDin WFar
I - 'Lemoinei'	NWea
lewisii	CPLG GKir
- L 1896	WPGP
'Limestone' **new**	MRav
maculatus	GKir
- 'Mexican Jewel'	CPLG WPGP
madrensis	LHop MRav
'Manteau d'Hermine' (d) ΨH4	Widely available
'Marjorie'	EBee
mexicanus	EBee WSHC
- B&SWJ 10253	WCru
- 'Rose Syringa'	CGHE CPLG WPGP
microphyllus	CBot CDul CMCN CMHG EBee ELan EPfP GKir LAst LRHS MAsh MGos MRav MWhi NHol SLon SPer SReu SSpi WBVN WHCG WPat WSHC
- var. ***occidentalis***	NLar
'Miniature Snowflake' (d)	MAsh WPat
'Minnesota Snowflake' (d)	CBcs EBee ECtt EQua EWes GKir LBuc LRHS LSRN MRav NEgg NHol NLar NPro SBch SPur WDin WFar
'Mont Blanc'	CBcs EBee EWTr MRav NCGa WFar
'Mrs E.L. Robinson' (d)	CMac EBee ECtt GKir LAst LBuc LLHF LRHS MAsh NEgg NLar WBor WPat
'Natchez' (d)	CMac EBee ECtt MAsh WDin WPat
'Oeil de Pourpre'	MRav
palmeri	WPGP
pekinensis	CPLG
'Perryhill'	MRav
'Polar Star'	CBcs GBin
§ ***purpurascens***	EPfP EWes GQui LLHF MRav WPGP WPat
- BWJ 7540	WCru
× ***purpureomaculatus***	GKir LLHF MRav WPat
satsumi B&SWJ 10811 **new**	WCru
schrenkii	NLar WPGP
- B&SWJ 8465	WCru
§ 'Silberregen'	CAlb CDul CMac EBee EPfP EWTr GKir LAst LRHS MAsh MBar MGos MMuc MRav NCGa NHol NPro SMad SRms SWvt WFar WPat
Silver Showers	see *P.* 'Silberregen'
'Snow Velvet'	EBee ECrN EPfP LLHF LRHS MAsh
'Snowbelle' (d)	EBee LBMP LRHS MAsh MBri MWea NBro NHol SWvt
'Snowflake'	CWSG GKir NMoo
'Snowgoose' **new**	MAsh
'Souvenir de Billiard'	see *P. insignis*
subcanus	CPLG
- L 524	WPGP
'Sybille' ΨH4	CDul CMHG ECrN EPfP GKir LHop LRHS MRav MSwo SDix SPer SPoG SRms SSpi WHCG WKif WPat WSHC WSpi
tenuifolius	NLar
tomentosus	CPLG GKir WHCG WPGP
- B&SWJ 2707	WCru
- GWJ 9215	WCru
'Virginal' (d)	Widely available
'Voie Lactée'	MRav
White Icicle = 'Bialy Sopel'	CCCN WBrE
White Rock = 'Pekphil'	CDoC CMac CPLG CWSG EBee EQua GKir LAst LLHF LRHS MRav NMoo SLim SPer SPoG WPat
'Yellow Cab'	EBee MBri NEgg NLar SPoG WClo
'Yellow Hill'	EBee LRHS MAsh NEgg SBch SPoG

Philesia (*Philesiaceae*)

buxifolia	see *P. magellanica*
§ ***magellanica***	CBcs CPLG GGGa SSpi WCru WSHC
- 'Rosea'	CWib EPfP IBlr LRHS SSpi

Phillyrea (*Oleaceae*)

angustifolia	CBcs CDul CGHE CMCN EBee ELan EPfP ERom IFFs LRHS MBri MGos MRav SBig SEND SLPl SPer SSpi WDin WFar WPGP WSHC
- f. ***rosmarinifolia***	CCCN CPLG ELan EPfP EPla LAst MBri NLar SLPl WFar
- - 'French Fries' **new**	WPGP
decora	see *Osmanthus decorus*

§ ***latifolia*** CDul EBee EGFP ELan EPfP GGal LRHS MBri MWea NLar SAPC SArc SLPl SSpi WDin WFar WPGP
I - 'Rodrigueziensis' WCFE
media see *P. latifolia*

Philodendron (*Araceae*)

epipremnum see *Epipremnum pinnatum*
'Pink Princess' (v) **new** CBow
* ***rubrum*** XBlo
scandens 'Mica' XBlo
selloum EAmu XBlo
xanadu XBlo

Philotheca (*Rutaceae*)

buxifolia ECou

Phlebodium (*Polypodiaceae*)

§ ***aureum*** ♀H1 CSpe EShb WRic
- 'Mandaianum' WRic

Phleum (*Poaceae*)

bertolonii CRWN EBWF
pratense EHoe GQue NMir WSFF

Phlomis ✿ (*Lamiaceae*)

* ***anatolica*** LRHS NLar
* - 'Lloyd's Variety' CAbP CSam ELan LRHS MAsh SPer WPen
atropurpurea BWJ 7922 WCru
bourgaei 'Whirling Dervish' WCom
bovei subsp. ***maroccana*** CBot IFro WHal
bracteosa WCot
cashmeriana CBcs CBot EBee ECha EPfP LBMP LDai LRHS LSou MMuc NLar SMad WPtf WWEG WWlt
chrysophylla ♀H3 CAbP CBot ECha ELan EPfP LRHS MRav NLar SDix SPer WCFE WSpi
crinita EBee
'Edward Bowles' CDul ECha LRHS LSRN MRav NBid SLPl SWvt WCom
* 'Elliot's Variety' CPLG
fruticosa ♀H4 Widely available
- white-flowered ECrN
grandiflora CBot SEND
herba-venti MBri
italica Widely available
- 'Pink Glory' CMac LRHS
lanata ♀H3-4 CAbP CBgR EBee ELan EPfP LRHS SPer SPoG WEas WSHC
- 'Pygmy' CHVG LRHS MGos NPro
leucophracta 'Golden Janissary' WPGP
longifolia CBot EBee EGoo EPfP LHop LRHS LSou MGos NLar SEND SPer
- var. ***bailanica*** CSam
lycia LRHS
macrophylla SPhx
pratensis EBee
purpurea CAbP CArn CBot CPLG CSam EBee ELan EPfP LRHS MAsh MBri NBir SBch WCot
- ***alba*** CBot EPfP LHop LRHS
- subsp. ***almeriensis*** CMdw CPom
rotata GKev
§ ***russeliana*** ♀H4 Widely available
- 'Mosaic' (v) **new** EBee WCAu
samia Boiss. see *P. russeliana*
samia L. CEnt CPom EBee EBrs EWTr LBMP LDai LRHS NBPC NChi NGdn NLar SPoG WCot WHal WPtf
taurica GAbr NChi SDix
tuberosa CBcs CBot CFir CKno CPou EBee EBrs EPPr EPfP GKir LEdu LLWP LRHS LSRN NGdn NLar SBch SGSe SMrm SPet SWal WCAu WCot WFar WGwG WHoo WMnd WPGP WPtf
- 'Amazone' CFir CKno EBee ECha EHrv EPfP GBuc GMac LHop MAvo MRav NBid NCGa NOrc NSti SAga SMad SMrm SUsu WFar WMnd WSpi
- 'Bronze Flamingo' CMac EBee ECGP EHrv EPfP LAst LRHS LSou MAvo MRav NOrc SPoG SWal WMnd WPer WSpi
viscosa misapplied see *P. russeliana*

Phlox ✿ (*Polemoniaceae*)

adsurgens ♀H4 NCob WAbe WCom
- 'Alba' WAbe
- 'Mary Ellen' ITim
- 'Red Buttes' ECho
- 'Wagon Wheel' CWCL EBee ECho EPPr EPot EWes GGar GKir ITim LAst LRHS NSla NWCA SIng SMrm SPlb SRms SRot WAbe WCFE WClo WFar
amplifolia EBee NBre WFar
× ***arendsii*** 'Anja' WCot
- 'Babyface' NGdn
- 'Early Star' EBee LSou
- 'Eyecatcher' CPrp NBro NGdn
- 'Lilac Girl' NBre
- 'Lisbeth' SUsu WCot
- 'Luc's Lilac' CMHG ECtt GBin GBuc LLHF LRHS NBro NEgg NGdn SMeo SMrm SMrs SPhx SPoG STes WAul WWlt
§ - 'Miss Jill' (Spring Pearl Series) CSsd EBee EPfP MAvo NBPC NHol SPet WCot WTin
§ - 'Miss Karen' (Spring Pearl Series) NBro
§ - 'Miss Margie' (Spring Pearl Series) GMaP LEdu NBir
§ - 'Miss Mary' (Spring Pearl Series) EBrs ECtt EPfP GMaP LRHS MDKP NHol NPro
§ - 'Miss Wilma' (Spring Pearl Series) EPfP GMaP
- 'Paul' WCot
- 'Ping Pong' EBee LDai NBPC NBre NBro NPro STes
- 'Pink Attraction' CPrp MNrw NBro NCGa
- 'Purple Star' CPrp EBee
- 'Rosa Star' EBee NBre
- 'Sabine' EBee
- 'Suzanne' EBee
austromontana EPot GKev NHol NWCA
'Bavaria' LLHF
bifida ECho
- 'Alba' ECho LLHF LSou WFar
- blue-flowered ECho LRHS LSou SUsu
- 'Minima Colvin' ECho ECtt EPot
- 'Petticoat' CMea CPBP ECtt EPot LRHS MDKP WFar
- 'Ralph Haywood' CMea CWCL ECtt EPot GBuc ITim
- 'Starbrite' LRHS WFar
- 'Starcleft' **new** WRHF
- 'Thefi' EWes MNrw
'Black Buttes' GEdr
borealis see *P. sibirica* subsp. *borealis*
* - ***arctica*** EPot
bryoides see *P. hoodii* subsp. *muscoides*
caespitosa ECho EWes NDlv
- 'Zigeunerblut' **new** CPBP
canadensis see *P. divaricata*
carolina subsp. ***angusta*** SUsu

	- 'Bill Baker' ♀H4	Widely available
	- 'Magnificence'	CPrp EBee EWes GBuc GMac LRHS MDKP SMad STes WCot WSHC
	- 'Miss Lingard' ♀H4	CSam CWCL EBee ECtt GBuc LAst LRHS MAvo NBid NBir NGdn NHol NLar NSti SAga SMrm WAul WCot WFar WWEG
	'Casablanca'	SMrm
	'Charles Ricardo'	EWes GBuc GMac SUsu WHoo
	'Chattahoochee'	see *P. divaricata* subsp. *laphamii* 'Chattahoochee'
§	***condensata***	ECho WPat
	covillei	see *P. condensata*
	'Daniel's Cushion'	see *P. subulata* 'McDaniel's Cushion'
	diffusa	WAbe
§	***divaricata*** ♀H4	GBee GKir SBod SPlb
	- 'Blue Dreams'	CFir ECtt EHrv GBuc LRHS MNrw NCob SUsu WFar WHal WPGP WSHC WWlt
	- 'Blue Perfume'	CPrp EBee ECtt LSou NBro NCGa NGdn NLar SHGN SMrm WFar
	- 'Clouds of Perfume'	CMMP COIW CWCL EAEE EBee ECtt GMaP LAst LRHS LSRN MSCN NCGa NCob NEgg NLar SBod SMrm SPoG STes WClo WFar WWEG
	- 'Dirigo Ice'	EAEE EBee EHrv LHop LRHS MWte NLar SIng WFar WSHC
	- 'Eco Texas Purple'	EBee ECtt IPot NCGa NCob NPro SAga WFar WPGP WSHC WWlt
	- 'Fuller's White'	CWCL ECtt LRHS
	- subsp. ***laphamii***	CBot EWes WFar
§	- - 'Chattahoochee' ♀H4	CBot COIW CPrp CSpe CWCL EAEE EBee ECho ECtt ELan EPfP EPot EWes GBuc GMac LHop LRHS MCot MWat NCGa NLar SIng SMrm SPoG SRot WCFE WCom WFar WHoo
§	- 'Louisiana Purple'	WSHC
	- 'May Breeze'	CAby EBee ECho EHrv GCra GKir GMaP LHop LRHS MNrw NCGa NCob SIng SUsu WCom WFar WPGP WSHC WWEG WWlt
	- 'Plum Perfect'	EBee LLHF NBhm NBro WFar WPtf
*	- 'White Perfume'	CMMP CPrp CWCL EBee EWes IPot LAst LRHS LSou MDKP NBro NCGa NCob NLar SHGN SMrm STes WFar
	douglasii	GKir NPol NWCA SRms
	- 'Alba'	GJos
	- 'Apollo'	CTri ECho ECtt LLHF NMen
	- 'Boothman's Variety' ♀H4	ECha ECho ECtt EDAr ELan EPfP EPot MLHP MWat NMen SRms WAbe WCom
	- 'Crackerjack' ♀H4	CMea CStu ECho ECtt EDAr ELan ELon EPfP EPot GAbr GJos GKev GKir GMaP LRHS MAsh MHer MLHP NBir NEgg NMen SIng SPoG SRGP WFar
	- 'Eva'	CMMP CPBP ECho ECtt EDAr EPot GMaP LRHS LSRN MSCN NBir NMen NPri NWCA SRGP WCom WFar
	- 'Galaxy'	ECho
	- 'Georg Arends'	ECtt EPot GJos
	- 'Holden Variety'	ECtt
	- 'Ice Mountain'	CPBP ECho ECtt ELan EPot GMaP LRHS NEgg NHol NWCA SIng SPoG SRot WFar WRHF
	- 'Iceberg' ♀H4	ECho GJos NMen
	- 'Lilac Cloud'	ECtt EDAr GJos NPro SIng WAbe
	- Lilac Queen	see *P. douglasii* 'Lilakönigin'

§	- 'Lilakönigin'	ECho
	- 'Napoleon'	CPBP ECho ECtt EPot LLHF NHol NMen WAbe
	- 'Ochsenblut'	ECho EPot LLHF LRHS MHer MLHP WAbe
	- 'Red Admiral' ♀H4	ECho ECtt EPfP EWes GEdr GKev GKir GMaP LRHS MWat NMen WCFE WFar WRHF
	- 'Rose Cushion'	ECho EDAr EWes MHer NMen
	- 'Rose Queen'	ECho
	- 'Rosea'	ECho EDAr ELan GEdr LRHS NMen NPol WBVN WFar
	- 'Silver Rose'	ECho GEdr MWat NWCA
	- 'Sprite'	SRms
	- 'Tycoon'	see *P. subulata* 'Tamaongalei'
	- 'Violet Queen'	ECho EWes WFar
	- 'Waterloo'	ECho ECtt EPot NMen
I	- 'White Admiral'	ECtt EPot LRHS LSRN NPro SIng
	drummondii 'Classic Cassis'	NPri SPoG
	'Fancy Feelings' (Feelings Series)	NBro NCob WHil
	glaberrima 'Morris Berd'	CDes EBee WPGP
	hoodii	ECho GKev
§	- subsp. ***muscoides***	ECho
*	'Hortensia'	LRHS
	'Kelly's Eye' ♀H4	CMMP CPBP ECho ECtt EPot GEdr NBir NHol NMen SPoG WBVN WCom WFar
	kelseyi	ECho WAbe WPat
	- 'Lemhi Purple'	CPBP
	- 'Rosette'	ECho EPot MDKP NMen WFar WPer
	Light Pink Flame = 'Bareleven'PBR	EPfP LRHS SPoG
	Lilac Flame = 'Barten'PBR	SPoG
	longifolia subsp. ***brevifolia***	CPBP
	'Louisiana'	see *P. divaricata* 'Louisiana Purple'
	maculata	NOrc WPer
	- 'Alba'	SPoG
	- 'Alpha' ♀H4	CHrt CPrp CSam CWCL EBee ECha ECtt EPfP GCal GCra GGar GKir GMaP LRHS NCGa NHol NLar NOrc SPer SWvt WAul WCAu WFar WSHC WWlt
	- Avalanche	see *P. maculata* 'Schneelawine'
	- 'Delta'	CCVN EBee EPfP GBuc LRHS LSou NBPC NHol SBch SPer SRkn SWvt WBor WFar
	- 'Natascha'	Widely available
	- 'Omega' ♀H4	CPLG CPrp EAEE EBee ECtt EWTr GBuc GGar GKir LRHS MMuc NGdn NHol NLar SBch SMad SPer SPoG SWvt WAul WCAu WFar WSHC WSpi WWEG
	- 'Princess Sturdza' ♀H4	MWte SDix
	- 'Reine du Jour'	CSam GMac LPla LSou MDKP SAga SPhx SUsu WSHC
	- 'Rosalinde'	EAEE EBee ECtt ELon GBuc LRHS MMuc NCob NHol NLar SBch SRGP STes SWvt WCAu WFar WSHC WWEG
§	- 'Schneelawine'	GKir SPlb
	'Matineus'	SPhx
	'Millstream'	see *P.* × *procumbens* 'Millstream'
	'Millstream Jupiter'	ECho
	'Minnie Pearl'	LRHS
	muscoides	see *P. hoodii* subsp. *muscoides*
	nana 'Mary Maslin'	WCom
	nivalis 'Jill Alexander'	CMea SAga

	Name	Suppliers
	- 'Nivea'	EPot GJos LRHS LSou
	paniculata	ECha GCra NBid SDix SMeo WCAu WCot WTin
	- 'Aida'	EBee
	- var. ***alba***	CMoH MAvo SDix SMeo WCot WTin
	- 'Alba Grandiflora' ♀H4	EHrv GMaP MAvo NCob WCot WEas WHoo
	- 'All in One' **new**	LSou
	- 'Amethyst' misapplied	see *P. paniculata* 'Lilac Time'
	- 'Amethyst' Foerster	CFir CSam EBee EHrv LAst LRHS NBir NLar NOrc NPri SPet SWat WCAu WFar
I	- 'Aureovariegata Undulata' (v)	WCot
	- 'Balmoral'	EBee ECtt EPfP GCra GKir LRHS MLHP MRav NCob NEgg NSti SBch SMrs SPoG SWat SWvt WSpi WWEG
	- 'Barnwell'	SWat
	- 'Becky Towe' PBR (v)	CBow EBee ECtt ELon IMon LHop LLHF LOck LRHS LSou NEgg NLar SPoG WCot
	- 'Bill Green'	LRHS
	- 'Blauer Morgen' **new**	IPot
	- 'Blue Boy'	EBee ECGP ECtt EPfP GMaP LAst LRHS MDKP MSCN NBir NBro NChi NEgg NGby NGdn NLar SMrm WBrE WClo WCot WFar WHil WMnd
	- 'Blue Evening'	LSou
	- 'Blue Ice' ♀H4	EBee ELan MSCN NBro
	- 'Blue Paradise'	Widely available
	- 'Blushing Bride'	SRms
	- 'Border Gem'	CBcs CMac EBee ECtt GKir LRHS MAvo MCot MRav MSpe MWat NChi NCob NHol NLar NVic SDix SPur SWat SWvt WBrk WHrl WWEG
	- 'Branklyn'	EBrs GCra GKir LRHS
	- 'Brigadier' ♀H4	CPrp CTri EBee ECtt ELan GMaP LRHS MCot MDKP MSpe MWat NCob NEgg NGdn NVic SBch SMrm SPer SRms WCAu WFar
	- 'Bright Eyes' ♀H4	Widely available
	- 'Burgi'	SDix
	- 'Candy Floss'	LLHF NCob
	- 'Caroline van den Berg'	LRHS SRms
	- 'Cecil Hanbury'	NLar SRms
	- 'Cherry Pink' **new**	LRHS
	- 'Chintz'	SRms
	- 'Cinderella'	EBee ECtt
§	- 'Cool of the Evening'	EBee WKif
	- 'Cosmopolitan' **new**	MAsh MBri
	- Count Zeppelin	see *P. paniculata* 'Graf Zeppelin'
	- 'Danielle'	CSBt EBee LSou MWea
	- 'Darwin's Choice'	see *P. paniculata* 'Norah Leigh'
	- 'David'	Widely available
	- 'David's Lavender' **new**	LRHS
	- 'Delilah' PBR	EBee NPri
	- 'Discovery'	EBee EHrv EWes IPot LRHS MCot MRav NCob NEgg SBch SPur STes SWat WCAu
	- 'Dodo Hanbury-Forbes' ♀H4	GKir
	- 'Doghouse Pink'	SDix
	- 'Dresden China'	MAvo SWat
§	- 'Düsterlohe'	CElw CSBt CSam EBee ECtt GBuc IPot NBir NGdn NLar NSti SMrm SPer STes SWat WCAu WCot WHil WHoo
	- 'Eclaireur' misapplied	see *P. paniculata* 'Düsterlohe'
	- 'Eclaireur' Lemoine	SWat
	- 'Eden's Crush'	CHrt NBre NVic
	- 'Eden's Flash'	EBee ECtt LRHS MSpe
	- 'Eden's Smile'	EBee MSCN
	- 'Elisabeth' (v)	EBee LSRN SPoG SRGP
	- 'Elizabeth Arden'	MAvo NLar SWat
	- 'Elizabeth Campbell' **new**	GCal
	- 'Empty Feelings' PBR (Feelings Series)	EBee NBro NCob
	- 'Etoile de Paris'	see *P. paniculata* 'Toits de Paris' Symons-Jeune
	- 'Europa'	EBee ECtt ELan LRHS MCot NBir NCob NGdn NHol NLar SPer SPoG WCAu WFar
	- 'Eva Cullum'	EBee ECtt EPfP GCra GKir GMaP LHop LRHS MArl MCot NBPC NHol NLar NMoo SBch SPer SPet SPoG SWat WCot WWEG
	- 'Eva Foerster' **new**	LRHS
	- 'Eventide' ♀H4	CMac CSam CWCL EBee ECGP ECtt EPfP GKir LRHS MArl MCot MRav NCob SBch SPer SPet SPoG SPur SWat WCAu WCot
	- 'Excelsior'	LRHS MRav
	- 'Fairy's Petticoat'	LRHS MWat
	- 'Ferris Wheel'	MWea
	- 'Flamingo'	EBee ECtt EWTr LRHS NGby NLar SWvt
	- 'Fondant Fancy'	MBri SPoG
	- 'Franz Schubert'	CHrt CSam EBee ECtt EPfP EWTr GCra GKir LRHS MCot MLHP MRav MWat NBir NGdn NLar NSti SBch SPer SPhx STes SWat SWvt WCot WFar WKif WWEG WWlt
§	- 'Frau Alfred von Mauthner'	COIW ECtt SMrm
	- 'Frosted Elegance' (v)	ECtt LSou MAvo
	- 'Fujiyama'	see *P. paniculata* 'Mount Fuji'
	- 'Glamis'	MWat
	- 'Goldmine' PBR (v)	ELan LRHS MCCP NSti
§	- 'Graf Zeppelin'	ECtt ELan LRHS NGby SRms
	- 'Grenadine Dream'	LLHF NVic SPoG
	- 'Harlequin' (v)	CBcs EBee ECha ECtt EHoe ELon GBuc GMaP LAst LRHS MCCP MCot NBPC NBid NBro NEgg NLar NSti SGSe SPer SPoG WCom WCot WFar WWlt
	- 'Hesperis'	CMdw EBee ECha GBin SMeo SMrm SPhx WFar
	- 'Inspiration' **new**	LRHS
	- 'Iris'	CMoH GBuc SRms WCot
	- 'Judy'	LSRN NBro
	- 'Jules Sandeau'	LRHS MBri
§	- 'Juliglut'	CSpr SWat WCot
	- July Glow	see *P. paniculata* 'Juliglut'
	- 'Junior Dance'	LSou NGdn
	- 'Junior Dream'	LSou
	- 'Junior Fountain' **new**	LSou
	- 'Katarina'	CElw ECtt NLar
	- 'Katherine'	CHar LRHS NLar
	- 'Kirchenfürst'	CElw LRHS MBri NBir SBch
	- 'Kirmesländler'	EBee ECtt GBin LRHS NLar SWat
	- 'Lads Pink'	SDix
	- 'Lady Clare'	SRms
	- 'Landhochzeit'	EBee GBin WFar
*	- 'Laura'	CMMP EBee ECtt EPfP IPot LRHS NBPC NBro NPri NVic SGSe SMrm SPet SPoG SRGP SRkn STes WFar WHoo WMnd WTin
§	- 'Lavendelwolke'	CSam EBee GCal NBir NLar SWat
	- Lavender Cloud	see *P. paniculata* 'Lavendelwolke'
	- 'Le Mahdi' ♀H4	ELan LRHS MRav MWat SMeo SRms SWat
	- 'Lichtspel'	SAga SMeo SPhx

	Name	Suppliers
§	- 'Lilac Time'	EBee EHrv EWll LSRN MDKP MWat NLar NMoo SWat SWvt WWEG
	- 'Little Boy'	CElw EBrs ECtt LRHS LSou MDKP MNrw NLar WFar
	- 'Little Laura'	CElw CMHG CWGN EBee ECtt LRHS LSRN MCCP MWea NLar NOrc WCot
	- 'Little Princess'	ELon LLHF LRHS NLar SMrm SRGP WMnd
	- 'Lizzy'[PBR]	NLar
	- 'Manoir d'Hézèques'	WCot
	- 'Mary Christine' (v)	CDes EBee NBid
	- 'Mary Fox'	CSam LRHS
	- 'Mia Ruys'	LRHS MArl MLHP
	- 'Midnight Feelings' (Feelings Series)	LLHF NBro NCob NLar
	- 'Mies Copijn'	GMaP WFar
	- 'Milly van Hoboken'	WKif
	- 'Miss Elie'	LAst NBre NGdn SGSe SPoG WFar WHoo WWlt
	- 'Miss Holland'	LAst MWea NBPC NGdn SPet STes WWEG
	- 'Miss Jessica'	LAst LRHS STes
	- 'Miss Jill'	see *P.* × *arendsii* 'Miss Jill'
	- 'Miss Karen'	see *P.* × *arendsii* 'Miss Karen'
	- 'Miss Kelly'	CMMP EBee LRHS LSou MSpe MWat MWea SRGP WHoo
	- 'Miss Margie'	see *P.* × *arendsii* 'Miss Margie'
	- 'Miss Mary'	see *P.* × *arendsii* 'Miss Mary'
	- 'Miss Pepper'	CPrp CWCL EBee ECtt ELon LRHS LSou MMuc NGdn NLar SMrm SRkn WBor WFar WHil WWlt
	- 'Miss Universe'	MCCP NBre SGSe SPoG WWEG
	- 'Miss Wilma'	see *P.* × *arendsii* 'Miss Wilma'
	- 'Monica Lynden-Bell'	Widely available
	- 'Mother of Pearl' ♀[H4]	EBee ECtt ELan GQue IPot LRHS MSpe MWat NCob NEgg NHol NVic SPer SUsu WFar WWEG WWlt
§	- 'Mount Fuji' ♀[H4]	Widely available
	- 'Mount Fujiyama'	see *P. paniculata* 'Mount Fuji'
	- 'Mrs A.E. Jeans'	SRms
	- 'Natural Feelings'[PBR] (Feelings Series)	CSpe ELan MCCP MWea NBro NCob NLar WWlt
	- 'Newbird'	SRms WHal WHil WWEG
	- 'Nicky'	see *P. paniculata* 'Düsterlohe'
§	- 'Norah Leigh' (v)	Widely available
	- 'Orange Perfection'	see *P. paniculata* 'Prince of Orange'
	- 'Othello'	CSam EBee EBrs ECtt GBuc GKir LRHS NCob NSti SBch SUsu WFar WMnd WWlt
	- 'Otley Choice'	EBee ECtt LRHS MRav MWat NCob NHol NLar NVic SCoo SWat
	- 'Otley Purple'	MHer
	- 'P.D. Williams'	WCot
	- 'Pastorale'	LRHS WCot
	- 'Pax'	SMeo
	- 'Peppermint Twist'	CWCL MBri MNrw MWea NEgg SPoG WFut WWlt
	- 'Picasso' **new**	LSou
	- 'Pina Colada' **new**	MAsh
	- Pink Eye Flame = 'Barthirtyfive'[PBR] **new**	LSou
	- 'Pink Perfection' **new**	LRHS
	- 'Pink Posie' (v)	LRHS MBri WCot
	- 'Pinky Hill'	CElw LSou NPri
	- 'Pleasant Feelings'[PBR] (Feelings Series)	MBNS NBro NCob
	- 'Popeye'	ECtt LPla MBri NLar
§	- 'Prince of Orange' ♀[H4]	Widely available
	- 'Prospero' Foerster ♀[H4]	CHar CSam EBee EHrv LRHS MCot NBid SPer SRkn SWat
	- Purple Eye Flame = 'Barthirtythree'[PBR] **new**	LLHF LSou

	Name	Suppliers
	- 'Purple Kiss' **new**	MAsh
	- 'Rainbow'	ELon
	- 'Red Feelings'[PBR] (Feelings Series)	NBro NCob
	- 'Red Flame' **new**	LRHS LSou WCot
	- 'Red Riding Hood'	EBrs ECtt LAst LRHS MAvo MWea NBPC SPet
	- 'Rembrandt'	CPLG LRHS NBlu WCot
	- 'Rijnstroom'	CBcs EBee ECtt ELon GKir LRHS NLar SMrm WBrk WFar WSpi
	- 'Robert Poore'	GBin
	- 'Rosa Pastell'	CDes EHrv ELon LPla LSou MDun SPhx SUsu
	- 'Rosie's Pink' **new**	SMrm
	- 'Rowie'	NBid
	- 'Rubymine'[PBR] (v)	LLHF NCob
	- 'San Antonio'	LRHS
	- 'Sandringham'	CMac EBee EHrv EPfP GKir LRHS MArl MLHP MNrw MRav MSpe NBir NHol SBch SPer SPoG STes SWvt WCAu WWlt
§	- 'Schneerausch'	LPla SPhx
	- 'Septemberglut'	LRHS NLar
	- 'Silvermine' (v)	CBow MCCP NBro SDnm
	- 'Sir Malcolm Campbell'	EBee
	- 'Skylight'	EBee EHrv LRHS LSRN MAvo MWhi NBre NBro NVic SBch SDix SPer WAul
	- 'Snow Hare' **new**	LRHS
	- 'Snow White'	NBre NVic
	- Snowdrift	see *P. paniculata* 'Schneerausch'
	- 'Speed Limit 45'	WCot
	- 'Spitfire'	see *P. paniculata* 'Frau Alfred von Mauthner'
	- 'Starburst'	EBee NBro NGdn NLar
	- 'Starfire' ♀[H4]	Widely available
	- 'Steeple Bumpstead'	EBee LSou NCob WCot
	- 'Sternhimmel'	LPla
	- 'Sylvia' **new**	LRHS
	- 'Tempest' **new**	LRHS
	- 'Tenor'	CDes CFir CHar CTri EBee ECtt EPfP LAst LRHS MCot MDKP MSpe NCob NGdn NHol NLar NPri SBch SPet SPoG STes SWvt WBrE WCAu WFar WPGP WWEG
	- 'The King'	CElw EBee ECtt LRHS MAvo MDKP NBro NGby NLar SWat WCot WSHC WSpi
	- 'Toits de Paris' misapplied	see *P. paniculata* 'Cool of the Evening'
	- 'Toits de Paris' ambig.	MAvo
§	- 'Toits de Paris' Symons-Jeune	WSHC
	- 'Uspekh'	COIW CSam EBee EBrs ECtt EPPr EWes LRHS MCot MDKP MDun MRav NBro NCGa NCob NGdn NHol NOrc SAga SBch SPer SPoG SUsu WFar
	- 'Utopia'	CDes CSam ELon LPla NLar SMrm SPhx SUsu
	- 'Van Gogh'	CMdw EHrv
	- 'Velvet Flame' **new**	LSou
	- 'Violetta Gloriosa'	LPla MWte SMrm
	- 'Visions'	WHil
	- 'Watermelon Punch' **new**	MAsh MBri
	- 'Wendy House'	LLHF MNrw NCob SPoG
	- 'Wenn Schon Denn Schon'	EBee GBin
	- 'White Admiral' ♀[H4]	Widely available
	- White Flame = 'Bartwentynine'[PBR]	EBee EPPr EPfP LRHS LSou
	- 'Wilhelm Kesselring'	EBee ELon LRHS NBre WBor

	- 'William Ramsay'	LRHS
	- 'Windsor' ♀[H4]	EBee ECtt ELon EPfP GCal GKir LRHS MSpe NEgg NHol NLar SBch SCoo SPoG SRms SWvt WCAu WFar WSpi WWEG
	pilosa	NPro
	Pink Flame = 'Bartwelve'[PBR]	EBee EPfP LLHF LRHS LSou SPoG
	'Pride of Rochester'	GJos LHop LRHS
§	× ***procumbens*** 'Millstream' ♀[H4]	EPPr LRHS WClo
	- 'Variegata' (v)	ECha ECho LRHS MDKP NBlu NPri NWCA SPlb SRot SUsu
	Purple Flame = 'Barfourteen'[PBR]	EBee EPfP LRHS LSou SPoG
	'Sandra'	LRHS
	'Scented Pillow'	NHol SGSe WRHF
	'Sherbet Cocktail'	CWGN EKen MWea SPoG WCot
§	***sibirica*** subsp. ***borealis***	EDAr WAbe
	'Sileniflora'	EPot
	stansburyi dwarf	GKev
	stolonifera	MNrw
I	- 'Alba'	CBcs EBee EPfP
	- 'Ariane'	CWCL ECha EPPr LSou WCFE
	- 'Blue Ridge' ♀[H4]	CPLG CWCL EBee ECha ECtt EPPr EPfP EShb EWld GBuc GKir LRHS LSRN MCot MRav SRms
	- 'Bob's Motley' (v)	ECtt
	- 'Fran's Purple'	EBee ELon LRHS NBro WCFE WPGP
	- 'Home Fires'	EBee ECtt ELon EPPr EPfP LEdu LRHS MNrw NBro NLar SAga SMrm SPlb WFar
	- 'Mary Belle Frey'	CEnt EBee LRHS
	- 'Montrose Tricolor' (v)	EPPr NBre NBro
	- 'Pink Ridge'	LRHS MNrw NBir
	- 'Purpurea'	CWCL EBee EPPr EPfP LEdu LSou MMuc SGSe
	- variegated (v)	GKir
	- 'Violet Vere'	GBuc
	subulata 'Alexander's Surprise'	CMea ECho ECtt EDAr EPfP EPot LBee LRHS NBir SPlb SRGP
	- 'Amazing Grace'	CTri CWCL ECho EDAr EPfP EWes GKir LAst LHop LRHS MHer NLar SIng SPoG WAbe
	- 'Apple Blossom'	EDAr LRHS NPro SPet SPoG SRms WFar
	- 'Atropurpurea'	EDAr LIMB LRHS SPoG
	- Beauty of Ronsdorf	see *P. subulata* 'Ronsdorfer Schöne'
	- 'Betty'	ECtt
	- 'Blue Eyes'	see *P. subulata* 'Oakington Blue Eyes'
	- 'Bonita'	EAlp ECho ECtt EPot GJos GKir LRHS MMuc MWte
	- 'Bressingham Blue Eyes'	see *P. subulata* 'Oakington Blue Eyes'
	- 'Brightness'	ECho LRHS
	- 'Brilliant'	ECho SIng
	- subsp. ***brittonii*** 'Rosea'	GEdr
	- 'Candy Stripe'	see *P. subulata* 'Tamaongalei'
	- 'Cavaldes White'	SPoG
	- 'Drumm'	see *P. subulata* 'Tamaongalei'
	- 'Emerald Cushion'	CSam CTri CWCL ECho ECtt EDAr ELon GEdr GKir LRHS MDKP MWat NCGa WBVN
	- 'Emerald Cushion Blue'	CPLG EAlp ECho EPfP GJos LIMB LRHS NBir NMen NPri NPro SGar SPlb SPoG WAbe WClo WFar WPer
	- 'Fairy'	WPer
	- 'G.F. Wilson'	see *P. subulata* 'Lilacina'
*	- 'Holly'	ECtt EPot LLHF NHol NMen
	- 'Jupiter'	ECho
	- 'Kimono'	see *P. subulata* 'Tamaongalei'
§	- 'Lilacina'	CMea ECho ECtt GEdr GMaP LRHS MWat NLar
§	- 'Maischnee'	CMea CTri ECho ECtt EPfP LRHS MWat NHol SIng SPlb WFar
	- 'Marjorie'	ECho ECtt GEdr GJos LBee LRHS MAsh MHer NBir NWCA SIng SPoG SRGP WFar
	- May Snow	see *P. subulata* 'Maischnee'
§	- 'McDaniel's Cushion' ♀[H4]	Widely available
	- 'Mikado'	see *P. subulata* 'Tamaongalei'
	- 'Moonlight'	ECtt EDAr GJos WCom
	- 'Nettleton Variation' (v)	EAlp ECho EDAr EPPr EPfP EWes GKev GKir LHop LRHS MDKP MHer NBlu SIng SPlb SPoG SRot WBrE
§	- 'Oakington Blue Eyes'	GKir LRHS SRms
	- 'Pink Pearl'	EWes
	- 'Purple Beauty'	CMea CWCL EPot GGar GJos LIMB LLHF MWte SPoG WFar WSHC
	- 'Red Wings' ♀[H4]	ECho ECtt EPfP GKir LRHS NMen SIng SRms
§	- 'Ronsdorfer Schöne'	EPot LBee LLHF LRHS NBir
	- 'Samson'	LSRN MMuc
	- 'Sarah'	LLHF
	- 'Scarlet Flame'	CMea CSam ECho ECtt EDAr EPfP EPot NHol NPri SRGP WFar
	- 'Schneewittchen'	GKir
	- 'Snow Queen'	see *P. subulata* 'Maischnee'
§	- 'Tamaongalei'	CMea CPBP CTri CWCL ECho EDAr EPfP EPot EWes GGar GJos GKev GKir GMaP LAst LRHS MMuc MSCN NBlu NHol SCoo SIng SPet SPoG SRms STes WCFE WClo
	- 'Temiskaming'	CTri ECho ECtt EDAr EWes GEdr LBee LHop LRHS MLHP NMen SIng SPoG SRms WCom WSHC
	- 'Tschernobyl'	EPot
	- 'White Delight'	EAlp ECho ECtt EDAr EPfP GJos LAst LBee LRHS NBlu NMen SPet SPoG WClo WFar
	- 'Winifred'	NEgg
	- 'Zwergenteppich'	LLHF
	'Sweet William'	NCob NEgg SRGP
	'Swirly Burly' **new**	GQue WHlf
	'Tiny Bugles'	WPat
	'White Kimono' **new**	LRHS

Phoebe (*Lauraceae*)

	sheareri	WPGP

Phoenicaulis (*Brassicaceae*)

§	***cheiranthoides***	LLHF

Phoenix (*Arecaceae*)

	canariensis ♀[H1+3]	CBcs CPLG CTrC CTrG CWSG CWib EAmu EBee EPfP GAuc LPJP LPal LRHS MBri MCCP MREP NBlu NMoo SAPC SArc SBch SBst SEND SLim SPlb SPoG STrG WFar
	dactylifera (F)	CDTJ EAmu ETod LPal SBig
	reclinata	EAmu LPJP NPal XBlo
	roebelenii ♀[H1+3]	CBrP CDTJ CDoC CTsd EGxp LPal LRHS MBri SBig SMad
	- 'Multistem'	XBlo
	rupicola	EAmu LPal
	sylvestris	EAmu LPal
	theophrasti	CPHo EAmu LEdu LPJP LPal

Phormium ✿ (*Phormiaceae*)

§	'Alison Blackman'[PBR]	CAlb CBcs CBct CDoC CKno CSBt CTrC CWit EBee ESwi IBlr LHop LRHS LSRN MCCP MGos MREP

	Name	Suppliers
		MRav NBlu NScw NWsh SBch SCoo SPoG SWvt WClo
	'Amazing Red'	CTrC EBee ESwi IBal IBlr
	'Apricot Queen' (v)	Widely available
	Ballyrogan variegated (v)	IBlr
	'Black Edge'	IBlr MRav
	Black Velvet = 'Seivel' **new**	WClo
	'Bronze Baby'	Widely available
	'Buckland Ruby'	CBct CDoC
	'Carousel'	CTrC ESwi IBal
	'Chocolate Fingers'	CBcs WCot
	colensoi	see *P. cookianum*
§	***cookianum***	CHEx CTrC ECre EPfP GGar GKev GKir IBlr MGos SAPC SArc SCoo SEND WFar
	- 'Alpinum Purpureum'	see *P. tenax* 'Nanum Purpureum'
	- 'Black Adder' **new**	LRHS
	- dwarf	IBlr SLPl
	- 'Flamingo' (v)	CAlb CBcs CCCN CDTJ CSBt CTrC EBee ECre ELan ELon EPfP ESwi GKir IBal LRHS LSou MAsh MGos NPri SBch SLim SPer SPoG SRkn WCFE WCot WPat
	- 'Golden Wonder'	IBlr
	- subsp. ***hookeri*** 'Cream Delight' (v) ♀H3-4	Widely available
	- - 'Tricolor' (v) ♀H3-4	Widely available
	'Copper Beauty'	NMoo WDyG
	'Crimson Devil'	CBcs CTrC GGar IBal MREP SBch
	'Dark Delight'	CBcs CDoC IBlr LRHS
	'Dazzler' (v)	CBcs CDoC GKir IBlr LSou WCot
	'Duet' (v) ♀H3	CCCN CDoC CSBt CTrC CWib EBee EHoe ELon EPfP ESwi IBlr LHop LRHS MGos MREP SWvt
	'Dusky Chief'	CSBt CTrC ESwi IBal LRHS
	'Dusky Prince' **new**	LRHS
	'Dusky Princess'	ESwi LRHS
	'Emerald Isle'	CDoC
	'Evening Glow' (v)	CBcs CCCN CSBt CTrC EBee ELan EPfP EPla ESwi ETod GKir IBlr LFCN LRHS LSRN MAsh MBri MGos MREP NPri SPoG SRkn SWvt WCot WGrn WPat
	'Firebird'	ESwi IBlr LSRN SAga SWvt
	'Glowing Embers'	CTrC ELon ESwi IBal WGrn
	'Gold Ray'	CTrC ELon ESwi IBal IBlr LRHS MREP NLar SBch WGrn
	'Gold Sword' (v)	CBcs CCCN CDoC CMHG CSBt CTrC EBee EPfP ESwi IBal IBlr LRHS MAsh MBri MGos NEgg SBch
	'Golden Alison' PBR	see *P.* 'Alison Blackman'
	'Green Sword'	CCCN
	'Guardsman' (v)	IBlr
	'Jack Spratt' (v)	ECou EHoe ELan IBal SWvt WPrP
	'Jester' (v)	Widely available
	'Limelight'	SBch SWvt
§	'Maori Chief'	CSBt ELan EPfP ESwi LOck MAsh NMoo SWvt WFar WGrn WPat
§	'Maori Maiden' (v)	CAlb CBcs CCCN CChe CDoC CDul CTrC CTri EBee ECre EHoe EPfP ESwi ISea LAst MBri MGos MRav SBch SRkn SWvt WFar
§	'Maori Queen' (v)	CBcs CCCN CChe CDTJ CDoC CSBt CTrC EBee ELan EPfP ESwi IBlr LRHS MBri MGos MSwo NMoo NPri SBch SCoo SEND SPer SPoG SRkn SWvt WCot WFar WPGP
§	'Maori Sunrise' (v)	CBcs CCCN CDoC CKno CTrC EBee EPfP ESwi GKir IArd IBlr LAst LRHS LSRN MAsh MBrN MGos MRav NBlu NPri NScw SBch SCoo SEND SLim SPer SWvt WFar
	'Margaret Jones' PBR	CBcs CBct CCCN CTrC CWit EBee LSRN SLim
	'Merlot' PBR	EGxp LRHS
	'Peter Pan' **new**	NPri
	'Pink Panther' (v)	Widely available
	'Pink Stripe' (v)	CBcs CDoC CSBt EBee ECrN EQua ESwi IBlr LRHS MBri MGos NPal NPri SBch SPoG SWvt WCot
	'Platt's Black'	Widely available
	'Rainbow Chief'	see *P.* 'Maori Chief'
	'Rainbow Maiden'	see *P.* 'Maori Maiden'
	'Rainbow Queen'	see *P.* 'Maori Queen'
	'Rainbow Sunrise'	see *P.* 'Maori Sunrise'
	'Red Sensation'	EPfP LRHS MAsh WClo
I	'Rubrum'	CTrC ESwi GKir IBal LRHS
	'Stormy Dawn'	WCot
	'Sundowner' (v) ♀H3	Widely available
	'Sunset' (v)	CBcs CCCN CChe CSBt IBlr IFoB LAst SWvt WCot
	'Surfer' (v)	CBcs EHoe LHop MCCP WGrn
	'Surfer Boy'	LAst SPur
	'Surfer Bronze'	CCCN CSBt ETod IBal LSou MGos
	'Surfer Green'	CCCN CTsd ESwi IBal MGos WHer
	'Sussex Velvet' **new**	SCoo
	tenax ♀H4	Widely available
	- 'All Black' **new**	LRHS
	- 'Atropurpureum'	CEnt CHEx GKir LAst
	- 'Bronze'	CHEx SWal SWvt
	- 'Chocolate Dream' **new**	EPfP
	- 'Co-ordination'	CCCN EBee EPfP IBlr ISea
	- 'Deep Purple'	CHEx
*	- dwarf	IBlr SLPl
I	- 'Giganteum'	CHEx
*	- ***lineatum***	MMuc SEND
§	- 'Nanum Purpureum'	EHoe MMuc SEND
	- Purpureum Group ♀H3-4	Widely available
	- 'Radiance' (v)	IBlr
	- Sweet Mist = 'Phos2'	LBMP MAvo
	- 'Variegatum' (v) ♀H3-4	CDTJ CSBt CTrC EBee ELon EPfP ETod IBal IBlr LPal LRHS MGos MMuc NBlu NMoo SAPC SArc SBch SEND SPer SRms WBrE WFar WHoo
	- 'Veitchianum' (v)	IBlr LRHS SPer
	'Thumbelina'	CBcs CCCN ESwi IFoB LRHS MAsh WPat
	'Tom Thumb'	GGar SHGN WDin WPrP
	'Wings of Gold'	ESwi ETod IBal LRHS
	'Yellow Wave' (v) ♀H3	Widely available

Photinia ✿ (*Rosaceae*)

	Name	Suppliers
	arbutifolia	see *Heteromeles salicifolia*
	beauverdiana	CTho GKir SRms
	- var. ***notabilis***	EPfP MBri NLar
§	'Branpara' PBR	CTrC LRHS LSou WHar
	davidiana	CDul CMac CSam CTri ELan EPfP ISea MRav NLar SPer SRms WDin WFar
	- 'Palette' (v)	Widely available
	- var. ***undulata***	LRHS
	- - 'Fructu Luteo'	CAbP CSam CTrG EPfP EPla GGal MRav NLar WFar
	- - 'Prostrata'	CMac CTri ELan EQua MRav NLar WFar
	× ***fraseri***	CMCN
	- 'Allyn Sprite' PBR	LSou NEgg WClo WHar
I	- 'Atropurpurea Nana' **new**	MGos
	- 'Birmingham'	CMac EBee EWes GKir LRHS SRms WDin
	- 'Canivily'	CTrC EBee EMil EWes MGos NLar SBch SPad SPoG
*	- 'Ilexifolium'	ESwi
	- 'Little Red Robin' **new**	EGxp EShb LRHS MAsh NHol NPal SPoG

- Pink Marble = 'Cassini' (v) **new** — SBch
- 'Purple Peter' — CEnd LRHS
- 'Red Robin' ♀H4 — Widely available
- 'Red Select' — CAlb EQua LRHS MAsh NPri WPat
- 'Robusta' — CMac CTrC EPfP LRHS MAsh SWvt

I - 'Robusta Compacta' — MWea WFar

glabra — SArc

§ - 'Parfait' (v) — CAbP ELan ERas LRHS SPer WFar

- 'Pink Lady' — see *P. glabra* 'Parfait'
- 'Rubens' — ELan EPfP LRHS MAsh MRav SPer SSta WPat
- 'Variegata' — see *P. glabra* 'Parfait'

glomerata misapplied — see *P. prionophylla*

lasiogyna — CMCN

microphylla B&SWJ 11837 — WCru

- HWJ 564 — WCru

parvifolia — EPfP

§ ***prionophylla*** — CHEx GKir

'Redstart' — CAbP CMac EBee EPfP LRHS LSou MGos NEgg NHol NPro SLim SLon SPer SSta SWvt WMoo

§ ***serratifolia*** — CBcs CBot CHEx EBee EPfP GKir LRHS MBri NLar SAPC SArc SPer SPoG SSpi WFar WPGP

I - 'Compacta' **new** — WFar

- 'Jenny' — CTrC LRHS LSou NEgg

serrulata — see *P. serratifolia*

- Curly Fantasy = 'Kolcurl'[PBR] — EBee EMil LRHS MGos MRav NLar SPoG

'Super Hedge'[PBR] — see *P.* 'Branpara'

'Super Red' — CAlb CSBt EBee

villosa ♀H4 — CAbP CGHE CTho EBee GAuc GKir NPal SPoG

- B&SWJ 8665 — WCru
- var. ***laevis*** — CPLG EPfP
- - B&SWJ 8877 — WCru
- f. ***maximowicziana*** — EPfP GAuc

* - var. ***zollingeri*** B&SWJ 8903 — WCru

Phragmites (*Poaceae*)

from Sichuan, China — EPPr

§ ***australis*** — CBen CRWN CWat EBWF EMFW GFor LPBA MSKA NMir SVic SWat WMAq WPnP

- subsp. ***australis*** var. ***striatopictus*** — EPPr
- - 'Variegatus' (v) — CBen CKno CWCL CWat EBee ECGP EHoe EMFW EPPr EPla EShb LLWG LPBA LRHS MMoz MWhi NBir NWsh SMad WFar WWEG
- subsp. ***pseudodonax*** — EPPr

communis — see *P. australis*

karka — EPPr

- 'Candy Stripe' (v) — CBen EPPr MSKA
- 'Variegatus' (v) — NLar

Phuopsis (*Rubiaceae*)

§ ***stylosa*** — CHrt CSev CTri EBee ECha ELan ELon EPfP GAbr GMaP IFoB LBMP LRHS MHer MLHP NBid NBir NBro NChi SPoG SRms WCAu WCom WFar WMoo WPer

- 'Purpurea' — CElw EBee MNrw MRav NChi WCom

Phygelius ✿ (*Scrophulariaceae*)

aequalis — CFee MNrw MRav WMoo WPer

- ***albus*** — see *P. aequalis* 'Yellow Trumpet'
- 'Apricot Trumpet' — GKir
- 'Aureus' — see *P. aequalis* 'Yellow Trumpet'
- Cedric Morris form — SHom
- 'Cream Trumpet' — see *P. aequalis* 'Yellow Trumpet'
- 'Indian Chief' — see *P.* × *rectus* 'African Queen'
- 'Pink Trumpet' — EAro LRHS SCoo SMrm SPet
- 'Sani Pass' — CBcs CPom ECtt EPfP GMaP LSRN MBri MRav SCoo SHom SPer SPet SPlb SPoG SRms SWvt WSpi
- 'Trewidden Pink' ♀H4 — CChe CWib EBee ELan ELon EPfP LAst LRHS MHer MSCN NGdn SBch SGSe SHom SLim SWal SWvt WHoo WMnd WMoo WPGP WWEG

§ - 'Yellow Trumpet' ♀H3-4 — Widely available

Candy Drops Series **new** — LRHS

§ ***capensis*** ♀H3-4 — CDul CWib ELan EPfP GCra GGal MHer NLar SBch SGar SHom SPet SRms SUsu WFar WMnd WPer

- ***coccineus*** — see *P. capensis*
- orange-flowered — LHop SHom

Cherry Ripe = 'Blacher'[PBR] — LRHS LSou MBri

'Golden Gate' — see *P. aequalis* 'Yellow Trumpet'

'Madame Aerts' — WSHC

'Midas Touch' **new** — CBow NPri

New Sensation = 'Blaphy'[PBR] — LRHS MAsh SPoG SWvt WCot

§ × ***rectus*** — CFee CHrt EBee ECrN ECtt ELan

'African Queen' ♀H3-4 — EPfP GKir MLHP MRav MSwo NBir NBlu NGdn NHol SHom SMad SPlb SWvt WFar WKif WMnd WMoo WPer WWEG

- 'Aylesham's Pride' — SHom
- 'Devil's Tears' ♀H4 — CBcs CFee EBee ELan EPfP GKir LAst LRHS MBri MCot NEgg NHol SBch SGSe SHom SLim SPad SRot SWvt WMnd WMoo WPGP WPer
- 'Ivory Twist'[PBR] — LBuc LRHS SHom SPer
- 'Jodie Southon' — LSou SHom SUsu

* - 'Logan's Pink' — LSRN

- 'Moonraker' — CHrt CTri EBee ECtt ELan EPfP GBuc LAst LHop LRHS MBri MHer MRav MWat NEgg NGdn NLar SBch SGSe SHom SPlb SPoG SRms SRot WFar WKif WMoo WPGP
- 'Pink Elf' — ELan
- 'Raspberry Swirl'[PBR] — ELon EPfP LBuc LRHS SHom
- 'Salmon Leap' ♀H4 — CBcs CTri EBee ELan EPfP GKir LAst LRHS LSRN MBNS MBri MRav NEgg SBch SHom SLim SMrm SPad SPlb SRot SWal SWvt WFar WHoo WMnd WMoo WPer WWEG
- Somerford Funfair Apricot = 'Yapapr' — MAsh SWvt
- Somerford Funfair Coral = 'Yapcor'[PBR] — CDoC EAEE EBee GKev MAsh MBri NEgg NLar SIng SLim SPav SRkn SWvt WFar
- Somerford Funfair Cream = 'Yapcre'[PBR] — CDoC EBee EPfP LBMP LRHS MAsh NEgg NLar NPri SGSe SGar SIng SLim SPav SRkn SWvt WFar
- Somerford Funfair Orange = 'Yapor'[PBR] — EBee LBMP LRHS MAsh MBri NLar NPri SGSe SIng SLim SPav SPoG SWvt WFar
- Somerford Funfair Wine = 'Yapwin' — EBee ELan EPfP EShb GJos LHop LRHS LSou MAsh MBNS MBri NEgg NLar NPri SBch SGSe SGar SIng SLim SMrm SPav SPoG SRkn SWvt WFar
- Somerford Funfair Yellow = 'Yapyel'[PBR] — EBee LRHS MAsh MHav SLim SPoG SWvt
- 'Sunshine' — EBee ELan LRHS MDKP SHom SMrm WCom
- 'Sweet Dreams'[PBR] — LBuc LRHS SHom

§ - 'Winchester Fanfare' — CSBt EBee ECtt ELan EPfP GKir GMaP LRHS MRav MWat NGdn

	NHol NVic SLim SMrm SPer SWvt WFar WGwG WMoo WPer WWEG
- 'Winton Fanfare'	see *P.* × *rectus* 'Winchester Fanfare'
'Rory' **new**	LRHS

Phyla (*Verbenaceae*)

lanceolata	LLWG
§ ***nodiflora***	CEls CStu ECha NWCA SEND SIng WPer
§ - var. ***canescens***	WHal

Phylica (*Rhamnaceae*)

arborea 'Superba'	CBcs

Phyllanthus (*Euphorbiaceae*)

glaucus	MBri

× *Phylliopsis* (*Ericaceae*)

'Coppelia' ♀H4	GEdr GKev ITim WAbe
hillieri 'Askival'	WAbe
- 'Pinocchio'	GKir ITim WAbe WPat WThu
'Hobgoblin'	WAbe
'Mermaid'	ITim WThu
'Sprite'	WPat
'Sugar Plum'	CCCN CWSG EBee ITim LRHS NDlv NLar SSta SWvt WAbe WThu

Phyllitis see *Asplenium*

scolopendrium	see *Asplenium scolopendrium*

Phyllocladus (*Phyllocladaceae*)

alpinus	CBcs CDoC CDul ECou NLar
aspleniifolius	IDee

Phyllodoce (*Ericaceae*)

aleutica	ECho NMen SRms WThu
× ***alpina***	GKir
caerulea ♀H4	ECho NLar
- ***japonica***	see *P. nipponica*
* - var. ***japonica***	GKir WThu
- 'W.M. Buchanan's Peach Seedling'	GKir
empetriformis	ECho GKir MBar SRms WThu
× ***intermedia*** 'Fred Stoker'	GKir
§ ***nipponica*** ♀H4	NMen
- var. ***oblongo-ovata***	NMen
tsugifolia	NLar

Phyllostachys ✿ (*Poaceae*)

angusta	EPla MWht SBig WJun
arcana	EPla GKir WJun
- 'Luteosulcata'	CEnt CGHE EPla GBin LRHS MMoz MMuc MWht NLar NPal WJun WPGP
§ ***atrovaginata***	EPla ERod WJun
aurea ♀H4	Widely available
- 'Albovariegata' (v)	CDTJ ENBC EPla MREP WJun
- 'Flavescens Inversa'	EPla ERod MWht WJun
- 'Holochrysa'	CBrP CDTJ EPla ERod MWht WJun WPGP
- 'Koi'	CDTJ CEnt CGHE EPla ERod LPal LRHS MMoz MWht NMoo NPal SBig SEND WJun WPGP
aureocaulis	see *P. aureosulcata* f. *aureocaulis*, *P. vivax* f. *aureocaulis*
aureosulcata	CWib EBee EMui ENBC EPfP EPla ERod GKir LEdu LRHS MAsh MMoz MWht NMoo WBVN WJun WMoo
- f. ***alata***	see *P. aureosulcata* f. *pekinensis*
- 'Argus'	EPla
§ - f. ***aureocaulis*** ♀H4	Widely available
- 'Harbin'	EPla ERod
- 'Harbin Inversa'	CDTJ EPla ERod
- 'Lama Tempel'	CDTJ EPla WPGP
§ - f. ***pekinensis***	CMCo EPla MMoz NLar SBig SPer WPGP
- f. ***spectabilis*** ♀H4	Widely available
bambusoides	CDTJ EPla GKir SBig SDix WJun
- 'Albovariegata' (v)	EPla
- 'Allgold'	see *P. bambusoides* 'Holochrysa'
- 'Castilloni Inversa'	CGHE EAmu EPla ERod ETod EWes LEdu LPal MMoz MWht WJun WPGP
- 'Castillonii'	CBcs EAmu EBee ENBC EPla ERod EWes GKir LEdu LPal MMoz MWht NMoo NPal SAPC SArc SBig SDix SEND WJun WPGP
- 'Castillonis Inversa Variegata' (v) **new**	WJun
§ - 'Holochrysa'	CDTJ CDoC CEnt EPla ERod MGos MMoz MMuc MWht NMoo NPal SEND WJun WPGP
- 'Katashibo'	EPla
- 'Kawadana' (v)	EPla ERod WJun
- f. ***lacrima-deae***	CAgr CDTJ CTrC EBee EPfP EPla ETod GBin IMou
- 'Marliacea'	EPla ERod LPJP SBig WJun
- 'Subvariegata'	EPla WPGP
- 'Sulphurea'	see *P. bambusoides* 'Holochrysa'
- 'Tanakae'	CDTJ ENBC MMoz NLar NMoo SBig WPGP
- 'Violascens'	EPla NMoo SBig
bissetii	CAbb CAgr CBcs CDoC CEnt CMCo EAmu EBee ENBC EPfP EPla ERod GKir LPal LRHS MAsh MAvo MBrN MBri MCCP MGos MMoz MSwo MWht NMoo NWsh SPer WBVN WJun WPGP
circumpilis	EPla
congesta misapplied	see *P. atrovaginata*
decora	EBee ENBC EPla ERod LRHS MMoz MMuc MWht NLar NMoo NPal SEND WJun WPGP
dulcis	CEnt EPfP EPla ERod LEdu LPJP MWht SBig WDyG WJun WPGP
§ ***edulis***	CAgr CDTJ CTrC EPla ERod MMoz MWht SBig WJun WPGP
- 'Bicolor'	WJun
§ - 'Heterocycla'	XBlo
- f. ***pubescens***	see *P. edulis*
fimbriligula	EPla WJun
flexuosa	CEnt EPla GKir IMGH LRHS MWht WJun WPGP
glauca	CDTJ EPla ERod ETod LRHS MMoz MWht NLar NMoo NPal SBig WDyG
- f. ***yunzhu***	EPla ERod MWht WJun
heteroclada	CAgr CDTJ CEnt NMoo WJun
- 'Solid Stem' misapplied	see *P. purpurata* 'Straight Stem'
heterocycla	see *P. edulis* 'Heterocycla'
- f. ***pubescens***	see *P. edulis*
humilis	CBcs CDul CEnt EBee ENBC EPla ERod LRHS MCCP MGos MMoz MMuc MWhi MWht NLar NMoo NPal SBig WJun
incarnata **new**	WJun
iridescens	EPla NLar SBig WJun
kwangsiensis	EPla
lithophila	EPla
lofushanensis	EPla
makinoi	ERod
mannii	EPla MWht
meyeri	EPla LRHS
nidularia	EPla ERod MMoz SBig WJun
- f. ***farcta***	EPla

nigella	EPla
nigra ♀H4	Widely available
- 'Boryana'	CDoC CEnt CGHE EAmu EBee EPfP EPla GKir MGos MMoz MMuc MWht NMoo SBig SEND SWvt WFar WJun WMoo WPGP
- 'Fulva'	EPla
- 'Hale'	EPla MWht
- f. ***henonis*** ♀H4	EAmu EBee ENBC EPla ERod LPal LRHS MMoz MMuc MWht NLar NMoo SBig SEND WDyG WJun WPGP
- 'Megurochiku'	ENBC EPla ERod MWht WJun
- f. ***nigra***	EPla SPer
- f. ***punctata***	CDoC EBee ENBC EPfP EPla ERod MAvo MMuc MWht NGdn SEND WDyG WJun WMoo WPGP
- 'Tosaensis'	EPla
- 'Wisley'	EPla
nuda	EAmu EPla ERod GKir MMoz MWht NLar NPal NWsh WJun
- f. ***localis***	EPla MWht
parvifolia	CEnt EPla ERod MWht WJun WPGP
platyglossa	EPla ERod WPGP
praecox	EPla ETod NMoo WJun
- f. ***notata***	EPla
- f. ***viridisulcata***	EAmu EPla WJun
prominens	EPla
propinqua	CDoC CDul ENBC EPla ERod GBin LEdu MMoz MMuc MWht NMoo WJun
- 'Li Yu Gan'	EPla
* ***pubescens*** 'Mazel'	SPlb
§ ***purpurata*** 'Straight Stem'	EPla MWht
rubicunda	EPla WJun
rubromarginata	CDTJ CEnt EPla ERod LRHS MMuc MWht NLar WJun WPGP
'Shanghai 3'	EAmu ETod
stimulosa	EPla ERod MWht WJun
sulphurea	CDTJ GKir NMoo
- 'Houzeau'	EPla ERod
- 'Mitis'	LMaj
- 'Robert Young'	EPla
§ - f. ***sulphurea*** **new**	WJun
- 'Sulphurea'	see *P. sulphurea* f. *sulphurea*
§ - f. ***viridis***	EPla ERod MAsh MWht NMoo SBig
violascens	CBcs CEnt EPla ERod MMoz MWht SBig WJun WPGP
virella	EPla
viridiglaucescens	CBcs CDTJ EPfP EPla ETod GKir LRHS MAvo MBrN MMoz MMuc MWht NLar SBig SEND WJun
viridis	see *P. sulphurea* f. *viridis*
vivax	EPfP EPla ERod GKir GQui LEdu MMoz MREP MWht NLar SBig SEND WJun
§ - f. ***aureocaulis*** ♀H4	Widely available
- - 'Huanwenzii'	CDTJ CGHE CTrC EAmu EMui ENBC EPla ERod ETod MGos MMoz MWht NMoo NScw WJun
- 'Katrin'	LEdu
* - 'Sulphurea'	EPla XBlo

× *Phyllothamnus* (*Ericaceae*)

erectus	WAbe

Phymatosorus (*Polypodiaceae*)

§ ***diversifolius***	CGHE WPGP

Phymosia (*Malvaceae*)

§ ***umbellata***	CBot CRHN ERea

Phyodina see *Callisia*

Physalis (*Solanaceae*)

alkekengi ♀H4	CTri EBee EPfP GKir NBir NLar SWvt WFar
- var. ***franchetii***	CArn CMac CSBt EBee ECha ELan EPfP LAst LRHS MHer MWat NBir NBro NEgg NPri NVic SBch SPer SPoG SRms WCAu WClo WFar WMnd WOld WPer WTin
- - dwarf	LRHS NLar SPoG
- - 'Gigantea'	ECGP GBuc LRHS MNHC NChi NGBl NLar SPad SPlb WHil
- - 'Gnome'	see *P. alkekengi* var. *franchetii* 'Zwerg'
- - 'Variegata' (v)	ECtt EPla EWes LEdu MAvo NPro SEND WOld
§ - - 'Zwerg'	LRHS MBri
angulata B&SWJ 7016	LLHF WCru
campanula	EWld
- B&SWJ 10409	EWld WCru
edulis	see *P. peruviana*
§ ***peruviana*** (F)	CBod CCCN SBch SHDw SVic

Physaria (*Brassicaceae*)

didymocarpa	GKev

Physocarpus (*Rosaceae*)

malvaceus	EWes
monogynus	NLar
opulifolius	CDul IFFs
- 'Dart's Gold' ♀H4	Widely available
- 'Diablo d'Or'	CAlb CDoC EBee EMil LBuc LRHS MAsh NEgg NScw
- 'Diabolo' PBR ♀H4	Widely available
- Lady in Red = 'Tuilad' PBR	CMac CSBt EBee EWes LAst LHop LRHS LSqu MAsh MWea NHol SHar SLon SPoG
§ - 'Luteus'	CBot CDoC CSam CWib ISea MBar MRav SRms WDin WFar WMoo WPat
- 'Nugget' **new**	SGol
§ - 'Seward' PBR	EPfP MAsh MGos
- Summer Wine PBR	see *P. opulifolius* 'Seward'
- 'Tilden Park'	EBee
ribesifolius 'Aureus'	see *P. opulifolius* 'Luteus'

Physochlaina (*Solanaceae*)

orientalis	CAby EPPr WAul

Physoplexis (*Campanulaceae*)

§ ***comosa*** ♀H2-3	ECho EPot ITim NMen NSla

Physostegia (*Lamiaceae*)

angustifolia	NBre
§ ***virginiana***	CSBt CTri GBar GKir GMaP LHop LRHS MBNS SBch SGar SPoG SWat WBrk WFar WRHF
- 'Alba'	CBot CEnt COIW CSBt CTri EHrv EPfP EShb GAbr GBar GJos GMaP LEdu LRHS NBPC NChi NLar NOrc SMrm SPet SPlb WClo WHrl
§ - 'Crown of Snow'	CFir CMMP EBee ECtt GKir LRHS MBNS MHer MRav MSCN MWat NPri SBch SPoG SWal SWvt WFar WHil WPer
- 'Grandiflora'	CFir
- 'Miss Manners'	EAEE EBee ECtt LRHS MBNS MBri MCot NBre NCGa NCob SPer SRGP SUsu WCAu WHil
- 'Olympic Gold' (v)	LRHS MDKP MRav

	- 'Red Beauty'	EBee MDKP
	- 'Rose Crown'	LRHS
	- 'Rose Queen'	COIW CTri MWat NBre NChi WTin
	- 'Rosea'	CBot EBee GJos IFoB MDKP MMuc NBPC NBre SPoG SWal SWvt WClo WFar WHrl WPer WWEG
	- Schneekrone	see *P. virginiana* 'Crown of Snow'
	- 'Snow Queen'	see *P. virginiana* 'Summer Snow'
	- var. ***speciosa***	WFar
§	- - 'Bouquet Rose'	CPrp EBee ECha EHrv EPfP GKir LEdu LRHS MCot MNFA MRav NBir NHol SPer SWvt WAul WCAu WFar WGwG WMoo WWEG
	- - Rose Bouquet	see *P. virginiana* var. *speciosa* 'Bouquet Rose'
	- - 'Variegata' (v)	Widely available
§	- 'Summer Snow' ♀H4	CBcs CPrp EBee ECha ELan EPfP GKir LHop LRHS MBri NHol SRms SWat WBrk WCAu WCot WFar WMnd
	- 'Summer Spire'	EBee EHrv ELan LRHS NHol WFar
	- 'Vivid' ♀H4	Widely available
	- 'Wassenhove'	SMrm

Phyteuma (*Campanulaceae*)

	balbisii	see *P. cordatum*
	comosum	see *Physoplexis comosa*
§	***cordatum***	GJos
	hemisphaericum	ECho
	humile	EDAr
	nigrum	CEnt EBee ECho LLHF LRHS MNrw NBid WBor WPGP
	orbiculare	EBWF GEdr
	scheuchzeri	CDes CEnt CSpe EBee ECho EPfP EWld GEdr LRHS NOrc NPri NWCA SBch SGSe SGar SMad SRms WHoo WPGP
	sieberi	CPBP
	spicatum	CDes CEnt NBro

Phytolacca (*Phytolaccaceae*)

	acinosa	EWld GPoy NLar SWat WHil
	- HWJ 647	WCru
§	***americana***	CArn COld CSev EBee ELan EPfP GPoy MBNS MCot MHer NLar NMun SIde SMad SRms SWat WAbb WCru WFar WHil WJek WMnd WMoo
	- B&SWJ 8817A	WCru
	- 'Silberstein' (v)	CBct EBee LDai MBNS MHer NLar WCot
	- 'Variegata'	NBir
	bogotensis new	WHil
	clavigera	see *P. polyandra*
	decandra	see *P. americana*
	dioica	CHEx CPLG LEdu
	esculenta	LEdu LHop
	icosandra	EWld
	- B&SWJ 8988	WCru
	- B&SWJ 9033	WCru
	- Purpurascens Group B&SWJ 11251 new	WCru
	japonica B&SWJ 3005	NBid
	- B&SWJ 4897	WCru
	octandra B&SWJ 9514	WCru
	- B&SWJ 10151	WCru
§	***polyandra***	EWld NBid NBro NLar SRms WBor
	rivinoides B&SWJ 10264	WCru
	rugosa B&SWJ 7132	WCru

Piaranthus (*Asclepiadaceae*)

§	***decorus*** subsp. ***cornutus***	CFwr
	geminatus	CFwr
	ruschii	see *P. decorus* subsp. *cornutus*

Picea (*Pinaceae*)

§	***abies***	CCVT CChe CDul CLnd CMac CSBt CTri CWib EHul EMac EPfP GKir IFFs LAst LBuc LRHS MBar MBri MGos MMuc NEgg NWea SCoo SLim SPer SPoG WBVN WDin WEve WMou
	- 'Acrocona'	ECho EHul EOrn GKir MAsh MBar MBlu MBri MGos NLar SCoo WEve
	- 'Archer'	CKen
	- 'Argenteospica' (v)	ECho NHol NPCo
	- 'Aurea'	ECho EOrn MGos NPCo WEve
	- 'Capitata'	CKen MBar NLar
	- 'Ceejay's Gem'	SCoo
	- 'Clanbrassiliana'	CDoC CKen ECho MBar MGos NLar SCoo WEve WFar
	- Compacta Group	ECho LBee LRHS NPCo
I	- 'Congesta'	CKen
	- 'Crippsii'	CKen
I	- 'Cruenta'	CKen
	- 'Cupressina'	CKen
	- 'Diffusa'	CKen MBar NLar SCoo
	- 'Dumpy'	CKen MGos NLar
	- 'Elegans'	MBar
	- 'Ellwangeriana'	NLar WEve
	- 'Excelsa'	see *P. abies*
	- 'Fahndrich'	CKen CMen
	- 'Finedonensis'	MGos NHol NLar WEve
	- 'Formanek'	CDoC CKen CMen ECho NLar
	- 'Four Winds'	CAbP CKen NLar
	- 'Frohburg'	CKen ECho GKir MBar MGos
	- 'Globosa'	ECho MBar
	- 'Globosa Nana'	ECho LAst MGos
	- 'Goldstart'	MGos
	- 'Gregoryana'	CKen CMac ECho IMGH MBar NDlv WAbe
	- 'Heartland Gem'	CKen
	- 'Himfa'	NLar
	- 'Horace Wilson'	CKen CMen
	- 'Humilis'	CKen
	- 'Hystrix'	CMen NHol NLar
	- 'Inversa'	CDul CKen EBrs ECho EHul EOrn GKir LRHS MBar MBlu MGos SLim WEve
	- 'J.W. Daisy's White'	see *P. glauca* 'J.W. Daisy's White'
	- 'Jana'	CKen
	- 'Kral'	CKen
	- 'Little Gem' ♀H4	CDoC CKen CMen ECho EHul EOrn EPla GEdr GKir LBee LRHS MAsh MBar NHol NWea SCoo SLim SPer SPoG WEve WFar
	- 'Marcel'	CKen
	- 'Maxwellii'	EHul MBar
	- 'Mikulasovice'	NLar
	- 'Nana'	MBar
	- 'Nana Compacta'	CKen CMen ECho EHul LAst LBee MBar WFar
	- 'Nidiformis' ♀H4	CDoC CKen CMac CMen CSBt CTri ECho EHul EOrn GKir LAst LRHS MBar NBlu NHol NPCo NWea SCoo SLim SPer SPoG SRms WDin WEve WFar
	- 'Norrkoping'	CKen
	- 'Ohlendorffii'	CKen ECho EHul MBar MGos NLar SCoo
	- 'Pachyphylla'	CKen
	- 'Procumbens'	MBar
	- 'Pumila'	EOrn
	- 'Pumila Nigra'	ECho EHul LRHS MBar MGos SLim SPoG

	Name	Suppliers
	- 'Pusch'	CKen CMen NLar
	- 'Pygmaea'	CKen ECho LRHS MBar MGos NLar
	- 'Reflexa'	ECho EHul IMGH LRHS NHol NPCo WEve
	- 'Remontii'	NWea
	- 'Repens'	ECho LRHS MBar MBlu
	- 'Rydal'	CBcs CDoC CDul CKen MGos NHol NLar NWea WEve
	- 'Saint James'	CKen
	- 'Saint Mary's Broom'	CMen
	- 'Silberkugel' **new**	NLar
	- 'Sonnenberg' **new**	NLar
	- 'Starý Smolivec'	NLar
	- 'Tabuliformis'	MBar
	- 'Tompa'	EMil NLar
	- 'Tufty'	EOrn
	- 'Veitchii' **new**	NHol
	- 'Vermont Gold'	CKen NLar
	- 'Waugh'	MBar
	- Will's Dwarf	see *P. abies* 'Wills Zwerg'
§	- 'Wills Zwerg'	GKir SCoo
	ajanensis	GAuc
§	***alcoquiana*** var. ***alcoquiana***	GKir NWea
I	- 'Prostrata'	MBar
	- var. ***reflexa***	MPkF
	asperata	GKir NWea
	bicolor	see *P. alcoquiana* var. *alcoquiana*
I	- 'Prostrata'	MGos
	brachytyla	GKir
	breweriana ♀H4	Widely available
	- 'Emerald Midget'	NLar
	- 'Kohout's Dwarf'	CKen
	engelmannii	CDul GKir NWea
	- 'Compact'	EBrs GKir
	- subsp. ***engelmannii***	CKen GKir NPCo
	- 'Jasper'	NLar
	glauca	CDul CTri GKir WEve
	- Alberta Blue = 'Haal' PBR	CKen ECho EOrn GKir LRHS MAsh SLim WEve WFar
	- var. ***albertiana*** 'Alberta Globe'	CDoC CSBt ECho EHul EOrn EPla GKir LBee LRHS MAsh MBar MBri MGos NDlv NEgg NHol SCoo SLim SPoG WEve WFar
	- - 'Conica'	CBcs CDoC CMac CSBt ECho EHul EPfP EPla GKev GKir LAst LBee LRHS MAsh MBar MBri MGos NBlu NEgg NHol NWea SLim SPer SPoG STre WCFE WDin WEve WFar
	- - 'Gnome'	CKen WEve
	- - 'Laurin'	CDoC CKen ECho EOrn EPla LBee LRHS MAsh MBar MGos NHol NPCo WEve
	- - 'Tiny'	CKen EOrn MBar NHol WBor WEve WGor
	- 'Arneson's Blue Variegated' (v)	CDoC CKen LRHS MAsh SLim WFar WGor
	- 'Biesenthaler Frühling' **new**	NLar
	- 'Blue Planet'	CKen MGos NLar
	- 'Blue Wonder'	LRHS
	- 'Coerulea'	ECho GKir MBar NPCo
I	- 'Coerulea Nana'	ECho NLar
	- 'Cy's Wonder'	CKen
	- 'Echiniformis' ♀H4	CKen ECho LBee LRHS MBar MBri
	- var. ***glauca***	WEve
	- 'Goldilocks'	CKen
§	- 'J.W. Daisy's White'	CBcs CKen EBrs ECho EMil EOrn EPla GKir LRHS MAsh MGos NEgg NHol NLar SCoo SLim SPer SPoG WBor WEve WFar WGor
I	- 'Julian Potts Monstrosa'	NLar
	- 'Lilliput'	CKen ECho EHul EOrn MBar MBri MGos NLar
§	- 'Nana'	CKen
	- 'Piccolo'	CBcs CKen ECho GKir LRHS MAsh MGos NHol NLar SLim WEve
	- 'Pixie'	CKen WEve
	- 'Rainbow's End' (v)	CKen ECho EMil LRHS MGos NLar SLim WFar
	- 'Sander's Blue'	CKen ECho EOrn EPfP EPla LAst LBee LRHS MBri MGos SLim WEve WFar
	- 'Zuckerhut'	LRHS MBar MBri
	glehnii	GKir
	- 'Sasanosei'	CKen
	- 'Shimezusei'	CKen
	jezoensis	CKen CMen GKir MGos
	- subsp. ***hondoensis***	CMen GKir
	- 'Marianbad'	CKen
	- 'Yatsabusa'	CKen CMen
	koraiensis	GAuc GKir
	kosteri 'Glauca'	see *P. pungens* 'Koster'
	koyamae	GKir
	likiangensis	CDul EPfP GKir
	- var. ***balfouriana***	see *P. likiangensis* var. *rubescens*
§	- var. ***rubescens***	GKir MGos NHol
	mariana	GGar GKir NWea
	- 'Aureovariegata' (v)	ECho WFar
	- 'Austria Broom'	CKen
	- 'Doumetii'	EOrn
	- 'Fastigiata'	CKen EOrn
	- 'Nana' ♀H4	CDoC CKen CMac CMen ECho EHul EPfP EPot GEdr GKir IMGH LAst LRHS MAsh MBar MMuc MNrw NDlv NHol NWea SCoo SEND SLim SPoG WBrE WDin WEve WFar
I	- 'Pygmaea'	CKen
	× ***mariorika***	MBar
	- 'Gnom'	MGos
	- 'Machala'	ECho MGos
	meyeri	GKir
	morrisonicola	CKen GKir
	obovata	GAuc GKir
	- var. ***coerulea***	GAuc GKir NLar NWea
	omorika ♀H4	CBcs CCVT CDul CMCN EMac GKir IFFs MBar MGos NWea SPer SPoG WCFE WDin WEve WFar WMou
I	- 'Aurea'	ECho
	- 'Bruns'	GKir
	- 'Frohnleiten'	CKen
	- 'Frondenberg'	CKen ECho
	- 'Karel'	CKen MBri NLar
	- 'Minimax'	CKen ECho
	- 'Nana' ♀H4	ECho EHul GKir LRHS MAsh MBar MGos NPCo SCoo SLim SPoG WCFE WEve WFar
	- 'Pendula' ♀H4	CDoC ECho GKir MBar MBlu NLar NPal SLim SPoG SSta WEve
	- 'Pendula Bruns'	SLim
	- 'Peve Tijn'	LRHS MAsh NLar SPoG
	- 'Pimoko'	CKen GKir LRHS MGos NLar NPCo SCoo SLim
	- 'Pygmy'	CKen
	- 'Schneverdingen'	CKen
	- 'Tijn'	CKen SLim
	- 'Treblitsch'	CKen NLar
	orientalis ♀H4	CDul GKir NWea WMou
	- 'Aurea' (v) ♀H4	CMac ECho ECrN EHul ELan EPla GKir LRHS MBar MBri MGos NHol NPri SCoo SLim WDin
	- 'Aureospicata'	CDoC CTho ECho MBlu NPCo SCoo WEve

	- 'Bergman's Gem'	CKen
	- 'Early Gold' (v)	MBri WFar
	- 'Golden Start'	NLar SLim
	- 'Gowdy'	MBar NLar
	- 'Jewel'	CKen NLar
	- 'Kenwith'	CKen ECho
	- 'Mount Vernon'	CKen
	- Nana Group	SCoo
	- Pendula Group	MGos
	- 'Professor Langner'	CKen MAsh SLim
	- 'Skylands'	CDoC CKen ECho ELan GKir MAsh MBri MGos NHol NLar SLim SPoG WEve
	- 'Tom Thumb'	CKen NLar SLim
*	- 'Wittbold Compact'	LRHS
	- 'Wittboldt'	MAsh
	pungens	GKir MBar WDin WEve
	- 'Baby Blueeyes'	ECho WFar
	- 'Blaukissen'	CKen
	- 'Blue Mountain'	ECho LAst NScw
	- 'Blue Pearl'	NLar
	- 'Blue Trinket'	GKir
	- 'Drayer'	ECho
	- 'Edith'	CKen EBrs GKir IFFs LRHS NPCo SLim WFar
	- 'Endtz'	EBrs ECho
	- 'Erich Frahm'	CTri ECho GKir LRHS MAsh MBar MGos SLim WFar
	- 'Fat Albert'	CDul CWib ECho GKir LRHS MGos NEgg NLar NPCo SLim WFar
	- 'Frieda'	LRHS NLar SLim
	- Glauca Group	CDul CLnd CMac EMac GKir MBar NWea SCoo SPoG WBVN WDin WEve WFar WMou
	- - 'Glauca Procumbens'	CMen NLar
§	- - 'Glauca Prostrata'	ECho EHul GKir MBar SLim WEve
	- 'Glauca Globosa'	see *P. pungens* 'Globosa'
	- 'Globe'	CKen CMen GKir
I	- 'Globosa' ♀H4	CBcs CDoC CKen CSBt ECho EHul EOrn EPla GKir LBee LRHS MAsh MBar MBri MGos NPCo NPri NWea SCoo SLim SPer SPoG SRms WEve WFar
I	- 'Globosa Viridis'	ECho
	- 'Gloria'	CKen GKir
	- 'Hoopsii' ♀H4	CDul CSBt ECho EHul EPfP EPla GKir LAst LMaj LRHS MAsh MBar MGos NBlu NEgg NPCo NWea SLim SPoG SWvt WDin WEve WFar
	- 'Hoto'	EHul EOrn GKir MBar MGos
	- 'Iseli Fastigiate'	ECho GKir LRHS MAsh MBri MGos NPCo SCoo SLim SPer SPoG WEve
	- 'Iseli Foxtail'	NLar
§	- 'Koster' ♀H4	CDoC CSBt ECho EHul EPfP GKir LRHS MBar MGos NEgg NScw NWea SLim SPoG SRms WDin WEve WFar
	- 'Koster Fastigiata'	NEgg
	- 'Lucky Strike'	CDoC CKen ECho MGos NLar
	- 'Maigold' (v)	CKen EBrs ECho MAsh NLar SLim
	- 'Moerheimii'	ECho EHul MBar NLar WEve
	- 'Montgomery'	CKen ECho GKir MBar NLar WEve
	- 'Mrs Cesarini'	CKen NLar
	- 'Nimety'	CKen NLar
	- 'Oldenburg'	GKir LAst NEgg NLar NPCo NWea SLim
	- 'Procumbens'	CKen GKir
	- 'Prostrata'	see *P. pungens* 'Glauca Prostrata'
	- 'Prostrate Blue Mist'	WEve
	- 'Rovelli's Monument'	NLar
	- 'Saint Mary's Broom'	CKen NLar NPCo
	- 'Schovenhorst'	ECho EHul WFar
	- 'Snowkiss'	ECho NPCo WFar
	- 'Spek'	ECho GKir MGos
	- 'Thomsen'	ECho EHul GKir LRHS MAsh NScw
	- 'Thuem'	ECho EHul EPfP MGos NDlv NLar NPCo WEve WFar
	- 'Waldbrunn'	CKen ECho LRHS MAsh NLar SPoG WEve
	- 'Wendy'	CKen
	purpurea	GKir WEve
	retroflexa	GAuc NWea
	rubens	NLar NWea WEve
	schrenkiana	CMCN GKir
	sitchensis	CDul GKir IFFs NWea WMou
	- 'Nana'	CDoC ECho
	- 'Papoose'	see *P. sitchensis* 'Tenas'
	- 'Pévé Wiesje' **new**	NLar
	- 'Silberzwerg'	CKen ECho LRHS NLar SLim SPoG
	- 'Strypemonde'	CKen
§	- 'Tenas'	CDoC CKen EBrs ECho EOrn GKir LRHS NLar SLim SPoG
	smithiana	CDul CTho EPfP GKir ISea LRHS NLar NWea WEve
I	- 'Aurea'	MGos
	- 'Sunray'	SLim
	spinulosa	GKir
	wilsonii	CKen GKir NLar

Picrasma (*Simaroubaceae*)

	ailanthoides	see *P. quassioides*
§	***quassioides***	EPfP WPGP

Picris (*Asteraceae*)

	echioides	CArn WHer

Picrorhiza (*Scrophulariaceae*)

	kurrooa	GPoy

Pieris ✿ (*Ericaceae*)

	'Balls of Fire'	CMac
	'Bert Chandler'	CMac LRHS MAsh SPer SPoG SSpi WSpi
	'Brouwer's Beauty'	SLim
	'Firecrest' ♀H4	CMHG CTrG MMuc SSpi
	'Flaming Silver' (v) ♀H4	Widely available
	floribunda	GKir
	'Forest Flame' ♀H4	Widely available
	formosa B&SWJ 2257	WCru
	- var. ***forrestii***	CDoC CWib GLin ISea
	- - 'Jermyns'	CMac MRav
	- - 'Wakehurst' ♀H3	CAbP CDul CMac CTrG CTri CWSG ELon EPfP ISea LHyd LRHS MAsh MGos MRav MSnd SPer SPoG SSpi WFar WSpi
	Havila = 'Mouwsvila' (v)	CMac MGos NHol NLar WFar
	japonica	CMac GGal GKir MGos SArc SReu WDin
	- 'Astrid'	MGos
	- 'Bisbee Dwarf'	MBar NHol
	- 'Blush' ♀H4	GKir MBri MGos NHol
	- 'Bonfire'	CCCN CEnd EBee ELan EMil EQua LRHS MAsh MBri MGos NEgg NLar SBch SPoG
	- 'Brookside Miniature'	NHol
	- 'Carnaval' (v)	CCCN CDoC CEnd CMac CSBt CWib EBee ELan ELon GAbr ISea LBuc LRHS LSRN MAsh MGos NLar NPCo NPri SBch SCoo SPer SPoG SWvt WFar
	- 'Cavatine' ♀H4	CMHG GKir LRHS
§	- 'Christmas Cheer'	CMac EMil EQua GKir LSou MAsh NLar WFar WMoo

	- 'Cupido'	CDoC EMil GKir LRHS MAsh MBar MGos NHol NLar SBch SPoG WFar
	- 'Debutante' ♀H4	CBcs CWSG CWib EBee ELan EMil EPfP GKir IFFs LRHS MAsh MBri MDun MGos NHol NLar NPCo NPri SBch SCoo SPoG SSpi SWvt WFar
	- 'Don'	see *P. japonica* 'Pygmaea'
	- 'Dorothy Wyckoff'	CMHG CTrG CWSG GKir LRHS MDun NDlv NHol SSta
	- 'Flaming Star'	SWvt
	- 'Flamingo'	CMac LRHS MBar MGos NDlv NHol
	- 'Grayswood' ♀H4	EPfP LRHS NHol WFar
I	- 'Katsura'	Widely available
	- 'Little Heath' (v) ♀H4	Widely available
	- 'Little Heath Green' ♀H4	CChe CDoC CMac CSBt CTrG GKir LHyd LRHS MAsh MBar MGos MMuc NDlv NEgg NHol NPCo SBch SPer SPoG SWvt WFar WMoo
	- 'Minor'	MBar NHol WThu
	- 'Mountain Fire' ♀H4	Widely available
	- 'Passion'PBR	CEnd MAsh MGos SBch
	- 'Pink Delight' ♀H4	CAbP CDoC GKir LRHS LSRN LSou MAsh MBar MRav NEgg NMun SBch SRms WGwG
	- 'Prelude' ♀H4	CSBt CTrG CWSG EMil GKev GKir LRHS MAsh MSnd NHol NLar NMen SPad WAbe WFar
	- 'Purity' ♀H4	CBcs CDoC CMHG CMac CWSG GKir LRHS MAsh MBar MGos NEgg NHol SBch SReu SSta SWvt WDin WFar
§	- 'Pygmaea'	CMac GKev NHol SSta
	- 'Red Mill'	CEnd CWSG EPfP GKir LRHS MAsh MHav SPer SSpi WFar
	- 'Rokujo's Dwarf'	WAbe
	- 'Rosalinda'	MGos NLar WFar
	- 'Rosea'	LHyd
	- 'Sarabande' ♀H4	GKir LRHS MAsh MBar MGos NLar SPoG SSta
	- 'Scarlett O'Hara'	CSBt GKir MGos
	- 'Select'	MGos
	- 'Silver Mills'	MGos
	- 'Snowdrift'	LRHS
	- 'Spring Candy'	LRHS NPri
	- 'Spring Snow'	LRHS
	- Taiwanensis Group	CMHG EPfP GGar LRHS MAsh MBar MDun MMuc NLar SBch SRms SSta WFar
	- 'Temple Bells'	CSBt GKir LRHS MGos SBch
	- 'Tickled Pink'	GKir
	- 'Valley Rose'	CGHE CSBt ELan ELon EPfP GKir LLHF LRHS MAsh MGos MHav NLar NMun SPoG SSpi WFar WSpi
	- 'Valley Valentine' ♀H4	CBcs CDoC CDul CEnd CMac CSBt CTrh CWSG CWib EPfP LRHS LSRN MAsh MBri MGos MMuc NBlu NDlv NPCo SBch SCoo SLim SMad SPer SPoG SReu SSta SWvt WFar
	- 'Variegata' misapplied	see *P. japonica* 'White Rim'
	- 'Variegata' ambig.	MMuc
	- 'Variegata' (Carrière) Bean (v)	CMHG EPfP GKir LHyd LRHS MBar MGos MRav NHol SBch SPer SPoG SReu SSta WDin WFar WHar
	- 'Wada's Pink'	see *P. japonica* 'Christmas Cheer'
	- 'White Pearl'	CAbP CMac EPfP MGos
§	- 'White Rim' (v) ♀H4	CDul CMac CSBt EPfP IMon LRHS MAsh NHol SPlb WFar
	- 'William Buchanan'	MBar NHol WThu
	- var. ***yakushimensis***	NLar
	nana	GKir WThu
	'Tilford'	CMac

Pilea (*Urticaceae*)

*	'Anette'	MBri
	cadierei ♀H1	MBri
§	***microphylla***	EBak EShb
	muscosa	see *P. microphylla*
	peperomioides ♀H1	CSev
	repens	MBri

Pileostegia (*Hydrangeaceae*)

sp.	GGal
viburnoides ♀H4	Widely available
- B&SWJ 3565	WCru
- B&SWJ 3570 from Taiwan **new**	WCru
- B&SWJ 7132	WCru

Pilosella (*Asteraceae*)

§	***aurantiaca***	CArn CHrt CRWN CSsd EBWF ELan LEdu LRHS MHer NBid NOrc NPri SECG SGar SIde WCAu WFar WHer WMoo WSFF
§	- subsp. ***carpathicola***	GGar
§	***officinarum***	EBWF NBlu NRya
	× ***stoloniflora*** 'Phil Clark'	WAlt

Pimelea (*Thymelaeaceae*)

	coarctata	see *P. prostrata*
	ferruginea	ECou
	filiformis	ECou
	ligustrina	CTrC GGar
§	***prostrata***	CBcs CTrC CTri ECho ECou EPot LRHS MBar SRot WPer
	- 'Misty Blue' **new**	CTrC
	- f. ***parvifolia***	ECou
	tomentosa	ECou LRHS

Pimpinella (*Apiaceae*)

anisum	CArn SIde SVic
bicknellii	WPGP
flahaultii	EBee
major	EBWF
- 'Rosea'	CBow CDes CHrt CPLG CSpe EBee EDAr GCal GMac LDai LHop LPio LSou MAvo MBel NBPC NCGa NChi NCob NGdn SMrm SUsu WCot WFar WHal WPGP WWFP
saxifraga	NBre

pineapple see *Ananas comosus*

pineapple guava see *Acca sellowiana*

Pinellia (*Araceae*)

	cordata	CPom EBee EWTr LEdu MDKP NMen SChF WCot WCru WWst
	- pink-flowered	GEdr
	pedatisecta	CAby CDes EBee GEdr LFur LPio MDKP SChF WCot WFar
	pinnatisecta	see *P. tripartita*
	ternata	CStu EBee EBrs GEdr LEdu NMen WCot WFar WPnP
	- B&SWJ 3532	WCru
§	***tripartita***	CFee CPLG CStu EBee ECho EPPr LFur MDKP SChF WAbe WCot WPrP
	- B&SWJ 1102	WCru
	- 'Purple Face'	WCru
	- 'Silver Dragon'	GEdr

Pinguicula (*Lentibulariaceae*)

acuminata	SHmp

crassifolia CHew
crassifolia* × *emarginata SHmp
cyclosecta CHew CSWC SHmp
debbertiana SHmp
ehlersiae EFEx
esseriana CSWC EFEx
grandiflora CSWC EECP EFEx GCra GKev MCCP NMen NRya NWCA
hemiepiphytica CHew
heterophylla CHew SHmp
jaumavensis CHew
lauana CHew SHmp
leptoceras CFir
longifolia EFEx
  subsp. ***longifolia***
macrophylla CHew SHmp
macrophylla* × *zecheri SHmp
moctezumae SHmp
moranensis var. ***caudata*** EFEx
- moreana EFEx
- superba EFEx
* ***pilosa*** SHmp
rotundiflora CHew SHmp
'Tina' **new** LRHS
vulgaris EFEx
'Weser' CSWC LRHS NChu

pinkcurrant see *Ribes rubrum* (P)

Pinus ✿ (*Pinaceae*)

albicaulis 'Flinck' CKen
- 'Nana' see *P. albicaulis* 'Noble's Dwarf'
- 'No. 3' CKen
§ - 'Noble's Dwarf' CKen
aristata CDul CLnd CMen EHul EOrn GKir MAsh MBar MGos SCoo SMad STre WDin WEve
- 'Cecilia' CKen
- 'Kohout's Mini' CKen
- 'Sherwood Compact' CKen GKir MAsh NLar
- 'So Tight' CKen
armandii CAgr CDoC CDul CTrC GKev GKir NHim WPGP
- 'Gold Tip' CKen
attenuata GKir
austriaca see *P. nigra* subsp. *nigra*
N ***ayacahuite*** CKen GKir
- F&M 100A WPGP
balfouriana 'Dwarf Form' CKen
banksiana CDul GKir SCoo
- 'Arctis' NLar
- 'Chippewa' CKen ECho
I - 'Compacta' CKen
- 'H.J. Welch' CKen
- 'Manomet' CKen
- 'Neponset' CKen
- 'Schneverdingen' CKen
- 'Schoodic' ECho LRHS NLar SLim SPoG
- 'Uncle Fogy' ECho MGos NLar
- 'Wisconsin' CKen
brutia CDoC
- var. ***eldarica*** GAuc
bungeana CDoC CDul CLnd CMCN CTho EPfP GKir LRHS MBlu SLPl WEve
- 'Diamant' CKen
- 'June's Broom' CKen
canariensis EHul IDee
cembra CAgr CDul CLnd EHul GKir MBar NLar NWea STre WEve
- 'Aurea' see *P. cembra* 'Aureovariegata'
§ - 'Aureovariegata' (v) ECho LRHS NPCo SCoo SPoG WEve
- 'Barnhourie' CKen
- 'Blue Mound' CKen
- 'Chalet' CKen
- 'Compacta Glauca' ECho MBri
- Glauca Group SCoo WEve
* - 'Griffithii' WDin
- 'Inverleith' CKen
- 'Jermyns' CKen
- 'King's Dwarf' CKen
- 'Ortler' CKen
- 'Roughills' CKen
- 'Stricta' CKen ECho
- witches' broom CKen
communis 'Penrhyn' **new** WGwG
contorta CBcs CDoC CDul GKir IFFs MBar MGos NWea SPlb WDin WMou
- 'Asher' CDoC CKen ECho SCoo
I - 'Compacta' SCoo
- 'Frisian Gold' CKen SLim
- var. ***latifolia*** CDul CLnd GKir WDin
- 'Spaan's Dwarf' CKen ECho LRHS MGos NLar SCoo SLim SPoG WEve
coulteri ♀H4 CDul CMCN CTho ECho EPfP GKir LRHS SBig SCoo WThu
densiflora CDul CMCN CMac GAuc
- 'Alice Verkade' CDoC CMen ECho EHul GKir LRHS MAsh MBri NLar SCoo SLim WEve WFar
- 'Aurea' LRHS MBar MGos NLar SLim
- 'Golden Ghost' MAsh NLar SLim
- 'Jane Kluis' CKen ECho EHul EOrn EPla GKir LRHS MBri NHol NLar SCoo SLim WEve WFar
- 'Jim Cross' CKen
- 'Low Glow' CKen ECho EOrn LRHS NLar NPCo SLim
- 'Oculus-draconis' (v) ECho EOrn GKir LRHS MBar MGos NEgg NLar SLim WEve WFar
- 'Pendula' CKen ECho EOrn LRHS NEgg NLar SCoo SLim WEve WFar
I - 'Pygmaea' EOrn
* - 'Pyramidalis' ECho
- 'Umbraculifera' CDoC CMen ECho GKir IMGH LRHS MAsh MBar MGos NLar NPCo SCoo SSta WEve WFar
I - 'Umbraculifera Nana' ECho
§ ***devoniana*** CDoC LRHS SLim
edulis CAgr GAuc
- 'Juno' CKen
elliottii SBig
engelmanii 'Glauca' EBrs WFar
fenzeliana CKen
flexilis CDul NWea
- 'Firmament' ECho LRHS SLim SPoG
- 'Glenmore Dwarf' CKen
- 'Nana' CKen
- 'Tarryall' CKen
- 'Tinby Temple' **new** NLar
- 'Vanderwolf's Pyramid' CDoC MAsh NLar
- WB No 1 CKen
- WB No 2 CKen
gerardiana GAuc GKir
greggii EPfP IDee LRHS
griffithii see *P. wallichiana*
halepensis CDul GAuc
§ ***heldreichii*** ♀H4 CDoC CDul ECho GKir LRHS MBar MGos SCoo WFar
- 'Aureospicata' MBar NLar WEve
- 'Compact Gem' CDoC CKen EBrs ECho LBee MBar MBri MGos NLar SCoo SLim SSta WEve
- 'Dolce Dorme' CKen NLar
- 'Groen' CKen

	Name	Suppliers
	- 'Kalous'	NLar
	- var. ***leucodermis***	see *P. heldreichii*
	- - 'Irish Bell'	NLar
	- - 'Pirin 7'	NLar
	- 'Malink'	CKen ECho LRHS SLim
	- 'Ottocek'	CKen
	- 'Pygmy'	CKen ECho
	- 'Satellit'	CDoC CKen CTri ECho EHul EMil EOrn GKir LRHS MGos NLar NPCo SCoo SLim SPoG WEve
	- 'Schmidtii'	see *P. heldreichii* 'Smidtii'
§	- 'Smidtii' ♀H4	CDoC CKen CMen ECho EOrn GKir LRHS MAsh MBar MGos NLar SLim SPoG WEve
	- 'Zwerg Schneverdingen'	CKen NLar NPCo
	× ***holfordiana*** **new**	CDoC CDul
	jeffreyi ♀H4	CMCN CTho GAuc GKir GLin LRHS NWea
	- 'Joppi'	CKen NLar SLim
	koraiensis	GAuc GKir LRHS MBlu NWea SCoo SLim
	- 'Bergman'	CKen
	- 'Dragon Eye'	CKen
	- 'Jack Corbit'	CKen
	- 'Shibamichi' (v)	CKen
	- 'Silver Lining'	MAsh NPCo
	- 'Silveray'	NLar SLim
	- 'Silvergrey'	CKen
	- 'Winton'	CKen NLar SLim
	leucodermis	see *P. heldreichii*
	'Little Gold Star' **new**	EOrn
	magnifica	see *P. devoniana*
*	***meyerei***	GAuc
	monophylla	ECho
	- 'Tioga Pass' **new**	NLar
	montezumae ambig.	LRHS SAPC SArc
	montezumae Lamb.	SBig
	monticola 'Pendula'	CKen MBar
	- 'Pygmy'	see *P. monticola* 'Raraflora'
§	- 'Raraflora'	CKen
	- 'Skyline'	MBar NLar WEve
	- 'Windsor Dwarf'	CKen
	mugo	CArn CBcs CChe CDul CMac CSBt CTri EHul GKir MBar MGos NWea WBor WBrE WDin WEve WFar
	- 'Allgau'	CKen NLar
	- 'Amber Glow'	MAsh NLar
	- 'Benjamin'	CKen ECho MAsh MGos NLar SCoo
	- 'Bisley Green'	ECho NLar
	- 'Brownie'	CKen
	- 'Carsten'	CKen ECho EOrn LRHS MAsh MGos SCoo SLim WEve
	- 'Carsten's Wintergold'	CDoC EMil GKir LRHS MAsh MBri NLar SCoo SPoG WEve
	- 'Chameleon'	NLar
	- 'Corley's Mat'	CKen ECho GKir LAst LRHS NHol NLar SCoo SLim WEve
	- 'Dachstein 3'	NLar
	- 'Devon Gem'	ECho NPCo
	- 'Dezember Gold'	LRHS NLar SLim
	- 'Flanders Belle'	ECho SCoo SLim SPoG
	- 'Gnom'	CDul ECho EHul EOrn GKir IMGH LRHS MBar MBri MGos NEgg NPCo SCoo WDin WEve WFar
	- 'Gold Star' **new**	CMen SLim
	- 'Golden Glow'	CKen ECho MBri NLar SCoo SLim
	- 'Hesse'	ECho GKir SCoo
	- 'Hoersholm'	CKen ECho
	- 'Hulk' **new**	CKen
	- 'Humpy'	CKen CMen ECho EOrn GKir IMGH LBee LRHS MAsh MBar MBri MGos NPCo SCoo SLim WEve WFar
	- 'Ironsides'	CKen
	- 'Jacobsen'	CKen NLar
	- 'Janovsky'	CKen ECho EOrn SCoo
	- 'Kamila'	NLar
	- 'Kissen'	CKen ECho MGos NLar WEve
	- 'Kleiner Wimbachi' **new**	NHol
	- 'Klosterkotter'	ECho EOrn MGos NLar SCoo WFar
	- 'Kobold'	ECho NEgg NHol WFar
	- 'Krauskopf'	CKen
	- 'Laarheide'	ECho EOrn GKir SCoo WEve
	- 'Laurin'	CKen ECho
	- 'Little Lady'	NLar
	- 'Marand'	ECho
	- 'March'	CKen ECho EHul
	- 'Mini Mops'	CKen ECho NLar WEve
	- 'Minikin'	CKen EOrn MAsh
	- 'Mops' ♀H4	CMac CMen ECho EHul EPfP GKir LBee LRHS MAsh MBar MBlu MBri MGos NHol NPCo NPri NWea SCoo SLim SPer SPoG SSta WDin WEve WFar
	- 'Mops Midget'	CMen ECho EOrn LRHS MAsh NPCo WEve
	- var. ***mughus***	see *P. mugo* subsp. *mugo*
§	- subsp. ***mugo***	EMac EOrn GAuc IFFs MBar NBlu NWea WCFE WFar
	- 'Mumpitz'	CKen
	- 'Ophir'	CBcs CDoC CDul CKen CMen ECho EHul EOrn EPfP EPla GKir IMGH LAst LBee LRHS MBar MBri MGos NLar SCoo SLim SPer SSta WDin WEve WFar
	- 'Orange Sun'	MBri
	- 'Pal Maleter' (v)	ECho GKir LRHS MAsh NLar NPCo SCoo SLim SPoG
	- 'Paradekissen'	NPCo
	- 'Paul's Dwarf'	CKen
	- 'Picobello'	LRHS MAsh NLar SLim
	- 'Piggelmee'	CKen ECho NLar
	- Pumilio Group ♀H4	CDoC CDul CLnd ECho ECrN EHul EOrn IFFs LRHS MBar MGos NBlu NHol NWea SBch SCoo STre WBVN WCFE WDin WFar WMoo
	- 'Pygmy'	ECho
	- var. ***rostrata***	see *P. mugo* subsp. *uncinata*
	- 'Rushmore'	CKen
	- 'Schilderhaus'	NLar
	- 'Spaan'	CKen
	- 'Sunshine' (v)	CKen NLar
	- 'Suzi'	CKen
	- 'Trompenburg' **new**	NPCo
	- 'Tuffet'	ECho MGos NLar
	- 'Uelzen'	CKen NLar
§	- subsp. ***uncinata***	GAuc LMaj LRHS NWea SCoo SLim WFar
	- - 'Grüne Welle'	CKen ECho NLar SLim
	- - 'Paradekissen'	CKen NLar
	- 'Varella'	CKen EOrn LRHS NLar SCoo SLim
	- 'White Tip'	CKen ECho
	- 'Winter Gold'	CKen EBrs ECho EHul EOrn EPfP EPla LAst LRHS MGos NLar NPCo NWea SSta WEve WFar
	- 'Winter Sun'	ECho NLar
	- 'Winzig'	CKen
	- 'Zundert'	CKen ECho EHul GKir MBar MGos NLar WEve
	- 'Zwergkugel'	CKen
	muricata ♀H4	CDoC CDul CLnd GKir MGos NWea
	nigra ♀H4	CBcs CDul CLnd CMac CSBt CTri ECrN GKir LMaj LRHS MBar MGos SBch SCoo WBrE WDin WEve WMou

	- var. ***austriaca***	see *P. nigra* subsp. *nigra*
	- 'Bambino'	CKen
	- 'Black Prince'	CKen EBrs ECho EOrn GKir IMGH LBee LRHS MGos NLar NPCo SCoo SLim SPoG WEve WFar WGor
	- var. ***calabrica***	see *P. nigra* subsp. *laricio*
	- var. ***caramanica***	see *P. nigra* subsp. *pallasiana*
N	- 'Cebennensis Nana'	CKen
	- var. ***corsicana***	see *P. nigra* subsp. *laricio*
*	- 'Fastigiata'	GKir NPCo
	- 'Frank'	CKen ECho NLar
	- 'Globosa'	ECho
	- 'Green Tower'	NLar
	- 'Hornibrookiana'	CKen ECho NLar SCoo
	- 'Komet'	NLar SCoo
§	- subsp. ***laricio*** Υ^{H4}	CCVT CDoC CDul CKen CMac ECrN EMac IFFs LAst LRHS MBar MGos NWea SEND WMou
	- - 'Aurea'	MBlu MBri
	- - 'Bobby McGregor'	CKen ECho GKir
	- - 'Globosa Viridis'	ECho GKir LRHS NEgg NHol NPCo SLim
	- - 'Goldfingers'	CKen ECho LRHS NLar SLim
	- - 'Moseri'	CKen ECho EOrn LRHS SLim SSta
	- - 'Pygmaea'	CKen ECho EOrn WFar
	- - 'Spingarn'	CKen ECho
	- - 'Talland Bay'	CKen ECho
	- - 'Wurstle'	CKen
	- subsp. ***maritima***	see *P. nigra* subsp. *laricio*
	- 'Molette'	GKir
	- 'Nana'	ECrN LRHS MBri
§	- subsp. ***nigra***	CCVT CDoC CLnd CTho ECrN GKir IFFs MGos NLar NWea SBch SPer WFar
	- - 'Birte'	CKen
	- - 'Bright Eyes'	ECho EOrn GKir IMGH LBee LRHS SCoo SLim SPoG WEve
	- - 'Helga'	CKen NLar SCoo
	- - 'Schovenhorst'	CKen ECho
	- - 'Skyborn'	CKen
	- - 'Strypemonde'	CKen NPCo
	- - 'Yaffle Hill'	CKen ECho NLar
	- 'Obelisk'	CKen NLar SCoo
§	- subsp. ***pallasiana***	CDul NLar
	- 'Pierrick Bregeon' PBR	LRHS NLar
	- 'Richard'	CKen NLar
	- 'Rondello'	NLar
	- 'Spielberg'	NLar
	palustris	CDoC CDul CLnd LRHS MAsh SBig SLim
	parviflora	CTri EOrn GKir SPlb WDin WThu
	- 'Adcock's Dwarf' Υ^{H4}	CDoC CKen ECho GKir LRHS MGos NLar NPCo SCoo SLim SPoG WEve
	- Aizu-goyo Group	ECho
	- 'Al Fordham'	CKen
	- 'Aoi'	CKen CMen
	- 'Ara-kawa'	CKen CMen
	- 'Atco-goyo'	CKen
	- Azuma-goyo Group	CKen CMen
I	- 'Baasch's Form'	CKen MGos
	- 'Bergman'	CDoC ECho MAsh NLar
	- 'Blauer Engel'	CDoC ECho MBlu MGos NLar
	- 'Blue Giant'	ECho NLar
	- 'Bonnie Bergman'	CDoC CKen ECho GKir NLar WEve
	- 'Brevifolia'	NLar
	- 'Chikusa Goten' **new**	NLar
I	- 'Contorta'	EOrn
	- 'Dai-ho'	CKen
	- 'Daisetsusan'	CKen
	- 'Doctor Landis Gold'	CKen ECho
	- 'Dougal'	CKen
	- 'Fatsumo'	CKen
	- 'Fukai' (v)	CKen MAsh MGos NHol NLar
	- 'Fukiju'	CKen
	- Fukushima-goyo Group	CKen CMen
	- 'Fuku-zu-mi'	CKen ECho WEve
	- 'Fu-shiro'	CKen
	- 'Gimborn's Ideal' **new**	NLar
	- 'Gin-sho-chuba'	CKen
	- Glauca Group	CDoC ECho EHul LRHS MBar MBlu MBri MGos NPCo NPal STre WEve WFar
I	- 'Glauca Nana'	CKen
	- 'Goldilocks'	CKen ECho GKir NLar
	- 'Green Wave' **new**	CKen
	- 'Gyok-ke-sen'	CKen
	- 'Gyo-ko-haku'	CKen
	- 'Gyokuei'	CKen
	- 'Gyokusen Sämling'	CKen NLar
	- 'Gyo-ku-sui'	CKen CMen ECho
	- 'H2'	CKen
	- 'Hagaromo Seedling'	CKen CMen ECho MAsh NLar
	- 'Hakko'	CKen MGos
	- 'Hatchichi'	CKen
	- 'Hatsumari' **new**	NHol
	- 'Hatsumi'	NHol
	- 'Ibo-can'	CKen CMen
	- 'Ichi-no-se'	CKen
	- 'Iri-fune'	CKen
	- Ishizuchi-goyo Group	CKen
	- 'Ka-ho'	CKen ECho
	- 'Kanrico'	CKen
	- 'Kanzan'	CKen
	- 'Kiyomatsu'	CKen NLar
	- 'Kobe'	CKen ECho NLar WEve
	- 'Kokonoe'	CKen CMen
	- 'Kokuho'	CKen NLar
	- 'Koraku'	CKen
	- 'Kusu-dama'	CKen
	- 'Meiko'	CKen CMen ECho
	- 'Michinoku'	CKen
	- 'Momo-yama'	CKen
	- 'Myo-jo'	CKen
	- Nasu-goyo Group	CKen
	- 'Negishi'	CDoC CKen CMen GKir LRHS MAsh NLar SCoo SLim WEve
	- 'Nellie D.'	NLar
	- 'Ogon-janome'	CKen LRHS SLim SPoG
	- 'Ossorio Dwarf'	CKen
	- 'Regenhold'	CKen
	- 'Richard Lee'	CKen
	- 'Ryo-ku-ho'	CKen
	- 'Ryu-ju'	CKen NLar
	- 'Sa-dai-jin'	CKen
	- 'San-bo'	CKen ECho MGos
§	- 'Saphir'	CKen ECho
	- 'Schoon's Bonsai'	CDoC NLar
	- 'Setsugekka'	CKen
	- 'Shika-shima'	CKen
	- 'Shimada'	CKen
	- Shiobara-goyo Group	CKen
	- 'Shizukagoten'	CKen
	- 'Shu-re'	CKen
	- 'Sieryoden'	CKen
	- 'Smout'	CKen
	- 'Tani-mano-uki'	CKen
	- 'Tempelhof'	CTho GKir LMaj LRHS MAsh MBar NBlu NHol NLar NPCo
	- 'Tenysu-kazu'	CKen
	- 'Tokyo Dwarf'	CKen
I	- 'Torulosa'	LRHS
	- 'Tribune'	NLar
	- 'Venus'	EOrn

	Name	Suppliers
	– 'Walker's Dwarf'	CKen
	– 'Watnong'	CKen
	– 'Zelkova'	CMen ECho
	– 'Zui-sho'	CKen
	patula ♀H2-3	CBcs CCCN CDoC CDul CLnd CMCN GKir LAst LRHS NHim SAPC SArc SBch SBig SCoo SLim SPlb SPoG WEve WPGP
	peuce	GAuc GKir GLin MBar NLar NWea
	– 'Arnold Dwarf'	CKen
	– 'Cesarini'	CKen
	– 'Thessaloniki Broom'	CKen
	pinaster ♀H4	CBcs CDoC CDul CLnd EHul GKir IFFs MMuc
	pinea ♀H4	CAgr CArn CCVT CDoC CDul CKen CLnd CMac CTho ECrN ELau EPfP IFFs LEdu LMaj LRHS MGos NPri SAPC SArc SBch SCoo SEND WEve WPGP
	– 'Queensway'	CKen
	ponderosa ♀H4	CDul CLnd GAuc GKir WEve
	– var. ***scopulorum***	NWea
	pumila 'Buchanan'	CKen ECho
	– 'Draijer's Dwarf'	ECho EOrn GKir LRHS SCoo SLim WEve
	– 'Dwarf Blue'	ECho MAsh
	– 'Glauca' ♀H4	CKen MBar
	– 'Globe'	CDoC ECho LRHS MBri NLar
	– 'Jeddeloh'	CKen
	– 'Knightshayes'	CKen
	– 'Säntis'	CKen ECho
	– 'Saphir'	see *P. parviflora* 'Saphir'
	radiata ♀H3-4	CBcs CCVT CDoC CDul CLnd CSBt CTrC CTri ECrN ELan GKir IFFs LRHS SAPC SArc SBch SCoo SPer STre WDin WEve WFar
	– Aurea Group	CDoC CDul CKen ECho EOrn GKir LRHS MAsh MGos NEgg NPCo SCoo SLim SPoG WBor WEve WFar
	– 'Bodnant'	CKen
	– 'Isca'	CKen ECho
	– 'Marshwood' (v)	CKen ECho LRHS SLim
	resinosa 'Don Smith'	CKen
	– 'Joel's Broom'	CKen
	– 'Nana' **new**	NLar
	– 'Quinobequin'	CKen
	rigida	CMac
	roxburghii	CDoC WPGP
	sabineana	GAuc
	× ***schwerinii***	CDoC ECho MAsh MBri
	– 'Wiethorst'	CKen IArd LRHS NLar SLim SPoG
	sibirica	GKir
	– 'Blue Smoke' **new**	CKen
	– 'Mariko'	CKen
	strobiformis 'Coronado'	CKen
	– 'Loma Linda'	CKen
	strobus	CAlb CBcs CCVT CDul CLnd CMen GKir IFFs LRHS MBar MGos MMuc NWea SLim WDin WEve WFar
§	– 'Alba'	MGos SLim
	– 'Amelia's Dwarf'	CKen
	– 'Anna Fiele'	CKen
	– 'Bergman's Mini'	CKen NLar
	– 'Bergman's Pendula Broom'	CKen
I	– 'Bergman's Sport of Prostrata'	CKen
	– 'Bloomer's Dark Globe'	CKen
	– 'Blue Shag'	ECho EOrn GKir LRHS MBri MGos NLar SCoo SLim SPoG
	– 'Cesarini'	CKen
	– 'Compacta' **new**	NPCo
	– 'Densa'	CKen ECho MAsh
	– 'Dove's Dwarf'	CKen
	– 'Ed's Broom'	CKen
	– 'Elkins Dwarf'	CKen NHol
	– 'Fastigiata'	CKen ECho MBri
	– 'Golden Showers' **new**	NLar
	– 'Green Curls'	CKen
	– 'Green Twist' **new**	MAsh
	– 'Greg'	CKen ECho
	– 'Hershey'	CKen
	– 'Hillside Gem'	CKen
	– 'Himmelblau'	IArd LRHS MBlu NLar SLim
	– 'Horsford'	CKen ECho LRHS NLar SLim
	– 'Jericho'	CKen EOrn NLar
	– 'Julian Pott'	CKen
	– 'Julian's Dwarf'	CKen
	– 'Krügers Lilliput'	GKir LRHS NHol NLar SLim
	– 'Louie'	CKen LRHS MAsh NLar SLim
	– 'Macopin'	ECho EMil NLar SCoo
	– 'Mary Butler'	CKen NLar
	– 'Merrimack'	CKen ECho NLar
	– 'Minima'	CKen ECho EOrn LRHS MAsh MBar MBlu MBri MGos NLar NPCo NWea SCoo SLim SPoG WGor
	– 'Minuta'	CKen
	– 'Nana'	see *P. strobus* Nana Group
§	– Nana Group	MGos NPri WEve
	– 'Nana Compacta' **new**	LRHS
	– 'Nivea'	see *P. strobus* 'Alba'
	– 'Northway Broom'	CKen ECho LRHS SLim
	– 'Ontario'	MBlu
	– 'Pendula'	CKen IDee
I	– 'Pendula Broom'	CKen
	– 'Radiata'	CTri EHul EPla LRHS MBar NLar
	– 'Reinshaus'	CKen ECho
	– 'Sayville'	CKen
	– 'Sea Urchin'	CKen ECho SLim SPoG
	– 'Secrest'	NLar
	– 'Tiny Kurls' **new**	NLar
I	– 'Tortuosa'	NLar
	– 'Torulosa' **new**	MBlu
	– 'Uncatena'	CKen
	– 'Verkade's Broom'	CKen
	– 'Wendy'	NLar
	sylvestris ♀H4	Widely available
	– 'Abergeldie'	CKen
	– 'Alderly Edge'	CMen WEve WFar
	– 'Andorra'	CKen MGos
§	– 'Argentea'	CMen ECho LRHS SLim
§	– Aurea Group ♀H4	CDul CKen CMac CMen EBrs ECho EHul EMil EPfP GKir IMGH LRHS MAsh MBar MBlu MBri NEgg NHol NLar NPCo NWea SCoo SLim SPer SPoG SSta WEve WFar
	– 'Aurea'	see *P. sylvestris* Aurea Group
	– 'Avondene'	CKen ECho
	– 'Bergfield'	CMen ECho NLar
	– 'Beuvronensis' ♀H4	CMen ECho EOrn GKir IMGH LRHS MGos NEgg NHol NLar NPCo SCoo SLim WEve
	– 'Blue Sky'	NLar SLim
	– 'Bonna'	CLnd GKir LRHS SCoo SLim
	– 'Brevifolia'	MBar MGos
	– 'Buchanan's Gold'	CKen
	– 'Burghfield'	CKen CMen ECho WFar
	– 'Chantry Blue'	CDoC CMen ECho EHul EOrn GKir LAst LBee LRHS MAsh MBar MBri MGos NEgg NHol NLar NPCo SCoo SLim WEve WFar
	– 'Clumber Blue'	CKen
	– 'Compressa'	LRHS SLim
	– 'Corley'	ECho

	- 'Dereham'	CKen ECho
	- 'Doone Valley'	CKen ECho GKir MGos NEgg NPCo SCoo WEve WFar
	- 'Edwin Hillier'	see *P. sylvestris* 'Argentea'
	- Fastigiata Group	CDoC CDul CEnd CKen CMac CMen ECho EMil EOrn GKir IMGH LBee LRHS MAsh MBar MGos NPCo SCoo SLim SPoG WCFE WEve WFar
	- 'Frensham'	CKen ECho EOrn IMGH MAsh MGos NHol NLar NPCo SCoo WEve WFar
	- 'Globosa'	ECho GKir NPCo
	- 'Gold Coin'	CDoC CDul CKen CMen ECho EOrn EPfP GKir LRHS MAsh MGos NEgg NHol NLar NPCo SCoo SLim SPoG WEve WFar
	- 'Gold Medal'	CKen ECho GKir SLim WEve WFar
	- 'Grand Rapids'	CKen
	- 'Gwydyr Castle'	CKen
	- 'Hillside Creeper'	CKen ECho GKir LRHS SCoo SLim SPoG WEve
	- 'Humble Pie'	CKen
	- 'Inverleith' (v)	ECho EHul GKir LRHS MGos SCoo SLim SPoG WEve WFar
	- 'Jeremy'	CKen ECho EOrn GKir LRHS NEgg NHol NPCo SCoo SLim SPoG WEve
	- 'John Boy'	CMen ECho NLar
	- 'Kelpie'	ECho GKir LRHS SCoo SLim
	- 'Kenwith'	CKen ECho
	- 'Lakeside Dwarf'	CMen ECho
	- 'Lodge Hill'	CMen ECho EOrn GKir LRHS MAsh NPCo SCoo SLim WEve
	- 'Longmoor'	CKen ECho MGos NLar
	- 'Martham'	CKen CMen ECho WEve
	- 'Mitsch Weeping'	CKen
*	- 'Moseri'	ECho EOrn GKir LRHS MAsh NPCo
	- 'Mount Vernon Blue' **new**	NLar
	- 'Munches Blue'	CKen
	- 'Nana' misapplied	see *P. sylvestris* 'Watereri'
	- 'Nana Compacta'	CMen
§	- 'Nisbet's Gem'	CKen CMen ECho
	- 'Padworth'	CMen MGos NLar
	- 'Peve Heiheks'	NLar
	- 'Peve Miba'	NLar
I	- 'Pine Glen'	CKen
	- 'Piskowitz'	CKen
	- 'Pixie'	CKen ECho MGos NLar
I	- 'Prostrata'	LRHS NPCo SCoo
	- 'Pulham'	ECho
	- 'Pygmaea'	LRHS SCoo SLim
	- 'Reedham'	ECho
	- 'Repens'	CKen
	- 'Saint George'	CKen
	- 'Sandringham'	ECho
	- 'Saxatilis'	CKen CMen ECho EOrn GKir LRHS MAsh WEve
	- subsp. ***scotica***	GQue NWea
	- 'Scott's Dwarf'	see *P. sylvestris* 'Nisbet's Gem'
	- 'Scrubby'	ECho NLar
	- 'Sentinel'	CKen ECho SLim
	- 'Skjak I'	CKen NLar
	- 'Skjak II'	CKen ECho LRHS SCoo
	- 'Skogbygdi'	NLar
	- 'Slimkin'	CKen
	- 'Spaan's Slow Column'	CKen ECho GKir LRHS SCoo SLim
	- 'Tabuliformis'	ECho
	- 'Tage'	CKen ECho
	- 'Tanya'	CKen
	- 'Tilhead'	CKen ECho
	- 'Treasure'	CKen ECho
	- 'Trefrew Quarry'	CKen
	- 'Variegata' (v)	MGos
§	- 'Watereri'	ECho EHul GKir IMGH LAst LBee LRHS MAsh MBar MBri MGos NHol NPri SCoo SLim SPer WDin WFar
	- 'Westonbirt'	CKen CMen ECho EHul NLar WEve
	- 'Wishmoor'	ECho
	- 'Wolf Gold'	CKen ECho
	- 'Xawrey 1'	NLar
*	- 'Yaff Hill'	ECho GKir
	tabuliformis	CDul NMun STre
	taeda	GAuc NWea WPGP
	taiwanensis	CDoC
	thunbergii	CDul CLnd CMac CMen EHul ELan GAuc GKir IFFs MGos SEND STre
	- 'Akame'	CKen CMen
	- 'Akame Yatsabusa'	CMen
	- 'Aocha-matsu' (v)	CKen CMen NLar
	- 'Arakawa-sho'	CKen CMen
	- 'Awaji'	EOrn
	- 'Banshosho'	CKen CMen ECho EOrn GKir LRHS MGos NLar SLim WEve
	- 'Beni-kujaku'	CKen CMen
	- 'Compacta'	CKen CMen
	- var. ***corticosa*** 'Fuji'	CMen
	- - 'Iihara'	CMen
	- 'Dainagon'	CKen CMen
	- 'Eechee-nee'	CKen
	- 'Hayabusa'	CMen
	- 'Iwai'	CMen
	- 'Janome'	CMen
	- 'Katsuga'	CMen
	- 'Kotobuki'	CKen CMen EOrn GKir NLar NPCo WEve WFar
	- 'Koyosho'	CMen
	- 'Kujaku'	CKen CMen
	- 'Kyokko'	CKen CMen
	- 'Kyushu'	CKen CMen EOrn
	- 'Maijima'	NLar
	- 'Mikawa'	CMen
	- 'Miyajuna'	CKen CMen
	- 'Nishiki-ne'	CKen CMen
	- 'Nishiki-tsusaka'	CMen ECho
	- 'Oculus-draconis' (v)	CMen ECho NPCo
	- 'Ogon'	CKen CMen GKir LRHS NLar SLim
	- 'Porky'	CKen CMen
§	- 'Sayonara'	CMen ECho EOrn GKir LRHS MAsh NLar SCoo SLim SPoG
	- 'Senryu'	CKen CMen
	- 'Shinsho'	CKen CMen
	- 'Shio-guro'	CKen CMen EOrn MAsh
	- 'Suchiro'	EOrn NEgg NPCo
	- 'Suchiro Yatabusa'	CKen CMen ECho
	- 'Sunsho'	CKen CMen ECho
	- 'Taihei'	CKen CMen
I	- 'Thunderhead'	CKen CMen GKir LRHS MAsh NLar SLim
	- 'Yatsubusa'	see *P. thunbergii* 'Sayonara'
	- 'Ye-i-kan'	CKen
	- 'Yoshimura'	CMen
	- 'Yumaki'	CKen CMen ECho MGos SCoo
	torreyana	GAuc
	uncinata	see *P. mugo* subsp. *uncinata*
	- 'Etschtal'	CKen
	- 'Hexe' **new**	NHol
	- 'Hnizdo' **new**	NHol
	- 'Jezek'	CKen MAsh SLim
	- 'Kostelnicek'	NLar
	- 'Leuco-like'	CKen
	- 'Offenpass'	CKen
	- 'Susse Perle'	CKen
	virginiana	GAuc
	- 'Wate's Golden'	CKen NLar
§	***wallichiana*** ♀H4	Widely available

- SF 00001	ISea
- 'Densa'	NLar SLim
- 'Densa Hill'	LRHS
- 'Nana'	CKen EHul LRHS MBar NLar SCoo SLim SPoG WEve
- 'Umbraculifera'	MBri
- 'Zebrina' (v)	LRHS MAsh MBlu MGos NLar
yunnanensis	CDoC CTho LRHS WBor

Piper (*Piperaceae*)

auritum	GPoy
excelsum	see *Macropiper excelsum*

Piptanthus (*Papilionaceae*)

forrestii	see *P. nepalensis*
laburnifolius	see *P. nepalensis*
§ ***nepalensis***	CBcs CBot CDul CSBt CSpe EBee ECrN ELan EPau EPfP GGar GKir LHop LRHS MGos MSCN MWhi NBid SGar SMad SPer SPoG SRms WBVN
* ***tibetica*** new	ISea
tomentosus	MMHG WPGP

Pistacia (*Anacardiaceae*)

chinensis	EBtc EPfP
lentiscus	CArn CBcs EAro EBee ERom MGos SEND

Pistia (*Araceae*)

stratiotes	LPBA MSKA NPer SCoo

Pitcairnia (*Bromeliaceae*)

bergii	CHII
heterophylla	WCot

Pittosporum ✿ (*Pittosporaceae*)

anomalum	ECou
- (f)	ECou
- (m)	ECou
- 'Falcon'	ECou
- 'Raven' (f)	ECou
- 'Starling' (m)	ECou
* ***argyrophyllum***	LRHS
'Arundel Green'	CDoC CWSG EBee EJRN EPfP LFCN LRHS LSRN MAsh NHol SBch SLim SRms SWvt
bicolor	CTsd ECou GGal GQui SArc WBor WPGP
- 'Cradle' (f)	ECou
- 'Mount Field' (f)	ECou
buchananii	SGar
colensoi	ECou
- 'Cobb' (f)	ECou
- 'Wanaka' (m)	ECou
'Collaig Silver' new	EBee LRHS
crassifolium	CCCN CHEx CTrC ECou GGal LRHS WBrE WPGP
- 'Havering Dwarf' (f)	ECou
- 'Napier' (f)	ECou
- 'Variegatum' (v)	EShb WPat
crassifolium* × *tenuifolium	CWib ECou SWvt
'Crinkles' (f)	ECou
daphniphylloides	ELan
- B&SWJ 6789	WCru
- RWJ 9913	WCru
'Dark Delight' (m)	ECou
divaricatum	ECou
'Emerald Lake'	MGos
'Essex' (f/v)	ECou EJRN
eugenioides	CHEx CMHG CTrG GGar
- 'Mini Green'	CAlb CPen SBch WBrE
- 'Platinum' (v)	CBcs CCCN LRHS MGos
- 'Variegatum' (v) ♀H3	CAbb CAlb CBty CCCN CDoC CDul CHEx EBee EHoe EJRN EPfP ERas EWTr GGar GQui IArd ISea LRHS MBri MGos MREP NHol SBch SLim SPer SPoG WGob WPGP WSHC
'Garnettii' (v) ♀H3	Widely available
heterophyllum	CPen EBee ECou EWes SEND
- 'Ga Blanca'	CPen
- variegated (v)	EBtc ECou LRHS WSHC
'Holbrook' (v)	CSam
'Humpty Dumpty'	ECou EJRN
illicioides	WCru
var. ***angustifolium*** B&SWJ 6771	
- - RWJ 9846	WCru
- var. ***illicioides*** B&SWJ 6712	WCru
× ***intermedium*** 'Craxten' (f)	CCCN EBee ECou EJRN
lineare	ECou
michiei	ECou
- (f)	ECou
- (m)	ECou
- 'Jack' (m)	ECou
- 'Jill' (f)	ECou
'Nanum Variegatum'	see *P. tobira* 'Variegatum'
obcordatum	ECou
- var. ***kaitaiaense***	ECou
'Oliver Twist'	LFCN LRHS LSRN SBch SCoo
omeiense	ECou ECre EWes
'Peter Pan'	EJRN
pimeleoides var. ***reflexum*** (m)	ECou
'Purple Princess'	ECou EJRN
ralphii	CCCN CTsd ECou WPGP
- 'Green Globe'	ECou
- 'Variegatum' (v)	CGHE EPla LRHS SSpi WPGP
ralphii* × *tenuifolium new	ECou
'Saundersii' (v)	EQua LRHS SCoo
'Tadina Gold'	GKev
tenuifolium ♀H3	Widely available
- 'Abbotsbury Gold' (f/v)	CAbb CBty CCCN CDoC CMac CTri EBee ECou EHoe ELan EMil EWes LFCN LRHS MGos MREP MSwo SAga SBch SEND SLim SPer WSHC
- 'Atropurpureum'	ELan
- 'County Park'	CCCN LRHS WFar
- 'County Park Dwarf'	CBty CPen ECou EJRN EQua MAsh
- 'County Park Green' new	ELon
- 'Croxton'	CCCN
- 'Deborah' (v)	ECou EJRN LSou
- 'Dixie'	CPen ECou
§ - 'Eila Keightley' (v)	CMHG EJRN SAga
- 'Elizabeth' (m/v)	CAbP CBcs CDoC CMac CTrC EBee ECou EHoe EJRN IArd IMon ISea LAst LRHS LSRN MBri MGos MREP NHol NMun SBch SEND WClo
- 'French Lace'	CAlb CBcs CCCN EBee ECou EJRN ELan EMil ERas GAbr GKev LFCN LRHS MREP NHol NLar SBch SEND WFar
- 'Gold Edge' new	LRHS
- 'Gold Star'	CDoC ECou EGxp ELan LFCN LRHS MGos NHol NPal SBch SCoo SLim SPer SPoG WFar WMoo
- 'Golden Cut'	NLar
- 'Golden King'	CCCN CDoC CMHG CMac CSBt EBee EJRN EPfP LRHS LSou MAsh NEgg NHol NScw SBch SLim SPer SRms

- 'Golden Princess' (f) ECou EJRN
- 'Golf Ball' CTrC LRHS
- 'Green Elf' ECou EJRN
- 'Green Thumb' CMac CWSG EBee ELan
- 'Irene Paterson' (m/v) ♀H3 Widely available
- 'James Stirling' CCCN CPMA EBee ECou EPfP
- 'John Flanagan' see *P. tenuifolium* 'Margaret Turnbull'
- 'Limelight' (v) CBcs CSBt CSPN CWGN EBee EBtc IMon LHop LRHS LSRN MGos MREP NHol SPoG
- 'Loxhill Gold' CAbP CCCN CPen EBee IArd ISea LFCN LRHS LSou MGos NHol NScw
§ - 'Margaret Turnbull' (v) CBcs CPen CTrC ECou EJRN ELan EWes LRHS LSRN MBri MGos
- 'Marjory Channon' (v) CBty ELan EPfP LRHS LSRN
- 'Mellow Yellow' CAbP LRHS
- 'Moonlight' (v) CBcs CTrC EBee LRHS WDin
- 'Mountain Green' CMac LSou MGos SBch
- 'Nutty's Leprechaun' CCCN ELan
- 'Pompom' CCCN LRHS MAsh SRms WPat
- 'Purpureum' (m) CBty CCCN CMac CSBt CSam CTri EBee ECou EHoe EPfP ERas EWTr LAst LRHS LSRN MBri MREP NEgg SAga SBch SCoo SPer SPoG SRms WClo WSHC
- 'Silver Magic' (v) CBcs CPen CSBt EJRN EPfP LRHS MGos SBch
- 'Silver 'n' Gold' LRHS
- 'Silver Princess' (f) ECou EJRN
- 'Silver Queen' (f/v) ♀H3 Widely available
- 'Silver Sheen' (m) CBcs EBee ECou LRHS MGos
- 'Stevens Island' CBcs CTrC CWit LRHS MGos
- 'Stirling Gold' (f/v) ECou EPfP EWes
- 'Sunburst' see *P. tenuifolium* 'Eila Keightley'
- 'Tandara Gold' (v) CBcs CBty CCCN CDoC CDul CSBt CTrC EBee ECou EHoe EJRN ELan ELon EPfP ERas LFCN LRHS LSRN MGos SBch SLim SPoG WBrE WCot WFar WGob
- 'Tiki' (m) CBcs CCCN CDoC CTrC ECou LRHS
- 'Tom Thumb' ♀H3 Widely available
- 'Tresederi' (f/m) CCCN CTrC CTsd EBee ECou WFar
- 'Variegatum' (m/v) CBcs CDoC CSBt EBee ECou EQua LAst LRHS LSRN MGos MSwo SLim SPoG SWvt
- 'Victoria' (v) CBcs CCCN CDoC CTrC EBee LRHS LSRN MGos SPoG WFar
- 'Warnham Gold' (m) ♀H3 CBty CDoC CMac CSBt CWib EBee ECou ECrN EJRN ELan EPfP ISea LAst LRHS MAsh MCCP MGos SBch SLim SPer SPoG SSpi WAbe WClo WFar
- 'Wendle Channon' (m/v) CBty CCCN CMac CSBt EBee ECou EHoe EPfP EQua ERas LRHS NCGa NHol SLim SPer WGob WSHC
- 'Winter Sunshine' LRHS
- 'Wrinkled Blue' CTrC LRHS MGos MRav SBch WClo

tobira ♀H3 Widely available
- B&SWJ 4362 WCru
* - 'Cuneatum' CCCN CDoC CPLG CWGN EPfP LHop LRHS LSRN SAga
* - 'Nanum' CAlb CBcs CCCN CDoC CMac EBee ECou ELan EPfP ERom ETod IFFs LRHS MGos MREP SAPC SArc SBch SLim SPer SPoG WDin WFar
§ - 'Variegatum' (v) ♀H2-3 CAlb CBcs CBot CCCN CHII CMac CSam CWGN EBee ECou ECrN ELan EPfP GQui LHop LRHS LSRN MGos MREP SAga SBch SBod SDnm SLim SLon SPer SPoG SSta WSHC

truncatum ECre EWes
undulatum CHEx ECou
viridiflorum ECou EShb

Plagianthus (*Malvaceae*)

betulinus see *P. regius*
divaricatus CBcs CTrC ECou ECre WPGP
lyallii see *Hoberia lyallii*
§ ***regius*** CBcs SBig

Plagiorhegma see *Jeffersonia*

Planera (*Ulmaceae*)

aquatica EGFP

Plantago (*Plantaginaceae*)

asiatica 'Variegata' (v) GBuc NBro
coronopus EBWF
lanceolata EBWF NMir WSFF
- 'Dent's Downs Link' (v) WCot
- 'Golden Spears' CBre EBee
- 'Keer's Pride' (v) WCot
- 'Streaker' (v) WCot

major 'Atropurpurea' see *P. major* 'Rubrifolia'
- 'Bowles's Variety' see *P. major* 'Rosularis'
- 'Rosenstolz' CRow
§ - 'Rosularis' CArn CRow CSpe CSsd ILis LEdu MBNS MHer MTho NBro NChi NPri SPav WCom WHer
§ - 'Rubrifolia' CArn CHid CRow CSpe EBee EShb LDai MBNS MHer NBid NBro NChi SHlg WCAu WCom WHer WMoo WPer
- 'Subtle Streak' (v) WAlt
- 'Tony Lewis' WAlt

maritima EBWF WHer
media EBWF MHer
psyllium L. CArn
rosea see *P. major* 'Rosularis'
sempervirens MTho
triandra 'Wanaka' **new** IMou
uniflora Hook. f. WCom WCot

Platanthera (*Orchidaceae*)

bifolia NLAp
ciliaris NLAp
hologlottis EFEx
metabifolia EFEx

Platanus ✿ (*Platanaceae*)

× ***acerifolia*** see *P.* × *hispanica*
§ × ***hispanica*** ♀H4 CBcs CCVT CDul CLnd CMCN CTho EBee ECrN EMac EPfP EWTr LAst LBuc LMaj LRHS MGos MMuc NWea SEND SPer WDin WFar WMou
- 'Bloodgood' LRHS
- 'Pyramidalis' CTho
- 'Suttneri' (v) WMou

mexicana F&M 065 WPGP
orientalis ♀H4 CCVT CDul CLnd CMCN CTho EBee EPfP GKir LEdu NLar SLPl WDin WMou
- MSF 0028 from Sfendili, Crete WPGP
- 'Cuneata' IFFs
§ - f. ***digitata*** ♀H4 CDoC CDul CLnd CMCN EPfP ERod GKir MBlu SLPl SPur WFar WMou
- var. ***insularis*** WPGP

	– 'Laciniata'	see *P. orientalis* f. *digitata*
	– 'Minaret'	CDul WMou
	– 'Mirkovec'	CDoC GKir LRHS MBri SMad SPer WMou

Platycarya (*Juglandaceae*)

	strobilacea	CBcs CMCN NLar

Platycerium (*Polypodiaceae*)

	alcicorne misapplied	see *P. bifurcatum*
§	***bifurcatum*** ♀H1	CCCN LRHS MBri WRic XBlo
	'Lemoinei'	WRic

Platycladus (*Cupressaceae*)

§	***orientalis***	CDoC CKen CMac CSBt CWib
	'Aurea Nana' ♀H4	ECho EHul EPfP GKir ISea LBee LRHS MAsh MBar MBri MGos NBlu NHol NWea SLim SPoG WCFE WDin WEas WEve WFar
	– 'Autumn Glow'	CKen MAsh SCoo WGor
	– 'Beverleyensis'	NLar WEve
	– 'Blue Cone'	MBar
	– 'Caribbean Holiday'	MAsh
	– 'Collen's Gold'	EHul EOrn MBar
	– 'Conspicua'	CKen CSBt CWib ECho EHul MBar
	– 'Elegantissima' ♀H4	CDoC ECho EHul EOrn LBee LRHS MBar
	– 'Franky Boy'	CDoC LRHS MGos NHol NLar SLim SPoG
	– 'Golden Pillar'	EOrn
	– 'Golden Pygmy'	CKen EOrn MAsh
	– 'Juniperoides'	EHul MBar NHol
	– 'Kenwith'	CKen
	– 'Lemon 'n' Lime'	SCoo WEve
	– 'Madurodam'	MBar
	– 'Magnifica'	EHul
	– 'Meldensis'	CDoC CTri EHul MBar
	– 'Minima'	EHul WGor
	– 'Minima Glauca'	CKen MBar
	– 'Morgan' **new**	NLar
	– 'Purple King'	LRHS SCoo SLim
I	– 'Pyramidalis Aurea'	LBee LRHS NHol SCoo WEve
	– 'Raffles'	NHol
	– 'Rosedalis'	CKen CSBt ECho EHul EPfP IFFs LBee LRHS MAsh MBar SCoo SLim
	– 'Sanderi'	WCFE
	– 'Shirley Chilcott'	LBee MAsh
	– 'Sieboldii'	EHul
	– 'Southport'	LBee LRHS MAsh
	– 'Summer Cream'	CKen EHul MBar
	– 'Westmont' (v)	CKen EOrn NLar

Platycodon ✿ (*Campanulaceae*)

	grandiflorus ♀H4	CArn CMea CTri EBee ECha EPot GKev GKir LHop LRHS MHer MNrw NBlu NGBl SGar SIng SRms WHoo
	– 'Albus'	CBro CMac EBee ECho EPfP GKev LRHS SPer SWvt WHoo WPer
	– Apoyama Group ♀H4	ECho GKev LRHS NMen WHoo WPer
	– – 'Fairy Snow'	CMea EBee ECho ELan EShb GGar GKev LBMP NBre WEas WHoo WRHF
	– (Astra Series) 'Astra Blue'	CSpe ECho EPfP SPoG WHoo
	– – 'Astra Double Blue' (d)	CSpe
	– – 'Astra Pink'	LRHS SPoG WHoo
	– – 'Astra White'	SPoG WHoo
	– 'Blaue Glocke'	NBre
	– 'Blue Pearl'	WHoo
	– 'Blue Star' PBR **new**	LRHS
	– 'Florist Blue'	SGSe
	– 'Florist Rose'	SGSe WOut
	– 'Florist Snow'	SGSe
	– 'Fuji Blue'	CAby EBee NLar SPad SPur WWEG
	– 'Fuji Pink'	CBro CMea CPrp EAEE EBee ECho ELan EPfP LAst LHop LRHS MRav NLar SMrm SPad SPur SWvt WCAu WWEG
	– 'Fuji White'	EBee ECho ELan LAst NLar SMrm SPur WWEG
	– 'Hakone'	LAst MRav WHoo
	– 'Hakone Blue'	ECho NBre NLar SGSe SMrm
*	– 'Hakone Double Blue' (d)	CSpr EAEE EBee ELan LRHS MBNS SRms WCAu
	– 'Hakone White'	CPrp EBee ECho EPfP LAst LRHS MRav NLar NMen SGSe SMrm WHoo
	– 'Mariesii' ♀H4	CBro CSBt EAEE EBee ECho ECtt EPfP LAst LRHS NBir NEgg NMen SMrm SPer SPlb SRms SWvt WEas WHoo WPer WSHC WWEG
	– Mother of Pearl	see *P. grandiflorus* 'Perlmutterschale'
§	– 'Perlmutterschale'	CMMP CPrp EAEE EBee ECho EPfP IPot LBMP LRHS MRav WAul WHoo
	– 'Pink Star' **new**	LRHS
	– ***pumilus***	GKev NChi NWCA WHoo
	– 'Sentimental Blue'	CMac CWib EBee ECho EWll GKev NLar SPet
	– 'Shell Pink'	see *P. grandiflorus* 'Perlmutterschale'
	– white-flowered, double (d)	CBro
	– 'Zwerg'	ECho EShb LBMP NBre

Platycrater (*Hydrangeaceae*)

	arguta	WCru
	– B&SWJ 6266	WCru

Plectocephalus (*Asteraceae*)

	varians **new**	GCal

Plectranthus (*Lamiaceae*)

	from Puerto Rico	CArn
	ambiguus	EOHP
	– 'Manguzuku'	EOHP
	– 'Nico'	CSpe EOHP
	– 'Umigoye'	EOHP
	amboinicus	CArn EOHP NHor WDyG
*	– 'Variegatus' (v)	EOHP
	– 'Well Sweep Wedgewood' (v)	EOHP
	argentatus ♀H2	CDoC CMdw CPom CSam CSev CSpe EOHP MCot SDix SEND SGar SMrs WDyG WKif WWlt
	– 'Hill House' (v)	CHll CPne EOHP
	australis misapplied	see *P. verticillatus*
	barbatus 'Vicki' **new**	CPne
	behrii	see *P. fruticosus*
	Blue Angel = 'Edelblau' (Cape Angels Series)	EOHP
	caninus	NHor SPoG
	ciliatus	CPne EOHP EShb SGar WWlt
	– 'All Gold'	CPne
	– 'Easy Gold'	EOHP
	– 'Sasha' (v)	CCCN CDoC CHll ECtt EOHP EShb SPet
	'Cloud Nine' **new**	EOHP
	coleoides 'Marginatus'	see *P. forsteri* 'Marginatus'
	– 'Variegatus'	see *P. madagascariensis* 'Variegated Mintleaf'
	Cuban oregano	EOHP
	dolichopodus	EOHP
	ecklonii	EOHP WDyG

	- NJM 02.010	WPGP
	- 'Medley Wood'	EOHP
	ernstii	EOHP
	excisus	CDes EOHP IMou
§	***forsteri*** 'Marginatus'	EOHP EShb SGar
	frederici	see *P. welwitschii*
	'Frills'	EOHP
§	***fruticosus***	CPne EOHP
	- 'Behr's Pride' **new**	EOHP
	- 'James'	EOHP
	hadiensis 'Penge' **new**	EOHP
	- var. ***tomentosus*** 'Carnegie'	EOHP
	- - 'Ernst' **new**	EOHP
	- - green-leaved	EOHP
I	- 'Variegata' (v)	CPne
	- var. ***woodii***	EOHP
	madagascariensis	CPne EOHP
	- gold-leaved	EOHP
	- 'Lothlorien' (v) **new**	EOHP
§	- 'Variegated Mintleaf' (v) ♀H1	EOHP MNHC SPet SRms
	'Marble Ruffles'	EOHP EShb
	menthol-scented, large-leaved	EOHP
	menthol-scented, small-leaved	EOHP
	'Mona Lavender' **new**	EOHP
	mutabilis **new**	EOHP
§	***oertendahlii*** ♀H1	EBak EOHP EShb
	- silver-leaved	EOHP
	- 'Uvongo'	CPne
	ornatus	EOHP MCCP NHor NScw SWal
	- 'Pee Off'	EOHP
	- variegated (v) **new**	EOHP NScw
	prostratus **new**	EOHP
	purpuratus large-leaved **new**	EOHP
	- small-leaved **new**	EOHP
	rehmannii	EOHP
	saccatus	GFai
	- subsp. ***longitubus*** **new**	EOHP
	- subsp. ***pondoensis*** **new**	EOHP
	sinensis	LRHS
	spicatus	EOHP
	- 'Nelspruit'	EOHP
	strigosus **new**	EOHP
	Swedish ivy	see *P. oertendahlii*, *P. verticillatus*
§	***thyrsoideus***	ECre EOHP
§	***verticillatus***	CPne EOHP
	- 'Barberton' **new**	EOHP
	- 'Pink Surprise' **new**	EOHP
	Vick's plant	EOHP
§	***welwitschii***	NHor
	zatarhendii	EOHP
	zuluensis	CArn CDoC CFee CMdw CPne CSpe EOHP EShb SBch SMrs WBor WOld WPen
	- dark-leaved	EOHP
	- 'Sky' **new**	EOHP
	- 'Symphony'	CFee

Pleioblastus (*Poaceae*)

	akebono	see *P. argenteostriatus* 'Akebono'
§	***argenteostriatus*** 'Akebono'	CMCo
§	- 'Okinadake' (v)	EPla
§	- f. ***pumilus***	CDoC EHoe EPfP GKir MBlu MMoz MMuc MWht NHol SPlb WFar WJun WPer
	auricomus	see *P. viridistriatus*
	- 'Vagans'	see *Sasaella ramosa*
§	***chino***	EPla
	- var. ***argenteostriatus***	see *P. argenteostriatus* 'Okinadake'
	- f. ***aureostriatus*** (v)	EPla LEdu MGos MMoz
	- f. ***elegantissimus***	CDoC CEnt CFir CGHE CMCo ENBC EPla ERod MGos MMoz MMuc MWhi NMoo SBig SEND WJun WMoo WPGP WPnP
	- var. ***hisauchii***	EPla WJun
	- 'Kimmei'	EPla
	fortunei	see *P. variegatus* 'Fortunei'
	'Gauntlettii'	see *P. argenteostriatus* f. *pumilus*
	glaber 'Albostriatus'	see *Sasaella masamuneana* 'Albostriata'
	gramineus	EPla
§	***hindsii***	EPla ERod GBin MMoz NMoo SEND
§	***humilis***	ENBC GKir MWhi
	- var. ***pumilus***	see *P. argenteostriatus* f. *pumilus*
	kongosanensis 'Aureostriatus' (v)	EPla
	linearis	CAbb CBcs CMCo EAmu EPla ERod LPal LRHS MMoz MWht NMoo SBig WJun WMoo WPGP
	longifimbriatus	see *Sinobambusa intermedia*
	oleosus	EPla
§	***pygmaeus***	CBcs CDoC CDul CSam CTri EBee EHoe EHul ELan ENBC EPla GKev GKir LEdu LRHS MBar MBrN MGos MMoz MMuc MWhi NBro NGdn NWCA SBod SPer SRms WFar WMoo WPer
§	- 'Distichus'	CEnt EHul ENBC EPPr EPla LRHS MGos MMoz MMuc MWht NGdn NLar NMoo STes WJun WMoo
§	- 'Mirrezuzume'	CPLG WFar
*	- var. ***pygmaeus*** 'Mini'	WCot
§	***simonii***	CMCo EBee GBin LRHS MMoz MMuc MWhi MWht SPoG
	- 'Variegatus' (v)	EPla LRHS MBar NGdn SPer WJun WPGP
§	***variegatus*** (v) ♀H4	Widely available
§	- 'Fortunei' (v)	EPla MWhi
	- 'Tsuboii' (v)	CAbb CChe CDTJ CDoC EPPr EPla ERod GQui LAst LPal LRHS MAvo MBrN MBri MMoz MWhi MWht NMoo WFar WJun WMoo WPGP WPnP
§	***viridistriatus*** ♀H4	Widely available
	- 'Chrysophyllus'	EPla MMoz
	- f. ***variegatus*** (v)	SAga SWvt WMoo
	yixingensis	EPla

Pleione ✿ (*Orchidaceae*)

Adams gx	LYaf
albiflora	CFwr
Alishan gx 'Merlin'	LYaf
- 'Mother's Day'	LYaf
- 'Mount Fuji'	LYaf
Asama gx 'Red Grouse'	LYaf
Askia gx	LYaf
aurita	CFwr LYaf
Bandai-san gx	EPot LYaf
- 'Sand Grouse'	LYaf
× ***barbarae***	LYaf
Barcena gx	LYaf
Berapi gx 'Purple Sandpiper'	LYaf
Betty Arnold gx	LYaf
Brigadoon gx	LYaf
- 'Stonechat'	LYaf
- 'Woodcock'	LYaf
Britannia gx	LYaf
- 'Doreen'	EPot LYaf

§ ***bulbocodioides***	CFwr ERos IHer LYaf
– Pricei Group	see *P. formosana* Pricei Group
§ – 'Yunnan'	CFwr
Captain Hook gx	EPot LYaf
chunii	EFEx LYaf
× ***confusa***	LYaf
Danan gx	LYaf
Deriba gx	LYaf
Egmont gx 'Jay'	LYaf
Eiger gx	ERos LYaf
– cream-flowered	ERos LYaf
El Pico gx 'Pheasant'	LYaf
Erebus gx 'Redpoll'	LYaf
Etna gx 'Bullfinch'	LYaf
formosana ♀H2	CFir EBrs ECho EFEx EPot GBuc GGar LAma LEdu NCGa SAga SIng WFar WPGP
– Alba Group	CFwr EBrs ECho WFar
– – 'Claire'	EPot ERos LYaf
– – 'Snow Bunting'	LYaf
– 'Avalanche'	EPot
– 'Blush of Dawn'	LYaf
– 'Greenhill'	EPot LYaf
– 'Pitlochry'	LYaf
§ – Pricei Group	CStu ERos
– – 'Oriental Grace'	LYaf
– – 'Oriental Splendour'	LYaf
– 'Red Spot'	SIng
– 'Snow White'	LYaf
forrestii	CFwr EBrs EFEx EPot LAma
– from Vietnam **new**	CFwr
Fuego gx	EPot
Ganymede gx	LYaf
Gerry Mundey gx	EPot
– 'Tinney's Firs'	LYaf
§ ***grandiflora***	CFwr LYaf
Harlequin gx 'Norman'	LYaf
Hekla gx	ERos
– 'Partridge'	LYaf
hookeriana	CFwr
humilis	LYaf
Irazu gx 'Cheryl' **new**	EPot
Jorullo gx 'Long-tailed Tit'	LYaf
Keith Rattray gx 'Kelty'	LYaf
Kenya gx	LYaf
– 'Bald Eagle'	LYaf
Kilauea gx	LYaf
– 'Curlew'	LYaf
Kohala gx	LYaf
Krakatoa gx	LYaf
– 'Wheatear'	LYaf
Leda gx	LYaf
limprichtii ♀H2	CFwr EBrs EFEx EPot LYaf
maculata	CFwr EFEx WWst
Marco Polo gx	LYaf
Marion Johnson gx	EPot LYaf
Masaya gx	LYaf
Mauna Loa gx	LYaf
Mawenzi gx	LYaf
Myojin gx	LYaf
Novarupta gx	LYaf
– 'Raven' **new**	LYaf
Orizaba gx	LYaf
– 'Fish Eagle' **new**	LYaf
Paricutin gx	LYaf
pinkepankii	see *P. grandiflora*
Piton gx	EPot LYaf
§ ***pleionoides***	EPot LYaf
– 'Blakeway-Phillips'	EPot
pogonioides misapplied	see *P. pleionoides*
pogonioides (Rolfe) Rolfe	see *P. bulbocodioides*
praecox	CFwr
Quizapu gx 'Peregrine'	LYaf
Rainier gx	LYaf
Rakata gx 'Blackbird'	LYaf
– 'Redwing'	LYaf
– 'Rock Dove' **new**	LYaf
– 'Shot Silk'	LYaf
– 'Skylark'	LYaf
San Salvador gx	LYaf
Sangay gx	LYaf
Santorini gx	LYaf
saxicola	CFwr LYaf
scopulorum	CFwr EFEx
Shantung gx	CFir EPot LAma SIng
– 'Ducat'	LYaf
– 'Gerry Mundey'	LYaf
– 'Golden Plover'	LYaf
– 'Ridgeway'	LYaf
– 'Silver Anniversary'	LYaf
Sorea gx	LYaf
Soufrière gx	LYaf
speciosa Ames & Schltr.	see *P. pleionoides*
Stromboli gx 'Fireball'	EPot
Surtsey gx	EPot
Taal gx 'Red-tailed Hawk'	LYaf
× ***taliensis***	LYaf
Tarawera gx	LYaf
Tolima gx 'Moorhen'	LEdu LYaf
Tongariro gx	CPBP EPot ERos SIng
Versailles gx	EPot ERos
– 'Bucklebury' ♀H2	LYaf
– 'Heron'	LYaf
Vesuvius gx	EBrs EPot
– 'Aphrodite'	EPot
– 'Grey Wagtail'	LYaf
– 'Leopard'	LYaf
– 'Phoenix'	EPot LYaf
– 'Tawny Owl'	LYaf
Volcanello gx 'Honey Buzzard'	LYaf
– 'Song Thrush'	LYaf
Whakari gx **new**	LYaf
'Wharfedale Pine Warbler'	LYaf
yunnanensis misapplied	see *P. bulbocodioides* 'Yunnan'
yunnanensis (Rolfe) Rolfe	LYaf
Zeus Weinstein gx	LYaf
– 'Desert Sands'	LYaf

Pleomele see *Dracaena*

Pleurospermum (*Apiaceae*)

aff. ***amabile*** BWJ 7886	WCru
benthamii B&SWJ 2988	WCru
calcareum B&SWJ 8008	WCru

plum see *Prunus domestica*

Plumbago (*Plumbaginaceae*)

§ ***auriculata*** ♀H1-2	CBcs CCCN CHEx CRHN CSBt CTri CWSG EBak EBee ELan EPfP EShb ISea LRHS NPal SMrm SPer SPoG SRms SVic
– f. ***alba*** ♀H1-2	CBcs CBot CHEx CRHN CSev EBak EBee EPfP ERea EShb LRHS
* – ***aurea***	MRav
– 'Crystal Waters'	CCCN CDoC ERea EShb
– dark blue-flowered	CSpe
caerulea	CSpe
capensis	see *P. auriculata*
§ ***indica*** ♀H1	CCCN EShb LRHS
– ***rosea***	see *P. indica*
larpentiae	see *Ceratostigma plumbaginoides*

Plumeria (*Apocynaceae*)

sp.	WSFF
rubra ♀H1	CCCN EShb XBlo

Pneumatopteris (*Thelypteridaceae*)

pennigera	WRic

Poa (*Poaceae*)

alpina	NGdn NLar
chaixii	EHoe EPPr EPla GFor NLar SLPl
cita	GFor GMaP WPnP
colensoi	CKno EBee EHoe EPPr MAvo WPnP
×***jemtlandica***	EHoe EPPr
labillardierei	CKno CWCL EBee EBrs ECha EHoe EPPr GGar LRHS MAvo NWsh SEND SPer SUsu WDyG WMoo WPrP
trivialis	CRWN EBWF
I 'Variegata' (v)	SApp

Podalyria (*Papilionaceae*)

calyptrata	SPlb
sericea	SPlb

Podistera (*Apiaceae*)

nevadensis new	CPBP

Podocarpus (*Podocarpaceae*)

acutifolius	CBcs CDoC ECou GGar GKir MBar STre
- (f)	ECou
- (m)	ECou
alpinus R. Br. ex Hook. f.	NHol
andinus	see *Prumnopitys andina*
'Autumn Shades' (m)	ECou
'Blaze' (f)	CBcs CDoC ECou EMil LRHS MBrN NHol NLar SCoo SLim SPoG WFar
chilinus	see *P. salignus*
'Chocolate Box' (f)	ECou
'County Park Fire'PBR (f)	CBcs CDoC CWSG ECho ECou EMil EOrn EPfP IFFs LRHS MAsh MGos NEgg NHol SCoo SLim SPoG SWvt WEve WFar WGor WSpi
'County Park Treasure'	ECou
cunninghamii	CBcs ECou
- 'Kiwi' (f)	ECou MGos
- 'Roro' (m)	CBcs CDoC ECou
cunninghamii × ***nivalis*** (f)	ECou
dacrydioides	see *Dacrycarpus dacrydioides*
elongatus	CTrC IDee
- 'Blue Chip'	CBcs
'Flame'	CDoC ECho ECou NPCo SCoo
'Havering' (f)	CDoC ECou MGos
henkelii	CTrC EShb GGar
'Jill' (f)	ECou
latifolius	CAbb ECou EShb IDee
lawrencei	EHul GGar WThu
- (f)	ECou MBar
- 'Alpine Lass' (f)	ECou
- 'Blue Gem' (f)	CDoC ECou EOrn EPla IArd IDee IFFs LRHS MAsh MBar MGos MMuc NHol SCoo SLim WEve WFar
- 'Kiandra'	ECou
- 'Kosciuszko'	ECou
- 'Pine Lake'	ECou
- 'Red Tip'	CDoC EMil IFFs LRHS MAsh SCoo SLim STre WGor
'Lucky Lad'	ECou
'Macho' (m)	ECou
macrophyllus	CHEx EOrn NLar SAPC SArc SMad STre WFar
- (m)	ECou WFar
- 'Aureus'	CBcs
'Maori Prince' (m)	CDoC ECou MGos
nivalis	CBcs CDul CMac CTrC ECou EOrn EPla GCal GGar GKir MBar SCoo SRms STre
- 'Arthur' (m)	ECou
- 'Bronze'	CDoC ECou EPla MGos
- 'Christmas Lights' (f)	CKen ECou
- 'Clarence' (m)	ECou
- 'Cover Girl'	LRHS SPoG
- 'Green Queen' (f)	ECou
- 'Hikurangi'	CDoC
- 'Jack's Pass' (m)	ECou SCoo WFar
- 'Kaweka' (m)	ECou
- 'Kilworth Cream' (v)	CBcs CDoC CMen ECho ECou EMil LRHS MAsh MGos NHol NLar SCoo SLim SWvt WGor
- 'Little Lady' (f)	ECou
- 'Livingstone' (f)	ECou
- 'Lodestone' (m)	ECou
- 'Moffat' (f)	CBcs CDoC ECou
- 'Otari' (m)	CDoC ECou NLar
- 'Park Cover'	ECou
- 'Princess' (f)	ECou MBrN
- 'Ruapehu' (m)	CDoC ECou EPla
- 'Trompenburg'	NLar
nubigenus	CBcs
'Orangeade' (f)	CBcs CDoC MGos NHol NLar
'Red Embers'	CDoC ECho ECou NEgg SCoo WFar
* 'Redtip'	CMen SLim
§ ***salignus*** ♀H3	CBcs CBrd CDoC CDul CHEx CPLG EPfP EPla GGal IDee IFFs LRHS NMun SAPC SArc SLim WFar WPGP WSHC
- (f)	ECou WFar
- (m)	ECou
'Soldier Boy'	ECou
spicatus	see *Prumnopitys taxifolia*
'Spring Sunshine' (f)	CBcs CDoC ECou EPla MGos NLar
totara	CBcs CTrC ECou GGar IFFs LEdu WFar
- 'Albany Gold'	CTrC
- 'Aureus'	CBcs CDoC ECou EPla MBar SCoo WEve WFar
- 'Pendulus'	CDoC ECou
'Young Rusty' (f)	CBcs CDoC ECou EPla MAsh MGos NHol WEve

Podophyllum (*Berberidaceae*)

sp. new	WBor
aurantiocaule	GGGa
§ ***delavayi***	CAby CBct CFir CLAP EBee EBla EBrs ECho GEdr MDun NLar WCot WCru WSpi
difforme	CBct CLAP EBee GEdr WCru
emodi	see *P. hexandrum*
- var. ***chinense***	see *P. hexandrum* var. *chinense*
§ ***hexandrum***	CArn CBct CBro CHid COld CRow EBla EBrs ECha ECho EPot ERos GBBs GCra GKir GPoy LAma MBri MCot MRav NBid NBir NChi NMen SPhx SPoG WCon WCot WFar WPnP
§ - var. ***chinense***	CLAP CRow EBee EBla ECho GBuc GCal GEdr GKev IBlr ITim LEdu WCru WPtf
- - BWJ 7908	WCru
- - SDR 4409	GKev
- 'Chinese White'	WCot
- 'Majus'	CFir CLAP EBee EBrs LRHS SMad WCot WHal

I	- 'Nanum' **new**	LRHS
	'Kaleidoscope' (v)	CBow NBhm
	peltatum	CArn CBct CBro CHid CLAP COld CRow EBee EBla EBrs ECho EWTr EWld GBBs GEdr GPoy LAma LEdu NMyG NSti SPhx WBor WCon WCru WFar WPGP WPnP
	pleianthum	CAby CBct CLAP EBee GEdr WCot WCru
	- B&SWJ 282 from Taiwan	WCru
	- short	WCru WFar
	veitchii	see *P. delavayi*
	versipelle	CLAP EBee WCru WWst
	- 'Spotty Dotty'	CBct EBee GEdr GQue LFur LRHS NSti WCot WPrP

Podranea (*Bignoniaceae*)

	brycei	CRHN EShb
§	***ricasoliana***	CRHN ERea EShb MBri SPoG WBor

Pogonatherum (*Poaceae*)

§	***paniceum***	MBri
	saccharoideum	see *P. paniceum*

Pogostemon (*Lamiaceae*)

	from An Veleniki Herb Farm, Pennsylvania	CArn
§	***cablin***	GPoy
	patchouly	see *P. cablin*

Polemonium ✿ (*Polemoniaceae*)

	acutiflorum	see *P. caeruleum* subsp. *villosum*
	acutifolium var. ***nipponicum***	see *P. caeruleum* var. *nipponicum*
	ambervicsii	see *P. pauciflorum* subsp. *hinckleyi*
	'Apricot Beauty'	see *P. carneum* 'Apricot Delight'
N	***archibaldiae*** ♀H4	NBir SRms
	'Blue Pearl'	CElw CMea EBee ELan EPfP EShb LRHS MBel MBri MNrw NBro NCob NGdn NPol NPri SBch SGar SMrm SPer SPoG WClo WFar
§	***boreale***	EBee ECho GKir LRHS NPol SWvt WMoo
	- 'Heavenly Habit'	EBee GJos LRHS MWhi SHGN WWEG
	brandegeei misapplied	see *P. pauciflorum*
§	***brandegeei*** Greene	CCVN LFur SHGN WPer
	- subsp. ***mellitum***	see *P. brandegeei* Greene
§	***caeruleum***	Widely available
	- 'Bambino Blue'	EBee GKir LRHS NBre SWvt WPer
	- 'Blue Bell'	LRHS
	- Brise d'Anjou = 'Blanjou'PBR (v)	CMMP EBee EBrs ECrN ECtt EHrv ELan EPfP EShb EWes GKir LRHS MBri NBir NCGa NCob NPol SBch SPer SWvt WFar WWEG
	- subsp. ***caeruleum*** f. ***album***	CBre CPrp CSBt CWCL EBee ECha EHrv ELan EPfP GAbr MBNS MHer MNHC MRav NBro NPol NVic SBch SGar SPer SPoG SRms STes WCAu WMoo WPer
I	- f. ***dissectum***	NPol
	- 'Filigree Clouds' **new**	SMrm
	- 'Filigree Skies' **new**	GCal
	- var. ***grandiflorum***	see *P. caeruleum* subsp. *himalayanum*
§	- subsp. ***himalayanum***	GAbr NBur WMoo WPer WPtf
	- 'Humile'	see *P.* 'Northern Lights'
§	- var. ***nipponicum***	NPol WPer
	- 'Pam' (v)	CBow EBee WCot
	- 'Snow and Sapphires' (v)	LRHS MBri MCCP NPer SMrm SPav SWvt
§	- subsp. ***villosum***	NPol
	- subsp. ***vulgare***	NPol
	- white-flowered	GJos
	californicum	NPol
	carneum	CTri CWan ECGP ECha GCal GKir GMaP LBMP LRHS MCCP MNFA MNrw MTho NPol SPhx WAul WCAu WFar WMoo WPer
§	- 'Apricot Delight'	EBee GJos GMac LRHS MCCP MNrw NBir NGdn NPol SBch SGar SIde SPad SPoG STes WBVN WFar WHer WPer WPnP WPtf WSpi WWEG
	cashmerianum	see *P. caeruleum* subsp. *himalayanum*
	chartaceum	LLHF
	'Churchills'	CBre EBee WPGP WPrP WSHC
	'Dawn Flight'	NCot WFar
	delicatum	see *P. pulcherrimum* Hook. subsp. *delicatum*
	'Eastbury Purple'	CElw CWCL MAvo
	'Elworthy Amethyst'	CElw EBee NPol WPGP
	eximium	EBee LLHF
	flavum	see *P. foliosissimum* var. *flavum*
	foliosissimum misapplied	see *P. archibaldiae*
	foliosissimum A. Gray	IGor MNrw WPer
	- var. ***albiflorum***	see *P. foliosissimum* var. *alpinum*
§	- var. ***alpinum***	NBir NPol
	- 'Cottage Cream'	CBre NPol
§	- var. ***flavum***	NPol
	- var. ***foliosissimum***	EWes NPol
	- 'White Spirit'	NPol
	'Glebe Cottage Lilac'	CElw CHar EBee GCra NBir SBch WPGP
	grandiflorum	NPol
	'Hannah Billcliffe'	CDes CElw ECtt EWes MBrN NCot NPol WPGP
	'Heavenly Blue'	ECtt
§	'Hopleys'	GBar GCal NCot WFar
	× ***jacobaea***	EBee WCot WPGP WTin
	'Katie Daley'	see *P.* 'Hopleys'
	'Lambrook Mauve' ♀H4	Widely available
	'Mary Mottram'	NPol
	mellitum	see *P. brandegeei* Greene
	'North Tyne'	NChi NPol
§	'Northern Lights'	CSev CWCL EBee ELon EPPr EWes MCot MNrw NPol SBch SSvw SUsu WCot WFar WMoo WPGP
	'Norwell Mauve'	MNrw
	occidentale subsp. ***occidentale***	NPol
§	***pauciflorum***	CEnt EBee ECtt EHrv EPfP IFro LRHS MNrw MTho NBir NHol SPer WCAu WFar WMoo WPer
§	- subsp. ***hinckleyi***	GKev LRHS NPol SGar
§	- subsp. ***pauciflorum***	NPol SGar SPav
	- silver-leaved	see *P. pauciflorum* subsp. *pauciflorum*
	- 'Sulphur Trumpets'	ECtt SPav SWvt
	- subsp. ***typicum***	see *P. pauciflorum* subsp. *pauciflorum*
	'Pink Beauty'	CBre CMac ELan EPPr EPfP NBre NCob NCot NGdn NPol WWEG
	pulchellum Salisb.	see *P. reptans*
	pulchellum Turcz.	see *P. caeruleum*
	pulcherrimum misapplied	see *P. boreale*
	- 'Tricolor'	see *P. boreale*
	pulcherrimum Hook.	GCal NBro WPer
§	- subsp. ***delicatum***	MTho NPol
	- subsp. ***pulcherrimum***	LLHF NPol
§	***reptans***	CArn GBar GPoy MHer NBro NPol WAul WCom WFar WMoo WPer WPtf

	- 'Album'	see *P. reptans* 'Virginia White'
	- 'Blue Ice'	NPol
	- 'Firmament'	EBee WPGP
*	- 'Sky Blue'	NBro
	- 'Stairway to Heaven'PBR (v)	Widely available
	- 'Touch of Class'	CBow EBee MAsh
§	- 'Virginia White'	CBre CDes CElw CMea CSev EBee MAvo NChi NPol SUsu WFar WPGP
	- 'White Pearl'	EShb NPri WClo
	'Ribby'	NPol
	richardsonii misapplied	see *P.* 'Northern Lights'
	richardsonii Graham	see *P. boreale*
	'Sapphire'	CBre ELan LRHS MBrN NPol
	scopulinum	see *P. pulcherrimum* Hook. subsp. *delicatum*
	'Sonia's Bluebell'	CDes CElw CWCL EBee ECtt EWes LPio MAvo MDKP MNrw NPol NSti STes WPGP
	'Theddingworth'	MAvo NPol WFar
	vanbruntiae	NPol
	viscosum	GBuc NPol
	- f. ***leucanthum***	NPol
	yezoense	CBre NBre NCot NPol SPhx WFar
	- var. ***hidakanum***	NPol
	- - Bressingham Purple = 'Polbress'	CBow EBee EBrs ECtt ELan EWes GBin LHop LRHS MBNS MBri MCot NCGa NOrc NPri SBch WFar
	- - 'Purple Rain'	Widely available
	- 'Midnight Rain'	CSpe

Polianthes (*Agavaceae*)

	elongata new	WCot
§	***geminiflora***	EBrs LRHS
	tuberosa ♀H1-2	CBcs CCCN CSpe EBrs ECho IHer LRHS
	- 'The Pearl' (d)	EBrs ECho LAma WCot WHil WPGP

Poliomintha (*Lamiaceae*)

bustamanta	NBir SPhx
maderensis F&M 195	WPGP

Poliothyrsis (*Flacourtiaceae*)

sinensis ♀H4	CBcs CTho EBee EPfP LRHS MBri NLar SSpi WPGP

Pollia (*Commelinaceae*)

japonica	CBgR CWit WPnP

Polygala (*Polygalaceae*)

	calcarea	ECho LLHF WPat
	- Bulley's form	EPot LRHS
	- 'Lillet' ♀H4	ECho EPot EWes LHop LLHF LRHS NLAp NLar NMen NSla WFar WPat
	chamaebuxus ♀H4	CBcs ECho GKev GKir LSou MDKP MGos MWea NDlv NLar NSla NWCA SPoG SRms WBVN WSHC
I	- ***alba***	LBee LRHS LSou NLar SChF
§	- var. ***grandiflora*** ♀H4	CBcs CFir CMea ECho EPfP EPot GEdr GGar GKev GKir LBee LRHS MAsh MBar MDun MGos MWat NLAp NMen NSla SChF SIng SPoG WBVN WFar WPat WSHC
	- 'Kamniski'	ECho NLar
	- 'Loibl'	MAsh
	- 'Purpurea'	see *P. chamaebuxus* var. *grandiflora*
	- 'Rhodoptera'	see *P. chamaebuxus* var. *grandiflora*
§	× ***dalmaisiana*** ♀H1	CAbb CCCN CHEx CHll CRHN CSpe EBee EPfP SAga SGar WCFE
	myrtifolia	CCCN CTrC GFai MGos NWCA SGar SMrm SPlb
	- 'Grandiflora'	see *P.* × *dalmaisiana*
	'Rhubarb Rock'	GKir
	tenuifolia	CArn
	vayredae	CPBP
	virgata	ERea EShb

Polygonatum ✿ (*Convallariaceae*)

	acuminatifolium	EBla
	altelobatum	EBla
	- B&SWJ 286	WCru
	- B&SWJ 1886	WCru
	arisanense B&SWJ 3839	WCru
§	***biflorum***	Widely available
	- dwarf	EBla EPla
	canaliculatum	see *P. biflorum*
	cirrhifolium	CDes CFir CLAP CMdw CPom EBee EBla ELan EPot GBin GEdr GKir MAvo WCot WCru WPGP WPrP
	- red-flowered	NLar WCot WFar
	commutatum	see *P. biflorum*
	'Corsley'	CPou
	cryptanthum	EBla EPot WCru
	curvistylum	CAvo CBct CLAP CPom CStu EBla ECha EHrv EPPr GEdr IFoB IMou MNFA NLar NRya SPhx WCru WFar
	- CLD 761	GEdr
	cyrtonema misapplied	see *Disporopsis pernyi*
	cyrtonema Hua	CLAP
	- B&SWJ 271	MPoH WCru
*	***desoulavyi*** var. ***yezoense*** B&SWJ 764	MPoH WCru
	falcatum misapplied	see *P. humile*
	falcatum A. Gray	EBee EBla EPot NRya WHer WThu
	- B&SWJ 1077	WCru
	- silver-striped	CLAP EBee EPot GEdr LFur
	- - B&SWJ 5101	WCru
	- 'Variegatum'	see *P. odoratum* var. *pluriflorum* 'Variegatum'
	'Falcon'	see *P. humile*
	filipes	WCru
	fuscum	WCru
	geminiflorum	CBct CLAP CPom EBla WCru WFar
	- McB 2448	GEdr
	giganteum	see *P. biflorum*
	glaberrimum	CAvo CBct EBee EBla WCot WFar
§	***graminifolium***	CBct CLAP CPBP CPom EBee EBla EBrs ECho EPot ERos GEdr NMen SCnR WCot WCru
	- G-W&P 803	IPot
§	***hirtum***	CBct CLAP CPom EBla EBrs ECho EPPr EPla IFoB LEdu MAvo WCru WFar WTin
	- BM 7012	EBee MPoH
	hookeri	Widely available
	- McB 1413	GEdr
§	***humile***	CBct CLAP EBee EBla EBrs ECho EHrv EPPr EPfP ERos GCal GGar GKir IBal LHop LRHS NGdn NMen NMyG SGSe SMac WAul WCot WCru WFar WHil
I	- 'Variegatum' (v) new	CMac
§	× ***hybridum*** ♀H4	Widely available
	- 'Betberg'	CBct CLAP CRow EBla ECha EHrv EPPr IMou LPio NBir WCot
	- 'Flore Pleno' (d)	CBct EBla ELon WHer
	- 'Nanum'	CBct CHid EBla WCot
	- 'Purple Katie'	MPoH
§	- 'Striatum' (v)	Widely available
	- 'Variegatum'	see *P.* × *hybridum* 'Striatum'

- 'Wakehurst' EBla EHrv
- 'Weihenstephan' EBee EBla GCal
inflatum EBla ECho WCru
- B&SWJ 922 WCru
involucratum ECho WCru
- B&SWJ 4285 WCru
japonicum see *P. odoratum*
kingianum EBee
- yellow-flowered B&SWJ 6545 WCru
- - B&SWJ 6562 WCru
'Langthorns Variegated' (v) ELan
lasianthum EBee WCru WWst
- B&SWJ 671 WCru
latifolium see *P. hirtum*
leptophyllum KEKE 844 GEdr
maximowiczii CPom EBee EPPr GCal WCru
'Multifide' EBee
multiflorum misapplied see *P. × hybridum*
multiflorum L. CBcs CElw CMac CPrp CRow CSBt CWCL EBee EBrs ECha ECho EPla EPot GAbr GCal LAst MAvo MCot MRav NMyG NVic SEND SPlb SPoG SRms WBor WCAu WFar WHer WMoo
- CC 4572 WCot
- ***giganteum*** hort. see *P. biflorum*
* - 'Ramosissima' EBla
* ***nanum*** 'Variegatum' (v) CBcs CWCL ECho
nodosum EBla WCru
obtusifolium EBla
§ ***odoratum*** ♀H4 CAby CAvo CBct CBro CPom CRow CSWP EBee EBla EBrs ECho EHrv EPfP EPla GMaP LPio LRHS NBid NLar NRya WCru WFar WHil WPnP WWEG
- 'Angel's Wings' **new** MAvo
- 'Dunes Ijmuiden' **new** EBee
§ - dwarf ECho LEdu
- 'Flore Pleno' (d) ♀H4 CDes CLAP CPom CRow EBee EBla EBrs ECha ECho EHrv EPla LEdu MAvo SCnR WCot WFar WHoo WPGP WPnP WPrP WTin
- 'Grace Barker' see *P. × hybridum* 'Striatum'
- Kew form EPot
- var. ***pluriflorum*** GBuc
§ - - 'Variegatum' (v) ♀H4 Widely available
- 'Red Stem' ECho MPoH WCru
- 'Silver Wings' (v) CBct CLAP EBla ECha EHrv NBir
- 'Ussuriland' **new** GCal
officinale see *P. odoratum*
oppositifolium EBee EBla WFar
- B&SWJ 2537 WCru
§ ***orientale*** CBct CHid CLAP EBee EBla EBrs ECho WFar
pluriflorum see *P. graminifolium*
polyanthemum see *P. orientale*
prattii EBee EBla ECho
- CLD 325 GEdr
pubescens CBct EBee ECho WCru WThu
pumilum see *P. odoratum* dwarf
punctatum LEdu WFar
- B&SWJ 2395 CBct EBla WCru
roseum CDes CLAP CPom EPPr GEdr GKev SGSe WHer WPGP
- SBQE 310 MPoH
sewerzowii EBee EBla EPPr EPla
sibiricum CAvo CBct CPom EBla GEdr WCot WCru WFar
- DJHC 600 CDes
stenanthum **new** WWst
stenophyllum CAvo EBla WCru
stewartianum CLAP CPom EBee EPPr LFur NRya
aff. ***tessellatum*** B&SWJ 9752 WCru
tonkinense WFar
- HWJ 551 MPoH WCru
- HWJ 861 WCru
verticillatum CAvo CBct CBro CGHE CHid CRow EBla EBrs ECha EPPr EPfP EPla EPot GKir IFoB LBMP LEdu LRHS MNFA MNrw MRav MTho NWCA SMad WCom WCru WFar WPGP
- 'Giant One' EBee
- 'Himalayan Giant' CHid EBee EBla ECho IPot WFar WPnP
* - 'Roseum' GKir LRHS
- 'Rubrum' CArn CBct CLAP CRow EBee EBla EHrv EPPr EPla GEdr IPot LEdu LFur MAvo MTho NBid NGby NLar SPhx WCot WHil WPrP
- 'Serbian Dwarf' CBct CHid EBee EBla ECho IPot
aff. ***verticillatum*** CSpe
aff. ***wardii*** WCot
- B&SWJ 6599 WCru
zanlanscianense CBct EBee EBla WCru WFar

Polygonum (*Polygonaceae*)

affine see *Persicaria affinis*
amplexicaule see *Persicaria amplexicaulis*
aubertii see *Fallopia baldschuanica*
aviculare CArn
baldschuanicum see *Fallopia baldschuanica*
bistorta see *Persicaria bistorta*
capitatum see *Persicaria capitata*
compactum see *Fallopia japonica* var. *compacta*
equisetiforme misapplied see *P. scoparium*
filiforme see *Persicaria virginiana*
molle see *Persicaria mollis*
multiflorum see *Fallopia multiflora*
odoratum see *Persicaria odorata*
polystachyum see *Persicaria wallichii*
runciforme see *Persicaria runcinata*
§ ***scoparium*** CBcs CRow EPPr EPla ESwi SDys SIng WFar WOld WTin
tinctorium see *Persicaria tinctoria*
vacciniifolium see *Persicaria vacciniifolia*
weyrichii see *Persicaria weyrichii*

Polylepis (*Rosaceae*)

australis EBee EPla LEdu MBri SMad WCot WCru WPGP
- tall WPGP
pauta WPGP

Polymnia (*Asteraceae*)

sonchifolia LEdu

Polypodium ✿ (*Polypodiaceae*)

aureum see *Phlebodium aureum*
- 'Glaucum' CSpe WCot
australe see *P. cambricum*
§ ***cambricum*** EFer SGSe WCot WFib WRic WTin
- 'Barrowii' CBgR CLAP WAbe WFib
I - 'Cambricum' ♀H4 CBgR CLAP GCal WAbe WRic
- 'Cristatum' CLAP WFib
- (Cristatum Group) 'Grandiceps Forster' CLAP
- - 'Grandiceps Fox' ♀H4 WFib
- 'Hornet' GBin WFib
- 'Macrostachyon' CLAP EFer GBin NBid WFib
- 'Oakleyae' EFtx
- 'Omnilacerum Oxford' CLAP

	– 'Prestonii'	CBgR EBee WAbe WCot WFib
	– Pulcherrimum Group	CLAP WAbe WRic
	– – 'Pulcherrimum Addison'	GBin WAbe WFib
	– – 'Pulchritudine'	CLAP WAbe WCot
	– 'Richard Kayse'	CDes CLAP EBee WAbe WCot WFib WPGP
	– Semilacerum Group	WRic
	– – 'Carew Lane'	WFib
	– – 'Robustum'	WFib
	– 'Whilharris' ♀H4	CLAP WAbe
I	× ***coughlinii*** bifid	WFib
	formosanum	WRic
	glycyrrhiza	CLAP GPoy WFib
	– bifid	see *P.* × *coughlinii* bifid
	– 'Longicaudatum' ♀H4	CLAP EBee GBin WAbe WCot WFib
	– 'Malahatense'	CLAP
	– 'Malahatense' (sterile)	WAbe
	interjectum	CBgR CLAP EBee EBrs EFer LRHS MMoz NVic WPnP WRic
	– 'Cornubiense' ♀H4	CBgR CDes CLAP GEdr MMoz NBid NBir NHol NVic WAbe WTin
	– 'Glomeratum Mullins'	WFib
	× ***mantoniae***	WFib WIvy
	– 'Bifidograndiceps'	NBid WFib WRic
	scouleri	CLAP EFer NBro
	subauriculatum 'Knightii'	see *Goniophlebium subauriculatum* 'Knightiae'
	vulgare	Widely available
	– 'Bifidocristatum'	see *P. vulgare* 'Bifidomultifidum'
	– 'Bifido-multiceps' **new**	WCot
§	– 'Bifidomultifidum'	CBgR CBty CLAP CWCL GBin GCal GEdr LLWP LRHS MAsh MCCP MGos MRav NHol NLar STes WCot WWEG
*	– 'Congestum Cristatum'	SRms
	– 'Cornubiense Grandiceps'	GCal SRms WIvy WRic
*	– 'Cornubiense Multifidum'	EBee WCot
	– 'Elegantissimum'	NBid WFib
	– 'Parsley'	WCot
	– 'Trichomanoides Backhouse'	CLAP GCal WAbe WFib
	'Whitley Giant' **new**	WCot

Polypompholyx see *Utricularia*

Polystichum ✿ (*Dryopteridaceae*)

	BWJ 8182 from China	WCru
	acrostichoides	CBty CDTJ CDes CFwr CLAP CMHG EBee ERod GEdr GQui LRHS MBri NLar NMyG SBch WPGP WRic
	aculeatum ♀H4	CLAP CRWN EBee ECha EFer ELan EPfP ERod EShb GKir GMaP GQui LAst LRHS MAsh MBri MCot MGos NBid NEgg NHol NOrc SRms WAbe WFib WMoo WRic WWEG
I	– Densum Group	EFer
	– Grandiceps Group	EFer
	– 'Portia'	WFib
	andersonii	CLAP EBee EFtx NHol WRic
	bissectum	CPLG
	braunii	CBcs CMHG CWCL EBee EFtx EGol EQua GBin GMaP LRHS MAsh MMoz MMuc NHol NLar SBch WFib WPnP WRic
	caryotideum	see *Cyrtomium caryotideum*
	chilense **new**	EBee
	dracomontanum	WRic
	× ***dycei***	WRic
	falcatum	see *Cyrtomium falcatum*
	fortunei	see *Cyrtomium fortunei*
	imbricans	CLAP SArc
	interjectum	MRav
	makinoi	CCCN CLAP EBee LRHS NBid NHol WFib WRic
	munitum ♀H4	Widely available
	neolobatum	EFtx NVic WFib
	– BWJ 8182	WCru
	polyblepharum ♀H4	Widely available
	proliferum ambig.	CBty MAsh WPtf
	proliferum (R. Br.) C. Presl	CLAP EFtx GCal SBig WAbe WFib WPGP WRic
*	– ***plumosum***	LAst SPad
	richardii	GBin SBig WRic
	rigens	CBty CLAP CPrp EBee EFer LRHS LSou MAsh MMuc NDlv NHol NLar SBch SGSe SRms SRot WAbe WCru WFib WRic WWEG
	setiferum ♀H4	Widely available
§	– Acutilobum Group	CBgR CFwr CLAP CMHG CPrp EBee ECha EPla EWTr GMaP LRHS NHol SDix SMad SPer SRms STes WMoo WPGP WPnP WPrP
	– Congestum Group	CBgR CPrp GBin MMoz NCGa NEgg NHol SBch SPer SRms WFib WRic
	– 'Congestum'	CBty CFwr CLAP CWCL EBee EFtx ELan EMil EPPr EPfP ERod LBMP LRHS MAsh MDun MRav NBir NGdn NHol NMyG SMac SPoG WGor WMoo WPrP
	– 'Congestum Cristatum'	LAst
	– 'Cristatopinnulum'	CGHE CLAP EBee WPGP
	– Cristatum Group	CLAP EHrv SRms
	– Cruciatum Group	CLAP
	– Divisilobum Group	CBcs CFee CLAP CMHG CRow EFer ELan LPBA MGos MLHP MMoz NHol NVic SRms STre WAbe WAul WFar WFib WHoo WIvy WPGP WRic WTin
	– – 'Caernarvon'	CLAP
	– – 'Dahlem'	CBty CDoC CFwr CLAP EBee ECha EFer EFtx ELan EPfP EWTr GKev GKir GMaP LRHS MAsh MCot MDun MMoz NHol NMoo SPoG WAbe WFib WMoo WPnP WPtf WRic
	– – 'Divisilobum Densum' ♀H4	CBgR CLAP EHrv EPfP LRHS NBir NOrc
	– – 'Divisilobum Iveryanum' ♀H4	CLAP EFer NHol SRms WFib
	– – 'Divisilobum Laxum'	CLAP
	– – 'Divisilobum Wollaston'	CDTJ CLAP CWCL ETod GBin MAsh MRav NBid NHol NLar SMac
	– – 'Herrenhausen'	Widely available
	– – 'Madame Patti'	MMoz
	– – 'Mrs Goffey'	CGHE WFib WPGP
	– Foliosum Group	CLAP EBee EFer
	– 'Gracile'	MRav NBir
	– 'Grandiceps'	CGHE CLAP EBee EFer ELan WPGP
	– 'Hamlet'	WFib
	– 'Helena'	WFib
	– 'Hirondelle'	SRms
	– Lineare Group	GKir WFib
	– Multilobum Group	CLAP SRms WFib
	– 'Othello'	WFib
	– Perserratum Group	GBin NBid WFib
	– 'Plumo-Densum'	see *P. setiferum* 'Plumosomultilobum'
	– 'Plumosodensum'	see *P. setiferum* 'Plumosomultilobum'
	– Plumosodivisilobum Group	CLAP CRow ECha EGol GBin LSou NBid SGSe WAbe WFib
	– – 'Baldwinii'	CLAP WFib

	- - 'Bland'	WFib
I	- 'Plumosomultilobum'	Widely available
I	- (Plumosomultilobum Group) 'Plumosomultilobum Densum' new	WWEG
	- Plumosum Group	CBgR CGHE CLAP CMHG CSpe EBee EFer EFtx NOrc SAPC SArc SRot
	- - dwarf	CSBt
*	- ***plumosum grande*** 'Moly'	SRms
	- 'Portmeirion'	CLAP
	- Proliferum Group	see *P. setiferum* Acutilobum Group
*	- 'Proliferum Wollaston'	CBcs CBty CPrp EBee EMil LRHS MCot MMoz
	- 'Pulcherrimum Bevis' ♀H4	CDes CLAP CMea EBee ECGP GBin LRHS MAvo MRav NBid NGdn NMyG SDix SMad SUsu WCot WFib WPGP WPnP WRic
*	- 'Ramopinnatum'	CLAP
	- Rotundatum Group	CLAP
	- - 'Cristatum'	CLAP
	- - 'Rotundatum Ramosum'	CLAP
	- 'Smith's Cruciate'	CFwr CLAP GBin LLHF WFib
	- 'Wakeleyanum'	EBee EFer SRms
	tripteron	EBee
	tsussimense ♀H4	Widely available
	vestitum	CLAP CTrC GBin MMoz SBig WRic
	xiphophyllum	WAbe

Polyxena (*Hyacinthaceae*)

*	***brevifolia*** new	ECho
	corymbosa	CStu ECho NMen
§	***ensifolia***	EBrs ECho ERos LLHF
	longituba	ECho EDif
	odorata	CStu EBrs ECho NRya
	paucifolia new	ECho
	pygmaea	see *P. ensifolia*

Pomaderris (*Rhamnaceae*)

	apetala	CPLG
	elliptica	CPLG ECou
	kumeraho	CCCN

pomegranate see *Punica granatum*

Poncirus (*Rutaceae*)

§	***trifoliata***	CAgr CArn CBcs CCCN CDoC CTri EBee ELan EPfP IMGH LEdu LRHS MBlu MRav NEgg NWea SMad SPer SPlb SPoG WBVN WDin WFar WPGP WSHC

Ponerorchis (*Orchidaceae*)

	graminifolia	LAma WWst

Pontederia (*Pontederiaceae*)

	cordata ♀H4	CBen CHEx CRow CWat EHon ELan EMFW EPfP ILad LPBA MCCP MMuc MSKA NPer SCoo SPlb SWat WFar WMAq WPnP
	- f. ***albiflora***	CRow CWat EPfP LPBA MCCP NLar WMAq
	- 'Blue Spires'	MSKA SPer
§	- var. ***lancifolia***	CBen CRow EMFW EPfP LPBA MCCP MSKA NPer SWat WTin
	- 'Pink Pons'	CRow MSKA NLar
	dilatata	see *Monochoria hastata*
	lanceolata	see *P. cordata* var. *lancifolia*

Populus ✿ (*Salicaceae*)

	× ***acuminata***	WMou
	alba	CAlb CBcs CCVT CDoC CDul CLnd CMac CSBt CTho CTri CWib ECrN EMac GKir IFFs LBuc MBar NWea SPer WDin WMou
	- 'Bolleana'	see *P. alba* f. *pyramidalis*
§	- f. ***pyramidalis***	SRms WMou
§	- 'Raket'	CCVT CLnd CTho ECrN ELan SPer
	- 'Richardii'	CLnd EBtc ECrN GKir MAsh MBar SPer WCot WFar WMou
	- Rocket	see *P. alba* 'Raket'
	alba × ***grandidentata***	WMou
§	'Balsam Spire' (f) ♀H4	CAlb CDoC CDul CLnd CTho EMac GKir NWea WDin WMou
§	***balsamifera***	CCVT CDoC CSBt CTri ECrN EMac GKir LRHS MGos NWea SBch SPer SRms WCot WDin WFar
	- 'Vita Sackville West'	MBlu
	× ***berolinensis***	CDoC
	× ***canadensis***	ECrN
§	- 'Aurea' ♀H4	CDoC CDul CLnd CTho CWib EBee EMac IFFs MGos MRav NEgg SPer WDin WFar WMou
	- 'Aurea' × ***jackii*** 'Aurora'	WDin
	- 'Robusta' (m)	CDoC CDul CLnd CTri IFFs LBuc NWea WDin WMou
	- 'Serotina' (m)	CCVT CDoC CDul ECrN WDin WMou
	× ***candicans*** misapplied	see *P.* × *jackii*
	× ***canescens***	CDoC CDul CLnd ECrN MMuc NWea WDin WMou
	- 'Tower'	WMou
	× ***generosa*** 'Beaupré'	WMou
§	× ***jackii*** (f)	WDin
	- 'Aurora' (f/v)	CBcs CCVT CDul CLnd CMac CSBt CTrG ELan GKir LBuc LRHS MBar MBri MGos MMuc NPri NWea SBch SPer SRms WDin WFar WHar
	lasiocarpa ♀H4	CDoC CDul CEnd CGHE CMCN CPLG CSdC CTho EBee ELan EPfP IArd MBlu MRav SLPl SMad WMou WPGP
	maximowiczii	WMou
	nigra	CDul CLnd CMac CTho EMac EMil EPfP NWea WDin WSFF
	- (f)	ECrN SLPl
	- (m)	SLPl
	- subsp. ***betulifolia***	CCVT CDul CLnd CWan NWea WDin WMou
	- - (f)	ECrN WMou
	- - (m)	ECrN WMou
§	- 'Italica' (m) ♀H4	CAlb CCVT CDoC CDul CLnd CMac CSBt CTho CTri CWib ECrN ELan EMac GKir IFFs LBuc LRHS MGos NWea SBch SPer SRms WDin
	- 'Italica Aurea'	see *P. nigra* 'Lombardy Gold'
§	- 'Lombardy Gold' (m)	CEnd ECrN MBlu SMad
	- 'Pyramidalis'	see *P. nigra* 'Italica'
	'Serotina Aurea'	see *P.* × *canadensis* 'Aurea'
	simonii 'Fastigiata'	WMou
	- 'Obtusata'	WMou
	szechuanica	WMou
§	- var. ***tibetica***	WMou
	tacamahaca	see *P. balsamifera*
	'Tacatricho 32'	see *P.* 'Balsam Spire'
	tomentosa	WMou
	tremula ♀H4	CCVT CDoC CDul CLnd CMac CRWN CSBt CTho CTri CWib EBee ECrN ELan EMac EWTr GKir IFFs

		LBuc LRHS NWea SBch SPer WDin WHar WMou
§	- 'Erecta'	CDul CEnd CLnd CTho EBee LMaj MBlu MBri MMuc SMad WFar WMou
	- 'Fastigiata'	see *P. tremula* 'Erecta'
	- 'Pendula' (m)	CEnd CLnd CTho ECrN GKir WDin WMou
	trichocarpa	CDul ECrN LMaj NWea SPer
	- 'Fritzi Pauley' (f)	CDul CTho WMou
	violascens	see *P. szechuanica* var. *tibetica*
	yunnanensis	WMou

Portulaca (*Portulacaceae*)

	'Firegold'	SVil
	grandiflora 'Fairytales Cinderella' (Fairytales Series)	LSou
	oleracea	CArn MHer MNHC SIde SVic WJek
	- var. ***aurea***	MNHC WJek

Portulacaria (*Portulacaceae*)

	afra new	EShb
	- 'Variegata' (v)	EShb

Potamogeton (*Potamogetonaceae*)

	crispus	CWat EHon EMFW MSKA NSco WMAq
	natans	EMFW NSco SEND
	pectinatus	CWat

Potentilla ✿ (*Rosaceae*)

	CC 5226	GKev
	CC 5235	GKev
	CC 5356	EWld
	alba	CTri EBee ECha ECho ELan GBuc GCal GGar GMac MLHP MRav MWat NChi SPer WAul WPer
	alchemilloides	CMac LRHS WPer
	alpicola	WPer
	ambigua	see *P. cuneata*
	andicola	EBee
	anserina	CArn EBWF EGoo GBar MHer WHer
	- 'Golden Treasure' (v)	EBee WHer
	anserinoides	GCal WMoo WPer
	apennina new	EPot
	arbuscula misapplied	see *P. fruticosa* 'Elizabeth'
	- 'Beesii'	see *P. fruticosa* 'Beesii'
	'Arc-en-ciel'	CHid CKno COlW EBee ECtt GBuc GMac IFoB LRHS LSRN MAvo MBNS MBri MLHP NBPC NCGa NCob NEgg NLar NPro SHar STes WBor WCAu WFar WMoo WPnP WWFP
	argentea	CRWN EBWF GAuc GKir LRHS MBNS SPlb WFar
	arguta	EBee NBre
	argyrophylla	see *P. atrosanguinea* var. *argyrophylla*
	- 'Alfred Salter'	LRHS
*	- ***insignis rubra***	NWCA
	atrosanguinea	Widely available
§	- var. ***argyrophylla***	COlW CSam EBee ECha ELan EPPr EPfP GCal LHop LRHS MMuc MNFA NBir NBro NChi SMad SRms STes WClo WCom WFar WHil WMoo WPer
	- 'Fireball' (d)	GJos WPer
	- var. ***leucochroa***	see *P. atrosanguinea* var. *argyrophylla*
*	- 'Sundermannii'	CSpr LLHF
	aurea	EBee ECho ECtt EPfP LRHS MTho NLAp NMir NNor NWCA WBrk WPat
	- 'Aurantiaca'	EWes LRHS NBlu NLar SRot
§	- subsp. ***chrysocraspeda***	NMen
§	- 'Goldklumpen'	EAEE ECtt LRHS MRav NPro
	- 'Plena' (d)	LRHS SRot
	'Blazeaway'	EBee ECtt LBMP LRHS LSou MBNS NGdn NPro WFar
	brevifolia	NWCA
	calabra	EBee ECha EWes WHer
§	***cinerea***	CTri ECho LBee LLHF LRHS MMuc
	collina	LLHF
§	***crantzii***	CMea EBee MBar SRms
	- 'Nana'	see *P. crantzii* 'Pygmaea'
§	- 'Pygmaea'	ECho ECtt EPfP NBir NMen
§	***cuneata*** ♀H4	ECho GAbr LRHS MMuc MTho NWCA SIng WPer
	davurica 'Abbotswood'	see *P. fruticosa* 'Abbotswood'
	delavayi	LRHS MNrw
	detommasii	LLHF
	- MESE 400	EBee
	dickinsii	GKev NMen
	'Emilie'	CSpe EBee ECtt GCal GMac LRHS MBNS MBri NCob NGby NLar NPro SUsu SWvt WBor WFar
§	***erecta***	CArn CRWN CWan EBWF GBar GPoy
	eriocarpa	EBee ECho ECtt EPau GEdr NLAp NMen SPer WAbe WPat
	- var. ***tsarongensis***	WAbe
	- - CC 4627	EWld
	'Esta Ann'	EBee ECtt EPPr LHop LRHS MBNS MCot NCGa SRGP
	'Etna'	CEnt CHar CKno EBee ECtt ELan GMac LPio LRHS MLHP MNFA MNrw NBir NChi WCAu WCom WMoo WPGP WPer WPtf WWEG
	'Everest'	see *P. fruticosa* 'Mount Everest'
	'Fireflame'	ECha MRav NBre NLar WMoo
	fissa	EBee LFur MNrw NBir NBre SPhx
	'Flambeau' (d)	EBee ECtt EShb GCal GMac LDai LHop LRHS MNFA MRav NBre NCob NGdn NLar NPro WKif WMoo
	'Flamenco'	CSam CTri ECtt GKir GMac LRHS MArl MBNS MBri MLHP MNrw MRav NBir SAga WAbb WCom WFar WMoo
	fragariiformis	see *P. megalantha*
	fruticosa	LBuc MGan NWea
§	- 'Abbotswood' ♀H4	Widely available
	- 'Abbotswood Silver' (v)	LAst MSwo SLim WMoo
	- 'Alice'	LRHS
	- 'Annette'	CMac LRHS MBrN NPro
	- 'Apple Blossom'	CWib
	- var. ***arbuscula*** hort.	see *P. fruticosa* 'Elizabeth'
	- - 'Kingdon Ward'	LRHS
	- 'Argentea Nana'	see *P. fruticosa* 'Beesii'
	- 'Baby Bethan' PBR (d)	LLHF LRHS NHol WFar
	- 'Barnbarroch'	LRHS
§	- 'Beesii'	ELan EPfP ERas GGar LRHS MBar NCGa
	- 'Bewerley Surprise'	LRHS NBir WHCG
	- 'Chelsea Star' ♀H4	CMac LRHS LSRN MAsh MGos SBch
	- 'Chilo' (v)	LRHS NEgg WMoo
	- 'Clotted Cream'	MBar
	- var. ***dahurica*** W 1213	WPGP
	- - 'Hersii'	see *P. fruticosa* 'Snowflake'
	- - 'Rhodocalyx'	WFar

- 'Dart's Cream' MGan
- 'Dart's Golddigger' CTri SEND
- 'Daydawn' Widely available
§ - 'Elizabeth' CBcs CDoC CDul CSam CTri CWib EBee ELan EPfP GKir LAst LRHS LSRN MBar MGos MMuc MSwo NHol NWea SBch SCoo SPer SPoG SRms SWvt WBVN WCFE WDin WFar WMoo
- 'Farreri' see *P. fruticosa* 'Gold Drop'
- 'Floppy Disc' ELan EPfP LRHS MGos NHol
- 'Frances, Lady Daresbury' LRHS
- 'Glenroy Pinkie' CSam EPfP LRHS MRav NLar SCoo
§ - 'Gold Drop' CMac NHol
- 'Golden Dwarf' MGos
- 'Golden Spreader' GKir LRHS
- 'Goldfinger' CCVT CChe CDoC CMac CSBt EBee ELan EPfP GKir LHop LRHS MAsh MGos MRav MSwo MWat NEgg NHol NPri SCoo SLim SPer SPlb SPoG WAbe WDin WFar
- Goldkugel see *P. fruticosa* 'Gold Drop'
- 'Goldstar' CDul EQua GKir IArd LRHS MBri MGos NHol SBch SCoo SLon WFar WHCG
- 'Goldteppich' LBuc MBar
- 'Goscote' MGos
- 'Grace Darling' CAbP ELan EPfP EWes GGar LRHS NBir NEgg NHol SWvt WBrE WHCG WMoo
- 'Groneland' ♀H4 EPfP LRHS MAsh SPoG
- 'Haytor's Orange' CWib
- 'Hopleys Little Joker' WFar
- 'Hopleys Orange' ♀H4 CChe CDoC CEnt CHar EBee EPfP EWes GKir LHop LRHS MWat NHol NPri SCoo WFar WGor WMoo
- 'Hopleys Pink' LRHS
- 'Hurstbourne' NPro
- 'Jackman's Variety' ♀H4 CSam CWib LRHS MAsh SPoG SRms WRHF
- 'Janet' LRHS
- 'Jolina' LRHS
- 'Katherine Dykes' CDoC CDul CMac CTri CWib EBee EPfP GKir LBMP LRHS LSRN MBar MGos NEgg NWea SCoo SLim SLon SPer SPoG SRms WDin WFar WHar WMoo
* - 'King Cup' ♀H4 LRHS MAsh
§ - 'Klondike' CBcs CSBt EBee EPfP GKir MGan NEgg NWea WHil
- 'Knap Hill' see *P. fruticosa* 'Knap Hill Buttercup'
§ - 'Knap Hill Buttercup' LRHS
- 'Kobold' EBee MBar
* - 'Lemon and Lime' LRHS NBir NPro
- 'Limelight' ♀H4 CSBt EBee ELan EPfP LRHS LSou MAsh MRav MSwo NHol WClo WFar WHCG
- 'Longacre Variety' CMac CTri EQua MBar MSwo NWea SLPl
- 'Lovely Pink'PBR see *P. fruticosa* 'Pink Beauty'
§ - 'Maanelys' CSBt ELan EQua LRHS MGan NHol NWea SPer SRms WDin WHCG WMoo
- 'Macpenny's Cream' CMac
§ - 'Manchu' CDoC CMac MBar MRav MWat SLPl SPer SRms WCFE
- Mango Tango = 'Uman'PBR CDoC IMon LBuc LSRN NCGa SPoG
§ - Marian Red Robin = 'Marrob'PBR ♀H4 CDoC CSBt CWib EBee ELan EPfP GKir LAst LRHS MAsh MBri MRav MSwo MWat NCGa NEgg NHol NPri NWea SCoo SLim SLon SPer SPoG SWvt WDin
- 'Maybe' LRHS
- 'McKay's White' LRHS
- 'Medicine Wheel Mountain' ♀H4 EBee ELan EWes LRHS MAsh MGos MRav NHol NLar NPro SCoo SLim SPer SPoG WHCG
- 'Milkmaid' LRHS
- Moonlight see *P. fruticosa* 'Maanelys'
§ - 'Mount Everest' EQua NWea SLon SRms
- 'Nana Argentea' see *P. fruticosa* 'Beesii'
- 'New Dawn' CDoC MBri NCGa WFar
- 'Orange Star' LRHS
- 'Orangeade' EPfP LRHS MAsh NLar SPoG
- 'Peaches and Cream' WEas
* - 'Peachy Proud' NPro
- 'Penny White' ♀H4 **new** EPfP LRHS MAsh
§ - 'Pink Beauty'PBR ♀H4 CDoC CSBt EBee EGxp ELan ELon EPfP LRHS LSRN MAsh MBrN MRav NCGa NEgg NHol NPri SCoo SPer SPoG SWvt WClo WHar WMoo
- 'Pink Pearl' WMoo
- 'Pink Whisper' NPro
- 'Pretty Polly' CWSG ELan EPfP LAst LRHS MAsh MBar MGos MSwo NHol WDin WFar WMoo
- 'Primrose Beauty' ♀H4 CDoC CDul CMac EBee ECrN ELan EPfP GKir LAst LBMP LRHS LSRN MAsh MBar MRav MSwo NEgg NHol NPri SCoo SEND SLim SPer SPlb SPoG WClo WDin WFar WMoo
§ - Princess = 'Blink' CBcs CDul CWSG EBee ELan GKir LAst LBMP LRHS MAsh MBar MRav MSwo NBlu NEgg NHol SCoo SLim SPer SRms WBVN WDin WFar
- var. ***pumila*** GKev
- 'Red Ace' Widely available
- Red RobinPBR see *P. fruticosa* Marian Red Robin
- 'Royal Flush' NHol
- 'Snowbird' EBee EPfP LRHS MGos NPro SLim WFar
§ - 'Snowflake' CBcs WMoo
- 'Sommerflor' ♀H4 EPfP EQua LRHS MAsh NCGa
- 'Sophie's Blush' CChe LRHS MRav NHol NWea WDin WHCG WSHC
- 'Summer Sorbet' LRHS NPri
- 'Sunset' CBcs CMac CSam CWSG CWib EBee ECrN ELan EPfP GKir LRHS LSRN MBar MGos NBir NEgg NHol NWea SCoo SLim SPer SRms SSta WBVN WFar WMoo
- 'Super Ace' MGos
- 'Tangerine' Widely available
- 'Tilford Cream' CDoC CSBt CSam CTri EBee ELan EPfP EWTr GKir LAst LBMP LRHS LSRN MBar MSwo NBir NEgg NHol NPri SPer SRms WBVN WCFE WClo WDin WFar WHCG WMoo
- 'Tom Conway' CMac NLar WHCG
- 'Valley Gold' WClo
- var. ***veitchii*** CSBt
- 'Vilmoriniana' CBot CTri ELan EPfP GCal LRHS MLHP MRav NCGa SPer SPoG SSpi WAbe WHCG WPat WSHC WSpi
- 'Wessex Silver' CHar LRHS WHCG
- 'Whirligig' CMac WHCG
- 'White Rain' LRHS
- 'Wickwar Beauty' CWib
- 'Wickwar Trailer' EPot
- 'William Purdom' WHCG
- 'Wychbold White' LRHS
- 'Yellow Bird' ♀H4 LRHS MAsh MGos SPoG

Name	Suppliers
- 'Yellow Carpet'	LRHS
- 'Yellow Giant'	LRHS
'Gibson's Scarlet' ♀H4	Widely available
glandulosa	LRHS MNrw NBre WBrk
'Gloire de Nancy' (d)	IGor LHop LRHS MRav NBir NChi NCob WCom WPrP
'Gold Clogs'	see *P. aurea* 'Goldklumpen'
gracilis	WKif
'Hamlet'	EBrs LRHS
'Helen Jane'	GBuc GJos GKir LPio LRHS MHer NBir NGdn NLar NPro SAga STes WFar WMnd WPer
heptaphylla	NBre
'Herzblut'	EBee GBuc MNrw NLar
× ***hopwoodiana***	Widely available
* × ***hybrida*** 'Jean Jabber'	EBee EWll GBuc GMac MRav NBur NCob NLar NPro
hyparctica	MDKP
- ***nana***	LBee LRHS
'Jack Elliot'	LRHS NPro
'Light My Fire'	EBee EKen LLHF MAvo MBNS NMoo
* ***lutea***	NCob
'Mandshurica'	see *P. fruticosa* 'Manchu'
§ ***megalantha*** ♀H4	Widely available
- 'Gold Sovereign'	EBee EPfP LRHS LSou NPro SPoG
'Melton'	EBee MNrw NBir
* 'Melton Fire'	CEnt CWan ECtt EPfP EShb GJos GKir LAst LEdu MMuc MNHC NBir NBur SGar WClo WFar WMnd WMoo
'Monarch's Velvet'	see *P. thurberi* 'Monarch's Velvet'
'Monsieur Rouillard' (d)	CSam CWCL EBee ECtt GCra GKir IPot LRHS MNrw MRav MWat NCGa NGdn WCom WHoo WMnd
'Mont d'Or'	MRav
montana	WHer WPer
nepalensis	CEnt EHoe LAst MLHP NBPC NBro NChi NPro
- 'Flammenspiel'	WFar
- 'Master Floris'	GCal SAga WFar WHal
§ - 'Miss Willmott' ♀H4	Widely available
- 'Ron McBeath'	Widely available
- 'Roxana'	EBee ECGP ELan GBuc MRav NBro SRGP WAbb WFar WMoo WPer
- 'Shogran'	COIW EBee GAbr GBuc GJos GMac LAst LBMP LRHS MBNS NHol NLar NPro NVic SPad WHil WPtf
§ ***neumanniana***	CSpr EBWF NBir NPri
- 'Goldrausch'	LEdu MRav
§ - 'Nana'	ECho EPot GGar LBee LRHS MHer MMuc MWat NLAp NLar NMen NRya SPlb SPoG SRms WEas WFar WMoo WPat
- white-flowered	LAst
nevadensis	CTri ECho GEdr SRms WPer
nitida	GEdr NMen SRms WAbe
- 'Alba'	ECho EPot NCob NLAp NMen
- 'Lissadell'	EPot
- 'Rubra'	CFir ECho EDAr MWat NBir NLAp NWCA SRms WAbe WPat
nivalis	ECho
norvegica new	GAuc
* 'Olympic Mountains'	WPer
palustris	CWat EBWF EBee NLar WMoo
parvifolia new	LRHS
- 'Klondike'	see *P. fruticosa* 'Klondike'
pedata	LLWP NChi
pensylvanica	LLHF
'Pink Panther'	see *P. fruticosa* Princess
aff. ***polyphylla*** CHP&W 314	GKev
pulvinaris	EPot
recta	COIW EBWF MNHC NPri WTou
- 'Alba'	CEnt EGoo GMaP LAst LDai NBre NBur NCob NEgg WPer WPtf
- 'Citrina'	see *P. recta* var. *sulphurea*
- 'Macrantha'	see *P. recta* 'Warrenii'
§ - var. ***sulphurea***	CEnt CSsd EBee EGoo EWTr GMac IGor LAst LFur MHer MLHP MMuc MNFA MNrw NBir NBre SAga SIng SPhx WCAu WCom WFar WHal WHoo WMnd WMoo WPer WPtf WTin
§ - 'Warrenii'	CSBt EBee EPla GKir GMaP LAst LRHS MRav NBPC NBir NEgg SIng SPad SPer SPoG SRms WFar WHal WMoo WPer
reptans	CRWN EBWF
- 'Pleniflora' (d)	WAlt
'Roxanne' (d)	MHer
rupestris	CMea EBWF ECha MNrw NSti SGar WCAu WFar WHal WMoo WPer WPtf
simplex	EBee NBre
speciosa	EWes IGor WMoo
sterilis	CHid EBWF WSFF
* ***sundermanii*** new	WHrl
'Sungold'	ECho WHCG
tabernaemontani	see *P. neumanniana*
ternata	see *P. aurea* subsp. *chrysocraspeda*
thurberi	LRHS MBNS MCot MMHG MNrw NLar NMoo SPhx WMoo WSHC
§ - 'Monarch's Velvet'	Widely available
- 'Pirate's Gold'	NPro
tommasiniana	see *P. cinerea*
× ***tonguei*** ♀H4	Widely available
tormentilla	see *P. erecta*
'Twinkling Star'	EBee
verna	see *P. neumanniana*
- 'Pygmaea'	see *P. neumanniana* 'Nana'
villosa	see *P. crantzii*
'Volcan'	CMea EBee EWes MBri NChi NPro SAga SUsu WAbb WCAu WFar WHal WPGP
'White Queen'	GMac MNrw MRav NBre NBur NCob SHar SPur
'William Rollison' ♀H4	Widely available
willmottiae	see *P. nepalensis* 'Miss Willmott'
'Yellow Queen'	CBcs CMac CTri EBee EPfP GMaP LHop LRHS MNrw MRav NHol SPer WCAu WFar

Poterium see *Sanguisorba*

Name	Suppliers
sanguisorba	see *Sanguisorba minor*

Pouteria (*Sapotaceae*)

Name	Suppliers
costata new	ECou

Prasium (*Lamiaceae*)

Name	Suppliers
majus	CSpe

Pratia (*Campanulaceae*)

Name	Suppliers
§ ***angulata***	CTrC
- 'Jack's Pass'	ECho NEgg
§ - 'Treadwellii'	EAlp ECha ECho GEdr GGar LRHS SPlb WHal
- 'Woodside'	ECho ECou
angulata × ***pedunculata***	GGar
§ ***pedunculata***	CPLG CTri ECha ECho ECou ECtt EDAr ELan EPfP GGar GKir LBMP LBee LLWG LRHS MBar NChi NRya SIng SPet SPlb SPoG SRms WFar WMoo WPer WPtf

- 'County Park'	CEnt CSpe CTri EAlp ECha ECho ECou EDAr ELan EPfP GAbr GGar GKir LBMP LLWG LRHS MBar SIng SPlb SPoG SRms WHoo WMoo WPer
- 'Tom Stone'	MBNS
- 'White Stars'	SIng
perpusilla 'Fragrant Carpet'	ECou
- 'Summer Meadows'	ECou

Premna (*Verbenaceae*)

* ***vanrensburgii***	CCCN

Preslia see *Mentha*

Primula ✿ (*Primulaceae*)

Lismore 79-26	NHol
SDR 2709 (Cy) new	GKev
SDR 3239 (Cy) new	GKev
SDR 4735 (Cy) new	GKev
acaulis	see *P. vulgaris*
'Adrian Jones' (Au)	IPen NHol WAbe
advena var. ***eupryses*** new	GKev
agleniana (Cy)	GKev
'Alan Robb' (Pr/Prim/d)	ECtt EPfP GAbr MFie NGHP SPer SRGP WFar
albenensis (Au)	GKev
'Alexina' (*allionii* hybrid) (Au)	GKev MFie
algida (Al)	ECho GKev
§ ***allionii*** (Au) ♀H2	IPen LRHS NSum WAbe
- Hartside 383/3	NHol
- HNG 12	ITim
- 'Agnes' (Au)	NMen
- 'Aire Waves'	see *P.* × *loiseleurii* 'Aire Waves'
- 'Anna Griffith' (Au)	IPen MFie NRya NWCA WAbe
- 'Anne' (Au)	IPen NDlv
- 'Apple Blossom' (Au)	GAbr
- 'Archer' (Au)	IPen ITim NDlv NHol
- 'Austen' (Au)	NDlv NHol
- 'Avalanche' (Au)	IPen ITim WAbe
- 'Bill Martin' (Au)	IPen ITim NHol
- 'Blood Flake'	IPen
- Burnley form (Au)	NHol
- 'Claude Flight' (Au)	MFie
- 'Crowsley Variety' (Au)	NMen NWCA
- 'Crusader' (Au)	WThu
- 'Crystal' (Au)	WAbe
- 'Duncan' (Au)	ITim
§ - 'Edinburgh' (Au)	CPBP GKev IPen ITim NHol
- 'Edrom' (Au)	IPen ITim NHol
- 'Elizabeth Baker' (Au)	IPen ITim MFie
- 'Elizabeth Burrow' (Au)	WAbe
- 'Elizabeth Earle' (Au)	ITim WAbe
- 'Elliott's Large'	see *P. allionii* 'Edinburgh'
- 'Elliott's Variety'	see *P. allionii* 'Edinburgh'
- 'Fanfare' (Au)	IPen NHol
- 'Frank Barker' (Au)	NHol
- 'Gavin Brown' (Au)	IPen ITim
- 'Gilderdale Glow' (Au)	CPBP GKev
- 'Giuseppi's Form'	see *P. allionii* 'Mrs Dyas'
- 'Grandiflora' (Au)	GKev ITim
- 'Hartside' new	NHol
- 'Hartside 6' (Au)	IPen ITim
- 'Hartside 12' (Au)	IPen
- 'Hemswell' (Au)	NHol
- 'Hocker Edge' (Au)	NHol
- 'Huntsman' (Au)	MFie
- 'Joe Elliott' (Au)	IPen
- K R W	see *P. allionii* 'Ken's Seedling'
§ - 'Kath Dryden' (Au)	GKev IPen LLHF
§ - 'Ken's Seedling' (Au)	IPen NHol
- 'Little O' (Au)	NHol WAbe
- 'Margaret Earle' (Au)	NHol WAbe
- 'Marjorie Wooster' (Au)	IPen ITim MFie NWCA
- 'Martin' (Au)	IPen ITim
- 'Mary Berry' (Au)	CPBP IPen MFie NHol
- 'Molly' (Au)	IPen
§ - 'Mrs Dyas' (Au)	IPen NHol WAbe
- 'Peggy Wilson' (Au)	GKev NLar
- 'Pennine Pink' (Au)	MFie
- 'Perkie' (Au)	IPen
- 'Picton's Variety' (Au)	NDlv
- 'Pink Ice' (Au)	GCai ITim MFie NHol
- 'Praecox' (Au)	IPen
- 'Raymond Wooster' (Au)	NHol
- 'Scimitar' (Au)	NHol
- 'Snowflake' (Au)	CPBP GKev IPen ITim NHol NWCA WAbe
- 'Stanton House' (Au)	NDlv
- 'Tranquillity' (Au)	ITim MFie NHol WAbe
- 'Travellers' (Au)	IPen
- 'William Earle' (Au)	GKev ITim NDlv NHol
allionii × ***auricula***	ECho IPen NSum WFar
misapplied 'Blairside Yellow' (Au)	
allionii × ***auricula***	ECho
misapplied 'Old Red Dusty Miller' (Au)	
allionii × ***clusiana*** (Au)	ECho
allionii × ***hirsuta*** (Au)	NHol NLAp SIng
allionii × 'Lismore Treasure' (Au)	CPBP NWCA
allionii × ***pedemontana***	see *P.* × *sendtneri*
allionii × ***pubescens*** (Au)	ECho
allionii × 'Snow Ruffles' (Au)	ITim
allionii × 'White Linda Pope' (Au)	IPen MFie
alpicola (Si) ♀H4	CFee CLAP CRow CSWP CWCL EBee EPfP GAbr GAuc GEdr GGar GKev IPen LPBA LRHS MSnd NBid NBro NDlv NGdn NHol NLAp NSum NWCA SBch SPer WBVN
- var. ***alba*** (Si)	CRow CSWP EBee GAuc GBuc GEdr GGar GKev IPen LRHS MNrw MSnd NBid
§ - var. ***alpicola*** (Si)	CLAP CSWP EBee GBuc GCra GEdr GKev GKir IPen MNrw
- hybrids (Si)	STes
- 'Kevock Sky' (Si)	EBee GKev
- 'La Luna' (Si)	MMuc
- var. ***luna***	see *P. alpicola* var. *alpicola*
- var. ***violacea*** (Si)	CAby CFir CLAP CRow CSWP EBee GCra GGar GKev IPen MMuc MNrw MSnd NBid NHol NLAp WFar WPer
'Altaica'	see *P. elatior* subsp. *meyeri*
altaica grandiflora	see *P. elatior* subsp. *meyeri*
amethystina (Am)	GKev WAbe
amoena	see *P. elatior* subsp. *meyeri*
anisodora	see *P. wilsonii* var. *anisodora*
'April Rose' (Pr/Prim/d)	NBid
× ***arctotis***	see *P.* × *pubescens*
aurantiaca (Pf)	CFir EBee GBuc GEdr GKev GKir IPen SRms
aureata (Pe)	GKev WAbe
auricula L. (Au) ♀H4	EDAr IPen LRHS MFie MHer NBro NSla SPer SPet SPlb SPoG WAbe
- var. ***albocincta*** (Au)	EBee
- subsp. ***bauhinii*** (Au)	GAuc
auricula ambig. (Au)	CTsd GKev WRHF
auricula misapplied '2nd Vic' (Au/S)	SPop WFar WHil

– A74 (Au)	NCob NPri STre
– 'Abrigde' (Au/d)	WAln
– 'Abundance' (Au/A)	SPop
– 'Achates' (Au/A)	WAln
– 'Admiral' (Au/A)	WAln
– 'Adrian' (Au/A)	IPen LRHS MAsh MFie NBro SPop WHil
– 'Aga Khan' (Au/A)	WAln
– 'Agamemnon' (Au/A)	MAsh MFie WAln WCre
– 'Alamo' (Au/A)	MFie SPop WCre
– 'Alan Ball' (Au)	WCre
– 'Alan Ravenscroft' (Au/A)	MFie SPop WAln WFar WHil
– 'Alansford' (Au/A)	WAln
– 'Albert Bailey' (Au/d)	GAbr GCai IPen ITim MFie NEgg SPop WCre WHil
– 'Alexandra Georgina' (Au/A)	MFie WAln
– 'Alf' (Au/A)	MFie SPop WAln
– 'Alfred Charles' (Au/A)	WAln
– 'Alfred Niblett' (Au/S)	IPen
– 'Alice Haysom' (Au/S)	CWCL ELan GAbr GCai IPen MAsh SDnm SPav SPop WCre WFar WHil
– 'Alicia' (Au/A)	GAbr MFie NHol SDnm SPop WCre
– 'Alison Jane' (Au/A)	MFie WCre WHil
– 'Alison Telford' (Au/A)	WHil
– 'Allensford' (Au/A)	WCre
– 'Alloway' (Au/d)	WAln
– 'Almand' (Au/d)	WAln
– alpine mixed (Au/A)	EPfP GKir NBlu SRms
– 'Amber Waves' (Au) **new**	GAbr
– 'Amicable' (Au/A)	MFie NHol SPop WCre WHil
– 'Ancient Order' (Au/A)	WAln
– 'Ancient Society' (Au/A)	GAbr IPen NHol SPop WFar
– 'Andrea Julie' (Au/A)	IPen MFie SPop WCre WHil
– 'Andrew Hunter' (Au/A)	MFie SPop WAln
– 'Andy Cole' (Au/A)	SPop WAln
– 'Angel Eyes' (Au/St)	SPop
– 'Angela Gould' (Au)	GAbr MFie
– 'Angostura' (Au/d)	SPop
– 'Ann Taylor' (Au/A)	IPen
– 'Anne Hyatt' (Au/d)	GAbr MAsh WAln
– 'Anne Swithinbank' (Au/d)	WAln
– 'Annie Tustin' (Au/S) **new**	SPop
– 'Antoc' (Au/S)	SPop
– 'Anwar Sadat' (Au/A)	GAbr MFie WCre WFar WHil
– 'Apple Blossom' (Au/B) **new**	WHil
– 'Applecross' (Au/A)	IPen SPop WCre WFar WHil
– 'April Moon' (Au/S)	MAsh MFie SPop WAln
– 'April Tiger' (Au/St)	WAln
– 'Arabian Night' (Au/A)	WAln
– 'Arctic Fox'	MFie SPop WAln
– 'Argus' (Au/A)	GAbr LRHS MAsh MFie NHol SPop WCre
– 'Arlene' (Au/A)	WAln
– 'Arthur Delbridge' (Au/A)	MFie WFar
– 'Arundel Cross' (Au)	IPen NEgg
– 'Arundell' (Au/S/St)	EBee GAbr GCai ITim MAsh MFie NHol SPop WCre WFar WHil
– 'Arwen' (Au/A) **new**	SPop
– 'Ashcliffe Gem' (Au/A)	WAln
– 'Ashcliffe Gold' (Au/A)	WAln
– 'Ashwood Gold' (Au) **new**	MAsh
– 'Astolat' (Au/S)	EBee GAbr GKev IPen ITim NRya SDnm SPav SPop WCre WHil
– 'Athene' (Au/S)	IPen SPop WAln
– 'Atlantic' (Au/S)	NEgg
– 'Audacity' (Au/d)	WAln
– 'Aurora' (Au/A)	EDAr MFie WCre
– 'Austin' (Au/A)	IPen WAln
– 'Autumn Fire' (Au/A) **new**	SPop
– 'Aviemore' (Au/A)	SPop
– 'Avon Citronella' (Au)	SPop
– 'Avon Twist' (Au/d) **new**	SPop
– 'Avril' (Au/A)	SPop WAln
– 'Avril Hunter' (Au/A)	IPen MFie NHol SPop WCre WHil
– 'Aztec' (Au/d)	WAln
– 'Bacchante' (Au/d)	WAln
– 'Bacchus' (Au/A)	MFie SPop
– 'Baggage' (Au)	MAsh SPop
– 'Balbithan' (Au/B)	GAbr
– 'Baltic Amber' (Au)	MFie SPop
– 'Barbara Mason'	WAln
– 'Barbarella' (Au/S)	MAsh MFie SPop
– 'Barbarian' **new**	WFar
– Barnhaven doubles (Au/d)	CSWP GAbr NSum
– 'Barnhaven Gold' (Au)	IPen
– 'Basilio' (Au/S)	WAln
– 'Basuto' (Au/A)	IPen ITim MFie SPop WCre WHil
– 'Beatrice' (Au/A)	CTri EShb GAbr GCai IPen MFie NHol SPop WCre WFar WHil
– 'Beauty of Bath' (Au/S)	ITim WAln
– 'Bedford Lad' (Au/A)	WCre
– 'Beechen Green' (Au/S)	GAbr GCai ITim MAsh SPop WCre
– 'Behold' (Au)	WCre
– 'Bellamy Pride' (Au/B)	GAbr IPen MAsh SPop
– 'Belle Zana' (Au/S)	IPen MAsh MFie SPop WAln
– 'Ben Lawers' (Au/S)	SPop
– 'Ben Wyves' (Au/S)	NHol SPop WCre
– 'Bendigo' (Au/S)	MFie SPop WAln
– 'Bengal Rose' (Au/S) **new**	SPop
– 'Benny Green' (Au/S) **new**	SPop
– 'Bewitched' (Au/A)	MFie NHol WAln
– 'Big Ben' (Au/S)	ECho
– 'Bilbo Baggins' (Au/A)	SPop WAln
– 'Bill Bailey' (Au)	SPop WCre
– 'Bilton' (Au/S)	MAsh WCre
– 'Bingley Folk' (Au/B) **new**	SPop
– 'Bizarre' (Au)	WCre
– 'Black Ice' (Au/S)	WAln
– 'Black Jack'[PBR] (Au/d)	EBee LRHS
– 'Black Knight' (Au/d)	WAln
– 'Blackfield' (Au/S)	SPop
– 'Blackhill' (Au/S)	MFie SPop
– 'Blackpool Rock' (Au/St)	WAln
– 'Blairside Yellow' (Au/B)	ECho EWes LLHF NLAp WAbe
– 'Blakeney' (Au/d)	GCai MFie WAln
– 'Blossom' (Au/A)	GAbr MFie WFar
– 'Blue Bonnet' (Au/A/d)	GAbr SPop WAln WCre
– 'Blue Chips' (Au/S)	MAsh SPop WAln
– 'Blue Cliffs' (Au/S)	MAsh SPop WAln
– 'Blue Fire' (Au/S) **new**	SPop
– 'Blue Frills' (Au)	WAln
– 'Blue Heaven'	SPop WCre
– 'Blue Jean' (Au/S)	IPen MFie SPop
– 'Blue Moon' (Au/S)	WAln
– 'Blue Nile' (Au/S)	SPop WCre
– 'Blue Skies' (Au/St)	SPop
– 'Blue Velvet' (Au/B)	GAbr GKir IPen LLHF NBro WCre WHil
– 'Blue Wave' (Au/d)	MSCN
– 'Blue Yodeler' (Au/A)	SPop WHil
– 'Blush Baby' (Au/St)	SPop
– 'Bob Dingley' (Au/A)	WCre
– 'Bob Lancashire' (Au/S)	IPen MFie NHol SPop WCre
– 'Bold Tartan' (Au/St)	WAln
– 'Bollin Tiger' (Au/St)	WAln
– 'Bonafide' (Au/d)	WAln
– 'Bonanza' (Au/S)	WAln
– 'Bookham Firefly' (Au/A)	GAbr IPen MFie NHol NRya SPop WCre WFar WHil
– 'Boortree Bush' (Au)	WCre

- 'Border Bandit' (Au/B) new SPop
- 'Boromir' (Au/A) WAln
- 'Bradford City' (Au/A) EBee LRHS SDnm SPav
- 'Bradmore Bluebell' (Au) GAbr
- 'Bramley Rose' (Au/B) new SPop
- 'Branno' (Au/S) WAln
- 'Brasso' (Au) WAln
- 'Brazen Hussy' (Au/d) WAln
- 'Brazil' (Au/S) EBee GAbr IPen ITim LRHS MFie NHol SPav SPop WCre WHil
- 'Brazos River' (Au/A) MFie WAln
- 'Brenda's Choice' (Au/A) IPen MFie SPop WCre WFar
- 'Brentford Bees' (Au/St) WAln
- 'Bright Eyes' (Au/A) IPen MFie WCre
- 'Broad Gold' (Au/A) MFie SPop WAln WCre
- 'Broadwell Gold' (Au/B) EBee GAbr MAsh NLar SPop WCre
- 'Brompton' (Au/S) WAln
- 'Brookfield' (Au/S) IPen ITim MAsh MFie SPop WCre
- 'Broughton' (Au/S) MFie SPop
- 'Brown Ben' (Au) MFie WFar
- 'Brown Bess' (Au/A) GAbr GCai IPen MFie WCre WFar
- 'Brownie' (Au/B) CWCL NBir SDnm SPav SPop WHil
- 'Buccaneer' ECho
- 'Bucks Green' (Au/S) GAbr SPop
- 'Bunty' (Au/A) MFie
- 'Butterwick' (Au/A) GAbr GMaP IPen LRHS MFie NEgg SPav SPop
- 'C.G. Haysom' (Au/S) GAbr LRHS MAsh MFie NRya SPop WCre
- 'C.W. Needham' (Au/A) IPen MFie SPop WCre
- 'Calypso' (Au/d) SPop WAln
- 'Cambodunum' (Au/A) IPen MFie SPop WCre WFar WHil
- 'Camelot' (Au/d) EBee ECho ELan GCai LRHS MFie NBro NHol SPop WCre WFar
- 'Cameo' (Au/A) WCre
- 'Cameo Beauty' (Au/d) SPop
- 'Camilla' (Au/A) WAln
- 'Candida' (Au/d) IPen MFie SPop WCre
- 'Candy Stripe' (Au/St) new SPop
- 'Caramel' (Au/A) IPen WAln
- 'Cardinal Red' (Au/d) SPop
- 'Carioca' (Au/A) WAln
- 'Carmel' (Au/D) new SPop
- 'Carole' (Au/A) MFie WFar
- 'Carreras' (Au) MFie
- 'Catherine Redding' (Au/d) WAln
- 'Catherine Wheel' (Au/St) WAln
- 'Chaffinch' (Au/S) GAbr IPen SPop
- 'Chamois' (Au/B) GAbr IPen MFie WHil
- 'Chanel' (Au/S) new SPop
- 'Channel' (Au/S) WAln
- 'Chantilly Cream' (Au/d) WAln
- 'Charles Bronson' (Au/d) MFie WAln
- 'Charles Rennie' (Au/B) SPop WAln
- 'Charlie's Aunt' (Au/A) WAln
- 'Checkmate' (Au) MFie SPop WAln
- 'Chelsea Bridge' (Au/A) IPen MFie SPop WCre WHil
- 'Cheops' MFie NEgg
- 'Cherry' (Au/S) IPen
- 'Cherry Picker' (Au/A) MFie SPop WCre WFar
- 'Cheyenne' (Au/S) GAbr GAgs MAsh MFie WCre WFar
- 'Chiffon' (Au/S) IPen MAsh SPop
- 'Chiquita' (Au/d) MAsh SPop
- 'Chloris' (Au/S) WAln
- 'Chorister' (Au/S) CPBP EBee ECho GAbr GCai IPen ITim LRHS MFie NHol WHil
- 'Cicero' (Au/A) MFie SPop WAln
- 'Cindy' (Au/A) ECho
- 'Cinnamon' (Au/d) ITim MAsh MFie SPop WCre
- 'Cinnamon' (Au/S) GAbr
- 'Ciribiribin' (Au/A) WAln
- 'Clare' (Au/S) IPen MAsh MFie SPop
- 'Clatter-Ha' (Au/d) MAsh WHil
- 'Claudia Taylor' (Au) SPop
- 'Clouded Yellow' (Au/S) SPop WAln
- 'Cloudy Bay' (Au) LRHS WCot WFar
- 'Cloverdale' (Au/d) WAln
- 'Clunie' (Au/S) IPen WCre
- 'Clunie II' (Au/S) IPen WFar
- 'Cobden Meadows' (Au/A) WAln WCre
- 'Coffee' (Au/S) IPen MAsh MFie NRya WCre WFar
- 'Colbury' (Au/S) SPop
- 'Colonel Champney' (Au/S) SPop
- 'Comet' (Au/S) IPen
- 'Connaught Court' (Au/A) EBee WAln
- 'Conservative' (Au/S) GAbr IPen WFar
- 'Consett' (Au/S) IPen MFie WHil
- 'Coppi' (Au/A) IPen SPop WAln
- 'Coral Sea' (Au/S) MAsh WAln
- 'Cornmeal' (Au/S) MFie WAln WHil
- 'Corntime' (Au/S) WAln
- 'Corporal Jones' (Au/S) SPop
- 'Corporal Kate' (Au/St) WAln
- 'Corrie Files' (Au/d) MAsh MFie WAln
- 'Cortez Silver' (Au/S) WAln
- 'Cortina' (Au/S) ECho GAbr GCai IPen MAsh MFie NRya SDnm SPav SPop WCre WFar WHil
- 'County Park Red' (Au/B) ECou
- 'Coventry Street' (Au/S) new MAsh
- 'Crackley Tagetes' (Au/d) ECho
- 'Craig Dhu' (Au/B) SPop
- 'Craig Vaughan' (Au/A) MFie NHol SPop
- 'Cranbourne' (Au/A) SPop
- 'Crecy' (Au/A) MFie SPop WAln
- 'Crimson Glow' (Au/d) MAsh MFie SPop WAln
- 'Cuckoo Fair' GAbr IPen SPop WCre
- 'Cuckoo Fare' (Au/S) WAln
- 'Cuddles' (Au/A) MFie WAln
- 'Curry Blend' (Au/B) GAbr GAgs
- 'Cutie Pie' (Au/St) new MAsh
- 'Cuttlefish' (Au/St) new SPop
- 'Daftie Green' (Au/S) GAbr GAgs IPen
- 'Dakota' (Au/S) MFie
- 'Dales Red' (Au/B) GAbr MFie NHol SDnm SPop WAln WHil
- 'Dan Tiger' (Au/St) MAsh MFie WAln
- 'Daniel' (Au/A) WAln
- 'Daphnis' (Au/S) GAbr WAln
- 'Dark Eyes' (Au/d) MFie SPop WAln
- 'Dark Lady' (Au/A) WAln
- 'Dark Red' (Au/S) IPen
- 'David Beckham' (Au/d) SPop WAln
- 'Decaff' (Au/St) WAln
- 'Deckchair' (Au) SPop
- 'Dedham' (Au/d) WAln
- 'Delilah' (Au/d) GAbr ITim MAsh MFie SPop WHil
- 'Denise' (Au/S) WAln
- 'Denna Snuffer' (Au/d) GAbr
- 'Devon Cream' (Au/d) ECho LRHS MFie SPop WFar
- 'Diane' (Au/A) MFie
- 'Digby' (Au/d) WAln
- 'Digit' (Au/d) WAln
- 'Dilemma' (Au/A) SPop
- * - 'Dill' (Au/A) WAln
- 'Dilly Dilly' (Au/A) SPop WAln
- 'Divint Dunch' (Au/A) IPen MFie SPop WCre WFar WHil
- 'Doctor Duthie' (Au/S) SPop WAln
- 'Doctor Lennon's White' (Au/B) GAbr IPen MFie SPop WHil

- 'Dolly Viney' (Au/d) GAbr WAln
- 'Donhead' (Au/A) MFie SPop WCre WFar
- 'Donna Clancy' (Au/S) SPop
- 'Dorado' (Au/d) WAln
- 'Doreen Stephens' (Au/A) MFie WAln WFar
- 'Doris Jean' (Au/A) MFie WFar
- 'Dorothy' (Au/S) WAln
- 'Doublet' (Au/d) ECho GAbr GCai IPen MFie NHol SPop WCre WFar WHil
- 'Doubloon' (Au/d) ECho
- 'Doublure' (Au/d) GAbr SPop WHil
- 'Douglas Bader' (Au/A) MFie SPop WCre WHil
- 'Douglas Black' (Au/S) GAbr MFie SPop WCre WHil
- 'Douglas Blue' (Au/S) WAln
- 'Douglas Green' (Au/S) CWCL IPen SPop
- 'Douglas White' (Au/S) MFie SPop
- 'Dovedale' (Au/S) WAln
- 'Dowager' (Au/A) MFie
- 'Doyen' (Au/d) MAsh MFie WAln WFar
- 'Drax' (Au/A) WAln
- 'Dubarii' (Au/A) MFie WAln
- 'Duchess of Malfi' (Au/S) SPop
- 'Duchess of York' (Au) GBuc
- * - 'Dusky' (Au) WFar
- 'Dusky Girl' (Au/A) WAln
- 'Dusky Maiden' (Au/A) GAbr GCai LRHS MFie SPop WCre WHil
- 'Dusky Yellow' (Au/B) ECho
- 'Dusty Miller' (Au/B) EBee ECho LRHS MRav NBir NHol
- 'Eastern Promise' (Au/A) GCai MFie SPop WFar WHil
- 'Ed Spivey' (Au/A) WCre
- 'Eddy Gordon' (Au/A) WAln
- 'Eden Alexander' (Au/B) MFie
- 'Eden Carmine' (Au/B) MFie
- 'Eden David' (Au/B) MFie SPop WHil
- 'Edith Allen' (Au/A) WAln
- 'Edith Major' (Au/d) MFie
- 'Edward Sweeney' (Au/S) WAln
- 'Eglinton' WCre
- 'Elf Star' (Au/A) SPop
- 'Eli Jenkins' (Au) WAln
- 'Elizabeth Ann' (Au/A) GAbr SPop
- 'Ellen Thompson' (Au/A) GAbr MFie SPop WCre WFar
- 'Elsie' (Au/A) WCre
- 'Elsie May' (Au/A) MAsh MFie SPop WCre
- 'Elsinore' (Au/S) IPen MAsh WCre
- 'Emberglow' (Au/d) WAln
- 'Embley' (Au/S) SPop
- 'Emery Down' (Au/S) ITim SPop
- 'Emily' (Au/d) LRHS SIng
- 'Emmett Smith' (Au/A) WAln
- 'Enlightened' (Au/A) MFie
- 'Envy' (Au/S) MFie NHol WAln
- 'Erica' (Au/A) IPen ITim MFie SPop WCre
- 'Erjon' (Au/S) MFie SPop WAln
- 'Error' (Au/S) MFie WAln
- 'Etna' (Au/S) WAln
- 'Ettrick' (Au/S) WAln
- 'Eventide' (Au/S) EBee MAsh SPop
- 'Everest Blue' (Au/S) GAbr MAsh SPop WCre
- 'Excalibur' (Au/d) SPop WAln WFar
- 'Eyeopener' (Au/A) MFie SPop WAln WCre
- 'Fabuloso' (Au/St) **new** SPop
- 'Fairy' (Au/A) WAln
- 'Fairy Moon' (Au/S) IPen WAln
- 'Fairy Queen' (Au/S) **new** WAln
- 'Falaraki' (Au/A) SPop WAln
- 'Faloonside' (Au) WCre
- 'Falstaff' (Au/d) WAln
- 'Fanciful' (Au/S) MFie WHil
- 'Fancy Free' (Au) SPop
- 'Fandancer' (Au/A) WAln
- 'Fanfare' (Au/S) MAsh MFie SPop WAln
- 'Fanny Meerbeck' (Au/S) GAbr GCai IPen LRHS MFie SPop WFar
- 'Faro' (Au/S) MAsh WAln
- 'Favourite' (Au/S) GAbr IPen MAsh MFie NHol SPop WCre WFar WHil
- 'Fen Tiger' (Au/St) SPop
- 'Fennay' (Au/S) WAln
- 'Ferrybridge' (Au/A) IPen
- 'Fiddler's Green' (Au) GAbr SPop
- 'Figaro' (Au/S) MAsh MFie SPop WAln
- 'Finchfield' (Au/A) IPen MFie NHol
- 'Firecracker' (Au) WAln
- 'Firenze' (Au/A) MFie SPop
- 'Firsby' (Au/d) MAsh SPop WAln WCre
- 'First Lady' (Au/A) WAln
- 'Fishtoft' (Au/d) MFie WAln
- 'Fitzroy' (Au/d) SPop
- 'Fleminghouse' (Au/S) GAbr MAsh MFie SPop
- 'Forest Burgundy' (Au/d) **new** SPop
- 'Forest Cappuccino' (Au/d) **new** SPop
- 'Forest Duet' (Au/d) **new** SPop
- 'Forest Lemon' (Au/d) SPop
- 'Forest Pines' (Au/S) WAln
- 'Forest Shade' (Au/d) **new** SPop
- 'Fradley' (Au/A) IPen MFie WAln
- 'Frank Bailey' (Au/d) MAsh SPop WAln
- 'Frank Crosland' (Au/A) MFie WCre WFar
- 'Frank Faulkner' (Au/A) WAln
- 'Frank Jenning' (Au/A) WAln
- 'Fred Booley' (Au/d) GAbr IPen MAsh MFie NHol SPop WCre WFar WHil
- 'Fred Livesley' (Au/A) WAln
- 'Fresco' (Au/A) SPop
- 'Friskney' (Au/d) WAln
- 'Frittenden Yellow' (Au/B) GAgs SPop WFar
- 'Fuller's Red' (Au/S) MAsh SPop WCre WFar WHil
- 'Funny Valentine' (Au/d) IPen MAsh MFie SPop
- 'Fuzzy' (Au/St) WAln
- 'G.L. Taylor' (Au/A) IPen
- 'Gaia' (Au/d) SPop WAln
- 'Gail Atkinson' (Au/A) **new** SPop
- 'Galatea' (Au/S) WAln
- 'Galen' (Au/A) WFar
- 'Ganymede' (Au/d) WAln
- 'Gary Pallister' (Au/A) MAsh WAln
- 'Gavin Ward' (Au/S) MAsh WAln
- 'Gay Crusader' (Au/A) GAbr MFie SPop WCre WFar
- 'Gazza' (Au/A) WAln
- 'Gee Cross' (Au/A) GAbr IPen
- 'Geldersome Green' (Au/S) GCai SPop WFar
- 'General Champney' (Au) WCre
- 'Generosity' (Au/A) MFie SPop
- 'Geordie' (Au/A) WAln
- 'George Harrison' (Au/B) SPop
- 'George Jennings' (Au/A) MFie WAln
- 'George Swinford's Leathercoat' (Au/B) WHil
- 'Geronimo' (Au/S) IPen MAsh MFie SPop WCre
- 'Ghost Grey' (Au) WCre
- 'Gimli' (Au/A) **new** WAln
- 'Girl Guide' (Au/S) WAln WHil
- 'Gizabroon' (Au/S) CWCL EBee GAbr GCai LRHS MFie NEgg SDnm SPav SPop WCre WFar
- 'Glasnost' (Au/S) WAln
- 'Gleam' (Au/S) ECho EDAr GCai ITim LLHF MFie SPop WCre WFar WHil
- 'Glencoe' (Au/S) ECho
- 'Gleneagles' (Au/S) GCai IPen SPop WAln WCre

- 'Glenelg' (Au/S) GAbr ITim MAsh MFie SPop WCre WHil
- 'Glenluce' (Au/S) SPop
- 'Gnome' (Au/B) GAgs IPen NHol
- 'Gold Seal' (Au/d) **new** SPop
- 'Gold Seam' (Au/A) MFie WAln
- 'Golden Boy' (Au/A) WAln
- 'Golden Chartreuse' (Au/d) GAbr
- 'Golden Fleece' (Au/S) GAbr GCai MAsh MFie SPop
- 'Golden Hill' (Au/S) MAsh SPop
- 'Golden Hind' (Au/d) MFie NBro SPop WCre
- 'Golden Splendour' (Au/d) IPen ITim MAsh MFie SPop WCre WFar WHil
- 'Golden Wedding' (Au/A) IPen MFie SPop WAln
- 'Goldwin' (Au/A) WAln
- 'Gollum' (Au/A) MAsh MFie WAln
- 'Good Report' (Au/A) MAsh MFie SPop WFar WHil
- 'Gorey' (Au/A) MFie
- 'Grabley' (Au/S) SPop WAln
- 'Grandad's Favourite' (Au/B) SPop
- 'Green Elg' (Au) NHol
- 'Green Finger' (Au/S) MFie SPop
- 'Green Goddess' (Au/St) WAln
- 'Green Isle' (Au/S) GAbr IPen MFie SPop WCre WFar
- 'Green Jacket' (Au/S) IPen WCre
- 'Green Magic' (Au/S) WAln
- 'Green Meadows' (Au/S) SPop WAln
- 'Green Parrot' (Au/S) SPop
- 'Green Shank' (Au/S) IPen SPop WFar
- 'Greenfield's Fancy' (Au) EBee
- 'Greenfinger' (Au/S) WAln
- 'Greenheart' (Au/S) SPop
- 'Greenpeace' (Au/S) SPop
- 'Greenways' (Au/S) WAln
- 'Greswolde' (Au/d) **new** SPop
- 'Greta' (Au/S) CStu EBee ECho GAbr IPen ITim NHol SPop WCot WFar WHil
- 'Gretna Green' (Au/S) SPop
- 'Grey Bonnet' (Au/S) SPop
- 'Grey Dawn' (Au/S) SPop WAln
- 'Grey Edge' ECho
- 'Grey Friar' (Au/S) WAln
- 'Grey Hawk' (Au/S) IPen MFie SPop
- 'Grey Lady' (Au/S) WAln
- 'Grey Lag' (Au/S) WHil
- 'Grey Monarch' (Au/S) GAbr GCai MAsh MFie SPop
- 'Grey Owl' (Au/S) WAln
- 'Grizedale' (Au/S) WAln
- 'Grüner Veltliner' (Au/S) SPop
- 'Guinea' (Au/S) GAbr IPen SPop
- 'Gwen' (Au/A) SPop WAln WCre
- 'Gwen Baker' (Au/d) MFie SPop WCre
- 'Gwenda' (Au/A) SPop WAln WHil
- 'Gypsy Rose Lee' (Au/A) WAln
- 'Habanera' (Au/A) SPop WCre WFar
- 'Hadrian's Shooting Star' (Au/d) WAln
- 'Haffner' (Au/S) MAsh SPop
- 'Hallmark' (Au/A) MFie WAln
- 'Handsome Lass' (Au/St) SPop
- 'Hardley' (Au/S) WAln
- 'Harmony' (Au/B) MFie NBro NHol
- 'Harry Hotspur' (Au/A) IPen MFie SPop WFar WHil
- 'Harry 'O'' (Au/S) MFie SPop WCre
- 'Harvest Glow' (Au/S) IPen SPop WHil
- 'Hawkwood' (Au/S) CPBP CWCL GAbr IPen MAsh MFie NEgg SDnm SPav SPop WFar WHil

* - 'Hazel' (Au/A) IPen MFie SPop WCre
- 'Headdress' (Au/S) GAbr MFie SPop WCre
- 'Heady' (Au/A) MFie WHil
- 'Heart of Gold' (Au/A) MAsh MFie SPop WAln
- 'Hebers' (Au) SPop WAln
- 'Helen' (Au/S) GAbr IPen MFie SPop WHil
- 'Helen Barter' (Au/S) MFie SPop
- 'Helen Ruane' (Au/d) EBee GAgs SPop WAln WCre WFar
- 'Helena' (Au/S) IPen MAsh MFie SPop WFar WHil
- 'Helena Dean' (Au/d) MAsh WAln
- 'Her Nibs' (Au/St) **new** MAsh
- 'Hermia' (Au/A) **new** MFie
- 'Hetty Woolf' (Au/S) ECho GAbr NHol WCre
- 'Hew Dalrymple' (Au/S) SPop
- 'High Hopes' (Au) WAln
- 'Highland Park' (Au/A) **new** SPop
- 'Hinton Admiral' (Au/S) IPen SPop WAln
- 'Hinton Fields' (Au/S) CPBP CWCL EBee EShb GAbr GCai IPen LRHS MAsh MFie NEgg SDnm SPav SPop WCre WFar WHil
- 'Hoghton Gem' (Au/d) WAln
- 'Holyrood' (Au/S) GAbr IPen ITim SPop
- 'Honey' (Au/d) NBro NEgg SPop WAln
- 'Honeymoon' (Au/S) WAln
- 'Hopleys Coffee' (Au/d) GAbr GCai SPop WAln WCre
- 'Hurstwood Midnight' (Au) MFie

* - 'Hyacinth' (Au/S) LRHS
- 'Iago' (Au/S) SPop WAln
- 'Ian Greville' (Au/A) IPen MAsh SPop WAln
- 'Ibis' (Au/S) WAln WCre
- 'Ice Maiden' (Au) MFie SPop WAln
- 'Idmiston' (Au/S) ECho MAsh MFie SPop WFar
- 'Ilona' (Au/d) **new** SPop
- 'Imari Stripe' (Au/St) **new** MAsh
- 'Immaculate' (Au/A) SPop WAln WHil
- 'Impassioned' (Au/A) MFie SPop WAln WFar
- 'Impeccable' (Au/A) WAln
- 'Imperturbable' (Au/A) MFie SPop WAln
- 'Indian Love Call' (Au/A) IPen ITim MFie SPop WCre WFar WHil
- 'Isabel' (Au/S) WAln
- 'Isabella' (Au) WAln
- 'Jack Dean' (Au/A) MFie NHol SPop WAln WCre WFar WHil
- 'James Arnot' (Au/S) IPen MFie NRya SPop WFar WHil
- 'Jane' (Au/S) WAln
- 'Jane Myers' (Au/d) WAln WHil
- 'Janet' (Au) ECho GEdr
- 'Janie Hill' (Au/A) GAbr MFie SPop WCre
- 'Jean Fielder' (Au/A) SPop
- 'Jean Jacques' (Au/A) WAln
- 'Jean Walker' (Au/B) SPop
- 'Jeanne' (Au/A) MFie
- 'Jeannie Telford' (Au/A) MFie SPop WHil
- 'Jenny' (Au/A) EBee ECho GEdr IPen ITim MFie SPop WCre WFar
- 'Jersey Bounce' (Au/A) WAln
- 'Jesmond' (Au/S) WAln
- 'Jessie' (Au/d) WAln
- 'Joan Elliott' (Au/A) GAbr
- 'Joanne' (Au/A) MFie WCre
- 'Joe Perks' (Au/A) IPen MFie SPop WAln WFar WHil
- 'Joel' (Au/S) IPen ITim MFie SPop WAln WCre
- 'John Stewart' (Au/A) MFie SPop
- 'John Wayne' (Au/A) MAsh MFie WCre WFar WHil
- 'John Woolf' (Au/S) ECho
- 'Jonathon' (Au/A) WAln
- 'Joy' (Au/A) ECho IPen LLHF MAsh SPop WCre WFar WHil
- 'Joyce' (Au/A) GAbr IPen MFie SPop WCre WFar
- 'Julia' (Au/S) MAsh
- 'June' (Au/A) WAln
- 'Jungfrau' (Au/d) WAln
- 'Jupiter' (Au/S) MAsh SPop WAln

- 'Just Steven' (Au/A) WAln
- K85 (Au/S) ITim SPop
- 'Karen' (Au) **new** GAgs
- 'Karen Cordrey' (Au/S) EBee ECho GAbr GKev IPen MAsh MFie NHol SDnm SPav SPop WCre WFar WHil
- 'Karen McDonald' (Au/A) MFie SPop
- 'Kath Dryden' see *P. allionii* 'Kath Dryden'
- 'Kathy' (Au/A) ITim
- 'Kelso' (Au/A) MFie
- 'Ken Chilton' (Au/A) MFie WAln WFar WHil
- 'Kentucky Blues' (Au/d) SPop
- 'Kercup' (Au/A) MFie SPop WCre
- 'Kerry' **new** GKev
- 'Kevin Keegan' (Au/A) MFie SPop
- 'Key West' (Au/A) SPop WAln
- 'Khachaturian' (Au/A) WAln
- 'Kilby' (Au/A) **new** SPop
- 'Kim' (Au/A) IPen MFie
- 'King Cole' (Au/S) **new** CStu
- 'Kingcup' (Au/A) MFie SPop WCre
- 'Kingfisher' (Au/A) MFie SPop WHil
- 'Kintail' (Au/A) MFie
- 'Kiowa' (Au/S) SPop
- 'Kirklands' (Au/d) ITim MFie SPop
- 'Klondyke' (Au/A) WAln
- 'Kohinoor' (Au) MFie
- 'Königin der Nacht' (Au/St) MFie WAln
- 'Lady Daresbury' (Au/A) MFie SPop WFar
- 'Lady Day' (Au/d) SPop
- 'Lady Diana' (Au/S) WAln
- 'Lady Emma Monson' (Au/S) ITim
- 'Lady Joyful' (Au/S) WCre
- 'Lady of the Vale' (Au/A) WAln
- 'Lady Penelope' (Au/S) WAln
- 'Lady Zoë' (Au/S) MAsh MFie NHol SPop WAln WCre
- 'Lambert's Gold' (Au) SPop
- 'Lamplugh' (Au/d) IPen
- 'Lancelot' (Au/d) SPop WAln
- 'Landy' (Au/A) MFie SPop WCre
- 'Langley Park' (Au/A) IPen MFie SPop WHil
- 'Lara' (Au/A) MFie WAln
- 'Laredo' (Au/A) WAln
- 'Larry' (Au/A) MFie SPop WAln WCre WFar
- 'Last Chance' (Au/St) SPop
- 'Lavender Lady' (Au/B) IPen NEgg SPav
- 'Lavenham' (Au/S) WAln
- 'Laverock' (Au/S) MFie NBir NBro NEgg NHol WCre WHil
- 'Laverock Fancy' (Au/S) GAgs GCai IPen ITim NHol
- 'Lazy River' (Au/A) WAln
- 'Leather Jacket' (Au) GAbr GAgs
- 'Lechistan' (Au/S) ECho GAbr IPen ITim MAsh MFie SPop WCre
- 'Lee' (Au/A) IPen WAln WCre
- 'Lee Clark' (Au/A) MFie WAln
- 'Lee Paul' (Au/A) GAbr GCai IPen LRHS MAsh MFie NHol SPop WCre WHil
- 'Lee Sharpe' (Au/A) IPen MFie SPop WAln
- 'Lemmy Getatem' (Au/d) SPop
- 'Lemon Drop' (Au/S) ITim MAsh NBro SPop
- 'Lemon Sherbet' (Au/B) SPop WHil
- 'Lepton Jubilee' (Au/S) GAbr WAln
- 'Leroy Brown' (Au/A) WAln
- 'Lester' (Au/d) SPop
- 'Letty' (Au/S) WAln
- 'Leverton' (Au/d) WAln
- 'Lichfield' (Au/A/d) IPen SPop WAln WCre
- 'Light Hearted' (Au) MFie WFar
- 'Light Music' (Au/d) WAln
- 'Lila' (Au/S) WAln
- 'Lilac Domino' (Au/S) GAbr IPen ITim MFie NEgg SPop WAln WFar WHil
- 'Lillian Hill' (Au/A) WAln
- 'Lima' (Au/d) MFie WAln
- 'Limelight' (Au/A) SPop WAln
- 'Limelight' (Au/S) IPen WAln
- 'Lincoln Bullion' (Au/d) **new** SPop
- 'Lincoln Charm' (Au) GAbr
- 'Lincoln Chestnut' (Au/d) SPop
- 'Lincoln Imp' (Au/d) SPop
- 'Lincoln Imperial' (Au/d) **new** SPop
- 'Lindley' (Au/S) ITim MAsh
- 'Lindsey Moreno' (Au/S) WAln
- 'Ling' (Au/A) MFie SPop WCre
- 'Lintz' (Au/B) MAsh MFie
- 'Linze 2' (Au/S) **new** MFie
- 'Lisa' (Au/A) IPen MFie SPop WCre WFar WHil
- 'Lisa Clara' (Au/S) EBee GAbr GAgs GCai IPen ITim MAsh MFie SPop WFar
- 'Lisa's Smile' (Au/S) GCai ITim MFie SPop
- 'Little Rosetta' (Au/d) WAln
- 'Lockyer's Gem' (Au/B/St) **new** NEgg
- 'Lofty' (Au/St) **new** MAsh
- 'Lord Saye and Sele' (Au/St) GAbr GCai IPen ITim MAsh MFie NEgg SPop WCre WHil
- 'Lothlorien' (Au/A) WAln
- 'Louisa Woolhead' (Au/d) SPop
- 'Lovebird' (Au/S) CPBP CWCL GAbr ITim LRHS MAsh MFie SPop
- 'Lucky Strike' (Au) WAln
- 'Lucy Locket' (Au/B) CWCL EBee IPen LRHS NEgg NHol WCre
- 'Ludlow' (Au/S) GAbr
- 'Lynn' (Au/A) WAln
- 'Lynn Cooper' (Au) WFar
- 'MacWatt's Blue' (Au/B) GAbr IGor IPen MFie SPop
- 'Madelaine Palmer' (Au/d) SPop
- 'Maggie' (Au/S) GAbr ITim SPop WCre
- 'Magnolia' (Au/B) WCre
- 'Maid Marion' (Au/d) MAsh WCre
- 'Maizie' (Au/S) WAln
- 'Mandarin' (Au/A) MFie SPop WCre WFar WHil
- 'Mansell's Green' (Au/S) WAln
- 'Margaret' (Au/S) GAbr
- 'Margaret Faulkner' (Au/A) GAbr GCai MFie WCre
- 'Margaret Irene' (Au/A) IPen SPop WAln WCre
- 'Margaret Martin' (Au/S) IPen MAsh MFie SPop WAln
- 'Margot Fonteyn' (Au/A) SPop WAln
- 'Marie Crousse' (Au/d) CMea CPBP CSsd GMaP LRHS MFie NHol SPop WCre WFar
- 'Marigold' (Au/d) WFar
- 'Marion Howard Spring' (Au/A) MFie WAln WCre
- 'Marion Tiger' (Au/St) WAln
- 'Mark' (Au/A) IPen MAsh MFie NBro SPop WCre WFar
- 'Marmion' (Au/S) GAgs IPen ITim MFie SPop WAln WFar WHil
- 'Martha Livesley' (Au/A) WAln
- 'Martha's Choice' (Au/A) WAln
- 'Martin Fish' (Au) WCre
- 'Martin Luther King' (Au/S) CWCL
- 'Mary' (Au/d) GAbr SPop
- 'Mary Taylor' (Au/S) WAln
- 'Mary Zach' (Au/S) MFie WHil

- 'Matthew Yates' (Au/d) CWCL EBee GAbr GCai IPen LRHS MAsh MFie NHol NPri SBch SDnm SPav SPop WCot WCre WHil
- 'Maureen Millward' (Au/A) IPen MFie SPop WCre
- 'May' (Au/A) WAln WCre
- 'Mazetta Stripe' (Au/S/St) GAbr ITim MFie NLar SPop
- 'Meadowlark' (Au/A) ITim MFie SPop WAln WCre WFar
- 'Mease Tiger' (Au/St) GAbr WAln
- 'Megan' (Au/d) WAln
- 'Mellifluous' (Au) MFie WAln WCre WFar WHil
- 'Melody' (Au/S) IPen SPop
- 'Mere Green' (Au/S) WAln
- 'Merlin' (Au/A) EBee IPen
- 'Merlin' (Au/S) MFie WAln
- 'Merlin Stripe' (Au/St) IPen SPop WCre WHil
- 'Merridale' (Au/A) GAbr MFie WCre
- 'Mersey Tiger' (Au/S) GAbr ITim MAsh MFie SPop WCre WHil
- 'Metha' (Au/A) WAln
- 'Mexicano' (Au/A) WAln
- 'Michael' (Au/S) MAsh MFie SPop WAln
- 'Michael Wattam' (Au/S) WAln
- 'Mick' (Au/A) MAsh MFie WAln
- 'Midland Marvel' (Au/St) **new** SPop
- 'Midnight' (Au/A) WAln
- 'Mikado' (Au/S) IPen MAsh MFie WCre WHil
- 'Milkmaid' (Au/A) WMAq
- 'Millicent' (Au/A) MFie WAln WFar
- 'Mink' (Au/A) MFie WFar
- 'Minley' (Au/S) CPBP GAbr GCai MFie NBir NBro NEgg NHol SPop WCre
- 'Minstead' (Au/S) **new** SPop
- 'Minstrel' (Au/S) MAsh MFie WCre
- 'Mipsie Miranda' (Au/d) SPop
- 'Mirabella Bay' (Au/A) WAln
- 'Mirandinha' (Au/A) MFie WAln
- 'Miriam' (Au/A) SPop WAln
- 'Miss Bluey' (Au/d) SPop WAln
- 'Miss Newman' (Au/A) SPop WAln
- 'Miss Pinky' SPop
- 'Mojave' (Au/S) CWCL GAbr IPen MFie NEgg NHol NRya SPop WCre
- 'Mollie Langford' (Au/A) MFie SPop WAln WHil
- 'Monet' (Au/S) WAln
- 'Moneymoon' (Au/S) IPen WCre WHil
- 'Monica' (Au/A) MFie
- 'Monk' (Au/S) MFie
- 'Monk's Eleigh' (Au/A) WAln
- 'Moody Cow' (Au/St) **new** MAsh
- 'Moon Fairy' (Au) **new** MAsh
- 'Moonglow' (Au/S) LRHS MAsh
- 'Moonlight' (Au/S) GAbr WAln
- 'Moonriver' (Au/A) NHol SPop WAln WCre WFar
- 'Moonshadow' (Au/d) WAln
- 'Moselle' (Au/S) MAsh WAln
- 'Mr A' (Au/S) SPop WHil
- 'Mr Greenfingers' (Au) WCre
- 'Mrs Harris' (Au/B) **new** WAln
- 'Mrs J.H. Watson' (Au) WCre
- 'Mrs L. Hearn' (Au/A) GAbr IPen SPop
- 'Mrs R. Bolton' (Au/A) WFar
- 'Murray Lanes' (Au/A) WAln
- 'My Buddy' (Au/St) **new** SPop
- 'My Fair Lady' (Au/A) MFie WAln
- 'Nankenan' (Au/S) ITim MFie WAln
- 'Neat and Tidy' (Au/S) ECho GAbr LRHS MAsh MFie NHol NRya SPop WCre WFar
- 'Nefertiti' (Au/A) IPen MFie SPop WAln WHil
- 'Nessun Dorma' (Au/A) SPop WAln
- 'Neville Telford' (Au/S) GAbr IPen MAsh MFie WFar WHil
- 'Nick Drake' (Au/d) **new** SPop
- 'Nickity' (Au/A) GAbr IPen ITim MAsh MFie SPop WFar
- 'Nicola Jane' (Au/A) SPop WAln
- 'Nigel' (Au/d) GAbr MFie
- 'Night and Day' (Au/S) SPop
- 'Nightwatch' (Au/S) **new** WAln
- 'Nightwink' (Au/S) WAln
- 'Nil Amber' **new** SPop
- 'Nina' (Au/A) WAln
- 'Nita' (Au/d) WAln
- 'Nocturne' (Au/S) IPen LRHS NBro NHol SPop
- 'Nona' (Au/d) SPop
- 'Nonchalance' (Au/A) MFie SPop WHil
- 'Norma' (Au/A) MFie
- 'Notability' (Au/A) ITim WAln
- 'Notable' (Au/A) WAln
- 'Nymph' (Au/d) MFie SPop
- 'Oake's Blue' (Au/S) MAsh
- 'Oakie' (Au/S) WAln
- 'Oban' (Au/S) ITim SPop
- 'Oikos' (Au/B) SPop
- 'Ol' Blue Eyes' (Au/St) WAln
- 'Old Clove Red' (Au/B) GAbr GAgs MFie
- 'Old Cottage Blue' (Au/B) GAbr WFar
- 'Old England' (Au/S) MFie SPop
- 'Old Gold' (Au/S) GAbr IPen NHol WFar
- 'Old Irish Blue' (Au/B) ECho IGor NEgg
- 'Old Irish Scented' (Au/B) GAbr IGor IPen NBro
- 'Old Irish Yellow' (Au) **new** NEgg
- 'Old Pink Dusty Miller' (Au/B) GAbr IPen

§ - 'Old Purple Dusty Miller' (Au/B) GAbr

- 'Old Red Dusty Miller' (Au/B) GAbr LLHF SPop WHil
- 'Old Red Elvet' (Au/S) GAbr SPop WAln
- 'Old Smokey' (Au/A) SPop WAln WHil
- 'Old Suffolk Bronze' (Au/B) GAbr GAgs WHil
- 'Old Yellow Dusty Miller' (Au/B) EWes GAbr GCai IPen NBro NHol NRya
- 'Olivia' (Au/d) SPop
- 'Olton' (Au/A) IPen MFie
- 'Optimist' (Au/St) SPop
- 'Opus One' (Au/A) WAln
- 'Orb' (Au/S) GAbr IPen ITim MAsh MFie SPop
- 'Ordvic' (Au/S) WAln
- 'Orlando' (Au/S) MFie SPop WAln
- 'Orwell Tiger' (Au/St) IPen SPop
- 'Osbourne Green' (Au/B) GAbr GCai MFie SPop WCre WHil
- 'Otto Dix' (Au/A) WAln
- 'Overdale' (Au/A) WAln
- 'Paddlin Madeleine' (Au/A) WAln
- 'Pagoda Belle' (Au/A) WAln
- 'Paleface' (Au/A) IPen ITim MFie WAln WCre
- 'Pam Tiger' (Au/St) WAln
- 'Panache' (Au/S) WAln
- 'Papageno' (Au/St) WAln
- 'Paphos' (Au/d) MAsh SPop
- 'Paradise Yellow' (Au/B) GEdr NEgg SPop
- 'Paragon' (Au/A) ITim WHil
- 'Party Time' (Au/S) IPen WAln
- 'Pastiche' (Au/A) MFie WCre
- 'Pat' (Au/S) SPop
- 'Pat Barnard' (Au) IPen
- 'Patience' (Au/S) ITim SPop WHil
- 'Patricia Barras' (Au/S) WAln
- 'Pauline' (Au/A) MFie
- 'Pauline Taylor' (Au/d) WAln

- 'Pegasus' (Au/d)	SPop WAln
- 'Peggy' (Au/A)	GAbr WHil
- 'Peggy's Lad' (Au/A)	WAln
- 'Pequod' (Au/A)	SPop WAln
- 'Peter Beardsley' (Au/A)	WAln
- 'Peter Hall' (Au/d)	WAln
- 'Phantom' (Au)	WAln
- 'Pharaoh' (Au/A)	GAgs MFie SPop WAln WFar
- 'Phyllis Douglas' (Au/A)	IPen ITim MFie NEgg SPop WCre WHil
- 'Piccadilly' (Au/S) **new**	MAsh
- 'Pierot' (Au/A)	IPen MFie SPop WCre
- 'Piers Telford' (Au/A)	CWCL EBee GAbr GCai IPen LRHS MFie NEgg SBch SDnm SPav SPop WCre
- 'Piglet' (Au)	GAbr
- 'Pink Fondant' (Au/d)	WAln
- 'Pink Lady' (Au/A)	MFie NBro SPop
- 'Pink Panther' (Au/S)	WAln
- 'Pinkie' (Au/A)	WAln
- 'Pinstripe'	IPen SPop WCre WHil
- 'Pioneer Stripe' (Au/S)	IPen
- 'Pippin' (Au/A)	GAbr IPen MFie NBro SPop WCre WFar
- 'Pixie' (Au/A)	IPen MFie WAln
- 'Plain Jane' (Au) **new**	MAsh
- 'Playboy' (Au/A)	WAln
- 'Plush Royal' (Au/S)	WAln
- 'Polestar' (Au/A)	MFie SPop WCre WFar WHil
- 'Pop's Blue' (Au/S/d)	NEgg SPop
- 'Portree' (Au/S)	GAbr SPop
- 'Pot o' Gold' (Au/S)	CPBP EBee ECho IPen ITim MAsh MFie NEgg SPop WCre WFar WHil
- 'Prague' (Au/S)	GAbr IPen MAsh MFie NBir NHol SPop
- 'Pretender' (Au/A)	SPop WAln
- 'Pride of Poland' (Au/S) **new**	LRHS SPop
- 'Prince Bishop' (Au/S)	WAln
- 'Prince Charming' (Au/S)	IPen MFie SPop
- 'Prince John' (Au/A)	MAsh MFie NBro NHol SPop WCre WFar WHil
- 'Prometheus' (Au/d)	MAsh MFie NRya SPop WAln WCre WHil
- 'Prosperine' (Au/S) **new**	MAsh
- 'Purple Dusty Miller'	see *P. auricula* 'Old Purple Dusty Miller'
- 'Purple Emperor' (Au/A)	MFie
- 'Purple Frills' (Au)	MFie
- 'Purple Glow' (Au/d)	WAln
- 'Purple Haze'	SPop
- 'Purple Prose' (Au/St)	MFie SPop
- 'Purple Rain' (Au) **new**	MAsh
- 'Purple Sage' (Au/S)	GCai ITim MFie NHol
- 'Purple Velvet' (Au/S)	CWCL IPen NHol SPop
- 'Quatro' (Au/d)	SPop WAln
- 'Queen Alexandra' (Au/B)	GAbr GAgs
- 'Queen Bee' (Au/S)	GAbr MFie WFar
- 'Queen of Sheba' (Au/S)	WAln
- 'Queen's Bower' (Au/S)	SPop
- 'Quintessence' (Au/A)	MFie WAln WCre
- 'Rab C. Nesbitt' (Au/A)	WAln
- 'Rabley Heath' (Au/A)	GAgs GCai MFie SPop
- 'Rachel' (Au/A)	GAbr WAln
- 'Rajah' (Au/S)	EBee ECho GAbr IPen LRHS MAsh MFie NEgg NHol SPop WCre WFar WHil
- 'Raleigh Stripe' (Au/St)	GAgs IPen WAln
- 'Ralenzano' (Au/A)	WAln
- 'Rameses' (Au/A)	IPen MFie WAln WCre
- 'Rebecca Hyatt' (Au/d)	WAln
- 'Red Admiral' (Au)	WAln
- 'Red and White Stripe' (Au/S/St)	WFar
- 'Red Arrows' (Au)	WAln
- 'Red Beret' (Au/S)	LRHS
- 'Red Embers' (Au/S)	WAln
- 'Red Gauntlet' (Au/S)	GAbr GCai IPen ITim LRHS MFie MRav NHol SPop WFar
- 'Red Mark' (Au/A)	MFie
- 'Red Rum' (Au/S)	GAbr
- 'Red Sonata' (Au/S) **new**	SPop
- 'Red Vulcan' (Au)	WCre
- 'Red Wire'	MAsh SPop
- 'Redcar' (Au/A)	GAbr MFie WAln WCre
- 'Redstart' (Au/S)	IPen ITim
- 'Redstart' (Au/B)	ITim
- 'Regency' (Au/A)	WAln
- 'Regency Dandy' (Au/St) **new**	SPop
- 'Regency Emperor' (Au/St) **new**	SPop
- 'Remus' (Au/S)	ECho ELan GAbr GCai IPen ITim LLHF MAsh MFie NEgg NHol SPop WCre WFar WHil
- 'Rene' (Au/A)	GAbr IPen MFie WCre
- 'Respectable' (Au/A)	WAln
- 'Reverie' (Au/d)	WAln
- 'Reynardyne' (Au/d) **new**	SPop
- 'Riatty' (Au/d)	GAbr WAln
- 'Richard Shaw' (Au/A)	IPen
- 'Ring of Bells' (Au/S)	WAln
- 'Risdene' (Au)	IPen
- 'Rita' (Au/S)	WAln
- 'Robert Lee' (Au/A)	WAln
- 'Roberto' (Au/S)	MAsh WAln
- 'Robin Hood Stripe' (Au/St)	SPop
- 'Robinette' (Au/d)	SPop
- 'Rock Sand' (Au/S)	ECho GCai MFie WFar WHil
- 'Rodeo' (Au/A)	CStu IPen SPop WPat
- 'Rolts' (Au/S)	EBee ECho GAbr GKev IPen MAsh MFie NBro NHol SDnm SPav SPop WCre WFar WHil
- 'Rondy' (Au/S)	MFie
- 'Ronnie Johnson' (Au)	WAln
- 'Ronny Simpson'	WCre
- 'Rosalie' (Au)	SPop
- 'Rosalie Edwards' (Au/S)	MFie SPop
- 'Rose Conjou' (Au/d)	GAbr IPen MFie SPop WAln WFar
- 'Rose Kaye' (Au/A)	GAbr IPen SPop
- 'Rosebud' (Au/S)	GAbr
- 'Rosemarket Rackler' (Au/B) **new**	SPop
- 'Rosemary' (Au/S)	MAsh MFie SPop WCre WHil
- 'Rosewood' (Au) **new**	WCre
- 'Rothesay Robin' (Au/A)	WAln
- 'Rowena' (Au/A)	GCai IPen MFie NBro SDnm SPav SPop WCre WHil
- 'Roxborough' (Au/A)	CWCL IPen WAln
- 'Roxburgh' (Au/A)	MFie SPop WCre
- 'Roy Keane' (Au/A)	IPen MFie SPop
- 'Royal Mail' (Au/S)	MAsh SPop WAln
- 'Royal Marine' (Au/S)	WAln
- 'Royal Velvet' (Au/S)	GAbr GAgs IPen NHol WHil
- 'Ruby Hyde' (Au/B)	GAbr
- 'Rumbled' (Au/St) **new**	MAsh
- 'Rusty Dusty' (Au)	GAbr GAgs IGor
- 'Ryecroft' (Au/A)	WAln
- 'Sabrina' (Au/A)	WAln
- 'Saginaw' (Au/A)	WAln
- 'Sailor Boy' (Au/S)	MFie SPop
- 'Saint Boswells' (Au/S)	GAbr NRya SPop WAln
- 'Saint Elmo' (Au/A)	MFie

– 'Saint Quentin' (Au/S)	WAln
– 'Sale Green' (Au/S)	MFie
– 'Sally' (Au/A)	WAln
– 'Sam Gamgee' (Au/A)	WAln
– 'Sam Hunter' (Au/A)	SPop WAln
– 'Samantha' (Au/A)	WAln
– 'Sandhills' (Au/A)	MFie WAln WCre WHil
– 'Sandmartin' (Au/S)	MFie
– 'Sandra' (Au/A)	ECho ELan GAbr IPen MAsh MFie SPop WCre WHil
– 'Sandra's Lass' (Au/A)	SPop WAln
– 'Sandwood Bay' (Au/A)	GAbr GCai LRHS MFie NBro NEgg NHol SPop WCre WHil
– 'Sarah Gisby' (Au/d)	MFie SPop
– 'Sarah Lodge' (Au/d)	GAbr IPen MAsh SPop
– 'Satin Doll' (Au/d)	MFie SPop
– 'Scipio' (Au/S)	WAln
– 'Scorcher' (Au/S)	IPen SPop WAln
– 'Searchlight' (Au)	WCre
– 'Second Victory' (Au)	WCre
– 'Serenity' (Au/S)	MFie NHol WCre
– 'Sergeant Wilson' (Au)	SPop WAln
– 'Shalford' (Au/d)	MFie SPop WCre WFar
– 'Sharman's Cross' (Au/S)	MFie WAln
– 'Sharon Louise' (Au/S)	IPen MAsh WCre
– 'Sheila' (Au/S)	ECho GAbr MAsh SPop WCre WFar WHil
– 'Shere' (Au/S)	MFie SPop WCre
– 'Shergold' (Au/A)	MFie WCre
– 'Sherwood' (Au/S)	GAgs GCai IPen MAsh MFie SPop WHil
– 'Shirley' (Au/S)	SPop WAln
– 'Shotley' (Au/A)	MFie SPop
– 'Show Bandit' (Au/St) **new**	SPop
– 'Showman' (Au/S)	WAln
– 'Sibsey' (Au/d)	CWCL MAsh SPop WAln
– 'Sidney' (Au/A)	WAln
– 'Silas' (Au/B)	SPav
– 'Silmaril' (Au)	SPop WAln
– 'Silver Rose' (Au) **new**	MAsh
– 'Silverway' (Au/S)	ITim MAsh SPop WHil
– 'Simply Red' (Au)	IPen MAsh MFie SPop WAln
– 'Sir John' (Au/A)	MAsh MFie WFar WHil
– 'Sir John Hall'	MFie
– 'Sir Robert' (Au/d)	WAln
– 'Sirbol' (Au/A)	GAgs IPen MFie SPop WCre WFar
– 'Sirius' (Au/A)	CWCL GAbr IPen LRHS MFie NHol NRya SPop WCre WFar
– 'Skipper' (Au/d)	SPop
– 'Skylark' (Au/A)	GAbr IPen ITim SPop WAln WCre WHil
– 'Slim Whitman' (Au/A) **new**	WAln
– 'Slioch' (Au/S)	ECho GAbr IPen ITim MAsh MFie NHol SPop WCre
– 'Slip Anchor' (Au/A)	WAln
– 'Smart Tar' (Au/S)	WAln
– 'Snooty Fox' (Au/A)	IPen MFie SPop
– 'Snooty Fox II' (Au/A)	MFie
– 'Snowy Owl' (Au/S)	GAbr MFie SPop WCre
– 'Soliloquy' (Au) **new**	MAsh
– 'Somersby' (Au/d)	SPop WAln
– 'Soncy Face' (Au/A)	MFie WAln
– 'Sonny Boy' (Au/A)	WAln
– 'Sophie' (Au/d)	SPop WAln
– 'South Barrow' (Au/d)	GAbr ITim SPop WCre
– 'Sparky' (Au/A)	WAln
– 'Spartan' (Au)	WAln
– 'Spitfire' (Au/S) **new**	MAsh
– 'Spokey' (Au)	IPen
– 'Spring Meadows' (Au/S)	GAbr MAsh MFie NEgg NHol SPop
– 'Springtime' (Au/A)	SPop WAln
– 'Standish' (Au/d)	GAbr
– 'Stant's Blue' (Au/S)	GCai IPen MAsh MFie NBro WFar
– 'Star Wars' (Au/S)	MAsh MFie NHol SPop WAln
– 'Starburst' (Au/S)	WAln
– 'Starling' (Au/B)	GAbr IPen SPop
– 'Starry' (Au/S)	WCre
– 'Stella Coop' (Au/d)	WAln
– 'Stoke Poges' (Au/A)	WAln
– 'Stoney Cross' (Au/S)	SPop
– 'Stonnal' (Au/A)	MFie SPop
– 'Stormin Norman' (Au/A)	MFie SPop WAln
– 'Stripey' (Au/d)	IPen NHol WAln
– 'Stromboli' (Au/d)	SPop
– 'Subliminal' (Au/A)	WAln
– 'Sue' (Au/A)	MFie WCre WFar
– 'Suede Shoes' (Au/S) **new**	SPop
– 'Sugar Plum Fairy' (Au/S)	GAbr GAgs WHil
– 'Sultan' (Au/A)	WAln
– 'Summer Sky' (Au/A)	SPop WCre
– 'Summer Wine' (Au/A)	MFie
– 'Sumo' (Au/A)	GAgs MAsh MFie SPop WAln WCre WFar WHil
– 'Sunflower' (Au/A/S)	GAbr ITim MAsh MFie SPop WCre
– 'Sunsplash' (Au)	WCre
– 'Super Para' (Au/S)	GAbr IPen MFie SPop WHil
– 'Superb' (Au/S)	MFie WAln
– 'Susan' (Au/A)	MFie WCre
– 'Susannah' (Au/d)	CWCL GCai GMaP IPen LRHS MFie NHol NPri SDnm SPav SPop WCre WFar
* – 'Sweet Chestnut' (Au/S)	WAln
– 'Sweet Georgia Brown' (Au/A)	SPop WAln
– 'Sweet Pastures' (Au/S)	ECho GAbr IPen MFie NHol SPop WCre
– 'Sword' (Au/d)	CWCL ECho GAbr IPen ITim MAsh MFie NHol SPop WAln WCre WFar WHil
– 'Symphony' (Au/A)	MFie SPop WFar WHil
– 'T.A. Hadfield' (Au/A)	MFie SPop WFar WHil
– 'Taffeta' (Au/S)	CWCL EBee LRHS MAsh SDnm SPav WAln
– 'Tall Purple Dusty Miller' (Au/B)	SPop
– 'Tally-ho' (Au/A)	WAln
– 'Tamar Mist' (Au) **new**	MAsh
– 'Tamino' (Au/S)	MFie WAln
– 'Tandem' (Au/St)	WAln
– 'Tarantella' (Au/A)	MFie SPop
– 'Tawny Owl' (Au/B)	NBro
– 'Tay Tiger' (Au/St)	GAbr MAsh MFie SPop
– 'Teawell Pride' (Au/d)	ITim SPop
– 'Ted Gibbs' (Au/A)	MFie WAln WCre
– 'Ted Roberts' (Au/A)	MFie SPop WCre WFar
– 'Teem' (Au/S)	GAbr IPen MAsh SPop
– 'Temeraire' (Au/A)	MFie WAln
– 'Tenby Grey' (Au/S)	WCre
– 'Tender Trap' (Au/A)	WAln
– 'Terpo' (Au/A)	MFie WAln
– 'The Argylls' (Au/St) **new**	SPop
– 'The Baron' (Au/S)	GCai IPen ITim MFie SPop WCre WFar WHil
– 'The Bishop' (Au/S)	GAgs IPen SPop WHil
– 'The Bride' (Au/S)	MFie
– 'The Cardinal' (Au/d)	WAln
– 'The Czar' (Au/A)	MFie
– 'The Egyptian' (Au/A)	IPen SPop WAln WHil
– 'The Hobbit' (Au/A)	WAln
– 'The Maverick' (Au/S)	MFie
– 'The Raven' (Au/S)	ITim MAsh MFie SPop WCre
– 'The Sneep' (Au/A)	IPen MFie SPop WCre WFar
– 'The Snods' (Au/S)	EBee IPen MFie SPop
– 'The Wrekin' (Au/S)	WAln

Name	Suppliers
– 'Thetis' (Au/A)	MFie SPop WCre WFar
– 'Thirlmere' (Au/d)	WAln
– 'Three Way Stripe' (St)	GAbr WCre WHil
– 'Thunderstorm' (Au) **new**	MAsh
– 'Thutmoses' (Au/A)	WAln
– 'Tiger Tim' (Au/St)	WAln
– 'Tim' (Au)	IPen
– 'Tinker' (Au/S)	WAln
– 'Tinkerbell' (Au/S)	IPen MAsh MFie SPop WCre WFar
– 'Titania' (Au)	SPop
– 'Toffee Crisp' (Au/A)	IPen WAln
– 'Tom Farmer' (Au)	WCre
– 'Tomboy' (Au/S)	IPen MAsh SDnm SPop
– 'Toolyn' (Au/S)	WAln
– 'Tosca' (Au/S)	EBee GCai IPen MAsh NRya SPop WFar WHil
– 'Trish'	GAbr
– 'Trojan' (Au/S)	MAsh WCre
– 'Trouble' (Au/d)	EBee GMaP IPen LRHS MAsh MFie NRya SPop WCre WHil
– 'Troy Aykman' (Au/A)	MFie SPop WAln
– 'Trudy' (Au/S)	GAbr GCai IPen ITim MAsh MFie SPop WCre WHil
– 'True Briton' (Au/S)	IPen MFie SPop WCre
– 'Trumpet Blue' (Au/S)	MFie SPop WFar
– 'Tumbledown' (Au/A)	MFie
– 'Tummel'	MFie SPop WAln WHil
– 'Twiggy' (Au/S)	GCai NRya SPop WAln
– 'Tye Lea' (Au/S)	WAln
– 'Typhoon' (Au/A)	IPen MFie SPop WCre
– 'Uncle Arthur' (Au/A)	MFie WAln
– 'Unforgettable' (Au/A)	MFie WAln
– 'Upton Belle' (Au/S)	IPen MAsh MFie SPop WAln WFar
– 'Ushba' (Au/d) **new**	SPop
– 'Valerie' (Au/A)	IPen MFie SPop
– 'Valerie Clare'	WAln WHil
– 'Vee Too' (Au/A)	GAbr MFie SPop WFar WHil
– 'Vega' (Au/A)	SPop WAln
– 'Vein' (Au/St)	WAln
– 'Velvet Moon' (Au/A)	MFie WAln WFar
– 'Venetian' (Au/A)	MFie SPop WAln WFar WHil
– 'Venus' (Au/A)	WAln
– 'Vera' (Au/A)	SPop
– 'Verdi' (Au/A)	WAln
– 'Vesuvius' (Au/d)	IPen SPop
– 'Victoria' (Au/S)	WAln
– 'Victoria de Wemyss' (Au/A)	MFie WCre WHil
– 'Victoria Park' (Au/A)	WAln
– 'Virginia Belle' (Au/St)	WAln
– 'Vivian' (Au/S)	WAln
– 'Vulcan' (Au/A)	ECho MAsh MFie NBro SPop
– 'Walter Lomas' (Au/S)	WAln
– 'Walton' (Au/A)	GAbr LRHS MAsh MFie SPop WCre WFar WHil
– 'Walton Heath' (Au/d)	ECho IPen MAsh MFie SPop WCre WFar
– 'Waltz Time' (Au/A)	MFie
– 'Wanda's Moonlight' (Au/d)	WAln
– 'Warwick' (Au/S)	MAsh MFie SPop
– 'Watchett' (Au/S)	MAsh WAln
– 'Wayward' (Au/S)	WCre
– 'Wedding Day' (Au/S)	ITim MFie WAln
– 'Wentworth' (Au/A)	IPen WAln
– 'Whistle Jacket' (Au/S)	SPop WAln
– 'White Ensign' (Au/S)	ECho GAbr IPen ITim SPop WCre WFar
– 'White Water' (Au/A)	MFie SPop WAln
– 'White Wings' (Au/S)	GCai ITim MFie SPop
– 'Whitecap' (Au/S)	WAln
– 'Whoopee' (Au/A)	WAln
– 'Wichita Falls' (Au/A)	WAln
– 'Wilf Booth' (Au/A)	MFie SPop WAln WFar
– 'William Gunn' (Au/d) **new**	MFie SPop
– 'Wilson's Wonder' (Au) **new**	MAsh
– 'Wincha' (Au/S)	GCai MFie NEgg SPop WCre WFar
– 'Windways Mystery' (Au/B)	GAbr
– 'Winifrid' (Au/A)	GAbr LRHS NHol SPop WCre WFar
– 'Witchcraft' (Au)	SPop
– 'Woodmill' (Au/A)	IPen MFie SPop WAln
– 'Wycliffe Midnight' (Au)	GAbr
– 'Wye Hen' (Au/St)	SPop WAln
– 'Wye Lemon' (Au/S)	SPop
– 'X2' (Au)	WHil
– 'Yellow Hammer' (Au/S)	WAln
– 'Yellow Isle' (Au/S)	WAln
– 'Yellow Ribbon' **new**	WAln
– 'Yitzhak Rabin' (Au/A)	WAln WHil
– 'Yorkshire Grey' (Au/S)	IPen MFie NBro
– 'Zambia' (Au/d)	ECho GAbr ITim MFie SPop WCre
– 'Zircon' (Au/S)	MAsh WAln
– 'Zodiac' (Au/S)	WAln
– 'Zoe' (Au/A)	WAln
– 'Zoe Ann' (Au/S)	WAln
– 'Zorro' (Au/St)	WAln
auriculata (Or)	EBee GKev
– subsp. ***olgae*** (Or) **new**	GKev
'Barbara Barker' (Au)	GEdr NMen
'Barbara Midwinter' (Pr)	CDes GAbr GEdr SHar WAbe
Barnhaven Blues Group (Pr/Prim) $\mathbb{Y}^{H4}$	CSWP EBla GAbr
Barnhaven doubles (Pr/Prim/d)	CSWP
Barnhaven Gold-laced Group	see *P.* Gold-laced Group Barnhaven
Barnhaven hybrids	NSum
Barnhaven Traditional Group (Pr)	CSWP
'Beatrice Wooster' (Au)	GAbr GKir IPen LRHS MFie NDlv NLAp NWCA WFar
'Beeches' Pink'	GAbr
beesiana (Pf)	Widely available
– 'Golden' **new**	LRHS
(Belarina Series) 'Belarina Butter Yellow' (Pr/Prim/d)	CWCL EPfP EWll GAbr LAst NLar SIng SMrm SVil WHil
– 'Belarina Cobalt Blue' (Pr/Prim/d)	CWCL EWll SIng WHil
– 'Belarina Cream' (Pr/Prim/d)	CWCL EWll LLHF SIng SMrm SVil WHil
– 'Belarina Pink Ice' (Pr/Prim/d)	CWCL EWll LHop SIng SVil WHil
– 'Belarina Rosette Nectarine' (Pr/Prim/d)	CWCL ECtt EWll SIng SMrm SVil WHil
'Belinda'	ITim
bella (Mi) SDR 4542	GKev
bellidifolia (Mu)	EBee GEdr IPen
§ – subsp. ***hyacinthina*** (Mu)	WAbe
beluensis	see *P.* × *pubescens* 'Freedom'
§ × ***berninae*** 'Windrush' (Au)	WAbe
'Bewerley White'	see *P.* × *pubescens* 'Bewerley White'
bhutanica	see *P. whitei* 'Sherriff's Variety'
'Big Red Giant' (Pr/Prim/d)	ECtt
bileckii	see *P.* × *forsteri* 'Bileckii'
'Blue Riband' (Pr/Prim)	CDes EBee LLHF WFar
'Blue Sapphire' (Pr/Prim/d)	LRHS MFie
'Blutenkissen' (Pr/Prim)	GAbr GEdr
'Bon Accord Cerise' (Pr/Poly/d)	GAbr

	'Bon Accord Purple' (Pr/Poly/d)	WFar
	boothii (Pe)	NSum
	- EN 382	WThu
	- ***alba*** (Pe)	LLHF
	- subsp. ***repens*** (Pe)	CEnt MNrw
	'Boothman's Ruby'	see *P.* × *pubescens* 'Boothman's Variety'
§	***bracteosa*** (Pe)	GKev ITim
	Bressingham (Pf)	WFar
	brevicula (Cy) SDR 4770	GKev
	'Broadwell Milkmaid'	WAbe
	'Broadwell Pink' (Au)	WAbe
	'Broadwell Ruby' (Au)	WAbe
	'Bronwyn' (Pr/Prim)	WCot
	'Broxbourne'	MFie NHol
	'Buckland Wine' (Pr/Prim)	CElw
	× ***bulleesiana*** (Pf)	Widely available
	- Moerheim hybrids (Pf)	WFar
	bulleyana (Pf) ♀H4	Widely available
	- SDR 4261	GKev
	burmanica (Pf)	EBee GAbr GBuc GEdr GGar GKir IPen MMuc SRms SWat WFar WMoo
	'Butterscotch' (Pr/Prim)	CSWP
	'Caerulea Plena' (Pr/Prim)	GCal NBid
	Candelabra hybrids (Pf)	CBre CBro CHar CWCL ECho GAbr GGar GKir ITim LRHS LSou MNHC NBir NCob NGdn SGSe SMrm SPet SWal SWat WFar WPtf
	- orange-flowered (Pf) **new**	SMrm
	Candy Pinks Group (Pr/Prim)	CSWP
	capitata (Ca)	CMMP CMac CSWP CSpe EBee ECho EPfP GAbr GKev IPen NWCA SPer SPoG WFar WGwG WWFP
	- dark-flowered (Ca)	WCot
	- subsp. ***mooreana*** (Ca)	CFir CLAP CTsd EAlp IPen LBMP LRHS NDlv NGdn NLAp NSum SBch SMrm SPet SPlb SRot STes WHil WHrl WPtf
	- 'Norverna Blue' (Ca) **new**	CSpr
	'Captain Blood' (Pr/Prim/d)	CAby CDes ECtt EKen EPfP MFie WClo WFar
	carniolica (Au)	EPot GKev WCot
	Casquet mixture (Pr/Prim)	CSWP
	cernua (Mu)	GKev IPen
	Chartreuse Group (Pr/Poly)	CSWP GAbr
§	***chionantha*** (Cy) ♀H4	CLAP EBee EPfP EWTr GAbr GAuc GCra GGar GKev GKir LRHS NBPC NBir NCGa NCob NGdn NHol SBch WAbe WFar WGwG WPtf
	- SDR 4610	GKev
	- SDR 4847	GKev
	- subsp. ***chionantha*** (Cy)	EBee IPen
§	- subsp. ***melanops*** (Cy)	EBee GAuc
§	- subsp. ***sinopurpurea*** (Cy)	CLAP EBee GGar GKev GKir IPen MDKP NCGa NLar NSum SBch SPer WAbe WBVN WHil WPer
	- - SDR 1659	GKev
	- - SDR 2747	GKev
	chungensis (Pf)	CLAP CWCL EBee EPfP GBuc GCra GEdr GGar GKev GKir IPen LRHS NBPC NDlv NGdn NHol SBch SRms SWvt WAbe WMoo WSpi
§	***chungensis*** × ***pulverulenta*** (Pf)	CHid CLAP EBee GBuc GEdr GKir LRHS NBPC NHol NLar WMnd WWEG
	× ***chunglenta***	see *P. chungensis* × *P. pulverulenta*
	'Clarence Elliott' (Au)	CDes CPBP GKev IPen ITim MAsh MFie NMen WAbe WFar
	clarkei (Or)	GEdr GKev
	clusiana (Au)	GKev
	- 'Murray-Lyon' (Au)	NMen
	cockburniana (Pf) ♀H4	CBcs EBee EBla GAuc GEdr GGar GKev GQui IPen NGdn SRms SWat WAbe WFar
	- hybrids (Pf)	SWat
	- yellow-flowered (Pf)	EBee GEdr GKev GMac IPen
	concholoba (Mu)	GKev NLAp
	'Corporal Baxter' (Pr/Prim/d)	EPfP LLHF NLar
	cortusoides (Co)	CLAP EBee GAbr GCra GKev GKir IPen LFur LSou NLar SRms
	- SDR 4228	GKev
	Cowichan Amethyst Group (Pr/Poly)	CDes CSWP EBee NCGa
	Cowichan Blue Group (Pr/Poly)	CSWP NCGa
	Cowichan Garnet Group (Pr/Poly)	CDes CSWP GBuc NCGa WPGP
	Cowichan Red Group (Pr/Poly)	WFar
	Cowichan Venetian Group (Pr/Poly)	CDes CSWP NCGa WFar
	Cowichan Yellow Group (Pr/Poly)	NCGa WCot
	'Coy' (Au)	WAbe
	'Craven Gem' (Pr/Poly)	GBuc
	Crescendo Series (Pr/Poly)	GAbr WHil
	'Crimson Velvet' (Au)	GAbr IPen ITim NLAp
	crispa	see *P. glomerata*
	cuneifolia (Cu)	GKev
	darialica (Al)	EBee GKev LLHF
	'Dark Rosaleen' (Pr/Poly)	ECGP ECtt GAbr ITim LLHF NBPC SUsu WCot
	'David Valentine' (Pr)	EBla GAbr GBuc WCot
	'Dawn Ansell' (Pr/Prim/d)	CDes CRow CWCL EBla ECtt EPfP GAbr MFie MRav NBir NGHP SRGP WFar WHer WHil
	Daybreak Group (Pr/Poly)	CSWP NCGa
	deflexa (Mu)	IPen
	denticulata (De) ♀H4	Widely available
	- var. ***alba*** (De)	CBcs CTri CWCL CWat EBee ECha ECho EPfP GAbr GCra GGar GMaP LRHS MFie MWat NBid NCob NHol NOrc NPri SMrm SPer SPoG WClo WMoo WPer WWEG
	- blue-flowered (De)	CWCL ECho GAbr GKir LRHS NLar NPri SMrm WFar
	- 'Bressingham Beauty' (De)	LRHS
	- 'Glenroy Crimson' (De)	CLAP EBee LLHF SRms SWvt WCom
	- 'Karryann' (De/v)	CBow EBee SUsu WCot
	- lavender-flowered (De) **new**	LRHS
	- lilac-flowered (De)	ECho EHon MWat NCob NPri SMrm SPoG WWEG
	- 'Prichard's Ruby' (De)	NCob
	- purple-flowered (De)	ECho WMoo
	- red-flowered (De)	ECho GGar GKir MFie NBir NOrc WBor WMoo
	- 'Robinson's Red' (De)	GBuc
	- 'Ronsdorf' (De)	LBMP LRHS NBPC
	- rose-flowered (De)	GKir
	- 'Rubin' (De)	CHrt CWCL CWat ECho EHon GAbr GMaP LRHS MBrN MLHP NChi NCob SMrm SPer SPoG SRms WPer WWEG
	- 'Rubinball' (De)	EBee LRHS NHol
	deorum (Au)	GKev
	× ***deschmannii***	see *P.* × *vochinensis*
	'Desert Sunset' (Pr/Poly)	CSWP NCGa
	'Devon Cream' (Pr/Prim)	WFar

	Name	Suppliers
	'Don Keefe'[PBR]	CBod ECGP ECtt GBin GEdr GMac LLHF LSou MBNS MFie NBPC NGdn NLar WCot WFut
	'Dorothy' (Pr/Poly)	MRav
	'Double Lilac'	see *P. vulgaris* 'Lilacina Plena'
	dryadifolia (Dr) SDR 4422	GKev
	'Duckyls Red' (Pr/Prim)	GBuc WHal
	'Dusky Lady'	CLAP MBri WFar
	'Early Bird' (*allionii* hybrid) (Au)	IPen ITim
	'Easter Bonnet' (Pr/Prim)	NBid WCot
	edelbergii (Sp)	ITim
	edgeworthii	see *P. nana*
§	***elatior*** (Pr) 𝕐[H4]	CRWN CRow CSev EBWF EBee ECho GKev GKir MHer MNrw NChi NCob NEgg NLAp NMen NPri SBch SPer SPoG SRms SWvt WBrk WCot WFar WGwG WHil WPtf
	- SDR 3584	GKev
	- hose-in-hose (Pr/d)	NBid
	- hybrids (Pr)	GAbr MWat
I	- 'Jessica'	WCot WHil
	- subsp. ***leucophylla*** (Pr)	EBee ECho SBch
§	- subsp. ***meyeri*** (Pr)	EBee GKev GKir LLHF
	- subsp. ***pallasii*** (Pr)	GAuc
	'Elizabeth Browning' **new**	WCot
	'Elizabeth Killelay'[PBR] (Pr/Poly/d)	Widely available
	'Ellen Page' (Au)	MFie
	'Ethel Barker' (Au)	IPen ITim MFie NDlv NHol NLAp
	'Eugénie' (Pr/Prim/d)	ECtt GAbr LLHF MFie NLar SRGP
	'Fairy Rose' (Au)	IPen ITim NHol WAbe
	farinosa (Al)	EBee GKir IPen NGdn NSum SPoG WFar
	fasciculata (Ar)	GEdr GKev NWCA
	- CLD 345	WAbe
	'Fife Yellow' (Pr/Prim/d)	GBuc
	'Fire Opal'	EBrs LRHS
	Firefly Group (Pr/Poly)	NCGa WCot
§	***firmipes*** (Si)	EWes IPen
§	***flaccida*** (Mu)	GAuc GEdr GGGa GKev IPen NLAp WAbe
	Flamingo Group (Pr/Poly)	CSWP NCGa
	florida (Y)	NCob
	florindae (Si) 𝕐[H4]	Widely available
	- SDR 4626	GKev
	- bronze-flowered (Si)	GKir GQui NBir SWat
	- buff-flowered (Si)	GAuc
	- hybrids (Si)	CMac EHrv GAbr GEdr GKir GMaP ITim LBMP NCob NHol WHil
	- Keillour hybrids (Si)	CLAP NGdn WPtf
	- magenta-flowered (Si)	MDKP
	- 'Muadh' (Si)	MMuc
	- orange-flowered (Si)	CSam GCal GKev GMac IPen LLWG MDKP MNrw WFar WMoo
	- peach-flowered (Si)	MDKP
	- 'Ray's Ruby' (Si)	CHar CLAP EBee GBuc GEdr MDKP MNrw NBir NGdn SWat WWFP
	- red-flowered (Si)	GBin GBuc GGar GKev IPen LLWG NBid NLar NSum WCom WFar
	- terracotta-flowered (Si)	CSWP NGdn
	Footlight Parade Group (Pr/Prim)	CSWP
	forbesii (Mo)	WCot
	- CC 4084	CPLG
	forrestii (Bu)	EBee GAuc GKev IPen WAbe
	- SDR 4304	GKev
§	×***forsteri*** 'Bileckii' (Au)	LRHS NBir NWCA SRms
	- 'Dianne' (Au)	EDAr GAbr GBuc GKev NBro NHol NRya WAbe
	'Francisca' (Pr/Poly)	Widely available
	'Freckles' (Pr/Prim/d)	NGHP SWat

	Name	Suppliers
	frondosa (Al) 𝕐[H4]	ECho GCra IPen LRHS NLAp NMen NWCA WAbe
	'Garnet' (*allionii* hybrid) (Au)	MFie
	'Garryarde Guinevere'	see *P.* 'Guinevere'
	'Garryarde Crimson'	GEdr LLHF
	gemmifera (Ar)	GKev
	geraniifolia (Co)	CLAP GEdr
§	'Gigha' (Pr/Prim)	CLAP CSWP CSpe EBee GCal
	glaucescens (Au)	EPot GKev NSum
§	***glomerata*** (Ca)	ECho GBuc GKev IPen
	- CC 3843	GKev
	- GWJ 9213	WCru
	'Glowing Embers' (Pf)	GKev LLHF LRHS NBir
	glutinosa All.	see *P. allionii*
	glutinosa Wulfen (Au)	GKev
	Gold-laced Group (Pr/Poly)	Widely available
§	- Barnhaven (Pr/Poly)	EBla GAbr GKir NBPC NBir
	- Beeches strain (Pr/Poly) 𝕐[H4]	NCob
	gracilipes (Pe)	CDes CLAP MDKP NHol SRms WAbe
	- L&S 1166	WAbe
	- early-flowering (Pe)	GCra WAbe
	- late-flowering (Pe)	CLAP GCra
	- 'Major'	see *P. bracteosa*
	- 'Minor'	see *P. petiolaris* Wall.
	graminifolia	see *P. chionantha*
	Grand Canyon Group (Pr/Poly)	GAbr
	grandis (Sr)	IPen
	'Green Lace' (Pr/Poly)	NBhm WCot
	'Groenekan's Glorie' (Pr/Prim)	GAbr GEdr NBir NSum WFar
§	'Guinevere' (Pr/Poly) 𝕐[H4]	CSam EBee EBla EBrs EHoe EPfP GAbr GEdr GKir GMaP LRHS LSou MAvo MBri MFie NBPC NBid NBir NBro NCGa NHol NSla SPer SPlb WCom WCot WFar WHil WHoo WPat
	'Hall Barn Blue' (Pr/Prim)	EAlp GAbr GEdr NBPC NHol NMyG
§	***halleri*** (Al)	EBee GKev IPen LFur MDKP NDlv NLAp NSum WAbe
	- 'Longiflora'	see *P. halleri*
	Harbinger Group (Pr/Prim)	CSWP
	Harbour Lights mixture (Pr/Poly)	CSWP NCGa
	Harlow Carr hybrids (Pf)	CSWP EPfP GMac GQui LRHS NDlv NSla SPoG WMoo
	Harvest Yellows Group (Pr/Poly)	NCGa WCot
	'Helmswell Abbey' (Au)	GKev
	helodoxa	see *P. prolifera*
	'Hemswell Blush' (Au)	CSpe GKev ITim NLAp NLar WCre
	'Hemswell Ember' (Au)	CPBP NDlv NHol NLAp NRya
	heucherifolia (Co)	GAuc IPen
	- SDR 3224	GKev
	hidakana (R)	GEdr
	'High Point' (Au)	NMen
	hirsuta (Au)	IPen
	- red-flowered (Au)	MMuc NLAp
	- subsp. ***valcuvianensis*** (Au) **new**	EPot
	hookeri (Pe) **new**	GKev
	hose-in-hose (Pr/Poly/d)	CSWP MNrw
	'Hyacinthia' (Au)	IPen MFie NLar
	hyacinthina	see *P. bellidifolia* subsp. *hyacinthina*
	ianthina	see *P. prolifera*
	iljinskyi	GKev
	incana (Al)	EBee
	Indian Reds Group (Pr/Poly)	CSWP

	'Ingram's Blue' (Pr/Poly)	WPen
	Inshriach hybrids (Pf)	CMHG CSWP LRHS NSum WFar
	integrifolia (Au)	GBuc GEdr GKev
	integrifolia × ***minima*** 'Kilchuimin' (Au)	GEdr
§	'Inverewe' (Pf) ♀H4	CRow GBin GCra GKev GQui NBir NBre NChi NMun SUsu WCom
	involucrata	see *P. munroi*
	ioessa (Si)	EWes GCra GQui NGdn
	– var. ***hopeana*** (Si)	EBee GKev
	– hybrids (Si)	NLAp
	'Iris Mainwaring' (Pr/Prim)	ECtt GAbr GCra GEdr LLHF NHol NWCA WCot
	irregularis (Pe)	GKev WAbe
	Jack in the Green Group (Pr/Poly)	CLAP CSWP MNrw WBor WFar
	– Barnhaven (Pr/Poly)	EBla
	Jackanapes Group (Pr/Poly)	EBla
	'Jackie Richards' (Au)	MFie NHol
	japonica (Pf)	CMHG CRow CSam ECha GAuc GGar GQui IPen LPBA LRHS MNHC MSCN NBro NGdn NHol SUsu SWat WAbe WBrE WFar WHil WMoo WPer
	– 'Alba' (Pf)	CPrp CTri EBee ECho EHrv EPfP EWTr GAuc GCal GEdr GGar GKir IPen MFie NDlv NGdn NPri SBch SPer WAbe WFar WHil WWEG
	– 'Apple Blossom' (Pf)	CCVN CFir CMHG CWCL EBee EShb GCal GEdr GKev GKir IPen LBMP LHop LRHS MBNS MBri MFie NCGa NGdn NHol NPri SBch SWvt WFar WHoo WPnP
*	– 'Carminea' (Pf)	COIW CWCL EBee GBuc GEdr GGar GKev GKir IPen MFie MSCN NBro NCGa NGdn NLar WFar
	– 'Fuji' (Pf)	CSWP NBro
	– 'Fuji' hybrids (Pf)	NLar
	– hybrids (Pf)	CMac GCra GKir MRav
	– 'Jim Saunders' (Pf)	SLon
	– 'Merve's Red' (Pf)	CAby EBee WPGP
	– 'Miller's Crimson' (Pf) ♀H4	Widely available
	– 'Oriental Sunrise' (Pf)	CMil CSWP EBee GKev LLHF
	– pale pink-flowered (Pf)	NSum
	– 'Peninsula Pink' (Pf)	IPen
	– 'Pink Pagoda' (Pf) new	ITim
	– 'Pinkie' (Pf)	IPen
	– 'Postford White' (Pf) ♀H4	Widely available
	– Redfield strain (Pf)	IPen WHil
	– red-flowered (Pf)	IPen WAbe
	– 'Splendens' (Pf)	IPen
	– 'Valley Red' (Pf)	GBuc IPen ITim LRHS
	jesoana (Co)	EWld GGar GKev LLHF
	– B&SWJ 618	WCru
	– var. ***pubescens*** (Co)	EBee GKev
	'Joan Hughes' (*allionii* hybrid) (Au)	WAbe
	'Joanna'	ECou MHer
	'Johanna' (Pu)	GAbr GBuc GEdr GKev LLHF NGdn NHol NSum NWCA WAbe
	'John Fielding' (Sr × Pr)	CBro CElw GAbr GEdr MCot
	'Jo-Jo' (Au)	MFie NHol WAbe
	juliae (Pr)	ECho EDAr GEdr GKev LHop LRHS NBid NSum NWCA SPlb WAbe
I	– 'Millicent' (Pr)	WCot
	– white-flowered (Pr)	NSum
	'Ken Dearman' (Pr/Prim/d)	ECtt EPfP LRHS NBir NGHP SIng SRGP WClo
	kewensis (Sp) ♀H2	GKev WAbe
	'Kinlough Beauty' (Pr/Poly)	GAbr GEdr LLHF NRya NWCA WEas
§	***kisoana*** (Co)	CLAP EBla GKev IPen LLHF WCru
	– var. ***alba*** (Co)	CLAP EBee
	– var. ***shikokiana***	see *P. kisoana*
	– 'Velvet' (Co)	CLAP GEdr
	'Kusum Krishna'	GEdr
	'Lady Greer' (Pr/Poly) ♀H4	CMac CSam EBee EDAr EPfP GBuc GEdr GKev LLWP MCot MHer NChi NGdn NLAp NRya NWCA SAga SMac WFar WHer WHil
§	***latifolia*** (Au)	GKev
	latisecta (Co)	GEdr IPen
§	***laurentiana*** (Al)	CTsd EBee GAuc GKev NMen
	'Lea Gardens' (*allionii* hybrid) (Au)	IPen MFie NHol
	'Lee Myers' (*allionii* hybrid) (Au)	IPen NDlv
	leucophylla	see *P. elatior*
	'Lilac Domino' (Au)	IPen
	'Lilian Harvey' (Pr/Prim/d)	CElw EPfP SPer
	'Lindum Moonlight'	ITim MFie
	'Lindum Serenade' (Au)	WThu
	'Lingwood Beauty' (Pr/Prim)	CAby GAbr WAbe
	'Lismore Bay' (Au)	GKev
	'Lismore Jewel' (Au)	NMen WAbe
	'Lismore Treasure' (Au)	NMen WAbe
	'Lismore Yellow' (Au)	CPBP WAbe
	'Little Egypt' (Pr/Poly)	NCGa
	littoniana	see *P. vialii*
	× ***loiseleurii*** 'Aire Mist' (Au)	CPBP GKev IPen MAsh NHol NLAp NMen NRya NSum WAbe WHil
§	– 'Aire Waves' (Au)	ITim NHol NLAp NMen
	– 'Pink Aire Mist' (Au)	WHil
	– 'White Waves' (Au)	IPen
	longiflora	see *P. halleri*
	longipes (Cy)	GKev
	luteola (Or)	EBee ECho EWTr GGar GKev GKir LLHF NGdn NSum WFar WPer
	macrocalyx	see *P. veris*
	macrophylla (Cy)	EBee GKev
	'MacWatt's Claret' (Pr/Poly)	GAbr LLWP
	'MacWatt's Cream' (Pr/Poly)	CSWP EBee EBla GAbr GCra GEdr GKir LHop LRHS SIng WCot
	magellanica (Al)	EBee GKev NGdn WAbe
	'Maisie Michael' new	LLHF
	mandarin red-flowered (Pf)	CSWP
	marginata (Au) ♀H4	CPne ECho GEdr GKev GKir IPen LHop LRHS MFie MMuc NDlv NHol NLAp NSum SBch SIng WAbe WFar
	– from the Dolomites (Au)	NHol
	– 'Adrian Evans' (Au)	CStu ITim
	– ***alba*** (Au)	LRHS MFie NBro NDlv NHol NLAp NRya WFar
	– 'Baldock's Purple' (Au)	IPen
	– 'Barbara Clough' (Au)	GEdr IPen ITim MFie WFar
	– 'Beamish' (Au) ♀H4	NBro NHol NRya WCom
	– 'Beatrice Lascaris' (Au)	MFie NRya WAbe WCom
	– 'Boothman's Variety' (Au)	CTri ECho NLAp WCom
	– 'Caerulea' (Au)	MFie NLAp WAbe
	– 'Clear's Variety' (Au)	IPen WCom
	– cut-leaved (Au)	NHol WCom
	– 'Doctor Jenkins' (Au)	IPen NHol NLar NRya
	– 'Drake's Form' (Au)	IPen ITim NLAp NLar NRya
	– dwarf (Au)	GEdr LRHS MFie
	– 'Earl L. Bolton'	see *P. marginata* 'El Bolton'
§	– 'El Bolton' (Au)	IPen NHol
	– 'Elizabeth Fry' (Au)	IPen WCom
	– 'F.W. Millard' (Au)	WCom
	– 'Grandiflora' (Au)	IPen NHol
	– 'Highland Twilight' (Au)	IPen NSla WAbe
	– 'Holden Variety' (Au)	IPen MFie NDlv NHol NRya WCom

	Name	Suppliers
	- 'Ivy Agee' (Au)	IPen NLAp NRya
	- 'Janet' (Au)	GEdr NLAp WCom
	- 'Jenkins Variety' (Au)	ECho
	- 'Kesselring's Variety' (Au)	CMMP ECho GEdr IPen MFie NDlv NLAp WAbe WCom WFar WTin
	- 'Laciniata' (Au)	IPen ITim LRHS
	- lilac-flowered (Au)	IPen
	- 'Linda Pope' (Au) ♀H4	IPen ITim MAsh NBir NDlv NHol NLAp NSla NSum SIng WAbe WCom
	- maritime form (Au)	IPen
	- 'Millard's Variety' (Au)	IPen ITim NHol WCom
	- 'Miss Fell' (Au)	IPen
	- 'Miss Savory' (Au)	WCom
	- 'Mrs Carter Walmsley' (Au)	NRya
	- 'Mrs Gatenby' (Au)	NWCA
	- 'Nancy Lucy' (Au)	WAbe
	- 'Napoleon' (Au)	GEdr IPen ITim MFie MSCN
	- 'Prichard's Variety' (Au) ♀H4	ECho GEdr IPen ITim LRHS MFie MSCN NCob NDlv NLAp NMyG NRya NWCA WAbe WFar
	- 'Rosea' (Au)	IPen
	- 'Sheila Denby' (Au)	IPen ITim NLAp
	- violet-flowered (Au)	ECho
	- 'Waithman's Variety' (Au)	IPen NLAp NRya
	- wild-collected (Au)	MFie NHol
	'Marianne Davey' (Pr/Prim/d)	MRav WKif
	'Marie Crousse' (Pr/Prim/d)	CPBP CWCL EPfP LBMP SRGP WFar WHal
	Marine Blues Group (Pr/Poly)	CSWP NCGa
	'Maris Tabbard' (Au)	IPen NLar
	'Mars' (*allionii* hybrid) (Au)	NDlv NHol NRya
	'Marven' (Au)	GEdr IPen MFie
	'Mary Anne'	GAbr
	'Mauve Mist' (Au)	MAsh
	Mauve Victorians Group (Pr/Poly)	CSWP
	maximowiczii (Cy)	GBuc GKev
	megalocarpa (Cy)	GKev
	melanops	see *P. chionantha* subsp. *melanops*
	× ***meridiana*** (Au)	NHol
§	- 'Miniera' (Au)	IPen MFie SIng
	'Mexico'	LLHF WCot
	Midnight Group	CSWP NCGa
	'Miniera'	see *P.* × *meridiana* 'Miniera'
	minima (Au)	NBro NLar NSla WAbe
	- var. ***alba*** (Au)	NRya
	minima × ***wulfeniana***	see *P.* × *vochinensis*
	minor (Cy) SDR 1586	GKev
	'Miss Indigo' (Pr/Prim/d)	CAby CWCL ECtt EPfP GAbr GMaP MFie MRav NGHP SGar SPer WCot WFar WPtf
	mistassinica (Al) **new**	CPBP
	- var. ***macropoda***	see *P. laurentiana*
	miyabeana (Pf)	GKev IPen
	modesta var. ***faurieae*** (Al)	GAuc IPen NWCA
	- var. ***faurieae*** f. ***leucantha*** (Al)	GKev
	- 'Nemuro-koza-kura' (Al/v)	CBow
	mollis (Co)	EBee GKev
	'Moorland Apricot' **new**	WMoo
	moupinensis	CLAP EBee GGGa WAbe
	- SEH 086	WCot
*	'Mrs Eagland'	GAbr
	'Mrs Frank Neave' (Pr/Prim)	GEdr IPen
	'Mrs McGillivray' (Pr/Prim)	GAbr
§	***munroi*** (Ar)	CDes EBee EWld GEdr GKev IPen WAbe
§	- subsp. ***yargongensis*** (Al)	GAuc GGar GKev IPen LRHS MSnd
	- - SDR 3096	GKev
	muscarioides (Mu)	EBee GKev IPen MFie
	Muted Victorians Group (Pr/Poly)	CSWP NCGa
§	***nana*** (Pe)	GKev IPen
	- 'Alba' (Pe)	WAbe
	- blue-flowered (Pe)	GKev
	New Pinks Group (Pr/Poly)	CSWP GAbr NCGa
	'Nightingale'	NHol
	nipponica (Su)	GEdr
	nivalis Pallas	see *P. chionantha*
§	***nivalis*** (Fed.) Halda subsp. ***xanthobasis*** (Cy)	EBee
	nutans Delavay ex Franch.	see *P. flaccida*
	obconica (Ob)	LRHS
	- Touch Me Series (Ob) **new**	LRHS
	obtusifolia (Cy)	EBee
	'Old Port' (Pr/Poly)	CElw EBee GKev LLWP NMen WCot WPat
	Old Rose Victorians Group (Pr/Poly)	CSWP
	orbicularis (Cy)	GKev
	'Oriental Sunset'	MDKP
	Osiered Amber Group (Pr/Prim)	CSWP GAbr
	'Our Pat' (Pr/Poly/d)	GAbr
	palinuri (Au)	IPen WCom
	palmata (Co)	GEdr
	Paloma Series	LRHS
	'Pamilata'	EBee
	'Paris '90' (Pr/Poly)	CDes CSWP NCGa
	parryi (Pa)	EBee GKev NLAp
	- NNS 04-422	WCot
	- NNS 04-423	WCot
	'Peardrop' (Au)	NHol
	pedemontana (Au)	GKev
	- 'Alba' (Au)	WPat
	'Perle von Bottrop' (Pr/Prim)	GAbr
	petelotii **new**	GKev
	'Peter Klein' (Or)	GBuc GEdr LLHF NHol WAbe WTin
	petiolaris misapplied	see *P.* 'Redpoll'
§	***petiolaris*** Wall. (Pe)	GCra GKev MDun NSum NWCA WAbe
	- Sherriff's form	see *P.* 'Redpoll'
	'Petticoat'	NCGa NLar SPer
	'Pincushion'	GEdr
	'Pink Aire' (Au)	MFie NMen NRya WCom
	'Pink Fairy' (Au)	IPen ITim
	'Pink Ice' (*allionii* hybrid) (Au)	CPBP GKev ITim MFie NHol NRya
	pinnata	GKev
	poissonii (Pf)	CBen CTri EBee ELan GAuc GCra GEdr GGar GKev GKir GMac GQui IBal IPen LPBA LRHS MSnd NGby NGdn NHol SBch SPad WAbe WGwG WPtf WShi
	- ACE 2030	EPot
	- SDR 5126	GKev
	polyneura (Co)	EBee GEdr GGar IGor IPen MSnd NGdn SRms WCot
	'Port Wine' (Pr)	EBla GAbr GCra
	'Powdery Pink'	LRHS
	prenantha (Pf)	EBee LLHF
§	***prolifera*** (Pf) ♀H4	Widely available
§	× ***pubescens*** (Au) ♀H4	EAlp IPen LRHS NGdn NLAp SBch WPer

	Name	Suppliers
	– 'A.E. Matthews' (Au)	NHol
	– 'Apple Blossom' (Au)	IPen MFie
	– 'Balfouriana' (Au)	NHol
§	– 'Bewerley White' (Au)	EBee ECho EPfP IPen NDlv NHol NLAp WCre WFar
	– 'Blue Wave' (Au)	IPen MFie
§	– 'Boothman's Variety' (Au)	CTri ECho EPfP LRHS MFie NDlv NLAp NMyG WCom WFar WHoo WTin
	– 'Carmen'	see *P.* × *pubescens* 'Boothman's Variety'
	– 'Chamois' (Au)	MFie
	– 'Christine' (Au)	CDes CMea GKev IPen ITim MFie NBir NDlv NSum WCot
	– 'Cream Viscosa' (Au)	NDlv NLAp WCom
	– 'Deep Mrs Wilson' (Au)	CPBP MFie WCom
	– 'Faldonside' (Au)	IPen MFie NDlv NSum WCom
§	– 'Freedom' (Au)	CTri ECho GKev IPen LRHS MFie NBir NDlv NHol NLAp NLar SRms WCom
	– 'George Harrison' (Au)	MFie
	– 'Harlow Car' (Au)	CMea CPBP GQui IPen MFie NDlv NSum NWCA WFar WTin
	– 'Joan Danger' (Au)	IPen ITim
	– 'Joan Gibbs' (Au)	ECho IPen ITim LRHS MFie NLAp
	– 'Lilac Fairy' (Au)	IPen ITim NDlv NHol
	– 'Mrs J.H. Wilson' (Au)	GEdr MFie NDlv NHol NRya
	– 'Pat Barwick' (Au)	GKir IPen MFie NHol NLAp WTin
	– 'Peggy Fell' (Au)	WHil
	– 'Rufus' (Au)	ECho EWes WCot
	– 'S.E. Matthews' (Au)	NHol
	– 'Sid Skelton' (Au)	IPen
	– 'Snowcap' (Au)	CPBP IPen
	– 'Sonya' (Au)	IPen
	– 'The General' (Au)	CTri IPen MFie SPop
§	– 'Wedgwood' (Au)	GAbr IPen MFie
	– 'Winifred' (Au)	LRHS NHol SPop
	– yellow-flowered (Au)	IPen
	pulchella (Pu)	GKev
	pulverulenta (Pf) ♀^{H4}	Widely available
	– Bartley hybrids (Pf) ♀^{H4}	CBot CDes GBuc LRHS LSou NBre
	– 'Bartley Pink' (Pf)	GBuc ITim
	'Quaker's Bonnet'	see *P. vulgaris* 'Lilacina Plena'
	'Rachel Kinnen' (Au)	IPen MFie SIng WFar
	'Ravenglass Vermilion'	see *P.* 'Inverewe'
	'Red Velvet' (Pr/Prim/d)	CWCL
§	'Redpoll' (Pe)	CLAP WAbe
	reidii (So)	GEdr GKev NSla
	– CC 4624	GKev
	– var. ***williamsii*** (So)	IPen LLHF
	'Reverie' (Pr/Poly)	CSWP NCGa
	'Rheniana' (Au)	IPen SIng
	'Romeo' (Pr/Prim)	CLAP WCot
	rosea (Or) ♀^{H4}	CAby CBot CElw CRow EBee ECho EMFW EPfP GAuc GEdr IPen LRHS MFie MMuc NBid NBir NLAp NRya NVic
	– 'Delight'	see *P. rosea* 'Micia Visser-de Geer'
	– 'Gigas' (Or)	GBuc LRHS NHol WFar
	– 'Grandiflora' (Or)	CPrp EAlp ECho EHon EPfP GGar GKev LPBA LRHS NCGa NDlv NWCA SBch SIng SPoG SRms SWal SWat WFar WHil WPer
§	– 'Micia Visser-de Geer' (Or)	LRHS WTin
§	***rotundifolia*** (Cf)	IPen
	'Rowallane Rose' (Pf)	GBuc IGor
I	'Rowena'	GCra LLHF WCot
	roxburghii	see *P. rotundifolia*
	'Roy Cope' (Pr/Prim/d)	EPfP GAbr NBir SGar SRGP WFar
	rubra	see *P. firmipes*
	rusbyi (Pa)	EBee GKev MFie NWCA
	– subsp. ***ellisiae*** (Pe)	IPen

	Name	Suppliers
	scandinavica (Al)	EBee GAuc
§	'Schneekissen' (Pr/Prim)	GAbr GCra GEdr IPen LRHS MHer NBro NCGa NChi NGHP NMyG NPro WHil
	scotica (Al)	GAuc NSla WAbe
	secundiflora (Pf)	CLAP CWCL EBee ELan GCra GEdr GGar GKev GKir LPBA LRHS NLAp SPer SPlb SRms SWat WFar WGwG WMoo
	– B&SWJ 7547	WCru
	– SDR 4401	GKev
	– SDR 4435	GKev
§	× ***sendtneri*** (Au)	MFie
	× ***serrata***	see *P.* × *vochinensis*
	serratifolia (Pf)	GGGa
	– SDR 5165	GKev
	sibthorpii	see *P. vulgaris* subsp. *sibthorpii*
	sieboldii (Co) ♀^{H4}	CEnt CSpr ECho GKev MAsh MCot MFie MLHP MNrw NMen NRya NWCA SMac SRms WAbe WFar
	– 'Akinoysool' (Co) **new**	WFar
	– 'Ankoan' (Co) **new**	WFar
	– 'Asahi' (Co) **new**	WFar
	– 'Ayanami' (Co) **new**	WFar
	– 'Bide-a-Wee Blue' (Co)	NBid
	– 'Bijyonomai' (Co) **new**	WFar
	– 'Blacksmith's Blue' (Co)	EBla
I	– 'Blue Lagoon' (Co)	EBee EBrs GKir LLHF LRHS MMHG
	– 'Blue Shades' (Co)	IPen NMen
	– blue-flowered (Co)	CLAP CWCL ECho NMen
	– 'Blush' (Co)	CLAP
	– 'Bureikou' (Co) **new**	WFar
	– 'Carefree' (Co)	CLAP IPen LLHF NBro NLar NMen
	– 'Cherubim' (Co)	CAby CLAP EBee GCra GKir LLHF LRHS MMHG
	– 'Dancing Ladies' (Co)	CAby CLAP CMil CSWP EBla IPen MFie NBro WFar
	– 'Dart Rapids' (Co) **new**	CDes
	– 'Duane's Choice' (Co)	CDes CLAP
	– 'Edasango' (Co) **new**	WFar
	– 'Edomurasaki' (Co) **new**	WFar
	– 'Frilly Blue' (Co)	EBrs LRHS
	– 'Galaxy' (Co)	NBro NRya
	– 'Geisha Girl' (Co)	CAby CFir CLAP CSpe EBla EBrs GKir LRHS MRav NLar WAbe WFar
	– 'Ginhukurin' (Co) **new**	WFar
	– 'Godaisyo' (Co) **new**	WFar
	– 'Hatagarasi' (Co) **new**	WFar
	– 'Higurias' (Co) **new**	WFar
	– 'Hinokoromo' (Co) **new**	WFar
	– 'Hujikosi' (Co) **new**	WFar
	– 'Hutaezuru' (Co) **new**	WFar
	– 'Inikina White' (Co) **new**	WFar
	– 'Inokima Minoura' (Co) **new**	WFar
	– 'Izuto' (Co) **new**	WFar
	– 'Jyuuyuunovtage' (Co) **new**	WFar
	– 'Kaedegari' (Co) **new**	WFar
	– 'Kansenden' (Co) **new**	WFar
	– 'Karagoromo' (Co) **new**	WFar
	– 'Kokoroiki' (Co) **new**	WFar
	– 'Kosijimoyuki' (Co) **new**	WFar
	– 'Kotonosirabe' (Co) **new**	WFar
	– 'Kourohou' (Co) **new**	WFar
	– 'Kurama' (Co) **new**	WFar
	– f. ***lactiflora*** (Co)	CDes CLAP EBee IPen NBro NMen SRot WFar WPGP WTin
	– 'Lilac Sunbonnet' (Co)	CLAP EPfP LLHF LRHS NWCA WFar
	– 'Lisujyanome' (Co) **new**	WFar
	– 'Maiougi' (Co) **new**	WFar
	– 'Makazebeni' (Co) **new**	WFar

- 'Managuruma' (Co) **new** WFar
- 'Manakoora' (Co) CLAP CSWP EBee IPen NBro NSum WFar
- 'Mangetu' (Co) **new** WFar
- 'Masasino' (Co) **new** WFar
- 'Matunoyuki' (Co) **new** WFar
- 'Mihonokoji' (Co) **new** WFar
- 'Mikado' (Co) CLAP EBee EBrs GCra GKir IPen LRHS WFar
- 'Mikininonomare' (Co) **new** WFar
- 'Mitanohikari' (Co) **new** WFar
- 'Miyakowakare' (Co) **new** WFar
- 'Miyuki' (Co) **new** WFar
- 'Musasi' (Co) **new** WFar
- 'Myoutiriki' (Co) **new** WFar
- 'Okinatomo' (Co) **new** WFar
- 'Pago-Pago' (Co) CDes CLAP EBee IPen MFie NBro WFar
- 'Pink Laced' (Co) **new** WFar
- 'Purple Back' (Co) EBee
- 'Rasyoumon' (Co) **new** WFar
- 'Rock Candy' (Co) **new** WFar
- 'Sakuragana' (Co) **new** WFar
- 'Sasanari' (Co) **new** WFar
- 'Senyuu' (Co) **new** WFar
- 'Seraphim' (Co) CLAP EBee EBrs GKir LRHS MMHG
- 'Shirousasi' (Co) **new** WFar
- 'Sikoubai' (Co) **new** WFar
- 'Sinipukurn' (Co) **new** WFar
- 'Sinnkirou' (Co) **new** WFar
- 'Sinseiu' (Co) **new** WFar
- 'Siritonbo' (Co) **new** WFar
- 'Sitikenjin' (Co) **new** WFar
- 'Snowflake' (Co) CLAP EBrs LRHS MMHG NLar NMen NSla WAbe WFar
- 'Sotodorihime' (Co) **new** WFar
- 'Sousiarai' (Co) **new** WFar
- 'Spring Blush' (Co) **new** GEdr
- 'Spring Rose' (Co) **new** GEdr
- 'Spring Song' (Co) **new** GEdr
- 'Sumida No Hatu' (Co) **new** WFar
- 'Sumisonegawa' (Co) **new** WFar
- 'Sweetie' (Co) **new** WFar
- 'Syunkou' (Co) **new** WFar
- 'Syutyuka' (Co) **new** WFar
- 'Tagonoura' (Co) **new** WFar
- 'Tah-ni' (Co) CMil NBro NSum
- 'Tatutanoy' (Co) **new** WFar
- 'Tidoriasobi' (Co) **new** WFar
- 'Tokinohina' (Co) **new** WFar
- 'Toyonoharu' (Co) **new** WFar
- 'Tukinomiyaka' (Co) **new** WFar
- 'Winter Dreams' (Co) CLAP CSWP NBid NBro NSum WFar
- 'Yukiguruma' (Co) **new** WFar

sikkimensis (Si) ♀H4 CEnt CRow ECho EPot EWTr GAuc GEdr GGar GKev GKir IPen LRHS MNrw MSnd NGdn NSum SBch SPer SPoG WFar WPnP
- ACE 1422 GBuc
- CC&McK 1022 GQui
- SDR 2819 GKev
- SDR 3099 GKev
- SDR 3233 GKev
- SDR 4414 GKev
- SDR 4528 from high altitude GKev
- SDR 4763 GKev
- SDR 4919 GKev
- from Bhutan GCra
- var. ***pseudosikkimensis*** (Si) IPen
- var. ***pudibunda*** (Si) EBee GEdr
- 'Tilman Number 2' (Si) CWCL GAbr

aff. ***sikkimensis*** (Si) CBot GKir ITim
- ACE 2176 GBuc

Silver-laced Group (Pr/Poly) ECGP LBMP STes SWvt WCot WFar WPtf

'Silverwells' (Pf) GEdr

simensis (Sp) CPBP GKev ITim

sinolisteri **new** GKev

sinopurpurea see *P. chionantha* subsp. *sinopurpurea*

'Siobhan' **new** WCot

'Sir Bedivere' (Pr/Prim) CDes GAbr GBuc NLar WCot

smithiana see *P. prolifera*

'Snow Carpet' see *P.* 'Schneekissen'

'Snow White' (Pr/Poly) GEdr MRav

Snowcushion see *P.* 'Schneekissen'

'Snowruffles' ITim

sonchifolia (Pe) CFir CLAP MDun WCot
- from Tibet (Pe) MDun

aff. ***soongii*** (Cy) SDR 4849 EBee

sorachiana see *P. yuparensis*

souliei (Y) SDR 4767 GKev

'Sparkling Eyes' WCot

spectabilis (Au) EBee EPot GEdr GKev
- SDR 2415 GKev

Spice Shades Group (Pr/Poly) CSWP GKir NCGa WCot

'Stradbrook Charm' (Au) CPBP MFie NHol WCre WFar WThu

'Stradbrook Dainty' (Au) MFie NHol WFar

'Stradbrook Dream' (Au) ITim MFie NLAp WFar

'Stradbrook Lilac Lustre' (Au) MFie

'Stradbrook Lucy' (Au) IPen ITim NHol WFar

'Stradbrook Mauve Magic' (Au) MFie

Striped Victorians Group (Pr/Poly) CSWP NCGa

'Sue Jervis' (Pr/Prim/d) CWCL MRav NBir NCGa NGHP NLar NSum SPer WGwG WHal WPrP

suffrutescens (Su) WAbe

'Sunshine Susie' (Pr/Prim/d) CWCL EPfP GAbr MRav NCGa NGHP SIng SPer SRGP WHil

szechuanica (Cy) GKev
- SSSE 292 EBee

takedana (Bu) LLHF

'Tantallon' (Pe) CLAP LLHF

Tartan Reds Group (Pr/Prim) CSWP

'Tawny Port' (Pr/Poly) CLAP GAbr GBuc NBro SRms WCom

'Tie Dye' (Pr/Prim) CDes CElw EBla ECGP GAbr GBin GEdr LRHS LSou MNrw NBPC NBhm NCGa NLar SMrm SPoG SUsu WCot WFar

'Tipperary Purple' (Pr/Prim) GAbr GEdr

'Tomato Red' (Pr/Prim) WCot

'Tony' (Au) CPBP IPen MFie WAbe WCom

'Top Affair' (Au/d) IPen WAln

'Tournaig Pink' (Pf) GGar

tyrolensis (Au) **new** GKev

* ***urumiensis*** GKev

'Val Horncastle' (Pr/Prim/d) CWCL ECtt EPfP EWTr GMaP NCGa NGHP NLar SIng SPer WCot

× ***venusta*** **new** GKev

§ ***veris*** (Pr) ♀H4 Widely available
- subsp. ***columnae*** (Pr) EBee

	– feather-petalled (Pr)	WCot
	– hybrids (Pr)	LBMP SGar
	– 'Katy McSparron' (Pr/d)	CMea CSsd EBee GCra GKir LRHS WBor WCot
	– subsp. ***macrocalyx*** (Pr)	EBee GKev NWCA
	– orange-flowered (Pr)	MHer WMoo
	– red-flowered (Pr)	CSpr NBid NGdn SPer WCom WMoo
	– 'Sunset Shades' (Pr)	CAby NGHP NLar SBch WFar WPer
	vernalis	see *P. vulgaris*
	verticillata (Sp)	GKev IPen
§	***vialii*** (So) ♀H4	Widely available
	'Victoriana Black and Gold' **new**	LRHS
	'Victoriana Red and Gold' **new**	LRHS
	'Victoriana Scarlet and Gold' **new**	LRHS
	villosa var. ***commutata*** (Au) **new**	GKev
	Violet Victorians Group (Pr/Poly)	CSWP
	viscosa All.	see *P. latifolia*
§	× ***vochinensis*** (Au)	CFee NWCA
§	***vulgaris*** (Pr/Prim) ♀H4	Widely available
	– var. ***alba*** (Pr/Prim)	CRow NSla WAbe WBrk
	– 'Alba Plena' (Pr/Prim)	CRow GAbr GBuc GCal GGar IGor MBri NSum
	– 'Alex Brenton' (Pr/d)	LHop
	– green-flowered	see *P. vulgaris* 'Viridis'
§	– 'Lilacina Plena' (Pr/Prim/d)	CBot CDes EPfP GAbr GCal GMaP LLHF MFie MRav NCGa NGHP NSum SPer WFar
	– 'Lutea' (Pr/Prim)	GAbr
§	– subsp. ***sibthorpii*** (Pr/Prim) ♀H4	CMHG CSam EBee EBla EBrs ECho GAbr GBuc GEdr IPen ITim LLWP LRHS MHer MLHP MRav NBro NChi NGHP NHol NMyG SIng SRms WEas WHil
	– 'Taigetos' (Pr/Prim) **new**	CBro
§	– 'Viridis' (Pr/Prim/d)	CDes CFir CRow EBla
	walshii (Mi)	GKev
	waltonii (Si)	CLAP CMil EBee GBuc GEdr GKev IPen LFur LRHS MDKP MNrw NBPC NCGa NWCA SBch WPtf
	'Wanda' (Pr/Prim) ♀H4	CBcs CTri EBla ECho GAbr GCra LBMP LLWP MCot MHer NBid NBlu NVic SRGP SRms WBrk WCFE WCom WEas WFar WHil WTin
	Wanda Group (Pr/Prim)	ECho
	'Wanda Hose-in-hose' (Pr/Prim/d)	EBla GAbr GCra LLWP MMHG NBir NChi SSvw WBor WHer WHil
	'Wanda Jack in the Green' (Pr/Prim)	CLAP WCot WFar
	wardii	see *P. munroi*
	warshenewskiana (Or)	CLAP EBee ECtt GEdr GGar GKev MNrw NCob NHol NLAp NMen NRya NWCA WAbe WGwG
	watsonii (Mu)	EBee EWes GKev LFur NLAp SWat WPtf
	– ACE 1402	IPen
	– SDR 1673	GKev
	'Wedgwood'	see *P.* × *pubescens* 'Wedgwood'
	'Welsh Blue'	CSpe
	'Wharfedale Bluebell' (Au)	NBir NRya
	'Wharfedale Butterfly' (Au)	NHol
	'Wharfedale Crusader' (Au)	ITim NHol
	'Wharfedale Gem' (*allionii* hybrid) (Au)	ITim MFie NLAp NRya
	'Wharfedale Ling' (*allionii* hybrid) (Au)	CPBP ITim MFie NHol NLar NRya
	'Wharfedale Sunshine' (Au)	ITim MFie
	'Wharfedale Superb' (*allionii* hybrid) (Au)	ITim NLAp
	'Wharfedale Village' (Au)	CStu NLAp WThu
	'White Linda Pope' (Au)	MAsh NMen WCom
	'White Wanda' (Pr/Prim)	GAbr
§	***whitei*** 'Sherriff's Variety' (Pe)	CLAP
	'William Genders' (Pr/Poly)	GAbr GEdr
	wilsonii (Pf)	CSam CTri CTsd GBuc GKev GKir LDai MDKP MSnd NBPC NCGa NDlv SGSe SWat WBVN WGwG WHoo
§	– var. ***anisodora*** (Pf)	CLAP EBee GKev GKir GQui IPen NGdn WHrl WPtf
	'Windrush'	see *P.* × *berninae* 'Windrush'
	'Winter White'	see *P.* 'Gigha'
	'Wisley Crimson'	see *P.* 'Wisley Red'
§	'Wisley Red' (Pr/Prim)	CElw
	wollastonii (So)	GKev
	wulfeniana (Au)	EPot GEdr GKev
	xanthobasis	see *P. nivalis* (Fed.) Halda subsp. *xanthobasis*
	yargongensis	see *P. munroi* subsp. *yargongensis*
	yunnanensis (Y)	GKev
§	***yuparensis*** (Al)	EBee IPen NWCA
	– white-flowered (Al)	GKev
	zambalensis (Ar)	GKev IPen
	– SDR 4531	GKev

Prinsepia (*Rosaceae*)

	sinensis	CArn CBcs CFee MBlu NLar SLon WSHC
	utilis	CTrC CTrG

Prionosciadium (*Apiaceae*)

	thapsoides B&SWJ 10345	WCru

Pritchardia (*Arecaceae*)

	affinis	XBlo
	pacifica **new**	XBlo

Pritzelago (*Brassicaceae*)

	alpina	GEdr NBlu NPro

Prosopis (*Mimosaceae*)

	chilensis **new**	IDee

Prostanthera (*Lamiaceae*)

	aspalathoides	CTsd ECou EWes
	'Badja Peak'	CTrC CTsd LRHS MAsh WAbe WKif
	baxteri	ECou
	cuneata ♀H4	Widely available
	– 'Alpine Gold'	CMHG CWSG LAst NMun SPoG WBrE WFar
	– Kew form	WPGP
*	***digitiformis***	CTsd ECou
	incisa	CTsd SBch SHDw
	– 'Rosea'	EOHP SBod
	'La Provence' PBR **new**	LRHS
	lasianthos	CBcs CDoC CHll CTsd ECou EWes LRHS SAga SBch SHDw
	– 'Kallista Pink'	CTsd
	– var. ***subcoriacea***	CPLG CRHN
	latifolia **new**	CTsd
	'Mauve Mantle'	ECou
	melissifolia	CArn CTsd ECre
§	– var. ***parvifolia***	CBcs ECre WAbe
	'Mint Delight'	LRHS
	'Mint Royale'	LRHS
	'Mint-Ice'	LRHS
	nivea	ECou
	ovalifolia ♀H2	ECou

I	- 'Variegata' (v)	CPLG CTsd ECou GGar
	'Poorinda Ballerina'	CAlb CDoC CTsd CWSG CWit EBee ECou EOHP LRHS MGos MNHC SPoG WFar WGrn
	'Poorinda Petite' **new**	CTsd LRHS
	rotundifolia ♀H2	CHEx CSBt CSev CTrG CTri CTsd CWSG EBee ECho EOHP ESwi MNHC MSCN NGHP SEND SPer WGrn
	- 'Chelsea Girl'	see *P. rotundifolia* 'Rosea'
§	- 'Rosea' ♀H2	CDoC CSBt CTrC CTrG CTsd EBee ECou GGar NHol SPoG
	scutellarioides 'Lavender Lady'	ECou
	sericea	LRHS
	sieberi misapplied	see *P. melissifolia* var. *parvifolia*
	sieberi Benth.	CTsd
	walteri	EBee ECou LRHS

Protea (*Proteaceae*)

	aurea	SPlb
	burchellii	SPlb
	'Christine'	CTrC
	coronata	SPlb
	cynaroides	CBcs CCCN CHEx CTrC IDee LRHS SBig SPlb
	effusa	SPlb
	eximia	CBcs LRHS SPlb
	grandiceps	CBcs CCCN LRHS SPlb
	lacticolor	SPlb
	laurifolia	SPlb
	nana	SPlb
	neriifolia	CCCN SPlb
I	- 'Alba'	CTrC
	- 'Ruby'	CTrC
	- 'Snowcrest'	CTrC
	obtusifolia	SPlb
	'Pink Ice'	CTrC
	repens	SPlb
	subvestita	CTrC SPlb
	susannae	SPlb
	venusta	CTrC

Prumnopitys (*Podocarpaceae*)

§	***andina***	GKir IFFs WThu
	elegans	see *P. andina*
§	***taxifolia***	CDoC CTrC ECou

Prunella (*Lamiaceae*)

§	***grandiflora***	CHby CPrp ECha GBar GKir MHav SBch SWat WCHb WFar WPGP WWEG
	- 'Alba'	CSBt EBee ECha EPfP GMaP NGHP NLar SPer WCAu WCHb WFar
	- 'Altenberg Rosa' **new**	EBee
	- 'Bella Deep Rose'	WFar
	- 'Blue Loveliness'	EBee GBee GKir WCHb WWEG
	- 'Carminea'	EBee ECtt NGby SBch SPer
	- light blue-flowered	GBar NLar WFar
	- 'Loveliness' ♀H4	CDoC CMac EBee ECha ECtt GKir GMaP LRHS MNFA MRav NBro NGdn NSti NVic SPer SPlb SRGP WCAu WFar
	- 'Pagoda'	CEnt CSpe NBre NLar WCHb
	- 'Pink Loveliness'	CPrp EBee SRms WCHb
	- 'Rosea'	CElw CSBt EBee EPfP WOut
	- 'Rubra'	EBee GAbr NGHP NLar WPer
	- violet-flowered **new**	EPfP
	- 'White Loveliness'	CMac CPrp LRHS WPer WWEG
	incisa	see *P. vulgaris*
*	'Inshriach Ruby'	GBin
	laciniata	WCHb
§	***vulgaris***	CArn CRWN EBWF GBar GPoy MHer MNHC NLan NMir NPri NSco SECG WCHb WHer WMoo
	- f. ***leucantha***	GBar WAlt WHer
	- 'Marbled White' (v)	WAlt
	- 'Ruth Wainwright' (v)	WCHb
	- variegated (v)	WAlt
	- 'Voile'	WAlt
	× ***webbiana***	see *P. grandiflora*
	- 'Gruss aus Isernhagen'	EBee

Prunus ✿ (*Rosaceae*)

	'Accolade' ♀H4	Widely available
§	'Amanogawa' ♀H4	Widely available
	americana	EMui
	amygdalus	see *P. dulcis*
	armeniaca 'Alfred' (F)	EMui ERea GTwe MGos SDea SKee SPer
	- var. ***ansu*** 'Flore Pleno' (d)	ERea LAst
	- 'Blenheim' (F)	ERea
	- 'Bredase' (F)	CWib EMil ERea SDea
	- 'Early Moorpark' (F)	CAgr CTho CWib EPfP ERea GTwe IFFs LAst LRHS MBri SDea SLon
	- 'Farmingdale' (F)	ERea SDea
	- Flavorcot = 'Bayoto'PBR (F)	CAgr CSut SPer
	- 'Garden Aprigold' (F)	EMui MGos NPri SPoG
	- 'Goldcot' (F)	CAgr EPfP ERea LRHS MBri MCoo SDea SKee WHar
	- 'Golden Glow' (F)	CAgr CTho EMui ERea GTwe LAst LRHS MBri MCoo MWat SKee
	- 'Goldrich' (F)	CAgr
	- 'Hargrand' (F)	CAgr SVic
	- 'Harogem' (F)	CAgr
	- 'Hemskirke' (F)	SKee
	- 'Hongaarse' (F)	SDea
	- 'Isabella' (F)	CAgr ERea MBri MCoo MGos
	- 'Moorpark' (F) ♀H3	CEnd CSBt CTri CWib EMui ERea GKir GTwe LAst LBuc LRHS MAsh MGos MRav SDea SKee SPer
	- 'New Large Early' (F)	EMui ERea SDea SEND SKee
	- 'Petit Muscat' (F)	ERea
	- 'Tomcot' (F)	CAgr CTho EMui LBuc MBri MCoo SFam SKee SPoG WBVN
	- 'Tross Orange' (F)	CWib SDea
	avium ♀H4	Widely available
	- 'Amber Heart' (F)	SKee
	- 'August Heart' (F)	SKee
	- 'Bigarreau Gaucher' (F)	IFFs SKee
§	- 'Bigarreau Napoléon' (F)	GTwe SCrf SKee SVic
	- 'Birchenhayes'	see *P. avium* 'Early Birchenhayes'
	- 'Black Eagle' (F)	CTho SKee
	- 'Black Elton' (F)	SKee
	- 'Black Heart' (F)	CWib
	- 'Black Tartarian' (F)	SKee
	- 'Bottlers'	see *P. avium* 'Preserving'
	- 'Bradbourne Black' (F)	ECrN SCrf SKee
	- 'Bullion' (F)	CEnd CTho
	- 'Burcombe' (F)	CEnd CTho
	- 'Caroon' (F)	SKee
	- Celeste = 'Sumpaca'PBR (D)	CAgr CTri EMil EMui ERea GTwe LRHS MBri NLar SDea SKee SPoG
	- 'Cherokee'	see *P. avium* 'Lapins'
	- 'Colney' (F) ♀H4	ERea GTwe NLar SFam SKee WJas
	- 'Crown Morello' (F)	ERea
	- 'Dun' (F)	CTho
§	- 'Early Birchenhayes' (F)	CEnd CTho
	- 'Early Rivers' (F)	CSBt CWib ECrN GTwe LAst LSRN NLar SDea SKee SVic
	- 'Elton Heart' (F)	CTho SKee
	- 'Emperor Francis' (F)	ECrN
	- 'Fice' (F)	CEnd CTho

	Plant	Suppliers
	- 'Florence' (F)	SKee
	- 'Goodnestone Black' (D) **new**	SKee
	- 'Governor Wood' (F)	GTwe SKee
	- 'Grandiflora'	see *P. avium* 'Plena'
	- 'Greenstem Black' (F)	CTho
	- 'Hannaford' (D/C)	CTho
	- 'Hertford' (F) ♀H4	SFam SKee
	- 'Inga' (F)	SFam SKee
	- 'Kentish Red' (F)	CTho SKee
	- 'Kordia' (D) **new**	SKee
§	- 'Lapins' (F)	CAgr CDul CTho CTri ECrN EMui GTwe LAst MAsh NLar SDea SFam SKee SPoG WHar WJas
	- 'May Duke'	see *P.* × *gondouinii* 'May Duke'
	- 'Merchant' (F) ♀H4	ECrN SKee
	- 'Merton Favourite' (F)	SKee
	- 'Merton Glory' (F)	CDul CSBt ECrN EMui ERea GTwe IFFs LRHS MAsh MGos SCrf SFam SKee WHar
	- 'Merton Late' (F)	SKee
	- 'Merton Marvel' (F)	SKee
	- 'Merton Premier' (F)	SKee SVic
	- 'Merton Reward'	see *P.* × *gondouinii* 'Merton Reward'
	- 'Nabella' (F)	WJas
	- 'Napoléon'	see *P. avium* 'Bigarreau Napoléon'
	- 'Newstar' (F)	EMui
	- 'Noble' (F)	SKee
	- 'Noir de Guben' (F)	ECrN GTwe SKee
	- 'Noir de Meched' (D)	SKee
	- 'Old Black Heart' (F)	SKee
	- 'Penny' (F)	CAgr EMui LRHS SKee
§	- 'Plena' (d) ♀H4	Widely available
§	- 'Preserving' (F)	CTho
	- 'Regina' (F)	CSut
	- 'Ronald's Heart' (F)	SKee
	- 'Roundel Heart' (F)	SKee
	- 'Schauenburger' (F)	SKee
	- 'Small Black' (F)	CTho
	- 'Starkrimson' (F)	ECrN
	- 'Stella' (F) ♀H4	Widely available
	- 'Stella Compact' (F)	CWib ECrN LAst LSRN SDea WHar
	- 'Strawberry Heart' (F)	SKee
	- 'Summer Sun' (D) ♀H4	CAgr CSut CTho CTri EMil EMui ERea GBut GTwe LBuc LRHS MAsh MBri MCoo NLar SCoo SDea SFam SKee SPoG WHar
	- 'Summit' (F)	SKee
	- 'Sunburst' (F)	CAgr CCVT CDul CEnd CMac CTho CTri CWib ECrN EMil EMui GTwe LAst LBuc LRHS LSRN MAsh MBri SCoo SDea SFam SKee SPoG SVic WHar WJas
	- 'Sweetheart' (F)	CAgr CDul EMui GTwe LRHS LSRN MAsh MBri SKee SPoG
	- 'Sylvia' (F)	CAgr SFam
	- 'Turkish Black' (F)	SKee
	- 'Van' (F)	CSBt ECrN GTwe SKee
	- 'Vega' (F)	CAgr ERea GTwe IFFs LBuc SFam SKee WJas
	- 'Waterloo' (F)	CTho SKee
	- 'White Heart' (F)	CTho CWib ECrN SKee
	- 'Zweitfrühe' (F)	GKir
	'Beni-yutaka'	CEnd CTho GKir LRHS MAsh SCoo SLim
	besseyi	CAgr GAuc
	'Blaze'	see *P. cerasifera* 'Nigra'
	× ***blireana*** (d) ♀H4	CDoC CDul CEnd CTri EPfP ERea EWTr LAst LRHS MAsh MBri MGos MRav MSwo MWat NLar NWea SBch SCoo SPer SPoG WCFE WFar WHar
	- 'Saling Hall' (d) **new**	ERea
	'Blushing Bride'	see *P.* 'Shōgetsu'
	'Candy Floss'	see *P.* 'Matsumae-beni-murasaki'
	cerasifera	CDul CRWN CTri ECrN EMac GKir IFFs LBuc MAsh NWea SEND SPer SVic WDin
	- 'Cherry Plum' (F)	CTri ECrN SDea SKee
	- 'Crimson Dwarf'	GKir SCoo SWvt
	- 'First' (F)	CAgr
	- 'Golden Sphere' (F)	CAgr CTho EMui LRHS MBri
	- 'Gypsy' (F)	CAgr CTho EMui LRHS MBri SPoG
	- 'Hessei' (v)	CBow CEnd EBee LRHS MAsh MBri MGos MRav SBch SCoo SPoG
§	- Myrobalan Group (F)	ECrN EMui MRav SDea
	- - 'Magda Jensen' (C)	CAgr
§	- 'Nigra' ♀H4	Widely available
	- 'Pendula'	CTho ECrN WFar
§	- 'Pissardii'	CWib ECrN GKir IFFs LAst LMaj LRHS MBar NBea NWea SCoo SFam SLim WFar WJas
*	- 'Princess'	CWSG EMui
	- 'Rosea'	LRHS
	- 'Spring Glow'	CCVT CEnd EBee EPfP LRHS MAsh MSwo SBch SCoo SLim
	cerasus 'Maynard' (F) **new**	LSRN
	- 'Montmorency' (F)	SKee
	- 'Morello' (C) ♀H4	Widely available
	- 'Nabella' (F)	MAsh SKee
	- 'Rhexii' (d)	CDul CLnd ECrN MAsh MBri MGos NEgg NPCo SPer SPoG
	'Champagne Dream'	SCoo
	'Cheal's Weeping'	see *P.* 'Kiku-shidare-zakura'
	'Chocolate Ice'	see *P.* 'Matsumae-fuki'
§	× ***cistena*** ♀H4	CCVT CDul CSBt CWSG EBee ELan EPfP LAst LRHS MDun MGan MGos MSwo SBch SCoo SPlb SPoG WDin
	- 'Crimson Dwarf'	see *P.* × *cistena*
	'Collingwood Ingram'	GKir MBri MGos SPoG
	conradinae	see *P. hirtipes*
	'Daikoku'	GKir
	davidiana	SPlb
	domestica 'Allgroves Superb' (D)	ERea
	- 'Angelina Burdett' (D)	ERea GTwe SDea SKee
	- 'Anna Späth' (C/D)	SKee
	- 'Ariel' (C/D)	SDea SKee
	- 'Autumn Compote' (C)	SKee
	- 'Avalon' (D)	CAgr CCVT ECrN GTwe SDea SKee
	- 'Beauty' (D) **new**	CSut
	- 'Belgian Purple' (C)	SKee
	- 'Belle de Louvain' (C)	CDul CTho CTri ECrN EMil ERea GTwe SDea SKee
	- 'Birchenhayes' (F)	CEnd
	- 'Black Diamond'	see *P. salicina* 'Black Diamond'
	- 'Blaisdon Red' (C)	CTho GTwe
	- 'Blue Rock' (C/D) ♀H4	MCoo SKee
	- 'Blue Tit' (C/D) ♀H4	CAgr CTho EMui ERea GTwe SDea SKee
	- 'Bonne de Bry' (D)	SKee
§	- 'Bountiful' (C)	ERea
	- 'Brandy Gage' (C/D)	SKee
	- 'Bryanston Gage' (D)	CTho SKee
	- 'Burbank's Giant'	see *P. domestica* 'Giant Prune'
	- 'Burcombe' (F)	CEnd
	- 'Cambridge Gage' (D) ♀H4	CAgr CCVT CDoC CDul CTri CWib ECrN EMui EPfP ERea GKir GTwe IFFs LAst LRHS MAsh MBri MGan MWat NPri SCoo SCrf SDea SFam SKee SPer SPoG WHar WJas
	- 'Chrislin' (F)	CAgr CTho

	- 'Coe's Golden Drop' (D)	CCAT ECrN EMui ERea GTwe IFFs LAst MBri MGos MRav SDea SFam SKee SPer
	- 'Count Althann's Gage' (D)	ECrN ERea GTwe NEgg SDea SFam SKee
	- 'Cox's Emperor' (C)	SKee
	- 'Crimson Drop' (D)	ERea SKee
	- 'Cropper'	see *P. domestica* 'Laxton's Cropper'
	- 'Curlew' (C)	SDea SKee
	- 'Czar' (C) ♀^{H4}	CAgr CCAT CCVT CDoC CDul CMac CSBt CTri CWib ECrN EMui EPfP GBut GKir GTwe IFFs LAst LBuc MGos NPri NWea SDea SEND SFam SKee SPer SPoG SVic WHar
	- 'Delikya' (D) **new**	ERea
	- 'Denbigh Plum' (D)	WGwG
	- 'Denniston's Superb'	see *P. domestica* 'Imperial Gage'
	- 'Diamond' (C)	SKee
	- 'Dittisham Black' (C)	CAgr CTho
	- 'Dittisham Ploughman' (C)	CTho SKee
	- 'Dunster Plum' (F)	CAgr CTho CTri CWib
	- 'Early Favourite' (D/C)	ERea
	- 'Early Green Gage' (D)	NEgg
	- 'Early Laxton' (C/D) ♀^{H4}	ECrN ERea GTwe LAst SDea SFam SKee
	- 'Early Prolific'	see *P. domestica* 'Rivers's Early Prolific'
	- 'Early Rivers'	see *P. domestica* 'Rivers's Early Prolific'
	- 'Early Transparent Gage' (C/D)	CCAT CSBt CTho ECrN EMil EMui ERea GTwe IFFs LAst LBuc LRHS MBri MCoo SCoo SDea SFam SKee
	- 'Early Victoria' (C/D)	SDea
	- 'Edwards' (C/D) ♀^{H4}	CTri CWib ECrN GTwe NEgg SDea SKee
	- 'Excalibur' (D)	CAgr ECrN GTwe SDea SKee
§	- German Prune Group (C)	MCoo SKee
§	- 'Giant Prune' (C)	CCAT ECrN GTwe SDea SKee
I	- 'Godshill Big Sloe' (F)	SDea
	- 'Godshill Blue' (C)	SDea
	- 'Godshill Minigage' (F)	SDea
	- 'Golden Transparent' (D)	CTho GTwe MCoo SFam SKee
	- 'Goldfinch' (D)	GTwe MCoo SKee
	- 'Gordon Castle'	MCoo
	- Green Gage Group	see *P. domestica* Reine-Claude Group
	- - 'Lindsey Gage' (F)	WBVN
	- 'Grey Plum' (F)	CAgr CTho
	- 'Grove's Late Victoria' (C/D)	CCAT
	- 'Guinevere' (F) **new**	LRHS
	- 'Guthrie's Late Green' (D)	SKee
	- 'Hays' (C/D) **new**	ERea
	- 'Herman' (C/D)	CAgr ECrN EMil GKir GTwe LAst LRHS MBri MCoo SDea
	- 'Heron' (F)	ECrN GTwe SKee
	- 'Impérial Epineuse' (D)	SKee
§	- 'Imperial Gage' (C/D) ♀^{H4}	CAgr CCAT CSBt CTho CTri ECrN EMui ERea GTwe LRHS MAsh MGos NLar SDea SFam SKee WHar
	- 'Italian Prune' (F)	MCoo
	- subsp. ***italica***	EMui
	- 'Jan James' (F)	CEnd
	- 'Jefferson' (D) ♀^{H4}	CAgr ECrN EMui GTwe LAst NLar SDea SFam SKee SVic
*	- 'Jubilaeum' (D)	CAgr EMui GTwe SCoo SKee
	- 'Kea' (C)	CAgr CTho SKee
	- 'Kirke's' (D)	CCAT CTho CTri GTwe SDea SFam SKee
	- 'Landkey Yellow' (F)	CAgr CTho
	- 'Langley Gage' (F)	CAgr ECrN SDea
	- 'Late Muscatelle' (D)	ERea SKee
	- 'Late Transparent Gage' (D)	SKee
	- 'Laxton's Bountiful'	see *P. domestica* 'Bountiful'
§	- 'Laxton's Cropper' (C)	CTri GTwe LAst MCoo SKee
	- 'Laxton's Delight' (D) ♀^{H4}	GTwe
	- 'Laxton's Gage' (D)	SDea SKee
	- 'Mallard' (D) ♀^{H4}	SKee
	- 'Manaccan' (C)	CAgr CTho
	- 'Marjorie's Seedling' (C) ♀^{H4}	Widely available
	- 'McLaughlin' (D)	SKee
	- 'Merton Gage' (D)	SKee
	- 'Merton Gem' (C/D)	SKee
	- 'Monarch' (C)	SKee
	- Old English gage **new**	LAst
	- 'Olympia' (C/D)	SKee
	- 'Ontario' (C/D)	SKee
	- 'Opal' (D) ♀^{H4}	CAgr CCAT CCVT CDoC CDul CMac CWSG CWib ECrN EMui ERea GBut GTwe IFFs LBuc LRHS MBri MGos MWat NWea SCoo SCrf SDea SEND SFam SKee SPoG WHar
	- 'Orleans' (C)	SKee
	- 'Oullins Gage' (C/D) ♀^{H4}	Widely available
	- 'Pershore' (C) ♀^{H4}	CAgr CCAT CTho CWib ECrN ERea GTwe LAst MBri NEgg SDea SFam SKee WHar WSpi
	- 'Pond's Seedling' (C)	CSBt SDea SKee
	- 'President' (C/D)	SDea SKee
	- 'Priory Plum' (D)	SDea
	- 'Purple Pershore' (C)	CAgr CCAT CTri CWib ECrN ERea GTwe IFFs NEgg SDea SFam SKee WSpi
	- 'Quetsche d'Alsace'	see *P. domestica* German Prune Group
	- 'Reeves' (C) ♀^{H4}	GTwe MCoo SFam SKee
	- 'Reine-Claude Dorée'	see *P. domestica* Reine-Claude Group
§	- Reine-Claude Group (C/D)	CSBt ECrN EMui GKir GTwe MGos SDea SFam SKee SPer
	- - 'Old Green Gage'	see *P. domestica* (Reine-Claude Group) 'Reine-Claude Vraie'
	- - 'Reine-Claude de Bavais' (D)	CCAT CTho CTri ERea GTwe SDea SFam SKee
	- - 'Reine-Claude de Vars' (D)	SVic
	- - 'Reine-Claude Violette' (D)	ECrN ERea SKee
§	- - 'Reine-Claude Vraie' (C/D)	CAgr CCAT CCVT CMac CSBt CWib ECrN EMui EPfP ERea GKir LAst LRHS MAsh SPoG WJas
§	- - 'Willingham Gage' (C/D)	CMac ERea GTwe SKee
§	- 'Rivers's Early Prolific' (C)	CAgr CSBt CTho CTri ECrN EPfP ERea GTwe MAsh MCoo NWea SCoo SDea SKee WHar
	- 'Royale de Vilvoorde' (D)	SKee
	- 'Sanctus Hubertus' (D) ♀^{H4}	CTri ECrN EPfP GTwe SDea SKee
	- 'Severn Cross' (D)	GTwe SKee
	- 'Stanley' (C/D)	SVic
	- 'Stella'	CCVT CDul GKir LAst NEgg NPri
	- 'Stint' (C/D)	SKee
	- 'Swan' (C)	ECrN GTwe SKee
	- 'Syston White'	MGos
	- 'Thames Cross' (D)	CSut SKee
	- 'Transparent Gage' (D)	ECrN SKee
	- 'Upright' (F)	CEnd
	- 'Utility' (D)	SKee

	- 'Valor' (C/D) ♀H4	ECrN
	- 'Verity' (D/C)	SKee
	- 'Victoria' (C/D) ♀H4	Widely available
	- 'Violetta'PBR (C/D)	CAgr EMui GTwe SKee
	- 'Warwickshire Drooper' (C)	CAgr CTho CWib ERea GTwe LAst LRHS NEgg SDea SFam SKee WBVN
	- 'Washington' (D)	SDea SKee
	- 'White Magnum Bonum' (C)	SDea
	- 'Willingham'	see *P. domestica* (Reine-Claude Group) 'Willingham Gage'
§	***dulcis***	CDul CLnd CTri CWSG CWib ECrN EMui EPfP LAst LRHS MREP MWat NBea NWea SBch SCoo SCrf SDea SEND SFam SVic WBVN WDin
	- 'Ai' (F)	CAgr
	- 'Ardechoise' (F)	CAgr
	- 'Ferraduel' (F)	CAgr
	- 'Ferragnes' (F)	CAgr
	- 'Lauranne' (F)	CAgr
	- 'Macrocarpa' (F)	ECrN
	- 'Mandaline' (F)	CAgr
*	- 'Phoebe' (F)	CAgr
	- 'Princesse' (F)	EMil
	- 'Supernova' (F)	CCCN
	- 'Titan' (F)	ECrN
	- 'Tuono' (F)	CCCN
	Easter Bonnet = 'Comet'PBR	CTri EPfP LBuc LRHS NPri
	Fragrant Cloud	see *P.* 'Shizuka'
	fruticosa 'Globosa'	LRHS NHol
	'Fugenzō'	CSBt GKir
	glandulosa 'Alba Plena' (d)	CEnd CSBt EBee ECrN LRHS MAsh NBea SPlb SPoG SRms SWvt WCFE WDin
	- 'Rosea Plena'	see *P. glandulosa* 'Sinensis'
§	- 'Sinensis' (d)	CAlb CEnd CPLG CSBt EBee LRHS SPoG SRms WDin
§	× ***gondouinii*** 'May Duke' (F)	CTho SKee SVic
§	- 'Merton Reward' (F)	ERea SKee
	'Gyoikō'	CEnd GKir
	'Hally Jolivette'	CEnd ELan GKir LRHS MAsh NWea SPoG WDin
	'Hillieri'	ECrN MBar MGos
	'Hillieri Spire'	see *P.* 'Spire'
	'Hilling's Weeping'	EBee
§	***hirtipes***	CEnd CLnd LRHS
	'Hokusai'	EPfP GKir
	Hollywood	see *P.* 'Trailblazer'
	'Horinji'	GKir LRHS MBri SCoo
	'Ichiyo' (d) ♀H4	CDul ECrN EPfP GKir LAst MAsh MBri SCoo SCrf SPer SPoG
	ilicifolia	WCot
	subsp. ***ilicifolia*** NNS 05-607 **new**	
	incisa	CTri NBea NEgg NWea SPer WSpi
	- 'Ariane'	LMaj
	- 'Beniomi'	MRav
	- 'February Pink'	CAbP CPMA LRHS MRav WDin
	- 'Fujima'	CSBt EBee LAst SBch WSpi
	- 'Kojo-no-mai'	Widely available
	- 'Mikinori'	CEnd CSBt GKir LRHS MAsh MBlu NLar SCoo WFar WSpi
	- 'Oshidori' (d)	CSBt EPfP GKir LRHS MBri MGos MRav NEgg NLar SLim SPoG SRms
	- 'Paean'	NLar
	- 'Pendula'	GKir LRHS SCoo
	- 'Praecox' ♀H4	CSBt CTho CWSG EPfP GKir LRHS MWat SCoo
	- 'The Bride'	CEnd CWSG GKir LRHS MAsh MBri SCoo

§	- f. ***yamadae***	CPMA LBMP LRHS MAsh MBri NLar WSpi
	insititia (F)	CRWN IFFs
	- 'Abergwyngregin' (C)	WGwG
	- 'Black Bullace' (F)	EMui
§	- 'Bradley's King Damson' (C)	SKee
	- bullace (C)	NWea SDea
	- 'Countess' (C)	CTri
	- 'Dittisham Damson' (C)	CTho
	- 'Farleigh Damson' (C) ♀H4	CAgr CWib ECrN EMil ERea GKir GTwe LAst LBuc LRHS MAsh MMuc NWea SDea SEND SFam SKee SPer SVic WJas
	- 'Godshill Damson' (C)	SDea
	- 'Golden Bullace'	see *P. insititia* 'White Bullace'
	- 'King of Damsons'	see *P. insititia* 'Bradley's King Damson'
	- 'Langley Bullace' (C)	CAgr CDul CTho ECrN EMui ERea GTwe NLar SKee
	- 'Lisna' (C)	CTri
	- 'Merryweather Damson' (C)	Widely available
	- 'Mirabelle de Nancy' (C)	CAgr CTho CTri ERea GTwe LAst LMaj SDea SFam SKee
	- 'Mirabelle de Nancy (Red)' (C)	SDea
§	- 'Prune Damson' (C) ♀H4	CAgr CDoC CDul CTho CTri CWSG ECrN EMui GBut GTwe LAst LBuc LRHS MAsh MBri MMuc MWat NLar SDea SFam SKee SPer WHar WJas
	- 'Shepherd's Bullace' (C)	CAgr CTho ERea SKee
	- 'Shropshire Damson'	see *P. insititia* 'Prune Damson'
	- 'Small Bullace' (C)	CAgr SKee
§	- 'White Bullace' (C)	CAgr ERea SKee
	- 'Yellow Apricot' (C)	ERea SKee
§	***jamasakura***	CDul
	'Jō-nioi'	CDul CEnd CTho MBri
§	'Kanzan' ♀H4	Widely available
§	'Kiku-shidare-zakura' ♀H4	Widely available
	Korean hill cherry	see *P. verecunda*
	'Kulilensis Ruby'	GKir SLPl
	'Kursar' ♀H4	CDul CLnd CSBt CTho CTri EBee EMui EPfP GKir LRHS LSRN MAsh MBri NLar NWea SBch SCoo SCrf SLim SPer SPoG
	laurocerasus ♀H4	CBcs CCVT CChe CDul CMac CPMA CTrG CWSG EBee ECrN ELan EMac EPfP GKir IFFs LAst LRHS MGos MRav NBea NWea SEND SPer SPoG SReu WFar WMoo WMou
	- 'Angustifolia'	WDin
	- 'Aureovariegata'	see *P. laurocerasus* 'Taff's Golden Gleam'
	- 'Camelliifolia'	CTri EPla EQua MBlu WCFE WCom WHCG
N	- 'Castlewellan' (v)	CAlb CBot CDoC CDul CTri ELon EPfP EPla LAst LHop LRHS MBar MGos MRav MSwo NHol NPro SBch SDix SLim SPer SPoG SSta WCom WDin WFar WGrn WHar WMoo
	- 'Caucasica'	CEnd MGos SBch
	- 'Cherry Brandy'	GKir MRav SLPl WDin
	- Dart's Lowgreen	see *P. laurocerasus* Low 'n' Green
	- Etna = 'Anbri'PBR	CMac EBee EPfP IFFs LBuc LRHS LSou MAsh MBri MGos MWat NPri SBch SWvt
	- 'Gajo'PBR	NPro SPer WBor
	- Genolia = 'Mariblon'PBR **new**	MAsh

	Name	Suppliers
	- 'Green Marble' (v)	CPMA CTri EBee EHoe
	- 'Herbergii'	IFFs MAsh NLar
§	- 'Latifolia'	CHEx EQua SLPl
§	- Low 'n' Green = 'Interlo'	MRav
	- 'Magnoliifolia'	see *P. laurocerasus* 'Latifolia'
	- 'Mano'	MGos NLar
	- 'Marbled White'	see *P. laurocerasus* 'Castlewellan'
	- 'Miky'	CPMA
	- 'Mischeana'	SLPl
	- 'Mount Vernon'	CTri MBar MBlu MGos WDin
	- 'Novita'	EPfP
	- 'Otinii'	CHEx
	- 'Otto Luyken' ♀H4	Widely available
	- 'Prostrata' **new**	NHol
	- Renault Ace = 'Renlau'	MGos
	- 'Reynvaanii'	CPMA MBri
	- 'Rotundifolia'	Widely available
	- 'Schipkaensis'	SLPl SPer
§	- 'Taff's Golden Gleam' (v)	CBow CPMA
	- 'Van Nes'	CPMA EBee IFFs MAsh NLar WDin
	- 'Variegata' misapplied	see *P. laurocerasus* 'Castlewellan'
	- 'Variegata' ambig. (v)	CWib SRms
	- 'Whitespot'	MMuc
	- 'Zabeliana'	CAlb CDul CMac CTri EBee ECrN EPfP GKir LRHS MBar MGos MSwo NEgg NHol NWea SPer SRms WDin WFar
	litigiosa	CEnd GKir LRHS MBri SCoo SPoG
	'Little Pink Perfection'	CDul LRHS MBri SCoo
	lusitanica ♀H4	Widely available
	- subsp. ***azorica***	CDoC CPLG EQua GKir MRav WFar WPGP
	- 'Myrtifolia'	CTri EBee ECrN EPfP EPla EQua GKir LRHS MBri MRav SWvt WCFE WDin WMoo
	- 'Variegata' (v)	CBcs CBot CDul CMac CTri CWib EBee EHoe ELan GKir LAst LHop LRHS MGos MLHP MRav MSwo NHol SBch SDix SLim SPer SPoG SSta WDin WFar WMoo
	maackii	EPfP MMuc SEND SSpi WDin
	- 'Amber Beauty'	CBcs CDoC CDul EBee EPfP GBin GKir LMaj MRav SBch SCoo WDin WFar
	mahaleb	IFFs
	'Mahogany Lustre'	see *P. serrula* 'Mahogany Lustre'
	mandshurica	EGFP ERea GKir
	maritima	GAuc
§	'Matsumae-beni-murasaki'	EMil GKir NLar SCoo
	'Matsumae-beni-tamanishiki'	GKir
§	'Matsumae-fuki'	EMil GKir LRHS MBri NPal NWea SLim SPoG
§	'Matsumae-hanagasa'	CEnd GKir LRHS MAsh MBri NLar
	maximowiczii B&SWJ 10967	WCru
	'Mount Fuji'	see *P.* 'Shirotae'
	mume	CMCN CMen WDin
	- 'Beni-chidori'	CEnd CWib EBee EPfP LRHS MAsh MBlu MBri MGos NBea NLar SCoo SLim SPoG WJas WPGP
*	- 'Ken Kyo'	LRHS
*	- 'Kyo Koh'	LRHS
§	- 'Omoi-no-mama' (d)	CEnd CMen LRHS
	- 'Omoi-no-wac'	see *P. mume* 'Omoi-no-mama'
	- 'Pendula'	ECrN
	myrobalana	see *P. cerasifera* Myrobalan Group
	nipponica var. ***kurilensis*** 'Brilliant'	CBcs GKir LRHS MAsh MBri MGos NLar SBch SCrf
	- var. ***kurilensis*** 'Ruby'	CBcs CEnd GKir MBri MGos NEgg WFar

	Name	Suppliers
	'Okame' ♀H4	CChe CDul CLnd CMac CSam CTho EBee ECrN ELon EPfP GKir LAst LHop LRHS MAsh MGos MRav NWea SBch SCoo SCrf SLPl SLim SPer SPoG WFar
*	'Okame Harlequin' (v)	SBch SLim SPoG
	'Okumiyako' misapplied	see *P.* 'Shogetsu'
	padus	CCVT CDul CLnd CMac CRWN CSBt CTri ECrN EMac GKir IFFs LAst LBuc MGos MSwo NBea NWea WDin WMou
	- 'Albertii'	CCVT GKir MMuc SCoo
	- 'Colorata' ♀H4	CBcs CDoC CDul CEnd CSam CTho ECrN ELan EMil EWTr GKir LBuc LHop LMaj LRHS MAsh MGos SCoo SPer WCot WDin WFar WPat
	- 'Grandiflora'	see *P. padus* 'Watereri'
	- 'Purple Queen'	CEnd ECrN EQua SCoo
§	- 'Watereri' ♀H4	CCVT CDoC CDul CEnd CLnd CMCN CMac CTho CWib EBee ECrN ELan EPfP EWTr LAst LHop LMaj LRHS NWea SCoo SLim SPer SPoG WDin
	'Pandora' ♀H4	CDul CLnd EBee ECrN EPfP GKir LAst LRHS MAsh MBri MGos MRav MSwo NBea NPCo NWea SBch SCoo SCrf SEND SPer SPoG WFar
	pendula	SCrf
	- var. ***ascendens*** 'Rosea'	EBee
§	- 'Pendula Rosea' ♀H4	CDoC CDul CEnd CTri CWib EPfP GKir LAst LRHS MAsh SCrf SPer WFar WJas
§	- 'Pendula Rubra' ♀H4	CDoC CDul CLnd CSBt CWib EBee ECrN EPfP GKir LAst LHop LRHS MBri MGos MSwo SBch SCoo SLim SPer SPoG WFar WPat
§	- 'Stellata'	LRHS MAsh MBri SPer
	pensylvanica	LMaj
	persica 'Amsden June' (F)	CWib EBtc ERea GTwe SDea SFam SKee
	- 'Avalon Pride' (F) **new**	CSut
	- 'Barrington' (F) **new**	ERea
	- 'Bellegarde' (F)	ERea GTwe SDea SFam
	- 'Bonanza' (F)	EMui ERea LSRN
	- 'Cardinal' (F/d) **new**	ERea
	- 'Clara Meyer'	CTri
	- 'Darling' (F)	SVic
	- 'Dixi Red' (F)	CAgr ERea
	- 'Doctor Hogg' (F)	ERea SDea
	- 'Duke of York' (F) ♀H3	CTri ERea GTwe LRHS SDea SFam SKee
	- 'Dymond' (F)	ERea
	- 'Early Alexander' (F)	ERea
	- 'Flat China' (F)	ERea
	- 'Foliis Rubris' (F)	CDul LRHS WPGP
	- 'Francis' (F)	SKee
	- 'Garden Lady' (F)	ERea GTwe SKee SPoG
	- 'Hale's Early' (F)	ERea GTwe MRav MWat SEND SFam SKee SPer
	- 'Hylands' (F)	ERea SDea
	- 'Johnny Brack' (F) **new**	ERea
	- 'Kestrel' (F)	ERea
	- 'Madison' (F) **new**	ERea
	- 'Melred' (F)	MGos
	- 'Mesembrine' PBR (F)	EMui
	- 'Natalia' (F)	SDea
	- var. ***nectarina*** Crimson Gold (F)	SDea
	- - 'Early Blaze' (F) **new**	ERea
	- - 'Early Gem' (F)	ERea SDea
	- - 'Early Rivers' (F) ♀H3	ERea GTwe LSRN SDea SPer
	- - 'Elruge' (F)	ERea GTwe SDea

	- - 'Fantasia' (F)	ERea SDea
	- - 'Fire Gold' (F)	ERea SDea
	- - 'Flavortop' (F) **new**	ERea
	- - 'Garden Beauty' (F/d)	EMui MGos SPoG
	- - 'Humboldt' (F)	ERea GTwe SDea SKee
	- - 'John Rivers' (F)	GTwe SDea SFam
	- - 'Lord Napier' (F) ♀H3	CAgr CDoC CSBt CTri CWSG CWib EMui EPfP ERea GKir LAst LBuc LRHS MAsh MGos MWat SDea SFam SKee SPer SPoG SVic WHar
	- - 'Nectared' (F)	CWib ERea
	- - 'Nectarella' (F)	EMui ERea SKee
	- - 'Pineapple' (F)	CAgr CTri ERea GTwe SDea SFam SKee SPoG
	- - 'Red Gold' (F) **new**	ERea
	- - 'Ruby Gold' (F)	ERea SDea
	- - 'Terrace Ruby' (F)	MGos SPoG
	- - 'Violette Hâtive' (F) **new**	ERea
	- 'Peregrine' (F) ♀H3	CAgr CSBt CTri CWSG CWib EMui EPfP ERea GKir GTwe IFFs LAst LBuc LRHS MAsh MBri MGos MWat SDea SFam SKee SPer SPoG WJas
	- 'Pink Peachy' (F)	NLar
	- 'Red Haven' (F)	CAgr CWib ERea GTwe SDea SKee SVic
	- 'Redwing' (F)	CAgr ERea
	- 'Reliance' (F)	SDea
	- 'Robin Redbreast' (F)	SDea
	- 'Rochester' (F) ♀H3	CAgr CSBt CWSG CWib EMui ERea GTwe LAst LRHS LSRN MBri SDea SFam SKee SPer SPoG
	- 'Royal George' (F)	GTwe SFam
	- 'Sanguine de Savoie' (F)	EMui
	- 'Saturne' (F)	EMui ERea SKee SPoG
	- 'Springtime' (F)	ERea SDea
	- 'Terrace Amber' (F)	EMui MGos SPoG
	- 'Terrace Diamond' (F)	MGos SPoG
	- 'Terrace Garnet' (F)	MGos SPoG
	- 'White Peachy' (F)	NLar
	× ***persicoides*** 'Angélique'	EMil GKir
	- 'Ingrid' (F)	CAgr EBtc LBuc LRHS MBri MCoo SCoo
	- 'Pollardii'	NWea WJas
	- 'Robijn' (F)	CAgr ECrN LBuc
	- 'Spring Glow'	CDoC MBri MWea NWea WJas
	'Pink Champagne' **new**	LRHS
	'Pink Parasol'	see *P.* 'Matsumae-hanagasa'
	'Pink Perfection' ♀H4	CBcs CDul CLnd CSBt CWSG CWib EBee ECrN EPfP GKir LAst LRHS MAsh MBri MGos MWat NLar SBch SCrf SPer WDin WFar WHar WJas
	'Pink Shell' ♀H4	CLnd EBee ECrN EPfP GKir LRHS MAsh MBri SFam SPur
	pissardii	see *P. cerasifera* 'Pissardii'
	'Pissardii Nigra'	see *P. cerasifera* 'Nigra'
	prostrata	GAuc
*	- 'Anita Kistler'	ECho
*	- var. ***discolor***	NLar
	pseudocerasus 'Cantabrigiensis'	ECrN
	pumila var. ***depressa***	EMil MRav NLar NPro
	'Rebecca'	SPoG
	'Royal Burgundy' (d)	CCVT CDul CEnd CLnd CMac CWSG EBee ECrN EMil EPfP GKir LAst LRHS LSRN MAsh MBri MDun MGos MWat SBch SCoo SLim SPer SPoG SPur WFar WHar
	rufa	CDul CPMA CTho EBee EBtc LRHS SSpi
	salicina	ERea
	- 'Beauty'	ERea
§	- 'Black Diamond' (F)	SDea
	- 'Methley' (D)	ERea
	- 'Satsuma' (F)	ERea
	- 'Shiro' (D)	ERea
	sargentii ♀H4	Widely available
	- 'Charles Sargent'	GKir
	- 'Columnaris'	GKir LRHS MAsh
	- 'Rancho'	CLnd SCoo SLim WFar
	× ***schmittii***	ECrN SCoo SPer WJas
	'Sekiyama'	see *P.* 'Kanzan'
	serotina	CDul IFFs NLar
§	***serrula*** ♀H4	Widely available
	- Dorothy Clive form	EBee LRHS LSRN
§	- 'Mahogany Lustre'	WFar WPat
	- var. ***tibetica***	see *P. serrula*
	serrula × ***serrulata***	CBcs CTho
	serrulata (d)	MGos
	- 'Erecta'	see *P.* 'Amanogawa'
	- 'Grandiflora'	see *P.* 'Ukon'
	- 'Longipes'	see *P.* 'Shōgetsu'
	- 'Miyako' misapplied	see *P.* 'Shōgetsu'
N	- var. ***pubescens***	see *P. verecunda*
	- 'Rosea'	see *P.* 'Kiku-shidare-zakura'
	- var. ***spontanea***	see *P. jamasakura*
	'Shidare-zakura'	see *P.* 'Kiku-shidare-zakura'
	'Shimizu-zakura'	see *P.* 'Shōgetsu'
	'Shirofugen' ♀H4	CBcs CDoC CDul CLnd CMCN CMac CSBt CTho CWSG CWib EBee ECrN EPfP GKir LBuc LRHS MAsh MBri MRav MWat SBch SCrf SEND SPer SPoG WDin WFar WHar WJas
§	'Shirotae' ♀H4	Widely available
§	'Shizuka'	CMac CWSG CWib EMil GKir LRHS MBri SCoo SLim SPer SPoG
§	'Shōgetsu' ♀H4	CBcs CDul CEnd CLnd CSBt CTho CWSG EBee ECrN ELan EPfP GKir LAst LMaj MAsh MBri MRav NBlu NEgg NLar SBch SCrf SEND SFam SLim SPer SPoG WDin
	'Shosar'	CEnd CWib ECrN GKir LAst LRHS MAsh NLar SCoo SPer
	× ***sieboldii*** 'Caespitosa'	GKir
	'Snow Goose'	CDoC EBee GKir LAst LMaj LRHS NEgg SCoo WFar
	'Snow Showers'	CEnd CMac CWSG EBee EMui GKir LRHS MAsh MBri MNHC MWat NWea SBch SPer SPoG
	spinosa	CCVT CDoC CDul CMac CRWN CTri ECrN EMac EPfP GKir LBuc MAsh MBar MBlu NWea SBch SPer SPoG SVic WDin WFar WMou
	- 'Plena' (d)	CEnd CTho MBlu
	- 'Purpurea'	CTho MBlu MBri NHol WDin WFar WHCG WMou WPat
§	'Spire' ♀H4	CCVT CDoC CDul CLnd CMac CSBt CTho CWib EBee ECrN EPfP GKir LAst LBuc LRHS MAsh MGos MSwo NBlu NWea SBch SCoo SEND SPer WDin WFar WJas
	× ***subhirtella***	LAst
	- var. ***ascendens***	see *P. pendula* var. *ascendens*
	- 'Autumnalis' ♀H4	Widely available
	- 'Autumnalis Rosea' ♀H4	Widely available
	- 'Falling Stars' **new**	LRHS
	- 'Fukubana'	CLnd CMac EBee ECrN EPfP GKir LRHS MAsh
	- 'Pendula' misapplied	see *P. pendula* 'Pendula Rosea'
	- 'Pendula Plena Rosea' (d)	CMac LAst LRHS
	- 'Pendula Rosea'	see *P. pendula* 'Pendula Rosea'
	- 'Pendula Rubra'	see *P. pendula* 'Pendula Rubra'
N	- 'Rosea'	CLnd MRav
	- 'Stellata'	see *P. pendula* 'Stellata'
	'Sunset Boulevard'	GKir

'Taihaku' 𝕐H4	Widely available
'Taki-nioi'	ECrN
'Taoyame'	GKir
tenella	CAgr ECrN ELan WCot
- 'Fire Hill'	CPMA CSBt CWib ECho ELan EPfP LRHS MGos MRav SPer SSpi WCFE WCot WDin WJas WSpi
tibetica	see *P. serrula*
tomentosa	CAgr ECrN LLHF MAsh NPri
§ 'Trailblazer' (C/D)	CEnd CLnd CSBt ECrN LAst LRHS MSwo SPer
triloba	CBcs CWib ECrN EGxp LAst LBuc LRHS NHol NPri NWea SBch WDin
- 'Multiplex' (d)	ECho EWTr MGos SRms WJas
- Rosemund = 'Korros'	SCrf
§ 'Ukon' 𝕐H4	CBcs CDoC CDul CLnd CMCN CMac CTho CTri EBee ECrN EPfP EWTr GKir LRHS MAsh MBri MGos MMuc MRav MWat NEgg NWea SBch SCrf SPer WDin WFar WHar
'Umineko'	CDoC CLnd CWib ECrN GKir GQue LRHS MGos SCoo SLPl SPer WDin WHar
§ ***verecunda***	CLnd NWea WJas
- 'Autumn Glory'	CTho NBea
virginiana 'Schubert'	CDul CLnd EBee ECrN EWTr LRHS SCoo WFar WJas WPat
'White Cloud'	CDul
yamadae	see *P. incisa* f. *yamadae*
× ***yedoensis***	CDul LMaj LRHS MRav SBch SPer
- 'Ivensii'	CBcs CDul CSBt CWib EBee EWTr GKir LMaj LRHS MAsh NEgg NWea SCoo SPer WDin
- 'Moerheimii'	GKir
- 'Pendula'	see *P.* × *yedoensis* 'Shidare-yoshino'
- 'Perpendens'	see *P.* × *yedoensis* 'Shidare-yoshino'
§ - 'Shidare-yoshino'	CCVT CDul CEnd CLnd CSBt EBee ECrN GKir LRHS MBar MBri MGos MRav MSwo MWat NWea SBch SLim
§ - 'Somei-Yoshino' 𝕐H4	CCVT CLnd CTho CTri CWSG EBee ECrN EPfP GKir LAst MAsh MBri NWea SLim SPer WDin WHar WJas
'Yoshino'	see *P.* × *yedoensis* 'Somei-Yoshino'
'Yoshino Pendula'	see *P.* × *yedoensis* 'Shidare-yoshino'

Psacalium (*Asteraceae*)

pinetorum B&SWJ 10269 **new**	WCru

Pseuderanthemum (*Acanthaceae*)

carruthersii var. ***atropurpureum*** 'Rubrum'	CSpe LSou NPri WHil
- - 'Variegatum' (v)	WHil
laxiflorum	CCCN
reticulatum orange-flowered	CCCN

Pseudocydonia (*Rosaceae*)

§ ***sinensis***	CMen NLar

Pseudofumaria see *Corydalis*

alba	see *Corydalis ochroleuca*
lutea	see *Corydalis lutea*

Pseudogynoxys (*Asteraceae*)

§ ***chenopodioides***	CCCN ELan

Pseudolarix (*Pinaceae*)

§ ***amabilis*** 𝕐H4	CDoC CEnt CMCN CTho ECrN EHul EPfP GKir GQue IFFs LRHS MBar MBlu MBri MPkF NHol NPCo NWea SBch SLim SPoG SSpi WFar WPGP
kaempferi	see *P. amabilis*

Pseudomuscari see *Muscari*

azureum	see *Muscari azureum*

Pseudopanax (*Araliaceae*)

(Adiantifolius Group) 'Adiantifolius'	CBcs CDoC CHEx CTrC ESwi GQui
- 'Cyril Watson' 𝕐H1	CBcs CDoC CHEx EBee ELan LRHS SBig WCot
arboreus	see *Neopanax arboreus*
chathamicus	CDoC CHEx SAPC SArc
crassifolius	CAbb CBcs CBot CBrP CDTJ CHEx CTrC CWit EAmu EBee ESwi GBin LRHS SAPC SArc SBig
- var. ***trifoliolatus***	CHEx
discolor	CWit ECou LEdu
ferox	CAbb CBcs CBrP CDTJ CTsd CWit EAmu ESwi GBin IDee SAPC SArc SBig SMad
'Forest Gem' **new**	CTrC
laetus	see *Neopanax laetus*
lessonii	CBcs CHEx ECou ELan
- 'Gold Splash' (v) 𝕐H1	CBcs CDoC CDul CHEx CTrC EBee ELan LRHS SBig SEND
- 'Nigra'	CTrC
- 'Rangitira'	CBcs CTrC CWit IDee LRHS SBig
'Linearifolius'	CHEx CTrC LEdu
'Purpureus' 𝕐H1	CDoC CHEx CTrC ESwi
'Sabre'	CHEx CTrC EBee
'Trident'	CDoC CHEx CTrC ECou LEdu SBig

Pseudophoenix (*Arecaceae*)

* ***nativo***	MBri

Pseudosasa (*Poaceae*)

amabilis misapplied	see *Arundinaria gigantea*
§ ***amabilis*** (McClure) Keng f.	EPla WFar
§ ***japonica*** 𝕐H4	Widely available
§ - 'Akebonosuji' (v)	CEnt CGHE EPla MMoz MWht NMoo WJun WPGP
I - var. ***pleioblastoides***	EPla MWht
- 'Tsutsumiana'	CHEx CMCo EBee ELon EPla ERod LRHS MMoz MWht NLar NMoo SBig WJun
- 'Variegata'	see *P. japonica* 'Akebonosuji'
orthotropa	see *Sinobambusa orthotropa*
usawai	EPla WJun
viridula	MWht NMoo

Pseudotsuga (*Pinaceae*)

menzesii 'Dandy Doug' **new**	MAsh
- 'Trunkee Broom' **new**	MAsh
§ ***menziesii*** 𝕐H4	CBcs CDul CLnd ECrN EMac EPfP GKir IFFs MBar MBlu MMuc NWea WDin WFar WMou
- 'Bhiela Lhota'	CKen NLar
- 'Blue Wonder'	CKen
- 'Densa'	CKen
- 'Fastigiata'	CKen
- 'Fletcheri'	CKen LRHS
- 'Geijsteren' **new**	NLar
- var. ***glauca***	CDul GKir
- 'Glauca Pendula'	MGos
I - 'Gotelli's Pendula'	CKen
- 'Graceful Grace'	CKen

- 'Idaho Gem'	CKen
- 'Julie'	CKen
- 'Knaphill'	GKir NLar
- 'Little Jamie'	CKen
- 'Little Jon'	NHol
- 'Lohbrunner'	CKen
- 'McKenzie'	CKen
- 'Nana'	CKen
- 'Oudemansii'	GKir NLar
- Pendula Group	NPCo
- 'Stairii'	CKen
- 'Uwes Golden' **new**	NLar
- 'Young's Broom' **new**	NHol
taxifolia	see *P. menziesii*

Pseudowintera (*Winteraceae*)

§ ***colorata***	CBcs CDoC CMac CPLG CWib GCal GGar GKir IDee IMGH ISea LBuc LRHS MRav WCru WFar WFoF
- 'Marjorie Congreve' **new**	IMon
- 'Mount Congreve'	CBcs IArd LBuc LRHS MBri NLar
- 'Red Leopard'	LRHS

Psidium (*Myrtaceae*)

cattleyanum	see *P. littorale* var. *longipes*
friedrichsthalianum (F)	ERea
guajava (F)	CCCN ERea XBlo
littorale (F)	ERea
- var. ***littorale*** (F)	EShb
§ - var. ***longipes*** (F)	CCCN ERea XBlo

Psilotum (*Psilotaceae*)

nudum	ECou

Psoralea (*Papilionaceae*)

glabra	SPlb
glandulosa	CArn CMdw WSHC
oligophylla	SPlb
pinnata	CHEx CPLG CTrC CTrG IDee SEND

Psychotria (*Rubiaceae*)

capensis	CPLG EShb

Ptelea (*Rutaceae*)

trifoliata	CArn CBcs CDul CLnd CMac CTho CWib ECrN EMil EPfP IFFs IMGH MBlu MBri SHlg SPer SRms SSpi WDin WPGP
- 'Aurea' ♀H4	CAbP CBcs CBot CCVT CDul CEnd CLnd CMac CPLG CPMA EBee ELan EMil EPfP EWTr GBin GKir LHop LRHS MAsh MBlu MBri SPer SPoG SSpi WDin WPat
- 'Fastigiata'	EPfP

Pteracanthus see *Strobilanthes*

Pteridophyllum (*Papaveraceae*)

racemosum	EBee EFEx EPot GEdr WCru

Pteris (*Pteridaceae*)

from Yunnan	CLAP
§ ***actiniopteroides*** **new**	WCot
angustipinna B&SWJ 6738	WCru
biaurita	EShb
cretica ♀H1+3	CHEx EShb SAPC SArc
- var. ***albolineata*** ♀H1	EShb GQui SRms XBlo
- 'Parkeri'	EShb
- 'Rowei'	XBlo
dentata	WRic
ensiformis 'Victoriae'	EShb
esquirolii	WCot
marbled-fronded **new**	
gallinopes	CLAP
henryi	see *P. actiniopteroides*
nipponica	WRic
* ***staminea***	XBlo
tremula	CHEx EShb GQui SRms WRic
umbrosa	WRic
vittata	SRms
wallichiana	CGHE CHEx CLAP WPGP

Pterocarya (*Juglandaceae*)

fraxinifolia ♀H4	CBcs CDul CLnd CMCN CTrG ECrN EGFP EPfP LMaj MBlu MBri MMuc WDin
- IDS 02	WHCr
× ***rehderiana***	CTho MBlu WMou
stenoptera	CBcs CDTJ CDul CMCN CTho EGFP
- 'Fern Leaf'	EPfP MBlu SMad WMou WPGP

Pterocephalus (*Dipsacaceae*)

depressus	CPBP WPat
parnassi	see *P. perennis*
§ ***perennis***	CMea ECho MHer NBir NMen NRya NWCA SIng SRms WEas WHoo
- subsp. ***perennis***	EGoo WHrl
pinardii	NWCA

Pterostylis (*Orchidaceae*)

coccinea	ECho
curta	CStu ECho LLHF SCnR

Pterostyrax (*Styracaceae*)

corymbosa	CBcs CPMA IArd IDee MBlu MBri NLar SSpi WFar
hispida ♀H4	CAbP CBcs CDoC CDul CEnd CMCN CMac CPMA CWib EBee EPfP EPla IArd IDee LAst LRHS MBlu MBri MGos MRav NLar SSpi SSta WDin WFar WPGP

Ptilostemon (*Asteraceae*)

afer	CMdw EHrv SMrm
§ ***diacantha***	EBee IFoB LRHS NBPC NBre NPri WCot WSpi
echinocephalus	GKir MDKP NBhm NBre

Ptilotrichum see *Alyssum*

spinosum 'Roseum'	see *Alyssum spinosum* 'Roseum'

Ptilotus (*Amaranthaceae*)

exaltatus **new**	SPlb

Puccinellia (*Poaceae*)

distans	EBWF

Pueraria (*Papilionaceae*)

montana var. ***lobata***	CArn

Pulicaria (*Asteraceae*)

§ ***dysenterica***	CArn EBWF MHer NMir SIde WCHb WSFF

Pulmonaria (*Boraginaceae*)

affinis 'Margaret'	NCob
angustifolia ♀H4	CMac EBee EPfP GKev GKir GMaP LRHS MNrw NOrc SRms WTin
* - ***alba***	IFoB
- 'Azurea'	CBro CElw EBee ELan EPPr EPfP GMaP LAst LRHS MBNS MCot MNHC MRav NBro NCGa SBch

		SIng SMrm SPer SRms WCAu WCFE WFar WMnd
	- 'Blaues Meer'	CSam EBee EPfP GAbr GBuc GKir LLWG
	- 'Munstead Blue'	CElw CLAP CMac ECha EHrv MRav MTho NCob NHol NRya SRms
	'Apple Frost'	CLAP EBee GEdr LRHS NBhm NLar NSti WWEG
	'Barfield Regalia'	CMHG EBee IGor LLHF NSti SDys WCru
	'Benediction'	CDes LLHF NSti
§	'Beth's Blue'	WCAu
	'Beth's Pink'	ECha GAbr WFar
	'Big Blue' **new**	WCAu
	'Blauer Hügel'	CElw LLHF NSti
	'Blauhimmel'	GCra
	'Blue Buttons'	CBow CFir EBee ECtt EPla
	'Blue Crown'	CElw CLAP CSev EBee EHrv EWes GBuc WCAu
	'Blue Ensign'	Widely available
	'Blue Moon'	see *P. officinalis* 'Blue Mist'
	'Blue Pearl'	LRHS
	'Blueberry Muffin'	CSpe
	'Bonnie'	CMea SAga
	'Botanic Hybrid'	WCru
	'British Sterling'	EBee
	Cally hybrid	CElw CLAP GCal NBre NSti WCru
	'Cedric Morris'	CElw
	'Chintz'	CLAP CSam GBuc SMrm
	'Cleeton Red'	NSti
	'Coral Springs'	GKir LLHF LRHS MAvo NSti
	'Corsage'	ECtt
	'Cotton Cool'	Widely available
	'De Vroomen's Pride' (v)	EBee WMnd
	'Diana Clare'	Widely available
	'Elworthy Rubies'	CElw EPPr
	'Excalibur'	EBee ECtt EHrv EPPr GBuc LRHS NLar WWEG
	'Fiona'	MAvo WCAu WWEG
	'Glacier'	CBro CElw CMoH EBee EPfP LRHS NSti WWEG
	'Hazel Kaye's Red'	LLWP NSti
	'Highdown'	see *P.* 'Lewis Palmer'
	'Ice Ballet' (Classic Series)	EBee GEdr LRHS
	'Joan's Red'	CElw WTin
§	'Lewis Palmer' ♀H4	CBro CMHG CMea CSam EBee ECtt ELan GCal GKir GMaP LRHS MAvo MNHC MSpe NBid NBir NHol SPoG SRGP WBrk WCAu WCFE WCot WHoo WTin WWEG
	'Lime Close'	SAga
	'Little Blue'	NSti
	'Little Star'	EBee GBuc NBre NSti SRGP SUsu WFar
	longifolia	CArn CBot CBro CFee CHar EAEE EBee ECha EHoe ELan EPfP GAbr GKev LLWP LRHS NBir NOrc NSti WBrk WEas WFar
§	- 'Ankum'	CElw CLAP CSam EPfP EPla GBuc GKir MRav NBir NSti WCot WMoo WSHC WWEG WWlt
	- 'Ballyrogan Blue'	IBlr
	- 'Bertram Anderson'	CBgR CPrp CSsd EBee ECtt ELon GKir GMaP LRHS NBir NVic SPer SRGP SWvt WBrk WFar WMnd WWEG
	- subsp. ***cevennensis***	CLAP EBee EBrs EPfP GKir LRHS MBNS MBel MBri MCot NCGa NSti SBch WPtf WWEG
	- 'Coen Jansen'	see *P. longifolia* 'Ankum'
	- 'Coral Spring'	EBee GKir NBre
	- 'Dordogne'	CLAP GBuc GKir LRHS NBir NLar
	- 'Howard Eggins'	EBee
	'Lovell Blue'	NCot
	'Majesté'	Widely available
	'Margery Fish' ♀H4	CBro CHar CLAP CSam EBee EPfP GKir LRHS MBNS MBel SPer WMnd
	'Mary Mottram'	CElw ECtt ELan NBir NPol NSti WMnd
	'Matese Blue'	CLAP
	'Mawson's Blue'	CLAP ECha EWes GKir GMac MRav MWat MWea NBir NChi SWvt WBrk WEas WMoo WRHF WSHC
	'May Bouquet'[PBR]	LLHF NSti
	'Melancholia'	IBlr
	'Merlin'	CLAP
§	'Milchstrasse'	CLAP
	Milky Way	see *P.* 'Milchstrasse'
	mollis	CBot CLAP CSWP EBee ECGP EGoo GCal MNrw NSti WCru
	- 'Royal Blue'	MRav
	- 'Samobor'	CLAP
	'Moonshine'[PBR]	NSti
	'Moonstone'	CLAP
	'Mountain Magic'[PBR]	ECtt EWll NSti SIde
	'Mournful Purple'	EHrv
	'Mrs Kittle'	CElw CMMP EAEE EBee EPPr GBuc IFoB LRHS MBel MRav NBir NSti SDys WBrk WCAu WFar WMnd WWEG WWlt
	'Mystique'	EBee NSti
	'Netta Statham'	ECha LLHF NSti
	'Northern Lights'[PBR]	SHar
	'Nürnberg'	LRHS WWEG
	officinalis	CArn CBro CHby GBar GPoy IFoB MHer MLHP MNHC NChi NVic SIde WBrk WFar
	- 'Alba'	ELan WBrk
	- 'Bamberg' **new**	EBee
§	- 'Blue Mist'	CBro CElw CLAP EBee ECha ELan GBuc GMaP NBir WAbb WBrk WCot WHoo WMnd WMoo WTin
	- 'Bowles's Blue'	see *P. officinalis* 'Blue Mist'
	- Cambridge Blue Group	EBee GMaP LRHS MRav MWat NBir NLar WCot WPtf
*	- 'Frühlingslied'	EBee
	- 'Stillingfleet Gran'	LLHF NSti
	- 'White Wings'	CElw CLAP EBee GKir LRHS MRav NLar SIde WFar
	- 'Wuppertal'	EBee
	'Oliver Wyatt's White'	CLAP EBee SRGP
	Opal = 'Ocupol'	Widely available
	'Polar Splash'	EBee GBin GKir SIde SRot WFar
	'Raspberry Splash'[PBR]	CBct CLAP CPom EBee EGxp LRHS NLar NSti SGol SHar SIde SMrm SPoG
*	'Rowlatt Choules'	MAvo
	'Roy Davidson'	CLAP CSam EBee ECtt EHrv EPPr GKir GMac LHop LRHS NBir NCGa NSti SRGP SWvt WFar WPtf
	rubra ♀H4	CBcs CElw CPom CSWP ECha ELan EShb GAbr GKir LLWP MLHP MMuc MWte NBid NCob NOrc NSti SRms WCAu WFar WTin
	- var. ***alba***	see *P. rubra* var. *albocorollata*
§	- var. ***albocorollata***	CBre EBee EBtc ECha EHrv GAbr MBel NBid SHar WBrk WCru WFar WWEG
	- 'Ann'	CLAP NMoo WCru WFar WTin
	- 'Barfield Pink'	CBro ELan GBar GCal GKir IFro MBel NBir NLar WHlf WRHF
	- 'Barfield Ruby'	GBuc MAvo

– 'Bowles's Red'	CBot CPrp EBee ECtt EHrv EPfP GKir IFoB LAst LRHS MRav NBir NGdn NSti SIde SPer STes WFar WMnd
– 'David Ward' (v)	Widely available
– 'Rachel Vernie' (v)	CLAP CPom CPou MAvo WBrk
– 'Redstart'	Widely available
§ ***saccharata***	ECha EHrv ELan GMaP IFro LRHS NEgg SIde SRms WFar
– 'Alba'	CBro CElw ECha GBuc MMuc SRms
– Argentea Group ♀H4	CBro CSev CTri EBee ELan EPfP GMaP LRHS MRav MTho NGdn WBrk WCAu WWEG
– 'Brentor'	EBee
– 'Clent Skysilver'	EBee
– 'Dora Bielefeld'	Widely available
– 'Frühlingshimmel'	CBro CElw EBee ECtt GKir LRHS MRav WCAu WFar
– 'Glebe Cottage Blue'	CElw
– 'Jill Richardson'	ELan
– 'Leopard'	CElw CEnt CLAP CMac CMea CSam EBee ECtt GBuc GMaP LLWG LRHS MBel NBir NBre SApp SBch SPad SRGP SRot WBrk WClo WCot WFar WHoo WWEG
– 'Mrs Moon'	CTri CWib EBee ECtt ELon EPfP GMaP LAst LRHS MBNS MHer NBPC NBlu NOrc NPri SBch SPer SRGP SWvt WCAu WMnd WWEG
– 'Old Rectory Silver'	CLAP NBir
– 'Picta'	see *P. saccharata*
– 'Pink Dawn'	CMHG LRHS WMnd
– pink-flowered	WCru
– 'Reginald Kaye'	CElw ECha EWes MAvo MNrw
– 'Silverado'PBR	EBee ECtt GEdr GKir LRHS MHer NOrc
– 'Stanhoe'	EWes
– 'White Barn'	see *P.* 'Beth's Blue'
'Saint Ann's'	CElw LLHF NBre NSti WCru
'Samurai'	EBee GBin GEdr MBNS NSti WCAu WPtf
'Silver Lance'	GKir LRHS
'Silver Maid'	WCAu
'Silver Sabre'	IBlr
'Silver Surprise'	WCot
'Sissinghurst White' ♀H4	Widely available
'Smoky Blue'	CLAP EBee ECtt EPfP MBNS MRav NBPC NMoo SMrm SWat WFar WMnd WWEG
'Spilled Milk'	EBee NBre NLar
'Spotted Bob' **new**	WCAu
'Stillingfleet Meg'	CLAP EAEE EBee ECGP ECtt LAst LRHS MAvo MBNS MBel MCot NCob NHol NSti SRGP WFar
'Tim's Silver'	EBee ECtt
'Trevi Fountain'	CBct CLAP EBee EShb GJos GKev GKir LRHS NBre NSti SIde SMrm SPoG SRot WCot WPtf
'Victorian Brooch'PBR	CBct CLAP COIW EBee GAbr GKir GQue LRHS LSou NEgg NLar NSti SIde WFar WPtf WSpi
'Weetwood Blue'	CBre CLAP EBee EPfP EPla MNrw
'Wendy Perry'	CElw
'Wisley White'	CElw

Pulsatilla (*Ranunculaceae*)

alba	CBro NWCA
albana	CBro LHop LRHS
– 'Lutea'	EBee GKev
alpina	CBot ECho SRms WPat
– SDR 5408	GKev
§ – subsp. ***apiifolia*** ♀H4	EBee ELan IFro
– subsp. ***sulphurea***	see *P. alpina* subsp. *apiifolia*
ambigua	EBee GKev LLHF
bungeana	EBee GKev
– subsp. ***astragalifolia***	EBee
caucasica	LRHS
cernua	CBro EBee GBuc LHop LRHS
× ***gayeri***	ECho LLHF NBir
georgica	GEdr
halleri ♀H4	EBee ECho GKev LRHS WRHF
– subsp. ***slavica*** ♀H4	EBee GEdr GKev LRHS NWCA
lutea	see *P. alpina* subsp. *apiifolia*
montana	GBuc LLHF NMen SPlb
multifida	GBuc
§ ***patens***	EDAr LLHF
pratensis	CDes GPoy SRms
– subsp. ***nigricans***	LHop LRHS WFar
rubra	ECho GKev NGHP SPad SRot
turczaninovii	GBuc LLHF
§ ***vernalis*** ♀H2	ECho EPot GBuc NSla NWCA WAbe
violacea **new**	GKev
§ ***vulgaris*** ♀H4	Widely available
– 'Alba' ♀H4	Widely available
– 'Barton's Pink'	CBro EWes GKir LHop LRHS SIng
– 'Blaue Glocke'	EWll GEdr MCot MWat NLar NPri SMrm SWvt WFar WHil WRHF
– 'Eva Constance'	CBro GKev LHop LRHS SIng
– 'Gotlandica'	LLHF
– subsp. ***grandis***	CBot LRHS NMen
– – 'Budapest Seedling'	WCom
– – 'Papageno'	CBot CSpe EAEE EAlp EBee ECho ELon GMaP LAst LBMP LRHS NCGa NHol NLar SMrm SRot WFar WHil
– Heiler hybrids	CPrp EAEE EBee LBMP LRHS MRav NCGa NEgg NGdn WHal
– Red Clock	see *P. vulgaris* 'Röde Klokke'
§ – 'Röde Klokke'	EBee ECtt GEdr GKev LRHS MCot MWat MWhi NBPC NHol NLar NPri SMrm SWvt WHil WSpi
– ***rosea***	GAbr
– Rote Glocke	see *P. vulgaris* 'Röde Klokke'
– var. ***rubra***	Widely available
§ – 'Weisse Schwan'	ECho GKir GMaP NHol NMen
– White Swan	see *P. vulgaris* 'Weisse Schwan'
zimmermannii	NWCA

pummelo see *Citrus maxima*

Punica (*Lythraceae*)

granatum	CBcs CHEx CMen CTsd EPfP ERom LRHS MGos MREP SDnm SLim STre SVic WBVN WSHC
– 'André le Roi' (F)	SLPl
– 'Chico'	CBcs SEND
– 'Fina Tendral'	CCCN ERea
– 'Legrelleae' (d)	SEND SLPl
– 'Maxima Rubra'	IFFs
– var. ***nana*** ♀H3	CAgr CArn CCCN CMen EBtc EPfP EShb LRHS MREP SMrm SRms WPat
– f. ***plena*** (d)	CBcs LRHS MRav WCFE WPat
– – 'Flore Pleno Luteo' (d)	LRHS

Purshia (*Rosaceae*)

mexicana F&M 092	WPGP
aff. ***mexicana***	WSHC
– B&SWJ 9040	WCru

Puschkinia (*Hyacinthaceae*)

scilloides	EBrs ECho NBir
– 'Aragat's Gem'	EBrs ECho WWst
§ – var. ***libanotica***	CBro EBrs ECho EPfP EPot IHer LAma LRHS SMrm SPer WShi
– – 'Alba'	EBrs ECho EPot LAma SPer WCot

Puya (*Bromeliaceae*)

sp.	EBee
RCB/Arg L-3	WCot
RCB/Arg L-5	WCot
RCB/Arg S-2	WCot
alpestris	CBrP CCCN CHEx CTrC EAmu EBee EShb ETod SAPC SBig WPGP
berteroana	CBcs CCCN CDTJ EBee EShb ETod SPlb
chilensis	CAbb CBcs CCCN CDTJ CDoC CHEx CTrG EAmu EBee LRHS SAPC SArc SPlb WBor
coerulea	CCCN CDTJ CFir EAmu EBee ELon LEdu
gilmartiniae	WCot
laxa	SChr
mirabilis	CDTJ CHEx CTrC EBee ESwi
venusta	CCCN CDTJ EBee ETod SPlb

Pycnanthemum (*Lamiaceae*)

flexuosum new	EBee
muticum	LBMP MAvo
pilosum	CArn EBee ELau MHer NBre NLar NPri SBch SIde SWal
tenuifolium	NBre
virginianum	GCal

Pycnostachys (*Lamiaceae*)

reticulata	EOHP EShb
urticifolia	ECre EOHP EWes

Pyracantha (*Rosaceae*)

Alexander Pendula = 'Renolex'	LHop MRav MSwo SRms WFar
angustifolia	NMun WCFE
§ ***atalantioides***	SPlb WCFE
- 'Aurea'	ERas
'Brilliant'	EBee EPfP SCoo
'Buttercup'	EPla
coccinea	EBee
§ - 'Lalandei'	GKir
- 'Red Column'	Widely available
- 'Red Cushion'	MGos MRav SRms
crenulata	WCFE
Dart's Red = 'Interrada'	CSBt EBee GKir SBch SLim SPoG
'Fiery Cascade'	LRHS SPoG SRms
gibbsii	see *P. atalantioides*
'Gold Rush'	MAsh
'Golden Charmer' ♀H4	EBee ECtt EPfP GKir LRHS MAsh MGan MGos MSwo NBlu NEgg NLar NPri NWea SBch SCoo SPer SPoG SRms SWvt WDin WFar WGwG WRHF
'Golden Sun'	see *P.* 'Soleil d'Or'
'Harlequin' (v)	WFar
'Knap Hill Lemon'	CChe MBlu
koidzumii 'Victory'	MGos NBlu WClo
'Mohave'	CChe CMac CTri EBee ECrN ELan ELon GKir LRHS MAsh MBar MGan MNHC MWat NPri SCoo SLim SPer SRms SWvt WDin
'Mohave Silver' (v)	CWSG ELan LAst LOck LRHS MAsh MWat
'Molten Lava'	MBri
'Monrovia'	see *P. coccinea* 'Lalandei'
'Mozart'	EBee
'Navaho'	EPfP GKir SCoo
'Orange Charmer'	CTri EBee ELan EPfP GKir LHop LRHS MGan MGos MWat NBlu SPer SPlb WFar
'Orange Glow' ♀H4	Widely available
* 'Red Pillar'	GKir
'Renault d'Or'	LRHS SLPl
rogersiana ♀H4	EBee ECrN EPfP MRav WFar
- 'Flava' ♀H4	CSBt EBee ECrN EPfP ERas LRHS MAsh MBar NEgg NMun SBch SPoG
'Rosedale'	EBee LRHS
Saphyr Jaune = 'Cadaune'PBR	CAlb CBcs CCVT CDoC CEnd CSBt CWSG EBee EMil EPfP ERas GKir LRHS MAsh MGos MRav SCoo SPer
Saphyr Orange = 'Cadange'PBR ♀H4	CAlb CBcs CCVT CDoC CEnd CSBt CWSG EBee EMil EPfP ERas GKir LRHS MAsh MBri MGos MRav NCGa NEgg SCoo SPer WClo
Saphyr Panache = 'Cadvar'PBR (v)	EBee
Saphyr Rouge = 'Cadrou'PBR ♀H4	CAlb CBcs CCVT CDoC CEnd CSBt CWSG EBee EMil EPfP ERas GKir MAsh MBri MGos MRav NCGa NPri SCoo SPer WClo WFar
'Shawnee'	CSBt CWib EBee LRHS MSwo MWat
§ 'Soleil d'Or'	Widely available
'Sparkler' (v)	CSBt EGxp EHoe LAst MGos WFar
'Teton' ♀H4	CMac CWSG EBee ECrN ELan EPfP EPla GKir LAst LRHS MAsh MBar MBri MSwo MWat NEgg SPoG SRms WDin WFar
'Ventoux Red'	SCoo
'Watereri'	LRHS NWea SLPl WFar WSpi
'Yellow Sun'	see *P.* 'Soleil d'Or'

Pyrenaria (*Theaceae*)

spectabilis	see *Tutcheria spectabilis*

Pyrethropsis see *Rhodanthemum*

hosmariense	see *Rhodanthemum hosmariense*

Pyrethrum see *Tanacetum*

Pyrola (*Ericaceae*)

minor	NMen
rotundifolia	WHer

Pyrostegia (*Bignoniaceae*)

venusta	CCCN

Pyrrocoma (*Asteraceae*)

clementis	EBee

Pyrrosia (*Polypodiaceae*)

caudifrons new	WCot
lingua	WRic
polydactyla	EBee

Pyrus ✿ (*Rosaceae*)

amygdaliformis	CTho
- var. ***cuneifolia***	CLnd EBee
betulifolia	CMCN WJas
calleryana 'Bradford'	CLnd
- 'Capital'	LMaj
- 'Chanticleer' ♀H4	Widely available
- 'Chanticleer' variegated (v)	CLnd
communis (F)	CCVT CDul CTri EMac IFFs LBuc NWea SPer SPlb WMou
- 'Abbé Fétel' (D)	SKee
- 'Baronne de Mello' (D)	CTho SFam
- 'Beech Hill' (F)	CDul CLnd EBee ECrN EPfP SPer
- 'Belle Guérandaise' (D)	SKee
- 'Belle Julie' (D)	SKee
- 'Berllanderi Green' (Perry) new	WDol
- 'Berllanderi Red' (Perry) new	WDol

	Cultivar	Suppliers
	- 'Beth' (D) ♀H4	CAgr CDoC CMac CSBt CTri CWib ECrN EMil EMui EPfP ERea GKir GTwe LAst LBuc LRHS MAsh MBri MGos NPri SDea SFam SKee SPer SPoG WHar
	- 'Beurré Alexandre Lucas' (D)	SKee
	- 'Beurré Bedford' (D)	SKee
	- 'Beurré d'Amanlis' (D)	SKee
	- 'Beurré d'Avalon' (D)	SKee
	- 'Beurré de Beugny' (D)	SKee
	- 'Beurré de Naghin' (C/D)	SKee
	- 'Beurré Diel' (D)	SKee
	- 'Beurré Dumont' (D)	CAgr SFam
	- 'Beurré Giffard' (D)	CAgr
	- 'Beurré Gris d'Hiver' (D)	SKee
	- 'Beurré Hardy' (D) ♀H4	CAgr CCAT CCVT CDoC CDul CMac CSBt CTho CTri CWib ECrN EMui ERea GKir GTwe IFFs LAst MBri MGan MMuc MWat NEgg SDea SEND SFam SKee SPer
	- 'Beurré Jean van Geert' (D)	GKir
	- 'Beurré Mortillet' (D)	SKee
	- 'Beurré Rance' (F)	SKee
	- 'Beurré Six' (D)	SKee
	- 'Beurré Superfin' (D) ♀H4	ECrN GTwe LRHS MCoo SFam SKee
	- 'Bianchettone' (D)	SKee
	- 'Bishop's Thumb' (D)	SDea SKee
	- 'Black Worcester' (C)	GTwe SDea SFam SKee WJas
	- 'Blakeney Red' (Perry)	SDea
	- 'Blickling' (D)	SKee
	- 'Brandy' (Perry)	CAgr SDea SKee
	- 'Bristol Cross' (D)	CAgr GTwe SKee
§	- 'Butirra Precoce Morettini' (D)	SDea
	- 'Calebasse Bosc' (F)	SKee
	- 'Cannock' (F)	CCAT
	- 'Catillac' (C) ♀H4	CAgr CTho GTwe SFam SKee
	- 'Chalk'	see *P. communis* 'Crawford'
	- 'Chapman's Orange' (Perry) **new**	WDol
	- 'Charneaux' (F)	SVic
	- 'Clapp's Favourite' (D)	CTho ECrN SKee SVic
	- 'Concorde'[PBR] (D) ♀H4	Widely available
	- 'Conference' (D) ♀H4	Widely available
§	- 'Crawford' (D)	SKee
	- 'Deacon's Pear' (D)	SDea
	- Delbardélice = 'Delété' **new**	LRHS
	- 'Devoe' (D)	SDea
	- 'Docteur Jules Guyot' (D)	CAgr ECrN SDea SKee
	- 'Doyenné d'Eté' (D)	ERea LRHS MCoo SFam SKee
	- 'Doyenné du Comice' (D) ♀H4	Widely available
	- 'Duchesse d'Angoulême' (D)	SKee
	- 'Durondeau' (D)	ERea GTwe SDea SFam SKee
	- 'Early Saint Brides' (Perry) **new**	WDol
	- 'Easter Beurré' (D)	SKee
	- 'Emile d'Heyst' (D)	GBut GTwe MCoo
	- 'Fertility' (D)	CLnd ERea SKee
	- 'Fertility Improved'	see *P. communis* 'Improved Fertility'
	- 'Fondante d'Automne' (D)	CAgr CTho LRHS SKee
	- 'Forelle' (D)	ERea SKee
	- 'Glou Morceau' (D)	CAgr ECrN EMui ERea GTwe MCoo MWat SDea SFam SKee
	- 'Glow Red Williams' (D)	SFam
	- 'Gorham' (D) ♀H4	CAgr CTho ECrN GTwe MCoo SFam SKee
	- 'Gratiole de Jersey' (D)	CTho
	- 'Green Pear of Yair' (D)	SKee
	- 'Gregoire Bordillon' (D) **new**	SKee
	- 'Gwehelog' (Perry) **new**	WDol
	- 'Gwehelog Red' (Perry) **new**	WDol
	- 'Hacon's Imcomparable' (D)	SKee
	- 'Harrow Delight' (D)	SDea
	- 'Harvest Queen' (D/C)	SDea
	- 'Hendre Huffcap' (Perry)	CCAT
	- 'Hessle' (D)	CAgr GTwe MCoo NWea SDea SFam SKee
§	- 'Improved Fertility' (D)	CAgr CDoC GTwe SDea
	- Invincible = 'Delwinor' (D/C)	CAgr CDul CSut CTho EMui LBuc LRHS MBri MCoo SPoG
	- 'Jargonelle' (D)	CAgr CTho ECrN GTwe LRHS SDea SFam SKee
	- 'Jeanne d'Arc' (D)	SVic
	- 'Joséphine de Malines' (D) ♀H4	CAgr GTwe SDea SFam SKee
	- 'Kieffer' (C)	CAgr
	- 'Laxton's Foremost' (D)	CAgr SKee
	- 'Laxton's Satisfaction' (D)	SFam
	- 'Légipont' (F)	CAgr
	- 'Little Cross Huffcap' **new**	WDol
	- 'Louise Bonne of Jersey' (D) ♀H4	CAgr CDoC CMac CTri ECrN EMui GBut GTwe LAst LRHS MGos SDea SFam SKee
	- 'Maréchal de Cour' (D) **new**	SKee
	- 'Marguérite Marillat' (D)	SDea
	- 'Max Red Bartlett'	MCoo
	- 'Merton Pride' (D)	CAgr CTho CTri ECrN GTwe LRHS MCoo MWat SDea SFam SKee
	- 'Monmouthshire Burgundy' (Perry) **new**	WDol
	- 'Moonglow' (D/C)	CAgr ERea MCoo SDea
	- 'Moorcroft' (Perry)	SKee
	- 'Morettini'	see *P. communis* 'Butirra Precoce Morettini'
	- 'Nouveau Poiteau' (C/D)	CAgr CTho ECrN GTwe SKee
	- 'Nye Russet Bartlett' (F)	CAgr
	- 'Onward' (D) ♀H4	CAgr CCAT CDul CLnd CTho CTri CWib ECrN EMil EMui GTwe MAsh MBri NEgg NWea SDea SFam SKee SPoG WHar
	- 'Ovid' (D)	CAgr
§	- 'Packham's Triumph' (D)	CAgr CDoC CTri CWib ECrN GTwe LAst LRHS SDea SVic
	- 'Passe Crassane' (D)	SKee
	- 'Pear Apple' (D)	SDea
	- 'Petit Muscat' **new**	SKee
	- 'Pitmaston Duchess' (C/D) ♀H4	ECrN GTwe LRHS MCoo SDea SKee
	- 'Potato Pear' (Perry) **new**	WDol
	- 'Red Comice' (D/C)	GTwe SKee
	- 'Red Sensation Bartlett' (D/C)	EMui GTwe LBuc LRHS SKee
	- 'Redbald' (D) **new**	SKee
	- 'Robin' (C/D)	ERea SDea SKee
	- 'Santa Claus' (D)	SDea SFam SKee
	- 'Seckel' (D)	SFam SKee
	- 'Sierra' (D)	CAgr
	- 'Snowdon Queen' (D)	WGwG
	- 'Souvenir du Congrès' (D)	CAgr
	- 'Starkrimson' (D) **new**	SKee
	- 'Swan's Egg' (D)	SKee
	- 'Terrace Pearl'	EMui MGos SPoG

	- 'Thompson's' (D)	SFam SKee
	- 'Thorn' (Perry)	CAgr LRHS
	- 'Triomphe de Vienne' (D)	SFam
	- 'Triumph'	see *P. communis* 'Packham's Triumph'
	- 'Uvedale's St Germain' (C)	SKee
	- 'Vicar of Winkfield' (C/D)	GTwe SDea SKee
	- 'Virgouleuse' (D) **new**	SKee
	- 'Welsh Gin' (Perry) **new**	WDol
	- 'Williams' Bon Chrétien' (D/C) 🏆H4	Widely available
	- 'Williams Red' (D/C)	EMui GTwe SKee
	- 'Windsor' (D) **new**	SKee
	- 'Winter Nelis' (D)	CAgr CTri CWib ECrN GKir GTwe LRHS MAsh SDea SFam SKee
	cordata	CDul
	elaeagnifolia	LRHS
	- var. ***kotschyana***	CDul CEnd GKir LRHS SLim
	- 'Silver Sails'	CLnd EBee EMil GKir LAst LRHS MAsh MBlu MGos NLar SCoo SPur SSpi
	fauriei **new**	LRHS
	nivalis	CDul CLnd CTho EBee ECrN EPfP LMaj MBri MRav SCoo SPer SPur
	- 'Catalia'	EBee LRHS MAsh MBri NLar SCoo
	pyraster	CDul
	pyrifolia	GAuc
	- '20th Century'	see *P. pyrifolia* 'Nijisseiki'
	- 'Chojuro' (F)	ERea
	- 'Hosui' (F)	SVic
	- 'Kosui' (F)	ERea SVic
	- 'Kumoi' (F)	LRHS SDea
§	- 'Nijisseiki' (F)	ERea SVic
	- 'Shinko' (F) **new**	ERea
	- 'Shinseiki' (F)	CAgr CLnd EMui ERea MAsh SDea SKee
	- 'Shinsui' (F)	ERea SDea SKee
*	***salicifolia*** var. ***orientalis***	CTho
	- 'Pendula' 🏆H4	Widely available
	ussuriensis	CTho GAuc LRHS

Q

Qiongzhuea see *Chimonobambusa*

Quercus ✿ (*Fagaceae*)

	NJM 05.013A **new**	WPGP
	acerifolia	EPfP
§	***acuta***	CBcs IArd
	acutifolia	SBir
	acutifolia* × *mexicana	SBir
	acutissima	CBcs CLnd CMCN EPfP MBri SBir
	aegilops	see *Q. ithaburensis* subsp. *macrolepis*
	affinis	EPfP SBir
	agrifolia	CDul CMCN EBtc SBir
	alba	CDul CMCN SBir WDin
	aliena	CMCN SBir
	alnifolia	CDul SBir
	arkansana	SBir
	austrina	SBir
	× ***beadlei***	see *Q.* × *saulii*
	berberidifolia	SBir
	bicolor	CDul CMCN EPfP SBir WDin
§	× ***bimundorum*** 'Crimschmidt' **new**	MBlu
	borealis	see *Q. rubra*
	breweri	see *Q. garryana* var. *breweri*
	buckleyi	CMCN MBri SBir
	× ***bushii***	CMCN EPfP MBlu MBri SBir
	- 'Silhouette' **new**	SBir
	canariensis 🏆H4	CBcs CLnd CMCN CTho CTrG EPfP GKir LRHS WMou WPGP
	canbyi	CMCN
	castaneifolia	CDul CMCN EPfP IFFs SBir WDin
	- 'Green Spire' 🏆H4	CDoC CMCN CTho EPfP GKir IArd LRHS MBlu SBir SEND SMad
	cerris	CBcs CCVT CDoC CDul CLnd CMCN EBee ECrN EMac EPfP GKir IFFs LAst LMaj MGos NWea SEND SPer STre WDin WFar WMou
	- 'Afyon Lace'	MBlu MBri
§	- 'Argenteovariegata' (v)	CDul CEnd CMCN CTho EBee ELan EMil EPfP GKir LRHS MAsh MBlu MBri NLar SMad SPoG WPat
*	- 'Marmorata'	SBir
	- 'Variegata'	see *Q. cerris* 'Argenteovariegata'
	- 'Wodan'	EPfP GKir MBlu
	chenii	CMCN EGFP
	chrysolepis	CMCN EPfP
	coccifera	CDul CGHE CMCN EPla SSpi WDin WPGP
	coccinea	CBcs CDul CMCN CTho CTri ECrN EPfP GKir IFFs MMuc MWht NBea NEgg NWea SBir SLim SPer WDin WPat
	- 'Splendens' 🏆H4	CDoC CDul CEnd CHll CMCN CPMA CTri ELan EPfP EWTr LRHS MAsh MBlu MBri SPer WDin WPat
	crassipes	SBir
	Crimson Spire	see *Q.* × *bimundorum* 'Crimschmidt'
	dalechampii **new**	SBir
	× ***deamii***	SBir
	dentata	CMCN EPfP
	- 'Carl Ferris Miller'	CBcs CMCN EPfP GKir MBlu MBri SBir WPat
	- 'Pinnatifida'	CMCN EPfP GKir IDee MBlu SMad WPat
	- 'Sir Harold Hillier'	MBlu MBri
	douglasii	CMCN
	dumosa	CMCN
	elliottii	SBir
	ellipsoidalis	CMCN MBri SBir
	- 'Hemelrijk'	CDoC EPfP MBlu MBri
	emoryi	CDul CMCN
	engelmannii	CMCN
	fabrei	CMCN SBir
	faginea	EGFP
	falcata	CDul CMCN EBtc EPfP SBir
	- var. ***pagodifolia***	see *Q. pagoda*
	× ***fernaldii***	CMCN MBlu
	frainetto	CCVT CDoC CDul CLnd CMCN CTho EBee ECrN EPfP GKir IFFs ISea LMaj LRHS NWea SBir SEND SPer WDin WMou
	- 'Hungarian Crown' 🏆H4	CMCN EPfP GKir MBlu MBri SBir SMad
	- 'Tortworth'	MBri SMad WMou
	- 'Trump'	CLnd CMCN
	gambelii	CMCN EGFP
	garryana	CMCN
§	- var. ***breweri***	EGFP
	- var. ***fruticosa***	see *Q. garryana* var. *breweri*
	georgiana	CMCN EPfP SBir
	glandulifera	see *Q. serrata*
§	***glauca***	CMCN EPfP SAPC SArc SBir WPGP
	gravesii	CMCN EPfP SBir

	Name	Suppliers
	grisea	CDul CMCN
	× ***hastingsii***	CMCN SBir
	× ***hawkinsiae***	SBir
	× ***haynaldiana*** new	SBir
	hemisphaerica	CDul CMCN EPfP SBir
	× ***heterophylla***	CMCN EPfP SBir
	× ***hickelii***	CMCN EPfP LRHS SBir
	hinckleyi	WDin
§	× ***hispanica***	CLnd GKir
	- 'Ambrozyana'	CDul CMCN LRHS SMad WDin
	- 'Bloemendaal' new	MBlu
	- 'Diversifolia'	CMCN EPfP MBlu
	- 'Fulhamensis'	CMCN GKir MBlu SBir
§	- 'Lucombeana' ♀H4	CBcs CDul CMCN CSBt CTho EPfP IDee LRHS MBlu SBir SPer
§	- 'Pseudoturneri'	CBcs CDul EBee EPfP EWTr GKir MBlu
	- 'Suberosa'	CTho
	- 'Waasland'	MBri SBir
	- 'Wageningen'	CMCN EPfP MBri SBir
	hypoleucoides	EPfP MBri
	ilex ♀H4	Widely available
	ilicifolia	CMCN EPfP SBir
	imbricaria	CDul CMCN EPfP SBir
	incana Roxb.	see *Q. leucotrichophora*
	× ***introgressa***	SBir
	ithaburensis	EPfP
§	- subsp. ***macrolepis***	CMCN LEdu SBir
	- - 'Hemelrijk Silver'	SBir
	× ***jackiana***	EPfP
	kelloggii	CBcs CMCN
	× ***kewensis***	CDul CMCN LMaj SBir
	laceyi new	SBir
	laevigata	see *Q. acuta*
	laevis	CMCN EPfP SBir
	'Langtry'	SBir
§	***laurifolia***	CDul CMCN EPfP
	laurina	SBir
§	***leucotrichophora***	CMCN GKir SBir WCFE
	liaotungensis	see *Q. wutaishanica*
	× ***libanerris***	SBir
	- 'Rotterdam'	CDul CMCN
	libani	CMCN EPfP WDin
	lobata	CMCN EGFP LEdu
	× ***lucombeana***	see *Q.* × *hispanica*
	- 'William Lucombe'	see *Q.* × *hispanica* 'Lucombeana'
	× ***ludoviciana***	CMCN EPfP GKir MBri SBir
	lyrata	CMCN
	'Macon'	GKir
	macranthera	CLnd CMCN EPfP SBir
	macrocarpa	CDul CMCN EPfP MBri SMad
	- var. ***macrocarpa***	SBir
	macrolepis	see *Q. ithaburensis* subsp. *macrolepis*
	marilandica	CBcs CEnd CMCN EPfP GKir IFFs MBlu SBir WPGP
	'Mauri'	MBri
	mexicana	CDul CMCN SBir
§	***michauxii***	CDul CMCN GKir LRHS MBlu SBir
	mongolica	GKir MBlu SBir
	- subsp. ***crispula*** var. ***grosseserrata***	CMCN
	muhlenbergii	CDul CMCN LRHS MBlu SBir
	× ***mutabilis***	SBir
	myrsinifolia	see *Q. glauca*
	myrtifolia	EPfP SBir
	nigra	CMCN SBir
	- 'Beethoven' new	MBlu
	nuttallii	see *Q. texana*
	obtusa	see *Q. laurifolia*
	oglethorpensis	SBir

	Name	Suppliers
§	***pagoda***	CMCN SBir
	palustris ♀H4	CCVT CDoC CDul CLnd CMCN CSam CTho ECrN EMac EPfP EWTr GKir IArd IFFs LMaj LRHS MAsh MBlu MMuc NEgg NWea SBir SPer STre WDin
*	- 'Compacta'	EPfP
	- 'Green Dwarf'	CMCN MBlu
	- 'Pendula'	CEnd CMCN
	- 'Swamp Pygmy'	CMCN EPfP MBlu
	- 'Windischleuba' new	MBlu
	parvula new	SBir
	pedunculata	see *Q. robur*
	pedunculiflora	see *Q. robur* subsp. *pedunculiflora*
§	***petraea*** ♀H4	CDoC CDul CLnd ECrN EMac EPfP GKir IFFs IMGH LBuc MBlu NLar NWea SPer WDin WFar WMou
	- 'Acutiloba'	SBir
§	- 'Insecata'	CDoC CDul CEnd CMCN MBlu
	- 'Laciniata'	see *Q. petraea* 'Insecata'
§	- 'Purpurea'	CDul CMCN GKir MBlu
	- 'Rubicunda'	see *Q. petraea* 'Purpurea'
§	***phellos***	CDul CLnd CMCN EBtc ECrN EPfP LRHS MBlu MBri SBir SLPl SPoG WDin
	phillyreoides	CBcs CDul CMCN EPfP IDee SBir SLPl
	polymorpha	CDul CMCN
	'Pondaim'	CMCN GKir MBri SBir
	pontica	CMCN EPfP GKir LLHF MBlu WPat
	prinoides	CMCN
	prinus misapplied	see *Q. michauxii*
§	***prinus*** L.	CMCN EPfP
	pubescens	CMCN EMac SBir
	pumila Michx.	see *Q. prinus* L.
	pumila Walt.	see *Q. phellos*
	pyrenaica	CDul CMCN CTho EBtc MBri
	- 'Pendula'	CMCN EPfP WDin
	Regal Prince	see *Q.* × *warei* 'Long'
	rhysophylla	CMCN EBee EPfP GKir MBlu SBir WPGP
	- 'Maya' new	ELan EWTr MBri SBir
	× ***riparia***	SBir
§	***robur*** ♀H4	Widely available
	- 'Argenteomarginata' (v)	CDul CMCN MBlu SMad WPat
	- 'Atropurpurea'	EBee MGos NWea WDin
*	- 'Compacta'	MBlu
	- 'Concordia'	CBcs CDoC CDul CEnd CLnd CMCN EBee EBtc ELan EPfP GKir LRHS MAsh MBlu NLar NWea SMad WDin
*	- ***dissecta***	CMCN
	- 'Facrist'	SBir
	- f. ***fastigiata***	CDoC CDul CLnd CTho EBee ECrN EPfP GKir IMGH LRHS MBar MGos NWea SBir SCoo SLPl SLim SPer SPoG WDin WFar
	- - 'Koster' ♀H4	CDoC CDul CMCN CTri EPfP LMaj MBlu NWea SPoG
	- 'Filicifolia' misapplied	see *Q. robur* 'Pectinata'
	- 'Filicifolia'	see *Q.* × *rosacea* 'Filicifolia'
	- var. ***haas***	CDul
	- 'Irtha'	EPfP
	- 'Menhir'	MBlu
§	- 'Pectinata'	EPfP GKir LRHS MBlu WDin
§	- subsp. ***pedunculiflora***	CMCN SBir
	- 'Pendula'	CEnd CMCN MBlu MGos
	- 'Purpurascens'	CEnd CMCN
	- 'Purpurea'	MBlu

* - 'Pyramidalis Punctata' IArd
- 'Raba' CMCN
- 'Rita's Gold' MBlu SMad
§ - 'Salfast' MBlu
- 'Salicifolia Fastigiata' see *Q. robur* 'Salfast'
- Sherwood oak clone SMad
- 'Strypemonde' CMCN
- f. ***variegata*** (v) CPMA MGos
- - 'Fürst Schwarzenburg' (v) MBlu
I - 'Zeelandia' new SBir
robur* × *macrocarpa SBir
× ***virginiana***
§ × ***rosacea*** 'Filicifolia' CEnd GKir NLar WPat
rotundifolia EPfP
- NJM 03.009 WPGP
§ ***rubra*** ♀H4 Widely available
- 'Aurea' CDul CEnd CMCN CPMA EBee EPfP MBlu
- 'Boltes Gold' CPMA MBlu
- 'Cyrille' SBir
- 'Magic Fire' EPfP MBlu MBri SBir
* - 'Sunshine' CMCN MBlu MBri WPat
rugosa CDul CMCN SBir
× ***runcinata*** SBir
sadleriana GKir
salicina WPGP
sartorii SBir
§ × ***saulii*** CMCN SBir
× ***schochiana*** EPfP
× ***schuettei*** SBir
§ ***serrata*** CDoC CMCN EGFP MBri SBir
sessiliflora see *Q. petraea*
shumardii CDul CMCN EPfP MBlu MBri SBir SGol
sinuata SBir
subsp. ***breviloba*** new
stellata CMCN EPfP SBir
suber CBcs CCVT CDoC CDul CLnd CMCN CTho ELan EPfP EPla GGal IArd IFFs ISea LEdu LMaj LRHS MGos MREP SAPC SArc SEND WDin WPGP
- 'Cambridge' WMou
- 'Sopron' MBlu WMou
§ ***texana*** CMCN EPfP SBir
- 'New Madrid' MBlu MBri
trojana CMCN SBir
× ***turneri*** CDoC CLnd CMCN CTho EPfP LRHS MBri WDin WMou WSpi
- 'Pseudoturneri' see *Q.* × *hispanica* 'Pseudoturneri'
variabilis CMCN EPfP SGol
velutina CDul CLnd CMCN CPMA CTho EPfP IDee LRHS SBir WPGP
- 'Albertsii' MBlu
- 'Rubrifolia' CMCN EPfP
'Vilmoriana' GKir IArd
virginiana CMCN SBir
× ***warburgii*** EPfP
× ***warei*** SBir
§ - 'Long' new MBlu
- 'Windcandle' MBlu WHil
wislizeni CBcs CDul CMCN SBir
§ ***wutaishanica*** CDul CMCN

Quillaja (*Rosaceae*)

saponaria CArn CCCN CTrG EBee IDee

quince see *Cydonia oblonga*

Quisqualis (*Combretaceae*)

indica CCCN

R

Racosperma see *Acacia*

Ramonda (*Gesneriaceae*)

§ ***myconi*** ♀H4 CLAP CPBP ECho EWes GEdr GKev LLHF LSou NLAp NLar NMen NSla SChF SIng SRms WAbe
- var. ***alba*** CLAP ECho MTho WKif WThu
- 'Jim's Shadow' WAbe
- 'Rosea' CLAP
nathaliae ♀H4 CLAP WAbe WThu
- 'Alba' CLAP NSla WAbe
pyrenaica see *R. myconi*
serbica ECho WThu

Randia (*Rubiaceae*)

formosa CCCN

Ranunculus ✿ (*Ranunculaceae*)

abnormis WAbe
aconitifolius CSpe EBee ECha ECho GBBs GCra GKev GKir GMaP NLar SHar SWat WHal WMnd WMoo WSHC WSpi
- 'Flore Pleno' (d) ♀H4 CBgR CFir CSpe EBee ECha ECho EHrv EPfP GAbr GBBs GBuc GCal GKir GMaP GMac IGor LPla LRHS MLHP MRav NBir WBor WCAu WCot WFar WHer WHil WMoo WPnP WSHC
acris EBWF NBir NLan NMir NPer
* - 'Citrinus' CElw CEnt LRHS MCot MMHG NCGa NRya SHar WHal WMoo
- 'Cricket' (v) WAlt
- 'Farrer's Yellow' CRow
- 'Flore Pleno' (d) ♀H4 CBgR CDes CElw CFee CRow EBee ECha ECho EHrv ELan EPPr EPfP GBuc GQue LRHS MCot MRav NBid NBro NGdn NRya SPoG SRms WCAu WCom WFar WHil WMoo WSpi
- 'Hedgehog' EBee ECho EPPr LSou WPrP
- 'Stevenii' CFee CRow EPPr IGor SDix WHal WSHC
- 'Sulphureus' CBre ECha WEas WFar WHal
adoneus var. ***alpinus*** new EPot
alpestris ECho GEdr NMen NRya
amplexicaulis CAby ERos GMaP NMen WAbe
- 'Grandiflorus' new LRHS
aquatilis CWat EHon EMFW MSKA NSco SWat WPnP
× ***arendsii*** 'Moonlight' SRot SUsu WSHC
asiaticus EBrs
baurii ECho
bilobus NMen
buchananii GKev
bulbosus NSco
§ - 'F.M. Burton' EBee EHrv NRya
- ***farreri*** see *R. bulbosus* 'F.M. Burton'
- 'Speciosus Plenus' see *R. constantinopolitanus* 'Plenus'
calandrinioides ♀H2-3 CBgR EBee ECho EWes NBir WAbe WCot
- SF 137 WCot
§ ***constantinopolitanus* 'Plenus'** (d) CElw CRow ECha GCal MBel MBri MRav NBid NBro NRya WCot WEas WFar WMoo
cortusifolius NCGa SWat
crenatus ECho GAuc GEdr NMen NRya WAbe

	creticus	ECho
	crithmifolius new	GKev
	extorris 'Flore Pleno'	CDes EBee
	ficaria	CArn CRow CTri EBWF GBar LRHS MHer NChi NMir NSco WHer WShi
	- 'Aglow in the Dark'	CHid EBee
	- var. ***albus***	CHid CRow CSam ELon ERos LEdu LRHS NRya SIng WAlt
	- anemone-centred	see *R. ficaria* 'Collarette'
	- 'Ashen Primrose'	CRow EBee
§	- var. ***aurantiacus***	CBgR CRow EBee ECha ECho ERos LRHS MRav NLar NRya SIng SPhx SRms WAbe WFar WPtf
	- 'Bantam Egg'	CRow
	- 'Blackadder'	CRow
	- 'Bowles's Double'	see *R. ficaria* 'Double Bronze', 'Picton's Double'
	- 'Brambling'	CBre CHid CLAP CRow ECho LEdu LRHS MRav SBch SIng SSvw WAlt WPrP
	- 'Brazen Child'	CRow EBee MDKP
	- 'Brazen Daughter'	CRow
	- 'Brazen Hussy'	Widely available
	- 'Bregover White'	CRow
	- 'Budgerigar'	CRow
	- subsp. ***bulbilifer*** 'Chedglow'	CRow MDKP
	- 'Bunch' (d)	CRow
	- 'Cartwheel' (d)	CRow
	- 'Champernowne Giant'	CRow
	- 'Chocolate Cream'	CRow
§	- subsp. ***chrysocephalus***	CRow ECha ELon LRHS NRya SBch SIng WCot WFar
	- 'Clouded Yellow' (v)	CRow
	- 'Coffee Cream'	CRow EBee
	- 'Coker Cream'	CRow
§	- 'Collarette' (d)	CHid CRow CStu EBee ECho ELon ERos GBar GBuc LEdu LRHS MTho NBir NMen NRya WAbe WCom WFar
	- 'Coppernob'	CBre CHid CRow ECha ECho ELon LRHS MDKP SBch SIng WCot WFar
	- 'Corinne Tremaine'	WHer
	- 'Crawshay Cream'	CRow EBee
	- 'Cupreus'	see *R. ficaria* var. *aurantiacus*
	- 'Damerham' (d)	CHid CRow LRHS
	- 'Dappled Grey'	GKir WAlt
	- 'Deborah Jope'	CRow ECha SUsu
	- 'Diane Rowe'	LRHS
	- 'Dimpsey'	CRow
§	- 'Double Bronze' (d)	CBgR CHid CRow CStu EBee ECho ERos GBuc LEdu LRHS MDKP MTho NBir NLar NRya SIng
	- double cream-flowered	see *R. ficaria* 'Double Mud'
§	- 'Double Mud' (d)	CBgR CBow CHid CLAP CRow CStu ERos GBuc LEdu LRHS MTho NRya SIng WAbe WCom WFar WHal WSHC
	- double yellow-flowered	see *R. ficaria* Flore Pleno Group
	- double, green-eyed (d)	CHid CRow GKir LEdu
	- 'Dusky Maiden'	CRow LRHS NLar SBch SIng WFar
	- 'E.A. Bowles'	see *R. ficaria* 'Collarette'
	- 'Elan' (d)	CDes CRow EBee
	- subsp. ***ficariiformis***	LRHS
§	- Flore Pleno Group (d)	CBgR CFee CHid CRow CStu CTri EBee ECha ECho ELan ELon EPPr ERos LRHS NRya NSti SBch SIng SRms WAbe WCot WFar
	- 'Fried Egg'	CRow
	- 'Green Petal'	CHid CRow CStu EBee ECho EPPr EPot GBuc GKir LEdu LRHS MCot MDKP MHer MTho NBir NLar NRya SIng WHal WHer WHil
	- 'Greencourt Gold' (d)	CRow
	- 'Holly'	see *R. ficaria* 'Holly Green'
	- 'Holly Bronze'	CRow
§	- 'Holly Green'	CRow ECho
	- 'Hoskin's Miniature'	CRow
	- 'Hoskin's Variegated' (v)	CRow
	- 'Hyde Hall'	LRHS NLar SBch SIng WFar WPrP
	- 'Jake Perry'	CDes EBee
	- 'Jane's Dress'	CHid CRow
	- 'Ken Aslet Double' (d)	CDes CRow EBee LEdu LRHS WHal
	- 'Lambrook Black'	WHer
	- 'Laysh On' (d)	CRow
	- 'Lemon Queen'	CHid SIng
	- 'Leo'	LRHS MDKP
	- 'Limelight'	CRow
	- 'Little Southey'	CRow
	- subsp. ***major***	see *R. ficaria* subsp. *chrysocephalus*
	- 'Melanie Jope'	EBee
	- 'Mimsey' (d)	CRow EBee
	- 'Mobled Jade'	CHid CRow EBee
	- 'Mud'	MDKP
	- 'Newton Abbot'	CBre CRow
I	- 'Nigrifolia'	EBee MDKP
	- 'Oakenden Cream'	CRow
	- 'Old Master'	CBow EBee NCGa WCot
	- 'Orange Sorbet'	CRow LEdu LRHS NLar
§	- 'Picton's Double' (d)	CRow CStu GBar MTho NRya WAbe
	- 'Primrose'	CHid CRow LRHS MTho NLar NRya SIng
	- 'Primrose Elf'	CRow EBee ECha
	- 'Quantock Brown'	CBgR
	- 'Quillet' (d)	CRow
	- 'Ragamuffin' (d)	CDes CRow EBee LEdu WPrP
	- 'Randall's White'	CBgR CRow CSWP CStu MCot MRav MTho NCGa SHar WCom WFar WPtf WSHC
	- 'Rowden Magna'	CRow
	- 'Salad Bowl' (d)	CRow
	- 'Salmon's White'	CBre CRow EBee ECho ELan EPPr LRHS MRav NBir NLar NRya SIng WFar WHal WHer WHrl WPtf
	- 'Samidor'	CRow
	- 'Sheldon'	CRow
	- 'Sheldon Silver'	CHid CRow
	- 'Silver Collar'	LEdu
	- 'Single Cream'	LRHS
	- 'Suffusion'	CRow
	- 'Sutherland's Double' (d)	CRow
	- 'Sweet Chocolate'	CRow
	- 'Torquay Elf'	CRow EBee
	- 'Tortoiseshell'	CHid CRow EBee MDKP WCom WFar WPtf
	- 'Trenwheal' (d)	CRow
	- 'Tubby'	WAlt
	- 'Undercurrent' (v)	WAlt
	- 'Winkworth'	LRHS
	- 'Wisley Double'	see *R. ficaria* 'Double Bronze'
	- 'Wisley White'	NSti
	- 'Witchampton'	CDes
	- 'Yaffle'	CBre CHid CRow EBee LRHS MDKP SIng
	flammula	CBen CRow CWat EBWF EHon EMFW LPBA MSKA NSco SWat WPnP
	- subsp. ***minimus***	CRow
	gouanii	NRya
	gramineus ♀H4	EBee ECho EDAr ERos EWTr GBuc GEdr GKir GMaP LBee LRHS MNrw

	MTho MWat NMen NRya SMrm SPhx SRms SUsu WCAu WCom WFar WHil WPer
- 'Pardal'	SCnR WFar
* ***guttatus***	NMen
illyricus	EBee ECha EDAr EPPr NRya WHal
insignis	EBee
kochii	EBee ECho EPot
lanuginosus	EPPr
lingua	CFir COld EBWF EMFW MCCP NSco SPlb WSFF
- 'Grandiflorus'	CBen CRow EHon LPBA MMuc MSKA NPer SWat WHal WMAq WPnP
lyallii	GGar GKev WAbe
macauleyi	GEdr
millefoliatus	CPBP EBee ECho ERos GBuc MTho NMen
montanus double-flowered (d)	EBee EBrs LRHS SHar WCot
- 'Molten Gold' ♀H4	CStu ECho ECtt GMaP MRav MTho NRya
muelleri new	ECou
parnassiifolius	GKev NMen WAbe
platanifolius	EBrs LRHS SPhx
pyrenaeus	NMen
repens 'Boraston O.S.' (v)	WCHb
- 'Broken Egg' (v)	WAlt
- 'Buttered Popcorn' (v)	CBow CRow EBee NLar WMoo WSpi
- 'Cat's Eyes' (v)	CDes EBee WAlt
- 'Dinah Myte' (v)	WAlt
- 'Gloria Spale'	CBre CRow WAlt
- 'In Vein' (v)	WAlt
- 'Joe's Golden'	WAlt
- var. ***pleniflorus*** (d)	CBre CRow GGar SPhx WAlt WEas WFar
- semi-double (d)	WAlt
- 'Snowdrift' (v)	CDes EBee LEdu MAvo
- 'Time Bomb' (v)	WAlt
- 'Timothy Clark' (d)	CBre WAlt WSHC
sardous	EBWF
sceleratus	EBWF WHer
seguieri	GKev WAbe
serbicus	EBee EPPr
speciosus 'Flore Pleno'	see *R. constantinopolitanus* 'Plenus'

Ranzania (*Berberidaceae*)

japonica	EBee WCru

Raoulia (*Asteraceae*)

australis misapplied	see *R. hookeri*
australis Hook.f. ex Raoul	CEnt EDAr EPot GEdr GKir ITim LRHS MBar MWat NWCA SIng WHoo
- 'Calf'	GKev
§ - Lutescens Group	ECha ECho EPot SMad
glabra	EPot
haastii	ECho ECou
§ ***hookeri***	ECha ECho ECou EPot GAbr GEdr ITim LRHS NWCA SMad SPlb SRms WAbe WPat
- var. ***laxa***	EWes
× ***loganii***	see × *Leucoraoulia loganii*
lutescens	see *R. australis* Lutescens Group
monroi	EPot
petriensis	ECho WAbe
× ***petrimia*** 'Margaret Pringle'	WAbe
subsericea	ECho ECou EWes NMen NWCA
tenuicaulis	ECha ECou EPot SPlb

Raoulia × *Leucogenes* see × *Leucoraoulia*

raspberry see *Rubus idaeus*

Ratibida (*Asteraceae*)

columnifera	CRWN EBee EPfP LRHS LSou MSCN NBre SPav SPet
- 'Cheyenne Yellow'	EBrs
- f. ***pulcherrima***	CSpe EBee EPfP LBMP LSou MNFA NBre SGSe SPav SPet WWEG
- 'Red Midget'	EBrs MWat SPav SUsu
- red-flowered	SPav
pinnata	CEnt CRWN CSam EBee EPfP LRHS LSRN MSCN SMad SMrs SPav SPet SPhx SPlb WCAu WHal WMnd
tagetes	SPav

Ravenala (*Strelitziaceae*)

madagascariensis	EAmu LPal XBlo

Ravenea (*Arecaceae*)

rivularis	CCCN EAmu LPal XBlo

Rechsteineria see *Sinningia*

redcurrant see *Ribes rubrum* (R)

Rehderodendron (*Styracaceae*)

macrocarpum	CTrG

Rehmannia (*Scrophulariaceae*)

angulata misapplied	see *R. elata*
§ ***elata*** ♀H2	CBot CFir CSam CSpe EBee ELan EPfP IDee LAst LBMP LHop LLWP LPio LRHS MHer MNHC NOrc SGSe SGar SHGN SHlg SIng SPav WBor WCAu WEas WFar WWEG WWlt
- 'White Dragon'	CSpe LPio
piasezkii	CTsd

Reineckea (*Convallariaceae*)

§ ***carnea***	CDes CFee CFir CHid CHll CPLG CStu EBee ECha ELan EPPr EPla ERos GEdr GGar IDee IMou LEdu MAvo MMuc NSti SDys SGSe SPlb SUsu WCru WPGP WPtf WTin
- B&SWJ 4808	ELon WCru
- SDR 330	GKev
- 'Baoxing Booty' new	WCru
aff. ***carnea*** BWJ 8096 from Sichuan	WCru
- 'Variegata' (v)	EShb WCot

Reinwardtia (*Linaceae*)

§ ***indica***	CCCN CHll CPLG EBee ERea EShb SMrm
trigyna	see *R. indica*

Reseda (*Resedaceae*)

alba	MHer
lutea	SIde
luteola	CHby EBWF GBar GPoy MHer NSco WCHb WHer WSFF

Restio (*Restionaceae*)

brunneus	EBee
festuciformis	EHoe
subverticillatus	see *Ischyrolepis subverticillata*
tetraphyllus	CBct CFir CTrC EBee EHoe GCal SPoG WDyG

Reynoutria see *Fallopia*

Rhamnus (*Rhamnaceae*)

	alaternus	WFar WPGP
	var. ***angustifolia***	
§	- 'Argenteovariegata' (v) ♀H4	Widely available
	- 'Variegata'	see *R. alaternus* 'Argenteovariegata'
	californica	NLar
	cathartica	CCVT CDul CLnd CTri ECrN EMac EPfP LBuc NLar NWea WDin WMou WSFF
	frangula	see *Frangula alnus*
	imeretina	CGHE WPGP WPat
	lycioides	GAuc
	subsp. ***oleoides*** new	
	pallasii	NLar
	pumila	NLar
	taquetii	NLar

Rhaphiolepis (*Rosaceae*)

	× ***delacourii***	CMHG CMac CWSG CWib EBee ELan EPfP LRHS MWea SRms WHCG
	- 'Coates' Crimson'	CDoC CTsd EBee ELan EMil EPfP LAst LHop LRHS SEND WPat WSHC
	- Enchantress = 'Moness'	CMHG CSam CTsd EBee ELan EPfP ERas LRHS MAsh MBri MRav
	- 'Pink Cloud'	CBcs LRHS
	- 'Spring Song'	SLon
	indica	ERom SEND
	- B&SWJ 8405	WCru
	- 'Coppertone'	see *Eriobotrya* 'Coppertone'
	- Springtime = 'Monme'	LRHS SEND SPer SPur WDin
	umbellata ♀H2-3	CBcs CBot CFee CHEx CSam CTri CWib EBee ELan EMil EPfP EWTr GKir LAst LHop LRHS MAsh SEND SLon WFar WHCG WPGP WPat WSHC
	- f. ***ovata*** B&SWJ 4706	WCru

Rhaphithamnus (*Verbenaceae*)

	cyanocarpus	see *R. spinosus*
§	***spinosus***	EBee EPfP GBin GGar GKir IArd IDee LRHS

Rhapidophyllum (*Arecaceae*)

	hystrix	CBrP LPal NPal

Rhapis ✿ (*Arecaceae*)

§	***excelsa*** ♀H1	EAmu LPal NPal WCot XBlo
	multifida	LPal

Rhazya (*Apocynaceae*)

	orientalis	see *Amsonia orientalis*

Rheum ✿ (*Polygonaceae*)

	CC 5243	EWld
	GWJ 9329 from Sikkim	WCru
	HWJK 2354 from Nepal	WCru
	SDR 1863	GKev
	SDR 2817	GKev
	SDR 5004	GKev
	from India new	GCal
§	'Ace of Hearts'	Widely available
	'Ace of Spades'	see *R.* 'Ace of Hearts'
	acuminatum	EBee
	- HWJCM 252	WCru
	alexandrae	CFir EBee EWes GCal GCra LPio NCGa NChi
	- BWJ 7670	WCru
	- SDR 4602	GKev
	- SDR 4757	GKev
	altaicum	LEdu
	'Andrew's Red'	GTwe
§	***australe***	CAgr CFir CRow EBee GCal LEdu LPBA LPio LRHS NBro NLar WCot WFar WHoo WMnd
N	× ***cultorum***	see *R.* × *hybridum*
	delavayi	EBee GCal GKev
	- BWJ 7592	WCru
	- SDR 4602	GKev
	emodi	see *R. australe*
	forrestii	GAuc
§	× ***hybridum***	SEND
	- 'Amerikanske Kaempe' new	LRHS
	- 'Amstel Seedling' new	LRHS
	- 'Appleton's Forcing'	GTwe LRHS
	- 'Baker's All Season'	GTwe LRHS
	- 'Bedford Scarlet' new	LRHS
	- 'Brandy Carr Scarlet'	ECrN MRav NGHP NHol
	- 'Brown's Crimson' new	LRHS
	- 'Brown's Red' new	LRHS
	- 'Canada Red'	GTwe LRHS
	- 'Carter's Forcing' new	LRHS
	- 'Cawood Advance' new	LRHS
	- 'Cawood Castle' new	LRHS
	- 'Cawood Delight'	GKir GTwe LRHS NGHP
	- 'Cawood Ensign' new	LRHS
	- 'Cawood Oak' new	LRHS
	- 'Champagne'	CAgr EMil EPfP GTwe LRHS NGHP SBch SPer WSpi
*	- 'Champagne Rood' new	LRHS
	- 'Collis's Ruby' new	LRHS
	- 'Coutt's Red Stick' new	LRHS
	- 'Crimson Queen' new	LRHS
	- 'Crimson Wine' new	LRHS
	- 'Cutbush's Seedling' new	LRHS
	- 'Dawe's Challenge' new	LRHS
	- 'Daw's Champion'	GTwe LRHS
	- 'Donkere Bloedrede Zoet' new	LRHS
	- 'Early Champagne'	LRHS
	- 'Early Cherry'	GTwe LRHS
	- 'Early Devon' new	LRHS
	- 'Early Mitchell' new	LRHS
	- 'Early Superb' new	LRHS
	- 'Early Victoria' new	LRHS
	- from Burston Hall new	LRHS
	- 'Exhibition Red' new	LRHS
	- 'Fenton's Special'	CTri GTwe LRHS MCoo MRav NGHP NHol
*	- 'Frambozenrood Limburg' new	LRHS
	- from Isle of Ely Horticultural Institute new	LRHS
	- from Sherburn Park new	LRHS
	- 'German Wine'	LRHS
	- 'Giant Grooveless Crimson' new	LRHS
	- 'Glaskin's Perpetual'	CAgr CWib LBuc MAsh
	- 'Goliath'	LRHS
	- 'Grandad's Favorite' ♀H4	EBrs LRHS
	- 'Green Jam' new	LRHS
	- 'Greengage'	GTwe LRHS
	- 'Guardsman' new	LRHS
	- 'Hadspen Crimson'	CBct WCot
	- 'Hammond's Early'	GTwe LRHS
	- 'Harbinger'	GTwe LRHS NGHP
	- 'Hawke's Champagne' ♀H4	GTwe LRHS
	- 'Holsteiner Blut'	ECho LRHS

- 'J.B. Coutt's Seedling' new	LRHS
- 'Kentville' new	LRHS
- 'Larne' new	LRHS
- 'Laxton's No 1' new	LRHS
- 'Linnaeus' new	LRHS
- 'Livingstone'[PBR]	EPfP LRHS
- 'Mac Red' ♕H4	GTwe LRHS
- 'Marshall's Early' new	LRHS
- 'McDonald' new	LRHS
- 'Merton's Banner' new	LRHS
- 'Merton's Broadleaf' new	LRHS
- 'Merton's Foremost' new	LRHS
- 'Merton's Yardstick' new	LRHS
- 'Mitchell's Early Albert' new	LRHS
- 'Mitchell's Royal Albert' new	LRHS
- 'Mrs McKenzie' new	LRHS
- 'Perpetual' new	LRHS
- 'Prince Albert'	GTwe LRHS NEgg NGHP
- 'Queen Victoria' new	LRHS
* - 'Ras Versteeg' new	LRHS
- 'Raspberry Red'	LRHS NBlu
- 'Red Champagne'	EPfP LRHS NGHP WSpi
- 'Red Prolific'	GTwe
- 'Reed's Champagne' new	LRHS
- 'Reed's Early Superb' ♕H4	GTwe LRHS
- 'Riverside Giant' new	LRHS
- 'Rosenhagen' new	LRHS
- 'Ruby' new	LRHS
- 'Seedling Piggot' new	LRHS
- 'Stein's Champagne' ♕H4	GTwe LRHS
- 'Stockbridge' new	LRHS
- 'Stockbridge Arrow'	CSut CTri GTwe LRHS NEgg NGHP
- 'Stockbridge Bingo'	GTwe LRHS
- 'Stockbridge Cropper' new	LRHS
- 'Stockbridge Emerald'	GTwe LRHS
- 'Stockbridge Guardsman'	GTwe
- 'Stockbridge Harbinger' new	LRHS
- 'Stockbridge Smith' new	LRHS
- 'Stott's Monarch' new	LRHS
- 'Strawberry'	EMil EMui GTwe LRHS NBir
- 'Strawberry Red'	LRHS
- 'Strawberry Surprise'	GTwe
- 'Sutton's Cherry Red'	GTwe LRHS
- 'The Appleton' new	LRHS
- 'The Sutton'	CWib GTwe LRHS
- 'Timperley Early' ♕H4	CDoC CMac CSBt CTri CWib ECrN EMil EMui EPfP GKir GTwe LRHS MAsh MGos MMuc MRav NEgg NGHP NPri SBch SCoo SDea SKee SPer SPoG
- 'Tingley Cherry'	GTwe
- 'Valentine'	LRHS MAsh
- 'Victoria'	CAgr CDoC CTri CWib ELau EMil EPfP GTwe LBuc LRHS MAsh MCoo MHer MNHC NGHP NHol SPoG SVic WHar
- 'Vinrabarber Svenborg' new	LRHS
- 'Vroege Engelse' new	LRHS
- 'Zwolle Seedling'	GTwe
kialense	CBct CDes GCal NBid NSti WPGP WPnP
moorcroftianum	EBee
nobile SDR 4750	GKev
officinale	CArn CBct CHEx GCal LRHS MBri SIde SWat
palmatum	CArn CBcs CWat EBee ECha ELan EMFW EPfP GCra GMaP LAst LPBA LRHS MNHC MRav NGdn SWat WCAu WCot WFar
- 'Atropurpureum'	see *R. palmatum* 'Atrosanguineum'
§ - 'Atrosanguineum' ♕H4	CBct CBot CMac CMea CRow EBee ECha ELan EPfP EPla GBuc GCal GKir IFro LBMP LPBA LRHS MBri MMuc MRav NBid NBro NEgg SPlb SWat WCru WMnd
- 'Bowles's Crimson'	CBct GKir LBuc LRHS MBri MRav NBid WCot
- 'Red Herald'	CBct GKir LBuc LRHS WCot WWEG
- 'Rubrum'	CBct EBee GKir LRHS MCCP NBir NCGa NChi NHol WFar
- 'Savill'	CBct GKir LBuc LRHS MBri MRav WWEG
- var. ***tanguticum***	Widely available
- - 'Rosa Auslese'	WHil
rhaponticum	NLar
ribes	EBee GBin WCot
spiciforme	GKev
subacaule	NLar
tataricum	LEdu

Rhinanthus (*Scrophulariaceae*)

minor	GJos NSco

Rhodanthe (*Asteraceae*)

§ ***anthemoides***	ECou SEND

Rhodanthemum (*Asteraceae*)

from High Atlas, Morocco	SIng
'African Eyes'	EBee ECho EPfP GGar LBuc LRHS MAvo MGos NBhm NPri SPoG SRot SUsu
§ ***atlanticum***	ECho EWes
§ ***catananche***	CCCN EBee ECho EWes MBNS SRot
§ - 'Tizi-n-Test'	ECho LRHS WCFE WKif
- 'Tizi-n-Tichka'	CPBP ECho EWes LRHS
§ ***gayanum***	CCCN ECho EWes
- 'Flamingo'	see *R. gayanum*
§ ***hosmariense*** ♕H4	CCCN EBee ECha ECho EDAr ELan EPfP GGar GMaP LHop LRHS MCot MWat NBlu NPri SCoo SEND SMrm SPer SPoG SRms SRot WAbe WCom WHoo WPat

Rhodiola (*Crassulaceae*)

SDR 4742	GKev
SDR 4759	GKev
SDR 4901	GKev
SDR 5015	GKev
amablis	GAuc
crassipes	see *R. wallichiana*
cretinii HWJK 2283	WCru
§ ***fastigiata***	EBee GCal NMen NWCA
§ ***heterodonta***	ECha ELan MRav WCot
himalensis misapplied	see *R.* 'Keston'
himalensis (D. Don) Fu	CTri EBee GKev
- HWJK 2258	WCru
§ ***ishidae***	CTri
§ 'Keston'	CTri
§ ***kirilovii***	LRHS
- var. ***rubra***	LRHS
§ ***pachyclados***	EAlp EBur ECho ECtt EDAr EPot GJos GKir GMaP LBee LRHS MBar MHer NBir NHol NRya SEND SPlb SRot WAbe WCom WEas WFar WPer
aff. ***purpureoviridis***	WFar
- BWJ 7544	WCru
rhodantha	LBMP
§ ***rosea***	Widely available
semenovii	NLar

sinuata HWJK 2318 WCru
- HWJK 2326 WCru
§ ***trollii*** LRHS SPlb WAbe
§ ***wallichiana*** MLHP NBid
- GWJ 9263 WCru
- HWJK 2352 WCru

Rhodochiton (*Scrophulariaceae*)

§ ***atrosanguineus*** ♀H1-2 CBcs CCCN CEnd CHEx CSpe ELan EPfP ERas GGar LRHS MAsh SGar SPer SPoG WBor
volubilis see *R. atrosanguineus*

Rhodocoma (*Restionaceae*)

arida CBct CCCN
capensis CAbb CBct CCCN CFir CPen CPrp CSpe CTrC CTsd EAmu EBee
fruticosa CTrC
gigantea CCCN CPen CTrC EBee ESwi IDee

Rhododendron ✿ (*Ericaceae*)

'A. Gilbert' SHea
'A.J. Ivens' see *R.* 'Arthur J. Ivens'
'Abegail' MGos SLdr
'Abendsonne' MDun
aberconwayi LMil SLdr SReu
- 'His Lordship' GGGa LHyd LMil MSnd
acrophilum GGGa
(V) Argent 2768
'Ada Brunieres' (K) CSdC
'Addy Wery' (EA) ♀H3-4 CDoC ECho MBar MGos SLdr
adenogynum GGGa LMil MSnd SLdr
§ - Adenophorum Group EMui
- - F 20444 SLdr
adenophorum see *R. adenogynum* Adenophorum Group
adenopodum GGGa SLdr
adenosum NHol
- R 18228 GGGa
'Admiral Piet Hein' SReu
'Adonis' (EA/d) CMac LMil MBar NLar NMun SLdr SPoG
'Adriaan Koster' (hybrid) SHea
aeruginosum see *R. campanulatum* subsp. *aeruginosum*
aganniphum GGGa MSnd
- var. ***flavorufum*** MDun MSnd
- 'Rusty' MSnd
× ***agastum*** PW 98 LMil
'Aida' (R/d) CSBt SReu
'Aksel Olsen' CTri GEdr GKir LRHS MBar MDun
'Aladdin' (EA) CMac ECho NEgg SLdr WBrE WFar
'Aladdin' (*auriculatum* hybrid) GGGa
Aladdin Group SReu
'Albatross' LHyd
Albatross Group IDee LMil SLdr SReu
'Albatross Townhill Pink' LMil
'Albert Schweitzer' ♀H4 CDoC CWri GGGa GKir LMil MBar MDun SLdr WFar
albrechtii (A) GGGa LMil SLdr SReu
- Whitney form (A) LMil
'Album Elegans' MSnd
'Alena' GGGa LMil
'Alex Hill' CBcs
'Alexander' (EA) ♀H4 LMil LSRN MAsh MGos SLdr SReu
'Alfred' CWri LMil LRHS MAsh NMun
'Alice' (EA) LHyd SLdr
'Alice' (hybrid) ♀H4 CMac CSBt LHyd LMil SHea SLdr SReu
Alison Johnstone Group CBcs GGGa GGar MDun MSnd SLdr SReu
'Aloha' MBar NDlv
'Alpine Gem' LHyd
Alpine Gem Group GQui SLdr
§ ***alutaceum*** GGGa
var. ***alutaceum*** Globigerum Group R 11100
§ - var. ***iodes*** MSnd
§ - var. ***russotinctum*** MDun NHim
- - R 158 SLdr
§ - - Triplonaevium Group USDAPI 59442/R10923 GGGa
amagianum (A) LMil
'Amber Rain' (A) **new** SLdr
ambiguum LMil MSnd SLdr SReu
I - 'Crosswater' LMil
- 'Golden Summit' GGGa
- 'Jane Banks' LMil
'Ambrosia' (EA) CSBt
'America' MBar MDun SHea WFar
'Amity' CSBt CWri ECho LMil MAsh MBri MLea MSnd NPCo SLdr WFar WGwG
'Amoenum' (EA/d) CBcs CDoC CMac CSBt CTrG ECho LHyd LMil MAsh MBar MGos MSnd SLdr SPer WFar
'Amoenum Coccineum' (EA/d) SLdr SReu
Amor Group LHyd SHea
'Amoretto' MDun
'Anah Kruschke' GGGa MAsh SLdr SPoG
'Analin' see *R.* 'Anuschka'
'Anchorite' (EA) SLdr
* 'Andrae' SReu
'Angelo' LHyd LMil
Angelo Group CWri LHyd LMil SLdr SReu
Anita Group SHea
'Anita Dunstan' MLea
'Ann Callingham' (K) CSdC
'Ann Lindsay' NLar SReu
'Anna Baldsiefen' ELon MGos NLar NPCo SPoG SReu
'Anna H. Hall' MDun
'Anna Rose Whitney' CBcs CTri CWri GKir LHyd LRHS MAsh MBar MDun MGos MSnd NEgg NPri
'Annabella' (K) ♀H4 CSdC LMil MDun
annae GGGa LMil MSnd
'Anne Frank' (EA) MGos WFar
'Anne George' LHyd
'Anne Teese' GGGa IDee LMil SLdr
'Annegret Hansmann' GGGa
'Anneke' (A) EPfP LMil MDun SLdr SReu SSta WFar
anthopogon LMil
- 'Betty Graham' GGGa
I - 'Crosswater' LMil
- subsp. ***hypenanthum*** LMil MDun
- - 'Annapurna' GGGa
§ ***anthosphaerum*** SLdr SReu
'Antilope' (Vs) CWri ECho LMil MAsh MDun MGos MLea NEgg NHol NLar SLdr SPer SReu SSta WBVN
'Antonio' LMil
§ 'Anuschka' EMil GKir LRHS MAsh MDun MMuc
anwheiense CWri LHyd SHea
aperantum F 27022 GGGa
apodectum see *R. dichroanthum* subsp. *apodectum*
'Apotrophia' SLdr
'Apple Blossom' ambig. CMac
'Apple Blossom' Wezelenburg (M) NHol SLdr

N	'Appleblossom' (EA)	see *R.* 'Ho-o'
	'Apricot Blaze' (A)	MDun NHol
	'Apricot Fantasy'	LMil MDun
	'Apricot Nectar' (V) **new**	MDun
	'Apricot Surprise'	CTri LMil LRHS MAsh
	'Apricot Top Garden'	SLdr
	'April Dawn'	GGGa
	'April Glow'	LHyd
	'April Showers' (A)	LMil
I	'Arabella'	MAsh
	'Arabesk' (EA)	MAsh MBri SLdr WFar
	araiophyllum KR 4029	LMil
	arborescens (A)	GGGa LHyd LMil
	- pink-flowered (A)	LMil
	arboreum	CDoC CHEx CWri GGGa LMil LRHS MDun MSnd NHim SLdr SReu
	- 'Blood Red'	MSnd SLdr
	- subsp. ***cinnamomeum***	CDoC GGGa GGar IDee LMil MSnd SLdr SReu
	- - var. ***album***	LHyd SLdr SReu
	- - var. ***cinnamomeum*** Campbelliae Group	NLar SLdr
	- - var. ***roseum***	GGGa
*	- - - ***crispum***	SLdr
	- - - 'Tony Schilling'	LMil NLar SLdr SReu
	- subsp. ***delavayi***	GGGa LMil MSnd SLdr
	- - C&H 7178	GGGa
	- - var. ***delavayi*** **new**	GLin
	- - var. ***peramoenum*** AC 5577 **new**	GLin
	- 'Heligan'	CWri SReu
	- mid-pink-flowered	SLdr
§	- subsp. ***nilagiricum***	GGGa GLin SLdr
	- var. ***roseum***	SHea SLdr
§	- subsp. ***zeylanicum***	SLdr
	arboreum × ***grande***	SLdr
	'Arctic Fox' (EA)	GGGa
§	'Arctic Glow'	GKir
	'Arctic Regent' (K)	CSdC GQui
	'Arctic Tern'	see × *Ledodendron* 'Arctic Tern'
§	***argipeplum***	GGGa SLdr
	'Argosy' Ψ^{H4}	LMil SLdr SReu
	argyrophyllum	CWri GKir MSnd SLdr
	- subsp. ***argyrophyllum***	SLdr
	- - W/A 1210	SLdr
§	- subsp. ***hypoglaucum***	GGGa LHyd
	- - JN	GGGa
	- subsp. ***nankingense***	GGGa
	- - 'Chinese Silver' Ψ^{H4}	CDoC IDee LHyd LMil MDun MSnd SReu
	arizelum	GGGa GKir LMil MDun MSnd NHim SLdr
	- BASEX 9580	GGGa
	- R 25	GGGa
	- subsp. ***arizelum*** Rubicosum Group	LMil MDun
	armitii (V) Woods 2518	GGGa
	'Arneson Gem' (M)	CBcs CDoC GGGa ISea LMil LRHS MAsh NLar SLdr
	'Arneson Pink'	ISea NLar
	'Arpege' (Vs)	LMil MDun NLar SLdr SReu
	'Arthur Bedford'	CBcs SLdr SReu
§	'Arthur J. Ivens'	SLdr
	'Arthur Osborn'	GGGa SSpi
	'Arthur Stevens'	SLdr
	'Asa-gasumi' (EA)	LHyd
	'Ascot Brilliant'	SLdr
	asterochnoum C&H 7051	GGGa
	- EGM 314	LMil
	Asteroid Group	SLdr
	'Astrid'	LMil LSRN
	atlanticum (A)	GGGa LMil
	- 'Seaboard' (A)	IDee LMil
	atlanticum × ***canescens***	GKev
	Augfast Group	ISea SLdr
	'August Lamken'	MDun
	augustinii	CTrG CWri GGGa ISea LHyd LMil MLea MSnd SLdr SSpi SSta
	- subsp. ***augustinii*** C&H 7048	GGGa
§	- subsp. ***chasmanthum***	GGGa MDun
	- compact EGM 293	LMil
§	- Electra Group	CDoC GGGa IDee LHyd LMil MDun SLdr
	- Exbury best form	LHyd LMil MDun SReu
§	- subsp. ***hardyi***	GGGa
	- pale lilac-flowered	SLdr
§	- subsp. ***rubrum***	GGGa
*	- 'Trewithen'	LMil
I	- 'Werrington'	SLdr SReu
	- white-flowered	LHyd
§	***aureum***	GGGa LMil SLdr
	auriculatum	CBcs GGGa GKir IDee LHyd LMil MDun MSnd NHim NLar SLdr SReu SSpi SSta WBVN
	- PW 50	GGGa
	- Reuthe's form	SReu
	auriculatum × ***hemsleyanum***	GGGa
	auritum	GGGa MSnd SLdr
	'Aurora' (K)	SLdr
	'Aurore de Royghem'	LMil
	austrinum (A)	IDee LMil NLar
	- yellow-flowered (A)	LMil
	'Autumn Glow' (EA)	LMil
	'Autumn Gold'	SLdr
	'Avalanche' Ψ^{H4}	LMil SLdr SReu
	Avocet Group	LMil SLdr
	'Award'	LMil
	'Aya-kammuri' (EA)	LHyd
	Azamia Group	LHyd
	Azor Group	LHyd SHea SReu
	Azrie Group	SLdr
§	'Azuma-kagami' (EA)	ISea LHyd LMil LRHS SLdr WFar
	'Azurika'	SPoG
	'Azurro'	GGGa LMil NLar
	'Azurwolke'	LMil
	'B. de Bruin'	SHea
	'Babette'	see *R.* (Volker Group) 'Babette'
	'Babuschka'	LMil
	'Baden-Baden'	CMac CTri ECho GEdr GKir LHyd MAsh MBar MDun MGos MSnd NEgg NHol NMun SLdr SPoG WFar
	'Bagshot Ruby'	SHea SLdr SReu
	baileyi	GGGa SLdr
	bainbridgeanum	SLdr
*	'Baker's Lavender' (EA)	CTrh
	'Balalaika'	MDun
	balangense EN 3530	GGGa
	balfourianum	GGGa SLdr
	'Bali' **new**	MDun
	'Baltic Amber' (A)	GGGa
	'Balzac' (K)	CDoC CSam ECho MAsh MGos MLea NEgg SLdr SPer SPur WBVN
	'Bambi'	LSou SLdr SReu
	'Banana Ripe' **new**	MDun
	'Bandoola'	SReu
	'Barbara Coats' (EA)	SLdr
	'Barbarella'	MDun
	barbatum	CDoC CHEx CWri GGGa GGar IDee LHyd LMil MDun MSnd SLdr
	- B&SWJ 2160	WCru
	- B&SWJ 2237	WCru
	- B&SWJ 2624	WCru

'Barbecue' (K)	LMil
Barclayi Group	SLdr
'Barmstedt'	CWri MAsh
'Barnaby Sunset'	GGGa LMil LRHS
'Bashful' ♀H4	CBcs CSBt ECho EMui EPfP LSou MGos SLdr
§ ***basilicum***	CDoC GGGa GKir IDee LMil LRHS NLar SLdr
- AC 616	MSnd
'Basilisk' (K)	SLdr
× ***bathyphyllum*** Cox 6542	GGGa
bauhiniiflorum	see *R. triflorum* var. *bauhiniiflorum*
beanianum	GGGa
- KC 122	GGGa
- compact	see *R. piercei*
'Beatrice Keir'	LMil MDun SReu
'Beattie' (EA)	LMil SLdr
Beau Brummel Group	LMil SHea
'Beaulieu Manor'	GQui
'Beautiful Day' **new**	MDun
'Beautiful Dreamer' **new**	MDun
'Beauty of Littleworth'	LHyd SHea SReu
'Beefeater'	SLdr
'Beefeater' × ***yakushimanum***	SLdr
beesianum	GGGa SLdr
'Beethoven' (EA) ♀H3-4	CTrG LHyd MSnd SLdr SReu
'Belkanto'	CDoC MDun SPoG
'Belle Heller'	SLdr
'Bengal'	ECho GEdr GKir LRHS MAsh MBar MDun NDlv NHol SReu
'Bengal Beauty' (EA)	GQui SLdr
'Bengal Fire' (EA)	CMac SLdr
'Beni-giri' (EA)	CMac
'Bergensiana'	SReu
'Bergie Larson'	CBcs ECho LMil MAsh MDun MLea MMuc NPCo SLdr
bergii	see *R. augustinii* subsp. *rubrum*
'Berg's 10'	MLea
'Berg's Yellow'	CWri ECho ISea LMil MDun MGos MLea MMuc MSnd WBVN WFar
'Berlinale'	MDun
'Bernstein'	MAsh SPoG WFar
'Berryrose' (K) ♀H4	CBcs CMac CSBt CTri CWri ECho EPfP GKir LMil MAsh MBar MGos MLea NLar SLdr SPer WBVN WFar
Berryrose Group	LRHS MDun
'Bert's Own'	SLdr
'Beryl Taylor'	GGGa
'Betty' (EA)	CTrG LHyd
'Betty Anne Voss' (EA)	ECho GKir LHyd LSRN MGos NPri SCoo SLdr SReu
'Betty Wormald'	CMac CSBt ECho GKir LHyd LMil MBri MGos MLea MMuc MSnd SHea SLdr SPer WBVN
bhutanense CH&M	GGGa
Bibiani Group	SHea SLdr
'Bijou de Ledeberg' (EA)	CMac
'Billy Budd'	SLdr
'Birthday Girl'	ECho LMil LSRN MAsh MDun MLea SBod SPoG
'Biskra'	SHea
Biskra Group	GGGa LMil
'Blaauw's Pink' (EA) ♀H3-4	CDoC CMac CSBt ECho EPfP GKir GQui LHyd LMil MBar MBri MGos MSnd NPCo SLdr SPer SPlb SPoG SReu SRms WFar
'Black Hawk' (EA)	CBcs CTrG
'Black Knight' (A)	SLdr
'Black Magic'	CDoC CWri LMil
'Black Sport'	MLea
Blaue Donau	see *R.* 'Blue Danube'
'Blazecheck'	MGos SCoo
'Blewbury' ♀H4	LHyd LMil MDun SLdr SReu SSta
'Blue Beard'	SLdr
'Blue Bell'	SHea
'Blue Boy'	CDoC LMil MDun
'Blue Chip'	LHyd SLdr
§ 'Blue Danube' (EA) ♀H3-4	CDoC CMac CSBt CTrG CTri ECho EPfP GKir LHyd LMil LRHS MAsh MBar MBri MDun MGos MSnd NBlu NPCo NPri SLdr SPer SPoG SReu SSta WFar
'Blue Diamond'	CMac CSBt ECho ELon GKir LHyd LRHS LSRN MLea NPCo SPer WGwG
Blue Diamond Group	CBcs ECho EPfP LRHS MAsh MBar MDun MGos MSnd NHol SLdr SReu SRms
'Blue Haze'	LHyd
'Blue Monday'	SLdr
'Blue Moon'	LMil SLdr
'Blue Peter' ♀H4	CSBt CWri ECho EMil EPfP GGGa LHyd LMil LRHS MBar MDun MGos MLea SBod SLdr SPer SReu SSta
'Blue Pool'	LMil MBar
Blue Ribbon Group	CMHG ISea SLdr
'Blue Star'	GGar LHyd MDun MLea NMen
'Blue Steel'	see *R. fastigiatum* 'Blue Steel'
Blue Tit Group	CBcs CDoC CSBt CTrG EPfP GKir LHyd LRHS LSou MBar MDun MSnd NHol SLdr SReu SSta STre
Bluebird Group	CMac CSBt MBar MDun MGos NHol NWCA SLdr SRms
'Bluette'	MDun MLea NDlv
'Blurettia'	CDoC CWri LMil LRHS MMuc
'Blutopia'	LMil
'Bob Bovee'	NLar
'Bob's Blue'	MDun
'Boddaertianum'	LHyd SHea SLdr SReu
'Bodnant Yellow'	LMil
'Bonfire'	SHea SLdr SReu
boothii	GGGa
'Bo-peep'	CMac GQui LHyd LMil SReu
Bo-peep Group	CBcs SLdr
'Borde Hill' (R)	SHea
'Boskoop Ostara'	CBcs LMil MGos
'Boule de Neige'	MDun
'Bouquet de Flore' (G) ♀H4	CDoC CSdC EPfP LMil MBar SReu
'Bow Bells' ♀H4	ECho EPfP GEdr GKir LMil LRHS NHol NLar NPri SHea SLdr WFar
Bow Bells Group	CSam ISea LHyd MBar MDun MGos MLea
'Bow Street'	SHea
brachyanthum subsp. ***hypolepidotum***	GGGa LMil
brachycarpum	GLin SLdr
- 'Roseum Dwarf'	GGGa
'Brambling'	GGGa
'Brazier' (EA)	LHyd MSnd SLdr
'Brazil' (K)	CSBt EMil SLdr
'Brazilia' **new**	MAsh
'Bremen'	LMil
'Briane' (EA) **new**	GGGa
'Bric-à-brac'	CMac LHyd MDun WThu
Bric-à-brac Group	CBcs SLdr
'Bridesmaid' (O)	EPfP SPoG
'Bright Forecast' (K)	CWri NLar SLdr
'Brigitte'	CWri GGGa LMil LRHS LSRN MAsh MDun SLdr
'Brilliant' (EA)	MGos
'Brilliant' (hybrid)	MGos NHol WFar
'Brilliant Blue' (EA)	MAsh

'Britannia'	CBcs CSBt CSam CWri EPfP GKir LHyd MBar SHea SPer SReu WFar
'Britannia' × ***griersonianum***	SLdr
'Brocade'	CSam LHyd LMil MDun MSnd SHea SLdr
'Bronze Fire' (A)	NHol SLdr SReu
'Brown Eyes'	ECho ISea MDun MLea MMuc SLdr WFar
'Bruce Brechtbill' 🏆H4	CDoC CWri ECho GGGa LMil MAsh MBri MDun MGos MMuc NHol NLar NPCo SLdr SReu SSta
'Bruce Hancock' (Ad)	ECho
§ 'Bruns Gloria'	LMil MDun
'Bruns Schneewitchen'	SReu
'Buccaneer' (EA)	SLdr
'Bud Flanagan'	MDun
'Buketta'	GGGa MDun
bullatum	see *R. edgeworthii*
bulu C&V 9503	GGGa
'Bungo-nishiki' (EA/d)	CMac
bureavii 🏆H4	GGGa GKir GLin IDee LHyd LMil MDun MGos MSnd NHim SLdr SReu SSta
- SF 517	ISea
- 'Ardrishaig'	GGGa
bureavii × Elizabeth Group	SReu
bureavii × ***yakushimanum***	MSnd SReu
bureavioides	GKir LMil MSnd SReu
- Cox 5076	GGGa
burmanicum	GGGa MDun
'Busuki'	LMil
'Butter Brickle'	LMil MDun MLea WBVN WFar
'Butter Yellow'	ECho MDun
'Buttercup' (K)	MBar
'Buttered Popcorn'	MDun
'Butterfly'	MDun SHea SLdr
'Buttermint'	CWri ECho GQui MDun MGos MLea WBVN WFar
'Buttons and Bows' (K)	GGGa
'Buzzard' (K)	CSdC LMil
'Byron' (A/d)	SLdr
'Caerhays Lavender'	CBcs
caesium	SLdr
calendulaceum (A)	GKev LMil
- red-flowered (A)	LMil
- yellow-flowered (A)	IDee LMil
Calfort Group	SLdr
'Calico' (K)	CSdC SLdr
caliginis (V)	GGGa
callimorphum	GGGa LMil
- var. ***myiagrum*** F 21821a	SLdr
calophytum 🏆H4	GGGa GKir IDee ISea LMil LRHS MSnd NHim SLdr
- EGM 343	LMil
- var. ***openshawianum*** C&H 7055	GGGa
- pink-flowered <u>**new**</u>	LRHS
calostrotum	CWri WAbe
- SF 357	ISea
- subsp. ***calostrotum***	GKev
- 'Gigha' 🏆H4	GGGa ISea LLHF LMil LRHS MAsh MDun MGos SLdr WAbe
§ - subsp. ***keleticum*** 🏆H4	CDoC CTrG GEdr LRHS MBar MDun MGos WAbe WFar
- - F 21756	SLdr
- - R 58	LMil
§ - - Radicans Group	GEdr MBar MDun MLea NHol WAbe WThu
- - - USDAPI 59182/R11188	MLea
- subsp. ***riparium***	GLin
- - SF 95089	ISea
- - Calciphilum Group	GGGa MDun WThu
§ - - Nitens Group	CDoC GBin GGGa IDee MAsh NDlv NMen WAbe
caloxanthum	see *R. campylocarpum* subsp. *caloxanthum*
'Calsap'	GGGa
Calstocker Group	LMil
camelliiflorum	GGGa MDun
'Campanile'	MDun
campanulatum	LMil MDun MSnd SLdr SReu WAbe
- HWJCM 195	WCru
§ - subsp. ***aeruginosum***	GGGa LMil MDun SLdr SReu
- ***album***	SLdr
- 'Knaphill'	MSnd
§ 'Campfire' (EA)	SLdr
Campirr Group	LHyd
campylocarpum	GGGa IDee LMil MDun MSnd SLdr SReu
- B&SWJ 2462	WCru
- from East Nepal	MDun
§ - subsp. ***caloxanthum***	GGGa LMil MDun SLdr
- - KR 6152	LMil
campylogynum 🏆H4	GKev LMil MLea NHim NMen NMun NPCo SSpi WAbe
- SF 95181	ISea
- 'Album'	see *R.* 'Leucanthum'
- 'Bramble'	MDun
- Charopoeum Group	GGGa MBar MDun WThu
- - 'Patricia'	ECho EPot LLHF LMil MDun WThu
- claret-flowered	MDun
§ - Cremastum Group	CTrG GGGa LHyd
- - 'Bodnant Red'	MDun
- Myrtilloides Group	CDoC ECho GGGa GQui LHyd LMil MAsh MDun MGos MSnd NMen NMun NWCA SLdr SReu WAbe
- pink-flowered	MBar WAbe
- salmon pink-flowered	ECho GEdr MDun
camtschaticum	GAuc GGGa LMil MBri
- from Hokkaido, Japan	NMen
- var. ***albiflorum***	GGGa NMen
- red-flowered	GGGa
canadense (A)	GGGa SLdr
- f. ***albiflorum*** (A)	GGGa LMil
- dark-flowered (A)	LMil
- 'Deer Lake' (A)	SReu
'Canary'	SReu
canescens (A)	LMil
'Cannon's Double' (K/d) 🏆H4	CBcs CWri LHyd LMil LRHS MAsh MBri MDun MGos MLea NLar SLdr SPer
'Canzonetta' (EA) 🏆H4	ECho GGGa LMil LRHS MAsh MGos NMun WBrE
'Capistrano'	GGGa
'Caprice' (EA)	SReu
'Captain Jack'	GGGa SLdr
'Caractacus'	MBar WFar
'Carat' (A)	SLdr SReu
cardiobasis	see *R. orbiculare* subsp. *cardiobasis*
'Carita Charm'	SLdr
'Carita Golden Dream'	LMil
Carita Group	SHea SReu
'Carita Inchmery'	LHyd SHea SLdr
'Carmen'	CWri ECho GEdr GGGa GKir ISea LHyd LMil MAsh MBar MDun MGos MLea NHol NPCo SLdr SReu SRms WBVN
carneum	GGGa
'Carnival' (EA)	CBcs
'Caroline'	EMui

	Name	Suppliers
	'Caroline Allbrook' ♀^{H4}	CWri ECho EMil EPfP GGGa LHyd LMil MAsh MBri MDun MGos MLea MSnd NEgg NHol NLar SLdr SPoG WBVN
	'Caroline de Zoete'	LHyd SHea
	carolinianum	*R. minus* var. *minus*, see *R. minus* var. *minus* Carolinianum Group
	'Cary Ann'	CBcs CTri CWri GKir LRHS MAsh SLdr SReu WFar
	'Casablanca' (EA)	SLdr
	'Cassata'	LMil LRHS MDun
	'Cassley' (Vs)	LMil LRHS
	'Castle of Mey'	SLdr
	catacosmum	GGGa
	catawbiense	GGGa GKev LHyd MSnd SLdr
	'Catawbiense Album'	CTri CWri GGGa GKir MAsh WFar
	'Catawbiense Boursault'	MAsh SLdr WFar
	'Catawbiense Grandiflorum'	CWri EMil GKir LMil MAsh NMun WFar
	'Catherine Hopwood'	SLdr
§	***caucasicum*** 'Cunningham's Sulphur'	MDun
	'Caucasicum Pictum'	GGGa LHyd LMil MBar SLdr
	'Cavalcade'	GKir
	Cavalier Group	MDun
	'Cayenne' (EA)	SLdr
	'Cecile' (K) ♀^{H4}	CBcs CDoC CMac CSam CWri ECho EMil GKir LHyd LMil MBar MBri MDun MGos MSnd NBlu SBod SLdr SPer SReu WBVN
	'Celestial' (EA)	CMac
	'Centennial'	see *R.* 'Washington State Centennial'
	cephalanthum	GGGa LMil
	- subsp. ***cephalanthum*** SBEC 0751	WAbe
	- - Crebreflorum Group	GGGa LMil WAbe
	- - Nmaiense Group C&V 9513	GGGa
	- subsp. ***platyphyllum***	GGGa
	cerasinum	GGGa ISea LMil MSnd
	- C&V 9504	GGGa
	- SF 95067	ISea
	- 'Cherry Brandy'	MSnd
	'Cetewayo' ♀^{H4}	CWri LMil SReu
	chaetomallum	see *R. haematodes* subsp. *chaetomallum*
	chamaethomsonii	GGGa LMil
	- CCH&H 8195	GGGa
	- var. ***chamaethauma*** KW 5847	LMil
	chameunum	see *R. saluenense* subsp. *chameunum*
§	'Champagne' ♀$^{H3-4}$	CSBt EPfP GKir LHyd LMil LRHS MAsh MDun SHea SLdr SReu
	championiae	GGGa
	'Chanel' (Vs)	MDun SReu SSta
	changii	GGGa
	'Chanticleer' (EA)	SLdr SReu
	chapaense	see *R. maddenii* subsp. *crassum*
	'Chapeau'	LMil
	charitopes	GGGa LMil
§	- subsp. ***tsangpoense***	GGGa GQui NHol
	'Charlemagne' (G)	SLdr
*	'Charlotte de Rothschild' (A)	SLdr
	Charmaine Group	NHol
	'Charme La'	GGGa
	chasmanthum	see *R. augustinii* subsp. *chasmanthum*
	'Cheer'	CWri LRHS MAsh MBar MMuc NEgg SLdr SReu WFar
	'Cheerful Giant' (K)	MGos
	'Chelsea Reach' (K/d)	CSdC
	'Chelsea Seventy'	LRHS MAsh MSnd NLar SLdr
	'Cherie' (EA) **new**	MAsh
	'Cherokee'	SLdr
	'Cherries and Cream'	LMil
	'Cherry Cheesecake' **new**	GGGa
	'Cherry Drop' (EA)	LRHS MAsh
	'Cherry Float' **new**	MDun
	'Chetco' (K)	LMil SLdr
	'Chevalier Félix de Sauvage' ♀^{H4}	LMil SHea SReu
	'Cheyenne'	SLdr
	'Chiffchaff'	LHyd WAbe
	'Chikor'	CBcs CSBt CTrG ECho GGGa GKir MBar MBri MDun MGos MSnd NHol SLdr WFar
	China Group	SReu
	'China A'	SLdr
	'Chinchilla' (EA)	GQui
	'Chink'	CBcs MBar MDun SLdr
	'Chionoides'	CMac GGGa SLdr
	'Chipmunk' (EA/d)	GKir LRHS MAsh
	'Chippewa' (EA)	CTri LMil
	'Chocolate Ice' (K/d)	SLdr
	'Choremia' ♀^{H3}	LHyd LMil MLea SHea SLdr SReu
	'Chorister' (K)	SLdr
	'Chorus Line'	MDun
	'Chris' (EA)	SLdr
	christi (V)	GGGa
	'Christina' (EA/d)	LMil NHol NLar SLdr SReu
	'Christmas Cheer' (EA/d)	see *R.* 'Ima-shojo'
	'Christmas Cheer' (hybrid)	CBcs CDoC CMac CSBt CWri EMil GGGa GGal GKir LHyd LMil MAsh MGos MLea MSnd NLar SLdr SReu
	'Chromatella'	SLdr
	chrysanthum	see *R. aureum*
	chryseum	see *R. rupicola* var. *chryseum*
	chrysodoron	GGGa LMil
	ciliatum	CBcs CTrG GGGa IDee LMil SLdr
	'Cilpinense' ♀$^{H3-4}$	CMac CSBt CWri ECho EPfP GEdr GGGa LHyd LMil LRHS NPri SHea SPoG SReu WBVN WBrE
	Cilpinense Group	CBcs MAsh MBar MDun MMuc MSnd SLdr SPer WFar
	cinnabarinum	LMil MDun MSnd SLdr
	- subsp. ***cinnabarinum***	MDun SLdr
	- - BL&M 234	LMil
	- - 'Aestivale'	LMil
	- - Blandfordiiflorum Group	GGGa LMil MSnd SLdr
§	- - 'Conroy'	GGGa LMil MDun MLea SReu
	- - 'Nepal'	LHyd LMil
	- - Roylei Group	GGGa LHyd LMil MDun NHim SLdr
	- - - 'Magnificum'	MDun
	- - - 'Vin Rosé'	LMil MDun
§	- subsp. ***tamaense*** KW 21021	GGGa
§	- subsp. ***xanthocodon***	IDee LMil MDun MSnd NHim SLdr
§	- - Concatenans Group	GGGa LHyd LMil MDun MSnd NHim SLdr
	- - - C&V 9523	GGGa
	- - - KW 5874	LMil
	- - - 'Amber'	MDun
	- - - 'Copper'	SLdr
	- - 'Daffodilly'	LHyd
	- - Purpurellum Group	GGGa MDun MSnd SLdr
	Cinnkeys Group	GGGa MDun
	Cinzan Group	LMil SReu
	'Circus'	MDun
	citriniflorum	LMil
	- R 108	GGGa LMil

- Brodick form	LMil
- var. ***citriniflorum***	LMil
- var. ***horaeum***	SLdr
- - F 21850*	GGGa
'Citronella'	SLdr
'Claret Bumble'	MSnd
clementinae	GGGa MDun MSnd
- F 25705	LMil
- SDR 3230	GKev
'Cliff Garland'	GQui LMil
'Coccineum Speciosum' (G) ♀H4	CDoC CMac CSBt CSdC GGGa IDee LMil LRHS SLdr
coelicum F 25625	GGGa
coeloneuron	GGGa LMil MDun
- EGM 334	LMil
'Colin Kenrick' (K/d)	CSdC SLdr
collettianum H&W 8975	GGGa
'Colonel Coen'	CWri GKir LMil MBri MGos MLea MSnd WBVN
Colonel Rogers Group	LHyd SLdr SReu
'Colyer' (EA)	SLdr
(Comely Group) 'Golden Orfe'	SLdr
- yellow-flowered **new**	LHyd
complexum F 15392	GGGa
'Comte de Gomer' (hybrid)	CBcs
concatenans	see *R. cinnabarinum* subsp. *xanthocodon* Concatenans Group
concinnum	CWri LHyd MDun SLdr
- Pseudoyanthinum Group	GGGa GQui LMil MDun SLdr
'Connie' (EA) **new**	MAsh
'Conroy'	see *R. cinnabarinum* subsp. *cinnabarinum* 'Conroy'
'Constable'	LHyd
'Contina'	GGGa
'Conversation Piece' (EA) **new**	SLdr
cookeanum	see *R. sikangense* var. *sikangense* Cookeanum Group
'Coral Mist'	GGGa LMil MDun
'Coral Reef'	SLdr SReu
'Coral Sea' (EA)	MDun SLdr SReu
coriaceum	GGGa LMil MSnd SLdr
- R 120	MSnd
'Corneille' (G/d) ♀H4	CSBt LMil SLdr
'Cornish Cracker'	SLdr
Cornish Cross Group	LHyd SLdr SReu
Cornish Early Red Group	see *R.* Smithii Group
'Cornish Red'	see *R.* Smithii Group
Cornubia Group	SLdr
'Corona'	SHea
'Coronation Day'	LMil SHea SLdr SReu
'Corry Koster'	SHea
coryanum	GGGa
- SF 99067	ISea
- 'Chelsea Chimes'	MSnd SLdr
'Cosmopolitan'	CWri LMil LRHS MAsh MBar MDun MGos MMuc SLdr SPoG SReu
Cote Group (A)	SLdr
'Cougar' **new**	MDun
'Countess of Athlone'	SLdr
'Countess of Derby'	MDun SHea SReu
'Countess of Haddington' ♀H2	CBcs ISea LMil MDun SLdr
'Countess of Stair'	WFar
cowanianum	GGGa WAbe
Cowslip Group	CTri CWri LMil LRHS MBar MDun MGos MLea MSnd SLdr SReu
coxianum C&H 475B	GGGa
'Cranbourne'	LHyd SReu
'Crane' ♀H4	EPfP GGGa GKir GQui LLHF LMil LRHS MAsh MDun NPri

crassum	see *R. maddenii* subsp. *crassum*
'Cream Crest'	GQui LMil MDun WFar
'Cream Glory'	LHyd MDun
'Creamy Chiffon'	CWri ECho LHyd MDun MGos MLea
§ 'Creeping Jenny'	ECho GGGa GGal GGar LHyd MBar MDun SLdr
cremastum	see *R. campylogynum* Cremastum Group
'Crest' ♀H3-4	GGGa LHyd LMil MDun MGos SLdr
'Crete' ♀H4	LMil MDun
'Crimson Pippin'	LMil
crinigerum	GGGa IDee LHyd LMil MDun
'Crinoline' (K)	SReu
'Crinoline' (EA)	SLdr
'Croceum Tricolor' (G)	CSdC
Crossbill Group	CBcs
* ***crossium***	SReu
'Crosswater Belle'	LMil
'Crosswater Red' (K)	LMil
cubittii	see *R. veitchianum* Cubittii Group
cucullatum	see *R. roxieanum* var. *cucullatum*
cumberlandense (A)	GGGa IDee LMil
- 'Sunlight' (A)	LMil MBri
cuneatum	GGGa
'Cunningham's Blush'	GGGa
'Cunningham's Sulphur'	see *R. caucasicum* 'Cunningham's Sulphur'
'Cunningham's White'	CBcs CSBt CSam CTri CWri ELan EMil EPfP GGGa GKir LMil LRHS MAsh MBar MDun MGos MMuc MSnd NPri SLdr SPer SPoG SReu WFar
'Cupcake'	see *R.* 'Delp's Cupcake'
'Cupreum Ardens' (G)	CSdC
'Curlew' ♀H4	CMac CSBt EPfP GEdr GGGa GKir ISea LMil LRHS MAsh MBar MBri MDun MGos MSnd NHol SLdr SReu SSpi WBVN WFar
cyanocarpum Bu 294	GGGa
'Cynthia' ♀H4	CBcs CMac CSBt CSam CWri ECho EPfP GGGa GKir ISea LHyd LMil LSRN MBar MBri MDun MGos MSnd NEgg SLdr SPer SReu SSta
'Daimio' (EA)	LHyd
'Dairymaid'	SReu
dalhousieae	GGGa SLdr
§ - var. ***rhabdotum***	GGGa SLdr
Damaris Group	SLdr
'Damaris Logan'	see *R.* 'Logan Damaris'
'Damozel'	SHea SLdr
'Danger' **new**	SLdr
'Daphne Daffarn'	SHea
'Daphne Millais'	SHea SLdr
'Dartmoor Blush'	SReu
'Dartmoor Pixie'	SReu
'Dartmoor Rose'	SReu
dasycladum	see *R. selense* subsp. *dasycladum*
dasypetalum	MBar MDun NDlv
dauricum 'Arctic Pearl'	GGGa
- 'Mid-winter' ♀H4	GGGa LHyd
'David' ♀H4	LHyd SHea SLdr SReu
davidii	GGGa LMil SLdr
- EN 4213	GGGa
davidsonianum ♀H3-4	GGGa LMil SLdr SSpi
- Bodnant form	LMil MDun
- 'Caerhays Blotched'	SLdr
- 'Caerhays Pink'	GGGa SLdr
- 'Ruth Lyons'	LMil
'Daviesii' (G) ♀H4	CBcs CDoC CSBt CSam CSdC CTri CWri ECho EPfP GGGa GKir GQui IDee LHyd LMil LRHS MAsh MBri

		MDun MLea NPCo SLdr SPer SPoG SReu SSpi WBVN WBrE WFar
	'Dawn's Delight'	SLdr
*	'Day Dawn'	GKir SReu
	'Day Dream'	SHea SReu
	'Daybreak' (K)	GQui
N	'Daybreak'	see *R.* 'Kirin'
	'Dear Grandad' (EA)	CTri LMil MAsh NPri SCoo
	'Dear Grandma'	LMil
	'Dearest' (EA)	LRHS NPri
	'Debutante'	NHol
	decorum ♀H4	CDoC GGGa ISea LLHF LMil LRHS MDun MSnd SLdr SReu
	- Bu 286	NHol
	- C&H 7023	GGGa
	- 'Cox's Uranium Green'	SReu
§	- subsp. ***diaprepes***	LHyd
	- - 'Gargantua'	SReu
	- late-flowering	LMil
	- pink-flowered	SLdr
	decorum* × *yakushimanum	SLdr SReu
	degronianum	GGGa
§	- subsp. ***degronianum***	LMil SLdr
	- - 'Gerald Loder'	LHyd
§	- subsp. ***heptamerum***	GGGa MDun
	- - 'Ho Emma'	LMil MDun
	- - 'Oki Island'	LMil
	- 'Rae's Delight'	LMil
	dekatanum	GGGa
	deleiense	see *R. tephropeplum*
	'Delicatissimum' (O)	CBcs CDoC CWri ECho GGGa GQui MLea MMuc NEgg NLar NPCo SLdr SPer WBVN WBrE WGwG
§	'Delp's Cupcake'	NLar
	dendricola	SLdr
	- KW 20981	GGGa
	dendrocharis	NHim
	- Cox 5016	GGGa NHol WAbe
	- Glendoick Gem = 'Gle002'	GGGa
*	'Denny's Rose' (A)	LMil MDun SReu
	'Denny's Scarlet'	MDun SReu
	'Denny's White'	LMil MDun NHol SLdr SReu
	denudatum	GLin
	- C&H 7118	GGGa
	- C&H 70102	GGGa
	- EGM 294	LMil
	- SEH 334	LMil
	desquamatum	see *R. rubiginosum* Desquamatum Group
	'Devisiperbile' (EA)	SLdr
	'Dexter's Champagne' **new**	MDun
	'Dexter's Spice'	MDun
	'Dexter's Springtime' **new**	MDun
	'Dexter's Vanilla' **new**	MDun
	'Diadem' (V)	MAsh
	(Diamant Group) 'Diamant Enzianblau' (EA)	LMil
	- lilac-flowered (EA)	ECho LMil MLea
	- pink-flowered (EA)	ECho LMil LRHS MDun MGos MLea SLdr
§	- purple-flowered (EA)	ECho LMil MDun MGos MLea SLdr
§	- red-flowered (EA)	ECho LMil MDun MLea SLdr
	- rosy red-flowered (EA)	ECho
	- white-flowered (EA)	ECho MDun MLea SLdr
	'Diamant Purpur'	see *R.* Diamant Group purple-flowered
	'Diamant Rot'	see *R.* Diamant Group red-flowered
	'Diana Pearson'	LHyd
	'Diane'	CMac
	diaprepes	see *R. decorum* subsp. *diaprepes*
	dichroanthum	GGGa LMil MDun SLdr SReu
§	- subsp. ***apodectum***	GGGa LMil
	- subsp. ***dichroanthum*** SBEC 545	GGGa
§	- subsp. ***scyphocalyx***	LMil NLar SLdr
	- - F 24546	GGGa
	- subsp. ***septentrionale*** JN 575	GGGa
	didymum	see *R. sanguineum* subsp. *didymum*
	'Dietrich'	WFar
	dimitrum	MDun
	'Diny Dee'	MGos
	'Diorama' (Vs)	LMil SReu SSta
	'Directeur Charles Baumann'	SLdr
§	'Directeur Moerlands' (M)	SLdr
	discolor	see *R. fortunei* subsp. *discolor*
	'Doc'	CMac EPfP GKir MAsh MBar MDun MGos NDlv SLdr SReu WFar
	'Doctor A. Blok'	SLdr
	'Doctor Ernst Schäle'	GGGa
	'Doctor H.C. Dresselhuys'	EMil MBar
	'Doctor M. Oosthoek' (M) ♀H4	CSBt SLdr SReu
	'Doctor Stocker'	MSnd
	'Doctor V.H. Rutgers'	MBar MDun WFar
	'Don Giovanni'	NLar
	'Don Quixote' (K)	CSdC MAsh
	'Doncaster'	GKir MBar MGos SHea WFar
	'Donna Hardgrove' **new**	MDun
	'Dopey' ♀H4	CBcs CSBt CWri ECho EMui EPfP GGGa GGar GKir LHyd LMil LRHS MAsh MBar MBri MDun MGos MLea MSnd NDlv NEgg NHol SLdr SReu WBVN
	'Dora Amateis' ♀H4	CBcs CDoC ECho GGGa GKir LMil LRHS MAsh MBar MGos MSnd NHol NPri SLdr SReu
	Dormouse Group	CBcs ECho LMil MAsh SHea SLdr SReu WBVN WFar
	'Dorothea'	SLdr
	'Dorothy Hayden' (EA)	SLdr
	'Dorset Sandy' (EA)	LMil
	'Dörte Reich'	GGGa
	'Double Beauty' (EA/d)	SReu SSta
	'Double Damask' (K/d) ♀H4	SLdr
	'Double Date' (d)	SLdr
	double yellow-flowered	SLdr
	'Douglas McEwan'	MDun SLdr
	'Dracula' (K)	GGGa
	Dragonfly Group	SReu
	Dragonfly Group × ***serotinum***	SLdr
	'Drake's Mountain'	MBar MDun MLea
	'Dreamland' ♀H4	CBcs CDoC CSBt CWri ECho EMil GKir LMil LRHS MAsh MDun MGos MLea MSnd NLar SLdr SReu WFar
	'Driven Snow' (EA)	SLdr
	'Drury Lane' (K)	GQui LMil
	dryophyllum misapplied	see *R. phaeochrysum* var. *levistratum*
	'Duchess of Teck'	SReu
	'Dusky Dawn'	SLdr
	'Dusky Orange'	MDun SReu
	'Dusty'	MDun
	'Dusty Miller'	GKir LHyd LRHS MAsh MBar MDun MGos MSnd NDlv NLar SLdr
	'Earl of Athlone'	SHea SReu
	'Earl of Donoughmore'	MDun SReu SSta

	Name	Suppliers
	'Early Beni' (EA)	LHyd
	'Ebony Pearl'	CBcs ECho GBin MGos WGwG
	eclecteum	LMil MDun SLdr
	- Cox 6054	GGGa
	- 'Rowallane Yellow'	SLdr
§	***edgeworthii*** ♀H2-3	GGGa ISea NHim SLdr WAbe
	- KC 0106	GGGa
	'Edith Bosley'	GGGa NLar
	Edmondii Group	LHyd
	'Edmund de Rothschild' **new**	NMun
	'Edna Bee' (EA)	LMil
	'Effner'	LMil
	'Egret' ♀H4	ECho GGGa LMil MBar MDun MGos MLea NLar SLdr WThu
	'Eider'	GGGa SLdr SReu
	'Eileen'	LMil
	'El Camino'	ECho LMil MMuc MSnd NPCo SLdr
	'El Greco'	SLdr
	Eldorado Group	GQui
	Electra Group	see *R. augustinii* Electra Group
	elegantulum	GGGa LMil MDun MSnd
	'Elfin Gold'	SReu
	'Elisabeth Hobbie' ♀H4	ECho GEdr GGGa GKir LMil MBar MDun
	Elizabeth Group	CBcs GGGa LHyd LMil MAsh MBar SBod SLdr SPer SReu WFar
N	'Elizabeth' (EA)	CMac CSBt EPfP MGos SLdr
	'Elizabeth'	CTri CWri ECho GKir LRHS LSRN MGos NHol NPri SHea
	'Elizabeth de Rothschild'	MDun SLdr
	'Elizabeth Jenny'	see *R.* 'Creeping Jenny'
	'Elizabeth Lockhart'	ECho GEdr GQui MBar MDun MGos NMun
	'Elizabeth of Glamis'	GGGa
	'Elizabeth Red Foliage'	CTri GGGa GKir LHyd LMil LRHS MAsh MDun SPer SReu
	elliottii	GGGa
	Elsae Group	SLdr
	'Else Frye'	GGGa
	'Elsie Lee' (EA/d) ♀H3-4	CSBt CTrh ECho GGGa LHyd LMil MAsh NPCo SLdr
	'Elsie Pratt' (A)	MBar NHol
	'Elsie Straver'	MDun NHol SLdr SReu
	'Elsie Watson'	GGGa
	'Elspeth'	LHyd
	'Emasculum'	LMil SLdr SReu
	Emerald Isle Group	SReu
	'Emma Williams'	CBcs
	'Endsleigh Pink'	CBcs LMil
	'English Roseum'	SLdr
	'Erato'	GGGa LMil
	eriocarpum 'Jitsugetsuse' (EA)	LHyd
	eriogynum	see *R. facetum*
	eritimum	see *R. anthosphaerum*
	'Ernest Inman'	LHyd LMil SLdr
	erosum	GGGa SLdr
	'Esmeralda'	CMac CTrG
	Ethel Group	SLdr
	'Etna' (EA)	SLdr
	'Etta Burrows'	CWri GGGa MDun
	'Euan Cox'	GGGa
	euchroum	MSnd
	eudoxum	GGGa MSnd
	'Eunice Updike' (EA)	LHyd
	'Europa'	SReu
	'Eurydice' **new**	SHea
	eurysiphon	MSnd
	- Arduaine form	GGGa
	'Evelyn Hyde' (EA)	LMil SLdr
	'Evening Fragrance' (A)	LMil SReu
	'Everbloom' (EA)	SLdr
	'Everest' (EA)	LHyd LMil SLdr SPoG
	'Everestianum'	GGGa MBar SHea SLdr
	'Everitt Hershey' (A)	SLdr
§	'Everlasting'	SReu
	Everred = '851C'PBR	GGGa
	exasperatum KC 0116	GGGa
	- KC 0126	GGGa
	- KW 8250	GGGa
	'Exbury Calstocker'	LMil
	'Exbury Naomi'	LHyd LMil SLdr
	'Exbury White' (K)	GQui
	excellens	LMil
	- AC 146	GGGa
	- KR 7616	ISea
	- SF 92074	ISea
	- SF 92079	ISea
	eximium	see *R. falconeri* subsp. ***eximium***
	'Exotic'	MDun
	'Exquisitum' (O) ♀H4	CBcs CDoC CWri ECho EPfP GGGa LMil MBri MLea NLar SLdr WBVN WBrE
	exquisitum	see *R. oreotrephes* Exquisitum Group
	faberi	GGGa LMil SLdr
	'Fabia' ♀H3	CMac GGGa LMil MDun SHea
	Fabia Group	CWri MDun SLdr
	'Fabia Roman Pottery'	MDun
§	'Fabia Tangerine'	MDun MLea SReu
	'Fabia Waterer'	LMil SLdr
§	***facetum***	GGGa LMil MDun
	- KR 7593	LMil
	'Faggetter's Favourite' ♀H4	LMil MDun SHea SReu SSta
	Fairy Light Group	LMil SLdr
	'Falcon'	see *R.* (Hawk Group) 'Hawk Falcon'
	falconeri ♀H3-4	CBcs CDoC CHEx CWri GGGa ISea LMil MDun MGos MSnd NHim NPCo SLdr SPer WBVN
	- from East Nepal	MDun
§	- subsp. ***eximium***	CDoC GGGa LMil MDun NLar
	'Falling Snow'	MDun
	'Fanny'	see *R.* 'Pucella'
	'Fantastica' ♀H4	CDoC CWri ELan EMil EPfP GGGa GKev LHyd LMil LRHS MAsh MBri MDun MLea MSnd NPCo
	fargesii	see *R. oreodoxa* var. *fargesii*
	'Fashion'	CTrG SLdr
	fastigiatum	GEdr ISea LMil MBar MLea MSnd
	- C&H 7159	GGGa
	- SBEC 804/4869	GGGa MDun WThu
§	- 'Blue Steel' ♀H4	CBcs CTri CWri ECho GKir ISea LMil LRHS MAsh MDun MGos NPCo SPlb SReu WPat
	'Fastuosum Flore Pleno' (d) ♀H4	CBcs CMac CSBt CWri EPfP GGGa GKir ISea LHyd LMil MBar MDun MGos MLea MSnd SHea SLdr SPer SPoG SReu SSta WFar
	'Fatima'	LMil
	faucium	GGGa ISea LMil
	- KR 6229	LMil
	'Favorite' (EA)	LHyd MSnd NMun SLdr
	'Fawley' (K)	SLdr
	'Fedora' (EA)	CBcs SLdr
	'Fénelon' (G)	SLdr
	ferrugineum	GGGa LHyd LMil MBar MGos
	- 'Plenum' (d)	MDun
	'Festivo'	MDun
	'Feuerwerk' (K)	EMil SLdr
	fictolacteum	see *R. rex* subsp. *fictolacteum*
	Fire Bird Group	SHea SLdr
	'Fire Rim'	GGGa

	'Fireball' (K) ♀H4	CBcs CDoC CSam CTri CWri GGGa GKir LHyd LMil LRHS MAsh MBri MGos MLea NDlv NMun SBod SLdr SPer SPoG WBrE
	'Fireball' (hybrid)	SLdr
	Firedrake Group	SReu
	'Firefly' (EA)	see *R.* 'Hexe'
	'Fireglow'	CSBt CSdC LMil MAsh SLdr WFar
	'Firelight' (hybrid)	LMil LRHS
	'Fireman Jeff'	SLdr
	'Firetail'	SHea
	'Flaming Bronze'	SReu
	'Flaming Gold'	EPfP GGGa LRHS NPri
	Flamingo Group	SLdr
§	***flammeum*** (A)	LMil
	'Flanagan's Daughter'	GKir LMil LRHS
	'Flautando'	LMil MDun
	Flava Group	see *R.* Volker Group
	flavidum	SLdr
	- Cox 6143	GGGa
	- 'Album'	SLdr WThu
	fletcherianum 'Yellow Bunting'	GGGa
	aff. ***flinckii***	MAsh
	- AC 5441	GLin
	floccigerum	GGGa LMil SLdr
	'Floradora' (M)	SReu
	'Floriade'	LHyd
	'Floriade' × ***yakushimanum***	SLdr
	floribundum	LMil MSnd NHim SLdr
	- EGM 294	LMil
	- 'Swinhoe'	SLdr
	'Florida' (EA/d) ♀H3-4	CMac LMil LRHS SReu WFar
	'Flower Arranger' (EA)	LMil MAsh SCoo
I	'Fluidum'	MDun
	formosum	CBcs GGGa GQui SLdr
§	- var. ***formosum*** Iteaphyllum Group	GGGa
	- - 'Khasia'	GGGa
	- var. ***inaequale*** C&H 301	GGGa
	forrestii	GGGa MSnd
	- KR 6113	LMil
	- subsp. ***forrestii***	LMil
	- - Repens Group	GGGa GKev LMil SLdr
	- - - 'Seinghku'	GGGa WThu
	- Tumescens Group	GGGa WThu
	- - C&V 9517	GGGa
	'Fortune'	LHyd
	Fortune Group	SLdr
	fortunei	GGGa LHyd LMil MDun SLdr
§	- subsp. ***discolor*** ♀H4	GGGa LMil LRHS MDun MSnd SLdr
	- - PW 34	GGGa
	- - (Houlstonii Group) 'John R. Elcock'	IDee LMil
	- subsp. ***discolor*** × 'Lodauric Iceberg'	SLdr
	- 'Foxy'	SLdr
	- 'Lu-Shan'	MDun
	- 'Mrs Butler'	see *R. fortunei* 'Sir Charles Butler'
§	- 'Sir Charles Butler'	LMil MDun SLdr
	'Fox Hunter'	SLdr
	fragariiflorum C&V 9519	GGGa
	- LS&E 15828	GGGa
	'Fragrans' (Ad)	SLdr
	'Fragrant Star' (A)	GGGa SLdr
	'Fragrantissimum' ♀H2-3	CBcs CMac CSBt CTrG CTsd CWri GGGa GGal GGar ISea LHyd LMil MDun MRav MSnd NLar NMun SLdr
	'Francesca'	GGGa
	Francis Hanger (Reuthe's) Group	SLdr SReu
	'Frank Baum'	SReu
	'Frank Galsworthy' ♀H4	LMil SReu
	'Frans van der Bom' (M)	SLdr
	'Fraseri' (M)	SLdr
	'Fred Hamilton'	CWri MDun
	'Fred Nutbeam' (EA)	LMil
	'Fred Peste'	CDoC ECho GKir LMil MAsh MBri MDun MGos MLea MSnd NPCo SReu
	'Fred Wynniatt'	LHyd SLdr
	'Frere Organ' (G)	SLdr
	'Freya' (R/d)	LMil
	'Frieda' (EA)	SLdr
	'Frigata' (A)	SLdr
	'Frilled Petticoats'	SReu
	'Frilly Lemon' (K/d)	MDun NLar
	'Fritz Quihou' (A) **new**	LMil
	'Frosted Orange' (EA)	LMil MAsh
	'Frosthexe'	GGGa
	'Frühlingstraum'	LHyd
	'Fulbrook'	LMil
	fulgens	GGGa LMil MDun MSnd
	fulvum ♀H4	CDoC GGGa IDee LHyd LMil MDun MSnd NLar SLdr SReu SSta
	- KR 7614	LMil
	- subsp. ***fulvoides***	LMil
	- - Cox 6532	GGGa
§	'Fumiko' (EA)	CBcs CSBt LMil LRHS MAsh MBar MDun MGos MLea MMuc NMun NPCo WFar
	'Furnivall's Daughter' ♀H4	CMac CSBt CWri ECho EPfP GGGa GKir LHyd LMil MBar MDun MGos MLea MMuc MSnd NLar SHea SLdr SPer SReu SSta WFar
	'Fusilier'	SHea SReu
	'Gabrielle Hill' (EA)	MAsh MGos SLdr
	'Gaiety' (EA)	LMil SReu
	'Galactic'	SLdr
	galactinum	LMil MDun
	- EN 3537	GGGa
	'Gandy Dancer'	CWri MDun SLdr
	'Garden State Glow' (EA/d)	SLdr
	'Garibaldi'	SHea
	'Garnet'	SHea
	'Gartendirektor Glocker'	CWri ECho GGGa MAsh MDun MSnd SLdr
	'Gartendirektor Rieger' ♀H4	CWri GGGa LMil MDun SHea SReu
	'Gauche' (A)	GQui SLdr
	'Gaugin'	GQui
	Gaul Group	SLdr
	'Gay Lady'	SLdr
	'Geisha' (EA)	GKir MBar
	'Geisha Lilac'	see *R.* 'Hanako'
	'Geisha Orange'	see *R.* 'Satschiko'
	'Geisha Pink'	see *R.* 'Momoko'
	'Geisha Purple'	see *R.* 'Fumiko'
	'Geisha Red'	see *R.* 'Kazuko'
	'Geisha White'	see *R.* 'Hisako'
	'Gena Mae' (A/d)	GGGa SLdr
	'General Eisenhower'	SHea SReu
	'General Eric Harrison'	SLdr
	'General Practitioner'	MSnd SLdr
	'General Sir John du Cane'	SHea
	'General Wavell' (EA)	CMac SLdr
	'Gene's Favourite'	SReu
	genestierianum CC&H 8080	GGGa
	'Genoveva'	LMil
	'Geoffrey Millais'	LMil

	Name	Suppliers
	'Georg Arends' (Ad)	GKir LRHS SLdr
	'George Haslam'	SLdr
	'George Hyde' (EA)	LMil LRHS LSRN MGos SCoo
	'George Reynolds' (K)	MLea SLdr
	'Georgette'	LHyd SLdr
§	× ***geraldii***	SLdr
	'Germania'	EMil LMil LRHS MAsh MBar NPri SPoG SReu
	Gertrud Schäle Group	CDoC CTri GEdr MBar MDun SHea SReu
	Gibraltar Group	CTri
	'Gibraltar' (K) ♀H4	CBcs CDoC CMac CSBt CTri CWri EMil EPfP GGGa GKir LMil LRHS MAsh MBar MBri MDun MGos MLea SLdr SPer SReu SSta WFar
	giganteum	see *R. protistum* var. *giganteum*
	'Gilbert Mullie' (EA)	LMil
I	'Gill's Arboreum'	SLdr
	'Gill's Crimson'	SHea SLdr SReu
	'Ginger' (K)	CSBt CWri LMil LRHS
	'Ginny Gee' ♀H4	CBcs CDoC CSBt CWri ECho EPfP EPot GEdr GGGa GGar GKir LHyd LMil LRHS MAsh MBar MDun MGos MLea MSnd NEgg NHol SLdr SReu SSta WFar
	'Gipsy King'	SHea SLdr
§	'Girard's Hot Shot' (EA)	ECho GQui MAsh MGos SReu WFar
	'Girard's Hot Shot' variegated (EA/v)	ECho GGGa LMil MAsh NMun
	'Glacier' (EA)	MGos
	glanduliferum C&H 7131	GGGa
	- EGM 347	LMil
	'Glanzblatt'	MDun
	glaucophyllum	GGGa LMil MDun MSnd SLdr
	- B&SWJ 2638	WCru
	- var. ***album***	GGGa
	- Borde Hill form	LMil
§	- subsp. ***tubiforme***	NMun
	Glendoick Butterscotch = 'Gle003'	GGGa
	Glendoick Dream = 'Gle005' (EA)	GGGa
	Glendoick Ermine = 'Gle006' (EA)	GGGa
	Glendoick Frolic = 'Gle007'	GGGa
	Glendoick Garnet = 'Gle008' (EA)	GGGa
	Glendoick Glacier = 'Gle009' (EA)	GGGa
	Glendoick Goblin = 'Gle010' (EA)	GGGa
	Glendoick Gold = 'Gle011'	GGGa
	Glendoick Honeydew = 'Gle012'	GGGa
	Glendoick Ice Cream = 'Gle013'	GGGa
	Glendoick Mystique = 'Gle014'	GGGa
	Glendoick Petticoats = 'Gle015'	GGGa
	Glendoick Rosebud = 'Gle022' (EA) **new**	GGGa
	Glendoick Ruby = 'Gle016'	GGGa
	Glendoick Silver	GGGa
	Glendoick Snowflakes = 'Gle001' (EA) **new**	GGGa
	Glendoick Vanilla = 'Gle017'	GGGa
	Glendoick Velvet = 'Gle017'	GGGa

	Name	Suppliers
	'Gletschernacht'	CWri
	glischrum	GGGa MSnd
	- subsp. ***glischroides***	GGGa LMil
	- subsp. ***glischrum***	GGGa
§	- subsp. ***rude***	GGGa MSnd
	- - C&V 9524	GGGa
	globigerum	see *R. alutaceum* var. *alutaceum* Globigerum Group
	'Glockenspiel' (K/d)	SLdr
	glomerulatum	see *R. yungningense* Glomerulatum Group
	'Gloria'	see *R.* 'Bruns Gloria'
	'Gloria Mundi' (G)	SHea
	'Glory of Littleworth' (Ad)	LMil
	'Glowing Embers' (K)	CDoC CMac CSam CTri CWri ECho EMil GKir LRHS MAsh MBri MDun MLea NHol SLdr SPur SReu WBVN
	Goblin Group	SLdr
	'Gog' (K)	CSBt SLdr
	'Gold Mohur'	SLdr SReu
§	'Goldbukett'	GGGa LHyd MAsh
	'Golden Bee'	GGGa NHol
	'Golden Belle'	CWri MDun
	Golden Bouquet	see *R.* 'Goldbukett'
	'Golden Clipper'	LHyd
	'Golden Coach'	CWri ECho MDun MGos SBod SLdr SPer WBVN
	'Golden Eagle' (K)	CBcs CDoC ECho GGar LMil LRHS MDun MGos SLdr WBVN
	'Golden Flare' (A)	CBcs CDoC CSBt CSam CWri ECho LRHS MAsh MBri MLea MMuc NBlu NDlv NEgg NMun NPCo SLdr WBrE
	'Golden Fleece'	SReu
	'Golden Gate'	CDoC CSBt ECho MDun MMuc SReu WFar
	'Golden Horn' (K)	GQui
	'Golden Lights' (A)	CWri ECho LMil MAsh MBri MDun MGos NEgg NPCo SBod WBVN WGwG
	'Golden Melodie'	MDun
	'Golden Orfe'	LHyd
	Golden Oriole Group	NHol
§	- 'Talavera'	SSpi
	'Golden Oriole Talavera'	see *R.* (Golden Oriole Group) 'Talavera'
	'Golden Princess'	LMil MDun NHol
	'Golden Ruby'	ECho MGos SPer
	'Golden Splendour'	LMil
	'Golden Sunlight'	see *R.* 'Directeur Moerlands'
	'Golden Sunset' (K)	CMac CSdC ECho LMil LRHS MAsh MDun MGos MLea NHol NLar SLdr SPur
	'Golden Torch' ♀H4	CBcs CDoC CMHG CSBt CWri ECho EPfP GGar GKir LHyd LMil LRHS MAsh MBri MDun MGos MLea MSnd NDlv NPri SLdr SPer SPoG SReu SSta WBVN WFar
	'Golden Wedding'	CBcs CSBt CWri ECho LHyd LMil LSRN MAsh MDun MGos MLea NDlv NPCo SBod SLdr SPoG WBVN
	'Golden Wit'	MDun MMHG MMuc NEgg
	'Goldfinch' (K)	SLdr
	'Goldfinger'	MDun MGos
	'Goldflamme'	SLdr
	'Goldflimmer' (v)	CDoC EMil GGGa LMil LRHS MAsh MGos MLea NBlu NPri SLdr SPoG SReu WFar
	'Goldfort'	SReu
	'Goldika'	LMil LRHS
	'Goldkollier'	MDun

Name	Suppliers
'Goldkrone' 🏆[H4]	CWri EPfP GGGa LHyd LMil LRHS MAsh MDun MGos MLea SLdr SPoG SReu
Goldschatz = 'Goldprinz'	EMil GGGa LMil
'Goldstrike'	LMil SLdr
'Goldsworth Crimson'	LHyd
'Goldsworth Orange'	CSBt CWri ECho GGGa MGos SBod SLdr
'Goldsworth Yellow'	CSBt MGos
'Goldtopas' (K)	LMil LRHS
'Goldzwerg'	MDun
'Golfer'	CWri GGGa LMil MLea
'Gomer Waterer' 🏆[H4]	CDoC CMac CSBt CSam CWri ECho EPfP GGGa GKir ISea LHyd LMil LRHS MAsh MBar MDun MGos MLea MMuc MSnd SBod SLdr SPer SPoG SReu SSta WBVN WFar
gongshanense	GGGa
'Gorbella'	MAsh
'Gordian'	MDun
Gowenianum Group (Ad)	LMil SLdr
'Grace Seabrook'	CSBt CSam CTri CWri ECho GGGa GKir LHyd MDun MGos MMuc NPCo SBod SLdr SPer SReu WBVN
gracilentum (V)	GGGa
'Graciosum' (O)	SReu
'Graf Lennart'	LMil MDun
'Graffito'	LMil MDun
'Graham Thomas'	LMil SReu
'Grand Slam'	ECho ISea MDun MLea MSnd WBVN
grande	GGGa MSnd SLdr
- pink-flowered	MSnd
'Grandeur Triomphante' (G)	CSdC
gratum	see *R. basilicum*
'Graziella'	GGGa LMil MDun
'Greensleeves'	LMil LRHS
'Greenway' (EA)	CBcs SLdr
'Grenadier'	SHea
'Greta' (EA)	LHyd
'Gretzel'	SReu
griersonianum	CBcs GGGa LHyd LMil MDun
griersonianum* × *yakushimanum	SLdr
griffithianum	GGGa SLdr
'Gristede' 🏆[H4]	ECho LMil LRHS MDun NHol SLdr SReu
groenlandicum	see *Ledum groenlandicum*
'Grosclaude'	CMac SHea
'Grouse' × ***keiskei*** var. ***ozawae*** 'Yaku Fairy'	ECho
'Grumpy'	CBcs CSBt CWri ECho EMil EMui GGGa GKir LHyd LMil LRHS MAsh MBar MGos NDlv SBod SLdr SReu
'Gudrun'	MDun
'Guelder Rose'	SLdr
'Gumpo' (EA)	CBcs CMac MAsh
'Gumpo Pink' (EA)	SLdr
'Gumpo White' (EA)	LRHS MAsh MGos NLar
'Gwenda' (EA)	CTri LHyd SLdr
'Gwillt-king'	CBcs
'H.H. Hume' (EA)	SLdr
habrotrichum	GGGa LMil
'Hachmann's Anastasia'	LMil MDun
'Hachmann's Brasilia'	EMil LMil MDun SReu
'Hachmann's Charmant'	LMil MDun SPoG
'Hachmann's Constanze'	EMil LMil
'Hachmann's Diadem'	LMil LRHS
'Hachmann's Eskimo'	LMil LRHS
'Hachmann's Feuerschein'	LMil
'Hachmann's Junifeuer'	LMil MDun
'Hachmann's Kabarett'	LMil MDun
'Hachmann's Marianne'	LMil
'Hachmann's Marlis' 🏆[H4]	EMil LHyd LMil LRHS MAsh SReu
§ 'Hachmann's Polaris' 🏆[H4]	CDoC LHyd LMil MBri MDun NLar
'Hachmann's Porzellan' 🏆[H4]	EMil LMil
§ 'Hachmann's Rokoko' (EA)	GGGa LMil MAsh
haematodes	GGGa LHyd LMil LRHS MDun MSnd SRms
- 'Blood Red'	SLdr
§ - subsp. ***chaetomallum***	GGGa LMil SLdr
- - JN 493	GGGa
- subsp. ***haematodes***	LMil
- - SBEC 585	GGGa
'Haida Gold'	SLdr SReu
'Halfdan Lem'	CBcs CDoC ECho GGGa LHyd MAsh MBri MDun MGos MLea MMuc MSnd SLdr SPer SReu SSta WBVN
'Halopeanum'	LMil SHea SLdr
'Hamlet' (M)	LMil
'Hampshire Belle'	LMil
'Hana-asobi' (EA)	LHyd SLdr
§ 'Hanako' (EA)	GEdr GKir LRHS MBar MDun MGos MLea NDlv
hanceanum 'Canton Consul'	GGGa
- Nanum Group	CBcs GGGa
'Hanger's Flame' (A)	LMil
'Hansel'	CDoC CWri ECho GQui LMil MAsh MDun WFar
haofui Guiz 75	GGGa
Happy Group	CMac ECho
'Hardijzer Beauty' (Ad)	SLdr
hardyi	see *R. augustinii* subsp. *hardyi*
'Harkwood Moonlight'	LMil
'Harkwood Premiere'	GGGa
'Harkwood Red' (EA)	SLdr
Harmony Group	SLdr
'Harry Tagg'	CTrG SLdr
'Harvest Moon' (K)	GKir MDun SCoo SLdr SReu
'Harvest Moon' (hybrid)	CSBt MBar SReu
'Hatsu-giri' (EA)	CMac LHyd LMil MAsh MBar SLdr SPoG SReu
(Hawk Group) 'Hawk Buzzard'	SLdr
§ - 'Hawk Falcon'	SReu
'Heather Macleod' (EA)	SLdr
heatheriae	IDee LMil NHim
- KR 6150	GGGa
- KR 6158	GGGa
- KR 6176	LMil
heftii	SLdr
'Helen Close' (EA)	SLdr
'Helen Curtis' (EA)	MAsh SLdr SReu
'Helene Schiffner' 🏆[H4]	GGGa LMil SReu
heliolepis	GGGa LMil
- SF 489	ISea
- SF 516	ISea
- var. ***fumidum***	see *R. heliolepis* var. *heliolepis*
§ - var. ***heliolepis***	LMil
- - CN&W 1038	ISea
'Hello Dolly' **new**	MDun
hemidartum	see *R. pocophorum* var. *hemidartum*
hemitrichotum	WThu
hemsleyanum	GGGa IDee LMil MDun MSnd NHim SLdr
heptamerum	see *R. degronianum* subsp. *heptamerum*
'Herbert' (EA)	CMac
'Heureuse Surprise' (G)	SLdr
§ 'Hexe' (EA)	CTrh

'High Summer'	LMil
'Hilda Margaret'	SReu
'Hilda Niblett' (EA)	MGos SPoG
'Hille'	LMil
'Hino-crimson' (EA) ♀H3-4	CBcs CDoC CMac CSBt CTrG CTri LMil MAsh MBar MBri MGos NHol SLdr SPer SPoG SReu SSta WFar
'Hinode-giri' (EA)	CBcs CMac CSBt LHyd SLdr SReu WFar
'Hinode-no-taka' (EA)	LHyd
N 'Hinomayo' (EA) ♀H3-4	CBcs CMac CTrG CTri EPfP GKir GQui LHyd LMil MBar MSnd SLdr SReu SSta
'Hino-scarlet'	see *R.* 'Campfire'
'Hino-tsukasa' (EA)	SLdr
hippophaeoides	LMil MDun MSnd NHim SLdr WAbe WFar WGwG
- F 22197a	SLdr
- Yu 13845	GGGa LMil MDun
- 'Bei-ma-shan'	see *R. hippophaeoides* 'Haba Shan'
- 'Blue Silver'	EGxp GGGa LMil LRHS MAsh NLar NMun
- Glendoick Iceberg = 'Gle019'	GGGa
§ - 'Haba Shan' ♀H4	GGGa LMil MDun
- var. ***hippophaeoides*** Fimbriatum Group	NMun
hirsutum	GGGa LMil
- f. ***albiflorum***	GGGa SReu
- 'Flore Pleno' (d)	ECho GEdr MAsh MBar MDun
hirtipes	GGGa LMil
- C&V 9546	GGGa
- KR 5219	LMil
§ 'Hisako' (EA)	GEdr MDun NDlv
hodgsonii	GGGa GKir IDee LMil MDun NHol SLdr
- TSS 9	SLdr
- TSS 42A	SLdr
'Holden'	MAsh WFar
'Homebush' (K/d) ♀H4	CBcs CDoC CMac CTri CWri EPfP GGGa LHyd LMil LRHS MAsh MBar MBri MDun MGos NPCo SLdr SPer SPoG SSta WBVN
'Honey Butter'	LMil
'Honeysuckle' (K)	MBar NHol SReu
hongkongense	GGGa
§ 'Ho-o' (EA)	CBcs NLar SLdr
hookeri	CTrG SReu
- Tigh-na-Rudha form	GGGa
'Hope Findlay'	LHyd
'Hoppy'	CBcs CSBt CWri GKir ISea LMil MAsh MDun MGos MLea MSnd NMun SLdr SPoG WBVN
'Horizon Monarch' ♀H3-4	CDoC CWri EMil GGGa LHyd LMil LRHS MDun
horlickianum	GGGa
'Hortulanus H. Witte' (M)	CSBt SReu WFar
'Hot Shot'	see *R.* 'Girard's Hot Shot'
'Hot Shot Variegated' (EA/v)	CDoC EMil NEgg NPri SLdr
'Hotei' ♀H4	CDoC CSBt CWri ECho EPfP GGGa GKir LHyd LMil LRHS MAsh MBar MDun MGos NEgg NPCo NPri SHea SReu WBVN WFar
'Hotspur' (K)	CSBt CSam CWri ECho GBin MGos NLar SLdr SPer
Hotspur Group (K)	LHyd
'Hotspur Red' (K) ♀H4	CDoC LMil MAsh NEgg NPCo SReu
'Hotspur Yellow' (K)	SReu
huanum	LMil
- C&H 7073	GGGa
- EGM 316	LMil
'Hugh Koster'	CSBt MGos SLdr
aff. ***huidongense*** KR 7315	LMil
'Hullaballoo'	LMil
'Humboldt'	WFar
Humming Bird Group	CBcs CMHG GEdr GGar LHyd MBar MDun NHol SLdr SRms
hunnewellianum	MSnd
'Hussar'	CWri
'Hyde and Seek'	GQui
'Hydie' (EA/d)	LMil MGos SPoG
'Hydon Amethyst'	LHyd
'Hydon Ben'	LHyd
'Hydon Comet'	LHyd
'Hydon Dawn' ♀H4	CDoC CWri GGGa GKir LHyd LMil MAsh MDun MGos MLea MSnd NDlv SHea SReu SSta
'Hydon Glow'	LHyd
'Hydon Gold'	LHyd
'Hydon Haley'	LHyd
'Hydon Hunter' ♀H4	LHyd LMil MLea MSnd NDlv SHea SLdr SReu SSta
'Hydon Juliet'	LHyd
'Hydon Mist'	LHyd
'Hydon Pearl'	LHyd
'Hydon Pink'	SHea
'Hydon Rodney'	LHyd
'Hydon Salmon'	LHyd
'Hydon Velvet'	LHyd LMil SReu
hylaeum	MSnd
- BASEX 9659	GGGa
Hyperion Group	SReu SSta WFar
hyperythrum	GGGa LHyd MDun SLdr
- ETOT 196	MDun
hypoglaucum	see *R. argyrophyllum* subsp. *hypoglaucum*
'Ice Cube'	ECho MBri MDun MMuc NLar WFar
'Ice Music' **new**	GGGa
'Iceberg'	see *R.* 'Lodauric Iceberg'
'Idealist'	CWri SReu
'Ightham Gold'	SReu
'Ightham Peach'	SReu
'Ightham Purple'	SReu
'Ightham Yellow'	MDun SHea SLdr SReu
'Igneum Novum' (G)	SReu
'Il Tasso' (R/d)	SLdr
§ 'Ilam Melford Lemon' (A)	LMil
§ 'Ilam Ming' (A)	LMil
'Ilam Violet'	LHyd LMil
'Imago' (K/d)	CSdC SLdr
§ 'Ima-shojo' (EA/d)	CMac CSBt LHyd LRHS MAsh
impeditum	CBcs CSBt CWib ECho GGGa GQui LHyd LRHS MBar MDun MGos MLea MSnd SLdr SPer SReu SSta WBVN WBrE WFar
- F 29268	GGGa
- 'Blue Steel'	see *R. fastigiatum* 'Blue Steel'
- 'Indigo'	LLHF MAsh MDun MGos NPCo WAbe
- 'Pygmaeum'	GEdr WAbe WThu
- Reuthe's form	SReu
- 'Williams'	NMun SLdr
imperator	see *R. uniflorum* var. *imperator*
'Impi'	MSnd NMun SReu
Impi Group	MDun NLar
'Inamorata'	SLdr
indicum (EA)	LRHS
§ - 'Macranthum' (EA)	LHyd SLdr
insigne ♀H4	GGGa GLin IDee LMil MDun MSnd NLar
- Reuthe's form	SReu
insigne* × *yakushimanum	SReu

Name	Suppliers
Intrepid Group	SReu
intricatum	GGGa
Intrifast Group	GGGa LHyd
'Invitation' **new**	MDun
iodes	see *R. alutaceum* var. *iodes*
'Irene Koster' (O) 🏆^{H4}	CDoC CSBt CWri EPfP GGGa ISea LHyd LMil LRHS MBri MDun MLea NEgg NHim NLar SBod SLdr WBrE
'Irish Mist'	GGGa
'Irohayama' (EA) 🏆$^{H3-4}$	CMac GQui LHyd LMil LRHS MAsh NPri
irroratum	LMil SLdr
- subsp. ***irroratum*** C&H 7100	GGGa
* - subsp. ***kontumense*** var. ***ningyuense***	GLin
* - - - EGM 339	SLdr
- 'Polka Dot'	GGGa LHyd LMil SLdr
- subsp. ***yiliangense*** EGM 339 **new**	LMil
'Isabel' **new**	NPri
'Isabel Pierce'	CWri
Isabella Group	SLdr WFar
'Isabella Mangles'	LHyd
'Isola Bella'	GGGa
iteaphyllum	see *R. formosum* var. *formosum* Iteaphyllum Group
'Ivery's Scarlet'	GKir
'Ivette' (EA)	CMac LHyd
Iviza Group	SReu
'J.C. Williams'	CBcs
'J.G. Millais'	SLdr
'J.J. de Vink'	SHea
'J.M. de Montague'	see *R.* 'The Hon. Jean Marie de Montague'
'J.R.R. Tolkien'	SLdr
'Jabberwocky'	LHyd
'Jack Skilton'	LHyd SLdr
'Jacksonii'	ISea MBar SHea SLdr
Jalisco Group	SLdr
'Jalisco Elect'	CWri SLdr
'Jalisco Emblem'	SLdr
'Jalisco Goshawk'	SHea SLdr
'Jalisco Janet'	SHea SLdr
'James Barto'	LHyd SLdr
'James Burchett' 🏆^{H4}	LMil LRHS SLdr SReu
'James Gable' (EA)	MAsh SLdr
'Jan Bee'	SLdr
'Jan Dekens'	SReu
'Jan Steen' (M)	SLdr
'Janet Blair'	CWri MDun SLdr
'Janet Ward'	LHyd SReu
'Janine Alexandre Debray'	SLdr
japonicum (A. Gray) Valcken	see *R. molle* subsp. *japonicum*
- Schneider var. ***japonicum***	see *R. degronianum* subsp. *heptamerum*
- var. ***pentamerum***	see *R. degronianum* subsp. *degronianum*
'Jason'	SLdr
javanicum (V)	GGGa
'Jean Marie Montague'	see *R.* 'The Hon. Jean Marie de Montague'
'Jeff Hill' (EA)	ECho MMuc SReu
'Jenny'	see *R.* 'Creeping Jenny'
'Jeremy Davies'	SReu
'Jervis Bay'	SReu
'Jingle Bells'	GGGa MDun
'Joan Paton' (A)	SLdr
'Joanna' **new**	MMuc
'Jock'	SLdr
Jock Group	CBcs CMHG

Name	Suppliers
'Jock Brydon' (O)	GGGa LMil NLar SLdr
'Jock Coutts' (K)	CSdC
'Johann Sebastian Bach' (EA)	SLdr
'Johann Strauss' (EA)	GKir
'Johanna' (EA) 🏆^{H4}	CBcs CDoC CTri GGGa GKir LMil LRHS MAsh MBar MMHG NHol NLar NPri SLdr SPer SReu
'John Cairns' (EA)	CMac LHyd MBar SLdr
'John Walter'	MBar SHea SLdr
'John Waterer'	SHea WFar
'Johnny Bender'	SLdr
johnstoneanum	CBcs GGGa GGal LMil MSnd NMun SLdr
- KW 7732	SLdr
- 'Double Diamond' (d)	LMil
'Jolie Madame' (Vs)	CSam CWri ECho LMil LRHS MAsh MBri MLea NHim NLar SLdr SPur SReu
'Josefa Blue'	GGGa
'Joseph Baumann' (G)	CSdC SLdr
'Joseph Hill' (EA)	ECho NHol SReu
'Josephine Klinger' (G)	CSdC SReu
'Jubilant'	SHea
'Jubilee'	SLdr
Jubilee Queen Group	SLdr
'June Fire' (A)	MDun SReu
'Jungfrau'	CWri
'Junifee'	MDun
kaempferi (EA)	CBcs LHyd LMil
- 'Damio'	see *R. kaempferi* 'Mikado'
§ - 'Mikado' (EA)	LMil SLdr SReu
- orange-flowered (EA)	CMac
'Kakiemon' (EA)	LHyd
'Kalinka'	EMil LMil LRHS MAsh MDun NHol NLar SPoG
'Kaponga'	MGos
'Karalee' **new**	MDun
'Karen Triplett'	LMil
'Karin'	MDun SLdr
'Karin Seleger'	GGGa
'Kasane-kagaribi' (EA)	LHyd
kasoense HECC 10009	GGGa
- HECC 10040	GGGa
'Kate Waterer' 🏆^{H4}	CWri MBar MDun MGos NBlu SReu WFar
'Katharine Fortescue'	LHyd
'Kathleen' van Nes (EA)	LHyd SLdr
'Katisha' (EA)	LHyd SLdr
'Katy Watson'	SReu
kawakamii (V)	GGGa
§ 'Kazuko' (EA)	GEdr LMil LRHS MAsh MBar MDun MGos MLea NBlu NDlv WFar
'Keija'	SLdr
keiskei	LLHF
- compact	SLdr
- var. ***ozawae*** 'Yaku Fairy' 🏆^{H4}	GGGa ITim LMil MDun WThu
keleticum	see *R. calostrotum* subsp. *keleticum*
'Ken Janeck' 🏆^{H4}	GGGa MDun
§ ***kendrickii***	GGGa MDun
'Kentucky Colonel'	SLdr
'Kermesinum' (EA)	CTri LMil LRHS MAsh MBar MGos NMun SLdr SPlb SReu
I 'Kermesinum Album' (EA)	MBar MGos SReu
I 'Kermesinum Rosé' (EA)	CSBt ECho GGGa LMil MAsh MBar MDun MGos MLea SLdr SReu
'Kerrigan's Super Red' (EA) **new**	CTrh
kesangiae	LMil MDun
- AC 110	MSnd

- CH&M 3058	GGGa
- CH&M 3099	GGGa
- var. ***album*** KCSH 0362	GGGa
Kewense Group	CSBt LHyd
keysii	GGGa MDun SLdr
- EGM 064	LMil
- KC 0115	GGGa
'Kilian' (A) **new**	LRHS
'Kilimanjaro'	GGGa LHyd LMil SHea SReu
'Kimbeth'	GGGa
'Kimigayo' (EA)	LHyd
'King Fisher'	NMun
'King George' Loder	see *R.* 'Loderi King George'
'King George' van Nes	SReu
'King of Shrubs'	NLar
kingianum	see *R. arboreum* subsp. *zeylanicum*
'Kings Ride'	LHyd
'Kingston'	MDun
§ 'Kirin' (EA/d)	CBcs CMac CSBt LHyd LMil SLdr
'Kirishima' (EA)	SRms
'Kiritsubo' (EA)	LHyd
'Kitty Cole'	SLdr
kiusianum (EA) $\mathbb{Y}^{H4}$	LHyd LMil SReu SRms
- 'Album' (EA)	LHyd LMil SReu
- 'Hillier's Pink' (EA)	LMil
'Kiwi Majic'	LMil MDun
'Klondyke' (K) $\mathbb{Y}^{H4}$	CBcs CSBt CTri EMil EPfP GGGa GKir LMil LRHS MAsh MDun MGos NPri SBod SLdr SReu
'Kluis Sensation' $\mathbb{Y}^{H4}$	CMac CSBt LHyd MDun MSnd NHol SHea SLdr SReu
'Kluis Triumph'	SLdr SReu
'Knap Hill Apricot' (K)	CSdC LMil
'Knap Hill Red' (K)	CDoC LMil
'Knap Hill White' (K)	CSdC
'Kobold' (EA)	SLdr
'Koichiro Wada'	see *R. yakushimanum* 'Koichiro Wada'
'Kokardia'	EMil LMil NLar
kongboense	GGGa WAbe
- C&V 9540	GGGa
'Königstein' (EA)	LMil
§ 'Koningin Emma' (M)	LMil NLar
§ 'Koningin Wilhelmina' (M)	SLdr
konori var. ***phaeopeplum*** (V)	GGGa
'Koromo-shikibu' (EA)	GGGa GKir
'Koromo-shikibu White' (EA)	GGGa
'Koster's Brilliant Red' (M)	CSBt EPfP LMil MGos SReu
'Kupferberg'	GGGa
§ 'Kure-no-yuki' (EA/d)	CSBt CTrG EPfP LHyd LMil MAsh
'Lackblatt'	see *R.* (Volker Group) 'Lackblatt'
lacteum	LMil MDun SLdr
- SBEC 345	GGGa
'Lady Alice Fitzwilliam' $\mathbb{Y}^{H2-3}$	CBcs CEnd CMHG CMac CTrG GGGa IDee ISea LHyd LMil
Lady Bessborough Group	SLdr
'Lady Bowes Lyon'	SLdr
Lady Chamberlain Group	MSnd SLdr
'Lady Chamberlain Salmon Trout'	see *R.* 'Salmon Trout'
'Lady Clementine Mitford' $\mathbb{Y}^{H4}$	CSBt CWri ECho EPfP GQui LHyd LMil LRHS MAsh MBri MDun MGos MLea MMuc SHea SLdr SPer SPoG SReu
'Lady Digby'	CWri
'Lady Eleanor Cathcart'	SHea SLdr
'Lady Grey Egerton'	SHea
'Lady Longman'	LHyd SHea
'Lady Louise' (EA)	SLdr
'Lady Primrose'	SReu
'Lady Robin' (EA)	SLdr
'Lady Romsey' $\mathbb{Y}^{H4}$	LMil MSnd SLdr
'Lady Rosebery' (K)	CSdC MDun
Ladybird Group	SReu
laetum (V)	GGGa
Lamellen Group	LHyd SLdr
'Lampion'	GGGa
'Lamplighter'	SHea SLdr SReu
lanatoides	LMil
- C&C 7548	GGGa
- C&C 7574	GGGa
- C&C 7577	GGGa
- KR 6385	LMil
§ ***lanatum***	ECho GGGa LMil MDun
- CH&M 3080	GGGa
- dwarf, cream-flowered	GGGa
- Flinckii Group	see *R. lanatum*
'Langworth'	CWri ECho GQui ISea LMil MAsh MDun MGos MLea MSnd SLdr SReu
lanigerum	LMil MDun MSnd SReu
- C&V 9530	GGGa
- KW 8251	GGGa
lapponicum Confertissimum Group	GGGa
- Parvifolium Group from Siberia	GGGa WAbe
'Lapwing' (K)	SLdr
'Laramie'	GGGa
'Lascaux'	SReu
'Late Love' (EA)	CDoC MGos
§ ***latoucheae*** (EA) PW 86	GGGa
laudandum var. ***temoense***	GGGa
Laura Aberconway Group	SHea SLdr
'Laura Morland' (EA)	LHyd
'Lava Flow'	LHyd
'Lavender Girl' $\mathbb{Y}^{H4}$	CMac GGGa LHyd LMil MSnd NLar SHea SLdr SReu SSta
'Lavender Lady' (EA)	CTrG
'Lavendula'	GGGa
'Le Progrès'	LMil LRHS
'Lea Rainbow'	MLea
'Ledifolium'	see *R.* × *mucronatum*
'Ledifolium Album'	see *R.* × *mucronatum*
'Lee's Dark Purple'	CSBt CWri LMil LRHS MAsh MBar MDun WFar
'Lee's Scarlet'	LMil
'Lem'	SReu
'Lemon Dream'	LMil MDun
* 'Lemon Drop' (A)	GGGa
'Lemon Lights' (A)	LMil
'Lemon Marmalade' **new**	MDun
'Lemon Meringue' **new**	LMil
'Lemonora' (M)	CBcs LRHS MBri
'Lem's 121'	MDun
'Lem's 45'	CWri ECho ISea MDun SLdr
'Lem's Cameo' $\mathbb{Y}^{H3}$	GGGa LHyd LMil LRHS MDun SReu SSta
'Lem's Monarch' $\mathbb{Y}^{H4}$	CBcs CDoC CWri GGGa GKir LHyd LMil MBri MDun MGos MLea SReu SSta WBVN
'Lem's Tangerine'	CDoC LMil
'Lemur' (EA)	ECho GEdr GGGa MAsh MDun MLea NHol SReu WThu
'Leni'	LRHS MAsh
'Leny' (EA)	NHol
'Leo' (EA)	GQui LHyd SLdr
'Leonardslee Giles'	SLdr
'Leonardslee Primrose'	SLdr
Leonore Group	SReu

lepidostylum	CBcs CMac CWri GGGa LMil MBar MDun NHim NHol SLdr SReu WFar
lepidotum	GGGa GKev MDun WAbe
– Elaeagnoides Group	GGGa
– yellow-flowered McB 110	WThu
§ ***leptocarpum***	GGGa
leptothrium	GGGa
Letty Edwards Group	CSBt SLdr SReu
§ 'Leucanthum'	GGGa WThu
leucaspis	GGGa LHyd MDun NMun SLdr SReu
levinei	GGGa
'Lewis Monarch'	GQui
'Lila Pedigo'	CWri ECho MBri MDun MGos MLea MSnd SPer WBVN WFar
'Lilac Time' (EA)	MBar SLdr
liliiflorum Guiz 163	GGGa
'Lily Marleen' (EA)	CTri LRHS SCoo SReu
'Linda' ♀H4	CBcs CSam CTri ECho EPfP GGGa LMil LRHS LSRN MAsh MBar MDun MGos SLdr
'Linda Lee'	SLdr
'Linda R' (EA)	NPri
lindleyi	CBcs GQui LHyd
– L&S	GGGa
– 'Dame Edith Sitwell'	LMil
'Linearifolium'	see *R. stenopetalum* 'Linearifolium'
Lionel's Triumph Group	LMil SLdr
'Little Beauty' (EA)	SLdr
'Little Ben'	ECho GEdr MBar MDun
'Loch Awe'	GGGa
'Loch Earn'	GGGa
'Loch Laggan'	GGGa
'Loch Leven'	GGGa
'Loch Linnhe' **new**	GGGa
'Loch Lomond'	GGGa
'Loch Morar'	GGGa
'Loch o' the Lowes'	GGGa MBri MDun MGos WFar
'Loch Rannoch'	GGGa MGos WBVN WFar
'Loch Tummel'	GGGa
lochiae (V)	GGGa
'Lochinch Spinbur'	GQui
Lodauric Group	SLdr SReu
§ 'Lodauric Iceberg' ♀H3-4	LMil SLdr SReu
'Lodbrit'	SReu
Loderi Group	SLdr
'Loderi Fairy Queen'	SLdr
'Loderi Fairyland'	LHyd
'Loderi Game Chick' ♀H3-4	LHyd MDun SLdr SReu
'Loderi Georgette'	SLdr
'Loderi Helen'	SLdr
§ 'Loderi King George' ♀H3-4	CBcs CDoC CMac CSBt CWri ECho GGGa IDee ISea LHyd LMil LRHS MDun MGos MLea MSnd SLdr SPer SReu SSta
'Loderi Patience'	SLdr
'Loderi Pink Coral'	LMil SLdr
'Loderi Pink Diamond' ♀H3-4	CDoC CWri GGar LMil MDun SLdr
'Loderi Pink Topaz' ♀H3-4	LHyd SLdr
'Loderi Pretty Polly'	CWri SLdr
'Loderi Princess Marina'	SLdr
'Loderi Sir Edmund'	LHyd SLdr
'Loderi Sir Joseph Hooker'	LHyd SLdr
'Loderi Titan'	SLdr SReu
'Loderi Venus' ♀H3-4	CWri GGGa LHyd MDun SLdr SReu SSta
'Loderi White Diamond'	LHyd SLdr
'Loder's White' ♀H3-4	CWri GGGa LHyd LMil MDun MLea SHea SLdr SReu SSta
§ 'Logan Damaris'	LHyd SLdr SReu
longesquamatum	GGGa MSnd SLdr

longipes	LMil SLdr
– EGM 336	LMil
– var. ***longipes*** C&H 7072	GGGa
– – C&H 7113	GGGa
longistylum	GGGa
'Looking Glass'	MDun
'Lord Roberts' ♀H4	CBcs CDoC CMac CSBt CTri CWri ECho EPfP GGGa GKir ISea LMil LRHS MAsh MBar MGos MLea MSnd NEgg SHea SLdr SReu WFar
'Lord Swaythling'	LHyd SLdr
'Loreley'	NLar
'Lori Eichelser'	GEdr MDun
'Lorna' (EA)	GQui LMil
'Louis Pasteur'	SReu
'Louisa' (EA)	MAsh
'Louisa Hill' (EA)	MGos
'Louise' (EA)	SLdr
'Louise Dowdle' (EA)	SLdr
'Love Poem'	GGGa
'Lovely William'	CMac LMil MSnd SLdr
lowndesii	WAbe
luciferum CER 9935	GGGa
'Lucinda'	MDun
'Lucy'	NMun
'Lucy Lou'	GGGa
ludlowii	GGGa
ludwigianum	GGGa
'Lullaby' (EA)	GKir
'Lumina'	NLar
'Lunar Queen'	LHyd SLdr
Luscombei Group	SLdr
luteiflorum	MSnd
– KW 21556	GGGa
lutescens	CBcs LMil LRHS MDun MSnd SHea SLdr SReu SSta WAbe
– C&H 7124	GGGa
– 'Bagshot Sands' ♀H3-4	GGGa LHyd LMil
luteum (A) ♀H4	Widely available
– 'Golden Comet' (A)	GGGa
lyi KR 2962	GGGa
× ***lysolepis***	NMun
* 'Mac Ovata'	CMac
maccabeanum ♀H3-4	CBcs CDoC CWri GGGa GGar GKir IDee ISea LHyd LMil LRHS MBri MDun MLea MSnd NHim NLar NPCo SLdr SPer SReu SSpi SSta WBVN WFar WHer
– SEH 27	GGGa
– SEH 52	GGGa
– deep cream-flowered	SLdr
– Embley form	SLdr
– Reuthe's form	SReu
– Tower Court form	SLdr
maccabeanum × ***wardii*** **new**	GGGa
maccabeanum × ***sinogrande***	SReu
macgregoriae (V) Woods 2646	GGGa
macranthum	see *R. indicum* 'Macranthum'
'Macranthum Roseum' (EA)	MMHG
macrophyllum	GGGa
macrosmithii	see *R. argipeplum*
maculiferum	GGGa SLdr
'Madame Masson'	CDoC CTri CWri ECho EMil GGGa GKir ISea LMil LRHS MAsh MBri MDun MGos MLea MSnd NPCo NPri SBod SLdr SPer SPoG SReu SSta WBVN WFar
'Madame van Hecke' (EA)	CTri GKir LMil MAsh MBri SLdr WFar

	maddenii	CDoC LMil SLdr
§	- subsp. ***crassum***	CBcs GGGa GLin SLdr
§	- - Obtusifolium Group	GKev
§	- subsp. ***maddenii*** Polyandrum Group	CBcs GGal GQui ISea LHyd NMun SLdr
	'Madeline's Yellow'	SLdr
	'Mademoiselle Masson'	WFar
	'Magic Flute' (EA)	LRHS MGos
I	'Magic Flute' (V)	LMil NPri SCoo
	'Magnificum' (O)	SLdr
	magnificum	SReu
	'Maharani'	GGGa MDun
§	***makinoi*** ♀H4	GGGa GKir LHyd LLHF LMil LRHS MDun SLdr SReu SSpi SSta
	- 'Fuju-kaku-no-matsu'	MGos NLar
	'Malahat'	MSnd
	mallotum	GGGa IDee LHyd LMil LRHS MDun MSnd SLdr SReu
	- BASEX 9672	GGGa
	- Farrer 815	GGGa
	'Malwine'	MDun
	Mandalay Group	LHyd SHea
	'Mandarin Lights' (A)	LMil MBri NPri SLdr
	manipurense	see *R. maddenii* subsp. *crassum* Obtusifolium Group
	maoerense	GGGa
	'Marcel Ménard'	CDoC EMil GGGa LMil LRHS MAsh NLar NPri SReu WFar
	'Marchioness of Lansdowne'	SHea
	'Marcia'	SLdr
	'Mardi Gras'	CDoC GGGa MAsh MLea NEgg NLar NPCo
	Margaret Dunn Group	CWri
	'Margaret Falmouth'	SReu
	'Margaret George' (EA)	LHyd
	'Marianne' (EA/d)	LRHS MAsh
	'Maricee'	GGGa WAbe
	'Marie Curie'	LMil SReu
	'Marie Hoffman' **new**	LMil
	'Marie Starks' **new**	MDun
	'Marilee' (EA)	CDoC ECho LRHS MAsh MGos SLdr
	Mariloo Group	SLdr
	'Marinus Koster'	MDun SLdr
	'Marion Street' ♀H4	LHyd LMil SLdr SReu
	'Markeeta's Flame'	MDun
	'Markeeta's Prize' ♀H4	CDoC CWri ECho EPfP GGGa ISea LMil LRHS MBri MDun MGos MLea NPri SHea SLdr SReu WBVN
	'Marley Hedges'	GGGa LMil
	'Marlies' (A)	SLdr
	'Marmot' (EA)	ECho MBar MDun MLea NLar
	'Mars'	GGGa SLdr SReu
	'Martha Hitchcock' (EA)	SRms
	'Martha Isaacson' (Ad) ♀H4	LMil MGos SReu
	'Martine' (Ad)	MGos
	martinianum	SLdr
	aff. ***martinianum*** KW 21557	GGGa
	'Maruschka' (EA)	LMil LRHS NMun
	'Mary Drennen'	MDun
	'Mary Fleming'	MDun SBod SLdr
	'Mary Helen' (EA)	LHyd LMil LRHS MAsh SCoo
	'Mary Meredith' (EA)	LHyd
	'Mary Poppins' (K)	CTri LMil LRHS MAsh SCoo SLdr
	'Maryke'	LMil MDun
	'Marylou' **new**	MDun
	'Master of Elphinstone' (EA)	SLdr
	Matador Group	SLdr SReu
	'Matador'	LHyd LMil SHea
	maximum	GGGa
	- SDR 2205	GKev
§	'Maxwellii' (EA)	CMac SLdr
	'May Day' ♀H3-4	CMac MAsh NEgg NLar SHea
	May Day Group	CBcs CWri ISea MDun MGos MSnd SLdr
	'May Glow'	MGos
	May Morn Group	SReu
	'Mayor Johnstone'	CTri LRHS MAsh NPri
	'Mazurka' (K)	SLdr
	meddianum	GGGa
	- var. ***atrokermesinum*** KW 2100a	GGGa
	Medea Group	SLdr
	Medusa Group	GGGa MDun SHea SLdr SReu
	megacalyx	GGGa
	'Megan' (EA)	ECho MAsh MMuc NLar SLdr WGwG
	megaphyllum	see *R. basilicum*
	megeratum	GGGa SLdr SReu
	- 'Bodnant'	WAbe
	mekongense	GGGa
	- KR 5044	LMil
	- var. ***mekongense***	SReu
	- - Viridescens Group	see *R. viridescens*
§	- var. ***melinanthum***	SReu
	- var. ***rubrolineatum***	LMil
	'Melford Lemon'	see *R.* 'Ilam Melford Lemon'
	'Melidioso'	LMil MDun
	'Melina' (EA/d)	LMil
	melinanthum	see *R. mekongense* var. *melinanthum*
	mengtszense	MSnd
	'Merganser' ♀H4	GGGa GKev LMil LRHS MDun MLea NDlv NHol SReu WAbe WThu
	'Merley Cream' **new**	MDun
	'Meteor' elepidote	SHea
	metternichii	see *R. degronianum* subsp. *heptamerum*
	- var. ***pentamerum***	see *R. degronianum* subsp. *degronianum*
	'Mi Amor'	LMil
	'Miami' (A)	SLdr
	'Michael Hill' (EA)	LHyd MAsh
	'Michael Waterer'	MDun MSnd SLdr
	'Michael's Pride'	CBcs GQui LMil
	micranthum	GGGa MDun SLdr
	microgynum F 14242	GGGa
	microleucum	see *R. orthocladum* var. *microleucum*
	micromeres	see *R. leptocarpum*
	microphyllum (V) **new**	ISea
	'Midnight Mystique'	GGGa MDun
	'Midnight Ruby' **new**	GGGa
	'Midsummer'	CWri SHea SLdr
	'Midsummer Mermaid' (A) **new**	GGGa
	'Mikado' (EA)	see *R. kaempferi* 'Mikado'
	'Millennium' (A) **new**	GGGa
	'Milton' (R)	LMil SLdr
	mimetes	GKev
	'Mimi' (EA)	CMac LHyd
	'Mimra'	SLdr
	'Mina van Houtte' (G)	SLdr
	'Mindy's Love'	LMil MDun
	'Ming'	see *R.* 'Ilam Ming'
	'Minterne Cinnkeys'	MDun
	minus	GQui
	- SDR 2228	GKev
§	- var. ***minus***	SLdr
	- - (Carolinianum Group) 'Epoch'	LMil
§	- - Punctatum Group	MBar
	'Miss Muffet' (EA)	SLdr

	'Moerheim' ♀H4	CBcs CWri ECho LRHS LSou MBar MGos NHol NPCo NPri SReu WBVN WBrE
§	'Moerheim's Pink'	LHyd LMil MDun NHol SLdr
	'Moidart' (Vs)	LMil
	'Moira Salmon' (EA)	LHyd
§	***molle***	GGGa LMil SLdr
	subsp. ***japonicum*** (A)	
	- - JR 871	GGGa
	- subsp. ***molle*** (A)	LMil
	- - C&H 7181	GGGa
	mollicomum F 30940	SLdr
	'Mollie Coker'	CWri SLdr
	Mollis orange-flowered (M)	MBar SRms
	Mollis pink-flowered (M)	MBar NBlu SRms
	Mollis red-flowered (M)	MBar NBlu SRms
	Mollis salmon-flowered (M)	GGGa GQui
	Mollis yellow-flowered (M)	GQui MBar SRms
	'Molly Ann'	ECho GEdr GGGa MDun MGos MSnd SLdr
	'Molten Gold' (v)	LMil LRHS NPri
§	'Momoko' (EA)	GKir NBlu
	monanthum CCH&H 8133	GGGa
	'Monica'	CBcs
	monosematum	see *R. pachytrichum* var. *monosematum*
	montroseanum	CDoC IDee LMil MDun NHim SLdr SSpi WCru
*	- 'Baravalla'	GGGa
	- white-flowered	SLdr
	'Moon Maiden' (EA)	ECho GQui NLar SLdr
	Moonshine Group	SLdr
	'Moonshine'	SReu
	'Moonshine Bright'	LHyd MDun
	Moonstone Group	CBcs CWri MBar MDun MLea SLdr
	- pink-tipped	GEdr
	'Moonwax'	CWri SLdr
§	'Morgenrot'	EMil EMui GGGa LSou MAsh MGos SReu WFar
	morii	GGGa LHyd MDun
	'Morning Cloud' ♀H4	CAbP ECho EPfP LHyd LMil LRHS MAsh MBar NDlv NHol NPri SReu
	'Morning Magic'	LHyd MDun SLdr
	Morning Red	see *R.* 'Morgenrot'
	'Moser's Maroon'	CWri ECho MGos MLea NLar SLdr SPoG WBVN
	'Mossman' **new**	MDun
	'Motet' (K/d)	CSdC SLdr
	'Mother of Pearl'	SHea SLdr SReu
	'Mother's Day' (EA) ♀H4	CBcs CDoC CMac CSBt CTri ECho EPfP GKir GQui LHyd LMil LRHS MAsh MBar MBri MDun MGos MSnd NEgg NHol NPCo NPri SLdr SPer SPoG SReu SSta WFar
	Moulten Gold = 'Blattgold'	GGGa
	'Mount Everest'	GGGa LHyd LMil SReu SSta
	'Mount Rainier' (K)	SLdr SReu
	'Mount Saint Helens'	LMil NLar
	'Mount Seven Star'	see *R. nakaharae* 'Mount Seven Star'
	'Mountain Star'	SLdr
	moupinense	GGGa GLin IDee LHyd LMil SLdr SReu
	'Mrs A.C. Kenrick'	SHea SLdr
	'Mrs A.T. de la Mare' ♀H4	CSBt GGGa LHyd LMil MDun NHol SHea SLdr SReu SSta
	'Mrs Betty Robertson'	CMac ECho LMil MDun MGos MMuc SLdr SReu
	'Mrs C.B. van Nes'	SReu
	Mrs C. Whitner Group	SLdr
	'Mrs C. Whitner' × Tally Ho Group	SLdr

	'Mrs Charles E. Pearson' ♀H4	CSBt LMil MSnd SHea SLdr SReu
	'Mrs Davies Evans' ♀H4	CWri LHyd MBar SReu SSta
	'Mrs Dick Thompson'	SReu
	'Mrs Donald Graham'	SReu
	'Mrs E.C. Stirling'	SRms
	'Mrs Emil Hager' (EA)	LHyd SLdr
	'Mrs Furnivall' ♀H4	CBcs CDoC CWri ECho EPfP GGGa GKir LHyd LMil MAsh MDun MGos MLea MMuc SHea SLdr SReu
	'Mrs G.W. Leak'	CSBt CSam CWri EPfP GGGa GKir LHyd LMil MDun MLea SHea SLdr SReu
	'Mrs Henry Agnew'	SLdr
	'Mrs J.C. Williams' ♀H4	LMil
	'Mrs J.G. Millais'	LMil MDun SHea
	'Mrs James Horlick'	CWri
	'Mrs Kingsmill'	SLdr
	'Mrs Lionel de Rothschild' ♀H4	CWri MDun SReu
	'Mrs P.D. Williams'	SReu
	'Mrs Peter Koster' (M)	SLdr WFar
	'Mrs R.S. Holford' ♀H4	SHea SLdr
	'Mrs T.H. Lowinsky' ♀H4	CDoC CMac CSBt ECho EPfP GGGa GKir LMil MAsh MDun MGos MLea MMuc MSnd NLar SHea SLdr SPer SReu SSta
	'Mrs W.C. Slocock'	GKir MDun SLdr
§	× ***mucronatum*** (EA)	CBcs LHyd SLdr SRms
	'Mucronatum'	see *R.* × *mucronatum*
	mucronulatum	CBcs GGGa MSnd
	- var. ***chejuense***	see *R. mucronulatum* var. *taquetii*
	- 'Cornell Pink' ♀H4	GGGa LHyd WFar
§	- var. ***taquetii***	GGGa
	'Muncaster Hybrid'	NMun
	'Muncaster Mist'	LHyd
	'Munstead' **new**	LHyd
	nakaharae (EA)	MSnd SLdr SReu
	- 'Mariko' (EA)	LHyd MBar NHol WThu
§	- 'Mount Seven Star' (EA) ♀H4	ECho GGGa LHyd LMil MAsh MGos NHol SLdr WAbe
§	- orange-flowered (EA)	ECho LMil LRHS MAsh MGos MMuc NDlv NPri SReu
	- pink-flowered (EA)	ECho LMil MGos NDlv NLar SLdr SPer SReu SSta
	- red-flowered (EA)	ECho MGos
	'Nakahari Orange'	see *R. nakaharae* orange-flowered
	'Nancor'	CBcs
	'Nancy' (EA) **new**	MAsh
	'Nancy Buchanan' (K)	SLdr
	'Nancy Evans' ♀H3-4	CDoC CSBt CWri ECho EPfP GGGa GKir LHyd LMil LRHS MAsh MDun MLea NLar NPCo NPri SLdr SReu SSpi WFar
	'Nancy of Robinhill' (EA)	SReu
	'Nancy Waterer' (G) ♀H4	EPfP LMil NLar SPoG SReu
	'Nanki Poo' (EA)	LHyd SLdr
	Naomi Group	CWri LHyd MSnd SHea SLdr
	'Naomi' (EA)	GQui MSnd SLdr
	'Naomi Astarte'	MDun SLdr
	'Naomi Hope'	SLdr
	'Naomi Nautilus'	LMil
	'Naomi Stella Maris'	LHyd
	'Narcissiflorum' (G/d) ♀H4	CSBt EPfP IDee LHyd LMil NLar
	'Naselle'	GGGa SReu
	'Nassau' (EA/d)	LMil MAsh
	'Nelda Peach' **new**	MDun
	neriiflorum	GGGa MDun MSnd SReu
	- subsp. ***neriiflorum***	GKir
	- - L&S 1352	GGGa
§	- subsp. ***phaedropum***	MDun
	- - CCH&H 8125	GGGa

	Name	Suppliers
	nervulosum Sleumer (V)	GGGa
	'Nestor'	SReu
	'New Comet'	LHyd SLdr
	'New Moon'	SReu
	'Newcomb's Sweetheart'	LMil MDun
	'Niagara' (EA) ♀H3-4	CMac EPfP LHyd LMil MAsh MGos SLdr SPoG
	'Nichola' (EA)	SReu
	'Nico' (EA)	CMac LRHS
	'Nicoletta'	LMil
	'Night Sky'	CDoC ECho GGGa LHyd LMil LRHS MAsh MDun MGos MLea MSnd NPCo SLdr WBVN
	'Nightingale'	LMil SReu
	nigroglandulosum	GGGa
	nilagiricum	see *R. arboreum* subsp. *nilagiricum*
	'Nimbus'	LMil SLdr
	Nimrod Group	SLdr
	'Nippon'	SLdr
	'Nishiki' (EA)	CMac
	nitens	see *R. calostrotum* subsp. *riparium* Nitens Group
	nitidulum var. ***omeiense***	MSnd
	- - KR 185	GGGa
	nivale subsp. ***boreale*** Ramosissimum Group	GGGa
	niveum ♀H4	GGGa IDee LMil LRHS MDun MSnd SLdr SReu
	- B&SWJ 2611	WCru
	- B&SWJ 2659	WCru
	- B&SWJ 2675	WCru
	- 'Nepal'	LHyd
	nobleanum	see *R.* Nobleanum Group
§	Nobleanum Group	GGGa LHyd LMil MDun MSnd SLdr SSta
	'Nobleanum Album'	GGGa GGal LHyd LMil SReu SSta
	'Nobleanum Coccineum'	GGal SLdr SReu
	'Nobleanum Lamellen'	SLdr
	'Nobleanum Venustum'	CSBt LHyd LMil SReu SSta
	'Nordlicht' (EA)	SLdr
	'Norfolk Candy'	LMil MDun
	'Noriko' (EA)	SLdr
N	'Norma' (R/d) ♀H4	SReu
	Norman Shaw Group	LHyd
	'Norph' **new**	MDun
	'Northern Hi-Lights' (A)	LMil MBri SLdr
	'Northern Lights'	see *R.* 'Arctic Glow'
	'Northern Star'	LHyd
	'Nova Zembla'	CDoC CTri ECho EMil EPfP GGGa GKir ISea LMil LRHS MAsh MBar MGos NEgg NPri SLdr SPer SPoG SReu SSta WBrE
	nudiflorum	see *R. periclymenoides*
	nudipes	LMil
	nuttallii	GGGa GLin LMil SLdr
	'Oban'	GEdr ITim LMil MDun WAbe WThu
	Obtusum Group (EA)	LHyd SLdr
	occidentale (A) ♀H4	GGGa GGal IDee LMil LRHS MDun SSpi
	- SIN 1830	GLin
	ochraceum	LMil
	- C&H 7052	GGGa
	- EGM 312	LMil
	'Odee Wright'	CTri CWri LRHS MAsh MDun NLar SLdr SReu
	'Odoratum' (Ad)	MLea
	'Oh! Kitty'	CWri ECho MDun MLea NPCo
	'Oi-no-mezame' (EA)	LHyd
	'Old Copper'	CWri SLdr
	'Old Gold' (K)	ECho LRHS SLdr SReu
	'Old Port' ♀H4	CWri GGGa LHyd LMil SHea
	'Olga' ♀H4	CBcs LHyd LMil MDun SHea SLdr SReu SSta
	'Olga Mezzitt' **new**	LHyd
	'Olga Niblett' (EA)	LMil MGos SReu
	oligocarpum Guiz 148*	GGGa
	'Olin O. Dobbs'	SReu
	'Olive'	LHyd
	'Olympic Flame' (EA)	LMil
	Olympic Lady Group	LHyd MLea SLdr
	Omar Group	MBar
§	'One Thousand Butterflies'	MDun SLdr
	'Oporto'	SLdr
	'Opossum' (EA) **new**	GGGa
	'Orange Beauty' (EA) ♀H3-4	CBcs CDoC CMac CSBt ECho GGGa GKir LHyd LMil MAsh MBar MGos MSnd SLdr SReu WBVN WFar
	'Orange Flirt' **new**	MDun
	'Orange King' (EA)	CTrh LMil MAsh MGos SLdr SPoG
	'Orange Marmalade' **new**	MDun
	'Orange Sunset'	MDun
	'Orangengold'	MDun
	orbiculare ♀H3-4	GGGa LHyd LMil MDun MSnd SLdr
	- C&K 230	GGGa
§	- subsp. ***cardiobasis***	MDun SLdr
	- Sandling Park form	SReu
	'Orchid Lights'	GKir LRHS MAsh
	'Oregon' (EA)	SLdr
	oreodoxa	LMil
§	- var. ***fargesii*** ♀H4	GGGa LHyd LMil SLdr
	- var. ***oreodoxa***	LMil
	- - EN 4212	GGGa
	oreotrephes	CBcs IDee ISea LHyd LMil MDun MSnd NHim SHea SLdr SReu
	- 'Bluecalyptus'	GGGa
§	- Exquisitum Group	CBcs SLdr SReu
	- 'Pentland'	GGGa LMil
	Orestes Group	SLdr
	'Orient' (K) **new**	SLdr
§	***orthocladum*** var. ***microleucum***	GGGa WThu
	- var. ***orthocladum*** F 20488	GGGa
	'Oryx' (O)	CSdC SLdr
	'Osaraku Seedling' (EA)	EPfP GKir LRHS
	'Osmar' ♀H4	GGGa MGos MSnd SReu
	'Ostara'	MDun MGos
	'Ostergold'	LMil
	'Oudijk's Sensation'	CBcs CWri ECho GQui MAsh MDun MGos MMuc NPCo SLdr WBVN WBrE
	ovatum CN&W 548	ISea
	'Oxydol' (K)	MBri MMuc SLdr
§	***pachypodum***	GGGa
	pachysanthum ♀H4	CDoC LHyd LMil LRHS MDun MSnd NHim NLar SLdr SReu SSpi
	- RV 72/001	GGGa SLdr
	- 'Crosswater'	IDee LMil MDun
	pachysanthum × ***yakushimanum***	GGGa SReu
	pachytrichum	GGGa SLdr
	- W 1435	SLdr
§	- var. ***monosematum***	SLdr SReu
	'Pacific Gold' **new**	MDun
	'Palestrina' (EA) ♀H3-4	CBcs CMac CSBt ECho EPfP GKir LHyd MAsh MGos NHol NPCo SLdr SPer SReu SSta WFar
	'Pallas' (G)	SReu
	'Pamela Miles' (EA)	LHyd
	'Pamela Robinson'	LHyd
	'Pamela-Louise'	LHyd
	'Pancake'	CMac

	Name	Suppliers
	'Panda' (EA) ♀H4	CSBt CTri ECho EPfP GGGa GKir LHyd LMil LRHS MAsh MBar MDun MLea NDlv SReu
	'Papaya Punch'	LMil MDun
	'Paprika Spiced'	CWri ECho ISea LMil MDun MGos MLea NLar NPCo WFar
	'Paris'	LHyd
	'Parkfeuer' (A)	LMil LRHS SLdr
	parmulatum	LMil MDun
	- 'Ocelot'	GGGa LHyd MDun
	parryae	GGGa
	'Patty Bee' ♀H4	CBcs CSBt CSam CTri CWri ECho EPfP EPot GEdr GGGa GGar GKir IDee ISea LHyd LMil LRHS MAsh MBar MDun MGos MLea NHol NPri SPoG SReu SSpi SSta WFar
	patulum	see *R. pemakoense* Patulum Group
	'Pavane' (K)	SLdr
	'Peace'	GGGa
	'Peach Blossom'	see *R.* 'Saotome'
	'Peach Charm' **new**	MDun
	'Peach Lady'	SLdr
	'Peep-bo' (EA)	LHyd SLdr
	'Peeping Tom'	MDun SReu
	'Peggy' **new**	MDun
	pemakoense	CSBt CTrG GGGa IDee MBar MDun MSnd NHol SLdr SReu WAbe
§	- Patulum Group	MBar SLdr
	'Pemakofairy'	WThu
	pendulum LS&T 6660	GGGa
	Penelope Group	SReu
	'Penheale Blue' ♀H4	CWri GGGa LMil MDun NLar
	'Penjerrick Cream'	LHyd SLdr
	'Pennsylvannia' (A)	GGGa
	'Penny'	SReu
	pentaphyllum (A)	LMil NMun
	'Peppina'	GGGa
	'Percy Wiseman' ♀H4	Widely available
	'Perfect Lady'	LMil
§	***periclymenoides*** (A)	GGGa GKev LMil
	'Persil' (K) ♀H4	CBcs CMac CSBt CWri ECho EPfP GGGa GKir LHyd LMil LRHS MAsh MBar MBri MDun MGos MLea NBlu NHim SCoo SLdr SPer SReu WBVN WBrE
	'Peter Bee'	GGGa
	'Peter Berg'	MGos
	'Peter John Mezitt'	see *R.* (PJM Group) 'Peter John Mezitt'
	'Peter Koster' (M)	SHea WFar
	'Peter Koster' (hybrid)	CWri SLdr WFar
	petrocharis Guiz 120	GGGa
	'Petrouchka' (K)	MDun SLdr
	'Pfauenauge'	LMil MDun
	phaedropum	see *R. neriiflorum* subsp. *phaedropum*
	phaeochrysum	GGGa MSnd SLdr
	- var. ***agglutinatum***	GGGa GKev
§	- var. ***levistratum***	SLdr SReu
	'Phalarope'	GEdr MBar SLdr SReu
	'Phipp's Yellow' **new**	MDun
	'Phoebe' (R/d)	SLdr SReu
	'Phyllis Korn'	CWri LHyd LMil MDun NLar SLdr
	'Piccolo' (K/d)	CSdC
§	***piercei***	LMil MDun MSnd
	- KW 11040	GGGa
	Pilgrim Group	LMil
	'Pineapple Delight' **new**	MDun
	pingianum	SLdr
	- KR 184	GGGa
	'Pink Bride'	SLdr
	'Pink Cameo'	CWri

	Name	Suppliers
	'Pink Cherub' ♀H4	ECho EMui MBar MDun SLdr SReu
	'Pink Delight'	GQui NLar
I	'Pink Delight' (A)	MAsh MGos SLdr
	'Pink Drift'	CSBt ECho LMil MBar MDun MGos NHol NPCo SLdr SPer WBrE
	'Pink Gin'	LMil MDun
	'Pink Glory'	SLdr
	'Pink Lady' ambig. (A)	SReu
	'Pink Leopard'	SLdr
	'Pink Mimosa' (Vs)	SLdr
	'Pink Pancake' (EA) ♀H4	ECho EPfP GKir GQui LMil LRHS MAsh MGos NPri SLdr
	'Pink Pearl' (EA)	see *R.* 'Azuma-kagami'
	'Pink Pearl' (hybrid)	CBcs CMac CSBt CTri CWri ECho EPfP GGGa GKir LMil LRHS MAsh MBar MBri MDun MGos MMuc MSnd NPri SHea SLdr SPer SPoG SReu SSta WBVN WFar
	'Pink Pebble' ♀H3-4	CBcs LHyd MAsh MDun MLea
	'Pink Perfection'	CMac MBar MGos MSnd SHea SLdr SReu WFar
	'Pink Photo'	SLdr
	'Pink Polar Bear'	CBcs LMil LRHS
	'Pink Sensation'	MDun
	'Pintail'	GGGa IDee LMil LRHS
	'Pipit'	GGGa
	'Pippa' (EA)	CMac CTrG
	'PJM Elite'	LHyd NLar
	PJM Group	MDun
§	- 'Peter John Mezitt' ♀H4	LHyd SLdr
	platypodum	GGGa
	'Pleasant White' (EA)	LMil NMun
	'Plover'	GGGa
	pocophorum	GGGa MSnd SLdr
§	- var. ***hemidartum***	GGGa MSnd
	- var. ***pocophorum***	SLdr
	'Point Defiance'	CWri ECho GGGa LMil MDun MSnd NLar SLdr SPer WBVN
	'Polar Bear' (EA)	MBar MDun SLdr
	'Polar Bear' ♀H3-4	CBcs CSBt CSam IDee ISea LHyd LMil LRHS MGos SReu WBVN
	Polar Bear Group	CMac CWri ECho GGGa LMil MLea MSnd SLdr
	'Polaris'	see *R.* 'Hachmann's Polaris'
	'Polaris' (EA)	SReu
	'Polarnacht'	CDoC LMil MDun
	poluninii	GGGa
	polyandrum	see *R. maddenii* subsp. *maddenii* Polyandrum Group
§	***polycladum*** Scintillans Group	LHyd MBar MDun MLea NHol SLdr
	- - 'Policy' ♀H4	GGGa SReu
	polylepis	GGGa MSnd
	- C&K 284	GGGa
	'Polynesian Sunset' **new**	MDun
	ponticum	CBcs CDul CMac CTri MBar MGos SBch SPer SReu WFar
	- AC&H 205	GGGa
	- 'Foliis Purpureis'	SReu
	- 'Graziella' **new**	MDun
§	- 'Variegatum' (v)	CBcs CMac CSBt CTri EMil EPfP GGGa LMil LRHS MAsh MBar MDun MGos MLea MSnd NPri SBch SLdr SPoG SReu SRms SSta WFar
	'Pooh-Bah' (EA)	LHyd
	'Pook'	LHyd
	'Popocatapetl'	SReu
	'Potlatch'	GGGa
	poukhanense	see *R. yedoense* var. *poukhanense*
	'Praecox' ♀H4	CBcs CSBt ECho EPfP GGGa GKev ISea LHyd LMil LRHS MAsh MBar

	MDun MGos MMuc NBlu NHol NPri SLdr SPer SPoG SReu SSta WFar
praestans	GGGa LMil MDun SLdr
praevernum	GGGa
prattii	SLdr
- 'Perry Wood'	LMil
'Prawn'	SReu
Prelude Group	SLdr
preptum	GGGa SLdr
'President Roosevelt' (v)	CSBt EPfP GKir LRHS MAsh MDun MGos MLea NMun NPri SPer SPoG SReu WFar
'Pride of Leonardslee'	SLdr
'Pridenjoy'	LMil
primuliflorum	GGGa WAbe
- 'Doker-La'	LMil WAbe
'Prince Camille de Rohan'	LMil SHea
'Prince Henri de Pays Bas' (G)	CSdC SLdr
'Princess Alice'	CBcs LHyd
'Princess Anne' ♀H4	CMHG CSam ECho EPfP GEdr GGGa LMil LSou MAsh MBar MDun MGos MLea MSnd SLdr SPer SPoG SReu SSta
'Princess Galadriel'	SLdr
'Princess Ida' (EA)	LHyd
'Princess Juliana'	ECho MGos MLea MMuc
'Princess Margaret of Windsor' (K)	GQui LMil
'Princess Margaret Toth'	CSdC
principis	LMil SLdr
- C&V 9547	GGGa
- 'Lost Horizon'	CDoC LMil MDun
§ - Vellereum Group	SLdr
§ ***prinophyllum*** (A)	IDee LMil LRHS
'Prins Bernhard' (EA)	MAsh SLdr
'Prinses Juliana' (EA)	MMuc SLdr SReu WFar
'Professor Hugo de Vries' ♀H4	SHea SLdr SReu
'Professor J.H. Zaayer'	MGos
pronum	GGGa
- R.B. Cooke form	GGGa
- Towercourt form	GGGa
'Prostigiatum'	SLdr
prostratum	see *R. saluenense* subsp. *chameunum* Prostratum Group
proteoides	GGGa
protistum	SLdr
- KR 1986	GGGa
§ - var. ***giganteum***	SReu
pruniflorum	GGGa
prunifolium (A)	GGGa LMil SLdr
przewalskii	GGGa
- subsp. ***dabanshanense***	GGGa
pseudochrysanthum ♀H4	GGGa LHyd LMil MSnd SLdr SReu SSta
pseudociliipes	GGGa
'Psyche' (EA)	MDun
Psyche Group	see *R.* Wega Group
'Ptarmigan' ♀H3-4	CBcs ECho GEdr GGGa IDee LHyd LMil MAsh MBar MGos MLea MSnd NHol SLdr SPoG SReu SSta WFar
pubicostatum	GLin LMil
- CN&W 906	ISea
§ 'Pucella' (G) ♀H4	CWri SLdr
pudorosum L&S 2752	GGGa
'Pulchrum Maxwellii'	see *R.* 'Maxwellii'
pumilum	GGGa LLHF MDun WAbe WThu
'Puncta'	SLdr
punctatum	see *R. minus* var. *minus* Punctatum Group
'Purple Cushion' (EA) **new**	LRHS
'Purple Diamond'	see *R.* Diamant Group purple-flowered
'Purple Gem'	LRHS SPoG
purple Glenn Dale (EA)	SLdr
'Purple Heart'	LMil
'Purple Queen' (EA/d)	MAsh
'Purple Splendor' (EA)	CMac MGos MMuc SLdr
'Purple Splendour' ♀H4	CBcs CSBt CWri ECho EPfP IDee LHyd LMil MAsh MBar MDun MGos MLea MMuc NEgg NPCo SPer SPoG SReu SSta WBVN WFar
'Purple Triumph' (EA) ♀H3	LMil SLdr SReu SSta
'Purpurkissen' (EA)	LMil
'Purpurtraum' (EA) ♀H4	GGGa LMil
'Quail'	GGGa
Quaver Group	SRms
'Queen Alice'	MDun NLar
'Queen Elizabeth II' ♀H4	LHyd
Queen Emma	see *R.* 'Koningin Emma'
'Queen Mary'	MBar MDun SHea
'Queen Mother'	see *R.* 'The Queen Mother'
'Queen of England' (G)	CSdC
'Queen of Hearts'	LHyd SHea SLdr SReu
'Queen Souriya'	SLdr SReu
Queen Wilhelmina	see *R.* 'Koningin Wilhelmina'
'Queenswood Centenary'	LMil
'Quentin Metsys' (R)	SLdr
quinquefolium (A)	GGGa LMil MSnd
'Raby' (A)	LMil
racemosum ♀H4	LMil MBar MDun MSnd SLdr
- SSNY 47	GGGa
- 'Rock Rose' ♀H3-4	CWri GGGa LHyd LMil
racemosum × ***tephropeplum***	MBar
'Racil'	MBar MDun MGos
'Racine' (G)	SLdr
'Racoon' (EA) ♀H4	GGGa GKir
radicans	see *R. calostrotum* subsp. *keleticum* Radicans Group
'Rainbow'	MDun SLdr
'Ramapo' ♀H4	CDoC ECho GGGa LMil LRHS MAsh MBar MDun MGos NHol SPer SReu
ramsdenianum	SLdr
'Raphael de Smet' (G/d)	SReu
'Rashomon' (EA)	LHyd
'Raspberry Ripple'	SReu
'Rasputin'	GGGa
'Raymond Burfield'	SLdr
'Razorbill' ♀H4	CDoC ECho GGGa LHyd LMil LRHS MGos
'Recital'	GGGa
recurvoides	GGGa LHyd LMil MDun MSnd SLdr SReu
- Keillour form	GGGa
'Red and Gold'	GGGa
'Red Arrow'	LHyd
'Red Carpet'	LMil SLdr
'Red Dawn'	LRHS MAsh
'Red Delicious'	CWri GGGa LMil WBVN
'Red Diamond'	see *R.* Diamant Group red-flowered
'Red Fountain' (EA)	ECho MGos
'Red Glow'	LHyd
'Red Glow' × ***yakushimanum***	SLdr
'Red Jack'	CWri GGGa LMil
'Red Panda' (EA)	GGGa
'Red Pimpernel' (EA)	SLdr
'Red Sunset' (EA/d)	SLdr
'Red Wood'	GGGa
'Redwing' (EA)	CDoC MAsh
'Reich's Charmant'	GGGa

'Rendezvous' ♀H4	LMil SLdr SReu
'Rennie' (A)	ECho MGos MLea
'Renoir' ♀H4	CSBt LHyd LMil SLdr SReu
'Replique' (Vs)	SLdr
reticulatum (A)	CBcs GGGa LMil MSnd SReu
- 'Sea King' (A)	LHyd
retusum (V)	GGGa
'Reuthe's Purple'	LHyd NHol SReu WAbe WThu
'Rêve d'Amour' (Vs)	MDun SReu SSta
'Rex' (EA)	MAsh SLdr WFar
rex	CDoC GGGa IDee LMil LRHS MDun NHim SLdr
- EGM 295	LMil
§ - subsp. ***fictolacteum*** ♀H3-4	CDoC GGGa LMil MDun NHim NLar SLdr SReu
- - Miniforme Group	MDun
- subsp. ***gratum***	LMil
- yellow-flowered AC 2079	LMil
- - AC 901	MDun
rex × ***yakushimanum***	SReu
rhabdotum	see *R. dalhousieae* var. *rhabdotum*
'Ria Hardijzer'	LMil
'Ribera' (R)	SLdr
rigidum	GLin ISea
* - ***album***	LMil
'Ring of Fire'	CWri ECho ISea LMil MDun MGos MLea SLdr WBVN
'Ripe Corn'	SLdr SReu
ripense (EA)	LHyd
'Riplet'	MDun NDlv
'Ripples' (EA)	CTrh
ririei	GGGa LHyd LMil SLdr SReu
- AC 2036	LMil
'Robert Croux'	SLdr
'Robert Keir'	SLdr
'Robert Korn'	MDun
'Robert Seleger'	GGGa LMil LRHS MAsh SReu
'Robert Whelan' (A)	MDun NHol SReu
'Robin Hill Frosty' (EA)	SLdr
'Robinette'	CBcs CWri ECho LMil MAsh SLdr
'Rocket'	CDoC CTri ECho MAsh MDun MGos MLea SLdr WBVN
'Rokoko'	see *R.* 'Hachmann's Rokoko'
'Romany Chai' **new**	SHea
Romany Chai Group	LHyd
'Romany Chal'	SHea
'Rosa Mundi'	CSBt
Rosalind Group	CMac
'Rosalinda' (EA) **new**	SLdr
'Rosata' (Vs) ♀H4	MDun SLdr SReu SSta
'Rose Bud'	CSBt CTri MDun
'Rose de Flandre' (G)	SLdr
'Rose Elf'	MDun NDlv WThu
'Rose Glow' (A)	GKir MDun SReu
'Rose Gown'	SReu
'Rose Greeley' (EA)	CDoC ECho GQui SLdr SReu WFar WGwG
'Rose Haze' (A)	MDun SLdr SReu
'Rose Torch' (A)	MDun SReu
roseatum F 17227	GGGa
'Rosebud' (EA/d) ♀H3-4	CBcs CMac LHyd MBar MGos MSnd NHol SLdr SReu
'Rosemary Hyde' (EA)	LMil
'Rosenkavalier'	LHyd
roseotinctum	see *R. sanguineum* subsp. *sanguineum* var. *didymoides* Roseotinctum Group
roseum	see *R. prinophyllum*
'Roseum Elegans'	CDoC EMil MAsh MBar NBlu NMun NPri WFar
'Rosy Dream'	CWri ECho MAsh MDun MMuc MSnd
'Rosy Fire' (A)	LMil NHol SReu
'Rosy Lea'	MLea
'Rosy Lights' (A)	CTri LMil SBod SLdr
'Rothenburg'	CSam LHyd MDun SLdr
rothschildii	CDoC GGGa LMil
- C&Cu 9312	GGGa
'Rouge'	SHea
rousei (V)	GGGa
roxieanum	IDee LMil MSnd SReu
§ - var. ***cucullatum***	GKir MDun
- - CN&W 695	LMil
- - SBEC 350	GGGa
- var. ***oreonastes*** ♀H4	GGGa LMil MDun MSnd SSta
- - USDAPI 59222/R11312	GGGa
- - Nymans form	SReu
- var. ***parvum***	GGGa
'Royal Blood'	LHyd SLdr
'Royal Command' (K)	CBcs CWri LMil LRHS MBar MDun SLdr
Royal Flush Group	CBcs
'Royal Lodge' (K)	SLdr
'Royal Mail'	SHea
'Royal Ruby' (K)	CWri ECho MAsh MGos MLea SLdr
'Roza Stevenson'	LHyd LMil SLdr
'Rubicon'	CWri ECho GQui MAsh MDun MMuc SLdr
rubiginosum	CBcs GGGa LHyd LMil LRHS MSnd
§ - Desquamatum Group	CBcs LHyd SLdr
- pink-flowered	LMil
- white-flowered	LMil
rubineiflorum	GGGa
'Rubinetta' (EA)	LMil WFar
'Ruby F. Bowman'	CBcs SReu
'Ruby Hart'	GGGa LSRN MDun NHol SReu
Ruddigore Group	LHyd
rude	see *R. glischrum* subsp. *rude*
'Ruffles and Frills'	MDun
rufum	GGGa SLdr
rupicola	SLdr
§ - var. ***chryseum***	GGGa LHyd
- var. ***muliense*** Yu 14042	GGGa
russatum ♀H4	CBcs EPfP GGGa LMil MDun MSnd NMun SLdr WAbe WFar
- blue-black-flowered	LMil
- 'Purple Pillow'	CSBt
russotinctum	see *R. alutaceum* var. *russotinctum*
'Sabina'	SLdr
'Sacko'	CWri GGGa LLHF LMil MAsh MDun NHol WBVN
'Saffrano'	NLar
'Saffron Queen'	CBcs CTrG ISea SLdr
'Sahara' (K)	CSdC LMil
'Saint Breward'	CTrG GQui LHyd MDun MLea SLdr
'Saint Merryn' ♀H4	CTrG ECho GGGa LHyd MDun
'Saint Minver'	SLdr
'Saint Tudy'	EPfP LHyd MDun SLdr
'Salmon Queen' (M)	WFar
'Salmon Sander' (EA)	SLdr
§ 'Salmon Trout'	LMil
'Salmon's Leap' (EA/v)	CMac CSBt GKir GQui LHyd LMil LRHS NPri SLdr SReu WAbe WFar
saluenense	GGGa LMil MSnd SLdr WThu
- JN 260	GGGa
§ - subsp. ***chameunum***	GGGa SLdr
§ - - Prostratum Group	GGGa WAbe
'Sammetglut'	CWri SReu
'Samuel Taylor Coleridge' (M)	NLar
'Sanderling'	GGGa
'Sandling'	LHyd
'Sang de Gentbrugge' (G)	CSdC SReu
sanguineum	GGGa LMil MDun MSnd NHim SLdr

§	- subsp. ***didymum***	GGGa MDun
§	- subsp. ***sanguineum*** var. ***didymoides*** Roseotinctum Group USDAPI 59038/R10903	GGGa
	- - var. ***haemaleum***	CWri GGGa LMil
	- - var. ***sanguineum*** F 25521	LMil
	'Santa Maria'	ECho LMil MAsh SReu SSta WBrE
	'Santorina'	MDun
§	'Saotome' (EA)	CMac LHyd
	'Sapphire'	CBcs CSBt CTrG GEdr MBar MDun NDlv SLdr SRms WThu
	'Sappho'	CBcs CMac CSBt CWri ECho EPfP GBin GGGa GKir ISea LHyd LMil LRHS MAsh MBar MBri MDun MGos MLea MSnd NEgg NPCo SLdr SPer SReu SSta WBVN WFar
	'Sapporo'	LMil
	'Sarah Boscawen'	SReu
	sargentianum	GGGa LMil WAbe WThu
	- 'Whitebait'	GGGa WAbe
	'Sarita Loder'	LHyd
	'Sarled' ♀H4	GGGa LMil SHea WThu
	Sarled Group	SRms WAbe
	'Saroi' (EA)	SLdr
	'Sarsen' (K)	CSdC
	'Satan' (K) ♀H4	CSBt SReu
§	'Satschiko' (EA) ♀H4	CBcs CSBt GEdr GGGa GKir LMil LRHS MAsh MBar MDun MGos MLea NDlv NMun
	Satsuki type (EA)	ECho
	'Saturne' (G)	SLdr
	scabrifolium	CTrG
§	- var. ***spiciferum***	GGGa NMun WAbe
	- - SF 502	ISea
	'Scandinavia'	LHyd SHea
	'Scarlet Wonder' ♀H4	CBcs CDoC CMHG CSBt CWri ECho EPfP GEdr GGGa GKir IDee ISea LMil LRHS LSou MAsh MBar MBri MDun MGos MSnd NHol NPri SHea SLdr SPer SPoG SReu WFar
	schistocalyx F 17637	MSnd
	schlippenbachii (A)	CBcs CTrG GGGa LMil SLdr SSpi
	- 'Sid's Royal Pink' (A)	LMil MDun
	'Schneekrone' ♀H4	EMil GGGa LMil LRHS MAsh MDun
	'Schneeperle' (EA)	LMil
	'Schneespiegel'	MDun
	'Schubert' (EA)	MBar
	scintillans	see *R. polycladum* Scintillans Group
	'Scintillation'	CWri GGGa LMil MAsh MBar MDun MGos MLea MMuc MSnd NLar SLdr
	scopulorum	SLdr
	- C&C 7571	GGGa
	- KW 6354	GGGa
	- SF 99032	ISea
	'Scotian Bells'	GGGa
	scottianum	see *R. pachypodum*
	'Scout' (EA)	MAsh NMun SLdr
	scyphocalyx	see *R. dichroanthum* subsp. *scyphocalyx*
	searsiae	SLdr
	'Seaview Sunset'	GGGa
	'Seb'	SLdr
	'Second Honeymoon'	CBcs CWri ECho LMil MLea MSnd SReu WFar
	'Seikai' (EA)	SLdr
	seinghkuense CCH&H 8106	GGGa
	- KW 9254	GGGa
	selense	GGGa
§	- subsp. ***dasycladum***	MSnd
	- subsp. ***jucundum***	GGGa MDun
	semibarbatum **new**	GLin
	semnoides	GGGa LMil SLdr
	'Senator Henry Jackson'	GGGa MLea
	'Sennocke'	LHyd LMil
	'September Song'	CBcs CMac CSBt CWri ECho GGGa LMil MAsh MBri MDun MGos MLea MMuc NHol NPCo SLdr WBVN WFar
	serotinum	GLin LHyd LMil SReu
	- C&H 7189	GGGa
	serpyllifolium (A)	CBcs
	'Sesostris' (G)	CSdC
	'Sesterianum'	CMHG SLdr
	'Seta'	CAbP CBcs LHyd SHea WThu
	Seta Group	SLdr SReu
	setosum	GGGa MDun WAbe
	'Seven Stars'	CSBt
	'Shamrock'	CDoC EPfP GEdr GKir ISea LRHS MAsh MBar MDun MGos MLea NEgg NMun SLdr SPoG SReu WFar
	'Sheila' (EA)	CSBt MAsh NPri
	shepherdii	see *R. kendrickii*
	sherriffii	GGGa MDun MSnd
	'Shiko' (EA)	MAsh
	'Shiko Lavender' (A)	LMil SPoG
	Shilsonii Group	SReu
	'Shi-no-noe' (EA)	SLdr
	'Shintoki-no-hagasane' (EA)	LHyd
	'Shrimp Girl'	GKir LHyd MDun MSnd SLdr SReu
	sichotense	GAuc GGGa ISea
	sidereum	GGGa
	siderophyllum	GLin
	sikangense	MSnd SLdr
	- var. ***exquisitum***	GGGa GLin MDun
§	- var. ***sikangense*** Cookeanum Group	SLdr
§	'Silberwolke' ♀H4	LMil LRHS LSou MAsh SReu
	Silver Cloud	see *R.* 'Silberwolke'
	'Silver Edge'	see *R. ponticum* 'Variegatum'
	'Silver Fountain' (EA)	LMil
	'Silver Glow' (EA)	CMac
	'Silver Jubilee' ♀H4	CBcs LHyd LMil
	'Silver Moon' (EA)	SLdr
	'Silver Queen' (A)	ECho LMil MGos NEgg SLdr
	'Silver Sixpence'	CBcs CSBt ECho EPfP GKir ISea LRHS MAsh MBar MDun MGos MSnd NPCo SLdr SPoG SReu
	'Silver Skies'	LMil
	'Silver Slipper' (K) ♀H4	CBcs GKir LHyd LMil MAsh MBri MDun MLea NHol NLar SPoG SReu SSta WFar
	'Silver Thimbles' (V)	GGGa
	'Silverwood' (K)	LMil
	'Silvester' (EA)	LMil MAsh MBri SLdr
	'Silvia' ambig. **new**	MDun
	'Simona'	MDun SReu
	simsii (EA)	CMac LMil SLdr
	sinofalconeri	GGar IDee LMil LRHS
	- C&H 7183	GGGa
	- KR 7342	LMil
	- SEH 229	LMil
	sinogrande ♀H3	CBcs CDoC CHEx CWri GGGa GKev IDee LHyd LMil LRHS MBri MDun NLar NPCo SLdr WFar
	- KR 4027	LMil
	'Sir Charles Lemon' ♀H3-4	CBcs CDoC CWri ECho GKir LHyd LMil MAsh MDun MGos MLea NPCo SHea SLdr SPer SReu
	'Sir Robert' (EA)	NPri SLdr
	'Sir William Lawrence' (EA)	SReu

'Skookum'	MBri MDun MGos WBVN
'Sleepy'	CBcs CSBt ECho MAsh MGos MSnd NDlv
smirnowii	GGGa LMil MSnd SHea SReu
smithii	see *R. argipeplum*
§ Smithii Group	CWri SReu
'Sneezy'	CBcs CSBt CWri ECho EPfP GGGa GKir LHyd LRHS MBar MGos MSnd NHol SBod SLdr WFar
'Snipe'	CBcs CTri ECho GEdr ISea LMil LRHS MAsh MBar MDun MGos NHol SLdr SReu
'Snow' (EA)	MBar SLdr
'Snow Hill' (EA)	GQui LHyd LMil MAsh
'Snow Lady'	CBcs ECho EPfP GEdr GGar GQui MAsh MBar MDun MGos SLdr SPoG SReu WBVN
'Snow Pearl' **new**	LRHS MAsh
'Snow Queen'	LMil
Snow Queen Group	SReu
Snow White Group	LMil
'Snowbird' (A)	GGal LMil
'Snowflake' (EA/d)	see *R.* 'Kure-no-yuki'
'Snowstorm'	MAsh NPCo
'Soho' (EA)	CSdC GQui
'Soir de Paris' (Vs)	CSBt GGGa LHyd LMil MBar MBri MDun MLea NDlv NHim NHol NLar SBod SLdr SReu SSta WBVN WBrE WFar
'Soldier Sam'	SReu
'Solidarity'	ECho MBri MDun MGos MLea WBVN
'Solway' (Vs)	CSdC LMil
'Son de Paris' (A)	GQui
'Sonata'	CWri GGGa MDun SReu
'Songbird'	LHyd LMil MAsh MBar MDun SLdr SReu
'Sophie Hedges' (K/d)	SLdr
sororium (V) KR 3085	LMil
Souldis Group	MDun
souliei	GKir LMil MDun
- deep pink-flowered	GGGa
'Southern Cross'	SLdr
'Souvenir de D.A. Koster'	SLdr
'Souvenir de Doctor S. Endtz' ♀H4	MBar SHea SLdr
'Souvenir du Président Carnot' (G/d)	SLdr
'Souvenir of Anthony Waterer' ♀H4	MDun SHea SReu
'Souvenir of W.C. Slocock'	SReu
'Sparkler' (Vs)	GGGa
speciosum	see *R. flammeum*
'Spek's Orange' (M) ♀H4	MGos
sperabile var. ***weihsiense***	GGGa SLdr
sperabiloides	GGGa
sphaeranthum	see *R. trichostomum*
sphaeroblastum	GGGa
- var. ***wumengense***	GLin ISea MDun
- - CN&W 968	GGGa
spiciferum	see *R. scabrifolium* var. *spiciferum*
'Spicy Lights' (A)	LMil
spilotum	GGGa
'Spinner's Glory'	MAsh
spinuliferum	GGGa
- SF 247	ISea
'Spitfire'	MDun NHol SReu
'Splendens' (G)	CSdC
'Spring Beauty' (EA)	CMac SLdr SReu
'Spring Magic'	SLdr
'Spring Pearl'	see *R.* 'Moerheim's Pink'
'Spring Rose'	SLdr

'Spring Sunshine'	LMil
'Springbok'	LHyd
'Springday'	CMac
'Squirrel' (EA) ♀H4	CDoC ECho GEdr GGGa GKir LHyd LMil MAsh MDun MGos MLea NDlv NHol SLdr SReu
'Squirrel' tall (EA)	SLdr
Stadt Essen Group	LMil
stamineum	GGGa
'Stanley Rivlin'	LHyd
'Starbright Champagne'	LMil
'Starcross'	LHyd
'Starfish'	SReu
'Statuette'	MDun
§ ***stenopetalum*** 'Linearifolium' (A)	CMac LHyd LMil NMun SLdr WAbe
stenophyllum	see *R. makinoi*
stewartianum	GGGa LMil MDun SLdr
'Stewartstonian' (EA)	CMac CTrh LHyd MBar NHol SPoG SReu SSta WFar
'Stoat' (EA)	GQui MDun
'Stopham Girl' (A)	LMil
'Stopham Lad' (A)	LMil
'Stranraer'	MDun
'Strategist'	SHea SLdr
'Strawberry Cream'	GGGa
'Strawberry Ice' (K) ♀H4	CBcs CDoC CSBt CWri ECho EPfP GGGa GKir LMil LRHS MAsh MBar MBri MDun MGos MMHG NEgg SLdr SPer SReu
'Strawberry Sundae'	MAsh MLea MMuc NEgg SLdr WBVN
strigillosum	GGGa GLin LMil MDun MSnd
- C&H 7035	GGGa
- EGM 338	LMil
- Reuthe's form	SReu
subansiriense C&H 418	GGGa
suberosum	see *R. yunnanense* Suberosum Group
succothii	MDun SLdr
'Suede'	MDun
'Sui-yohi' (EA)	LHyd
sulfureum SBEC 249	GGGa
'Sulphamer'	SLdr
'Summer Blaze' (A)	SLdr SReu
'Summer Flame'	SReu
'Summer Fragrance' (O) ♀H4	LMil LRHS MDun NHol SReu SSta
'Summer Snow'	MDun
'Sun Chariot' (K)	CBcs CSam LMil MLea MMHG SReu
'Sun of Austerlitz'	SHea SLdr
'Sunbeam' (hybrid)	SReu
'Sunny' (V)	GGGa
(Sunrise Group) 'Sunrise'	SLdr
'Sunset Pink' (K)	LHyd SLdr
'Sunspot' **new**	MDun
'Sunte Nectarine' (K) ♀H4	ECho GQui ISea LHyd LMil LRHS MBri MDun MLea NLar NPri SLdr
superbum (V)	GGGa
'Surprise' ambig. (EA)	CDoC CTri SLdr
'Surprise' B.Y. Morrison (EA)	CTrh
'Surrey Heath'	CBcs CDoC CSBt CWri ECho EMil EPfP GKir LMil LRHS MAsh MBar MDun MGos MMuc MSnd NDlv NMun SLdr
'Susan' ♀H4	CSBt CWri GGGa LHyd LMil MDun SLdr SPer SReu
'Susannah Hill' (EA)	CBcs CDoC MGos SLdr
sutchuenense	GGGa IDee LMil MDun NHim SLdr
- var. ***geraldii***	see *R.* × *geraldii*
'Swamp Beauty'	CWri ECho MAsh MDun MLea MMuc WBVN WGwG

Name	Suppliers
'Swansong' (EA)	CMac
'Sweet Simplicity'	CWri SHea
'Sweet Sue'	SLdr SReu
'Swift'	ECho GGGa GQui LLHF LMil LRHS MAsh NHol NPCo SReu WBVN
'Sword of State' (K)	CWri
'Sylphides' (K)	CMac MDun SLdr
'Sylvester'	CTri LMil LRHS MGos NMun SReu
'Sylvia' (EA/d)	MAsh
'T.S. Black' (EA)	SLdr
taggianum 'Cliff Hanger'	LMil
'Takasago' (EA/d)	LHyd
taliense	GGGa LMil MDun
Tally Ho Group	SHea
tamaense	see *R. cinnabarinum* subsp. *tamaense*
'Tama-no-utena' (EA)	LHyd
'Tamarindos'	LMil
'Tanager' (EA)	SLdr
'Tangerine'	see *R.* 'Fabia Tangerine'
'Tangiers' (K)	SLdr
'Tarantella'	LMil NEgg
'Taurus' ♀H4	CDoC CWri ECho GGGa LMil LRHS MAsh MDun MGos MLea MSnd NPCo SLdr WBVN
taxifolium (v)	GGGa
'Tay' (K)	SLdr
'Teal'	ECho GEdr MBar MDun MGos MLea NHol
'Teddy Bear'	CWri GGGa GGar LMil MDun MLea
temenium	MDun
- var. ***gilvum*** 'Cruachan'	GGGa
'Temple Belle'	CBcs CWri ECho GKev MDun
Temple Belle Group	CSam GEdr LHyd NDlv SLdr
§ ***tephropeplum***	GGGa MDun
- USDAPQ 3914/R18408	GGGa
- Deleiense Group	see *R. tephropeplum*
'Tequila Sunrise'	LHyd LMil
'Terra-cotta'	LMil
'Terra-cotta Beauty' (EA)	CTrG
'Tessa'	CBcs ECho MAsh MMuc WBrE
Tessa Group	LMil MGos
'Tessa Roza' (EA) ♀H4	GGGa GQui LHyd
thayerianum	GGGa
§ 'The Hon. Jean Marie de Montague' ♀H4	CSam CWri EPfP GKir LMil MAsh MBri MDun MGos MLea MSnd NLar SHea SLdr SReu
'The Master' ♀H4	LHyd SReu
§ 'The Queen Mother'	LHyd
thomsonii	CDoC GGGa IDee LHyd LMil MDun NHol SLdr SReu
- B&SWJ 2465	WCru
- B&SWJ 2638	WCru
- SDR 3929	GKev
- subsp. ***lopsangianum***	GGGa
- subsp. ***thomsonii*** L&S 2847	GGGa
'Thor'	MDun SReu
'Thousand Butterflies'	see *R.* 'One Thousand Butterflies'
'Thunderstorm'	LHyd SReu
'Tibet' ♀H3-4	GQui LMil MBar MDun
'Tidbit' ♀H4	CMac GGGa LMil MGos MLea MSnd SLdr
'Timothy James'	GKir
'Tina Heinje'	EMil
'Tinkerbird'	GGGa
'Tinsmith' (K)	SLdr
'Tit Willow' (EA)	GKir LHyd LRHS MAsh NPri SCoo
titapuriense **new**	GGGa
'Titian Beauty'	CBcs CDoC CSBt CWri ECho EPfP GGGa ISea LHyd LMil LRHS MAsh MDun MGos MSnd NDlv NEgg NPCo NPri SBod SLdr SPer WBrE WFar
'Titipu' (EA)	LHyd
'Titness Delight'	SLdr
'Tolkien'	SReu
'Tom Hyde' (EA)	LMil
'Top Banana'	MDun SLdr
'Topsvoort Pearl'	SReu
'Torchlight' (EA)	LMil
'Toreador' (EA)	CTrG SLdr
'Tornado'	WFar
'Torridon' (Vs)	LMil
'Tortoiseshell Champagne'	see *R.* 'Champagne'
'Tortoiseshell Orange' ♀H3-4	CBcs CSBt EMil LHyd LMil MDun SHea SPoG SReu SSta
'Tortoiseshell Salome'	SHea SLdr SReu
'Tortoiseshell Scarlet'	MDun SReu
'Tortoiseshell Wonder' ♀H3-4	CSBt EPfP LMil LRHS MAsh NPri SHea SLdr SReu
'Totally Awesome' (K)	SLdr
'Toucan' (K)	CSBt MDun SLdr
'Tower Beauty' (A)	LHyd SLdr
'Tower Dainty' (A)	LHyd
'Tower Daring' (A)	LHyd SLdr
'Tower Dexter' (A)	LHyd
'Tower Dragon' (A)	LHyd LMil SLdr
traillianum	GGGa MSnd
'Treecreeper'	GGGa
'Tregedna Red'	SReu
'Trelawny'	SLdr
'Trewithen Orange'	MDun SLdr
trichanthum	GGGa NHim
- 'Honey Wood'	LMil SLdr
trichocladum	ISea NMun
§ ***trichostomum***	GGGa SSpi WAbe
- Ledoides Group	LMil
- - 'Collingwood Ingram' (EA) ♀H4	LMil
triflorum	GGGa ISea LMil MDun
- C&V 9573	GGGa
- SF 95149	ISea
§ - var. ***bauhiniiflorum***	CBcs GGGa MSnd NHim SLdr
'Trilby'	SReu
trilectorum	GGGa
- HECC 56	GGGa
'Trill' (EA)	SLdr
'Trinidad'	MDun
triplonaevium	see *R. alutaceum* var. *russotinctum* Triplonaevium Group
'Tromba'	LMil
'Trude Webster'	GGGa
tsangpoense	see *R. charitopes* subsp. *tsangpoense*
tsariense	GGGa LMil MSnd
- var. ***trimoense***	GGGa IDee LMil MDun MSnd
- - KW 8288	LMil
- 'Yum Yum'	GGGa SLdr
§ ***tsusiophyllum***	GGGa
'Tsuta-momiji' (EA)	LHyd SLdr
tubiforme	see *R. glaucophyllum* subsp. *tubiforme*
'Tuffet'	SLdr SReu
'Turacao'	GGGa MGos
'Turnstone' **new**	GGGa
'Twilight Pink'	SLdr
'Ukamuse' (EA/d)	LHyd
'Ulrike Jost'	MDun
'Umpqua Queen' (K)	MBri SLdr
ungernii	GGGa SLdr
§ ***uniflorum*** var. ***imperator*** KW 6884	GGGa

	Name	Suppliers
	'Unique' (G)	ECho EPfP ISea MGos MMuc NHol SLdr SPer
	'Unique' (*campylocarpum* hybrid) ♀H4	CBcs CSam GGGa LHyd LRHS MAsh MBri MDun MSnd SHea SLdr SReu SSta
	'Unique Marmalade'	ECho LMil MAsh SLdr WBVN
	uvariifolium	GGGa SLdr
	- Cox 6519	GGGa
	- var. ***griseum***	IDee LMil
	- - C&C 7506	GGGa
	- - KR 3774	LMil
	- - KR 3782	LMil
	- 'Reginald Childs'	LMil SLdr
	- 'Yangtze Bend'	GGGa
	vaccinioides (V) CCH&H 8051	GGGa
	'Valentine' (EA)	GGGa
	valentinianum	CBcs GGGa MSnd SLdr WAbe
	- F 24347	MSnd
	- var. ***oblongilobatum*** C&H 7186	LMil
	'Van' LMil NLar	
	'Van Nes Sensation'	LMil
	Vanessa Group	GGal LMil SReu
	'Vanessa Pastel' ♀H3-4	CMac GGGa LHyd LMil MDun SReu
	'Vanilla Spice' **new**	MDun
	vaseyi (A) ♀H3-4	CBcs GGGa LMil SLdr
	- 'White Find'	GGGa
	- white-flowered (A)	LMil
	'Vayo' (A)	SLdr
	veitchianum	GGGa
§	- Cubittii Group	GGGa SLdr
	- - 'Ashcombe'	LHyd
	- KNE Cox 9001	GGGa
	'Veldtstar'	LHyd
	vellereum	see *R. principis* Vellereum Group
	venator	GGGa MDun
	'Venetian Chimes'	CSBt ECho MDun MGos MSnd NMun SLdr SPoG SReu
	vernicosum	GGGa MSnd
	- JN 180	GGGa
	- SF 415	ISea
	'Veryan Bay'	CBcs
	'Vespers' (EA)	CTrh
	vialii (A)	GGGa
	'Victoria Hallett'	SLdr SReu
	'Vida Brown' (EA/d)	CMac SLdr SReu WThu
	'Viking' (EA)	LHyd
	'Viking Silver'	GGGa
	'Vinecourt Dong'	ISea
	'Vinecourt Dream' (M) **new**	MMuc
	'Vinecourt Duke' (R/d)	CWri ECho LRHS MAsh MDun MLea MMuc NEgg NLar NPCo NPri SBod WBVN
	'Vinecourt Troubador' (K/d)	CWri LMil MAsh MDun NPCo SBod WBVN
	'Vineland Dream' (K/d)	CWri ECho
	'Vineland Fragrance'	MDun SLdr
	'Vintage Rosé' ♀H4	LMil MLea SLdr SPoG SReu
	'Violet Longhurst' (EA)	LHyd
	'Violetta' (EA)	SLdr
	Virginia Richards Group	CWri LRHS MAsh MGos SLdr SReu
§	***viridescens***	MSnd NHim
	- 'Doshong La'	GGGa LMil
	viscidifolium	GGGa
	'Viscosepalum' (G)	CSdC SLdr
	viscosum (A) ♀H4	CBcs GGGa GQui IDee LMil MDun MLea MMHG SReu WBVN WBrE
	- 'Grey Leaf' (Vs)	LMil
	- var. ***montanum*** (A)	IBlr
	- f. ***rhodanthum*** (A)	LMil
	- 'Roseum' (Vs)	LMil
	'Viscount Powerscourt'	SLdr
	'Viscy' ♀H4	CSBt CWri ECho EMil EPfP GGGa GQui LHyd LMil MBri MDun MGos MSnd NLar WBVN WBrE
§	Volker Group	CWri LMil LRHS MAsh MBar MDun SReu SSta WFar
§	- 'Babette'	LMil
§	- 'Lackblatt'	LMil MBri
	'Vulcan' ♀H4	EPfP GGGa LMil MLea
	'Vulcan' × ***yakushimanum***	SReu
	'Vuyk's Rosyred' (EA) ♀H4	CBcs CDoC CMac CTri GKir GQui LHyd LMil LRHS MAsh MBar MGos NHol SLdr SPer SPoG SReu WFar
	'Vuyk's Scarlet' (EA) ♀H4	CBcs CDoC CMac CSBt CTri EPfP GKir GQui LHyd LMil LRHS MAsh MBar MDun MGos MSnd NHol NPri SLdr SPer SPlb SReu SSta WFar
	'W.E. Gumbleton' (M)	SReu
	'W.F.H.' ♀H4	CWri LMil MDun SLdr
	'Walküre'	LMil
	wallichii	GGGa MDun SLdr
	- DM 21	LMil
	- Heftii Group **new**	GLin
	Walloper Group	SReu
	'Wallowa Red' (K)	ECho GBin LMil MLea SLdr
	'Wally Miller'	ECho ISea MAsh MDun SReu WFar
	aff. ***walongense*** C&H 373	GGGa
	wardii	CBcs GGGa GKir IDee ISea LHyd LMil MDun MSnd NHim SHea SLdr
	- KR 4913	LMil
	- KR 5268	LMil
	- L&S	SReu
	- var. ***puralbum***	GGGa MSnd
	- var. ***wardii***	LMil
	- - Litiense Group	SLdr
	- - - CN&W 1079	ISea
	'Ward's Ruby' (EA)	CTrh SLdr
§	'Washington State Centennial' (A)	MBri
	wasonii	GGGa LHyd LMil MSnd
	- f. ***rhododactylum*** KW 1876	GGGa
	- var. ***wenchuanense*** C 5046	GGGa
	'Water Baby' (A) **new**	LRHS
	'Water Girl' (A) **new**	GGGa
	'Waterfall'	SLdr
	watsonii	GGGa
	- Cox 5075	GGGa
	wattii	GGGa
	'Waxbill'	GGGa
	'Waxwing'	SLdr
	websterianum Cox 5123	GGGa
	'Wee Bee' ♀H4	CDoC CSBt ECho EPot GEdr GGGa GGar GKev GKir LLHF LMil LRHS MAsh MDun MLea NDlv NHol NPCo SLdr SReu
§	Wega Group	LHyd
	'Wendy'	MAsh
	'Western Lights' (A)	LMil
	'Westminster' (O)	LMil
	'Weston's Pink Diamond' (d)	GGGa LMil
	weyrichii (A)	GGGa LMil
	'What a Dane' **new**	GGGa
	'Wheatear'	GGGa
	'Whidbey Island'	LMil
	'Whisperingrose'	GEdr LMil LRHS MDun NDlv NLar
	'White Bird'	ISea
	'White Brocade' **new**	MDun
	'White Frills' (EA)	ECho SLdr
	White Glory Group	SLdr

'White Gold' GGGa MDun
'White Grandeur' (EA) CTrh
'White Lady' (EA) LMil MBar
'White Lights' (A) ♀H4 EPfP GKir LMil LRHS NPri
'White Pearl' (EA) **new** SLdr
'White Perfume' (A) MDun SReu
'White Rosebud' (EA) SReu WFar
'White Swan' (K) MGos SLdr
'White Swan' (hybrid) SReu
'White Wings' GQui SLdr
'Whitethroat' (K/d) ♀H4 CSdC CWri ECho EPfP GQui ISea LMil LRHS MDun MLea MMHG NEgg SLdr SPer WBVN
'Whitney's Dwarf Red' SLdr
'Wigeon' GGGa LMil LRHS NHol
wightii GGGa GLin MDun MSnd
'Wild Affair' MDun
'Wilgen's Ruby' CDoC CSBt GKir LMil MBar MGos MSnd NHol SHea SLdr WFar
'Willbrit' CBcs CWri ECho LHyd MAsh MGos SLdr WBVN WBrE
'William III' (G) SLdr
williamsianum ♀H4 CBcs CMac CTrG CWri ECho GBin GEdr LMil MBar MDun MLea NHim SLdr SReu SRms SSpi WFar
- Caerhays form LMil MDun
- 'Special' GGGa
'Willy' (EA) SLdr
wilsoniae see *R. latoucheae*
Wilsonii Group CTrG
wiltonii ♀H4 GGGa IDee LHyd LMil MDun NLar SLdr
- CC&H 3906 GGGa
'Windlesham Scarlet' LHyd SLdr
'Windsor Hawk' CWri
'Windsor Lad' SHea SReu
'Windsor Sunbeam' (K) CWri
'Wine and Roses'PBR GGGa
'Wings of Gold' **new** MDun
'Winsome' (hybrid) ♀H3 CBcs GGGa LHyd NPri SHea SReu
Winsome Group CMac CWri LRHS MAsh MBar MDun MSnd SLdr SSta
'Winston Churchill' (M) MBar NHol SReu
'Wintergreen' (EA) GKir MMuc
'Wishmoor' SReu
'Wisley Blush' LMil LRHS
'Wisley Pearl' **new** LRHS
'Witch Doctor' LMil MDun
'Witchery' GGGa
'Wojnar's Purple' SLdr
'Wombat' (EA) ♀H4 CTri EPfP GGGa GKir LHyd LMil LRHS MAsh MGos NHol NLar NPri SLdr SReu
wongii GGGa GQui SLdr
'Woodcock' SHea SLdr
'Wren' ECho GEdr GGGa LMil LRHS MAsh MBar MDun MGos MLea SReu WBVN
'Wryneck' (K) CSdC SLdr SReu
xanthocodon see *R. cinnabarinum* subsp. *xanthocodon*
xanthostephanum GGGa
CCH&H 8070
- KR 3095 LMil
- KR 4462 LMil
'Yaku Angel' MDun
'Yaku Incense' ECho LMil MAsh MBri MDun MLea MMuc MSnd
'Yaku Prince' ECho MAsh MDun MGos SLdr WFar
yakushimanum CBcs CMHG CSBt CWri ECho GGGa GKir IDee ISea LHyd LMil LRHS MAsh MBar MBri MDun MGos MLea MMuc MSnd NHim NHol SLdr SPer SReu SSta WFar
- 'Berg' MDun
- Exbury form CMac SReu
- Exbury form SReu
× ***roxieanum*** var. ***oreonastes***
- FCC form see *R. yakushimanum* 'Koichiro Wada'
§ - 'Koichiro Wada' ♀H4 CMac EPfP GGGa GGar GKir LHyd LMil LRHS MAsh MDun MGos NHol SLdr SReu
- 'Mist Maiden' GGar
- 'Schneekissen' ♀H4 **new** SLdr
- 'Snow Mountain' SReu
'Yaye-hiryu' (EA) LHyd
§ ***yedoense*** var. ***poukhanense*** SLdr SReu
'Yellow Cloud' (A) SBod
'Yellow Hammer' ♀H4 CBcs CMac CTrG ECho EPfP ISea LHyd LMil MDun SLdr WBrE WFar
Yellow Hammer Group CWri GGGa MGos MSnd SLdr SPer SReu SSta
'Yellow Petticoats' MDun
'Yellow Rolls Royce' MDun
'Yol' SLdr
'Youthful Sin' ISea
yuefengense GGGa
yungningense MDun
§ - Glomerulatum Group SLdr
yunnanense CBcs GGGa GGal GGar IDee ISea LMil LRHS MDun MSnd SLdr SSpi
- AC 751 MDun
- C&H 7145 GGGa
- SDR 4957 GKev
- SDR 4960 GKev
- SF 379 ISea
- SF 400 ISea
- SF 96102 ISea
- 'Openwood' ♀H3-4 LMil
- pink-flowered GGGa
- 'Red Throat' SLdr
- red-blotched LMil
§ - Suberosum Group SLdr
- white-flowered GGGa LMil
zaleucum LMil MDun
- AC 685 MDun
- F 15688 GGGa
- KR 2687 GGGa
- KR 3979 LMil
- SF 347 ISea
- SF 578 ISea
'Zanna' SHea
zeylanicum see *R. arboreum* subsp. *zeylanicum*

Rhodohypoxis ✿ (*Hypoxidaceae*)

'Andromeda' EWes
baurii ♀H4 CAvo CMea CPBP ECho GEdr IBal ITim LRHS MTho NBir NMen NSla NWCA SPoG SRms WAbe WFar
- 'Abigail' EWes
- 'Alba' CMea ECho IBal NMen
- 'Albrighton' ECho ERos EWes GEdr IBal ITim LAma NHol NMen SIng WAbe WPat
- 'Apple Blossom' CFwr CPen EBrs ECho EPot ERos EWes IBal LBee LRHS NHol NLar NMen SCnR SIng WAbe WFar
- var. ***baurii*** EWes LBee SIng
- 'Bridal Bouquet' (d) EWes NHol WAbe WFar
- 'Coconut Ice' EPot EWes
- var. ***confecta*** CPen ECho EWes LRHS NHol SIng

- 'Daphne Mary'	EWes
- 'David Scott'	EWes
- 'Dawn'	CPen EBrs ECho EPot EWes GEdr IBal LAma NLar NMen SIng WAbe WFar
- 'Douglas'	CPen EBrs ECho EPfP EWes GEdr IBal ITim LAma LRHS NHol NMen SIng WAbe WClo WFar
- 'Dulcie'	CPen EBrs ECho EWes GEdr LRHS SCnR SUsu WAbe WFar
- 'Emily Peel'	CFwr EBrs ECho EWes LLHF NHol WAbe
- 'Eva-Kate'	ECho ERos EWes LAma SIng WAbe WFar WPat
- 'Fred Broome'	EBrs ECho EPot EWes GEdr LAma LRHS NHol NMen SIng WAbe WFar WPat
- 'Goliath'	EWes
- 'Harlequin'	ECho EPot EWes GEdr IBal LAma LAst LRHS NHol NMen SIng WAbe WFar
§ - 'Helen'	ECho EPot EWes GEdr IBal NHol SIng WAbe WFar
- 'Lily Jean' (d)	CEnt CFwr CStu EBrs ECho EPfP EWes GEdr IBal LRHS NCGa NLar SIng WCot WFar
- 'Margaret Rose'	ECho EWes IBal LLHF NHol NMen WAbe WFar
- 'Mars'	EWes NHol
- 'Pearl'	ECho NLar
- 'Perle'	ECho ERos EWes GEdr NHol SCnR WAbe
- 'Pictus'	ECho EPot EWes GEdr IBal LAma LBee LRHS NHol WAbe WFar WPat
- 'Pink Pearl'	EPot EWes IBal NHol WAbe
- 'Pink Pictus' **new**	MSCN
- pink-flowered	EBrs ITim NLAp WCru
- var. ***platypetala***	CStu EBrs ECho EPfP EPot EWes GEdr IBal LRHS NHol NMen WAbe WFar
- - Burtt 6981	EWes
- var. ***platypetala*** × ***milloides***	IBal LLHF NHol WAbe
- 'Rebecca'	ECho EWes
- 'Red King'	EWes IBal
- red-flowered	EBrs ECho MSCN NLAp SPlb
- 'Ruth'	CEnt EBrs ECho EWes IBal LAma NHol WAbe WFar
- 'Susan Garnett-Botfield'	ECho EPot EWes GEdr IBal NMen WAbe WFar
- 'Tetra Red'	CEnt EBrs ECho EPot EWes IBal LRHS NHol NMen SIng WAbe WFar
- 'The Bride'	EWes
- white-flowered	EBrs ECho EPot NLAp NMen
'Betsy Carmine'	CPen GEdr IBal WAbe WFar
'Bright Eyes' (d)	EWes
'Burgundy'	SIng
'Candy Stripe'	ECho EWes GEdr SIng
'Carina'	EWes
'Confusion'	EWes NHol WAbe WFar
'Dainty Dee' (d)	EWes
deflexa	CPBP CPen ECho EWes GEdr IBal ITim LRHS NHol SCnR SIng WAbe WFar
'Donald Mann'	ECho EWes LLHF NHol NMen WAbe
double, red-flowered (d)	CStu
'Dusky'	CFwr EBrs EWes GEdr
'E.A. Bowles'	CPen ECho EWes IBal NMen NSla WAbe WFar
'Ellicks'	IBal
'Garnett'	ECho EWes IBal NMen WAbe
'Goya' (d)	NWCA WPat
'Great Scot'	ECho ERos EWes GEdr GGar IBal ITim NMen WAbe WFar
'Hebron Farm Biscuit'	see *Hypoxis parvula* var. *albiflora* 'Hebron Farm Biscuit'
'Hebron Farm Cerise'	see × *Rhodoxis* 'Hebron Farm Cerise'
'Hebron Farm Pink'	see × *Rhodoxis hybrida* 'Hebron Farm Pink'
'Hinky Pinky'	CFwr GEdr
'Holden Rose'	ECho NHol
hybrids	CWCL ELan MWat
'Jupiter'	GEdr
'Kiwi Joy' (d)	CFwr CStu EWes IBal LLHF NCGa NHol NMen WFar
'Knockdolian Red'	NHol
'Lily Fan' **new**	WFar
'Midori'	EWes GEdr SUsu
milloides	CEnt EBrs ECho EPfP EPot EWes GEdr GKev IBal ITim LBee LRHS NHol NLAp NMen NWCA SIng WAbe WFar
- 'Claret'	CEnt CSam CStu ECho EWes IBal ITim LLHF NCGa NHol SAga SIng SUsu WAbe WFar WPat
- 'Damask'	CStu EWes SAga
- 'Drakensberg Snow'	EWes
- giant	ECho WFar
'Monty'	ECho EWes GEdr SIng WAbe
'Mystery'	EWes NHol WAbe
'Naomi'	EWes
'New Look'	EBrs ECho ERos EWes GEdr IBal LAst LLHF NMen SIng WAbe WFar WGor
'Pearl White'	ECho IBal
'Pink Ice'	GEdr IBal
'Pink Star' **new**	WFar
'Pinkeen'	ECho EPot EWes GEdr IBal LLHF SIng WAbe WFar
'Pinkie'	IBal
'Pintado'	EWes
'Raspberry Ice'	NHol
'Rosie Lee'	EWes WAbe
'Shell Pink'	EWes IBal ITim NHol WAbe
'Snow'	EWes
'Snow White'	EWes NHol
'Starlett'	EWes NHol
'Starry Eyes' (d)	CStu ECho EWes
'Stella'	EBrs ECho EPot ERos EWes GEdr IBal NHol NMen NSla SIng WAbe WClo
'Tetra Pink'	ECho EWes IBal NHol SIng WAbe
'Tetra Rose'	GEdr WFar
'Tetra White'	see *R. baurii* 'Helen'
thodiana	CStu ECho EPot ERos EWes GEdr IBal NHol NMen SCnR SIng WAbe WFar
'Twinkle Star Mixed'	LRHS
'Two Tone'	EWes
'Venetia'	CMea ECho IBal NHol NSla WAbe
'Westacre Picotee'	EWes
'White Prince'	IBal
'Wild Cherry Blossom'	CFwr ECho EWes SIng

Rhodohypoxis × *Hypoxis* see × *Rhodoxis*

R. baurii × ***H. parvula***	see × *Rhodoxis hybrida*

Rhodophiala (*Amaryllidaceae*)

§ ***advena***	EPot
- F&W 9579	WCot
bagnoldii	WCot
§ ***bifida***	SCnR WCot

chilensis	WCot
- F&W 9700	WCot
elwesii	WCot
fulgens	WCot
'Harry Hay'	WCot
montana	CFee
pratensis	EBee
serotina F&W 9586 new	WCot
splendens new	WCot

Rhodora see *Rhododendron*

Rhodothamnus (*Ericaceae*)

chamaecistus	WAbe
sessilifolius	WThu

Rhodotypos (*Rosaceae*)

kerrioides	see *R. scandens*
§ ***scandens***	CBot CPLG CTri CWib EBee ELan EPfP EPla EShb EWTr IMGH LRHS MBri MMHG MWea NHol NLar SEND SLon SSpi WCru WPat WSHC

× *Rhodoxis* ✿ (*Hypoxidaceae*)

'Aurora'	EWes
'Bloodstone'	EWes NHol
'Hebron Farm Biscuit'	see *Hypoxis parvula* var. *albiflora* 'Hebron Farm Biscuit'
§ 'Hebron Farm Cerise'	ERos EWes GEdr NMen NWCA SIng WFar
'Hebron Farm Rose'	LLHF
§ ***hybrida***	CPen CPne EBrs ECho EWes IBal NMen NWCA SIng WAbe
- 'Aya San'	EWes SIng
§ - 'Hebron Farm Pink'	CBro ECho ERos EWes GEdr IBal NHol NMen SCnR SIng WAbe WFar
- 'Hebron Farm Red Eye'	EWes GEdr SCnR SIng WAbe WFar
- 'Pink Stars'	SIng
- 'Ruby Giant'	SIng
- 'White Knight'	SIng
- 'White Stars'	SIng
'Little Pink Pet'	EWes

Rhoeo see *Tradescantia*

Rhopalostylis (*Arecaceae*)

baueri	CBrP LPal
sapida	CBrP CTrC CWit LPal
- 'East Cape'	SBig

rhubarb see *Rheum* × *hybridum*

Rhus (*Anacardiaceae*)

ambigua	EPfP
- B&SWJ 3656	WCru
- large-leaved B&SWJ 10884	WCru
§ ***aromatica***	CArn EBtc ELan LRHS NLar
chinensis	CDoC CMCN EPfP NLar
copallina	EBtc ELan EPfP LRHS
coriaria	CArn EPfP NLar
cotinus	see *Cotinus coggygria*
glabra	CArn CBcs CDoC EBtc EPfP MGos SBch SPer WDin
- 'Laciniata' misapplied	see *R.* × *pulvinata* Autumn Lace Group
- 'Laciniata' ambig.	GLin
- 'Laciniata' Carrière	NLar
glauca	EShb
N ***hirta***	see *R. typhina*
incisa	SPlb
integrifolia	CArn
krebsiana new	WHil
leptodictya	WHil
magalismontana	EShb
potaninii	CBod EPfP GKir MAsh SBch
§ × ***pulvinata*** Autumn Lace Group	EBee EPfP MGos WFar WPat
- 'Red Autumn Lace' ♀H4	GKir LBuc LRHS MBlu MBri MRav SBch SPer
§ ***radicans***	CArn COld GPoy WHer
succedanea	CDTJ SSpi
toxicodendron	see *R. radicans*
trichocarpa	EPfP
trilobata	see *R. aromatica*
N ***typhina*** ♀H4	CBcs CDoC CDul CHEx CLnd CMac CTrG CTri EBee ECrN ELan EPfP GKir LRHS MAsh MBar MGos MRav NBea NBlu NEgg NPri NWea SBch SPer SPoG SSta WBrE WDin WFar
§ - 'Dissecta' ♀H4	CBcs CDoC CDul CLnd CMac EBee ECrN ELan EPfP EWTr GKir IFFs LAst LRHS MBar MBri MGan MGos MRav MWat NBea NBlu NEgg NPri SBch SEND SPer SPoG WDin WFar
- 'Laciniata' hort.	see *R. typhina* 'Dissecta'
- Radiance = 'Sinrus'PBR	LRHS MAsh MBlu
- Tiger Eyes = 'Bailtiger'PBR	EBee ELan EMil EPfP LBuc LRHS MAsh MBlu MBri MGos SCoo SGol SPoG SWvt
§ ***verniciflua***	EGFP NLar SSpi

Rhynchelytrum see *Melinis*

Rhynchospora (*Cyperaceae*)

alba new	GAuc
colorata	CRow LLWG NPer SGar SHom WHal
latifolia	CKno SBch SHDw

Ribes ✿ (*Grossulariaceae*)

alpinum	CPLG EMac IFFs MRav MWht NWea SPer SRms WDin WGwG
- 'Aureum'	CAbP EHoe NEgg WCot WDin
- 'Schmidt'	EBee
americanum	SBch
- 'Variegatum' (v)	EHoe ELan NHol WPat
aureum hort.	see *R. odoratum*
* - 'Roxby Red'	MCoo
'Ben Hope'PBR (B)	CAgr EMui
'Black Velvet' (D)	CAgr IFFs MCoo
§ × ***culverwellii*** (F)	CAgr CWib EMil EMui GTwe IFFs LBuc LEdu MAsh SDea SPoG SVic
divaricatum	CAgr GPri LEdu
gayanum	CPMA NLar
× ***gordonianum***	Widely available
himalense GWJ 9331	WCru
jostaberry	see *R.* × *culverwellii*
laurifolium	CBcs CBot CDoC CDul CEnd CPLG EBee ELan EQua ERas GKir LAst MBri MRav NLar SPer WBVN WDin WFar WHCG WSHC WSpi
- (f)	CMac EPfP
- (m)	EPfP WPat
- 'Mrs Amy Doncaster'	WCot
- Rosemoor form	CDoC CSam LRHS SPoG SSpi WCot WHCG WPGP
longeracemosum new	GGGa
malvifolium	SEND
menziesii	CHll EWes WCot
nigrum	SEND
- 'Baldwin' (B)	CDoC CTri ECrN EPfP LRHS MAsh NLar SDea SKee SPer SPoG

	Name	Suppliers
	- 'Barchatnaja' (B)	CAgr
	- 'Ben Alder'PBR (B)	CAgr CWib GKir LRHS MAsh SDea
	- 'Ben Connan'PBR (B) 🏆H4	CAgr CSBt CWib EMil EMui EPfP ERea GKir GPri GTwe LRHS LSRN MAsh MBri MGos NLar NPri SCoo SDea SKee SPer SPoG
	- 'Ben Gairn'PBR (B)	CAgr CSBt MCoo
	- 'Ben Lomond'PBR (B) 🏆H4	CAgr CSBt CTri CWib ECrN EMil EMui GPri GTwe LAst LBuc LRHS MAsh MGos MRav NEgg NPri SBch SDea SKee SPer SVic
	- 'Ben More' (B)	CAgr CWib MBri SDea
	- 'Ben Nevis' (B)	CAgr CTri CWib GTwe SDea SKee
	- 'Ben Sarek'PBR (B) 🏆H4	CAgr CDoC CSBt CSut CTri CWib ECrN EMil EMui ERea GTwe LBuc LRHS LSRN MAsh MGos MRav NLar NPri SDea SKee SPer SPoG
	- 'Ben Tirran'PBR (B)	CAgr CDoC CSBt CWib ERea GKir LBuc LRHS MAsh MBri MGos NLar SPoG
	- 'Black Reward' (B)	CAgr MCoo
	- 'Boskoop Giant' (B)	CAgr GTwe MGan NBlu NEgg SPer
*	- 'Byelorussian Sweet' (B)	CAgr
	- 'Consort' (B)	CAgr
*	- 'Hystawneznaya' (B)	CAgr
	- 'Jet' (B)	CAgr GTwe NEgg SPer
*	- 'Kosmicheskaya' (B)	CAgr
	- 'Pilot Alexander Mamkin' (B)	CAgr
	- 'Seabrook's' (B)	CAgr MGan
	- 'Titania' (B)	EMui
	- 'Tsema' (B)	MCoo
	- 'Wellington XXX' (B)	CAgr EMil GTwe LBuc MGan SPer
§	***odoratum***	CBcs CBgR CDoC CDul CSBt CWib EBee ECrN ELan EPfP EWTr IDee LRHS MAsh MBar MGan MGos MRav NCGa NWea SBch SPer SPoG SRms SSpi WDin WFar WGwG WHCG WPat
	- 'Crandall'	CAgr LEdu
	'Pink Perfection' **new**	CMCN
	praecox	CBcs SEND
	rubrum 'Blanka' (W)	CAgr CSut LRHS
	- 'Cascade' (R)	CAgr
	- 'Cherry' (R)	CAgr MCoo
	- 'Fay's New Prolific' (R)	GTwe
	- 'Hollande Rose' (P)	GTwe
	- 'Jonkheer van Tets' (R) 🏆H4	CAgr CSBt CWib EMil EMui EPfP GTwe IArd IFFs LRHS LSRN MAsh MCoo NLar SDea SEND SKee SPer
	- 'Junifer' (R)	CAgr EMui GTwe SKee
	- 'Laxton's Number One' (R)	CAgr CTri EMui GPri GTwe LRHS LSRN MAsh MGan SDea SPer SPoG
	- 'Laxton's Perfection' (R)	MCoo
	- 'October Currant' (P)	GTwe
	- 'Raby Castle' (R)	GTwe
	- 'Red Lake' (R) 🏆H4	CAgr CTri CWib EPfP ERea GPri GTwe IFFs LBuc LRHS MGan MGos MNHC NEgg NLar SDea SKee SPer SPoG
	- 'Redstart' (R)	CAgr CSBt CTri CWib GKir GTwe LBuc LRHS MAsh NLar SDea SKee SPoG
	- 'Rondom' (R)	CAgr SDea SVic
	- 'Rosetta' (R)	MCoo
	- 'Rovada' (R)	CAgr CSBt CSut CWib EMil EMui ERea GKir GTwe IFFs MAsh SKee
	- 'Stanza' (R) 🏆H4	CAgr GTwe MCoo SDea SEND
	- 'Transparent' (W)	GTwe
§	- 'Versailles Blanche' (W)	CAgr CSBt CTri CWib EMui EPfP GTwe LBuc LRHS LSRN MAsh MBri MGan MGos NPri SDea SEND SKee SPer SPoG
	- 'White Dutch' (W)	ERea MCoo
	- 'White Grape' (W) 🏆H4	ERea GTwe
	- 'White Pearl' (W)	MCoo SDea SVic
	- White Versailles	see *R. rubrum* 'Versailles Blanche'
	- 'Wilson's Long Bunch' (R)	GTwe
	sanguineum	CDul EMac MBar NEgg WBVN WFar WMoo
I	- 'Atrorubens Select'	MBri
	- 'Brocklebankii'	CAbP CMac CPLG ELan EPfP LRHS MGos MRav NHol SAga SLim SPer WCFE WPat WPen WSHC
	- double-flowered	see *R. sanguineum* 'Plenum'
	- 'Flore Pleno'	see *R. sanguineum* 'Plenum'
	- 'King Edward VII'	Widely available
	- 'Koja'	EBee GBin LBuc LRHS LSRN MGos NPri SPoG
	- 'Lombartsii'	MRav
§	- 'Plenum' (d)	CBot
	- 'Poky's Pink'	CMac EWTr LRHS MGos MRav
	- 'Pulborough Scarlet' 🏆H4	CBcs CDoC CMac CWSG EBee ECrN ELan EPfP EWTr GKir LAst LRHS MAsh MGan MGos MNHC MRav MWat NBir NEgg NPri SBch SLim SPer SPlb SPoG SRms SWvt WFar WMoo
	- 'Red Bross'	MAsh SWvt
	- 'Red Pimpernel'	EBee LBMP LRHS LSRN MAsh MBNS SCoo SPoG SWvt
	- 'Taff's Kim' (v)	LRHS
	- 'Tydeman's White'	CPLG CSBt ELan EPfP MBar MGos NPri SDnm SSpi WSHC
	- var. ***variegata***	CMac
	- White Icicle = 'Ubric' 🏆H4	Widely available
	speciosum 🏆H3	Widely available
	uva-crispa 'Achilles' (D)	GTwe
	- 'Admiral Beattie' (F)	GTwe NEgg
	- 'Annelii' (F)	CAgr SDea
	- 'Bedford Red' (C/D)	GTwe
	- 'Bedford Yellow' (C/D)	GTwe
	- 'Beech Tree Nestling' (D)	GTwe
	- 'Blucher' (D)	GTwe
	- 'Bright Venus' (D)	GTwe
	- 'Broom Girl' (D)	GTwe
	- 'Captivator' (C)	GTwe MAsh NEgg SDea
	- 'Careless' (D) 🏆H4	CSBt EMil EMui GKir GTwe LRHS LSRN MAsh MGan MGos MNHC NPri SDea SKee SPer
	- 'Catherine'	SDea
	- 'Cook's Eagle' (C)	GTwe
	- 'Cousen's Seedling' (D)	GTwe
	- 'Criterion' (D)	GTwe
	- 'Crown Bob' (C/D)	GTwe MGan
	- 'Dan's Mistake' (D)	GTwe
	- 'Drill' (D)	GTwe
	- 'Early Sulphur' (D)	GTwe NGHP SDea
	- 'Firbob' (D)	GTwe NEgg
	- 'Forester' (D)	GTwe
	- 'Freedom' (C)	GTwe
	- 'Gipsy Queen' (D)	GTwe
	- 'Glenton Green' (D)	GTwe
	- 'Golden Ball' (D)	SDea
	- 'Golden Drop' (D)	GTwe
	- 'Green Gem' (C/D)	GTwe
	- 'Green Ocean' (D)	GTwe
	- 'Greenfinch' (C) 🏆H4	CAgr EMui GTwe SDea
	- 'Guido' (F)	GTwe
	- 'Gunner' (C/D)	GTwe NEgg
	- 'Heart of Oak' (F)	GTwe

- 'Hedgehog' (D)	GTwe
- 'Hero of the Nile' (D)	GTwe
- 'High Sheriff' (D)	GTwe
- 'Hinnonmäki' (F)	CAgr CSBt LBuc MAsh SPer
- 'Hinnonmäki Grön'	NBlu
- 'Hinnonmäki Gul' (D)	CAgr CSut EMil ERea GKir LBuc MAsh MGos NBlu SDea SKee SPer SPoG
- 'Hinnonmäki Röd' (C/D)	CAgr CSut EMil ERea GTwe LBuc LRHS MAsh MBri MCoo SDea SPer SPoG SVic
- 'Howard's Lancer' (C/D)	GTwe SDea
- 'Invicta' (C) ♀H4	CAgr CDoC CMac CSBt CSut CTri CWSG EMil EMui EPfP ERea GKir IFFs LBuc LRHS LSRN MAsh MBri MGan MGos MRav NEgg NGHP NPri SCoo SDea SKee SPer SPoG WBVN
- 'Ironmonger' (D)	GTwe
- 'Jubilee' (C/D)	LBuc MGos
- 'Keen's Seedling' (D)	GTwe
- 'Keepsake' (C/D)	GTwe SDea WBVN
- 'King of Trumps' (F)	GTwe
- 'Lancashire Lad' (C/D)	GTwe
- 'Langley Gage' (D)	GTwe MCoo NEgg
- 'Laxton's Amber' (D)	GTwe
- 'Leveller' (D) ♀H4	CTri EMui GKir GTwe IFFs LAst LBuc LRHS MAsh MCoo MGan MGos SDea SPer
- 'London' (C/D)	GTwe
- 'Lord Derby' (C/D)	GTwe
- 'Martlet' (F)	CAgr GTwe LBuc LRHS MCoo MNHC SKee SPoG
- 'May Duke' (C/D)	SDea
- 'Mitre' (D)	GTwe
- 'Pax'PBR (D)	CAgr CDoC CSBt EMui EPfP GKir GTwe LBuc LRHS SDea SKee
- 'Peru' (D)	GTwe
- 'Pitmaston Green Gage' (D)	GTwe
- 'Plunder'	GTwe
- 'Queen of Trumps' (D)	GTwe
- var. ***reclinatum*** 'Aston Red'	see *R. uva-crispa* 'Warrington'
- 'Red Champagne'	GTwe
- 'Remarka' (C/D)	EMui
- 'Rifleman' (D)	GTwe
- 'Rokula'PBR (C/D)	CDoC EMui GTwe LRHS MBri SDea
- 'Rosebery' (D)	GTwe
- 'Scotch Red Rough' (D)	GTwe
- 'Scottish Chieftan' (D)	GTwe
- 'Snow' (F)	EPfP SCoo
- 'Snowdrop' (D)	GTwe
- 'Spinefree' (C)	GTwe
- 'Surprise' (D)	GTwe
- 'Telegraph' (F)	GTwe
- 'Tom Joiner' (F)	GTwe
- 'Victoria' (C/D)	GTwe
§ - 'Warrington' (F)	GTwe
- 'Whinham's Industry' (C/D) ♀H4	CMac CSBt CTri EMil EMui ERea GKir GPri GTwe IFFs LAst LBuc LRHS LSRN MAsh MGos MRav NEgg NGHP NPri SDea SPer WBVN
- 'White Eagle' (C/D)	IFFs
- 'White Lion' (C/D)	GTwe
- 'White Transparent' (C)	GTwe
- 'Whitesmith' (C/D)	CTri ERea GTwe MCoo MGan SDea
- 'Woodpecker' (D)	GTwe NEgg
- 'Yellow Champagne' (D)	GTwe
viburnifolium	NLar
'Worcesterberry' (C)	EMui IFFs MGos SDea SPer

Richea (*Epacridaceae*)

dracophylla	SAPC

Ricinocarpos (*Euphorbiaceae*)

pinifolius	ECou

Ricinus (*Euphorbiaceae*)

communis	CDTJ SBch
- 'Carmencita' ♀H3	SGar
- 'Carmencita Pink'	CDTJ
- 'Carmencita Red'	CDTJ EShb SBch
- 'Dominican Republic'	CDTJ
- 'Gibsonii'	CDTJ SBst SHlg SMrm
- 'Impala'	CDTJ CSpe SBst SMrm
- 'New Zealand Black'	CDTJ
- 'Zanzibariensis'	CDTJ EShb

Riocreuxia (*Asclepiadaceae*)

torulosa	CCCN SPlb

Robinia (*Papilionaceae*)

× ***ambigua***	SSpi
§ ***boyntonii***	LSRN
§ ***hispida***	CDul CEnd CLnd CWib ECrN ELan EPfP EWTr LRHS MAsh MBlu SPer SPoG SSpi WDin WJas
- 'Macrophylla'	CEnd
- 'Rosea' misapplied	see *R. boyntonii*, *R. hispida*
- 'Rosea' ambig.	CBcs CBot EBee
kelseyi	CDul EBee EWes SPer WSpi
× ***margaretta*** Casque Rouge	see *R.* × *margaretta* 'Pink Cascade'
§ - 'Pink Cascade'	CCVT CDoC CDul CEnd CLnd CMac EBee ECrN EPfP LAst LMaj LRHS MAsh MBlu MGos MREP SBch SBod SCoo SCrf SEND SLim SPer SPoG WDin WFoF
pseudoacacia	CCVT CDul CLnd EBee ECrN ELan EMac LBuc MCoo NEgg SEND SPlb WDin WFar
- 'Bessoniana'	CDul EBee ECrN LAst LMaj SCoo
- 'Fastigiata'	see *R. pseudoacacia* 'Pyramidalis'
- 'Frisia' ♀H4	Widely available
- 'Inermis' hort.	see *R. pseudoacacia* 'Umbraculifera'
§ - 'Lace Lady'PBR	CSBt CWSG EBee ELan EPfP LRHS MAsh MBri MGos NLar SCoo SLim SPoG
§ - 'Pyramidalis'	EBee
- 'Rozynskiana'	CDul LRHS
- 'Tortuosa'	CDul CEnd EBee EBtc ECrN ELan EMil LAst LRHS MBlu MGos SBch SMad SPer
- 'Twisty Baby'PBR	see *R. pseudoacacia* 'Lace Lady'
§ - 'Umbraculifera'	CDul CLnd ECrN EMac EMil LMaj LRHS MBri MGos SCoo
- 'Unifoliola'	LMaj
× ***slavinii*** 'Hillieri' ♀H4	CDoC CDul CEnd CLnd EBee ECrN ELan EPfP EWTr LRHS LSRN MAsh MBlu MBri MGos SBch SCrf SEND SPer SPoG WSpi

Rochea see *Crassula*

Rodgersia ✿ (*Saxifragaceae*)

ACE 2303	GBuc
CLD 1329	NHol
CLD 1432	NHol
aesculifolia ♀H4	Widely available
- green bud	IBlr

- var. ***henrici***	CLAP CRow EBee LPio LRHS MRav NBro NMyG SWat WMoo
- - hybrid	EWTr GBuc ITim NHol NLar WAul WHil WWEG
- pink-flowered	SSpi
- 'Red Dawn'	IBlr
- 'Red Leaf'	GCal IFoB LRHS
'Badenweiter' new	ECha
'Blickfang'	IBlr
'Bloody Mary' new	EPPr
'Borodin'	EBee
Cally strain	EDAr GCal
'Die Anmutige'	CLAP CRow
'Die Schöne'	CLAP EBee GBin NLar
'Die Stolze'	EBee GBin
'Elfenbeinturm'	EBee IBlr
'Fascination' new	IBlr
'Herkules'	CAby CSam EBee ECha ECtt EHoe ELon GBin GCal GMaP IFoB LSou MBNS NEgg NLar SSpi WCot WGwG WPnP WWEG
'Irish Bronze' ♀H4	CLAP EBee EBrs GBin GKir LBMP LPio LRHS MBNS WAul WCAu WFar WMoo WPnP
'Koriata'	IBlr
'Kupfermond'	CRow IBlr
'La Blanche'	CAby EBee ECtt ELon EWTr LLWG LOck LRHS MCot NCGa NEgg NGdn SPer SPoG WCot WGwG WPnP WWEG
'Maigrün'	IBlr
nepalensis	CLAP IBlr MDun
'Panache'	IBlr
'Parasol'	CLAP CMac GBin GBuc IBlr NHol SSpi WPGP
pinnata	Widely available
- B&SWJ 7741A	WCru
- L 1670	CLAP SSpi
- SDR 3301	GKev
- from Himalaya	GCal
- from SW China	GCal
- 'Alba'	EBee GCal IBlr MBel NHol WMAq
- 'Buckland Beauty'	CDes IBlr LRHS SSpi WPGP
- 'Cally Salmon'	EWes GCal IBlr
- 'Chocolate Wing'	CLAP EBee ECtt EPPr EPfP ESwi EWTr GBin IPot LLWG LPio MAvo MBNS MBel MDun MWhi NBhm NEgg NGdn NMRc NMoo SMrm SPoG WBor WClo WCot WFar WMoo
- 'Crûg Cardinal'	GCal WCru
- 'Elegans'	EBee EHoe ELan EMFW EPfP EPla GKir GMaP IBlr LRHS MRav NEgg NHol NOrc SGSe SPer SWvt WAul WHil WPnP
- 'Fireworks'	CFir CHid CLAP CMoH EBee ECtt ELan GBin IMou IPot LRHS SPer WFar
- hybrids	LRHS
- 'Jade Dragon Mountain'	IBlr
- 'Maurice Mason'	CLAP CMoH EBee IBlr WWEG
- 'Mont Blanc'	IBlr
- Mount Stewart form	IBlr
- 'Perthshire Bronze'	IBlr
- pink-flowered	WCru
- 'Rosea'	IBlr
- 'Superba' ♀H4	Widely available
- white-flowered	GAbr SWat WCru
pinnata × ***sambucifolia***	IBlr
podophylla ♀H4	Widely available
- SDR 5158	GKev
- 'Braunlaub'	CLAP EBee MBNS NBro SMad WFar WMoo WPnP WWEG
- 'Bronceblad'	IBlr
- Donard selection	GBin IBlr MBri WPGP
- 'Rotlaub'	CDes CLAP CRow EBee GBin IBlr IMou LRHS WBor WMoo WPGP
- 'Smaragd'	CDes CLAP CRow EBee GBin GCal IBlr LRHS MRav NLar
purdomii hort.	CLAP EBrs GCal GKir LRHS WPGP
'Reinecke Fuchs'	IBlr
'Rosenlicht'	CRow EBee
'Rosenzipfel'	IBlr
sambucifolia	CBcs CLAP CMac CRow EBee EMFW GBee GCal GKir LEdu LRHS MLHP NEgg NLar NSti SMac SPer SWat WCAu WFar WMoo WPnP
- B&SWJ 7899	WCru
- dwarf pink-flowered	IBlr
- dwarf white-flowered	IBlr
- 'Mountain Select'	EBee GCal WFar
tabularis	see *Astilboides tabularis*

Rohdea (*Convallariaceae*)

japonica	CHEx WCot WPGP
- B&SWJ 4853	WCru
- B&SWJ 5091	WCru
- 'Godaishu' (v)	WCot
- 'Gunjaku' (v)	WCot
- 'Lance Leaf'	EPla
- long-leaved	WCot WFar
- 'Miyakonojo' (v)	EBee WCot
- 'Talbot Manor' (v)	CBct EBee EBla WCon WCot
- 'Tama-jishi' (v)	WCot
- 'Tuneshige Rokujo' (v)	WCot
watanabei B&SWJ 1911	WCru

Romanzoffia (*Hydrophyllaceae*)

californica	EBee
§ ***sitchensis***	CTri MAvo
suksdorfii E. Greene	see *R. sitchensis*
tracyi	CDes CLAP EBee GGar NRya WCon WPrP
unalaschcensis	CLAP EBee GKir NWCA SRms WPer WPtf

Romneya (*Papaveraceae*)

coulteri ♀H4	Widely available
§ - var. ***trichocalyx***	CFir CGHE EBee WPGP
§ - 'White Cloud' ♀H4	EBee ELan SMad WPGP WSpi
× ***hybrida***	see *R. coulteri* 'White Cloud'
trichocalyx	see *R. coulteri* var. *trichocalyx*

Romulea (*Iridaceae*)

amoena 'Nieuwoudtville'	ECho
autumnalis	ECho
barkerae 'Paternoster'	ECho
battandieri	EBrs ECho
bulbocodium	CBro ECho WAbe
- var. ***clusiana***	EBrs ECho
- var. ***crocea***	CStu EBrs ECho
* - 'Knightshayes'	SCnR
campanuloides	EDif
citrina from Tweerivier new	ECho
columnae	EBrs ECho
congoensis new	GCal
cruciata	ECho
var. ***intermedia*** 'Somerset West' new	
dichotoma	ECho
diversiformis 'Komsberg' new	ECho
gigantea	CStu

kamisensis ECho
leipoldtii ECho
linaresii ECho
- subsp. ***graeca*** WWst
longituba see *R. macowanii*
* ***luteoflora*** var. ***sanguinea*** EBee ECho NMen
§ ***macowanii*** EBrs ECho
montana **new** ECho
namaquensis ECho
nivalis EBrs ECho
obscura var. ***blanda*** ECho
- var. ***obscura*** ECho
- var. ***subtestacea*** ECho
ramiflora CPBP CPLG EBrs ECho WWst
requienii NMen
rosea ECho
sanguinalis from Tweerivier **new** ECho
subfistulosa from Roggeveld **new** ECho
tempskyana CPBP EBrs ECho WWst
unifolia from Roggeveld **new** ECho

Rorippa (Brassicaceae)

amphibia MSKA
nasturtium-aquaticum WMAq

Rosa ✿ (Rosaceae)

UNK 22 from East Himalaya GCal
UNK 229 from East Himalaya GCal
A Shropshire Lad = 'Ausled'PBR (S) LRHS LStr MAsh MBri MJon NEgg SSea SWCr WClo
A Whiter Shade of Pale = 'Peafanfare'PBR (HT) ESty MJon SMrm SWCr
Abbeyfield Gold = 'Korquelda'PBR (F) MGos
Abbeyfield Rose = 'Cocbrose'PBR (HT) ♀H4 GCoc MGan MRav SMrm SPer
Abigaile = 'Tanelaigib' (F) LSRN MJon
Abraham Darby = 'Auscot'PBR (S) CGro EBee EPfP EWTr LAst LRHS LStr MAsh MBri MJon MRav MWat NEgg NLar SEND SMrm SPer SPoG SWCr WAct WClo WHCG
Absent Friends = 'Dicemblem'PBR (F) IDic MWat
acicularis GAuc
'Adam Messerich' (Bb) SLon SWCr WHCG
'Adélaïde d'Orléans' (Ra) ♀H4 CRHN EBee LRHS MBri MCot MRav SEND SFam SPer WAct WHCG
Admirable = 'Searodney' (Min) MJon
'Admiral Rodney' (HT) MGan
Agatha Christie = 'Kormeita'PBR (ClF) MGos
'Aglaia' (Ra) WHCG
'Agnes' (Ru) ♀H4 CGro EBee ECnt ELon EPfP EWTr GCoc IArd LRHS MAsh MGan MRav NLar SMrm SPer SPoG SRGP SSea SWCr WAct WHCG
'Agnès Schilliger' MRav
'Aimée Vibert' (N) CSam EBee MRav NLar SPer SWCr WAct WHCG
'Alain Blanchard' (G) MGan WHCG
Alan Titchmarsh = 'Ausjive'PBR (S) CSBt ESty LRHS MAsh MBri MJon SCoo SMrm SPer SWCr WClo
§ × ***alba*** 'Alba Maxima' (A) GCoc LRHS MGan MRav NLar SFam SPer SSea SWCr WAct WHCG
§ - 'Alba Semiplena' (A) ♀H4 LRHS MBri MGan SPer SWCr WAct WHCG
- Celestial see *R.* 'Céleste'
- 'Maxima' see *R.* × ***alba*** 'Alba Maxima'
'Albéric Barbier' (Ra) ♀H4 CRHN CSBt CSam EBee ECnt ELan EPfP LRHS LStr MBri MGan MJon MRav MWat NBir NPri NWea SMad SMrm SPer SPoG SSea SWCr WAct WHCG
'Albertine' (Ra) ♀H4 Widely available
'Alchymist' (S/Cl) CPou EBee EPfP LRHS MAsh MGan MRav NLar SMrm SPer WAct WHCG
Alec's Red = 'Cored' (HT) CBcs CGro CSBt CTri CWSG GCoc LAst LRHS LSRN LStr MAsh MGan MJon MRav MWat NPri SMrm SPer SPoG SRGP SWCr
Alexander = 'Harlex' (HT) ♀H4 CGro GCoc LGod LStr MGan MJon MRav SPer SSea SWCr
'Alexander von Humboldt' (Cl) MGan NLar
'Alexandre Girault' (Ra) CRHN LRHS MAsh MBri NLar SPer WHCG
'Alfred de Dalmas' misapplied see *R.* 'Mousseline'
'Alfresco'PBR (ClHT) CSBt LGod SSea SWCr
'Alida Lovett' (Ra) LRHS
Alison = 'Coclibee'PBR (F) GCoc LSRN SWCr
§ 'Alister Stella Gray' (N) EPfP EWTr MBri MCot MGan MMuc NEgg NLar SLon SPer SSea SWCr WAct WHCG
'Allgold' (F) GKir MGan SMrm
Alnwick Castle = 'Ausgrab'PBR (S) EPfP LRHS LStr MBri MJon SCoo SSea SWCr WClo
'Aloha' (ClHT) ♀H4 CBcs CGro CTri EBee ELon EPfP ESty LAst LRHS LStr MAsh MBri MCot MGan MRav NLar SMrm SPer SPoG SSea SWCr WAct
alpina see *R.* ***pendulina***
'Alpine Sunset' (HT) CTri ELon ESty MAsh MRav SPer SPoG SWCr
altaica Willd. see *R.* ***spinosissima***
Altissimo = 'Delmur' (Cl) EBee MGan SPer SSea SWCr WAct
'Amadis' (Bs) WHCG
Amanda = 'Beesian' (F) ESty LSRN
'Amazing Grace' (HT) SWCr
'Ambassador Nogami' (S) **new** EBls
Amber Abundance = 'Harfizz'PBR (Abundance Series) (S) ESty MRav SWCr
Amber Cover = 'Poulbambe'PBR (Towne & Country Series) (GC) SWCr
Amber Nectar = 'Mehamber'PBR (F) MAsh MJon SWCr
Amber Queen = 'Harroony'PBR (F) ♀H4 CGro CSBt CTri EPfP GCoc IArd LGod LStr MAsh MBri MGan MJon MRav MWat NPri SMrm SPer SWCr
Amber Star = 'Manstar' (Min) MJon
Ambridge Rose = 'Auswonder' (S) LRHS
'Amélia' see *R.* 'Celsiana'
Amelia = 'Poulen011'PBR (Renaissance Series) (S) ECnt SWCr
'American Pillar' (Ra) CGro CSBt CSam CTri CWSG EBee ECnt ELan EPfP EWTr LRHS LStr MAsh MGan MRav SPer SPoG SSea SWCr WBor WKif
'Amy Robsart' (RH) MGan
'Andersonii' (*canina* hybrid) WAct
'Andrea' (ClMin) MJon
anemoniflora see *R.* × ***beanii***
'Angel Gates' (Ra) WAct

	Name	Suppliers
	Angela Rippon = 'Ocaru' (Min)	CSBt SPer
	'Angela's Choice' (F)	MGan SWCr
	Anisley Dickson = 'Dickimono'PBR (F) ♀H4	IDic LGod MGan SPer
	Ann = 'Ausfete'PBR (S)	LRHS
	Anna Ford = 'Harpiccolo' (Min/Patio) ♀H4	CWSG LStr MGan SPer SWCr
	Anna Livia = 'Kormetter'PBR (F) ♀H4	EBls ECnt MGos
	Anne Boleyn = 'Ausecret'PBR (S)	LRHS MAsh MBri NEgg SCoo
	'Anne Cocker' (F)	GCoc
	Anne Harkness = 'Harkaramel' (F)	MGan SPer
	'Anne of Geierstein' (RH)	MGan NHaw WAct
	Annick = 'Fryfrenzy'PBR (F)	SWCr
	Antique '89 = 'Kordalen'PBR (ClF)	MGos
	Aperitif = 'Macwaira'PBR (HT)	ECnt ESty MJon
	Aphrodite = 'Tanetidor' **new**	ESty
	apothecary's rose	see *R. gallica* var. *officinalis*
	'Apple Blossom' (Ra)	MGan WHCG
	'Apricot Nectar' (F)	MGan NHaw SPer
	'Apricot Silk' (HT)	CTri MGan SPer
	Apricot Sunblaze = 'Savamark' (Min)	CSBt
	'Archiduc Joseph' misapplied	see *R.* 'Général Schablikine'
	Ards Beauty = 'Dicjoy' (F)	SPer
	'Arethusa' (Ch)	EBee SLon SWCr
§	***arkansana*** var. ***suffulta***	GAuc WHCG
	'Arthur Bell' (F) ♀H4	CSBt EPfP ESty GKir IArd LAst LStr MAsh MGan MGos MRav MWat NEgg NPri SPer SPoG SRGP SSea SWCr WBor
	'Arthur de Sansal' (DPo)	WHCG
	arvensis	CCVT CRWN IFFs LBuc NHaw NWea WAct
	'Astra Desmond' (Ra)	WTin
	Audrey Wilcox = 'Frywilrey' (HT)	CSBt
	'Auguste Gervais' (Ra)	LRHS SPer WHCG
	Austrian copper rose	see *R. foetida* 'Bicolor'
	Austrian yellow	see *R. foetida*
	'Autumn Delight' (HM)	WHCG
	Autumn Fire	see *R.* 'Herbstfeuer'
	'Autumn Sunlight' (ClF)	MGan SPer
	'Autumn Sunset' (S/Cl)	MJon
	'Autumnalis'	see *R.* 'Princesse de Nassau'
	'Avignon' (F)	ECnt
	Avon = 'Poulmulti'PBR (GC) ♀H4	ELan EPfP GCoc MJon MRav SPer SWCr WHCG
	Awakening = 'Probuzení' (Cl)	ECGP MGan NLar SWCr WHCG
	'Ayrshire Splendens'	see *R.* 'Splendens'
	'Baby Bio' (F/Patio)	SWCr
	'Baby Darling' (Min)	MGan
	Baby Gold Star (Min)	see *R.* 'Estrellita de Oro'
	Baby Love = 'Scrivluv'PBR (yellow) (Min/Patio) ♀H4	CTri LGod
	Baby Masquerade = 'Tanba' (Min)	MGan MJon MRav SMrm SPer SWCr
	Babyface = 'Rawril'PBR (Min)	ESty
	'Ballerina' (HM/Poly) ♀H4	CGro CSBt EBee ECnt ELan EPfP ESty EWTr GCoc LGod LRHS LSRN LStr MAsh MBri MGan MJon MRav MWat NEgg NPri SMrm SPer SSea SWCr WAct WClo WHCG WKif
	Ballindalloch Castle = 'Cocneel'PBR (F)	GCoc
	'Baltimore Belle' (Ra)	CRHN WAct WHCG
	banksiae (Ra)	CPou GQui SRms
	- SF 96051	ISea
	- ***alba***	see *R. banksiae* var. *banksiae*
§	- var. ***banksiae*** (Ra/d)	CBot CPou CSBt CTri EBee ELan EPfP ERea LRHS LStr SEND SPer
	- 'Lutea' (Ra/d) ♀H3	Widely available
	- 'Lutescens' (Ra)	ERea
	- var. ***normalis*** (Ra)	CBot CSBt LRHS SLon WCot WHer
I	- 'Rosea'	NLar
	'Bantry Bay' (ClHT)	CSBt EBee ELan LSRN LStr MGan SLon SPer SSea SWCr
	Barbara Austin = 'Austop'PBR (S)	LRHS
	Barbara Windsor = 'Ganleon' (F) **new**	ECnt MGan SWCr
	Barkarole = 'Tanelorak'PBR (HT)	CSBt ESty LStr
	'Baron de Wassenaer' (CeMo)	MGan
	'Baron Girod de l'Ain' (HP)	EBee ELon ESty LAst LRHS MGan MRav NEgg NHaw NLar SMrm SPer SWCr WAct WHCG
	'Baroness Rothschild' (HP)	see *R.* 'Baronne Adolph de Rothschild'
	'Baroness Rothschild' (HT)	see *R.* Baronne Edmond de Rothschild
	'Baroness Rothschild' ambig.	see *R.* Baronne Edmond de Rothschild, Baronne Edmond de Rothschild, Climbing
§	'Baronne Adolph de Rothschild' (HP)	MGan MRav SWCr
§	Baronne Edmond de Rothschild = 'Meigriso' (HT)	EBee MGan WAct
§	Baronne Edmond de Rothschild, Climbing = 'Meigrisosar' (Cl/HT)	CSBt
	'Baronne Prévost' (HP)	SFam WHCG
	Baroque Floorshow = 'Harbaroque'PBR (S)	CGro MRav
§	× ***beanii*** (Ra)	EPla SMad
	'Beauté' (HT)	MGan
	Beautiful Britain = 'Dicfire'PBR (F)	CWSG LStr MGan MHav MRav SWCr
	Beautiful Sunrise = 'Bostimebide'PBR (ClPatio)	MAsh SWCr
	Behold = 'Savahold' (Min)	MJon
	'Bel Ange' (HT)	MGan
§	Bella = 'Pouljill'PBR (Renaissance Series) (S)	CPou EPfP
	'Belle Amour' (AxD)	SWCr WHCG
	Belle Blonde = 'Menap' (HT)	MGan SPer
	'Belle de Crécy' (G) ♀H4	CPou CSam EBee GKir LRHS LStr MAsh SFam SMrm SPer SPoG SWCr WAct WHCG
	'Belle des Jardins' misapplied	see *R.* × *centifolia* 'Unique Panachée'
	Belle Epoque = 'Fryyaboo'PBR (HT)	LStr MGan MJon SWCr
	'Belle Isis' (G)	MRav SPer
	'Belle Poitevine' (Ru)	MCot
§	'Belvedere' (Ra)	CPou MGan SPer WAct WBor WHCG
	Benita = 'Dicquarrel' (HT)	IDic

Name	Suppliers
Benjamin Britten = 'Ausencart'PBR (S)	CSBt EPfP LRHS MBri MJon NEgg SWCr WClo
Benson and Hedges Gold = 'Macgem' (HT)	CWSG
Benson and Hedges Special = 'Macshana'PBR (Min)	ECGP MJon
Berkshire = 'Korpinka'PBR (GC) ♀H4	LStr MGan SWCr
Beryl Joyce = 'Tan96145'PBR (HT) **new**	ESty
Best of Friends = 'Pouldunk'PBR (HT)	ECnt LSRN SWCr
Best Wishes = 'Chessnut'PBR (Cl/v)	CSBt EBls LSRN MGan SWCr
Bettina = 'Mepal' (HT)	MGan
Betty Boop = 'Wekplapic'PBR (F)	MJon SRGP SWCr
Betty Driver = 'Gandri'PBR (F)	MGan
Betty Harkness = 'Harette'PBR (F)	LStr SSea
'Betty Prior' (F)	GCoc MGan
§ Bewitched = 'Poulbella'PBR (Castle Series) (F)	ECnt EPfP SWCr
Bianco = 'Cocblanco'PBR (Patio/Min)	GCoc MRav MWat SPoG
Big Purple = 'Stebigpu'PBR (HT)	ECnt ESty MJon SWCr
Birthday Boy = 'Tan97607'PBR (HT)	CGro ESty LSRN LStr MRav
Birthday Girl = 'Meilasso'PBR (F)	ESty LSRN LStr MJon MRav MWat SMrm SRGP SSea SVic SWCr
Birthday Wishes = 'Guesdelay' (HT)	CTri LRHS MAsh MBri SWCr
Bishop Elphinstone = 'Cocjolly' (F)	GCoc
Black Baccara = 'Meidebenne'PBR	EGxp ESty SMrm SWCr
Black Beauty = 'Korfleur' (HT)	MJon
'Black Ice' (F)	CGro MGan SWCr
'Black Jack' (Ce)	see *R.* 'Tour de Malakoff'
Black Jade = 'Benblack' (Min/Patio)	MJon
'Blairii Number Two' (ClBb) ♀H4	EPfP LRHS MRav NEgg NLar SPer WAct WHCG WKif
'Blanche de Vibert' (DPo)	EBee
'Blanche Double de Coubert' (Ru) ♀H4	CDul CSBt CSam CTri EBee ECnt ELan EPfP GCoc LBuc LSRN LStr MGan MJon NEgg SPer SSea SWCr WAct WEas WHCG
'Blanche Moreau' (CeMo)	MGan NHaw NLar SLon SPer WAct
'Blanchefleur' (CexG)	MRav
'Blesma Soul' (HT)	CSBt
'Blessings' (HT) ♀H4	CBcs CGro CSBt LSRN LStr MAsh MGan MGos MJon MRav MWat SMrm SPer SRGP SWCr
'Bleu Magenta' (Ra) ♀H4	EBee EWTr IArd LRHS MRav NLar SWCr WAct WHCG WKif
'Blonde Bombshell' (F)	SPoG SWCr
'Bloomfield Abundance' (Poly)	CPou ECGP EPfP MGan MRav SPer SWCr WAct WHCG WHer
'Blossomtime' (Cl)	SMad SPer
Blue for You = 'Pejamblu' (F)	ECnt ESty LRHS LStr MAsh MBri MGan MJon NPri SWCr
Blue Moon = 'Tannacht' (HT)	CGro CTri ELan GCoc MGan MGos MHav MJon MRav NPri SMad SPer SPoG SWCr
Blue Peter = 'Ruiblun'PBR (Min)	ESty MJon MWat
'Blush Damask' (D)	WHCG
'Blush Noisette'	see *R.* 'Noisette Carnée'
'Blush Rambler' (Ra)	CSBt EBee EPfP MGan SPer SWCr WAct WHCG
'Blushing Lucy' (Ra)	SMrm SWCr WAct WHCG
Blythe Spirit = 'Auschool'PBR (S)	MBNS MBri NEgg SWCr
'Bobbie James' (Ra) ♀H4	EBee EPfP LRHS LStr MBri MGan MJon MRav NEgg NLar SEND SPer SPoG SRGP WAct WHCG
Bonica = 'Meidomonac'PBR (GC) ♀H4	Widely available
§ Bonita = 'Poulen009'PBR (Renaissance Series) (S)	ECnt
'Bonnie Scotland' (HT)	MGan
Boogie-Woogie = 'Poulyc006'PBR (Courtyard Series) (Cl)	ECnt LRHS MAsh MBri SWCr
'Born Again' **new**	MRav
'Botzaris' (D)	SFam
'Boule de Neige' (Bb)	CBcs CGro EBee ECnt ELan ELon EPfP GCoc LRHS LSRN LStr MAsh MBri MGan MRav SFam SMrm SPer SWCr WAct WHCG
'Bouquet d'Or' (N)	EBee
'Bouquet Tout Fait' misapplied	see *R.* 'Nastarana'
'Bouquet Tout Fait' (N)	EBee WHCG
'Bourbon Queen' (Bb)	SWCr
Bowled Over = 'Tandolgnil'PBR (F)	ESty MGan SWCr
Boy O Boy = 'Dicuniform' (GC)	IDic
§ ***bracteata***	CHll CRHN EWes GQui WHCG
Brass Ring	see *R.* Peek-a-boo
Brave Heart = 'Horbondsmile' (F)	MRav SPoG
Breath of Life = 'Harquanne'PBR (ClHT)	CGro CSBt CTri CWSG ELan EPfP LGod LStr MGan MRav SPer SWCr
Breathtaking = 'Hargalore'PBR (HT)	SWCr
§ 'Brenda Colvin' (Ra)	ISea
'Brian's Star' (F)	MGan SWCr
Bride = 'Fryyearn'PBR (HT)	ESty GCoc LSRN LStr MGan MRav SWCr
Bridge of Sighs = 'Harglowing'PBR (Cl)	ECnt ESty LStr MAsh MBri NPri SPoG SWCr
Bright Day = 'Chewvermillion'PBR (ClMin)	MAsh SSea
Bright Fire = 'Peaxi'PBR (Cl)	SPer SSea SWCr
Bright Future = 'Kirora' (Cl) **new**	ESty MJon
Bright Smile = 'Dicdance' (F/Patio)	MGan MRav SPer
Brilliant Pink Iceberg = 'Probril' (F)	EBee LStr SWCr
'Brindis' (ClF)	MGan SWCr
Britannia = 'Frycalm'PBR (HT)	ECnt MAsh MJon SWCr
Broadlands = 'Tanmirsch'PBR (GC)	MGan NLar SLon SWCr
Brother Cadfael = 'Ausglobe'PBR (S)	EBls LRHS LStr MBri NEgg NLar SCoo SPer SSea SWCr WClo
Brown Velvet = 'Maccultra'PBR (F)	ESty MJon SMrm SPer SWCr
§ ***brunonii*** (Ra)	CPLG EWes WCot
– CC 5147	EWld GKev
– 'Betty Sherriff' (Ra)	GGar

Name	Suppliers
§ - 'La Mortola' (Ra)	EBee MRav SPer
Brush-strokes = 'Guescolour' (F)	ESty SWCr
'Buff Beauty' (HM) ♀[H4]	Widely available
Burgundy Ice = 'Prose'[PBR] (F)	CGro CSBt EBee EBls ECnt ESty GCoc LGod LShp LStr MGan MRav MWat SMrm SPoG SWCr
'Burma Star' (F)	MGan SWCr
burnet, double pink	see *R. spinosissima* double pink-flowered
burnet, double white	see *R. spinosissima* double white-flowered
Bush Baby = 'Peanob'[PBR] (Min)	LGod LStr SWCr
Buttercup = 'Ausband'[PBR] (S)	LRHS SWCr
Buxom Beauty = 'Korbilant'[PBR] (HT)	ECnt ESty GCoc LRHS MAsh MBri MGos MJon MWat NPri SCoo SPoG SWCr
'C.F. Meyer'	see *R.* 'Conrad Ferdinand Meyer'
californica (S)	GAuc
- 'Plena'	see *R. nutkana* 'Plena'
'Callisto' (HM)	SWCr WHCG
§ Calypso = 'Poulclimb'[PBR] (Cl)	ECnt SWCr
'Camayeux' (G)	CPou EBee ECnt LRHS NLar SPer SWCr WHCG
Cambridgeshire = 'Korhaugen'[PBR] (GC)	LStr SPer SSea SWCr
'Camélia Rose' (Ch)	WHCG
Camille Pisarro = 'Destricol' (F)	LRHS MRav SPoG
'Canary Bird'	see *R. xanthina* 'Canary Bird'
'Candy Stripe' (HT)	NBlu
canina (S)	CArn CCVT CDul CGro CLnd CRWN CTri EMac EPfP GKir IFFs LBuc MRav NWea SMrm SPer SPoG WMou
'Cantabrigiensis' (S) ♀[H4]	CSam EBee EPfP LRHS NLar SLon SPer SSea SWCr WAct WHCG
'Capitaine John Ingram' (CeMo) ♀[H4]	SLon SMrm SWCr WHCG
Caramella = 'Korkinteral'[PBR] (HT)	MGos
'Cardinal de Richelieu' (G) ♀[H4]	Widely available
Cardinal Hume = 'Harregale' (S)	MGan NHaw
Carefree Days = 'Meirivouri' (Patio)	EPfP LRHS MAsh MBri SPoG SWCr
'Caring' (Patio)	SWCr
Caring for You ambig.	LSRN
Caring for You = 'Coclust'[PBR] (HT)	GCoc
'Carmenetta' (S)	NHaw WAct
'Carol' (Gn)	see *R.* 'Carol Amling'
§ 'Carol Amling' (Gn)	LSRN MJon
carolina	LHop NHaw SLPl WHCG
'Caroline Testout'	see *R.* 'Madame Caroline Testout'
Caron Keating Rose = 'Harkoral' (S) **new**	SWCr
Cascade = 'Poulskab'[PBR] (ClMin)	ECnt SWCr
§ Casino = 'Macca' (ClHT)	CTri ELon LAst MAsh MGan MHav MRav SPer SPoG SWCr
'Castle Apricot'[PBR]	see *R.* Lazy Days
'Castle Cream'	see *R.* Perfect Day
'Castle Fuchsia Pink'[PBR]	see *R.* Bewitched
'Castle Lilac'[PBR]	see *R.* Lambert Castle
Castle of Mey = 'Coclucid' (F)	GCoc
'Castle Red'[PBR]	see *R.* Krönberg
'Castle Shrimp Pink'[PBR]	see *R.* Fascination = 'Poulmax'
'Castle Yellow'[PBR]	see *R.* Summer Gold
§ 'Cécile Brünner' (Poly) ♀[H4]	CTri ELan GCoc LRHS LSRN LStr MCot MGan NLar SMad SMrm SPer SSea SWCr WAct WHCG
§ 'Céleste' (A) ♀[H4]	EPfP GCoc LRHS LStr MRav NLar SEND SFam SWCr WAct WHCG
'Célina' (CeMo)	MGan
'Céline Forestier' (N) ♀[H3]	CPou EBee MRav SFam SPer SPoG WHCG
§ 'Celsiana' (D)	CPou CSam LRHS SFam SPer SWCr WAct WHCG
Centenary = 'Koreledas'[PBR] (F) ♀[H4]	MGos SPer
§ × ***centifolia*** (Ce)	CArn LRHS MRav SMad SWCr WHCG
§ - 'Cristata' (Ce) ♀[H4]	ECnt EPfP LRHS LStr MBri MRav NLar SFam SPer SWCr WAct WHCG
§ - 'De Meaux' (Ce)	MRav NLar SPer SWCr WAct WHCG
§ - 'Muscosa' (CeMo)	GCoc LRHS LStr MGan MRav SEND SFam SWCr WAct
§ - 'Shailer's White Moss' (CeMo)	LRHS MGan SFam WHCG
- 'Spong' (Ce)	SWCr
§ - 'Unique' (Ce)	SWCr
§ - 'Unique Panachée' (Ce)	MGan SWCr
'Centifolia Variegata'	see *R.* × *centifolia* 'Unique Panachée'
Centre Stage = 'Chewcreepy'[PBR] (S/GC)	MJon
'Cerise Bouquet' (S) ♀[H4]	LRHS MGan MRav SPer SWCr WAct WHCG WKif
Champagne Cocktail = 'Horflash'[PBR] (F) ♀[H4]	SPer SWCr
'Champagne Dream' (Patio)	SWCr
Champagne Moments = 'Korvanaber'[PBR] (F)	CBcs CGro CSBt EBee EBls ECnt ELan EPfP ESty GCoc LGod LRHS LSRN LStr MAsh MGan MGos MJon MRav MWat NPri SMrm SPer SPoG SSea SWCr
'Champneys Pink Cluster' (China hybrid)	LRHS SFam
Chandos Beauty = 'Harmisty'[PBR] (HT)	ECnt ESty GCoc LStr SWCr
'Chanelle' (F)	MGan SDix SPer SWCr
Chantal Merieux = 'Masmaric' (Generosa Series) (S)	MRav
Chapeau de Napoléon	see *R.* × *centifolia* 'Cristata'
'Chaplin's Pink Climber' (Cl)	MGan
Charity = 'Auschar' (S)	LRHS
Charles Austin = 'Ausles' (S)	MRav WAct WHCG
Charles Darwin = 'Auspeet'[PBR] (S)	MAsh MBri MJon NEgg SCoo SPer SWCr WClo
Charles de Gaulle	see *R.* Katherine Mansfield
'Charles de Mills' (G) ♀[H4]	CSam EBee ECnt ELan EPfP EWTr GCra LRHS LShp LStr MBri MGan MRav NLar SFam SPer SRGP SSea SWCr WAct WHCG
Charles Rennie Mackintosh = 'Ausren'[PBR] (S)	CSBt LRHS MAsh NEgg SWCr
Charlie's Rose = 'Tanellepa' (HT)	ESty SWCr
Charlotte = 'Auspoly'[PBR] (S) ♀[H4]	EPfP ESty LRHS LSRN MAsh MBri MJon NEgg SCoo SPer SSea SWCr WClo
Charmant = 'Korpeligo'[PBR] (Min)	LRHS

Name	Suppliers
Chartreuse de Parme = 'Delviola' (S)	MRav
'Château de Clos-Vougeot' (HT)	IArd
Chatsworth = 'Tanotax'[PBR] (Patio/F)	MHav MRav MWat SMrm SPer SSea SWCr
§ Cheek to Cheek = 'Poulslas'[PBR] (Courtyard Series) (ClMin)	MAsh SWCr
Cheerful Charlie = 'Cocquimmer'[PBR] (F)	LSRN MRav SWCr
Chelsea Belle = 'Talchelsea' (Min)	MJon
Cherry Brandy '85 = 'Tanryrandy'[PBR] (HT)	CSBt MGan
Cheshire = 'Fryelise'[PBR] (HT)	GCoc MJon SWCr
Chester Cathedral = 'Franshine' (HT)	MJon SMrm
'Chevy Chase' (Ra)	WAct
Chianti = 'Auswine' (S)	MGan NLar WAct WHCG
Chicago Peace = 'Johnago' (HT)	MGan SWCr
Child of Achievement[PBR]	see *R.* Bella
Childhood Memories = 'Ferho' (HM/Cl)	SWCr
Chilterns = 'Kortemma'[PBR] (GC)	SWCr
'Chinatown' (F/S) 𝕐H4	CGro CSBt LStr MAsh MGan MRav SPer SPoG SWCr
chinensis misapplied	see *R.* × *odorata*
- 'Mutabilis'	see *R.* × *odorata* 'Mutabilis'
- 'Old Blush'	see *R.* × *odorata* 'Pallida'
Chloe = 'Poulen003'[PBR] (Renaissance Series) (S)	CPou ECnt SLon SWCr
'Chloris' (A)	CPou
Choir of Angels	see *R.* Our Jane
'Chorus Girl' (F)	MBri
Chris = 'Kirsan'[PBR] (Cl)	EBee ECnt ESty LSRN MGan MJon SWCr WGor
'Christine Gandy' (F)	MGan
Christopher = 'Cocopher' (HT)	GCoc SWCr
Christopher Columbus = 'Meinronsse' (HT)	IArd
Christopher Marlowe = 'Ausjump'[PBR] (S)	LRHS MAsh MBri SCoo
Cider Cup = 'Dicladida'[PBR] (Min/Patio) 𝕐H4	CTri ESty IDic LStr SWCr
'Cinderella' (Min)	CSBt MGan
Cinderella = 'Korfobalt' (Cl) **new**	MJon
'Cinderella' ambig.	MGos SWCr
City Lights = 'Poulgan'[PBR] (Patio)	CSBt
'City of Cardiff' (HT)	MGan
'City of Leeds' (F)	CWSG MAsh MGan SPer
City of London = 'Harukfore'[PBR] (F)	CSBt SPer SWCr
City of York = 'Direktör Benschop' (Cl)	MCot
Clair Matin = 'Meimont' (ClS)	WAct
Claire Austin = 'Ausprior' (S) **new**	LRHS MBri
'Claire Jacquier' (N)	SFam SPer SWCr WHCG
Claire Rayner = 'Macpandem' (F/Patio)	MJon
Claire Rose = 'Auslight'[PBR] (S)	CGro LRHS LSRN MJon MRav SMrm SPer

Name	Suppliers
Claire's Dream = 'Guesideal'	SWCr
Claret = 'Frykrisfal' (HT)	ESty GCoc LStr SWCr
Clarinda = 'Cocsummery'[PBR] (F)	GCoc SWCr
Claude Monet = 'Jacdesa' (HT)	LRHS MRav SPoG
Cleo = 'Beebop' (HT)	LSRN MJon
Cleopatra = 'Korverpea'[PBR] (HT)	MGos
'Cliff Richard' (F)	ESty LSRN SWCr
'Climbing Allgold' (ClF)	SLon SWCr
'Climbing Arthur Bell' (ClF) 𝕐H4	CSBt CTri ESty GCoc LAst LGod MAsh MGan SPer SPoG SSea SWCr
'Climbing Ballerina' (Ra)	CSBt MGan SWCr
'Climbing Blue Moon' (ClHT)	LAst MGan MHav SWCr
'Climbing Cécile Brünner' (ClPoly) 𝕐H4	CSBt CTri EBee ECnt EPfP LRHS LStr MGan MRav NLar SPer SSea SWCr WAct WHCG
§ 'Climbing Columbia' (ClHT)	ERea EShb SPer WHCG
'Climbing Crimson Glory' (ClHT)	CPou MGan SWCr WAct
§ 'Climbing Devoniensis' (ClT)	CPou
'Climbing Ena Harkness' (ClHT)	CTri GCoc LRHS MBri MGan MRav SEND SPer SPoG SSea SWCr
'Climbing Etoile de Hollande' (ClHT) 𝕐H4	CSBt CSam CTri CWSG EBee EPfP GCoc LRHS LStr MAsh MBri MGan MJon MRav MWat SFam SMad SPer SPoG SSea SWCr WClo
Climbing Fragrant Cloud = 'Colfragrasar' (ClHT)	CBcs ELan MGan
'Climbing Home Sweet Home' (ClHT)	LSRN
'Climbing Iceberg' (ClF) 𝕐H4	CGro CSBt ELan EPfP ESty IArd LRHS LSRN LStr MAsh MGan MJon MRav MWat NEgg SMrm SPer SPoG SSea SWCr WAct WClo WHCG
'Climbing Jazz'[PBR]	see *R.* That's Jazz
'Climbing Josephine Bruce' (ClHT)	MGan SWCr
'Climbing la France' (ClHT)	MRav
§ 'Climbing Lady Hillingdon' (ClT) 𝕐H3	ECGP EPfP LRHS MGan MRav NEgg NLar SFam SMad SPer SSea SWCr WAct WHCG
'Climbing Lady Sylvia' (ClHT)	CSBt EPfP LRHS MGan SPer
'Climbing Little White Pet'	see *R.* 'Félicité Perpétue'
'Climbing Madame Butterfly' (ClHT)	LRHS MGan NLar SPer
'Climbing Madame Caroline Testout' (ClHT)	CPou CTri LRHS MAsh MRav NPri SPer SWCr
'Climbing Masquerade' (ClF)	EBee MGan MHav MRav NEgg SPer SSea SWCr
'Climbing Mrs Herbert Stevens' (ClHT)	LRHS MRav SMrm SPer WHCG
'Climbing Mrs Sam McGredy' (ClHT) 𝕐H4	CSBt EWTr MGan
'Climbing Ophelia' (ClHT)	SPer
Climbing Orange Sunblaze = 'Meiji Katarsar'[PBR] (ClMin)	SPer
'Climbing Pascali' (ClHT)	MGan
§ 'Climbing Paul Lédé' (ClT)	LRHS SWCr
'Climbing Peace' (ClHT)	CSBt SPer
§ 'Climbing Pompon de Paris' (ClMinCh)	CBot CTri LHop LRHS MGan MRav SEND SLPl SMrm SPer WHCG
'Climbing Ruby Wedding'	LSRN

	Name	Suppliers
	'Climbing Shot Silk' (ClHT) ♀[H4]	CSBt MGan SPer SWCr
§	'Climbing Souvenir de la Malmaison' (ClBb)	CPou SPer WAct WHCG
	'Climbing Sterling Silver' (ClHT)	MGan
	'Climbing Sutter's Gold' (ClHT)	MGan
	'Climbing White Cloud'[PBR]	see *R.* White Cloud = 'Korstacha'
	Clodagh McGredy = 'Macswanle'[PBR] (F)	MJon
	Cloud Nine = 'Fryextra'[PBR] (HT)	ECnt GCoc LGod SMrm SWCr
	Cocktail = 'Meimick' (S)	MGan
	'Coconut Ice' (HT)	SWCr
	'Colby School' (F)	EBls
	Colchester Beauty = 'Cansend' (F)	ECnt
	Colchester Castle = 'Poulcs008'[PBR]	ECnt
	colonial white	see *R.* 'Sombreuil'
	'Columbia' **new**	CPou
	'Columbian'	see *R.* 'Climbing Columbia'
	'Commandant Beaurepaire' (Bb)	LRHS WKif
	common moss	see *R.* × *centifolia* 'Muscosa'
	Commonwealth Glory = 'Harclue'[PBR] (HT)	SWCr
	'Compassion' (ClHT) ♀[H4]	Widely available
*	'Compassionate' (F)	EWTr MRav
	'Complicata' (G) ♀[H4]	CTri EPfP EWTr LRHS LStr MBri MCot MGan MRav SFam SMrm SPer SWCr WAct WHCG
	'Comte de Chambord' misapplied	see *R.* 'Madame Knorr'
	Comtes de Champagne = 'Ausufo'[PBR] (S)	LRHS MBri SCoo
	'Comtesse Cécile de Chabrillant' (HP)	CPou SWCr
	'Comtesse de Lacépède' misapplied	see *R.* 'Du Maître d'Ecole'
§	'Comtesse de Murinais' (DMo)	LRHS SFam
	Comtesse de Ségur = 'Deltendre' (S)	MRav
§	'Comtesse du Caÿla' (Ch)	SSea
	'Comtesse Vandal' (HT)	WAct
	Concert[PBR]	see *R.* Calypso
	'Conditorum' (G)	SFam WAct
	Congratulations = 'Korlift' (HT)	CSBt ECnt IArd LSRN LStr MGan MGos MJon MRav NPri SMrm SPer SRGP SSea SVic SWCr
	Connie = 'Boselftay'[PBR] (F)	EGxp MGan SWCr
§	'Conrad Ferdinand Meyer' (Ru)	CSBt MGan NHaw SPer
	Conservation = 'Cocdimple'[PBR] (Min/Patio)	GCoc LAst SWCr
	Constance Finn = 'Hareden'[PBR] (F)	MRav SWCr
	'Constance Spry' ♀[H4]	EBee ELan EPfP LRHS LStr MBri MGan MJon MMuc MRav MWat NEgg NLar NPri SFam SMrm SPer SWCr WAct WHCG
§	'Cooperi' (Ra)	CAbP CWib EWTr GGal LRHS MCot SPer SSea WAct WHCG WKif WPGP
	Cooper's Burmese	see *R.* 'Cooperi'
	'Coral Satin' (Cl)	MGan
	Cordelia = 'Ausbottle'[PBR] (S)	LRHS MBri

	Name	Suppliers
	'Cornelia' (HM) ♀[H4]	CBcs CSBt CSam CTri EBee EPfP EWTr IArd LAst LRHS LStr MAsh MCot MGan MJon MRav MWat SFam SMrm SPer SRGP SSea SWCr WAct WHCG
	Coronation Street = 'Wekswetrup' (F)	MJon
	'Coronet' (F)	WAct WHCG
	Corvedale = 'Ausnetting'[PBR] (S)	LRHS
	cottage maid	see *R.* × *centifolia* 'Unique Panachée'
	Cottage Rose = 'Ausglisten'[PBR] (S)	CGro LRHS LSRN MBri MRav SWCr
	Countess of Wessex = 'Beacream' (S)	SWCr
	Courage = 'Poulduf'[PBR] (HT)	ECnt
	Courvoisier = 'Macsee' (F)	CSBt
	Crathes Castle = 'Cocathes' (F)	GCoc
	Crazy for You = 'Wekroalt'[PBR] (F)	ESty LGod LSRN MAsh MJon SRGP SSea SWCr
	Cream Abundance = 'Harflax'[PBR] (Abundance Series) (F)	ESty LStr SWCr
	'Cream of the Crop' (Patio) **new**	SWCr
	'Cream Silk' (F/Patio)	SWCr
	Crème Anglaise = 'Ganang'[PBR] (Cl)	ECnt MGan
	Crème Brûlée = 'Ganbru'[PBR] (Cl)	MGan
	Crème de la Crème = 'Gancre'[PBR] (Cl)	CSBt EBls ECnt ESty GCoc MGan MJon MRav SPer SWCr WAct
	'Crépuscule' (N)	SWCr WHCG
	crested moss	see *R.* × *centifolia* 'Cristata'
	Crimson Cascade = 'Fryclimbdown'[PBR] (Cl)	ESty LRHS MAsh MBri MGan MRav MWat SPer SPoG SSea SWCr WHCG
	crimson damask	see *R. gallica* var. *officinalis*
	'Crimson Descant' (Cl)	ECnt SWCr
	'Crimson Globe' (Mo)	MGan
	'Crimson Glory' (HT)	EBee MGan SWCr WClo
	'Crimson Shower' (Ra) ♀[H4]	CSam EWTr LRHS MBri MGan MMuc MRav NEgg SMrm SPer SWCr WAct WHCG WHer
	'Cristata'	see *R.* × *centifolia* 'Cristata'
	Crocus Rose = 'Ausquest'[PBR] (S)	ELon EPfP LRHS LStr MAsh MBri MGos MRav NEgg SWCr WClo
	Crown Princess Margareta = 'Auswinter'[PBR] (S)	EBee ECnt EPfP LRHS MBri MJon NEgg SCoo SPer SSea SWCr WClo
	cuisse de nymphe	see *R.* 'Great Maiden's Blush'
	'Cupid' (ClHT)	EWTr SPer
I	'Cutie' (Patio)	SMrm SWCr
	Cymbeline = 'Auslean' (S)	SPer
	Dacapo = 'Poulcy012'[PBR] (Courtyard Series) (ClPatio)	ECnt
	'D'Aguesseau' (G)	SWCr
	'Dainty Bess' (HT)	EBee EWTr SSea SWCr
	'Dainty Maid' (F)	SWCr
	× ***damascena*** var. ***bifera***	see *R.* × *damascena* var. *semperflorens*
§	- var. ***semperflorens*** (D)	EBee MRav NLar SSea SWCr WAct WHCG WKif
	- 'Trigintipetala' misapplied	see *R.* 'Professeur Emile Perrot'
§	- 'Versicolor' (D/d)	MGan SEND SFam SPer SSea SWCr
	'Dame de Coeur' (HT)	NBlu SWCr
	Dame Wendy = 'Canson' (F)	MGan

Dames de Chenonceau = 'Delpabra' (S) — MRav
'Danaë' (HM) — CSam SWCr WHCG
Dancing Queen = 'Fryfeston' (ClHT) — ECnt GCoc LGod MAsh MBri MWat NPri SMrm SWCr
Danny Boy = 'Dicxcon'PBR (Patio) — IDic MJon WGor
'Danse du Feu' (Cl) — CBcs CSBt CTri CWSG EBee ELan EPfP EWTr GKir LGod LRHS LStr MAsh MGan MJon MRav NPri SMrm SPer SPoG SWCr
'Daphne Gandy' (F) — MGan
Darcey Bussell = 'Ausdecorum' (S) **new** — CSBt ESty LRHS MBri SWCr WClo
'Dart's Defender' (Ru) — SLPl
David Whitfield = 'Gana'PBR (F) — MGan SWCr
Dawn Chorus = 'Dicquasar'PBR (HT) ♀H4 — CGro CSBt CWSG ECnt EPfP ESty IDic LGod LRHS LStr MAsh MBri MGan MRav MWat SPer SPoG SWCr
'Daybreak' (HM) — CTri SWCr WAct WHCG
Dazzling Delight = 'Cocuseful'PBR (F) — SWCr
'De la Grifferaie' — WAct
'De Meaux' — see *R.* × *centifolia* 'De Meaux'
§ 'De Resht' ♀H4 — CPou CTri ECnt EPfP GKir LRHS MAsh MCot MGan MJon MRav NLar SMrm SPer SSea SWCr WAct WHCG WKif
'Dearest' (F) — CBcs CSBt MGan MHav MRav SMrm SPer SWCr
'Debbie Thomas' (HT) — MJon
Deb's Delight = 'Legsweet'PBR (F) — LSRN MJon
'Debutante' (Ra) — CSam EBee EWTr LRHS SMrm WHCG
'Deep Secret' (HT) ♀H4 — CBcs CGro CSBt CTri CWSG EBee ECnt EPfP ESty GCoc LRHS LStr MAsh MGan MJon MRav NPri SMrm SPer SPoG SRGP SWCr
Dentelle de Malines = 'Lenfro' (S) — LRHS WAct
Desert Island = 'Dicfizz'PBR (F) — GCoc IDic
'Designer Sunset' (Patio) — SWCr
§ 'Desprez à Fleurs Jaunes' (N) — EBee IArd LRHS MGos MRav NEgg NLar SFam SPer SWCr
'Devon Maid' (ClHT) — SWCr
'Devoniensis' (ClT) — see *R.* 'Climbing Devoniensis'
'Diamond Celebration' **new** — LSRN SWCr
Diamond Days Forever = 'Fryjess' (F) **new** — ESty
'Diamond Jubilee' (HT) — CSBt MGan SWCr
Diamond — ESty GCoc LSRN LStr MGan MGos MJon SWCr
'Diamond Wishes'PBR — see *R.* Misty Hit
Dick's Delight = 'Dicwhistle' (GC) — ESty IDic LSRN MJon SMrm SWCr
Die Welt = 'Diekor' (HT) — MJon
'Directeur Alphand' (HP) — WHCG
Dizzy Heights = 'Fryblissful'PBR (Cl) — GCoc MAsh MGan MRav MWat SMrm SPer SWCr
Doctor Goldberg = 'Gandol' (HT) — MGan
Doctor Jo = 'Fryatlanta'PBR (F) — SWCr
'Doctor John Snow' (HT) — MGan
'Don Charlton' (HT) — NEgg
'Don Juan' (ClHT) — MGan SWCr
'Doris Tysterman' (HT) — CGro CTri LStr MGan SMrm SPer SRGP SWCr
Dorothy = 'Cocrocket'PBR (F) — GCoc LSRN MRav
'Dorothy Perkins' (Ra) — CGro CTri GCoc LRHS MGan MRav NLar NPer SPer SSea SWCr WHCG
'Dorothy Wheatcroft' (F) — MGan
§ 'Dortmund' (ClHScB) ♀H4 — EPfP LGod LRHS MGan NHaw SWCr WAct
Double Delight = 'Andeli' (HT) — CGro ESty GCoc MGan MJon SPer SPoG SWCr
'Dream Girl' (Cl) — SFam
Dream Lover = 'Peayetti'PBR (Patio) — ESty MJon SMrm SWCr
'Dreaming Spires' (Cl) — CSBt SPer SWCr
Drummer Boy = 'Harvacity'PBR (F/Patio) — MGan SPer SWCr
§ 'Du Maître d'Ecole' (G) — EBee ELon MRav SWCr WHCG WHer
Dublin Bay = 'Macdub' (Cl) ♀H4 — CSBt CTri ECnt ELan EPfP EWTr GKir IArd LAst LGod LRHS LStr MAsh MBri MGan MJon MRav SMrm SPer SSea SWCr WAct WBor
'Duc de Guiche' (G) ♀H4 — CSam EWTr SFam SLon SPer WHCG WHer
Duchess of Cornwall = 'Tan97157' (HT) — CSBt ESty SWCr
'Duchess of Portland' — see *R.* 'Portlandica'
Duchess of YorkPBR — see *R.* Sunseeker
'Duchesse d'Angoulême' (G × Ce) — SFam
'Duchesse de Buccleugh' (G) — MRav WAct
§ 'Duchesse de Montebello' (G) ♀H4 — EBee NLar SFam SLon SPer WHCG
'Duchesse de Verneuil' (CeMo) — SFam
'Duke of Wellington' (HP) — EBee SWCr WHCG
'Duke of Windsor' (HT) — MGan MHav SPer SWCr
§ 'Duplex' (S) — LRHS WAct WHCG
'Dupontii' (S) — MGan NLar SFam SPer WAct
'Dupuy Jamain' (HP) — WHCG
'Dusky Maiden' (F) — MCot SWCr WHCG
Dusty Springfield = 'Horluvdust' (F) — MGan
'Dutch Gold' (HT) — CWSG MGan MHav SPer SWCr
'E.H. Morse' — see *R.* 'Ernest H. Morse'
'Easlea's Golden Rambler' (Ra) ♀H4 — ECGP EPfP LRHS MRav NEgg SLon SPoG WAct WHCG
'Easter Morning' (Min) — SPer
Easy Going = 'Harflow'PBR (F) — IArd MAsh MRav SWCr
'Eblouissant' (Poly) — MGan
'Eddie's Jewel' (*moyesii* hybrid) — MGan SWCr
'Eden Rose' (HT) — MGan
Eden Rose '88 = 'Meiviolin'PBR (ClHT) — MJon SPer SWCr
Edith Holden = 'Chewlegacy'PBR (F) — ESty SPer
eglanteria — see *R. rubiginosa*
Eglantyne = 'Ausmak'PBR (S) ♀H4 — CSBt EBls EPfP ESty GCoc LRHS MBri MJon MRav SMrm SPer SPoG SWCr WClo
'Eleanor' (Patio) — SLon
'Eleanor' (Min) — EWTr
Eleanor = 'Poulberin'PBR (S) — ECnt SLon SWCr
§ ***elegantula*** 'Persetosa' (S) — NLar SPer SWCr WAct WHCG
Elfe = 'Tanelfe' (HT) — NHaw

	Name	Suppliers
§	Elina = 'Dicjana'PBR (HT) 🏆H4	CSBt EBee ECnt IDic LGod LStr MGan MGos MJon MRav SPer SPoG SWCr
	Elizabeth = 'Coctail'PBR (F)	GCoc SWCr
	'Elizabeth Harkness' (HT)	CWSG MGan SPer SWCr
	Elizabeth of Glamis = 'Macel' (F)	CGro CTri CWSG GCoc MGan MHav SPer SWCr
	Elizabeth Stuart = 'Maselstu' (Generosa Series) (S)	LSRN MRav
	Elle = 'Meibderos'PBR (HT)	ESty LSRN SWCr
	'Ellen Poulsen' (Poly)	MGan
	'Ellen Willmott' (HT)	EBee MCot SPer SWCr
	'Elmshorn' (S)	CBcs MGan WHCG
	Eloise = 'Kirsandra' **new**	ESty
	'Else Poulsen' (F)	WHCG
	Emanuel = 'Ausuel' (S)	SPer
	Emilien Guillot = 'Masemgui' (Generosa Series) (S)	MRav
	'Emily Gray' (Ra)	CGro CTri EBee ECnt EPfP GKir LRHS LStr MAsh MGan MRav SEND SPer WAct WHCG
	Emily Victoria = 'Boshipeacon' **new**	MGan
	Eminence = 'Gaxence' (HT) **new**	NBlu
	'Empereur du Maroc' (HP)	MRav WHCG
	Empress Michiko = 'Dicnifty'PBR (HT)	ESty IDic
	'Ena Harkness' (HT)	CTri ELan LRHS MGan SRGP SWCr
§	'Enfant de France' (HP)	MCot
	English Garden = 'Ausbuff'PBR (S)	CGro EBee EPfP EWTr LRHS MGos MRav MWat SLon SMrm SPer SWCr
	'English Miss' (F) 🏆H4	CSBt CTri EBee ECnt EPfP ESty LAst LStr MAsh MGan MJon MRav SPer SPoG SWCr
	'Erfurt' (HM)	MGan SPer SWCr WHCG
§	'Erinnerung an Brod' (S)	WHCG
§	'Ernest H. Morse' (HT)	CSBt CTri CWSG GCoc LAst MGan MJon MRav NBlu SPer SPoG SSea SWCr
	'Ernest May' (HT)	SSea
	Escapade = 'Harpade' (F) 🏆H4	SWCr
	Especially for You = 'Fryworthy'PBR (HT)	CSBt CTri ELon ESty GCoc LGod LRHS LSRN LStr MAsh MBri MGan NPri SCoo SMrm SRGP SSea SWCr
	Essex = 'Poulnoz'PBR (GC)	MRav SPer SWCr
§	'Estrellita de Oro' (Min)	SPer SWCr
	'Etain' (Ra)	ECnt
§	'Etendard' (Cl)	MGan MRav SPer SPoG SWCr WAct
	Eternal Flame = 'Korassenet'PBR (F)	MGos
	Eternally Yours = 'Macspeego'PBR (HT)	ECnt MJon
	'Ethel' (Ra)	CPou EBee SWCr
	'Etoile de Hollande' (HT)	ELan EWTr GKir LRHS NEgg NLar NPri SLon SMrm WAct
	'Eugénie Guinoisseau' (Mo)	CPou EWTr WHCG
	Euphoria = 'Intereup'PBR (GC/S)	GCoc IDic SWCr
	'Europeana' (F)	MGan
	Evelyn = 'Aussaucer'PBR (S) 🏆H4	CSBt EPfP ESty EWTr GCoc LRHS LSRN MGan MJon MRav MWat NEgg SMrm SPer SWCr
§	Evelyn Fison = 'Macev' (F)	CSBt CTri ELan MGan MRav SPer SWCr
	Evening Light = 'Chewpechette'PBR (ClMin)	MAsh
	Evening Light = 'Tarde Gris' (ClMin)	LRHS MBri SSea
	'Excelsa' (Ra)	CSBt CTri EPfP GKir IArd LGod MAsh MGan MRav NWea
	'Eyecatcher' (F)	EBee
	'F.E. Lester'	see *R.* 'Francis E. Lester'
§	'F.J. Grootendorst' (Ru)	LRHS MGan NEgg SPer WAct
	Fairhope = 'Talfairhope' (Min)	MJon
	Fairy Prince = 'Harnougette' (GC)	ESty
	Fairy Queen = 'Sperien' (Poly/GC)	IDic MAsh
	'Fairy Rose'	see *R.* 'The Fairy'
	Fairy Snow = 'Holfairy' (S)	SWCr
	Fairyland = 'Harlayalong' (Poly)	MGan
	Falstaff = 'Ausverse'PBR (S)	CSBt ECnt EPfP LRHS LStr MBNS MBri MGos MJon MRav NEgg SMrm SSea SWCr WClo
	'Fantin-Latour' (*centifolia* hybrid) 🏆H4	CTri EBee ECnt ELan EPfP EWTr GCoc GCra LAst LRHS LStr MBri MCot MGan MRav MWat NEgg SFam SMad SMrm SPer SSea SWCr WAct WHCG WKif
	farreri var. ***persetosa***	see *R. elegantula* 'Persetosa'
	Fascination = 'Jacoyel' (Castle Series) (HT)	LStr MBri SCoo
§	Fascination = 'Poulmax'PBR (F) 🏆H4	CSBt EBee ECnt EPfP LRHS MGan MGos MRav MWat SPer SRGP SWCr
	Father's Favourite = 'Gandoug' **new**	MGan SWCr
§	Favourite Hit = 'Poululv'PBR (Patio)	MAsh
	fedtschenkoana misapplied	SPer WAct WHCG
	fedtschenkoana Regel	SLPl
	Fée des Neiges	see *R.* Iceberg
	'Felicia' (HM) 🏆H4	CSBt CSam CTri EBee ECnt ELan EPfP GCoc GKir LRHS LStr MAsh MCot MGan MGos MJon MRav SFam SMrm SPer SWCr WAct WHCG WKif
	'Félicité Parmentier' (AxD) 🏆H4	EBee LRHS MBri MGan MRav NLar SFam SPer SWCr WAct WHCG
§	'Félicité Perpétue' (Ra) 🏆H4	CBcs CSBt EBee ELan EPfP GCoc GKir ISea LRHS LShp LStr MAsh MGan MRav NEgg SEND SFam SPer SPoG SSea SWCr WAct WHCG
	Felicity Kendal = 'Lanken' (HT)	MHav MJon
	'Fellemberg' (ClCh)	WHCG
	Fellowship = 'Harwelcome'PBR (F) 🏆H4	ECnt ESty LGod LStr MGan MJon MRav SCoo SSea SWCr
	'Ferdinand Pichard' (Bb) 🏆H4	CPou CSBt ECnt ELon EPfP ESty EWTr LAst LRHS MBri MCot MGan MJon MRav MWat NEgg SPer SPoG SSea SWCr WAct WFoF WHCG WKif
	Ferdy = 'Keitoli'PBR (GC)	MRav SPer
	Fergie = 'Ganfer'PBR (F/Patio)	MGan SWCr
I	'Fern's Rose' (F)	SWCr
	ferruginea	see *R. glauca* Pourr.
	Festival = 'Kordialo'PBR (Patio)	ESty LStr MRav SPer SPoG SWCr
	Fetzer Syrah Rosé = 'Harextra'PBR	ESty
	Fiery Hit = 'Poulfiry'PBR (PatioHit Series) (Min)	MAsh SWCr
	Fiesta = 'Macfirinlin' (Patio)	MJon

Name	Suppliers
filipes	GAuc
- 'Brenda Colvin'	see *R.* 'Brenda Colvin'
§ - 'Kiftsgate' (Ra) ΨH4	Widely available
§ 'Fimbriata' (Ru)	CPou ECGP ELon EWTr NLar SPer SSea SWCr WAct
Fiona = 'Meibeluxen'PBR (S/GC)	LSRN SWCr
'First Great Western' (HT)	ESty LStr SWCr
'First Love' (HT)	MGan
'Fisher and Holmes' (HP)	WAct WHCG
Fisherman's Friend = 'Auschild'PBR (S)	SPer
Flashdance = 'Poulyc004'PBR (ClMin)	ECnt LRHS SWCr
'Flora McIvor' (RH)	MGan NHaw
'Flore' (Ra)	CRHN
'Florence Mary Morse' (S)	SDix
Florence Nightingale = 'Ganflor'PBR (F)	MGan SPer
'Flower Carpet Amber' **new**	MAsh SCoo SWCr
'Flower Carpet Coral'PBR (GC)	CGro ECnt GCoc LRHS MAsh MBri MWat SCoo SWCr
Flower Carpet Gold = 'Noalesa'PBR (GC)	ECnt GCoc LRHS MAsh MBri SPoG SWCr
Flower Carpet PinkPBR	see *R.* Pink Flower Carpet
Flower Carpet Red Velvet = 'Noare'PBR (GC)	CGro ECnt ELan EPfP GCoc LRHS LStr MAsh MBri MGan MWat SCoo SPer SPoG SWCr
§ Flower Carpet Sunshine = 'Noason'PBR (GC)	CGro CTri ELan EPfP GCoc LRHS LStr MWat SCoo SPer
Flower Carpet White = 'Noaschnee'PBR (GC) ΨH4	CGro CTri ELan EPfP GCoc LRHS LStr MAsh MBri MGan SCoo SPer SPoG SWCr
Flower Power = 'Frycassia'PBR (Patio)	CSBt ECnt ESty GCoc LRHS LStr MAsh MJon MRav MWat NPri SPoG SWCr
§ *foetida* (S)	EBee NHaw
§ - 'Bicolor' (S)	CArn LRHS NHaw NLar
§ - 'Persiana' (S)	MGan NHaw SPer
foliolosa	SLPl WHCG
Fond Memories = 'Kirfelix'PBR (Patio)	ESty LSRN LStr MJon SWCr
For You With Love = 'Fryjangle' (Patio)	MGan SWCr
Forever Royal = 'Franmite' (F)	ESty
Forever Young = 'Jacimgol'PBR (F)	IDic
Forget Me Not = 'Coccharm' (HT) **new**	GCoc
forrestiana	LRHS WHCG
'Fountain' (HT/S)	MGan SPer SWCr
Fragrant Cloud = 'Tanellis' (HT)	CGro CTri CWSG EPfP ESty GCoc LRHS LStr MAsh MBri MGan MGos MJon MRav MWat NPri SMrm SPer SPoG SSea SWCr
'Fragrant Delight' (F) ΨH4	CSBt ELan ELon GCoc LStr MGan MJon MRav MWat SPer SPoG SWCr
Fragrant Dream = 'Dicodour'PBR (HT)	CGro ESty IDic LStr MGan MRav SWCr
Fragrant Memories = 'Korpastato'PBR (HT/S)	CSBt GCoc LRHS MGos SCoo SWCr
Fragrant Plum = 'Aroplumi' (HT)	SSea
'Francesca' (HM)	LRHS MGan SFam SPer SWCr WAct WHCG
Francine Austin = 'Ausram'PBR (S/GC)	LRHS MAsh MBri NEgg SPer WAct
'Francis Dubreuil' (T)	MCot

Name	Suppliers
§ 'Francis E. Lester' (HM/Ra) ΨH4	CRHN CSam EBee EPfP EWTr LRHS MBri MJon NLar SMrm SPer SRGP SSea SWCr WAct WClo WHCG
× *francofurtana* misapplied	see *R.* 'Impératrice Joséphine'
- 'Empress Josephine'	see *R.* 'Impératrice Joséphine'
'François Juranville' (Ra) ΨH4	CPou CRHN CSBt EPfP EWTr GGal LAst LRHS LShp LStr MBri MGan MRav NLar SLon SMrm SPer SWCr WAct
§ 'Frau Karl Druschki' (HP)	WAct
'Fred Loads' (F/S) ΨH4	MGan MRav SMrm
Freddie Mercury = 'Batmercury' (HT)	LSRN MJon NEgg
Free Spirit = 'Fryjeru' (F) **new**	ECnt GCoc
Freedom = 'Dicjem'PBR (HT) ΨH4	CGro CTri EBls ECnt GCoc IDic LGod LStr MGan MGos MRav MWat SPer SRGP SVic SWCr
'Frensham' (F)	LStr MGan SSea SWCr
Fresh Pink (Min/Poly)	MGan
Friend for Life = 'Cocnanne'PBR (F) ΨH4	GCoc LSRN MJon MRav SMrm
'Fritz Nobis' (S) ΨH4	LRHS LStr MGan MRav NHaw NLar SPer SWCr WAct WKif
Frothy = 'Macfrothy'PBR (Patio)	ECnt MJon
'Fru Dagmar Hastrup' (Ru) ΨH4	CDul CSBt EBee ECnt ELan EPfP GCoc LBuc LRHS LStr MGan MJon NEgg NLar SPer SWCr WAct WHCG
'Frühlingsanfang' (PiH)	CTri WAct
'Frühlingsgold' (PiH) ΨH4	CBcs ELan EPfP EWTr GCoc LRHS LStr MGan MRav NLar NWea SPer SPoG SWCr WAct WHCG WKif
'Frühlingsmorgen' (PiH)	EWTr GCoc LStr MGan SLon SMad SPer SSea SWCr WKif
Fulton Mackay = 'Cocdana'PBR (HT)	GCoc MGan
Fyvie Castle = 'Cocbamber' (HT)	GCoc
'Gail Borden' (HT)	MGan SWCr
§ *gallica* var. *officinalis* (G) ΨH4	CAbP CArn CSam CTri EPfP GCoc GPoy LRHS MAsh MBri MGan MJon MRav NLar SFam SPer SSea SWCr WAct WHCG
§ - 'Versicolor' (G) ΨH4	Widely available
Galway Bay = 'Macba' (ClHT)	EBee LRHS MAsh MGan MRav SMad SPer SWCr
§ Garden News = 'Poulrim'PBR (HT)	ECnt SWCr
Gardeners Glory = 'Chewability' (Cl) **new**	ESty MJon
'Gardenia' (Ra)	EWTr LRHS SPer SWCr WHCG
'Gardiner's Pink' (Ra)	MCot WHCG
'Garnette Carol'	see *R.* 'Carol Amling'
'Garnette Pink'	see *R.* 'Carol Amling'
'Gaujard'	see *R.* Rose Gaujard
'Gelbe Dagmar Hastrup'PBR	see *R.* Yellow Dagmar Hastrup
'Général Kléber' (CeMo)	SFam SPer WAct
§ 'Général Schablikine' (T)	SWCr WAct
Genesis = 'Fryjuicy' (Patio)	ECnt ESty LRHS MAsh MBri MJon SWCr
N *gentiliana* misapplied	see *R.* 'Polyantha Grandiflora'
N *gentiliana* H. Lév. & Variot	see *R. multiflora* var. *cathayensis*
Gentle Hermione = 'Ausrumba'PBR	LRHS MBri SMrm WClo
Gentle Touch = 'Diclulu'PBR (Min/Patio)	CSBt CWSG IDic MRav SPer SWCr
Geoff Hamilton = 'Ausham'PBR (S)	ESty LRHS LStr MAsh MBNS MBri NEgg SCoo SMrm SPer SSea SWCr WClo

George Best = 'Dichimanher' (Patio)	IDic LSRN MJon SMrm
'Georges Vibert' (G)	EBee
Geraldine = 'Peahaze' (F)	MHav
'Geranium' (*moyesii* hybrid) ♀^{H4}	CBcs CDul CSam EBee ELan EPfP GCoc GKir IArd LGod LRHS LStr MAsh MBri MGan MJon MRav NBlu NPri NScw SEND SMrm SPer SPoG SSea SWCr WAct WHCG
Gerbe d'Or	see *R.* Casino
Gertrude Jekyll = 'Ausbord'^{PBR} (S) ♀^{H4}	Widely available
'Ghislaine de Féligonde' (Ra/S)	CPou CSam EWTr LStr MCot MGan NLar SPer SWCr WHCG WPen
Ghita^{PBR}	see *R.* Millie
Ginger Syllabub = 'Harjolina'^{PBR} (Cl)	ECnt ESty GCoc SPoG SWCr
Gipsy Boy	see *R.* 'Zigeunerknabe'
giraldii	GAuc
Glad Tidings = 'Tantide'^{PBR} (F)	CSBt CWSG MGan MRav SPer SWCr
Glamis Castle = 'Auslevel'^{PBR} (S)	CBcs CTri LRHS LStr MBri NEgg NPri SCoo SPer SWCr WClo
glauca ambig.	EMac
§ ***glauca*** Pourr. (S) ♀^{H4}	Widely available
'Glenfiddich' (F)	CSBt CTri CWSG GCoc LStr MBri MRav NPri SPer SWCr
'Glenn Dale' (Cl)	EBee
Glenshane = 'Dicvood' (GC/S)	IDic MRav
Global Beauty = 'Tan 94448' (HT)	MRav SMrm SWCr
'Gloire de Dijon' (ClT)	CGro CSBt CTri CWSG EBee ECnt ELan EPfP GKir LAst LGod LRHS LStr MBri MGan MJon MRav NEgg NPri SMad SMrm SPer SWCr WAct WHCG
'Gloire de Ducher' (HP)	MGan NHaw WAct WHCG
'Gloire de France' (G)	MRav WHer
'Gloire de Guilan' (D)	WAct
'Gloire des Mousseuses' (CeMo)	EBee LRHS SFam WHCG
'Gloire Lyonnaise' (HP)	EBee SLon WHCG
'Gloria Mundi' (Poly)	NEgg SWCr
Gloriana = 'Chewpope'^{PBR} (ClMin)	CGro ECnt ESty LRHS MAsh MBri MJon MRav MWat SCoo SMrm SPer SPoG SSea SWCr
Glorious = 'Interictira'^{PBR} (HT)	ESty IDic MJon SWCr
'Glory of Seale' (S)	SSea
Glowing Amber = 'Manglow' (Min)	ESty MJon
glutinosa	see *R. pulverulenta*
Goddess of Love = 'Horradhe' (S)	SWCr
'Goldbusch' (RH)	MGan
'Golden Anniversary' (Patio)	LRHS LStr MAsh SPer SPoG SWCr
Golden Beauty = 'Korberbeni'^{PBR} (F)	ESty MAsh MBri MGos
Golden Beryl = 'Manberyl' (Min)	MJon
Golden Celebration = 'Ausgold'^{PBR} (S) ♀^{H4}	CGro CSBt CWSG EBee ECnt EPfP ESty GCoc LGod LRHS LSRN LStr MAsh MBri MJon MRav NLar SMad SMrm SPer SPoG SRGP SSea SWCr WClo
Golden Future = 'Horanymoll'^{PBR} (Cl)	SWCr
Golden Gate = 'Korgolgat'^{PBR} (ClHT)	ECnt ESty LStr MGos MJon SWCr
Golden Jewel = 'Tanledolg'^{PBR} (F/Patio)	ESty MAsh MBri SPoG SWCr
Golden Jubilee = 'Cocagold' (HT)	CTri GCoc MRav SWCr
Golden Kiss = 'Dicalways'^{PBR} (HT)	GCoc IDic
Golden Memories = 'Korholesea'^{PBR} (F)	CBcs CGro CSBt EBls ESty GCoc LGod LRHS LStr MGos MJon MRav NPri SCoo SPer SWCr
§ Golden Penny = 'Rugul' (Min)	MGan
'Golden Rambler'	see *R.* 'Alister Stella Gray'
'Golden Salmon' (Poly)	MGan
'Golden Showers' (Cl) ♀^{H4}	Widely available
Golden Symphonie = 'Meitoleil' (Min/Patio)	SWCr
Golden Tribute = 'Horannfree' (F)	MGan
Golden Trust = 'Hardish'^{PBR} (Patio)	LStr MWat
Golden Wedding = 'Arokris'^{PBR} (F/HT)	CGro CSBt CTri CWSG ECnt ELan EPfP GCoc IArd LGod LRHS LSRN LStr MAsh MGan MGos MJon MRav MWat NEgg NPri SMrm SPer SPoG SRGP SSea SVic SWCr WBor WClo
'Golden Wedding Celebration' (F)	ESty LSRN SPoG SWCr
'Golden Wings' (S) ♀^{H4}	CTri EBee ELan EPfP GCoc LRHS LStr MAsh MGan MJon MRav NLar SEND SMad SPer SSea SWCr WAct WHCG
'Goldfinch' (Ra)	ELan EPfP LRHS LStr MBri MRav NEgg NLar SMrm SPer SPoG SWCr WHCG
Goldstar = 'Candide' (HT)	ECnt MGan
Good as Gold = 'Chewsunbeam'^{PBR} (ClMin)	CSBt EBee ECnt ESty LStr MBri MJon SPer SRGP SWCr
Good Life = 'Cococircus'^{PBR} (HT)	GCoc SCoo SPer
Good Luck = 'Burspec' (F/Patio)	GCoc SPer SWCr
Good News 95 = 'Chespink'^{PBR}	SWCr
Good Wishes^{PBR}	see *R.* Favourite Hit
Gordon Snell = 'Dicwriter' (F)	IDic
Gordon's College = 'Cocjabby'^{PBR} (F) ♀^{H4}	ESty GCoc MJon
'Grace Abounding' (F)	LSRN
Grace = 'Auskeppy'^{PBR} (S)	CSBt EPfP ESty LRHS LSRN LStr MBri MJon NEgg SPer SRGP SSea SWCr WClo
Gracious Queen = 'Bedqueen' (HT)	GCoc SWCr
Graham Thomas = 'Ausmas'^{PBR} (S) ♀^{H4}	CGro CSBt EBee ECnt EPfP EWTr GCoc LAst LGod LRHS LSRN LStr MAsh MBri MCot MGan MJon MRav MWat NEgg NPri SMrm SPer SPoG SSea SWCr WAct WClo WHCG WKif
Grande Amore = 'Korcoluma'^{PBR} (HT)	CSBt MGos SWCr
Grand-mère Jenny = 'Grem' (HT)	MGan
'Grandpa Dickson' (HT)	CBcs CWSG LGod MAsh MGan MJon MRav NPri SPer SRGP SWCr
Granny's Favourite (Patio/F)	LSRN SWCr
Great Expectations = 'Jacdal' (F)	EBee SPoG
Great Expectations = 'Lanican' (HT)	CBcs

	Great Expectations = 'Mackalves'PBR (F)	CSBt ECnt EPfP GCoc IArd LGod LStr MAsh MJon MRav SCoo SPer SWCr
§	'Great Maiden's Blush' (A)	GCoc MRav MWat NLar SFam WAct
	Greenall's Glory = 'Kirmac'PBR (F/Patio)	MJon MRav SMrm
	'Greenmantle' (RH)	WAct
	Greetings = 'Jacdreco'PBR (F)	IDic MAsh MRav SRGP SWCr WBor
	Grenadine = 'Poulgrena'PBR (HT)	ECnt
	Grimaldi = 'Delstror' (F)	LRHS
	'Grootendorst'	see *R.* 'F.J. Grootendorst'
	'Grootendorst Supreme' (Ru)	SPer
N	'Gros Chou de Hollande' (Bb)	WHCG
	Grouse = 'Korimro'PBR (S/GC) ♀H4	EPfP GCoc LRHS NLar SEND SPer SWCr WAct
	'Gruss an Aachen' (Poly)	EPfP LStr MGan NLar SPer SWCr WAct WHCG
	'Gruss an Teplitz' (China hybrid)	SPer WHCG
	Guardian Angel	SWCr
	'Guinée' (ClHT)	CSBt EBee ECnt ELan ELon EPfP EWTr GKir LAst LRHS LStr MAsh MGan MRav NPri SMrm SPer SPoG SSea SWCr WHCG
	Guletta	see *R.* Golden Penny
	Guy Savoy = 'Delstrimen'PBR (F)	MRav
	Gwen Mayor = 'Cocover'PBR (HT)	GCoc
	Gwent = 'Poulurt'PBR (GC)	CSBt ELan GCoc LSRN LStr SEND SPer SWCr WAct
§	***gymnocarpa*** var. ***willmottiae***	MGan SPer SSea WAct WHCG
	Gypsy Boy	see *R.* 'Zigeunerknabe'
N	'Hakuun' (F/Patio) ♀H4	MGan MHav SMad SWCr
	'Hamburger Phönix' (Ra)	CGro MGan SPer WAct
	Hampshire = 'Korhamp'PBR (GC)	MGan SWCr
	Hand in Hand = 'Haraztec'PBR (Patio/Min)	MAsh MWat SPoG SWCr
	Handel = 'Macha' (Cl) ♀H4	CGro CSBt CTri CWSG ELan EPfP LAst LRHS LStr MAsh MGan MJon MRav NEgg SPer SPoG SSea SWCr WBVN WBor
	Hanky Panky = 'Wektorcent'PBR	CGro EBls ESty GCoc LRHS MAsh MBri MJon MRav NPri SWCr
	Hannah Gordon = 'Korweiso'PBR (F)	EBls ECnt MGan MHav SPer SWCr
	'Hanne' (HT)	NBlu
	'Hansa' (Ru)	ECGP EMil GCoc LBuc MGan SPer SWCr WHCG
	Happy Anniversary ambig.	LSRN
	Happy Anniversary = 'Bedfranc'PBR	LSRN MJon NPri SWCr
	Happy Anniversary = 'Delpre' (F)	CGro CTri LRHS LStr MAsh MBri MRav SPoG SSea
	'Happy Birthday' (Min/Patio)	CWSG ESty LSRN LStr MGan SPoG SWCr
	Happy Child = 'Auscomp'PBR (S)	CWSG LRHS MJon
	Happy Retirement = 'Tantoras'PBR (F)	CGro ESty GCoc LRHS LSRN LStr MAsh MGan MRav MWat SCoo SMrm SPoG SSea SWCr
	'Happy Thought' (Min)	CWSG
	Happy Times = 'Bedone'PBR (Patio/Min)	LRHS SPoG
§	× ***harisonii*** 'Harison's Yellow' (PiH)	SPer
§	- 'Williams Double Yellow' (PiH)	GCoc MGan WAct
	Harlow Carr = 'Aushouse'PBR	LGod LRHS MAsh SCoo WClo
	Harlow Carr = 'Kirlyl' (F)	MBri
	'Harry Edland' (F)	SSea SWCr
	'Harry Wheatcroft' (HT)	CGro MGan SPer SWCr
	Harvest Fayre = 'Dicnorth'PBR (F)	CTri IDic MGan SPer
	Havana Hit = 'Poulpah032'PBR	MAsh
	'Headleyensis' (S)	SLon WHCG
	Heart of Gold = 'Coctarlotte'PBR (HT)	EBee ECnt GCoc MRav SWCr
	Heartbeat '97 = 'Cocorona'PBR (F)	SWCr
	Heather Austin = 'Auscook'PBR (S)	LRHS
	Heavenly Rosalind = 'Ausmash'PBR (S)	LRHS
§	'Hebe's Lip' (DSwB)	MGan WAct
	'Helen Knight' (*ecae* hybrid) (S)	MAsh NPri SSea
	helenae	CTri MGan NLar SPer SWCr
	- hybrid	WHCG
	Hello = 'Cochello' (Min/Patio)	SWCr
	'Helping Hands' (F) **new**	SWCr
§	'Henri Martin' (CeMo)	LRHS MGan NEgg NLar SLon SMrm SPer SWCr WAct WHCG
	Henri Matisse = 'Delstrobla' (HT)	LRHS MRav SPoG
	Her Majesty = 'Dicxotic'PBR (F)	IDic
§	'Herbstfeuer' (RH)	CPou SPer SWCr
	Heritage = 'Ausblush'PBR (S)	CGro ELan ELon EPfP GCoc LGod LRHS LStr MBri MRav NEgg SLon SMrm SPer SPoG SSea SWCr WHCG
	'Hermosa' (Ch)	LAst LRHS MRav SWCr WHCG
	Hertfordshire = 'Kortenay'PBR (GC) ♀H4	ELan MJon MRav NPri SPer SWCr
	'Hiawatha' (Ra)	SWCr
§	'Hidcote Yellow' (Cl)	LRHS SWCr
	Hide and Seek = 'Diczodiac'PBR (F)	IDic
	High Flier = 'Fryfandango'PBR (Cl)	SWCr
	High Flyer = 'Jacsat' (Cl) **new**	SRGP
	High Hopes = 'Haryup'PBR (Cl) ♀H4	ECnt EPfP LRHS LStr MAsh MGan MJon SPer SPoG SSea SWCr WHCG
	'High Society' (HT)	SWCr
	'Highdownensis' (*moyesii* hybrid) (S)	ELan SPer
	Highfield = 'Harcomp' (Cl)	SPer SWCr
	Hole-in-one = 'Horeagle' (F)	LSRN SWCr
	holy rose	see *R.* × *richardii*
	Honey Bunch = 'Cocglen'PBR (F)	GCoc LStr MRav SPer SPoG SRGP SWCr
	Honey Dijon = 'Weksproulses' (F) **new**	CSBt ECnt ESty GCoc
	Honeybun = 'Tan98264'PBR (Patio)	ESty
	Honeymoon	see *R.* 'Honigmond'
§	'Honigmond' (F)	CWSG SWCr
	'Honorine de Brabant' (Bb)	CPou LRHS SPer SWCr WHCG WKif
	Hospitality = 'Horcoff'PBR (F)	ESty

	Name	Suppliers
	Hot Chocolate = 'Wekpaltez' (F)	CSBt EBee EBls ECnt EGxp ELan ELon EPfP ESty GCoc LBuc LGod LRHS LStr MAsh MBri MGan MGos MJon MRav MWat NPri SCoo SMrm SPoG SRGP SSea SWCr
	Hot Stuff = 'Maclarayspo' (Min)	MJon SWCr
	Hot Tamale = 'Jacpoy' (Min)	MJon
	House Beautiful = 'Harbingo'PBR (Patio)	SMrm
	'Hugh Dickson' (HP)	CPou NLar SWCr
	hugonis	see *R. xanthina* f. *hugonis*
	- 'Plenissima'	see *R. xanthina* f. *hugonis*
	Humanity = 'Harcross'PBR (F)	MRav
	'Hunter' (Ru)	WAct
	Hyde Hall = 'Ausbosky'PBR	LGod LRHS SCoo
	I Love You = 'Geelove' (HT)	SWCr
	Ice Cream = 'Korzuri'PBR (HT) ŸH4	CSBt CWSG ECnt GCoc LStr MGan MGos MJon MRav SPoG SWCr
§	Iceberg = 'Korbin' (F) ŸH4	CBcs CGro CSBt CTri CWSG ECnt EPfP ESty GCoc LAst LGod LRHS LStr MAsh MGan MGos MJon MRav MWat NPri NWea SMrm SPer SPoG SSea SWCr WAct
	'Iced Ginger' (F)	MGan SPer
	'Illusion' (Cl/F)	SWCr
§	'Impératrice Joséphine' ŸH4	CSam EWTr LRHS MRav NLar SFam SWCr WAct WHCG
	In Memory Of	LSRN
	Incognito = 'Briincog' (Min)	MJon
	Indian Summer = 'Peaperfume'PBR (HT) ŸH4	CSBt CWSG ESty GCoc LGod MHav MRav MWat SMrm SPoG SWCr
	'Indigo' (DPo)	CPou WHCG
	Ingrid Bergman = 'Poulman'PBR (HT) ŸH4	CTri ECnt EPfP LRHS LStr MAsh MBri MGan MGos MJon MRav SMrm SPoG SRGP SWCr
	Innocence = 'Cocoray'PBR (Patio)	GCoc
	Intrigue = 'Korlech'PBR (F)	LStr SWCr
	Invincible = 'Runatru'PBR (F)	MGan
	'Ipsilanté' (G)	WAct
	'Irène Watts' (Ch)	CPou ECre EPfP EWTr LSRN NLar SSea SWCr WAct WHCG
	Iris = 'Coczero' (HT) **new**	ECnt
	Iris = 'Ferecha' (HT)	GCoc LSRN SWCr
	Irish Eyes = 'Dicwitness'PBR (F)	CBcs CWSG EPfP ESty IArd IDic LGod LStr MAsh MBri MGan MJon MRav MWat NPri SCoo SPer SSea SWCr
	Irish Hope = 'Harexclaim'PBR (F)	SWCr
	Irish Wonder	see *R.* Evelyn Fison
	Irresistible = 'Tinresist' (Min/Patio)	MJon
	Isabella = 'Poulisab'PBR (Renaissance Series) (S)	CPou ECnt EPfP SWCr
	IsisPBR (HT)	see *R.* Silver Anniversary = 'Poulari'
	Isn't She Lovely (HT) **new**	ESty GCoc IDic
	'Ispahan' (D) ŸH4	CFee EPfP LRHS MBri NEgg NLar SFam SLPl SLon SPer SWCr WAct WHCG
	Jack's Wish = 'Kirsil' (HT)	MJon
§	× ***jacksonii*** 'Max Graf' (GC/Ru)	EPfP LRHS MGan SMad WAct
	- Red Max GrafPBR	see *R.* Rote Max Graf
§	- White Max Graf = 'Korgram'PBR (GC/Ru)	WAct
	Jacobite rose	see *R.* × *alba* 'Alba Maxima'
	Jacqueline du Pré = 'Harwanna'PBR (S) ŸH4	EBee ECnt EPfP ESty EWTr GCoc MCot MGan MJon MRav NLar SPer SWCr WAct WHCG
N	'Jacques Cartier' misapplied	see *R.* 'Marchesa Boccella'
	James Galway = 'Auscrystal'PBR (S)	CSBt CWSG ELon LRHS LStr MAsh MBri NEgg SCoo SSea SWCr WClo
	'James Mason' (G)	CSam
	'James Veitch' (DPoMo)	WHCG
	Jane Asher = 'Peapet' (Min/Patio)	SWCr
	Janet = 'Auspishus'PBR (S)	LRHS LSRN MBri SSea SWCr
§	'Japonica' (CeMo)	SWCr
§	Jardins de Bagatelle = 'Meimafris' (HT)	LSRN MJon MRav
	Jasmina = 'Korcentex' (Cl)	ESty MGos MJon SWCr
	'Jaune Desprez'	see *R.* 'Desprez à Fleurs Jaunes'
	Jayne Austin = 'Ausbreak'PBR (S)	CSBt CWSG LRHS SPer SWCr
	JazzPBR	see *R.* That's Jazz
	Jean = 'Cocupland'PBR (Patio)	GCoc SWCr
	Jean Kenneally = 'Tineally' (Min)	MJon
	'Jean Mermoz' (Poly)	SWCr
	'Jenny Duval' misapplied	see *R.* 'Président de Sèze'
	'Jenny's Dream' (HT)	LGod
	Jenny's Rose = 'Cansit' (F)	ECnt MGan SWCr
	'Jens Munk' (Ru)	NHaw WAct
	Jillian McGredy = 'Macarnhe' (F)	MJon
	Jill's Rose = 'Ganjil'PBR (F)	LSRN MGan SWCr
	'Jimmy Greaves' (HT)	MGan
	Joëlle Marouani = 'Masjoma' (Generosa Series) (S)	MRav
	John Clare = 'Auscent'PBR (S)	LRHS
	John Gibb = 'Coczorose' (F)	GCoc
	'John Hopper' (HP)	SWCr
	Johnnie Walker = 'Frygran'PBR (HT)	SWCr
	'Jolly Roger' (F)	SWCr
	'Josephine Bruce' (HT)	CBcs CSBt LGod LRHS MGan SWCr
	'Joseph's Coat' (S/Cl)	IArd LAst LGod LStr MGan SRGP SWCr
	'Journey's End' (HT)	MGan SWCr
	'Jubilee Celebration' (F)	EPfP
	Jubilee Celebration = 'Aushunter'PBR (S)	CSBt EPfP ESty LRHS MAsh MBri SSea WClo
	Jude the Obscure = 'Ausjo'PBR (S)	CSBt ELon ESty LRHS MBri MJon NEgg SWCr WClo
	'Julia's Rose' (HT)	CGro LSRN LStr MGan MJon SPer SWCr
	'Juno' (Ce)	SWCr WHCG
	'Juno' (Ch) **new**	CPou
	'Just for You' (F)	SWCr
	Just for You = 'Moryou' (Min)	LSRN
	'Just Jenny' (Min)	MJon
	'Just Joey' (HT) ŸH4	CBcs CGro CSBt CWSG ECnt ELan EPfP GCoc IArd LGod LRHS LStr MAsh MBri MGan MJon MRav MWat NEgg NPri SMrm SPer SPoG SRGP SSea SWCr WClo
	Just Married	SPoG SWCr
	'Kanegem' (HT)	NBlu
	'Karlsruhe' (Cl)	SSea
	'Katharina Zeimet' (Poly)	CPou CTri MGan NLar WAct WHCG
§	Katherine Mansfield = 'Meilanein' (HT)	CSBt
	'Kathleen Ferrier' (F)	MGan

'Kathleen Harrop' (Bb) EBee ELon LStr NLar SFam SMrm SPer SRGP SSea SWCr WAct WHCG
Kathleen's Rose = 'Kirkitt' (F) MJon
Kathryn McGredy = 'Macauclad' (HT) ESty MJon
Kathryn Morley = 'Ausclub'PBR (F) LRHS
'Katie' (ClF) MGan SWCr
N 'Kazanlik' misapplied see *R.* 'Professeur Emile Perrot'
Keep Smiling = 'Fryflorida' (HT) GCoc LGod LStr MAsh SMrm SRGP SWCr
Keepsake = 'Kormalda' (HT) MGan MJon
'Keith Maughn' **new** EBls
§ Kent = 'Poulcov'PBR (Towne & Country Series) (S/GC) ♀H4 CSBt ECnt ELan EPfP ESty EWTr GCoc LSRN LStr MGan MJon MRav MWat SMrm SPer SPoG SWCr WAct WHCG
'Kew Rambler' (Ra) CRHN CSam MMuc MRav SEND SFam SMrm SPer WHCG
'Kiese' (*canina* hybrid) NHaw
'Kiftsgate' see *R. filipes* 'Kiftsgate'
'Kilworth Gold' (HT) MGan
Kind Regards = 'Peatiger' (F) LSRN
King's Macc = 'Frydisco'PBR (HT) SWCr
'King's Ransom' (HT) CSBt MGan MHav MRav SPer SPoG SWCr
Knock Out = 'Dadler' (F) MAsh SWCr
§ 'Königin von Dänemark' (A) ♀H4 ECnt ELon EPfP GCoc LRHS MAsh MBri MRav NEgg NLar SMrm SPer SSea SWCr WAct WHCG
'Kordes' Robusta' see *R.* Robusta
Korona = 'Kornita' (F) SPer
'Korresia' (F) CSBt CTri EBee ECnt EPfP ESty GCoc LGod LStr MAsh MBri MGan MGos MJon MRav SPer SPoG SWCr
Kristin = 'Benmagic' (Min) MJon
§ Krönberg = 'Poultry'PBR (Castle Series) (F) EPfP
'Kronprinzessin Viktoria von Preussen' (Bb) EBee WHCG
L.D. Braithwaite = 'Auscrim'PBR (S) ♀H4 CBcs ELan EPfP GCoc LAst LGod LRHS LStr MBNS MBri MGan MJon MRav MWat NLar NPri SMrm SPer SWCr WAct WClo WHCG
'La Belle Distinguée' (RH) WHCG
'La Belle Sultane' see *R.* 'Violacea'
'La Mortola' see *R. brunonii* 'La Mortola'
'La Perle' (Ra) CRHN
'La Reine Victoria' see *R.* 'Reine Victoria'
'La Rubanée' see *R.* × *centifolia* 'Unique Panachée'
La Sévillana = 'Meigekanu' (F/GC) EBee SPer WAct
'La Ville de Bruxelles' (D) ♀H4 LRHS SFam SLon SPer WHCG
Lady Emma Hamilton = 'Ausbrother'PBR (S) EPfP ESty LRHS MAsh MBri SCoo SWCr
'Lady Gay' (Ra) EWTr SWCr WBor WHCG
'Lady Hillingdon' (T) SMrm
'Lady Hillingdon' (ClT) see *R.* 'Climbing Lady Hillingdon'
'Lady Iliffe' (HT) MGan SWCr
Lady in Red = 'Sealady' (Min) MJon
'Lady Love '95' (Patio) SWCr
Lady MacRobert = 'Coclent' (F) GCoc
§ Lady Meillandina = 'Meilarco' (Min) CSBt
Lady of Megginch = 'Ausvolume' (S) **new** LRHS MBri SWCr WClo
Lady Penelope = 'Chewdor'PBR (ClHT) CSBt ELon MAsh MJon SSea SWCr
§ 'Lady Penzance' (RH) ♀H4 CBcs MGan SPer SWCr WAct
Lady Rachel = 'Candoodle' (F) ECnt
Lady Rose = 'Korlady' (HT) MAsh SWCr
Lady Sunblaze see *R.* Lady Meillandina
'Lady Sylvia' (HT) LRHS MGan NEgg SPer
'Lady Waterlow' (ClHT) EWTr NLar WHCG
laevigata (Ra) NLar SWCr
Laguna = 'Koradigel'PBR (Cl) MGos MJon
L'Aimant = 'Harzola'PBR (F) ♀H4 CSBt ESty GCoc LGod LStr MGan MRav SWCr
'Lamarque' (N) CPou
§ Lambert Castle = 'Poulcs006'PBR (F) SWCr
Lancashire = 'Korstesgli'PBR (GC) ♀H4 ECnt ESty GCoc LGod LSRN LStr MGan MRav SMrm SWCr
Laura Anne = 'Cocclarion' (HT) GCoc SWCr
Laura Ford = 'Chewarvel'PBR (ClMin) ♀H4 CGro CTri LRHS LStr MAsh MGos MHav MJon MRav MWat NPri SPer SPoG SRGP SSea SWCr
'Laure Davoust' (Ra) CPou
'Lavender Lassie' (HM) ♀H4 CPou CSam EBee MGan SPer SSea SWCr WHCG
Lavender Symphonies SWCr
LaviniaPBR see *R.* Lawinia
§ Lawinia = 'Tanklewi'PBR (ClHT) ♀H4 CSBt EPfP LStr MAsh MRav NPri SPer SWCr
'Lawrence Johnston' see *R.* 'Hidcote Yellow'
§ Lazy Days = 'Poulkalm'PBR (F) EBee ECnt SWCr
Lea = 'Poulren019' **new** ECnt
Leaping Salmon = 'Peamight'PBR (ClHT) CGro CSBt EBee ELan ELon ESty GCoc LAst LGod LStr MGan MRav SPer SWCr
'Leda' (D) ELon NLar SFam SPer SWCr WAct
'Lemon Pillar' see *R.* 'Paul's Lemon Pillar'
Léonardo de Vinci = 'Meideauri'PBR (F) CSBt
'Léontine Gervais' (Ra) CAbP CRHN LRHS MBri NLar WAct
'Leo's Eye' EPfP SWCr
Leslie's Dream = 'Dicjoon' (HT) IDic
'Leverkusen' (Cl) ♀H4 EWTr LRHS MGan MRav SMrm SPer SPoG SWCr WAct WHCG
'Ley's Perpetual' (ClT) EBee SWCr
Lichfield Angel = 'Ausrelate' (S) LRHS MAsh MBri SCoo WClo
Lichtkönigin Lucia = 'Korlillub' (S) SSea
Life Begins at 40! = 'Horhohoho' (F) LSRN SWCr
Light Fantastic = 'Dicgottago' (F) GCoc IDic SWCr
'Lilac Charm' (F) SWCr
'Lilac Dream' (F) SWCr
Liliana = 'Poulsyng'PBR (S) ECnt SWCr
Lilli Marlene = 'Korlima' (F) CSBt CWSG ECGP MGan MHav SPer SWCr
Lincoln Cathedral = 'Glanlin'PBR (HT) MJon SPer SWCr
Lincolnshire Poacher = 'Glareabit' (HT) NEgg
'Lionheart' (HT) SWCr
Lisa = 'Kirdisco' (F) LSRN MJon
'Little Buckaroo' (Min) SPer SWCr
Little Cherub = 'Tan00814' (Patio) ESty SWCr

Name	Suppliers
'Little Flirt' (Min)	MGan SWCr
'Little Gem' (DPMo)	MGan
Little Jackie = 'Savor' (Min)	MJon
Little Muff = 'Horluisbond' (Min)	MJon
Little Rambler = 'Chewramb'PBR (MinRa) ♀H4	CSBt ECnt ESty LRHS LStr MBri MGan MGos MJon MMuc MRav MWat SCoo SPer SSea SWCr
'Little White Pet'	see *R.* 'White Pet'
Little Woman = 'Diclittle'PBR (Patio)	IDic LStr
'Lolabelle' **new**	CPou
'Long John Silver' (Cl)	SSea
longicuspis misapplied	see *R. mulliganii*
longicuspis Bertol. (Ra) AC 2097	GGar
§ - var. ***sinowilsonii*** (Ra)	GCal GGar
aff. ***longicuspis***	EBee
- AC 1808	GGar
Lord Byron = 'Meitosier' (ClHT)	LStr SSea
'Lord Penzance' (RH)	CGro MGan NHaw SPer WAct
Lorna = 'Cocringer' (F)	GCoc SWCr
'L'Ouche' misapplied	see *R.* 'Louise Odier'
'Louis XIV' (Ch)	MCot WHCG
Louisa Stone = 'Harbadge' (S)	SWCr
§ 'Louise Odier' (Bb)	EBee ECnt ELon EPfP IArd LRHS LStr MBri MCot MGan MJon MRav MWat NLar SFam SPer SSea SWCr WAct WBor WHCG WKif
Love & Peace = 'Baipeace'PBR (HT)	ELan ESty SWCr
Love Knot = 'Chewglorious'PBR (ClMin)	CSBt ECnt ESty MAsh MJon MRav Wat SCoo SRGP SSea SWCr WGor
§ Lovely Bride = 'Meiratcan'PBR (Patio)	MAsh MBri SPoG SWCr
Lovely Fairy = 'Spevu'PBR (Poly/GC)	IDic WAct
Lovely Lady = 'Dicjubell'PBR (HT) ♀H4	CSBt EBee EBls ECnt ESty IDic LStr MGan MJon MRav MWat SRGP SSea SWCr
Lovely MeidilandPBR	see *R.* Lovely Bride
'Lovers' Meeting' (HT)	MGan MRav SPer SRGP SSea SWCr
Loving Memory = 'Korgund'PBR (HT)	CGro CSBt CWSG ECnt ESty GCoc IArd LSRN LStr MGan MGos MJon MRav MWat NPri SPer SPoG SRGP SVic SWCr
'Lucky' (F) **new**	ESty LStr
Lucky! = 'Frylucy' (F) **new**	CSBt ECnt
Lucy = 'Kirlis' (F)	MJon
'Lykkefund' (Ra)	WHCG
Macartney rose	see *R. bracteata*, *R.* The McCartney Rose
Macmillan Nurse = 'Beamac' (S)	ESty
'Macrantha' (Gallica hybrid)	LRHS SPer WAct
macrophylla	WAct
- B&SWJ 2603	WCru
'Madame Alfred Carrière' (N) ♀H4	Widely available
'Madame Alice Garnier' (Ra)	CPou EBee SPer
'Madame Butterfly' (HT)	MGan SFam SPer SSea
§ 'Madame Caroline Testout' (HT)	GKir LRHS MGan SFam SMad SPoG WAct
'Madame de la Roche-Lambert' (DPMo)	CPou WAct WHCG
'Madame de Sancy de Parabère' (Bs)	EWTr IArd SFam SWCr
'Madame Ernest Calvat' (Bb)	CPou
'Madame Eugène Résal' misapplied	see *R.* 'Comtesse du Cayla'
Madame Figaro = 'Delrona' (S)	MRav
§ 'Madame Grégoire Staechelin' (ClHT) ♀H4	CWSG ECnt ELan EPfP LAst LRHS LStr MBri MGan MJon MRav NEgg SFam SMrm SPer SWCr WAct WHCG
'Madame Hardy' (ClD) ♀H4	CPou CSBt EBee ECnt EPfP EWTr GCoc LRHS LStr MBri MGan MJon MRav NEgg NLar SFam SMrm SPer SSea SWCr WAct WHCG
'Madame Isaac Pereire' (ClBb) ♀H4	CSBt CTri EBee ECnt EPfP ESty GCoc GKir LRHS LStr MAsh MBri MCot MGan MJon MRav MWat SFam SMad SMrm SPer SPoG SSea SWCr WAct WHCG
§ 'Madame Knorr' (DPo) ♀H4	CPou EBee ECnt EPfP GKir LRHS MAsh MCot MRav NLar SEND SMrm SPer SSea WAct WHCG
'Madame Laurette Messimy' (Ch)	WHCG
'Madame Lauriol de Barny' (Bb)	MGan MRav NHaw NLar SFam SLon SWCr WHCG
'Madame Legras de Saint Germain' (AxN)	CPou EBee LRHS NLar SFam SPer WAct WHCG
'Madame Louis Lévêque' (DPMo)	NLar SWCr WAct WHCG
'Madame Pierre Oger' (Bb)	EBee ECnt LRHS LStr MAsh MGan MRav SPer SWCr WAct
'Madame Plantier' (AxN)	CPou LRHS MRav NHaw NLar SPer SWCr WHCG
'Madame Scipion Cochet' (T)	EWTr WHCG
'Madeleine Seltzer' (Ra)	ECGP MGan
'Madge' (HM)	SDix
Magic Carpet = 'Jaclover'PBR (S/GC) ♀H4	CWSG ECnt ELan GCoc IDic MGan MGos MRav MWat SMrm SPer SPoG SSea SWCr
Magic Hit = 'Poulhi004'PBR (Min)	LRHS MAsh
'Magnifica' (RH)	LRHS MGan
'Maid of Kent'PBR (Cl)	CSBt MJon SCoo SPer SWCr
'Maiden's Blush' (A) ♀H4	CArn CTri ELan GKir LRHS MAsh MGan NPri SFam SPer SSea SWCr WHCG
'Maiden's Blush, Great'	see *R.* 'Great Maiden's Blush'
'Maigold' (ClPiH) ♀H4	CBcs CGro CTri CWSG EBee ECnt ELan EPfP GCoc GKir LGod LRHS LStr MAsh MCot MGan MJon MRav MWat SMad SPer SPoG SWCr WAct WHCG
Make a Wish = 'Mehpat'PBR (Min/Patio)	ESty LStr
Maltese rose	see *R.* 'Cécile Brünner'
Malvern Hills = 'Auscanary'PBR (Ra)	CSBt LRHS MAsh MBri MGan MJon SPer SSea SWCr WAct WClo
Mama Mia! = 'Fryjolly' (HT) **new**	ECnt ESty GCoc
Mandarin = 'Korcelin'PBR (Min)	ESty LStr MRav
'Manning's Blush' (RH)	WAct
Manou Meilland = 'Meitulimon' (HT)	SSea
Many Happy Returns = 'Harwanted'PBR (S/F) ♀H4	CBcs CGro CSBt CWSG ECnt ELan EPfP GCoc LGod LRHS LSRN LStr MAsh MGan MGos MJon MRav NPri SPer SPoG SRGP SSea SVic SWCr
§ 'Marchesa Boccella' (DPo) ♀H4	CPou CSam CTri EBee ELon EPfP GKir LRHS MAsh MBri MCot MGan MGos NLar NPri SPer SPoG SSea SWCr WAct WHCG

'Marcia Gandy' (HT) MGan
'Maréchal Davoust' (CeMo) SFam
'Maréchal Niel' (N) ERea EShb EWTr SPer WHCG
'Margaret' (HT) MGan SWCr
Margaret Merril = 'Harkuly' (F) ♀H4 CBcs CGro CSBt CTri CWSG EBee ECnt ELan EPfP ESty GCoc IArd LGod LRHS LStr MAsh MBri MGan MJon MRav MWat SMrm SPer SPoG SRGP SSea SWCr WBor
'Marguerite Hilling' (S) ♀H4 CTri EPfP MGan MRav NLar SPer SSea SWCr WAct WHCG
Maria McGredy = 'Macturangu'PBR (HT) MJon
'Mariae-Graebnerae' SLPl
'Marie Louise' (D) SFam WHCG
'Marie Pavič' (Poly) CPou WHCG
Marilyn Monroe = 'Weksunspat' (HT) MJon
Marjorie Fair = 'Harhero' (Poly/S) ♀H4 EPfP MAsh MGan MRav SWCr WBor
Marjorie Marshall = 'Hardenier'PBR MRav
'Marlena' (F/Patio) GCoc
Marry Me = 'Dicwonder'PBR (Patio) ♀H4 IDic
'Martian Glow' (F/S) MGan NLar
'Martin Frobisher' (Ru) NHaw SSea
I 'Mary' (Poly) LStr
Mary Magdalene = 'Ausjolly'PBR (S) LRHS
'Mary Manners' (Ru) NLar SPer
Mary Rose = 'Ausmary'PBR (S) ♀H4 CGro CSBt CWSG ELan ELon EPfP GCoc LGod LRHS LStr MBri MCot MGan MJon MRav MWat NPri SMrm SPer SPoG SSea SWCr WClo WKif
'Masquerade' (F) CWSG ELan MGan SMrm SPer SSea SWCr
Matangi = 'Macman' (F) ♀H4 MGan
Matawhero MagicPBR see *R.* Simply the Best
'Max Graf' see *R.* × *jacksonii* 'Max Graf'
'Maxima' see *R.* × *alba* 'Alba Maxima'
'May Queen' (Ra) CPou LRHS MAsh MBri MGan MRav NLar SEND SFam SPer SWCr WHCG
Mayor of Casterbridge = 'Ausbrid'PBR (S) LRHS
'McCartney Rose'PBR see *R.* The McCartney Rose
'Meg' (ClHT) EBee EWTr LRHS LSRN MCot MGan SPer SRGP SWCr WAct WHCG
'Meg Merrilies' (RH) MGan NLar SWCr WAct
'Megiddo' (F) MGan
'Meicobuis'PBR see *R.* Terracotta = 'Meicobuis'
Melody Maker = 'Dicqueen'PBR (F) CWSG IDic MHav SWCr
Memento = 'Dicbar' (F) ♀H4 MGan SWCr
'Memoriam' (HT) MGan SWCr
'Memories Are Made of This' (F) MGan
Memory Lane = 'Peavoodoo'PBR (F) SWCr
'Mermaid' (Cl) ♀H3-4 CBcs CGro CSBt CTri ECnt ELon EPfP EWTr LHop LRHS LStr MBri MGan MJon SMrm SPer SPoG SSea SWCr WAct WHCG
§ Message = 'Meban' (HT) SWCr
'Meteor' (F/Patio) MGan
§ 'Mevrouw Nathalie Nypels' (Poly) ♀H4 LRHS LStr MRav SPer SWCr WHCG WKif
Michael Fish = 'Kirgale' (F) MJon
'Michèle Meilland' (HT) NBlu
Michelle Chetcuti = 'Kirchief' (HT) MJon
Midnight Blue = 'Wekfabpur' (S) **new** MJon
§ Millie = 'Poulren013'PBR (Renaissance Series) (S) ECnt SWCr
'Mills and Boon' (F) MGan
'Minnehaha' (Ra) LGod SWCr
Minnie Pearl = 'Savahowdy' (Min) MJon
mirifica stellata see *R. stellata* var. *mirifica*
Mischief = 'Macmi' (HT) MGan SPer SWCr
Miss Alice = 'Ausjake'PBR (S) LRHS SWCr
Miss Dior = 'Harencens'PBR (S) MRav
Miss Flippins = 'Tuckflip' (Min) MJon
Missing You = 'Horcakebread' (F) MGan SWCr
§ 'Mister Lincoln' (HT) LGod MGan SPer SSea
§ Misty Hit = 'Poulhi011'PBR (PatioHit Series) (Patio) ECnt LRHS LSRN MAsh SWCr
'Mojave' (HT) MGan
'Moje Hammarberg' (Ru) MJon WAct
Molineux = 'Ausmol'PBR (S) ♀H4 CSBt ECnt EPfP LRHS MAsh MBri SMrm SSea SWCr WClo
'Monique' (HT) MGan
'Moonlight' (HM) CTri EBee ELan EWTr LRHS MGan MRav SPer SWCr WAct WHCG
'Morgengruss' (Cl) MGan SPer SWCr
Moriah = 'Ganhol'PBR (HT) MGan
'Morletii' (Bs) MRav WHCG
'Morning Jewel' (ClF) ♀H4 GCoc MGan MJon SPer SWCr
Morning Mist = 'Ausfire' (S) SSea
§ 'Morsdag' (Poly/F) LSRN LStr MJon SPoG SWCr
Mortimer Sackler = 'Ausorts'PBR (S) LRHS MBri MJon SCoo SWCr WClo
moschata (Ra) MRav SSea WAct WHCG
- 'Autumnalis' see *R.* 'Princesse de Nassau'
- var. ***nepalensis*** see *R. brunonii*
I 'Mother's Day' **new** SRGP
Mother's Day see *R.* 'Morsdag'
Mother's Joy = 'Horsiltrop' (F) LSRN
Mountain Snow = 'Aussnow' (Ra) LRHS
Mountbatten = 'Harmantelle' (F) ♀H4 CWSG ELan EPfP LGod LRHS LStr MAsh MGan MJon MRav NPri SPer SPoG SSea SWCr
§ 'Mousseline' (DPoMo) CPou EBee MRav NLar SPer SWCr WHCG
'Mousseuse du Japon' see *R.* 'Japonica'
moyesii (S) CTri ELan GCra GKir ISea MGan NEgg NWea SPer WAct
- 'Evesbatch' (S) WAct
'Mozart' (HM) SWCr WHCG
'Mr Bluebird' (MinCh) MGan SWCr
'Mr Lincoln' see *R.* 'Mister Lincoln'
'Mrs Anthony Waterer' (Ru) SPer SWCr WAct WHCG
'Mrs Arthur Curtiss James' (ClHT) EBee
'Mrs Eveline Gandy' (HT) MGan
'Mrs Honey Dyson' (Ra) EWTr WHCG
'Mrs John Laing' (HP) EPfP LRHS NLar SFam SLon SPer SWCr
'Mrs Oakley Fisher' (HT) EWTr MCot SDix SMrm SPer SWCr WAct
'Mrs Sam McGredy' (HT) LRHS MGan NEgg SSea
'Mullard Jubilee' (HT) MGan SWCr
§ ***mulliganii*** (Ra) ♀H4 EPfP SPer WAct WHCG

	multibracteata (S)	WHCG
	multiflora (Ra)	IFFs LBuc NHaw NWea WAct
§	– var. ***cathayensis*** (Ra)	WBor WHCG
§	– 'Grevillei' (Ra)	SPer SWCr
	– 'Platyphylla'	see *R. multiflora* 'Grevillei'
	'Mum in a Million'	LRHS MAsh MBri NPri SPoG SWCr
	Mummy[PBR]	see *R.* Newly Wed
	mundi	see *R. gallica* 'Versicolor'
	Munstead Wood = 'Ausbernard' **new**	LRHS
	'Mutabilis'	see *R.* × *odorata* 'Mutabilis'
	'My Choice' (HT)	MGan SWCr
	My Everything = 'Coccastle' (F)	ESty GCoc
	My Love = 'Cogamo' (HT)	MJon
	My Mum = 'Webmorrow'[PBR]	EGxp ESty MGan SMrm SWCr
	My Valentine = 'Mormyval' (Min)	LSRN LStr
	Myriam = 'Cocgrand' (HT)	GCoc
	Mystery Girl = 'Dicdothis' (HT) **new**	ECnt ESty IDic
	Mystique = 'Kirmyst' (F)	EBls MJon
	Nahéma = 'Deléri' (Cl)	MRav SMrm SWCr
	'Nan of Painswick'	WAct
	nanothamnus	WCot
	'Narrow Water' (Ra)	CPou EBee NLar SWCr WAct WHCG
§	'Nastarana' (N)	EBee
	'Nathalie Nypels'	see *R.* 'Mevrouw Nathalie Nypels'
	'National Trust' (HT)	CBcs IArd MAsh MGan MJon MWat SMrm SPer
	'Nelson's Pride' (F)	EBls
	'Nestor' (G)	SWCr
	'Nevada' (S) ♀H4	CSBt CTri EBee ECnt ELan EPfP GCoc IArd LGod LStr MCot MGan MJon MRav SPer SSea SWCr WAct WHCG
	Never Forgotten = 'Gregart' (HT)	SWCr
	New Age = 'Wekbipuhit'[PBR] (F)	CSBt ESty MJon SWCr
	New Arrival	see *R.* 'Red Patio'
	'New Arrival' (Patio/Min)	MGan SWCr
	New Beginnings = 'Korprofko' (F) **new**	GCoc
§	'New Dawn' (Cl) ♀H4	Widely available
	New Life = 'Cocwarble' (F) **new**	GCoc
	'New Look' (F)	MGan
	New Zealand = 'Macgenev'[PBR] (HT)	MJon SWCr
§	Newly Wed = 'Dicwhynot'[PBR] (Patio)	IDic LStr MJon
	News = 'Legnews' (F)	MGan SWCr
	Nice Day = 'Chewsea'[PBR] (ClMin) ♀H4	CGro CSBt CWSG ELon EPfP ESty LGod LRHS LStr MAsh MRav MWat SPer SRGP SSea SWCr
	'Nicola' (F)	MGan SWCr
	Night Light = 'Poullight'[PBR] (Courtyard Series) (Cl)	ECnt MGan MRav SWCr
	Night Sky = 'Dicetch'[PBR] (F)	IDic SSea
	Nina = 'Mehnina'[PBR] (S)	LSRN SWCr
	Nina Nadine = 'Kirhand' (F)	MJon
	Nina = 'Poulren018' (Renaissance Series) (S)	ECnt
	'Nina Weibull' (F)	SWCr
	nitida	EMac MGan NHaw NWea SEND SPer SSea SWCr WAct WHer
	Noble Antony = 'Ausway'[PBR] (S)	LRHS LStr MBri MJon SWCr
§	'Noisette Carnée' (N)	CSam EPfP GCra LRHS LStr MAsh MBNS MGan MJon MRav NLar SLPl SPer SSea SWCr WAct WClo
	Norfolk = 'Poulfolk'[PBR] (GC)	EWTr SPer SWCr
	'Norma Major' (HT)	MJon
	Northamptonshire = 'Mattdor'[PBR] (GC)	MGan
	'Northern Lights' (HT)	GCoc SWCr
	Nostalgia = 'Savarita' (Min)	CGro MAsh MGan
	Nostalgie = 'Taneiglat'[PBR] (HT)	EBee EBls ECnt EGxp ESty LStr MBri MJon MRav SPoG SSea SWCr
	'Nottingham Millennium' (F)	MGan
	'Nozomi' (ClMin/GC) ♀H4	CGro CTri ELan ESty GCoc MGan MJon MRav SMad SMrm SPer SPoG SWCr WAct
	'Nuits de Young' (CeMo) ♀H4	GCoc LRHS SFam SWCr WAct WHCG
	'Nur Mahal' (HM)	SWCr WHCG
§	***nutkana*** 'Plena' (S/D) ♀H4	EPfP MGan NLar SWCr WAct WHCG
	'Nymphenburg' (HM)	SPer SWCr
	Octavia Hill = 'Harzeal'[PBR] (F/S)	EWTr MRav SPer SWCr
§	× ***odorata***	SVic
§	– 'Mutabilis' (Ch) ♀H3-4	CRHN EBee ECre EPfP EWTr GCoc GGal LRHS MBri MCot MGan MRav MWat SMrm SPer SPoG SSea SWCr WAct WBor WCFE WCot WHCG WKif
§	– 'Pallida' (Ch)	EPfP EWTr GCoc LRHS MCot MRav SPer SSea SWCr WAct WHCG
§	– Sanguinea Group (Ch)	WHCG
	– – 'Bengal Crimson' (Ch)	ECGP EPfP EWTr LRHS WCot
	– – 'Bob's Beauty' (Ch) **new**	WCot
§	– 'Viridiflora' (Ch)	EBee LRHS SLon SMad SPer SSea SWCr WHCG
	Odyssey = 'Franski'[PBR] (F)	ESty MJon
	'Oeillet Panaché' (Mo)	WAct
	officinalis	see *R. gallica* var. *officinalis*
	'Oklahoma' (HT)	MGan SWCr
	old blush China	see *R.* × *odorata* 'Pallida'
	old cabbage	see *R.* × *centifolia*
	Old John = 'Dicwillynilly' (F)	IDic
	old pink moss rose	see *R.* × *centifolia* 'Muscosa'
	Old Port = 'Mackati'[PBR] (F)	IArd MJon
	old red moss	see *R.* 'Henri Martin'
	old velvet moss	see *R.* 'William Lobb'
	old yellow Scotch (PiH)	see *R.* × *harisonii* 'Williams Double Yellow'
	Olympic Palace = 'Poulymp'[PBR] (Palace Series) (F)	EBee ECnt
	'Omar Khayyám' (D)	MRav
	omeiensis	see *R. sericea* subsp. *omeiensis*
	'One Another' (F)	MGan
	One Promise = 'Frannite'[PBR] **new**	LRHS MAsh MBri NPri SWCr
	Open Arms = 'Chewpixcel'[PBR] (ClMin) ♀H4	ESty MAsh MBri MJon SPer SSea SWCr
	'Ophelia' (HT)	LRHS MGan
	'Orange Sensation' (F)	CTri CWSG MGan MHav SWCr
§	Orange Sunblaze = 'Meijikatar'[PBR] (Min)	CSBt MGan SPer
	Oranges and Lemons = 'Macoranlem'[PBR] (S/F)	CGro CSBt EBls ECnt ELan LGod LStr MAsh MGan MJon SPoG SSea SWCr
	'Orient Express' (HT)	CWSG
	Othello = 'Auslo'[PBR] (S)	SLon SWCr WAct
	'Our Beth' (S)	EBls

Name	Suppliers
'Our Dream' (Patio)	MAsh
Our George = 'Kirrush' (Patio)	MJon
§ Our Jane = 'Horengland' (F) **new**	SWCr
Our Jubilee = 'Coccages' (HT)	ESty SVic SWCr
Our Love = 'Andour' (HT)	CWSG
Our Molly = 'Dicreason' (GC/S)	IDic LSRN MGan MJon SWCr
Oxfordshire = 'Korfullwind'PBR (GC) ♀H4	LStr MRav MWat
Paddy McGredy = 'Macpa' (F)	MGan
Paddy Stephens = 'Macclack'PBR (HT)	MJon
Painted Moon = 'Dicpaint' (HT)	ESty
Panache = 'Poultop'PBR (Patio)	ECnt LRHS LStr MAsh SMrm SWCr
Papa Meilland = 'Meisar' (HT)	CGro CSBt MGan MHav SPer SWCr
Paper Anniversary (Patio)	LSRN
Papi Delbard = 'Delaby' (Cl)	MRav
§ 'Para Ti' (Min)	MGan MJon SPer SWCr
I 'Parade' (Cl) ♀H4	MRav SMrm SWCr WHCG
'Paradise' (Patio)	SPoG SWCr
Paradise = 'Wezip' (HT)	MGan
'Parkdirektor Riggers' (Cl)	EWTr LStr MBri MGan NLar SPer SWCr WHCG
'Parkjuwel' (CeMo)	MGan
Parson's pink China	see *R.* × *odorata* 'Pallida'
Partridge = 'Korweirim'PBR (GC)	MGan SPer SWCr WAct
'Party Girl' (Min)	MJon
Pas de Deux = 'Poulhult'PBR (Courtyard Series) (ClF)	LRHS MAsh
Pascali = 'Lenip' (HT)	CTri GCoc MGan MJon MRav MWat NPri SMrm SPer SSea SWCr
Pat Austin = 'Ausmum'PBR (S) ♀H4	CSBt EBee ECnt EPfP LRHS LStr MAsh MBNS MBri MRav NEgg NLar SPoG SRGP SWCr WClo
Pathfinder = 'Chewpobey' (GC)	MJon
Patricia Kent = 'Harmerry'PBR (S) **new**	MJon
Patricia = 'Korpatri' (F)	SWCr
Paul Cézanne = 'Jacdeli' (S)	LRHS
'Paul Crampel' (Poly)	MGan WAct
'Paul Lédé' (ClT)	see *R.* 'Climbing Paul Lédé'
Paul McCartneyPBR	see *R.* The McCartney Rose
'Paul Neyron' (HP)	EBee SPer SWCr
Paul Shirville = 'Harqueterwife'PBR (HT) ♀H4	ELan ELon MGan SPer SRGP SWCr
'Paul Transon' (Ra) ♀H4	CPou CRHN EBee EPfP EWTr LRHS MBri NEgg NLar SPer WClo WHer
§ 'Paulii' (Ru/GC)	WAct
'Paulii Alba'	see *R.* 'Paulii'
'Paulii Rosea' (Ru/GC)	MGan WAct
'Paul's Himalayan Musk' (Ra) ♀H3-4	CPLG CRHN CSBt CSam CTri EBee ECnt EPfP IArd ISea LRHS LStr MBri MGan MJon MRav NEgg SFam SMrm SPer SPoG SSea SWCr WAct WBVN WBor WClo WHCG WKif
§ 'Paul's Lemon Pillar' (ClHT)	EBee LAst LRHS NLar SMrm SPer SSea SWCr
'Paul's Scarlet Climber' (Cl/Ra)	CGro CSBt ELan EPfP EWTr GKir LAst LStr MAsh MGan MJon MRav NBlu NPri SEND SPer SRGP SWCr
'Paul's Single White Perpetual' (Ra)	WHCG
'Pax' (HM)	CPou SWCr WAct WHCG WKif
Peace = 'Madame A. Meilland' (HT) ♀H4	CGro CSBt ECnt ELan EPfP ESty GCoc LGod LRHS LStr MAsh MBri MGan MJon MRav MWat NEgg NPri SMrm SPer SPoG SRGP SSea SWCr WBor
Peace Sunblaze (Min)	see *R.* Lady Meillandina
Peacekeeper = 'Harbella'PBR (F)	CSBt MRav
Peachy = 'Macrelea' (HT) **new**	MAsh SWCr
§ Pearl Abundance = 'Harfrisky'PBR (F)	ESty SWCr
Pearl Anniversary = 'Whitston'PBR (Min/Patio)	CSBt ESty LSRN LStr MRav MWat SWCr
Pearl Drift = 'Leggab' (S)	SMrm SPer SWCr WHCG
Pearl = 'Kortershi' **new**	SWCr
Pearl Meidiland = 'Meiplatin' (S)	SWCr
PeaudoucePBR	see *R.* Elina
§ Peek-a-boo = 'Dicgrow' (Min/Patio)	MGan SPer
Peer Gynt = 'Korol' (HT)	MGan SWCr
Pegasus = 'Ausmoon'PBR (S)	LRHS SSea
§ ***pendulina***	LBuc NHaw
- 'Nana'	NHol
'Penelope' (HM) ♀H4	CSBt CSam CTri EBee ECnt ELan EPfP GCoc LRHS LSRN LStr MAsh MBri MCot MGan MGos MJon MRav MWat NPri SFam SMrm SPer SRGP SSea SWCr WAct WHCG WKif
Penny Lane = 'Hardwell'PBR (Cl) ♀H4	CSBt ECnt EPfP ESty GCoc LAst LGod LRHS LStr MAsh MBri MGan MGos MJon MRav MWat NPri SCoo SMrm SPer SPoG SSea SWCr
Pensioner's Voice = 'Fryrelax'PBR (F)	MGan SWCr
× ***penzanceana***	see *R.* 'Lady Penzance'
Perception = 'Harzippee'PBR (HT)	SWCr
Perdita = 'Ausperd' (S)	ESty LRHS MJon MRav
Perennial Blue = 'Mehblue'	ECnt ESty SMad SMrm SSea SWCr
§ Perfect Day = 'Poulrem' (F)	ECnt SWCr
Perfecta = 'Koralu' (HT)	MGan
§ 'Perle d'Or' (Poly) ♀H4	ECGP EPfP MGan NLar SDix SLon SMad SPer SWCr WAct WHCG
Perpetually Yours = 'Harfable'PBR (Cl)	CGro LStr MRav MWat SCoo
Persian yellow	see *R. foetida* 'Persiana'
Peter Pan = 'Chewpan'PBR (Min)	MAsh MJon MWat NPri SWCr
Peter Pan = 'Sunpete' (Patio)	EPfP LRHS NPri SPoG
'Petite de Hollande' (Ce)	NLar SPer SWCr WHCG
'Petite Lisette' (CexD)	NLar
'Petito' (F) **new**	SMrm
Phab Gold = 'Frybountiful'PBR (F)	ESty GCoc MAsh
Pheasant = 'Kordapt'PBR (GC)	GCoc MGan MJon SPer WAct
Phillipa = 'Poulheart'PBR (S)	ECnt SWCr
Phoebe (Ru)	see *R.* 'Fimbriata'
'Phyllis Bide' (Ra) ♀H4	CAbP EBee ECGP EPfP IArd LRHS LStr MBri MGan MJon NLar SPer SSea SWCr WAct WHCG WKif
Picasso = 'Macpic' (F)	MGan NHaw

Name	Source codes
Piccadilly = 'Macar' (HT)	CGro CSBt CTri MGan MRav SPer SWCr WBor
Piccolo = 'Tanolokip' PBR (F/Patio)	CGro ESty LStr MBri MJon MRav SWCr
'Picture' (HT)	MGan SPer SWCr
Pigalle '84 = 'Meicloux' (F)	SWCr
'Pilgrim' PBR	see *R.* The Pilgrim
pimpinellifolia	see *R. spinosissima*
- double yellow-flowered	see *R.* × *harisonii* 'Williams Double Yellow'
- 'Harisonii'	see *R.* × *harisonii* 'Harison's Yellow'
Pink Abundance = 'Harfrothy' PBR (Abundance Series) (F)	ESty LStr
Pink Bells = 'Poulbells' PBR (GC)	GCoc SPer
'Pink Bouquet' (Ra)	CRHN
'Pink Favorite' (HT)	CSBt MGan SPer SWCr
Pink Fizz = 'Poulycool' (ClPatio)	ECnt MAsh SWCr
§ Pink Flower Carpet = 'Noatraum' PBR (GC) 🏆H4	CGro CSBt CTri ECnt ELan GCoc LRHS LStr MAsh MBri MGan NPri SCoo SPer SPoG SWCr
'Pink Garnette'	see *R.* 'Carol Amling'
'Pink Grootendorst' (Ru) 🏆H4	EBee EPfP LRHS MGan NEgg NLar SPer SWCr WAct WHCG
§ Pink Hit = 'Poultipe' PBR (Min/Patio)	ECnt LRHS MAsh SWCr
Pink La Sevillana = 'Meigeroka' PBR (F/GC)	WAct
'Pink Medley' (F)	MAsh
pink moss	see *R.* × *centifolia* 'Muscosa'
'Pink Parfait' (F)	MGan SPer
Pink Peace = 'Meibil' (HT)	NBlu SWCr
'Pink Perpétué' (Cl)	CBcs CGro CSBt CTri ECnt ELan EPfP GCoc GKir LRHS LStr MAsh MGan MJon MRav SPer SPoG SWCr WAct
'Pink Showers' (ClHT)	WAct
Pink Skyliner = 'Franwekpink' PBR (ClPatio)	EBls MJon
Pirouette = 'Poulyc003' PBR (Cl)	EBee ECnt MAsh SWCr
'Playboy' (F)	GCoc SWCr
Pleine de Grâce = 'Lengra' (S)	LRHS
Poetry in Motion = 'Harelan' PBR (HT)	EBls
Polar Star = 'Tanlarpost' PBR (HT)	CSBt ECnt LGod LStr MAsh MGan MRav MWat SWCr
× ***polliniana***	SLPl
'Polly' (HT)	MGan
§ 'Polyantha Grandiflora' (Ra)	LRHS
pomifera	see *R. villosa* L.
'Pompon de Paris' (ClMinCh)	see *R.* 'Climbing Pompon de Paris'
Port Sunlight = 'Auslofty' (HM) **new**	LRHS WClo
Portland rose	see *R.* 'Portlandica'
§ 'Portlandica' (Po)	CTri GKir LRHS MAsh SPer SWCr WAct WHCG
Portmeirion = 'Ausguard' PBR (S)	LRHS SCoo
Pot o' Gold = 'Dicdivine' (HT)	SPer SWCr
Pour Toi	see *R.* 'Para Ti'
'Precious Memories' (Min)	SWCr
Precious Moments = 'Lyopr' (Min)	SWCr
'Precious Platinum' (HT)	LGod MJon SPer SWCr
§ 'Président de Sèze' (G) 🏆H4	CPou NLar SFam SWCr WAct WHCG
'President Herbert Hoover' (HT)	ESty
Pretty in Pink = 'Dicumpteen' PBR (GC)	ECnt IDic SWCr
Pretty Jessica = 'Ausjess' (S)	CGro LRHS MJon MRav SMrm SPer
Pretty Lady = 'Scrivo' PBR (F) 🏆H4	LStr MJon SSea
Pretty Polly = 'Meitonje' PBR (Min) 🏆H4	CGro EPfP ESty LRHS LStr MAsh MBri MGan MRav MWat SPer SPoG SRGP SWCr
Pride of England = 'Harencore' PBR (HT)	EBls GCoc MJon SWCr
Pride of Scotland = 'Macwhitba' (HT)	GCoc MJon
'Prima Ballerina' (HT)	CGro CSBt CTri CWSG GCoc LRHS LStr MAsh MGan SPer SSea SWCr
primula (S) 🏆H3-4	MGan MJon NLar SSea WAct WHCG
'Prince Camille de Rohan' (HP)	WHCG
'Prince Charles' (Bb)	SWCr WKif
Prince Regent = 'Genpen' (S)	SSea
Princess Alexandra of Kent = 'Ausmerchant' **new**	LRHS MBri SWCr WClo
Princess Alexandra = 'Pouldra' PBR (Renaissance Series) (S)	CTri ECnt EPfP SWCr
Princess Alice = 'Hartanna' (F)	MGan
Princess Nobuko = 'Coclistine' PBR (HT)	GCoc SWCr
'Princess of Wales' (HP)	EPfP
Princess of Wales = 'Hardinkum' PBR (F) 🏆H4	EPfP LRHS LStr MAsh MBri MGan MRav NPri SCoo SPer SWCr
Princess Royal = 'Dicroyal' PBR (HT)	IDic
§ 'Princesse de Nassau' (Ra)	WAct WHCG
'Princesse Louise' (Ra)	CRHN SFam
'Princesse Marie' misapplied	see *R.* 'Belvedere'
Priory Rose = 'Nostpri' **new**	SWCr
§ 'Professeur Emile Perrot' (D)	CArn EBee SMad WAct
'Prolifera de Redouté' misapplied	see *R.* 'Duchesse de Montebello'
'Prosperity' (HM) 🏆H4	CSam CTri EPfP GCoc LRHS MCot MGan MJon MRav SPer SWCr WAct WHCG
Prospero = 'Auspero' (S)	NLar
§ ***pulverulenta***	GAuc
'Pure Abundance' (F)	SWCr
Pure Bliss = 'Dictator' PBR (HT)	ECnt IDic MGan SWCr
Pure Gold = 'Harhappen' PBR (F) **new**	CSBt
'Purezza' (Ra)	NLar
'Purity' (Cl)	EBee
'Purple Beauty' (HT)	MGan
Purple Skyliner = 'Franwekpurp' PBR (ClS)	ESty MJon SSea
Purple Tiger = 'Jacpurr' PBR (F)	ESty IDic LStr SMrm SWCr
'Purpurtraum' (Ru)	WHCG
Quaker Star = 'Dicperhaps' (F)	IDic
quatre saisons	see *R.* × *damascena* var. *semperflorens*
'Quatre Saisons Blanche Mousseuse' (DMo)	SWCr WAct
Queen Elizabeth	see *R.* 'The Queen Elizabeth'

	Name	Suppliers
	Queen Mother = 'Korquemu'PBR (Patio) ♀H4	CSBt ELan EPfP GCoc LGod LStr MGan MRav SMrm SPer SPoG SWCr
	Queen of Denmark	see *R.* 'Königin von Dänemark'
	Queen of Sweden = 'Austiger'PBR	ECnt LRHS MAsh MBri MJon SPer SWCr WClo
	'Rachel' ambig.	GCoc
	'Rachel' (HT)	EBls LSRN
	Rachel = 'Tangust'PBR (HT)	CSBt ESty LStr MJon MRav SPoG SWCr
	Racy Lady = 'Dicwaffle'PBR (HT)	IDic MJon
	Radio Times = 'Aussal'PBR (S)	ESty LRHS
	'Ragamuffin' (Patio) **new**	LShp
	Rainbow Magic = 'Dicxplosion'PBR (Patio)	IDic
	'Ralph Tizzard' (F)	SSea
	'Rambling Rector' (Ra) ♀H4	Widely available
	Rambling Rosie = 'Horjasper' (Ra)	EBls ECnt ESty LGod LSRN MJon SWCr
	'Ramona' (Ra)	SWCr
	'Raspberry Royale' (F/Patio)	SWCr
	'Raubritter' ('Macrantha' hybrid)	CAbP ECGP LRHS SPer SWCr WAct WHCG
	Ray of Hope = 'Cocnilly'PBR (F)	GCoc LGod
	Ray of Sunshine = 'Cocclare'PBR (Patio)	GCoc SWCr
	Raymond Blanc = 'Delnado' (HT)	LRHS
	'Raymond Chenault' (Cl)	CGro MGan SWCr
	Rebecca (Patio)	ESty LSRN
	'Rebecca Claire' (HT)	LSRN SWCr
	Reconciliation = 'Hartillery'PBR (HT)	SRGP SWCr
	Red AbundancePBR	see *R.* Songs of Praise
	Red Bells = 'Poulred'PBR (Min/GC)	SPer
	Red Blanket = 'Intercell' (S/GC)	GCoc SPer WAct
	Red Caviar = 'Poulfl001'PBR (HT)	EBee
	Red Devil = 'Dicam' (HT)	MAsh MGan MJon SCoo SPoG SWCr
	Red Eden Rose = 'Meidrason'PBR (Cl)	ESty SSea
	'Red Facade' (Cl)	MAsh
	Red Finesse = 'Korvillade'PBR	MAsh MGos
	'Red Grootendorst'	see *R.* 'F.J. Grootendorst'
	Red Hot = 'Weksacquem' (Patio) **new**	MJon
	'Red Max Graf'PBR	see *R.* Rote Max Graf
	red moss	see *R.* 'Henri Martin'
	Red New Dawn	see *R.* 'Etendard'
§	'Red Patio' (FPatio)	LSRN
	Red Rascal = 'Jacbed'PBR (S/Patio)	CSBt ECGP IDic
	red rose of Lancaster	see *R. gallica* var. *officinalis*
	Redouté = 'Auspale'PBR (S)	LRHS SWCr
	Reflections = 'Simref' (F)	SWCr
	Regensberg = 'Macyoumis'PBR (F/Patio)	MBri MGan MJon SPer SWCr
	'Reine des Centfeuilles' (Ce)	SFam
	'Reine des Violettes' (HP)	CGro CPou EBee ELon EPfP GKir IArd LRHS LStr MAsh MBri MCot MGan MRav NLar SPer SPoG SWCr WAct WBor WHCG
§	'Reine Victoria' (Bb)	EPfP LRHS LStr MBri MCot MGan SPer SWCr
	Remember Me = 'Cocdestin'PBR (HT) ♀H4	CSBt CWSG ECnt ESty GCoc IArd LGod LSRN LStr MBri MGan MGos MJon MRav MWat NEgg NPri SPer SPoG SRGP SWCr
§	Remember = 'Poulht001'PBR (HT)	ECnt EPfP LRHS MAsh SWCr
	Remembrance = 'Harxampton'PBR (F) ♀H4	CTri EBls ESty LGod LRHS LSRN LStr MAsh MGan MJon MRav NPri SPer SPoG SRGP SWCr
	Renaissance = 'Harzart'PBR (HT)	CSBt GCoc LStr MWat SWCr
	'René André' (Ra)	CPou CRHN EBee
	'Rescht'	see *R.* 'De Resht'
	'Rêve d'Or' (N)	CSam SLon SPer
	Rhapsody in Blue = 'Frantasia'PBR (S)	CGro CSBt EBee ECnt ELan ELon EPfP ESty GCoc LAst LGod LRHS LStr MAsh MBri MGan MGos MJon MRav MWat NPri SCoo SMad SMrm SPer SPoG SSea SWCr
§	× ***richardii***	MGan MRav WAct WHCG
	Rick Stein = 'Tan96205'PBR (HT)	LSRN LStr SWCr
	'River Gardens'	NPer
	Rob Roy = 'Cocrob' (F)	GCoc MGan SPer SWCr
	Robbie Burns = 'Ausburn' (PiH)	WAct
	'Robert le Diable' (Ce × G)	NLar SPer SWCr WAct
	'Robin Hood' (HM)	SWCr
§	Robusta = 'Korgosa' (Ru)	ECnt MGan SWCr
	Rockabye Baby = 'Dicdwarf' (Patio)	ESty IDic SWCr
	Romance = 'Tanezamor'PBR (S)	MRav
	'Rosa Mundi'	see *R. gallica* 'Versicolor'
	Rosabell = 'Cocceleste'PBR (F/Patio)	ESty GCoc SWCr
	Rosarium Uetersen = 'Kortersen' (ClHT)	MJon
§	'Rose d'Amour' (S) ♀H4	CFee SWCr
	'Rose de Meaux'	see *R.* × *centifolia* 'De Meaux'
	'Rose de Rescht'	see *R.* 'De Resht'
	'Rose du Maître d'Ecole'	see *R.* 'Du Maître d'Ecole'
	'Rose du Roi' (HP/DPo)	WAct WHCG
§	Rose Gaujard = 'Gaumo' (HT)	LGod MAsh MGan NBlu SWCr
	Rose of Picardy = 'Ausfudge' (S)	LRHS MBri SSea
*	'Rose of Yunnan' (Ra)	WAct
	Rose Pearl = 'Korterschi'PBR (S)	MGan
	'Rose-Marie Viaud' (Ra)	CFee CPou CSam EBee SWCr WHCG
	'Rosemary Gandy' (F)	MGan
	Rosemary Harkness = 'Harrowbond'PBR (HT)	ESty LStr MRav SMrm
	'Rosemary Rose' (F)	SPer
	Rosemoor = 'Austough'PBR	CSBt LGod LRHS MAsh MBri SSea WClo
	Rosendal = 'Pouldahle'PBR (F)	EBee
	Rosenprofessor SieberPBR	see *R.* The Halcyon Days Rose
	'Roseraie de l'Haÿ' (Ru) ♀H4	Widely available
	Roses des Cisterciens = 'Deltisse'	MRav
	Rosy Cushion = 'Interall' (S/GC) ♀H4	CSam EWTr LRHS MGan SPer SWCr WAct WHCG
	Rosy Future = 'Harwaderox' (F/Patio)	CSBt SWCr
	'Rosy Mantle' (Cl)	CSBt MGan SPer SWCr

Name	Suppliers
§ Rotary Sunrise = 'Fryglitzy' (HT)	CSBt MBri
§ Rote Max Graf = 'Kormax'PBR (GC/Ru)	CDul EPfP WAct
roxburghii (S)	EPfP GAuc LEdu MGan WAct WHCG
- f. ***normalis*** (S)	CFee
'Royal Albert Hall' (HT)	GCoc
Royal Celebration = 'Wekbiphitsou' (F)	MJon
Royal CopenhagenPBR	see *R.* Remember = 'Poulht001'
'Royal Gold' (ClHT)	MGan
'Royal Occasion' (F)	SPer SWCr
Royal William = 'Korzaun'PBR (HT) ♀H4	CSBt ELan ESty GCoc LGod LStr MAsh MBri MGan MGos MJon MRav MWat NPri SPer SWCr WBor
§ ***rubiginosa***	CArn CCVT CDul CRWN EBee EMac EPfP GPoy IFro ILis LBuc MHer MJon MRav NWea SFam SPer SWCr WAct WMou
rubrifolia	see *R. glauca* Pourr.
'Rubrotincta'	see *R.* 'Hebe's Lip'
rubus (Ra)	ISea
- SF 96062	ISea
§ - var. ***glandulifera***	WAct
- ***velutescens***	see *R. rubus* var. *glandulifera*
Ruby Anniversary = 'Harbonny'PBR (Patio)	CSBt CWSG EBls ESty LRHS LStr MAsh MHav MRav MWat SCoo SPoG SRGP SVic SWCr
Ruby Celebration = 'Peawinner'PBR (F)	CWSG EBls ESty MJon MRav MWat SMrm SWCr
Ruby Ruby	see *R.* Ruby Slippers
§ Ruby Slippers = 'Weksactrumi' (Min)	MAsh
'Ruby Wedding' (HT)	CBcs CGro CSBt CTri CWSG ECnt ELan EPfP GCoc IArd LGod LRHS LSRN LStr MAsh MBri MGan MGos MJon MRav NPri SMrm SPer SPoG SSea SVic SWCr WBor WClo
'Ruby Wedding Anniversary' (F)	LSRN
rugosa (Ru)	CDul CLnd CTri EMac EPfP GGar GKir IFFs LBuc LRHS MAsh MBri MHer MRav NWea SBch SPlb SVic SWCr
- 'Alba' (Ru) ♀H4	CBcs CCVT CDul CTri EBee ECnt ELan EMac EPfP EWTr GBin GKir LAst LBuc LRHS LStr MCot MGan MJon MRav NWea SBch SMrm SPer SPoG SSea SVic SWCr WAct
- 'Rubra' (Ru) ♀H4	CBcs CCVT CTri CWib EPfP GKir LAst LBuc LRHS LStr MGan SBch SMrm SPer SPoG SVic WAct
- Sakhalin form	MCCP
'Rugosa Atropurpurea' (Ru)	GKir SBch
'Rugspin' (Ru)	WAct
Rugul = 'Guletta' (Min) **new**	MJon
'Rumba' (F)	SWCr
'Rural England' (Ra)	EBls
'Russelliana' (Ra)	SFam SWCr WKif
Safe Haven = 'Jacreraz'PBR (F)	ECnt IDic MGan
Saint Alban = 'Auschesnut'PBR (S)	CSBt
Saint Boniface = 'Kormatt' (F/Patio)	CSBt
'Saint Catherine' (Ra)	CFee
Saint Cecilia = 'Ausmit'PBR (S)	LRHS LStr SMrm SWCr
Saint Dunstan's Rose = 'Kirshru' (S)	MJon
Saint Edmunds RosePBR	see *R.* Bonita
Saint Helena = 'Canlish' (F)	ECnt
Saint John = 'Harbilbo'PBR (F)	CSBt MRav
Saint John's rose	see *R.* × *richardii*
Saint Mark's rose	see *R.* 'Rose d'Amour'
Saint Swithun = 'Auswith'PBR (S)	LRHS MBri MJon SSea SWCr WClo
'Salet' (DPMo)	WHCG
'Sally Holmes' (S) ♀H4	EBee ECnt EPfP GCoc MGan MJon MRav SPer SSea SWCr WAct WHCG
Sally Kane = 'Frygroovy' (HT) **new**	ECnt
Sally's Rose = 'Canrem' (HT)	EBee ECnt LSRN
SalsaPBR	see *R.* Cheek to Cheek
Salvation = 'Harlark'PBR	ECnt ESty SWCr
Samaritan = 'Harverag'PBR (HT)	CSBt ESty MRav SPoG SWCr
sancta	see *R.* × *richardii*
'Sander's White Rambler' (Ra) ♀H4	CRHN CSam CTri EBee ECGP EPfP LRHS LStr MGan MRav NLar SPer SWCr WAct WHCG
Sandra = 'Carsandra'	EPfP SLon
'Sanguinea'	see *R.* × *odorata* Sanguinea Group
Sarah (HT)	see *R.* Jardins de Bagatelle
'Sarah van Fleet' (Ru)	CTri EBee EPfP GCoc IArd LRHS LStr MCot MGan MGos MRav MWat NEgg NLar SMad SPer SWCr WAct
Sarah, Duchess of YorkPBR	see *R.* Sunseeker
Savoy Hotel = 'Harvintage'PBR (HT) ♀H4	CGro ECnt LStr MGan MRav SMrm SPer SPoG SWCr
'Scabrosa' (Ru) ♀H4	EBee ECnt GCoc GKir LAst LRHS MAsh MGan MJon NLar SLon SPer SPoG SSea SWCr WAct WHCG
Scarborough Fair = 'Ausoran' (S)	SWCr
Scarlet Fire	see *R.* 'Scharlachglut'
Scarlet Glow	see *R.* 'Scharlachglut'
Scarlet Hit = 'Poulmo'PBR (PatioHit Series) (P)	ECnt LRHS MAsh
Scarlet Patio = 'Kortingle'PBR (Patio)	ESty LRHS MAsh SWCr
Scarlet Queen Elizabeth = 'Dicel' (F)	CBcs MRav
'Scented Abundance' (F)	SWCr
'Scented Air' (F)	MGan SPer
Scented Carpet = 'Chewground'PBR (GC)	ECnt ESty MJon SMrm
Scented Memory = 'Poulht002'PBR (HT)	ECnt LRHS MAsh MBri SWCr
Scentimental = 'Wekplapep'PBR (F)	ESty LStr MAsh MBri MRav SCoo SSea SWCr
Scent-sation = 'Fryromeo'PBR (HT)	CWSG GCoc LGod LRHS LStr MAsh MBri MGan MRav NPri SCoo SPoG SWCr
Scepter'd Isle = 'Ausland'PBR (S) ♀H4	CSBt ECnt LRHS MAsh MBri SCoo SPer SSea SWCr WClo
§ 'Scharlachglut' (ClS) ♀H4	CPou LRHS MCot MGan MRav SPer SWCr WAct WHCG
* ***schmidtiana***	CFee
Schneewittchen	see *R.* Iceberg
§ 'Schneezwerg' (Ru) ♀H4	CGro GCoc MGan MGos MRav NLar SPer SSea SWCr WAct WHCG
'Schoolgirl' (Cl)	CBcs CGro CSBt CTri ELan EPfP GCoc GKir LAst LRHS LStr MAsh MGan MJon MRav MWat NEgg NPri SPer SPoG SWCr
'Schratel' **new**	LRHS
Scotch pink (PiH)	WAct
Scotch rose	see *R. spinosissima*

	Scotch yellow (PiH)	see *R.* × *harisonii* 'Williams Double Yellow'
	'Seagull' (Ra) ΥH4	CGro CTri CWSG ECnt EPfP ESty LAst LGod LRHS LStr MAsh MGan MJon MRav MWat NPri NWea SLon SMad SMrm SPer SPoG SSea SWCr WAct WHCG WHer
	'Seale Pink Diamond' (S)	SSea
	'Sealing Wax' (*moyesii* hybrid)	NLar WAct
	Selfridges = 'Korpriwa' (HT)	MJon
	'Semiplena'	see *R.* × *alba* 'Alba Semiplena'
	sericea (S)	CFee GBin WHCG
	- var. ***morrisonensis*** B&SWJ 7139	WCru
§	- subsp. ***omeiensis*** BWJ 7550	WCru
	- - f. ***pteracantha*** (S)	CSBt ELan EPfP EWTr GGar MGan MRav NLar NWea SMad SPer SPoG SSea SWCr WAct
	- - - 'Atrosanguinea' (S)	CArn WBor
	sertata	GAuc
	setipoda (S)	WAct WHCG
	seven sisters rose	see *R. multiflora* 'Grevillei'
	Seventh Heaven = 'Fryfantasy'PBR (HT)	GCoc SWCr
	Sexy Rexy = 'Macrexy'PBR (F) ΥH4	CGro CSBt EPfP ESty GCoc LRHS LSRN LStr MAsh MBri MGan MJon MRav SMrm SPer SPoG SWCr
	'Shailer's White Moss'	see *R.* × *centifolia* 'Shailer's White Moss'
	Sharifa Asma = 'Ausreef'PBR (S)	CSBt EBee ELan ELon LRHS LStr MBNS MBri MRav NEgg SLon SMrm SPer SWCr WAct
	Sheila's Perfume = 'Harsherry'PBR (HT/F)	CGro EBee ECnt GCoc LStr MGan MJon MRav SPer SPoG SRGP SWCr
	'Sherbert Fizz' (Patio)	SWCr
	Shine On = 'Dictalent'PBR (Patio) ΥH4	CSBt ECnt ESty IDic LStr MAsh SPoG SWCr
	Shining Light = 'Cocshimmer'PBR (Patio)	GCoc MRav SCoo
	Shocking Blue = 'Korblue' (F)	CSBt MGan MJon SPer
	Shona = 'Dicdrum' (F)	IDic
	'Shot Silk' (HT)	MGan SWCr
	Showtime = 'Baitime'	MAsh SWCr
	Shrimp Hit = 'Poulshrimp'PBR (Patio)	ECnt MAsh
	'Shropshire Lass' (S)	LRHS
	Silver Anniversary ambig.	LSRN
§	Silver Anniversary = 'Poulari'PBR (HT) ΥH4	CGro CSBt CTri EBee EBls ECnt ELan GCoc LRHS LSRN LStr MAsh MGan MGos MJon MRav MWat NPri SCoo SMrm SPer SPoG SSea SWCr WClo
	Silver Ghost = 'Kormifari'PBR (S)	MGos
	'Silver Jubilee' (HT) ΥH4	CGro CSBt EBee EPfP GCoc IArd LGod LRHS LStr MAsh MGan MJon MRav SPer SPoG SVic SWCr
	'Silver Lining' (HT)	ELon SRGP SWCr
	'Silver Moon' (Cl)	CRHN
	'Silver Wedding' (HT)	CWSG ELan GCoc IArd MHav MRav NBir NEgg SMrm SPer SRGP SVic SWCr WBor
	'Silver Wedding Celebration' (F)	CTri ESty
	Silver WishesPBR	see *R.* Pink Hit
	Simba = 'Korbelma' (HT)	MGan
	'Simplex Multiflora'	CWib
	Simply Heaven = 'Diczombie'PBR (HT)	ESty GCoc IDic SWCr
§	Simply the Best = 'Macamster'PBR (HT)	CGro CSBt EBls ECnt ELan ESty GCoc LGod LSRN LStr MAsh MGos MJon MRav MWat NPri SCoo SMrm SPer SPoG SRGP SWCr
§	Singin' in the Rain = 'Macivy' (F)	MJon
	sinowilsonii	see *R. longicuspis* var. *sinowilsonii*
	'Sir Cedric Morris' (Ra)	EBee SSea WAct
I	'Sir Galahad' white-flowered (F)	MRav
	'Sir Joseph Paxton' (Bb)	CAbP
	'Sir Paul Smith' (Cl)	EBls
	Sir Walter Raleigh = 'Ausspry' (S)	MRav SMrm
	Sister Elizabeth = 'Auspalette' (S)	LRHS MBri SCoo
	Skylark = 'Ausimple' **new**	LRHS MBri WClo
	'Skyrocket'	see *R.* 'Wilhelm'
	Smarty = 'Intersmart' (S/GC)	CAbP SPer WAct
	'Smooth Angel' (HT)	MGan
	Smooth Lady = 'Hadlady' (HT)	MGan
	Smooth Melody = 'Hadmelody' (F)	LAst
	Smooth Prince = 'Hadprince' (HT)	LAst
	'Smooth Velvet' (HT)	LAst
	Snow Carpet = 'Maccarpe' (Min/GC)	MJon SSea
	'Snow Dwarf'	see *R.* 'Schneezwerg'
	Snow Goose = 'Auspom'PBR (Cl/S)	CSBt LRHS MBri SSea SWCr
	Snow Hit = 'Poulsnows'PBR (Min/Patio)	ECnt LRHS SWCr
	'Snow Queen'	see *R.* 'Frau Karl Druschki'
	Snow Sunblaze = 'Meigovin' (Min)	CSBt SPer
	Snowball = 'Macangeli' (Min/GC)	MJon
	Snowcap = 'Harfleet'PBR (Patio)	ESty
	'Snowdon' (Ru)	LRHS
	'Snowdrift' W.R. Smith (Ra)	WHCG
	'Snowflake' (Ra)	WHCG
	Soft Cover = 'Poultco10' **new**	SWCr
	'Soldier Boy' (Cl)	CPou SWCr WHCG
	Solitaire = 'Macyefre'PBR (HT)	MJon
§	Solo Mio = 'Poulen002'PBR (Renaissance Series) (S)	CTri ECnt SWCr
§	'Sombreuil' (ClT)	EBee EPfP IArd LRHS MBri MRav NEgg NLar SFam SPer SSea SWCr WAct WHCG
	Something Special = 'Macwyo'PBR (HT)	EBee ECnt ESty GCoc MJon SWCr
	Song and Dance (HT)	ESty GCoc SWCr
§	Songs of Praise = 'Harkimono'PBR (Abundance Series) (F)	ESty SWCr
	Sonia	see *R.* Sweet Promise
	'Sophia'PBR	see *R.* Solo Mio = 'Poulen002'
	'Sophie's Perpetual' (ClCh)	CPou LRHS MGan MGos SLon SPer SWCr WAct WHCG
	Sophy's Rose = 'Auslot'PBR (S)	ESty LRHS LSRN LStr MBri MJon NEgg SPer SSea SWCr
	soulieana (Ra/S) ΥH3-4	WAct WKif
	'Soupert et Notting' (DPoMo)	LRHS MRav SPer SWCr WAct
	'Southampton' (F) ΥH4	EPfP LSRN LStr MAsh SSea SWCr

Name	Suppliers
'Souvenir d'Alphonse Lavallée' (ClHP)	WHCG
'Souvenir de Brod'	see *R.* 'Erinnerung an Brod'
'Souvenir de Claudius Denoyel' (ClHT)	MGan SPer WAct
'Souvenir de Jeanne Balandreau' (HP)	CPou
'Souvenir de la Malmaison' (ClBb)	see *R.* 'Climbing Souvenir de la Malmaison'
'Souvenir de la Malmaison' (Bb)	EPfP GCoc LRHS MCot MGan MRav NLar SPer SWCr WAct
Souvenir de Louis Amade = 'Delilac' (S)	MRav
'Souvenir de Madame Léonie Viennot' (ClT)	EBee MRav SPoG
'Souvenir de Saint Anne's' (Bb)	EWTr SWCr WAct WHCG
'Souvenir di Castagneto' (HP)	MRav
'Souvenir du Docteur Jamain' (ClHP)	CPou CSBt EBee ECGP ELan ELon EPfP ESty EWTr LStr MGan MRav NLar SFam SMrm SPer SPoG SSea SWCr WAct WHCG WKif
Spangles = 'Ganspa'PBR (F)	MGan NHaw SWCr
'Spanish Beauty'	see *R.* 'Madame Grégoire Staechelin'
Sparkling Scarlet = 'Meihati' (ClF)	ELan MAsh
Special Anniversary = 'Whastiluc'PBR (HT)	CGro ELon EPfP ESty GCoc LRHS MAsh MBri MRav MWat NPri SCoo SPoG SRGP SWCr
Special Child = 'Tanaripsa'	LStr SWCr
Special Friend = 'Kirspec'PBR (Patio)	ESty GCoc LStr MGan MJon MWat SWCr
'Special Moment' (F) **new**	SWCr
Special Occasion = 'Fryyoung'PBR (HT)	ESty GCoc LRHS MAsh MBri MGos MRav MWat SMrm SWCr
'Spectabilis' (Ra)	WHCG
Spek's Centennial (F)	see *R.* Singin' in the Rain
SpellboundPBR	see *R.* Garden News
'Spencer' misapplied	see *R.* 'Enfant de France'
Spice of Life = 'Diccheeky'PBR (F/Patio)	IDic
§ ***spinosissima***	CDul EBee EMac GKir IFFs LBuc MGan NHaw NWea SPer SPoG SSea WAct WCot WHCG
- 'Andrewsii' ♀H4	MRav WAct
§ - double pink-flowered	WBor
§ - double white-flowered	CNat ECha GCoc IGor WAct
- 'Dunwich Rose'	EPfP LRHS MGan MJon SPer SWCr WAct WHCG
- 'Falkland'	ECha GCra
- 'Mary, Queen of Scots'	MGan SRms WAct
- 'Robbie'	WAct
- 'Single Cherry'	SSea
- 'Variegata' (v)	CArn
- 'William III'	EWes GCra SLPl
Spirit of Freedom = 'Ausbite'PBR (S)	ESty LRHS MAsh MBri NEgg SSea SWCr WClo
§ 'Splendens' (Ra)	EBee SLPl WAct
'Stanwell Perpetual' (PiH)	CSam EBee EPfP EWTr GCoc LStr MCot MRav NLar SEND SPer SSea SWCr WAct WHCG
'Star of Waltham' (HP)	SWCr WHCG
'Star Performer'PBR (ClPatio)	CSBt ECnt ESty MAsh MJon SMrm SRGP SSea SWCr
Stardust = 'Peavandyke'PBR (Patio/F)	ESty SWCr
Starina = 'Megabi' (Min)	MGan
Starlight Express = 'Trobstar'PBR (Cl)	MAsh MBri MRav MWat SCoo SPer SPoG SWCr
Starry Eyed = 'Horcoexist' (Patio)	MGan SWCr
Stella (HT)	MGan SWCr
§ ***stellata*** var. ***mirifica***	EBee MGan SSea
'Sterling Silver' (HT)	MGan
Strawberries and Cream = 'Geestraw' (Min/Patio)	ELan ESty
Strawberry Fayre = 'Arowillip'PBR (Min/Patio)	ESty LStr MRav SPoG
Strawberry Hill = 'Ausrimini' (S)	ESty LRHS MBri SCoo SWCr
Stunning = 'Poulpm004'PBR (HT) **new**	SWCr
§ Sue Hipkin = 'Harzazz'PBR (HT)	ESty SWCr
Suffolk = 'Kormixal'PBR (S/GC)	CGro CSBt ELan GCoc LStr MGan MRav MWat SPer SSea SWCr WAct
suffulta	see *R. arkansana* var. *suffulta*
Sugar and Spice = 'Peaallure'PBR (Patio)	SPoG
Sugar Baby = 'Tanabagus'PBR (Patio)	ESty SMrm SWCr
Sugar 'n' Spice = 'Tinspice' (Min)	MRav
Suma = 'Harsuma' (GC)	ESty MJon SMrm WAct
Summer Breeze = 'Korelasting'PBR (Cl)	MGos
Summer Dream = 'Frymaxicot'PBR (F)	CSBt
Summer Fragrance = 'Tanfudermos'PBR (Castle Series) (HT)	CSBt ELon SWCr
§ Summer Gold = 'Poulreb'PBR (F)	ECnt SWCr
'Summer Holiday' (HT)	SWCr
Summer Love = 'Franluv' (F)	CBcs
Summer Memories = 'Koruteli'PBR (Palace Series) (F)	MGos
Summer Snow = 'Weopop' (Patio)	MJon
Summer Song = 'Austango'PBR (S)	LRHS MAsh MBri MJon SWCr WClo
Summer Wine = 'Korizont'PBR (Cl) ♀H4	CSBt EBee ECnt GKir LRHS MAsh MGan MGos MJon NPri SCoo SPer SPoG SWCr
Summertime = 'Chewlarmoll'PBR (Patio/Cl)	CGro CSBt ECnt ELan GCoc LGod LRHS LStr MAsh MGan MGos MJon MRav MWat NPri SCoo SMrm SPer SPoG SWCr
Sun Hit = 'Poulsun'PBR (PatioHit Series) (Patio)	CSBt ECnt LRHS MAsh MRav SMrm SWCr
'Sunblaze'PBR	see *R.* Orange Sunblaze
Sunblest = 'Landora' (HT)	LRHS MAsh MRav SMrm SWCr
Suncharm = 'Harfab'PBR (Patio) **new**	SWCr
'Sunny Abundance'	SWCr
Sunrise = 'Kormarter'PBR (Cl)	CGro ESty MBri MWat SWCr
§ Sunseeker = 'Dicracer'PBR (F/Patio)	EPfP IDic LRHS MAsh MRav SPoG SWCr
Sunset Boulevard = 'Harbabble'PBR (F) ♀H4	CSBt ECnt LGod LStr MAsh MBri MGan MRav SCoo SPer SWCr
Sunset CelebrationPBR	see *R.* Warm Wishes
'Sunshine' (Poly)	MGan
'Sunsilk' (F)	SWCr
Sunsplash = 'Cocweaver'PBR (F)	MRav SMrm SPoG SWCr

	Name	Suppliers
	Super Dorothy = 'Heldoro' (Ra)	ESty LSRN MJon SSea SWCr
	Super Elfin = 'Helkleger'[PBR] (Ra) 🏆H4	LStr MGan MJon MRav SMrm SPer SSea SWCr
	Super Excelsa = 'Helexa' (Ra)	ESty LRHS LStr MGan MJon SPoG SSea SWCr
	Super Fairy = 'Helsufair'[PBR] (Ra)	EBee ECnt ESty LStr MGan MJon MRav SMrm SPer SSea SWCr
	Super Sparkle = 'Helfels'[PBR] (Ra)	ECnt LStr SSea
§	Super Star = 'Tanorstar' (HT)	LStr MGan MJon MRav SRGP SWCr
	'Surpasse Tout' (G)	EWTr SWCr
§	'Surpassing Beauty of Woolverstone' (ClHP)	WHCG
	Surprise = 'Presur'[PBR] (Fs/HT)	SWCr
	Surrey = 'Korlanum'[PBR] (GC) 🏆H4	CSBt ECnt ELan EPfP ESty LGod LSRN LStr MGan MRav MWat NLar SMrm SPer SPoG SSea SWCr WAct
	Susan = 'Poulsue' (S)	ECnt SLon SWCr
	Sussex = 'Poulave'[PBR] (GC)	CSBt GCoc LStr MGan MRav NPri SMrm SPer SPoG SWCr
	'Sutter's Gold' (HT)	MGan
	Swan Lake = 'Macmed' (Cl)	EBee ECnt ELan EPfP LGod LStr MGan MHav MRav NPri SMad SMrm SPer SWCr
	Swany = 'Meiburenac' (Min/GC) 🏆H4	ESty LSRN MGan SPer SWCr WHCG
	Sweet Cover = 'Poulweeto'[PBR] (Towne & Country Series)	SWCr
	Sweet Dream = 'Fryminicot'[PBR] (Patio) 🏆H4	CGro CSBt CTri ECnt ELan EPfP ESty GCoc LGod LStr MAsh MBri MGan MJon MRav MWat NPri SMrm SPer SPoG SRGP SSea SWCr
	'Sweet Fairy' (Min)	CSBt
	Sweet Haze = 'Tan97274'[PBR]	CGro CSBt ESty GCoc LGod LRHS LStr MAsh MGan MJon MRav MWat NPri SCoo SMrm SPoG
	Sweet Juliet = 'Ausleap'[PBR] (S)	CSBt CWSG ELon ESty LGod LRHS MCot MJon SMrm SPer SWCr
*	'Sweet Lemon Dream' (Patio)	CTri
	Sweet Magic = 'Dicmagic'[PBR] (Min/Patio) 🏆H4	CGro CSBt CTri EPfP IDic LStr MAsh MBri MGan MJon MRav NPri SMrm SPoG SWCr
	Sweet Memories = 'Whamemo' (Patio)	CTri ECnt EPfP ESty LGod LRHS LStr MAsh MJon MRav NPri SCoo SMrm SPer SPoG SRGP SWCr
§	Sweet Promise = 'Meihelvet' (GC)	MGan SPer
	Sweet Remembrance = 'Kirr' (HT)	LStr
	'Sweet Repose' (F)	MGan
	'Sweet Revelation'[PBR]	see *R.* Sue Hipkin
	Sweet Symphonie = 'Meibarke'[PBR] (Patio)	SWCr
	'Sweet Velvet' (F)	MGan
	'Sweet Wonder' (Patio)	EPfP MAsh MBri SMrm SPoG SWCr
N	Sweetheart = 'Cocapeer' (HT)	GCoc
	'Sweetie' (Patio)	SWCr
	sweginzowii	GAuc
	'Sydonie' (HP)	EBee WHCG
	'Sympathie' (ClHT)	MGan MGos SMrm SPer SSea SWCr
	Tall Story = 'Dickooky'[PBR] (F) 🏆H4	IDic MJon SWCr WHCG
	Tango = 'Macfirwal' (F)	MJon
	Tango Showground = 'Chewpattens'[PBR] (GC)	SSea
	Tapis Jaune	see *R.* Golden Penny
	Tatoo = 'Poulyc002'[PBR] (Cl/Patio)	EBee ECnt SWCr
	Tatton = 'Fryentice'[PBR] (F)	EBls ESty MJon MRav SMrm SPoG SWCr
	Tawny Tiger = 'Frygolly'[PBR] (F)	CGro GCoc SWCr
	Tea Clipper = 'Ausrover' (S)	CSBt ESty LRHS MBri SCoo SSea SWCr WClo
	Tear Drop = 'Dicomo'[PBR] (Min/Patio)	IDic LStr MGan SWCr
	Teasing Georgia = 'Ausbaker'[PBR] (S)	ECnt EPfP ESty LRHS LSRN MBri MJon SCoo SMrm SRGP SSea SWCr WClo
	'Telstar' (F)	MGan
	Temptress = 'Korramal' (Cl)	MAsh MGos MJon
	Tenacious = 'Macblackpo'[PBR] (F)	ESty LStr MJon
	'Tequila Gold' **new**	SMrm
	Tequila Sunrise = 'Dicobey'[PBR] (HT) 🏆H4	CGro CTri EBls ECnt ELan EPfP IDic LRHS LStr MAsh MGan MJon MRav SMrm SPer SPoG SWCr
§	Terracotta = 'Meicobuis'[PBR] (HT)	ESty SMrm SWCr
	Tess of the d'Urbervilles = 'Ausmove'[PBR] (S)	LRHS LStr MBri NEgg SCoo SMrm SPer SWCr WClo
	'Tessa' (F)	MGan SWCr
	Thank You = 'Chesdeep'[PBR] (Patio)	ESty LStr MGan SPoG SRGP SWCr
§	That's Jazz = 'Poulnorm'[PBR] (Courtyard Series) (ClF)	ECnt MAsh MBri MJon MWat SMrm SWCr
	The Alexandra Rose = 'Ausday'[PBR] (S)	LRHS SSea
	The Attenborough Rose = 'Dicelope'[PBR] (F)	IDic
	'The Bishop of Bradford' (ClPiH)	EBee ECnt
	The Brownie Rose = 'Harlassie'[PBR] (F) **new**	SWCr
	The Compass Rose = 'Korwisco'[PBR] (S)	MGos
	The Compassionate Friends = 'Harzodiac'[PBR] (F)	SWCr
	The Countryman = 'Ausman'[PBR] (S)	ELon LRHS LStr SMrm SSea SWCr
	The Dark Lady = 'Ausbloom'[PBR] (S)	LRHS MAsh NEgg SPer SWCr WClo
	'The Doctor' (HT)	MGan
	The Dove = 'Tanamola'[PBR] (F)	MGan
	'The Ednaston Rose' (Cl)	WHCG
§	'The Fairy' (Poly) 🏆H4	CSBt CTri EBee ECnt ELan EPfP IFFs LAst LGod LRHS LStr MAsh MCot MGan MJon MRav MWat SEND SMad SMrm SPer SSea SWCr WAct WCFE WHCG
	'The Garland' (Ra) 🏆H4	CRHN EBee EPfP EWTr LRHS MBri NLar SFam SPer WHCG
	The Generous Gardener = 'Ausdrawn'[PBR] (S)	EPfP LRHS MBri SCoo SWCr WClo
	The Gold Award Rose = 'Poulac008' (Palace Series) (Patio)	ECnt
§	The Halcyon Days Rose = 'Korparesni'[PBR] (F)	MGos
	The Herbalist = 'Aussemi' (S)	LRHS SSea
	The Ingenious Mr Fairchild = 'Austijus'[PBR] (S)	LRHS MBri SCoo SWCr

	The Jubilee Rose = 'Poulbrido'PBR (F)	ECnt SCoo
	'The Lister Rose' (F)	MGan
	The Maidstone Rose = 'Kordauerpa'	SCoo SMrm
	'The Margaret Coppola Rose'PBR	see *R.* White Gold
	The Mayflower = 'Austilly'PBR (S)	CSBt LRHS LStr MBri MJon SSea SWCr
§	The McCartney Rose = 'Meizeli'PBR (HT)	LStr MHav MJon SDix SPer SWCr
	'The New Dawn'	see *R.* 'New Dawn'
	The Painter = 'Mactemaik'PBR (F)	LStr MJon
§	The Pilgrim = 'Auswalker'PBR (S)	CSBt CSam EPfP ESty LRHS LStr MAsh MBri MJon SPer SSea SWCr WClo WHCG
	The Prince = 'Ausvelvet'PBR (S)	LRHS NLar SPer SSea SWCr
	The Prince's Trust = 'Harholding'PBR (Cl)	LStr MBri MJon SPoG
§	'The Queen Elizabeth' (F)	CBcs CGro CSBt CTri CWSG GCoc LGod LRHS LStr MAsh MBri MGan MJon MRav MWat NPri SPer SWCr WBor
	The Rotarian	see *R.* Rotary Sunrise
I	'The Rugby Rose' (HT)	MGan SWCr
	The Schofield Rose = 'Weksacsodor' (F) **new**	MJon
	The Shepherdess = 'Austwist'PBR	LRHS MBri MJon SSea WClo
	The Soham RosePBR	see *R.* Pearl Abundance
	The Soroptimist Rose = 'Benstar' (Patio)	MJon
	The Times Rose = 'Korpeahn'PBR (F) ♀H4	ECnt LGod LStr MGan MGos MJon MRav SPer SWCr
	'Thérèse Bugnet' (Ru)	NHaw
	Thinking of You = 'Frydandy'PBR (HT)	EBls ESty GCoc LGod LRHS LStr MAsh MGan NPri SRGP SVic SWCr
	'Thisbe' (HM)	EWTr SPer WAct WHCG
	Thomas Barton = 'Meihirvin' (HT)	LStr
	'Threave' (B)	CPou EWTr SWCr WHCG
	Three Cheers = 'Dicdomino'PBR (F)	IDic
	'Three Wishes' **new**	MAsh SWCr
	threepenny bit rose	see *R. elegantula* 'Persetosa'
	Thumbs Up = 'Hornothing' (S)	EBls
	tibetica	GAuc
	Tickled Pink = 'Fryhunky' (F)	CGro CSBt EBee EBls ECnt EPfP GCoc LGod LRHS LSRN LShp MAsh MBri MGan MJon MRav NPri SCoo SMrm SPer SPoG SRGP SWCr
	Tigris = 'Harprier' (*persica* hybrid) (S)	WAct
	Times Past = 'Harhilt'PBR (Cl)	ELon ESty GCoc LStr MGan MJon MRav SPoG SWCr
	'Tina Turner' (HT)	MJon
	Tintinara = 'Dicuptight'PBR (HT)	ECnt IDic
	Tip Top = 'Tanope' (F/Patio)	MGan SPer SWCr
	'Tipo Ideale'	see *R.* × *odorata* 'Mutabilis'
	Titanic = 'Macdako'PBR (F)	MJon
	'Toby Tristam' (Ra)	CRHN
	Together Forever = 'Dicecho'PBR (F)	GCoc IDic
	'Tom Marshall'	EBee WHCG
	Too Hot to Handle = 'Macloupri' (S/Cl)	MJon
	Top Marks = 'Fryministar'PBR (Min/Patio)	CGro CSBt CTri GCoc LAst LGod LStr MGan MJon MRav MWat NPri SCoo SPer SWCr
	'Top of the Bill' (Patio)	SWCr
	Topaz JewelPBR	see *R.* Yellow Dagmar Hastrup
	Toprose = 'Cocgold'PBR (F)	GCoc MAsh
	'Topsi' (F/Patio)	SPer
	'Touch of Glamour' (Patio)	SWCr
§	'Tour de Malakoff' (Ce)	CPou LRHS MRav NLar SFam SPer WAct WHCG WKif
	Tower Bridge = 'Haravis' (HT)	ESty
	'Trade Winds' (HT)	MGan SWCr
	TraditionPBR	see *R.* Tradition '95
§	Tradition '95 = 'Korkeltin'PBR (Cl) ♀H4	MGos
	'Treasure Trove' (Ra)	CRHN LRHS MGan MJon NLar SWCr WAct
	'Trier' (Ra)	CPou EBee WHCG
	'Trigintipetala' misapplied	see *R.* 'Professeur Emile Perrot'
	triphylla	see *R.* × *beanii*
	Troika = 'Poumidor' (HT) ♀H4	CSBt ELan EPfP LRHS LStr MAsh MBri MGan MRav SPer SPoG SWCr
	'Tropicana'	see *R.* Super Star
	Trumpeter = 'Mactru' (F) ♀H4	CSBt EBee ECnt IArd LRHS LStr MAsh MBri MGan MJon MRav SPer SPoG
	'Tuscany' (G)	GCoc SPer WAct WHCG
	'Tuscany Superb' (G) ♀H4	CPou CSBt CSam EBee EPfP EWTr GCra LAst LRHS MBri MCot MGan MRav NChi NLar SEND SMrm SPer SSea SWCr WAct WHCG WKif
	Twenty-one Again! = 'Meinimo'PBR (HT)	LSRN SWCr
	Twice in a Blue Moon = 'Tan96138'PBR (HT)	CGro CSBt EBee EBls ECnt ESty LGod MAsh MBri MGan MJon MRav SCoo SMrm SPoG SSea SWCr
	Twist = 'Poulstri'PBR (Courtyard Series) (ClPatio)	CGro EBee ECnt ESty MAsh SWCr
	Tynwald = 'Mattwyt' (HT)	LStr MGos MJon SPer
	Uncle Walter = 'Macon' (HT)	SWCr
	UNICEF = 'Cocjojo'PBR (F)	GCoc
	'Unique Blanche'	see *R.* × *centifolia* 'Unique'
	Valencia = 'Koreklia'PBR (HT) ♀H4	CSBt ECnt
	Valentine Heart = 'Dicogle'PBR (F) ♀H4	CSBt ESty IArd IDic LRHS MAsh MBri MGos MRav SPoG SRGP SWCr
	Valiant Heart = 'Poulberg' (F)	ECnt
	Vanilla Twist = 'Dicghost' (F)	IDic
	Varenna Allen = 'Harmode' (F) **new**	ECnt
	'Variegata di Bologna' (Bb)	EPfP LRHS MRav SLon SSea SWCr WAct
	'Vatertag' (Min)	LSRN
	'Veilchenblau' (Ra) ♀H4	CRHN CSBt EBee ECnt ELan EPfP LGod LRHS LStr MAsh MGan MRav NEgg NLar NPri SMrm SPer SPoG SSea SWCr WAct WBor WHCG WKif
	Velvet Abundance (F)	SPoG SWCr
	Velvet Fragrance = 'Fryperdee'PBR (HT)	CSBt ECnt ESty GCoc LRHS LStr MGan MJon MRav SMrm SPoG SWCr
	'Verschuren' (HT/v)	MJon
	versicolor	see *R. gallica* 'Versicolor'
	Versigny = 'Masversi' (Generosa Series) (S)	MRav
	'Victor Madeley' (F)	MGan
	Vidal Sassoon = 'Macjuliat'PBR (HT)	MGan MJon SWCr
	'Village Maid'	see *R.* × *centifolia* 'Unique Panachée'

	Name	Suppliers
§	***villosa*** L.	CArn WAct
§	'Violacea' (G)	EBee LRHS WAct WHCG
	'Violette' (Ra)	CPou CRHN EWTr LRHS SPer SWCr WHCG
	virginiana 𝕐H4	CFee GAuc GCal IFFs LBuc MGan NHaw NWea SPer SWCr WAct WHCG
	- 'Harvest Song'	NHaw
	- 'Plena'	see *R.* 'Rose d'Amour'
	'Viridiflora'	see *R.* × *odorata* 'Viridiflora'
	Waltz = 'Poulkrid'[PBR] (Courtyard Series) (ClPatio)	ECnt LRHS
	'Waltz Time' (HT)	SWCr
	Wandering Minstrel = 'Harquince' (F)	SWCr
	Warm Welcome = 'Chewizz'[PBR] (ClMin) 𝕐H4	CGro ECnt EPfP ESty LGod LRHS LSRN LStr MAsh MBri MGan MGos MJon MRav MWat SMad SMrm SPer SPoG SRGP SSea SWCr
§	Warm Wishes = 'Fryxotic'[PBR] (HT) 𝕐H4	CSBt ECnt ESty GCoc LGod LRHS LSRN LStr MAsh MBri MGan MGos MHav MJon MRav NPri SMrm SPoG SRGP SWCr WBor
	'Warrior' (F)	MGan SPer
	Warwickshire = 'Korkandel'[PBR] (GC)	SPer SWCr
	webbiana	SPer WHCG
	Wedding Celebration = 'Poulht006' (HT)	ECnt SWCr
	'Wedding Day' (Ra)	CRHN CSBt CSam CTri EBee ECnt ELan EPfP ESty LRHS LStr MAsh MBNS MBri MGan MGos MJon MRav MWat NEgg NPri SMrm SPer SPoG SSea SWCr WAct WHCG
	Wee Cracker = 'Cocmarris'[PBR] (Patio)	GCoc LGod SWCr
	Wee Jock = 'Cocabest' (F/Patio)	GCoc
	'Weetwood' (Ra)	CRHN SPer
	Weisse Wolcke[PBR]	see *R.* White Cloud = 'Korstacha'
	Welcome Home = 'Koraubala'[PBR] (F)	MGos
	Well-Being = 'Harjangle'[PBR] (S)	CSBt ELon ESty MJon SWCr
	'Wendy Cussons' (HT)	CGro CTri CWSG GCoc MGan MRav SPer SWCr
	Wenlock = 'Auswen' (S)	SPer
	'West Country Millennium' (F)	MGan
	Westerland = 'Korwest' (F/S) 𝕐H4	ECGP MGan MJon MRav SWCr WAct
	Where the Heart Is = 'Cocoplan'[PBR] (HT)	ESty SWCr
	'Whisky Gill' (HT)	MGan
	Whisky Mac = 'Tanky' (HT)	CBcs CGro CSBt CTri CWSG ELan GCoc MGan MHav MJon MRav NPri SPer SPoG SWCr
	'White Bath'	see *R.* × *centifolia* 'Shailer's White Moss'
	'White Cécile Brünner' (Poly)	WHCG
	'White Christmas' (HT)	MGan SWCr
§	White Cloud = 'Korstacha'[PBR] (S/ClHT) 𝕐H4	CSBt ECnt EPfP ESty LGod LRHS MAsh MGos MJon MWat SPoG SWCr WHCG
	White Cloud = 'Savacloud' (Min)	MBri
	'White Cockade' (Cl)	EWTr GCoc MGan SMrm SPer SWCr
	White Cover[PBR]	see *R.* Kent
	White Diamond = 'Interamon'[PBR] (S)	EBee ECnt IDic MGan
§	White Gold = 'Cocquiriam'[PBR] (F)	CSBt GCoc MRav SPoG
	'White Grootendorst' (Ru)	LRHS WAct
	White Knight	see *R.* Message = 'Meban'
	'White Lace' (Patio)	SWCr
	White Max Graf[PBR]	see *R.* × *jacksonii* White Max Graf
	white moss	see *R.* × *centifolia* 'Shailer's White Moss', *R.* 'Comtesse de Murinais'
§	'White Pet' (Poly) 𝕐H4	CSBt EBee ECnt EPfP ESty EWTr GCoc LRHS LStr MBri MCot MGan MJon MRav SEND SMrm SPer SWCr WAct WKif
	white Provence	see *R.* × *centifolia* 'Unique'
	'White Queen Elizabeth' (F)	SWCr
	white rose of York	see *R.* × *alba* 'Alba Semiplena'
	White Skyliner = 'Franwekwhit'[PBR] (ClS)	EBls MJon
	'White Wings' (HT)	EWTr MGan SWCr WAct WHCG WKif
	'White Wonderland' **new**	SWCr
N	***wichurana*** (Ra)	GCal GLin MGan SWCr WHCG
	- 'Cally Anemone' (d) **new**	GCal
	- 'Variegata' (Ra/v)	CBow CSWP MJon
*	- 'Variegata Nana' (Ra/v)	MRav
	'Wickwar' (Ra)	CSWP EBee EWTr GCal GGal WAct WHCG
	Wild Edric = 'Aushedge'[PBR] (Ru)	LRHS MBri SCoo SWCr
	Wild Rover = 'Dichirap'[PBR] (F)	ESty IDic LStr
	Wild Thing = 'Jactoose' (S) **new**	IDic
	Wildeve = 'Ausbonny'[PBR] (S)	LRHS MBri SWCr WClo
	Wildfire = 'Fryessex' (Patio)	ECnt ESty LGod LRHS MAsh MBri MJon SWCr
§	'Wilhelm' (HM)	MRav SPer WHCG
	'William Allen Richardson' (N)	WHCG
	'William Cobbett' (F)	SSea
§	'William Lobb' (CeMo) 𝕐H4	CPou CRHN EBee EPfP EWTr LRHS LStr MBri MCot MGan MRav NEgg SPer SSea SWCr WAct WHCG WKif
	William Morris = 'Auswill'[PBR] (S)	CSBt LRHS MAsh MBri MJon NEgg SMrm SWCr
	William Shakespeare 2000 = 'Ausromeo'[PBR] (S)	CSBt EBee ECnt EPfP ESty LGod LRHS LStr MAsh MBNS MBri NEgg SCoo SSea SWCr
	William Shakespeare = 'Ausroyal'[PBR] (S)	LRHS SPer WClo
	'William Tyndale' (Ra)	EBee WHCG
	'Williams' Double Yellow'	see *R.* × *harisonii* 'Williams Double Yellow'
	willmottiae	see *R. gymnocarpa* var. *willmottiae*
	Wilton = 'Eurosa'	SWCr
	Wiltshire = 'Kormuse'[PBR] (S/GC) 𝕐H4	CSBt ECnt ESty LSRN LStr MJon MRav NPri SLon SMrm SSea SWCr
	Winchester Cathedral = 'Auscat'[PBR] (S)	CGro CSBt EBee ECnt ELon EPfP ESty EWTr LGod LRHS LStr MAsh MBri MRav MWat NEgg NLar SPer SPoG SSea SWCr WClo
	Windflower = 'Auscross' (S)	LRHS
	Windrush = 'Ausrush' (S)	MJon SPer SWCr WAct WHCG
	Wine and Dine = 'Dicuncle' (GC)	IDic
	Winter Magic = 'Foumagic' (Min)	MJon

	Name	Suppliers
	'Wintoniensis' (*moyesii* hybrid)	WAct WHCG
	Wishing = 'Dickerfuffle'^{PBR} (F/Patio)	IDic MGan
	Wisley = 'Ausintense'^{PBR} (S)	CSBt LRHS MJon SCoo SSea
	With All My Love = 'Coczodiac'^{PBR} (HT)	CSBt ESty GCoc LStr
	With Love = 'Andwit' (HT)	SWCr
	With Thanks = 'Fransmoov'^{PBR} (HT)	SRGP SWCr
	'Woburn Abbey' (F)	CWSG SSea
	'Wolley-Dod'	see *R.* 'Duplex'
	Woman o'th' North = 'Kirlon' (F/Patio)	MJon
	Wonderful = 'Poulpmt005'^{PBR} (HT)	EBee ECnt SWCr
	Wonderful News = 'Jonone'^{PBR} (Patio)	ESty MJon
§	***woodsii***	WHCG
	- var. ***fendleri***	see *R. woodsii*
	'Woolverstone Church Rose'	see *R.* 'Surpassing Beauty of Woolverstone'
	Worcestershire = 'Korlalon'^{PBR} (GC)	GCoc MGan MJon MRav SPer SSea SWCr WAct
§	***xanthina*** 'Canary Bird' (S) Υ^{H4}	Widely available
§	- f. ***hugonis*** Υ^{H4}	CTri MGan NHaw SPer SWCr WAct
	X-rated = 'Tinx' (Min)	MJon
	Yellow Button = 'Auslow' (S)	WAct
	'Yellow Cécile Brünner'	see *R.* 'Perle d'Or'
§	Yellow Dagmar Hastrup = 'Moryelrug'^{PBR} (Ru)	EBee MGan MJon SPer SWCr WAct
	'Yellow Doll' (Min)	SWCr
*	'Yellow Dream' (Patio)	SPoG
	Yellow Floorshow = 'Harfully'^{PBR} (GC)	MRav
	Yellow Flower Carpet^{PBR}	see *R.* Flower Carpet Sunshine
	'Yellow Patio' (Min/Patio)	LRHS LStr MAsh SPoG SWCr
	yellow Scotch	see *R.* × *harisonii* 'Williams Double Yellow'
	Yellow Sunblaze = 'Meitrisical' (Min)	CSBt
	'Yesterday' (Poly/F/S) Υ^{H4}	EWTr MAsh MGan SWCr
	York and Lancaster	see *R.* × *damascena* 'Versicolor'
	Yorkshire = 'Korbarkeit'^{PBR} (GC)	GCoc LGod LStr MRav MWat
	'Yorkshire Lady' (HT)	MJon NEgg
	'Yvonne Rabier' (Poly) Υ^{H4}	LStr MGan MRav SPer SWCr WAct WHCG WKif
	'Zéphirine Drouhin' (Bb)	Widely available
§	'Zigeunerknabe' (S)	ECnt ELan MGan MRav NLar SPer SWCr WAct WHCG
	Zorba = 'Poulyc008'^{PBR} (Patio/Cl)	EBee SWCr
	'Zweibrücken' (Cl)	MGan

Roscoea ✿ (*Zingiberaceae*)

	Name	Suppliers
	ACE 2539	GEdr
	alpina	CBro CLAP CPLG CPrp EBee EBrs ECho EHrv EPPr ERos GBuc GEdr GGar GKev GKir LFur LRHS MTho NGdn NLAp NMen NWCA SRms WCru
	- CC 3667	GEdr GKev
	- pink-flowered	IBlr LFur
	- purple-flowered	IBlr
	- short	WCru
§	***auriculata***	Widely available
	- B&SWJ 2594	WCru
	- brown-stemmed × ***purpurea***	IBlr
	- early-flowering	IBlr NCot WCru
	- 'Floriade'	CLAP EBee GBuc GMac IBlr LRHS SPoG
	- green-stemmed × ***purpurea***	IBlr
	- late-flowering	WCru
	- 'Special'	CLAP
	- 'White Cap'	EBee
	auriculata × ***australis***	IBlr
	australis	CFir ELon GBuc GEdr MNrw NMyG WCru
	- pink-flowered	NCot
	- - KW 22124	IBlr
	- purple-flowered KW 22124	IBlr
	australis × ***humeana*** **new**	IBlr
	'Ballyrogan Lavender'	IBlr
	'Ballyrogan Purple' **new**	IBlr
	'Beesiana'	Widely available
	'Beesiana' dark-flowered	ERos IBlr
	'Beesiana' pale-flowered	ECho ERos EWld LEdu WCru
	'Beesiana' white-flowered	CBct CDes CFwr CLAP EBee EBrs EHrv EPfP EPot GEdr IBlr MMHG NBir NGdn NMyG WPGP
	Blackthorn strain	IBlr
	brandisii	EBee EBrs ECho IBlr WWst
	capitata	CLAP IBlr
	cautleyoides Υ^{H4}	Widely available
	- CLD 772	IBlr
I	- 'Alba'	NGdn NLAp WCot
	- f. ***atropurpurea*** **new**	IBlr
	- - 'Giraffe' **new**	IBlr
	- 'Doge Purple' **new**	IBlr
	- 'Early Purple'	CDes CLAP EBee ECho WPGP
	- 'Early Yellow'	EBee
	- 'Himalaya'	CLAP EBee
	- hybrid	ECho MBel
	- 'Jeffrey Thomas'	CBct CFwr CLAP CSam EBee EBrs ECha ECho ELon EPPr EPot GBuc GCal GEdr IBlr MLHP NBhm NMyG SRGP WCot
	- 'Kew Beauty' Υ^{H4}	CDes CFir CLAP CMea CPLG EBee EPfP GCal GEdr GKir LRHS MTho NMyG SRms WCom WCot WPGP
	- late, lavender-flowered	IBlr
	- late, yellow-flowered	IBlr
	- 'Lemon Giraffe' **new**	IBlr
	- 'Paars'	NBhm
	- 'Pennine Purple' **new**	IBlr
	- plum-flowered	IBlr
	- var. ***pubescens***	IBlr
	- 'Purple Giant'	CLAP EBee EWll NMyG WCot
	- purple-flowered	CAby GBuc IBlr
	- 'Reinier'	CAby CLAP EBee GBuc GCal IBlr WCot
	- f. ***sinopurpurea*** **new**	IBlr
	- 'Vanilla'	EBee NMyG
	- 'Washfield Purple'	IBlr
	- 'Yeti'	CLAP EBee NMyG
	cautleyoides × ***humeana***	CLAP IBlr LRHS
	cautleyoides × ***scillifolia*** dark-flowered	IBlr
	debilis var. ***debilis***	IBlr
	forrestii f. ***forrestii***	IBlr
	- f. ***purpurea***	IBlr
	- f. ***purpurea*** × ***humeana*** **new**	IBlr
	'Gestreept'	CLAP
	humeana Υ^{H4}	CBct CBro CLAP CSam EBrs ECho ERos GAuc GBuc GEdr LAma LRHS MBri NMyG WCFE WCot WThu WWst
	- ACE 2539	IBlr

- CC 1820	IBlr
- f. ***alba***	IBlr
- cream-flowered **new**	WWst
- Forrest's form	IBlr
- lavender-flowered	IBlr
- 'Long Acre Sunrise'	CLAP
- f. ***lutea***	CLAP GEdr IBlr
- pink-flowered	IBlr
- 'Purple Streaker'	CAby CDes CLAP EBee WPGP
- 'Rosemoor Plum'	CDes CLAP EBee GEdr
- 'Snowy Owl'	CLAP WCot
- f. ***tyria***	IBlr
- - 'Inkling'	GBuc WWst
'Ice Maiden' **new**	IBlr
'Monique'	CDes CLAP EBee IBlr NMyG WPGP
'Petite Purple' **new**	IBlr
praecox	IBlr
procera misapplied	see *R. auriculata*
procera Wall.	see *R. purpurea*
'Purple King'	EBee WCot
§ ***purpurea***	Widely available
- CC 1757	IBlr
- CC 3667	WCot
- HWJK 2020	WCru
- HWJK 2169	WCru
- HWJK 2175	WCru
- HWJK 2400	WCru
- HWJK 2401	WCru
- HWJK 2407	WCru
- KW 13755	IBlr
- MECC 2	IBlr
- MECC 10	IBlr
- f. ***alba*** **new**	GEdr
- 'Brown Peacock'	CDes CLAP EBee IBlr NMyG WPGP
- 'Dalai Lama' **new**	EBee
- var. ***gigantea***	CLAP IBlr
- - CC 1757	MNrw
- 'Himalayan Delight' **new**	IBlr
- 'Nico'	CLAP EBee ELan IBlr
- 'Niedrig'	EBee IBlr
- pale-flowered	EBla
- 'Peacock'	CLAP EBee IBlr NMyG WFar
- 'Peacock Eye'	CLAP EBee IBlr
- var. ***procera***	see *R. purpurea*
- 'Red Gurkha'	CDes CLAP IBlr
- Rosemoor form	CLAP WWst
- short	CLAP IBlr
- tall	CLAP NLAp WCru WPGP
- 'Typico' **new**	IBlr
- 'Vincent'	EBee WCot
- 'Wisley Amethyst'	CLAP CPrp EBee GEdr IBlr LRHS MBri NCot NMyG WWst
schneideriana	IBlr MLul WThu
- robust form **new**	IBlr
scillifolia	CBro CDes CFir CPBP ECho ERos GBuc GKev GKir LAma LFur LHop LRHS MAvo MTho NBir NGdn NMen WPrP
- subsp. ***atropurpurea*** **new**	GEdr
- dark-flowered	CPom CStu EBee EHrv IBlr NMyG WCru WPGP WThu
- 'Deep Purple' **new**	WWEG
- pink-flowered	EBee ECho EHrv ERos GEdr IBlr IFoB NMen NMyG WCot WHil WPrP
aff. ***scillifolia*** purple-flowered **new**	IBlr
'Speckles' **new**	IBlr
tibetica	CFir CLAP EBee GEdr GKev IBlr LRHS WCru WThu
- ACE 2538	IBlr
- SDR 467	GKev
aff. ***tibetica***	IBlr NMyG
aff. ***tibetica*** f. ***albo-purpurea*** **new**	IBlr
tumjensis	CLAP EBee EWes IBlr WPGP
wardii	CPLG IBlr

rosemary see *Rosmarinus officinalis*

Rosenia (*Asteraceae*)

humilis **new**	CPBP

Rosmarinus ✿ (*Lamiaceae*)

corsicus 'Prostratus'	see *R. officinalis* Prostratus Group
lavandulaceus misapplied	see *R. officinalis* Prostratus Group
officinalis	Widely available
- SDR 5234	GKev
- var. ***albiflorus***	CArn CPrp CSev EBee ELau EOHP EPfP GBar GPoy LRHS MBar MHer MNHC SBch SDow SHDw SHGN SLim SPlb STre WCHb WClo WGwG
- - 'Lady in White'	CSBt EBee ELan EPfP GBar LRHS MHer NGHP SDow SEND SPer SPoG WGwG WJek
- 'Alderney'	GBar MHer SDow
§ - var. ***angustissimus*** 'Benenden Blue' 🏆H4	CSBt CWan CWib EAro EBee EGoo EOHP EPfP GBar GPoy LRHS SBch SDix SEND SPer SPlb STre SUsu WGwG WPnn WSpi
- - 'Corsican Blue'	CAlb CArn EBee ELan EPfP GBar GPoy LRHS MHer MNHC MRav NGHP SBch SDow SHDw SIde SPer WBrE WPer WRHF
* - 'Argenteovariegatus' (v)	WPGP
- 'Aureovariegatus'	see *R. officinalis* 'Aureus'
§ - 'Aureus' (v)	CBow GBar WCHb WCom WJek
- 'Baby P.J.'	EOHP
- 'Barbecue'[PBR]	ELau MHer NGHP SIde
- 'Blue Lagoon'	EBee ELau EOHP MHer MNHC NGHP SIde WCHb WGwG WJek WPnn
- 'Blue Rain'	CBod EAro GPWP LRHS MHer NGHP SIde WPnn
- 'Boule'	CArn CBod CPrp ELau MHer SDow WCHb WGwG WJek
- 'Capercaillie'	SDow
- 'Collingwood Ingram'	see *R. officinalis* var. *angustissimus* 'Benenden Blue'
- 'Cottage White'	WGwG
- dwarf, blue-flowered	ELau GBar
- dwarf, white-flowered	WCHb
- 'Farinole'	CArn CBod CPrp ELau GBar MNHC
- 'Fastigiatus'	see *R. officinalis* 'Miss Jessopp's Upright'
- 'Fota Blue'	CArn CBod CBow CPrp CTsd CWib EAro ELau GBar IArd LRHS MHer MNHC NGHP NHol SAga SBch SDow SHDw SIde SPoG WCHb WFar WGwG WJek WPnn
- 'Frimley Blue'	see *R. officinalis* 'Primley Blue'
- 'Genges Gold' (v)	ECtt MHer SBch
- 'Golden Rain'	see *R. officinalis* 'Joyce DeBaggio'
- 'Gorizia'	CBcs GBar LRHS SDow WGwG WPnn
- 'Green Ginger'	CBod CPrp EBee ELan ELau EOHP EPfP GBar GBin LHop LRHS MAsh MHer MNHC MRav MSCN NGHP NPer SDow SPer SPoG WCHb WFoF WGwG WMnd WPnn
- 'Guilded'	see *R. officinalis* 'Aureus'
- 'Gunnel's Upright'	GBar

	- 'Haifa'	CBod EBtc ECtt ELau GGar NGHP SIde WCHb WPnn
	- 'Heavenly Blue'	GBar
	- 'Henfield Blue'	SBch SHDw
	- 'Iden Blue'	SIde
	- 'Iden Blue Boy'	SIde
	- 'Iden Pillar'	SIde
§	- 'Joyce DeBaggio' (v)	MHer SDow WGwG
	- 'Ken Taylor'	SPhx
	- 'Lady in Blue'	WGwG
	- ***lavandulaceus***	see *R. officinalis* Prostratus Group
	- 'Lilies Blue'	GPoy
	- 'Lockwood Variety'	see *R. officinalis* (Prostratus Group) 'Lockwood de Forest'
	- 'Majorca Pink'	CBcs CChe CSBt CSam CSpe CWan EBee EGoo ELau GBar GGar GPWP LRHS MCot MHer MNHC NPri SDow SEND SIde SPer SRms WCHb WGwG
	- 'Maltese White'	WCot
	- 'Marenca'	ELau MNHC WCHb
	- 'McConnell's Blue' 🏆H4	CAlb CArn CDoC CPrp EBee ELan ELau EShb GBar LHop LRHS MAsh MGos MNHC SBch SDow SHDw WCHb WFar WGwG WHoo WPGP
*	- 'Miss Jessopp's Prostrate'	GKir
§	- 'Miss Jessopp's Upright' 🏆H4	Widely available
	- 'Mrs Harding'	CBod
	- 'Pointe du Raz'	CAbP EBee ELan EMil EPfP LRHS MAsh SChF SPoG WSpi
§	- 'Primley Blue'	CArn CMea CPrp CSam CSev CTsd CWSG EBee ECtt ELau GBar LSou MNHC MRav NGHP SIde SPoG WCHb WFar WPer WSpi
§	- Prostratus Group	Widely available
	- - 'Capri'	CAbP CDul CSBt ECtt ELau IMon LRHS MAsh MBrN MHer NGHP SPoG
	- - 'Gethsemane'	SIde
	- - 'Jackman's Prostrate'	CBcs ECtt
§	- - 'Lockwood de Forest'	GBar LSou WGwG
	- f. ***pyramidalis***	see *R. officinalis* 'Miss Jessopp's Upright'
	- ***repens***	see *R. officinalis* Prostratus Group
	- 'Rex'	CBod ELau
	- 'Roman Beauty'	CBcs EBee LAst LRHS LSRN NPri SPoG WSpi
	- 'Roseus'	CArn CEnt CPrp CWib EBee ELan ELau EMil EPfP GPoy LHop LRHS MAsh MHer MNHC NEgg SBch SDow SHGN SLim SPoG SUsu WAbe WClo WGwG WHer WMnd WPer WPnn
	- 'Russell's Blue'	WFar
	- 'Salem'	CBod MHer
	- 'Sea Level'	CBod ELau MHer WCHb WGwG
	- 'Severn Sea' 🏆H4	Widely available
	- 'Shimmering Stars'	SDow
	- 'Silver Sparkler'	WCom WPat
	- Silver Spires = 'Wolros'	MNHC WFar
	- 'Sissinghurst Blue' 🏆H4	CArn CDul CSev CWan EBee ECha ECrN ELan ELau EPfP GBar LRHS MHer MLHP MNHC MRav NGHP SBch SDow SIde SLim SPer SPlb SRms WCHb WClo WCom WGwG
	- 'Sissinghurst White'	WGwG
	- 'South Downs Blue'	SBch SHDw
	- 'Spanish Snow'	WGwG
	- 'Sudbury Blue'	EAro EBee ELau EPfP GBar MNHC NGHP SBch SDow SHDw WEas WFar WJek WPnn
	- 'Trusty'	CWan GBar LRHS
	- 'Tuscan Blue'	Widely available
	- 'Variegatus'	see *R. officinalis* 'Aureus'
	repens	see *R. officinalis* Prostratus Group

Rostrinucula (*Lamiaceae*)

	dependens	EPfP EWes MBri NLar
	B&SWJ 11739 from northern Vietnam **new**	WCru
	sinensis	CPLG

Rosularia ✿ (*Crassulaceae*)

	sp.	MWat
	from Sandras Dag	CWil LBee LRHS
§	***aizoon***	LRHS
	alba	see *R. sedoides* var. *alba*
	alpestris	WThu
	from Rhotang Pass	
§	***chrysantha***	EBur EDAr EPot LRHS NMen SFgr SPlb
	- number 1	CWil
	crassipes	see *Rhodiola wallichiana*
	libanotica RCB RL 20 **new**	WCot
§	***muratdaghensis***	EBur LRHS
	pallida A. Berger	see *R. chrysantha*
	pallida Stapf	see *R. aizoon*
	pallida ambig.	SFgr
	platyphylla misapplied	see *R. muratdaghensis*
	sedoides	CWil LRHS MBar SIng
§	- var. ***alba***	ECho EDAr EPot GGar LRHS WTin
	sempervivum	CWil ECho EWes NMen
§	- subsp. ***glaucophylla***	CWil WAbe WThu
	spatulata hort.	see *R. sempervivum* subsp. *glaucophylla*

Rothmannia (*Rubiaceae*)

capensis	EShb

Rubia (*Rubiaceae*)

peregrina	CArn GPoy
tinctorum	CArn CHby EOHP GBar GPoy MHer SWat WCHb WSFF

Rubus ✿ (*Rosaceae*)

RCB/Eq C-1	WCot
SDR 4635	GKev
alceifolius Poir.	CFee SDys
arcticus	EBee ECtt EPPr GAuc GEdr GGar MCCP NLAp NLar SHar SRms SRot WCru WPat
- subsp. ***stellatus***	GAuc
× ***barkeri***	ECou
'Benenden' 🏆H4	Widely available
'Betty Ashburner'	CAgr CBcs CDoC CDul EBee ECrN EPfP EWTr GQui LAst LBuc MGos MRav MWhi NHol SLPl SPer WDin WMoo WTin
biflorus 🏆H4	EPfP EWes LEdu MBlu SEND WPGP
'Black Butte'	CSut EMil EMui GPri SDea SVic
'Boatsberry'	SDea
boysenberry, thornless (F)	CMac EMil EMui ERea GPri GTwe LBuc LSRN MGan NPri SDea SPer
buergeri B&SWJ 5555	WCru
calophyllus	CDul WPGP
calycinoides Hayata	see *R. rolfei*
calycinoides Kuntze **new**	EBtc
chamaemorus	GAuc GPoy
cockburnianus (F)	CArn CBcs CTri CWib EBee ELan EPfP GCra GKir IFoB LBuc MRav MSwo NHol NSti NWea SPer SPlb SRms WDin WEas WFar WSpi

	Name	Suppliers
	- 'Goldenvale' ♀H4	Widely available
	crataegifolius	CWan MRav WPat
	deliciosus	WFar
	discolor Himalayan berry (F)	ERea
	'Emerald Spreader'	GKir SBod WMoo
	flagelliflorus	MBar
	fockeanus misapplied	see *R. rolfei*
	formosensis B&SWJ 1798	WCru
N	***fruticosus*** agg.	WSFF
	- 'Adrienne' (F)	CAgr CSBt EMui MAsh
	- 'Ashton Cross' (F)	CDoC GTwe LBuc
	- 'Bedford Giant' (F)	CSBt ECrN GTwe LRHS MAsh MGan MGos SEND SKee SPoG
	- 'Black Satin' (F)	CAgr LRHS MCoo NLar SDea SVic
	- 'Chester' (F)	LRHS SKee
	- 'Fantasia'PBR (F) ♀H4	EMui
	- 'Godshill Goliath' (F)	SDea
	- 'Helen' (F)	CAgr CSut EMil EMui MAsh SDea
	- 'Himalayan Giant' (F)	ERea GTwe MGan MRav NEgg NLar SDea SPer
	- 'John Innes' (F)	MCoo
	- 'Kotata' (F)	EMil MRav
	- 'Loch Ness'PBR (F) ♀H4	CAgr CMac CWib EMil EMui ERea GKir GTwe IArd LBuc LRHS MAsh MCoo NPri SCoo SDea SKee
	- 'Merton Thornless' (F)	CSBt CWib ERea GTwe LSRN MAsh MGan MGos
	- 'No Thorn' (F)	SDea
	- 'Oregon Thornless' (F)	CAgr CCVT CDoC CSBt CWib ECrN EMui EPfP GTwe LRHS MAsh MRav NEgg NLar SCoo SDea SKee SPoG SRms
	- 'Parsley Leaved' (F)	SDea
*	- 'Sylvan' (F)	EMil MCoo MGos SPer
	- 'Thornfree' (F)	CAgr CDoC CTri LRHS NLar SDea SKee
	- 'Variegatus' (v)	CBot CMac EPla MBlu SMad WCot
	- 'Veronique' (F)	EMui
	- 'Waldo' (F)	CAgr CSBt CWib ECrN EMui LBuc LSRN MAsh MBri MGos SDea
	aff. ***gachetensis*** B&SWJ 10603	WCru
	'Golden Showers'	CWib
	henryi	CBot EBla EPla LRHS MRav NLar NSti SMac SPoG WCot
	- var. ***bambusarum***	EBee EPla MCCP MRav NHol NVic WCru
	'Hildaberry' (F) **new**	GPri
	hupehensis	SLPl
	ichangensis	CBcs CBot EPla LEdu
	idaeus	GPoy
	- 'All Gold' (F)	CAgr CSut EMil ERea GPri LRHS MAsh MNHC SVic
	- 'Aureus' (F)	ECha ELan EPla EWes MRav NBid SMac WCot WFar WMoo
	- 'Autumn Bliss'PBR (F) ♀H4	Widely available
	- 'Fallgold' (F)	CWib EMui EPfP MCoo MMuc SKee SPer SPoG
	- 'Galante'PBR (F)	EMui
	- 'Glen Ample'PBR (F) ♀H4	CAgr CMac CSBt CSut CTri CWSG CWib EMil EMui EPfP ERea GPri GTwe LBuc LEdu LRHS LSRN MAsh MBri MCoo NPri SCoo SDea SKee SPer SPoG SVic
	- 'Glen Clova' (F)	CAgr CSBt CTri CWib ECrN GKir GTwe MAsh MGan MGos MRav SKee SPer SPoG SVic
	- 'Glen Garry' (F) **new**	LRHS
	- 'Glen Lyon'PBR (F)	CWib EMui GTwe LBuc LRHS MAsh MBri SCoo
	- 'Glen Magna'PBR (F)	CAgr CSBt CWSG CWib EMui ERea LBuc MAsh MBri MNHC SCoo SDea SKee SPoG
	- 'Glen Moy'PBR (F) ♀H4	CAgr CSBt CTri CWib EMil EMui EPfP ERea GTwe LRHS LSRN MAsh MGos MNHC NEgg NPri SCoo SDea SKee
	- 'Glen Prosen'PBR (F) ♀H4	CAgr CSBt CWib ECrN EMui GKir GTwe LRHS MAsh MBri MGos MRav NEgg NPri SCoo SDea SKee SPer
	- 'Glen Rosa' (F)	ERea
	- 'Heritage' (F)	CWib MAsh MGos SCoo
	- Himbo Top = 'Rafzaqu'PBR (F)	ERea
	- 'Joan J'PBR (F)	CMac CSut EMil ERea
	- 'Joan Squire' (F)	LRHS SKee
	- 'Julia' (F)	GTwe MCoo
	- 'Leo'PBR (F) ♀H4	CSBt CTri CWib EMui GTwe LRHS MAsh MGos SCoo SKee SPer
	- 'Malling Admiral' (F) ♀H4	CSBt CTri CWib EMui GKir GTwe LSRN MAsh SCoo SKee SPer
	- 'Malling Delight' (F)	CSBt CWib MAsh SCoo
	- 'Malling Jewel' (F) ♀H4	CSBt CWib EMui GKir GTwe LBuc MAsh MGan SDea SKee SPer
	- 'Malling Promise' (F)	CWib
	- 'Octavia'PBR (F)	CAgr CSBt EMil EMui LBuc LRHS MAsh MCoo MNHC SPoG
	- 'Polka'PBR (F)	CSut EMui SKee SVic
	- 'Redsetter' (F)	EMui
	- 'Summer Gold' (F)	GTwe
	- 'Tulameen' (F)	CAgr CSBt CWib EMil EMui LSRN MAsh MBri NPri SCoo SKee SPoG SVic
	- 'Valentina' (F)	EMil
	- 'Zeva Herbsternte' (F)	CWib MAsh
	irenaeus	EBla LRHS SSpi
	Japanese wineberry	see *R. phoenicolasius*
	'Jermyn's Jubilee' **new**	SLPl
	'Karaka Black'PBR	LBuc SVic
	'Kenneth Ashburner'	CDoC NLar SLPl WTin
	'King's Acre Berry' (F)	EMui
	laciniatus	EPla
	leucodermis NNS 00-663	EPPr
	lineatus	CBot CDTJ CDoC CWib EPfP EWes LRHS MCot NSti SMad WCru WDin WPGP
	- B&SWJ 11261 from Sumatra	WCru
	- HWJ 892 from Vietnam	WCru
	- HWJK 2045 from Nepal	WCru
	- from Nepal	GCra
	× ***loganobaccus*** 'Brandywine'	SDea
	- 'Ly 59' (F) ♀H4	ECrN EMui EPfP GTwe MRav SDea SKee SPer SRms
	- 'Ly 654' (F) ♀H4	CSBt GTwe LBuc MBri MGos NEgg NPri SDea SPer
	- thornless (F)	CAgr CTri CWSG CWib GPri GTwe MAsh MGan SDea SPoG SVic
	'Malling Minerva' (F)	CMac CSut
	'Margaret Gordon'	MRav
	microphyllus 'Variegatus' (v)	MRav WPat
§	***nepalensis***	CAgr CDoC EBee GCra LEdu
	- from Nepal	GCra
	nutans	see *R. nepalensis*
	occidentalis 'Haut' **new**	GPri
	- 'Jewel' **new**	GPri
	odoratus	CPLG EBee ELan EPPr EPfP EWTr LEdu MBlu MRav NBid NPal SPer WBor WCot WFar WHCG WTin

	parviflorus	CArn
	- double-flowered (d)	EPPr WCru
	- 'Sunshine Spreader'	EHoe WPat
	parvus	GGar
	pectinellus var. ***trilobus***	CFee EWld LEdu NLar
	- - B&SWJ 1669B	WCru
	peltatus	CGHE NLar WPGP
	pentalobus	see *R. rolfei*
§	***phoenicolasius***	CAgr CCCN CMac EMui EPfP EPla EWTr GTwe LEdu LHop LRHS MBlu MCoo MGan MRav SDea SPer SPoG SVic WAbb WHCG WPGP
§	***rolfei***	CTri EPPr MBar
	- B&SWJ 3546 from Taiwan	WCru
	- B&SWJ 3878 from the Philippines	WCru
	- 'Emerald Carpet'	CAgr NLar SBod
	rosifolius	CSpe
	- 'Coronarius' (d)	CFee CHar CSpe ECrN ELan LRHS LSou MRav NPro WCot WFar
	sachalinensis	GAuc
	sanctus	CNat
	setchuenensis	CFee CMCN EWes MBri
	'Silvan' (F) ♀H4	EMui GPri GTwe SEND
	spectabilis	CBcs CSev CWib EBee ELan EPPr EPla EWTr LEdu MMuc MRav WFar WSHC WWFP
	- 'Flore Pleno'	see *R. spectabilis* 'Olympic Double'
	- 'Golden Ruby' new	SGol
§	- 'Olympic Double' (d)	Widely available
	splendidissimus B&SWJ 2361	WCru
	squarrosus	ECou
*	***stelleri***	GAuc
	'Sunberry' (F)	CCCN GTwe SDea
	swinhoei B&SWJ 1735	WCru
	taiwanicola	EDAr GEdr
	- B&SWJ 317	GBin WCru
	Tayberry Group (F) ♀H4	CSBt CTri ECrN EMui GTwe LSRN MAsh MGan MGos NLar NPri SPer SRms SVic
	- 'Buckingham' (F)	CSut EMil EMui GTwe LBuc LRHS MAsh SPoG SVic
	- 'Medana Tayberry' (F)	CAgr EMui EPfP ERea GPri LRHS SDea SKee SPoG
§	***thibetanus*** ♀H4	Widely available
	- 'Silver Fern'	see *R. thibetanus*
	treutleri B&SWJ 2139	WCru
	tricolor	CAgr CBcs CDul CSBt CTri CWib EBee ECrN EPfP GKir MBlu MMuc MRav MSwo NEgg NHol SDix SMac SPer WDin WHCG WMoo
	trilobus B&SWJ 9096	WCru
	'Tummelberry' (F)	EMil GTwe MCoo SVic
	ulmifolius	GCal MBlu MRav MSwo NSti SDix
	'Bellidiflorus' (d)	WAbb WEas WHrl
	'Veitchberry' (F)	GTwe
	xanthocarpus	NLar
	'Youngberry' (F)	SDea
	'Youngberry' thornless (F) new	GPri

Rudbeckia ✿ (*Asteraceae*)

	Autumn Sun	see *R. laciniata* 'Herbstsonne'
	californica	WPer
	- var. ***intermedia*** from Anthony Brooks	WCot
	deamii	see *R. fulgida* var. *deamii*
	fulgida	GKir NNor
	- 'City Garden' new	EBee MAsh
§	- var. ***deamii*** ♀H4	Widely available
	- var. ***fulgida***	CMea EBee EPfP SBch SMad
§	- var. ***speciosa*** ♀H4	CKno CMMP CSam EBee ECha ECtt ELan EPfP GAbr MMuc NBPC SBch SPlb SRms SWal WEas WFar WMoo WPer WPtf WTin WWEG
I	- var. ***sullivantii*** 'Goldschirm' new	EBee
	- - 'Goldsturm' ♀H4	Widely available
	- Viette's Little Suzy = 'Blovi'	EBee EBrs GKir LRHS
	gloriosa	see *R. hirta*
	'Golden Jubilee'	LRHS
§	***hirta***	CHar CHrt LRHS NBir
	- 'Autumn Colours' (mixed)	CMea LRHS
	- 'Cherokee Sunset' (d)	CSpe LRHS
	- 'Chim Chiminee'	LBMP LRHS
	- 'Goldilocks'	LRHS
	- 'Indian Summer' ♀H3	LRHS SPav
	- 'Irish Eyes'	SPav
	- 'Marmalade'	LBMP LRHS NGBl
	- 'Prairie Sun'	EPfP LBMP LRHS NGBl SAga
	- 'Rustic' new	LRHS
	- 'Sonora'	LRHS WHal
	- 'Toto' ♀H3	LRHS SPav SWvt
	- 'Toto Lemon'	LRHS
	- 'Toto Rustic'	LRHS
	July Gold	see *R. laciniata* 'Juligold'
	laciniata	CElw CHVG CKno CMac CSam EBee EBrs ELan EPPr GCal GKir GQue LEdu LRHS MDKP MMuc NLar NOrc SPhx WCot WMoo WOld WWEG
	- var. ***digitata*** new	IMou
	- 'Golden Glow'	see *R. laciniata* 'Hortensia'
	- 'Goldquelle' (d) ♀H4	Widely available
§	- 'Herbstsonne' ♀H4	Widely available
§	- 'Hortensia' (d)	EBee GQue MAvo MRav WHoo WOld WWEG
§	- 'Juligold'	CPrp EBee IPot LBMP LRHS MAvo MBNS NBre NEgg NGdn SPoG WFar WWEG
	- 'Starcadia Razzle Dazzle'	EBee
	maxima	CDes CKno COIW CSpe EBee ECha GMac IFoB LEdu LHop LRHS MAvo MBri MCCP NCGa NLar NPri NSti SAga SDix SMad SMrm SPhx SPlb SPoG WBor WCot WFar WWEG
	missouriensis	NBre SBch SUsu
	mollis	EBee LRHS NBre
	newmannii	see *R. fulgida* var. *speciosa*
	nitida	EShb WSpi
	occidentalis	LBMP LRHS NBre NVic WPer
	- 'Black Beauty' PBR	CBcs EBee EHrv EPfP GKir NBhm NMoo NSti WMnd WSpi
	- 'Green Wizard'	Widely available
*	***paniculata***	EBee LLHF NBre WCot
	purpurea	see *Echinacea purpurea*
	speciosa	see *R. fulgida* var. *speciosa*
	subtomentosa	CDes CSam EBee EWes GCal LPla LRHS MAvo MDKP MNFA NBre NSti STes WCAu WOld
	- 'Henry Eilers' new	EBee EPfP MBNS MWea NBhm
	- 'Loofahsa Wheaten Gold'	WCot
	'Takao'	CEnt CWCL EBee LSou MAvo MBel MDKP MNrw MWea NLar SPoG WBor
	triloba ♀H4	CDes CEnt CMea CSam EBee ECha EPfP EShb LRHS MNrw NBPC NCGa NGdn SGSe SMad SMrm SMrs SPet SUsu WCAu WCot WFar WMoo WPGP WTin

rue see *Ruta graveolens*

Ruellia (*Acanthaceae*)

amoena	see *R. brevifolia*
§ ***brevifolia***	CSpe ECre EShb
humilis	EBee EPPr EShb NLar WHil
macrantha	CCCN EShb
makoyana ♀H1	CSev EShb MBri WHil
tweediana	EShb WHil

Rumex (*Polygonaceae*)

acetosa	CArn CHby CSev CWan EBWF ELau GBar GPoy LRHS MCoo MHer MMuc MNHC NBir NGHP NPri NSco SBch SIde WHer WSFF
- 'Abundance'	ELau
- subsp. ***acetosa*** 'Saucy' (v)	WAlt WCot
- 'De Belleville'	CPrp NPri
- 'Profusion'	GPoy MHer
- subsp. ***vinealis***	EBee WCot
acetosella	CArn EBWF MNHC NMir WSFF
alpinus	EBee LEdu SPhx WCot
flexuosus	CSpe CSpr EBee GCal LBMP MDKP NLar WJek
hydrolapathum	CArn EBWF EMFW LPBA MMuc MSKA SPlb WSFF
patientia	CArn
sanguineus	CTri EPfP EShb LBMP LPBA MSKA NBlu NCob NLar WFar WMAq
- var. ***sanguineus***	CArn CBgR CElw CRow CSev EBee ELan IFoB MHer MNrw MTho NBro NHol SGSe WHer
'Schavel'	LEdu
scutatus	CArn CHby CPrp CSev ELau GPoy MNHC SBch SIde SPlb WHer WJek
- 'Silver Shield'	CBod CRow ELau MHer SIde WCHb WJek

Rumohra (*Davalliaceae*)

sp.	SEND
adiantiformis ♀H1	CCCN EBee EFtx LRHS SEND WFib WRic
- RCB/Arg D-2	WCot

Ruscus ✿ (*Ruscaceae*)

aculeatus	Widely available
- (f)	WFar WGrn WMou
- (m)	WCFE WMou
- hermaphrodite	EPfP EPla EWes GCal MBri SMad WPGP WPat WThu
- var. ***aculeatus*** 'Lanceolatus' (f)	GCal
- var. ***angustifolius***	EPla
- - (f)	EPla
- 'Christmas Berry'	ELan EPfP NLar
- 'John Redmond'[PBR]	Widely available
* - 'Wheeler's Variety' (f/m)	CPMA MRav
hypoglossum	LRHS SEND WPGP WSpi
hypophyllum	LRHS
× ***microglossum*** (f)	CDul
racemosus	see *Danae racemosa*

Ruspolia (*Acanthaceae*)

hypocrateriformis new	CCCN
seticalyx	EShb

Russelia (*Scrophulariaceae*)

§ ***equisetiformis*** ♀H1	CHII EShb
- 'Lemon Falls'	EShb
juncea	see *R. equisetiformis*

Ruta (*Rutaceae*)

chalepensis	CArn
corsica	CArn
graveolens	CArn CWan EPfP GBar GPoy MNHC NBlu NPri SBch SIde WJek WPer
- 'Jackman's Blue'	CBcs CDul CPrp CSev EHoe ELan EOHP EPfP GKir GMaP GPoy LAst MGos MHer MRav MSwo SBch SLim SRms WMnd WSpi
- 'Variegata' (v)	CBot CBow CWan ELan EOHP GBar LRHS MNHC NPer WCom WJek

Ruttya (*Acanthaceae*)

fruticosa new	CCCN

× *Ruttyruspolia* (*Acanthaceae*)

'Phyllis van Heerden'	GFai
* ***lutea*** new	CCCN

Rytidosperma (*Poaceae*)

* ***arundinaceum***	EShb

S

Sabal (*Arecaceae*)

§ ***bermudana***	EAmu
causiarum	EAmu
etonia	LPal
§ ***mexicana***	EAmu
minor	CBrP CHEx CPHo EAmu ETod LPal MREP NPal SBig
palmetto	CDoC EAmu LPal
princeps	see *S. bermudana*
rosei	LPal
texana	see *S. mexicana*
uresana	LPal

Saccharum (*Poaceae*)

arundinaceum	CKno EPPr
§ ***baldwinii***	GCal GFor
brevibarbe var. ***contortum***	GCal
ravennae	EBee GCal GFor MWhi SApp SEND SMad SMrm SPlb
strictum (Baldwin) Nutt.	see *S. baldwinii*

Sadleria (*Blechnaceae*)

cyatheoides	WRic

sage see *Salvia officinalis*

sage, annual clary see *Salvia viridis*

sage, biennial clary see *Salvia sclarea*

sage, pineapple see *Salvia elegans*

Sageretia (*Rhamnaceae*)

§ ***thea***	CMen STre
theezans	see *S. thea*

Sagina (*Caryophyllaceae*)

boydii	ECho
subulata	ECho SVic

§	- var. ***glabrata*** 'Aurea'	CMea CTri EAlp ECha ECho ECtt EDAr GKir GMaP LRHS SIng SPoG SRms WEas WFar WPer

Sagittaria (*Alismataceae*)

	'Bloomin Babe'	CRow
	graminea 'Crushed Ice' (v)	CRow
	japonica	see *S. sagittifolia*
	latifolia	COld LPBA NPer SMad
*	***leucopetala*** 'Flore Pleno' (d)	NLar NPer
§	***sagittifolia***	CBen CRow CWat EHon EMFW EPfP LLWG LPBA MSKA NSco WMAq WPnP
	- 'Flore Pleno' (d)	CBen CRow CWat EMFW LPBA WMAq
	- var. ***leucopetala***	WMAq

Saintpaulia (*Gesneriaceae*)

'Arctic Frost'	WDib
'Bangle Blue'	WDib
'Beatrice Trail'	WDib
'Betty Stoehr'	WDib
'Blue Dragon'	WDib
'Bob Serbin' (d)	WDib
'Bohemian Sunset'	WDib
'Buffalo Hunt'	WDib
'Centenary'	WDib
'Cherries 'n' Cream'	WDib
'Chiffon Fiesta'	WDib
'Chiffon Mist' (d)	WDib
'Chiffon Moonmoth'	WDib
'Chiffon Stardust'	WDib
'Chiffon Vesper'	WDib
'Coroloir'	WDib
'Delft' (d)	WDib
'Electric Dreams'	WDib
'Gillian'	WDib
'Golden Glow' (d)	WDib
'Halo' (Ultra Violet Series)	WDib
'Halo's Aglitter'	WDib
ionantha **new**	LRHS
'Irish Flirt' (d)	WDib
'King's Trail' (d) **new**	WDib
'Lemon Drop' (d)	WDib
'Lemon Whip' (d)	WDib
'Love Spots'	WDib
'Lucky Lee Ann' (d)	WDib
'Ma Chérie' **new**	LRHS
'Ma Mars'	WDib
'Marching Band'	WDib
'Mermaid' (d)	WDib
'Midget Lillian' (v)	WDib
'Midnight Flame'	WDib
'Midnight Waltz'	WDib
'Ness' Crinkle Blue'	WDib
'Nubian Winter'	WDib
'Otoe'	WDib
'Powder Keg' (d)	WDib
'Powwow' (d/v)	WDib
'Rainbow Limelight'	WDib
'Ramblin' Magic' (d)	WDib
'Rapid Transit' (d)	WDib
'Rhapsodie Clementine'	WDib
'Rob's Bamboozle'	WDib
'Rob's Calypso Beat'	WDib
'Rob's Cloudy Skies' (d)	WDib
'Rob's Dandy Lion'	WDib
'Rob's Denim Demon'	WDib
'Rob's Dust Storm' (d)	WDib
'Rob's Firebrand'	WDib
'Rob's Gundaroo' (d)	WDib
'Rob's Heat Wave' (d)	WDib
'Rob's Hopscotch'	WDib
'Rob's Ice Ripples' (d)	WDib
'Rob's June Bug'	WDib
'Rob's Loose Goose'	WDib
'Rob's Love Bite'	WDib
'Rob's Macho Devil'	WDib
'Rob's Mad Cat' (d)	WDib
'Rob's Red Bug' (d/r)	WDib
'Rob's Rinky Dink' (d)	WDib
'Rob's Sarsparilla' (d)	WDib
'Rob's Seduction'	WDib
'Rob's Shadow Magic' (d)	WDib
'Rob's Smarty Pants'	WDib
'Rob's Sticky Wicket'	WDib
'Rob's Toorooka' (d)	WDib
'Rob's Twinkle Pink'	WDib
shumensis	WDib
'Sky Bandit' (d)	WDib
'Sky Bells' (v)	WDib
'Sweet Amy Sue' (d) **new**	WDib
'Taffeta Blue' (d) **new**	WDib
'The Madam'	WDib
'Tippy Toe' (d)	WDib

Salicornia (*Chenopodiaceae*)

europaea **new**	SVic

Salix ✿ (*Salicaceae*)

	acutifolia	ELan EQua IFFs WDin
	- 'Blue Streak' (m) ♀H4	CEnd CWiW CWon EPfP EWes LRHS MBlu NBir NHol NLar SWat WFar
	- 'Lady Aldenham No 2'	EPla
	- 'Pendulifolia' (m)	WPat
	aegyptiaca	CDoC CWon EBtc ECrN MBlu NWea WMou
	alba	CCVT CDul CLnd CWiW ECrN EMac GGal IFFs LBuc LMaj NWea WDin WMou
	- f. ***argentea***	see *S. alba* var. *sericea*
	- 'Aurea'	CLnd CTho CWon WIvy WMou
	- 'Belders' (m)	IFFs
	- var. ***caerulea***	CDul CLnd CWon NWea WMou
	- - 'Wantage Hall' (f)	CWiW CWon
	- 'Cardinalis' (f)	CWiW CWon GQue IFFs ISea SWat
	- 'Chermesina' hort.	see *S. alba* var. *vitellina* 'Britzensis'
	- 'Dart's Snake'	ELan EPfP EPla LRHS MAsh MBrN MRav NLar SCoo WCot
	- 'Golden Ness'	LRHS MBlu
	- 'Hutchinson's Yellow'	CDoC CTho CWon ECrN EQua MGos NLar SCoo SLim WDin
	- 'Liempde' (m)	NWea
	- 'Raesfeld' (m)	CWiW CWon
	- 'Saint Oedendrode'	CWon
§	- var. ***sericea*** ♀H4	CBcs CDoC CDul CLnd CTho CWon EPfP MBlu MRav NWea SPer WDin WIvy WMou
	- 'Splendens'	see *S. alba* var. *sericea*
	- 'Tristis' misapplied	see *S.* × *sepulcralis* var. *chrysocoma*
§	- 'Tristis' ambig.	CCVT CLnd CTri ELan GKir LRHS MBri MGos MRav MSwo NLar NWea SLim SRms SWat WDin WFar WHar
	- 'Tristis' Gaud.	MMuc
	- var. ***vitellina*** ♀H4	CDul CTri CWon EMac EPfP GQue IFFs LBuc MBNS MBrN NWea SLon SWat WDin WIvy WMoo
§	- - 'Britzensis' (m) ♀H4	Widely available
	- - 'Nova'	SWat
§	- - 'Yelverton'	CWon LRHS SWat
	- 'Vitellina Pendula'	see *S. alba* 'Tristis' ambig.

	- 'Vitellina Tristis'	see *S. alba* 'Tristis' ambig.
§	***alpina***	EBee ECho NBir
	'Americana'	CWiW
	amplexicaulis 'Pescara' (m)	CWiW
	amygdaloides	CWiW CWon
	'Aokautere'	see *S.* × *sepulcralis* 'Aokautere'
	apennina 'Cisa Pass'	CWon
	apoda	CWon
	- (m)	ECho NWCA WPer
§	***arbuscula***	CWon EBee ECho GAuc LRHS NWCA WDin
	arctica var. ***petraea***	NLAp WPat
	arenaria	see *S. repens* var. *argentea*
	aurita	GAuc IFFs NLar NWea
	babylonica	CDul CEnd CTrG CWon WMou
	- 'Annularis'	see *S. babylonica* 'Crispa'
	- 'Bijdorp'	MBri NLar
§	- 'Crispa'	CDul CWon ELan LHop LRHS MBri NPro SMad WCom WFar
	- 'Pan Chih-kang'	CWiW NLar
	- var. ***pekinensis***	CWon
	- - 'Snake'	CWon
§	- - 'Tortuosa' ♀H4	Widely available
*	- 'Tortuosa Aurea'	MCCP SWvt
	× ***balfourii***	CWon
	bebbiana	CWon
	'Blackskin' (f)	CWiW
	bockii	EBee EBtc ELan LLHF LRHS MBar MMuc WFar
§	'Bowles's Hybrid'	WMou
	'Boydii' (f) ♀H4	CWon EBee ECho EPfP EPot GAbr GEdr GKir ITim LEdu MGos NBir NLAp NMen NRya NSla SIng SRms WAbe WFar WPat
§	'Boyd's Pendulous' (m)	CWib
	burjatica	CWon
	- 'Germany'	CWon
	- 'Korso'	CWon
	caesia	EMac NWCA WIvy
	× ***calodendron*** (f)	CWon
	candida	CWon GAuc
	cantabrica	CWon
	caprea	CBcs CCVT CDul CLnd CTri CWon ECrN EMac EPfP IFFs LBuc LMaj NWea SPer STre WDin WMou WSFF
	- 'Black Stem'	CDul
	- 'Curlilocks'	MBar
§	- 'Kilmarnock' (m)	Widely available
	- var. ***pendula*** (m)	see *S. caprea* 'Kilmarnock' (m)
	caprea × ***lanata***	CWon
	× ***capreola***	CWon
	cashmiriana	CWon GAuc GEdr WPat
	caspica	CWon
*	- ***rubra nana***	SWat
	× ***cernua***	NWCA
	chaenomeloides	EBrs
	'Chrysocoma'	see *S.* × *sepulcralis* var. *chrysocoma*
	cinerea	CBcs CDoC CWon ECrN EMac GKir IFFs LBuc NWea STre WDin
	- 'Bude'	CWon
	- subsp. ***oleifolia*** × ***hibernica***	CWon
	- 'Tricolor' (v)	CArn NPro
	cordata	CWon ECrN SLPl WDin
	- 'Purpurescens'	CWon
	× ***cottetii***	EBee GAuc LRHS MBar WDin
	daphnoides	CCVT CDoC CDul CLnd CMac EBee EMac EPfP EWTr GKir IFFs MBrN MGos MMuc MSwo NWea SEND SPer SRms STre SWat WDin WFar WJas WMou WSFF
	- 'Aglaia' (m)	CBcs CWon ECrN GQue MGos WIvy
	- 'Continental Purple'	CWon
	- 'Lady Aldenham'	CWon
	- 'Meikle' (f)	CWiW SWat
	- 'Netta Statham' (m)	CWiW CWon
	- 'Ovaro Udine' (m)	CWiW
	- 'Oxford Violet' (m)	CWon ECrN WIvy
	- 'Pendulifolia'	CWon
	- 'Purple Heart'	CWon
	- 'Sinker'	WIvy
	- 'Stewartstown'	CWiW
	- 'Wynter Bloom'	CWon
	× ***dasyclados***	CWon
	- 'Grandis'	NWea
	discolor	CWon
§	× ***doniana*** 'Kumeti'	CWiW
	'E.A. Bowles'	see *S.* 'Bowles's Hybrid'
	× ***ehrhartiana***	CNat CWon
§	***elaeagnos***	CCVT CDoC CLnd CTho CTri ECrN EPfP GKir LRHS MBlu MBrN SLon SPer SWat WDin WFar WMou
§	- subsp. ***angustifolia*** ♀H4	CDul CWon EBee ELan EPfP GKir GQue IFFs MBar MMuc MRav MSwo NLar NPCo NWea SEND SRms STre WIvy
	- 'Angustifolia'	see *S. elaeagnos* subsp. *angustifolia*
	'Elegantissima'	see *S.* × *pendulina* var. *elegantissima*
	× ***erdingeri***	EPla
	eriocephala 'American Mackay' (m)	CWiW
	- 'Green USA'	CWon
	- 'Kerksii' (m)	CWiW CWon
	- 'Mawdesley' (m)	CWiW
	- 'Russelliana' (f)	CWiW CWon
§	'Erythroflexuosa'	CBcs CDoC CEnd CWon EBee ELan EPfP IFFs LAst LBMP LHop LRHS MAsh MBar MGos MRav NWea SBch SLim SMad SPer SPoG SWat WDin WFar WHer WPat
	exigua	Widely available
	fargesii	CAbP CBot CDoC CEnd CFee CMac CWon EBee ELan EPfP GKir LEdu LHop LRHS MAsh MBlu MGos MRav NBid NEgg NPCo SDix SMad SPoG SSpi WCru WFar WPGP WPat
	fargesii × ***magnifica***	WPGP
§	× ***finnmarchica***	GAuc GEdr NWCA WAbe
	× ***forbyana***	CWon
	formosa	see *S. arbuscula*
	fragilis	CCVT CDul CLnd ECrN EMac IFFs LMaj MRav NWea WDin WMou
§	- var. ***furcata***	CTri CWon GBin GKev WPat
	- 'Legomey'	WIvy
	× ***fruticosa*** 'McElroy' (f)	CWiW
	fruticulosa	see *S. fragilis* var. *furcata*
	'Fuiri-koriyanagi'	see *S. integra* 'Hakuro-nishiki'
	furcata	see *S. fragilis* var. *furcata*
	glabra	CWon
	glauca	CNat
	glaucophylloides	CWon
	glaucosericea	EPla
	'Golden Curls'	see *S.* 'Erythroflexuosa'
	gracilistyla	CTho CWon ECrN LRHS NWea SCoo SLPl WMou
§	- 'Melanostachys' (m)	Widely available
	× ***grahamii*** 'Moorei' (f)	NWCA
	× ***greyi***	NPro NWCA
	hastata (f)	SWat

	- 'Wehrhahnii' (m) ♀H4	CBcs CMea CWib CWon EBee EChо ELan EPfP GCra GKir LEdu LRHS MBar MBlu MRav MSwo MWhi NBir NPCo NWea SPer SWat WCFE WDin WFar WPat WPer
	helvetica ♀H4	CBcs CMac EBee ECho EGxp ELan EPfP GAbr LRHS MBar MBlu MMuc MRav NBir NEgg NWCA NWea SPer WAbe WDin WFar WPat
	herbacea	ECho GAuc GEdr NMen
	hibernica	see *S. phylicifolia*
I	***himalayas***	CWon
	× ***hirtei*** 'Delamere'	CWon
	- 'Rosewarne'	CWon
	hookeriana	CDul CLnd CTho CWon EBee ELan MBlu MBrN MBri SLPl WCFE WIvy WMou WPGP WTin
	humilis var. ***microphylla***	CWon
	× ***hungarica***	CWon
	incana	see *S. elaeagnos*
	integra	CWon
	- 'Albomaculata'	see *S. integra* 'Hakuro-nishiki'
	- 'Flamingo'PBR	SPoG
§	- 'Hakuro-nishiki' (v)	Widely available
	- 'Pendula' (f)	CEnd MAsh MBri
	irrorata	CDul CLnd CWon EBee ECrN EPfP GKir IFFs MBlu MRav MSwo SWat WCom
	'Jacquinii'	see *S. alpina*
	kinuyanagi (m)	CWon ELan WIvy
§	***koriyanagi***	CWiW CWon
	'Kumeti'	see *S.* × *doniana* 'Kumeti'
	'Kuro-me'	see *S. gracilistyla* 'Melanostachys'
	× ***laestadiana***	GAuc
	laggeri	CWon
	lanata ♀H4	CBcs CBot CMac CMea CWon EBee ECho ELan EPfP GAbr GAuc GGar GKir LRHS MAsh MGos MRav NBir NEgg NHol NMen NWea SPer SSta SWat WAbe WCFE WDin WFar
	- 'Drake's Hybrid'	NMen
	- 'Mrs Mac' (m)	CWon
	lapponum	EBee GAuc GEdr GKir NWea SRms WAbe
	lasiandra	CWon
	× ***laurina*** (f)	CWon
§	***lindleyana***	GKir
	lineariistipularis	CWon
	lucida	CWon ECrN
	mackenzieana	CWon
	magnifica ♀H4	CDul CEnd CGHE CLnd CMCN CTho CWon EBee ELan EMil EPfP EPla EWTr GKir IArd IDee IFFs LEdu LRHS MSnd NWea SMad SPoG SSpi SWat WDin WFar WMou WPGP WSpi
	'Mark Postill' (f)	CDoC CWon EBee EMil GKir LRHS MBNS MMuc
	matsudana 'Tortuosa'	see *S. babylonica* var. *pekinensis* 'Tortuosa'
	- 'Tortuosa Aureopendula'	see *S.* 'Erythroflexuosa'
	'Melanostachys'	see *S. gracilistyla* 'Melanostachys'
	× ***meyeriana***	CWon WIvy
	- 'Lumley' (f)	CWiW
	mielichhoferi	CWon
	× ***mollissima*** var. ***hippophaifolia*** 'Jefferies' (m)	CWiW
	- - 'Notts Spaniard' (m)	CWiW
	- - 'Stinchcombe'	WIvy
	- - 'Trustworthy' (m)	CWiW
	- var. ***undulata*** 'Kottenheider Weide' (f)	CWiW
	moupinensis	CWon EPfP IArd IDee MBri NLar WAbe
	- EDHCH 97.319	WPGP
	aff. ***moupinensis*** from Vietnam	WPGP
§	***myrsinifolia***	EBee MBlu MMuc
	- subsp. ***alpicola***	CWon
	myrsinites var. ***jacquiniana***	see *S. alpina*
	myrtilloides 'Pink Tassels' (m)	ECho GEdr MAsh NWCA SIng
	myrtilloides × ***repens***	see *S.* × *finnmarchica*
	nakamurana var. ***yezoalpina***	CEnd CFee CWon EBee ELan EMil EPot EWes GEdr LRHS MBlu MRav NHol NLar NPro NWCA WAbe WFar WPat
	nepalensis	see *S. lindleyana*
	nigra	CWon
	nigricans	see *S. myrsinifolia*
	nivalis	see *S. reticulata* subsp. *nivalis*
	'Onusta' (m)	EBee EWTr
	× ***ovata***	NMen
§	× ***pendulina*** var. ***elegantissima***	CTho CWon SWat
	pentandra	CBot CDul CLnd ECrN GKir IFFs NWea WDin WFar WMou
	- 'Patent Lumley'	CWiW CWon
	petiolaris	CWon
	'Philip's Fancy'	NWCA
§	***phylicifolia***	ECrN GKir NWea WMou
	- 'Malham' (m)	CWiW CWon
§	***purpurea***	CCVT CDul EMac GKir IFFs NWea SRms WDin WGwG WMou
	- 'Brittany Green' (f)	CWiW CWon
	- 'Continental Reeks'	CWiW WIvy
	- 'Dark Dicks' (f)	CWiW CWon NLar WIvy
	- 'Dicky Meadows' (m)	CWiW CWon WIvy
	- 'Goldstones'	CWiW NLar WIvy
	- f. ***gracilis***	see *S. purpurea* 'Nana'
	- 'Green Dicks'	CWiW CWon WIvy
	- 'Helix'	see *S. purpurea*
	- 'Howki' (m)	CWon WMou
	- 'Irette' (m)	CWiW
	- 'Jagiellonka' (f)	CWiW WIvy
	- var. ***japonica***	see *S. koriyanagi*
	- subsp. ***lambertiana***	CWiW WIvy
	- 'Lancashire Dicks' (m)	CWiW
	- 'Leicestershire Dicks' (m)	CWiW
	- 'Light Dicks'	CWiW CWon
	- 'Lincolnshire Dutch' (f)	CWiW
§	- 'Nana'	EMac EPfP IFFs MMuc NLar NWea SLPl SLon SPer SPur STre WFar WMoo
	- 'Nancy Saunders' (f)	CTho CWiW CWon EBee EHoe EPla GBuc GCal MBNS MBlu MBrN MRav NLar NPro NSti SCoo SMad SUsu WCot WIvy
I	- 'Nicholsonii Purpurascens'	CWon
	- 'Pendula' ♀H4	CCVT CEnd CWib CWon EBee ECrN EMil LAst LRHS MAsh MBar MBri MGos MSwo NBlu NWea SBch SPer WDin
	- 'Read' (f)	CWiW
	- 'Reeks' (f)	CWiW CWon
	- 'Richartii' (f)	CWiW CWon
	- 'Uralensis' (f)	CWiW CWon
	pyrenaica	EBee EWes NWCA WAbe
	pyrenaica × ***retusa***	ECho
	pyrifolia	CWon NWea
	rehderiana	CWon

	reinii	CWon
	repens	ECho EMac GAuc NWea SRms STre SWat WDin WGwG
§	- var. ***argentea***	CWon EPfP EQua EWes GAuc IFFs LRHS MMuc MRav NWCA SPer STre WDin WFar
	- 'Armando'PBR	LRHS MGos
	- 'Iona' (m)	LRHS
	- ***pendula***	see *S.* 'Boyd's Pendulous' (m)
	- 'Voorthuizen' (f)	CWib ECho LAst MBar MGos WDin
	reticulata ♀H4	ECho EPot GKir NBir NLAp NMen WAbe
§	- subsp. ***nivalis***	NWCA
	retusa	CTri ECho GAuc NBir NLAp
	retusa × ***serpyllifolia***	EPot NWCA
	'Robin Redbreast'	CWon
	rosmarinifolia misapplied	see *S. elaeagnos* subsp. *angustifolia*
§	× ***rubens*** var. ***basfordiana***	GKir
	- 'Basfordiana' (m)	CDoC CDul CLnd CTho CWiW CWon EWes MBNS SWat WMou
	- 'Bouton Aigu'	CWiW
	- 'Farndon'	CWiW
	- 'Farndon Red'	CWon
	- 'Flanders Red' (f)	CWiW CWon
	- 'Fransgeel Rood' (m)	CWiW CWon
	- 'Glaucescens' (m)	CWiW
	- 'Golden Willow'	CWiW CWon
	- 'Hutchinson's Brown'	CWon
	- 'Jaune de Falaise'	CWiW CWon
	- 'Jaune Hâtive'	CWiW
	- 'Laurina'	CWiW
	- 'Natural Red' (f)	CWiW CWon
	- 'Parsons'	CWiW
	- 'Rouge Ardennais'	CWiW CWon
	- 'Rouge Folle'	CWiW
	- 'Russet' (f)	CWiW
	× ***rubra***	CWiW
	- 'Abbey's Harrison' (f)	CWiW
	- 'Continental Osier' (f)	CWiW CWon
	- 'Eugenei' (m)	CDul ECrN GQui MBlu SWat WIvy WMou
	- 'Fidkin' (f)	CWiW
	- 'Harrison's' (f)	CWiW
	- 'Harrison's Seedling A' (f)	CWiW
	- 'Mawdesley'	CWiW
	- 'Mawdesley Seedling A' (f)	CWiW
	- 'Pyramidalis'	CWiW
	sachalinensis 'Kioryo'	CWon
	salvaefolia	CWon
	× ***sanguinea***	see *S.* × *rubens* var. *basfordiana*
	× ***savensis***	CWon
	Scarlet Curls = 'Scarcuzam'	CWon WPat
	schwerinii	CWon
	- 'Hilliers'	CWon
	scouleriana	CWon
	× ***sepulcralis***	NWea
§	- 'Aokautere'	CWiW
	- 'Caradoc'	CWiW
§	- var. ***chrysocoma***	Widely available
	× ***sericans***	CWon
	× ***seringeana*** new	CWon
	serissaefolia	CWon
	serpyllifolia	CTri NMen WAbe WPat
	serpyllum	see *S. fragilis* var. *furcata*
	'Setsuka'	see *S. udensis* 'Sekka'
	silesiaca	CWon
	× ***simulatrix***	EPot GAuc MBar NWCA
	sitchensis	NWea
	× ***smithiana***	CLnd GKir NWea
	songarica	GKir
	× ***stipularis*** (f)	NWea
	'Stuartii'	MBar NMen NWCA SRms
	subopposita	EBee EBtc ELan EWes MBar MMuc SLon STre WGwG
	thomasii	GAuc
	triandra	CWon IFFs WMou
	- 'Black German' (m)	CWiW
	- 'Black Hollander' (m)	CWiW NLar WIvy
	- 'Black Maul'	CWiW
	- 'Brilliant'	CWon
	- 'Champion B'	CWon
	- 'Grisette de Falaise'	CWiW
	- 'Grisette Droda' (f)	CWiW
	- 'Houghton's Black'	CWon
	- 'Light French'	CWon
	- 'Long Bud'	CWiW
	- 'Noir de Challans'	CWiW
	- 'Noir de Touraine'	CWiW CWon
	- 'Noir de Villaines' (m)	CWiW CWon WIvy
	- 'Oliveacea'	CWon
	- 'Rouge d'Orléans'	CWon EBtc
	- 'Sarda d'Anjou'	CWiW
	- 'Semperflorens' (m)	CWon NLar
	- 'Whissander'	CWiW WIvy
	- 'Zwarre Driebast'	CWon
	× ***tsugaluensis*** 'Ginme' (f)	CWon SLPl WPat
	udensis	NWea
§	- 'Sekka' (m)	CWon EBee ELan EPfP IFFs MBlu NBir NWea STre SWat WFar WIvy WMou
	uva-ursi	WAbe
	viminalis	CCVT CLnd CMac CWon ECrN EMac IFFs LBuc NWea SVic WDin WMou
	- 'Black Satin'	CWon
	- 'Brown Merrin'	WIvy
	- 'Gigantea' (m)	CWon
	- 'Green Gotz'	CWiW WIvy
	- 'Reader's Red' (m)	WIvy
	- 'Regalis'	CWon
	- 'Riefenweide'	WIvy
	- 'Romanin'	CWon
	- 'Yellow Osier'	WIvy
	vitellina 'Pendula'	see *S. alba* 'Tristis' ambig.
	waldsteiniana	GAuc MBar NWCA
	× ***wimmeriana***	SRms
	'Yelverton'	see *S. alba* var. *vitellina* 'Yelverton'
*	***zatungensis***	CWon

Salsola (*Chenopodiaceae*)

	soda	CArn

Salvia ✿ (*Lamiaceae*)

	ACE 2172	SPin
	CD&R 1162	CAby SPin
	CD&R 1458	SPin
	CD&R 1495	SHGN SPin
	CD&R 3071	SPin
	DJH 93T	SPin
	PC&H 226	SPin
	acetabulosa	see *S. multicaulis*
	adenophora	SPin
	aerea	CPom
	aethiopis	EAro EWes SDnm SPav SPin WOut
§	***africana***	GGar SPin WDyG
	africana-caerulea	see *S. africana*
	africana-lutea	see *S. aurea*
	agnes	SPin
	algeriensis	CSpe SBch SPin
	amarissima	EWld SPin
	'Amber'	EBee SPin SUsu
	ambigens	see *S. guaranitica* 'Blue Enigma'

	ampelophylla B&SWJ 10751	WCru
§	***amplexicaulis***	EAro EPyc EWld MWea NLar SBch SMrm SPin WPer
	amplifrons	EWld SPin
	angustifolia Cav.	see *S. reptans*
	angustifolia 'Anthony Parker'	MAJR SAga SDys WOut
	apiana	CArn EAro EOHP EPyc MDKP MHer SAga SGar SPin
	argentea ♀H3	CArn CBcs CSpe EBee EBla ECha ELan EPfP EShb GMaP LAst LRHS SAga SBch SGar SMad SPav SPer SPin SWat WCAu WCHb WCom WFar WMnd WPer WWEG
	arizonica	EAro GCal MHom SDys SPin
	aspera	SPin
	atrocyanea	CSpe EPyc EWld LPio MAJR MAsh SDys SGar SPin WHal WKif WWlt
§	***aurea***	CHll CSev EShb LPio SAga SGar SPin SWal
	- 'Kirstenbosch'	CDes CSev CWGN EAro EBee ECtt EWld MBel SDys SPin WGwG WKif WOut WPGP WPer
	aurita	SPin
	- var. ***galpinii***	SPin
	austriaca	SPin
§	***azurea***	CRWN CSpe LRHS SBod SMrm SPin
	- var. ***grandiflora***	SPin
	bacheriana	see *S. buchananii*
§	***barrelieri***	EOHP SPin
	'Belhaven'	GCal SPin WDyG
	bertolonii	see *S. pratensis* Bertolonii Group
	bicolor Des.	see *S. barrelieri*
	'Black Knight'	CWGN MAvo SDys SPin SUsu
	blancoana	CBot CMea ECha ELau GBar LPla MBel MHer SAga SBch SDys SPin
	blepharophylla	CSpe EAro EBee ECtt EPyc EShb LHop LPio MCot MHer MSCN NGHP SAga SBch SDnm SPav SPin SRkn WCom
	- 'Diablo'	ECtt SAga SDys SPin
	- 'Painted Lady'	CWGN MAsh MSpe SDys SPin WOut WWlt
	'Blue Chiquita'	CWGN SDys SPin
	'Blue Sky'	EWld SDys
	'Blue Vein'	NPri
	bracteata	SPin
	brandegeei	SPin
	broussonetii	SPin
§	***buchananii*** ♀H1+3	CHll CSWP CSam CSpe EAro EPfP EPyc EShb EWld GQui LHop LPio MAsh MBel MHer MRav MSpe NGHP SAga SPav SPin SPoG SRkn WCom WFar
	bulleyana Diels	CPLG CSev EDAr EWes EWld LEdu MBel MDKP MMHG NGHP NLar SDnm SPav WCru WFar
	bulleyana misapplied	see *S. flava* var. *megalantha*
	cacaliifolia ♀H1+3	CPLG CRHN CSam CSpe EBee ECtt EPyc EWld GBar MAsh MHer MNrw MSCN NGHP SAga SBch SDnm SGar SPer SPin SRkn SUsu WCom WSHC WWlt
	cadmica	SPin
	caerulea misapplied	see *S. guaranitica* 'Black and Blue'
	caerulea L.	see *S. africana*
	caespitosa	NMen SPin
	campanulata	CPom EWld GKev SPin
	- B&SWJ 9232	WCru
	- CC&McK 1071	CFir
	- DJHC C394	SPin
	- GWJ 9294	SPin WCru
	canariensis	CSpe EAro EShb IDee IGor SPin WOut
	- f. ***candidissima***	SPin
	candelabrum ♀H3-4	CAbP CArn CMea CSpe EWTr MHer SAga SBch SPav SPin WCHb WKif WWlt
	candidissima	SPin
	canescens	EAro
	cardinalis	see *S. fulgens*
	carduacea	SPin
	carnea	EWld SPin
	- from Valle de Bravo, Mexico	SDys
	castanea	SPin
	caudata	SPin
	cedrosensis	SDys
§	***chamaedryoides***	CSev CWGN EBee EPyc LPio MHom NGHP SDnm SDys SGar SPet SPhx SPin
	- aff. var. ***isochroma***	EAro MAsh SDys SPin
	- 'Marine Blue'	MAsh MCot SDys SPin
	- silver-leaved	CSpe SPin
	aff. ***chamaedryoides*** B&SWJ 9032 from Guatemala	SPin WCru
	chamaedryoides × ***microphylla***	EAro
	chamelaeagnea	GFai SDys SHar SPin WPrP
	chapalensis	MAJR SAga SPin
	cheinii	SPin
	chiapensis	CSpe MAJR MAsh SAga SDys SPin WWlt
	chinensis	see *S. japonica*
	'Christine Yeo'	CDes EBee ECtt ELon EPPr EPfP EPyc EWld GGar MAsh MDKP MHer MSpe NGHP SAga SBch SDys SGar SPav SPin SWal WDyG WMnd WPGP
	cinnabarina	SPin
	cleistogama misapplied	see *S. glutinosa*
	clevelandii	EAro EWes MHer SPav WHil
	- 'Winnifred Gilman'	CWGN EAro SDys
	clinopodioides	SPin
	coahuilensis misapplied	see *S. greggii* × *serpyllifolia*
	coahuilensis ambig.	CAby LSou MAsh SAga SGar SMeo SMrm SPin SRkn WSHC
	coahuilensis Fernald	EAro WHil
	coccinea	CBot SPin
	- 'Brenthurst'	SDys SPin
	- 'Coral Nymph' (Nymph Series)	ECtt EPyc LDai SDnm SDys SPav SPin
	- 'Forest Fire'	SDys
	- 'Lactea'	CBot
	- 'Lady in Red' (Nymph Series) ♀H3	ECtt SDys SPav
*	- 'Snow Nymph' (Nymph Series)	ECtt
	columbariae	SPin
	concolor misapplied	see *S. guaranitica*
	concolor Lamb. ex Benth.	CDes EWld GCal GGar MHom SPin WDyG WPGP WSHC
	confertiflora	CBow CDes CHEx CSam CSpe CWCL EBee ECtt ELan EPyc EShb EWld GCal LPio MAsh MCot MHer MHom NGHP SAga SDys SGar SPin SRkn SWal WCom WDyG WPGP WWlt
	corrugata	CBcs CDes CPne CSam CSpe EBee EPyc EShb EWld GCal IDee MAsh MBel MHer MSpe NGHP SAga SDys SPin SRkn SWal WPGP WWlt
	'Crème Caramel'	CWGN EPyc MAsh MHom SDys

	Name	Suppliers
	cruickshanksii	SPin
	aff. ***curtiflora*** B&SWJ 10356 **new**	WCru
	cyanescens	CMea CPBP EPot EWld GKev SPin
	cyanicalyx	SDys SPin
	daghestanica	LFur SDys SPin
I	***dangitalis***	CPLG
	- SDR 4332	EBee
	darcyi misapplied	see *S. roemeriana*
	darcyi J. Compton	CAby CHll CSpe EBee EPyc EWes EWld LPio SAga SDys SPin WHil WSHC WWlt
	davidsonii	SPin
	dentata	SDys SPin
	desoleana	EAro SPin
	digitaloides BWJ 7777	SPin WCru
	discolor ♀H1	Widely available
*	- ***nigra***	CArn CMdw
	disermas	SDys SPin SPlb
	- pink-flowered **new**	SPin
	disjuncta	SPin
	- 'Chimbango'	SDys
	divinorum	CBow EOHP GPoy NGHP
	dolichantha	CSpe CTsd EAro EDAr EPyc GAuc MAvo MDKP SBod SEND SGar SPin WMoo WPtf
	- 'Breckland Skies' **new**	EPPr
	dolomitica	SPav SPin
	dombeyi	CHll CPne CWGN EAro EWld SDys SPin WCom
	dominica	SAga SPin
	dorisiana	CPne CSpe EAro ELan EOHP MAsh SDys SPin
	eigii	SPin
	elegans	ELau EWes GBee GCra MAJR MHom SAga
	- 'Honey Melon'	CAby EOHP MAsh NGHP SDys SUsu
§	- 'Scarlet Pineapple'	Widely available
	- 'Sonoran Red'	EAro SDys
	- 'Tangerine'	CArn CPrp CWan ELau EOHP EPyc GBar LFol LSou MHer MNHC NGHP SBch SDnm SPin SWal WGwG
	evansiana BWJ 8013	SPin
	'Eveline'	NCGa
	excelsa	SPin
	fallax	SPin
	farinacea	EPfP SPin
	- 'Reference' **new**	CSpr
	- 'Strata'	SDys
	- 'Victoria' ♀H3	LRHS MCot SDys SGar
§	***flava*** var. ***megalantha***	ELan LEdu LSRN MNrw NGdn SPin WPer
	- - BWJ 7974	WCru
	florida	SPin
	forreri	CDes EAro EBee EPyc MAsh SAga SBHP SDys SPin WPGP
	- 'Karen Dyson'	SDys
§	***forsskaolii***	Widely available
	- white-flowered	SPin
§	***fruticosa***	CArn EAro ELau EPyc LRHS SIde SPin
§	***fulgens*** ♀H3	EWld GBar ILis MAsh MHom NGHP SAga SBHP SBch SGar SPin SRkn WFar WOut WWlt
	gesneriiflora	CAby ECtt EWld SDys SPin WCom WOut
	- 'Tequila'	MAJR SPin
	gilliesii	SPin
	glabrescens	SPin
	- B&SWJ 10919	WCru
	- 'Momobana'	EBee
	- 'Shi-ho'	EBee
	glechomifolia	SPin
	'Gloomy'	SPin
§	***glutinosa***	CArn CSpe EAro EBee ECtt EPPr EPyc EWld GCal IMou LDai MCot MNrw NBro SAga SPav SPin SWal WCAu WCom WGwG WPer
	graciliramulosa	SPin
	gracilis	SPin
	grahamii	see *S. microphylla* var. *microphylla*
	gravida	SPin
	greggii	ECtt EWes EWld LRHS MHer NGHP SBod WPer
	- CD&R 1148	EAro MCot SDys
	- 'Alba'	EBee LPio NGHP SAga SDys SPin
	- 'Blush Pink'	see *S. microphylla* 'Pink Blush'
	- 'Caramba' (v)	CBow EAro EBee EPyc LRHS NGHP SAga SDnm SHGN SPav SPoG
	- 'Devon Cream'	see *S. greggii* 'Sungold'
	- 'Diane'	MAsh
	- 'Icing Sugar' **new**	EPPr LRHS NPri
	- 'Lipstick' **new**	MAsh
	- 'Magenta'	MDKP WHil
	- 'Magnet'	SPin
	- (Navajo Series) 'Navajo Bright Red'	EPyc
*	- - 'Navajo Cream'	EAro EPyc SAga
*	- - 'Navajo Dark Purple'	EAro EPyc SAga
	- - Navajo Pink = 'Rfds019'	SGar
	- - Navajo Salmon Red = 'Rfds016'	EPyc
*	- - 'Navajo White'	EPyc
	- 'Peach' misapplied	see *S.* × *jamensis* 'Pat Vlasto'
	- 'Peach'	CDes CSpe CWGN ELau EPfP EPyc LHop MAsh MBel MCot MHer NGHP SAga SDnm SGar SPav SPet SPin WCom WMnd WPGP WWlt
	- 'Pink Preference' **new**	MAsh
	- salmon-flowered	EPyc
	- 'Sierra San Antonio'	see *S.* × *jamensis* 'Sierra San Antonio'
	- 'Sparkler' (v)	EPfP LRHS MAsh SBch
	- 'Stormy Pink'	CAby CDes CHll CSpe CWGN EPyc MCot MSpe SAga WCom WIvy WPGP WSHC WWlt
§	- 'Sungold'	CWGN EAro ECtt EPfP EPyc LHop LRHS MAsh MHom MWte NGHP SBch SDys SHGN SHom SPin WMnd
	- variegated (v)	EHoe
	greggii × ***lycioides***	see *S. greggii* × *serpyllifolia*
§	***greggii*** × ***serpyllifolia***	CAbP CSpe EPyc LRHS MCot SAga SDys SGar SPin WPGP
	grewiifolia	SPin
§	***guaranitica***	CBcs CBot CEnt CHEx ECtt EPyc EShb GCra LRHS SAga SDnm SDys SPav SPer SPin SWal WCHb WKif WPGP WWlt
	- 'Argentina Skies'	ECtt EPPr EPyc LPio MSpe SAga SDys SMrm SPin WWlt
§	- 'Black and Blue'	COIW CPne CRHN CSWP CSev CWCL EBee ECtt EPPr EPfP EPyc GCal LPio LRHS MAvo NGHP SAga SBch SDnm SGar SPav SPin SUsu SWal WPGP WPer WSHC
§	- 'Blue Enigma' ♀H3-4	Widely available
	- 'Indigo Blue'	ECtt EPfP MAsh MBel SPin WWlt
	- 'Purple Splendor'	EShb
	- purple-flowered	CSam
	haematodes	see *S. pratensis* Haematodes Group
	haenkei	SPin
	- 'Prawn Chorus'	CSpe MAJR SAga SPin

	heerii	SPin
	heldreichiana	SPin
	henryi	SPin
	hians	CPom EAro EBee GBar GCra MBel MDKP MNrw SBch SDnm SGar SPav SPin SRms WKif WPer
	- CC 1787	SPin
	hierosolymitana	SPin
	hirtella	SPin
	hispanica misapplied	see *S. lavandulifolia*
	hispanica L.	CSam SPin
	holwayi	SPin
	- B&SWJ 8995	WCru
	horminum	see *S. viridis* var. *comata*
	huberi	SPin
	indica	SPin
	'Indigo Spires'	CHll CMHG CSpe CWGN ECtt EPPr EShb EWld LPio MAsh MBel MCot MHom SAga SDys SMrm SPhx SPin WDyG WPen WSHC WWlt
	interrupta	MBel MHer SAga SPin WPen
	involucrata ♀H3	CFir CPom CSev CSpe GCra GQui MCot MHom NBro NBur SBch SDys SPet SPin WHrl WSHC
	- 'Bethellii' ♀H3-4	Widely available
	- 'Boutin' ♀H3	MAJR MAsh MBel MHom SAga SDys
§	- 'Hadspen'	CBot CHll CRHN CSam CSpe EWes GCal MAJR SPin WCom WKif WWlt
	- 'Joan'	CWGN MAsh SDys SPin
	- 'Mrs Pope'	see *S. involucrata* 'Hadspen'
*	- var. ***puberula***	MAJR MHom SDys SPin
	iodantha	SDys SPin
	- 'Louis Saso'	SPin
	iodochroa	CDes EBee WPGP
	- B&SWJ 10252	SPin WCru
	× ***jamensis***	CAby CWGN EAro ELau EPyc EWes EWld LBuc MAvo MWea NPri SAga SDys SMrm SPin
	- 'Cherry Queen'	CSpe EAro EBee EPyc MAsh SAga SDys SPin WWlt
	- 'Dark Dancer'	CWGN LPio MAsh MSpe SDys WWlt
	- 'Desert Blaze' (v)	CAbP CBow CDes CWGN EAro EBee ECtt EPyc MCot MHer NCGa NGHP SDys SMrm SPin WCom WGrn WPGP
	- 'Devantville'	CAby
	- 'Dysons' Orangy Pink'	CAby CSpe MAsh SAga SPin
§	- 'Hot Lips' **new**	CDes CHVG CPom CWGN ELon IMon LRHS NPri SBch SEND SGar SHom SRkn WHrl WPGP
	- 'James Compton'	EAro EPyc MHom SDys SGar
	- 'La Luna'	CEnt CPom CSam CTri CWGN EAro EBee ECtt EPfP EPyc EShb EWld LHop LPio MCot MHer MHom SDys SEND SGar SHGN SPin WCom WMnd WPGP WSHC
	- 'La Siesta'	EAro EBee NGHP SDys
	- 'La Tarde'	CAby CEnt CTri MAsh MHom NGHP SBch SDys
	- 'Lemon Sorbet'	SDys
	- 'Los Lirios' ♀H3-4	CPom CSpe CTri EAro EBee EPyc SAga SDys SMrm SPin WCom
	- 'Maraschino'	CAbP EAro EBee EPfP EPyc LPio LRHS MAsh SDys SMrm SPin WMnd WWlt
*	- 'Mauve'	EPyc SAga SDys
	- 'Moonlight Over Ashwood' (v)	EAro EPyc MAsh SBHP SDys SPin WSHC WWlt
	- 'Moonlight Serenade'	CAby EAro EPyc MAsh MWea SAga SBch SDys SHGN WHoo
§	- 'Pat Vlasto'	EAro EBee EPyc MHom MWea NGHP SDys SPin
	- 'Peter Vidgeon'	CWGN SDys SPin
	- 'Pleasant Pink'	CSev EPyc MAsh SAga SDys SPin
	- 'Plum Wine'	MAsh
	- 'Raspberry Royale' ♀H3-4	CDes CPom CSev CWGN EAro EBee ECtt EPfP EPyc GBar LHop LRHS MAsh MBel MCot MHer NGHP SDnm SGar SMrm SPav SPin SWal WCom WHoo WMnd WSHC
	- 'Red Velvet'	CAby EBee ECtt ELon EWld MAsh MHer MHom NGHP SUsu WEas WHrl WSHC WWlt
	- 'Señorita Leah'	EPyc SDys SUsu
§	- 'Sierra San Antonio'	CWGN EAro ECtt EPfP LRHS MAsh MHom MWea SAga SBHP SDys SMrm SUsu
§	- 'Trebah'	CDes CPom CSpe ECre EPyc MAsh MCot MHom MWea SAga SDys SGar SMrm SPav SPin SRot WIvy WPGP WWlt
	- 'Trenance'	CAby ECre EPyc LRHS MHom SDys SGar SPav SPin SRot WHil WSHC
	- white-flowered	SPin
§	***japonica***	SPin
	- 'Alba'	SPin
	'Jean's Purple Passion'	SPin
	judaica	SPin WGrn
	jurisicii	CArn CWib EAro EBee EPyc SPav SPin WJek
	- pink-flowered	CSpe SPin
	karwinskyi	SPin
	- B&SWJ 9081	WCru
	keerlii	SPin
	koyamae	SPin
	- B&SWJ 10919	WCru
	kuznetzovii	EBee
	'Lady Strybing'	SPin
	lanceolata	EAro SPin WWlt
	lanigera	SPin
	lasiantha	SPin
§	***lavandulifolia***	Widely available
	lavanduloides	SPin
	- B&SWJ 9053	WCru
	lemmonii	see *S. microphylla* var. *wislizeni*
	leptophylla	see *S. reptans*
	leucantha ♀H1	CArn CBow CHrt CPne CRHN CSam CSev CSpe EBee ELan EShb GBar GGar LPio MBel MCot MHer MRav MSCN SAga SDys SPav SPin SRkn SWal
	- 'Eder' (v)	MAJR SDys SPin
	- 'Midnight'	IFoB
	- 'Purple Velvet'	GGar MAJR MAsh MHer MHom NGHP SDix SDys SPin WOut WWlt
	- 'San Marcos Lavender'	SPin
	- 'Santa Barbara'	CHll CWGN SDys
	leucocephala	SPin
	leucophylla NNS 01-375	SPin
	littae	SPin
	longispicata	SPin
	longistyla	SPin
	lycioides misapplied	see *S. greggii* × *serpyllifolia*
	lycioides A. Gray	CAbP CHll LPio SDys SEND SPhx SPin WCom WDyG
	lyrata	EOHP SGar SPin
	- 'Burgundy Bliss'	see *S. lyrata* 'Purple Knockout'
§	- 'Purple Knockout'	CBow CKno EAro EBee EPPr EPfP EPyc EShb GKev LAst LHop NGHP SBch SBod SGar SMrm SPav SPhx SPin SWal
	- 'Purple Vulcano'	see *S. lyrata* 'Purple Knockout'

	macellaria misapplied	see *S. microphylla*
	macellaria Epling	CSam
	macrophylla	GCal SPin WPGP
	madrensis	MAJR SPin
	- 'Dunham'	GCal SDys
	melissodora	SDys SPin
	mellifera	CArn SPin
	'Merieaux' **new**	NPri
	merjamie	SPin
	- 'Mint-sauce'	EAro GBar LHop LRHS WFar WPer
	mexicana	SPin
	- B&SWJ 10288	WCru
	- T&K 550	CBot
	- 'Lollie Jackson'	MAJR
	- var. ***minor***	EWld MAJR SPin
	- 'Snowflake'	MAJR
	- 'Tula'	SDys
	meyeri	EWld MAJR MHom SPin WWlt
§	***microphylla***	CArn CHrt CMHG CMac CPom CPrp CTri CWan EAro ELau EOHP EWes GBar GGar LAst LFol LHop MHer MSCN NSti SPet WCor WHCG WPer
	- CD&R 1141	SPin
	- 'Belize'	EAro MAsh NGHP WWlt
	- 'Cerro Potosi'	CMdw CPom CSev CSpe ELon EPyc LPio LRHS MAsh NGHP SAga SDys SGar SPin SUsu WClo WDyG WPen WWlt
	- 'Dieciocho de Marzo'	SDys
	- 'Hot Lips'	see *S. × jamensis* 'Hot Lips'
	- 'Huntington'	EOHP SPin
	- hybrid, purple-flowered	CPom
	- 'Kew Red' ♀H3-4	CFir CHVG CSpe CWGN MNrw MWea NGHP SBch SPin WHoo WHrl WPen
	- 'La Trinidad'	SDys
I	- 'Lutea'	MAsh
	- 'Maroon'	CWGN SDys
§	- var. ***microphylla***	CFee CRHN CSev CSpe CTri CWib EBee ECtt ELan EOHP EPfP LRHS LSRN MAvo MCot MHer MNHC MRav NGHP SGar SPav SPin SRkn WCFE WFar WPer WSHC
	- - 'La Foux'	ECtt MCot MWea SBch SDys SMeo SMrm SPhx WCom
	- - 'Newby Hall' ♀H3-4	CAby CDes EBee ECtt EPyc EShb EWes MWea NGHP SDys SPhx SPoG WPGP
N	- var. ***neurepia***	see *S. microphylla* var. *microphylla*
	- 'Orange Door'	EPyc SDys SUsu
	- 'Oregon Peach'	EPfP LRHS
	- 'Oxford'	NGHP SDys SPin
§	- 'Pink Blush' ♀H3-4	CAby CBot EAro EBee ECtt ELan EPfP EPyc IMon LAst LRHS MAsh MBel MCot MHer MHom NGHP SMrm SPin WCom WHil WKif WPGP WSHC WWlt
	- 'Pleasant View' ♀H3-4	CAby EPyc MAsh MBel
	- 'Robin's Pride'	SDys
	- 'Rodbaston Current Purple' **new**	MSpe
	- 'Rosy Cheeks'	WOut
§	- 'Ruth Stungo' (v)	ECre
	- 'San Carlos Festival'	CDes CPom EAro ECtt EPyc MAsh NGHP SBch SDys SPin WPGP WWlt
	- 'Trelawny Rose Pink'	see *S.* 'Trelawney'
	- 'Trelissick Creamy Yellow'	see *S.* 'Trelissick'
	- 'Trewithen Cerise'	see *S.* 'Trewithen'
	- 'Variegata' splashed	see *S. microphylla* 'Ruth Stungo'
	- 'Violette' **new**	EPfP
	- 'Wild Watermelon'	CWGN EAro EPyc MAsh SAga SDys
§	- var. ***wislizeni***	CPom EPyc SDys SPin WWlt
	- 'Zaragoza'	SPin
	miltiorhiza	CArn CSpe SPin
	miniata	CSev CSpe MAJR SBHP SDys SPin
	misella	CSpe SPin WHil
	mohavensis	SPin
	moorcroftiana	SDnm WCot
	muelleri misapplied	see *S. greggii × serpyllifolia*
	muelleri Epling	EAro EBee EPyc
	muirii	SHar SPin
	'Mulberry Jam'	CDes CHll CMdw CSev CSpe CWGN EAro EBee ECtt EPyc EWes EWld GCal LPio MAJR MAsh MHer MHom SAga SDys SPin SRkn SUsu WKif WPGP WSHC WWlt
§	***multicaulis*** ♀H4	EPyc SPin WCot WEas
	munzii	CFir SPin
*	***murrayi***	CAbP SPin
	namaensis	EAro SDys SPin
	nana B&SWJ 10272	SPin WCru
	napifolia	EBee GKev LBMP SAga SBod SDnm SPav SPhx SPin WGwG WPer
	'Nazareth'	EAro SPin
	nemorosa	EBee EPyc LRHS SPin SRms
	- 'Amethyst' ♀H4	CHar EBee ELon EPPr EPfP GBBs LAst LRHS MBel MRav NMoo SAga SDys SPhx WCAu WCot WKif WSHC WWEG WWlt
	- Blue Mound	see *S. × sylvestris* 'Blauhügel'
	- 'Caradonna'	Widely available
	- East Friesland	see *S. nemorosa* 'Ostfriesland'
	- 'Lubecca' ♀H4	EBee EBrs ECGP ECtt EHrv EPfP EShb LHop LRHS MCot NEgg NLar SMrm SPer WCAu WFar WMnd WWEG
	- Marcus = 'Haeumanarc'PBR	CSpe EBee ECtt ELan EPfP EPyc LAst LRHS LSRN LSou MBNS MBri NLar SBch SDys WFar WSHC
	- 'Midsummer'	EWld
§	- 'Ostfriesland' ♀H4	Widely available
	- 'Phoenix Pink'	SPhx
	- 'Pink Friesland'	EBee EPPr GQue LHop LRHS LSou NPri
	- 'Plumosa'	see *S. nemorosa* 'Pusztaflamme'
	- 'Porzellan' ♀H4	ECtt
§	- 'Pusztaflamme' ♀H4	CWGN EBee ECha ECtt EPPr EPfP NOrc SMrm SUsu WWEG
	- 'Rose Queen'	ECtt GKir LAst LBMP LRHS MCot NBir SDys SPer SWat WFar
	- 'Rosenwein'	EAro EBee GBuc LDai LRHS MAvo MDKP MNrw NBPC NGdn SMrm SPhx
	- 'Royal Distinction'	EBee ECtt SUsu
	- 'Schwellenburg'	EBee EPfP LHop LRHS NBPC NMoo SUsu
	- 'Sensation Rose'	CCVN CWGN EBee EBrs GBin LLHF LRHS LSou WCot
§	- subsp. ***tesquicola***	ECha EPyc LRHS LSRN MNFA MWhi NGdn NLar SMrm SPhx WFar WPtf
	- 'Wesuwe'	EBee EPPr NGby
	neurepia	see *S. microphylla* var. *microphylla*
	nilotica	EAro EBee SPin SWal
	nipponica B&SWJ 5829	SPin WCru
	- 'Fuji Snow' (v)	CBow EBee EPyc LSou
	- var. ***trisecta***	SPin
	nubicola	CPLG EBee EPPr EWld GPoy LDai SPin WOut
	nutans	SPin
	'Nymans Yellow' **new**	LRHS
	oblongifolia B&SWJ 10315	WCru
	officinalis	Widely available

	- 'Albiflora'	CArn CBod CBot ECtt EOHP GBar SBch SPin WCHb WJek WPer
N	- 'Aurea' ambig.	CWib ECho GKir GPoy MBar
	- 'Berggarten'	CArn CPrp EBee ECha ELau EPfP GBar GBee GCal LHop LPio LRHS MBri MHer MRav SDix SPhx SPin WHer WMnd
	- 'Blackcurrant'	LSou
§	- broad-leaved	CBot CSWP ELau MHer SWat WClo WJek
	- 'Crispa'	EOHP SPin WCHb
	- 'Extrakta'	SPhx
	- 'Grandiflora'	CFir EAro
	- 'Grete Stolze'	EBee IMou LPla
§	- 'Icterina' (v) ♀H4	Widely available
	- 'Kew Gold'	MRav
	- ***latifolia***	see *S. officinalis* broad-leaved
	- narrow-leaved	see *S. lavandulifolia*
	- 'Nazareth'PBR	ELau
*	- 'Pink Splash' (v)	CBow WCHb
	- ***prostrata***	see *S. lavandulifolia*
	- 'Purpurascens' ♀H4	Widely available
	- 'Purpurascens Variegata' (v)	WEas
	- 'Robin Hill'	GBar
	- 'Rosea'	CArn EOHP WCHb
	- 'Tricolor' (v)	Widely available
	- 'Variegata'	see *S. officinalis* 'Icterina'
	- variegated (v)	CBow ECho
	ombrophila new	SPin
	omeiana	WFar
	- BWJ 8062	SPin WCru
	- 'Crûg Thundercloud'	WCru
	oppositiflora misapplied	see *S. tubiflora*
	oppositiflora ambig.	MAJR SAga SDys SPin
	orbignaei	SPin
	oxyphora	SDys SPin
	pachyphylla	SPin
§	***patens*** ♀H3	Widely available
	- 'Alba' misapplied	see *S. patens* 'White Trophy'
	- 'Blue Angel'	EAro EWes IFoB MSwo WWEG
	- 'Cambridge Blue' ♀H3	Widely available
	- 'Chilcombe'	CSam EBee ECtt EPyc EWTr MCot SAga SDys SPin WCom WWlt
	- 'Dot's Delight' new	SHar SPin WHlf
	- 'Guanajuato'	CBcs CHVG CSam CSpe EBee EPyc EShb EWes GMaP IFoB LAst LPio MAsh MHer NGHP NPri SAga SBch SDnm SDys SMad SMrm SPin SPoG SRkn SRot SUsu WHoo WSHC
	- lavender-flowered	SBch
	- 'Oxford Blue'	see *S. patens*
	- pink-flowered new	SPin
	- 'Royal Blue'	see *S. patens*
	- 'Southern Lights' new	MAJR
	- tall	SUsu
§	- 'White Trophy'	CBcs EBee ELan EPyc EShb EWld LRHS MBNS MHer NGHP SDnm SDys SPer SPin SWal WCom WFar
	pauciserrata	SPin
	penstemonoides	SDys
	personata	SPin
	'Peru Blue'	CSpe SDys
	'Phyllis' Fancy'	LPio MAsh SDys
	pinguifolia	SPin
	'Pink Ice'	CPom
	pisidica	SPin
	platystoma	SPin
	plectranthoides	SPin
	pogonochila	CPom SPin
	polystachya	SPin
	- B&SWJ 8985	WCru
*	'Powis Castle'	MHom
	praeclara	SPin
	pratensis	CAby CArn CWib EBWF EBee ELan EPyc GJos MHer MNHC NChi SECG SGar SPin WPer
	- 'Albiflora'	CDes
§	- Bertolonii Group	EPyc SPin
§	- Haematodes Group ♀H4	ECha ELan EPyc LDai MNrw NLar SBch SDnm SPav SPin SRms WPer
	- 'Indigo' ♀H4	CDes CPrp EBee ECGP ECtt EPPr EPfP LRHS MCot MRav NEgg NLar SPhx SPin SUsu WMnd WPGP
	- 'Lapis Lazuli'	CDes EAro EBee EWes NBre SPhx WFar WKif
	- 'Pink Delight'PBR	EBee LRHS NCGa
	- 'Rose Rhapsody' (Ballet Series)	CAby EAro EBee EDAr GJos LBMP LDai NCGa WFar WHil
	- 'Rosea'	ECha LRHS MHer SPhx SPin
	- 'Swan Lake' (Ballet Series)	CBod CMHG EAro EBee NCGa NChi NHol SAga SPhx SPin SPlb WHil WPer
	- 'White Swan'	CAby
	pratensis* × *transylvanica	GJos
	procurrens new	SPin
	prostrata	EOHP
	prunelloides	SPin
	przewalskii	CPom EAro EWld GBar LRHS MCCP MCot NMRc SAga SDnm SGar SPhx SPin WPer
	- BWJ 7920	SPin WCru
	pubescens new	SPin
	pulchella	MAJR SPin
	'Purple Majesty'	CHll CSev CWGN EPPr EShb LHop LPio MAvo MBel SAga SDys SMrm SPhx SPin SRkn WKif WWlt
	'Purple Queen'	LRHS LSou MSpe SDys SPoG WWlt
	purpurea	LSRN SPin
	radula new	SPin
	ranzaniana	SPin
	recognita	CBot LFur SPin WSHC
	recurva	SPin
	red-flowered B&SWJ 10375 from Guatemala new	WCru
	reflexa	SPin
	regeliana misapplied	see *S. virgata* Jacq.
	regeliana Trautv.	MBel NBir SPin
	regla	MAJR MAsh NGHP SDys SPin WHil WPGP
	- 'Jame'	SPin
	- 'Mount Emory'	SPin
	- 'Royal'	SPin
	repens	EAro EBee EPyc IGor SDys SPhx SPin WOut
	- var. ***repens***	SGar
§	***reptans***	CSpe SPin WPer
	- from Mexico	SDys
	- from Western Texas	CWGN SDys
	retinervia	SPin
	ringens	EAro SDys SPin
	riparia misapplied	see *S. rypara*
	roborowskii	SPin
§	***roemeriana*** ♀H3	CPBP CSpe EBee EPyc IFoB NWCA SAga SDnm SDys SPin WPGP
	- 'Hot Trumpets' new	LRHS WHil
	roscida	SPin
	'Rose Queen' ambig.	MRav
	'Royal Bumble' new	IPot
	rubescens	SDys SPin
	rubiginosa	SDys SPin
	runcinata	EAro EPyc SPin

	rutilans	see *S. elegans* 'Scarlet Pineapple'
§	***rypara***	CPom EAro SDys SPin
	sagittata	SDys SPin WOut WWlt
*	***sauntia***	SPin
	Savannah Series **new**	LRHS
	scabiosifolia	SPin
	scabra	CFir SDys SPin WOut
	schlechteri **new**	SPin
	sclarea	CArn CHby ECtt GPoy LRHS MHer MNHC NGHP NGdn SECG SIde SPin WCHb WPer
	- var. ***sclarea***	CKno EBee EBla ECtt
	- short **new**	WHil
	- var. ***turkestaniana*** **new**	WWEG
	- var. ***turkestanica*** hort.	CSev CSpe EBee EHrv ELan EPfP EWTr LBMP LRHS LSRN MBri MCot MRav NEgg NGdn SBch SGar SMad SMrm SPav SPer SWal SWat WCAu WCom WEas WHil WKif WMnd WPer
§	- 'Vatican White'	EAro EBee EBrs EPfP LDai LRHS MWat SBch SDnm SMad SPav WMnd WPer WSHC
	- white-bracted	CWib NGHP NLar SBod SPin SWal SWvt
*	***scordifolia***	SPin
	scutellarioides	SPin
	semiatrata misapplied	see *S. chamaedryoides*
	semiatrata ambig.	IFoB LPio
	semiatrata Zucc.	CDes CSpe EWld SAga SDys SPin
	serpyllifolia	SDys SPin
	- white-flowered	WOut
	sessei	SPin
	setulosa	SPin
	'Silas Dyson'	CSpe CWGN EPyc EWld LPio LRHS MWea SAga SBch SDys SPin
	'Silke's Dream'	CWGN EAro EBee ECtt EPyc EWld MAsh MWea SBHP SDys SPin SUsu WPen WWlt
	sinaloensis	EPyc MAsh SBch SDys SPin WFar WHil
	- 'Blue Eyes'	LRHS
	somalensis	SDys SHar SPin WPen
	spathacea ♀H3-4	MDKP SDys SPhx SPin
	splendens	SPin
	- 'Dancing Flame' (v)	EPyc
	- 'Helen Dillon'	SDys
	- 'Peach'	SDys SPin
	- 'Salsa Burgundy' (Salsa Series)	WWlt
§	- 'Van-Houttei' ♀H3	CSpe ECre EPyc GCal MBel SDys SPin WWlt
	sprucei	SPin
	squalens	SPin
	stachydifolia	SPin
§	***staminea***	SDys SPhx SPin
	stenophylla	EAro SPin WHil WPer
	'Stephanie'	SDys
	stepposa	SPin
	stolonifera **new**	SPin
	striata	COlW SPin
	styphelus	SPin
*	***suberecta***	WHil
	subpalmatinervis **new**	SPin
	subrotunda	SDys SPin WHil
	summa **new**	CPBP
	× ***superba*** ♀H4	CBot CPrp CSBt EBee ECtt ELan EPfP EPyc LAst LEdu LRHS MBri MHer MWat SDix SHar SPer SRms WHoo WWEG
	- 'Adrian'	CMHG CPrp EBee ECtt LRHS SMrm

	- 'Dear Anja'	LHop SAga SPhx
	- 'Merleau'	EBee EPyc LRHS
	- 'Merleau Rose'	LRHS
	- 'Rubin' ♀H4	ECtt MBNS NBre SMrm SPhx
I	- 'Superba'	CSev ECha ECtt EHrv MRav SMrm SPhx SRkn WCAu
	× ***sylvestris***	LAst SGar SPin
§	- 'Blauhügel' ♀H4	CHar EBee ECha ECtt ELan EPfP EShb MArl NPri SBch SMrm SPhx WCAu WPer WWEG
§	- 'Blaukönigin'	EBee EPfP GMaP LAst LBMP LRHS MWat NLar NMir NVic SBch SPet SPhx SPlb SPoG SWvt WHil WPer WWEG
	- Blue Queen	see *S.* × *sylvestris* 'Blaukönigin'
	- 'Lye End'	ECtt MWat WCot
§	- 'Mainacht' ♀H4	Widely available
	- May Night	see *S.* × *sylvestris* 'Mainacht'
	- 'Negrito'	EBee EWll NGdn SMrm
	- 'Rhapsody in Blue' PBR	EBee LRHS MBNS NLar WFar
	- 'Rose Queen'	CMac CMea EBee ECha ECtt ELan EPfP EShb LHop LRHS NOrc SBch SCoo SPet SPhx SPoG SWvt WPer WWEG
	- 'Rügen'	CMac EBee EPyc
	- 'Schneehügel'	CMac CSBt EBee ECha ELan ELon EPPr EPfP GMaP LAst LRHS MBNS MRav NBre NCob NEgg NMoo NPri NPro SMrm SPer WCAu WMnd WWEG
	- 'Tänzerin' ♀H4	EBee ELon EPPr EPyc SDys SUsu WCot
	- 'Viola Klose'	CHar CMHG CPrp CWGN EBee EBrs ECha ECtt EShb GBuc LRHS LSRN MBri MCot NCGa NGdn NLar WCAu
	tachiei hort.	see *S. forsskaolii*
	'Tammy'	SPin
	taraxacifolia	SDys SPin
	tesquicola	see *S. nemorosa* subsp. *tesquicola*
	tianschanica	SPin
	tiliifolia	EAro SEND SPav SPin SRms
	tingitana	SDys SPin
	tomentosa	SPin
	transcaucasica	see *S. staminea*
	transsylvanica	IMou LDai MSpe SDnm SGar SPav SPhx SPin STes WCAu WPer
	- 'Blue Spire'	EBee ECtt MCot MWhi SPad SPav SPur
	'Trebah Lilac White'	see *S.* × *jamensis* 'Trebah'
§	'Trelawney'	EPyc LRHS MHom SDys SPav SPin SRot WHil
§	'Trelissick'	ECre EPyc LHop LRHS MAsh MHom SDys SPav SPin SRot WHil WWlt
§	'Trewithen'	CPLG CPom ECre EPyc LRHS SPav SPin SPoG SRot
	trijuga	SPin
	triloba	see *S. fruticosa*
	tubifera	MAsh SAga SPin
§	***tubiflora*** ♀H1+3	EPyc MAJR SPin WWlt
	uliginosa ♀H3-4	Widely available
	- 'African Skies'	CChe EBee MNrw SPin WDyG
	urica	CSpe EWld MAJR SDys SPav SPin
	- short	CMdw CSpe SDys
	'Valerie'	SDys
	'Van-Houttei'	see *S. splendens* 'Van-Houttei'
	'Vatican City'	see *S. sclarea* 'Vatican White'
	verbenaca	CArn EBWF EPyc MHer NMir NSco SPin WOut WPer
	- pink-flowered	SPhx

	verticillata	EBee EGoo EHrv EPyc LEdu LRHS SDys SEND SPin WPer
§	- 'Alba'	CAbP EBee ECtt EPPr EPfP EShb GJos GQue LBMP LRHS MBel MCot MRav NGdn SPer SPin WCAu WPer
	- subsp. ***amasiaca***	SGar
	- 'Hannay's Blue'	EPPr SMrm
	- 'Hannay's Purple'	EPPr
	- 'Purple Rain'	Widely available
	- 'Smouldering Torches'	EBee LPla
	- 'White Rain'	see *S. verticillata* 'Alba'
	villicaulis	see *S. amplexicaulis*
	villosa	SPin
§	***virgata*** Jacq.	SGar SPin WOut
	viridis	MNHC SPin
§	- var. ***comata***	MCot NGHP SIde WJek
	- var. ***viridis***	SBod WHrl
	viscosa ambig.	EPyc
	viscosa Jacq.	SPin
	- 'Framboise'	MCot
	vitifolia B&SWJ 10236 **new**	WCru
	wagneriana	MAJR SPin
	warszewicziana **new**	SGar
	'Waverly'	CDes CHll CSpe EWld MAJR MAsh MCot SAga SDys SUsu WCom WOut WWlt
	xalapensis	SPin
	yunnanensis BWJ 7874	WCru
	aff. ***yunnanensis***	SPin

Salvinia (*Salviniaceae*)

	sp.	LPBA
	natans	MSKA

Sambucus ✿ (*Caprifoliaceae*)

	adnata	SDix WFar
	caerulea	see *S. nigra* subsp. *caerulea*
	callicarpa	NLar
	chinensis B&SWJ 5960	WCru
	ebulus	GKir LEdu NLar SMad
	formosana	LEdu
	- B&SWJ 1543	WCru
§	***javanica*** B&SWJ 4047	WCru
	kamtschatica	WBVN
	mexicana B&SWJ 10349	WCru
	nigra	CArn CBcs CCVT CDul EMac GKir GPoy IFFs NWea SBch SIde WDin WFar WMou WSFF
	- 'Albomarginata'	see *S. nigra* 'Marginata'
	- 'Albovariegata' (v)	CDoC CMac EBee SEND WMoo
*	- 'Ardwall'	CAgr GCal
N	- 'Aurea' ♀H4	CBcs CDul CLnd CSBt CWan ELan EMac EPfP GKir MBar MRav NWea SPer WDin WFar WMoo
	- 'Aureomarginata' (v)	CBgR ECrN ELan EPPr EPfP ISea MRav MSnd NLar NSti SBch WCFE WFar
	- 'Bradet'	CAgr
	- 'Cae Rhos Lligwy'	CAgr WHer
§	- subsp. ***caerulea***	EPfP WSpi
	- subsp. ***canadensis*** 'Aurea'	CWib MBar NWea WHar
	- - 'Goldfinch'	LRHS
	- - 'John's'	CAgr
	- - 'Maxima'	EWes SMad SMrm WCot
	- - 'York' (F)	CAgr WCot
	- 'Donau'	CAgr
§	- 'Eva'PBR	Widely available
	- 'Frances' (v)	EPPr WCot
	- 'Franzi'	CAgr
	- 'Fructu Luteo'	NLar
§	- 'Gerda'PBR ♀H4	Widely available
	- 'Godshill' (F)	CAgr SDea
	- 'Haschberg'	CAgr
	- 'Heterophylla'	see *S. nigra* 'Linearis'
	- 'Ina'	CAgr
	- 'Körsör' (F)	NLar
	- f. ***laciniata*** ♀H4	CDul CPLG EBee ELan EPPr EPfP EPla GCal GKir LRHS MBlu MMuc MRav NBea NGHP NSti NWea SDix SLon SPoG WCFE WCot WDin WFar WPGP
§	- 'Linearis'	CPMA ELan EPla MRav NLar
	- 'Long Tooth'	CDul
	- 'Madonna' (v)	CBgR CMac EBee LRHS LSou MBlu MGos MRav NLar SBch WCot
§	- 'Marginata' (v)	CBcs CDul CWan CWib EHoe GKir MBar MHer MRav SDix SLon SPer WCot WDin WFar
	- 'Marion Bull' (v)	CDul
I	- 'Marmorata'	NLar
I	- 'Monstrosa'	NLar SMad
	- 'Plena' (d)	WCot
	- f. ***porphyrophylla*** 'Black Beauty'PBR	see *S. nigra* 'Gerda'
	- - 'Black Lace'PBR	see *S. nigra* 'Eva'
§	- - 'Guincho Purple'	CBcs CDoC CDul CTri CWib EBee ECrN EHoe ELan EPPr EPfP GKir LRHS MBar MCCP MHer MRav NBlu NHol SPlb WDin WFar WMoo
	- - 'Purple Pete'	CDul
	- - 'Thundercloud'	CBcs CDul CMHG EBee EWes LBMP LRHS MAsh MBri NChi NLar NPro WCot WFar WPat
	- 'Pulverulenta' (v)	CBgR CBow CDoC CWib EPPr EPla GCal GKir LHop LRHS MRav NLar SPer WCot WFar
	- 'Purpurea'	see *S. nigra* f. *porphyrophylla* 'Guincho Purple'
	- 'Pyramidalis'	CPMA EPla NLar SMad
	- 'Sambu' (F)	CAgr
	- 'Samdal' (F)	CAgr
	- 'Samidan' (F)	CAgr
	- 'Samnor' (F)	CAgr
	- 'Sampo' (F)	CAgr
	- 'Samyl' (F)	CAgr
*	- 'Tenuifolia'	MRav
	- 'Urban Lace'	CAgr
	- 'Variegata'	see *S. nigra* 'Marginata'
	- f. ***viridis***	CAgr CBgR
	racemosa	EPfP NWea
	- 'Aurea'	EHoe
	- 'Crûg Lace'	WCru
	- 'Goldenlocks'	EWes LRHS MGos MSwo NLar SPer
	- 'Plumosa Aurea'	CBcs CMac CPLG CSBt CTri CWib EBee ECrN ELan EPfP GCra GKir LRHS MBri MRav MSwo MWhi NHol NPri NWea SLim SReu SSta WCFE WDin WFar
	- 'Sutherland Gold' ♀H4	Widely available
	- 'Tenuifolia'	CPMA CSWP ELan EPfP LRHS NLar WPGP WPat
	tigranii	NLar
	wightiana	see *S. javanica*

Samolus (*Primulaceae*)

	repens	CPBP ECou LLHF
	valerandi	EBWF

Sandersonia (*Colchicaceae*)

	aurantiaca	CAvo CFFs CPne EBrs ECho EPot LAma LRHS

Sanguinaria (*Papaveraceae*)

canadensis	Widely available
- f. ***multiplex*** (d)	CDes CLAP EBrs ECho ERos GEdr GKir IFro LRHS NBir WCom WSHC WWst
- - 'Plena' (d) ♀H4	CBct CBro CSpe CWCL EBee ECho ELon GCra GKev GPoy LAma LRHS NCGa NHol NMen NRya SIng SPer SPoG WAbe WBVN WFar WPGP WPat WTin

Sanguisorba ✿ (*Rosaceae*)

sp.	SUsu
§ ***albiflora***	CCVN CDes CHar CKno CRow EBee EBla ELan GBuc LPla LRHS MAvo MRav NGdn NLar NPro SMrm SPhx SWat WCom WFar WMoo WPGP
armena	CElw EBee EBla EWes MAvo MBel MNrw SSvw WTin
benthamiana	CHEx
canadensis	CDes CKno CMac CRow EBee EBla ECha EPPr EPfP GCal GMaP GPoy LPio LPla MAvo NBir NVic SMeo SPer SPhx SWat WAul WCAu WFar WMoo WOld WTin
* ***caucasica***	EBee EPPr EWes LBMP LEdu LPla NBre SPhx
'Chocolate Tip'	EBee EBla IPot NBro
'Dark Knight'	WCHb
hakusanensis	CDes CHar CKno EBee EBla GBBs GCal GKev IFro IPot LEdu MAvo MNFA MNrw NBir NBre NBro NChi NPro SMeo WCot WFar WPGP WTin
- B&SWJ 8709	WCru
'John Coke'	NLar
'Korean Snow'	MNFA SPhx SUsu
magnifica Schischk. & Kom.	CDes EWes GCal LEdu WPGP
- ***alba***	see *S. albiflora*
menziesii	Widely available
- 'Dali Marble' (v)	CBow CCVN EBee ECtt
§ ***minor***	CArn CHby CPrp EBee EBla ELau GBar GKir GPoy MDun MHer MNHC NBro NGHP NMir SIde SPlb WCHb WGwG WHer WMoo WWEG
- subsp. ***minor***	EBWF
obtusa	Widely available
- 'Chatto'	EBee
- white-flowered	CDes MAvo WPGP
officinalis	CArn CKno COIW CWan EBWF EBee EBla EHrv EPPr GBar GQue LEdu LPio MHer MNFA NMir NPro SPer SPhx SWat WCAu WFar WMoo WWEG
- CDC 262	CAby LPla
- CDC 282	SPhx
- CDC 292	WCot
- from Mongolia **new**	LEdu
- 'Arnhem'	CKno CMdw EBla EPPr LEdu LPla MAvo SMeo SMrm SPhx SUsu WCot WTin
- 'False Tanna'	CWib WFar
- 'Lemon Splash' (v)	CBow EBee EBla WCom WCot
- 'Martin's Mulberry'	CDes EWes
- 'Pink Tanna'	CDes CElw CKno CPrp EBee EBla EPPr GBBs LEdu LFur MAvo MCot MDKP NBhm NBid NBre NBro NGHP NSti SMrm SPhx SUsu WCot WMoo WTin
- 'Red Thunder'	EBee EPPr IPot LFur MAvo NCGa NLar WWEG
- 'Shiro-fukurin' (v)	CDes EBee MAvo WCot
parviflora	see *S. tenuifolia* var. *parviflora*
pimpinella	see *S. minor*
'Pink Brushes'	EBla NLar SPhx
riishirensis	EBee
sitchensis	see *S. stipulata*
§ ***stipulata***	EBee GCal GKir LRHS MNrw NGby WCAu
'Tanna'	Widely available
'Tanna' seedling	EPPr EShb
tenuifolia	CEnt EBla GBBs GCal GKir IFro LRHS MCot MDun NLar NPro SBHP SHGN SMrm SPhx WMoo
- 'Alba'	CDes CKno EBee EBla EWes GBuc GCal GQue IMou LPio MAvo MRav NPro SMad SPhx WCom WCot WFar WOld WWEG
- 'Big Pink'	GCal MNrw
§ - var. ***parviflora***	CDes EBee LEdu MAvo MNrw NCob NLar SMeo WPGP WTin
- - white-flowered	EBla
- 'Pink Elephant'	CDes CHar CKno EBee EBla ECtt EPPr GBin LDai LEdu MAvo NLar SMad WCAu WPGP WTin
- var. ***purpurea*** **new**	CDes
- 'Purpurea'	CKno EBee EBla EPPr LEdu MAvo MDun NLar WCAu WCom WCot WFar WPGP
- 'Stand Up Comedian'	EBee MAvo NLar
- 'Sturdy Guard' **new**	EBee
- 'White Elephant'	EBla

Sanicula (*Apiaceae*)

coerulescens	NBhm
europaea	EBWF EBee GBar GPoy NSco WHer WTin

Sansevieria (*Dracaenaceae*)

trifasciata 'Golden Hahnii' (v) ♀H1	EShb MBri
- 'Hahnii' ♀H1	EShb
- var. ***laurentii*** (v) ♀H1	MBri
- 'Moonshine' ♀H1	EShb
zeylanica	EShb

Santolina (*Asteraceae*)

benthamiana	EAro
§ ***chamaecyparissus*** ♀H4	Widely available
- var. ***corsica***	see *S. chamaecyparissus* 'Nana'
- 'Double Lemon' (d)	EBee EPfP WSpi
- 'Lambrook Silver'	CArn CDoC EBee ECtt EGoo EOHP EPfP LBMP LRHS MAsh MBNS NHol SBch SCoo SLim SPoG
- 'Lemon Queen'	CArn CDoC EBee EGoo EPfP GBar LRHS MAsh MGos MNHC MSwo NBir NPri SBch SIde SWat WCHb WFar WGwG WPer WSpi
- subsp. ***magonica***	GKir
§ - 'Nana' ♀H4	CPrp EBee ECho EPfP LRHS MAsh MBar MHer MRav MSwo SPoG SRms SWat WGrn WPer
- var. ***nana*** 'Weston'	ECho
- 'Pretty Carol'	CAbP EBee ECtt ELan EMil EPfP GBar GGar LRHS LSRN LSou MAsh MBri NGHP SIde WFar
- 'Small-Ness'	CMea CStu EBee ECho EGoo ELan EPfP EPot EWes GBar GEdr LRHS MAsh MHer NLAp SIng SPer SPoG STre SWvt WAbe WCom WPer
incana	see *S. chamaecyparissus*

pectinata	see *S. rosmarinifolia* subsp. *canescens*
pinnata	CArn CSev MHer WPer
§ - subsp. ***neapolitana*** ♀H4	CArn CSBt CSev CWib EBee ECha ECho ECrN ELan EPfP GBar LRHS MBri MNHC NCob NPri SDix SIde WEas WHCG WMnd WTin WWEG
- - cream-flowered	see *S. pinnata* subsp. *neapolitana* 'Edward Bowles'
§ - - 'Edward Bowles'	Widely available
- - 'Sulphurea'	CArn CMea EBee ECGP ECrN EGoo EPfP LRHS MAsh NCob NGHP SBch SPer SPhx SPoG WKif WPer
rosmarinifolia	CArn CDoC CDul CWan EBee ECrN GPoy LRHS MRav MSCN NGHP SLon SPlb SRms STre WCHb WCom
§ - subsp. ***canescens***	EBee EPfP LRHS WPer
- 'Lemon Fizz'	EPPr LSou NPol NPri SBch SPoG
§ - subsp. ***rosmarinifolia***	CPrp CSev ECha ECrN EGoo ELan EPfP GBar LRHS MHer MRav SBch SDix SIde SPer SPoG SWvt WBrE WCHb WDin WFar WGwG WHoo
- - 'Primrose Gem' ♀H4	CBcs CDoC CPrp CSBt CSam CTri EBee ECha ECho ECrN EPfP GBar LHop LRHS MAsh MRav MSwo MWat NCob NPri SBch SPer SPoG SWvt WCot WPer WSpi
- - white-flowered	SSvw
tomentosa	see *S. pinnata* subsp. *neapolitana*
virens	see *S. rosmarinifolia* subsp. *rosmarinifolia*
viridis	see *S. rosmarinifolia* subsp. *rosmarinifolia*

Sanvitalia (*Asteraceae*)

Aztekengold = 'Starbini'PBR	LAst WGor
'Little Sun'	SPet
procumbens 'Irish Eyes'	CSpe
'Sunbini'PBR	CSpe LSou NPri SVil WGor

Sapindus (*Sapindaceae*)

mukorossi	CBcs
saponaria var. ***drummondii***	EGFP

Saponaria (*Caryophyllaceae*)

'Bressingham' ♀H4	EAlp ECho ECtt EDAr EPfP EPot LBee LRHS NBlu NLAp NMen WAbe WPat
Bressingham Hybrid **new**	LRHS
caespitosa	ECho EDAr EPot EWes
× ***lempergii*** 'Max Frei'	CAbP CSam EBee ELon EWTr GBuc LSou MRav NCob SAga SDix SPhx WOld WSHC
lutea	GKev
ocymoides ♀H4	CMea EBee ECha ECho ECtt EDAr EHon EPfP GAbr GBar LRHS MLHP MNHC NBlu NMen NPri NVic SIng SPer SPlb SPoG SRms SRot SWal WBor WCFE WFar WPer
- 'Alba'	EBee ECha ECho WFar
- 'Rubra Compacta' ♀H4	WAbe
- 'Snow Tip'	ECho ECtt EDAr EPfP NGdn NLar SBch
- 'Splendens'	ECho
officinalis	CArn CBre CHby CWan EBWF GBar GPoy LEdu MHer MLHP NGHP NPri SIde SPlb WFar WHer WMoo WPer
- 'Alba Plena' (d)	CBre EBee EBrs ECha EWTr GBar GGar LRHS NLar SHar WCHb WFar WHer WPer WPtf WTin
- 'Betty Arnold' (d)	EBee ECtt EWes GMac WCot WFar WTin
§ - 'Dazzler' (v)	GBar WCHb WHer WWEG
- 'Rosea Plena' (d)	Widely available
- 'Rubra Plena' (d)	CBre ELan EWes MWhi NBre NGHP SHar WCHb WHer WTin
- 'Variegata'	see *S. officinalis* 'Dazzler'
× ***olivana*** ♀H4	CPBP EAlp ECho EPot LRHS MTho NLAp NMen WPat
pamphylica	MNrw
'Rosenteppich'	CPBP ECtt WPat
zawadskii	see *Silene zawadskii*

Saposhnikovia (*Apiaceae*)

divaricata	CArn

Sarcocapnos (*Papaveraceae*)

enneaphylla	LSRN

Sarcococca ✿ (*Buxaceae*)

confusa ♀H4	Widely available
hookeriana ♀H4	CPLG CTrG EPfP EWld IFoB LAst LRHS LSRN MBlu MDun MSwo NPri SBch WAbe WFar WPGP
- B&SWJ 2585	WCru
- HWJK 2393	WCru
- Sch 2396	EPla
- var. ***digyna*** ♀H4	Widely available
- - 'Purple Stem'	CHar CPLG CPMA CTri EBee EPfP EPla ERas LRHS MGos MRav NLar SCoo SPoG WCru WDin
* - - 'Schillingii'	CPMA LRHS WCru
- var. ***hookeriana***	CPMA
- - GWJ 9369	WCru
- - Sch 1160	CGHE
- var. ***humilis***	Widely available
orientalis	CAbP CBcs CMCN CPLG CPMA ELan EPfP EPla LRHS MAsh MGos SPoG SSpi WFar WPGP WSpi
'Roy Lancaster'	see *S. ruscifolia* var. *chinensis* 'Dragon Gate'
ruscifolia	CBcs CBgR CDul CMCN CPLG CPMA CSBt EBee ECrN ELan EPfP EPla ERas EWTr GKir LAst LRHS MAsh MGos MRav NEgg NPri SLim SLon SPer SRms SSpi WCru WFar
- var. ***chinensis*** ♀H4	CPMA CSam EPfP EPla SLon WCru WFar WPGP
- - L 713	EPla
§ - - 'Dragon Gate'	CDoC CGHE CPLG CPMA EBee ELan EPfP EPla LLHF LRHS LSRN MAsh MBlu SLim SLon SPoG SReu SSta WCru WPGP WPat
saligna	CBcs CPMA EBtc EPfP EPla LRHS NLar SLon WCru
vagans B&SWJ 7285	WCru
wallichii	CGHE CPLG CPMA EBee MBlu WPGP
- B&SWJ 2291	WCru
- GWJ 9427	WCru

Sarcostemma (*Asclepiadaceae*)

viminale	EShb

Sarmienta (*Gesneriaceae*)

repens ♀H2	CGHE CPLG WAbe WPGP

Sarothamnus see *Cytisus*

Sarracenia ✿ (*Sarraceniaceae*)

× ***ahlesii***	CHew

alata	CHew CSWC EECP MCCP NChu SHmp WSSs
- all green	SHmp
- 'Black Tube'	WSSs
- heavily-veined	SHmp WSSs
- pubescent	CSWC EECP NChu WSSs
- 'Red Lid'	CSWC EECP NChu WSSs
- 'Red Lid' × ***flava*** red pitcher	EECP
- wavy lid	SHmp WSSs
- white-flowered	WSSs
alata × ***flava*** var. ***maxima***	CSWC NChu
× ***areolata***	CHew CSWC NChu WSSs
× ***catesbyi*** ♀H1	CHew CSWC NChu SHmp WSSs
× ***courtii***	CSWC NChu
'Dixie Lace'	CSWC
'Evendine'	CSWC
× ***excellens*** ♀H1	CSWC NChu WSSs
× ***exornata***	CSWC NChu
flava ♀H1	CSWC MCCP NChu WSSs
- all green giant	see *S. flava* var. *maxima*
- var. ***atropurpurea***	EECP WSSs
- 'Burgundy'	MYeo WSSs
- var. ***cuprea***	CSWC NChu WSSs
- var. ***flava***	CHew EECP WSSs
§ - var. ***maxima***	CHew CSWC EECP NChu WSSs
- var. ***ornata***	CHew CSWC EECP NChu SHmp WSSs
- var. ***rubricorpora***	CHew EECP NChu SHmp WSSs
- var. ***rugelii***	CHew EECP MYeo SHmp WSSs
- veinless	CSWC
× ***harperi***	CSWC NChu
'Juthatip Soper'	LRHS SHmp WSSs
'Ladies in Waiting'	CSWC
leucophylla ♀H1	CHew CSWC NChu SHmp WSSs
- from Okaloosa Co., Florida	SHmp
- 'Deer Park Alabama'	SHmp
- green	WSSs
- ***popei***	EECP
- pubescent	WSSs
- 'Schnell's Ghost'	WSSs
- 'Tarnok' new	WSSs
leucophylla × ***oreophila***	CSWC EECP NChu
'Lynda Butt'	SHmp WSSs
× ***miniata***	EECP SHmp
minor	CSWC EECP NChu SHmp WSSs
- var. ***minor***	CHew
§ - 'Okee Giant'	CSWC MYeo NChu WSSs
- var. ***okeefenokeensis***	CHew
- 'Okefenokee Giant'	see *S. minor* 'Okee Giant'
minor × ***oreophila***	CSWC
× ***mitchelliana*** ♀H1	WSSs
× ***moorei***	CHew WSSs
- 'Brook's Hybrid'	CHew CSWC EECP NChu WSSs
oreophila	CHew CSWC MYeo NChu SHmp WSSs
oreophila × ***purpurea*** subsp. ***venosa***	CSWC NChu
× ***popei***	CSWC NChu
psittacina	CHew CSWC EECP LRHS NChu SHmp WSSs
* - f. ***heterophylla***	CSWC MYeo
purpurea	LRHS NWCA SPlb
- subsp. ***purpurea***	CHew CSWC MCCP NChu SHmp WSSs
- - f. ***heterophylla***	CSWC MYeo WSSs
- subsp. ***venosa***	CHew CSWC SHmp WSSs
- - var. ***burkii***	CSWC NChu WSSs
× ***readii***	SHmp WSSs
- 'Farnhamii'	CSWC EECP NChu
× ***rehderi***	SHmp
rubra	CSWC EECP NChu WSSs
- subsp. ***alabamensis***	CHew CSWC NChu SHmp WSSs
- subsp. ***gulfensis***	CHew CSWC NChu SHmp WSSs
* - - f. ***heterophylla***	CSWC WSSs
- subsp. ***jonesii***	CSWC EECP NChu WSSs
* - - f. ***heterophylla***	CSWC WSSs
- subsp. ***rubra***	CHew CSWC WSSs
- subsp. ***wherryi***	CHew CSWC EECP NChu WSSs
- - giant	WSSs
- - yellow-flowered	CSWC WSSs
'Umlanftiana'	CSWC

Saruma (*Aristolochiaceae*)

henryi	CAby CDes CLAP CMea CPom EBee EWTr LSou MAvo SUsu WCot WCru WPGP WSHC

Sasa (*Poaceae*)

chrysantha misapplied	see *Pleioblastus chino*
disticha 'Mirrezuzume'	see *Pleioblastus pygmaeus* 'Mirrezuzume'
glabra f. ***albostriata***	see *Sasaella masamuneana* 'Albostriata'
kagamiana	NLar
kurilensis	CMCo EBee EPla LPal MWhi MWht NMoo WFar WJun
§ - 'Shima-shimofuri' (v)	CMCo EPPr EPfP EPla ERod MMoz MWht WJun
- 'Shimofuri'	see *S. kurilensis* 'Shima-shimofuri'
- short	EPla
nana	see *S. veitchii* f. *minor*
nipponica	WJun
oshidensis	EPla
§ ***palmata***	CAbb CDul COld CTrG CWib EBee EHoe MCCP MMuc MWhi SBch WDin WFar WHer WPnP
- f. ***nebulosa***	CBcs CBct CDoC CFir CHEx EHul ENBC EPfP EPla EWes MBrN MMoz MWht NMoo SAPC SArc WDyG WFar WJun WMoo WPnP
quelpaertensis	EPla MWht
tessellata	see *Indocalamus tessellatus*
tsuboiana	CDoC EBee ENBC EPla GQui LPal MMoz MWht NGdn NLar SBig WDyG WFar WMoo
§ ***veitchii***	CAbb CBcs CKno CTrC CTrG EBee ECha EHoe ENBC EPfP EPla GKir LEdu LRHS MMoz MMuc MREP MRav MWht NMoo SPer WDin WFar WJun WMoo
§ - f. ***minor***	EBee MCCP WMoo

Sasaella (*Poaceae*)

glabra	see *S. masamuneana*
§ ***masamuneana***	ENBC EPla
§ - 'Albostriata' (v)	CDoC CEnt CMCo CWib EBee ENBC EPPr EPla ERod LEdu LPal LRHS MBar MCCP MMoz MWht NGdn NMoo SBig WDyG WFar WJun WMoo WPGP
- f. ***aureostriata*** (v)	EPla MMoz NPal
§ ***ramosa***	CHEx EPla LEdu MCCP MMoz MWht NMoo WDin

Sassafras (*Lauraceae*)

albidum	CArn CBcs CCCN CMCN EPfP LEdu LRHS MAsh MBri SBch WPGP
tzumu	CGHE WPGP

satsuma see *Citrus unshiu*

Satureja ✿ (*Lamiaceae*)

coerulea ♀H4	CWan ECho EWes NBir

douglasii EOHP GBar SBch SHDw WJek
- 'Indian Mint'[PBR] MHer NGHP
hortensis CBod GPoy ILis MHer MNHC SBch SIde WJek
- 'Selektion' LLWP
montana CArn CHby CPrp CWan ECho ELau GKev GPoy ILis LLWP MBri MHer MNHC NGHP NMen SBch SDix SEND SHGN SIde SRms SVic WCHb WPer
* - ***citriodora*** GPoy MHer
§ - subsp. ***illyrica*** WJek WPer
- prostrate, white-flowered NGHP
- 'Purple Mountain' GPoy LLWP MHer
- ***subspicata*** see *S. montana* subsp. *illyrica*
parnassica LLWP WPer
repanda see *S. spicigera*
seleriana SDys
§ ***spicigera*** CArn CBod CPBP CPrp ECho ELau EPot GBar GEdr LEdu LFol LLWP MHer NBir NMen SHGN SIde WCHb WJek WPer
thymbra CArn SBch SHDw
§ ***viminea*** EOHP

Saurauia (*Actinidiaceae*)

subspinosa CHEx

Sauromatum (*Araceae*)

guttatum see *S. venosum*
§ ***venosum*** CDes CMea CPLG CStu EAmu EBee EBrs ECho EShb GCal LAma LEdu LFur LRHS SBig SHaC WCot WCru WPGP

Saururus (*Saururaceae*)

cernuus CBen CHEx CRow CWat EHon ELan EMFW EPfP LPBA SRms SWat WMAq
chinensis CRow

Saussurea (*Asteraceae*)

albescens WCot
costus CArn
deltoidea WWJ 11652 **new** WCru

savory, summer see *Satureja hortensis*

savory, winter see *Satureja montana*

Saxegothaea (*Podocarpaceae*)

conspicua CDoC CDul ECou GBin IDee IFFs

Saxifraga ✿ (*Saxifragaceae*)

'Ada' (× *petraschii*) (7) NMen
'Aemula' (× *borisii*) (7) NMen
§ 'Afrodite' (*sempervivum*) (7) EPot
aizoides (9) ECho
- var. ***atrorubens*** (9) ECho
aizoon see *S. paniculata*
'Aladdin' (× *borisii*) (7) NMen
'Alan Hayhurst' (8) WAbe WFar
'Alan Martin' (× *boydilacina*) (7) ECho EPot MHer NMen
'Alba' (*oppositifolia*) (7) ECho ELan EWes ITim NDlv NHol NLAp NWCA WAbe
'Alba' (× *apiculata*) (7) ECho EDAr EPot LRHS MHer NLAp NMen NRya SPlb WAbe WCom WFar WPat
'Alba' (× *arco-valleyi*) see *S.* 'Ophelia'
'Albert Einstein' (× *apiculata*) (7) NMen
'Albertii' (*callosa*) see *S.* 'Albida'
§ 'Albida' (*callosa*) (8) ECho LRHS WAbe
'Albrecht Dürer' (Lasciva Group) (7) **new** EPot WAbe
'Aldebaran' (× *borisii*) (7) NMen
'Aldo Bacci' (Milford Group) (7) NMen
'Alfons Mucha' (7) EPot NMen
'Allendale Acclaim' (× *lismorensis*) (7) EPot NDlv NMen
'Allendale Accord' (*diapensioides* × *lilacina*) (7) NDlv NMen NWCA
'Allendale Allure' (7) NMen
'Allendale Amber' (7) NMen
'Allendale Andante' (× *arco-valleyi*) (7) NMen
'Allendale Angel' (× *kepleri*) (7) NMen WAbe
'Allendale Argonaut' (7) NDlv NMen
'Allendale Ballad' (7) NMen WAbe
'Allendale Ballet' (7) NMen
'Allendale Bamby' (× *lismorensis*) (7) NMen
'Allendale Banshee' (7) NMen
'Allendale Beau' (× *lismorensis*) (7) CPBP NMen
'Allendale Beauty' (7) CPBP NMen
'Allendale Betty' (× *lismorensis*) (7) NMen
'Allendale Billows' (7) NMen
'Allendale Blossom' (× *limorensis*) (7) NMen
'Allendale Bonny' (7) NMen WAbe
'Allendale Boon' (× *izari*) (7) NMen
'Allendale Bounty' (7) NMen
'Allendale Bravo' (× *lismorensis*) (7) NMen WAbe
'Allendale Cabal' (7) NMen
'Allendale Celt' (× *novacastelensis*) (7) NMen
'Allendale Charm' (Swing Group) (7) CPBP NMen WAbe
'Allendale Chick' (7) NMen
'Allendale Comet' (7) NMen
'Allendale Dance' (7) NMen
'Allendale Desire' (7) WAbe
'Allendale Divine' (7) WAbe
'Allendale Dream' (7) EPot NMen
'Allendale Duo' (7) NMen WAbe
'Allendale Elegance' (7) NMen
'Allendale Elf' (7) NMen
'Allendale Elite' (7) NMen
'Allendale Enchantment' (7) NMen
'Allendale Envoy' (7) NMen WAbe
'Allendale Epic' (7) EPot NMen WAbe
'Allendale Fairy' (7) NMen
'Allendale Fame' (7) NMen
'Allendale Fancy' **new** WAbe
'Allendale Frost' (7) NMen
'Allendale Garnet' (7) NMen
'Allendale Ghost' (7) NMen
'Allendale Goblin' (7) NMen NWCA WAbe
'Allendale Grace' (7) NMen WAbe
'Allendale Gremlin' (7) NMen
'Allendale Harvest' (7) NMen
'Allendale Hobbit' (7) EPot NMen WAbe
'Allendale Host' (7) NMen WAbe
'Allendale Icon' (× *polulacina*) (7) WAbe
'Allendale Imp' (7) WAbe

Name	Suppliers
'Allendale Ina' (7)	NMen WAbe
'Allendale Joy' (× *wendelacina*) (7)	NMen
'Allendale Pearl' (× *novacastelensis*) (7)	NMen
'Allendale Ruby' (7)	NMen
'Allendale Snow' (× *rayei*) (7)	NMen
'Alpenglow' (7)	NMen
alpigena (7)	EPot
'Amitie' (× *gloriana*) (7)	CFee NMen
andersonii (7)	NDlv NMen NRya
'Andrea Cesalpino' (Renaissance Group) (7)	NMen
× ***andrewsii*** (8×11)	MTho
angustifolia Haw.	see *S. hypnoides*
'Anna' (× *fontanae*) (7)	NMen WAbe
'Anne Beddall' (× *goringiana*) (7)	NMen
'Antonio Vivaldi' (7)	NMen WAbe
'Aphrodite' (*sempervivum*)	see *S.* 'Afrodite'
× ***apiculata*** *sensu stricto* hort.	see *S.* 'Gregor Mendel'
'Apple Blossom' (15)	ECtt GKev NPro NRya SPoG WGor
'Arabella' (× *edithae*) (7)	ECho
'Archdale' (*paniculata*) (8)	EAlp
§ 'Arco' (× *arco-valleyi*) (7)	NMen
× ***arco-valleyi*** *sensu stricto* hort.	see *S.* 'Arco'
× ***arendsii*** purple-flowered (15)	LRHS NNor
§ 'Aretiastrum' (× *boydii*) (7)	NDlv NMen
aretioides (7)	NMen
'Argia Romani' (7) **new**	NMen
'Ariel' (× *hornibrookii*) (7)	NMen
'Arthur' (× *anglica*) (7)	NMen
'Assimilis' (× *petraschii*) (7)	NMen
'August Hayek' (× *leyboldii*) (7)	NMen
'Aurea Maculata' (*cuneifolia*)	see *S.* 'Aureopunctata'
'Aurea' (*umbrosa*)	see *S.* 'Aureopunctata'
§ 'Aureopunctata' (× *urbium*) (11/v)	CMac CTri ECha ECho ELan GBuc GKir GMaP LBMP LRHS MBel MHer MRav NHol SBch SPer SPlb SPoG SRms WCom WMoo
'Autumn Tribute' (*fortunei*) (5)	CLAP WAbe WFar
'Ayer's Rock' (7) **new**	WAbe
'Balcana' (*paniculata*) (8)	EPot
'Baldensis'	see *S. paniculata* var. *minutifolia*
'Ballawley Guardsman' (15)	SIng
§ 'Beatrix Stanley' (7)	LRHS MHer NDlv NHol NLAp NMen NRya WGor
'Becky Foster' (× *borisii*) (7)	NMen
'Bellisant' (× *hornibrookii*) (7)	NMen
'Berenika' (× *bertolonii*) (7)	NMen
'Beryl' (× *anglica*) (7)	NMen
'Bettina' (× *paulinae*) (7)	NMen
× ***biasolettoi*** *sensu stricto* hort.	see *S.* 'Phoenix'
× ***bilekii*** (7)	ECho NMen
'Birch Baby' (15)	SIng
'Black Beauty' (15)	CMea CMoH LRHS MHer SIng
'Black Ruby' (*fortunei*) (5)	Widely available
'Blackberry and Apple Pie' (*fortunei*) (5)	CBct CBod CElw CLAP EBee ECtt GEdr IBal LOck LRHS MBrN MLHP MNrw NBro NHol NMen NMyG SWvt WAul WCot WFar WWEG
'Blaník' (× *borisii*) (7)	NMen
'Blanka' (× *borisii*) (7)	NMen
'Bob Hawkins' (15/v)	EAlp EDAr LRHS NHol
§ 'Bodensee' (× *hofmannii*) (7)	EPot NDlv WPat
'Bohdalec' (× *megaseiflora*) (7)	NMen
'Bohemia' (7)	ECho NMen
× ***borisii*** *sensu stricto* hort.	see *S.* 'Sofia'
'Bornmuelleri' (7)	NMen
'Boston Spa' (× *elisabethae*) (7)	ECho ECtt LRHS MHer NDlv NLAp NMen SPlb WPat
'Brailes' (× *poluanglica*) (7)	NMen
'Brian Arundel' (Magnus Group) (7) **new**	NMen
'Bridget' (× *edithae*) (7)	ECho LRHS NDlv NMen SIng
'Brimstone' (7) **new**	NMen
'Brno' (× *elisabethae*) (7)	EPot NMen
'Brookside' (*burseriana*) (7)	EPot NMen
brunoniana	see *S. brunonis*
§ ***brunonis*** (1) CC 5315	EWld
- CC&McK 108	NWCA
'Bryn Llwyd'	WAbe
bryoides (10)	ECho NRya
× ***burnatii*** (8)	LRHS NDlv NMen NPro WGor
burseriana (7)	ECho NLAp WAbe WGor
'Buster' (× *hardingii*) (7)	NMen
'Buttercup' (× *kayei*) (7)	EPot NLAp NMen NWCA WHoo
× ***byam-groundsii*** (7)	WFar
caesia misapplied (× *fritschiana*)	see *S.* 'Krain'
caesia L. (8)	SRms
§ ***callosa*** (8) $\mathbb{Y}^{H4}$	ECho EDAr GEdr MDKP MHer MLHP NHol NLAp WAbe WEas WFar WPat WTin
- subsp. ***callosa*** (8)	ECho
§ - - var. ***australis*** (8)	NBro NHol NMen
- var. ***lantoscana***	see *S. callosa* subsp. *callosa* var. *australis*
- ***lingulata***	see *S. callosa*
'Cambridge Seedling' (7)	NDlv NMen
'Camyra' (7)	WAbe
× ***canis-dalmatica***	see *S.* 'Canis-dalmatica'
§ 'Canis-dalmatica' (× *gaudinii*) (8) $\mathbb{Y}^{H4}$	CSsd CStu ECho ECtt EGoo EPot GEdr GGar LRHS NDlv NHol NMen NWCA WGor WPer
§ 'Carmen' (× *elisabethae*) (7)	NDlv NMen WAbe
§ 'Carniolica' (*paniculata*) (8)	GKir MBar NBro NHol NMen NWCA WCom
carolinica	see *S.* 'Carniolica' (*paniculata*)
cartilaginea	see *S. paniculata* subsp. *cartilaginea*
'Castor' (× *bilekii*) (7)	NMen
'Cathy Reed' (× *polulacina*) (7)	NMen
caucasica (7)	ECho
cebennensis (15) $\mathbb{Y}^{H2}$	EPot NMen NRya
cespitosa (15)	WAbe
'Chambers' Pink Pride'	see *S.* 'Miss Chambers'
'Charles Chaplin' (7)	ECho NMen WAbe
'Cheap Confections' (*fortunei*) (4)	CBct CLAP EBee ECtt EWll GAbr GEdr LFur LLHF LRHS NHol NMen WBor WCot WFar WMoo WOld WPGP WWEG
§ ***cherlerioides*** (10)	ECtt NRya NVic WFar
'Cherry Pie' (*fortunei*) (5)	CBct CLAP EBee GAbr LLHF LOck LRHS MNrw NBir NMyG WCot
'Cherrytrees' (× *boydii*) (7)	NMen WAbe
* 'Chetwynd' (*marginata*) (7)	NMen
'Chez Nous' (× *gloriana*) (7/v)	NMen
'Chodov' (7)	EPot NMen
'Christine' (× *anglica*) (7)	ECho NDlv NHol NLAp NMen

	cinerea (7)	EPot NMen WAbe
	'Cio-Cio-San' (Vanessa Group) (7)	NMen
	'Citronella' (7)	ECho WAbe
	'Claire Felstead' (*cinerea* × *poluniniana*) (7)	NMen
	'Clare Island' (*rosacea*) (15)	SIng
	'Clare' (× *anglica*) (7)	NMen
§	'Clarence Elliott' (*umbrosa*) (11) ♀H4	CMea CTri EBee ECho EWes GAbr GCal GJos GKev GMaP LRHS MDKP MHer NHol NRya NVic WCom WFar WHoo WPat WWEG
	'Claude Monet' (Impressio Group) (7)	CPBP WAbe
	'Claudia' (× *borisii*) (7)	NMen
	'Cleo' (× *boydii*) (7)	NMen
§	× ***clibranii*** hort. (15)	SIng
	'Cloth of Gold' (*exarata* subsp. *moschata*) (15)	ECha ECho ECtt EDAr ELan GMaP LAst LRHS MAsh MBar MHer NHol NMen NRya SIng SPer SPlb SPoG SRms WAbe WFar
	cochlearis (8)	CTri GEdr LRHS NBro NDlv NMen SBch WAbe WCom WPer
	'Cockscomb' (*paniculata*) (8)	EAlp ECho NHol NMen NRya WAbe
	columnaris (7)	NMen WAbe
	'Combrook' (× *poluanglica*) (7)	NMen
	'Coningsby Queen' (× *hornibrookii*) (7)	NMen
	continentalis (15)	NWCA
	'Conwy Snow' (*fortunei*) (5)	CLAP WAbe WFar
	'Conwy Star' (*fortunei*) (5)	CLAP WAbe WFar
	'Coolock Gem' (7)	NMen WAbe
	'Coolock Jean' (7) **new**	NMen WAbe
	'Coolock Kate' (7)	NMen WAbe
	'Cordata' (*burseriana*) (7)	NMen
	'Corona' (× *boydii*) (7)	NMen
	'Corrennie Claret' (15)	EWes
	'Correvoniana' Farrer (*paniculata*) (8)	EDAr MHer MSCN WFar
	cortusifolia (5)	CLAP ECho LRHS
	- B&SWJ 5879	WCru
	- var. ***stolonifera*** (5)	ECho GCal
	- - B&SWJ 6205	WCru
	'Cotton Crochet' (*fortunei*) (5/d)	CBct EBee ECtt GEdr LRHS NMyG WBor WCot WFar WOld
	cotyledon (8)	ECho LRHS MAsh NHol WCFE WEas WPer
§	'Cranbourne' (× *anglica*) (7) ♀H4	ECho EPot LRHS NHol NLAp NMen NWCA SIng WCom WPat
	'Cream' (*paniculata*) (8)	ECho LRHS
	'Cream Seedling' (× *elisabethae*) (7)	ECho NDlv NMen
	'Crenata' (*burseriana*) (7)	EPot LRHS NDlv NMen
	'Crimscote-love' (*poluanglica*) (7)	NMen
	'Crimson Diall' (× *irvingii*) (7) **new**	NMen
	'Crimson Rose' (*paniculata*)	see *S.* 'Rosea' (*paniculata*)
§	***crustata*** (8)	EAlp ECho MDKP NMen WThu
	- var. ***vochinensis***	see *S. crustata*
	'Crystal Pink' (*fortunei*) (5/v)	CBct CMil EBee ECtt EHrv GAbr GEdr LOck LRHS MNrw NBro NMen NMyG SGSe WCot WFar WOld
	'Crystalie' (× *biasolettoi*) (7)	LRHS NDlv NMen NRya WPat
	'Cultrata' (*paniculata*) (8)	NBro
	'Cumulus' (*iranica* hybrid) (7) ♀H4	EDAr EPot NMen WAbe
	cuneata (15)	NHol
§	***cuneifolia*** (11)	ECho GGar GKir IMou LBee LRHS MHer MWat NDlv NHol NSti NWCA WCom WFar WPer
	- var. ***capillipes***	see *S. cuneifolia* subsp. *cuneifolia*
§	- subsp. ***cuneifolia*** (11)	ECtt
*	- var. ***subintegra*** (11)	ECho
	'Cuscutiformis' (*stolonifera*) (5)	CAby CElw CHid EBee EBla EWld GEdr MBel SBch SIng SMad SMrm SRms WCru WPGP
	cymbalaria (2)	EBur SIng
	dahurica	see *S. cuneifolia*
	'Dainty Dame' (× *arco-valleyi*) (7)	LRHS NDlv NMen NWCA
	'Dana' (× *megaseiflora*) (7)	NHol NMen
	'Dartington Double' (15/d)	EWes LRHS WFar
	'Dartington Double White' (15/d)	NHol
	'David' (7)	NMen
	'Dawn Frost' (7)	EPot NDlv NLAp NMen
	'Delia' (× *hornibrookii*) (7)	EPot NMen
§	'Denisa' (× *pseudokotschyi*) (7)	NMen
	densa	see *S. cherlerioides*
	'Densa' (*hypnoides*) (15)	EAlp
	'Dentata' (× *geum*)	see *S.* 'Dentata' (× ***polita***)
§	'Dentata' (× *polita*) (11)	CSpe ECha ECho GCal GGar NVic WMoo WWEG
	'Dentata' (× *urbium*)	see *S.* 'Dentata' (× ***polita***)
	desoulavyi (7)	NMen
	diapensioides (7)	WAbe
	dinnikii (7)	EPot NMen WAbe
	× ***dinninaris*** (7)	NMen
	'Dobruška' (× *irvingii*) (7)	NMen
	'Doctor Clay' (*paniculata*) (8)	LRHS NMen NRya
	'Doctor Ramsey' (8)	ECtt EWes GEdr LRHS NBro NDlv NHol NMen WGor WPnn
	'Donald Mann' (15)	EWes
	'Donnington Chalice' **new**	NMen
	'Donnington Gold' **new**	NMen
	'Donnington Veil' **new**	NMen
	'Dorothy Milne' (7)	NMen
	'Drakula' (*ferdinandi-coburgi*) (7)	LRHS NDlv NMen SIng
	'Dubarry' (15)	EWes NRya WPnn
	'Dulcimer' (× *petraschii*) (7)	NMen
	'Edgar Irmscher' (7)	NDlv NMen
	'Edith' (× *edithae*) (7)	ECho LRHS
	'Edward Elgar' (× *megaseiflora*) (7)	NHol NMen
	× ***elegantissima***	see *S.* × *clibranii* hort.
	'Elf' (7)	see *S.* 'Beatrix Stanley'
	'Eliot Hodgkin' (× *millstreamiana*) (7)	NMen
	× ***elisabethae*** Sünd. (7)	EDAr
	× ***elisabethae*** *sensu stricto* hort.	see *S.* 'Carmen'
	'Elizabeth Sinclair' (× *elisabethae*) (7)	EPot NMen
	'Ellie Brinckerhoff' (× *hornibrookii*) (7)	NMen
	'Elliott's Variety'	see *S.* 'Clarence Elliott' (***umbrosa***)
§	'Ernst Heinrich' (× *heinrichii*) (7)	NMen
	'Esther' (× *burnatii*) (8)	CMea GEdr GKev LRHS NHol NMen NWCA SRGP WPnn
§	'Eulenspiegel' (× *geuderi*) (7)	EPot NHol NMen
	'Eva Hanzliková' (× *izari*) (7)	NMen
	exarata (15)	LRHS NMen WAbe

	Name	Suppliers
	- subsp. ***moschata*** 'Elf' (15)	ECtt EPfP NHol NMen SIng SRms WGor
	'Excellent' (Exclusive Group) (7) **new**	EPot
	fair maids of France	see *S.* 'Flore Pleno'
	'Fairy' (*exarata* subsp. *moschata*) (15)	CMea ECtt ELan EPot GKir WCom
	'Faldonside' (× *boydii*) (7) ♀^{H4}	NDlv NLAp NMen NRya WPat
	'Falstaff' (*burseriana*) (7)	NDlv NHol NRya WAbe
	×***farreri*** (15)	EPot GEdr
§	'Faust' (× *borisii*) (7)	NMen
	'Favorit' (× *bilekii*) (7)	NMen
§	***federici-augusti*** subsp. ***grisebachii*** (7) ♀$^{H2-3}$	ECho EPot GKev NSla WAbe WCom WFar
	'Ferdinand' (× *hofmannii*) (7)	NMen
	ferdinandi-coburgi (7) ♀^{H4}	ECtt EPot NDlv NRya WAbe
§	- subsp. ***chrysosplenifolia*** var. ***rhodopea*** (7)	EPot LRHS NDlv NMen
	- var. ***pravislavii***	see *S. ferdinandi-coburgi* subsp. *chrysosplenifolia* var. *rhodopea*
	- var. ***radoslavoffii***	see *S. ferdinandi-coburgi* subsp. *chrysosplenifolia* var. *rhodopea*
	'Findling' (15)	EPfP LRHS NHol NMen SPoG WAbe
	'Firebrand' (× *kochii*) (7)	NMen WAbe
	'Five Color' (*fortunei*)	see *S.* 'Go-nishiki'
§	***flagellaris*** (1)	NMen WAbe
	'Flavescens' misapplied	see *S.* 'Lutea' (*paniculata*)
	×***fleischeri*** (7)	NMen
§	'Flore Pleno' (*granulata*) (15/d)	CFir EBee EWes MAvo NBir SIng SUsu WAbe WFar
	'Flowers of Sulphur'	see *S.* 'Schwefelblüte'
	'Flush' (× *petraschii*) (7)	WAbe
	fortunei (5) ♀^{H4}	CHEx CLAP CMac ECho EWTr GKir GMaP NBir NLAp SRms WAbe WCru WMoo
	- B&SWJ 6346	WCru
	- f. ***alpina*** (5)	CLAP
	- - from Hokkaido (5)	CLAP WCru
	- var. ***koraiensis*** (5) B&SWJ 8688	WCru
	- 'Musgrove Pink'	CLAP
	- var. ***obtusocuneata*** (5)	CLAP EBee ECho LLHF NMen WAbe
	- f. ***partita*** (5)	CLAP GEdr WCru
	- var. ***pilosissima*** (5) B&SWJ 8557	WCru
	- pink-flowered (5)	CLAP WAbe WFar
	- var. ***suwoensis*** (5)	CLAP
	'Foster's Gold' (× *elisabethae*) (7)	NMen WAbe
	'Four Winds' (15)	EWes LRHS SPoG WCom
	'Francesco Redi' (7)	NMen WAbe
	'Francis Cade' (8)	GAbr WAbe
	'Frank Sinatra' (× *poluanglica*) (7)	NMen
	'Franzii' (× *paulinae*) (7)	NMen
	'Freckles'	GKev
	'Friar Tuck' (× *boydii*) (7)	NMen
	'Friesei' (× *salmonica*) (7)	EPot NMen
	×***fritschiana*** (8)	GEdr NMen
	'Fumiko' (*fortunei*) (5)	CLAP WAbe WCru
	'Funkii' (× *petraschii*) (7)	NMen
	'Gaertneri' (× *mariae-theresiae*) (7)	NMen
	'Gaiety' (15)	EAlp GKir LRHS SPoG WFar
	'Galahad' (× *elizabethae*) (7) **new**	NMen
	'Galaxie' (× *megaseiflora*) (7)	NDlv NMen
	'Ganymede' (*burseriana*) (7)	NMen
	'Gelber Findling' (7)	EPot LRHS
	'Gem' (× *irvingii*) (7)	NDlv NMen
	'General Joffre'	see *S.* 'Maréchal Joffre'
	'Geoff Wilson' (× *biasolettoi*)	NMen
	'George Gershwin' (Blues Group) (7) **new**	NMen
	georgei (7)	NMen WAbe
	'Gertie Pritchard' (× *megaseiflora*)	see *S.* 'Mrs Gertie Prichard'
	×***geuderi*** *sensu stricto* hort.	see *S.* 'Eulenspiegel'
§	×***geum*** (11)	CHid MLHP MRav WCor WFar WMoo
	- Dixter form (11)	ECha WFar WWEG
	'Gleborg' (15)	EWes SPoG
	'Gloria' (*burseriana*) (7) ♀^{H4}	LRHS NMen NSla SIng WCom WPat
	×***gloriana*** *sensu stricto* hort. (7)	see *S.* 'Godiva'
	'Gloriana'	see *S.* 'Godiva'
	'Gloriosa' (× *gloriana*) (7)	see *S.* 'Godiva'
§	'Godiva' (× *gloriana*) (7)	NMen
	'Goeblii' (7)	NDlv
	'Gold Dust' (× *eudoxiana*) (7)	ECho NLAp NMen NRya WCom
	'Golden Falls' (15/v)	EWes LRHS NHol SPlb SPoG
	Golden Prague (× *pragensis*)	see *S.* 'Zlatá Praha'
§	'Go-nishiki' (*fortunei*) (5)	EBee LLHF
	'Goring White' (7)	NMen
	'Gothenburg' (7)	LBMP NMen
	'Grace Farwell' (× *anglica*) (7)	ECho LRHS MBar NDlv NHol NMen NRya NWCA WCom WHoo
	'Grace' (× *arendsii*) (15/v)	see *S.* 'Seaspray'
	granulata (15)	CRWN EBWF ECho EDAr GJos NMir NSco WAbe WFar
	'Gratoides' (× *grata*) (7)	NMen
§	'Gregor Mendel' (× *apiculata*) (7) ♀^{H4}	CMea CSam ECho ECtt EPot LRHS NDlv NHol NLAp NMen SRms WAbe WCom WFar WHoo
	grisebachii	see *S. federici-augusti* subsp. *grisebachii*
	'Haagii' (× *eudoxiana*) (7)	CTri ECho GKev NDlv NLAp NMen
	'Harbinger' (7)	WGor
	'Hare Knoll Beauty' (8)	ECho GKev ITim LRHS NLAp NMen NRya WAbe
	'Harley' (7) **new**	NMen
	'Harlow Car' (7)	NMen NSla
	'Harold Lloyd' (7) **new**	NMen
	'Harry Marshall' (× *irvingii*) (7)	NDlv NHol NMen
	'Hartswood White' (15)	LRHS MWat
	'Harvest Moon' (*stolonifera*) (5)	CBow CHEx WHer
	'Hedwig' (× *malbyana*) (7)	NMen
	×***heinreichii*** *sensu stricto* hort.	see *S.* 'Ernst Heinrich'
	'Hi-Ace' (15/v)	ECtt EDAr LRHS MHer SPlb
	'Highdownensis' (*cotyledon*) (8)	NDlv
	'Hime' (*stolonifera*) (5)	WCru
	'Hindhead Seedling' (× *boydii*) (7)	LRHS NDlv NMen SIng
	hirsuta (11)	EBla EWTr EWld GGar IFro LRHS MMuc WCru
§	'Hirsuta' (*paniculata*) **new**	EPot
	'Hirsuta' (× *geum*)	see *S.* × ***geum***
	'Hirtella' misapplied	see *S.* 'Hirsuta'
	'Hirtella' Ingwersen (*paniculata*) (8)	EPot
	'Hirtifolia' (*paniculata*) **new**	GJos

Name	Suppliers
'His Majesty' (× *irvingii*) (7)	NMen WCom WFar
'Hiten' (*fortunei*) new	GKev
'Hocker Edge' (× *arco-valleyi*) (7)	ITim NDlv NMen
'Holden Seedling' (15)	ECtt EWes
'Honington' (× *poluanglica*) (7)	NMen
× ***hornibrookii*** (7)	WPat
hostii (8)	ECho EDAr LRHS MAsh NHol NLAp WTin
- subsp. ***hostii*** (8)	GAuc GEdr
- - var. ***altissima*** (8)	STre
- subsp. ***rhaetica*** (8)	EPot GBin NBro NDlv NMen
'Hradčany' (× *megaseiflora*) (7)	NMen
'Hsitou Silver' (*stolonifera*) (5)	CFee EBee EPPr MDKP WCru
'Hunscote' (× *poluanglica*) (7)	NMen
hybrid JB 11	NMen
§ ***hypnoides*** (15)	SPoG WAbe
hypostoma (7)	WAbe
'Iceland' (*oppositifolia*) (7)	EWes WAbe
'Icicle' (× *elisabethae*) (7)	NMen
'Idlecote' new	NMen
'Ignaz Dörfler' (× *doerfleri*) (7)	NMen WAbe
imparilis (5)	CLAP EHrv GEdr WCru
'Ingeborg' (15)	ECha LRHS SIng
iranica (7)	EPot NMen
- pink-flowered (7)	CPBP
'Irene Bacci' (× *baccii*) (7)	NMen
'Iris Prichard' (× *hardingii*) (7)	WAbe
× ***irvingii*** (7)	ECho NDlv
× ***irvingii*** *sensu stricto* hort.	see *S.* 'Walter Irving'
'Ivana' (× *caroliquarti*) (7)	NMen
'James Bremner' (15)	LRHS
'Jan Neruda' (× *megaseiflora*) (7)	NMen
'Jan Palach' (× *krausii*) (7)	NMen
'Jason' (× *elisabethae*) (7)	NMen
'Jenkinsiae' (× *irvingii*) (7) ♀H4	CFee ECho EDAr EPot LRHS NDlv NLAp NMen NRya SIng WAbe WCom WPat
§ 'Johann Kellerer' (× *kellereri*) (7)	CFee NDlv
'John Byam-Grounds' (Honor Group) (7) new	WAbe
'John Tomlinson' (*burseriana*) (7)	NMen
'Jorg' (× *biasolettoi*) (7)	EPot
'Josef Čapek' (× *megaseiflora*) (7)	NMen
'Josef Mánes' (× *borisii*) (7)	NMen
'Joy'	see *S.* 'Kaspar Maria Sternberg'
'Judith Shackleton' (× *abingdonensis*) (7)	NDlv NHol NMen WAbe
'Juliet'	see *S.* 'Riverslea'
§ ***juniperifolia*** (7)	CMea ECho ECtt EDAr GAbr LRHS NDlv NLAp NWCA SRms
'Jupiter' (× *megaseiflora*) (7)	LRHS NDlv NLAp NMen
'Kampa' (7)	NMen
karadzicensis (7)	NMen
'Karasin' (7)	NMen
'Karel Čapek' (× *megaseiflora*) (7)	EPot LRHS NDlv NMen NRya NSla
'Karel Stivín' (× *edithae*) (7)	NMen
'Karlštejn' (× *borisii*) (7)	NDlv
§ 'Kaspar Maria Sternberg' (× *petraschii*) (7)	LRHS NMen WPat
'Kath Dryden' (7)	ECho ECtt GKev NHol
'Kathleen Pinsent' (8) ♀H4	ECho NWCA WCom
'Kathleen' (× *polulacina*) (7)	NLAp WAbe WFar
× ***kellereri*** *sensu stricto* hort.	see *S.* 'Johann Kellerer'
'Ken McGregor' (7) new	WAbe
'Kestoniensis' (× *salmonica*) (7)	NMen
'Kew Gem' (× *petraschii*) (7)	ECho NMen
'Kewensis' (× *kellereri*) (7)	NDlv NMen
'Kineton' (× *poluanglica*) (7)	NMen
'King Lear' (× *bursiculata*) (7)	EPot LRHS NMen
'Kingscote White' (15)	SIng
'Kinki Purple' (*stolonifera*) (5)	EBee EHrv ELon EWld GGar WCru
'Knapton Pink' (15)	ECtt EDAr EPfP NPro NRya SIng SPoG WAbe WCom WFar
'Knapton White' (15)	SIng SPoG
'Knebworth' (8)	ECho
* 'Koigokora' (*fortunei*) (5)	WOld
'Kokaku' (fortunei)	LLHF
* 'Kosumosu' (*fortunei*) (5)	WOld
kotschyi × ***wendelboi*** new	EPot
§ 'Krain' (× *fritschiana*) (8)	ECho
'Krákatit' (× *megaseiflora*) (7)	NMen
'Krasava' (× *megaseiflora*) (7)	EPot NMen
'Kyrilli' (× *borisii*) (7)	NMen
'Labe' (× *arco-valleyi*) (7)	EPot LRHS NMen
'Ladislav Čelakovský' (7)	NMen
'Lady Beatrix Stanley'	see *S.* 'Beatrix Stanley'
'Lagraveana' (*paniculata*) (8) ♀H4	ECtt EDAr LRHS MMuc NDlv NRya WGor
× ***landaueri*** *sensu stricto* hort.	see *S.* 'Leonore'
'Latonica' (*callosa*) (8)	EPot
'Lemon Hybrid' (× *boydii*) (7)	NMen
'Lemon Spires' (7)	NMen
'Lenka' (× *byam-groundsii*) (7)	NMen NSla
'Leo Gordon Godseff' (× *elisabethae*) (7)	LRHS NDlv NMen
§ 'Leonore' (× *landaueri*) (7)	LRHS WFar
'Letchworth Gem' (× *urbium*) (11)	ECho GCal NWCA
'Lidice' (7)	NDlv NMen WHoo
'Lilac Time' (× *youngiana*) (7)	NMen WAbe
lilacina (7)	NMen WCom
'Lindau' (7)	NMen
lingulata	see *S. callosa*
'Lismore Carmine' (× *lismorensis*) (7)	NDlv NMen NWCA
'Lismore Gem' (× *lismorensis*) (7)	ECho NMen
'Lismore Mist' (× *lismorensis*) (7)	NMen
'Lismore Pink' (× *lismorensis*) (7)	NDlv NMen NWCA
* 'Little Piggy' (*epiphylla*) (5)	WCru
'Lohengrin' (× *hoerhammeri*) (7)	NMen
'Lohmuelleri' (× *biasolettoi*) (7)	GKev
'Long Acre Pink' (*fortunei*) (5)	CLAP
longifolia (8)	ECho EPot GKev NSla WGor
- hybrids new	GKev

	Name	Suppliers
	'Louis Armstrong' (Blues Group) (7)	EPot NMen WAbe
	Love Me	see *S.* 'Miluj Mne'
	lowndesii (7)	WAbe
	'Loxley' (*poluanglica*) (7)	GEdr NMen
	'Ludmila Šubrová' (× *bertolonii*) (7)	NMen
	'Lusanna' (× *irvingii*) (7)	GKev
	'Lutea' (*aizoon*)	see *S.* 'Lutea' (*paniculata*)
	'Lutea' (*diapensioides*)	see *S.* 'Primulina', 'Wilhelm Tell'
	'Lutea' (*marginata*)	see *S.* 'Faust'
§	'Lutea' (*paniculata*) (8) ΥH4	EAlp ECho EDAr EHoe EPot GEdr GMaP NBro NDlv NHol WFar
§	'Luteola' (× *boydii*) (7) ΥH4	NDlv WAbe
	'Lužnice' (× *poluluteopurpurea*) (7)	NMen
	lychnitis **new**	EBee GKev
	macedonica	see *S. juniperifolia*
	'Magdalena' (× *thomasiana*) (7)	NMen
	'Major' (*cochlearis*) (8) ΥH4	LRHS WGor
	'Major Lutea'	see *S.* 'Luteola'
	'Marc Chagall' (Decora Group) (7)	NMen WAbe
§	'Maréchal Joffre' (15)	GAbr IMon LAst NEgg WCom
	'Margarete' (× *borisii*) (7)	NMen
	marginata (7)	WAbe
	- var. ***balcanica***	see *S. marginata* subsp. *marginata* var. *rocheliana*
	- subsp. ***marginata*** var. ***boryi*** (7)	EPot LRHS NMen WAbe
	- - var. ***coriophylla*** (7)	EPot NMen NWCA WAbe
§	- - var. ***rocheliana*** (7)	LRHS NDlv NMen SAga
	'Maria Callas' (× *poluanglica*) (7)	WGor
	'Maria Luisa' (× *salmonica*) (7)	CFee NDlv NMen NWCA
	'Marianna' (× *borisii*) (7)	CMea NDlv NHol NMen NRya
	'Maroon Beauty' (*stolonifera*) (5)	EBee ECtt EPPr MDKP NBre WCot
	'Mars' (× *elisabethae*) (7)	NMen
	'Marshal Joffre'	see *S.* 'Maréchal Joffre' (15)
	'Marsilio Ficino' (Milford Group) (7) **new**	NMen
§	'Martha' (× *semmleri*) (7)	NMen
	'Mary Golds' (Swing Group) (7)	EDAr WGor
	matta-florida (7)	NMen
	'May Queen' (7)	NMen
	× ***megaseiflora*** *sensu stricto* hort.	see *S.* 'Robin Hood'
	'Melrose' (× *salmonica*) (7)	NMen
	mertensiana (6)	GEdr NBir WCru
	'Meteor' (7)	NDlv NRya
	micranthidifolia (4)	CLAP EBee WPGP
	'Millstream' (8)	NWCA
	'Millstream Cream' (× *elisabethae*) (7)	ECho NMen
§	'Miluj Mne' (× *poluanglica*) (7)	ECho NDlv NHol NMen
	'Minor' (*cochlearis*) (8) ΥH4	LRHS MAsh NHol NMen NWCA SIng WGor WPat
	'Mirko Webr' (Harmonia Group) (7) **new**	NMen
§	'Miss Chambers' (× *urbium*) (11)	WCot WMoo WPen WSHC
	'Mona Lisa' (× *borisii*) (7)	NMen WAbe
	'Monarch' (8) ΥH4	MAsh WAbe
	'Moonlight' (× *boydii*)	see *S.* 'Sulphurea'
	'Morava' (7)	NMen
	Mossy Group (15) **new**	LRHS
*	'Mossy Pink'	NBlu SPoG
	'Mossy Red'	LRHS SPoG
	'Mossy Triumph'	see *S.* 'Triumph'
	'Mossy White' **new**	LRHS
	'Mother of Pearl' (× *irvingii*) (7)	ECho NDlv NLAp NMen
	'Mother Queen' (× *irvingii*) (7)	NLAp NMen WPat
	'Mount Hood' (*fortunei*) **new**	LRHS
	'Mount Nachi' (*fortunei*) (5)	CBct CDes EBee EBrs EPfP EWes GAbr GEdr GMaP IBal LFur LOck LRHS MLHP NBhm NBro NMen NMyG SPoG SUsu WAbe WClo WCot WFar WPGP WPer WSpi WWEG
§	'Mrs Gertie Prichard' (× *megaseiflora*) (7)	NMen
	'Mrs Helen Terry' (× *salmonica*) (7)	EPot LRHS NDlv NMen
	'Mrs Leng' (× *elisabethae*) (7)	MDKP NMen
	mutata	EPot
	subsp. ***demissa*** **new**	
	'Myra Cambria' (× *anglica*) (7)	NDlv NHol NMen
	'Myra' (× *anglica*) (7)	ECho LRHS NHol NMen NWCA WHoo WPat
	'Myriad' (7)	EPot NMen
	'Nancye' (× *goringiana*) (7)	NDlv NMen WAbe
§	***nelsoniana*** (4)	NHol
	'Nimbus' (*iranica*) (7)	NMen
	'Niobe' (× *pulvilacina*) (7)	NMen
	'Notata' (*paniculata*) (8)	NLAp
	'Nottingham Gold' (× *boydii*) (7)	EPot NHol NMen
	'Obristii' (× *salmonica*) (7)	NDlv NMen NRya
§	***obtusa*** (7)	EPot MHer NMen
	'Ochroleuca' (× *elisabethae*) (7)	NMen
	'Odysseus' (*sancta*) (7)	NMen
	'Olymp' (*scardica*) (7)	NMen
	'Opalescent' (7)	NMen
§	'Ophelia' (× *arco-valleyi*) (7)	NMen
	oppositifolia (7)	ECho EPot GKir MWat NLAp NSla SPlb SRms WAbe WCom WFar
I	- 'Holden Variety'	NHol
	- subsp. ***oppositifolia*** var. ***latina*** (7)	ECho NLAp
	'Oriole' (× *boydii*) (7)	NMen
	'Orjen' (*paniculata* var. *orientalis*) (8)	GEdr
	'Ottone Rosai' (Toscana Group) (7)	NMen
	'Oxhill' (7)	NMen
§	***paniculata*** (8)	ECho EDAr EHoe GGar GKev GMaP MDKP MWat NDlv NLAp NSla SPlb SRms WAbe WFar WHoo
§	- subsp. ***cartilaginea*** (8)	GKev NHol WAbe
	- subsp. ***kolenatiana***	see *S. paniculata* subsp. *cartilaginea*
§	- var. ***minutifolia*** (8)	CPBP CTri ECho LRHS MBar MSCN MWat NBro NDlv NHol NLAp NMen NRya NWCA SPlb WAbe
	paradoxa (15)	EPot GEdr LRHS NHol WGor
	'Parcevalis' (× *finnisiae*) (7×9)	WAbe
	'Parsee' (× *margoxiana*) (7)	EPot NDlv NMen
	'Paula' (× *paulinae*) (7)	NMen
	'Peach Blossom' (7)	NDlv NMen NRya
	'Peach Melba' (7)	EAlp EPot NMen WAbe WFar
*	'Peachy Head'	NMen WAbe
	'Pearly Gates' (× *irvingii*) (7)	NDlv NMen
	'Pearly Gold' (15)	NRya WFar

	Name	Suppliers
	'Pearly King' (15)	GMaP LRHS WAbe WFar
	× ***pectinata*** Schott, Nyman & Kotschy	see *S.* 'Krain'
	'Penelope' (× *boydilacina*) (7)	CMea ECho EPot LRHS NMen WCom WHoo WPat
	pensylvanica (4)	GCal GCra IMou
	'Perikles' (7)	NMen
	'Peter Burrow' (× *poluanglica*) (7) ♀H4	CPBP ECho NMen
	'Peter Pan' (15)	EAlp EDAr EPfP GJos GMaP MHer NHol NMen NPro NRya SIng SPoG WFar WPat WPnn
	'Petra' (7)	EPot NMen WFar
§	'Phoenix' (× *biasolettoi*) (7)	LRHS WThu
	'Pilatus' (× *boydii*) (7)	NMen
	'Pink Cloud' (*fortunei*) (5)	CLAP WAbe WFar
	'Pink Haze' (*fortunei*) (5)	CLAP WAbe
	'Pink Mist' (*fortunei*) (5)	CLAP WAbe WFar
	'Pink Pagoda' (*nipponica*) (5)	CDes CLAP EBee GEdr WCot WCru WPGP
	'Pink Pearl' (7)	CMea NMen
	'Pixie' (15)	CTri ECtt LRHS NHol NMen SIng SPoG SRms
	'Pixie Alba'	see *S.* 'White Pixie'
	'Plena' (*granulata*)	see *S.* 'Flore Pleno'
	'Pollux' (× *boydii*) (7)	EPot NMen
	poluniniana (7)	WAbe
	poluniniana × 'Winifred' (× *poluanglica*) (7)	ECho
	'Pompadour' (15)	LRHS NPro
	'Popelka' (subsp. *marginata* var. *rocheliana*) (7)	LRHS NMen
	porophylla (7)	NMen
	- aff. var. ***thessalica***	see *S. sempervivum* f. *stenophylla*
	aff. ***porophylla*** (7)	NWCA
	'Precious Piggy' (*epiphylla*) (5)	WCru
	'Primrose Bee' (× *apiculata*) (7)	EPot ITim
	'Primrose Dame' (× *elisabethae*) (7)	ECho ITim MDKP NMen WAbe WCom
	'Primulaize' (9×11)	MHer MWat NMen
	'Primulaize Salmon' (9×11)	NDlv NHol WCom WHoo WPer
§	'Primulina' (× *malbyana*) (7)	NMen
	primuloides	see *S.* 'Primuloides'
§	'Primuloides' (*umbrosa*) (11) ♀H4	ECho EDAr GKir MMuc NMen SPoG SRms SWvt WFar
	'Prince Hal' (*burseriana*) (7)	ECho EDAr EPot LRHS NDlv NMen WCom
	'Princess' (*burseriana*) (7)	EDAr LRHS NMen WCom
	'Probynii' (*cochlearis*) (8)	EPot MWat NDlv NMen WAbe
	'Prospero' (× *petraschii*) (7)	NMen
	× ***prossenii*** *sensu stricto* hort.	see *S.* 'Regina'
	× ***proximae*** 'Květy Coventry' (7) **new**	EPot
	- 'Slzy Coventry'	EPot WAbe
	× ***pseudokotschyi*** *sensu stricto* hort.	see *S.* 'Denisa'
	'Pseudoscardica' (× *wehrhahnii*) (7)	NMen
	'Pseudo-valdensis' (*cochlearis*) (8)	WAbe
	pubescens (15)	LRHS WAbe
	- subsp. ***iratiana*** (15)	CPBP NLAp
	punctata Sternbo. (4)	see *S. nelsoniana*
*	***punctissima***	NHol
	'Pungens' (× *apiculata*) (7)	EPot NDlv NMen
	'Purple Piggy' (*epiphylla*) (5)	CFee CLAP WCru
	'Purpurea' (*fortunei*)	see *S.* 'Rubrifolia'
§	'Pygmalion' (× *webrii*) (7)	WGor
	'Pyramidalis' (*cotyledon*) (8)	EPfP EWTr SRms
	'Pyrenaica' (*oppositifolia*) (7)	ECho NMen
	'Quarry Wood' (× *anglica*) (7)	EPot NHol NMen
	'Radvan Horný' (× *cullinanii*) **new**	WAbe
	'Rainsley Seedling' (8)	EPot GKev ITim NBro NMen
	ramulosa (7)	NMen
	'Red Poll' (× *poluanglica*) (7)	ITim NDlv NMen NRya NWCA
*	'Regent'	WAbe
§	'Regina' (× *prossenii*) (7)	MHer NMen
	retusa (7)	NMen WAbe
	'Rex' (*paniculata*) (8)	NHol
§	'Riverslea' (× *hornibrookii*) (7)	LRHS NMen WAbe
§	'Robin Hood' (× *megaseiflora*) (7)	CFee CPBP LRHS NMen WHoo WPat
	'Rokujō' (*fortunei*) (5)	CLAP EBee NLar NPro WFar
	'Romeo' (× *hornibrookii*) (7)	NMen
	'Rosa Tubbs'	GKev
	rosacea (15)	EDAr
	'Rosea' (*cortusifolia*) (5)	CLAP
§	'Rosea' (*paniculata*) (8) ♀H4	GMaP LBMP LBee NBro NDlv NHol NSla SRms WFar
	'Rosea' (× *stuartii*) (7)	NDlv NMen
	'Rosemarie' (7)	ECho NMen
	'Rosenzwerg' (15)	WFar
	'Rosina Sündermann' (× *rosinae*) (7)	EPot NDlv NMen
	rotundifolia (12)	EBee GMaP MDKP NHol
	- subsp. ***chrysospleniifolia*** var. ***rhodopea*** (12)	WCru
	'Roy Clutterbuck' (7)	NMen
	'Rubella' (× *irvingii*) (7)	EPot
	'Rubra' (*aizoon*)	see *S.* 'Rosea' (*paniculata*)
§	'Rubrifolia' (*fortunei*) (5)	CLAP CSpe EBee ECha ECtt EHoe GAbr GEdr IBal LAst LOck LRHS MBri NMen NMyG SAga SGSe SMad SPet SWvt WAbe WBor WClo WCot WCru WFar WWEG
*	'Ruby Red'	NPro
*	'Ruby Wedding' (*cortusifolia*) (5)	CLAP WCru WFar
	rufescens (5)	EHrv GEdr
	- BWJ 7510	WCru
	- BWJ 7684	WCru
	'Rusalka' (× *borisii*) (7)	NMen
	'Russell Vincent Prichard' (× *irvingii*) (7)	NMen
	'Ruth Draper' (*oppositifolia*) (7)	WAbe WFar
	'Ruth McConnell' (15)	CMea LRHS WCom
	'Saint John's' (8)	EBur ECho GEdr
	'Saint Kilda' (*oppositifolia*) (7)	ITim
	× ***salmonica*** *sensu stricto* hort.	see *S.* 'Salomonii'
§	'Salomonii' (× *salmonica*) (7)	NDlv NMen SRms
	'Samo' (× *bertolonii*) (7)	NMen
	sancta (7)	ECho EPot LRHS NMen SRms WAbe
	- subsp. ***pseudosancta*** (7)	see *S. juniperifolia*
	- - var. ***macedonica***	see *S. juniperifolia*
	'Sandpiper' (7)	NMen
	'Sanguinea Superba' (× *arendsii*) (15) ♀H4	SIng
	'Sara Sinclair' (× *arco-valleyi*) (7)	CMea

	Name	Suppliers
	'Šárka' (7)	NMen
	sarmentosa	see *S. stolonifera*
	'Sartorii'	see *S.* 'Pygmalion'
	'Saturn' (× *megaseiflora*) (7)	NMen WFar
	'Sázava' (× *poluluteopurpurea*) (7)	NMen
	scardica (7)	NBro NMen WAbe
	- var. ***dalmatica***	see *S. obtusa*
§	'Schelleri' (× *petraschii*) (7)	NMen
	'Schneeteppich' (15)	WCom
§	'Schwefelblüte' (15)	GMaP LRHS NPri NWCA SPoG WCom WPat
	scleropoda (7)	EPot NMen
§	'Seaspray' (× *arendsii*) (15/v)	EWes
	'Seissera' (*burseriana*) (7)	EPot NMen
	'Semafor' (× *megaseiflora*) (7)	NMen
	× ***semmleri*** *sensu stricto* hort.	see *S.* 'Martha'
	sempervivum (7)	NGdn NMen NWCA WAbe WTin
§	- f. ***stenophylla*** (7)	ECho MHer
	sendaica (5)	CLAP WCru
	- B&SWJ 7448	GEdr
	'Sergio Bacci' (7) **new**	NMen
	'Sherlock Holmes' (7) **new**	WAbe
§	'Silver Cushion' (15/v)	CMea CTri EDAr ELan GGar GKir LAst LRHS MBar NEgg NPri NPro SBch SPer SPlb SPoG WAbe WFar
	'Silver Edge' (× *arco-valleyi*) (7)	NMen
	'Silver Maid' (× *engleri*)	GEdr NMen
	'Silver Mound'	see *S.* 'Silver Cushion'
	'Silver Velvet' (*fortunei*) (5)	CLAP CMil EBee ECtt GAbr GEdr LOck LRHS NMyG SMad WCot
	'Sir Douglas Haig' (15)	SIng
	'Sissi' (7)	CPBP
	'Slack's Ruby Southside' (Southside Seedling Group) ♀H4	MDKP NLAp NSla WFar
	'Snowcap' (*pubescens*) (15)	EPot WAbe
	'Snowdon' (*burseriana*) (7)	NMen
	'Snowflake' (Silver Farreri Group) (8) ♀H4	NDlv WAbe
§	'Sofia' (× *borisii*) (7)	EPot NMen WFar
	'Sorrento' (*marginata*) (7)	NMen
	Southside Seedling Group ♀H4	CMea ECho EDAr EPfP GAbr GEdr GGar GKir GMaP LHop LRHS MAsh MBar MHer MMuc NBro NHol NMen NRya NWCA SIng SPer SPet SPoG SRms WCom WCot WHoo WPat WTin
	- 'Southside Star' ♀H4	WAbe WFar
	'Spartakus' (× *apiculata*) (7)	NDlv
	spathularis (11)	CEnt EBee WCom WCot WEas
	'Speciosa' (*burseriana*) (7)	NDlv
	'Splendens' (*oppositifolia*) (7) ♀H4	ECho EPfP NDlv NHol NLAp NWCA SRms WAbe WPat
	'Spotted Dog'	see *S.* 'Canis-dalmatica'
	'Sprite' (15)	SPoG
	spruneri (7)	LRHS NMen WAbe WCom
	- var. ***deorum*** (7)	NMen
	'Stansfieldii' (*rosacea*) (15)	EAlp LRHS NMen SPlb SPoG WFar
	'Star Dust' (7) **new**	EPot
	stenophylla subsp. ***stenophylla***	see *S. flagellaris*
	stolitzkae (7)	NMen WAbe
§	***stolonifera*** (5) ♀H2	CArn CCVN CEnt CHEx CSpe ECho EShb EWTr GBin LDai NBro SDix SWvt WFar WMoo WPnn
	stribrnyi (7)	NMen WAbe
	- JCA 861-400	NWCA
	'Sturmiana' (*paniculata*) (8)	NMen SRms
	'Sue Drew' (*fortunei*)	LLHF
	'Suendermannii Major' (× *kellereri*) (7)	LRHS NRya
	'Suendermannii' (× *kellereri*) (7)	LRHS NDlv
	'Sugar Plum Fairy' (*fortunei*) (5)	EBee EHrv EShb LFur LOck LRHS WCot
§	'Sulphurea' (× *boydii*) (7)	LRHS NMen SIng WCom WPat
	'Sunset' (*anglica*) (7)	WAbe
	'Swan' (× *fallsvillagensis*) (7)	NMen
	'Sylva' (× *elisabethae*) (7)	NMen
	'Tábor' (× *schottii*) (7)	NMen
	'Tamayura' (*fortunei*) (5)	CLAP
	'Teide' (Swirly Group) (7) **new**	NMen
	'Tenerife' (Swirly Group) (7) **new**	NMen
	'Theoden' (*oppositifolia*) (7) ♀H4	ECho EWes NLAp NWCA WAbe
	'Theresia' (× *mariae-theresiae*) (7)	NDlv NMen
	'Thorpei' (× *gusmusii*) (7)	NMen
	'Timmy Foster' (× *irvingii*) (7)	NHol NMen
	tombeanensis (7)	NMen
	'Tricolor' (*stolonifera*) (5) ♀H2	CBow CHEx EBak LRHS
	trifurcata (15)	GGar
	'Tristan' (*stribrnyi*)	GKev
§	'Triumph' (× *arendsii*) (15)	ECtt EPfP GMaP LRHS NEgg NPri SPoG WBVN
	'Tully' (× *elisabethae*) (7)	NLAp WGor WPat
	'Tumbling Waters' (8) ♀H4	ECho EPot GAbr LHop LRHS NHol NMen NSla SIng WAbe WFar WGor WPat
§	'Tvoje Píseň' (× *poluanglica*) (7)	ECho NDlv NMen
§	'Tvůj Den' (× *poluanglica*) (7)	ECho NDlv NMen WAbe
§	'Tvůj Polibek' (× *poluanglica*) (7)	ECho MDKP NDlv NMen
§	'Tvůj Přítel' (× *poluanglica*) (7)	ECho NDlv
§	'Tvůj Úsměv' (× *poluanglica*) (7)	ECho NDlv NMen
§	'Tvůj Úspěch' (× *poluanglica*) (7)	ECho NDlv NHol NMen WAbe
	'Tycho Brahe' (× *doerfleri*) (7)	NDlv NMen WAbe
	'Tysoe' (7)	NMen
	umbrosa (11)	CMac CTri EBee ECGP ECho EDAr GKir LAst LEdu LRHS MMuc MRav SBch SPlb SPoG SRms SWvt WCAu WFar WMoo
*	- ***subintenger***	EBee
	'Unique'	see *S.* 'Bodensee'
	× ***urbium*** (11) ♀H4	CHEx CTri EBee ECho ELan EPfP EWTr GMaP LAst LEdu LRHS NSti SBch SIng SPer SRms WBrk WCor WFar WPer WWEG
	'Vaccariana' (*oppositifolia*) (7)	ECho
	'Václav Hollar' (× *gusmusii*) (7)	NMen
	'Vahlii' (× *smithii*) (7)	NMen
	'Valborg'	see *S.* 'Cranbourne'
	'Valentine'	see *S.* 'Cranbourne'
	'Valerie Finnis'	see *S.* 'Aretiastrum'
	'Valerie Keevil' (× *anglica*) (7)	NMen
	vandellii (7)	EPot

I 'Variegata' (*cuneifolia*) (11/v) — ECho ECtt EPfP GGar LRHS MBar NBlu NHol NVic SPet SPlb SPoG WFar WMoo WPer
'Variegata' (*umbrosa*) — see *S.* 'Aureopunctata'
I 'Variegata' (× *urbium*) (11/v) — EBee ECho EPfP GGar LAst LRHS NLar SRms WEas WFar WWEG
'Večerní Hvězda' **new** — WAbe
veitchiana (5) — EBee GEdr NBro
'Vesna' (× *borisii*) (7) — NMen
'Vincent van Gogh' (× *borisii*) (7) — NMen
'Vladana' (× *megaseiflora*) (7) — EPot LRHS NMen SIng
'Vlasta' (7) — NMen
'Vlasta Burian' (7) **new** — WAbe
'Vltava' (7) — NMen
'Volgeri' (× *hofmannii*) (7) — NMen
'Vreny' (8) — GKev
'Vysoké Mýto' (7) **new** — WAbe
'Wada' (*fortunei*) (5) — CAbP CLAP CSam EAEE EBee ECtt EWTr GBuc GEdr LAst LFur LRHS MCot NBir NMyG SGSe SPer SPoG WBor WCot WFar WOld WPGP WWEG
'Wallacei' (15) — NMen
'Walpole's Variety' (8) — WPer
'Walter Ingwersen' (*umbrosa*) (11) — SIng SRms
§ 'Walter Irving' (× *irvingii*) (7) — EPot NHol NMen
'Wartosque' (*callosa*) (8) — EPot
'Welsh Dragon' (15) — WAbe
'Welsh Red' (15) — WAbe WFar
'Welsh Rose' (15) — WAbe
wendelboi (7) — EPot NMen
'Wendrush' (× *wendelacina*) (7) — NMen
'Wendy' (× *wendelacina*) (7) — NMen
'Wheatley Gem' (7) — NMen
'Wheatley Lion' (× *borisii*) (7) — NMen
'Wheatley Rose' (7) — LRHS
'White Alice' **new** — NBlu
'White Cap' (× *boydii*) (7) — NMen
'White Craggs' — NHol
'White Imp' (7) — NMen
§ 'White Pixie' (15) — EAlp ECtt EDAr EPfP GMaP LRHS MHer NHol NPri NPro NRya SIng SPlb SPoG SRms WFar
'White Star' (× *petraschii*) — see *S.* 'Schelleri'
'Whitehill' (8) ♡H4 — CMea EAlp ECho ECtt ELan GEdr GJos GKir GMaP ITim LBee LRHS MDKP NBro NHol NMen SPet WCom WFar WHoo WPat WPer WTin
§ 'Wilhelm Tell' (× *malbyana*) (7) — NMen
'William Boyd' (× *boydii*) (7) — NSla
'William Shakespeare' (Blues Group) (7) **new** — WAbe
'Winifred Bevington' (8×11) ♡H4 — ECho EDAr LHop LRHS MMuc NBro NDlv NHol NLAp NMen NRya SAga SMad WAbe WCom WFar WHoo WPer WPnn
'Winifred' (× *anglica*) (7) — ECho EPot NLAp NMen
'Winston Churchill' (15) — CElw CTri EPfP LRHS NHol SIng
I 'Winston Churchill Variegata' — LRHS NHol
'Winton' (× *paulinae*) (7) — NMen
'Wisley' (*federici-augusti* subsp. *grisebachii*) (7) ♡H2-3 — EPot NLAp NMen WPat
'Woodside Ross' (15) — ECtt
'Yellow Rock' (7) — NDlv NMen NRya
Your Day — see *S.* 'Tvůj Den'
Your Friend — see *S.* 'Tvůj Přítel'
Your Good Fortune — see *S.* 'Tvůj Úspěch'
Your Kiss — see *S.* 'Tvůj Polibek'
Your Smile — see *S.* 'Tvůj Úsměv'
Your Song — see *S.* 'Tvoje Píseň'
Your Success — see *S.* 'Tvůj Úspěch'
'Yuinagi' (*fortunei*) (5) — WOld
× ***zimmeteri*** (8×11) — ECho NMen
§ 'Zlatá Praha' (× *pragensis*) (7) — NDlv NMen NRya WAbe
'Zlin' (× *leyboldii*) (7) — NMen

Scabiosa (Dipsacaceae)

africana — CElw EWes LSou SHar
alpina L. — see *Cephalaria alpina*
argentea — EBee EWes LEdu SUsu WPGP
atropurpurea — CEnt EGoo LEdu SPav
- 'Ace of Spades' — CSpe CWCL EBee LRHS SMad SPav WPGP WSpi
- 'Beaujolais Bonnets' **new** — LAst SPer
§ - 'Chile Black' — Widely available
§ - 'Chilli Pepper' — CWCL EPfP LHop LRHS MGos NLar NPri SPoG SRGP WSpi
§ - 'Chilli Sauce' — CWCL EPfP LHop LRHS MGos NLar NPri SPoG
- dark-flowered — SPav
- 'Derry's Black' **new** — CSpe
- 'Nona' — LLHF
- 'Peter Ray' — CElw ECtt SPav WWlt
- 'Salmon Queen' — LRHS
- 'Summer Sundae' **new** — LRHS
banatica — see *S. columbaria*
'Blue Diamonds' — CKno LRHS WHil WSpi
Burgundy Bonnets = 'Scabon'PBR — EBee EGxp ILad LRHS LSou SPoG
§ 'Butterfly Blue' — CMHG EBee ECtt EPfP LBMP LRHS LSRN MBri NBPC NLar NMoo SCoo SMrm SPer SPoG SWvt WAul WCAu WCot WFar WWEG
caucasica — CMac EPfP GKev GKir LAst LEdu LRHS NBlu SPhx WFar WHoo
- var. ***alba*** — CBcs CBot CKno EBee EHrv EPfP GKir WFar WHal WHoo
- 'Blausiegel' — CSam EBee ECtt LAst LBMP MRav NBre NCob NGdn SPet WFar
- 'Bressingham White' — LRHS
- 'Clive Greaves' ♡H4 — CHar CTri EBee ECha ECtt EHrv ELan EPfP GKir LRHS MBri MRav NCob SPer SRms SWvt WCAu WCom WEas WFar WHlf WWEG
- 'Deep Waters' — CSpe EBee NBre NCGa SPad WPtf
- 'Fama' — CSpe CWib EShb LRHS NBir NLar SMrm SPlb SPoG SRms WFar WPtf WWEG
- 'Goldingensis' — GJos MHer NBre NGdn NPri WPer
- House's hybrids — CSBt GJos NGdn SRms
- 'Isaac House' — LRHS NLar SPoG
- 'Kompliment' — MWhi NBre NLar SMrm WWEG
- 'Lavender Blue' — NBPC WFar
- 'Miss Willmott' ♡H4 — CMMP CSam EBee ECha ECtt ELan EPfP EShb LBMP LHop LRHS MBri MHer MLHP MRav NCob SWvt WCAu WFar WMnd
- 'Moerheim Blue' — EBee

- Perfecta Series	CSpe CWib LRHS MMHG NGdn NLar SMrm SPoG SWat WBor
- - 'Perfecta Alba'	COIW CSpe CWib EBee ECtt GJos GKir GMaP GMac LAst LRHS MWat NChi NLar NOrc NPri SHGN SMrm SPad SPer SPoG STes SWat WPtf WWEG
- - 'Perfecta Lilac Blue'	CWib EPfP GMaP GMac SPer STes WWEG
- 'Stäfa'	CKno CMMP EBee ECha EShb EWTr LBMP LRHS MRav NEgg NLar SUsu WFar WHrl WMnd
'Chile Black'	see *S. atropurpurea* 'Chile Black'
'Chile Pepper'	see *S. atropurpurea* 'Chilli Pepper'
'Chile Sauce'	see *S. atropurpurea* 'Chilli Sauce'
'Chile Spice'	WHlf
cinerea	SPhx
§ ***columbaria***	EBWF EBee ECGP LRHS MBel MMuc MPet NBre NEgg NLan NMir NSco NWCA SECG SMrm SWal WHer WJek WSFF
- blue-flowered **new**	LRHS
- 'Flower Power'	EBee EWll
- 'Misty Butterflies'	COIW ECGP EDAr EPfP EShb GKev LHop LSou NEgg NGdn NLar NMoo SBch SPad STes WBor WBrE WFar WWEG
- 'Nana'	CMdw CMea EBee EGoo EShb GEdr LRHS NBir NGdn NLar NMen NPri SBch WCFE WFar WGwG WHil WHrl
§ - subsp. ***ochroleuca***	CBot CKno CSpe ECha EGoo EHrv EShb GCal LEdu LLWP LPio LRHS MBel MCot MRav MSpe NBir NLar NPri SGSe SMad SPhx SPoG SRms WCAu WCom WFar WHoo WPGP WTin
- - MESE 344	EBee
- - 'Moon Dance'	CMea CSam EBee EDAr EPPr EShb EWTr GCal GMac LBMP LLHF MNFA SBch
- 'Pincushion Pink'	NGdn NPri SGSe WFar WHil WWEG
cretica	CSpe
drakensbergensis	EBee EKen EWes SBch SGSe SPav WHrl
farinosa	CBot CDes ECtt LEdu LSou SAga SGar WFar WPer
gigantea	see *Cephalaria gigantea*
graminifolia	EBrs ECho EGoo GBuc GKev LRHS MDKP NBir NMen NWCA SBch SRms WHrl
- JM 990	EBee
- ***rosea***	EWes
'Helen Dillon'	EBee ECtt EWes LSou WWEG
incisa 'Pink Cheer'	LRHS
'Irish Perpetual Flowering'	EBee ECtt WCot WWEG
japonica	WPer
- var. ***acutiloba***	SPhx
- var. ***alpina***	CEnt CPrp EBee GBuc IBal NGdn NHol SBch SHGN SPet SPhx WAbe WHoo WTin
- - 'Blue Star' **new**	NBre NCGa
lachnophylla	GCal
'Little Emily'	ELon SUsu
lucida	EAEE EBee ECho ECtt EPfP EShb LRHS MRav NPri WCAu WHrl WPGP WPer
'Midnight'	CMea CSpe
'Miss Havisham'	EBee ECtt EWes LEdu LSou WPGP
'Monita Pink'	CMoH
montana (Bieb.) DC.	see *Knautia tatarica*
montana Mill.	see *Knautia arvensis*
ochroleuca	see *S. columbaria* subsp. *ochroleuca*
parnassi	see *Pterocephalus perennis*
'Peggotty'	ECtt
'Perpetual Flowering'	see *S.* 'Butterfly Blue'
Pink Buttons = 'Walminipink'	CFir EBee LRHS
'Pink Mist' PBR	CPrp EBee ECtt EPfP EWll LRHS MBri NBir NLar SCoo SMrm SPer SPoG SRms WCAu
pterocephala	see *Pterocephalus perennis*
rhodopensis	EBee
'Rosie's Pink'	ECtt
rumelica	see *Knautia macedonica*
'Satchmo'	see *S. atropurpurea* 'Chile Black'
speciosa 'Maharajah' **new**	NBre NCGa SPad
succisa	see *Succisa pratensis*
tatarica	see *Cephalaria gigantea*
tenuis	CSpe LPio SPhx
triandra	CSpe EBee LHop
ucranica	EShb

Scadoxus ✿ (*Amaryllidaceae*)

multiflorus	CPne EBrs LAma LRHS MBri WCot
§ - subsp. ***katherinae*** ♀H1	CPne ECho
§ - subsp. ***multiflorus*** ♀H1 **new**	LRHS
natalensis	see *S. puniceus*
§ ***puniceus***	CLak

Scaevola (*Goodeniaceae*)

aemula 'Blue Fan' PBR	see *S. aemula* 'Blue Wonder'
§ - 'Blue Wonder' PBR	NPer SWvt
- New Wonder = 'Newon' PBR	LAst
- 'White Fan'	LAst
- 'Zig Zag' PBR	CCCN LAst LSou
Blauer Facher = 'Saphira' PBR	CCCN LHop LRHS SMrm
'Brillant' PBR	LSou
crassifolia	SPlb
'Diamond'	LAst LSou
'Mini Blue'	CCCN
'Topaz Pink' **new**	LAst LSou

Schefflera (*Araliaceae*)

actinophylla ♀H1	SRms
alpina B&SWJ 8247	WCru
- HWJ 585	WCru
- HWJ 936	WCru
arboricola ♀H1	CHEx SEND XBlo
- 'Compacta'	MBri
- 'Gold Capella' ♀H1	MBri SEND XBlo
- 'Kalahari'	XBlo
- 'Trinetta'	MBri
brevipedicellata HWJ 870	WCru
chapana HWJ 983	WCru
delavayi	CHEx GLin
digitata	CTrC
elegantissima ♀H1	EShb
enneaphylla HWJ 1018	WCru
fantsipanensis B&SWJ 8228	WCru
gracilis HWJ 622	WCru
kornasii HWJ 918	WCru
lenticellata B&SWJ 9762 **new**	WCru
macrophylla B&SWJ 8210	WCru
- B&SWJ 9788	WCru
microphylla B&SWJ 3872	WCru
rhododendrifolia	CHEx
- GWJ 9375	WCru
taiwaniana	CHEx
- B&SWJ 3575	WCru

- B&SWJ 7096 WCru
- RWJ 10000 WCru
- RWJ 10016 WCru

Schima (*Theaceae*)

wallichii CBcs
subsp. ***liukiuensis***
- subsp. ***noronhae*** CCCN EPfP
var. ***superba***
- subsp. ***wallichii*** ISea
var. ***khasiana***

Schinus (*Anacardiaceae*)

molle CArn IDee
polygamus CBcs

Schisandra (*Schisandraceae*)

TH CHEx
arisanensis B&SWJ 3050 WCru
aff. ***bicolor*** BWJ 8151 WCru
chinensis CAgr CArn CBcs EBrs GPoy MSwo WBVN
- B&SWJ 4204 WCru
- SDR 3980 GKev
grandiflora CDoC EBee ELan EPfP LRHS MBlu NLar SCoo WGwG
- B&SWJ 2245 WCru
- var. ***cathayensis*** see *S. sphaerandra*
- 'Jamu' (m) WCru
- 'Lahlu' (f) WCru
grandiflora × ***rubriflora*** WCru
henryi subsp. ***yunnanensis*** B&SWJ 6546 WCru
aff. ***neglecta*** BWJ 7739 WCru
nigra see *S. repanda*
propinqua subsp. ***sinensis*** CBcs CBot CMac CSPN LEdu MBlu NLar WSHC
- - BWJ 8148 WCru
repanda B&SWJ 5897 WCru
rubriflora CHEx CSPN CTri CWSG EPfP GKir IFFs LRHS MBlu MGos SSpi WSpi
- (f) CBcs ELan EMil MGos WSHC
- (m) NHol
- BWJ 7557 WCru
§ ***sphaerandra*** BWJ 7898 WCru
sphenanthera ELan IMGH LRHS NLar WSHC
verrucosa see *Kadsura verrucosa*

Schivereckia (*Brassicaceae*)

doerfleri MWat

Schizachyrium (*Poaceae*)

§ ***scoparium*** CKno CSpe EBee ECGP EHoe EPPr EPau GCal IFoB LBMP LRHS MWhi NSti SGSe SMrm SUsu WCot
- 'Cairo' EBee
- 'Prairie Blues' **new** EPPr GQue

Schizanthus (*Solanaceae*)

porrigens CSpe

Schizocodon see *Shortia*

Schizopetalon (*Brassicaceae*)

walkeri CSpe

Schizophragma (*Hydrangeaceae*)

corylifolium CBcs NLar
hydrangeoides CBcs CDoC CDul EBee ELan EPfP EWTr GKir LRHS MBlu MGos NPal NPri SLim SLon SPer SPoG SSpi SSta SWvt WDin
- B&SWJ 5489 WCru
- B&SWJ 5732 WCru
- B&SWJ 5954 WCru
- B&SWJ 6119 from Yakushima, Japan WCru
- B&SWJ 8505 from Korea WCru
- B&SWJ 8522 from Ulleungdo, Korea WCru
- from Korea MBri
- 'Brookside Littleleaf' see *Hydrangea anomala* subsp. *petiolaris* var. *cordifolia* 'Brookside Littleleaf'
- 'Iwa Garami' EBee MBri NLar
- 'Moonlight' Widely available
* - f. ***quelpartensis*** B&SWJ 1160 WCru
- - B&SWJ 8771 WCru
- 'Roseum' ♀H4 Widely available
integrifolium ♀H4 CBcs CMac EBee ELan EPfP EWTr LRHS NLar SSpi WPGP WSHC
- var. ***fauriei*** NLar WSHC
- - B&SWJ 1701 WCru
aff. ***megalocarpum*** BWJ 8150 WCru

Schizostachyum (*Poaceae*)

§ ***funghomii*** EPla MMoz MMuc SEND WPGP

Schizostylis ✿ (*Iridaceae*)

§ ***coccinea*** Widely available
- f. ***alba*** Widely available
- 'Anne' WHoo
- 'Ballyrogan Giant' CFir EBee ECho GBuc IBlr MAvo NCot NHol WPGP WSHC
- 'Big Moma' CPrp GMac NCot
- 'Brick Red' **new** MAvo
- 'Cardinal' NHol WFar
- 'Caroline' NCot
- 'Cindy Towe' EBee GBuc
- 'Countesse de Vere' EBee NCot
- 'Crawshaw Chance' **new** LRHS
- 'Elburton Glow' CPrp GMac NCot WFar WHoo
- 'Fenland Daybreak' Widely available
- 'Gigantea' see *S. coccinea* 'Major'
- 'Good White' EBee MAvo NBir
- 'Grandiflora' see *S. coccinea* 'Major'
- 'Hilary Gould' CPrp GBuc MAvo NCGa NCot WFar WHal WHil WWEG
- 'Hint of Pink' MAvo MDKP
- 'Jack Frost' EBee GMac MAvo NCGa WMoo
- 'Jennifer' ♀H4 CBro CElw CPrp CTri EBee ECho EHrv EPfP ERos EShb GAbr LPio LRHS LSou MAvo MRav NCGa SApp SBch SMrm SRms SUsu SWvt WFar WHil WMoo WOld WSpi WWEG
- late-flowering SIng
- 'Maiden's Blush' CPrp EBrs ECGP ECtt EHrv GBuc GKir LRHS LSou MAvo MCot MDKP NCot NHol NLar SPet WFar
§ - 'Major' ♀H4 Widely available
* - 'Marietta' NCot
- 'Mollie Gould' EAEE EBee EBla ECtt EHrv EKen ELon EShb GCra LBMP LPio LRHS MAvo MMHG NBre NCGa NCot NHol NLar SCoo SRGP WFar WHil WPrP WTin WWEG
- 'Mrs Hegarty' Widely available
- 'November Cheer' CMac CPrp CSpr EBrs IBlr LRHS NBir NCot NLar WFar WWEG
- 'Oregon Sunset' CPrp EBee GBuc MDKP

- 'Pallida'	CMil CPom CSam ECha ECtt EHrv ELan GBuc MLHP MRav MWea NBir NCot NLar WFar
- 'Pink Marg'	CPrp GMac MAvo NCot
- 'Pink Princess'	see *S. coccinea* 'Wilfred H. Bryant'
- 'Professor Barnard'	CCCN CFee CHar CPrp CSpe EBee ECho ELon EPfP EShb GAbr MAvo MBNS MSpe NBir NCot NEgg SApp SMrm SWal WFar WHil WMoo WOld WPnn
- 'Red Dragon'	GAbr GBuc LLHF NCGa NCot NHol WCon WFar WHoo
- 'Salmon Charm'	EBrs GBin GBuc LRHS NCGa WFar WMoo
- salmon-flowered	NCot
- 'Salome'	CPrp NCot
- 'Silver Pink'	IBlr
- 'Snow Maiden'	CAbP CElw EBee ECtt GAbr GBuc GGar GKev LRHS MAvo NCot SPav
- 'Strawberry'	CPrp NCot SPav
§ - 'Sunrise' ♀H4	Widely available
- 'Sunset'	see *S. coccinea* 'Sunrise'
- 'Tambara'	CMdw CPou CPrp CSam EBee EHrv GAbr GBuc MAvo MWea NCot NLar SApp SMrm WFar
- 'Vera'	NCot
- 'Viscountess Byng'	CBcs CBro CPrp CTri EBee ECho ELon EPau GAbr IBlr IGor LAst LRHS MSCN NBir NCot NLar SMrm SPav SPer WFar WPer
- 'Wilfred H. Bryant'	Widely available
- 'Zeal Salmon'	CBro CFee CFir CPou CPrp ECha EPot GAbr GMac LHop MAvo NBir NCot NHol SApp WFar WHil
* ***rosea***	CChe EBrs ERCP

Schoenoplectus (*Cyperaceae*)

§ ***lacustris***	CWat EBWF EMFW GFor MSKA SVic
§ - subsp. ***tabernaemontani***	EBWF SPer
- - 'Albescens' (v)	CBen CKno CWat EBee EMFW LPBA MSKA SWal SWat WHal WPrP
- - 'Zebrinus' (v)	CBen CBot CKno CWat EHon ELan EMFW EPfP LPBA LRHS MMuc MSKA NScw SPlb SWat WFar WHal WMAq WPrP

Schoenus (*Cyperaceae*)

pauciflorus	CWCL EBee ECou EHoe EPPr EWes NOak WMoo WPGP WPrP

Sciadopitys (*Sciadopityaceae*)

verticillata ♀H4	Widely available
- 'Compacta' new	LRHS
- 'Firework'	CKen
- 'Globe'	CKen
- 'Gold Star'	CKen
- 'Goldammer'	NLar
- 'Golden Rush'	CKen ECho MAsh MGos NLar WEve
- 'Goldmahne'	CKen
- 'Grüne Kugel'	CKen ECho NLar SLim
- 'Jeddeloh Compact'	CKen
- 'Kugelblitz'	WEve
- 'Kupferschirm'	CKen ECho NLar
- 'Mecki'	CKen ECho WEve
- 'Megaschirm'	CKen
- 'Ossorio Gold'	CKen ECho WEve
- 'Perlenglanz' new	NLar
- 'Picola'	CKen ECho MAsh NLar
- 'Pygmy'	CKen
- 'Richie's Cushion'	CKen ECho WEve
- 'Shorty'	CKen
- 'Speerspitze'	CKen
- 'Starburst'	CKen
- 'Sternschnuppe'	CKen ECho MAsh NLar SLim WEve
- 'Wintergreen'	CKen

Scilla (*Hyacinthaceae*)

adlamii	see *Ledebouria cooperi*
× ***allenii***	see × *Chionoscilla allenii*
amethystina	see *S. litardierei*
amoena	EBrs ECho WCot
aristidis from Algeria	ECho
autumnalis	CAvo CDes CPom CStu EBWF EBrs ECho EPot ERos LAma LRHS NRya WShi WThu
- JCA 0.872.602	WCot
- from Crete	ECho
- from Morocco	ECho
- subsp. ***fallax***	EBrs ECho
bifolia ♀H4	CAvo CBro CFFs CPom CStu EBrs ECho EPot LAma LLWP LRHS SPhx WCot WShi
- RS 156/83	ECho WWst
- 'Alba'	EBrs ECho EPot SPhx
- 'Norman Stevens'	SCnR
- 'Rosea'	CStu EBrs ECho EPot LAma LLWP LRHS MWat
bithynica ♀H4	WShi
campanulata	see *Hyacinthoides hispanica*
caucasica new	WWst
chinensis	see *S. scilloides*
cilicica	CStu ECho ERos SPhx
greilhuberi	CStu EBrs ECho ERos WAbe WCot WWst
haemorrhoidalis	WCot
hohenackeri	EBee ERos SPhx WThu
- BSBE 559	WWst
- BSBE 811	WCot
hughii	EBrs ECho
hyacinthoides	EBrs ECho ERos WBVN WCot WWst
ingridiae	ECho ERos WWst
- var. ***taurica***	ECho ERos WWst
italica	see *Hyacinthoides italica*
japonica	see *S. scilloides*
latifolia from Morocco	ECho
libanotica	see *Puschkinia scilloides* var. *libanotica*
liliohyacinthus	CBro CRow EBrs ECho IBlr MMHG SSvw WSHC WShi WWst
- 'Alba'	ERos
lingulata	CStu ECho ERos NMen WCot
- var. ***ciliolata***	CBro EBrs ECho EPot ERos
§ ***litardierei*** ♀H4	CBgR CPom CStu EBrs ECho EPPr EPot ERos LAma MBri NMen SBch SPhx WShi
- ***hoogiana***	ERos
- 'Orjen'	EBrs ECho
lutea hort.	see *Ledebouria socialis*
madeirensis new	CLak
mauritanica	ECho WWst
melaina	WCot
cf. ***mesopotamica*** new	WWst
messeniaca	CPom
- Hoa 0168	WWst
- MS 38 from Greece	WCot
mischtschenkoana ♀H4	CAvo CBro CHid ECho EPot LAma LRHS MBri SPer WBVN
- 'Armenia'	EBrs
§ - 'Tubergeniana' ♀H4	CMea EBrs ECho GKev SPhx WCot
- 'Zwanenburg'	ECho
monophyllos	CStu ECho
- var. ***tingitana***	ERos

morrisii	ECho ERos
natalensis	see *Merwilla plumbea*
non-scripta	see *Hyacinthoides non-scripta*
numidica	EBrs ECho
nutans	see *Hyacinthoides non-scripta*
obtusifolia	EBrs ECho WCot
- subsp. ***intermedia***	ECho
persica ♀H4	CPom EBrs ECho ERos LPio SPhx WCot
peruviana	Widely available
- S&L 285	WCot
- SB&L 20/1	WCot
- 'Alba'	CBcs CBro CFwr CSWP CSpe CStu ECho LPio LRHS MTho SMrm WCot WWst
* - var. ***ciliata***	WCot
- 'Grand Bleu'	CFwr
- var. ***ifniensis***	WCot
- var. ***venusta*** S&L 311/2	WCot
pratensis	see *S. litardierei*
puschkinioides	ECho
ramburei	EBrs ECho
reverchonii	EBrs ECho ERos WWst
- from Spain	WCot
rosenii	EBrs ECho LRHS
§ ***scilloides***	EBrs ECho ERos SCnR
- B&SWJ 8812	WCru
siberica ♀H4	CAvo CFFs EBrs ECho EPfP GAbr IHer LAma LRHS MWat SBch SMrm SPer SPhx WShi
- 'Alba'	CBro EBrs ECho EPfP EPot LAma LRHS MWat SBch WShi
- subsp. ***armena***	ECho
- subsp. ***siberica*** 'Penza' **new**	LRHS
- 'Spring Beauty'	CBro CMdw CMea EBrs ECho EPot GKev LAma LRHS MBri SPhx SRms
'Tubergeniana'	see *S. mischtschenkoana* 'Tubergeniana'
verna	CDes EBWF EBrs ECho ERos WHer WShi WThu
vicentina	see *Hyacinthoides vicentina*
violacea	see *Ledebouria socialis*

Scindapsus (*Araceae*)

aureus	see *Epipremnum aureum*
pictus (v)	LRHS MBri

Scirpoides (*Cyperaceae*)

§ ***holoschoenus***	CRWN EBWF

Scirpus (*Cyperaceae*)

cernuus	see *Isolepis cernua*
holoschoenus	see *Scirpoides holoschoenus*
lacustris	see *Schoenoplectus lacustris*
- 'Spiralis'	see *Juncus effusus* f. *spiralis*
maritimus	see *Bolboschoenus maritimus*
tabernaemontani	see *Schoenoplectus lacustris* subsp. *tabernaemontani*

Scleranthus (*Illecebraceae*)

biflorus	CTrC ECho EDAr EWes GGar NDlv NWCA SPlb WPer
perennis	ECho
uniflorus	CTrC ECho EShb NHol NWCA SMad SPlb WPrP

Sclerochiton (*Acanthaceae*)

harveyanus	EShb

Scoliopus (*Trilliaceae*)

bigelowii	SCnR WHal WWst
hallii	EBee EBrs GEdr NMen SCnR WCot WCru WWst

Scolopendrium see *Asplenium*

Scopolia (*Solanaceae*)

anomala	CArn
carniolica	CArn CAvo CFir COld ELan GKir GPoy LEdu MBlu MPhe NChi NLar NSti SPhx SPlb WCru WFar WPGP WSHC
- from Poland	LEdu
§ - var. ***brevifolia***	EHrv EPPr GBin LEdu LRHS SDys SPhx WTin
- - WM 9811	MPhe
- subsp. ***hladnikiana***	see *S. carniolica* var. *brevifolia*
- 'Zwanenburg'	EBrs EHrv EPPr EPot EWes LEdu SPhx
lurida	see *Anisodus luridus*

Scorzonera (*Asteraceae*)

suberosa subsp. ***cariensis***	CPBP

Scrophularia (*Scrophulariaceae*)

aquatica	see *S. auriculata*
§ ***auriculata***	EBWF EPfP LPBA MHer NMir NPer WHer
§ - 'Variegata' (v)	CArn CBcs EBee ECha ECtt EHoe ELan EPfP GCal GKir LPBA LRHS MAvo MDun MHer NBid NCob NEgg NSti SDnm SPer SPoG SRms WFar WSHC WWlt
buergeriana 'Lemon and Lime' misapplied	see *Scrophularia buergeriana* 'Lemon and Lime', *Teucrium viscidum* 'Lemon and Lime'
§ - 'Lemon and Lime' (v) **new**	NEgg
calliantha	MDKP
canina SDR 5466 **new**	GKev
cf. ***canina*** **new**	EBee
grandiflora	EWld NBre WCot WFar
nodosa	CArn CRWN EBWF EBee GPoy NMir NSco WHer
- ***variegata***	see *S. auriculata* 'Variegata'
scopolii	EBee

Scutellaria ✿ (*Lamiaceae*)

albida	EBee
§ ***alpina***	CPBP ECho GEdr GJos LRHS SPlb SRms SRot WGor WPer
- 'Arcobaleno'	GKev LLHF LRHS SMrm SUsu
- 'Greencourt'	WPat
- 'Moonbeam'	GEdr SMrm
- 'Rosea' **new**	LRHS
altissima	CArn ECha ELan ELon GBuc GKev GKir MMuc NBro SBod SMrm SPlb WCHb WPtf
'Amazing Grace'	EWes
baicalensis	CArn EBee GJos GKev GPoy MAvo MWhi SMrm WPer WPtf
canescens	see *S. incana*
columnae	EBee
costaricana	EShb
diffusa	ECtt WPer
formosana 'China Blue'	EPfP LRHS
galericulata	CWan EBWF GPoy MHer NVic WCHb
hastata	see *S. hastifolia*
§ ***hastifolia***	CTri ECho ECtt WPer
§ ***incana***	CBct CPom CSam EBee ECGP EHrv ELan ELon EPPr GMaP LHop LPla MWea SMrm SUsu WCot
indica	WCFE

	- var. ***japonica***	see *S. indica* var. *parvifolia*
§	- var. ***parvifolia***	CPBP EBee EBur ECho EWes GEdr LRHS NWCA SRot
	- - 'Alba'	CPBP ECho LLHF LRHS
	lateriflora	CArn GBar GPoy MNHC NMun WCHb WJek
	maekawae	CSpe EBee WPGP
	- B&SWJ 557a	WCru
	novae-zelandiae	ECou
	oreophila new	GKev
	orientalis	CMdw CMea ECtt GCal GEdr WAbe WPat
	- subsp. ***bicolor***	ECtt NWCA
	- subsp. ***pinnatifida***	GEdr NWCA
	ovata new	EBee
	pontica	CPBP GEdr GKev SBch SMrm WFoF
	prostrata	LLHF WPat
	scordiifolia	CEnt CMea CSam EBee ECha ECho EDAr GEdr IMou LRHS NRya NWCA SBHP SHGN SRms WCom WFar WHal WHoo WTin
	- 'Seoul Sapphire'	CSpe EWes GAbr LRHS LSou WBVN WPtf
	sevanensis new	EPot WCot
	'Sherbert Lemon' new	SRot
	strigillosa	EBee
	suffrutescens 'Texas Rose'	CPBP CSpe LLHF LRHS MWea SIng SRot
	supina	see *S. alpina*
	tournefortii	ECtt LLWP WPtf
*	***zhongdianensis***	WPtf

seakale see *Crambe maritima*

Sebaea (*Gentianaceae*)

rehmanii new	SPlb
thomasii	WAbe

Securigera see *Coronilla*

Sedastrum see *Sedum*

Sedum ✿ (*Crassulaceae*)

	B&SWJ 737	EGoo
	NS 622	NWCA
	'Abbey Dore'	CAby EBee EBrs EGoo ELan EPfP GCal LPla LRHS NBPC NCGa NGby NWsh SBch SPoG SRkn WAbb WBor WHoo WPGP
	acre	CTri EBWF ECho GJos GPoy LEdu LRHS MBar MHer MNHC NBlu NMir SEND SPlb
	- 'Aureum'	ECho EDAr EHoe EPfP LAst MBar NLar NPri SIng SPer SPoG WFar WPat
	- 'Elegans'	ECtt GKir NBlu
	- 'Golden Queen'	EAlp LRHS SPlb SPoG
	- 'Minus'	ECho EDAr
§	- subsp. ***neglectum*** var. ***majus***	CChe EPfP IPot LSou NLar
	- 'Oktoberfest'	GJos
	adolphi	EPfP
	aizoon	EAro ECho GCal GKir LAst NBre SIde SPlb WBVN WFar
	- 'Aurantiacum'	see *S. aizoon* 'Euphorbioides'
§	- 'Euphorbioides'	ECha ECtt EGoo ELan LDai MHer MRav NLar SAga SEND SGar SPer SPlb WFar WTin
	albescens	see *S. forsterianum* f. *purpureum*
	alboroseum	see *S. erythrostictum*
§	***album***	EAlp EBWF LRHS NBro NMir WPer
	- 'Coral Carpet'	EAlp ECho ECtt EDAr EPfP EPot GJos GKev MBar MRav MWat NRya SFgr SPoG WCot WFar
	- subsp. ***gypsicola***	see *S. gypsicola*
§	- subsp. ***teretifolium*** var. ***murale***	CTri MBar STre
	altissimum	see *S. sediforme*
*	***altum***	NBre WFar
	amplexicaule	see *S. amplexicaule* subsp. *tenuifolium*
§	- subsp. ***tenuifolium***	EBur
	anacampseros	EGoo NHol SEND SUsu WPer
	- B&SWJ 723	WCru
	anglicum	EBWF
	athoum	see *S. album*
	atlanticum	see *S. dasyphyllum* subsp. *dasyphyllum* var. *mesatlanticum*
	'Autumn Charm'	see *S.* (Herbstfreude Group) 'Lajos'
	Autumn Joy	see *S.* (Herbstfreude Group) 'Herbstfreude'
	balfourii HWJ 824	WCru
	'Bertram Anderson' ♀H4	Widely available
	beyrichianum misapplied	see *S. glaucophyllum*
	bithynicum 'Aureum'	see *S. hispanicum* var. *minus* 'Aureum'
	'Blade Runner'	EBee
	brevifolium	GGar
§	- var. ***quinquefarium***	WAbe
	caeruleum	SIng
	'Carl'	CDes CKno CPrp EBee EBla EBrs ECha ECtt EGoo EPfP EShb EWTr GMaP LHop LRHS MRav NBro NCGa NCob NOrc NSti NWsh SAga SMrm SRGP WCot WHoo WMnd WMoo WWEG
	caucasicum	WAbb WCot WEas
	cauticola ♀H4	CSpe ECho EDAr GBuc GCal GEdr MBrN MHer MRav NBre NHol SRms SRot WAbe
	- from Lida	ECho
	- 'Coca-Cola'	CBct CCVN EAlp ECtt EHoe LAst LRHS NPri SBch SPoG WBor WFar
	- 'Lidakense' ♀H4	CMea CSam ECha ECho ECtt EPfP GAbr GKir LRHS MBri MLHP NHol NSla SBch SIng SPer SPlb SRot WCot WFar
	- 'Purpurine'	ECho GCal
	- 'Robustum'	see *S.* 'Ruby Glow'
	compressum	see *S. palmeri* subsp. *palmeri* tetraploid
	confusum Hemsl.	SChr SEND WFar
	crassipes	see *Rhodiola wallichiana*
	crassularia	see *Crassula setulosa* 'Milfordiae'
	'Crazy Ruffles'	EBee ECtt
	cryptomerioides B&SWJ 054	WCru
	cyaneum Rudolph	WAbe
	'Dark Jack'	EBee IPot LBuc LRHS MGos
	dasyphyllum	ECho EDAr NRya SPlb SRms STre
§	- subsp. ***dasyphyllum*** var. ***mesatlanticum***	GKev NBir
	- ***mucronatis***	see *S. dasyphyllum* subsp. *dasyphyllum* var. *mesatlanticum*
	debile	WAbe
	'Diamond Edge' (v)	EBee ECtt
	divergens	SMad
	douglasii	see *S. stenopetalum* 'Douglasii'
	drymarioides	NBre WWEG
	'Dudley Field'	MHer
	'Eleanor Fisher'	see *S. telephium* subsp. *ruprechtii*
	ellacombeanum	see *S. kamtschaticum* var. *ellacombeanum*

	Name	Suppliers
§	***erythrostictum***	CBot CWan MTho WAbb
	- 'Frosty Morn' (v)	Widely available
§	- 'Mediovariegatum' (v)	EBee EGoo ELan EShb LRHS MHer MNrw MRav NCob NWsh SPad SPoG SWvt WFar WMnd WMoo WPer WWEG
	'Evening Cloud'	EBee ECha
	ewersii	EBee ECho ECtt EDAr GMaP LRHS NBro NHol NLar SPlb
	- var. ***homophyllum*** 'Rosenteppich'	LBuc LRHS MBrN SWvt WCom
	fabaria	see *S. telephium* subsp. *fabaria*
	farinosum	GGar
	fastigiatum	see *Rhodiola fastigiata*
	forsterianum subsp. ***elegans***	SPlb
§	- f. ***purpureum***	NRya
	frutescens	STre
	furfuraceum	CStu NMen WAbe
	Garnet Brocade = 'Garbro'PBR	CCVN SPoG
§	***glaucophyllum***	WFar WPer
	'Gold Mound'	EPfP LAst LRHS MGos NLar SPoG SVil
	'Green Expectations'	EBee ECtt EShb LRHS MRav MWat NBre
§	***gypsicola***	EBee WPer
	'Harvest Moon'	EBur
	(Herbstfreude Group) 'Autumn Fire'	EBee
	- 'Beka' (v) **new**	MAsh
§	- 'Herbstfreude' ♀H4	Widely available
	- 'Jaws'PBR	CAby CKno EBee ECGP ECtt LSou SMrm WClo WCot
§	- 'Lajos' (v)	EBee LRHS MAsh
	heterodontum	see *Rhodiola heterodonta*
	hidakanum	ECtt EHoe EPot GGar GMaP NBro NHol NMen WHoo WPat WTin
	himalense misapplied	see *Rhodiola* 'Keston'
	hispanicum	EAlp ECho EDAr MHer NBre SPlb
	- ***glaucum***	see *S. hispanicum* var. *minus*
§	- var. ***minus***	ECho ECtt MBar MMuc SEND SIng SPlb
§	- - 'Aureum'	ECha ECho EDAr MBar NHol SPoG
	humifusum	EBur EPot NWCA SIng
§	***hybridum***	WEas
	'Indian Chief'	see *S.* (Herbstfreude Group) 'Herbstfreude'
	ishidae	see *Rhodiola ishidae*
	'José Aubergine'PBR	CPrp EBee IPot MAsh MBri NCGa
	'Joyce Henderson'	COlW EBee EBrs ECtt GKir GQue LHop LRHS MCot MRav NChi NCob NLar NVic SPer SRGP SUsu WBrk WCom WCot WEas WMoo WTin WWEG
	kamtschaticum ♀H4	EAlp ECho GAuc GJos MBar WFar
	- B&SWJ 10870	WCru
§	- var. ***ellacombeanum*** ♀H4	EDAr EGoo LRHS MMuc NMen SEND SMad WCot
	- - B&SWJ 8853	WCru
§	- var. ***floriferum*** 'Weihenstephaner Gold'	CEnt CTri ECho ECtt EDAr EGoo EPfP GAbr GEdr GGar GKir GMaP LRHS MBar MHer MRav MWat NBir NMen NPri NVic SIng SPlb SPoG SRms WFar WPat
	- var. ***kamtschaticum*** 'Variegatum' (v) ♀H4	CMea EAlp EBee ECho ECtt EDAr EHoe EPfP GKir LAst LBMP LRHS MHer MMuc MWat SIng SPoG SRms SRot SWvt WCom WEas
	kirilovii	see *Rhodiola kirilovii*
	lanceolatum	WPer
	lineare	LAst LRHS
	- 'Variegatum' (v)	LRHS
	'Little Gem'	see × *Cremnosedum* 'Little Gem'
§	***lydium***	CTri ECho GKir MBar MHer NBlu SFgr SPlb
	- 'Aureum'	see *S. hispanicum* var. *minus* 'Aureum'
	- 'Bronze Queen'	see *S. lydium*
	makinoi 'Ogon'	EBee LRHS
I	'Marchants Best Red' ♀H4	SUsu
	'Matrona' ♀H4	Widely available
	maweanum	see *S. acre* subsp. *neglectum* var. *majus*
	middendorffianum	ECho EDAr EGoo GKev LRHS MBrN MHer MWat NMen SPoG SRms SRot WFar
	'Moonglow'	ECtt NMen
	moranense	MMuc SEND
	morganianum ♀H1	EBak EShb STre
	'Munstead Red'	Widely available
	murale	see *S. album* subsp. *teretifolium* var. *murale*
N	***nevii*** A. Gray	SPlb
	nicaeense	see *S. sediforme*
	niveum **new**	NMen
	obcordatum	NMen
	obtusatum misapplied	see *S. oreganum*
§	***obtusatum*** A. Gray	EAlp ECtt GGar NBro NSla STre WFar WPnn
	- subsp. ***boreale*** NNS 01-123	NWCA
	oppositifolium	see *S. spurium* 'Album'
§	***oreganum***	ECha ECho EDAr GGar GKev GMaP MBar MHer MWat NMen SPlb SRms SRot STre
	- 'Procumbens'	see *S. oreganum* subsp. *tenue*
§	- subsp. ***tenue***	LEdu NHol NRya WAbe WPat
§	***oregonense***	EBur LRHS NMen
*	***oryzifolium*** 'Minus'	EAlp EBur
	oxypetalum	STre
	pachyclados	see *Rhodiola pachyclados*
	pachyphyllum	EPfP
	palmeri	CHEx CSpe LSou MRav NBir SChr SGar SSvw STre
§	- subsp. ***palmeri*** tetraploid	EDAr SEND
	'Pewter'	ECho
	pilosum	NMen
§	***pluricaule***	ECho LRHS SPlb SRms
	populifolium	ECha GCal GJos IMou MHer STre WCom WPer
	praealtum	GGar LRHS SChr SEND STre WCot
	pulchellum	SPlb
	quinquefarium	see *S. brevifolium* var. *quinquefarium*
	'Red Cauli' ♀H4	CKno EBee ECha EPPr GBin IPot LHop LPio LRHS MBNS MBri MCot NCGa NPro SPhx SPoG SUsu WCot WFar
	'Red Rum'	SMeo
	reflexum L.	see *S. rupestre* L.
	reptans	ECho NCob
	rhodiola	see *Rhodiola rosea*
	rosea	see *Rhodiola rosea*
	rubroglaucum misapplied	see *S. oregonense*
	rubroglaucum Praeger	see *S. obtusatum* A. Gray
	× ***rubrotinctum***	CHEx LRHS SChr
	- 'Aurora'	SChr
§	'Ruby Glow' ♀H4	Widely available
	'Ruby Port'	CSpe
§	***rupestre*** L.	EAlp EBWF ECho GGar LRHS MBNS MBar MWat SPlb SPoG WCor WFar

	- 'Angelina'	EBee EPPr EWes ILad IMou LRHS MAvo MGos MHer NBir NHol NPri NPro SPoG SRGP WCot
	- 'Monstrosum Cristatum'	NBir SMad WAlt
	ruprechtii	see *S. telephium* subsp. *ruprechtii*
	'Samuel Oliphant' (v)	WCot
	sarcocaule hort.	see *Crassula sarcocaulis*
	sarmentosum	ECho
§	***sediforme***	CArn EDAr LRHS
	- ***nicaeense***	see *S. sediforme*
	selskianum	GGar NBre SBch WFar
	sempervivoides	ECho
	'September Ruby' **new**	LRHS
	sexangulare	EAlp ECho EDAr GGar MBar MHer MMuc NRya SEND SFgr SIng SPlb SRms STre WFar WPer
	sibiricum	see *S. hybridum*
	sieboldii	EBee ECho
	- 'Mediovariegatum' (v) ♀[H2-3]	CHEx COIW EAlp ECho EWll MHer NCob NPri SPlb WFar
	'Silvermoon'	EBur ECtt NHol
	spathulifolium	CTri ECha ECho EPot MDKP NBlu
	- 'Aureum'	EBur ECho ECtt MWat WAbe
	- 'Cape Blanco' ♀[H4]	Widely available
	- 'Purpureum' ♀[H4]	Widely available
	spectabile ♀[H4]	CArn CChe CHEx CHrt CPrp CTri EBee ELan EPfP GJos GMaP LRHS MCot MHer MRav NCob NGdn SBch SGar SPlb SRms WBVN WBor WBrk WCAu WFar WSFF WTin WWEG
	- 'Album'	CHEx NCob
	- (Brilliant Group) 'Brilliant' ♀[H4]	CBcs CKno CMMP CSBt CTri EBee ECha ECtt ELan EPfP GKir LAst LBMP LRHS MBri MGos MRav NBlu NGdn NOrc SBch SMad SPer SPoG SWvt WCAu WFar WMoo WWEG
	- - 'Carmen'	EBee LRHS WMoo
	- - 'Hot Stuff'	NBhm
	- - 'Lisa'	EBee GBin NLar
	- - 'Meteor'	CPrp EBee MBNS MWat NLar SMrm WPer WWEG
	- - 'Neon'	EBee
	- - 'Pink Fairy'	WHil
	- - 'Rosenteller'	EBee NBre SMrm WFar
§	- - 'Septemberglut'	EBee EGoo LRHS NBre NSti WCot
	- - 'Steven Ward'	EBee EWes SRGP
	- 'Iceberg'	Widely available
*	- 'Mini'	ELan MRav
	- 'Pink Chablis'[PBR] (v)	EBee MAsh NBhm WCot
	- September Glow	see *S. spectabile* (Brilliant Group) 'Septemberglut'
	- 'Stardust'	CKno CPrp CTri EBee EBrs EPfP GKev GMaP LRHS MBNS MHer MRav NCGa NVic SMrm SPer SPet SPoG WFar WGor WWEG
	- 'Variegatum'	see *S. erythrostictum* 'Mediovariegatum'
	spinosum	see *Orostachys spinosa*
	spurium	CHEx ECho EGoo GJos MMuc NHol NPro SEND SGar SRms STre
§	- 'Album'	EGoo NRya
	- 'Atropurpureum'	ECha NCob WMoo
	- 'Coccineum'	EAlp ECho GJos LRHS MBar MNHC SEND WBVN
	- Dragon's Blood	see *S. spurium* 'Schorbuser Blut'
	- 'Erdblut'	LRHS NMen
	- 'Fuldaglut'	CTri EBee ECho EDAr EHoe EPfP GBuc GMaP GQue LRHS NRya SIng SMrm SPer WFar WMoo WPer WPnn WRHF
	- 'Green Mantle'	EBee ECha ECho EPfP
	- Purple Carpet	see *S. spurium* 'Purpurteppich'
	- 'Purpureum'	EGoo SRms
§	- 'Purpurteppich'	EBee ECho ECtt GJos LRHS MRav NBro NHol NLar SRms
	- 'Roseum'	EWll SRms
	- 'Ruby Mantle'	EWll GKev GKir SBch SPoG SWvt WBVN WMoo
§	- 'Schorbuser Blut' ♀[H4]	CMea EBee ECho ECtt EPau EPfP EPot GJos GKev GKir LRHS MCot MLHP MWat NBir NRya NVic SPlb SRGP SRms WEas WFar WHoo WTin
	- 'Summer Glory'	EAlp NLar
§	- 'Tricolor' (v)	CTri EAlp EBee ECha ECho EDAr EGoo EHoe GGar LAst MBar MHer MLHP MRav NBlu NHol NPri NRya SBod SIng SPlb SPoG STre WFar WMoo
	- 'Variegatum'	see *S. spurium* 'Tricolor'
	- 'Voodoo'	CChe CEnt EAlp EBee ECtt EWes LBMP MHer MSCN WFar WRHF
	stenopetalum	SPlb
§	- 'Douglasii'	MHer SRms
	'Stewed Rhubarb Mountain'	CPrp EAEE EBee EBla ECtt EPfP LBMP LDai LHop LRHS LSou MBNS MCot MNFA MRav NBro NOrc SBch SMrm SPoG WCot WFar WMoo WPGP WWEG
	stoloniferum	ECho
	'Sunset Cloud'	CHEx CMHG CSam EBee ECtt EWes GCal IPot LPla LRHS MRav NBre NCob
	takesimense B&SWJ 8518	WCru
	telephium	CArn NBir SRms
§	- Atropurpureum Group ♀[H4]	COIW EBee ELan EPfP MRav SWvt WCom WEas WWEG
	- - 'African Pearl' **new**	CPrp ECGP WCot WWEG
	- - 'Arthur Branch'	CPrp EBee EPPr GBin GBuc MTho WWEG
I	- - 'Atropurpureum Nanum' **new**	WWEG
	- - 'Black Emperor'	EBee
	- - 'Bon Bon'	CPrp EBee MBNS WPtf
	- - 'Bressingham Purple'	EBrs LRHS
	- - 'Chocolate'	EBee EPPr LRHS MBNS
	- - 'El Cid'	EBee EWes
	- - 'Hester'	WSpi WWEG
	- - 'Karfunkelstein'	CSam GBin SPhx SUsu
	- - 'Leonore Zuuntz'	EBee NBre
	- - 'Lynda et Rodney'	CKno EGoo EWes LRHS WCot
	- - 'Lynda Windsor'	CBct CBow EBee ECtt EHrv EPfP GAbr LHop LRHS MBNS NBhm NLar NMoo SPoG SRGP SWvt WFar
	- - 'Möhrchen'	CPrp EBee EHrv GMaP MRav NGdn NLar NWsh SBch SMrm SPoG WCom WFar WMnd WMoo
	- - 'Picolette'	EBee LRHS
	- - 'Postman's Pride'[PBR]	CAby CWGN EBee ECtt EPfP GQue IPot LBuc LRHS MCot MWat NCGa SMad SPoG SUsu WCot WWEG
§	- - 'Purple Emperor' ♀[H4]	Widely available
	- - 'Ringmore Ruby'	WCot WWEG
	- - 'Xenox'[PBR]	CAby EBee ECtt EKen EPfP EWTr EWll GBin IPot LRHS MAsh MBNS MCot SBch SPoG
	- Emperor's Waves Group	GQue NGdn WRHF
§	- subsp. ***fabaria***	MRav NWsh SMrm WAbb WCot WFar WWEG
	- - var. ***borderei***	CElw LPla SBch SPhx SUsu
	- 'Jennifer'	WCot
	- subsp. ***maximum***	CBot MGos
	- - 'Atropurpureum'	see *S. telephium* Atropurpureum Group

- - 'Gooseberry Fool' COlW CPrp EBee ECGP ECtt EGoo EPfP ETod EWTr GMaP LRHS NSti SBch SPhx WFar WWEG
- 'Roseum' WWEG
§ - subsp. ***ruprechtii*** COlW CPrp EBee ECha ECtt EGoo EPPr EPfP GAuc GMaP LRHS MCot MNFA MRav NSti SMeo SMrm SPer SPet SPhx WBVN WEas WFar WMoo WPer
- - 'Citrus Twist' EBee EBla ECtt LRHS LSou MBNS MRav NBhm WPtf
- - 'Hab Gray' CSpe EBee ECtt EWes GBin GQue LAst LRHS NBPC NLar SAga SMrm WClo WCot
- - 'Pink Dome' ECha
- 'Strawberries and Cream' Widely available
- subsp. ***telephium*** GCra LRHS
- 'Variegatum' (v) MDKP WHal
tenuifolium see *S. amplexicaule* subsp. *tenuifolium*
- subsp. ***ibericum*** see *S. amplexicaule* subsp. *tenuifolium*
ternatum WFar
trollii see *Rhodiola trollii*
urvillei Sartorianum Group MHer
ussuriense EBee ECha SUsu
- 'Chuwangsan' **new** WCru
- 'Turkish Delight' **new** EWll GJos
'Vera Jameson' ♀H4 Widely available
viviparum B&SWJ 8662 WCru
'Wallaceum' EAlp NBlu
'Washfield Purple' see *S. telephium* 'Purple Emperor'
'Weihenstephaner Gold' see *S. kamtschaticum* var. *floriferum* 'Weihenstephaner Gold'
weinbergii see *Graptopetalum paraguayense*
yezoense see *S. pluricaule*
'Zebra' **new** LOck LRHS

Seemannia see *Gloxinia*

Selaginella ✿ (*Selaginellaceae*)

apoda MBri
braunii CLAP WCot
helvetica CStu IMou
kraussiana ♀H1 CLAP EDAr GGar NHol WRic
- 'Aurea' CBty CCCN LRHS SMad WRic
- 'Brownii' ♀H1 CBty CCCN LRHS
- 'Gold Tips' CBty CCCN LRHS
lepidophylla EBrs SVic
moellendorfii WRic
sanguinolenta CStu SIng
uncinata ♀H1 CLAP WRic

Selago (*Scrophulariaceae*)

galpinii **new** CPBP

Selinum (*Apiaceae*)

carvifolium CMac EBee LDai LRHS NLar
tenuifolium see *S. wallichianum*
§ ***wallichianum*** CDes CHid CSpe EBrs ECGP EDAr EGoo ELan EShb EWTr GBuc GCal GCra GKir LRHS MWat NBPC NCGa NMRc SMad SMeo SPer SPhx SUsu WCot WFar WHil WPGP WPtf WWEG
- EMAK 886 EBee GPoy SDix
- HWJK 2224 WCru
- HWJK 2347 WCru

Selliera (*Goodeniaceae*)

radicans ECou EDAr GGar

Semele (*Ruscaceae*)

androgyna CHEx CRHN

Semiaquilegia (*Ranunculaceae*)

§ ***adoxoides*** CPom SHar
'Early Dwarf' EDif
§ ***ecalcarata*** CBot CDes CMea CPom ECho EShb GBBs GBuc GCal GGar GKev GKir LDai LFur LRHS NGdn SBch SRms SSvw WCru WFar WHal WPGP WPer
* - f. ***bicolor*** CPom WCru WFar
- 'Snowbell' WCru
simulatrix see *S. ecalcarata*

Semiarundinaria (*Poaceae*)

from Korea EPla
§ ***fastuosa*** ♀H4 CBcs CDoC CEnt CHEx CPMA EAmu EBee ENBC EPfP EPla ERod IMou LMaj LPal LRHS MBri MMoz MMuc MWht NMoo NVic SAPC SArc SEND SPlb WJun
- var. ***viridis*** CEnt EBee EPla ERod LPJP MWht SBig WCru WJun
kagamiana CDoC CMCo EBee ENBC EPla IMou MMoz MMuc MWhi MWht NMoo SBig WJun
§ ***lubrica*** MWht
makinoi CGHE EAmu EPla MWht WJun WPGP
nitida see *Fargesia nitida*
§ ***okuboi*** CEnt ENBC EPla ERod LPal MMoz MWht WJun
villosa see *S. okuboi*
yamadorii EPla ERod MMoz MWht WJun
- 'Brimscombe' EPla
yashadake CEnt EPla ERod WJun
- 'Gimmei' EPla
- f. ***kimmei*** CDoC CEnt ENBC EPla ERod LRHS MAsh MGos MMoz MMuc MREP MWht NMoo SBig SEND WDyG WFar WJun WMoo WPGP
I - - 'Inversa' **new** CEnt

Sempervivella see *Rosularia*

Sempervivum ✿ (*Crassulaceae*)

EKB 1727 MOne
from Andorra NHol
from Sierra Nova NDlv
'Abba' CMea MOne WHal WPer
acuminatum see *S. tectorum* var. *glaucum*
'Adelaar' CWil NMen
'Adelmoed' CWil SFgr
'Adeltruid' NHol
'Adlerhorst' NHol
'Aglow' MHom MOne NMen
'Aladdin' CWil GEdr MOne NMen SRms
'Albernelli' NHol SFgr
'Alchimist' MOne
'Alcithoë' MOne
'Aldo Moro' CWil ECha EDAr GAbr LBee LRHS MHom MOne NMen SFgr WIvy
'Alidae' MOne
allionii see *Jovibarba allionii*
'Alluring' GAbr MOne
'Alpha' LBee LRHS MOne NHol NMen SFgr SIng SRms STre WHal WPer WTin
altum CWil LRHS MHom NMen SPlb
'Amanda' CWil ECha MOne NMen SIng SRms WHoo WPer WTin

	Name	Suppliers
	'Ambergreen'	NMen
	andreanum	see *S. tectorum* var. *alpinum*
	'Apache' Payne	see *Jovibarba heuffelii* 'Apache'
	'Apache' Haberer	MOne NMen
	'Apollo'	NHol SFgr
	'Apple Blossom'	CMea ECha MOne NMen
	arachnoideum ♀H4	Widely available
	- from Cascade Piste 7	MOne
	- 'Ararat'	SDys
	- 'Boria'	MOne
	- var. ***bryoides***	CWil LRHS MBrN NMen WAbe WIvy WPer
	- 'Clärchen'	EPot NHol NMen NSla SFgr WAbe
	- cristate	CWil
*	- ***densum***	EDAr LRHS MBrN MSCN NRya WAbe WFar
	- subsp. ***doellianum***	see *S. arachnoideum* subsp. *tomentosum* var. *glabrescens*
	- form No 1	ECho
	- 'Laggeri'	see *S. arachnoideum* subsp. *tomentosum* (C.B. Lehm. & Schnittsp.) Schinz & Thell.
	- 'Opitz'	WCom WPer
	- 'Peña Prieta'	NHol
	- red	NMen
	- 'Red Wings'	ECha MOne NMen SRms
	- 'Rubrum'	CHEx GGar GKir GMaP LRHS MAsh MOne SPlb
	- 'Sultan'	MOne
	- subsp. ***tomentosum*** misapplied	see *S.* × *barbulatum* 'Hookeri'
§	- subsp. ***tomentosum*** (C.B. Lehm. & Schnittsp.) Schinz & Thell. ♀H4	CHEx CWil LRHS MHer NHol NMen NPer SFgr SIng SPlb SRms WAbe WGor WPer
	- - GDJ 92.04	CWil
§	- - var. ***glabrescens***	NMen SDys WPat
	- - 'Minus'	NHol NMen SIng
§	- - 'Stansfieldii'	GAbr LRHS NMen SDys SIng STre WHal
§	- 'White Christmas'	CWil MHer
	arachnoideum × ***calcareum***	CWil NHol NMen WIvy WTin
	arachnoideum × ***montanum***	see *S.* × *barbulatum*
	arachnoideum × ***nevadense***	CWil SDys
	arachnoideum × ***pittonii***	CWil NHol NMen WAbe
	arenarium	see *Jovibarba arenaria*
	armenum	MOne NMen
	- var. ***insigne***	MOne
	'Arondina'	CWil
	'Aross'	CMea GAbr NMen
	'Arrowheads Red'	MOne
	'Artist'	CWil MOne NMen SFgr SIng
	arvernense	see *S. tectorum*
	'Ashes of Roses'	EGoo EPot GKev MHom MOne NMen WAbe WGor WPer
	'Asteroid'	CWil MOne NMen
	'Astrid'	CWil
	atlanticum	MHom NDlv NMen NSla SRot
	- from Atlas Mountains, Morocco	CWil MOne
	- from Oukaïmeden, Morocco	CWil GAbr MOne NHol NMen WTin
	- 'Edward Balls'	CWil MOne SDys SFgr
	'Atlantis' ambig.	NHol
	'Atropurpureum' ambig.	CHEx CWil EDAr GAbr GEdr MBrN MOne NMen SRms WGor WIvy WPer
	'Averil'	CWil
	'Averley'	MOne
	'Aymon Correvon'	MOne
	balcanicum	CWil EDAr MOne NMen WIvy
	ballsii	LRHS NMen
	- from Kambeecho, Greece	MHom
	- from Smólikas, Greece	CWil MHom MOne NMen
	- from Tschumba Petzi, Greece	CWil MHom MOne SDys
	'Banderi'	MOne
	'Banjo'	MOne
	'Banyan'	LRHS
	'Barbarosa'	CWil MOne
§	× ***barbulatum***	NMen SDys WCom WPer
§	- 'Hookeri'	CTri CWil EPot MOne MSCN NLar NMen SFgr SIng WAbe WPer
	'Bascour Zilver'	CMea CWil ECha LBee MOne SFgr SIng WHal
	'Beaute'	MOne
	'Bedivere'	CPBP CWil LBee LRHS MOne NMen SRms
	'Bedivere Crested'	CWil
*	'Bedley Hi'	MHom MOne
	'Bella Donna'	MHom MOne NHol NMen WPer
	'Bella Meade'	CWil MOne NMen SFgr SRms WPer
	'Bellotts Pourpre'	CWil NHol
	'Bennerbroek'	MOne
	'Benny Hill'	CWil MOne
	'Bernstein'	CWil MHer MOne SFgr WHal
	'Beta'	MHom MOne NHol NMen WAbe WPer WTin
	'Bethany'	CWil MOne NHol NMen WHal
	'Bicolor' ambig.	EPfP
	'Big Mal'	NHol
	'Big Slipper'	MOne NHol
	'Binstead'	MOne NHol
	'Birchmaier'	NMen SFgr
	'Black Beauty'	EPot
	'Black Cap'	MOne
	'Black Claret'	NHol
	'Black Knight'	LBee LRHS MHer SPlb SRms WHal
	'Black Mini'	CWil EPot GAbr MDKP NBir NMen SRms WAbe
	'Black Mountain'	CHEx CWil LBee LRHS MOne SIng
	'Black Prince'	ECha
	'Black Velvet'	WCom WIvy WPer
	'Bladon'	WPer
	'Blari'	MOne
	'Blood Sucker'	WGor
	'Blood Tip'	CHEx CMea CWil ECha GAbr GCra GKev LBee LRHS MHer NHol NMen NRya SPoG SRms WFar WGor WHal WPer
	'Blue Boy'	CWil ECha EPPr EPot GAbr LBee LRHS MOne NHol NMen SFgr SRms WCom WPer
	'Blue Moon'	MOne NMen
	'Blue Time'	GEdr MOne SFgr WHoo WTin
	'Blush'	EDAr MOne
	'Boissieri'	see *S. tectorum* subsp. *tectorum* 'Boissieri'
	'Bold Chick'	MOne
	'Booth's Red'	CHEx MOne NMen SIng WGor
	'Boreale'	see *Jovibarba hirta* subsp. *borealis*
	borisii	see *S. ciliosum* var. *borisii*
	borissovae	CWil MHom NMen SDys
	'Boromir'	CWil MOne
	'Boule de Neige'	NMen
	'Bowles's Variety'	WCom WPer
	'Braune Maus' **new**	SFgr
	brevipilum from Turkey	MOne

'Bright Eyes'	MOne
'Britta'	MOne SDys
'Brock'	CWil ECha LRHS MHer MHom NHol WPer
'Bronco'	CHEx CWil ECho GAbr LBee LRHS MHom MOne NMen SRms WCot WFar WPGP
'Bronze Pastel'	CWil ECha MHom MOne NMen NSla SFgr SRms SRot WGor WTin
'Bronze Tower'	NHol
'Brown Owl'	CWil ECho MOne NHol SRms WFar
'Brownii'	MOne NMen WPer WTin
'Brunette'	ECho GAbr
'Burgundy'	ECha MOne
'Burgundy Velvet'	MOne
'Burnatii'	see *S. montanum* subsp. *burnatii*
'Burning Desire'	WGor
'Butterfly'	MOne
'Café'	CWil EGoo NHol NMen SFgr SIng SRms WIvy WPer
× ***calcaratum***	SRms
calcareum	CMea CSam CWil EWll GKir LRHS MAsh MOne NBro NEgg NMen SPlb SPoG SRms SRot WFar WHoo WPer
- from Alps, France	CWil MOne
- from Calde la Vanoise, France	CWil MOne NMen
- from Ceüze, France	CWil MOne WIvy
- from Cherion	MOne
- from Cleizé, France	see *S. calcareum* 'Limelight'
- from Col Bayard, France	CWil GAbr MOne NMen
- from Colle St Michel, France	CWil MOne NMen SFgr
- from Gorges supérieures du Cians, France	CWil MOne NMen
- from Guillaumes, Mont Ventoux, France	CWil MOne NMen SFgr SRot WHoo
- from La Mata de la Riba, Spain	MOne
- from Mont Ventoux, France	CWil MOne
- from Petite Ceüse, France	SRot
- - GDJ 92.15	CWil
- - GDJ 92.16	CWil
- from Queyras, France	CWil MOne NMen
- from Route d'Annôt, France	CWil MOne NMen
- from Triora, Italy	CWil MOne NHol NMen
- 'Benz'	SDys
- 'Cristatum'	CStu
- 'Extra'	CHEx CWil GAbr GEdr MSCN SFgr SRot
- 'Greenii'	CWil GKev LRHS MOne NDlv NHol NMen SIng SPlb
§ - 'Grigg's Surprise'	CWil MHer MOne NMen WFar
§ - 'Limelight'	CMea CWil LRHS MOne NHol NMen SIng SPoG WHal WIvy WPer WTin
- 'Monstrosum'	see *S. calcareum* 'Grigg's Surprise'
- 'Mrs Giuseppi'	CWil ECho ETod GAbr LBee LRHS MOne NMen SFgr SRms STre WAbe WFar WPer
- 'Pink Pearl'	CWil MOne MSCN NMen SDys SFgr WIvy WTin
- 'Sir William Lawrence'	CMea CPBP CWil ECho EDAr NMen SFgr WAbe WHal WHoo WIvy WPer WThu WTin
'Caldera'	NHol
californicum	SIng
* ***calopticum*** × ***nevadense***	WTin
'Cameo'	see *Jovibarba heuffelii* var. *glabra* 'Cameo'
'Canada Kate'	CWil NHol WPer
'Cancer'	MOne
'Candy Floss'	CWil MOne NMen WGor
cantabricum	CWil NMen WThu
- subsp. ***cantabricum*** from Leitariegos, Spain	CWil GAbr MHom MOne NMen
- - from Peña de Llesba, Spain GDJ 93.13	CWil
- - from Pico del Lobo, Spain	CWil
- from Cuengas Piedras	MOne
- from Cuevas del Sil, Spain	CWil MOne
- from Navafria, Spain	CWil MOne NHol SIng WTin
- from Peña Prieta, Spain	MOne NMen
- from Piedrafita, Spain	MOne
- from Riaño, Spain	CWil GAbr
- from San Glorio, Spain	CWil GAbr MOne NMen
- from Santander, Spain	NHol
- from Ticeros	MOne NMen
- from Tizneros, Spain	CWil
- from Valvarnera, Spain	MOne NMen
- subsp. ***guadarramense***	see *S. vicentei* subsp. *paui*
- - from Pico del Lobo, Spain, No 1	MOne SRot
- - from Pico del Lobo, Spain, No 2	MOne
- - from Valvanera, Spain, No 1	CWil NMen
cantabricum × ***montanum*** subsp. ***stiriacum***	WEas WTin
cantabricum × ***montanum*** subsp. ***stiriacum*** 'Lloyd Praeger'	CWil
- subsp. ***urbionense***	CWil GEdr
- - from El Gatón, Spain	CWil
- - from Picos de Urbión, Spain	CWil MOne NMen
'Canth'	NHol
'Caramel'	MOne
* × ***carlsii***	MOne
'Carluke'	MOne
'Carmen'	GAbr MOne SFgr
'Carneum'	MOne NHol
'Carnival'	MOne NMen WPer
caucasicum	CWil GEdr GKir MHom MOne NMen SPoG
'Cauticola'	MOne
'Cavo Doro'	CWil MOne SFgr
'Celon'	MOne
'Centennial'	MOne
'Chalon'	MOne
charadzeae	CWil LBee LRHS MOne NHol
'Cherry Frost'	ECho MOne NDlv NMen SFgr STre WAbe
'Cherry Glow'	see *Jovibarba heuffelii* 'Cherry Glow'
'Chivalry'	MOne
'Chocolate'	MOne NHol WAbe WPer
§ × ***christii***	MOne NHol NMen
'Christmas Time'	MOne NHol SFgr
ciliosum ♀H4	CMea CPBP CWil ECho GMaP NMen NRya
- from Alí Butús, Bulgaria	SDys
§ - var. ***borisii***	CWil EPfP GCal GKev NDlv NMen NRya WAbe WHal
- var. ***galicicum*** 'Mali Hat'	NMen WPer
ciliosum × ***ciliosum*** var. ***borisii***	CTri NMen
ciliosum × ***grandiflorum***	CWil MOne NMen

ciliosum* × *marmoreum	NMen
ciliosum* × *tectorum	WTin
'Cindy'	MOne SRms
'Circlet'	CWil MOne NMen
'Cistaceum'	WEas
'Clara Noyes'	MOne WFar WPer
'Clare'	MHer MOne
'Claudine'	MOne
'Clemanum'	MOne
'Cleveland Morgan'	ECha LRHS MHom MOne NBro NMen
'Climax' ambig.	ECho EPfP MHom MOne NMen WFar
'Cobweb Capers'	MHom MOne
'Cobweb Centres'	MOne NMen
'Cochise'	MOne
'Collage'	MOne NHol WPer
'Collecteur Anchisi'	MOne NHol SDys SFgr
'Commander Hay' ♀H4	CHEx COlW EDAr EPfP ETod EWes GAbr GCra GKev LHop LRHS MBNS MHom MOne MSCN NMen NPer SRGP SRms STre WEas WHal WIvy WPer
'Comte de Congae'	MOne NMen
'Concorde' **new**	LRHS
'Congo'	MOne NMen SFgr
'Conran'	NHol
'Corio'	MOne
'Cornstone'	ECha NHol
'Corona'	CWil MOne NHol SFgr SRms WPer
'Corsair'	CWil ECha GEdr GKev MBrN MOne NMen SFgr WGor WIvy WPer WTin
'Cranberry'	MOne
'Cresta'	MOne
'Crimson King'	SFgr
'Crimson Velvet'	CHEx CMea LBee LRHS MOne NHol SFgr WCom WPer
§ 'Crispyn'	CWil EPot LBee LRHS MHer MHom MOne NHol NMen SFgr WEas WPer
'Croky'	MOne
'Croton'	WPer
'Cupream'	CWil NDlv SRms WPer
'Czakor'	NHol
'Dakota'	CWil MOne NHol NMen SFgr
'Dallas'	CWil MOne NHol NMen SRms
'Damask'	CWil LBee LRHS MOne NMen SFgr WPer
'Dame Arsac'	MOne
'Dancer's Veil'	MOne
'Darjeeling'	CWil
'Dark Beauty'	CMea CWil ECha LRHS MOne MSCN NMen WAbe WCot WGor WHal WPer
'Dark Cloud'	CWil GAbr LBee LRHS MOne WHoo WIvy WPer
'Dark Point'	CWil MHom MOne NMen SFgr WCom
'Darkie'	CWil SFgr WPer
davisii	ECha
'Deep Fire'	CWil MOne NHol NMen SRms WAbe WIvy WTin
× ***degenianum***	GAbr MOne NMen SFgr WPer
'Delta'	NMen WHoo WTin
densum	see *S. tectorum*
'Devon Jewel'	WGor
'Diamant'	MOne
'Diane'	CWil SFgr
'Director Jacobs'	CWil EDAr MOne NHol NMen SFgr WEas WPer WTin
'Doctor Roberts'	NHol
dolomiticum	NMen
- from Rif Sennes, Italy	MOne
dolomiticum* × *montanum	CWil GKev MOne NBro NMen SFgr WTin
'Donarrose'	NHol SFgr
'Downland Queen'	CWil MOne NHol
'Dragoness'	MOne
'Duke of Windsor'	MOne NMen SFgr
'Dusky'	MOne
'Dyke'	CTri CWil GAbr MOne NHol NMen SFgr WHal
dzhavachischvilii	MOne NMen
'Edge of Night'	CWil NHol SRms
'Eefje'	CWil
'El Greco'	MOne
'El Toro'	ECha MHom SIng
'Elene'	MOne
'Elgar'	MOne WIvy WPer
'Elizabeth'	WPer
'Elvis'	CWil GAbr NMen SFgr
'Emerald Giant'	CWil MOne NHol SFgr SRms WPer WTin
'Emerson's Giant'	CWil MOne NMen
'Emma Jane'	MOne
'Emmchen'	CWil
'Engle's'	CMea CTri ECha LRHS MHer MOne NMen SRms WHal WPer
'Engle's 13-2'	MOne NBro NHol NMen
'Engle's Rubrum'	CPBP EPot LBee NHol NMen
erythraeum	CMea LRHS MHom NHol NMen SPlb WHal
- from Pirin, Bulgaria	MOne NMen SIng
- from Rila, Bulgaria	NMen
- 'Red Velvet'	MOne
'Excalibur'	MOne NMen WIvy
'Exhibita'	CWil MOne SDys SRms
'Exorna'	CWil ECha MHom MOne NMen SFgr WEas WIvy WPer
'Fair Lady'	CWil MHom MOne NMen
'Fairy'	EPot
'Fame'	MOne NHol
'Fat Jack'	CWil
× ***fauconnettii***	CWil EDAr NHol NMen SFgr SIng
- 'Thompsonii'	CWil MOne NHol NMen SIng
'Feldmaier'	GAbr MOne
'Festival'	MOne NMen
'Feu de Printemps'	MOne
'Fiery Furness'	MOne
'Fiesta' ambig.	WHal
fimbriatum	see *S.* × *barbulatum*
'Finerpointe'	MOne
'Fire Glint'	CWil GEdr MOne NHol SIng SRms WIvy
'Firebird'	MOne NMen SFgr
'Firefly'	MOne
'First Try'	MOne
'Flaming Heart'	CWil EDAr MBrN MOne NMen WGor WPer
'Flamingo'	ECha MOne NMen
'Flamme'	MOne
'Flanders Passion'	ECha EPot LBee LRHS NMen SRms WPer
'Flasher'	WPer
'Fluweel'	MOne
'Fontanae'	MOne
'Forden'	CHEx MOne MSCN SFgr WGor
'Ford's Amiability'	SDys
'Ford's Shadows'	SDys
'Ford's Spring'	CWil MOne NHol NMen WIvy WPer
'Freckles'	MOne
'Freeland'	WPer
'Frigidum'	NDlv

'Frolic' MOne
'Fronika' CWil
'Frost and Flame' NHol
'Frosty' CWil MOne SFgr SRms
'Fuego' CWil MHom MOne SFgr
× ***funckii*** CHEx CWil EDAr MBrN MOne NHol NMen SDys SIng WPer WTin
'Furryness' MOne
'Fuzzy Wuzzy' MOne
'Gallivarda' CWil MSCN
'Gambol' NHol
'Gamma' CHEx CWil LBee LRHS NHol NMen SDys SIng SRms WEas WTin
'Garnet' ECho WIvy WPer
'Gay Jester' CTri CWil MOne SFgr WHoo WTin
'Gazelle' WIvy WPer
'Genevione' CWil
'Georgette' CWil ECha NMen WPer
'Ginger' MOne
'Ginnie's Delight' CWil NMen
'Gipsy' CWil MOne
giuseppii LBee MHer NHol NMen WPer
- from Coriscao, Spain LRHS
- - GDJ 93.17 CWil
- from Cumbre de Cebolleda GDJ 93.04 CWil
- from Peña Espigüete, Spain CWil MOne NMen SDys
- from Peña Prieta, Spain CWil MOne NMen
'Gizmo' CWil SFgr
'Glaucum' see *S. tectorum* var. *glaucum*
'Gleam' MOne
'Gloriosum' ambig. GAbr SFgr WPer
'Glowing Embers' CWil MHom MOne NMen WHal WPer
'Goldie' MOne
'Gollum' MOne
'Granada' NMen
'Granat' CWil LRHS MHer MOne NMen SRms WCom WIvy WPer
'Granby' CWil ECho LBee LRHS MOne NMen SDys
grandiflorum CWil NMen SIng WPer
- from Valpine MOne NMen
- 'Fasciatum' CWil MOne NMen
- 'Keston' MOne
grandiflorum* × *montanum see *S.* × *christii*
grandiflorum* × *tectorum see *S.* × *hayekii*
'Grannie's Favourite' MOne
'Grape Idol' CWil
'Grapetone' MHom NMen SDys WHal
'Graupurpur' CWil
'Green Apple' CWil GAbr MHom NMen SDys
'Green Dragon' LRHS MSCN
'Green Gables' WPer
'Green Ice' CWil
'Greenwich Time' NMen
* ***greigii*** EPot GKir
'Grenadier' MOne
'Grey Dawn' LRHS MHom
'Grey Ghost' NMen WIvy WPer
'Grey Green' CWil NHol
'Grey Lady' CElw CMea CWil
'Grey Owl' GMaP LRHS
'Grey Velvet' CWil
'Greyfriars' CMea EPot EWll LBee LRHS NMen SFgr WGor WPer
'Greyolla' CWil WPer
'Gruaud Larose' NHol
'Grünrand' MOne
'Grünschnabel' MOne
'Grünspecht' MOne
'Gulle Dame' CWil SFgr
'Halemaumau' CWil MOne
I 'Hall's Hybrid' CWil GAbr NBro SRms STre
'Hall's Seedling' GKir
'Happy' CWil MOne NMen SFgr SRms WGor WIvy WPer WThu
'Hart' CWil NHol SRms WTin
'Hartside' MOne
'Haullauer's Seedling' MOne
'Havana' NMen
§ × ***hayekii*** MOne
'Hayling' LRHS MOne NHol NMen SRms WPer
'Heavenly Joy' NHol
'Heigham Red' CWil EPPr LBee LRHS MOne NHol NMen WPer
'Heliotroop' MOne SDys SRot
helveticum see *S. montanum*
'Hester' CHEx CWil ECho GAbr MBrN NBro NMen SRms WFar
'Hey-hey' EPot LBee LRHS MBrN NMen SIng SPlb SRms WPer
'Hidde' CWil SFgr WIvy WPer
'Hidde's Roosje' MOne NMen
'Hirsutum' see *Jovibarba allionii*
hirtum see *Jovibarba hirta*
'Hispidulum' MOne
'Hookeri' see *S.* × *barbulatum* 'Hookeri'
'Hopi' CWil MOne NHol SRms
'Hortulanus Smit' NMen
'Hugo' SIng
'Hullabaloo' MOne SFgr
'Hurricane' CWil MOne WIvy WPer
'Icicle' CHEx CMea LRHS MSCN NBro NHol NMen SIng SRms WAbe WGor
imbricatum see *S.* × *barbulatum*
'Imperial' CWil MHom
ingwersenii MHom MOne
ingwersenii* × *pumilum CWil
- from Spain MOne NMen
'Interlace' MOne
'Iophon' LBee LRHS MOne
'Irazu' CWil GAbr LRHS MOne NMen SDys SFgr SRms WPer
'Irene' **new** SFgr
'Isaac Dyson' SDys SRot
italicum MHom NMen
'Itchen' MOne NMen
'Iwo' CHEx NMen SFgr WIvy
'Jack Frost' CWil MOne NBro NMen SFgr
'Jacquette' CWil
'Jade' ambig. MOne
'Jamie's Pride' WGor
'Jane' MOne
'Jelly Bean' CWil MOne NMen SFgr
'Jet Stream' CWil EPPr LRHS NMen SDys SPlb WGor
'Jewel Case' CWil LRHS MOne NMen SRms
'John T.' MOne WEas
'Jolly Green Giant' MHom MOne
'Jo's Spark' NSla
'Jubilee' CMea CWil ECho EDAr ELan EPot GKev MHer NHol NMen SRms STre WGor WPer
'Jubilee Tricolor' NHol NMen SFgr WAbe
'Jungle Fires' CWil EPot ITim NHol SDys SRms WHoo
'Jungle Shadows' EDAr
'Jurato' NHol
'Justine's Choice' CWil SRms

'Kalinda'	MHom NMen
'Kappa'	CTri MOne NBro NHol NMen SDys SRot WPer
'Katmai'	CWil NHol
'Kelly Jo'	CWil EWll NBro NMen WFar WTin
'Kelut'	MOne
'Kermit'	MHom NMen
'Kerneri'	NHol
'Kibo'	MOne WIvy
'Kimble'	WPer
kindingeri	CWil MHom NMen NWCA
'King George'	CTri CWil ECha GKir ITim LBee LRHS MOne NMen SFgr SRms STre WGor WHal WHoo WPer WTin
'Kip'	CMea ECha NMen WGor WIvy WPer
'Kismet'	NMen
'Koko Flanel'	CWil SFgr
'Kolagas Mayfair'	MOne
'Korspel Glory 4'	CWil
'Korspelsegietje'	CWil GAbr
kosaninii	CWil MOne NHol NMen SFgr WPer WTin
- from Koprivnik, Slovenia	MOne MSCN NMen SDys WAbe
- 'Hepworth'	NHol
'Krakeling'	MOne
'Kramer's Purpur'	NMen
'Kramer's Spinrad'	CHEx CMea CWil ECha GAbr LBee LRHS MOne NMen NWCA SDys SFgr SIng STre WEas WHoo WIvy WTin
'La Serenissima'	MOne
'Lady Kelly'	CMea MOne NMen WIvy
'Launcelot'	ECha WPer
'Lavender and Old Lace'	CHEx CWil GAbr LRHS MSCN NMen SFgr WPer
'Laysan'	CWil NHol
Le Clair's hybrid No 4	NMen
'Lennik's Glory'	see *S.* 'Crispyn'
'Leocadia's Nephew'	MOne NMen
'Leocadia's Niece'	MOne
'Leon Smits'	CWil
'Les Yielding'	MOne
'Lilac Time'	CWil GAbr LRHS MHer MOne NMen SFgr SPlb SRms WHal WIvy WPer
'Limbo'	CWil
'Lion King'	CWil MSCN
'Lipari'	CElw ECha EPot NMen SRms
'Lipstick'	NMen
'Lively Bug'	CWil GEdr LBee LRHS MSCN SDys WCom WGor WPer
'Lloyd Praeger'	see *S. montanum* subsp. *stiriacum* 'Lloyd Praeger'
'Lonzo'	CWil SRms
'Lorraine' **new**	LRHS
'Lustrous'	MOne
'Lynn's Choice'	CWil GAbr MOne SFgr SIng WHal WIvy WPer
macedonicum	NDlv NMen WTin
- from Ljuboten, Macedonia/Kosovo	CWil MOne NMen
'Madeleine'	CWil
'Magic Spell'	CWil MOne NMen
'Magical'	CWil
'Magnificum'	CWil NMen WGor
'Mahogany'	CHEx CTri CWil ECho EDAr GKev LBee LRHS MHer MOne NHol NMen NWCA SFgr SRms STre SWal WEas WGor WHal WIvy
'Maigret'	CWil WPer
'Majestic'	CWil LBee LRHS NMen
'Major White'	CHEx
'Malby's Hybrid'	see *S.* 'Reginald Malby'
'Marella'	WPer
'Maria Laach'	CWil SIng
'Marijntje'	CWil NHol NMen WPer
'Marjorie Newton'	CWil WPer
§ ***marmoreum***	ECho EPot GKev LBee LRHS NMen SRms STre WFar WHal WPer
- from Kanzan Gorge, Bulgaria	EPot MOne NHol NMen SIng
- from Monte Tirone, Italy	LRHS SDys
- from Okol, Albania	MOne NMen
- 'Brunneifolium'	CWil EGoo GAbr GCal LBee LRHS MOne NHol NMen SIng WIvy WPer
- 'Bruno' **new**	STre
- subsp. ***marmoreum*** var. ***dinaricum***	MHer NMen
'Matador'	MOne
'Mate'	NMen
'Maubi'	CHEx
'Mauna Kea'	WPer
'Mauvine'	MOne NHol
'Mayfair Imp'	MOne
'Medallion'	MOne SFgr
'Meisse'	ECho MOne
'Melanie'	CWil MBrN NMen WIvy
'Mercury'	CWil GAbr LRHS NBro NHol NMen SRms
'Merkur'	MOne
'Merlin'	MSCN
'Midas'	CWil ECha GEdr LRHS SFgr
'Milá'	CWil
'Minaret'	MOne
'Mini Frost'	CWil NMen SIng WPer
'Missouri Rose'	NHol
'Mixed Spice'	CWil
'Moerkerk's Merit'	CWil GAbr NHol NMen
'Mondstein'	CWil GMaP MOne SFgr SRms WIvy WPer
'Monique'	WPer
'Montage'	CWil
§ ***montanum***	LRHS NMen WPer
- from Arbizion	CWil MOne
- from Windachtal, Germany	CWil NMen
§ - subsp. ***burnatii***	CWil MHom MOne NMen WIvy
- 'Caesar' **new**	MSCN
- subsp. ***carpaticum***	CWil
- - 'Cmiral's Yellow'	MSCN NMen SFgr WAbe WCom WIvy
* - Fragell form	SFgr
- from Monte Tirone	LBee
- from Monte Tonale, Italy	CWil
- subsp. ***montanum***	CWil
- 'Rubrum'	see *S.* 'Red Mountain'
- subsp. ***stiriacum***	CWil GEdr MOne NMen SFgr SIng
§ - - 'Lloyd Praeger'	CWil LBee LRHS MOne NMen SDys SFgr WIvy WPer
montanum* × *tectorum var. ***boutignyanum*** GDJ 94.15	CWil
'Moondrops'	CWil
'More Honey'	CWil NMen SFgr SRms
'Morning Glow'	CMea WGor WHal WPer
'Mount Hood'	LRHS SRms WHal
'Mrs Elliott'	MOne
'Mulberry Wine'	CWil LBee LRHS NHol WHoo
'Mystic'	CWil MBrN NMen WPer
'Neon'	CWil
nevadense	CWil EPot MOne NMen SFgr SRms
- from Puerto de San Francisco	CWil MOne

- from Calar de Santa Barbara, Spain GDJ 96A-07	CWil
- var. ***hirtellum***	CWil NMen SIng
'Nico'	CWil SRms
'Night Raven'	CMea WIvy WPer
'Nigrum'	see *S. tectorum* 'Nigrum'
'Niobe'	MOne SFgr WHal
'Noir'	CWil EDAr NBro NMen WAbe
'Norbert'	CWil EDAr SRms WIvy WPer
'Norne'	MOne
'Nörtofts Beauty'	MOne
'Nouveau Pastel'	CMea CWil MOne NMen WHal WPer
'Novak'	CWil
'Octet'	CWil MOne NMen SIng
octopodes	NBir SIde
- var. ***apetalum***	CWil GAbr MOne MSCN NMen SIng SRms WIvy
'Oddity'	CPBP CWil ECha ETod MBrN MHer NMen WCot WHal WPer
'Ohio Burgundy'	ECha LRHS MOne NDlv NMen WAbe WPer WTin
'Old Rose'	MOne
'Olivette'	ECha NMen WPer WTin
'Omega'	MOne WPer
'Ornatum'	EPot MHer MHom MOne NMen SRms WAbe WEas WHal WIvy WPer
ossetiense	CWil GAbr MOne NMen
'Othello'	CTri EPfP GCra NBir STre WCot WPer WTin
'Pacific Feather Power'	NMen
'Pacific Purple Shadows'	CWil
'Packardian'	CWil GKev MOne NHol NMen SFgr WIvy
'Painted Lady'	CWil
'Palissander'	EDAr GAbr MOne NMen SFgr WPer
'Pam Wain'	MHom NMen
'Panola Fire'	WFar
'Parade'	MOne
'Paricutin'	SDys
'Passionata'	CWil SFgr
'Pastel'	CWil NMen SIng
patens	see *Jovibarba heuffelii*
'Patrician'	CWil LBee LRHS SRms
'Peggy'	CWil WGor
'Pekinese'	CWil EDAr EPot GEdr ITim LRHS NBro NHol NMen SIng SRms WEas WGor WPer
'Peterson's Ornatum'	MOne SDys
'Petsy'	CWil SRms
'Pilatus'	ECha EWes LBMP SRms WFar WPer
× ***piliferum*** 'Hausmannii'	MOne
'Pink Astrid'	CWil
'Pink Button'	CWil
'Pink Cloud'	CWil LRHS NMen SRms
'Pink Dawn'	MOne
'Pink Delight'	MOne
'Pink Flamingoes'	MOne SRot
'Pink Lemonade'	CWil MHom
'Pink Mist'	WPer
'Pink Puff'	CWil MHom MOne NMen SRms
'Pippin'	CMea CWil SRms WPer
'Piran'	CWil MOne
pittonii	CMea CWil EPot GAbr NMen WHal
'Pixie'	CPBP CWil MOne NDlv NMen SFgr WIvy WPer
'Plum Frosting'	WGor
'Plum Mist'	NHol
'Plumb Rose'	CWil MOne NMen WIvy WPer
'Pluto'	CWil LBee LRHS NHol
'Polaris'	CWil MHom
'Poldark'	MOne
'Pompeon'	MOne
'Ponderosa'	CWil
'Pottsii'	CWil MOne
I 'Powellii'	MOne SIng
'Procton'	MOne
'Proud Zelda'	GAbr MOne NMen
'Průhonice'	CWil MOne SRms WFar
'Pseudo-ornatum'	LBee LRHS SRms
'Pumaros'	NMen SDys
pumilum	CWil LRHS MBar NMen
- from Adyl-Su, Chechnya, No 1	CWil
- from Armkhi	SDys
- from El'brus, Russia, No 1	CWil
- from Techensis	CWil NMen
- 'Sopa'	CWil MOne NMen
'Purdy'	MHom MSCN WAbe
'Purdy's 50-6'	CWil GAbr
'Purdy's 70-40'	MOne
'Purple Beauty'	EPot MOne
'Purple King'	MHom SDys
'Purple Queen'	CWil EDAr LRHS
'Pygmalion'	CWil SIng
'Queen Amalia'	see *S. reginae-amaliae*
'Quintessence'	CWil NHol SFgr SRms
'Racey'	CWil
'Ragtime'	MOne
'Ramses'	MOne SDys
'Raspberry Ice'	CMea LBee LRHS MSCN NBro NHol NMen WPer
'Rauer Kulm'	CWil
* 'Rauheit'	MOne WFar
'Rauhreif'	WFar
'Red Ace'	CWil ECha GEdr LRHS NBro NMen SFgr SRms WFar WPer
'Red Beam'	CWil LRHS MOne MSCN
'Red Chips'	MHom
'Red Cross'	MOne
'Red Delta'	CWil MOne NBir NMen SFgr WCot
'Red Devil'	CWil ECha LRHS MOne NHol NMen SFgr SPlb WHoo WPer WTin
'Red King'	MOne
'Red Lion'	CWil GEdr SFgr
'Red Lynn'	CWil
§ 'Red Mountain'	CWil LBee LRHS MOne SRms
'Red Pink'	CWil MOne
'Red Robin'	EDAr GMaP LRHS MOne SIng
'Red Rum'	SIng WPer
'Red Shadows'	LBee LRHS WPer WTin
'Red Spider'	CWil MHom NBro NMen
'Red Summer'	MOne
'Regal'	MOne NMen
'Regina'	NMen
reginae	see *S. reginae-amaliae*
§ ***reginae-amaliae***	CWil NHol NMen
- from Kambeecho, Greece, No 2	NMen SDys
- from Mavri Petri	CWil MOne SDys
- from Sarpun, Turkey	CWil NMen SDys WTin
- from Vardusa, Serbia	CWil SDys
§ 'Reginald Malby'	CTri ECho GMaP LRHS NMen SFgr SRms WIvy
'Reinhardt'	CMea CWil ECha EDAr EPot GEdr LRHS MBrN MHer MOne NMen SIng SPlb SRms WFar WHal WHoo WIvy WPer
'Remus'	CWil ECha ELan MOne NMen SDys SFgr SRms WGor
'Rex'	NMen
'Rhöne'	CWil LBee LRHS MOne

*	***richardii***	MBar
	'Risque'	CWil LBee LRHS WPer
	'Rita Jane'	CWil ECha MHom MOne NMen SFgr SIng WTin
	'Robin'	ITim LBee LRHS NBro NHol SRms WTin
	'Ronny'	CWil
	'Rose Splendour'	NHol
	× ***roseum***	MOne
	- 'Fimbriatum'	CWil GAbr LBee LRHS NDlv NHol SFgr WEas
	'Rosie'	CMea CPBP CWil EPot GAbr GEdr ITim LBee LRHS MOne NHol NMen SIng SRms WHal WHoo WPer WTin
	'Rotkopf'	CWil MOne MSCN NHol NMen SFgr SRms
	'Rotmantel'	SDys WTin
	'Rotsandsteinriese'	MOne
	'Rotund'	CWil GEdr
	'Rouge'	NMen
	'Royal Mail'	MOne
	'Royal Opera'	CWil EDAr MOne NMen
	'Royal Ruby'	ECha LBee LRHS MSCN NMen SRms WIvy
	'Royale' **new**	SFgr
	'Rubellum'	CWil MOne
	'Rubellum Mahogany'	SFgr
	'Rubikon Improved'	MOne
	'Rubin'	CMea CTri ECha EGoo EPfP GGar MAsh MSCN NBir NBlu NEgg NMen NPri NWCA SPoG SRms WAbe WClo WEas WPer
I	'Rubra Ash'	CWil MOne NMen WAbe WTin
	'Rubrum Ray'	CWil MOne SRms
*	'Ruby Glow'	EDAr
	'Russian River'	WHoo WTin
	'Rusty'	CWil SFgr
	ruthenicum	LRHS MHom
	- 'Regis-Fernandii'	ECho
	'Safara'	CWil
	'Saffron'	MOne NMen
	'Saga'	MHom MOne
	'Sanford's Hybrid'	MOne
	'Sarah'	MOne NMen
	'Sarotte'	CWil
	'Sassy Frass'	NMen
	'Saturn'	MOne NMen
	schlehanii	see *S. marmoreum*
	schnittspahnii	MOne
	× ***schottii***	MOne
	'Seminole'	CWil MOne
	'Serena'	MOne
	'Sha-Na'	CWil
	'Sharon's Pencil'	CWil
	'Sheila'	GAbr
	'Shirley Moore'	CWil MOne SFgr WTin
	'Shirley's Joy'	NMen WTin
	'Sideshow'	CWil MOne
	'Sigma'	MOne
	'Silbering'	LBMP
	'Silberkarneol' misapplied	see *S.* 'Silver Jubilee'
	'Silberspitz'	CWil LRHS MHer MHom NBro NMen SPlb WPer
	'Silver Cup'	CWil SFgr WIvy
§	'Silver Jubilee'	CMea CWil ECha EDAr GAbr LRHS NBro NDlv SPlb SRms WGor
	'Silver Queen'	CWil SFgr
	'Silver Shadow'	WGor
	'Silver Thaw'	CWil ECha EDAr LRHS NMen SFgr SIng
	'Silverine'	CWil
	'Silvertone'	CWil
	'Simonkaianum'	see *Jovibarba hirta*
	'Sioux'	CPBP CWil GAbr LBee LRHS MBrN NMen SIng WFar WHal WIvy WPer WTin
	'Skrocki's Bronze'	GAbr LRHS WPer
	'Slabber's Seedling'	CWil
	'Small Wonder'	CWil
	'Smaragd'	CWil ECha LBee LRHS WFar
	'Smokey Jet'	SFgr
	'Snowberger'	CMea CWil EPot LRHS MOne NMen SFgr SIng SRms WGor WHal WPer
	'Soarte'	MOne
	soboliferum	see *Jovibarba sobolifera*
	'Soothsayer'	CWil MOne NMen
	sosnowskyi	CWil MOne NMen
	'Spanish Dancer'	NMen
	'Speciosum'	MOne
	'Spherette'	CWil MBrN NMen WAbe WPer
	'Spice'	MOne
	'Spinellii'	MOne WThu WTin
	'Spiver's Velvet'	MOne
	'Sponnier'	MOne
	'Springmist'	CMea CWil EPot GAbr GMaP LRHS MBrN MOne NBlu SFgr SRms WGor WPer WTin
	'Sprite'	CWil GEdr MOne NMen SDys WIvy WTin
	'Squib'	CWil MSCN
	stansfieldii	see *S. arachnoideum* subsp. *tomentosum* 'Stansfieldii'
	'Starion'	CWil MOne
	'Starshine'	MHer NHol NMen SFgr
	'State Fair'	CWil NHol NMen WCom WIvy WPer
*	***stoloniferum***	GAbr
	'Strawberry Fields'	MOne
	'Strider'	CWil GAbr WTin
	'Stuffed Olive'	CWil MOne SDys SRot
I	'Subanum'	MOne
	'Sun Waves'	CWil MOne NHol SDys SFgr
	'Sunray Magic'	WGor
	'Sunrise'	MOne
	'Super Dome'	CWil
	'Supernova'	MOne
	'Syston Flame'	CWil NMen
	'Tambimuttu'	MOne
	'Tarita'	CWil
	'Tarn Hows'	MOne
§	***tectorum*** ♀H4	CArn CHby CSam CTri CWil ECho EDAr ELan EPfP GKev GKir GPoy LBee LRHS MBar MHer MNHC NBlu NMen SBch SIde SIng SPlb STre WFar WJek
	- from Eporn	CWil MOne NMen
§	- var. ***alpinum***	CWil LRHS MHom MOne NBro NHol NMen SIng
	- - from Sierra del Cadi, Spain	MOne NHol
	- var. ***andreanum***	CWil
	- 'Atropurpureum'	ECho ELan NHol NMen WCom WTin
	- 'Atrorubens'	NHol
	- 'Atroviolaceum'	EDAr NHol NLar NMen WFar WIvy WTin
*	- 'Aureum'	SFgr
	- var. ***boutignyanum*** from Route de Tuixén, Spain GDJ 94.04	CWil
	- - from Sant Joan de Caselles, Andorra GDJ 94.02	CWil
	- - GDJ 94.03	CWil
	- var. ***calcareum***	ECho MOne

	- subsp. ***cantalicum***	SRms
§	- var. ***glaucum***	MOne NDlv
§	- 'Nigrum'	LBee LRHS MHer MOne NBro NHol NMen SDys SRms WGor WTin
	- 'Red Flush'	CWil EDAr GKir MBrN NMen SDys SFgr SPoG WFar WPer
	- 'Royanum'	GAbr MSCN
*	- subsp. ***sanguineum***	EDAr
	- 'Sunset'	CMea EDAr NMen SDys SFgr WHal
	- subsp. ***tectorum***	MOne
§	- - 'Boissieri'	CWil NMen SRms WIvy
	- - 'Triste'	CHEx CWil LBee LRHS MOne NMen SRms WFar
	- 'Violaceum'	MHom SIng SRms STre WGor
	tectorum × ***zeleborii***	WTin
	'Tederheid'	LBMP MOne
	'Telfan'	MOne NMen
	'Tenburg'	MOne
	'Terracotta Baby'	CWil SFgr
	'Thayne'	NMen
	'The Platters'	CWil
	'The Rocket'	CWil
	× ***thompsonianum***	CWil NHol NMen SFgr
	'Thunder'	CWil
	'Tiffany'	NHol WPer
	'Tiger Bay'	NHol
	'Tina'	WPer
	'Tip Top'	CWil GEdr SFgr
	'Titania'	CWil NBro NMen WHal WTin
	'Tombago'	MOne
	'Topaz'	CWil ECha LBee LRHS MOne NMen SFgr SRms
	'Tordeur's Memory'	CWil LBee LRHS MOne NMen
	'Trail Walker'	CWil LBee LRHS MOne SRms
	transcaucasicum	CWil
	'Tree Beard'	CWil
	'Tristesse'	CWil EDAr GAbr MOne NMen SFgr WGor
	'Truva'	CWil MOne NMen SFgr
	'Tumpty'	WGor
	'Twilight Blues'	CWil LRHS SFgr
	'Undine'	CWil SFgr
	× ***vaccarii***	CWil NMen
	'Van der Steen'	GAbr
	'Vanbaelen'	CWil GAbr NMen SDys
	'Vanessa'	CWil
	× ***versicolor***	NHol
	'Veuchelen'	CWil MOne
	vicentei	MHom NMen WFar WTin
	- from Gaton	LBee LRHS MOne NMen
§	- subsp. ***paui***	NSla
	'Victorian'	MOne
	'Video'	CWil MHom NMen SFgr
	'Virgil'	CWil EDAr GAbr MBrN NMen SDys SIng WAbe WCot WGor WPer WTin
I	'Virginius'	CWil GAbr
	'Warners Pink'	MDKP
	'Watermelon Rind'	MOne
	webbianum	see *S. arachnoideum* subsp. *tomentosum* (C.B. Lehm. & Schnittsp.) Schinz & Thell.
	'Webby Flame'	CWil
	'Webby Ola'	NMen
	'Wega'	NMen
	'Weirdo'	CWil
	'Wendy'	MOne NMen
	'Westerlin'	CWil ECha MOne NMen SIng
	'White Christmas'	see *S. arachnoideum* 'White Christmas'
	'White Eyes'	NMen
	'Whitening'	NMen
I	'Woolcott's Variety'	CWil ECho GAbr LRHS MDKP MOne MSCN NBir NMen SFgr WFar WPer WTin
	wulfenii	CWil NMen
*	- ***roseum***	EDAr
	'Xaviera'	CWil
	zeleborii	SDys WHal
	'Zenith'	CWil GAbr SFgr SRms
	'Zenobia'	MHom
	'Zenocrate'	WHal
	'Zepherin'	CWil MSCN
	'Zilver Moon'	CWil NMen
	'Zircon'	NMen
	'Zone'	CHEx NMen
	'Zorba'	NMen
	'Zulu'	ECha SFgr

Senecio (*Asteraceae*)

	B&SWJ 10703 from Colombia	WCru
	amplectens var. ***holmii*** **new**	LFur
§	***articulatus***	EShb SGar STre
	bidwillii	see *Brachyglottis bidwillii*
	buchananii	see *Brachyglottis buchananii*
	candicans	see *S. cineraria*
	chrysanthemoides	see *Euryops chrysanthemoides*
§	***cineraria***	LRHS NBlu
	- 'Ramparts'	EBee
	- 'Silver Dust' ♀H3	EPfP SBch
	- 'White Diamond'	ECha
*	***coccinilifera***	SBch
	compactus	see *Brachyglottis compacta*
	confusus	see *Pseudogynoxys chenopodioides*
	crassissimus	EShb
	doria	EShb LRHS WFar WHrl
	fistulosus	LEdu
	formosoides B&SWJ 10736	WCru
	formosus B&SWJ 10700	WCru
	- B&SWJ 10746	WCru
	gerberifolius B&SWJ 10357 **new**	WCru
	- B&SWJ 10361	WCru
	grandifolius	see *Telanthophora grandifolia*
	'Gregynog Gold'	see *Ligularia* 'Gregynog Gold'
	greyi misapplied	see *Brachyglottis* (Dunedin Group) 'Sunshine'
	greyi Hook.	see *Brachyglottis greyi* (Hook. f.) B. Nord.
	heritieri DC.	see *Pericallis lanata* (L'Hér.) B. Nord.
	hoffmannii	EShb
	integrifolius subsp. ***capitatus***	SPlb
	kleiniiformis	EShb
	laxifolius hort.	see *Brachyglottis* (Dunedin Group) 'Sunshine'
	leucostachys	see *S. viravira*
	macroglossus	CHIl EShb WFar
	- 'Variegatus' (v) ♀H1	ERea EShb
	maritimus	see *S. cineraria*
	monroi	see *Brachyglottis monroi*
	niveoaureus B&SWJ 714	WCru
	petasitis	CHEx CTrC
	polyodon	CCCN CSpe CSpr EBla EPPr EShb GBin GMac ILad LBMP MNrw MWea NCGa NLar WMoo WPGP WWEG
	- S&SH 29	CFir EBee SAga
	- subsp. ***subglaber***	EBee EWes
	przewalskii	see *Ligularia przewalskii*

pulcher	CDTJ CDes CGHE CSam LEdu MNrw MTho SHar SMrm SUsu WCot WPGP
reinholdii	see *Brachyglottis rotundifolia*
rowleyanus	EBak EShb STre
scandens	CBre CCCN CPLG EShb MNrw WPGP
scaposus	WCot
seminiveus	EBee
§ ***serpens***	CStu EShb SEND
§ ***smithii***	CHid CRow ELan EWld GBee NBid WCot WCru WFar
spedenii	see *Brachyglottis spedenii*
squalidus	WHer
'Sunshine'	see *Brachyglottis* (Dunedin Group) 'Sunshine'
talinoides	EShb
subsp. ***cylindricus*** 'Himalaya'	
tanguticus	see *Sinacalia tangutica*
§ ***viravira*** ♀H3-4	CWan EBee EGoo EPfP ERas EShb MCot SMad SMrm SPer WEas WSHC

Senna (*Caesalpiniaceae*)

alata B&SWJ 9772	WCru
alexandrina	CCCN EShb LRHS WPGP
§ ***corymbosa***	CBcs CBot CCCN CHEx CRHN CSpe CTri
× ***floribunda***	LRHS
§ ***marilandica***	CArn CBod EBee ELan EWes WHil
obtusa (Roxb.) Wight	EBee
retusa	CHEx
septemtrionalis	CCCN LRHS WPGP

Sequoia (*Cupressaceae*)

sempervirens ♀H4	CBcs CDoC CDul CLnd CMCN CMac CMen CTho CTrG ECrN EHul EPfP ERom EWTr IFFs ISea LMaj LRHS MBar MMuc NMun SPoG WDin WEve WMou
- 'Adpressa'	CDoC CSli CTho EHul EOrn EPfP EPla IDee IFFs LRHS MAsh MBar MBri MGos NHol NWea SCoo SLim WFar
- 'Cantab'	SLim
- 'Prostrata'	CDoC CSli EOrn LRHS MAsh MMuc SLim WFar

Sequoiadendron (*Cupressaceae*)

giganteum ♀H4	Widely available
- 'Bajojeka'	NLar
- 'Barabits Requiem'	GKir IDee LRHS MBlu NLar SLim SMad
- 'Blauer Eichzweig'	NLar SLim
- 'Blue Iceberg'	CKen
- 'Bultinck Yellow'	NLar SMad
- 'Conrad Appel'	NLar
- 'French Beauty'	NLar
- 'Glaucum'	CDoC CTho EMil LRHS MAsh MBlu MBri NLar SLim SMad SPoG
* - 'Glaucum Compactum'	MBlu
- 'Greenpeace'	MBlu NLar
- 'Hazel Smith'	IArd IDee SMad
- 'Little Stan'	CKen NLar
- 'Pendulum'	CDoC CDul CKen ERod GKir LRHS MBlu MGos NLar SLim SMad SWvt
- 'Peve Bonsai'	NLar
- 'Philip Curtis'	NLar
- 'Powdered Blue'	NLar
- 'Variegatum' (v)	GKir MAsh MGos
- 'Von Martin'	NLar

Serapias (*Orchidaceae*)

lingua	SCnR

Serenoa (*Arecaceae*)

repens	CBrP EAmu LPal

Seriphidium (*Asteraceae*)

caerulescens var. ***gallicum***	CEls
§ ***canum***	CEls MHer
§ ***ferganense***	CEls
§ ***fragrans***	CEls
§ ***maritimum***	CArn GGar GPWP ILis MHer
- var. ***maritimum***	CEls
§ ***nutans***	CEls MCot MRav
§ ***tridentatum***	CArn EBee
- subsp. ***tridentatum***	CEls
tripartitum var. ***rupicola***	CEls
§ ***vallesiacum*** ♀H4	CEls EBee SUsu WEas

Serissa (*Rubiaceae*)

foetida	see *S. japonica*
§ ***japonica***	STre
- ***rosea***	STre
- 'Variegata' (v)	STre
- 'White Snow'	MGos

Serratula (*Asteraceae*)

bulgarica new	WCot
coronata	EBee LRHS
- subsp. ***insularis*** f. ***alba***	EBee GAbr
§ ***seoanei***	CKno CMea CPom EBee ECha EDAr LHop LPla LRHS MHer MLHP MRav MWat SAga SBch SDix SPhx SRms SUsu WCot WEas WFar WPGP WPat WPrP WTin
shawii	see *S. seoanei*
tinctoria	CArn GBar NLar NMir WOut
- subsp. ***macrocephala***	EBee EBrs LRHS SHGN
wolffii	EBee

Serruria (*Proteaceae*)

florida	SPlb

Sesamum (*Pedaliaceae*)

indicum	CArn

Sesbania (*Papilionaceae*)

punicea	CCCN CSpe

Seseli (*Apiaceae*)

elatum	CSpe LPio
- subsp. ***osseum***	LPio
globiferum	LPio
gummiferum	CArn CBot CHid CSpe EBee LDai LPio SDix SEND SPhx WPtf
hippomarathrum	LPio SPhx SUsu WHoo WHrl WPGP
libanotis	CSpe EBee LEdu LPio LPla NLar SAga SBch SPhx
montanum	CDes CSpe EBee IMou WPGP

Sesleria (*Poaceae*)

§ ***argentea***	EHoe
autumnalis	EBee LEdu LPla SPhx
caerulea	CSam EAlp EBee EHoe ELan EPfP GFor LEdu MBar MMoz MWhi NLar WPtf
- 'Malvern Mop'	EBee WHrl WPGP WWEG
* ***candida***	EPPr
cylindrica	see *S. argentea*
glauca	EHoe NLar NOak NPro SBch WPer

heufleriana CWCL EBee EHoe EPPr EPla GFor NLar SLPl SPlb WWEG
insularis EPPr EShb
'Morning Dew' EBee GCal
nitida CKno EBee EHoe GFor LBMP LEdu MMoz SApp SPhx WPGP
rigida EHoe
sadleriana EBee EPPr EWes GFor

Setaria (*Poaceae*)

italica WTou
macrostachya ♀H3 CKno LLWP SBch SPhx SUsu
palmifolia CAby CHEx CHll CKno SDix SGSe WCot WDyG
- BWJ 8132 WCru
viridis CHrt CSpe NSti WCot WTin

Setcreasea see *Tradescantia*

shaddock see *Citrus maxima*

Sharon fruit see *Diospyros kaki*

Shepherdia (*Elaeagnaceae*)

argentea CBcs NLar

Shibataea (*Poaceae*)

chinensis CBcs EBee
kumasaca CAbb CBcs CDoC CEnt CHEx EBee ENBC EPfP EPla ERod GCal IBal LEdu LPal LRHS MBrN MCCP MMoz MWht NMoo NVic SBig SLPl WJun WPGP
- 'Aureostriata' EPla
lancifolia CMCo EPla WJun

Shortia (*Diapensiaceae*)

galacifolia IBlr
- var. ***brevistyla*** IBlr
soldanelloides IBlr
- var. ***ilicifolia*** IBlr
- var. ***intercedens*** new EBee
- 'Kuju' EBee
- var. ***magna*** IBlr
uniflora EBee IBlr
- var. ***orbicularis*** 'Grandiflora' IBlr

Sibbaldia (*Rosaceae*)

procumbens GAuc GKev GKir

Sibbaldiopsis (*Rosaceae*)

tridentata 'Lemon Mac' SIng
- 'Nuuk' MBar

Sibthorpia (*Scrophulariaceae*)

europaea CGHE CHEx CPLG

Sidalcea (*Malvaceae*)

'Brilliant' CBcs CHar EBee EPfP LAst LRHS MDKP MNrw NBPC NBir NPri SPer WMoo WWEG
candida CSam EBee ECtt ELan EPfP GCra GGar GMaP LAst LEdu LFur LHop LRHS MBNS MCot MRav NEgg NGdn NSti SMrm SPer SPoG STes SUsu WCAu WCot WPtf WSpi
- 'Bianca' CBot CMea EBee EHrv EShb MSCN NBPC NPri WFar WHal WMoo WPer WWEG
'Candy Girl' EBee WBor
'Croftway Red' CFir EBee ELan EPfP GCra GGar LRHS MAvo MCot NBro NCob NGdn NHol SAga SMrm SPet SWvt WAul WFar WMoo
cusickii WOut
'Elsie Heugh' ♀H4 Widely available
* ***grandiflora*** EBee
hendersonii EBee
hickmanii subsp. ***anomala*** EBee
'Little Princess'PBR CElw CFir EBee EPfP EWes GKir LBuc LLWG LRHS LSou MBNS NCGa NLar SPoG WFar
'Loveliness' CMMP EBee ECtt ELan EShb LHop LRHS LSou MAvo MRav NBro NCob NGdn NHol NLar SAga SBch
malviflora SEND SRms WBVN
- 'Alba' WFar
'Monarch' MDKP WFar
'Moorland Rose Coronet' WMoo
'Mr Lindbergh' EBee EPfP LRHS MAvo NHol SAga WFar
'Mrs Borrodaile' CMac EBee ECtt GBuc LAst LRHS MBel MLHP MRav NBro NCob NGdn NHol NPro SMrm WFar WMoo WSpi WWEG
'Mrs Galloway' WFar
'Mrs T. Alderson' EBee WFar WMoo
'My Love' ECha SMrm
'Oberon' EBee GBuc LRHS MRav WFar
oregana NBid NGdn
- subsp. ***spicata*** WFar WMoo
'Party Girl' Widely available
'Präriebrand' LSou SAga
'Purpetta' COIW EBee NGBl NLar NPro STes WPer
'Reverend Page Roberts' MRav WCot WFar WWEG
'Rosaly' CEnt EBee GAbr IFoB LBMP LRHS NLar SBch STes WFar WGor WHal WPer
'Rosanna' EBee GAbr GMaP LRHS NLar SBch SPhx WHal WPer WPtf
'Rose Bud' CElw EBee
'Rose Queen' CKno EBee ECha LHop LRHS MAvo MCot MRav NBro NCob NHol SPer SRms WCAu WFar
'Rosy Gem' ECtt LRHS NBre WFar
Stark's hybrids LRHS SRms
'Sussex Beauty' CSam EBee GMac LRHS MArl MAvo MBel MLHP MRav NEgg NGdn SMrm SPer WAul WFar WMoo
'Wensleydale' new LRHS
'William Smith' ♀H4 CSam EBee ECha ECtt EPfP EWes GKir LAst LRHS MBel MCot MRav NCGa NChi NCob NGdn NOrc SMrm SPer SPhx WBVN WFar WMoo WWEG
'Wine Red' CFir CKno CMHG EBee EShb IPot LAst LRHS MAvo MCot MDKP NCob NEgg NGdn SBch SWvt WCAu WFar WSpi WWEG

Sideritis (*Lamiaceae*)

hyssopifolia EBee
syriaca CArn NBre

Sieversia (*Rosaceae*)

§ ***pentapetala*** GEdr WAbe
reptans see *Geum reptans*

Silaum (*Apiaceae*)

silaus NMir

Silene (*Caryophyllaceae*)

	SDR 4329	GKev
	SDR 5162 new	GKev
	from Uzbekistan new	GCal
	acaulis	EAlp ECho EDAr LRHS MTho NLAp NLar NMen SRms WAbe
§	- subsp. **acaulis**	ECho SPlb SRms
	- 'Alba'	ECho EWes NLan NMen WAbe WPat
	- 'Blush'	NHol NLAp NMen WAbe
	- subsp. **elongata**	see *S. acaulis* subsp. *acaulis*
	- 'Frances'	EPot GMaP NLAp NMen NRya NSla NWCA WAbe
	- 'Francis Copeland'	ECho NMen
	- 'Helen's Double' (d)	ECho EDAr EPot
*	- **minima**	EPot
	- 'Mount Snowdon'	ECho EDAr ELan EPfP EPot EWes GGar GKir GMaP LBee LRHS NLAp NLar NMen NRya NWCA SPlb SPoG SRms SRot WHoo WPat
	- 'Pedunculata'	see *S. acaulis* subsp. *acaulis*
	alba	see *S. latifolia*
§	**alpestris**	EBee MBar MTho SRms SRot WFar WMoo WThu
	- 'Flore Pleno' (d) ♀H4	EWes LBee LRHS NSla WAbe WPat
	araratica	WAbe
	argaea	WAbe
	× **arkwrightii**	see *Lychnis* × *arkwrightii*
	armeria	WHer
	- 'Electra'	CSpe
	asterias	GBuc GCal GCra IGor MNrw NBid NBre WPer
	- MESE 429	EBee GBin
	atropurpurea	see *Lychnis viscaria* subsp. *atropurpurea*
	bellidioides	WPGP
	californica	EBee
	caroliniana	CHrt
	- 'Hot Pink' new	LRHS
	- subsp. **wherryi**	GAuc WFar
	chungtienensis	EBee
§	**compacta**	NLar
§	**davidii**	CPBP EBee GKev
	dinarica	GKev
§	**dioica**	CArn CRWN EBWF EGoo LEdu MHer MNHC NLan NLar NMir NVic SECG SWat WMoo WSFF WShi
	- 'Clifford Moor' (v)	ECtt EHoe NSti SCoo
	- 'Compacta'	see *S. dioica* 'Minikin'
	- 'Firefly' new	LRHS
§	- 'Flore Pleno' (d)	GCra MRav MTho NBid NBro NChi NGdn SMrm WEas WFar WHoo WTin
§	- 'Graham's Delight' (v)	MSCN WCHb
	- 'Inane'	CDes EBee WAlt WPGP
	- 'Innocence' new	NChi
	- f. **lactea**	MHer
§	- 'Minikin'	ECha EGoo LRHS WAlt WTin
	- 'Pat Clissold' (v)	WCHb
	- 'Pembrokeshire Pastel' (v)	WAlt
	- 'Purple Prince' new	CBow SMrm
	- 'Richmond' (d)	EBee GBuc NBre
	- 'Rosea Plena' (d)	CBre MTho NCob
	- 'Rubra Plena'	see *S. dioica* 'Flore Pleno'
	- 'Thelma Kay' (d/v)	CFee CSev EBee ECtt EWes GBuc MDun NBid NBre NLar WMoo WPGP WWFP
	- 'Underdine'	EBee EWes
	- 'Valley High' (v)	CBow EWes WHer
	- 'Variegata'	see *S. dioica* 'Graham's Delight'
	elisabethae	EPot GKir NBlu
§	**fimbriata**	CFir CSpe EBee EHrv ELan EPyc EShb LEdu LPla MCot MMHG MNFA MRav NChi NSti SAga SMrm WAbb WCot WKif WMoo WPGP WPen WPtf WRHF WSHC WTin
	hookeri	GKev
	- Ingramii Group	WAbe
	inflata	see *S. vulgaris*
	italica	WCot
	kantzeensis	see *S. davidii*
	keiskei	LFur
	var. **akaisialpina** new	
	- var. **minor**	CPBP EWes LRHS MTho WAbe
	laciniata	LRHS
	- 'Jack Flash'	MWea WHrl
§	**latifolia**	CArn EBWF NMir NSco
	- subsp. **alba**	MNHC SECG
	maritima	see *S. uniflora*
	maroccana	CRWN
	moorcroftiana	EBee
	multifida	see *S. fimbriata*
	noctiflora	EBWF
	nutans	EBWF SRms WHer WSFF
	orientalis	see *S. compacta*
	parishii var. **latifolia** NNS 03-556	NWCA
	petersonii	EPot
	- NNS 06-534	NWCA
	pusilla	NLar WAbe
	quadridentata misapplied	see *S. alpestris*
	regia	NBre WPGP
	rubra	see *S. dioica*
	schafta ♀H4	CHrt CTri EAlp ECha ECho ECtt EPfP GGar LRHS NBid NBlu NCob NPri NWCA SRms WAbe WFar WHoo WPer
	- 'Abbotswood'	see *Lychnis* × *walkeri* 'Abbotswood Rose'
	- 'Persian Carpet'	SBch WRHF
	- 'Robusta'	WAbe
	- 'Shell Pink'	ECha EPot EWes GJos LBee LRHS LSou MBNS NCob NLar NWCA WAbe WCom WHoo
	sieboldii	see *Lychnis coronata* var. *sieboldii*
*	**tenuis**	GBuc
	- ACE 2429	GBuc
§	**uniflora**	EBWF ECho ECtt EPfP GGar LRHS MCot MMuc MWat NBro SBch SECG SPlb SRms WFar WMoo
	- from Madeira new	GGar
	- 'Alba Plena'	see *S. uniflora* 'Robin Whitebreast'
I	- 'Compacta'	CEnt ECho NDlv WMoo
§	- 'Druett's Variegated' (v)	CHrt CMea CTri EAlp ECha ECho ECtt EDAr EPfP EWes GBuc LAst LBee LRHS MBar MHer NBid NBlu NLAp NMen NPri NVic SIng SPad SPet SPlb SPoG SRms WFar WPat
	- 'Flore Pleno'	see *S. uniflora* 'Robin Whitebreast'
	- pink-flowered	LRHS
§	- 'Robin Whitebreast' (d)	EBee ECha ECho ECtt EPfP GCal MBar MTho NBid NBro NPri SRms SRot WMoo WPer WSHC
	- 'Rosea'	EBee ECtt EPfP GGar GKev GKir MMuc SPlb SRot WFar WPer
	- 'Silver Lining' (v)	GBuc
	- 'Swan Lake' (d)	LRHS
	- 'Variegata'	see *S. uniflora* 'Druett's Variegated'
	- Weisskehlchen	see *S. uniflora* 'Robin Whitebreast'
	- 'White Bells'	CTri ECtt WHoo WKif WSHC
	virginica	GKev

	viridiflora new	LFur
§	***vulgaris***	CRWN EBWF LEdu MHer NLan NMir NSco SECG
	- subsp. ***maritima***	see *S. uniflora*
	wallichiana	see *S. vulgaris*
	'Wisley Pink'	ECtt
	yunnanensis	SPhx WSHC
§	***zawadskii***	GBuc GKev MDKP NHol SWal WTin

Silphium (*Asteraceae*)

	integrifolium	EBee NBre SAga SMad WCot WOld
	laciniatum	CArn EBee NBre SMad SMrm SPhx
	perfoliatum ♀H4	CArn COld EBee ELon GPoy IMou NBre NCob NLar SMrm SPhx SUsu WCot WFar WOld WWEG
	radula new	EBee
	terebinthinaceum	EPPr SMad SPhx WCot
	trifoliatum	EBee

Silybum (*Asteraceae*)

	marianum	CArn CSpe EBee ELan EPfP GAbr GPWP GPoy LRHS MNHC MSCN NGHP SECG SHlg SIde SPav WCom WFar WHer WTou
	- 'Adriana'	SHlg SPav

Simmondsia (*Simmondsiaceae*)

	chinensis	CArn EOHP

Sinacalia (*Asteraceae*)

§	***tangutica***	CSam EBee ECha EPPr GGar MBel MWhi NBid NBro NCGa NChi SDix WAbb WCru WFar

Sinarundinaria (*Poaceae*)

	anceps	see *Yushania anceps*
	jaunsarensis	see *Yushania anceps*
	maling	see *Yushania maling*
	murielae	see *Fargesia murielae*
	nitida	see *Fargesia nitida*

Sinningia (*Gesneriaceae*)

	sp. new	EABi
*	***caerulea***	WDib
	canescens ♀H1	ERea WDib
§	***cardinalis***	EBak WDib
	- 'Innocent'	WDib
	conspicua new	WDib
	'Kaiser Wilhelm'	LRHS
	nivalis	WDib
	speciosa 'Blanche de Méru'	LRHS
	- 'Kaiser Friedrich'	LRHS
	tubiflora	CSpe LPio

Sinobambusa (*Poaceae*)

§	***intermedia***	EPla
*	***orthotropa***	EPla WPGP
	rubroligula	EPla NMoo WPGP
	tootsik	EPla WJun
§	- 'Albostriata' (v)	EPla LPJP WJun
	- 'Variegata'	see *S. tootsik* 'Albostriata'

× *Sinocalycalycanthus* (*Calycanthaceae*)

	raulstonii 'Hartlage Wine'	CPMA EPfP MBri NLar SSpi
	'Venus'	EPfP LRHS SSpi

Sinocalycanthus (*Calycanthaceae*)

	chinensis	CBcs CMCN CMac CPMA EBee ELan EPfP IArd IDee IMGH LRHS MBlu MBri MMHG NLar SSpi WBVN WPGP

Sinofranchetia (*Lardizabalaceae*)

	chinensis	CBcs WCru

Sinojackia (*Styracaceae*)

	xylocarpa	CBcs MBri NLar WFar

Sinowilsonia (*Hamamelidaceae*)

	henryi	NLar

Siphocampylus (*Campanulaceae*)

	foliosus CDPR 3240	WPGP
	- RCB RA S-4	WCot

Siphocranion (*Lamiaceae*)

§	***macranthum***	CDes EBee EWes WPGP

Sison (*Apiaceae*)

	amomum	CBre

Sisyrinchium ✿ (*Iridaceae*)

	× ***anceps***	see *S. angustifolium*
§	***angustifolium***	CMHG EBee EBur ECha ECho LBMP LPBA MBar MCot NBir NChi NLAp NLar SChF SPlb SRms WBrk WPer WPtf
	- ***album***	ECho MCot NChi NLar
	- 'Lucerne'	EBee
§	***arenarium***	CMea CPBP EBur MAvo
	atlanticum	NBro SUsu WPer
	bellum hort.	see *S. idahoense* var. *bellum*
	bermudiana	see *S. angustifolium*
	- 'Album'	see *S. graminoides* 'Album'
	'Biscutella'	CBod CKno CPrp CSsd CTri EBee EBur ECho ECtt EPfP GKir GMaP LEdu LHop NMen NRya SAga SIng SPad SPlb SPoG SWal SWvt WFar WHal WHoo WKif
	'Blue France'	EPot
	'Blue Ice'	CMea CPBP CWCL EAlp EBur EDAr LRHS MAvo NLAp WAbe WMoo WPat WPer
	boreale	see *S. californicum*
	brachypus	see *S. californicum* Brachypus Group
	'Californian Skies'	Widely available
§	***californicum***	CBen EBur ECho EHon EMFW EPfP GAbr LPBA LRHS MBar NBro NHol SMrm WFar WMAq WPer
§	- Brachypus Group	CMac EAlp EBee ECho ECtt EDAr EPfP GAbr GKir MMuc MWat NBir NBlu NLAp NLar NPri NVic SGar SPad SPlb SPoG SWal SWvt WMoo
*	***capsicum***	CPLG
§	***chilense***	ERos
	coeleste	EBur
	coeruleum	see *Gelasine coerulea*
	commutatum	ECho MNrw SGar
	convolutum	GGar
	- B&SWJ 9117	WCru
	cuspidatum	see *S. arenarium*
	'Deep Seas'	SUsu
	demissum	EBur
	depauperatum	EBur LFur MNrw WHer WPer
	'Devon Blue'	ECho
	'Devon Skies'	CHid CWCL EBur ECho MDKP MWea NMen SBch SIng SWvt WAbe WFar
	douglasii	see *Olsynium douglasii*
	'Dragon's Eye'	CKno CMea CPBP EBur EWes MAvo MBrN SIng SMrm SRot WPer
	'E.K. Balls'	Widely available

	elmeri	EBur
	'Emmeline'	EBur
	filifolium	see *Olsynium filifolium*
	graminoides	EBur IFoB NBro WPer
§	- 'Album'	EBur NBro WPer
	grandiflorum	see *Olsynium douglasii*
	'Hemswell Sky'	EBur ECho EHoe NRya
	'Iceberg'	EAro EBur EShb LPla MWat SBch SUsu
	idahoense	ECha ECho EDAr GAbr GEdr LRHS LSou MHer NRya SPlb SRms
§	- var. ***bellum***	CKno EBur ECho EPfP GGar IFro LBMP LRHS NPri SGar SPet SRms WCom WMoo WPat WPer
	- - pale-flowered	CKno LPla SUsu
	- - 'Rocky Point'	CElw CSpe EAro EBee EBur EWes GJos LRHS MMuc NLAp SPoG SRot WCom WFar WHoo WPat
	- var. ***macounii***	EBee GEdr LRHS WFar
§	- - 'Album' 🏆^{H4}	CMea CSsd EAlp EBur ECho EMFW ERos GAbr GKev LRHS MTho MWat NLAp SPet WAbe WCom WFar WPat WPer
	iridifolium	see *S. micranthum*
	junceum	see *Olsynium junceum*
	littorale	CPLG EBur NLar WPer
	macrocarpon misapplied	see *S. macrocarpum*
	macrocarpon 🏆$^{H2-3}$	CPBP LRHS NMen
§	***macrocarpum***	CFee CSsd EBur ECho ERos MDKP SWal WPer
	'Marie'	EBur
	'Marion'	CElw CKno CMea CPBP MAvo MBrN NLar SBch SMrm SPet SRot WPer
	'May Snow'	see *S. idahoense* var. *macounii* 'Album'
	'Miami'	EBur
§	***micranthum***	CBro EBur ECho LFur
	montanum	ECho ERos
	montanum × ***nudicaule***	CFee EBur ECho GAbr MNrw NLAp NRya SRot WPer
	'Mrs Spivey'	EBee EBur ECho ECtt MBar MHer NBir
	'North Star'	see *S.* 'Pole Star'
	palmifolium	CBgR CBod CDes CSpe CSsd EBee EBur EWTr GAbr MDKP MHer MNrw MWea SGar SPoG WCot
	- JCA 2.880.010	WPGP
	patagonicum	CPLG EBur EDAr ERos GBuc WPer
§	'Pole Star'	CFee CSpe EBee EBur ECho GGar WFar WPer
	'Quaint and Queer'	COIW CPLG CWCL EBee EBur ECha ECho ECtt EHoe EShb MBrN MLHP MNFA MSCN MTho NBir NBro NChi NLAp SWvt WMnd WMoo WPer WSHC
	'Raspberry'	CMea CSpe EBee EBur
	'Sapphire'	NPri WFar
	scabrum	see *S. chilense*
	'Sisland Blue'	EBur EWes
§	***striatum***	Widely available
§	- 'Aunt May' (v)	Widely available
	- 'Variegatum'	see *S. striatum* 'Aunt May'
	aff. ***unispathaceum*** B&SWJ 10683 **new**	WCru

Sium (*Apiaceae*)

	sisarum	ELau GPoy MHer

Skimmia ✿ (*Rutaceae*)

	anquetilia	CMac MBar
	arborescens GWJ 9374	WCru
	- subsp. ***nitida*** B&SWJ 8239	WCru
	arisanensis B&SWJ 7114	WCru
	× ***confusa***	WFar
	- 'Kew Green' (m) 🏆^{H4}	Widely available
	japonica	CDul CMHG CMac CWib GQui LRHS MGan MGos NScw SReu SSta WDin WFar WHCG
	- (f)	CMac CTrG CTri ELan EPfP GGal SRms
	- (m)	GGal
	- B&SWJ 5053	WCru
	- 'Alba'	see *S. japonica* 'Wakehurst White'
	- 'Bowles's Dwarf Female' (f)	CMHG EPfP MBar MBri MGos MRav MWht NHol SLim SLon
	- 'Bowles's Dwarf Male' (m)	CMHG EPla MBar NHol SLim
	- 'Bronze Knight' (m)	CMac EQua LRHS MBar MBri MRav NHol SLim WFar
	- 'Cecilia Brown' (f)	WFar
	- 'Chameleon'	LRHS NHol
*	- 'Claries Repens'	LRHS
	- compact (f)	GGal
	- 'Dad's Red Dragon'	NHol
	- 'Emerald King' (m)	MBar MBri WFar
N	- 'Foremanii'	see *S. japonica* 'Veitchii'
§	- 'Fragrans' (m) 🏆^{H4}	CDoC CMac CSBt CTri CWib EBee ECrN EPfP GKir LRHS MAsh MBar MBri MGos MRav NHol NPri NWea SBch SLim SPer SPoG SWvt WFar WGob WGwG
	- 'Fragrant Cloud'	see *S. japonica* 'Fragrans'
	- 'Fragrantissima' (m)	WFar
	- 'Fructu Albo'	see *S. japonica* 'Wakehurst White'
	- 'Godrie's Dwarf' (m)	CWSG EBee EMil EPfP IArd LRHS WFar
	- 'Highgrove Redbud' (f)	MBar MGos
	- var. ***intermedia*** f. ***repens***	WFar
	- - B&SWJ 5560	WCru
	- 'Keessen' (f)	WFar
	- 'Kew White' (f)	CAbP CDoC CWib EBee EPfP EQua GKir IArd LRHS MAsh MGos NHol NPal SLon SPer SRms SWvt WCFE WDin WFar WHCG
	- Luwian = 'Wanto'	EBee LRHS NHol WCFE WFar
	- 'Magic Marlot'^{PBR} (v) **new**	EBee EGxp LRHS MAsh MGos SPoG
	- 'Marlot' (m)	EBee EPfP LRHS MAsh NLar SPoG
	- 'Nymans' (f) 🏆^{H4}	CDoC CEnd CSam EBee ELan EPfP GKir LBMP LRHS MAsh MBar MBri MRav NCGa SLim SPer SPoG SReu SRms SSpi SSta WBVN WFar WGob
	- 'Obovata' (f)	EPla
	- Obsession = 'Obsbolwi'^{PBR}	EBee
	- 'Pigmy' (f)	CPLG
	- 'Red Dragon' (f)	CMac
	- 'Red Princess' (f)	EPla LAst WFar
*	- 'Red Riding Hood'	LBMP LRHS MAsh NHol SLon
	- 'Redruth' (f)	CBcs CDoC CMac CSBt CSam EBee EQua GKir ISea LAst LHop MAsh MBar MGos MWat NHol SBch SSta WFar
§	- subsp. ***reevesiana***	Widely available
	- - B&SWJ 3763	WCru
	- - 'Chilan Choice' (f/m)	EPfP LRHS SLim SSta
	- - 'Fata Morgana' (m)	MGos
	- - var. ***reevesiana*** B&SWJ 3544	WCru
	- - 'Robert Fortune' (f/m)	MBar
§	- Rogersii Group	CMac CTri MBar
	- - 'Dunwood'	MBar
	- - 'George Gardner'	LRHS MBar
	- - 'Helen Goodall' (f)	MBar
	- - 'Nana Mascula' (m)	CTri MGos

	- - 'Rockyfield Green'	MBar
	- - 'Snow Dwarf' (m)	MBar WFar
	- 'Rubella' (m) ♀H4	Widely available
	- 'Rubinetta' (m)	EBee EPfP GKir IArd LRHS LSRN MAsh MBar MGos NHol SLim WFar
	- 'Ruby Dome' (m)	LRHS MBar NHol WFar
	- 'Ruby King' (m)	CDoC CSBt ECrN EQua IArd LSRN MBar MHav NHol NLar
	- 'Scarlet Dwarf' (f)	LRHS MBar NHol
	- 'Scarlet Queen' (f)	CWib
	- 'Snow White'PBR **new**	EGxp MAsh
	- 'Tansley Gem' (f)	EPfP LRHS MAsh MBri MWht SPoG SSta WFar
	- 'Thelma King'	GKir WFar
§	- 'Veitchii' (f)	CBcs CDul CMac CSBt CTri CWSG EBee ELan EPfP GKir IArd LRHS LSRN MBar MGos MRav MWat NHol SEND SLim SPer SPoG SWvt WDin
§	- 'Wakehurst White' (f)	CBcs CMHG CMac CSBt CTri EBee EPfP GKir LRHS MBar MRav SLim SLon SPer SReu SSpi WFar
	- 'White Gerpa'	MGos
	- 'Winifred Crook' (f)	EPla GKir MBar MBri SLim WFar
	- 'Winnie's Dwarf'	MGos
	- 'Wisley Female' (f)	CTri ECtt NHol WFar
	laureola	CDoC CPLG CSam EBee MRav NHol SRms WFar WSHC
	- GWJ 9364	WCru
	- 'Borde Hill' (f)	LRHS
	- subsp. ***multinervia*** B&SWJ 8259	WCru
*	***mica***	ISea SLim
	'Olympic Flame'	CWSG EWTr GKir LRHS MAsh MBlu MGos SPoG WFar
	reevesiana	see *S. japonica* subsp. *reevesiana*
	rogersii	see *S. japonica* Rogersii Group

Smilacina see *Maianthemum*

Smilax (*Smilacaceae*)

sp.	WBor
B&SWJ 6628 from Thailand	WCru
F&M 051	WPGP
from Thailand	LEdu
aspera	CArn CMac EBee EPla EShb EWld LEdu WCru WPGP
china B&SWJ 4427	WCru
discotis	CBcs SEND
glaucophylla B&SWJ 2971	WCru
nipponica B&SWJ 4331	WCru
rotundifolia	LEdu
sieboldii	LEdu MRav
- B&SWJ 744	WCru

Smithiantha (*Gesneriaceae*)

	'Extra Sassy'	EABi
	'Little One'	EOHP WDib
	'Multiflora'	EABi WDib
	'Santa Clara'	EABi
I	'Temple Bells'	EABi

Smyrnium (*Apiaceae*)

olusatrum	CArn CSev CSpe EBWF EBee GBar GPWP MHer MNHC SIde STre SWat WHer
perfoliatum	CHid CSpe EBee EHrv ELan EWes LPio NBir SDix SMrm WCot WEas WFar WHal WSHC
rotundifolium	CArn LPio WCot

Solandra (*Solanaceae*)

	grandiflora misapplied	see *S. maxima*
	hartwegii	see *S. maxima*
§	***maxima***	CCCN CHll EShb

Solanum (*Solanaceae*)

	atropurpureum	CDTJ CSpe WHil
	conchifolium hort.	see *S. linearifolium*
	crispum	NBir SGar WDin
	- 'Autumnale'	see *S. crispum* 'Glasnevin'
	- 'Elizabeth Jane Dunn' (v)	WCot WSHC
§	- 'Glasnevin' ♀H3	Widely available
	- 'Variegatum' (v)	WGwG
	dulcamara	CArn EBWF GPoy
	- var. ***album*** **new**	LSRN
	- 'Variegatum' (v)	CMac CWan EBee ECrN EHoe EPfP LRHS MAsh NSti SPoG WFar WSHC
	hispidum	CHEx
	jasminoides	see *S. laxum*
	laciniatum	CArn CCCN CDTJ CHEx CPLG CSev CSpe EShb EWes GGal GGar MCot SAPC SArc SBch SBig SBst SGar SPav SPlb WHil WKif WWlt
§	***laxum***	EBee EShb GGal LRHS MSwo NSti SPer SPoG SRms SWvt WDin WSHC
	- 'Album' ♀H3	Widely available
	- 'Album Variegatum' (v)	CWib ELan LRHS NBlu NSti WSHC
*	- 'Aureovariegatum' (v)	EBee EPfP EShb LBMP MGos NEgg SBch SCoo SLim SPlb
	- 'Coldham'	EShb SMad
	- 'Creche ar Pape' **new**	ECha
§	***linearifolium***	EWld MAsh WCot WPGP
	muricatum (F)	CCCN EShb
	pseudocapsicum 'Thurino'	EPfP LRHS
	- variegated (v)	EShb
	pyracanthum	CDTJ SMad
	quitoense (F)	CDTJ SBig SMad
§	***rantonnetii***	CCCN CHll ELan EPfP EShb IDee LHop LRHS MCot SEND SPoG
	- 'Royal Robe'	CBcs CRHN CTri
	- 'Variegatum' (v)	EShb MSCN WCom WCot
	salicifolium	EShb
	seaforthianum	EShb
	sisymbriifolium	CDTJ WWlt
	aff. ***stenophyllum*** B&SWJ 10744	WCru
	wendlandii	CHll EShb

Solaria (*Alliaceae*)

sp.	GCal

Soldanella (*Primulaceae*)

	alpina	EBee ECho GCra GKev GKir MTho NMen SIng SRms WAbe
	- SDR 3504	GKev
I	- 'Alba'	ECho WAbe
	carpatica	EBee ECho GKev LLHF WAbe
	- 'Alba'	ECho MDKP NSla WAbe
	- hybrid **new**	NMen
	carpatica* × *pusilla	CPBP ECho NHol NMen NRya
	carpatica* × *villosa	ECho MDKP
	cyanaster	ECho GEdr GJos NMen NRya WAbe
	dimoniei	CFee EBee ECho GKev ITim NMen NSla WAbe
	hungarica	ECho MTho WAbe
	minima	ECho GJos NDlv NMen NSla WAbe
	montana	EBee ECho EDAr GEdr GJos GKev LLHF MDun MTho NLar NMen
	pindicola	ECho EWes GBuc NDlv NMen NWCA WAbe WFar

pusilla	EBee GKev
* - ***alba***	ECho
'Spring Symphony' **new**	GEdr
'Sudden Spring'	WAbe
villosa	CDes EBee ECho GAbr GGar GKev LEdu LRHS MTho NHol NRya SBch WFar WPtf WSHC

Soleirolia (*Urticaceae*)

soleirolii	CHEx CTri EPot LPBA LRHS MCCP MWhi SIng SMad SPer STre SVic WHer
- 'Argentea'	see *S. soleirolii* 'Variegata'
§ - 'Aurea'	CTri EPot SIng STre
- 'Golden Queen'	see *S. soleirolii* 'Aurea'
- 'Silver Queen'	see *S. soleirolii* 'Variegata'
§ - 'Variegata' (v)	EShb LPBA WHer

Solenomelus (*Iridaceae*)

chilensis	see *S. pedunculatus*
§ ***pedunculatus***	CFee WPGP
segethii	ERos

Solenopsis (*Campanulaceae*)

axillaris	see *Isotoma axillaris*

Solenostemon ✿ (*Lamiaceae*)

'Alice Horn'	NHor
'Angel of the North'	NHor
'Anglo Saxons' **new**	NCob
'Autumn'	NHor
'Autumn Gold'	NHor
'Autumn Rainbow'	WDib
'Avril Lagivine' **new**	NCob
'Beauty' (v)	NHor WDib
'Beauty of Lyons'	NHor
'Beckwith's Gem'	NHor
'Billy Elliot'	NHor
'Bizarre Croton' (v)	NHor
'Black Dragon'	LSou NHor NPri
'Black Heart'	NHor WDib
'Black Prince'	EShb NHor WDib
'Brightness' (v)	NHor
'Brilliant' (v)	NHor WDib
'Bronze Gloriosus' (v)	NHor
'Bronze Pagoda' **new**	NHor
'Brooklyn Horror' **new**	NHor
'Burning Bush' **new**	NHor
'Buttercup'	NHor WDib
'Buttermilk' (v) ♀H1	NHor
'Carnival' (v)	NHor WDib
'Carousel' (v)	NHor
'Castle Eden'	NHor
'Catherine Cookson'	NHor
'Chamaeleon' (v)	NHor WDib
'City of Durham' (v)	NHor
'City of Leeds' **new**	NCob
'City of Liverpool'	NHor
'City of Middlesbrough' (v)	NHor
'City of Newcastle'	NHor
'City of Sunderland'	NHor WDib
'City of York' **new**	NHor
'Combat' (v)	NHor SVil WDib
'Coppersmith'	NHor
'Crimson Ruffles' (v) ♀H1	NHor WDib
'Crimson Velvet'	NHor
'Crinkly Bottom'	NHor
'Crown of Bohemia'	NHor
'Dairy Maid' (v)	NHor
'Darwells Charm' **new**	NCob
'Darwells Glory' **new**	NCob
'Dazzler' (v)	NHor WDib
'Display'	NHor WDib
'Doctor Louise' **new**	NCob
'Doctor Wu' **new**	NHor
'Dracula'	NHor
'Duke of Swirl' **new**	NHor
'Durham Autumn' **new**	NHor
'Durham Gala'	NHor WDib
'Eclipse' **new**	NHor
'Ella Darwell' **new**	NCob
'Ella's Fire'	NHor
'Etna' (v)	NHor
'Fire Fingers'	NHor
'Firebrand' (v) ♀H1	NHor
'Firedance' (v)	NHor
'Firefly'	NHor
'Firelight' **new**	WDib
'Flamenco Dancer'	NHor
'Flamestitch'	CSpe
'Flirtin' Skirts' **new**	NHor
'Forest Flame' **new**	NHor
'Freckles' (v)	NHor WDib
'Funfair' (v)	NHor
'George Harrison' **new**	NHor
'Gertrude Jekyll'	NHor
'Gloriosus'	NHor
'Glory of Luxembourg' (v) ♀H1	NHor
'Goody Goody' **new**	NHor
'Grape Expectations' **new**	NHor
'Green Mars' (v)	NHor
'Hannay Harding'	NHor
'Harvest Time' (v)	NHor
'Hidden Poppy' **new**	NCob
'Holly' (v)	NHor
'Illumination' **new**	NHor
'Inky Fingers' (v)	EShb NHor WDib
'Jean' (v)	NHor
'Joseph's Cloak' **new**	NHor
'Joseph's Coat' (v)	NHor
'Juliet Quartermain'	NHor WDib
'Jupiter'	NHor
'Kate Adie'	NHor
'Kentish Fire' (v)	NHor WDib
'Killer Klown' **new**	NHor
'Kiwi Fern' (v)	EShb NHor WDib
'Klondike'	NHor
Kong Series	SPoG
- 'Kong Rose'	NPri
'Laing's Croton' (v)	NHor WDib
'Lemon Dash'	NHor
'Lemondrop'	NHor
'Leopard' (v)	NHor
'Lindisfarne'	NHor
'Lord Falmouth' ♀H1	NHor WDib
'Luke Darwell' **new**	NCob
'Lukey Boy' **new**	NCob
'Luminous'	NHor
'Mardigras'	NHor
'Margaret Horn' **new**	NHor
'Marks Tiger' **new**	NCob
'Masquerade'	NHor
'Maximas Barker' **new**	NCob
'Melody' (v)	NHor WDib
'Midas'	NHor
'Midnight'	NHor
'Mission Gem' (v)	NHor SVil
'Morris Cullen' **new**	NHor
'Mrs Pilkington' (v)	NHor WDib
'Muriel Pedley' (v)	NHor WDib
'Nettie' (v)	NHor

	Name	Suppliers
	'Paisley Shawl' (v) Υ^{H1}	NHor WDib
	'Palisandra'	CSpe
	'Panache' **new**	NHor
	pentheri	NHor
	'Percy Roots'	NHor
	'Peter Wonder' (v)	NHor SVil WDib
	'Phantom'	NHor
	'Pheasant's Eye' (v)	NHor
	'Picturatus' (v) Υ^{H1}	NHor WDib
	'Pineapple Beauty' (v) Υ^{H1}	NHor WDib
	'Pineapplette' Υ^{H1}	EShb NHor WDib
	'Pink Chaos' **new**	NHor
	'Pink Devil' (v)	NHor
	'Pink Shawl'	NHor
	'Primrose Cloud' (v)	NHor
	'Primrose Spire' (v)	NHor
	'Prince Bishop' **new**	NHor
	'Purple Oak'	NHor
	'Red Angel'	WDib
	'Red Croton' (v)	NHor WDib
	'Red Mars'	NHor WDib
	'Red Nettie' (v)	NHor WDib
	'Red Rosie'	NHor WDib
	'Red Velvet'	EShb NHor WDib
	'Ringleader' **new**	NHor
	'Rose Blush' (v)	NHor WDib
	'Rosie'	NHor
	'Roy Pedley'	NHor WDib
	'Royal Scot' (v) Υ^{H1}	NHor WDib
	'Royal Velvet' **new**	NHor
	'Salmon Plumes' (v)	NHor WDib
	'Saturn'	LAst NHor SVil WDib
	'Scarborough Fair' **new**	NHor
	'Scarlet Ribbons'	NHor
	scutellarioides 'Molten Lava'PBR (v)	NHor
	'Sedona'PBR **new**	CSpe
	'Solar Sunrise' **new**	NHor
	'Speckles' (v)	NHor
	'Spire' (v)	NHor
	'Strawberry Jam'	NHor
	'Sunbeam' (v)	NHor
	'Tees Valley' **new**	NHor
	'The Cardinal' **new**	NHor
	'The Durham Angel'	NHor WDib
	'Theresa Horn'	NHor
	thyrsoideus	see *Plectranthus thyrsoideus*
	'Timotei'	NHor WDib
	'Tom Cooke'	NHor
	'Treales' (v)	NHor WDib
	'Tynesider' **new**	NHor
	'Vesuvius'	NHor
	'Vicky Darwell' **new**	NCob
	'Volcano'	NHor
	'Walter Turner' (v) Υ^{H1}	NHor SVil WDib
	'Weardale' **new**	NHor
	'Wearsider' **new**	NHor
	'White Gem' (v)	NHor
	'White Pheasant' (v)	NHor
	'Winsome' (v)	NHor WDib
	'Winter Sun' (v)	NHor WDib
	'Wisley Flame'	NHor WDib
	'Wisley Tapestry' (v) Υ^{H1}	NHor WDib
	'Yellow Croton' (v)	NHor

Solidago (*Asteraceae*)

	Name	Suppliers
	Babygold	see *S.* 'Goldkind'
	brachystachys	see *S. cutleri*
	caesia	EBee EWes LHop NBir WMoo WOld WTin
	canadensis	CTri ELan MMuc NBre SEND SPlb WFar WHer
	– var. ***salebrosa*** **new**	LRHS
	– var. ***scabra***	MAvo WOld WTin
	'Citronella'	ECtt NBPC
	'Cloth of Gold'	CMac EBee ECho ECtt GKir LRHS NPro SWvt WMnd WOld
§	'Crown of Rays'	CPrp ECtt LRHS MRav WFar WMnd WWEG
§	***cutleri***	EBee ECho ELan GEdr LRHS MBar MTho MWat NLar SPlb SRms WFar WPat
I	– ***nana***	ECho EWes
	'Ducky'	EBee NBPC
	'Early Bird'	WFar
	'Featherbush'	LRHS
§	***flexicaulis***	GMaP
	– 'Variegata' (v)	CWan EBee ECtt ELan EPfP GKir GMaP LRHS NLar NWsh WFar WHer WOld WPer WWEG
	'Gardone' Υ^{H4}	WFar
	gigantea	WFar WPer
	glomerata	NBre NLar NNor SMrm WPer
	Golden Baby	see *S.* 'Goldkind'
§	'Golden Dwarf'	COIW LRHS SPoG WPtf WWEG
	'Golden Falls'	LRHS
	'Golden Fleece'	see *S. sphacelata* 'Golden Fleece'
	Golden Gate = 'Dansolgold'	LRHS
	'Golden Thumb'	see *S.* 'Queenie'
	'Golden Wings'	CBre
	'Goldenmosa' Υ^{H4}	CAby CMac CSBt EBee ECtt EPfP EWes GKev GMaP LRHS MRav SPer SSvw WCot WFar WOld
	'Goldilocks'	NPri SRms
§	'Goldkind'	CMMP CSBt CTri EBee ECho ECtt EPfP EShb GAbr GKir IMon LRHS MCot MMuc MNHC MWhi NBPC NEgg NNor NOrc SBch SEND SWal SWvt WBrk WFar WWEG
	Goldzwerg	see *S.* 'Golden Dwarf'
	'Harvest Gold'	CAby CElw
	hybrida	see × *Solidaster luteus*
*	***idahoensis*** **new**	EBee
	latifolia	see *S. flexicaulis*
	'Laurin'	EBee EPfP LRHS MBri NLar WTin
	'Ledsham'	CAby EBee ECtt LEdu LRHS MCot NBre SPoG WMnd
	'Lemore'	see × *Solidaster luteus* 'Lemore'
	'Leraft'	EBee
	'Linner Gold'	NBre
	'Little Lemon' **new**	GCal
	ohioensis	EBee
*	'Peter Pan'	LRHS WFar
§	'Queenie'	ECha ECho MHer MLHP NBre NPro NVic SRms WWEG
	rigida	LRHS NBre SMrm WCot WPer
	roanensis	NBre
	rugosa	ECha MBNS MMuc NBre SEND SPhx WCot
	– 'Fireworks'	CBgR CBre CHVG CMHG COIW CPrp CSam EBee EBrs ECtt ELon EPPr GCal GQue LRHS MAvo MBNS MNFA NBPC NCGa SUsu WBrk WCot WFar WHil WHoo WOld WTin WWEG WWlt
	sciaphila	NBre
	sempervirens	WCot WFar
	– 'Goldene Wellen'	EBee
	shortii	EBee
	simplex subsp. ***simplex*** var. ***nana***	NWCA WPer
	'Sonnenschein'	NBre
	'Spätgold'	EBee

speciosa	LRHS NBre WPer
spectabilis var. ***confinis***	EBee
§ ***sphacelata***	CBcs EBee IMou LRHS NBre SPoG
'Golden Fleece'	WFar WMnd WWEG
spiraeifolia	NBre
Strahlenkrone	see *S.* 'Crown of Rays'
'Summer Sunshine'	WWEG
Sweety = 'Barseven'PBR	MBri
'Tom Thumb'	CMac MRav SRms WEas
uliginosa	EShb NBre
ulmifolia	EBee NBre
virgaurea	CArn CSam EBWF EBee GPoy MHer MNHC NBre NLar NSco SMrm WHer WPer
- subsp. ***alpestris*** var. ***minutissima***	NBre WPat
- var. ***cambrica***	see *S. virgaurea* subsp. *minuta*
§ - subsp. ***minuta***	GBin
§ - 'Variegata' (v)	EHoe NPro
vulgaris 'Variegata'	see *S. virgaurea* 'Variegata'
'Yellow Springs' **new**	GJos
'Yellowstone'	EBee

× *Solidaster* (*Asteraceae*)

hybridus	see × *S. luteus*
§ ***luteus***	CBgR EBee MBri SRms WEas WFar WHil
§ - 'Lemore' ♀H4	CHrt CMea CPrp EBee ELan EPfP GBuc GMaP GMac GQue LAst LDai LHop LRHS MBrN MWat NCGa NPri NWsh SPer WCot WFar
'Super'	CAby CPrp EBee WCot

Sollya (*Pittosporaceae*)

fusiformis	see *S. heterophylla*
§ ***heterophylla*** ♀H1	Widely available
- 'Alba'	CBcs CCCN EBee ELan EPfP LRHS SPer SPoG SWvt
- mauve-flowered	ECou
- 'Pink Charmer'	EBee ELan ERea LRHS MAsh SPer SPoG
- pink-flowered	CCCN CHII CSPN EPfP LBMP LRHS SEND SPad SWvt

Sonchus (*Asteraceae*)

fruticosus	CHEx GGar
giganteus	CHII
pinnatus	SPlb

Sophora (*Papilionaceae*)

§ ***davidii***	CBcs CGHE CPLG CWib EBee EBtc EPfP EWTr LHop LRHS MBlu MGos MWea SEND SPoG WPGP WSHC
fulvida	ECou
howinsula	ECou
japonica	see *Styphnolobium japonicum*
- 'Dot' **new**	LRHS
- 'Pendula'	ELan EMil LMaj LRHS MBlu MGos
§ 'Little Baby'	CAbP CWib EBee EMil EPfP LAst LBuc LRHS LSRN MCCP MGos MWea SBch SDix SPoG SWvt WGrn WPGP WPat
longicarinata	ECou
macrocarpa	EBee GQui
microphylla	CArn CHEx CTri EBee ECou EPfP LHop LRHS SEND WBVN WHer WPGP
- 'Dragon's Gold'	CBcs EBee ECou ELan EPfP LRHS MAsh SCoo SPoG SSpi SSta WDin
- 'Early Gold'	GQui
molloyi	ECou
prostrata misapplied	see *S.* 'Little Baby'
prostrata ambig.	CBcs CGHE LRHS
prostrata Buch.	CBot CMac ECou
- Pukaki form	ECou
Sun King = 'Hilsop'PBR ♀H4	CBcs CCVT CWGN EBee ELan EMui EPfP EWes GKir LRHS LSRN MGos MWea NCGa NLar NPri SBch SCoo SLon SPoG
tetraptera ♀H3	CAbP CBcs CDul CFee CMac CTsd CWit EBee ECou EPfP GGal GQui ISea LRHS MWea SEND SRms WBVN WBor WPGP
viciifolia	see *S. davidii*

Sorbaria (*Rosaceae*)

SF 95205	ISea
aitchisonii	see *S. tomentosa* var. *angustifolia*
arborea	see *S. kirilowii*
aff. ***assurgens*** BWJ 8185	WCru
§ ***kirilowii***	CMac CPLG MRav NLar SMad SPer WBVN WDyG WOut
- AC 3433	MSnd
lindleyana	see *S. tomentosa*
rhoifolia	EPfP
sorbifolia	CAbP CBcs EBee ECrN GAuc GKir IFFs MBar MLHP MMuc NPro SEND SPer SPlb SPoG WDin WFar
- 'Sem'PBR	Widely available
- var. ***stellipila***	SLPl
- - B&SWJ 776	WCru
§ ***tomentosa*** CC 4547	WCot
§ - var. ***angustifolia*** ♀H4	CBcs CDul CTri CWan EBee ELan EPfP EWTr GAuc GKir LRHS MMuc MRav NHol NPro SEND SLon SPer WEas WFar WHer WSpi

× *Sorbopyrus* (*Rosaceae*)

auricularis	CTho
- 'Shipova' (F)	CAgr

Sorbus ✿ (*Rosaceae*)

CLD 1437	GAuc
Guiz 119	GKir
MF 96072	GKev
SDR 5114	GKev
alnifolia	CLnd CMCN EBee EPfP MBlu SLPl
- B&SWJ 10948	WCru
- 'Red Bird' **new**	MBlu
americana	CLnd NWea
- 'Belmonte'	GKir
amoena	GKir
- CLD 311	GKir
aff. ***amurensis*** B&SWJ 8665	WCru
anglica	CDul CNat GKir
apiculata	GKir
- CLD 310	GAuc GKir
'Apricot'	CEnd GKir
'Apricot Lady'	LRHS MAsh MGos
'Apricot Queen'	CLnd EBee ECrN EMil LAst NEgg WBor WFar
aria	CCVT CDul CLnd CSBt CTri ECrN EMac EPfP GAuc GKir IFFs LBuc MBar MGan MGos MMuc MSnd NWea WDin WMou
- 'Aurea'	CLnd MGos WFar
- 'Chrysophylla'	CDul CSBt EBee ECrN GKir LRHS MGos NWea SLim SPer SPoG
- 'Decaisneana'	see *S. aria* 'Majestica'
- 'Lutescens' ♀H4	Widely available

	Name	Suppliers
	- 'Magnifica'	CDoC CTho ECrN ELan LMaj NEgg SCoo WDin WJas
§	- 'Majestica' ♀H4	CCVT CDoC CDul CLnd CMac CTho EBee ECrN GKir LHop LRHS MAsh NWea SCoo SPer SPoG WHar WJas
	- 'Mitchellii'	see *S. thibetica* 'John Mitchell'
	× ***arnoldiana*** 'Cerise Queen'	GKir
	- 'Golden Wonder'	see *S.* 'Lombarts Golden Wonder'
	aronioides misapplied	see *S. caloneura*
	arranensis	CNat GKir
§	***aucuparia***	Widely available
	- 'Aspleniifolia'	CBcs CCVT CDul CLnd CMCN CMac CSBt CWSG EBee ECrN GKir IFFs LAst LRHS MAsh MGos MRav MWat NPCo NWea SBch SLim SPer SPoG WDin WFar WJas
	- 'Beauty of Banff'	GKir
§	- 'Beissneri'	CAgr CDul CLnd GBin GKir MBri MGos NLar NPCo NWea SCoo SLon SPoG
	- Cardinal Royal = 'Michred'	CCVT CDoC ECrN GKir GQui LRHS NEgg SBch SCoo WJas
	- 'Crème Lace'	GKir SCoo
	- 'Dirkenii'	CDul CWSG GBin GKir IFFs LRHS MAsh WDin WJas
§	- var. ***edulis*** (F)	CDul CLnd CTho ECrN LBuc LMaj MGos SCoo WDin
	- - 'Rossica' misapplied	see *S. aucuparia* var. *edulis* 'Rossica Major'
§	- - 'Rossica Major'	CDul ECrN GQui SCoo WFar
§	- 'Fastigiata'	CEnd CLnd CMac CTri ECrN EPfP GKir LAst LMaj LRHS MAsh MGos NPCo WDin WFar
	- var. ***heteromorpha***	GAuc
	- 'Hilling's Spire'	CTho GKir
	- 'Pendula'	CDul EBee
	- ***pluripinnata***	see *S. scalaris* Koehne
	- var. ***rossica*** Koehne	see *S. aucuparia* var. *edulis*
	- 'Scarlet King'	see *S.* × *thuringiaca* 'Scarlet King'
	- 'Sheerwater Seedling' ♀H4	CCVT CDoC CDul CLnd CMCN CSBt EBee ECrN ELan EPfP GKir IFFs LAst LHop LMaj LRHS MGos MMuc MRav MSwo NBlu NPri SBch SLim SSta WDin WFar
	- var. ***xanthocarpa*** ♀H4	CLnd ECrN EPfP LMaj WDin
	Autumn Spire = 'Flanrock'	CDoC CLnd CWSG GKir LRHS MAsh MBri MGos NLar SBch SCoo SPoG WHar
	'Bellona'	WPat
	bissetii	GKir
	'Boyne Bay'	GKir
	'Brilliant Yellow'	GKir
	bristoliensis	GAuc GKir
	'Burka'	see *Aronia* × *Sorbus*, 'Burka'
	californica	GKir
§	***caloneura***	EPfP GKir MBlu SSpi WPGP
	carmesina 'Emberglow'	GKir LRHS
	'Carpet of Gold'	CLnd GKir
	cashmiriana Hedl. ♀H4	Widely available
	chamaemespilus	GAuc WPat
	'Chamois Glow'	GKir WJas
	'Chinese Lace'	Widely available
§	***commixta***	CBcs CDul CEnd CLnd CMCN CSto CTho EBee ECrN EPfP GAuc GKir IFFs LAst LRHS MBar MBlu MGos MMuc MSwo NBea SLim SPer SPoG WDin WJas
	- B&SWJ 8496	WCru
	- 'Embley' ♀H4	CBcs CCVT CDul CMCN CMac CSBt CSam CTho CTri ECrN ELan EPfP GKir LHop MBar MBlu MGos MMuc MRav NEgg NPCo NWea SMHT SPer WDin WFar
	- 'Jermyns'	GKir
	- 'Ravensbill'	GKir LRHS MAsh WHar WMou
	- var. ***rufoferruginea***	GKir GQui
	- - B&SWJ 6078	WCru
	conradinae misapplied	see *S. pohuashanensis* (Hance) Hedlund
	conradinae Koehne	see *S. esserteauana*
	'Copper Kettle'	GKir MAsh MBri MWat NLar SCoo SPoG WHar
	'Coral Beauty'	CDul CLnd
	'Covert Gold'	CEnd CLnd
	croceocarpa	CDul GKir
	'Croft Coral' new	NPal
	cuspidata	see *S. vestita*
*	***decora*** 'Grootendorst'	CDul
	- var. ***nana***	see *S. aucuparia* 'Fastigiata'
	devoniensis	CDul CNat CTho GKir LRHS
	- 'Devon Beauty'	CAgr
	discolor misapplied	see *S. commixta*
	discolor (Maxim.) Maxim.	CLnd EBee GAuc GKir MAsh MBlu NWea WJas
	- MF 96172	GKir
	domestica	CDul EPfP IFFs WDin
§	- f. ***pyrifera***	WMou
	- 'Pyriformis'	see *S. domestica* f. *pyrifera*
	- 'Rosie'	CAgr
	'Eastern Promise'	CSam CWSG EBee ECrN GKir LRHS MAsh MBlu MBri MWat NLar NWea SCoo SLim SMHT WDin WJas
§	***eburnea*** Harry Smith 12799	GKir GQui
	eminens	CDul CNat
	epidendron	GKir
§	***esserteauana***	CTho EPfP WPat
	- 'Flava'	GKir
	'Fastigiata'	see *S. aucuparia* 'Fastigiata', *S.* × *thuringiaca* 'Fastigiata'
	folgneri	CEnd
	- 'Emiel'	EPfP MBlu MBri
	- 'Lemon Drop'	CDul CEnd CLnd CPMA CWSG EPfP GKir LRHS MAsh NLar SCoo SMad SSpi
§	***foliolosa***	CLnd EPfP GKir NWea SCoo
	forrestii	EPfP GKir NBea NLar SLPl SMHT
*	***fortunei***	CLnd
	fruticosa Crantz	CSto GAuc
I	***fruticosa*** McAllister	CEnd CLnd EBee EPfP EWTr GKev GKir NWea WJas
	- 'Koehneana'	see *S. koehneana* C.K. Schneid.
	'Ghose'	CEnd CLnd GKir LRHS SCoo SPer SSpi
	glabrescens new	CSto
	glabriuscula	GGal GKir
	'Glendoick Gleam'	GGGa
	'Glendoick Glory'	GGGa
	'Glendoick Ivory'	GGGa
	'Glendoick Pearl'	GGGa
	'Glendoick Ruby'	GGGa
	'Glendoick Spire'	GGGa
	'Glendoick White Baby'	GGGa
	glomerulata	LLHF
	'Golden Wonder'	see *S.* 'Lombarts Golden Wonder'
	gonggashanica	EPfP GKir
*	***gorrodini***	CLnd
§	***graeca***	GAuc GKir SEND
	'Granatnaja'	see × *Crataegosorbus* 'Granatnaja'
	granulosa HWJ 1041	WCru
	harrowiana	GKir WPat

Harry Smith **new**	LRHS
'Harvest Moon'	GQui
hedlundii	CPLG EBtc GBin GKir LRHS MGos NLar WPGP
helenae	GKir
hemsleyi	CDul CLnd CPLG GKir WPGP
- 'John Bond'	GKir MBri SPoG
× ***hostii***	CLnd MRav SPer
hupehensis C.K. Schneid. ♀H4	CBcs CDul CEnd CLnd CMCN CMac CTho CTri EBee ECrN EPfP GKev GKir LHop LRHS MBar NHol NWea SBch SLPl WCru WDin WFar WHar WJas WPat
- 'November Pink'	see *S. hupehensis* 'Pink Pagoda'
§ - var. ***obtusa*** ♀H4	CBrd CCVT CDoC CDul CLnd EPfP GCal GKev GKir NEgg NPCo SSpi WDin
§ - 'Pink Pagoda'	CDoC CDul CLnd CWSG EBee ECrN EMui EPfP GKir IArd LRHS LSRN MAsh MBlu MDun MGos MMuc MRav MWat NWea SBch SCoo SLim SLon SPer SPoG WBor WDin WFar
- red-berried	GGal
- 'Rosea'	see *S. hupehensis* var. *obtusa*
× ***hybrida*** misapplied	see *S.* × *thuringiaca*
hybrida L.	ECrN
- 'Gibbsii' ♀H4	CDoC CLnd EBee ELan EPfP GAuc GKir LRHS MAsh MBri SPur WHar
insignis	CDoC EPfP WPat
intermedia	CCVT CDul CLnd CSBt CTho CTri CWib ECrN GKir IFFs MGos NBlu NWea SEND WDin WHar WMou
- 'Brouwers'	ELan LMaj LRHS
japonica B&SWJ 10813	WCru
- B&SWJ 11048	WCru
'Joseph Rock'	Widely available
§ × ***kewensis***	CDul CLnd NWea SMHT SPlb
'Kirsten Pink'	CLnd CWib EBee ECrN GKir SMHT SPer WFar
koehneana hort.	see *S. fruticosa* McAllister
§ ***koehneana*** C.K. Schneid. ♀H4	CBcs CLnd ECrN GKir GQui IDee LRHS MAsh NBlu NMen NWea SCoo WPat WTin
aff. ***koehneana***	see *S. eburnea*
'Kukula'	GKir
kurzii	GKir
- KR 1501	GKir
lanata misapplied	see *S. vestita*
lancastriensis	CDul CNat GKir
latifolia	CLnd ECrN WDin
- 'Henk Vink'	LMaj
'Leonard Messel'	GKir MAsh MBri SCoo
'Leonard Springer'	ECrN EPfP GKir GQui
leptophylla	CDul GKir
ligustrifolia HWJ 984	WCru
'Likjornaja'	EPfP
§ 'Lombarts Golden Wonder'	CBcs CDoC CDul CLnd MAsh NWea WJas
matsumurana misapplied	see *S. commixta*
matsumurana (Makino) Koehne	GKir
megalocarpa	CDoC CPMA EPfP SSpi WPGP WPat
meliosmifolia B&SWJ 11771	WCru
microphylla GWJ 9252	WCru
minima	GKir
monbeigii (Card.) Yü	GAuc GKir
moravica 'Laciniata'	see *S. aucuparia* 'Beissneri'
mougeotii	GKir
§ ***munda***	CMCN GBin GKir SCoo
nova CLD 1437	GAuc
aff. ***ovalis*** H 1948 **new**	GKev
'Peachi-Ness'	CLnd
'Pearly King'	CBcs CTho LRHS MAsh NBea WJas
pekinensis	see *S. reticulata* subsp. *pekinensis*
§ 'Pink Pearl'	CDul GKir LRHS
'Pink-Ness'	EBee GKir LRHS NLar SCoo SPoG
pogonopetala Koehne	GAuc GKir
pohuashanensis misapplied	see *S.* × *kewensis*
§ ***pohuashanensis*** (Hance) Hedlund	GKir WPat
porrigentiformis	CDul
poteriifolia	GAuc GKir WPat
prattii misapplied	see *S. munda*
prattii Koehne	CDul GKev GKir WPat
- var. ***subarachnoidea***	see *S. munda*
* ***pseudobalsomnensis***	CBcs
pseudofennica	GKir
pseudohupehensis	GKir
pseudovilmorinii	GBin GKir
- MF 93044	SSpi
- SDR 4232	GKev
randaiensis	CSto GQui SPlb
- B&SWJ 3202	NHol SSpi WCru
'Red Tip'	CDul MWat
reducta ♀H4	CBcs CEnd CSWP EPfP GAbr GAuc GBin GKev GKir GQui LRHS MBlu NHol NWCA SCoo SPer SPoG WDin WFar
reflexipetala misapplied	see *S. commixta*
rehderiana misapplied	see *S. aucuparia*
rehderiana Koehne	CDul CLnd GKir
§ ***reticulata*** subsp. ***pekinensis***	GKir
rosea	EMui GKir LRHS
- 'Rosiness'	CLnd EPfP GKir LRHS MBri SCoo SLim
'Rowancroft Coral Pink'	CDul EBee MBar MGos
rufopilosa	GKir WPat
'Salmon Queen'	CLnd
sambucifolia	GAuc
sargentiana ♀H4	CCVT CDul CEnd CLnd CMCN CTho CTri EBee ECrN ELan EPfP GKir IFFs LAst LRHS MBlu MBri MGos MRav MSwo NBea NWea SLim SMHT SMad SPer SSpi WDin WJas
scalaris ambig.	GAuc MGos
§ ***scalaris*** Koehne	CBcs CCVT CEnd CTho CTri EBee EPfP GKir LRHS MAsh MBlu MGos SBch SCoo SPer SPoG SSpi WDin WJas
'Schouten'	ECrN
scopulina misapplied	see *S. aucuparia* 'Fastigiata'
scopulina Greene wild-collected **new**	GKir
setschwanensis	CMCN GGGa GKir
'Signalman'	GKir
simonkaiana **new**	GAuc
subcuneata	CNat
'Sunshine'	CAlb CCVT CDoC CDul GKir LRHS MAsh MGos MMuc NLar WJas
thibetica	WPGP
§ - 'John Mitchell' ♀H4	CAgr CDul CEnd CLnd CMCN CWib EBtc ECrN EPfP GKir GQui LRHS MAsh MBlu MBri MGos MRav NBea NLar NWea SLim SMHT SPer SPoG WFar WJas WPat
aff. ***thibetica*** BWJ 7757a	WCru
thomsonii GWJ 9363	WCru
§ × ***thuringiaca***	GAuc NBea WMou

§	- 'Fastigiata'	CBcs CDul CLnd CMac CSBt EPfP MGos MMuc NEgg SCoo WDin WJas
§	- 'Scarlet King'	EBee
	tianschanica new	GAuc
	torminalis	CAlb CCVT CDul CLnd CMac CTho CTri EBee ECrN EMac EPfP GKir IFFs LRHS MBlu MBri MGos MMuc MRav MSnd NWea SCoo SEND SPer SPoG WFar WHar WMou WSpi
	umbellata	GKir
	- var. ***cretica***	see *S. graeca*
	ursina	see *S. foliolosa*
	× ***vagensis***	CLnd GKir WMou
	verrucosa	WCru
	var. ***subulata*** HWJ 579	
	- - HWJ 925	WCru
§	***vestita***	CLnd CTho GKir MBlu
	vexans	CDul CNat GBin
	vilmorinii ♀H4	Widely available
	- 'Robusta'	see *S.* 'Pink Pearl'
	wallichii SF 06035 new	ISea
	wardii	CBcs CLnd CTho EPfP GKir MBlu
	'White Swan'	MAsh
	'White Wax'	CDul CWSG EPfP GKir GQue LAst LRHS MGos SPer SPoG WDin WPat
	'Wilfrid Fox'	CLnd GKir SLPl
	wilmottiana	CDul GKir
	wilsoniana	CLnd GKir GQui
	- C 5018	GKir
	- C&H 7122	GKir
	'Wisley Gold'	CWSG LRHS MAsh MGos NLar SCoo SLim SPoG

Sorghastrum (*Poaceae*)

	avenaceum	see *S. nutans*
§	***nutans***	CKno CRWN CWCL GFor LEdu LRHS SMad
	- 'Indian Steel'	EBee ECha GFor GQue SGSe WWEG
	- 'Sioux Blue' new	EPPr

sorrel, common see *Rumex acetosa*

sorrel, French see *Rumex scutatus*

Souliea see *Actaea*

soursop see *Annona muricata*

Sparaxis (*Iridaceae*)

sp. new	ECho
bulbifera	ECho
'Colour Mill'	WHil
fragrans 'Napier' new	ECho
grandiflora ♀H2-3 new	LRHS
- subsp. ***acutiloba***	ECho
- subsp. ***fimbriata***	ECho
- subsp. ***grandiflora***	CGrW ECho
hybrids	LAma
parviflora	ECho
'Red Reflex' new	ECho
tricolor	EBrs ECho
variegata	ECho
subsp. ***metelerkampiae*** 'Rawsonville' new	
villosa	ECho

Sparganium (*Sparganiaceae*)

§	***erectum***	CRow CWat EHon EMFW LPBA NPer NSco SWat WMAq WSFF
	ramosum	see *S. erectum*

Sparrmannia (*Tiliaceae*)

africana ♀H1	CBcs CHEx CHll CTrG EAmu EShb LRHS MBri SDnm SPav

Spathipappus see *Tanacetum*

Spartina (*Poaceae*)

'Dafken'	EBee
patens	EPPr
pectinata	CHar GFor LRHS
- 'Aureomarginata' (v)	Widely available

Spartium (*Papilionaceae*)

junceum ♀H4	CArn CBcs CDoC CDul CEnd CTri EBee ECrN ELan EMil EPfP GCal LAst LRHS MGos MWat NSti SBch SDix SGar SMad SPer SPoG SRms WDin
- 'Brockhill Compact'	CDoC EMil LRHS

Spartocytisus see *Cytisus*

Spathantheum (*Araceae*)

orbignyanum	EBee LFur WCot

Spathiphyllum (*Araceae*)

'Viscount'	MBri
wallisii	LRHS MBri

Spathodea (*Bignoniaceae*)

campanulata	SPlb

spearmint see *Mentha spicata*

Speirantha (*Convallariaceae*)

§	***convallarioides***	CDes CGHE CLAP CPom CStu EBee ECho EHrv ELon EPPr ERos LEdu WCot WCru WPGP WPrP
	gardenii	see *S. convallarioides*

Spergularia (*Caryophyllaceae*)

purpurea	ECho
rupicola	EBWF ECho

Sphacele see *Lepechinia*

Sphaeralcea (*Malvaceae*)

	sp.	EBee
	ambigua	ELan
	'Childerley'	CSpe LHop SAga SMrs
	coccinea	SPlb
	fendleri	CBot CHll
	'Hopleys Lavender'	EBee LAst LHop LSou SAga SWvt WSHC
	'Hyde Hall'	EBee EPPr
	incana	CSpe SAga
	malviflora	CDTJ WPer
	miniata	CHll SAga SMrm
	munroana	CBot CDTJ CPom CSev ECGP ELan SAga SRkn WSHC
	- 'Dixieland Pink'	EBee
	- pale pink-flowered	ECtt
*	- 'Shell Pink'	CSpe ECGP
	'Newleaze Coral'	CSpe EBee LAst LHop LSou MAsh SAga SMrs SPoG SUsu SWvt
	'Newleaze Pink'	LHop SAga SRkn
	obtusiloba	CSpe SAga
	remota	CPLG SPlb
	umbellata	see *Phymosia umbellata*

Sphaeromeria (*Asteraceae*)

§	***capitata***	CPBP NWCA

Spigelia (*Loganiaceae*)

	marilandica	CDes EBee EWTr
	- 'Wisley Jester'	GKir LBuc LRHS MBri SCoo

Spilanthes (*Asteraceae*)

	acmella misapplied	see *Acmella oleracea*
	oleracea	see *Acmella oleracea*

Spiloxene (*Hypoxidaceae*)

	capensis 'Somerset West' **new**	ECho
	serrata 'Saldanha' **new**	ECho

Spiraea (*Rosaceae*)

	'Abigail'	CDoC
	albiflora	see *S. japonica* var. *albiflora*
	arborea	see *Sorbaria kirilowii*
	arcuata	EMac
§	'Arguta' ♀H4	Widely available
	× ***arguta*** 'Bridal Wreath'	see *S.* 'Arguta'
	bella	SLon WTin
	betulifolia	CDul MRav NHol WDin WHCG
	- var. ***aemiliana***	CBot CWSG EBee ECtt MAsh MGos SLPl WFar
	× ***billardii*** misapplied	see *S.* × *pseudosalicifolia*
	× ***bumalda*** 'Wulfenii'	see *S. japonica* 'Walluf'
	callosa 'Alba'	see *S. japonica* var. *albiflora*
	canescens	CPLG GKev
	- AC 1354	MSnd
§	***cantoniensis*** 'Flore Pleno' (d)	SLon
	- 'Lanceata'	see *S. cantoniensis* 'Flore Pleno'
	× ***cinerea*** 'Grefsheim' ♀H4	CDoC CSBt EBee ECtt LRHS MBri MMuc SLim SPer SPlb WCFE WDin
	crispifolia	see *S. japonica* 'Bullata'
	douglasii	CMac GAuc IFFs MBar
	formosana	WCru
	- B&SWJ 1597	CPLG
§	× ***foxii***	SLPl
	fritschiana	CMac SLPl SLon
	hayatana	SLon
	- RWJ 10014	WCru
	hendersonii	see *Petrophytum hendersonii*
	japonica	GKir SBod WFar
§	- var. ***albiflora***	CBcs CMac CSBt CTri CWib ELan EPfP GKir LBMP LRHS MBar MGos MMuc MRav MSwo MWat NEgg NPri SBch SEND SLim SPer SRms SWvt WDin WFar WHCG WMoo WSpi
	- 'Alpina'	see *S. japonica* 'Nana'
	- 'Alpine Gold'	GBin LRHS NPro
	- 'Anthony Waterer' (v)	Widely available
	- 'Barkby Gold'	MGos
	- 'Blenheim'	SRms
§	- 'Bullata'	CFee CMac EPfP GEdr MBar NWCA SRms WAbe
	- 'Candlelight' ♀H4	CAbP CSBt CWSG EBee EPfP GKir LAst LRHS MAsh MBri MGos NEgg NHol SBch SCoo SLim SPer SPoG SWvt WMoo
	- 'Coccinea'	ELon
	- 'Crispa'	EMil EPfP LRHS MBar NPro WFar WGrn WMoo
	- 'Dart's Red' ♀H4	GKir LRHS NPri WFar
	- 'Firelight'	CAbP CSBt EBee EHoe ELan EPfP GKir LAst LRHS MAsh MBri MGos MSwo NEgg NHol NPri SCoo SLim SPer SPoG SSta SWvt WDin WFar WMoo
§	- 'Genpei'	CChe CMac MAsh NBlu SPer
	- 'Gold Mound'	CChe CMac CPLG CWSG CWib EBee ECrN EHoe ELan EPfP GKir LBMP LRHS MBar MGos MMuc MRav MSwo NHol NPri SBch SCoo SPer SPlb SRms WDin WFar WHar
	- Golden Princess = 'Lisp'PBR ♀H4	CMac CTri CWSG EPfP GKir LBuc LRHS MAsh MBar MGos NBlu NEgg NPri SCoo SReu SRms SSta WCFE WDin WFar
	- 'Goldflame'	Widely available
	- 'Little Princess'	CBcs CDul CMac CWSG CWib EBee ECrN EMil GKir LRHS MAsh MBar MRav MSwo NHol NPri SCoo SLim SPer SRGP SRms SSta SWvt WBVN WDin WFar WHar WMoo
	- 'Macrophylla'	CEnt
	- Magic Carpet = 'Walbuma'PBR (v) ♀H4	EBee EBrs GKir LBuc LRHS MAsh NLar SCoo SPoG
	- 'Magnifica'	WHCG WPat
§	- 'Nana' ♀H4	CMac CSBt ECho GEdr MAsh MBar MRav SRms WPer
	- 'Nyewoods'	see *S. japonica* 'Nana'
	- 'Shiburi'	see *S. japonica* var. *albiflora*
N	- 'Shirobana' misapplied	see *S. japonica* 'Genpei'
N	- 'Shirobana'	see *S. japonica* var. *albiflora*
	- 'Snow Cap'	CWib
§	- 'Walluf'	CMac CPLG CTri CWib
	- 'White Cloud'	ELan
	- 'White Gold'PBR	CSBt EBee ELan EPfP LAst LRHS LSqu MAsh MBri NHol NPro SCoo SPer SPoG SWvt WHar WMoo
	'Margaritae'	SPer SWvt
	micrantha	CPLG
	nipponica	CBcs GKir LAst MBar
	- 'Halward's Silver'	EMil LBuc MGos MRav NHol NPro SLPl
	- 'June Bride'	NBlu
§	- 'Snowmound' ♀H4	Widely available
	- var. ***tosaensis*** misapplied	see *S. nipponica* 'Snowmound'
	- var. ***tosaensis*** (Yatabe) Makino	LHop SReu
	palmata 'Elegans'	see *Filipendula purpurea* 'Elegans'
	prunifolia (d)	CMac ECrN ELan MBlu MRav SLon SPer SPoG WCFE WDin WGrn WPat
	× ***pseudosalicifolia*** 'Triumphans'	MMuc
	salicifolia	WFar
	stevenii	SPer
	'Summersnow'	SLPl
	'Superba'	see *S.* × *foxii*
	tarokoensis	GAuc
	thunbergii ♀H4	CDul CTri CWib EBee ECrN EPfP MRav NWea SBch SCoo SLim SPer SRms WDin WGwG WHCG
	- 'Aurea' **new**	LRHS MAsh SPoG
	- 'Fujino Pink'	MAsh WDin
	- 'Mellow Yellow'	see *S. thunbergii* 'Ogon'
	- 'Mount Fuji'	CAbP CMac CWib EHoe MGos MRav NPro WFar
§	- 'Ōgon'	WFar WPen
	- 'Tickled Pink'	LRHS
	trilobata	EBee
	ulmaria	see *Filipendula ulmaria*
	× ***vanhouttei***	CBcs CDul CTri EBee EPfP LRHS MBar MMuc MRav MSwo SLim SPer SRms WDin WFar
	- 'Gold Fountain'	GBin LRHS NHol SCoo SPoG WFar

	– 'Pink Ice' (v)	CAbP CDoC CWib EHoe EPfP LAst LBMP LRHS MAsh MGos MRav NHol SBch SPer SPlb SPoG SWvt WDin WFar
	veitchii	MRav
	venusta 'Magnifica'	see *Filipendula rubra* 'Venusta'

Spiranthes (*Orchidaceae*)

	cernua	NGdn NLAp
	– var. ***odorata***	LSou SMrm
	– – 'Chadd's Ford'	Widely available
	spiralis	WHer

Spirodela (*Lemnaceae*)

§	***polyrhiza***	CWat

Spodiopogon (*Poaceae*)

	sibiricus	CKno EBee EHoe EPPr GFor LDai LEdu MWhi SGSe SMad
	– 'West Lake' **new**	IMou

Sporobolus (*Poaceae*)

	airoides	CKno EBee EHoe EPPr EShb GCal LPio MWea SGSe SMad WCot WHrl
	heterolepis	CKno EBee EHoe EShb GAbr GCal LPio MWhi SGSe SMad
	– 'Cloud'	GBin
I	– 'Wisconsin Strain' **new**	IMou
	wrightii	EBee EPPr MWhi

Sprekelia (*Amaryllidaceae*)

	formosissima	CFir CSpe CStu EBrs ECho LAma LEdu LRHS SPav

Stachys ✿ (*Lamiaceae*)

	B&SWJ 10300 from Guatemala	WCru
	aethiopica 'Danielle'	see *S. thunbergii* 'Danielle'
§	***affinis***	CAgr CArn CFir GPoy LEdu SVic
	albens	EBla IFro
	albotomentosa	EBee EBla LSou MDKP SHar WCHb WCot WWlt
	× ***ambigua***	EBWF
	balcanica	CDes EBee GKev
	– MESE	WPGP
	betonica	see *S. officinalis*
§	***byzantina***	Widely available
§	– 'Big Ears'	CBow EBee ECha EPfP EWTr GMaP LAst LHop MBri MRav MWat SBch SEND SGSe SMrm SPhx SPoG WBor WCAu WCFE WCot WFar WHoo WMnd WMoo WWEG
§	– 'Cotton Boll'	COIW EBee ECha GCal LRHS SBch SPer WCom WFar WWEG
	– 'Countess Helen von Stein'	see *S. byzantina* 'Big Ears'
	– gold-leaved	see *S. byzantina* 'Primrose Heron'
	– large-leaved	see *S. byzantina* 'Big Ears'
	– 'Limelight'	WCot
§	– 'Primrose Heron'	CMoH EBee ECha EPPr GKev LRHS MRav MSpe NBid NLar NOrc SMrm SWvt WCAu WFar WOut
	– 'Sheila McQueen'	see *S. byzantina* 'Cotton Boll'
	– 'Silky Fleece'	EBee ECha EDAr EPfP EShb GKir LBMP NBre SBch WWEG
	– 'Silver Carpet'	CBcs COIW EBee ECha EHoe EPfP EWTr GKir GMaP LAst LRHS LSRN MRav NOrc NSti SPer SPoG SRms SWat SWvt WCAu WCom WCot WFar WHoo WMnd WMoo WWEG
§	– 'Striped Phantom' (v)	CBow EBla WCHb WEas
	– 'Variegata'	see *S. byzantina* 'Striped Phantom'
	calcicola B&SWJ 10427 **new**	WCru
	chamissonis var. ***cooleyae***	EBee
	citrina	CMea EBee GCal LRHS
	coccinea	EBee ECtt EHrv EShb GBBs MCot SBch SDnm SPav SRkn WCHb WCot WMoo
	– B&SWJ 10418	WCru
	– 'El Salto'	WCom
	corsica	WPGP
	densiflora	see *S. monieri* (Gouan) P.W. Ball
§	***discolor***	CMea EBee IKil LRHS MBel MDKP NLar SBch WCot WOut WPer
	germanica	CPom EBee GPWP NBre
	– subsp. ***bithynica***	SMrm
	glutinosa	MDKP
	grandiflora	see *S. macrantha*
	heraclea	LRHS
	'Hidalgo'	CSpe SAga
	lanata	see *S. byzantina*
	lavandulifolia	WAbe
§	***macrantha***	Widely available
*	– 'Alba'	EBee ECha WMoo
	– 'Cally Splash' (v)	GCal
	– 'Hummelo'	see *S. officinalis* 'Hummelo'
*	– 'Nivea'	CSam EHrv ELan MMHG NBir
	– 'Robusta' ♀H4	CDes ELan GCal LRHS NBro NGdn SMrm WCot WWEG
	– 'Rosea'	CElw CMHG EBee ELan GBee GMaP LLWP MArl MAvo MLHP SPlb SWat WCFE WEas WPer
	– 'Superba'	CSpe EBee EBla ECtt EPfP GCra GMaP LAst LBMP LRHS MBri MMHG MRav MWhi NBPC NEgg SPer SWvt WBor WCAu WCHb WCom WCot WFar WMnd WMoo
	– 'Violacea'	LRHS MAvo MBrN NChi WCot WPGP
	mexicana misapplied	see *S. thunbergii*
	monieri misapplied	see *S. officinalis*
	monieri ambig.	CAbP CMMP EBee EShb GKev LBMP MSCN NLar NSti WPer
§	***monieri*** (Gouan) P.W. Ball	CEnt GBin LEdu LRHS WOut
*	– 'Rosea'	EBee NBre NLar
	nivea	see *S. discolor*
	obliqua	NBre WOut
§	***officinalis***	CArn CEnt CPrp CRWN CSev CWan EBWF EBee GBar GPoy LEdu MCot MHer MNHC NLan NMir SHlg WClo WHer
	– SDR 3554	GKev
	– 'Alba'	CArn EBee LEdu LRHS NBro STes WCHb WCom WFar WOut WTin
	– dwarf, white-flowered	GCal
§	– 'Hummelo'	EBee ECtt ELon EPPr EPfP GAbr GQue IKil LDai LHop LPla LSou MBel MDKP MRav NBPC NLar SAga SMrm SPhx SPoG SUsu WCAu WFar WWEG
	– mauve-flowered	WTin
	– 'Rosea'	CMea GCal NBro STes WCom WCot WFar WSHC WTin WWEG
	– 'Rosea Superba'	EBee ECha MDKP NBre SIng WCAu WCot WFar WMoo
	– 'Saharan Pink'	EBee EPfP LSou MHer WMoo WOut WWEG
	– 'Spitzenberg'	SUsu
	– 'Wisley White'	WCot
	olympica	see *S. byzantina*
	ossetica	CDes EBee
	palustris	CArn EBWF LPBA NLan NMir NSco
	'Pinkie'	LRHS
	recta	CEnt

	scardica MESE 362	MDKP
	setifera	EBee EBla NBre
	spicata	see *S. macrantha*
	stricta new	LRHS
	sylvatica	CArn EBWF NLan NMir NSco WHer
	- 'Hoskin's Variegated' (v)	WCHb
	- 'Huskers' (v)	LSou NBre
	- 'Shade of Pale'	WAlt
§	***thunbergii***	CDes EShb LEdu MBrN MDKP MWhi SBch SMeo SPhx SSvw SUsu WCot WPGP WPrP
§	- 'Danielle'	CBow EAro EBee ECtt LHop LIMB LRHS MHer NBre SRGP SRkn WMoo
	tuberifera	see *S. affinis*

Stachyurus (*Stachyuraceae*)

	chinensis	CBcs CMCN CPMA CTri CWib IArd IDee LRHS MGos NLar SPoG
	- 'Celina'	CPMA EMil LRHS MBlu MBri MGos NLar
	- 'Goldbeater'	NLar
	- 'Joy Forever' (v)	CBcs CDoC CDul CEnd CMCN CMac EBee EMil EPfP IArd IDee LLHF LRHS LSRN MBlu MBri MGos NLar SLim SPoG SSpi SSta SWvt WCot
	himalaicus	CBcs NLar
	- HWJCM 009	WCru
	- HWJK 2035	WCru
	aff. ***himalaicus*** HWJK 2052 new	WCru
	'Magpie' (v)	CPMA EPfP LRHS MBri MGos NLar SAga WCru
	praecox ♀H4	Widely available
	- B&SWJ 8898	WCru
	- B&SWJ 10899	WCru
	- var. ***leucotrichus***	CPMA NLar
	- var. ***matsuzakii***	CPMA NBhm NLar
	- - B&SWJ 2817	WCru
	- - B&SWJ 11229	WCru
	- 'Petra' new	CPMA
	retusus	CPLG NLar
	'Rubriflorus'	CPMA ELan EPfP LRHS MBri NLar SPoG WFar WPGP
	salicifolius	CBcs CGHE CPLG CPMA IDee MBri NLar SSpi WAbe WPGP
*	***sigeyosii*** B&SWJ 6915	WCru
	aff. ***szechuanensis***	CPLG
	- BWJ 8153	WCru
	yunnanensis	CBcs NLar SSpi WSHC

Stapelia (*Asclepiadaceae*)

	asterias	CFwr
	gettliffei	CFwr EShb
	gigantea ♀H1	CFwr
	grandiflora	CFwr
	- 'Flavirostris'	CFwr EShb
	hirsuta	CFwr EShb
	leendertziae	CFwr
	macowanii	CFwr
	marmoratum	see *Orbea variegata*
	mutabilis	CFwr
	variegata	see *Orbea variegata*

Staphylea (*Staphyleaceae*)

	bolanderi	CBcs
	bumalda	CBcs CPMA
	- B&SWJ 11053	WCru
	colchica	CBcs CDul EBee EBtc ELan EPfP EWTr EWes LRHS MGos MMHG NPal SMad SPer WCom WDin WKif WSHC
	- 'Rosea'	CBcs
	× ***coulombieri***	CBcs
	holocarpa	CPMA EPfP LHop MRav WFar
	- 'Innocence'	CBcs CDul NLar
N	- var. ***rosea***	CPMA EPfP MBri SMad
N	- 'Rosea'	CPMA MBlu NLar SSpi WSHC
	pinnata	CAgr CBcs CEnd CPMA EBtc EPfP SEND SMad WPat
	trifolia	CAgr CBcs NEgg

Statice see *Limonium*

Stauntonia (*Lardizabalaceae*)

	aff. ***chinensis*** DJHV 06175 new	WCru
	hexaphylla	CBcs CDoC CHEx CSam CTri CWGN EBee EPfP LRHS MAsh MBri SPer SPoG SReu SSpi SSta WBrE WSHC
	- B&SWJ 4858	WCru
	obovatifoliola B&SWJ 3685	WCru
	purpurea	NLar
	- B&SWJ 3690	WCru
	yaoshanensis HWJ 1024	WCru

Stegnogramma (*Thelypteridaceae*)

	pozoi	EBee EFer

Stellaria (*Caryophyllaceae*)

	graminea	EBWF
	holostea	CArn CRWN EBWF NMir NSco WPtf WShi

Stemmacantha (*Asteraceae*)

	carthamoides	CArn
§	***centaureoides***	EBee ECGP ECha GAbr GCal GQue LPla LRHS MBNS NBid NBre NVic SMeo SUsu WCAu WCot WSpi

Stenanthium (*Melanthiaceae*)

	robustum	WPGP

Stenocarpus (*Proteaceae*)

	sinuatus	EShb

Stenochlaena (*Blechnaceae*)

	palustris	MBri

Stenomesson (*Amaryllidaceae*)

§	***miniatum***	CStu WCot
	pearcei	WCot WPrP
	variegatum	WCot
	- yellow-flowered new	WCot

Stenotaphrum (*Poaceae*)

	secundatum	EShb
	- 'Variegatum' (v) ♀H1	EShb LSou WDyG

Stephanandra (*Rosaceae*)

	chinensis	SLon
	incisa	CBcs CPLG WHCG
§	- 'Crispa'	CDoC CDul CMac CTri EBee ECrN ELan EPfP EWTr LAst LHop LRHS MBar MBlu MRav NEgg NHol SPer SPoG WCFE WDin WFar WHCG WMoo
	- 'Dart's Horizon'	SLPl
	- 'Prostrata'	see *S. incisa* 'Crispa'

tanakae CAlb CBcs CDoC CDul CMac CPLG CTri EBee ELan EPfP EWTr LAst MBar MBlu MRav NEgg SLPl SLon SPer WDin WFar WHCG

Stephania (*Menispermaceae*)

rotunda B&SWJ 2396 — WCru
sinica BWJ 8094 **new** — WCru

Stephanotis (*Asclepiadaceae*)

floribunda ♀H1 — CBcs CCCN EBak LRHS MBri

Sterculia (*Sterculiaceae*)

rupestris — see *Brachychiton rupestris*

Sternbergia (*Amaryllidaceae*)

'Autumn Gold' — EBrs ECho LAma
candida — CBro EBrs ECho
§ ***clusiana*** — EBrs ECho
colchiciflora — EBrs ECho
fischeriana — CBro EBrs ECho
greuteriana — EBrs ECho EPot WWst
lutea — CAvo CBro CPBP CStu EBrs ECho EPot ERCP EWes LAma LRHS MAsh MCot MHer NWCA SDix SPhx WEas WTin
- Angustifolia Group — CBro CDes CMea EBee EBrs ECho WCot
macrantha — see *S. clusiana*
sicula — CBro CStu EBrs ECho EPot MAsh NRya
- 'Arcadian Sun' **new** — ECho WWst
- var. ***graeca*** — EBrs ECho
- - from Crete — ECho
- 'John Marr' — WThu

Stevia (*Asteraceae*)

rebaudiana — CArn EOHP GPoy MDKP WCot

Stewartia ✿ (*Theaceae*)

gemmata — see *S. sinensis*
'Korean Splendor' — see *S. pseudocamellia* Koreana Group
koreana — see *S. pseudocamellia* Koreana Group
malacodendron ♀H4 — EPfP LRHS SSpi
monadelpha — CMen LLHF SSpi
ovata — LRHS SSpi
pseudocamellia ♀H4 — Widely available
- B&SWJ 11044 — WCru
§ - Koreana Group ♀H4 — CDul CEnd CMCN ECrN EPfP GAuc LRHS MBri MDun NLar SSpi WDin WFar WPGP
- 'Ogisu' **new** — NLar
pteropetiolata — WPGP
rostrata — CBcs CPMA ELan IArd IDee MBlu MBri MPkF NLar SSpi
serrata — CMen IArd IDee MPkF NBhm
§ ***sinensis*** ♀H4 — CBcs CDul CPMA EPfP MBlu MBri NLar SSpi SSta

Stigmaphyllon (*Malpighiaceae*)

ciliatum — CCCN
littorale — CCCN

Stipa (*Poaceae*)

F&M 248 — WPGP
arundinacea — see *Anemanthele lessoniana*
barbata — CKno CMea CSpe EBee ECha EHoe EPPr EWes LRHS MAvo SApp SPer SUsu WClo WKif WPGP
- 'Silver Feather' — NWsh SLim
* ***boysterica*** — CFee
brachytricha — see *Calamagrostis brachytricha*
§ ***calamagrostis*** — Widely available
- 'Algau' — GBin
- 'Lemperg' — EPPr IMou
canescens — SPhx
capillata — CKno EAlp EBee EPPr GCal GFor LRHS SMad SWal WPGP
- 'Brautschleier' — CHrt CWib SWal WPtf
* - 'Lace Veil' — LRHS
caudata — EBee
chrysophylla F&W 9321 — WPGP
columbiana — MBel
comata — EBee MSnd
elegantissima — CKno EHoe GFor LRHS
extremiorientalis — CKno ECha EPPr GFor MRav SLPl SMad
* ***gerardi*** — SApp
gigantea ♀H4 — Widely available
- 'Gold Fontaene' — CDes CFir CKno EBee ECha EPPr EWes MAvo MMoz MNrw SBch SMad SPhx SUsu WCot WMoo WPGP WPrP
- 'Pixie' — ELon MAvo NWsh SApp SPhx
grandis — CKno ECha GBin GFor WMoo WPer
ichu — SDix
- F&M 32 — WPGP
joannis — GCal
lasiagrostis — see *S. calamagrostis*
lessingiana — CHrt CPLG EAlp EBee EHoe EHul EPPr LFur MWhi NLar SEND WMoo WPGP
offneri — EBee EPPr EWes SSvw
pekinense — EBee
pennata — CKno CMea EPPr GFor WWEG
pontica — SPhx
pseudoichu RCB/Arg K2-2 — WCot
- RCB/Arg Y-1 — WCot
pulcherrima — CBow EPPr GAbr GCal LBMP LRHS MAvo
- subsp. ***pulcherrima*** — SPhx
- 'Windfeder' — CFir SLPl SMrm
ramosissima — CKno
robusta — EBee EPPr
splendens misapplied — see *S. calamagrostis*
splendens Trin. — EBee WFoF
stenophylla — see *S. tirsa*
stipoides — GGar
tenacissima — EBee ECha EHul GFor IFro NCob NPri SUsu WDin WMoo
tenuifolia misapplied — see *S. tenuissima*
tenuifolia Steud. — CHar CMea EBee EHul EPfP LRHS MBri MRav NBir NBro NHol NOak NSti SIng WCAu WHal WMoo
§ ***tenuissima*** — Widely available
- 'Wind Whispers' **new** — CSpe
§ ***tirsa*** — LRHS SPhx
turkestanica — EBee SBch SHDw SUsu SWat
ucrainica — GFor
verticillata — CKno

Stokesia ✿ (*Asteraceae*)

cyanea — see *S. laevis*
§ ***laevis*** — CMea CPou CPrp EBee ECGP ECha EPfP GAbr GKir GMac LRHS NLar SHGN SMrm SPet SPlb WBrE WCAu WClo WFar WMoo WPGP WPer WWEG
- 'Alba' — CMMP COIW CPrp EBee ECha EHrv ELan EPfP EWTr GKir LAst LRHS MMuc MRav SPad SPer SPhx STes

- 'Blue Star'	CBcs CMHG COIW CSam CWGN EBee ELan EPfP GGar LAst LBMP LLWG LRHS MBri MNFA MRav MWhi NHol NPri SAga SBch SPad SPer SPhx SPoG SWvt WMnd WMoo WSHC
- 'Klaus Jelitto'	CFwr EBee IPot LBuc LEdu LRHS SHar
- 'Mary Gregory'	Widely available
- 'Omega Skyrocket'	CPou EBee EWTr LRHS MBel NHol SHGN SMrm WFar WWEG
- 'Peach Melba'	EBee ECtt NCGa WMoo
- 'Purple Parasols'	CMMP COIW CWGN EBee EBrs ECtt EPfP EShb IKil IPot LAst LBMP LHop LLWG LPio LRHS NCGa NChi NSti SMrm SPhx SPoG STes SUsu SWvt WAul WFar WMoo WWEG
- 'Silver Moon'	COIW EAEE EBee ECtt EPfP EShb IPot LAst LPio LRHS NBir NHol SAga SPoG WAul WFar WWEG
- 'Träumerei'	CWGN EBee GMac LAst LRHS NHol SBch SMrm SPet WMnd WMoo WWEG
- 'Wyoming'	LRHS

Stranvaesia see *Photinia*

× *Stranvinia* see *Photinia*

Stratiotes (*Hydrocharitaceae*)

aloides	CWat EHon EMFW LPBA NPer NSco SVic SWat WMAq WPnP

strawberry see *Fragaria*

Strelitzia (*Strelitziaceae*)

alba	CCCN EAmu NScw
juncea	ERea XBlo
nicolai	CAbb CDTJ CFwr EAmu EShb LPal NPer SBig XBlo
reginae ♀H1	CAbb CBcs ELan ERea EShb LPal LRHS MREP NPal NPer NScw SAPC SArc SBig SChr SEND SPlb SRms XBlo
- var. ***citrina***	ERea
- 'Kirstenbosch Gold'	NPal XBlo

Streptocarpella see *Streptocarpus*

Streptocarpus ✿ (*Gesneriaceae*)

'Albatross' ♀H1	SBrm SDnm SPav WDib
'Alice'	SBrm WDib
'Alissa' **new**	WDib
'Amanda' Dibley ♀H1	SBrm WDib
'Amanda' Fleischle PBR (Marleen Series)	WDib
'Anne'	CSpe MCot SBrm WDib
'Athena'	CSpe SBrm WDib
'Awena' **new**	WDib
baudertii	WDib
'Beryl'	WDib
'Bethan' ♀H1	SBrm WDib
'Bicentenary'	SBrm
'Black Gardenia'	WDib
'Black Panther'	WDib
'Blue Bird'	SBrm
'Blue Gem'	WDib
'Blue Heaven'	SBrm WDib
'Blue Moon'	WDib
'Blue Nymph'	SBrm WDib
'Blue Pencil'	SBrm
§ 'Blue Upstart'	SBrm
'Blushing Bride' (d)	SDnm SPav WDib
* 'Boysenberry Delight'	WDib
'Branwen'	SBrm SDnm SPav WDib
'Brimstone'	SBrm
'Bristol's Black Bird'	SBrm WDib
'Bristol's Daisy Jane' **new**	SBrm
'Bristol's Ice Castle'	SBrm WDib
'Bristol's Petticoats' **new**	SBrm
'Bristol's Red Typhoon'	SBrm
'Bristol's Stormy Skies' **new**	SBrm
'Bristol's Very Best'	WDib
'Buttons'	SBrm
caeruleus	WDib
'Caitlin'	WDib
candidus	WDib
'Carol'	SBrm WDib
'Carolyn Ann'	SBrm
'Carys' ♀H1	SBrm WDib
'Catania' (Marleen Series)	WDib
'Catrin' ♀H1	SBrm WDib
caulescens	WDib
- var. ***pallescens***	EOHP WDib
'Charlotte'	SBrm WDib
'Chloe'	WDib
'Chorus Line' ♀H1	SDnm SPav WDib
'Christine' **new**	SBrm
'Clare'	WDib
'Clouds'	CSpe SBrm
'Concord Blue'	WDib
'Constant Nymph'	SBrm WDib
'Copper Knob'	SBrm
'Coral Flair'	WDib
'Cranberry Velvet'	SBrm
'Crystal Beauty' PBR	WDib
'Crystal Blush' PBR	WDib
'Crystal Charm' PBR	WDib
'Crystal Dawn' PBR	WDib
'Crystal Ice' PBR ♀H1	WDib
'Crystal Snow' PBR	WDib
'Crystal Wonder' PBR	WDib
cyaneus	WDib
- subsp. ***polackii***	WDib
'Cynthia' ♀H1	SBrm WDib
'Dainty Lady'	SBrm
'Daphne' ♀H1	WDib
'Dark Eyes Mary'	SBrm
'Demeter'	SBrm
denticulatus **new**	WDib
'Diana'	SBrm WDib
'Dinas'	SBrm WDib
'Double Trouble' **new**	SBrm
'Dreamtime' **new**	SBrm
dunnii	SGar WDib
'Eira'	WDib
'Eleanor' **new**	SBrm
'Elegance'	SBrm
'Elizabeth' **new**	SBrm
'Ella'	SBrm
'Ella Mae'	SBrm
'Ellie'	WDib
'Elsi'	SBrm SDnm SPav WDib
'Emily'	SBrm WDib
'Emma'	SBrm WDib
'Falling Stars' ♀H1	CSpe SBrm WDib
'Festival Wales'	SBrm WDib
'Fiona'	SBrm WDib
floribundus hort.	WDib
'Frances'	SBrm
'Franken Alison'	SBrm
'Franken Jenny'	SBrm
'Franken Kelly'	SBrm
'Franken Misty Blue'	SBrm

	Name	Suppliers
	'Franken Texas Sunset'	SBrm
	'Frosty Diamond'	SBrm WDib
	gardenii	WDib
	'Gillian'	SBrm
	glandulosissimus ♀H1	EOHP WDib
	'Gloria' ♀H1	CSpe SBrm WDib
	'Gower Daybreak'	SBrm
	'Gower Garnet'	SBrm
	'Gower Midnight'	SBrm
	'Grape Slush'	WDib
	'Gwen'	SBrm WDib
	'Hannah Ellis'	SBrm
	'Happy Snappy' ♀H1	SBrm SDnm SPav WDib
	'Heidi' ♀H1	SDnm SPav WDib
	'Helen' ♀H1	SBrm WDib
	'Huge White'	CSpe
	'Ida'	SBrm
	'Inky Fingers'	SBrm
	'Iona' **new**	WDib
	'Izzy'	SBrm
	'Jaco's Gem'	SBrm WDib
	'Jacquie'	WDib
	'Jane Elizabeth'	SBrm
	'Jennifer' ♀H1	SBrm SDnm SPav WDib
	'Jessica' **new**	WDib
	'Joanna'	SBrm WDib
	johannis	WDib
	'Josie'	SBrm
	'Judith'	SBrm
	'Julie'	WDib
	'Karen'	SBrm SDnm SPav WDib
	'Katie' **new**	SBrm WDib
	kentaniensis	WDib
	'Kerry's Gold'	SBrm
	'Kim' ♀H1	CSpe EShb MCot SBrm SDnm SPav WDib
	kirkii	WDib
	'Kisie'	SBrm
	'Lady Lavender'	SBrm
	'Largesse'	SBrm
	'Laura' ♀H1	SBrm WDib
	'Lemon Ice'	SBrm
	'Lisa' ♀H1	SBrm
	'Little Gem'	CSpe SBrm
	'Louise'	SBrm WDib
	'Lynette'	SBrm
	'Lynne'	SBrm WDib
	'Maassen's White' ♀H1	SBrm WDib
	'Magpie'	SBrm
	'Mandy'	SDnm SPav WDib
	'Margaret'	SBrm WDib
	'Marie'	SBrm WDib
	'Mary'	SBrm
	'Megan'	SBrm WDib
	'Melanie' Dibley ♀H1	SBrm WDib
I	'Melanie' Fleischle (Marleen Series)	WDib
	meyeri	WDib
	'Midnight Flame'	EShb SBrm WDib
	'Mini Nymph'	CSpe WDib
	'Misty Pink'	SBrm
	'Modbury Lady'	SBrm
	modestus	WDib
	'Molly'	SBrm
	'Mona' **new**	SBrm
	'Monica's Magic' **new**	SBrm
	'Moonlight'	SBrm WDib
	'Muse'	SBrm
	'Neptune'	SBrm WDib
	'Nerys'[PBR]	SBrm WDib
	'Nia'	CSpe SBrm WDib
	'Nicola'	SBrm WDib

	Name	Suppliers
	'Night Beacon' **new**	SBrm
	'Olga'	WDib
	'Olwen'	WDib
	'Orchid Lace' **new**	SBrm
	'Padarn'	WDib
	'Pale Rider'	SBrm
	'Party Doll'	SBrm WDib
	'Passion Pink'	SBrm WDib
	'Patricia'	SBrm
	'Paula' ♀H1	SBrm WDib
	pentherianus	WDib
	'Pink Fondant'	CSpe
	'Pink Souffle'	SBrm SDnm SPav WDib
	'Pink Upstart'	SBrm
	'Plum Crazy'	SBrm
	polyanthus subsp. ***dracomontanus***	WDib
	primulifolius	WDib
	- subsp. ***formosus***	WDib
	'Princesse' (Marleen Series)	WDib
	prolixus	WDib
*	'Purple Passion'	SBrm
	'Raspberry Dream'	SBrm
	rexii	WDib
	'Rhiannon'	CSpe SBrm SDnm SPav WDib
	'Rosebud'	SBrm WDib
	'Rosemary' (d)	SPav WDib
	'Roulette Cherry' (Roulette Series) **new**	WDib
	'Ruby' ♀H1	SBrm WDib
	'Ruby Anniversary'	SBrm
	'Ruffled Lilac'	CSpe SBrm
	'Ruffles'	SBrm
	'Sally'	SBrm WDib
	'Samantha'	SBrm
	'Sandra'	SBrm SDnm SPav WDib
	'Sarah'	SBrm SPav WDib
	saxorum ♀H1	CCCN EOHP EShb LSou MBri SRms WDib WFar
	- compact	CCCN EOHP WDib
	'Seren'	SBrm WDib
	'Shannon' **new**	SBrm
	'Sian'	SBrm SDnm SPav WDib
	silvaticus	WDib
	'Snow White' ♀H1	CSpe SDnm SPav WDib
	'Something Special'	SBrm SDnm WDib
	'Sophie'	WDib
	'Southshore'	SBrm WDib
	'Spider'	SBrm
	'Stacey'	SBrm
	'Stella' ♀H1	SBrm WDib
	'Stephanie'	CSpe MCot WDib
	stomandrus	WDib
	'Stormy'	SBrm
	'Strawberry Fondant'	SBrm
	'Sugar Almond'	CSpe SBrm
	'Sunsweet' **new**	SBrm
	'Susan' ♀H1	WDib
	'Swaybelle'	SBrm
	'Tanga'	SBrm
	'Targa' (Marleen Series) **new**	WDib
	'Tatan Blue'	SBrm
	'Terracotta'	SBrm
	'Texas Hot Chili'	SBrm WDib
	'Texas Sunrise'	SBrm
	thompsonii	WDib
	'Tina' ♀H1	SBrm SDnm SPav WDib
	'Tracey'	SBrm WDib
	'Turbulent Tide'	SBrm
	'Upstart'	see *S.* 'Blue Upstart'
	'Vanessa' **new**	SBrm
	variabilis	WDib

'Velvet Underground'	SBrm
'Vera'	SBrm
'Violet Lace'	CSpe SBrm
'Watermelon Wine'	WDib
wendlandii	WDib
'Wendy'	SBrm SPav WDib
'White Wings'	SBrm
'Wiesmoor Red'	WDib
'Winifred'	SBrm WDib

Streptopus (*Convallariaceae*)

amplexifolius	EBee EBrs ECho GBuc NMen WCru
roseus	EBee ECho
streptopoides	EBee

Streptosolen (*Solanaceae*)

jamesonii ♀H1	CHll CSev CSpe EBak ELan ERea EShb SAga
- 'Fire Gold'	ERea

Strobilanthes (*Acanthaceae*)

CC 4071	CPLG
CC 4573	CPLG
anisophylla	EShb WCot WSpi
atropurpurea misapplied	see *S. attenuata*
atropurpurea Nees	see *S. wallichii*
§ ***attenuata***	CBot CFir CSam ECha ECtt ELan EPfP EWll GCal GCra GKev GKir LHop LLWP LRHS MRav NSti SGSe SGar WCru WFar WMoo WPer WWlt
- dwarf	WCom
- subsp. ***nepalensis***	CHll CLAP MWhi WPrP WRHF
dyeriana ♀H1	CAbP CSpe EBak ECtt ELan EShb LRHS LSou SGar WCot WHil
flexicaulis	CDes EBee WPGP WPrP
- B&SWJ 354	WCru
gossypinus **new**	EShb
aff. ***inflata*** B&SWJ 7754 **new**	WCru
nutans	CDes CLAP CPom CPou CSpe EBee LSou NSti WPrP
aff. ***pentstemonoides*** HWJK 2019 **new**	WCru
rankanensis	CDes CFir CLAP EBee EPPr NGby SDys WHil WPrP
- B&SWJ 1771	WCru
violacea	CPrp WPer
§ ***wallichii***	CDes CLAP CMac EBee EPPr EWes EWld LSou NSti SUsu WCru WFar WPrP WSHC
'Wollerton' **new**	WWlt

Stromanthe (*Marantaceae*)

sanguinea	MBri
- 'Triostar' PBR (v)	XBlo
'Stripestar'	MBri

Strophanthus (*Apocynaceae*)

speciosus	CCCN CHll EShb

Strumaria (*Amaryllidaceae*)

aestivalis **new**	ECho
chaplinii **new**	ECho
karooica 'Komsberg' **new**	ECho
massoniella 'Reitfontein' **new**	ECho
truncata **new**	ECho

Struthiopteris (*Blechnaceae*)

niponica	see *Blechnum niponicum*

Stuartia see *Stewartia*

Stylidium (*Stylidiaceae*)

graminifolium	GGar SPlb
- 'Little Sapphire'	NOak
- 'Tiny Trina'	EBee LRHS NCGa NOak

Stylophorum (*Papaveraceae*)

diphyllum	CFwr CPBP CPou EBee EWld GEdr IMou MRav NMen WCru WFar WPnP
lasiocarpum	CPLG CPom CSpe CSpr EWes EWld LFur LRHS MWhi NBid SGar WCru WPrP

Styphelia (*Epacridaceae*)

colensoi	see *Leucopogon colensoi*

Styphnolobium (*Leguminosae*)

§ ***japonicum*** ♀H4	CAbP CBcs CDul CLnd CWib EPfP EWTr IDee LMaj LRHS MGos SPer SPlb WDin

Styrax (*Styracaceae*)

americanus	CBcs GAuc NLar
faberi	CBcs
formosanus	CGHE CTho EBee LRHS
- var. ***formosanus***	EPfP WPGP
- - B&SWJ 3803	WCru
- var. ***hayatiana*** B&SWJ 6823	WCru
hemsleyanus ♀H4	CAbP CBcs CTho ECrN EPfP GKir IArd IDee IMGH LRHS MBlu MDun MMuc NLar SPer SSpi WFar WPGP
japonicus ♀H4	CBcs CDoC CDul CEnd CMCN CPLG CTho CTri CWib EBee ELan EPfP GGal GKir LRHS MAsh MBlu MGos MRav NPal SPer SReu SSpi SSta WDin WFar WPGP WPat WSHC
- B&SWJ 4405	WCru
§ - Benibana Group ♀H4	SSta
- - 'Pink Chimes'	CBcs CMCN CMac CPLG CPMA ELan EPfP LRHS MBlu MBri NLar SCoo SPoG SSpi SSta
- 'Carillon'	CPMA LRHS MBlu
I - 'Compactus' **new**	SSpi
- 'Emerald Pagoda'	MBlu MBri NLar SSpi
- 'Fargesii'	CAlb CBcs CDoC CDul CPMA CTho ECrN EPfP IDee IMGH LRHS MDun SCoo
- 'Pendulus'	NLar
- 'Purple Dress'	NLar
- 'Roseus'	see *S. japonicus* Benibana Group
- 'Sohuksan'	WPGP
obassia ♀H4	CBcs CMCN CPne CTho EPfP GKir IArd IDee LRHS MBlu MBri MDun NLar SSpi
- B&SWJ 6023	WCru
odoratissimus	WPGP
officinalis **new**	CBcs
redivivus NNS 05-658 **new**	WCot
wuyuanensis	CBcs

Succisa (*Dipsacaceae*)

§ ***pratensis***	CArn EBWF EBee LEdu MHer MWea NLan NLar NMen NSco NWCA SBch SGSe SPhx SUsu WHer WHoo WSFF WTin

- ***alba***	EWes MDKP
- 'Derby Purple'	CSpe
- dwarf	GKev NRya WAbe
- 'Peddar's Pink'	EBee EWes SPhx WAlt

Succisella (*Dipsacaceae*)

inflexa	SPhx
- 'Frosted Pearls'	CSpr EBee EDAr LLWP MBNS MWat SHGN WHil

sunberry see *Rubus* 'Sunberry'

Sutera (*Scrophulariaceae*)

(Abunda Series) Abunda Blue Improved = 'Balabimblu'	NPri
- Abunda Colossal White = 'Balabowite' new	NPri
Cabana Trailing White = 'Sutcatrwhi'PBR	WGor
'Cinderella Strawberry'	NPri
(Copia Series) Copia Dark Pink = 'Dancop19'PBR	NPri
- Copia Double White (d) new	LAst LSou
- Copia Golden Leaves	NPri
- Copia Great Dark Pink new	LSou
- Copia Great Purple	LSou
- Copia Gulliver Lavender = 'Dangul16'PBR	LSou NPri
- Copia Gulliver Lilac	LSou
- Copia Gulliver White = 'Dangul14'PBR	LSou
cordata 'Blizzard'PBR	LRHS LSou
- Blue Showers = 'Bacoble'PBR	LAst
- Lavender Showers = 'Sunlav'	NPri
- 'Olympic Gold' (v)	ECtt SCoo SPoG
- 'Pink Domino'	ECtt SPet
§ - 'Snowflake'	ECtt LRHS NBlu NPer SCoo SPet SPoG
microphylla	CPBP
neglecta	SPlb WPGP
Suteranova Big Pink = 'Danova912'PBR (Suteranova Series)	NPri

Sutherlandia (*Papilionaceae*)

frutescens	CArn CBod CSpe SPlb
- 'Prostrata'	MBri WPat

Swainsona (*Papilionaceae*)

galegifolia	CHll
- 'Albiflora'	CSpe WWlt

sweet cicely see *Myrrhis odorata*

Syagrus (*Arecaceae*)

botryophora	XBlo
§ ***romanzoffiana***	CBrP EAmu LPal XBlo
weddeliana	see *Lytocaryum weddellianum*

× *Sycoparrotia* (*Hamamelidaceae*)

semidecidua	CBcs CPMA LRHS MBlu NLar SLPl WPGP
- 'Purple Haze'	MBri NLar

Sycopsis (*Hamamelidaceae*)

sinensis	CAbP CBcs CMCN CWib EBee EMil EPfP LRHS NLar SDnm SPoG SSpi WDin WFar WPGP WSHC

Symphoricarpos (*Caprifoliaceae*)

albus	CDul ECrN EMac GKir MSwo NWea SPoG WDin
- 'Constance Spry'	SRms
§ - var. ***laevigatus***	EPfP LBuc MBar
§ - 'Taff's White' (v)	WMoo
- 'Variegatus'	see *S. albus* 'Taff's White'
× ***chenaultii*** 'Hancock'	CMac EBee ECrN ELan EMac EPfP MBar MGos MMuc MRav MSwo NPro SLim SPer WDin
× ***doorenbosii*** 'Magic Berry'	EBee IFFs MBar MRav NWea
- 'Mother of Pearl'	EBee ELan EMac EPfP GKir IFFs MAsh MBar MGos MMuc MRav NBlu NWea SPer
- 'White Hedge'	CAlb CSBt EBee ELan IFFs LBuc MMuc NWea SPer SPlb SPoG
guatemalensis B&SWJ 1016	WCru
orbiculatus	SLon
- 'Albovariegatus'	see *S. orbiculatus* 'Taff's Silver Edge'
- 'Argenteovariegatus'	see *S. orbiculatus* 'Taff's Silver Edge'
- 'Bowles's Golden Variegated'	see *S. orbiculatus* 'Foliis Variegatis'
§ - 'Foliis Variegatis' (v)	CMac CTri EBee ECrN EHoe ELan EPfP MAsh MGos MRav SPer WDin WEas WSHC
§ - 'Taff's Silver Edge' (v)	EHoe MBar
- 'Variegatus'	see *S. orbiculatus* 'Foliis Variegatis'
rivularis	see *S. albus* var. *laevigatus*

Symphyandra see *Campanula*

asiatica	see *Hanabusaya asiatica*

Symphyotrichum see *Aster*

Symphytum (*Boraginaceae*)

asperum	ECha ELan MRav NLar WCHb WMoo
* ***azureum***	EBee ELan NLar WCAu WCHb WFar WMnd
'Belsay'	GBuc
'Belsay Gold'	SDix
caucasicum ♀H4	CElw CMHG ECha GBar GPoy IFro LEdu LRHS SBch SEND SIde SSvw WCHb WHer WHil WMoo WWlt
- 'Eminence'	EGoo WCHb
- 'Norwich Sky'	CKno CPLG EBee EWld WCHb
cordatum	EBee EPPr
'Denford Variegated' (v)	NBid
§ 'Goldsmith' (v)	Widely available
grandiflorum	CArn CMac CTri CWan EBee GPoy LEdu STes WGwG
* - 'Sky-blue-pink'	IFro NCot
'Grandiflorum' variegated (v) new	LRHS
'Hidcote Blue'	CBct CBre CPrp CTri EBee ECha ECtt EPfP EPla GBar ILis LBMP LRHS NBro NCGa NEgg NGHP NHol SBch SEND SLPl SPer SPoG WCAu WCru WMnd WMoo WPtf WWEG
§ 'Hidcote Pink'	CBct CPom CPrp EBee ECha ECtt EPla LBMP LRHS NBir NEgg NWsh SBch SLPl SPer SPoG WCAu WFar WMnd WMoo WPnP WWEG
'Hidcote Variegated' (v)	CMac WCHb

ibericum	CArn CSam EBee ECha EHrv EPfP EPla GBar GMaP GPoy LRHS NBlu NSti SGar SRms WCHb WMoo
- 'All Gold'	CArn EBrs ECha ECtt LRHS NWsh WMoo
- 'Blaueglocken'	CSev EBee ECha WMoo WPrP
- dwarf	CPrp IFro WMoo
- 'Gold in Spring'	EGoo NLar WCHb WFar
- 'Jubilee'	see *S.* 'Goldsmith'
- 'Lilacinum'	LRHS WHer
- 'Pink Robins'	WCHb
- 'Variegatum'	see *S.* 'Goldsmith'
- 'Wisley Blue'	CBcs EBee EPfP NLar WFar WMnd WMoo WWEG
'Lambrook Sunrise'	EAEE EBee LEdu LRHS MBri NBro WCot WFar WMoo WWEG
'Langthorns Pink'	CPom ELan GBuc GCal WCHb
'Mereworth'	see *S.* × *uplandicum* 'Mereworth'
officinale	CArn COld CSev CWan EBee GBar GJos GPoy MHer MNHC MNrw NGHP NPer NPri NSco SBch SHlg SIde SPoG SRms WHer
- 'Boraston White'	WCHb
- var. ***ochroleucum***	WHer
orientale	CPom GCal WCHb
peregrinum	see *S.* × *uplandicum*
'Roseum'	see *S.* 'Hidcote Pink'
'Rubrum'	CDes CEnt EBee EHrv ELan EPPr EPfP EWes GCra LAst LBMP LEdu LRHS MAvo MHer NCGa NGHP NOrc SBch SPer WCAu WCot WFar WGwG WPGP
tuberosum	CArn CBre CElw CEnt COld CPom CSam EPPr GPoy LEdu MHer MMuc NHol WBor WCHb WFar WHer
§ × ***uplandicum***	CSev CTri EBee ELan GBar GCra GPoy MHer SHlg SIde SVic WCHb WJek
- 'Axminster Gold' (v)	CDes CEnt CMea EWes LHop SUsu WPGP
- 'Bocking 14'	CAgr CBod CEnt CHby CPrp EOHP GAbr GBar SIde WSFF
- 'Droitwich' (v)	WCot
§ - 'Mereworth' (v)	CBct EBrs LRHS MMuc SMad WCHb
- 'Moorland Heather'	MAvo WMoo
- purple-flowered **new**	MMuc
- 'Variegatum' (v) ♀H4	CBot CMac ECtt ELan EPfP EWes GBuc LRHS MBri MTho NBir NGHP NGdn SDix WCHb WCot WFar WMoo WSpi

Symplocarpus (*Araceae*)

foetidus	EBee ECho

Symplocos (*Symplocaceae*)

paniculata	see *S. sawafutagi*
§ ***sawafutagi***	CBcs MBri NLar WPGP WPat

Syncarpha (*Asteraceae*)

argyropsis	GFai

Syneilesis (*Asteraceae*)

aconitifolia	CDes CFwr CLAP GEdr WCot WPGP
- B&SWJ 879	WCru
palmata	CDes CLAP EBee GEdr LEdu WCot
- B&SWJ 1003	WCru
subglabrata	LEdu
- B&SWJ 298	WCru
aff. ***tagawae*** B&SWJ 11191	WCru

Syngonium (*Araceae*)

'Maya Red'	MBri
podophyllum ♀H1	XBlo
- 'Silver Knight'	MBri
- 'Variegatum' (v)	MBri
'White Butterfly'	LRHS MBri

Synnotia see *Sparaxis*

Synthyris (*Scrophulariaceae*)

laciniata NNS 06-540	NWCA
missurica	CDes CLAP EBrs EPPr GBuc LRHS
- var. ***stellata***	CLAP EBee EHrv LEdu LRHS NGby NHol NWsh WFar WHal WPGP
- - 'Alba' **new**	WWEG
pinnatifida	GBuc NBir
reniformis	CLAP GBuc WPGP WWEG

Syringa ✿ (*Oleaceae*)

afghanica misapplied	see *S. protolaciniata*
afghanica C.K. Schneid.	IArd LRHS
'Alexander's Pink'	WGob
× ***chinensis*** **new**	MAsh
- 'Persian Lilac'	ECrN WDin WFar WGob WSpi
- 'Saugeana'	NLar SPer
emodi	CBot WHCG
- 'Aurea'	IArd IDee MGos NLar
- 'Aureovariegata'	see *S. emodi* 'Elegantissima'
§ - 'Elegantissima' (v)	CBcs CDoC CEnd CWGN EMil EPfP LLHF LRHS MAsh MDun NEgg SPoG SSpi WDin
- 'Variegata' **new**	LRHS
'Hagny'	WGob
× ***hyacinthiflora*** 'Clarke's Giant'	IDee
- 'Esther Staley' ♀H4	EBee EPfP MRav WGob
- 'Excel'	WGob
- 'Maiden's Blush'	EBee WGob
- 'Pocahontas'	EBee
Josée = 'Morjos 060f'	CDoC EBee EPfP EQua LBMP MAsh NLar SPoG SWvt WFar WGob WPat
× ***josiflexa***	CPLG
- 'Agnes Smith'	LAst LRHS NLar WGob
- 'Anna Amhoff'	GBin NLar
- 'Bellicent' ♀H4	CEnd CLnd EBee ELan EPfP GKir ISea LAst LRHS MBar MRav NLar NPri NSti SCoo SPer SPlb SPoG SRms SSpi SWvt WCFE WDin WGob WHCG WPat WPen WSpi
- 'James MacFarlane'	NLar WGob
- 'Lynette'	EPla NPro
- 'Redwine'	MGos NLar
§ - 'Royalty'	LRHS MAsh NLar WGob
josikaea	CMCN CSBt EBee MBar NLar SCoo SPer WGob WHCG WSpi
'Kim'	GKir MRav NLar
komarowii	NLar
- L 490	GGGa
§ - subsp. ***reflexa***	CDul EPfP EWTr LLHF MBar MGos SSpi WDin WFar WGob
§ × ***laciniata*** Mill.	CBot CPMA EBee EGxp ELan EPfP LAst LRHS MGos MMuc MRav MWea NLar SCoo SPer SPoG SSpi WCFE WGor WHCG WPGP
§ ***meyeri*** 'Palibin' ♀H4	Widely available
microphylla	see *S. pubescens* subsp. *microphylla*
'Minuet'	CBcs MGos NLar WGob
'Miss Canada'	EBee GKir MBri NLar WGob
oblata	CMCN
palibiniana	see *S. meyeri* 'Palibin'

patula misapplied	see *S. meyeri* 'Palibin'
patula (Palibin) Nakai	see *S. pubescens* subsp. *patula*
pekinensis	see *S. reticulata* subsp. *pekinensis*
× ***persica*** ♀H4	CDul CPLG CPMA CSam CTri EPfP EWTr GKir MGos MRav NBea NLar NPal SLon SPer
- 'Alba' ♀H4	CBot CPMA GQui MRav WFar WHCG WPat
- var. ***laciniata***	see *S.* × *laciniata* Mill.
pinnatifolia	CBcs CBot GKir IArd IDee MBri WHCG
× ***prestoniae*** 'Coral'	WFar
- 'Desdemona'	LRHS SSta
- 'Donald Wyman'	MBri WGob
- 'Elinor' ♀H4	CMHG EPfP LRHS MRav NSti SPer
- 'Helen'	MAsh
- 'Hiawatha'	MGos
- 'Isabella'	LRHS MGos SCoo
- 'Nike' **new**	LRHS
- 'Nocturne'	MGos WFar WGob
- 'Royalty'	see *S.* × *josiflexa* 'Royalty'
§ ***protolaciniata***	EShb LBMP LRHS MAsh MGos NLar WFar
- 'Kabul'	EPfP LRHS NLar
pubescens subsp. ***julianae*** 'George Eastman' **new**	LRHS
§ - subsp. ***microphylla***	GKir
- - 'Superba' ♀H4	Widely available
§ - subsp. ***patula***	CMac ECho EPfP LRHS MRav NWea SEND SLon SPoG WFar
- - 'Miss Kim' ♀H4	CDoC CSBt CWSG EBee ELan EMil EWTr IArd LAst LRHS LSRN MBri MGos MRav MSwo NBea NBlu NEgg NHol NLar SCoo SLim SPoG SSta WDin WFar WGob WHCG WPat
'Red Pixie'	CBgR LBuc LRHS MAsh MBri MGos MMHG SBch SCoo WGob
'Red Prince'	LRHS MAsh NPri
reflexa	see *S. komarowii* subsp. *reflexa*
reticulata	MBlu MBri WDin
- 'Ivory Silk'	CWSG EPfP LLHF NLar WGob
§ - subsp. ***pekinensis***	CBot CMCN GBin IDee WBVN
- - China Snow = 'Morton' **new**	MBri
- - 'Pendula'	IArd IDee
- - 'Yellow Fragrance'	MBri
× ***swegiflexa***	CDul CPLG NLar
sweginzowii	NLar SPer WFar WSpi
- 'Superba'	LAst WMoo
tomentella	NWea SRms
velutina	see *S. pubescens* subsp. *patula*
villosa	SPlb WBVN WDin WGob
vulgaris	ECrN EMac EWTr LBuc MBar NWea
- var. ***alba***	MBar
§ - 'Andenken an Ludwig Späth' ♀H4	Widely available
- 'Aurea'	EQua LBuc LRHS MRav NPro WFar
- Beauty of Moscow	see *S. vulgaris* 'Krasavitsa Moskvy'
- 'Belle de Nancy' (d)	CCCN CDul CWib EBee ELan ELon IFFs LAst MAsh MMuc MRav NEgg SEND SWvt WDin
- 'Charles Joly' (d) ♀H4	Widely available
- 'Comtesse d'Harcourt'	EQua MAsh
- 'Congo'	GKir MRav NMoo SEND SPer WGob
- Dentelle d'Anjou = 'Mindent' **new**	MAsh
- 'Edward J. Gardner' (d)	ECrN ELon
- 'Firmament' ♀H4	EBee ELan EPfP MRav NEgg SEND SPer WGob WSpi
- 'Hope'	see *S. vulgaris* 'Nadezhda'
- 'Katherine Havemeyer' (d) ♀H4	Widely available
- Kindy Rose = 'Gaby'[PBR]	EMil MAsh
§ - 'Krasavitsa Moskvy' (d)	EWes GKir LRHS MAsh MBri
- 'Lee Jewett Walker'	WGob
- 'Lois Amee Utley' (d)	LRHS
- 'Lucie Baltet'	MBri
- 'Madame Florent Stepman'	CMac NLar
- 'Madame Lemoine' (d) ♀H4	Widely available
- 'Masséna'	MRav SPer
- 'Maud Notcutt'	EWes
- 'Michel Buchner' (d)	CBcs CDul CWib EBee ELan GKir LAst MBar MGan MRav NLar SBch SCoo SLim SPer WBVN WGob
- 'Miss Ellen Willmott' (d)	MBri MRav
- 'Mrs Edward Harding' (d) ♀H4	ECrN EPfP EQua LAst LBuc MGos MRav NLar NWea SCoo SPer SRGP
§ - 'Nadezhda' (d)	LRHS
- 'Olivier de Serres' (d)	MBri
- 'Paul Deschanel' (d)	NLar
- 'Président Grévy' (d)	CDoC CLnd CMac EBee EMil MAsh MMuc SPer
- 'Primrose'	CBcs CBot CCCN CDul CMac CWib EBee ELan ELon EPfP GBin GKir IArd LAst LRHS MAsh MBri MGos MRav MSnd NEgg NLar SBch SCoo SEND SPer WDin WFar WGob WSpi
- 'Prince Wolkonsky' (d)	EBee EMil EPfP EQua LRHS MAsh WFar
- 'Princesse Sturdza'	EMil MAsh
- 'Sensation'	CBcs CDoC CSBt CWSG EBee ECrN ELon EPfP EWTr GKir IArd LAst LRHS LSRN LSou MGos MMuc MRav MSwo NEgg NLar NPri NWea SCoo SEND SLim SPer SPoG WGob WSpi
- 'Souvenir de Louis Spaeth'	see *S. vulgaris* 'Andenken an Ludwig Späth'
- 'Sweetheart' (d)	GKir
- variegated (v)	EWes
- variegated double (d/v)	WCot
- 'Vestale' ♀H4	EWes MRav
- 'Viviand-Morel' (d)	LLHF NEgg WGob
- 'Znamya Lenina'	MBri
wolfii	CArn EBtc MBri WBVN
yunnanensis	CPLG GGGa LLHF WSpi
- 'Prophecy'	WGob
- 'Rosea'	MBri WGob

Syzygium (*Myrtaceae*)

sp.	CMen
australe	ERom EShb IDee
jambos	EShb
paniculatum	CMen CPLG EShb IDee

T

Tabernaemontana (*Apocynaceae*)

coronaria	see *T. divaricata*
§ ***divaricata***	CCCN

Tacca (*Taccaceae*)

chantrieri	CCCN EAmu EBrs ECho EGxp
integrifolia	EAmu EBrs ECho

Tacitus see *Graptopetalum*

Tagetes (*Asteraceae*)

lemmonii	IMou SBch SHDw SMad

lucida	CArn EOHP IMou WJek
patula	LRHS
tenuifolia	CArn

Talbotia (*Velloziaceae*)

§ ***elegans***	CSpe EPot WFar

Talinum (*Portulacaceae*)

'Kingwood Gold'	CBow
okanoganense	CCCN GKev
paniculatum	CCCN
'Zoe'	CPBP

tamarillo see *Cyphomandra betacea*

tamarind see *Tamarindus indica*

Tamarindus (*Caesalpiniaceae*)

indica (F)	SPlb

Tamarix (*Tamaricaceae*)

africana	EBee EMil
chinensis	CSBt
gallica	CMen CSBt NWea SAPC SArc WSHC
hampeana	SEND
§ ***parviflora***	CMac EMil LRHS MGos SPoG
pentandra	see *T. ramosissima*
§ ***ramosissima***	CCCN CMac CTri EBee ECrN ELan EPfP MAsh MBar MBrN MWhi SLim SRms SSta WDin WSHC
- 'Pink Cascade'	CBcs CCCN CDul CSBt EBee ELon EMil EPfP GCal GKir LRHS MBlu MBri MGos MREP MRav NEgg SBch SPer SPoG SWvt WDin
- 'Rosea'	CBcs MGan SLon
§ - 'Rubra' ♀H4	CChe CDoC CWSG EMil EPfP GKir LRHS MGos NLar SEND SLon SPer WDin
- 'Summer Glow'	see *T. ramosissima* 'Rubra'
tetrandra ♀H4	CBcs CDul CMac CSBt CWSG CWib EBee ELan EMac EPfP LRHS MAsh MBar MBlu MBri MRav MSwo MWat NPer SBch SPer SPlb SRms SWvt WBrE WDin WFar WHar WMoo
- 'Africance'	ERom
- var. ***purpurea***	see *T. parviflora*

Tamus (*Dioscoreaceae*)

communis	CArn

Tanacetum ✿ (*Asteraceae*)

§ ***argenteum***	ECho MRav SIde
- subsp. ***canum***	ECho EWes LRHS
§ ***balsamita***	CArn COld CPrp EAro EBee ELan ELau GPWP GPoy LEdu MBri MHer MNHC SHGN WJek WPer WTin
§ - subsp. ***balsamita***	CBod GPoy SIde
§ - subsp. ***balsamitoides***	CBod CHby CPrp GBar MHer WJek
- var. ***tanacetoides***	see *T. balsamita* subsp. *balsamita*
- ***tomentosum***	see *T. balsamita* subsp. *balsamitoides*
capitatum	see *Sphaeromeria capitata*
§ ***cinerariifolium***	CArn CPrp CWan GBar GPoy MNHC
§ ***coccineum***	NBPC SPoG SRms WFar
- 'Alfred'	EBee
- 'Aphrodite' (d)	ECtt LRHS NEgg WCAu
- 'Beauty of Stapleford'	LRHS NEgg NOrc
- 'Bees' Pink Delight'	NEgg
- 'Brenda'	EBee EPfP MRav
- 'Duro'	GBuc LRHS
- 'Eileen May Robinson' ♀H4	EBee EPfP LHop LSRN NBre NGdn WCAu
- 'Evenglow'	ECtt EPfP
- 'H.M. Pike'	EBee ECtt EWll NOrc
- 'James Kelway' ♀H4	EBee ECtt ELan EPfP GKir LRHS MRav NBir SRms
- 'King Size'	SGar WFar
- 'Laurin'	LRHS
- 'Mont Blanc'	EBee
- Robinson's crimson **new**	LRHS
- - giant-flowered	GJos SRms
- - mixed **new**	WWEG
- - pink	CMdw EBee ELan EPfP GKir GMaP LRHS NBre SBch SGSe SRms WWEG
- - red	CSBt EBee EPfP GKir GMaP IMon LRHS MBNS NPri NVic SGSe SMrs SPur SRms SWvt WClo WWEG
- - rose	MBNS
- 'Scarlet Glow'	LRHS
- 'Snow Cloud'	ECtt ELan NBre WWEG
§ ***corymbosum***	GCal
- 'Festtafel'	EBee LPla
densum	ECho EDAr EPot NBlu WCFE
- subsp. ***amani***	EBee ECha ECho GBar GMaP LRHS MHer MWat NWCA SEND SRms
§ ***haradjanii***	ECho ECtt ELan SBch WHer
huronense	EBee
macrophyllum misapplied	see *Achillea grandifolia* Friv.
§ ***macrophyllum*** (Waldst. & Kit.) Sch.Bip.	ECtt EPPr LPla SPhx WCot WPer
niveum	CArn EAro ECha WCot
- 'Jackpot'	CSpe CWan CWib EAro EBee EPfP EWes MBri SHar SSvw
§ ***parthenium***	CArn CHby CWan EBWF ELau GPoy MHer MNHC NPer SBch SIde SPoG SRms SVic WHer
- 'Aureum'	CEnt CHid CPrp CRow CWan ECha ELan ELau EWes GBar GPoy MBri MHer MLHP MNHC NBlu NGHP SBch SIng SPer SPlb SRms WCot WEas WFar WHer WMoo WPer
- double white-flowered (d)	CSWP GBar MMuc MNHC NPer SEND SRms
- 'Golden Ball'	EPfP
- 'Plenum' (d)	EHrv SBch SIng
§ - 'Rowallane' (d)	ELan GBuc GMac MAvo MBri WCot
- 'Sissinghurst White'	see *T. parthenium* 'Rowallane'
- 'Snowball' (d)	EPfP IFro
- 'White Bobbles' **new**	LRHS
- 'White Bonnet' (d)	WEas
poteriifolium	EBee EBrs LRHS
§ ***ptarmiciflorum*** ♀H3-4	WCot
- 'Silver Feather'	MNHC WJek
tatsiense	GKev
* ***tommansii***	LRHS
vulgare	CArn CHby CSev ECtt ELau GPoy MHer MNHC NSco SBch SIde SVic WMoo WSFF
- 'All Gold'	SMad
- var. ***crispum***	CHby CPrp CWan EBee ELau GBar MHer MRav SIde SMad WFar WJek
- 'Golden Fleece' **new**	MAvo NSti SPer WCot
- 'Isla Gold' (v)	CBow CHVG EBee EPPr EWes GMaP LDai LHop MMuc MRav NBre SEND SMrm WCAu WCHb WCot WFar WMoo
- 'Silver Lace' (v)	CBow EBee GBar NBid NGHP WCHb WFar WHer WMoo

Tanakaea (*Saxifragaceae*)

radicans	EBee WCru

tangelo see *Citrus* × *tangelo*

tangerine see *Citrus reticulata*

tangor see *Citrus* × *nobilis* Tangor Group

Taraxacum (*Asteraceae*)

albidum DJH 452	CHid
coreanum	WPrP
faeroense	EPPr WCot
officinale agg.	CArn
- 'Tapeley' (v) **new**	CNat
rubrifolium	CSpe EPPr

Tarchonanthus (*Asteraceae*)

camphoratus	CTrC

tarragon see *Artemisia dracunculus*

Tasmannia see *Drimys*

Taxodium (*Cupressaceae*)

ascendens 'Nutans'	see *T. distichum* var. *imbricatum* 'Nutans'
distichum ♀H4	Widely available
- 'Cascade Falls' PBR	EMil LRHS MBlu MBri MGos NLar SLim
- 'Cave Hill' **new**	SLim
- 'Falling Waters' **new**	LRHS
- 'Hursley Park'	NLar SLim
- var. ***imbricatum***	CGHE CMCN EPfP LRHS WPGP
§ - - 'Nutans' ♀H4	CAlb CBcs CEnd CTho EPfP GKir ISea LRHS MAsh MBlu SCoo SLim SMad
- 'Little Leaf' **new**	NLar SLim
- 'Little Twister'	NLar
- 'Minaret'	MBlu
- 'Peve Minaret'	CDoC CMen EWTr LRHS MAsh MBri MGos NLar SLim
- 'Peve Yellow'	MBlu NLar
- 'Schloss Herten'	LRHS SLim
- 'Secrest'	CBcs LRHS MAsh MBlu MBri SLim
- Shawnee Brave = 'Mickelson'	MBlu NLar
mucronatum	CDoC CPLG
- F&M 198	WPGP

Taxus ✿ (*Taxaceae*)

baccata ♀H4	Widely available
- 'Adpressa' (f)	ECho
- 'Adpressa Aurea' (v)	CKen ECho GKir LRHS SCoo
- 'Adpressa Variegata' (m/v) ♀H4	CDoC ECho EHul
- 'Aldenham Gold'	CKen
- 'Amersfoort'	CDoC EOrn LRHS NHol NLar SCoo SLim
- 'Argentea Minor'	see *T. baccata* 'Dwarf White'
- Aurea Group	CDul NHol SRms STre
I - 'Aurea Pendula'	ECho EOrn GKir
I - 'Aureomarginata' (v)	CBcs CBow ECho EOrn MAsh NEgg SWvt
- 'Autumn Shades'	CBcs
- 'Bridget's Gold'	CKen
- 'Cavendishii' (f)	ECho
- 'Compacta'	EOrn EPla
- 'Corleys Coppertip'	CKen ECho EPot GKir LRHS MAsh MBar MRav NHol NLar SCoo SLim WEve WFar
- 'Cristata'	CKen NLar
- 'David'	IArd LRHS MBri NLar SCoo WEve
- 'Davie' **new**	LRHS
- 'Dovastoniana' (f) ♀H4	CMac MBar NLar NWea SCoo WMou
- 'Dovastonii Aurea' (m/v) ♀H4	CBcs ECho EOrn EPfP EPla GKir LRHS MBar MBlu MBri MGos NEgg NLar NPCo NPri NWea SCoo SLim WCFE WDin WFar
- 'Drinkstone Gold' (v)	EHul
§ - 'Dwarf White' (v)	ECho EOrn SCoo WGor
- 'Elegantissima' (f/v)	CTho ECho EHul EPfP LRHS NPCo NWea SCoo WFar
- 'Erecta' (f)	EHul
§ - 'Fastigiata' (f) ♀H4	Widely available
- Fastigiata Aurea Group	CLnd CMac CWib ECho EPfP GKev GKir IArd IFFs LBuc LMaj LRHS MAsh MGan MGos NHol NPri SRms STre WBrE WFar WHar
- 'Fastigiata Aureomarginata' (m/v) ♀H4	CDoC CDul CMac CSBt CTri ECho EHul EOrn EPfP GKir ISea LAst LBee LRHS MBar MBri MGos NWea SAga SBch SCoo SLim SLon SPer SPoG SWvt WCFE WDin WEve
- 'Fastigiata Robusta' (f)	CDoC CSBt ECho EPfP EPla GKir LRHS MBar MBri NHol NPCo SCoo SLim WEve WFar
- 'Goud Elsje'	CKen MBri NLar
- 'Green Column'	CKen
- 'Green Diamond'	CKen NLar
- 'Green Rocket'	EMil
- 'Hibernica'	see *T. baccata* 'Fastigiata'
- 'Icicle'	CBcs ECho EPla LRHS MAsh MGos NHol NLar SLim
- 'Itsy Bitsy'	CKen
- 'Ivory Tower'	CBcs CDoC CKen ECho ELan EPla LBee LRHS MAsh MGos NEgg NHol NLar NPCo SLim SPoG WEve WFar WGor
- 'Klitzeklein'	CKen
- 'Laurie'	SCoo
- 'Melfard'	CDoC
- 'Nutans'	CDoC CKen ECho EOrn GKir MBar SCoo SPoG
- 'Pendula'	MRav
- 'Prostrata'	CMac WFar
- 'Pygmaea'	CKen
- 'Repandens' (f) ♀H4	EHul IArd MBar NWea WCFE WDin WFar
I - 'Repens Aurea' (v) ♀H4	CDoC CKen CMac ECho ECrN EHul EOrn EPfP GKir LRHS MAsh MBar MGos NEgg SCoo WEve WFar
- 'Rushmore'	MBri
- 'Semperaurea' (m) ♀H4	CAgr CBcs CDoC CMac ECho EHul EOrn EPla GKir LBuc LRHS MAsh MBar MBri MGan MGos NHol NWea SCoo SLim SPoG WCFE WDin WFar
- 'Silver Spire' (v)	CKen MDKP
- 'Standishii' (f) ♀H4	Widely available
- 'Stove Pipe'	CKen
- 'Summergold' (v)	ECho EHul ELan EPfP EPla LRHS MAsh MBar MBri MGos MRav NBir NBlu NEgg NHol NLar SCoo SLim WDin WEve WFar
- 'Washingtonii' (v)	IArd MBar
- 'White Icicle'	EOrn MGos WGor
brevifolia	NHol
chinensis **new**	EGFP
cuspidata	CMen ECho GKir
- 'Aurescens' (v)	CKen EPla SRms
- 'Minuet'	CKen

- var. ***nana*** hort. ex Rehder	EOrn IFFs MBar
- 'Robusta'	EHul
- 'Straight Hedge'	CDoC EMil LRHS SLim
× ***media*** 'Brownii'	LBuc
- 'Hicksii' (f) ♀H4	CDul GKir LBuc LMaj LRHS MBar MGan MGos NBlu NWea SCoo SLim WFar
- 'Hillii'	MBar SCoo
- 'Lodi'	LBee LRHS
- 'Nixe' new	SLim
- 'Strait Hedge' (f)	CAgr

tayberry see *Rubus* Tayberry Group

Tecoma (*Bignoniaceae*)

capensis ♀H1	CSev
- 'Aurea'	CSev EShb
- 'Coccinea'	EShb
- 'Lutea'	EShb
cochabambensis RCB/Arg L-8	WCot
ricasoliana	see *Podranea ricasoliana*
stans	CWit ELon

Tecomanthe (*Bignoniaceae*)

speciosa	CHEx ECou

Tecomaria see *Tecoma*

Tecophilaea (*Tecophilaeaceae*)

cyanocrocus ♀H2	CAvo CBro EBrs ECho EPot IHer LAma LRHS NMin WCot
- 'Leichtlinii' ♀H2	CBro EBrs ECho EPot IHer LAma LRHS NMin SCnR
- 'Purpurea'	see *T. cyanocrocus* 'Violacea'
- Storm Cloud Group	CBro ECho
§ - 'Violacea'	CAvo CBro EBrs ECho EPot IHer LRHS NMin
violiflora	EBrs ECho LAma

Tectaria (*Dryopteridaceae*)

gemmifera	GQui

Telanthophora (*Asteraceae*)

§ ***grandifolia***	CHEx

Telekia (*Asteraceae*)

§ ***speciosa***	CFir CHar CHrt COIW CSam CSpe EBee EBrs ELan EPfP GAbr GKir LRHS MCCP MMuc NBro NChi SDix SLPl SPlb WCFE WFar WHer WHoo WMoo WPer WPtf WWEG

Telesonix see *Boykinia*

Teline see *Genista*

Tellima (*Saxifragaceae*)

grandiflora	Widely available
- 'Bob's Choice'	WCot
- 'Delphine' (v)	CBow EBee EPPr SAga WOut
- 'Forest Frost'	CBct CBow CMac EBee EPPr GCai LAst LBMP LHop NBre NGdn NHol NLar NOrc WClo WMoo WOut
- Odorata Group	CBre EBee ECha MRav NSti WCot WMoo WRHF WWEG
- - 'Howells'	WOut
- 'Purpurea'	see *T. grandiflora* Rubra Group
- 'Purpurteppich'	EBee EBrs ECha EHrv EPPr LAst LRHS MRav NGdn NVic WMnd WMoo WWEG
§ - Rubra Group	Widely available
- 'Silver Select'	EPPr

Telopea (*Proteaceae*)

'Dawn Fire'	CTrC
oreades	GGal SPlb
speciosissima	CBcs CCCN CTrC SPlb
- 'Red Embers'	CTrC
truncata	CBcs CCCN GGal SPlb WCru

Templetonia (*Papilionaceae*)

retusa	ECou

Temu see *Blepharocalyx*

Tetracentron (*Tetracentraceae*)

sinense	CBcs EPfP IArd IFFs LRHS MBri NLar WPGP

Tetradenia (*Lamiaceae*)

riparia	EOHP

Tetradium (*Rutaceae*)

§ ***daniellii***	CBcs CCVT CMCN EPfP IArd IDee IFFs NLar SSpi WPGP
* - ***henryi***	NLar
§ - Hupehense Group	CMCN CTho GBin GKir MBri MSnd SEND WDin
glabrifolium	WPGP
- B&SWJ 6882	WCru
ruticarpum	WPGP
- B&SWJ 3541	WCru
* ***velutinum***	NLar

Tetragonia (*Tetragoniaceae*)

tetragonoides	CArn

Tetragonolobus see *Lotus*

Tetraneuris (*Asteraceae*)

§ ***grandiflora***	ELon
scaposa	EPot LRHS

Tetrapanax (*Araliaceae*)

§ ***papyrifer*** ♀H2-3	CBcs CBrP CDTJ CHEx CTsd CWit ELon ESwi MBri NLar SAPC SArc SBig SBst XBlo
- B&SWJ 7135	WCru
- 'Empress'	WCru
- 'Rex'	CDTJ CGHE CHEx CPLG EAmu EGFP SMad WCot WCru WPGP
- 'Steroidal Giant' new	SBig

Tetrapathaea see *Passiflora*

Tetrastigma (*Vitaceae*)

obtectum	CCCN CTsd ECre ELon EShb EWes
voinierianum ♀H1	EShb MBri SAPC SArc WCot

Tetratheca (*Tremandraceae*)

thymifolia	ECou

Teucridium (*Verbenaceae*)

parvifolium	ECou

Teucrium (*Lamiaceae*)

* ***ackermannii***	CMea ECho LBee LRHS NMen NWCA WAbe WCom WEas WHoo WPat WTin
arduinoi	SEND
aroanium	ECho EPot GEdr MWat NMen NWCA WPat

asiaticum	EGoo
botrys	MHer
canadense	WWEG
chamaedrys misapplied	see *T.* × *lucidrys*
chamaedrys L.	CPom CPrp CSam CWan CWib EChо EGoo GBar GPoy LEdu LRHS LSRN MNHC MSwo NGHP NWCA SBch SLim SRms STre WBrk WJek WTin WWEG
- 'Nanum'	ECho NChi
- 'Rose Carpet'	EGoo WCom
- 'Summer Sunshine'	LBuc LRHS
- 'Variegatum' (v)	GBar WCHb WCom WPer
§ ***creticum***	ECho
divaricatum NS 614	NWCA
dunense	EAro
flavum	CArn EBee EDAr EGoo EPPr NBre SGar WCHb
fruticans	Widely available
- 'Azureum' Υ^{H3}	CAlb CBcs CBot CMMP COIW CWSG EBee ELan EPfP IMon LAst LRHS LSRN MRav SBch SEND SMad SPer SPoG WEas
- 'Compactum'	CChe CDoC EBee ELan LAst LRHS MCCP MGos SLon SPer SPoG WAbe WCFE WPGP
- 'Drysdale'	CDoC CSBt LRHS
hircanicum	Widely available
- 'Paradise Delight'	EBee ECtt EKen MAvo MBNS MBri NBPC NOrc NPro WBor
- 'Purple Tails'	CChe COIW CPrp CSpe CWib LSou MCot NBir NCob SMad SPoG SWal WWEG
§ × ***lucidrys***	CArn CMea CPom CSev CSpe CWan EBee ECha ECho EGoo ELan EPfP LAst LRHS MHer MNHC MRav NBlu NGHP SGar SIde SPer SPoG WCFE WEas WHoo
lucidum	GCal
marum	CArn CMea CTri NGHP NMen SHGN WJek
'Massif Central'	LRHS
massiliense misapplied	see *T.* × *lucidrys*
massiliense L.	EAro EBee WSHC
montanum	EGoo GBar SHGN
musimonum	EPot
nivale	EBee
orientale	EBee
polium	CPLG ECho MWat NLAp WCom WJek WPat WThu
- subsp. ***aureum***	NWCA
pyrenaicum	CMea CPBP CPom EBee ECho EPot EWes GEdr NWCA WPat
rosmarinifolium	see *T. creticum*
scordium	CNat
scorodonia	CArn COld CRWN EBWF EGoo GBar GPoy MCot MHer MNHC NMir WHer WJek
- 'Binsted Gold'	EBee EGoo EPPr LDai LSou NSti WAlt
- 'Crispum'	CWan GBar GKir LBMP MHer MMuc MNHC NBro NCob SBch SPer WBrE WCHb WClo WGrn WGwG WHoo WJek WKif WMnd WMoo WPer
- 'Crispum Marginatum' (v)	CBot COIW EBee ECGP ECha EGoo EHoe EHrv EPPr EPfP GBar ILis LHop LRHS MNrw MRav NHol NSti SBch WEas WFar WTin WWEG
- 'Spring Morn'	EBee
- 'Winterdown' (v)	CBow EBee EGoo LRHS NPro SBch WCHb
subspinosum	ECho GEdr LBee LLHF LRHS MWat NLAp NMen WAbe WCom WHoo WPat
§ ***viscidum*** 'Lemon and Lime' (v)	CBow EBee ECtt LHop LSou SDnm
webbianum	EBee ECho
'Winterdown'	LEdu SHGN WDyG

Thalia (*Marantaceae*)

dealbata	CBen CHEx CMdw CTrC EAmu EMFW LLWG LPBA MSKA NLar SBig SDix WMAq

Thalictrum (*Ranunculaceae*)

CC 4576	CPLG
CC 4577	WCot
SDR 1679	GKev
SDR 2706	GKev
from Afghanistan	see *T. isopyroides*
actaeifolium	CLAP CWib GMac MDKP
- B&SWJ 4664	WCru
- B&SWJ 6310	WCru
- var. ***brevistylum***	LSou
- - B&SWJ 8819	WCru
- - 'Twinkling Star'	EBee NCob
adiantifolium	see *T. minus* 'Adiantifolium'
alpinum	EBWF EDAr EPPr SBch
angustifolium	see *T. lucidum*
'Anne'^{PBR} **new**	IPot
aquilegiifolium	Widely available
- var. ***album***	CBot CMea COIW EBee ECha ELan EPfP GCra LAst LBMP LHop LRHS MMuc NBid SMrm SPhx WCAu WMnd WPer WPtf WSpi WWEG
- 'Gold Lace' **new**	EBee
* - 'Hybridum'	WFar WMoo WPer
- 'Purpureum'	CPom CSev LBMP LRHS NLar WHoo
* - var. ***sibiricum*** B&SWJ 11007	WCru
- 'Small Thundercloud'	GCal
- 'Thundercloud' Υ^{H4}	CBct CCVN CFir CMHG EAEE EBee ECtt EPfP GKir LFur LHop LRHS MAvo MBri MCot MDKP MDun MNFA NBPC NEgg NLar NSti SBch SMrm SPoG WBrE WCAu WCot WSpi WWEG
baicalense	CPom EBee
'Black Stockings'	EBee EShb LBMP LSou MAvo SPoG
chelidonii	GMaP LRHS
- HWJK 2216	WCru
clavatum	CLAP EBee WPGP
contortum	SDys
coreanum	see *T. ichangense*
cultratum	CDes MBel WPGP
- HWJCM 367	NLar WCru
dasycarpum	GMac MBel MDKP NBre NLar WFar WPnP
§ ***delavayi*** Υ^{H4}	Widely available
- BWJ 7903	WCru
- DJHC 473	WCru
- var. ***acuminatum*** BWJ 7535	WCru
- - BWJ 7971	WCru
- 'Album'	Widely available
- 'Ankum'	EBee
- var. ***decorum***	CDes CLAP CPom CWCL ELon EPPr GEdr GMac LPio MBel MCot NCGa NCob WCot WCru WSHC
- - BWJ 7770	WCru
- 'Hewitt's Double' (d) Υ^{H4}	Widely available
- var. ***mucronatum***	WCru

- - DJHC 473	WCru
- purple-stemmed BWJ 7748	WCru
diffusiflorum	CLAP GBuc GMac WCru WSHC
dioicum	WPnP
dipterocarpum misapplied	see *T. delavayi*
dipterocarpum Franch.	CMac EBee GKir MSCN WMnd
- ACE 4.878.280	CMil
elegans HWJK 2271	WCru
'Elin'	Widely available
fendleri	GBin GBuc
- NNS 06-547	WCot
- var. ***polycarpum***	WOut
filamentosum	EBee EPPr
- B&SWJ 777	WCru
- B&SWJ 4145	WCru
- var. ***yakusimense*** B&SWJ 6094	WCru
finetii	CLAP
aff. ***finetii***	CLAP
flavum	CMac CWan EBWF ECtt LRHS NBro SMrm SPhx SWat WBrE WShi WWEG
- 'Chollerton'	see *T. isopyroides*
§ - subsp. ***glaucum*** 🏆^{H4}	Widely available
- - dwarf	CDes
- 'Illuminator'	CDes CKno CTri EBee EPPr EPfP GKir LPio LRHS MArl MHer MRav SBch SMad SPoG WCAu WCom WCot WFar WPnP WPrP
flexuosum	see *T. minus* subsp. *minus*
foetidum	NBre
- BWJ 7558	WCru
foliolosum HWJK 2181	WCru
grandiflorum	NCob
honanense	EBee
§ ***ichangense*** B&SWJ 8203	WCru
* - var. ***minus***	WCru
- - 'Chinese Chintz'	WCru
- 'Purple Marble' new	WCot
§ ***isopyroides***	CFir CPom EBee EBrs GBin GBuc GCal GKev LAst LPio LRHS MNFA MRav NChi NGdn NMen WCot WDyG WSpi WTin WWEG
javanicum	LEdu
- B&SWJ 9506	WCru
- var. ***puberulum*** B&SWJ 6770	WCru
johnstonii B&SWJ 9127	WCru
kiusianum	Widely available
- Kew form	GBuc WSHC
koreanum	see *T. ichangense*
§ ***lucidum***	CKno CSpe EBee ECtt ELan EShb GCal GMac ILad LOck LPio LRHS MAvo MBel NBPC NBre NLar NSti SGar SHar SPhx WCot WFar
minus	CMHG EBWF EBee ECGP ELan GBuc GKir LPio LRHS MBel NBre SEND
§ - 'Adiantifolium'	CMac EBee GBuc MBel MRav NBre NCob NGdn NLar SHar SRms WFar WPer WWEG
- var. ***hypoleucum*** B&SWJ 8634	WCru
- subsp. ***kemense***	EBee
§ - subsp. ***minus***	NBre
§ - subsp. ***olympicum***	WPer
- subsp. ***saxatile***	see *T. minus* subsp. *olympicum*
- var. ***sipellatum*** B&SWJ 5051	WCru
morisonii	NBid
occidentale JLS 86255	MNrw
omeiense	CDes WPGP
- BWJ 8049	WCru
orientale	EWes
osmundifolium	WCru
petaloideum new	ECha EWTr GCal MDKP WCot
platycarpum B&SWJ 2261	WCru
polygamum	see *T. pubescens*
przewalskii	WCru
§ ***pubescens***	ECha GAuc GMaP LRHS NBre NCGa SHar SUsu WPrP
punctatum	CLAP LPio
- B&SWJ 1272	WCru
ramosum BWJ 8126	WCru
reniforme	CFir GBuc GMac WCot
- B&SWJ 2610	WCru
- GWJ 9311	WCru
- HWJK 2152	WCru
reticulatum	WCru
- BWJ 7407	WCru
rochebrunianum	Widely available
rubescens	EBee
sachalinense	CDes EBee MCCP SWal WOut WPGP
- RBS 0279	EKen
shensiense	GEdr
simplex var. ***brevipes*** B&SWJ 4794	WCru
speciosissimum	see *T. flavum* subsp. *glaucum*
* ***sphaerostachyum***	GKir GMac ILad LRHS MWhi SMrm WCot WHal
'Splendide' new	EBee EWTr MBel NBPC
squarrosum	CDes EBee LRHS WPGP
tenuisubulatum BWJ 7929	WCru
tuberosum	CDes CElw CMea EBee GBuc LLHF NLAp WAbe WPGP WPat
- 'Rosie Hardy'	WCot
tubiferum	EBee
uchiyamae	CDes CFwr EBee GBin LRHS WCot WPGP
urbainii new	EBee
yunnanense	WCru

Thamnocalamus (*Poaceae*)

aristatus	CGHE EPfP EPla WDyG WPGP
crassinodus	EPla SBig
- dwarf	EPla
- 'Gosainkund'	CEnt EPla
- 'Kew Beauty'	CAbb CDTJ CDoC CEnt CGHE CMCo EPfP EPla ERod MBrN MMoz MWht NPal SBig WCot WDyG WJun WPGP
- 'Lang Tang'	CEnt CGHE EPla ERod MMoz WJun WPGP
- 'Merlyn'	CDoC CEnt EPfP EPla ERod MMoz MWht WJun WPGP
falcatus	see *Drepanostachyum falcatum*
falconeri	see *Himalayacalamus falconeri*
funghomii	see *Schizostachyum funghomii*
khasianus	see *Drepanostachyum khasianum*
maling	see *Yushania maling*
spathaceus misapplied	see *Fargesia murielae*
§ ***spathiflorus***	CEnt EPla WJun
- subsp. ***nepalensis***	EPla MMoz SBig WPGP
§ ***tessellatus***	ENBC EPla MMoz SEND WDyG WJun

Thamnochortus (*Restionaceae*)

bachmannii	CTrC
cinereus	CTrC WPGP
insignis	CHEx SPlb WPrP
lucens	CTrC
rigidus	CCCN CTrC
spicigerus	CTrC IDee

Thapsia (*Apiaceae*)

decipiens	see *Melanoselinum decipiens*

Thea see *Camellia*

Thelypteris (*Thelypteridaceae*)

dentata	SGSe
kunthii	WRic
limbosperma	see *Oreopteris limbosperma*
palustris	CRWN EBee EMil LPBA NHol NVic NWsh SRms WFib WPnP WRic
phegopteris	see *Phegopteris connectilis*

Themeda (*Poaceae*)

japonica	EPPr SGSe
triandra	SMad

Thermopsis (*Papilionaceae*)

	caroliniana	see *T. villosa*
	chinensis	LRHS SPhx WHil
	- 'Sophie' new	EBee LRHS
	fabacea	see *T. lupinoides*
	lanceolata	CTri EBee EPfP GBin LRHS NBPC NCGa NPri NSti SAga SMrm SPhx WAul WCAu WFar WHil WHrl WPer
§	***lupinoides***	ECha EHrv EWTr EWld MBel MHer NBre WPer
	macrophylla	EBee
	- 'Agnina'	WCot
	mollis	CPLG LRHS NBid
	montana	see *T. rhombifolia* var. *montana*
§	***rhombifolia***	CMHG CWCL EAEE EBee ELan
	var. ***montana***	EPfP GCra GGar GMaP LBMP LHop LRHS MNrw MSCN NBir NBre NCGa NLar NOrc NPol NSti SBod SGSe SPer SPoG WAbb WBVN WHil WPer WWEG
§	***villosa***	CPom CWCL EBee MBel MRav NBre NGdn WCot WHil WHoo WPGP

Therorhodion see *Rhododendron*

Thevetia (*Apocynaceae*)

neriifolia	CCCN

Thladiantha (*Cucurbitaceae*)

dubia	GCra SDix
oliveri (f)	MSCN

Thlaspi (*Brassicaceae*)

biebersteinii	see *Pachyphragma macrophyllum*
fendleri	MNrw

Thryptomene (*Myrtaceae*)

baeckeacea	CCCN
saxicola	ECou
- 'F.C. Payne'	CBcs

Thuja ✿ (*Cupressaceae*)

	'Extra Gold'	see *T. plicata* 'Irish Gold'
	'Gnome'	IBal
	'Green Giant'	SLim
§	***koraiensis***	GKir GLin IDee IFFs LRHS MBar SCoo
	occidentalis	EMac IFFs NWea
	- 'Amber Glow'	CDoC CKen CSBt ECho LRHS MAsh MGos NHol NLar SCoo SLim SPoG WBor WEve
	- Aurea Group	MBar
	- 'Aureospicata'	EHul
	- 'Bateman Broom'	CKen
	- 'Beaufort' (v)	CKen EHul MBar
	- 'Brabant'	CDul IFFs LMaj LRHS NLar SCoo SLim
	- 'Brobecks Tower'	CKen NLar SLim
	- 'Caespitosa'	CKen ECho LRHS NHol NLar SCoo WEve WGor
	- 'Cristata Aurea'	CKen
	- 'Danica' ♀H4	CMac ECho EHul GKir MAsh MBar MMuc NWea SCoo SLim SRms WCFE WEve WFar
	- 'Degroot's Spire'	CKen NLar SLim
	- 'Dicksonii'	EHul
	- 'Douglasii Aurea' (v)	CKen
	- 'Ellwangeriana Aurea'	MGos
	- Emerald	see *T. occidentalis* 'Smaragd'
	- 'Ericoides'	CDoC CTri EHul MBar MGos SRms
	- 'Europa Gold'	CDoC CDul EHul MBar MGos NHol NLar SLim
	- 'Fastigiata'	MBar
	- 'Filiformis'	CKen
	- 'Globosa'	MBar
I	- 'Globosa Variegata' (v)	CKen MBar
	- 'Gold Drop'	CKen
	- 'Golden Globe'	CDoC EHul LRHS MBar MGos NHol SCoo SLim WDin
	- 'Golden Minaret'	EHul
	- 'Golden Tuffet'	CDoC ECho LRHS MGos SCoo SLim
	- 'Hetz Midget'	CKen ECho EHul LRHS MBar NHol NLar SCoo SLim SPlb WDin WFar
	- 'Holmstrup' ♀H4	CDoC CDul CMac CSBt CTri CWib EHul EOrn GKir LRHS MAsh MBar NBlu SBch SCoo SLim SPoG SRms WClo WDin WEve WFar
	- 'Holmstrup's Yellow'	EHul LRHS NHol SLim SPoG
	- 'Hoveyi'	CTri EHul
	- 'Linesville'	CKen
	- 'Little Champion'	EHul LBMP NLar
	- 'Little Gem'	EHul MGos NHol NLar SRms WDin
	- 'Lutea Nana' ♀H4	EHul MBar NDlv WCFE
	- 'Malonyana'	NLar
	- 'Marrisen's Sulphur'	EHul LRHS NLar SCoo SLim
	- 'Meineke's Zwerg' (v)	CKen NLar
	- 'Miky'	CKen
	- 'Mr Bowling Ball'	CDoC LRHS SCoo SLim
	- 'Ohlendorffii'	CDoC CKen EHul MBar NHol
I	- 'Pumila Sudworth'	NHol
I	- 'Pygmaea'	CKen MBar
	- 'Pyramidalis Aurea'	MGos NHol WEve
	- 'Pyramidalis Compacta'	EHul IFFs NWea WGor
	- 'Recurva Nana'	EHul MBar NHol
	- 'Rheingold' ♀H4	Widely available
§	- 'Smaragd' ♀H4	CDoC CDul CSBt CWib ECho ECrN EHul EOrn EPfP GKir IFFs LAst LBuc LRHS MAsh MBar MGos NBlu NWea SBch SCoo SLim SPer SPoG SWvt WCFE WEve WFar
*	- 'Smaragd Variegated' (v)	CKen
	- 'Smokey'	CKen

	– 'Southport'	CKen WEve
	– 'Spaethii'	EHul
	– 'Spiralis'	EHul MBar NLar WCFE
§	– 'Stolwijk' (v)	EHul MBar MGos SCoo
	– 'Sunkist'	CKen CMac CTri CWib ECho EHul GKir MAsh MBar MGos NEgg NHol SCoo SLim SPoG WFar
	– 'Teddy'	CDoC ECho LBee LRHS MAsh NHol NLar SCoo SLim SPoG WFar
	– 'Tiny Tim'	CDoC CMac CSBt CWib ECho EHul GKir IFFs MBar MGos NHol SCoo WEve WFar WGor
	– 'Trompenburg'	CSBt ECho EHul EOrn MAsh NLar SCoo
	– 'Wansdyke Silver' (v)	CMac EHul LRHS MBar SCoo SLim SPoG
	– 'Wareana'	CMac
	– 'Wareana Aurea'	see *T. occidentalis* 'Wareana Lutescens'
§	– 'Wareana Lutescens'	CWib EHul MBar MGos NHol
	– 'Woodwardii'	EHul MBar
	– 'Yellow Ribbon'	CKen CSBt EHul GKir IFFs LRHS MBar NLar SCoo SLim SPoG WEve WFar WHar
	orientalis	see *Platycladus orientalis*
	– 'Miller's Gold'	see *Platycladus orientalis* 'Aurea Nana'
	plicata	CCVT CDul CMac CSBt EHul EMac EPfP IFFs MBar MGos NWea SLim SPer WDin WMou
	– 'Atrovirens' ♀H4	CDul CTri ECrN IFFs LBee LBuc LMaj LRHS MAsh MBar MBri MGos MMuc SBch SCoo SLim SRms WDin WEve WHar
*	– 'Atrovirens Aurea'	SLim WEve
	– 'Aurea' ♀H4	EHul LBee LRHS MAsh SLim SPoG SRms
	– 'Brooks Gold'	CKen
	– 'Can-can' (v)	ECho NLar SCoo
I	– 'Cole's Variety'	CWib MBar MGos SLim
	– 'Collyer's Gold'	CDul CTri EHul NHol NLar SRms WEve
	– 'Copper Kettle'	CKen ECho EHul LRHS MAsh MBar NDlv NLar SCoo SLim WEve WGor
	– 'Cuprea'	CKen EHul MBar
	– 'Doone Valley'	CKen EHul MBar NDlv WFar
	– 'Excelsa'	CDul LMaj
	– 'Fastigiata' ♀H4	CDul CMac
	– 'Gelderland'	CTho ECho EHul LRHS NEgg NLar SCoo SLim WFar
	– Goldy = '4ever'PBR	MBri
	– 'Gracilis Aurea'	EHul
	– 'Grüne Kugel'	CDoC
	– 'Hillieri'	CDoC CDul MBar
§	– 'Irish Gold' (v) ♀H4	CDul CMac
	– 'Rogersii'	CDoC CKen CMac CTri ECho EHul EOrn EPfP GKir MAsh MBar MGos NHol SCoo SPoG SRms WFar
	– 'Stolwijk's Gold'	see *T. occidentalis* 'Stolwijk'
	– 'Stoneham Gold' ♀H4	CDoC CMac ECho EHul EOrn GKir LRHS MAsh MBar MGos MMuc NHol NPCo SLim SPer SPoG SRms WEve
	– 'Sunshine'	CKen
	– Verigold = 'Courtapli'	MMuc SEND
	– 'Whipcord'	CBcs ECho EMil LRHS NLar SCoo SLim WEve
*	– 'Windsor Gold'	EHul
	– 'Winter Pink' (v)	CKen NLar
	– 'Zebrina' (v)	CBcs CDoC CDul CMac CSBt CSli CTri CWib ECho EHul ELan EPfP GKir LRHS MAsh MBar MGos NEgg NWea SCoo SLim SPer SPoG SWvt WDin WEve WFar WHar
	plicata* × *standishii	CDul

Thujopsis (*Cupressaceae*)

	dolabrata ♀H4	CBcs CTrG EHul GKir IFFs MBar MMuc NEgg NLar NWea WBrE WDin WEve WFar WPGP
	– 'Aurea' (v)	CDoC CKen EHul LRHS MBar MGos NLar SCoo SLim WEve
	– 'Laetevirens'	see *T. dolabrata* 'Nana'
	– 'Melbourne Gold'	NLar WEve
§	– 'Nana'	CDoC CKen CMac EHul IFFs LRHS MBar MGos NHol NLar SCoo SLim SRms STre WEve WFar
	– 'Variegata' (v)	CFee CMac EHul EOrn LRHS MBar NLar NMun SCoo SLim SPoG WDin WEve WFar
	koraiensis (Nakai) hort.	see *Thuja koraiensis*

Thunbergia (*Acanthaceae*)

	alata	EPfP LRHS MBri SPoG WTou
	– 'African Sunset'	CSpe EShb LRHS SVil
	– 'Lemon'	SVil
	– 'Orange Beauty'	SVil
*	***arborea*** **new**	CCCN
	battiscombeii	CCCN ERea EShb
	coccinea	CCCN ERea
	erecta	CCCN ERea
	grandiflora ♀H1	CCCN CHll CTrG ELan EPfP ERea EShb WHil
	– 'Alba'	CCCN CHll EShb
	gregorii ♀H1+3	CCCN CHll CSpe ERea EShb WHil
	'Lemon Star'	LRHS
	'Moonglow' **new**	CCCN
	mysorensis ♀H1	CCCN ERea EShb
	natalensis	CCCN ERea EShb WHil
	'Orange Wonder' **new**	CCCN

thyme, caraway see *Thymus herba-barona*

thyme, garden see *Thymus vulgaris*

thyme, lemon see *Thymus citriodorus*

thyme, wild see *Thymus serpyllum*

Thymus ✿ (*Lamiaceae*)

	from Albania	CArn
	from Turkey	ECho EWes LLWP SBch SHDw
§	'Alan Bloom'	LLWP
	'Anderson's Gold'	see *T. pulegioides* 'Bertram Anderson'
	azoricus	see *T. caespititius*
	'Brigantes' **new**	LLWP
	'Caborn Fragrant Cloud' **new**	LLWP
	'Caborn Greenfinch' **new**	LLWP
	'Caborn Grey Lady' **new**	LLWP
	'Caborn Lilac Gem'	LLWP SBch SHDw
	'Caborn Pink Carpet'	LLWP
	'Caborn Rosanne'	LLWP
	'Caborn Wine and Roses' **new**	LLWP
§	***caespititius***	CArn ECho EDAr ELau GBar GMaP GPoy MHer NMen NRya SBch SPlb SRot WAbe WCHb WPer WWEG

	Name	Suppliers
	caespitosus	CTri GKir
	camphoratus	CArn CBod CMea ELau EWes GBar LAst MHer MNHC NGHP NMen SBch WJek WWEG
	- 'A Touch of Frost'	SBch SHDw
	- 'Derry'	CSpe
	capitatus	CArn MHer
	carnosus misapplied	see *T. vulgaris* 'Erectus'
	carnosus Boiss.	STre
	'Carol Ann' (v)	ECho ELau EWes GBar LLWP MNHC WWEG
	'Caroline'	SBch SHDw
	'Carshalton'	CWan
	ciliatus	LLWP WClo WPer
	cilicicus misapplied	see *T. caespititius*
	cilicicus ambig.	MNHC NMen WCHb WWEG
	cilicicus Boiss. & Bail.	CPBP EWes GBar WAbe
	citriodorus	CArn CHby CHrt CWan ECho EDAr ELau GBar GKir GPoy LLWP MBrN MHer MNHC MWat NGHP NPri SBch WBrE WJek WPer
	- 'Archer's Gold'	see *T. pulegioides* 'Archer's Gold'
	- 'Aureus'	see *T. pulegioides* 'Aureus'
	- 'Bertram Anderson'	see *T. pulegioides* 'Bertram Anderson'
§	- 'Golden King' (v)	CWan ECha ECho EDAr ELan GBar LHop LLWP LRHS MBar MBri MHer NGHP WCHb WHoo WPer WWEG
	- 'Golden Lemon' misapplied	see *T. pulegioides* 'Aureus'
	- 'Golden Lemon' (v)	CArn LLWP WJek
	- 'Golden Queen' (v)	ECho EDAr GGar GKev LRHS MHer MWat NBlu NGHP NPri SBch SPer SPet SRms WFar
	- 'Lemon Supreme'	LLWP
	- 'Lime'	LLWP
	- ***repandus***	see *T.* 'Rosemary's Lemon Carpet'
	- 'Silver King' (v)	ECho LLWP
	- 'Silver Posie'	see *T. vulgaris* 'Silver Posie'
	- 'Silver Queen' (v) ♀H4	CBcs CSam CWan EAlp ECha ECho EDAr ELan EPfP GBar GGar GKev GMaP LAst LRHS MBar MHer MNHC NBlu NGHP SBch SPlb WFar
	- 'Variegatus' misapplied	see *T. citriodorus* 'Golden King'
*	- 'Variegatus' (v)	GBar LHop LSRN MBri NBlu NGHP
	'Coccineus'	see *T.* Coccineus Group
N	Coccineus Group ♀H4	CArn CPrp CTri ECha ECho ECtt ELan ELau GKir GMaP LLWP LRHS MBar MBri MHer MNHC NBlu NGHP NHol NPri NRya SIng SPer SRms SRot WAbe WClo WHoo WPat WRHF
§	- 'Atropurpureus' misapplied	LLWP SBch SHDw
	- 'Bethany'	LLWP SGar
§	- 'Hardstoft Red' (v)	GBar
§	- 'Purple Beauty'	LLWP MHer NGHP
§	- 'Purpurteppich'	LLWP
§	- 'Red Elf'	ECho GAbr GBar MHer NGHP SBch WJek WWEG
	'Coccineus Major'	CMea CWan ECho EDAr LRHS MHer MNHC SIde WJek
	comosus misapplied	SBch SHDw WEas WPer
	'Cow Green'	LLWP SBch
	'Creeping Lemon'	ELau GBar LLWP MHer NGHP SBch SHDw WJek
	'Dark Eyes'	SBch SHDw
	'Dartmoor'	GBar LLWP SBch SHDw WWEG
	'Desboro'	GBar LLWP MHer NHol WWEG
	doerfleri	ECha LLWP
	- 'Bressingham'	CArn CMea CPrp CTri CWan ECho ECtt EDAr ELau GBar GKir LBee LLWP LRHS MHer MNHC NGHP NHol NPri SBch SPlb SRms SWal WClo WFar WPat WPer WWEG
	'Doone Valley' (v)	Widely available
	drucei	see *T. polytrichus* subsp. *britannicus*
	'E.B. Anderson'	see *T. pulegioides* 'Bertram Anderson'
	'Eastgrove Pink'	LLWP SBch SHDw
	'Emma's Pink'	LLWP
	erectus	see *T. vulgaris* 'Erectus'
	'Fragrantissimus'	CArn CEnt CHrt CMea CWan ELau GBar GGar GPoy LLWP MHer MNHC MWat NGHP NPri SHlg SIde SPlb WFar WJek WPer
	'Gibson's Cave'	LLWP
	'Glenridding'	LLWP
	'Gratian'	LLWP SBch SHDw
	'Hadrian' **new**	LLWP
	'Hans Stam'	LLWP
	'Hardstoft Red'	see *T.* (Coccineus Group) 'Hardstoft Red'
§	'Hartington Silver' (v)	CMea EAlp ECha ECho ECtt EPot EWes GBar GBuc GKir LBee LHop LRHS MHer MNHC NGHP NHol NRya SIng SPlb WFar WHoo WPer WWEG
	herba-barona	CArn CHrt CMea CPrp CTri CWan ECha EDAr ELau GBar GPoy LEdu LLWP MHer MNHC MWat NGHP NHol SIde SRms STre WPer WWEG
	- 'Bob Flowerdew'	LLWP
	- ***citrata***	see *T. herba-barona* 'Lemon-scented'
§	- 'Lemon-scented'	ECha GBar GPoy LLWP MHer SBch SHDw SIde WCHb
	'Highdown'	ECtt SBch SHDw
	'Highdown Adur'	SBch SHDw
	'Highdown Lemon'	SBch SHDw
	'Highdown Red'	SBch SHDw
	'Highdown Stretham'	SBch SHDw
	'Highland Cream'	see *T.* 'Hartington Silver'
	hirsutus	NBir
	'Jekka' **new**	WWEG
	'Kurt'	LLWP SBch SHDw
	'Lake District'	LLWP
I	'Lantanii'	LLWP SBch
	lanuginosus misapplied	see *T. pseudolanuginosus*
	'Lavender Sea'	ELau EWes LLWP
	'Lemon Caraway'	see *T. herba-barona* 'Lemon-scented'
	'Lemon Sorbet'	SBch SHDw
*	'Lemon Variegated' (v)	EDAr ELau EPfP GBar MNHC SPer SPoG WWEG
	'Lilac Time'	EWes GBar LLWP MHer NGHP SBch SHDw SIde SPlb WCHb WJek WWEG
	longicaulis	CArn ECha ELau GBar LLWP MHer WJek
	'Low Force'	LLWP
	'Marjorie'	LLWP
	marschallianus	see *T. pannonicus*
	mastichina	CArn GBar
	- 'Didi'	MHer
	membranaceus	CPBP
	micans	see *T. caespititius*
	minus	see *Calamintha nepeta*
	montanus Waldst. & Kit.	see *T. pulegioides*
	'Mountain Select'	LLWP SBch SHDw
	neiceffii	CMea ECha ELau GBar LLWP WWEG

	'New Hall'	SBch
	nummularius misapplied	see *T.*'Pat Milne'
	odoratissimus	see *T. pallasianus* subsp. *pallasianus*
	'Orange Balsam'	LLWP NHol
	'Orange Spice'	LLWP SBch SHDw SPoG WWEG
	pallasianus	ELau SBch SHDw
§	- subsp. ***pallasianus***	GBar
§	***pannonicus***	LLWP MHer WPer
§	'Pat Milne'	ELau LLWP
	'Peter Davis'	CArn CMea GBar LHop LRHS LSRN MBNS MHer MNHC NBir NGHP NHol SBch SIde WJek WRHF
	'Pink Ripple'	CBod CMea EAlp EDAr ELau EWes GBar LLWP MHer NGHP SBch SHDw SIde SIng WCHb WHal WHoo WJek WWEG
	polytrichus misapplied	see *T. praecox*
§	***polytrichus*** A. Kern. ex Borbás subsp. ***britannicus***	CArn ECho GPoy LSou SBch SHDw SPlb WAbe WJek WPer WWEG
	- - 'Minor'	ECho LLWP WPer
	- - 'Orkney White'	WAlt
§	- - 'Thomas's White' ♀H4	CTri ECho LLWP
	- - 'Timothy's White'	CEnt
	'Porlock'	CMea CPrp CTri CWan ECho ELau EPfP GBar GKir GMaP GPoy LLWP LRHS MHer MNHC NGHP SIde SRms WAbe WHoo WJek WPer WWEG
§	***praecox***	EBWF GBar GJos MHer NLan NMir NSco
	- subsp. ***arcticus***	see *T. polytrichus* subsp. *britannicus*
	- - 'Albus'	see *T. polytrichus* subsp. *britannicus* 'Thomas's White'
§	***pseudolanuginosus***	CArn CTri CWan EAlp ECha ECho EDAr EPot GBar GJos GMaP LBee LLWP LRHS MBNS MBri MHer MLHP MNHC NBir NGHP NHol SPlb SRms WHoo WPer WSpi WWEG
	- 'Hall's Variety'	GBar
§	***pulegioides***	CArn CBod CHby CHrt ELau GBar GGar GPoy LLWP MBri MHer MNHC NPri SBch SHDw SIde WClo WJek WPer
§	- 'Archer's Gold'	Widely available
§	- 'Aureus' ♀H4	EPot GBar GGar GKev GKir GMaP LAst LLWP LRHS MBar MBri MHer NBlu NWCA SBch SGar SPer SPlb STre WFar WHoo
§	- 'Bertram Anderson' ♀H4	CArn CMea CSam ECha ECho ECtt ELau EPfP GBar GKir GMaP LAst LLWP LRHS MHer NBir NGHP NHol NPri NRya NVic SBch SIde SPer SRGP SRms WAbe WFar WHoo WWEG
	- 'Foxley' (v)	CBod CBow CWan ECho EHoe ELau EPfP GBar LLWP LRHS LSou MHer MNHC NGHP NHol NPro SBch SHDw SIde SPlb WCHb WJek WWEG
	- 'Golden Dwarf'	LLWP
§	- 'Goldentime'	GBar LLWP NGHP SWal
	- 'Sir John Lawes'	LLWP MHer SBch SHDw
	- 'Sundon Hills'	LLWP
	- 'Tabor'	GBar GMaP MNHC NGHP SBch SHDw
	'Rasta' (v)	LLWP SIng
	'Redstart'	ECha ELau GBar LBee LLWP LRHS MHer NBlu NGHP SBch SHDw SIde WCHb WWEG
	richardii subsp. ***nitidus*** misapplied	see *T. vulgaris* 'Suditin'
	- - 'Compactus Albus'	see *T. vulgaris* 'Snow White'
	'Rosa Ceeping'	SBch SHDw
	'Rosalicht'	LLWP
	'Rosalind'	SBch SHDw
	'Rosedrift'	LLWP SBch SHDw
§	'Rosemary's Lemon Carpet'	CArn LLWP
	rotundifolius misapplied	see *T. vulgaris* 'Elsbeth'
	'Ruby Glow'	CEnt CHrt ELau EWes MHer SBch SHDw WFar WWEG
	serpyllum ambig.	CArn ELau GJos MBri NGHP SIde SPet SPlb SRms WJek WPer
	serpyllum L.	EAro GKev LLWP
	- var. ***albus***	CPrp ECha ECho ELau GBar GPoy LAst LLWP LRHS MNHC NGHP NHol NPri SIde SPer SRms WAbe WHoo WWEG
	- 'Albus Variegatus'	see *T.* 'Hartington Silver'
N	- 'Annie Hall'	CWan ECho EDAr ELau EPfP EPot GBar GGar LAst LLWP LRHS MHer NGHP NPri SBch SIde SPer STre WCFE WPer
	- 'Atropurpureus'	see *T.* (Coccineus Group) 'Atropurpureus' misapplied
	- 'August Moon'	LLWP
	- 'Barwinnock Snowdrift' (v)	GBar
	- ***coccineus*** 'Minor' misapplied	see *T.* Coccineus Group
	- - 'Minor' Bloom	see *T.* 'Alan Bloom'
	- 'Conwy Rose'	CPBP LLWP WAbe
N	- 'East Lodge'	LLWP MNHC
	- 'Elfin'	ECho EDAr EWes GKev LBee LRHS MBri SBch SPlb WAbe
N	- 'Fulney Red'	EWes
	- 'Goldstream' (v)	CMea ECho ELau EPfP GBar LHop LLWP LRHS MBar MBri MHer NBlu NGHP NHol SPlb SRms WCHb WHoo WPer
	- 'Iden'	WWEG
	- 'Lemon Curd'	CWan ELau GBar LLWP MHer MNHC NGHP NHol SBch SHDw SIde SPlb SPoG WCHb WFar WJek WWEG
§	- 'Minimalist'	CArn CMea CPBP CWan ECha ELau GBar LLWP MBri MHer MLHP MNHC NHol NRya SBch SIde SPer SPet SPlb SRot WBVN WCHb WClo WHoo WPat WPer
	- 'Minimus'	see *T. serpyllum* 'Minimalist'
§	- 'Minor'	CEnt CTri ECho ECtt GBar LLWP NMen NSla SBch SHDw WAbe
N	- 'Minor Albus'	ECho GBar
	- 'Minus'	see *T. serpyllum* 'Minor'
	- 'Petite'	EWes LLWP
N	- 'Pink Chintz' ♀H4	CMea CPrp ECha ECho ECtt EDAr ELau EPfP EPot GBar GBuc GKir GPoy LLWP LRHS MBar MBri MHer MNHC NGHP NPri SBch SIng SPer SPlb SPoG WClo WHoo WPer WWEG
	- 'Posh Pinky'	EDAr EPot LLWP NMen
	- 'Purple Beauty'	see *T.* (Coccineus Group) 'Purple Beauty'
	- 'Purpurteppich'	see *T.* (Coccineus Group) 'Purpurteppich'
	- 'Pygmaeus'	LLWP

	– 'Rainbow Falls' (v)	EPfP GBar LLWP MNHC NGHP NHol SBch SHDw SIde WRHF WWEG
	– 'Red Carpet'	EDAr NHol
	– 'Red Elf'	see *T.* (Coccineus Group) 'Red Elf'
	– 'Red Glow'	LLWP
	– 'Roger's Snowdrift'	LLWP
N	– 'Roseus'	GBar SIde
N	– 'Russetings'	CPrp EAlp ECtt ELau EPfP EPot GBar LLWP MBar MHer MNHC NGHP NHol SBch SIde SPer SRms WFar WHoo WWEG
N	– 'September'	LLWP MHer
N	– 'Snowdrift'	CArn CMea CWan ECho ECtt EDAr ELau EPfP EPot GBar LLWP MBar MHer MNHC MWat NHol NMen NRya SBch SIde SPlb WCFE WFar WJek WPat WPer WWEG
N	– 'Splendens'	LLWP
	– subsp. ***tanaensis***	CArn
	– 'Variegatus'	see *T.* 'Hartington Silver'
	– 'Vey'	ECho EWes GBar GMaP LLWP LRHS MHer SBch SHDw SIng WCHb WWEG
	sibthorpii	CArn
N	'Silver Posie'	see *T. vulgaris* 'Silver Posie'
	'Snowdonia Idris'	LLWP
	'Snowdonia Ifor'	LLWP
	'Snowdonia Imperial Beauty'	LLWP
	'Snowdonia Iorwerth'	LLWP
	'Snowdonia Isolde'	LLWP
	'Snowdonia Istyn'	LLWP
	'Snowdonia Lass'	LLWP SBch
	'Snowdonia Pedr'	LLWP
	'Snowdonia Pink Gem'	LLWP
	'Snowdonia Pryderi'	LLWP
	'Snowdonia Pwyll'	LLWP
	'Snowdonia Rhiannon' **new**	LLWP
	'Snowdonia Rowena'	LLWP
	'Snowman'	SBch
*	***valesiacus***	LLWP SBch SHDw WWEG
§	***villosus***	ECho
	vulgaris	Widely available
	– ***albus***	ECho GBar
	– 'Aureus' hort.	see *T. pulegioides* 'Goldentime'
	– 'Boule'	LLWP
*	– 'Compactus'	GPoy LLWP MNHC MRav
	– 'Deutsche Auslese'	LLWP
	– 'Diamantis'	LLWP
	– 'Dorcas White'	LLWP MHer WPer
§	– 'Elsbeth'	ECho ELau LLWP SBch SHDw
	– 'English Winter'	GBar MNHC SHlg SIde
§	– 'Erectus'	CArn GBar MHer WPer
	– French	ELau GGar LLWP MHer SBch SHDw SPlb
	– French, summer	SIde
	– 'Golden Pins'	GBar MHer
	– 'Lemon Queen'	ECho ELau
	– 'Lucy'	GBar LLWP MHer MNHC
	– 'Pinewood'	LLWP MHer SIde
	– 'Silver Pearl' (v)	ECho
§	– 'Silver Posie'	Widely available
§	– 'Snow White'	ELau EWes LLWP SBch SHDw
§	– 'Suditin'	STre
	'Widecombe' (v)	LLWP MHer SBch SHDw
	zygis	CArn

Tiarella (*Saxifragaceae*)

	'Black Velvet'PBR	GCai MBel NLar SPer WFar
	'Braveheart'	EBee WWEG
	collina	see *T. wherryi*
	cordifolia ♀H4	Widely available
	– 'Glossy'	CBct GBuc WPGP
	– 'Oakleaf'	CMoH EBee MBel NBre NBro
	– 'Rosalie'	see × *Heucherella alba* 'Rosalie'
	– 'Running Tapestry'	EBee WMoo
	– 'Slick Rock'	EPPr
	'Crow Feather'PBR	EBee
	'Cygnet'PBR	CBct CLAP EBee ECtt EPPr GCai LHop MBel SIng SPer SPoG SRot WFar
	'Dark Star'	ECtt NBre
	'Dunvegan'	EBee MBel WMoo
	'Elizabeth Oliver'	CLAP EBee
	'Freckles'	MRav
	'Hidden Carpet'	CHid
	'Inkblot'	EBee ELan LRHS MBel NBro WFar WMoo WSpi
	'Iron Butterfly'PBR	CBct CChe CLAP CMac CWCL EBee ECGP ECtt EPfP GBin GMaP LAst LBMP LRHS LSRN MRav NBro NCGa SGSe SMrm SPer SRot STes WFar WPGP WSpi
*	'Laciniate Runner'	CLAP
	'Martha Oliver'	CLAP EBee GBuc NBre SBch WPGP
	'Mint Chocolate'PBR	CLAP EBee ECha ECtt EHoe EHrv ELan EPfP GMaP LFur LOck LRHS MRav NGdn NLar SMrm SPer SWvt WAul WFar WPGP WWEG
	Morning Star = 'Tntia042'PBR	EWll LAst MBri SRot WFar
	'Neon Lights'PBR	CBow EWes NBPC SGol SPer SWvt
§	'Ninja'PBR	CHid CMac CWCL EBee EBrs ECha ECtt EHrv ELan GMaP LAst LFur LRHS MAvo MBel MDun MRav NLar NSti SPer SWvt WFar
	'Petite Pink Bouquet'	ECtt
	'Pink Bouquet'	CAbP CBow CLAP CMac CSpe EBee EBrs ECha ECtt EHrv GJos LBMP LRHS MBel MBri NHol SBch WFar WMoo WPnP
	'Pink Brushes'PBR	EBee LFur WPnP
	'Pink Skyrocket'PBR	CWGN EBee ECtt GCai GEdr LFur LLHF LOck LRHS NCob NGdn NHol SHar SMrm SPer WCot WGor
	'Pinwheel'	EBrs LRHS MRav NBre
	'Pirate's Patch'PBR	GCai LLHF NHol
	polyphylla	CBow CSsd ELan NBre NLar SBch SWal WFar WMoo
	– 'Baoxing Pink'	CBow WCru
	– 'Filigran'	EBee LRHS NHol NLar
	– 'Moorgrün'	GCal
	– pink-flowered	CLAP CMoH EHrv GBin
	– – BWJ 8088	WCru
	'Running Tiger'	EBee WWEG
	'Sea Foam'	NHol WSpi
	'Simsalabim'	EBee
	'Skeleton Key'	EBee
	'Skid's Variegated' (v)	CBow EBee ECtt EShb NSti SWvt WCot
	'Spanish Cross'PBR	NHol
	'Spring Symphony'PBR	CLAP CMac CWCL EBee ECtt EShb GBin GCai LAst LRHS LSou MBri NCGa NHol NLar NPer SHar SIng SMrm WFar WSpi
	Starburst = 'Tntia041'PBR	LAst SIng
	'Starfish'	MBel NBPC NBre WPrP
	'Sugar and Spice'PBR	EBee LSou NHol
	'Tiger Stripe'	EBee EPfP LRHS MRav NBro SPer WFar WMoo WPnP WSpi WWEG
	trifoliata	MRav NBre WFar
	– var. ***unifoliata***	WWEG
	'Viking Ship'PBR	see × *Heucherella* 'Viking Ship'

§ ***wherryi*** ♀H4 — CBcs CHrt COlW CRow EBee ECtt EHrv ELan EPfP GKir GMaP LAst LBMP LFur LRHS NBir NBro NHol NOrc NPri SBch SPer SPlb SRot SWvt WFar WMoo WPer WPnP WWEG
- 'Bronze Beauty' — CLAP GBuc MRav NPro SBch WFar WMoo WPGP WSpi
- 'Green Velvet' — ECha
- 'Heronswood Mist' (v) — CAbP CBct CBow CFir EBee ECtt GEdr GQue MBel SPer SWvt WCot WWEG
- 'Montrose' — NBre WPGP

Tibouchina (*Melastomataceae*)

grandifolia — CRHN EShb
heteromalla — CCCN
'Jules' — CBcs
organensis — CCCN CHll WPGP
paratropica — CRHN
semidecandra hort. — see *T. urvilleana*
§ ***urvilleana*** ♀H1 — CBcs CCCN CDoC CHEx CHrt CKno CRHN CSBt CTri EAmu EBak ECre ELan EPfP IFFs ISea MCot MREP NCGa SAPC SArc SDnm SEND SPer SRkn SRms WCot WHil
- 'Compacta' — CCCN
- 'Edwardsii' — LSou SMrm SUsu
- 'Nana' — CDoC
- 'Rich Blue Sun' — CSpe
- variegated (v) — CCCN LSou WCot

Tigridia ✿ (*Iridaceae*)

lutea — ECho
orthantha B&SWJ 10244 new — WCru
pavonia — CPLG CSpr EBrs ECho EDif EWll IGor LAma MBri
- 'Alba' — CSpe EBrs EDif
- 'Alba Grandiflora' — EBee EWll
- 'Aurea' — EBee
- 'Canariensis' — EBee EBrs
- 'Lilacea' — EBee EBrs ECho EWll
- 'Speciosa' — EBee

Tilia ✿ (*Tiliaceae*)

americana — CLnd CMCN GKir NWea SCoo
- 'Dentata' — CDul
- 'Nova' — CDoC
amurensis — CMCN GKir
- subsp. ***taquetii*** — GKir
argentea — see *T. tomentosa*
begoniifolia — see *T. dasystyla*
chenmoui — CMCN EPfP GKir MBlu WPGP
chinensis — CMCN GKir NPCo WPGP
chingiana — CDul CMCN GKir SBir SLon
cordata ♀H4 — CBcs CCVT CDul CLnd CMac CSBt CTho CTri EBee ECrN ELan EMac EPfP GKir IFFs LBuc LMaj LRHS MAsh MMuc MSwo NWea SBch SCoo SPer STre WDin WMou
§ - 'Böhlje' — CDul SLPl
- 'Dainty Leaf' — CDul
- 'Erecta' — see *T. cordata* 'Böhlje'
- 'Greenspire' ♀H4 — CCVT CDoC CDul CLnd CWib EBee ECrN LMaj
- 'Len Parvin' — WPGP
- 'Lico' — CMen LMaj
- 'Monto' — CMen
- 'Plymtree Gold' — CDul
- 'Roelvo' — CDul
- 'Swedish Upright' — CDul CLnd CTho
- 'Winter Orange' — CDul CEnd EBee ECrN GKir LAst MBlu MBri NPCo SBir SCoo
§ ***dasystyla*** — CMCN WPGP
× ***euchlora*** ♀H4 — CBcs CCVT CDul CLnd CMCN EBee ECrN EPfP GKir LAst LMaj NWea SPer WDin WFar
§ × ***europaea*** — CBcs CDul CLnd CRWN ELan EWTr NWea WMou
- 'Koningslinde' — CDul
- 'Pallida' — CDul CLnd CTho LMaj MBlu NWea WMou
- 'Wratislaviensis' ♀H4 — CDoC CDul CLnd EPfP GKir LRHS MAsh MBlu NWea
§ 'Harold Hillier' — MBlu
henryana — CDoC CDul CEnd CLnd CMCN CTho CWib EBee ECrN EMil EPfP ERod GKir IArd IDee LRHS MBlu MBri MMuc SBir WDin WPGP
§ ***heterophylla*** — CMCN CTho WPGP
- var. ***michauxii*** — CLnd GKir
'Hillieri' — see *T.* 'Harold Hillier'
insularis — CMCN GKir MBlu
japonica — CDul CMCN GKir WMou WPGP
kiusiana — CDul CMCN GKir MBlu MBri WPGP
mandshurica — CMCN WPGP
maximowicziana — GKir WPGP
mexicana — WPGP
miqueliana — CMCN
'Moltkei' — CLnd CMCN WPGP
mongolica — CDoC CDul CLnd CMCN CTho EBee EPfP GKir MBlu MMuc SCoo SMHT WPGP
monticola — see *T. heterophylla*
oliveri — CDul CMCN GKir LRHS MBlu NWea SBir WPGP
'Petiolaris' ♀H4 — CCVT CDoC CDul CEnd CLnd CMCN EBee ECrN ELan EPfP GKir MBlu MSwo NWea SPer WDin
platyphyllos — CCVT CDul CLnd CMCN CSBt CTho CTri EBee ECrN EMac EMil EPfP EWTr GKir IFFs LAst LBuc LRHS MMuc NWea SBch SCoo SPer WDin WMou
- 'Aurea' — CDul CLnd CTho ECrN MBlu
- 'Corallina' — see *T. platyphyllos* 'Rubra'
- 'Erecta' — see *T. platyphyllos* 'Fastigiata'
§ - 'Fastigiata' — CDul CTho ECrN SLPl
- 'Laciniata' — CDul CMCN CTho EBee GKir LMaj MBlu
* - 'Pendula' — CTho
§ - 'Rubra' ♀H4 — CDoC CLnd CTho ECrN EPfP GKir LBuc MGos NWea WDin WFar
- 'Tortuosa' — MBlu
§ ***tomentosa*** — CDul CLnd CMCN CTho ECrN ELan EMil GKir IFFs LMaj MMuc NWea SCoo SEND WDin WMou
- 'Brabant' ♀H4 — CDoC CDul EPfP EWTr LMaj WFar
tuan — CMCN
× ***vulgaris*** — see *T.* × *europaea*

Tilingia (*Apiaceae*)

ajanensis B&SWJ 11202 — WCru

Tillaea see *Crassula*

Tillandsia (*Bromeliaceae*)

aeranthos — SChr
albertiana new — LRHS
andreana new — LRHS
argentea ♀H1 — MBri
bergeri new — LRHS

brachycaulos LRHS
butzii LRHS
cacticola new LRHS
caput-medusae LRHS
circinnatoides LRHS
cyanea ♀H1 LRHS MBri
filifolia LRHS
gardneri new LRHS
harrisii new LRHS
ionantha LRHS
- var. ***scaposa*** see *T. kolbii*
juncea LRHS
§ ***kolbii*** LRHS
magnusiana LRHS
seleriana LRHS
streptophylla new LRHS
stricta new LRHS
tectorum new LRHS
usneoides SHmp
xerographica LRHS

Tinantia (*Commelinaceae*)

pringlei CDes EBee LEdu SDys WPGP WSHC
- AIM 77 WCot WPrP

Titanopsis (*Aizoaceae*)

calcarea ♀H1 CCCN EPfP

Tithonia (*Asteraceae*)

rotundifolia CSpe
- 'Torch' SMrm

Todea (*Osmundaceae*)

barbara WPGP WRic

Tofieldia (*Melanthiaceae*)

calyculata NHol
coccinea EBee GCal
nuda var. ***furusei*** new EBee
pusilla ERos

Tolmiea (*Saxifragaceae*)

menziesii EBee EWld MBri MCot NHol SPer SWal
- 'Goldsplash' see *T. menziesii* 'Taff's Gold'
- 'Maculata' see *T. menziesii* 'Taff's Gold'
§ - 'Taff's Gold' (v) ♀H4 CWan EHoe EOHP EShb GMaP LRHS MHer NBid NVic SPlb WHoo WTin
- 'Variegata' see *T. menziesii* 'Taff's Gold'

Tolpis (*Asteraceae*)

barbata CSpe

Tonestus (*Asteraceae*)

§ ***lyallii*** WPer

Toona (*Meliaceae*)

§ ***sinensis*** CArn CDul CEnd CGHE CTho CWib ELan EPfP SPoG WBVN WFar WPGP
- 'Flamingo' (v) CBcs EPfP IDee LBuc LRHS MAsh MGos NLar SMad SPoG SSta WCot

Torenia (*Scrophulariaceae*)

(Moon Series) Golden Moon = 'Danmoon16'PBR new LAst
- Purple Moon = 'Dantopur'PBR LAst LSou SVil
- Rose Moon = 'Dantoromoon' new LAst
- White Moon = 'Dantorwhite'PBR LAst
- Yellow Moon = 'Danmoon20'PBR LAst LSou
Summer Wave Series CCCN SCoo
(Vivia Series) 'Snow' new SVil
- 'Sol' new SVil

Torilis (*Apiaceae*)

japonica CBre EBWF

Torreya (*Taxaceae*)

grandis EGFP

Townsendia (*Asteraceae*)

alpigena new GKev
§ - var. ***alpigena*** CPBP EPot GKev
- var. ***caelilinensis*** NNS 06-551 GKev
formosa ECho GKev
incana WAbe
leptotes CPBP
montana see *T. alpigena* var. *alpigena*
nuttallii GKev
parryi GKev WAbe
§ ***rothrockii*** EPot NMen
spathulata CPBP
wilcoxiana misapplied see *T. rothrockii*

Toxicodendron (*Anacardiaceae*)

verniciflluum see *Rhus verniciflua*

Trachelium (*Campanulaceae*)

caeruleum ♀H1 CHrt SGar
- 'Black Knight' CSpe
- 'Purple Umbrella' CPLG
jacquinii subsp. ***rumelianum*** CPBP NWCA WPat

Trachelospermum ✿ (*Apocynaceae*)

from Nanking, China EShb
§ ***asiaticum*** ♀H2-3 Widely available
- B&SWJ 4814 WCru
- 'Golden Memories' CPLG CWGN EPfP LRHS LSRN LSqu MAsh MGos SLon SPoG SSpi SSta WPat
- 'Goshiki' (v) CBow EShb GQui WPat
- var. ***intermedium*** NPal WPGP
- - B&SWJ 8733 WCru
- 'Kulu Chiriman' WCot
'Chameleon' EGxp NPal
jasminoides ♀H3-4 Widely available
- B&SWJ 5117 WCru
- 'Big White Star' EPfP
§ - 'Japonicum' CSPN LRHS SLon SPoG WSHC
- 'Major' CSPN CTrG EBee ELan SSpi
* - 'Oblanceolatum' GCal
- 'Tricolor' (v) CBcs LRHS SWvt WCot WHil
- 'Variegatum' (v) ♀H3-4 Widely available
- 'Waterwheel' CWGN ELan LRHS SPoG SSpi WPGP WSHC
- 'Wilsonii' CBot CMac CPLG CSPN CSam EBee ELan EPfP EShb GCal LHop LRHS MCCP SBch SBod SLim SPer SPoG SWvt WCot WCru WHar WPGP
majus misapplied see *T. jasminoides* 'Japonicum'
majus Nakai see *T. asiaticum*

Trachycarpus (*Arecaceae*)

sp. new EAmu
from Manipur EAmu NExo
§ ***fortunei*** ♀H3-4 Widely available

latisectus	CBrP EAmu LPJP LPal NPal SBig
martianus	CTrC EAmu LPJP LPal SBig SChr
nanus	LPal
oreophilus	LPal
princeps	LPal
takil	CBrP EAmu EPla LPal NPal
wagnerianus	CBrP CDTJ CGHE CHid CPHo CPLG CTrC EAmu EBee EPla ETod LPJP LPal MREP NPal NScw SBig SChr SMad WPGP

Trachymene (*Apiaceae*)

coerulea	CSpe

Trachystemon (*Boraginaceae*)

orientalis	CBre CHEx CMac CPLG CSev EBee ECha EGol ELan EPfP IKil LEdu LHop MAvo MRav NBid SBig SDnm SMrm WBor WCru WDyG WFar WHer WMoo WPnP

Tradescantia ✿ (*Commelinaceae*)

albiflora	see *T. fluminensis*
× ***andersoniana*** W. Ludwig & Rohw. nom. inval.	see *T.* Andersoniana Group
§ Andersoniana Group	CSpr CWan CWib SPet SWal WPer
- 'Baby Doll'	GKir
- 'Bilberry Ice'	Widely available
- 'Blanca'	WWEG
- 'Blue and Gold'	CBcs COIW CSpe EBee ECtt ELon EPPr EPfP GBuc LAst LHop LRHS MNFA MRav NPri NSti SGSe SPoG WCAu WCot WFar WHil WWEG
- 'Blue Stone'	CMdw CMea CSBt EBee ECha ECtt MAvo MRav NPri SRms WFar WHoo WTin
- 'Blushing Bride'	EBee
- 'Bridal Veil'	CHll
- 'Caerulea Plena'	see *T. virginiana* 'Caerulea Plena'
- Carmine Glow	see *T.* (Andersoniana Group) 'Karminglut'
- 'Charlotte'	EBee EBrs ECha ECtt EMFW LRHS LSRN MCot NBre NBro NGdn SBch SRGP WCAu WMnd WWEG
- 'Chedglow'	WWEG
- 'Concord Grape'	Widely available
- 'Danielle'	EBee EPfP GMac
- 'Domaine de Courson'	EBee ECtt
- 'In the Navy'	LDai NBre NLar
- 'Innocence'	CMHG CSBt CTri EBee ECha ECtt ELan EMFW EPfP GCra GJos GMaP LAst LHop LRHS NBPC NBir NCGa NGdn NOrc NPri NSti SBch SPer SPoG STes WFar WMnd
- 'Iris Prichard'	CPrp EBee ELan EPfP GCra GMaP LAst LRHS NBre NCGa NLar SRGP WFar
- 'Isis' ♀H4	CBcs CHar CPrp CTri EBee ECGP ECtt ELan EPfP GCra GKir LBMP LRHS MMuc MRav NBir NCGa NGdn NOrc SBch SEND SPer WMnd WTin
- 'J.C. Weguelin' ♀H4	EBee EPfP GKir MCot NBir NBre NMRc SRms WCAu WMnd WWEG
§ - 'Karminglut'	EBee ECtt ELan EPfP GKir GMaP LAst MNrw NBir NGdn NOrc NVic SGSe SPad WHoo WWEG
- 'Leonora'	CWan EBee EPfP LRHS NLar
- 'Little Doll'	CWCL EBee ECtt GMac LAst MBel MDKP MNFA NBro NPri WFar WWEG
- 'Little White Doll'	CPrp CWCL EBee ECtt GMac LAst MBNS MDKP MNFA NBre WFar WWEG
- 'Mariella'	EBee GMac LAst
- 'Mrs Loewer'	MAvo
- 'Navajo Princess'	EBee
- 'Osprey' ♀H4	Widely available
- 'Pauline'	CHar EBee ECtt ELon EPla GKir LAst MNrw MRav NBir NLar WFar WHoo WTin WWEG WWlt
- 'Perinne's Pink'	CWCL EBee EBrs EPfP EWTr MBri NBPC NLar NSti SUsu WCAu
- 'Pink Chablis'PBR	CWCL EBee ECtt MAvo NBro NLar NMoo SMrm
- 'Purewell Giant'	CMac CMoH CTri EBee GBee LHop LRHS NBro NLar WGor WKif WMnd
- 'Purple Dome'	CHar CSsd EBee ECtt EMFW EPla GKir GMaP LAst LRHS MCot MMuc MRav NBir NBro NCGa NGdn SBch SEND SPoG STes WCAu WMnd WTin WWEG
- 'Red Grape'	COIW EBee ECtt EWll LRHS MWhi NPro NSti WBor WCAu WWEG
- 'Rosi'	EBee
- 'Rubra'	CPrp CSpr EBee NOrc SBod SRms
- 'Satin Doll'PBR	COIW EBee ECtt EPfP LRHS
- 'Sweet Kate'	CBct CHar CMac CWCL EBee ECtt LFur LRHS LSRN MBNS MCCP NBro SRGP WBor
- 'Sylvana'	EBee GMac SApp
- 'Temptation'	ECtt
- 'Valour'	CSBt EBee WFar
- 'Zwanenburg Blue'	EBee ECha ECtt EHrv ELan GBee GKir GMac LAst LRHS MCot MLHP NCGa SGSe SPlb WMnd WWEG
'Angel Eyes'	MBel MDKP
canaliculata	see *T. ohiensis*
§ ***fluminensis***	SChr
- 'Albovittata'	EShb
§ - 'Aurea' ♀H1	EShb
- 'Laekenensis' (v)	MBri
- 'Maiden's Blush' (v)	CSpe EShb SGar SRms WFoF
- 'Quicksilver' (v) ♀H1	EShb MBri
- 'Variegata'	see *T. fluminensis* 'Aurea'
longipes	EBee
§ ***ohiensis***	CFee EBee LPBA MAvo
pallida ♀H2-3	EOHP
- 'Kartuz Giant' **new**	WCot
§ - 'Purpurea' ♀H2-3	EShb
pendula	see *T. zebrina*
'Purple Sabre'	LAst SDys SMrm SRot
purpurea	see *T. pallida* 'Purpurea'
sillamontana ♀H1	EOHP MBri
spathacea	EShb
tricolor	see *T. zebrina*
virginiana	CMoH MWhi SGar
- 'Alba'	CMac GCal WPer
* - 'Brevicaulis'	ECha ECtt ERos GBuc NBre NBro WWEG
§ - 'Caerulea Plena' (d)	CHar CMHG EBee ELan EPfP EPla MRav NBPC NCGa SRms STes WFar WTin WWEG
- 'Rubra'	ECGP SPlb
§ ***zebrina*** ♀H1	EShb
- ***pendula***	see *T. zebrina*
- 'Purpusii' ♀H1	SRms

Tragopogon (*Asteraceae*)

crocifolius	CCVN CSpe SPhx WCot
porrifolius	EBWF GCal ILis SECG
pratensis	CArn EBWF NMir

Trautvetteria (*Ranunculaceae*)

carolinensis var. ***japonica***	CLAP EBee GEdr WCru WPrP
- var. ***occidentalis***	GEdr WCru

Triadica (*Euphorbiaceae*)

sebifera	CPLG

Trichopetalum (*Anthericaceae*)

§ ***plumosum***	CBro ECho

Trichostema (*Lamiaceae*)

dichotomum	WCot
RCB RL 15 new	

Tricuspidaria see *Crinodendron*

Tricyrtis ✿ (*Convallariaceae*)

B&SWJ 3229 from Taiwan	WCru
from Taiwan	WFar
'Adbane'	CBct CChe CLAP EBee ELan EPPr EWes GBBs GBuc GKev IKil NGdn NLar SGSe SMrm WFar WGwG WWEG
affinis	CLAP GAbr GBin GBuc GGar NLar
- B&SWJ 2804	WCru
- B&SWJ 5640	WCru
- B&SWJ 5645	WCru
- B&SWJ 6182	WCru
- B&SWJ 11169	WCru
- 'Early Bird'	LEdu WCru WFar
- 'Sansyoku'	GEdr
'Amanagowa'	CLAP
bakeri	see *T. latifolia*
'Blue Wonder'	EBee EWTr LRHS LSou NGdn NPro SPet
'Blueberry Mousse' new	EBee
dilatata	see *T. macropoda*
'Empress'	CBct COlW CSam CWCL EBee EBla ECha ELon EPfP EWes GBuc IBal LEdu LFur LRHS LSou MAvo MSCN NBPC NCob NEgg NHol NSti SGSe SMrm SPet WFar WWEG
flava	EBee LRHS WCru WFar
formosana ♀H4	Widely available
- B&SWJ 306	CLAP EBla MNrw WFar
- B&SWJ 355	WCru WFar
- B&SWJ 3073	WCru
- B&SWJ 3616	WCru
- B&SWJ 3712	WCru WFar
- B&SWJ 6705	see *T. formosana* 'Taiwan Toad'
- B&SWJ 6741	WCru
- B&SWJ 6970	WCru
- B&SWJ 7071	WFar
- RWJ 10109	WCru
- 'Autumn Glow' (v)	EBee
- dark-flowered	GAbr NCGa WFar
- 'Dark Beauty'	CDes CEnt CLAP CPLG CWCL EBee EHrv EWTr GBuc MAvo MBri MCot MSCN NBPC NPri NPro SMrm SMrs SPad SPur SUsu WFar WPGP WWEG WWFP
- 'Emperor' (v)	EBee
- 'Gilt Edge' (v)	Widely available
- f. ***glandosa***	WFar
- - B&SWJ 7084	WCru
- - 'Blu-Shing Toad'	WCru WFar
- var. ***grandiflora*** B&SWJ 6905	WCru WFar
- pale-flowered	CBct WFar WWEG
- 'Purple Beauty'	EBee LSou MDKP NMyG
- 'Samurai' (v)	CLAP CMil CWCL EPPr EWes NCGa NMoo WFar
- 'Shelley's'	CBct CLAP LRHS NBro SMrm WFar WPrP
- 'Small Wonder'	WCru WFar
- 'Spotted Toad'	WCru
§ - Stolonifera Group	CAvo CBcs CBro CMMP CMac EBee EHrv ELan EPfP GGar LEdu LRHS MCot NGdn NHol SDix WFar WMnd
- - B&SWJ 7046	WCru WFar
§ - 'Taiwan Toad' new	CLAP WPrP WFar
- 'Taroko Toad'	WCru WPrP
- 'Tiny Toad'	WCru WFar
- 'Variegata' (v)	CBct CBro CWan GBBs LEdu MMHG NBir NLar WBor WCru WFar
- 'Velvet Toad'	WCru WFar
'Golden Leopard'	CBct EBee EPfP LRHS NCGa NMyG NSti SPet
'Harlequin'	LEdu NLar WFar
§ ***hirta***	Widely available
- B&SWJ 2827	WCru
- B&SWJ 5971	WCru
- B&SWJ 11182	WCru
- B&SWJ 11227	WCru
- 'Alba'	CMac EHrv LRHS MAvo SBch SGSe WFar
- 'Albomarginata' (v)	CMac CPrp EAEE EBee EPPr EPfP EShb GCra LBMP LRHS MAvo MCot NEgg NHol NLar NMyG NSti SBch SGSe SWvt WFar WPGP
- 'Golden Gleam'	WCot WFar
- 'Makinoi Gold'	WFar
- 'Matsukaze'	CLAP CPom MAvo WFar
- 'Miyazaki'	CBct CFir CLAP CMac GBuc IMon LBMP LRHS MCot MHer MNrw NCGa NLar SMac SMrs WFar WWEG
- 'Taiwan Atrianne'	CSam EAEE EBee ECGP IPot LDai LRHS MDKP MRav NCGa NCob NEgg NHol WFar
- 'Variegata' (v)	CBct CTri EBrs ELon EWes GBuc GCra LRHS NLar WCot WFar WHrl WWEG
N Hototogisu	CBct CBro CLAP CPom EAEE EBee EBla ELan ELon EWTr LHop LRHS MCot MTho NBir NEgg NHol NLar NMyG SDnm SMrs SPav WFar WHil WMnd WSpi WWEG
ishiiana	CDes CLAP EBla WCot WCru WFar WPGP WSHC
- var. ***surugensis***	EBla LEdu WCru WFar
'Ivory Queen'	WFar
japonica	see *T. hirta*
'Kohaku'	CBct CLAP EBee EBla ELan EPPr EWes NPro SPav WCot WFar WPGP WWEG
lasiocarpa	CBct CLAP GBin LEdu MAvo NMyG WFar
- B&SWJ 3635	CLAP EBla WCru WFar
- B&SWJ 6861	WCru
- B&SWJ 7013	WCru WPrP
- B&SWJ 7103	WCru
- 'Royal Toad'	WCru
§ ***latifolia***	CDes EBee ELan GAbr GGar GMaP LEdu LRHS MNrw NGdn NLar SGSe SPoG WBVN WCru WFar WWEG
- B&SWJ 10996 from Japan	WCru

- from Japan WFar
- 'Yellow Sunrise' EBee EPPr NCGa
'Lemon Lime' (v) CBct CBro MDKP NPro SGSe SPav WFar WWEG
'Lightning Strike' (v) CBct EBee ECtt EWes GBuc LEdu LSou MDKP NBPC NCob NHol NMyG SPoG WCot WFar
'Lilac Towers' CBct EBrs ELan LRHS WCru WFar WWEG
macrantha CMil GBBs GGar GKev LRHS WCru WSHC
§ - subsp. ***macranthopsis*** CBct CLAP EBla EPot GBuc GEdr MDKP WCot WCru WFar
- - 'Juro' (d) WCru
macranthopsis see *T. macrantha* subsp. *macranthopsis*
N ***macropoda*** CBct EBee EBla ELan EPfP GAbr GBuc GMaP LEdu LRHS MAvo NGdn NWCA SGSe SMad WFar WMnd WWEG
- B&SWJ 1271 from Korea EBla WCru WFar
- B&SWJ 2804 from Japan WCru
- B&SWJ 5013 WCru WFar
- B&SWJ 5556 WCru
- B&SWJ 5847 from Japan WCru WFar
- B&SWJ 6209 WCru WFar
- B&SWJ 8700 WCru WFar
- B&SWJ 8829 from Korea WCru WFar
- from Yungi Temple, China CLAP EBla EPPr MDKP NCGa WCot WFar
- 'Tricolor' WCot
- variegated (v) CBow
maculata WFar
- HWJCM 470 WCru
- HWJK 2010 WCru
- HWJK 2411 WCru
'Mine-no-yuki' EBee
'Moonlight Treasure'[PBR] CLAP EBee NHol WCot
nana CLAP WCru
- 'Karasuba' EBee
- 'Raven's Back' WCru
'Niitaka' EBee
ohsumiensis CBct CDes CLAP CPom EBee EBla ECha GBuc GEdr LEdu MDKP MTho NMyG SBch SUsu WCru WFar WPGP
- 'Lunar Eclipse' GEdr
perfoliata CLAP LEdu WCru WFar
- 'Spring Shine' (v) WCru WFar
'Raspberry Mousse' CDes CLAP CWCL EBee EHrv EKen IPot LFur LHop MBNS MWea NMoo NMyG NSti SMrm WPGP
setouchiensis WCru WFar
'Shimone' CHid CLAP CPom EBee ECha ELan GBuc NCGa SGSe WFar WKif
'Shining Light' EBee
'Sinonome' EBee GBin IPot
stolonifera see *T. formosana* Stolonifera Group
suzukii WFar
- RWJ 10111 WCru
'Taipei Silk' CMac EBee EKen GAbr LRHS LSou NLar SBch
'Tojen' Widely available
'Tresahor White' CBct WFar
'Variegata' (*affinis* hybrid) (v) WFar WWEG
'Washfields' WFar WPGP
'White Towers' CBct CBro CHid CLAP CWCL EBee EBla ECha EHrv EPPr EPfP GBuc GKir LRHS MCot MRav NCGa NCob NEgg NHol NSti SBch SMrm SPer SPet SRms WAul WFar WWEG
'White Towers' spotted WBrE

Trifolium (Papilionaceae)

angustifolium CArn
dasyphyllum new LFur
fragiferum EBWF
incarnatum CSpe MHer
medium EBWF
ochroleucon CElw EBWF EBee EDAr EHrv EPPr GMaP LBMP LRHS MAvo MCCP MCot NSti SBch SGSe SSvw SWal WAul WCAu WCot WFar WMoo WWEG
pannonicum CBgR CCVN CMea EBee EHrv GCal NBre SUsu WFar WPGP WSHC WTin
pratense EBWF MHer NMir NSco SECG WSFF
- 'Dolly North' see *T. pratense* 'Susan Smith'
- 'Ice Cool' see *T. repens* 'Green Ice'
- 'Nina' EBee WAlt
- 'Purple Heart' new LRHS
- 'Speech House' (v) WAlt
- 'Splash' WAlt
§ - 'Susan Smith' (v) CBre CCCN EBee ECGP EHoe EWes GBuc GCal MNrw NGHP NSti SIng WFar
repens COld EBWF EHrv NSco SECG SVic WSFF
- 'Douglas Dawson' LDai
- 'Dragon's Blood' EBee NPro SIng SMrm SVil WFar
- 'Gold Net' see *T. pratense* 'Susan Smith'
- 'Good Luck' MTho
§ - 'Green Ice' CBre EAEE EBee EHoe GBuc LRHS MBNS MTho NBir NCob NSti WAlt WCHb WFar WHal
- 'Harlequin' (v) EBee EHoe GGar MHer MTho WAlt WCot WFar WMoo WOut WPer
- 'Hiccups' (v) WAlt
- pale pink-flowered WAlt
- 'Purple Velvet' EBee
- 'Purpurascens' CArn CBre CEnt EAEE ECGP EPfP GGar GMac ILis LLWG LRHS MAvo MBNS MHer NEgg NSti SPoG WKif
§ - 'Purpurascens Quadrifolium' CMea CSpe CWan EBee ECha ECho EHoe EPau EWes LBMP MCot NEgg NGHP NMir NPer NPri SIng SPer SPlb WAlt WCHb WFar
- 'Quadrifolium' EDAr
- 'Saint Patrick' CNat
- 'Tetraphyllum Purpureum' see *T. repens* 'Purpurascens Quadrifolium'
- 'Wheatfen' CBow CBre CRow EBee EHoe GBuc NPer WCot
- 'William' CBow CBre EBee ECGP EGoo LEdu SPur WAlt WCot WFar
rubens Widely available
- 'Drama' SUsu
- 'Peach Pink' CSpe EBee EShb LHop MBel MMHG NCob SPhx SUsu WCot
- 'Red Feathers' CSpr LFur LRHS MWat MWea SGSe SMad WWEG

Triglochin (Juncaginaceae)

maritimum CRWN EBWF
palustre CRWN

Trigonella (Papilionaceae)

foenum-graecum CArn SIde

Trillidium see *Trillium*

Trillium ✿ (*Trilliaceae*)

albidum	CAby CWCL EBee EBrs ECho ELon EPot GBuc GGar GMaP LLHF NMen SSpi WCru WHal
angustipetalum	EBrs WCru
apetalon	GEdr LAma WWst
camschatcense	EBee EBrs GBuc GEdr LAma WCru
- from Japan	WWst
§ ***catesbyi***	CBro CLAP CWCL EBee EBrs ECho EHrv EPot GEdr GGar IBal LAma LLHF NHol NMyG WWst
cernuum	CLAP ECho GCra IBal LRHS NMyG WCru WSHC
chloropetalum	CBro EBee GBBs LRHS SSpi WFar WKif WPGP
§ - var. ***giganteum*** ♀H4	CLAP GBuc GEdr GKev GKir NMen SSpi WCru WWst
- var. ***rubrum***	see *T. chloropetalum* var. *giganteum*
- white-flowered	ECha IBal
cuneatum	Widely available
decipiens	WWst
decumbens	WWst
discolor	WWst
erectum ♀H4	CArn CBcs CBro CLAP EBee EBla EBrs ECho EHrv EPot GBBs GBuc GEdr GGar GKev GMaP GPoy LAma LRHS MBri MCot MTho NHol NMen SIng SRot SSpi WCru WFar WPnP
- f. ***albiflorum***	CFir CLAP EBee EBrs ECho EPot GBuc GEdr GGar LAma NHol NMyG SIng SMrm SSpi WCru WWst
- 'Beige'	GKev IBal
- f. ***luteum***	CBct EPfP WWst
- red-flowered	IBal
erectum* × *flexipes	CAby CLAP EBee ECho EHrv GBuc GEdr GGar MNrw NMen SSpi WWst
flexipes	CLAP EBee EBrs ECho EHrv EPot GAuc GEdr IBal LAma LRHS NMen SSpi WCru
- erect	MNrw NMen WWst
- 'Harvington Selection'	EBee LRHS MBri WWst
foetidissimum	WWst
govanianum	WWst
grandiflorum ♀H4	Widely available
- 'Flore Pleno' (d)	CLAP ECha ECho GBuc MTho SCnR SPhx WWst
- 'Kath's Dwarf'	GEdr
- f. ***roseum***	EBrs WWst
- 'Snowbunting' (d)	EBrs EWes GKir LRHS MMHG WThu WWst
kurabayashii	CAby CBct CFir CPLG CWCL EBee EBrs ECho ELon GBuc GGar MNrw SSpi WBVN WCot WCru WHal WPGP WWst
lancifolium	WWst
ludovicianum	WWst
luteum ♀H4	CBcs CBro CLAP EBee EBla EBrs ECho EHrv EPfP EPot GBBs GBuc GEdr GGar GKev GKir GMaP LAma LRHS MBri NHol NMen NMyG SSpi WBor WCAu WCru WFar WPnP WWst
maculatum	WWst
nivale	WWst
ovatum	CLAP CWCL EBee ELon GBuc GGar NMen SSpi WBVN WHal
- f. ***hibbersonii***	CBro GBuc GCra NMen
- 'Roy Elliott'	EPot
parviflorum	ECho GEdr NMen
pusillum	CLAP EBee ECho ELan EPot EWTr GAuc GBBs GEdr GGar IBal NHol NMen WAbe WWst
- var. ***virginianum***	CLAP EBrs LAma WCru
recurvatum	CBcs EBee EBrs ECho EHrv EPot GAbr GBBs GEdr GGar GKev IBal LAma NHol NMen NMyG WCru WFar WPnP WWst
reliquum	WWst
rivale ♀H3	CBro CElw CLAP ECho EHrv GBBs GBuc ITim LLHF NMen WAbe WFar WWst
- pink-flowered	GEdr NMen
- 'Purple Heart'	CLAP GEdr
rugelii	CAby CBro CLAP EBee EBrs ECho EHrv EWes GAuc GBuc GMaP LAma NMen SSpi WCru WWst
- Askival hybrids	EBee EBrs ECho GBuc MNrw NMen SSpi WWst
- 'Orchard Pink' **new**	MNrw WWst
rugelii* × *vaseyi	EBee EHrv EWes GBuc MNrw NMen SSpi WWst
sessile	EBee EBrs ECho GBBs GBuc GKev GKir IBal LAma LRHS NBir NMen NMyG SMrm WCAu WFar WKif WPnP WSHC WShi WWst
- 'Rubrum'	see *T. chloropetalum* var. *giganteum*
simile	CBro CLAP EBee EBrs ECho LLHF LRHS MNrw SSpi WWst
smallii	EBee WWst
stamineum	ECho GEdr GGar IBal WWst
stylosum	see *T. catesbyi*
sulcatum	CBro CLAP EBee EBrs ECho EHrv EPot GAuc GBuc GEdr GGar GMaP IBal LRHS MBri MNrw NMen SSpi WCru WFar WWst
tschonoskii	EBrs ECho GBuc GEdr LAma NMen
underwoodii	WWst
undulatum	EBee ECho GEdr GGar LAma NHol NMen NMyG WCru WWst
vaseyi	CBro CLAP EBee EBrs ECho EHrv EPot EWes GAuc GBBs GBuc GEdr GGar LAma LRHS MBri MNrw NMen SSpi WCru WWst
- prostrate	MNrw WWst
viride	EBla GBBs IBal NGby WFar WPnP
viridescens	EBee EBrs ECho EPot GEdr LAma NMyG WFar WWst

Triosteum (*Caprifoliaceae*)

erythrocarpum **new**	EBee
himalayanum	CLAP EBee GCal GKev
- BWJ 7907	WCru
- SDR 4406	GKev
pinnatifidum	CLAP CPom EBee GCal IMou

Tripetaleia (*Ericaceae*)

§ ***bracteata***	GAuc

Tripsacum (*Poaceae*)

dactyloides	EPPr

Tripterospermum (*Gentianaceae*)

B&SWJ 11297 from Malaysia **new**	WCru
* aff. ***chevalieri*** B&SWJ 8359	WCru
cordifolium B&SWJ 081	WCru
fasciculatum B&SWJ 7197	WCru

aff. ***hirticalyx*** B&SWJ 8264	WCru
japonicum	LLHF WAbe
- B&SWJ 1168	WCru
- B&SWJ 10876	WCru
lanceolatum B&SWJ 085	WCru
- RWJ 9918	WCru
taiwanense B&SWJ 1205	WCru
- RWJ 10115	WCru

Tripterygium (*Celastraceae*)

regelii	CBcs NLar WPGP
- B&SWJ 5453	WCru
- B&SWJ 10921	WCru
wilfordii	WCru

Trisetum (*Poaceae*)

flavescens	GFor

Tristagma (*Alliaceae*)

nivale	EBee
- f. ***nivale*** F&W 9612	WCot
- - F&W 10284	WCot

Triteleia (*Alliaceae*)

	'4U'	CMea EBee ECho
	bridgesii	ECho GAuc
	californica	see *Brodiaea californica*
§	'Corrina'	CAvo CFFs CMdw EBee EBrs ECho EPot MNrw SMeo
	grandiflora	ECho WCot
	hyacinthina	EBee EBrs ECho ERos WCot
	- white-flowered	CStu
	ixioides	ECho ERos
	- 'Splendens'	EBee EBrs ECho NMen WHil
	- 'Starlight'	CAvo CFFs CSpe CSsd CTri EBee EBrs ECho EPot ERCP SBch SPer SPhx WHil
§	***laxa***	ECho GAuc WBVN
	- NNS 98-541	WCot
	- 'Allure'	EBee EBrs ECho IPot
§	- 'Koningin Fabiola'	CMea CPrp CTri EBee EBrs ECho EPfP EPot IPot LAma LRHS MBri NBir SBch SEND SMeo SPer SPhx WBrE WCot
*	- var. ***nimia*** NNS 00-743	WCot
	- Queen Fabiola	see *T. laxa* 'Koningin Fabiola'
	lilacina	ECho
§	***peduncularis***	EBee EBrs ECho SPhx
	- NNS 95-746	WCot
	'Rudy'	CAvo CMea EBee ECho
	× ***tubergenii***	EBrs ECho
	uniflora	see *Ipheion uniflorum*

Trithrinax (*Arecaceae*)

brasiliensis	EAmu LPJP LPal SBig
campestris	CBrP EAmu ETod LMaj LPal SBig

Tritoma see *Kniphofia*

Tritonia (*Iridaceae*)

crocata ♀H2-3	CPou EBrs ECho MAvo SBch
- 'Baby Doll'	CDes CPrp EBee EBrs LEdu WHil WPGP
- 'Bridal Veil'	EBrs EPot
- 'Pink Sensation'	CDes EBee EBrs ECho EPot WHil WPGP
- 'Plymouth Pastel'	CDes WPrP
- 'Prince of Orange'	CPou WPGP
- 'Princess Beatrix'	CDes WPGP
- 'Serendipity'	CDes CPrp EBee EBrs WCon
- 'Tangerine'	CDes EBee EBrs EPot WPGP

§	***disticha*** subsp. ***rubrolucens***	Widely available
	dubia new	WCot
	hyalina	CPou
	laxifolia	EBee EBrs ECho EPot LEdu
	lineata	CDes CPou EBee EBrs ECho WPGP WPrP
	- 'Parvifolia'	EBee
	pallida	ECho SPlb
	rosea	see *T. disticha* subsp. ***rubrolucens***
	securigera	ECho
	squalida	ECho

Trochetiopsis (*Sterculiaceae*)

§	***ebenus***	WPGP
	melanoxylon misapplied	see *T. ebenus*

Trochocarpa (*Epacridaceae*)

clarkei	WThu
thymifolia	WAbe
- red-flowered	WAbe WThu

Trochodendron (*Trochodendraceae*)

aralioides	CBcs CDoC CHEx CMac CSam CTho CWib EBee ECrN EPfP ERas LRHS MBri MGos MMuc SAPC SArc SDix SLPl SLon SMad SReu SSpi SSta WCot WDin WPGP WSHC
- B&SWJ 1651 from Taiwan	WCru
- B&SWJ 6727 from Taiwan	WCru

Trollius (*Ranunculaceae*)

	ACE 1187	GEdr
	SDR 4816	GKev
	acaulis	ECho EWes MTho WFar WPat
	asiaticus	EBee ECho GBuc GKev LRHS WFar
	aff. ***buddae*** BWJ 7958	WCru
§	***chinensis***	ECha GCal GKev GKir NChi SRms SWat
	- 'Golden Queen' ♀H4	Widely available
	× ***cultorum*** new	MAvo
	- 'Alabaster'	Widely available
	- 'Baudirektor Linne'	ECtt MRav NGdn WFar
	- Bressingham hybrids	LRHS WFar
	- 'Bressingham Sunshine' new	LRHS
	- 'Byrne's Giant'	EBee WFar WPnP
	- 'Canary Bird'	ELan EPfP GCal NGdn SRms WSpi
	- 'Cheddar'	EBee EBla ECtt EPPr EPfP GCal GKir MBNS MBri MCCP MMHG MRav NBPC NBro NEgg NLar NOrc NPri NPro SHar SMrm WFar WSpi WWEG
	- 'Commander-in-chief'	CDes LRHS WFar WPGP WPnP
	- 'Earliest of All'	CPrp CSam EBee EKen GKir NGby NGdn SPer SRms WFar WSHC WWEG
	- 'Etna'	EBee WFar WPnP WWEG
§	- 'Feuertroll'	CMea CPrp EBee ECha ECtt GKir LBMP LRHS MRav MSCN NBPC NCob NEgg NPro SPoG SUsu WFar
	- Fireglobe	see *T.* × *cultorum* 'Feuertroll'
	- 'Frühlingsbote' new	EBee
	- 'Golden Cup'	NBir NGdn
	- 'Golden Monarch'	WFar
	- 'Goldquelle' ♀H4	EBee EHon GKir
	- 'Goliath'	EWes NCob SMad WFar
	- 'Helios'	CSam
	- 'Lemon Queen'	CWat EBee ECtt EHrv EPfP EWTr GMaP LBMP LPBA LRHS MBri MNFA MRav NBPC NBlu SPer SWat WCAu WFar WSpi

- 'Meteor'	WFar
- new hybrids	WFar
- 'Orange Crest'	EBee GCal GKir WFar WHal WWEG
- 'Orange Globe'	EBee GAbr NBPC NCob NGby SMrm WFar
- 'Orange Glow'	SMad
- 'Orange Princess' ♀H4	CElw CWat EBee EPfP GKir GMaP LRHS MCCP NBro NLar NPri SPer SRms
- 'Orange Queen'	SWvt
- 'Prichard's Giant'	CMHG EBee EBla ECtt ELan NBro NEgg NGby WFar WSpi WWEG
§ - 'Superbus' ♀H4	EBee ECho ELan EPfP GKir GMaP LAst LRHS MBNS NGdn SPer WBrE WFar WMoo
- 'T. Smith'	EBee NBro NGby WFar
* - 'Taleggio'	SPhx
- 'Yellow Beauty'	WFar
europaeus	Widely available
- 'Superbus'	see *T.* × *cultorum* 'Superbus'
farreri new	GKev
hondoensis	EBee GCal LLHF LRHS NBur NLar NPro
ircuticus	EBee GKev
laxus	EWes
- 'Albiflorus'	NWCA
ledebourii misapplied	see *T. chinensis*
pumilus	EBee ECha ECho ELan GCal GGar GKir GMaP LRHS NWCA SBch SGSe SPer WAbe WClo WFar WPer
- ACE 1818	GBuc
- 'Wargrave'	EBee
ranunculoides	GKev
riederianus	LRHS
stenopetalus	CDes EBee EWes GKir MBri MNrw MRav NMyG WFar WPGP
vaginatus	GKev
yunnanensis	EBee GBuc GKev WFar WPnP
- SDR 4713	GKev
- f. ***eupetalus*** BWJ 7614	WCru
- orange-flowered	EBee GKev

Tropaeolum ✿ (*Tropaeolaceae*)

azureum	CCCN EPot MPoH
beuthii	MPoH
brachyceras	CCCN EBee ECho MPoH WCot
ciliatum ♀H1	CAvo CBro CCCN CFir CGHE CSam CSpr CStu EBrs ECho ELan EPot GCal MPoH MTho NBid WCot WCru WFar WHer WPGP
Gleam Series	MNHC
hookerianum subsp. ***austropurpureum***	ERos MPoH
- subsp. ***hookerianum*** F&W 9467	WPGP
incisum	CCCN EBee MPoH
majus Alaska Series (v) ♀H3	CPrp MNHC SBch SEND SIde WJek
- 'Apricot Twist' new	GBee
- 'Crimson Beauty'	CSpe
§ - 'Darjeeling Double' (d) ♀H4	GBee
- 'Darjeeling Gold'	see *T. majus* 'Darjeeling Double'
- 'Empress of India'	CPrp NBlu WJek
- 'Hermine Grashoff' (d) ♀H2-3	CSWP CSpe GBee GCal NPer
- 'Indian Ruby'	WCHb
- 'Margaret Long' (d)	CSpe GCal
* - 'Peaches and Cream'	CPrp WJek
- 'Red Wonder'	CCCN CSWP CSpe EPfP LSou NPri SMrm
- Tom Thumb mixed	MNHC WJek
pentaphyllum	CAvo CSpe ECho ELan EWes GCal GGar LFur LLHF MTho WCot
peregrinum	CSpe SBch
polyphyllum	CCCN EBee EPfP GBuc MAvo NBir SCnR WAbe WPGP
sessilifolium	EBee ECho
speciosum ♀H4	Widely available
sylvestre	EWld NVic
tricolor ♀H1	CAvo CCCN EBee EBrs ECho ELan EPot GCal GGar MAsh MTho WBor
tuberosum	CEnd EBrs ECho GPoy IHer MPoH
- var. ***lineamaculatum*** 'Ken Aslet' ♀H3	CBcs CBro CCCN CSpe EBee EBrs ECha ECho ELan EOHP EPfP EPot ERos GAbr GGar IFro IHer LAma LRHS MTho NPri SPoG WCom WCru WFar WPGP

Trymalium (*Rhamnaceae*)

ledifolium new	CTrC

Tsuga ✿ (*Pinaceae*)

canadensis	CDul EHul MBar NBlu NWea WDin WEve WMou
- 'Abbott's Dwarf'	CKen EOrn MGos NHol
§ - 'Abbott's Pygmy'	CKen
- 'Albospica' (v)	EOrn WFar WGor
- 'Arnold Gold Weeper'	CKen
- 'Aurea' (v)	MBar NHol NLar WEve
- 'Bacon Cristate'	CKen
- 'Baldwin Dwarf Pyramid'	MBar
- 'Beehive'	ECho WGor
- 'Bennett'	MBar
- 'Betty Rose' (v)	CKen
- 'Brandley'	CKen
§ - 'Branklyn'	CKen
- 'Cappy's Choice'	CKen
- 'Cinnamonea'	CDoC CKen
- 'Coffin'	CKen
- 'Cole's Prostrate'	CKen EOrn MAsh MBar NHol NLar SLim
- 'Coryhill'	ECho SCoo
- 'Creamey' (v)	CKen
- 'Curley'	CKen
- 'Curtis Ideal'	CKen
- 'Essex'	NHol NLar
* - 'Everitt's Dense Leaf'	CKen
- 'Everitt's Golden'	CKen
- 'Fantana'	ECho EHul LBee LRHS MAsh MBar NHol NLar SCoo SLim WEve
- 'Gentsch White' (v)	MGos NLar
- 'Gracilis'	WThu
- 'Horsford'	CKen NLar
- 'Horstmann' No 1	CKen
- 'Hussii'	CKen NHol NLar
- 'Jacqueline Verkade'	CKen NLar
- 'Jeddeloh' ♀H4	CDoC ECho EHul EOrn EPla IFFs LRHS MAsh MBar MGos NEgg NHol SCoo SLim SPoG WDin WEve
- 'Jervis'	CKen NHol NLar
- 'Julianne'	CKen
- 'Kingsville Spreader'	CKen
- 'Little Joe'	CKen
- 'Little Snow'	CKen
I - 'Lutea'	CKen
- 'Many Cones'	CKen
- 'Minima'	CKen
- 'Minuta'	CDoC CKen ECho EHul EOrn LBee MBar MGos NLar SCoo SPoG WGor
- 'Moon Frost' new	NLar
- 'Nana'	EHul WDin
- 'Palomino'	CKen NLar
- 'Pendula' ♀H4	CDoC CKen ECho EHul EOrn EPfP LRHS MAsh MBar SLim WDin WEve WFar

- 'Pincushion'	CKen
- 'Prostrata'	see *T. canadensis* 'Branklyn'
- 'Pygmaea'	see *T. canadensis* 'Abbott's Pygmy'
- 'Rugg's Washington Dwarf'	CKen SCoo
- 'Snowflake'	CKen MGos
- 'Stewart's Gem'	CKen
- 'Verkade Petite'	CKen
- 'Verkade Recurved'	CKen MBar NLar
- 'Von Helms' Dwarf'	CKen
- 'Warnham'	CKen ECho EOrn LBee LRHS MAsh SCoo
caroliniana 'La Bar Weeping'	CKen NLar
diversifolia 'Gotelli'	CKen
heterophylla ♀H4	CBcs CDoC CDul CLnd EPfP IFFs LBuc LRHS MBar NWea SPer STre WDin WEve
- 'Iron Springs'	CKen EOrn
- 'Laursen's Column'	CKen
- 'Thorsens Weeping'	CKen
menziesii (Mirb.) hort.	see *Pseudotsuga menziesii*
mertensiana	CDul
- 'Blue Star'	CKen NLar
- 'Elizabeth'	CDoC CKen
- 'Glauca'	CKen NLar
I - 'Glauca Nana'	CKen
I - 'Horstmann'	CKen
- 'Quartz Mountain'	CKen
sieboldii 'Baldwin'	CKen
- 'Green Ball'	CKen NLar
- 'Honeywell Estate'	CKen
- 'Nana'	CKen

Tsusiophyllum (*Ericaceae*)

tanakae	see *Rhododendron tsusiophyllum*

Tuberaria (*Cistaceae*)

lignosa	WAbe

Tulbaghia ✿ (*Alliaceae*)

acutiloba	CPen ERos MHom NHoy WPrP
'African Moon' **new**	NHoy
alliacea	CAvo EBla ECho ERos EShb MHom NHoy WCot
alliacea × ***violacea***	ECho
capensis	CPou EBee ERea ERos LPio MHom NBir NHoy WCot
cepacea × ***natalensis***	ERos
cernua CD&R 199	CDes WPrP
- hybrid	NHoy WPrP
cernua × ***violacea***	WPrP
§ ***coddii***	CDes EBee MHom NHoy WCot WPrP
coddii × ***violacea***	NHoy WPrP
cominsii	CPLG EDif ERea SBch SCnR WCom
- 'Harry Hay's Pink' **new**	NHoy
cominsii × ***violacea***	CAvo CPLG EBee ERos MHom NHoy WPrP
'Cosmic'	CPen CPou NHoy WPrP
'Crystal' **new**	NHoy
'Dreaming Spires' **new**	NHoy
dregeana	ERos NHoy WCot
'Elaine Ann' **new**	NHoy
'Enigma' **new**	NHoy
'Fairy Snow' **new**	CDes
'Fairy Star'	CDes EBee ERos EShb NHoy WCot WOut WPGP WPrP
fragrans	see *T. simmleri*
- 'Alba'	EBrs ELan EWTr
galpinii	CPen ERos NHoy NWCA WPrP
'Grey Dawn' **new**	NHoy
'Hazel'	CPen NHoy WPrP
'Janet' **new**	NHoy
'John May's Special'	CAby CDes CKno EBee EShb MHom NHoy SMrm SUsu WCot WPGP WPrP
leucantha	EBee ERos MHom NHoy NWCA WPrP
- H&B 11996	CDes WPrP
- from Sentinel Park, South Africa	WPrP
maritima	see *T. violacea* var. *maritima*
Marwood seedling	EBee MHom NHoy
montana	CDes CStu EBee NHoy WCot WPGP WPrP
natalensis	CPou CPrp EBee ECho NHoy WHoo
- B&V 421	CDes
- - clone 1 white-flowered	NHoy WPrP
- - clone 2 pink-flowered	NHoy WPrP
- CD&R 84	NHoy WPrP
- pink-flowered	ECho ERos MHom NHoy WPrP
natalensis × ***verdoorniae***	WPrP
natalensis × ***verdoorniae*** VOS 1966	WPrP
natalensis × ***violacea***	NHoy NWCA
poetica	see *T. coddii*
'Purple Eyes' **new**	WPrP
'Rainbow' **new**	NHoy
§ ***simmleri***	CBgR CPou EBee EBla EBrs ECho EHrv EPot EPyc ERea ERos EShb EWes GGar LAma LEdu LPio NHoy WCot
- 'Cheryl Renshaw'	CDes
- pink-flowered	CPen WPGP
- 'Snow Queen' **new**	CPrp
- white-flowered	CPen CPou EPot NHoy
'Snowball' **new**	NHoy
'Suzanne' **new**	NHoy
verdoorniae	ERos NHoy
violacea	Widely available
* - 'Alba'	EBee EBla EPPr ERos GCal LPio NHoy NLAp SMrm SWat WFar WHoo WTin
- 'Dissect White'	NHoy WPrP
I - 'Fine Form'	NHoy
* - ***grandiflora***	CAvo
- 'John Rider'	NHoy NWCA WPer
- 'Lowan' **new**	NWCA
* - var. ***maritima***	CPen CPrp EDif ERos EShb GGar MHom NBid NHoy NWCA SMrm WCot WPrP
- var. ***obtusa***	NHoy WPrP
- 'Pallida'	CAvo CBro CDes CMdw CPne CPou ECho LEdu LPio NHoy NWCA WPGP WPrP
- 'Pearl'	CPou NHoy WPrP
- 'Peppermint Garlic'	CDes
- RBGE form	MHom
- var. ***robustior***	CPou EBee EBla EWes NHoy WPrP
§ - 'Silver Lace' (v)	Widely available
- 'Variegata'	see *T. violacea* 'Silver Lace'
- var. ***violacea***	NHoy WPrP
- 'White Goddess'	CPou
- 'White Star'	EBee

Tulipa ✿ (*Liliaceae*)

'Abba' (2)	LRHS
'Absalon' (9)	LAma
'Abu Hassan' (3)	CAvo CFFs CMea EBrs ERCP LAma MBri SPhx

	Name	Suppliers
	acuminata (15)	CAvo CBro CFFs CHid EBrs ECho ERCP LAma LRHS MMHG NMin SPhx
	'Ad Rem' (4)	MBri
	'Addis' (14) ♀H4	LAma
	'African Queen' (3)	LAma
	agenensis	EBrs
	aitchisonii	see *T. clusiana*
	'Aladdin' (6)	LAma LRHS
	'Aladdin's Record' (6)	EBrs
	albertii (15)	EBrs ECho LAma NMin WWst
	aleppensis (15)	LRHS
	'Alfred Cortot' (12) ♀H4	LAma
	'Ali Baba' (14) ♀H4	LRHS
	'Allegretto' (11)	LRHS MBri
	altaica (15) ♀H4	EBrs ECho EPot LAma SBch
	amabilis	see *T. hoogiana*
	'Ancilla' (12) ♀H4	CBro LAma
	'Angélique' (11) ♀H4	CAvo CFFs CMea EBrs EPfP ERCP EWal LAma LRHS NBir SMeo SPer SPhx
	'Angel's Dream' **new**	LRHS
	'Annie Schilder' (3)	ERCP LRHS
	'Antoinette'PBR (5)	LRHS SPer
	'Apeldoorn' (4)	EBrs EGxp EWal LAma LRHS MBri
	'Apeldoorn's Elite' (4) ♀H4	EWal LAma LRHS MBri
	'Apricot Beauty' (1) ♀H4	CHid EBrs EPfP ERCP EWal LAma LRHS MBri MCot NBir SPer SPhx
	'Apricot Jewel'	see *T. linifolia* (Batalinii Group) 'Apricot Jewel'
	'Apricot Parrot' (10) ♀H4	CAvo CFFs EPfP LAma MBri SPer
	'Arabian Mystery' (3)	CAvo CFFs EBrs ERCP LAma LRHS SPhx
	'Artist' (8) ♀H4	EBrs ERCP LAma
	'Attila' (3)	EBrs LAma
	aucheriana (15) ♀H4	CBro EBrs ECho EPot ERos LAma LLHF NMin
	'Aurea'	see *T. greigii* 'Aurea'
	australis (15)	ECho
	aximensis (15)	EBrs ECho
	'Bacchus' (7)	LAma
	bakeri	see *T. saxatilis* Bakeri Group
	'Ballade' (6) ♀H4	CAvo CFFs EBrs ERCP LAma
	'Ballerina' (6) ♀H4	CAvo CBro CFFs CMea EBrs ECho EPfP ERCP LAma LRHS MBri SMeo SPer SPhx
	'Banja Luka' (4)	EBrs
	'Barcelona' (3) ♀H4 **new**	ERCP
	batalinii	see *T. linifolia* Batalinii Group
	'Beauty of Apeldoorn' (4)	LAma LRHS MBri
	'Beauty Queen' (1)	EBrs
	'Belicia' (2) **new**	LAma
	'Bellflower' (7)	LAma
	'Bernadette' (15) **new**	LRHS
	biebersteiniana (15)	EBrs ECho NMin
§	***biflora*** (15)	CBro CGrW EBrs ECho EPot GKev LAma LLHF LRHS
	bifloriformis (15)	EBrs ECho WWst
I	- 'Maxima' (15)	EBrs ECho NMin
	- 'Starlight' (15)	EBrs ECho IPot LRHS WWst
	'Big Chief' (4) ♀H4	LAma
	'Big Smile' (5)	LRHS
	'Bird of Paradise' (10)	EBrs
	'Black Hero' (11)	CAvo CFFs EBrs ERCP LAma LRHS MCot SMeo SPer SPhx
	'Black Horse' (5)	LAma
	'Black Jewel' (7)	ERCP
	'Black Parrot' (10) ♀H4	CAvo CBro CFFs CHid EBrs EPfP ERCP LAma LRHS MBri MCot SMeo SPer
	'Black Stallion' (11)	LAma
	'Blenda' (3)	EBrs
	'Bleu Aimable' (5)	CAvo CFFs EBrs ERCP
	'Blue Diamond' (11)	CAvo CFFs ERCP LRHS SPer
	'Blue Heron' (7) ♀H4	CAvo CFFs EBrs ERCP LAma MCot
	'Blue Parrot' (10)	CAvo CFFs EBrs EPfP ERCP EWal LAma LRHS
	'Blue Ribbon' (3)	CAvo CFFs LRHS
	Blueberry Ripple	see *T.* 'Zurel'
	'Boutade' (14)	NPer
	'Bridal Bouquet' **new**	LRHS
	'Bridesmaid' (5)	LAma
	'Burgundy' (6)	EBrs ERCP LAma LRHS SPhx
	'Burgundy Lace' (7)	EBrs LAma
	'Café Noir' (5)	ERCP LAma
	'Cairo'PBR	ERCP LRHS
	'Calgary' (3) ♀H4 **new**	LRHS
	'Calibra' (7)	LRHS
	'Calypso' (14) ♀H4	EBrs
	'Canasta' (7) **new**	LRHS
	'Candela' (13) ♀H4	LAma LRHS
	'Candy Club' (5)	EBrs LAma
	'Candy Prince'PBR **new**	LRHS
	'Cantata' (13)	CBro LAma
	'Cape Cod' (14)	EPfP LAma LRHS
	'Cardinal Mindszenty' (2)	ERCP
	carinata (15)	ECho LRHS
	'Carnaval de Nice' (11/v) ♀H4	CAvo CBro CFFs EBrs ERCP LAma LRHS MBri SPer
	'Carrousel' (7)	EBrs
	'Casablanca' (11)	CMea EBrs
	'Cassini' (3)	LAma
§	***celsiana*** (15)	EBrs ECho LAma WWst
	'China Pink' (6) ♀H4	CAvo CBro CFFs CMea EBrs EPfP ERCP LAma LRHS MBri SPhx
	'China Town' (8) ♀H4	EBrs ERCP LAma LRHS MBri
	'Christmas Marvel' (1)	EBrs LAma
	chrysantha Boiss. ex Baker	see *T. montana*
	'Claudia' (6)	EPfP LRHS
	'Cloud Nine' (5)	ECho LRHS
§	***clusiana*** (15)	CBro EBrs ECho ERCP IHer LAma MSSP NMin SPhx WHer
	- f. ***cashmeriana*** **new**	SPhx
	- var. ***chrysantha*** (15) ♀H4	CAvo CFFs CGrW CMea EBrs ECho LAma LRHS SBch SPhx WHoo WShi
	- - 'Tubergen's Gem' (15)	EBrs ECho EPot LAma LRHS MBri SPhx
	- 'Cynthia' (15) ♀H4	EBrs ECho EPot ERCP LAma LRHS MSSP NMin SPhx
	- 'Sheila' (15)	EBrs ECho NMin SPhx
§	- var. ***stellata*** (15)	ECho SPhx
	'Colour Spectacle'PBR (5)	LSou
	'Columbine' (5)	ECho LAma
	'Compostella' (14)	LRHS
	'Concerto' (13)	CBro EBrs MBri NPer
	'Corona' (12)	EBrs ECho
	'Couleur Cardinal' (3)	CBro EBrs LAma SMeo
	'Creme Upstar' (11)	LRHS
	cretica (15)	EBrs ECho EPot NMin WWst
	'Cum Laude' (5) **new**	LRHS
	'Cummins' (7)	ERCP
	'Curly Sue' (7)	CAvo CFFs ERCP LRHS
	'Czaar Peter' ♀H4	CAvo CFFs LRHS MBri NPer
	'Dancing Show' (8)	CAvo CFFs LAma
	dasystemon (15)	EBrs ECho LAma LLHF SBch
	dasystemonoides (15)	EBrs ECho WWst
	'Davenport' (7)	ERCP
	'David Teniers' (2)	ERCP
	'Daydream' (4) ♀H4	EGxp SPer
	'Daylight' (12)	EBrs
	'Deirdre' (8)	ERCP LRHS
	'Denise' (3) **new**	LRHS
	didieri misapplied	see *T. passeriniana*
	'Doll's Minuet' (8)	ERCP LAma SPer

'Don Quichotte' (3) ♀H4	MBri
'Donna Bella' (14) ♀H4	EPfP
'Dordogne' (5)	LRHS
'Double Dazzle' (2) **new**	LRHS
'Double Price' (2)	ERCP
'Douglas Bader' (5)	CAvo CFFs CMea
'Dreamboat' (14)	MBri
'Dreaming Maid' (3)	EGxp LAma LRHS
'Dreamland' (5) ♀H4	MBri
'Duc van Tol' (1)	IHer IPot
'Duc van Tol Aurora'	IHer
'Duc van Tol Red and Yellow' (I)	WHer
'Duc van Tol Rose' (1)	IHer LAma
'Duc van Tol Salmon' (1)	LAma
'Early Harvest' (12) ♀H4	CAvo CFFs
'Early Star' (14) ♀H4 **new**	CMea
'Easter Surprise' (14) ♀H4	MBri
edulis (15)	ECho
eichleri	see *T. undulatifolia*
'Electra' (5)	LAma MBri
'Elegans Alba' (6) **new**	LAma
'Elegant Lady' (6)	CAvo CFFs EBrs EPfP LAma LRHS SPer
'Esperanto' (8/v) ♀H4	LAma
'Estella Rijnveld' (10)	EBrs EGxp LAma LRHS MBri
'Esther' (5)	ERCP
'Eternal Flame' (2)	LAma
'Evita'PBR **new**	LRHS
'Exotic Emperor'	LAma
'Fancy Frills' (7) ♀H4	EBrs ERCP LAma LRHS
'Fantasy' (10) ♀H4	LAma LRHS
'Fashion' (12)	EPfP
'Fats Domino' (3)	EBrs
ferganica (15)	EBrs ECho EPot LAma NMin
* 'Finola' (11)	ERCP
'Fire Queen' (3) ♀H4	EBrs ERCP LAma
'First Impression' (14)	LRHS
'Flair' (1)	LAma
'Flaming Parrot' (10)	CAvo CFFs EBrs ERCP LAma LRHS MBri
I 'Flaming Purissima' (13)	CAvo CFFs LRHS
'Flaming Springgreen' (8) **new**	ERCP LRHS
'Flashback' (10) **new**	LRHS
'Florosa' (8)	ERCP
'Flowerdale' (14)	CAvo CFFs EBrs
'Foxtrot'PBR (2) **new**	ERCP
'Fringed Beauty' (7) ♀H4	ERCP
'Fritz Kreisler' (12)	LAma
'Frosta' (7)	ERCP
'Fulgens' (6)	EBrs
'Gabriella' (3)	LRHS
'Garden Party' (3) ♀H4	LAma
'Gavota' (3)	CAvo CBro CFFs EBrs EGxp EPfP ERCP LAma LRHS SPer
'Gemma' (10) **new**	LAma
'Generaal de Wet' (1)	EBrs IHer LAma MBri
'Georgette' (5)	LAma LRHS LSou MBri
'Gerbrand Kieft' (11) ♀H4	EBrs ERCP
'Giuseppe Verdi' (12)	EWal LAma MBri
'Glück' (12) ♀H4	ECho EWal LRHS
'Golden Apeldoorn' (4)	EWal LAma LRHS MBri SPer
'Golden Artist' (8)	EBrs EPfP LAma LRHS
'Golden Emperor' (13)	EBrs EPfP LAma LRHS SPer
'Golden Melody' (3)	EBrs LRHS MCot
'Golden Oxford' (4)	LAma
'Golden Parade' (4)	LAma
'Goudstuk' (12)	LAma
'Green Wave' (10)	CHid ERCP LAma LRHS
§ ***greigii*** 'Aurea' (14)	WWst
grengiolensis (15)	EBrs ECho LAma WWst
'Groenland' (8)	CAvo CBro CFFs ERCP LAma LRHS MBri MCot SPer
'Gudoshnik' (4)	LAma
hageri (15)	EBrs ECho LAma MBri
- 'Splendens' (15)	EBrs ECho EPot LAma
'Hamilton' (7) ♀H4	LAma
'Hans Dietrich Genscher' (3)	EBrs
'Hans Mayer' (4)	LRHS
'Happy Family' (3)	LAma LRHS
'Happy Generation' (3)	LAma MBri
'Happy Hour' (7)	ERCP
'Harry's Memory' (3) **new**	LRHS
'Havran' (5)	CAvo CFFs ERCP LAma
'Heart's Delight' (12)	CBro EBrs ECho EWal LAma MBri SBch
'Helmar' (3)	CAvo CFFs
'Hemisphere' (3) **new**	ERCP
'Hermitage' (3)	ERCP LAma
heweri (15)	EBrs ECho NMin
'Hillstar' (7) **new**	LRHS
'Holland Chic' **new**	LRHS
'Hollandia' (3)	LRHS
'Hollywood' (8)	LAma
§ ***hoogiana*** (15)	EBrs ECho WWst
§ ***humilis*** (15)	CBro CGrW ECho EWTr GKev LAma LRHS MBri SPhx WShi
- 'China Carol' (15)	ECho ERCP
- 'China Royal' (15) **new**	LRHS
- 'Eastern Spice' (15)	ECho NMin
- 'Eastern Star' (15)	EBrs ECho GKev LAma LRHS MBri SPhx
§ - 'Lilliput' (15)	CBro EBrs ECho EPot GKev LRHS NMin SPhx
- 'Magenta Queen' (15)	EBrs ECho LRHS SPhx
- 'Odalisque' (15)	EBrs ECho EPot ERCP GGar GKev LAma LRHS NMin SPhx
- 'Pegasus' (15)	EBrs NMin
- 'Persian Pearl' (15)	EBrs ECho EPfP EPot ERCP GKev LAma LRHS MBri NMin SBch SPer SPhx
* - 'Pink Charm' (15)	EBrs
§ - var. ***pulchella***	LRHS
- - Albocaerulea Oculata Group (15)	CMea CPou CSsd EBrs ECho EPot ERCP LAma LLHF LRHS NMin SPhx WWst
- 'Rosea' (15)	EBrs NMin
§ - Violacea Group (15)	CMea ECho EWal LAma MBri
- - black base (15)	CBro EBrs ECho EPot ERCP GKev LRHS MBri NMin
- - yellow base (15)	EBrs ECho EPot GKev LAma LRHS
- 'Zephyr' (15)	NMin
'Humming Bird' (8)	LAma
'Ile de France' (5)	LAma SPer
iliensis (15)	EBrs ECho EPot NMin WWst
'India' (3) **new**	ERCP
ingens (15)	EBrs ECho LAma SPhx WWst
'Insulinde' (9)	LAma
'Inzell' (3)	EBrs EPfP LAma
'Ivory Floradale' (4) ♀H4	EBrs LAma
'Jackpot' (3)	ERCP LRHS
'Jazz' (6) **new**	ERCP LRHS
'Jeantine' (12) ♀H4	EPfP
'Jewel of Spring' (4) ♀H4	LAma
'Joffre' (1)	MBri
'Johann Strauss' (12)	CBro ECho EWal LAma LRHS MBri
'John Peel' (3) **new**	LRHS
'Juan' (13) ♀H4	LRHS MBri
'Judith Leyster' (3) **new**	LRHS
julia (15)	ECho NMin
'Karel Doorman' (10)	LAma

	Name	Suppliers
	kaufmanniana (12)	CAvo CFFs EBrs ECho EPot
	- 'Ugam'	LRHS
§	'Kees Nelis' (3)	LRHS MBri
	'Keizerskroon' (1) ♀H4	IHer LAma
	kolpakowskiana (15) ♀H4	EBrs ECho EPfP EPot ERCP LAma LRHS MBri SBch
	kurdica (15)	EBrs ECho LAma LRHS WWst
	- purple-flowered (15)	ECho WWst
	- red-flowered (15)	WWst
	'La Courtine' (5)	LRHS
	'Lac van Rijn' (1)	IHer IPot LAma
*	'Lady Diana' (14)	MBri
	'Lady Jane' (15)	CAvo CBro CFFs EBrs ECho ERCP MSSP NMin SPer SPhx
	'Lady Night' (3) **new**	LRHS
	'Lambada' (7) ♀H4	LRHS
	lanata (15)	EBrs ECho NMin
	'Latvian Gold' (15)	EBrs ECho NMin
	'Leen van der Mark' (3)	LAma LRHS MBri
	'Libretto Parrot' (10)	LAma
	'Lilac Perfection' (11)	EBrs ERCP MBri
	'Lilac Wonder'	see *T. saxatilis* (Bakeri Group) 'Lilac Wonder'
	'Lilliput'	see *T. humilis* 'Lilliput'
	'Lilyrosa' (6)	EBrs
	linifolia (15) ♀H4	CAvo CFFs EBrs ECho EPfP EPot LAma LRHS MBri SBch SPhx WShi
§	- Batalinii Group (15) ♀H4	CBro EBrs ECho LAma MBri SPhx
§	- - 'Apricot Jewel' (15)	CBro CGrW EBrs ECho EPot GKev
	- - 'Bright Gem' (15) ♀H4	CAvo CBro CSam EBrs ECho EPot GKev LAma LRHS MBri SBch SPer SPhx
	- - 'Bronze Charm' (15)	CAvo CBro CFFs CMea EBrs ECho EPot IPot LAma MBri NMin SPhx
	- - 'Honky Tonk' (15)	CMea EBrs ECho NMin SPhx
	- - 'Red Gem' (15)	EBrs ECho GKev LAma SPhx
	- - 'Red Hunter' (15) ♀H4	ECho SPer
	- - 'Red Jewel' (15)	ECho
	- - 'Yellow Jewel' (15)	EBrs ECho GKev LAma SPhx
§	- Maximowiczii Group (15)	CBro EBrs ECho EPot LAma
	'Lipgloss' (3)	LAma
	'Little Beauty' (15) ♀H4	CAvo CBro CFFs CMea CSam EBrs ECho GGar GKev LAma LRHS MBri SBch WHoo
	'Little Princess' (15)	CAvo CBro CFFs CMea CSam EBrs ECho EPfP GGar LAma LRHS
	'Lovely Surprise' (14)	EBrs
	'Lucky Strike' (3)	MBri
	'Mabel' (9)	LAma
§	'Madame Lefeber' (13)	EBrs EWal LRHS MBri SPhx
	'Madonna' (10) **new**	LRHS
	'Magier' (5)	MBri
	'Maja' (7)	CAvo CFFs MBri
	'March of Time' (14)	MBri
	'Mariette' (6)	CBro LAma LRHS MBri
	'Marilyn' (6)	CAvo EBrs ERCP LAma LRHS SPhx
	marjolletii (15)	CAvo CBro CFFs EBrs ECho ERos LAma SPhx
	'Maroon' **new**	ERCP
	'Mary Ann' (14)	EBrs LAma
	'Maureen' (5) ♀H4	EBrs EGxp LAma LRHS
	mauritiana (15)	ECho
	- 'Cindy' (15)	EBrs ECho
	maximowiczii	see *T. linifolia* Maximowiczii Group
	'Maytime' (6)	CAvo CFFs LAma LRHS MBri
	'Maywonder' (11) ♀H4	MBri
	'Menton' (5)	EBrs LAma LRHS
	'Mickey Mouse' (1)	MBri
	'Miss Holland' (3)	MBri
	'Mistress' (3) **new**	LRHS
	'Mona Lisa' (6)	EBrs LAma LRHS
	'Monsella' (2)	EBrs LRHS
§	***montana*** (15)	EBrs ECho EPfP EPot LAma LRHS NMin
	- yellow-flowered	EBrs ECho WWst
	'Monte Carlo' (2) ♀H4	EWal LAma LRHS MBri
	'Montreux' (2)	ECho LAma
	'Moonshine' (6)	LRHS
	'Mount Tacoma' (11)	CBro EBrs EPfP ERCP EWal LAma LRHS MBri SPer SPhx
	'Mr Van der Hoef' (2)	LAma MBri
	'Muriel' (10) **new**	ERCP
	'My Support' (14) **new**	LRHS
	'Negrita' (3)	EGxp ERCP LAma LRHS MBri MCot SPer
	neustruevae (15)	CBro EBrs ECho EPot NMin SPhx
	'New Design' (3/v)	EBrs ERCP EWal LAma MBri SPer
	'New Look' (7)	EBrs
	'Ollioules' (4) ♀H4	EBrs LRHS
	'Orange Bouquet' (3) ♀H4	LAma LRHS MBri
	'Orange Breeze' (13)	LRHS
	'Orange Elite' (14)	LRHS MBri
	'Orange Emperor' (13) ♀H4	CAvo CFFs LAma MBri MCot SPer SPhx
	'Orange Favourite' (10)	CAvo CFFs LAma
	'Orange Princess' (11) ♀H4	ERCP LRHS
	'Orange Triumph' (11)	MBri
	'Oranje Nassau' (2) ♀H4	LAma MBri
	'Oratorio' (14) ♀H4	LRHS MBri
	orithyioides	ECho LRHS NMin
	orphanidea (15)	CGrW EBrs ECho LAma LRHS NMin SCnR SPhx
	- 'Flava' (15)	EBrs ECho EPot ERCP LAma SPhx
§	- Whittallii Group (15) ♀H4	CAvo CFFs EBrs ECho ERCP IPot LAma LRHS MMHG NMin SPhx
	ostrowskiana (15)	EBrs ECho LAma NMin WWst
	'Oxford' (4) ♀H4	LAma LRHS
	'Oxford's Elite' (4)	LAma LRHS
	'Paeony Gold' (11)	IPot
	'Page Polka' (3)	EBrs LRHS MBri
	'Pandour' (14)	MBri
	'Papillon' (9)	LAma
	'Parade' (4) ♀H4	MBri
§	***passeriniana*** (15)	EBrs ECho WWst
	'Passionale' (3)	EGxp EPfP LRHS
	patens	ECho
	'Paul Scherer' (3)	ERCP
	'Peach Blossom' (2)	CMea EBrs ERCP LAma MBri SPer
*	'Peaches and Cream'	SPer
	'Peppermintstick' (15) **new**	ERCP LRHS SPhx
	'Perestroyka' (5)	MBri
	persica	see *T. celsiana*
	'Philippe de Comines' (5)	LAma
	'Picture' (5) ♀H4	EBrs ERCP LAma
	'Pieter de Leur' (6)	EPfP LAma MBri SPer
	'Pimpernel' (8/v)	LAma LRHS
	'Pink Impression' (4) ♀H4	EBrs LAma LRHS MBri SPer
	'Pinocchio' (14)	LRHS MBri
	'Plaisir' (14) ♀H4	LAma MBri
	platystigma (15)	EBrs ECho LAma NMin
	polychroma	see *T. biflora*
	praestans (15)	EBrs ECho LAma SPer
	- 'Fusilier' (15) ♀H4	CBro EBrs ECho EPfP EPot EWal LAma LRHS MBri NBir SPhx
	- 'Unicum' (15/v)	EBrs ECho EPot ERCP EWal LAma MBri NMin SBch
	- 'Van Tubergen's Variety' (15)	EBrs ECho LAma SPhx
	- 'Zwanenburg Variety' (15)	EBrs ECho
	'Princeps' (13)	LAma MBri

Name	Suppliers
'Princesse Charmante' (14) ♀H4	EBrs MBri
'Prinses Irene' (3) ♀H4	CAvo CMea EBrs EGxp EPfP ERCP LAma LRHS MBri NBir SPer
'Professor Röntgen' (10)	LAma LRHS
pulchella	see *T. humilis* var. *pulchella*
- ***humilis***	see *T. humilis*
§ 'Purissima' (13) ♀H4	CAvo CBro CFFs EBrs EWal LAma LRHS MBri MCot SPer SPhx
'Purple Dream' (6) **new**	LRHS
'Purple Prince' (5)	EPfP
'Queen Ingrid' (14)	LRHS
'Queen of Night' (5)	CAvo CBro CFFs CMea EBrs EGxp EPfP ERCP EWal LAma LRHS MBri MCot SPer SPhx WPtf
'Queen of Sheba' (6) ♀H4	CMea LAma
'Rai' (10) **new**	LRHS
'Rajka' (6)	LRHS
'Recreado' (5)	CAvo CFFs EBrs ERCP SPhx
'Red Emperor'	see *T.* 'Madame Lefeber'
'Red Georgette' (5) ♀H4	LAma LSou MBri NBir
'Red Impression' PBR (4) ♀H4	LRHS
'Red Paradise' (1) ♀H4	LRHS
'Red Riding Hood' (14) ♀H4	CAvo CBro CFFs EBrs EGxp EPfP EWal LAma LRHS MBri NBir SPer SPhx
'Red Shine' (6) ♀H4	CAvo CBro LAma LRHS MBri
'Red Springgreen' (8)	LAma
Rembrandt mix (9)	MBri
'Renown Unique' (11)	ERCP LAma
rhodopea	see *T. urumoffii*
'Ringo'	see *T.* 'Kees Nelis'
'Robassa' (13)	EBrs
'Rockery Master' (14)	EBrs
'Rococo' (10)	ERCP LRHS MBri
'Royal Virgin' (3)	CAvo CFFs
'Salmon Impression' PBR (4)	LRHS
'Salmon Jewel' (3)	IPot
'Sapporro' (6)	LAma
saracenica	EBrs ECho
saxatilis (15)	CArn CBro EBrs ECho EPfP LAma MBri SMeo
§ - Bakeri Group (15)	CPou EBrs ECho IPot
§ - - 'Lilac Wonder' (15) ♀H4	CAvo CBro CFFs CSam EBrs ECho EPot ERCP GGar GKev LAma LRHS MBri SBch SPhx
'Scarlet Baby' (12)	EPfP LRHS MBri
'Schoonoord' (2)	LAma MBri
schrenkii (15)	CMea EBrs ECho EPot ERCP IHer LAma NMin WWst
'Shakespeare' (12)	CBro EBrs ECho LAma
'Shirley' (3)	CAvo CFFs EBrs EPfP ERCP EWal LAma LRHS MBri MCot SPer
'Shirley Dream' (3) **new**	EGxp
'Showwinner' (12) ♀H4	CAvo CBro CFFs EBrs LAma MBri
'Silver Standard' (1)	IHer
'Silverstream' (4)	LAma
sogdiana (15)	EBrs ECho GAuc LAma NMin WWst
'Sonnet' (6)	ERCP
'Sorbet' (5) ♀H4	EBrs LAma
sosnowskyi (15)	EBrs ECho
sprengeri (15) ♀H4	CAvo CBro CLAP CMea ECGP ECha ECho EPot ERCP ERas IPot LAma SCnR WHal WIvy WShi WTou
- Trotter's form (15)	WCot
'Spring Green' (8) ♀H4	CAvo CBro CFFs EBrs EGxp EPfP ERCP EWal LAma LRHS MBri MCot MMHG SPer SPhx
stellata	see *T. clusiana* var. *stellata*
'Stockholm' (2) ♀H4	LAma
'Stresa' (12) ♀H4	CAvo CBro CFFs EBrs LAma LRHS
subpraestans (15)	EBrs ECho LAma
'Sunwing'	LSou
'Super Parrot' (10)	LAma LRHS
'Swan Wings' (7)	EBrs ERCP LAma LRHS SPer
'Sweet Desire' (2)	EBrs
'Sweet Harmony' (5) ♀H4	MBri
'Sweetheart' (13)	CBro EBrs LRHS MBri SPer
sylvestris (15)	CArn CBro CHid EBrs ECho EPfP EPot ERCP LAma LRHS MBri NMin SPhx WCot WHer WShi
'Synaeda Stratego' (3) **new**	ERCP
systola (15)	EBrs ECho GAuc NMin WWst
tarda (15) ♀H4	CAvo CBro CFFs CHid EBrs ECho EPfP EWal GGar GKev LAma LSou MBri SBch SPhx
- 'Kazakhstan' (15)	EBrs
'Temple of Beauty' (5) ♀H4	EBrs
tetraphylla (15)	EBrs ECho
'Texas Flame' (10)	EBrs LRHS MBri
'Texas Gold' (10)	CHid EBrs LAma
'The First' (12)	CAvo CFFs EBrs
'The Lizard' (9)	LAma
'Theeroos' (2) **new**	LAma
'Tinka' (15)	CMdw CMea CSam EBrs ECho LSou NMin SPhx
'Toronto' (14) ♀H4	LAma LRHS LSou MBri
'Toulon' (13) ♀H4	MBri
'Très Chic' (6)	EBrs LRHS
'Trinket' (14) ♀H4	LAma
'Triumphator' (2)	EGxp
tschimganica (15)	EBrs ECho GAuc LAma LRHS WWst
tubergeniana (15)	EBrs ECho
- 'Keukenhof' (15)	EBrs ECho
turkestanica (15) ♀H4	CBro EBrs ECho EPfP EPot ERCP LAma MBri SBch SPhx WHoo
'Turkish Delight' (14)	NPer
'Typhoon' (3)	EBrs
'Uncle Tom' (11)	EGxp EPfP ERCP LAma LRHS MBri
§ ***undulatifolia*** (15)	EBrs ECho LAma LRHS
- 'Clare Benedict' (15)	EBrs ECho
- 'Excelsa' (15)	EBrs ECho
'Union Jack' (5) ♀H4	LAma
'United States' (14)	EBrs NPer
'Upstar' (11)	EBrs
urumiensis (15) ♀H4	CAvo CBro CFFs EBrs ECho EPot GKev LAma MBri NMin SBch SPhx WHoo
§ ***urumoffii*** (15)	ECho GAuc LAma
'Valentine' (3) ♀H4	LRHS
'Valery Gergiev' (7)	ERCP LRHS
'Verona' (2)	EBrs LRHS SPhx
'Viking' **new**	LRHS
violacea	see *T. humilis* Violacea Group
'Violet Bird' (8) **new**	ERCP
'Virichic' (8) **new**	ERCP LRHS
'Viridiflora' (8)	EBrs
vvedenskyi (15)	EBrs ECho EPot SPhx WWst
- 'Tangerine Beauty' (15) ♀H4	EBrs ECho LRHS MBri SBch SPhx
'Washington' (3)	EBrs ERCP
* 'Water Lily' **new**	ECho
'Weber's Parrot' (10)	MBri
'Weisse Berliner' (3)	CBro EBrs EPfP LAma LRHS
'West Point' (6) ♀H4	CAvo CBro CFFs EBrs ERCP LAma MBri
'White Dream' (3)	EBrs EPfP EWal LAma LRHS MBri
'White Elegance' (6)	LRHS SPer
'White Emperor'	see *T.* 'Purissima'
'White Parrot' (10)	CAvo CFFs EBrs ERCP LAma LRHS
'White Triumphator' (6) ♀H4	CAvo CBro CFFs CMea EBrs ERCP EWal LAma LRHS MCot NBir SMeo SPhx

	whittallii	see *T. orphanidea* Whittallii Group
	'Wildhof' (3) ♀^{H4} **new**	ERCP
	'Willemsoord' (2)	LAma MBri
	wilsoniana	see *T. montana*
	'Wirosa' (11) ♀^{H4}	LRHS
	'World's Favourite' (4)	LRHS
	'Yellow Emperor' (5)	MBri
	'Yellow Flight' (3)	LAma
	'Yellow Pompenette'^{PBR} (11)	ERCP
I	'Yellow Purissima' (13) ♀^{H4}	EPfP LRHS
	'Yokohama' (3)	EBrs LAma LRHS
	'Zampa' (14) ♀^{H4}	MBri
	'Zombie' (13)	LAma
	'Zomerschoon' (5)	EBrs LAma
§	'Zurel' (3)	CAvo EBrs EPfP ERCP LAma LRHS SPer

tummelberry see *Rubus* 'Tummelberry'

Tunica see *Petrorhagia*

Tupistra (*Convallariaceae*)

	aurantiaca	GEdr WCot
	- B&SWJ 2267	WCru WPrP
	- B&SWJ 2401	WCru
	chinensis 'Eco China Ruffles'	WCot
	fimbriata	WCot
	wattii B&SWJ 8297	WCru

Turraea (*Meliaceae*)

	obtusifolia	EShb

Tussilago (*Asteraceae*)

	farfara	CArn EBWF GBar GPoy MHer NMir NSco WHer WSFF

Tutcheria (*Theaceae*)

§	***spectabilis***	EPfP

Tweedia (*Asclepiadaceae*)

§	***caerulea*** ♀^{H2}	CBcs CDTJ CSpe SBch SGar SPad
	- pink-flowered	SPad

Typha (*Typhaceae*)

	angustifolia	CBen CKno CRow CWat EHon EMFW GFor LPBA MMuc NPer NSco SPlb SWat WFar WPnP
	gracilis	CBen EMFW LLWG
	latifolia	CBen CRow CWat EHon EMFW GFor LPBA MSKA NBir NLan NPer NSco SWat WDyG WFar WHer WMAq WPnP
	- 'Variegata' (v)	CBen CKno CRow CWat ELan EMFW LLWG LPBA MSKA NScw WCot WMAq
§	***laxmannii***	CBen CRow EMFW GFor LPBA MSKA NLan WPnP
	minima	CBen CFir CRow CSsd CWat EHoe EHon ELan EMFW EPfP LPBA MMuc MSKA NPer SCoo SMad SWat WFar WMAq WPnP
	shuttleworthii	CRow
	stenophylla	see *T. laxmannii*

Typhonium (*Araceae*)

	alpinum	EBee
	giganteum	WCot
	venosum **new**	SBst

Typhonodorum (*Araceae*)

	lindleyanum	XBlo

ugli see *Citrus* × *tangelo* 'Ugli'

Ugni (*Myrtaceae*)

§	***molinae***	CBcs CDul CFir CHll CPrp CSBt CTrC EBee ELan ELon GGal GGar GKev IDee IFFs LEdu LRHS MCCP MCoo MHer SBch SLPl SWvt WBor WCHb WDin WFar WJek WMoo WSHC
	- 'Flambeau'	CAgr EBee ELan EPfP LBMP LEdu LRHS MAsh MGos NLar SPoG SWvt

Ulex (*Papilionaceae*)

	europaeus	CArn CCVT CDoC CDul CRWN ECrN ELan EPfP GPoy LBuc MCoo MGos MMuc NEgg NWea SCoo WDin WHar WMou
§	- 'Flore Pleno' (d) ♀^{H4}	CBcs CBgR CDoC CDul CMac CSBt EBee EPfP GAbr GCal GGar IArd MBlu MGos NWea SPer SPoG WFar
	- 'Plenus'	see *U. europaeus* 'Flore Pleno'
	gallii	WDin
	- 'Mizen Head'	GGar MBlu MWhi SLon

Ulmus ✿ (*Ulmaceae*)

	Accolade = 'Morton' **new**	SGol
	alata	EGFP
	americana 'Princeton'	CKno
	crassifolia **new**	EGFP
	davidiana **new**	SSpi
	- var. ***japonica*** 'Prospector' **new**	SGol
	'Dodoens'	IArd MGos SCoo
	'Frontiez' **new**	SGol
§	***glabra***	CDul CRWN ECrN EMac IFFs NWea SCoo WDin
	- 'Camperdownii'	CDoC CMac EBee ECrN ELan GKir LAst
	- 'Exoniensis'	CTho
	- 'Gittisham'	CTho LRHS
	- 'Horizontalis'	see *U. glabra* 'Pendula'
	- 'Lutescens'	CDoC CEnd CTho CTri LRHS NWea SCoo SLim
§	- 'Pendula'	CMac
§	× ***hollandica*** 'Dampieri Aurea'	CBot CDul CEnd EBee ECrN ELan ELon EPfP GKir LBuc LRHS MAsh MBar MBlu MGos MRav NBlu NHol SPer SPoG WDin WPat
	- 'Jacqueline Hillier'	CBgR CDul CMac CSpe EBee ECho ELan LAst LMaj MBar MGos MRav SEND SLon STre WCFE WDin WFar WPat
	- 'Lobel'	CDul MGos
	- 'Wredei'	see *U.* × *hollandica* 'Dampieri Aurea'
	laevis	CDul ECrN
	Lutèce = 'Nanguen'	CDoC
	minor	CDul EMac IFFs
	- 'Dampieri Aurea'	see *U.* × *hollandica* 'Dampieri Aurea'
	- 'Silvery Gem' (v)	LRHS
	- 'Variegata' (v)	EBee SCoo
	montana	see *U. glabra*
	'Morton Glossy'	LRHS SGol

parvifolia	CMCN CMen STre WPGP
- 'Frosty' (v)	ECho
- 'Geisha' (v)	EBee ECho ELan MGos MRav WPat
§ - 'Hokkaido'	CMen LLHF NLAp NMen WAbe WPat WThu
- 'Pygmaea'	see *U. parvifolia* 'Hokkaido'
- 'Yatsubusa'	ECho EWes LLHF MRav NLar SIng STre WPat
procera	CTho ECrN LBuc LRHS MCoo MGos WDin WSFF
- 'Argenteovariegata' (v)	CDul MGos
- clone 2	SMad
pumila	EBee
'Regal' PBR **new**	SGol
rubra	CArn EGFP
'Sapporo Autumn Gold'	CDoC LBuc LMaj MRav WDin
serotina **new**	EGFP

Umbellularia (*Lauraceae*)

californica	CArn CPne EPfP GKir SSpi WSHC

Umbilicus (*Crassulaceae*)

rupestris	CArn CRWN EBWF NWCA SChr SECG WHer WShi

Uncinia (*Cyperaceae*)

from Chile	GCal
* ***cyparissias*** from Chile	NBir
divaricata	ECou
egmontiana	CHid EBee EBla EHoe EPPr EPau EPfP EShb GFor LBMP LRHS MNrw NWsh SHGN WFoF WGrn WHrl WMnd WMoo WWEG
lechleriana	GBin
N ***rubra***	Widely available
uncinata	CBcs CMMP ECha GFor NCob NHol SBod SDix
* - ***rubra***	CFir CKno COIW CTri CWCL EHrv ELon IFro LAst LRHS MMHG MNrw NCob NGdn NPri SBch SLim SMrm SPad SUsu SWvt WPGP

Ungnadia (*Sapindaceae*)

speciosa NJM 05.054 **new**	WPGP

Uniola (*Poaceae*)

latifolia	see *Chasmanthium latifolium*
paniculata	SApp

Urceolina (*Amaryllidaceae*)

miniata	see *Stenomesson miniatum*
peruviana	see *Stenomesson miniatum*

Urginea (*Hyacinthaceae*)

fugax	EBee
maritima	CArn CPou EBee EBrs ECho LAma LRHS MNrw WCot WHil
ollivieri	EBrs ECho

Urospermum (*Asteraceae*)

dalechampii	CDes CSam ECha LLWP LRHS SGar SUsu

Ursinia (*Asteraceae*)

alpina	CPBP
montana	NWCA

Urtica (*Urticaceae*)

dioica 'Brightstone Bitch' (v)	WAlt
- 'Danae Johnston' (v)	WAlt
- 'Dayglo Delight'	WAlt
- 'Dusting' (v)	WAlt
- 'Fearnvale Tigertooth' (v)	WAlt
- 'Good as Gold'	WAlt
- OGG mutant	WAlt
- 'Spring Fever'	WAlt
- 'Worn Gilding' (v)	WAlt

Utricularia (*Lentibulariaceae*)

sp.	EECP
alpina	CSWC SHmp
australis	EFEx
biloba	CHew
bisquamata	CSWC SHmp
- 'Betty's Bay'	CHew
blancheti	CSWC
calycifida	CSWC SHmp
dichotoma	CHew CSWC EFEx
exoleta R. Brown	see *U. gibba*
§ ***gibba***	EFEx
heterosepala	CHew
intermedia	EFEx
lateriflora	CHew EFEx
livida	CHew CSWC EECP EFEx SHmp
longifolia	CSWC SHmp
macrorhiza	CSWC
menziesii	EFEx
microcalyx	CHew SHmp
monanthos	CHew EFEx
nephrophylla	CHew SHmp
novae-zelandiae	CHew
ochroleuca	EFEx
paulineae	CHew
praelonga	CHew CSWC SHmp
prehensilis	CHew
pubescens	CSWC SHmp
reniformis	EFEx SHmp
- ***nana***	EFEx
sandersonii	CHew CSWC EECP SHmp
- blue-flowered	CSWC EECP
simplex	CHew
subulata	EFEx
tricolor	CHew CSWC SHmp
uniflora	CHew
vulgaris	EFEx
warburgii	CHew
welwitschii	CHew

Uvularia (*Convallariaceae*)

§ ***caroliniana***	ECho
disporum	EBee ECho
grandiflora ♀H4	Widely available
- dwarf	ECho IBlr
- gold-leaved	MAvo WWst
- var. ***pallida***	CAby CAvo CBct CLAP CPom CStu EBee ECha ECho EHrv EPPr EPot GBuc GCal GEdr IBlr LEdu LRHS MRav NCGa SMac SPhx SUsu WAbe WCru WFar WPGP WPnP
- 'Susie Lewis'	WCru
grandiflora × ***perfoliata***	ECho IBlr NBir
perfoliata	CBct CDes CLAP CPLG EBee ECha ECho EDAr EPPr EPfP EPla EPot EWTr GGar IBlr IMou LEdu MRav SIng WAbe WBrE WCru WPGP WPnP
pudica	see *U. caroliniana*
sessilifolia	CBct CLAP CPLG EBee ECho EPot GEdr IBlr IMou LEdu NMen SSvw WCru
- 'Cobblewood Gold' (v) **new**	WCru

V

Vaccinium ✿ (*Ericaceae*)

angustifolium var. ***laevifolium***	GLin
arctostaphylos	NLar SWvt
'Berkeley' (F)	CAgr CCCN CTrh CWib LBuc LSRN MBlu NLar NScw SDea SPoG
'Bluejay' (F)	CWib EMil GKir LRHS MAsh NLar SCoo SLon
'Blueray' (F)	CWib GPri
'Brigitta' (F)	CTrh ECrN EMil GTwe SPoG
'Chandler' (F)	CAgr CMac CTrh EMil ERea GPri SKee
corymbosum (F) ♀H4	CBcs EPfP LRHS MBar MGos MNHC SBch SCoo SReu SSta WBVN WDin
- 'Blauweiss-goldtraube' (F)	CSBt CWSG CWib EMil ERea LRHS LSRN MGos NLar SDea SPer SPoG SVic WBVN WFar
- 'Blue Duke' (F)	LSRN
- 'Bluecrop' (F)	Widely available
- 'Bluegold' (F)	EMil LRHS MGos SLon
- 'Bluetta' (F)	CAgr CTri CWib EMui GKir GPri GTwe MBri MGos SCoo SPoG WFar
- 'Coville' (F)	CWib EMui
- 'Darrow' (F)	CAgr CTrh GTwe LBuc SPoG
- 'Dixie' (F)	CSBt NScw
- 'Duke' (F) ♀H4	CTrh CWib ELan EMil EPfP GPri LRHS MAsh MGos
- 'Elizabeth' (F) **new**	GPri
- 'Elliott' (F)	LRHS MGos
- 'Grover' (F)	LRHS NLar NPri SPer
- 'Hannah's Choice' (F) **new**	GPri
- 'Jersey' (F)	CAgr CWib EPfP IFFs LRHS MAsh MCoo MGos NLar SCoo SDea SPer SVic
- 'Legacy' (F)	EMil LRHS
- 'Nelson' (F)	GPri SCoo
- 'Nui' (F)	EMui
- 'Patriot' (F)	CAgr CSBt CTrh CWib ECrN EMil GPri GTwe IFFs LBuc LRHS MBri MGos MRav NPri NScw SBch SCoo SPoG
- 'Pioneer' (F)	MBar
- 'Sierra' (F) **new**	GPri
- 'Spartan' (F) ♀H4	CTrh CWib EMil GTwe IFFs LRHS SCoo SKee
- 'Stanley' (F)	ELan LRHS MAsh
- 'Toro' (F)	CTrh EMil GPri GTwe LBuc LRHS MAsh MGos
- 'Weymouth' (F)	SDea
crassifolium	LRHS MAsh SPoG
subsp. ***sempervirens*** 'Well's Delight' (F)	
cylindraceum ♀H4	EPfP NLar WFar WPat
delavayi	ECho LRHS MAsh MBar NMen SReu SSta WAbe WFar WPat WThu
dunalianum	MMuc
- var. ***caudatifolium*** B&SWJ 1716	WCru
- var. ***megaphyllum*** HWJ 515	WCru
'Earliblue' (F)	CAgr CSBt ECrN EMil EMui LRHS MBri MGos NPri SDea WFar
floribundum	CBcs CDoC CMHG ECho GKir IDee LRHS MAsh NLar SPoG SSpi WPGP
glaucoalbum ♀H3-4	CAbP CDoC CMac EPfP GGGa GKir LRHS MAsh MBar MRav SMad SPer SPoG SSpi
* ***grandiflorum***	ECho
griffithianum	SReu SSta
'Groover'	LSRN
'Herbert' (F)	CMac CTrh EMil EMui GTwe LBuc MGos
macrocarpon (F)	CArn ECho ELan EMui GKir GTwe LRHS MAsh MBar MMuc NWCA SDea SPoG SRms
- 'CN' (F)	CAgr MGos NLar
- 'Early Black' (F)	EGxp EMui MGos
- 'Franklin' (F)	CAgr
- 'Hamilton'	GEdr LLHF NLAp NMen WAbe WThu
- 'Langlois' (F)	NLar
- 'McFarlin' (F)	EMui
- 'Olson's Honkers' (F)	CAgr NLar
- 'Pilgrim' (F)	CAgr CMac MAsh
- 'Red Star' (F)	CEnd EMui MCCP
'Misty' (F)	CAgr SPoG
mortinia	NMen
moupinense	CDoC ECho GKir LRHS MAsh NMen SPoG WAbe WPat WThu
- 'Variegatum' (v)	LLHF
myrsinites	ECho
myrtillus	CAgr GPoy MBar NWea WSFF
'Nimo Pink'	MBar
'Northland' (F)	CSBt CWib GTwe LRHS MAsh MBri NLar NScw SCoo SDea SPoG
nummularia	ECho GEdr LRHS MMuc NLar NMen SSpi WAbe WThu
ovalifolium	GAuc
ovatum	CBcs CMHG IDee LRHS MBar SSta
- 'Thundercloud'	CAbP LRHS MAsh SPoG
§ ***oxycoccos*** (F)	CAgr CArn GPoy MCoo MGos
'Ozarkblue' (F)	EMui
padifolium	WPGP
pallidum	IBlr
palustre	see *V. oxycoccos*
praestans	NHol
'Rubel' (F) **new**	LRHS NPri
'Sunrise' (F)	GTwe
'Sunshine Blue' (F)	CAgr CAlb ECrN EMui LBuc LRHS SKee
'Tophat' (F)	CCCN EMui LRHS
vitis-idaea	ECho EPfP EWes GGar GPoy MBar MGos NBlu NWea SPoG SVic WFar
- 'Autumn Beauty'	NLar
- 'Compactum'	EWes LLHF LSou
- Koralle Group ♀H4	CAgr EPfP MBar MBri NHol WPat
- subsp. ***minus***	GEdr GPri LRHS NLar NMen WAbe
- 'Red Pearl'	CAgr CSBt EPfP LRHS MAsh MGos
* - 'Variegatum' (v)	EWes NLAp
wrightii var. ***formosanum***	ECho

Vagaria (*Amaryllidaceae*)

ollivieri	ECho

Valeriana (*Valerianaceae*)

'Alba'	see *Centranthus ruber* 'Albus'
alliariifolia	EBee GCal NBro WCot
celtica **new**	GPoy
'Coccinea'	see *Centranthus ruber*
coreana	CFee WMoo
dioica	EBWF
hardwickii	EBee
jatamansii	GPoy SHlg
montana	NBro NRya SRms SWat

	officinalis	Widely available
	- subsp. ***sambucifolia***	CFee EPPr GCal MSpe SHar WHil WOut
*	- 'Variegata' (v)	WCHb
	phu 'Aurea'	Widely available
	pyrenaica	ECha EHrv EPPr GCal LRHS MMHG SPhx WCAu WCot WMoo
	saxatilis	CMea NLar NRya
	supina	NWCA
	wallrothii	CDes EBee WCot

Valerianella (*Valerianaceae*)

§	***locusta***	CArn GPoy
	olitoria	see *V. locusta*

Vallea (*Elaeocarpaceae*)

stipularis	CDoC CHII CTsd

Vallota see *Cyrtanthus*

Vancouveria (*Berberidaceae*)

chrysantha	CDes CFir CLAP CPLG CPom EBee ECha ERos GBuc MRav NLar NRya NWCA SMad WCon WCru WMoo
hexandra	CBct CFir CGHE CLAP CPLG CPom EBee ECha EHrv EPPr EPfP EPla ERos GBuc GEdr GKir LEdu LRHS NRya NSti NWCA WCru WMoo WPGP WWEG
planipetala	CLAP WCru

Vania see *Thlaspi*

campylophylla	CPBP

veitchberry see *Rubus* 'Veitchberry'

Velleia (*Goodeniaceae*)

paradoxa new	ECou

Vellozia (*Velloziaceae*)

elegans	see *Talbotia elegans*

Veltheimia ✿ (*Hyacinthaceae*)

§	***bracteata*** ♀H1	CAbb CHII CLak CMdw CPou EBak EBrs ECho IBlr NPal WCot
§	***capensis*** ♀H1	CSev
	viridifolia misapplied	see *V. capensis*
	viridifolia Jacq.	see *V. bracteata*

× *Venidioarctotis* see *Arctotis*

Venidium see *Arctotis*

Veratrum ✿ (*Melanthiaceae*)

SDR 4762 new	GKev
album ♀H4	CPne EBee EBrs ECha ECho GBuc GCal GPoy LEdu LRHS MRav NBid NChi SMad WBrE WCru WFar WHil WSHC
- var. ***flavum***	CAby SPhx WCru
- var. ***oxysepalum***	EBee WCru
californicum	EBee ECha GCal MNrw NBid WCot
- compact	MNrw
dolichopetalum B&SWJ 4195	WCru
formosanum	GEdr MNrw
- B&SWJ 1575	WCru
- RWJ 9806	WCru
grandiflorum B&SWJ 4416	WCru
longebracteatum	WCru
maackii	EBee GEdr
- var. ***japonicum***	see *V. schindleri*
- var. ***maackii*** B&SWJ 5831	WCru
- var. ***parviflorum***	GCal
mengtzeanum	CBct EBee WCot
nigrum ♀H4	Widely available
- B&SWJ 4450	WCru
§ ***schindleri***	WCru WWst
- B&SWJ 4068	WCru
stamineum	EBee WCru
viride	CHid ECha EWes GCal LRHS NMyG

Verbascum ✿ (*Scrophulariaceae*)

	adzharicum	NBur WHoo
	Allestree hybrids	EHrv
	'Annie May'	EBee EPfP LPio LSRN NOrc SPhx
	'Apricot Sunset'	LRHS SMrs SPhx WPGP
	'Arctic Summer'	see *V. bombyciferum* 'Polarsommer'
	arcturus	CFee
	'Aurora'	MAvo SJoh SPhx
	'Aztec Gold'	EBee MAvo SJoh SPhx WPGP
*	***bakerianum***	EBla ECtt
	'Bill Bishop'	ECho
	blattaria	EBWF EBee EHrv NBPC NBir SPav SWat WFar WHer WWEG
	- f. ***albiflorum***	CSpe EBee IFro LHop LLWP MNFA SGar SPlb WHer WMoo WTin WWEG
	- 'Pink White Blush'	LSou
	- pink-flowered	SPav
	- yellow-flowered	SPav SWat
	'Blushing Bride' PBR	ECtt LLHF LRHS LSou NBhm
§	***bombyciferum***	CBre CSev EBee ECha GMaP SRms
	- BSSS 232	WCru
*	- 'Arctic Snow'	SPav
§	- 'Polarsommer'	CSpe EBee EPfP GKir LRHS MBri NBir NVic SPav SPer SPet SRms SWat
	- 'Silver Lining'	NBur NLar NPer SDnm SPav
	'Broussa'	see *V. bombyciferum*
	'Buttercup'	EBee LRHS WFar
	'Caribbean Crush'	CMac EBee ECtt ELan EPfP EWTr EWll GKir LSou NBPC NLar NMoo SMrm SPav SPer WHil WHoo
	chaixii	CSam ECha ECtt EHrv GBuc GKir MMHG NBir WFar WMoo WPer
	- 'Album' ♀H4	Widely available
	- 'Blackberry Crush'	MDKP
	- 'Helene Bowles'	CHar
	- 'Sixteen Candles'	GQue LRHS NChi WHal WHil WPtf
	- 'Wedding Candles' new	SMrm
	chaixii × 'Wendy's Choice'	MDKP
	'Charles Harper'	SPhx
	'Charlotte'	SJoh
	'Cherokee'	MAvo SJoh
	'Cherry Helen' PBR	EBee EPfP LAst LRHS LSRN MBri NEgg NGdn NLar NMoo SBch SMrm SPer WSpi WWEG
	'Claire'	MAvo SJoh
	'Clementine'	SJoh SPhx
	'Coneyhill Yellow' new	EPPr
	(Cotswold Group)	CSam EAEE EBee ECtt EPfP GKir
	'Cotswold Beauty' ♀H4	LAst LRHS MRav MWat NGdn SPer WCAu WMnd WPGP
	- 'Cotswold Gem'	ECtt
	- 'Cotswold Queen'	CBcs CMMP EAEE EBee ECtt ELan EPPr EPfP EWTr LRHS MDKP MRav MWat NGdn SPer SPet SWvt WCAu WMnd WSpi WWEG
	- 'Gainsborough' ♀H4	Widely available
	- 'Mont Blanc'	EAEE EBee EHrv GMaP LAst LPio LRHS SWat WSpi

	Name	Suppliers
	- 'Pink Domino' ♀H4	CBot CPrp EBee ECtt EHrv ELan EPPr EPfP GKir GMaP LRHS MLHP MRav SDnm SPer SPet SWvt WCAu WFar WMnd WSpi WWEG
	- 'Royal Highland'	EBee ECtt EHrv ELan EPfP LPio LRHS NGdn NLar SDnm SPav SWvt WFar
	- 'White Domino'	EBee GKir SPer WHlf
	'Cotswold King'	see *V. creticum*
§	***creticum***	CSpe MDKP SDnm SGar SPav WCot WPGP
	- white-flowered **new**	WCot
	'Daisy Alice'	LPio
§	***densiflorum***	CArn EBee SPer WWEG
	'Dijon'	ECtt EWes
	dumulosum ♀H2-3	EPot GCal WAbe
	'Dusky Maiden'	NWCA
	'Ebenezer Howard'	LPio
	'Eleanor's Blush'	LRHS
	'Elektra'	MAvo SJoh
	'Ellenbank Jewel'	GMac
	epixanthinum	GKev LRHS LSou MCCP MDKP
	- MESE 552	EBee
	'Flower of Scotland'	ECtt LRHS
	'Golden Wings' ♀H2-3	ECtt ITim NMen WAbe
	Harptree smokey hybrids	CHar
	'Helen Johnson'	CBcs CMMP EBee ECtt EPfP GKir LAst LHop LRHS LSRN MRav NLar NPri SBch SCoo SMrm SPav SPer SRkn SWvt WCAu WFar WWEG
	'Hiawatha'	MAvo SJoh SMeo SPhx
	'High Noon'	SJoh
	× ***hybridum*** 'Banana Custard'	EAEE EBee ECtt GKir NGBl
	- 'Copper Rose'	EPfP LRHS MBri
	- 'Snow Maiden'	CTri EPfP LRHS MHer MWte SDnm WClo
	'Hyde Hall Sunrise'	EPfP LRHS MGos
	'Innocence'	MDKP
	'Jackie'	CBcs CHar CMac COIW EBee ECtt EHrv ELan GKir LAst LHop LRHS LSRN MBri NGdn NPri SBch SCoo SMrm SPav SPer SPoG SRGP WFar WHil WSpi WWEG
	'Jackie in Pink'	EWes GKir LBuc LRHS NMoo WFar
	'Jackie in Yellow'[PBR]	LLHF NMoo
	'Jolly Eyes'	EBee ECtt MBri WHlf
	'June Johnson'	EAEE EBee ECtt LRHS NGdn SHar
	'Kalypso'	MAvo SJoh SPhx
	'Klondike'	SJoh
	'Kynaston'	LRHS NGdn
	'Lavender Lass'	CMea ECtt NGdn
	'Letitia' ♀H3	CBcs CMea EBee ECho ECtt ELan EPot EWes GCal LRHS MAvo MTho NMen NWCA SIng SPav SRot SWvt WAbe WCom WKif WPat
	longifolium	WFar
	- var. ***pannosum***	see *V. olympicum*
*	***luridifolium***	EBee SPhx WPGP
	lychnitis	CArn GJos SPhx WHer WMoo
	'Megan's Mauve'	EBee EWll SWvt WSpi
	'Merlin'	ECtt MAvo SJoh WCot
	'Monster'	CDes WPGP
	'Moonlight'	ECtt
	'Moonshadow'	SJoh SPhx
	'Mystery Blonde'	MAvo SJoh SPhx
	nigrum	CArn EBWF EBee ECtt EPfP NGHP NLar SECG WBrE WMnd WMoo WPer
	- var. ***album***	NChi NGHP NLar WMoo
	'Norfolk Dawn'	ECtt EPfP LRHS MAvo NGdn SMrs SPhx WPGP
§	***olympicum***	CSam CWan EBee ECtt ELan EPfP GJos GKir LRHS MAvo MWat NGBl SDix SEND WBrE WCAu WCot WPer
	'Pandora'	EBrs LRHS
	'Patricia'	EBee LRHS SPhx WPGP
	'Petra'	SJoh SPhx WPGP
	phlomoides	SPhx
	phoeniceum	CArn ELan EPfP GJos GKev LRHS MNHC NBlu NBro SGar SPet SPlb SPoG SWal WBrE WEas WMoo WPer
*	- 'Album'	CSpe WCom
	- 'Antique Rose' **new**	WHrl
	- 'Flush of Pink'	ECtt
	- 'Flush of White'	CBot EBee ECtt EPPr EPfP GQue LBMP LRHS NGBl SDnm SPav SSvw WGor WMoo WWEG
	- hybrids	CBot CSpe CTri ECtt EGoo GMaP LBMP MSCN NEgg NGdn SRms SWat WFar WGor WPer
	- 'Rosetta'	EPfP LBMP LRHS NGBl SPad WHil WRHF
	- 'Violetta'	CMea CSpe EBee EPPr EPfP EWll GGar GMac IFro LAst LBMP NEgg NGdn NSti NVic SPav SPer STes WCAu WCFE WCom WCot WFar WGor WHil WHrl WMoo
	'Phoenix'	CTsd EBee WPGP
	'Pink Ice'	EPPr MAvo MDKP
	'Pink Kisses'	EBee LBuc LLHF LRHS LSRN LSou NBPC SBch
	'Pink Petticoats'	ECtt LBuc LRHS MGos SPoG
	'Plum Smokey'[PBR]	ECtt ELon LLHF LRHS WWEG
	'Primrose Cottage'	MBri SPhx
	'Primrose Path'	ECtt LRHS SBch SHar SRot
	pulverulentum	EBWF
	'Purple Prince'	ECtt
	pyramidatum	SPhx
	'Raspberry Ripple'	CMac EBee ECtt ELan LAst LBMP LLHF LRHS NMoo SPad SPav SPer WCot
	'Rosie'	EBrs LRHS NGdn SPoG
	'Royalty' **new**	LRHS
	'Sierra Sunset'	ECtt ELon WWlt
	'South Country'	SJoh
	'Southern Charm'	CChe EBee ECtt EGoo EWll GJos GKir GMaP LBMP MBri MCCP NChi SPad SPav SPoG STes WFar WHil WPtf WWEG
	'Spica'	NLar WSpi
	spicatum	CBot
	'Sugar Plum'[PBR]	CHar EBee ECtt EWll LAst LLHF WWEG
	'Summer Sorbet'	EBee ECtt ELan EPfP GKir LRHS LSou SPer SPoG
	Sunset shades	GJos
	thapsiforme	see *V. densiflorum*
	thapsus	CBgR COld CSev EBWF GPoy MHer MNHC NMir NSco SEND
	'Tropic Blush'	MAvo SJoh
	'Tropic Dawn'	MAvo SJoh
	'Tropic Moon'	SJoh
	'Tropic Rose'	MAvo SJoh
	'Tropic Spice'	MAvo SJoh
	'Tropic Sun'	MAvo SJoh
	'Twilight'	EBrs LRHS
	'Valerie Grace'	SPhx
	'Vernale'	CBot
	'Virginia'	SJoh
	wiedemannianum	CSpr EWTr

Verbena (Verbenaceae)

	Name	Suppliers
	(Aztec Series) Aztec Cherry Red = 'Balazcherd'PBR (G)	NPri
	- Aztec Coral = 'Balazcoral'PBR (G)	NPri
	- Aztec Pearl = 'Balazpearl'PBR (G)	SCoo
	- Aztec Plum Magic = 'Balazplum'PBR (G)	NPri
	- Aztec Red = 'Balazred' (G)	SCoo
	- Aztec Silver Magic = 'Balazsilma'PBR (G)	NPri SCoo
	'Betty Lee' (G)	ECtt
	'Blue Prince' (G)	CSpe MAsh SUsu
§	***bonariensis*** ♀H3-4	Widely available
	brasiliensis misapplied	see *V. bonariensis*
	canadensis 'Perfecta' (G)	CSpe
	'Candy Carousel' (G)	SPet
	chamaedrifolia	see *V. peruviana*
§	'Claret' (G) ♀H3	CAby CElw CSpe EBee ECtt ELan EPfP EShb LRHS LSRN LSou MAsh MCot MWea NPri SAga SBch SCoo SMeo SMrm SPhx SPoG SUsu WWEG
	(Corsage Series) 'Corsage Peach' (G/d)	LAst
	- 'Corsage Red' (G/d)	LAst
	- 'Corsage White' (G/d) **new**	LAst
	corymbosa	CAby CEnt CHid CHll CMMP CWCL EBee ECGP ECha EPPr LHop LRHS MDKP MMuc NLar SAga SBch SBod SPoG WCom WHil WPer WPtf WWEG
	- 'Gravetye'	CHrt EBee GBuc NChi NCob WFar
§	***dentatum*** 'Ralph Senior' **new**	NLar
	'Derby' **new**	MPet
	'Diamond Merci' (G)	EShb WHoo
	Donalena Lavender Grace (Donalena Series) (G) **new**	LAst
	'Edith Eddleman' (G)	EBee ECtt EPfP MNrw
	'Hammerstein Pink'	EBee EPfP
	hastata	CHar CSpe EBee ECtt EPfP GBar LEdu LHop LRHS MCot MNrw NCob NSti SGar SMeo SMrm SPhx SPlb SWat SWvt WFar WMnd WMoo WPer WSHC
*	- 'Alba'	CEnt EBee EPfP GBar GBuc GCal LDai MCot MDKP SMrm WCAu WMoo WPer
	- 'Blue Spires' **new**	WWEG
	- f. ***rosea***	CArn CElw CHar CKno CMea EBee ELan GBar GBuc LHop MAvo MBel MCot MDKP MLHP MRav NBPC NChi NCob SBch SMeo SMrm SPhx SUsu SWat WCAu WFar WMoo WSHC WWEG
	- - 'Pink Spires'	EKen EPfP LBMP LHop SPad WWEG
	'Homestead Purple' (G)	CChe CMac CSev EAEE EBee ECtt ENor EPfP EShb IMon LDai LRHS LSRN MCot SAga SBch SMrm SUsu SWvt WCot WWEG
	incompta	see *V. bonariensis*
	'Jenny's Wine'	see *V.* 'Claret'
	'La France' (G)	CSam EBee ECha ECtt EPfP EShb LSou MWea SAga SDix SMeo SMrm SPhx SUsu WHal WHoo WMnd WWEG
	lasiostachys	EBee
	litoralis	EBee LHop
	'Lois' Ruby'	see *V.* 'Claret'
	macdougalii	EGoo LHop MDKP SPhx
	officinalis	CArn CRWN CWan EBWF GBar GPWP GPoy MHer MNHC SIde WHer WJek WPer
	patagonica	see *V. bonariensis*
	'Peaches 'n' Cream' (G) ♀H3	MPet
§	***peruviana*** (G)	EBee ELan EPfP EShb LBMP LRHS MAsh SAga SChF SIng SRms
	'Pink Bouquet'	see *V.* 'Silver Anne'
	'Pink Parfait' (G)	EPfP LAst SAga SBch
	platensis (G)	GCal
	'Quartz Red Polka Dot' **new**	SBch
	'Red Cascade'	SPet
§	***rigida*** ♀H3	Widely available
	- 'Fliederblau' **new**	EBee
	- f. ***lilacina***	LSRN
	- - 'Lavender Haze' **new**	LRHS
	- - 'Lilac Haze'	CMac EBee EPfP LRHS NSti SPoG SRkn
	- - 'Polaris'	CHar EBee ELon EPfP EShb IPot LHop LSou MAvo MRav SHar SMrm SPhx SUsu
	Sandy Series (G) ♀H3	MPet
	'Seabrook's Lavender'	EBee EShb LRHS LSou MAsh MWea NPri SVil
§	'Silver Anne' (G) ♀H3	CHrt CSam ECtt LDai LSou MCot SMrm SUsu
§	'Sissinghurst' (G) ♀H2-3	CSam ECtt LAst MAsh NPri SAga SBch SIng SMrm SRms
	'Sissinghurst Pink'	IMon
	stricta	LRHS MDKP NLar
	Superbena Bushy Merlot = 'Usbena5002'PBR (Superbena Series) (G)	NPri
	(Tapien Series) Tapien Pink = 'Sunver'PBR (G)	LAst
	- Tapien Salmon = 'Suntapiro'PBR (G)	LAst LSou WGor
	- Tapien Sky Blue = 'Suntapilabu'PBR (G)	LAst LSou
	- Tapien Violet = 'Sunvop'PBR (G)	LAst LHop LSou
	- Tapien White = 'Suntapipurew'PBR (G)	LAst
	(Temari Series) Temari Blue = 'Sunmariribu'PBR (G)	LAst LSou
	- Temari Burgundy = 'Sunmariwaba'PBR (G)	LAst LSou
	- Temari Coral Pink = 'Sunmariripi'PBR (G)	LAst LSou
	- Temari Neon Red = 'Sunmarineopi'PBR (G)	LAst LSou
	- Temari Peaches and Cream = 'Sunmaripeach' (G) **new**	WGor
	- Temari Vanilla = 'Sunmarivani'PBR (G)	LSou
	- Temari Violet = 'Sunmariba'PBR (G)	WGor
	'Tenerife'	see *V.* 'Sissinghurst'
	'Tonic Pink Splash'	LSou
	venosa	see *V. rigida*
	Waterfall Blue = 'Dofall'	SMrm

Verbesina (*Asteraceae*)

alternifolia	CArn EBee
- 'Goldstrahl'	EPPr WPer
helianthoides	CSpr EWll LSou

Vernonia (*Asteraceae*)

§ ***arkansana***	CAby ECha EWes LRHS NLar SMad SMrm SPhx WBor
- 'Betty Blindeman'	EBee
- 'Mammuth'	CDes EBee ECtt EWes LHop NCob SMrm SPhx WPGP
baldwinii	EBee
crinita	see *V. arkansana*
fasciculata	EBee EShb EWes LPla LRHS MRav NLar SMrm WCot
gigantea	EBee EWes MMuc NLar SBHP WHrl
lettermannii 'Iron Butterfly' **new**	EBee
missurica	EBee
noveboracensis	EBee GQue NLar SGSe SGar SMad SMrm WPer
- 'Albiflora'	EBee EWes WPer

Veronica (*Scrophulariaceae*)

allionii **new**	GKev
amethystina	see *V. spuria* L.
anagallis-aquatica	EBWF NSco
armena	EBee ECho EWes LRHS MDKP MHer MWat NMen NWCA SBch WAbe WFar
arvensis 'Chedglow'	CNat
§ ***austriaca***	MBel NBre NChi WFar WMoo
- var. ***dubia***	see *V. prostrata*
- 'Ionian Skies'	CPBP CTri EBee ECha ECtt EGoo EPPr EWes GBuc GKir LBee LRHS MMuc MNrw NEgg SEND SGar SMrm SPer WAbe WCom WFar WKif WPat WPer WSHC WWEG
- 'Jacqueline'	NBre
§ - subsp. ***teucrium***	CArn CSam CTri EBee ECho MHav NDlv SRms WFar WHrl WPer
- - 'Crater Lake Blue' ♀H4	EBee ECtt ELan EPfP EShb GKir LEdu LHop LRHS MAvo MCot MRav NBre NVic SMrm SPhx SPlb SRms WCAu WCom WCot WEas WFar WMnd WPat WPer
- - 'Kapitän'	ECha GBuc LRHS MNrw NPro WFar WPer
- - 'Knallblau'	EBee NGby SMrm SSvw WFar
- - 'Royal Blue' ♀H4	EAEE EBee EPfP EShb GBuc GMaP LAst LRHS MWhi NCGa NSti SBch SRms WFar WMnd
'Baby Doll'[PBR]	LBuc LRHS MBNS MBri NBhm NLar
bachofenii	WTin
beccabunga	CArn CBen CWat EBWF EHon EMFW EPfP GPoy LPBA MSKA NMir NPer NSco SWat WHer WMAq WPnP WSFF
- var. ***limosa***	WAlt
'Bergen's Blue'	CMac GMac NLar SHGN SHar
Blue Bouquet	see *V. longifolia* 'Blaubündel'
'Blue Indigo'	ELan IBal NBre NGdn
'Blue Spire'	SWat WPer
bombycina	ECho
- subsp. ***bolkardaghensis***	CPBP NMen
caespitosa	CPBP
- subsp. ***caespitosa***	NMen WAbe
candida	see *V. spicata* subsp. *incana*
× ***cantiana*** 'Kentish Pink'	GBuc MHer WDyG WFar WMoo WPer WSpi WWEG
caucasica	MWat
chamaedrys	EBWF ECho NMir
§ - 'Miffy Brute' (v)	EBee NBir
- 'Pam' (v)	CBow ECtt WCHb
- 'Variegata'	see *V. chamaedrys* 'Miffy Brute'
- 'Waterrow'	WAlt
- 'Yorkley Wood'	WAlt
cinerea ♀H4	CMea GMaP MLHP SAga SBch WEas WHoo
dabneyi	CDes EBee WPGP
'Dark Martje'	EBee GBin WCot
'Darwin's Blue'[PBR]	GAbr LRHS MBNS NLar NMoo NOrc WHrl
'Ellen Mae'	CElw EBee ECtt EWes WCAu WMnd
'Eveline'[PBR]	EBee ECtt EPfP LSou NLar
exaltata	CMdw GBuc NBur NChi SMrm WCot WPer WSpi
'Fairytale'[PBR]	CWGN EPfP GMac IPot LRHS MAsh MAvo MBNS MBri MWea NSti SMrm WBor
filiformis 'Fairyland' (v)	EWes WCHb
formosa	see *Parahebe formosa*
§ ***fruticans***	ECho GJos NMen
fruticulosa	LLHF NWCA
gentianoides ♀H4	Widely available
- 'Alba'	CMea GCal LRHS NBre NChi NGby NSti
- 'Barbara Sherwood'	EBee EBrs EKen GBin GKir GMac LRHS MBel NBre WCAu WWEG
- 'Blue Streak'	EWll LRHS NDlv SGSe WRHF
- 'Lilacina'	EBee LRHS
- 'Nana'	CEnt EBee EPfP SRGP
- 'Pallida'	CSpr EBee EPfP MBrN MMuc MRav NMoo SEND SPlb WBor WFar WWEG
- 'Robusta'	EBee EHrv GMac LRHS NCGa NCob NEgg WCAu WCom WMnd
- 'Tissington White'	Widely available
- 'Variegata' (v)	CBcs EBee ECha ECho ECtt ELan EPfP GCra GKir GMaP LAst LBMP LRHS MHer MRav MSCN NBir NEgg NPri SPer SWat WBrE WCom WEas WFar WHoo WMnd WWEG
gigantea	CSpr
glauca **new**	EBee
grandis	EBee GAbr IFro LEdu MAvo MDKP MMuc MWhi NBur NChi NLar SWal WFar WHrl WMoo WPtf
× ***guthrieana***	CAbP NMen SRms WFar
hendersonii	see *V. subsessilis hendersonii*
incana	see *V. spicata* subsp. *incana*
* - 'Candidissima'	GCal
'Inspiration'	CMdw MBel NBre SMrm
'Inspire Blue' **new**	LSou
'Inspire Pink' **new**	LSou
kellereri	see *V. spicata*
kiusiana	CMHG EBee IFro MWhi NBPC NLar SPhx WHrl
* - var. ***maxima***	GQue LFur SGar
liwanensis	ECho NMen
- Mac&W 5936	EPot MDKP
longifolia	CHar CMea CSBt ECha ELan GCra LRHS MAvo MLHP NSti NVic WClo WFar WMoo
- 'Alba'	EBee EGoo ELan LBMP MMuc NGby NLar STes WMoo
§ - 'Blaubündel'	CMdw NDlv NGdn
- 'Blauer Sommer'	EAEE EBee LRHS MCot NEgg NGdn
§ - 'Blauriesin'	CCVN CTri EBee ECtt EPfP GMaP LRHS MBri NBre SPer SSvw WSpi

- blue-flowered **new** SGSe
- Blue Giantess see *V. longifolia* 'Blauriesin'
- 'Blue John' EBee GMac NBre NSti
- 'Fascination' ECtt LAst NGdn NPro
- 'Foerster's Blue' see *V. longifolia* 'Blauriesin'
- 'Joseph's Coat' (v) CBow EBee MBel NBre
- 'Lila Karina' EBee WPer
- 'Lilac Fantasy' EBee ECtt GMac GQue MBNS MSCN NGdn NSti WCAu
- 'Oxford Blue' EBee EGxp LRHS NBlu WHoo WRHF
- pink-flowered EShb STes
- 'Rose Tone' EGoo GJos MWea NLar SBHP SHlg WHal WHrl WMoo
- 'Rosea' LAst SBch WPer
- 'Schneeriesin' CHar CPrp EAEE EBee ECGP ECha EHrv GMaP LRHS MRav NBir NLar SPer

lyallii see *Parahebe lyallii*
'Martje' SMrm
'Mini Spires Blue' **new** EPfP LRHS
'Mini Spires Pink' **new** LRHS
montana EBWF
- 'Corinne Tremaine' (v) CBow EBee NBir NLar SAga SPoG SRms WHer
nummularia NBur
officinalis CArn EBWF
- 'Cream Crackers' (v) WAlt
- 'Pathlight' WAlt
oltensis CPBP ECho EDAr EPot EWes LLHF MHer NMen WAbe WPat
orchidea EBee SRms
orientalis subsp. ***orientalis*** NMen
ornata EGoo WPer
pectinata ECtt
- 'Rosea' ECho ECtt EWes WPer
peduncularis 'Oxford Blue' see *V. umbrosa* 'Georgia Blue'
perfoliata see *Parahebe perfoliata*
petraea 'Madame Mercier' CPrp SMrm SRot
'Pink Damask' CHar CSpe CWCL EBee ECtt ELan ELon EPfP GMaP LRHS MCot MRav MWat NCob NEgg NLar NSti SMrm SUsu WClo WFar WHoo WMnd WTin WWEG WWlt
pinnata 'Blue Eyes' LBee LRHS
- 'Blue Feathers' CEnt NCGa
porphyriana CSpe EBee MWea NCGa SMad WClo
prenja see *V. austriaca*
'Prince of Wales Feathers' NCGa
§ ***prostrata*** ♀H4 CEnt CMea CSam CTri ECho ECtt EPfP GJos LAst LBee LRHS MLHP NEgg NHol SRms WCom WEas WFar WHoo WMoo
- 'Alba' MLHP MWat WFar WHoo
- 'Aztec Gold' PBR CMac NBro NLar NPro
§ - 'Blauspiegel' CPBP LRHS
- 'Blue Ice' SMrm
- Blue Mirror see *V. prostrata* 'Blauspiegel'
- 'Blue Sheen' ECho ECtt GEdr LRHS NBir SIng WFar WMoo WPer
- 'Goldwell' LRHS
- 'Lilac Time' CSpr GMaP LHop LRHS NBir NLar SIng SRms WRHF
- 'Loddon Blue' ECho NVic SRms WPer
- 'Miss Willmott' see *V. prostrata* 'Warley Blue'
- 'Mrs Holt' CPBP ECho ECtt GEdr LHop LRHS MSCN NBir NHol NMen SIng SRGP SRms WAbe WBrk WCom WFar
- 'Nana' ECho ECtt EPot EWes MWat NMen WAbe
- 'Nestor' CTri ECGP ECtt EGoo NDlv WMoo
- 'Rosea' ECho MWat WPer
- 'Shirley Holt' GKir NBir
- 'Spode Blue' ♀H4 CMea ECho ECtt GMaP LHop LRHS NWCA SIng SPoG SRms WFar WMoo
- 'Trehane' CEnt EBee ECho ECtt EDAr EPfP LBee LHop LRHS MHer MWat NEgg NPri NRya SPlb SPoG SRms SRot WFar WMoo
§ - 'Warley Blue' ECho
* ***pseudolysimachion*** MHer WMoo
'Purpleicious' CWGN EBee EPfP LRHS MAvo MBri MWea SMrm WHlf
repens ECho GJos NBlu NPro SPlb WPer
'Rosalinde' CBot GBuc WPer
'Royal Pink' CBct MSCN NBid NLar NSti STes
rupestris see *V. prostrata*
saturejoides SRms WPer
saxatilis see *V. fruticans*
schmidtiana EShb WPer
- 'Nana' GKev
selleri see *V. wormskjoldii*
'Shirley Blue' ♀H4 CPrp CWib EBee ELan EPfP GAbr GKir LSRN MCot MHer MMuc MWat SPer SPhx SPoG SRGP SRms WCFE WClo WPer WWEG
sieboldiana SMrm
§ ***spicata*** CSam EBee ELan EPfP GJos LEdu LRHS MBNS MDun NBid SRms WBrk WCAu WFar WMoo WPer WTou WWEG
- 'Alba' EBee GJos MBNS MRav MWat NGby NLar WPer WTin WWEG
- 'Barcarolle' EBee ELan EPfP NGby
§ - 'Blaufuchs' ECtt
- 'Blue Bouquet' NBre NLar NPri WPtf
- Blue Fox see *V. spicata* 'Blaufuchs'
§ - 'Erika' CBct ECha ECtt EPfP GBuc IPot MWat NBid NBir NBre
§ - 'Glory' PBR EBee ECtt EPfP GKir LRHS LSou MAvo MBel MGos NBre NCGa NEgg NGdn NMoo SMrm SPad SPer WBrE WCot WWEG
- 'Heidekind' EBee ECha ECho ECtt EDAr ELan EPPr EPfP EPot GBuc LAst LHop LRHS MLHP MWat NBir NPri NVic NWCA SIng SMrm SPoG SRms SRot SWat WAbe WFar WHoo WTin
- 'High Five' PBR EBee IBal LRHS NBhm
- subsp. ***hybrida*** WCot WHer
§ - 'Icicle' CDes EBee MBrN NBre SUsu WHlf
§ - subsp. ***incana*** CMea CWan EBee ECho EHoe ELan EPfP EShb GJos LBMP SPlb SRms SWat WCFE WFar WMoo WPer WTin WWEG
- - 'Nana' ECha MLHP NBir SRms
- - 'Silbersee' MLHP WHil
- - 'Silver Carpet' CPrp EBee ECtt LAst LRHS LSou MRav NBre SPer WCom WMnd
- - 'Wendy' GCal LPla
- 'Nana Blauteppich' NBre NLar NVic NWCA
- 'Noah Williams' (v) ECtt GBuc NPro
- 'Pink Goblin' GQue NBre WPer
- 'Pink Panther' EBee MBNS NBhm SMrm WWlt
- Red Fox see *V. spicata* 'Rotfuchs'

	- 'Romiley Purple'	EBee LEdu LHop MBel NBre SPer WSpi WWEG
	- 'Rosalind'	NLar
	- ***rosea***	see *V. spicata* 'Erika'
	- 'Rosenrot'	ECho
§	- 'Rotfuchs'	CMHG CPrp EBee ECtt EHoe ELan EPfP GKir LAst LRHS MAvo MCot MRav NBPC NBir NMoo NOrc NPri SBch SMrm SPer SPoG SRms WCot WFar WPer WSHC WWEG
	- 'Royal Candles'PBR	see *V. spicata* 'Glory'
	- 'Sightseeing'	CWib GJos NBir NBre SPet SRms WFar
	- 'Twilight'	MBri
	- 'Ulster Blue Dwarf'	CBct EPfP LRHS MAsh MBri NPri WPtf
	- ***variegata*** (v)	MBel NBir
§	***spuria*** L.	NBur WPer
	stelleri	see *V. wormskjoldii*
	subsessilis	WPer
	- 'Blaue Pyramide'	EBee NBre WPtf
*	- ***hendersonii***	NBre NGby
	'Sunny Border Blue'	EAEE EBee EPfP GBuc LRHS MSpe NBre NLar WFar
	telephiifolia	ECho ECtt EWes MDKP NMen NWCA
	teucrium	see *V. austriaca* subsp. *teucrium*
	thessalica	ECho
	thymoides subsp. ***pseudocinerea***	NWCA
	umbrosa	WEas
I	- 'Alba'	WPer
§	- 'Georgia Blue'	Widely available
	virginica	see *Veronicastrum virginicum*
	'Waterperry Blue'	LRHS WFar WPer
	wherryi	WPer
	'White Icicle'	see *V. spicata* 'Icicle'
	'White Jolanda'	EBee ECtt EPfP MSCN NLar NPro NSti SMrm
	'White Spire'	CBot
	whitleyi	MMuc
§	***wormskjoldii***	EBee ECho ECtt EDAr GAuc MAvo MBrN NCGa NLar NMen NWCA SRms WPer
	- NNS 06-569	WCot
	- 'Alba'	EBee MLHP WPer

Veronicastrum (*Scrophulariaceae*)

	'Adoration' new	SPhx
	brunonianum	GCal
	japonicum	SGar
	- var. ***australe*** B&SWJ 11009	WCru
	latifolium	CDes EBee GCal LPio WCot WPGP WSHC
	- BWJ 8158	WCru
	sibiricum	CAby EBee ECha EShb GCal GQue LEdu NBid NBre WMoo
	- BWJ 6352	WCru
	- 'Red Arrows'	SPhx
	- var. ***yezoense***	MDKP
	- - RBS 0290	NPro
	villosulum	CPom EBee EWes IMou NBid NBro NLar SMrm WCru WSHC
§	***virginicum***	CArn CEnt CKno EBee ECtt EHrv GBBs GCra GPoy LRHS MBrN MLHP MMuc NBir NHol SRms WMoo WPer WWEG
	- 'Alboroseum'	WTin
	- 'Album'	Widely available
	- 'Apollo'	CBre EBee EBla ECtt EPPr EPfP GAbr GMaP LAst LPio MBel MBri MCot NBro NLar NOrc NSti SMrm WAul WBor WCAu WHrl WWEG
	- 'Diane'	GMaP LRHS NBre
	- 'Erica'	CCVN EBee ECtt EKen EPPr EPfP EWTr GBin GMac GQue LPio MBri NBPC NMoo NSti SMrm SPur WWlt
	- 'Fascination'	Widely available
	- var. ***incarnatum***	see *V. virginicum* f. *roseum*
	- 'Lavendelturm'	CAby CDes CSam EBee ECha GMaP IPot LHop LRHS MBri MCot NLar NSti SMad SMrm SPer SPhx WAul WCot WSpi
	- light blue-flowered new	SGSe
	- 'Pointed Finger'	GCal GMaP GMac LEdu NBre SMrm WWlt
§	- f. ***roseum***	CAby EBee EBla ECha ELan GMaP MBel MRav NBro SPer SPhx WClo WFar WKif WMoo
	- - 'Pink Glow'	CKno EBee EBla EBrs ECtt EHoe ELan ELon EPfP EWTr LBMP LHop LPla LRHS MMuc MRav NCGa NChi NGdn NSti SMrm SPer SPhx SPoG STes WCAu WFar WMnd WSpi
	- 'Spring Dew'	CBre EBee ECtt EPfP LPla NBid NBro NLar NPro WMnd
	- 'Temptation'	EBee GBin GMaP LRHS NBre NBro NLar NPro SUsu WCAu WTin WWEG
	'White Jolan'	CFir ECtt

Verschaffeltia (*Arecaceae*)

	splendida	XBlo

Vestia (*Solanaceae*)

§	***foetida*** ♀H1	CBcs CCCN CElw CHll CPLG CPom CSpe CTsd CWib EBee ELan ELon EMil EPfP LRHS MNrw NChi NLar SBig SDnm SGar WHil WPGP WPer WSHC
	lycioides	see *V. foetida*

Viburnum ✿ (*Caprifoliaceae*)

	B&SWJ 10290 from Mexico	WCru
	acerifolium	GAuc LLHF WFar WHCG WPat
	alnifolium	see *V. lantanoides*
	annamensis B&SWJ 8302	WCru
	atrocyaneum	CDul CGHE CPLG EBee NHol NLar SPoG WFar WHCG WPGP WPat
	- B&SWJ 7272	WCru
	awabuki	CHEx EBee EPfP EWTr MBlu MGos NLar WPGP
	- B&SWJ 8404	WCru
	- B&SWJ 11374 from Wabuka, Japan new	WCru
§	- 'Emerald Lustre'	CDoC CHEx WPat
	betulifolium	CAbP CBcs CMCN CPLG CPMA EBee EPfP EQua GAuc NHol NLar SMad WFar WHCG
	- 'Hohuanshan'	WCru
	bitchiuense	CPMA ELan NLar WPat
	× ***bodnantense***	CBot CMac CTri CWSG EBee LMaj MSnd SAga WHar
	- 'Charles Lamont' ♀H4	Widely available
	- 'Dawn' ♀H4	Widely available
	- 'Deben' ♀H4	CMac EBee EPfP EQua GKir LRHS SPer WDin WFar WPat

	bracteatum	NLar
	buddlejifolium	CMac EBee EPfP EWes GKir LRHS WCru WFar WHCG WPGP
	× ***burkwoodii***	Widely available
	- 'Anika'	NLar
	- 'Anne Russell' ♀H4	CAbP CBcs CEnd CPMA CTri EBee ECrN ELan EPfP EWes GKir IArd LRHS LSRN MAsh MGos MRav MSwo NHol NSti SCoo SLon SPer SPoG SSta SWvt WBrE WDin WFar
	- 'Chenaultii'	MRav WCru WDin
	- 'Compact Beauty'	CPMA EPfP MAsh WPat
	- 'Conoy'	CPMA MWat WPat
	- 'Fulbrook' ♀H4	CAbP CMHG EPfP GKir LRHS MAsh MGos NLar WDin WFar WPat
	- 'Mohawk'	CAbP CDoC CEnd CPMA EBee ELan EPfP IDee LRHS MAsh MBri NHol NLar SCoo SPoG SWvt WFar WPGP WPat WSpi
	- 'Park Farm Hybrid' ♀H4	CAbP CDoC CMac CPLG CPMA CSam CTri CWSG CWib EBee ECrN ELan EPfP ERas GKir LAst LBMP LRHS MAsh MRav MSwo NLar NSti SLPl SPer SRms WFar WPat WSpi
	× ***carlcephalum*** ♀H4	Widely available
	- 'Cayuga'	NLar WPat
*	- 'Variegatum' (v)	CPMA
	carlesii	CBcs CMac CTri CWib EBee EPfP GKir LAst LSRN LSou MBlu MGan MRav MSwo SCoo SLim SPer
	- B&SWJ 8838	WCru
	- 'Aurora' ♀H4	Widely available
	- 'Charis'	CPMA CSBt GKir LRHS NLar
	- 'Compactum'	CPMA LRHS NHol
	- 'Diana'	CDoC CEnd CMHG CMac CPMA EPfP GKir LRHS LSRN MAsh MBlu MRav NLar SPer SPoG WCFE WPGP WPat
	- 'Marlou'	CPMA NLar WPat
	cassinoides	EPfP GBin GKir WFar WPat
	- 'Bullatum' **new**	EPfP
	- 'Sear Charm'	WPat
	'Chesapeake'	CDoC CPMA EWes LRHS SEND WDin
	chingii	CGHE CPMA SLon WPGP
	cinnamomifolium ♀H3	CAbP CBcs CHEx CMac CPLG EBee EPfP GKir LRHS MAsh MBri NLar SAPC SArc SCoo SEND SLon SPer SPoG SSpi WFar WHCG WPGP WSHC
*	'Cornubia'	GGal
	cotinifolium	CPLG NLar WCot
	cylindricum	CBot CGHE EPfP EWTr GAuc GCal GKir LHop LRHS SSpi WCru WPGP
	- B&SWJ 6479 from Thailand	WCru
	- B&SWJ 7239	WCru
	- B&SWJ 9719 from Vietnam	WCru
	- BWJ 7778 from China	WCru
	- HWJCM 434 from Nepal	WCru
	- SDR 4712	GKev
	dasyanthum	EPfP GAuc IArd NLar
	davidii ♀H4	Widely available
	- (f)	CBcs CBot CDoC CMac CSBt ELan EPfP LAst MAsh MGos SPer SPoG SReu SRms SSta WPat
	- (m)	CBcs CBot CDoC CMac CSBt CWSG ELan EPfP GKir MAsh MGos MRav SPer SPoG SReu SRms SSta WPat
	- 'Angustifolium'	EQua WFar

	dentatum	EPfP GAuc
	- Autumn Jazz	see *Verbena dentatum* 'Ralph Senior'
	- Blue Muffin = 'Christom' **new**	MBri
	- Chicago Lustre	see *V. dentatum* 'Synnestvedt'
	- 'Moon Glo'	NLar
§	- 'Synnestvedt' **new**	NLar
	- 'White and Blue'	NLar
	dilatatum B&SWJ 4456	WCru
	- B&SWJ 8734	WCru
	- 'Erie'	EPfP NLar
	- 'Iroquois'	EPfP
	- 'Michael Dodge'	EPfP MBri NLar
	- 'Sealing Wax'	NLar
	edule **new**	GAuc
	erosum B&SWJ 3585	WCru
	erubescens	CAbP CPMA GKir IDee MBri WFar
	- B&SWJ 8281	WCru
	- var. ***gracilipes***	CPMA EPfP ERas WPat
	- 'Lloyd Kenyon'	NLar
	- 'Ward van Teylingen'	EPfP NLar
	'Eskimo'	CAbP CBcs CMac CWSG EBee ECrN EPfP EPla EWTr GKir LAst LRHS LSRN MAsh MBNS MGos MRav NBlu NMoo SLim SPoG SWvt WDin WFar WHCG
§	***farreri*** ♀H4	Widely available
	- 'Album'	see *V. farreri* 'Candidissimum'
§	- 'Candidissimum'	CBot CDul CMac ELan EPfP EWTr GKir IArd LHop LRHS MRav NLar SPer SPoG
	- 'December Dwarf'	CPMA
	- 'Farrer's Pink'	CAbP CPMA NHol
	- 'Fioretta'	NLar
	- 'Nanum'	CMac CPMA EBee EPfP LRHS MBar MBrN MRav MWat NHol NLar WFar WHCG WPat
	foetens	see *V. grandiflorum* f. *foetens*
	foetidum var. ***ceanothoides***	NLar
	- var. ***rectangulatum*** B&SWJ 1888	WCru
	- - B&SWJ 3451	WCru
	- - B&SWJ 3637	WCru
	fragrans Bunge	see *V. farreri*
	'Fragrant Cloud'	ECrN
	furcatum ♀H4	EPfP IArd MBri NLar WPat
	- B&SWJ 5939	WCru
	× ***globosum*** 'Jermyns Globe'	CAbP CDoC CMHG CMac EBee EPfP GKir LAst LRHS MBar MGos MRav NLar SLon SPoG WDin WFar WHCG WPGP
	grandiflorum	CPMA EPfP NLar WDin
	- HWJK 2163	WCru
§	- f. ***foetens***	CPMA EPfP
	harryanum	CAbP CMHG EBee EPfP MAsh MBNS NLar WCru WFar
	henryi	CAbP CPMA ECrN EPfP EWTr IDee MAsh NLar WDin WPat
	× ***hillieri***	MWhi WFar WHCG WKif
	- 'Winton' ♀H4	CAbP CDoC CEnd CMac CPMA CWib EBee EMil EPfP GKir LHop LRHS LSRN MBri MGos NPal SLon SPoG SSpi WDin WFar WPGP
	hupehense	GAuc
	'Huron'	MGos WPat
	ichangense	CPMA NLar
	japonicum	CMac CPLG EPfP LRHS NLar SLon SPoG WFar
	- B&SWJ 5968	WCru

	× ***juddii*** ♀H4	Widely available
	koreanum B&SWJ 4231	WCru
	lantana	CCVT CDul CLnd CRWN CTri CWib ECrN EMac GAuc GKir LAst LBuc NLar NWea SCoo SPer SPoG SVic WDin WFar WMou
	- 'Aureum'	ECtt EHoe LRHS MAsh MBlu NLar SCoo
	- 'Candy'	NLar
	- var. ***discolor***	NLar
	- 'Mohican'	NLar
	- 'Variefolium' (v)	CPMA
§	***lantanoides***	EPfP GKir NLar SSpi
	lentago	CAbP CMac NLar
	lobophyllum	EPfP NLar
	luzonicum B&SWJ 3930	WCru
*	- var. ***floribundum*** B&SWJ 8281	WCru
	- var. ***oblongum*** B&SWJ 3549	WCru
	macrocephalum	CEnd CPMA SLon WDin
	mariesii	see *V. plicatum* f. *tomentosum* 'Mariesii'
	nervosum B&SWJ 2251a	WCru
	nudum	EBee ECrN EPfP NLar
	- 'Pink Beauty'	CGHE CPMA CWSG EBee EMil LRHS LSRN MAsh NLar WFar WPGP WPat
	- 'Winterthur'	CPMA NLar
	odoratissimum misapplied	CBcs CHEx CPLG CSam EBee EPfP ERas IArd LRHS MWea SEND SMad SSpi WSHC
	odoratissimum Ker Gawl. RWJ 10046 **new**	WCru
	- 'Emerald Lustre'	see *V. awabuki* 'Emerald Lustre'
	'Oneida'	NLar WDin WPat
	opulus	Widely available
§	- var. ***americanum***	MBri
	- - 'Bailey's Compact'	MAsh WPat
	- - 'Hans'	NLar
	- - 'Phillips'	CAgr
	- - 'Spring Red' **new**	MBri NLar
	- - 'Wentworth'	CAgr
	- 'Apricot'	NLar
	- 'Aureum'	Widely available
	- var. ***calvescens*** B&SWJ 10544 **new**	WCru
	- 'Compactum' ♀H4	Widely available
*	- 'Harvest Gold'	EBee GKir SCoo SLim SPoG
	- 'Nanum'	CAbP CBcs CMea EBee ELan ELon EPfP EPla EShb GKir LAst MBar MRav NHol NLar NMen NPro WDin WFar WHCG WPat
	- 'Notcutt's Variety' ♀H4	EPfP GKir MBlu MGos SRms WPat
	- 'Park Harvest'	CDul EPfP GKir LRHS NLar SLPl WPat
§	- 'Roseum' ♀H4	Widely available
	- 'Sterile'	see *V. opulus* 'Roseum'
*	- 'Sterile Compactum'	LAst SWvt
	- 'Sunshine'	MBri
N	- 'Xanthocarpum' ♀H4	CBcs CDoC CDul CMHG CMac CPLG CSam EBee ELan EPfP LAst LHop LRHS MBar MBlu MGos MMuc MRav MSwo NGHP NMyG SBch SLPl SLon SPer SPoG SRms SWvt WDin WFar
	parvifolium	NLar
	pichinchense B&SWJ 10660	WCru
N	***plicatum***	CTri CWib GAuc MBar NLar WDin
	- 'Janny'	MBlu
	- 'Mary Milton'	NLar
	- 'Nanum'	see *V. plicatum* f. *tomentosum* 'Nanum Semperflorens'
	- 'Pink Sensation'	CPMA GGal NCGa NPal
§	- f. ***plicatum***	GKir
	- 'Popcorn'	CAbP CPMA EBee EPfP EWTr LRHS LSRN MAsh MRav SPoG SReu SSta WHCG WPat
	- 'Rosace'	MBlu MBri NLar SSpi
	- 'Shoshoni'	MBri NLar
N	- 'Sterile'	see *V. plicatum* f. *plicatum*
	- f. ***tomentosum***	EGxp EPfP EWTr WDin
	- - 'Cascade'	EBee EWTr LRHS MMHG NEgg NLar SSpi
	- - 'Dart's Red Robin'	ECtt LLHF WPat
	- - 'Elizabeth Bullivant'	LLHF LRHS MAsh SLon
	- - 'Grandiflorum'	CAbP CDoC EPfP GKir MBar NLar SPer WHCG WMoo
	- - 'Igloo' **new**	NLar
	- - 'Lanarth'	CBcs CDoC CDul CMac CPLG CSBt CTri CWSG CWib EBee ECrN ECtt EPfP EWTr GKir LHop LRHS LSRN MBlu MGos MNHC NLar SCoo SPer SPoG SWal SWvt WDin WFar
§	- - 'Mariesii' ♀H4	Widely available
	- - 'Molly Schroeder'	CPMA MBri NLar
§	- - 'Nanum Semperflorens'	CAlb CDoC CMac CWSG ECtt EPla IArd MBlu MGos NHol SBch SLPl SPer SPoG WFar WHCG WPat WSHC
	- - Newport = 'Newzam' **new**	NLar
	- - 'Pink Beauty' ♀H4	Widely available
	- - 'Rotundifolium'	MRav NLar WPat
	- - 'Rowallane'	EPfP MBri WPat
	- - 'Saint Keverne'	EBee
	- - 'Shasta'	CDoC CMCN EBee EPfP EWTr LRHS MBri NLar WDin WFar WSpi
	- - 'Summer Snowflake'	CDoC CEnd CWGN CWSG EBee ECrN EPfP LRHS MAsh MSwo NHol NPri SLim SPer SPoG WDin WFar WHCG
	- Triumph = 'Trizam' **new**	NLar
	- 'Watanabe'	see *V. plicatum* f. *tomentosum* 'Nanum Semperflorens'
	'Pragense' ♀H4	CAbP CBcs CDul CMCN EBee EPfP EQua GKir MBar MGos MMuc NBlu NHol SLon SPer WDin WFar WHCG WPat
	propinquum	CAbP NLar WFar
	- B&SWJ 4009	WCru
	prunifolium	NLar
	- 'Mrs Henry's Large'	CPMA NLar
	punctatum B&SWJ 9532	WCru
*	'Regenteum'	CWib
	× ***rhytidophylloides***	GKir WFar
	- 'Alleghany'	EBee NLar
	- Dart's Duke = 'Interduke'	EBee SLPl
	- 'Holland'	EBee
	- 'Willowwood'	EBee LRHS MAsh NLar SMad SPer WPat
	rhytidophyllum	CBcs CDul CHEx CMac CTri EBee ECrN EPfP GKir LHop LRHS MBar MGos MSwo NBlu NEgg SBch SCoo SPer SReu SRms WCFE WDin WFar WMoo
	- 'Aldenham'	GCal LSRN
	- 'Crathes Castle' **new**	NLar
	- 'Roseum'	CBot CPLG SLPl SWvt
	- 'Variegatum' (v)	CPMA NLar

	- 'Wisley Pink'	LRHS
	'Royal Guard'	LLHF NLar WPat
	sargentii	EPfP GAuc
	- B&SWJ 8695	WCru
	- f. ***flavum***	NLar
	- 'Onondaga' ♀H4	Widely available
	- 'Susquehanna'	EPfP NLar
	semperflorens	see *V. plicatum* f. *tomentosum* 'Nanum Semperflorens'
§	***setigerum***	EPfP GAuc IArd IDee NLar SLPl WPat
	- 'Aurantiacum'	EPfP NLar
	sieboldii	GAuc
	- B&SWJ 2837	WCru
	- 'Seneca'	EPfP NLar
	subalpinum	GKir NLar
	taiwanianum B&SWJ 3009	WCru
	ternatum new	EPfP
	theiferum	see *V. setigerum*
	tinoides B&SWJ 10757	WCru
	tinus	Widely available
	- 'Bewley's Variegated' (v)	CBcs EBee ECrN MGos MRav SPer
I	- 'Compactum'	SWvt
	- 'Eve Price' ♀H4	Widely available
	- 'French White' ♀H4	CDoC CMac CWSG EBee ELan ELon EPfP EPla LRHS MGos MRav SBch SCoo SLim SPoG SWvt WFar
	- 'Gwenllian' ♀H4	Widely available
	- 'Israel'	MBNS NLar SPer WFar
	- 'Little Bognor'	EBee NLar
	- 'Lucidum'	CBcs CPMA CSam EBee NLar WCFE WDin WFar
	- 'Lucidum Variegatum' (v)	CMac CPMA SLim
*	- 'Macrophyllum'	EBee EPfP LRHS NLar SPoG SWvt WFar
	- 'Pink Prelude'	EPla WSpi
	- 'Purpureum'	CDul CSBt EBee ECrN EHoe ELon EPfP EPla GKir IFFs LBMP LRHS MAsh MGos MSwo NEgg NHol SBch SCoo SLPl SLim SPer SPoG WBrE WDin WFar WMoo WPat
	- Spirit = 'Anvi'PBR	CAbP EBee LAst LRHS LSou MAsh MBri MGos NCGa NLar SBch SCoo SPoG
	- 'Spring Bouquet'	MAsh MGos NHol NLar
	- 'Variegatum' (v)	Widely available
	tomentosum	see *V. plicatum*
	trilobum	see *V. opulus* var. *americanum*
	urceolatum B&SWJ 6988	WCru
	utile	WFar WHCG WThu
	aff. ***venustum*** B&SWJ 10477	WCru
	wilsonii	IArd
	wrightii	EPfP MRav NLar WHCG WPat
	- B&SWJ 8780	WCru
	- 'Hessei'	WPat
	- var. ***stipellatum*** B&SWJ 5844	WCru

Vicia (*Papilionaceae*)

	cracca	EBWF NLan NMir NSco WSFF
	oroboides new	LRHS
	sativa	EBWF NSco
	sepium	NSco
	sylvatica	CBgR CPom EWes
	unijuga	CPom

Vigna (*Papilionaceae*)

§	***caracalla***	CCCN

Villarsia (*Menyanthaceae*)

	bennettii	see *Nymphoides peltata* 'Bennettii'

Vinca (*Apocynaceae*)

	balcanica new	IMou
	difformis ♀H3-4	CAlb CBgR CHar CPom CTri CWan EBee ECha LLWP LRHS MGos NCGa NPri SBch SDix WHer
*	- 'Alba'	CPom GKir SBch WCom
	- subsp. ***difformis***	WBrE
	- Greystone form	EPPr EPfP LHop MBNS NHol NLar SEND WCAu WGwG WRHF
	- 'Jenny Pym'	CAlb CBgR COlW CPom EBee EPPr EWes GBuc GGar LHop LRHS MAvo MBNS NHol SBch SEND SMad SPoG WCom WFar WRHF
	- 'Ruby Baker'	EBee LRHS NChi NPri WHrl
	- 'Snowmound'	CAlb COlW CWan EBee LRHS MRav SPoG
	'Hidcote Purple'	see *V. major* var. *oxyloba*
	major	CBcs CDul CMac CSBt CWib EBee ELan EPfP GKir GPoy LBuc LRHS MGan MGos MSwo NPri NWea SBch SPer SRms WDin WFar WGwG WMoo
	- 'Alba'	CMac CWib GBuc WEas
	- 'Caucasian Blue'	WPGP
	- 'Elegantissima'	see *V. major* 'Variegata'
§	- subsp. ***hirsuta*** (Boiss.) Stearn	CMac
	- var. ***hirsuta*** hort.	see *V. major* var. *oxyloba*
	- 'Jason Hill'	CAlb
§	- 'Maculata' (v)	CAlb CDoC COlW CSBt EBee EHoe LRHS LSou MBar MGos MRav MSwo NBPC NHol NPri SBch SEND SLim SPer SPoG SWvt WFar WMoo
§	- var. ***oxyloba***	CBgR CMac COlW COld CTri EBee ECtt ELan LHop MRav MWat SPoG SRms WFar WHer
	- var. ***pubescens***	see *V. major* subsp. *hirsuta* (Boiss.) Stearn
	- 'Reticulata' (v)	ELan
	- 'Surrey Marble'	see *V. major* 'Maculata'
§	- 'Variegata' (v) ♀H4	Widely available
	- Westwood form	CFee
	- 'Wojo's Jem' (v)	CDoC CMac EBee EWes LBuc LRHS LSRN MBri MGos NCGa SCoo SPoG SWvt WCot
	minor	CAlb CBgR CDoC CDul CMac ECrN ELan EPfP GAbr GKir GPoy LRHS MAsh MBar MGos NBlu NPri NWea SBch SVic WBrE WCAu WDin WFar
	- f. ***alba*** ♀H4	CAlb CBcs CBot CDoC CMac COlW EBee ECha EGoo EPfP GBar LBMP LRHS LSRN MAsh MBar MGos NEgg NPri SBch SHlg SPer SPoG STre WCom WCot WFar WPtf
	- 'Alba Aureovariegata'	see *V. minor* 'Alba Variegata'
	- f. ***alba*** Beth Chatto selection new	EPPr
	- - 'Gertrude Jekyll' ♀H4	Widely available
§	- 'Alba Variegata' (v)	CBgR CPLG EHoe EPla GGar GKir LSRN MBar MGos NGHP NHol NPro SRms STre WEas WFar WHoo
§	- 'Argenteovariegata' (v) ♀H4	Widely available
§	- 'Atropurpurea' ♀H4	Widely available
	- 'Aurea'	SPoG WFar
§	- 'Aureovariegata' (v)	CBcs CBot CMac EBee GAbr MBar MGos MRav NHol SPer SPlb WFar

	- 'Azurea'	CHid
§	- 'Azurea Flore Pleno' (d) ♀H4	Widely available
*	- 'Blue and Gold'	EAEE ECGP EGoo MAvo NBre
	- 'Blue Drift'	EWes MSwo WSpi
	- 'Blue Moon'	ECtt
	- 'Bowles's Blue'	see *V. minor* 'La Grave'
	- 'Bowles's Variety'	see *V. minor* 'La Grave'
	- 'Burgundy'	CFee SRms
	- 'Caerulea Plena'	see *V. minor* 'Azurea Flore Pleno'
	- 'Dartington Star'	see *V. major* var. *oxyloba*
	- 'Double Burgundy'	see *V. minor* 'Multiplex'
	- Green Carpet	see *V. minor* 'Grüner Teppich'
§	- 'Grüner Teppich'	WFar
	- 'Illumination' (v)	Widely available
§	- 'La Grave' ♀H4	Widely available
	- 'Marie'	MGos
§	- 'Multiplex' (d)	CAlb EBee ECtt EPPr EPla GBar LBuc LRHS MBar NChi NHol SRms WHrl
	- 'Purpurea'	see *V. minor* 'Atropurpurea'
	- 'Ralph Shugert'	EBee ELon EPfP EWes LRHS LSRN LSqu MAsh NLar SCoo SPoG
	- 'Rubra'	see *V. minor* 'Atropurpurea'
	- 'Sabinka'	CHid EGoo EPPr
	- 'Silver Service' (d/v)	CFee CHid CWan EBee GBuc MRav WCot WHoo
	- 'Variegata'	see *V. minor* 'Argenteovariegata'
	- 'Variegata Aurea'	see *V. minor* 'Aureovariegata'
	- 'White Gold'	EBee NHol NPro
	sardoa	CAlb CBgR EBee EPPr EWes

Vincetoxicum (*Asclepiadaceae*)

	forrestii	CPLG
§	***hirundinaria***	EBee EPPr GPoy LEdu WGwG
	nigrum	EWTr GCal NChi NMyG WCot WTin
	officinale	see *V. hirundinaria*
	scandens	CRHN

Viola ✿ (*Violaceae*)

	'Ada Segre' (Vt)	CGro
	'Admiral Avellan'	see *V.* 'Amiral Avellan'
	'Admiration' (Va)	WBou
	adunca	NWCA
	- var. ***minor***	see *V. labradorica* ambig.
§	***alba***	EWes NMen
	'Alethia' (Va)	GMac WBou
	'Alice' (Vt)	CGro
	'Alice Kate'	CAby WBou
	'Alice Witter' (Vt)	CBre CGro EBee ECha NChi
*	'Alison' (Va)	WBou
	'Amelia' (Va)	GKir WBou
	'Amethyst' (C)	EBee
I	'Amethyst' (Vt)	CGro
§	'Amiral Avellan' (Vt)	CGro
	'Annaleisia' (Vt)	CGro
I	'Annie' (Vt)	CBre CGro EBee LLHF
	arborescens	LFur
	'Ardross Gem' (Va)	CAby ECho ECtt GKir GMac WBou WEas
	arenaria	see *V. rupestris*
	'Arkwright's Ruby' (Va)	SRms
	'Ashvale Blue' (PVt)	CGro
	'Aspasia' (Va) ♀H4	CAby GMac WBou
	'Avril Lawson' (Va)	GKev GQue SHar WBou
	'Baby Blue'	NBlu
	'Baby Franjo'	NVic
	'Baby Lucia' (Va)	NVic SRms
	'Barbara' (Va)	WBou
	'Baroness de Rothschild' misapplied	see *V.* 'Baronne Alice de Rothschild'
	'Baroness de Rothschild' ambig. (Vt)	CGro
§	'Baronne Alice de Rothschild' (Vt)	GMaP SHar WCot
	'Beatrice' (Vtta)	WBou
	'Becky Groves' (Vt)	CGro
	'Beechy's Double White' (d)	CGro
	'Beetroot' (Vt) **new**	CGro
*	***bella***	WEas
§	'Belmont Blue' (C)	CEnt CSam CTri EAlp EBee ECtt EWes GCal GCra GMac IFro LHop LRHS MHer MMuc MRav MSCN NBir NCGa SMrm SPer SRkn SRms WBou WFar WSpi
§	***bertolonii***	WBou
	'Beshlie' (Va) ♀H4	EBee ECtt LRHS WBou WEas
	betonicifolia var. ***oblongosagittata***	CGro
	biflora	CMHG MTho
	'Black Bun'	WPGP
	'Blue Butterfly' (C)	GMac
	'Blue Moon' (C)	WBou
	'Blue Moonlight' (C)	CAby CElw GBuc GMac LRHS MMuc
	'Boughton Blue'	see *V.* 'Belmont Blue'
	'Bournemouth Gem' (Vt)	CBre CGro
§	'Bowles's Black' (T)	CArn CSWP CSpe EPfP GCal LBMP LEdu MMuc NBro NGHP NVic SRGP SRms WEas
	'Boy Blue' (Vtta)	ECtt
	'Bruneau' (dVt)	WCot
*	'Bryony' (Vtta)	WBou
	'Bullion' (Va)	EBee WBou
	'Burncoose Yellow'	WBou
	'Buttercup' (Vtta)	COlW ECtt GKir GMaP GMac LRHS LSRN MAsh NEgg SPoG WBou
	'Butterfly Wings' **new**	LRHS MAsh
	'Butterpat' (C)	GMac
	'Buxton Blue' (Va)	GBuc WBou
	'Candy' (Vt)	CGro
	canina	NBro NMir
*	- ***alba***	CBre
	'Carmine Witch' (Vt)	CGro
	'Carol' (Vt)	CGro
	'Carol Loxton' (Vt)	CGro
	'Catalina'	CGro ELon
	chaerophylloides 'Beni-zuru'	EBee
§	- var. ***sieboldiana***	CPMA
	'Charles W. Groves' (Vt)	CGro EBee ELon
	'Charlotte'	WBou
	'Chloe' (Vtta)	CGro
	'Christie's Wedding' (Vt) **new**	CGro
	'Christmas' (Vt)	CGro
	'Cinders' (Vtta)	CAby GMac
	'Clementina' (Va) ♀H4	MRav WBou
	'Cleo' (Va)	EBee WBou
	'Clive Farrell' (Vt)	CGro
	'Clive Groves' (Vt)	CGro CHid ELon
	'Coeur d'Alsace' (Vt)	CBre CGro EBee NCGa NLar WEas WHal
	'Colette' (Va)	WBou
	'Colombine' (Vt)	CGro NSti
	'Columbine' (Va)	EBee ECtt EPfP GKir GMaP GMac LRHS MAsh MHer NBir NBlu NEgg NPri SIng SPer SPoG WBou WClo WCot WFar WWlt
	'Comte de Chambord' (dVt)	SHar WFar
	'Connigar'	CSam
§	'Conte di Brazza' (dPVt)	CGro EHrv SHar WFar WHer
	'Cordelia' (Va)	WFar

	Name	Suppliers
	'Cordelia' (Vt)	CGro
	cornuta $\mathbb{Y}^{H4}$	CAby CElw CMea ECho EPot GGar GKev GKir LRHS MLHP MWat NBir NBro NChi NCob SBch SPoG SRms WBou WCom WFar WHoo WTou
	- Alba Group $\mathbb{Y}^{H4}$	Widely available
	- 'Alba Minor'	CAby CEnt CSsd EBee ECho EPfP EShb EWes GBuc GCal GMac IGor NBro NChi SHGN WAbe WFar
	- 'Blaue Schönheit' **new**	LRHS
	- blue-flowered	ECho MHer MLHP NCob SHGN WFar WMoo
	- 'Brimstone'	GMac
	- 'Cleopatra' (C)	CAby GAbr GMac
	- 'Clouded Yellow'	CAby GMac
	- 'Compton Lane'	WCom
	- 'Gypsy Moth' (C)	CAby GMac
	- 'Icy But Spicy'	EBee EHrv EWTr SMrm WBou WCot
	- Lilacina Group (C)	ECha MRav SWat WFar WMnd WPtf
	- 'Maiden's Blush'	CAby GMac
	- 'Minor' $\mathbb{Y}^{H4}$	CAby CSam GMac LRHS NBro WAbe WBou
	- 'Netta Statham'	CAby WBou
	- 'Pale Apollo' (C)	GMac
	- Purpurea Group	CMea ECha GBuc GCal NCob WMnd
	- 'Rosea'	ECha
	- 'Spider'	CAby GMac
	- 'Ulla' **new**	SBch
	- 'Victoria's Blush' (C)	CAby CSpe EBee ECtt EWTr GBuc GMaP GMac MMuc NBir WBou
	- 'Violacea'	GMac
	- 'Yellow King'	EHrv
	corsica	CEnt CSpe EBee NChi SHGN
*	'Cottage Garden' (Va)	LRHS
	'Crepuscle' (Vt)	CGro
§	***cucullata*** $\mathbb{Y}^{H4}$	ECho SRms WFar
§	- 'Alba' (Vt)	CBro CGro EBee ECho LLWP NBir NSti SRms
	- ***rosea***	EWes
*	- 'Striata Alba'	NBre NBro
	'Czar'	see *V.* 'The Czar'
	'Daisy Smith' (Va)	CAby WBou
	'Dancing Geisha' (Vt)	EBee EHrv EPfP
	'Danielle Molly'	WBou
	'Dawn' (Vtta)	CAby EBee ECtt GKir GMaP MAsh NEgg NPri SBch SIng SPer SPoG SRGP WBou WClo
	'Delicia' (Vtta)	WBou
	'Delphine' (Va)	NChi
	'Des Charentes' (Vt)	CGro
	'Desdemona' (Va)	GMac WBou
	'Devon Cream' (Va)	CAby WBou
	'Diana Groves' (Vt)	CGro
	'Dick o' the Hills' (Vt)	CGro
	dissecta	WCot
	- var. ***sieboldiana***	see *V. chaerophylloides* var. ***sieboldiana***
	'Donau' (Vt)	CBre CGro
	'Doreen' (Vt)	CGro
	'Double White' (dVt)	CGro
	dubyana	GBuc NChi
	'Duchesse de Parme' (dPVt)	CGro EBee IFro NWCA SHar SRms
	'Dusk'	WBou
	'E.A. Bowles'	see *V.* 'Bowles's Black'
	'Eastgrove Blue Scented' (C)	GMaP GMac NCob WBou WEas WOut WPtf WWFP
	'Eastgrove Ice Blue' (C)	WBou WEas
	'Eastgrove Twinkle' (C)	NCob WEas
	eizanensis	MTho
	'Elaine Quin'	MAsh NBlu NEgg NPri SPer SPoG SRGP WBou
§	***elatior***	CEnt CSWP EBee EBla EPPr GBuc IFro MNrw NChi WHil WPer WPtf WSHC
	'Elizabeth' (Va)	EBee ECtt GKir WBou
	'Elizabeth Bailes' (Vt)	CGro
	'Elliot Adam' (Va)	WBou
	'Emma' (Va)	CAby
	'Emperor Blue Vein'	EBee EPfP LSou
	'Emperor Magenta Red'	GJos LSou
	'Emperor White'	LSou
	erecta	see *V. elatior*
	'Eris' (Va)	NChi WBou
	'Etain' (Va)	COIW EAlp EBee ECho ECtt ELan EPfP EWes GBuc GMaP LAst LRHS MAsh NCob NEgg NPri SMrm SPer SPoG WBou WClo WEas
	'Fabiola' (Vtta)	GMac NBir
	'Famecheck Apricot'	CPom
*	'Fantasy'	WBou
	fargesii B&SWJ 6728	WCru
	'Fiona' (Va)	CAby EBee GMac MCot NChi NCob WBou
	'Fiona Lawrenson' (Va)	WBou
	'Florence' (Va)	NChi WBou
	(Foiolina Series) 'Foiolina Blue' **new**	LSou
	- 'Foiolina Orange' **new**	LSou
	- 'Foiolina Purple' **new**	LSou
	- 'Foiolina White' **new**	LSou
	'Foxbrook Cream' (C)	CAby GBuc WBou
	'Freckles'	see *V. sororia* 'Freckles'
	'Fred Morey' (Vt) **new**	CGro
	'George Lee' (Vt)	CGro
	'Gladys Findlay' (Va)	WBou
*	'Glenda'	WBou
	'Glenholme'	CAby GAbr GMac
	'Gloire de Verdun' (PVt)	CGro NWCA
	'Gloriole' (Vt)	CGro
	'Governor Herrick' (Vt)	CGro WCot
§	***gracilis***	NBir WFar
	- 'Lutea'	CSam
	- 'Major'	WBou
	'Green Goddess'^{PBR}	LRHS MAsh MWea SMrm SPoG WFar
	'Green Jade' (v)	NBir
	'Grey Owl' (Va)	LRHS WBou WPGP
	'Grovemount Blue' (C)	CElw CMea
	'Groves' Snow White' (Vt) **new**	CGro
§	***grypoceras*** var. ***exilis***	NGdn
	- - 'Sylettas'	CBow GGar NBPC
	- f. ***variegata*** (v)	NBir
	'Gustav Wermig' (C)	WBou
	'Hansa' (C)	NChi
	'Haslemere'	see *V.* 'Nellie Britton'
*	'Heaselands'	SMrm
§	***hederacea***	CTsd EBee ECho ECou GQui IFoB SRms WFar WPtf
	- blue-flowered	SIng
	- 'Putty Road' (Vt)	CGro
	'Helen' (Va)	ECtt
§	'Helen Mount' (T)	LBMP
	'Helena' (Va)	WBou
	'Hespera' (Va)	WBou
	heterophylla	see *V. bertolonii* subsp. ***epirota***
*	'Hetty Gatenby'	WBou
	hirsutula	EBla EHrv

I	– 'Alba'	EBla
I	– 'Purpurea'	EBla
	'Hudsons Blue'	CElw WEas
	'Huntercombe Purple' (Va) ♀H4	LHop LRHS MCot NBir SRms WBou WHal WKif
	'Iden Gem' (Va)	WBou
	'Inverurie Beauty' (Va) ♀H4	GMaP GMac NChi WBou
	'Irish Elegance'	see *V.* 'Sulfurea'
	'Irish Molly' (Va)	CBot CSpe EBee ECho ECtt ELan EPfP EWTr GGar GKev GKir GMac LRHS MAsh MHer NEgg NPri SIng SMrm SPer SPoG SRGP SRms WBou WClo WCom WFar WWlt
	'Isabel'	WBou
	'Isabella' (Vt)	CGro
	'Ivory Queen' (Va)	EBee GAbr GMac MRav WBou
	'Jack Sampson' (Vt)	CGro
	'Jackanapes' (Va) ♀H4	EBee ECho ECtt ELan EPfP GKir LRHS MAsh NEgg NPri SIng SPer SPoG SRms WBou WFar
	'Janet' (Va)	ECtt MAsh NBlu NPri SMrm SPer SPoG SRGP
	japonica	GGar
	'Jeannie Bellew' (Va)	ECtt SPer SRms WBou WFar WSpi
	'Jennifer Andrews' (Va)	WBou
	'Joanna' (Va)	WBou
	'John Raddenbury' (Vt)	GMaP
	'Johnny Jump Up'	see *V.* 'Helen Mount'
	jooi	CEnt CPBP EBee ECho EPfP GKev MWea NBir NMen SPhx SRms WPat WPtf
	'Josephine' (Vt)	CGro
	'Josie' (Va)	WBou
	'Joyce Gray' (Va)	WBou
	'Judy Goring' (Va)	GMac
	'Julia' (Va)	WBou
	'Julian' (Va)	CAby EBee GMac SRms WBou
	'Juno' (Va)	GMac
	'Jupiter' (Va)	EBee
	'Katerina' (Va)	WBou
	'Kerry Girl' (Vt)	CGro
	'Kim'	CGro
	'Kitten'	CAby GAbr GMac LRHS NChi WBou
	'Kitty White' (Va)	GMac
§	'Königin Charlotte' (Vt)	CGro COIW EBee EPfP GMac LBMP LRHS MCot MHer NChi NEgg NWCA WCot WFar WHil WMoo
	koreana	see *V. grypoceras* var. *exilis*
	'Kristina' (Vt) **new**	CGro
	'La France' (Vt)	CGro
N	***labradorica*** misapplied	see *V. riviniana* Purpurea Group
§	***labradorica*** ambig.	CHar ECho LRHS MCot MRav NBlu NPri SMrm WCAu WFar
N	– ***purpurea*** misapplied	see *V. riviniana* Purpurea Group
	lactiflora	EBee
	'Lady Hume Campbell' (PVt)	CGro NWCA WHer
	'Lady Jane' (Vt)	CGro
	'Lady Saville'	see *V.* 'Sissinghurst'
	'Laura' (C)	GBuc
	'Laura Cawthorne'	EBee
	'Lavender Lady' (Vt)	CBre CGro
	'Lavinia' (Va)	LRHS WBou
	'Lees Peachy Pink' (Vt)	CGro
	'Lemon Sorbet'	GBuc
	'Letitia' (Va)	EBee GMaP SRms WBou WFar
	'Lianne' (Vt)	CGro LLHF
	'Lindsay'	WBou
	'Lisa Tanner' (Va)	WBou
	'Lise Lazare' (Vt)	CGro
	'Little David' (Vtta) ♀H4	CAby CSam CTri ECtt GMac MCot SRms WBou WPGP
	'Lord Plunket' (Va)	WBou
	'Lorna Cawthorne' (C)	CAby WBou
	'Louisa' (Va)	GMac WBou
§	***lutea***	NChi WBou
	– subsp. ***elegans***	see *V. lutea*
	'Luxonne' (Vt)	CBre CGro EBee
	'Lydia Groves' (Vt)	CGro
	'Lydia's Legacy' (Vt)	CGro
	'Madame Armandine Pagès' (Vt)	CBre CGro EBee
	'Maggie Mott' (Va) ♀H4	ECha ECho ECtt GAbr GBuc GMac LHop LRHS SRGP WBou WFar WSpi WWFP
	'Magic'	CAby GBuc GMac LRHS WBou
	'Magnifico'	LRHS
	mandshurica	NWCA
	– 'Fuji Dawn' (v)	CBow SGSe WCot WPtf
	– f. ***hasegawae***	EPPr
	'Margaret' (Va)	WBou
	'Marie-Louise' (dPVt)	CDes CGro EBee GMaP SHar SRGP
I	'Mars'	CAbP ECtt GBin LSRN LSou WBor WFar
	'Mars' (Va)	EBee ECtt LRHS SBch SHGN SMrm SRGP WHer WSpi
	'Martin' (Va) ♀H4	CAby COIW EBee ECha ECtt GAbr GMaP GMac LHop LRHS LSRN MHer SPer SPoG SRGP WBou WClo WCom WFar
	'Mary Mouse'	WBou
	'Mauve Haze' (Va)	WBou
	'Mauve Radiance' (Va)	ECtt GMac NVic WBou
	'May Mott' (Va)	GMac WBou
	'Mayfly' (Va)	WBou
	'Melinda' (Vtta)	WBou
	'Melting Moments' (Va)	MAsh NEgg SIng SMrm WClo
	'Mercury' (Va)	SHGN WBou
	'Milkmaid' (Va)	CAby EBee EWTr LRHS NBir NBlu
	'Miss Brookes' (Va)	WBou
	'Mistress Mallory' (Vt)	CGro
	'Misty Guy' (Vtta)	NChi WBou
	'Molly Sanderson' (Va) ♀H4	CEnt COIW CSpe EAlp EBee ECha ECho ECtt ELan EPfP GGar GKir LAst LHop LRHS MHer MMuc MRav NEgg NPri SIng SPer SPlb SPoG SRGP WBou WClo WFar
	'Moonlight' (Va) ♀H4	CAby ECho ELan GKir LHop LRHS MHer MMuc WBou
	'Moonraker'	GMaP NBir
	'Morwenna' (Va)	ECtt WBou
	'Mrs Cotterell'	GBuc
	'Mrs David Lloyd George' (dVt)	CGro
	'Mrs Lancaster' (Va)	CAby EBee GMaP GMac LHop LSRN MAsh NBir NChi NPri SPoG SRGP SRms WBou
	'Mrs Pinehurst' (Vt)	CGro
	'Mrs R. Barton' (Vt)	CGro SHar
	'Mulberry' (Vt)	CGro
	'Myfawnny' (Va)	CAby CMea ECho ECtt ELan EWes GKir GMac LRHS SRms WBou WFar WSpi
	'Neapolitan'	see *V.* 'Pallida Plena'
§	'Nellie Britton' (Va) ♀H4	ECho ECtt SRms
	'Netta Statham'	see *V.* 'Belmont Blue'
	'Nora'	WBou
	'Norah Church' (Vt)	CGro
	'Norah Leigh' (Va)	EOHP WBou
	obliqua	see *V. cucullata*

	Name	Suppliers
	odorata (Vt)	CArn CBcs CBod CGro CRWN CSWP EBee EGoo EPfP GBar GPoy LRHS MRav NCob NMir NPri NSco SBch SIde SIng SPer SRms SVic WBor
	- 'Alba' (Vt)	CBre CGro CPom CSWP CWan EBee ECho ELan EPfP EShb GBar ILis MHer NCob NPri SRms WMoo
	- 'Alba Plena' (dVt)	EHrv LSou WHer
	- 'Albiflora'	CEnt
	- apricot-flowered	see *V.* 'Sulfurea'
	- 'Dawnie' (Vt)	CGro
	- var. ***dumetorum***	see *V. alba*
	- 'Katy'	CPom ELon SBch
	- 'King of Violets' (dVt)	CBre EBee EWll LSou MBel NCGa NEgg SHar SPer WClo WCot WFar
	- pink-flowered	see *V. odorata* Rosea Group
	- 'Red Devil'	WCot WFar
	- ***rosea***	see *V. odorata* Rosea Group
§	- Rosea Group (Vt)	CDes CEnt CGro CPom EBee GBar GMac IFoB LSou MBel MMuc MRav NEgg SIde SIng SMrm SPer WClo WCot
*	- subsp. ***subcarnea*** (Vt)	SEND
	- 'Sulphurea'	see *V.* 'Sulfurea'
	- 'Vin d'André Thorp' **new**	NBPC WCot
	- 'Weimar'	GBin
	'Opéra' (Vt)	CGro LLHF
	'Orchid Pink' (Vt)	CGro EBee GMaP
§	'Pallida Plena' (dPVt)	CGro
	palustris	CRWN WHer WSFF WShi
	'Pamela Zambra' (Vt)	GMaP SHar WPrP
	'Papilio' **new**	LAst
	papilionacea	see *V. sororia*
*	'Paradise Blue' (Vt)	CGro
	'Parchment' (Vt)	CGro
	'Parme de Toulouse' (dPVt)	CGro
	'Pasha' (Va)	GMac
	'Pat Creasy' (Va)	CAby WBou
	'Pat Kavanagh' (C)	CAby GAbr WBou
	'Patience'	WBou
	'Pearl Rose' **new**	ELon
	pedata	CBro WAbe WHil WPer
	- 'Bicolor'	WAbe
	pedatifida	CElw EBee MTho
	pensylvanica	see *V. pubescens* var. *eriocarpa*
	'Peppered-palms'	EHrv SGSe
	'Perle Rose' (Vt)	CGro EHrv EShb SHar
	'Petra' (Vtta)	CAby GMac
	'Phyl Dove' (Vt)	CGro
	'Pickering Blue' (Va)	WBou
	'Primrose Dame' (Va)	WBou
	'Primrose Pixie' (Va)	WBou
	'Prince Henry' (T)	MNHC
	'Prince John' (T)	MNHC
	'Princess Diana' (Vt) **new**	CGro
	'Princess Mab' (Vtta)	WBou
	'Princess of Prussia' (Vt)	CBre CGro
	'Princess of Wales'	see *V.* 'Princesse de Galles'
§	'Princesse de Galles' (Vt)	CGro CTri WHal
	'Pritchard's Russian' (Vt)	CGro
	'Prolific' (Vt)	CGro
§	***pubescens*** var. ***eriocarpa***	SRms WCot
	'Purple Wings' (Va)	WBou
	'Putty'	ECou
	Queen Charlotte	see *V.* 'Königin Charlotte'
	'Queen Victoria'	see *V.* 'Victoria Regina'
	'Raven'	GMac WBou
	'Rawson's White' (Vt)	CGro
	'Rebecca' (Vtta)	CSam CSpe EAlp EBee ECho ECtt ELan EPfP GKir GMaP GMac LAst LRHS LSRN MHer NBir NBlu NCGa NChi NCob NEgg NPri SPer SPoG SRGP SRms WBou WClo WEas WFar
	'Rebecca Cawthorne' (C)	EBee
	'Red Charm' (Vt)	EBee LRHS
	'Red Giant' (Vt)	CGro EBla EHrv LRHS MRav NEgg
	'Red Lion' (Vt)	CGro
	'Red Queen' (Vt)	CGro
	reichei	CRWN
	reichenbachiana	EBWF
	'Reine des Blanches' (dVt)	EBee ELon MBel NBPC NEgg NGdn SMrm SPer WClo WCot
	'Reine des Neiges' (Vt)	CGro
	reniforme	see *V. hederacea*
	'Richard Staples'	SRGP
	riviniana	CArn CRWN EBWF LFur MHer MMuc NSco WHer WJek WSFF WShi
	- dark pink-flowered	WAlt
	- 'Ed's Variegated' (v)	CBow EPPr WCot
§	- Purpurea Group	Widely available
	- white-flowered	EBee EWes MMuc WAlt
	'Rodney Davey' (Vt/v)	NBir
	'Rodney Marsh'	NBir
	'Roscastle Black'	CMea EBee ECtt GMaP GMac LRHS SBch SMrm SPoG WBou WCot WPGP WSpi
	'Rose Madder' (Vt)	CGro
	'Rosine' (Vt)	CGro
	'Royal Elk' (Vt)	CGro
	'Royal Robe' (Vt)	CGro
	'Rubra' (Vt)	CGro EWTr WPer WPtf
§	***rupestris***	CTri CWan ECho
*	- ***rosea***	CEnt CPom CSsd EBee EPfP EShb IFro LLWP MHer NWCA SBch SGSe STre WEas WOut
	'Saint Helena' (Vt)	CGro
	'Sally' (Vtta)	CGro
	schariensis	EWes
	selkirkii Pursh ex Goldie	GAuc NWCA
	- 'Variegata' (v)	GBuc NBir
	septentrionalis	see *V. sororia*
	'Serena' (Va)	WBou
	'Sherbet Dip'	WBou
	'Shirobana'	NBir
	'Sidborough Poppet'	CStu EWes
§	'Sissinghurst' (Va)	MHer NBir
	'Sisters' (Vt)	CGro
	'Smugglers' Moon'	CAby WBou
	'Sophie' (Vtta)	WBou
	'Sorbet Peach Frost' **new**	LAst
§	***sororia***	CGro EAEE EBee ECho EPPr LRHS MLHP MNrw NBir NBro WBrE WPtf
*	- 'Albiflora' ♀H4	CBre CGro CHid CSWP EBee EBrs ECho EPPr EPfP GGar LEdu MRav NWCA SPhx WCFE WClo WFar WJek WPer
	- 'Dark Freckles'	EBee ECho LHop SPhx WPtf
§	- 'Freckles'	Widely available
	- 'Priceana'	CBre CDes EAEE EBee ECGP ECha EPyc LRHS NBir NChi SMrm WCot WPGP WSpi
	- 'Red Sister'	MHer
	- 'Speckles' (v)	CBow EBla
*	'Spencer's Cottage'	WBou
	'Steyning' (Va)	WBou
	stojanowii	CEnt CSpe EBee ECho

suavis 'Catalonica White' (Vt) new — CGro
§ 'Sulfurea' (Vt) — CEnt CGro CPBP CPMA EBee ECho EShb LBMP LLWP MMHG NRya NWCA WCot WEas WFar WPer
'Sulphurea' lemon-flowered (Vt) — CGro
'Sultan' (Vt) new — CGro
'Susan Chilcott' (Vt) — CGro
'Susanne Lucas' (Vt) — CGro
'Susie' (Va) — WBou
'Swanley White' — see *V.* 'Conte di Brazza'
'Sybil' (SP) — WBou
'Sylvia Hart' — MTho
'Tanith' (Vt) — EBee
§ 'The Czar' (Vt) — CBre CGro ILis NChi WCot
'Tiger Eyes' (Va) — SPoG
'Tina' (Va) — EBee
'Titania' (Va) — CGro
'Tom Tit' (Va) — ECtt WBou
'Tony Venison' (C/v) — EBee MTho NBlu NEgg SPoG SRGP WBou WFar WHer WSpi
tricolor — CPrp EBWF ECho EPfP GBar GPoy MHer MNHC NGHP NPri NSco SBch SECG SIde WJek
'Vanessa' (Va) — GMac
velutina — see *V. gracilis*
verecunda — CLAP WSHC
- B&SWJ 604a — WCru
'Victoria Cawthorne' (C) — CAby CElw GAbr GBuc GMaP MCot MHer SHGN WBou WEas
§ 'Victoria Regina' (Vt) — CBre EPfP
'Virginia' (Va) — WBou
'Vita' (Va) — CAby GAbr GBuc GMac SRms WBou
'Wasp' (Va) — CAby GMac
'White Ladies' — see *V. cucullata* 'Alba'
'White Pearl' (Va) — SPhx WBou
'White Superior' — LRHS
'White Swan' (Va) — NChi
'Windward' (Vt) — CGro
'Winifred Jones' (Va) — WBou
'Winifred Warden' (Va) — WSpi
'Winifred Wargent' (Va) — NBlu
'Winona Cawthorne' (C) — CAby GMac
'Wisley White' — EBee EWes WFar
'Woodlands Cream' (Va) — GMac MHer NCob WBou
'Woodlands Lilac' (Va) — WBou
'Yellow Prince' — EAlp
'Zara' (Va) — WBou
'Zoe' (Vtta) — EBee ECtt LRHS NEgg NPri SMrm SPer SPoG SRGP WBou WFar

Viscaria (*Caryophyllaceae*)

vulgaris — see *Lychnis viscaria*

Vitaliana (*Primulaceae*)

§ ***primuliflora*** — ECho GKev NLAp NMen NRya NSla
- subsp. ***assoana*** — EPot GKev
- subsp. ***praetutiana*** — CPBP EPot NHol NMen NWCA WAbe WPat
- subsp. ***tridentata*** — NMen

Vitex (*Verbenaceae*)

agnus-castus — CAgr CArn CBcs COld EBee EOHP EShb GPoy LEdu LRHS LSou MCCP MHer MNrw SBch SEND SLon SPer WDin WFar WHer WSHC
- 'Alba' — CDul CWib EBee EPfP LRHS
- var. ***latifolia*** — CAlb CWib ELan ELon EPfP LRHS LSRN MAsh NLar NScw SBch SPoG WPGP
I - 'Rosea' — NLar
- 'Silver Spire' — CDul EBee ELan SPoG WPGP WSHC
incisa — see *V. negundo* var. *heterophylla*
lucens — CHEx
negundo — CArn EOHP
§ - var. ***heterophylla*** — EWes

Vitis ✿ (*Vitaceae*)

'Abundante' (F) — WSuV
'Alden' (O/B) — WSuV
'Amandin' (G/W) — WSuV
amurensis — CAlb EBee EPfP MBri NLar
- B&SWJ 4138 — WCru
'Atlantis' (O/W) — WSuV
§ 'Aurore' (W) — CAgr WSuV
'Baco Noir' (O/B) — CAgr GTwe SDea WSuV
'Bianca' (O/W) — MCoo WSuV
'Birstaller Muscat' (W) new — WSuV
Black Hamburgh — see *V. vinifera* 'Schiava Grossa'
* 'Black Strawberry' (B) — CAgr WSuV
§ 'Boskoop Glory' (O/B) ♀H4 — CMac ERea LBuc MAsh MCoo NBlu NPal SCoo SDea WSuV
'Brant' (O/B) ♀H4 — Widely available
'Brilliant' (B) — WSuV
'Buffalo' (B) — WSuV
'Canadice' (O/R/S) — SDea WSuV
'Cascade' — see *V.* Seibel 13053
Castel 19637 (B) — WSuV
'Chambourcin' (B) — WSuV
coignetiae ♀H4 — Widely available
- B&SWJ 4550 from Korea — WCru
- B&SWJ 4744 — WCru
- B&SWJ 10882 from Japan — WCru
- Claret Cloak = 'Frovit' PBR — CBcs EBee ELan EPfP GKir LRHS LSRN MAsh MRav NLar SCoo SPer SPoG SSpi WClo WPGP WPat WSpi
- cut-leaved — CMac
- var. ***glabrescens*** B&SWJ 8537 — WCru
- Sunningdale form — WSpi
'Dalkauer' (W) — WSuV
I 'Diamond' (B) — WSuV
'Dutch Black' (O/B) — WSuV
'Edwards No 1' (O/W) — WSuV
'Eger Csillaga' (O/W) — WSuV
'Einset' (B/S) — WSuV
ficifolia — see *V. thunbergii*
flexuosa B&SWJ 5568 — WCru
- var. ***choii*** B&SWJ 4101 — WCru
§ 'Fragola' (O/R) — CAgr CMac CTri EBee EPfP GTwe LOck LRHS MAsh MRav SDea SPer SRms WCom WSuV
'Gagarin Blue' (O/B) — CAgr EMui ERea GTwe SDea WSuV
'Glenora' (F/B/S) — CAgr WSuV
'Hecker' (O/W) — WSuV
henryana — see *Parthenocissus henryana*
'Himrod' (O/W/S) — CCCN ERea GTwe NPal SDea WSuV
'Horizon' (O/W) — WSuV
inconstans — see *Parthenocissus tricuspidata*
'Interlaken' (O/W/S) — CAgr ERea WSuV
'Johanniter' (W) new — WSuV
'Kempsey Black' (O/B) — CAgr WSuV
'Kozmapalme Muscatoly' (O/W) — WSuV
'Kuibishevski' (O/R) — WSuV
Landot 244 (O/B) — WSuV
Landot 3217 (O/B) new — WSuV

	'L'Arcadie Blanche' (W) **new**	WSuV
	'Léon Millot' (O/G/B)	CAgr CSBt EMui ERea LSRN SDea WSuV
	'Lucy Kuhlman' (B) **new**	WSuV
	'Maréchal Foch' (O/B)	EGxp WSuV
	'Maréchal Joffre' (O/B)	CAgr GTwe WSuV
	'Mars' (O/B/S)	WSuV
	'Merzling' (O/W)	WSuV
	'Munson R.W.' (O/R)	WSuV
	'Muscat Bleu' (O/B)	CCCN EMui LRHS WSuV
	'Nero'PBR	CAgr SBch
	'New York Muscat' (O/B) ♀H4	ERea WSuV
	'New York Seedless' (O/W/S)	WSuV
	'Niagara' (O/W)	WSuV
	'Niederother Monschrebe' (O/R)	WSuV
	Oberlin 595 (O/B)	WSuV
	'Orion' (O/W)	EMui LRHS MAsh WSuV
	'Paletina' (O/W)	WSuV
	parsley-leaved	see *V. vinifera* 'Ciotat'
	parvifolia	WPat
	'Perdin' (O/W)	WSuV
	'Phönix' (O/W)	CAgr EMil EMui GTwe LRHS MAsh MBri MGos NLar SKee SLim SPoG SVic WSuV
*	'Pink Strawberry' (O)	WSuV
	'Pirovano 14' (O/B)	GTwe SDea WSuV
§	'Plantet' (O/B)	WSuV
*	'Poloske Muscat' (W)	EMui ERea GTwe WSuV
	pseudoreticulata	WPGP
	purpurea 'Spetchley Park' (O/B)	CAgr WSuV
	quinquefolia	see *Parthenocissus quinquefolia*
	'Ramdas' (O/W)	WSuV
	Ravat 51 (O/W)	WSuV
	'Rayon d'Or' (O/W)	WSuV
	'Regent'PBR (O/S)	CAgr CWSG EMui GTwe LRHS MBri MCoo MGos NLar SKee SLim WSuV
	'Reliance' (O/R/S)	ERea WSuV
	'Rembrant' (R)	CAgr NPal WSuV
	riparia	CArn NLar
	'Romulus' (O/G/W/S)	WSuV
	'Rondo' (O/B)	CAgr EMui
	- EM 6494-5	WSuV
	'Saturn' (O/R/S)	WSuV
	'Schuyler' (O/B)	CAgr WSuV
	Seibel (F)	GTwe SDea
	Seibel 5279	see *V.* 'Aurore'
	Seibel 5409 (W)	WSuV
	Seibel 5455	see *V.* 'Plantet'
	Seibel 7053	WSuV
	Seibel 9549	WSuV
§	Seibel 13053 (O/B)	CMac LRHS MAsh SDea SEND WSuV
	Seibel 138315 (R)	WSuV
	'Seneca' (W)	WSuV
	'Serena' (O/W)	WSuV
§	'Seyval Blanc' (O/W)	CAgr GTwe SDea SEND SVic WSuV
	Seyve Villard 5276	see *V.* 'Seyval Blanc'
	Seyve Villard 12.375	see *V.* 'Villard Blanc'
	Seyve Villard ambig.	LRHS NPer
	Seyve Villard 20.473 (F)	LRHS MAsh NPer
	'Sirius' (B) **new**	WSuV
	'Solaris' (O/W)	WSuV
	'Stauffer' (O/W)	WSuV
	'Suffolk Seedless' (B/S)	ERea WSuV
	'Tereshkova' (O/B)	CAgr ERea SDea WSuV
	'Thornton' (O/S)	WSuV
§	***thunbergii*** B&SWJ 4702	WCru
	- 'Lobata' **new**	EBee
	'Triomphe d'Alsace' (O/B)	CAgr CSBt EMui NPer SDea WSuV
	'Trollinger'	see *V. vinifera* 'Schiava Grossa'
	'Vanessa' (O/R/S)	SDea WSuV
§	'Villard Blanc' (O/W)	WSuV
	vinifera	GKir LRHS MGos STrG
	- EM 323158B	WSuV
	- 'Abouriou' (O/B)	WSuV
	- 'Acolon' (O/B)	WSuV
	- 'Adelheidtraube' (O/W)	WSuV
	- 'Albalonga' (W)	WSuV
§	- 'Alicante' (G/B)	CMac EGxp ERea GTwe NPal SDea WSuV
	- 'Alphonse Lavalle' (O/B/S) **new**	LRHS
	- 'Apiifolia'	see *V. vinifera* 'Ciotat'
	- 'Appley Towers' (G/B)	ERea
	- 'Augusta Louise' (O/W)	WSuV
	- 'Auxerrois' (O/W)	WSuV
	- 'Bacchus' (O/W)	LRHS MBri NLar SDea SVic WSuV
	- 'Baresana' (G/W)	EGxp WSuV
	- 'Beauty'	CAgr
	- 'Black Alicante'	see *V. vinifera* 'Alicante'
	- 'Black Corinth' (G/B/S)	ERea
	- 'Black Frontignan' (G/O/B)	ERea WSuV
	- Black Hamburgh	see *V. vinifera* 'Schiava Grossa'
	- 'Black Monukka' (G/B/S)	ERea WSuV
	- 'Black Prince' (G/B)	WSuV
	- 'Blue Portuguese'	see *V. vinifera* 'Portugieser'
§	- 'Bouvier' (W)	WSuV
	- 'Bouviertraube'	see *V. vinifera* 'Bouvier'
	- 'Buckland Sweetwater' (G/W)	CDul ERea GTwe MGos SDea WSuV
	- 'Cabernet Sauvignon' (O/B)	LRHS MAsh MGos NPer SDea WSuV
	- 'Canon Hall Muscat' (G/W)	ERea
	- 'Cardinal' (O/R)	EMil WSuV
	- 'Carla' (O/R)	WSuV
	- 'Centennial' (O/N/S)	WSuV
	- 'Chardonnay' (O/W)	CAgr CCCN EMui LRHS MAsh NPer SDea SPer SVic WSuV
§	- 'Chasselas' (G/O/W)	LRHS MAsh SDea WSuV
	- 'Chasselas Blanc' (O/W)	SVic
	- 'Chasselas de Fontainebleau' (F)	CCCN EMil LRHS
	- 'Chasselas de Tramontaner' (F)	EMil LRHS
	- 'Chasselas d'Or'	see *V. vinifera* 'Chasselas'
	- 'Chasselas Rosé' (G/R)	SVic WSuV
	- 'Chasselas Rosé Royal' (O/R)	CCCN
	- 'Chasselas Vibert' (G/W)	WSuV
	- 'Chenin Blanc' (O/W)	WSuV
§	- 'Ciotat' (F)	ERea EShb MRav SDea WSuV
	- 'Cot Précoce de Tours' (O/B)	WSuV
	- 'Crimson Seedless' (R/S)	ERea LRHS WSuV
	- 'Csabyongye' (O/W)	WSuV
	- 'Dattier de Beyrouth' (G/W)	EMil WSuV
	- 'Dattier Saint Vallier' (O/W)	SVic WSuV
	- 'Dolcetto' (O/B)	WSuV
	- 'Dornfelder' (O/R)	CCCN CSut LRHS NLar WSuV
	- 'Dunkelfelder' (O/R)	WSuV
	- 'Early Van der Laan' (F)	CMac NBlu

- 'Ehrenfelser' (O/W)	WSuV
- 'Elbling' (O/W)	WSuV
- 'Exalta' (G/W/S)	CCCN WSuV
- 'Excelsior' (W)	WSuV
- 'Faber' (O/W)	WSuV
- 'Fiesta' (W/S)	WSuV
- 'Findling' (W)	WSuV
- 'Flame'	CAgr EMui
- 'Flame Red' (O/D)	CCCN
- 'Flame Seedless' (G/O/R/S)	CMac EMui LRHS SPoG WSuV
- 'Forta' (O/W)	WSuV
- 'Foster's Seedling' (G/W)	GTwe SDea SVic WSuV
- 'Freisamer' (O/W)	WSuV
- 'Frühburgunder' (O/B)	WSuV
- 'Gamay Hâtif des Vosges'	WSuV
- 'Gamay Noir' (O/B)	WSuV
- Gamay Teinturier Group (O/B)	WSuV
- 'Gewürztraminer' (O/R)	LRHS MAsh SDea WSuV
- 'Glory of Boskoop'	see *V.* 'Boskoop Glory'
- 'Golden Chasselas'	see *V. vinifera* 'Chasselas'
- 'Golden Queen' (G/W)	ERea
- 'Goldriesling' (O/W)	WSuV
- 'Grizzley Frontignan' (G/R) **new**	ERea
- 'Gros Colmar' (G/B)	WSuV
- 'Grüner Veltliner' (O/W)	WSuV
- 'Gutenborner' (O/W)	WSuV
- 'Helfensteiner' (O/R)	WSuV
- 'Huxelrebe' (O/W)	WSuV
- 'Incana' (O/B)	EBee ELon EPfP GCal MRav WCFE WCom WCot WSHC
- 'Italia' (O/W) **new**	LRHS
- 'Juliaumsrebe' (O/W)	WSuV
- 'Kanzler' (O/W)	WSuV
- 'Kerner' (O/W)	WSuV
- 'Kernling' (F)	WSuV
- 'King's Ruby' (F/S)	ERea WSuV
- 'Lady Downe's Seedling' (G/B)	ERea
- 'Lady Hastings' (G/B)	ERea
- 'Lakemont' (O/W/S)	CAgr CCCN CMac EMil EMui GTwe LRHS MBri SKee SPoG WBVN WSuV
- 'Lival' (O/B)	WSuV
- 'Madeleine Angevine' (O/W)	CAgr EMui GTwe LRHS LSRN MAsh MGos NPer SDea SVic WSuV
- 'Madeleine Celine' (B)	WSuV
- 'Madeleine Royale' (G/W)	WSuV
- 'Madeleine Silvaner' (O/W)	CSBt EMui GTwe LRHS MAsh MGos NPer SDea SPer WBVN WSuV
- 'Madresfield Court' (G/B)	ERea GTwe WSuV
- 'Merlot' (G/B)	LRHS SDea WSuV
§ - 'Meunier' (B)	WSuV
- 'Mireille' (F)	GTwe SDea WSuV
- 'Morio Muscat' (O/W)	WSuV
- 'Mrs Pearson' (G/W)	ERea
- 'Mrs Pince's Black Muscat' (G/B)	ERea
§ - 'Müller-Thurgau' (O/W)	EMui GTwe LRHS LSRN MAsh MGos NPri SDea SPer SVic WSuV
- 'Muscat Blanc à Petits Grains' (O/W)	SWvt WSuV
- 'Muscat Champion' (G/R)	ERea
- 'Muscat de Lierval' (O/B)	WSuV
- 'Muscat de Saumur' (O/W)	WSuV
- 'Muscat Hamburg' (G/B)	EMui ERea LHop LRHS LSRN MAsh MGos NScw SDea SWvt WSuV
- 'Muscat of Alexandria' (G/W)	CBcs CCCN CMac EMui ERea LRHS MRav NPal SDea SPer SVic
- 'Muscat Ottonel' (O/W)	WSuV
- 'Muscat Saint Laurent' (W)	WSuV
- 'Nebbiolo' (O/B)	WSuV
- 'No 69' (W)	WSuV
- 'Noblessa' (W) **new**	WSuV
- 'Noir Hâtif de Marseille' (O/B)	WSuV
- 'Olive Blanche' (O/W)	WSuV
- 'Oliver Irsay' (O/W)	ERea WSuV
- 'Optima' (O/W)	WSuV
- 'Ora' (O/W/S)	WSuV
- 'Ortega' (O/W)	CCCN WSuV
- 'Perle' (O/W)	WSuV
- 'Perle de Czaba' (G/O/W)	WSuV
- 'Perlette' (O/W/S)	CCCN CSut EMui ERea LRHS NPri WSuV
- 'Petit Rouge' (R)	WSuV
- 'Pinot Blanc' (O/W)	CCCN LRHS MAsh SVic WSuV
- 'Pinot Gris' (O/B)	SDea WSuV
- 'Pinot Noir' (O/B)	CCCN NPal SVic WSuV
§ - 'Portugieser' (O/B)	WSuV
- 'Précoce de Bousquet' (O/W)	WSuV
- 'Précoce de Malingre' (O/W)	CAgr SDea
- 'Prima' (O/B)	WSuV
- 'Primavis Frontignan' (G/W)	WSuV
- 'Purpurea' (O/B) ♀H4	Widely available
- 'Queen of Esther' (B)	GTwe LRHS MBri NLar SKee SLim SPoG WSuV
- 'Regner' (O/W)	WSuV
- 'Reichensteiner' (O/G/W)	SDea WSuV
- 'Riesling' (O/W)	CCCN MAsh SVic WSuV
- Riesling-Silvaner	see *V. vinifera* 'Müller-Thurgau'
- 'Rish Baba'	ERea
- 'Rotberger' (O/G/B)	WSuV
- 'Royal Muscadine' (G/O/W)	WSuV
- 'Saint Laurent' (G/O/W)	SVic WSuV
- 'Sauvignon Blanc' (O/W)	CCCN LRHS WSuV
- 'Scheurebe' (O/W)	WSuV
§ - 'Schiava Grossa' (G/B/D)	Widely available
- 'Schönburger' (O/W)	SDea SVic WSuV
- 'Schwarzriesling'	see *V. vinifera* 'Meunier'
- 'Sémillon'	LRHS MAsh
- 'Senator' (O/W)	WSuV
- 'Septimer' (O/W)	WSuV
- 'Shiraz' (B)	WSuV
- 'Siegerrebe' (O/W/D)	CAgr EMui GTwe LRHS MAsh NPer SDea SVic WSuV
- 'Silvaner' (O/W)	EMui WSuV
- 'Spetchley Red'	EBee WCot WCru WPGP WPat WSpi
- strawberry grape	see *V.* 'Fragola'
§ - 'Sultana' (W/S)	CAgr CCCN EMui GTwe SDea WSuV
- 'Theresa'	LRHS MBri SKee WSuV
- 'Thompson Seedless'	see *V. vinifera* 'Sultana'
* - 'Triomphe' (O/B)	EMui SVic
- 'Triomphrebe' (W)	WSuV
- 'Vitalis Gold'	MGos
- 'Vitalis Ruby'	MGos
- 'Wrotham Pinot' (O/B)	SDea WSuV
- 'Würzer' (O/W)	WSuV
- 'Zweigeltrebe' (O/B)	WSuV
* 'White Strawberry' (O/W)	WSuV
'Zalagyöngye' (W)	CAgr WSuV

Vriesea (*Bromeliaceae*)

carinata	MBri
hieroglyphica	MBri

× ***poelmanii***	MBri
× ***polonia***	MBri
saundersii ♀H1	MBri
splendens ♀H1	MBri XBlo
Tiffany Group new	LRHS
'Vulkana'	MBri

W

Wachendorfia (*Haemodoraceae*)

brachyandra	GCal GGar
thyrsiflora	CDes CFir CHEx CPLG CPen CPne CTsd EBee IGor LEdu WPGP

Wahlenbergia (*Campanulaceae*)

sp.	ECou
albomarginata	ECho ECou NWCA
- 'Blue Mist'	ECho ECou
ceracea	GKev NLAp
congesta	ECho GKev
cuspidata	GKev
gloriosa	ECho ECou LRHS NLAp WAbe WFar
gracilenta new	GKev
hederacea	GGar
pumilio	see *Edraianthus pumilio*
rivularis	GKev LLHF
- 'Snow-cap' new	GKev
§ ***saxicola***	CRow ECho
serpyllifolia	see *Edraianthus serpyllifolius*
stricta	ECou
tasmanica	see *W. saxicola*
undulata	CSpe
- 'Melton Bluebird' new	GJos

Walafrida (*Scrophulariaceae*)

myrtifolia	GFai

Waldsteinia (*Rosaceae*)

geoides	EBee EPPr EPfP LAst LRHS NBre NLar NPro SPer WWEG
ternata	Widely available
§ - 'Mozaick' (v)	EBee EWes NBid NBir NBre NPro
- 'Variegata'	see *W. ternata* 'Mozaick'

Wallichia (*Arecaceae*)

densiflora	LPal
disticha	LPal

walnut, black see *Juglans nigra*

walnut, common see *Juglans regia*

Wasabia (*Brassicaceae*)

wasabi	CArn GPoy LEdu

Washingtonia (*Arecaceae*)

'Filibusta' new	EAmu
filifera ♀H1	CAbb CCCN CDoC CPHo EAmu EShb ETod LPal LRHS MBri SAPC SArc SBig SEND SPlb
robusta	CBcs CTrC EAmu LPal LRHS NPal SBst SChr SPlb

Watsonia (*Iridaceae*)

aletroides	CBgR CDes CPen EBee EBrs ECho ERCP GCal GGar NCGa WCot WPGP
amatolae	IBlr
angusta	CDes CGHE CPen CPne CPrp EBee IBlr SGSe WPGP
- JCA 3.950.409	WCot
ardernei	see *W. borbonica* subsp. *ardernei* 'Arderne's White'
beatricis	see *W. pillansii*
I 'Best Red'	WCot
§ ***borbonica***	CAbb CPne CPou CPrp EShb GGal NCot SGar WCot
- subsp. ***ardernei*** misapplied	see *W. borbonica* subsp. *ardernei* (Sander) Goldblatt 'Arderne's White'
- subsp. ***ardernei*** (Sander) Goldblatt	EShb
§ - - 'Arderne's White'	CAby CBre CDes CGHE CPen CPrp EBee EBrs ECho ERos EShb GGar IBlr WPGP
- subsp. ***borbonica***	CAby CDes EBee IBlr WPGP
brevifolia	see *W. laccata*
coccinea Baker	see *W. spectabilis*
coccinea Herb. ex Baker	CPBP GGar WCot WPGP
densiflora	CPou CStu EShb IBlr IDee WCot
distans	EBee
'Flame'	NCGa
fourcadei	CPne EShb WPGP
fulgens	CPne LEdu
galpinii	CFir NCot WPGP
- lavender-flowered new	IBlr
- pink-flowered	CPrp IBlr
galpinii × ***knysnana*** new	IBlr
gladioloides	WPGP
§ ***humilis***	CDes CPBP CPou CPrp EBee WPGP
knysnana	CDes CPou CPrp EShb IBlr WCot WPGP
§ ***laccata***	CDes CFir CPBP CPne CPou CPrp EBee EShb GGar ITim WCot WHil WPGP
latifolia new	IBlr
lepida	CPou EBee IBlr
× ***longifolia*** JCA 03.952.850	WCot
marginata	CDes CPne CPou GGar WCot WPGP
- 'Star Spike'	WCot
meriania	CPen CPou ERCP GGal IBlr NCGa WCot
- var. ***bulbillifera***	CBgR CGHE CPne CPrp EBee EBrs ECho GAbr GCra GGal GGar GMac IBlr NCot WPGP
§ ***pillansii***	CAbb CGHE CHEx CPLG CPen CPne CPou CPrp ERos EShb IBlr SMrm WFar WMnd
- JCA 3.593.609	WCot
- hybrid new	WHil
- pink-flowered	CPrp
- red-flowered	GBin
pink-flowered	CDes EBee
pyramidata	see *W. borbonica*
roseoalba	see *W. humilis*
schlechteri	WPGP
§ ***spectabilis***	CPne WPGP
'Stanford Scarlet'	CDes CPne CPou CPrp CStu ELon GGar IBlr SChr SHom WPGP WSHC
stenosiphon	IBlr
strubeniae	IBlr
tabularis	CAbb IBlr
transvaalensis	EBee
'Tresco Dwarf Pink'	CDes CPrp CSam IBlr LEdu WCot WPGP
Tresco hybrids	CAbb CHll CPen CPne CSsd GGal LRHS WCFE
vanderspuyae	CPLG CPne CPou CPrp IBlr NCot WCot WPGP
'White Dazzler'	SApp

wilmaniae	CPne CPou CPrp EBee IBlr WPGP
zeyheri	WHil

Wattakaka see *Dregea*

Weigela ✿ (*Caprifoliaceae*)

CC 1231	CPLG
'Abel Carrière'	CMac CTri EBee ECtt EPfP EWes MMuc NWea WCFE WFar WSpi
'Anne Marie'	MGos
'Avalanche' misapplied	see *W.* 'Candida'
'Avalanche' Lemoine	see *W. praecox* 'Avalanche'
'Boskoop Glory'	GQui SPer
§ Briant Rubidor = 'Olympiade' (v)	CDoC CMac CSBt CWSG EBee ECtt EHoe EPfP GKir LAst LRHS MAsh MBNS MBar MGos MMuc MRav NCGa NEgg NHol NVic SLim SPer SPlb SPoG WFar
'Bristol Ruby'	CDul CMac CPLG CWib EBee ECrN ELan EPfP GKir LRHS MBar MGan MGos MHer MLHP MSwo NBir NBlu NPri NWea SBch SGar SLon SPer SPlb SRms WBVN WDin WFar WMoo
§ 'Candida'	CTri ELan EMil EWes MBar MRav NBlu NHol NLar SPer WSpi
Cappuccino = 'Verweig2'[PBR]	EBee EMil LBuc NBro NEgg NLar SGol SPoG
Carnaval = 'Courtalor'[PBR]	CBcs CWib EBee EQua GKir LRHS LSou MMuc NHol NLar SGol
'Conquête'	GKir SGol SLon
coraeensis	CHll MBlu MMHG WPat
- 'Alba'	SPer
decora	GQui
'Eva Rathke'	CAlb CTri GKir NBir NLar NWea
'Evita'	MBar MGos SGol WFar
Feline = 'Courtamon'	MBri SGol
florida	CDul CMac EPfP MBar MGos MMuc SPad WGwG
- B&SWJ 8439	WCru
- f. ***alba***	CBcs WFar
* - 'Albovariegata' (v)	CPLG LAst WBVN
- 'Bicolor'	CMac ELan
- 'Bristol Snowflake'	CDul CMac EBee EPfP GKir MBar MHer MMuc MSwo NBir NHol NLar SLon
- 'Foliis Purpureis' ♀H4	Widely available
- Minor Black = 'Verweig 3'[PBR]	LBuc MBri NBro NLar NMun SGol SPoG
- Monet = 'Verweig'[PBR] (v)	CDul EBee EGxp EMil EPfP LAst LBMP LBuc LRHS LSRN MAsh MBri MCCP MGos MMHG MPkF MRav NBro NCGa NLar NMun NPri SGol SLim SPoG WHar
- Moulin Rouge = 'Brigela'[PBR]	CBcs CDoC CSBt EPfP LBuc LRHS MBri MGos SGol
- 'Pink Princess'	LRHS MSwo
- Rubigold	see *W.* Briant Rubidor
- 'Samabor'	WFar
- 'Sunny Princess'	EQua NHol NMun SGol
- 'Suzanne' (v)	MGos NPro SGol
- 'Tango'	CPMA ECtt LRHS MAsh NHol NPro SGol
'Florida Variegata' (v) ♀H4	Widely available
florida 'Versicolor'	CMHG CMac CPLG CWib GQui SLon SMrm WFar WGor
- Wine and Roses = 'Alexandra'	CAbP CBcs CDoC CPLG CSBt EHoe ELan EMil EPfP EShb GKir LAst LRHS LSRN MAsh MBri MGos MRav MWat NCGa NEgg NLar NPri SBch SPoG SRGP SWvt WFar WGrn
'Gold Rush'	EHoe NHol NLar
'Golden Candy'	NPro
'Gustave Malet'	CMCN GQui
hortensis	CPLG
japonica 'Dart's Colourdream'	ECtt EWes GKir LAst LSou MMuc NHol SCoo SLim
'Jean's Gold'	EBee ELan MGos MRav SGol
'Kosteriana Variegata' (v)	CSBt EBee LRHS MAsh MBNS MMuc NEgg SBch SLon WFar
'Looymansii Aurea'	CMHG CPLG CTri EBee ELan EPfP GKir LAst SPer WDin WFar WHar
Lucifer = 'Courtared'[PBR]	CBcs CDoC NHol
maximowiczii	CPLG GQui
§ ***middendorffiana***	Widely available
'Minuet'	EBee EPfP LRHS MBar MGos MRav MSwo NPro SLPl
'Mont Blanc'	CBot MAsh MMHG
Nain Rouge = 'Courtanin'[PBR]	CBcs EBee MBri NHol SGol
'Nana Variegata' (v)	CPLG ECrN ELon EPfP LRHS MBar MBri MHav NBlu SBch SLPl WGwG
Naomi Campbell = 'Bokrashine'[PBR]	CBow GBin GKir MGos MMHG MWea NCGa NEgg NHol NLar SGol WFar WHar WMoo WRHF
'Newport Red'	EBee GKir MBNS MWat NWea WFar
Pink Poppet = 'Plangen'[PBR]	CAbP CSBt EKen EMil LAst LBMP LRHS LSRN LSou MAsh NHol NLar NPri SBch SCoo SGol SPoG SWvt
praecox	ECrN MWte
- B&SWJ 8705	WCru
§ - 'Avalanche'	ECtt SGar
'Praecox Variegata' (v) ♀H4	CChe CMac CTri ELan EPfP GKir LAst LRHS MAsh MRav NBir SBch SDix SPer SPoG SRms WCFE WFar WHCG WPat
'Red Prince' ♀H4	CAlb EBee ECrN ELan LBuc LRHS MGos MSwo NBlu NCGa NEgg NHol NLar SPoG
Rubidor	see *W.* Briant Rubidor
Rubigold	see *W.* Briant Rubidor
'Ruby Queen'[PBR]	CMac EBee EPfP
'Rumba'	CMac MRav NPro SGol
sessilifolia	see *Diervilla sessilifolia*
'Snowflake'	CAlb CChe EBee ECrN ECtt EWTr GKir MBNS NPro SRms WDin WFar
'Stelzneri' **new**	MMuc
subsessilis B&SWJ 1056	WCru
'Victoria'	CAlb CDul CMac CWib EBee ECrN ECtt EHoe ELan EPfP LAst LBMP LRHS MAsh MGos MSwo NBir NHol SBch SPer WBrE WFar WGor WHar WMoo
'Wessex Gold' (v)	WHCG

Weinmannia (*Cunoniaceae*)

racemosa **new**	IDee
- 'Kamahi'	CTrC
trichosperma	CBcs EBee IArd IFFs SAPC SArc SSpi

Weldenia (*Commelinaceae*)

candida	EBla ECho IBlr LLHF NMen SIng WAbe

Westringia (*Lamiaceae*)

angustifolia	ECou
brevifolia	ECou

	- var. ***raleighii***	ECou
§	***fruticosa*** 𝕐H1	CArn CBcs CCCN CTsd ECou EShb WJek
	- 'Smokie'	CTsd ECou
	- 'Variegata' (v)	GQui MNHC WJek
	longifolia	CCCN ECou
	rosmariniformis	see *W. fruticosa*
	'Smokie'	CCCN
	'Wynyabbie Gem'	EBee LRHS SEND

whitecurrant see *Ribes rubrum* (W)

Widdringtonia (*Cupressaceae*)

	cedarbergensis	CPne

Wigandia (*Hydrophyllaceae*)

	caracasana	CHll

Wikstroemia (*Thymelaeaceae*)

	gemmata	LRHS SCoo SSta

wineberry see *Rubus phoenicolasius*

Wisteria ✿ (*Papilionaceae*)

§	***brachybotrys***	SLau SLim
§	- Murasaki-kapitan	CEnd CTri CWGN EPfP MAsh WSpi
	- 'Pink Chiffon'	EPfP LRHS MAsh
	- 'Shiro-beni'	CTri LRHS MGos SEND
§	- 'Shiro-kapitan'	CBcs CEnd CSPN CTri CWGN EBee EPfP LRHS LSRN MBri MGos MRav NHol SCoo SLau SPer WPGP WPat
*	- 'White Silk'	CBcs EPfP LRHS LSRN MAsh MGos
§	'Burford'	CEnd CSPN CWGN EMui ERas LRHS LSRN MBri MGan MWat NHol SCoo SLau SLim WHar WPGP WSpi
	'Caroline'	CBcs CCCN CDoC CSBt CSPN CSam CWGN EBee EPfP ERas EWTr GKir LRHS LSRN MAsh MGos MRav NEgg NPCo SLau SPer SSpi WPGP WSHC
	floribunda	CBcs CRHN CWib ELan EPfP GGal MMuc NPCo WDin WFar
§	- 'Alba' 𝕐H4	Widely available
	- 'Black Dragon'	see *W. floribunda* 'Yae-kokuryū'
	- 'Burford'	see *W.* 'Burford'
*	- 'Cascade'	LRHS MGos NEgg WSpi
§	- 'Domino'	CEnd CMac CTri EBee ELon EPfP IArd LHop LRHS LSRN MAsh MBar MGan MGos MRav NHol SBch SCoo SEND SLau SLim SPer SSta WFar
	- 'Fragrantissima'	see *W. sinensis* 'Jako'
	- 'Geisha'	CBcs CEnd
	- 'Golden Dragon'	SLim
	- 'Goshiki' (v) new	CBcs
	- 'Hagoromo Nishiki' (V)	MGos
	- 'Harlequin'	CBcs CSPN EBee ECrN ELon GCal LRHS MAsh MGos NLar NPCo SBch SEND WFar
	- 'Hocker Edge'	SLau
	- 'Hon-beni'	see *W. floribunda* 'Rosea'
	- 'Honey Bee Pink'	see *W. floribunda* 'Rosea'
	- 'Honko'	see *W. floribunda* 'Rosea'
	- 'Issai'	LRHS LSRN MSwo
	- 'Issai Perfect'	LRHS LSRN MAsh NLar SCoo
	- 'Jakohn-fuji'	see *W. sinensis* 'Jako'
§	- 'Kuchi-beni'	CBcs CEnd CSBt CSPN EBee ELan LRHS LSRN MAsh MGos NEgg NHol NLar NPCo SCoo SEND SLau SPer SPoG
	- 'Lawrence'	CEnd CSPN EBee MBri NLar SLau
	- 'Lipstick'	see *W. floribunda* 'Kuchi-beni'
	- 'Longissima'	see *W. floribunda* 'Multijuga'
	- 'Longissima Alba'	see *W. floribunda* 'Alba'
	- 'Macrobotrys'	see *W. floribunda* 'Multijuga'
	- 'Magenta'	LRHS MAsh
§	- 'Multijuga' 𝕐H4	Widely available
	- Murasaki-naga	see *W. floribunda* 'Purple Patches'
	- 'Nana Richin's Purple'	CEnd SLau
	- 'Peaches and Cream'	see *W. floribunda* 'Kuchi-beni'
	- 'Pink Ice'	see *W. floribunda* 'Rosea'
§	- 'Purple Patches'	EBee MGos NPri
	- Reindeer	see *W. sinensis* 'Jako'
§	- 'Rosea' 𝕐H4	CBcs CDul CEnd CMac CSPN CWGN CWib EBee ECrN ELan EPfP IArd LRHS LSRN MBar MBri MGos MRav NBea NHol NPCo SLim SPer SPoG SWvt WDin WFar WSHC
	- 'Royal Purple'	CEnd LRHS MAsh MBri NLar SPoG WFar WGor
	- 'Russelliana'	CBcs EBee LRHS
	- 'Shiro-naga'	see *W. floribunda* 'Alba'
	- 'Shiro-nagi'	see *W. floribunda* 'Alba'
	- 'Shiro-noda'	see *W. floribunda* 'Alba'
	- 'Snow Showers'	see *W. floribunda* 'Alba'
	- 'Variegata' (v)	CWGN
N	- 'Violacea Plena' (d)	CBcs CDoC CMac ECrN EPfP EQua LRHS MGos NBlu NPri SPer SWvt WDin WFar
N	- 'Yae-kokuryū' (d)	Widely available
	× ***formosa***	CEnd MGan SLau SLim
	- 'Black Dragon'	see *W. floribunda* 'Yae-kokuryū'
	- 'Domino'	see *W. floribunda* 'Domino'
	- 'Issai' Wada pro parte	see *W. floribunda* 'Domino'
	- 'Kokuryū'	see *W. floribunda* 'Yae-kokuryū'
	- 'Yae-kokuryū'	see *W. floribunda* 'Yae-kokuryū'
	frutescens	EBee SLim WFar
	- 'Amethyst Falls' PBR	CEnd CWGN IArd LRHS SCoo
	- 'Magnifica'	see *W. macrostachya* 'Magnifica'
	Kapitan-fuji	see *W. brachybotrys*
	'Lavender Lace'	EBee EPfP LRHS LSRN MAsh NEgg NLar SLau WFar
	macrostachya	IArd
	'Clara Mack'	
§	- 'Magnifica'	WSpi
	multijuga 'Alba'	see *W. floribunda* 'Alba'
	'Showa-beni'	CEnd CWGN EBee EPfP LHop MGos SCoo SEND SLau SLim WPGP
	sinensis 𝕐H4	Widely available
	- 'Alba' 𝕐H4	CBcs CDoC CDul CMen CWib EBee ECrN ELan EPfP GKir ISea LAst LRHS LSRN MAsh MBar MGan MGos MNHC MWat NBlu NEgg NScw SEND SLau SLim SPer SPoG WDin WFar
	- 'Amethyst'	CBcs CEnd CSBt CSPN EBee EPfP LRHS LSRN MAsh MBri MGos MRav MWat NSti SLau SPer SReu WPat
	- 'Blue Sapphire'	CBcs CSPN EBee ISea LSRN NEgg NPCo SLau
*	- 'Caerulea'	GAuc
	- 'Consequa'	see *W. sinensis* 'Prolific'
§	- 'Jako'	CEnd MGos NHol
	- 'Oosthoek's Variety'	see *W. sinensis* 'Prolific'
I	- 'Pink Ice'	EWTr MAsh NEgg NPCo
	- 'Prematura'	see *W. floribunda* 'Domino'
	- 'Prematura Alba'	see *W. brachybotrys* 'Shiro-kapitan'

§ - 'Prolific' CDul CMac CSBt CSam CTri CWib EBee ELan EMac EPfP LBuc LRHS LSou MBri MGos MRav NBlu NHol SBch SCoo SEND SPer SSpi SWvt WFar WPGP WPat
- 'Rosea' LRHS LSRN MGos SPur SWvt WSpi
- 'Shiro-capital' see *W. brachybotrys* 'Shiro-kapitan'
'Tiverton' CBcs CWit EBee
venusta see *W. brachybotrys* 'Shiro-kapitan'
- 'Alba' see *W. brachybotrys* 'Shiro-kapitan'
- var. ***violacea*** misapplied see *W. brachybotrys* Murasaki-kapitan
- var. ***violacea*** Rehder see *W. brachybotrys* Murasaki-kapitan

Withania (*Solanaceae*)
somnifera CArn EOHP ERea GPoy

Wittsteinia (*Alseuosmiaceae*)
vacciniacea WCru

Wodyetia (*Arecaceae*)
bifurcata LPal XBlo

Wollemia (*Araucariaceae*)
nobilis EPfP ESwi LRHS MAsh WMou

Woodsia (*Woodsiaceae*)
obtusa CBty CDTJ CLAP CWCL EBee EFer EMil EWTr GMaP LRHS NBro NHol NLar NMyG SRot WPnP WRic WWEG
polystichoides ♀H4 GQui SRms WAbe

Woodwardia (*Blechnaceae*)
from Emei Shan, China CLAP
fimbriata Widely available
martinezii GLin
obtusa new SBch
orientalis WCot WFib
- var. ***formosana*** CLAP
- - B&SWJ 6865 WCru
radicans ♀H3 CAbb CHEx CHid CLAP EWes EWld GQui ISea SAPC SArc WFib WRic
unigemmata CHEx CLAP EWes EWld SAPC SArc WAbe WFib WHal WRic
virginica CLAP

Worcesterberry see *Ribes* 'Worcesterberry'

Wulfenia (*Scrophulariaceae*)
carinthiaca EBee ECho GEdr GKev NBir NHol NLar SBHP WPer
× ***schwarzii*** CDes EBee

Wurmbea (*Colchicaceae*)
recurva CStu ECho

X

Xanthium (*Asteraceae*)
sibiricum CArn

Xanthoceras (*Sapindaceae*)
sorbifolium ♀H3-4 CAgr CArn CBcs CBot CMCN CWib EBee ECrN ELan EPfP GKir IDee LRHS MBlu MBri SMad SPoG SSpi WDin WPat WSpi

Xanthocyparis see *Chamaecyparis*

Xanthorhiza (*Ranunculaceae*)
simplicissima CArn CBcs CGHE CRow EPfP GCal LEdu MBri NLar SDys SPer SSpi WPGP

Xanthorrhoea (*Xanthorrhoeaceae*)
australis SPlb
glauca CCCN CDTJ

Xanthosoma (*Araceae*)
sagittifolium CDTJ
violaceum CDTJ EAmu WWst

Xerochrysum (*Asteraceae*)
§ ***bracteatum*** 'Coco' CMHG CSpe MAJR WWlt
§ - 'Dargan Hill Monarch' CHll CMHG CSpe MAJR SRms WWlt
§ - 'Skynet' MAJR WWlt
- 'Wollerton' WWlt
'Sundaze Flame' new LSou

Xeronema (*Phormiaceae*)
callistemon CBcs CTrC

Xerophyllum (*Melanthiaceae*)
tenax GCal GGar NMen

Xylorhiza see *Machaeranthera*

Xyris (*Xyridaceae*)
torta WPGP

Youngberry see *Rubus* 'Youngberry'

Ypsilandra (*Melanthiaceae*)
cavaleriei CPLG EBee GEdr WCot
thibetica CDes CFir CGHE CPLG CSpe EBee EBla GEdr LAma LEdu LLHF LRHS SMad WCot WCru WPGP WSHC

Yucca ✿ (*Agavaceae*)
SDR 3701 GKev
aloifolia CCCN CDoC CHEx EAmu EBee ISea MGos MREP SAPC SArc SBch SBig SChr SEND SMad SPlb
§ - f. ***marginata*** (v) EAmu LPal MREP SArc SBig
- 'Purpurea' MAga SPlb
- 'Tricolor' (v) MREP
- 'Variegata' see *Y. aloifolia* f. *marginata*
angustifolia see *Y. glauca*
angustissima NNS 99-509 WCot
arizonica CBrP
baccata CCCN CTrC ETod LEdu
- NNS 99-510 WCot
baileyi GCal
carnerosana CTrC EAmu
§ ***elata*** CCCN CTrC EAmu ETod WPGP
§ ***elephantipes*** ♀H1 EAmu LRHS MBri SBch SEND
- 'Jewel' (v) EAmu SEND
faxoniana EAmu MAga WPGP
faxoniana × ***glauca*** MAga
filamentosa ♀H4 Widely available
- 'Antwerp' GCal
- 'Bright Edge' (v) ♀H3 Widely available

- 'Color Guard' (v)	CTrC LAst MBri NLar WCot WFar
- 'Garland's Gold' (v)	CBcs CCCN CDoC GQui MAsh MGos SBch SBig WCot WFar
- 'Variegata' (v) ♀H3	CBcs EPfP MGos SRms WDin WFar
filifera	EAmu ETod
flaccida	MGos MMuc SDix
- 'Golden Sword' (v) ♀H3	CBcs CDoC CHVG CMac CSBt CTrC CWSG EBee ECrN ELan EPfP GKir LAst LRHS LSRN MAsh MCCP MGos MSCN MSwo NBlu NMoo NScw SBch SLim SPer SPoG SWvt WCot
- 'Ivory' ♀H3-4	CBcs CDoC CEnd EBee ECtt ELan ELon EPfP GCal GKir LEdu LRHS LSRN MBlu MBri MGos MRav SBch SPer SRms SSta STre WMoo
× ***floribunda***	SAPC SArc
§ ***glauca***	CBrP EPfP GLin IFFs LEdu LRHS MBri NPal SAPC
* - var. ***radiosa***	CTrC
gloriosa ♀H4	CBcs CDoC CHEx CMac CTri EAmu EPfP EPla LRHS MGos MREP NPal NScw SAPC SArc SBch SEND SPer SPlb SPoG SWvt WBrE WBrk WCor
- 'Aureovariegata'	see *Y. gloriosa* 'Variegata'
§ - 'Variegata' (v) ♀H4	Widely available
guatemalensis	see *Y. elephantipes*
linearis	see *Y. thompsoniana*
'Nobilis'	CHEx SDix
pallida new	WPGP
radiosa	see *Y. elata*
recurvifolia ♀H4	CHEx EAmu EPfP GCal MGos SAPC SArc SBch
- 'Gold Stream' (v) new	WCot
rigida	CBrP EAmu WPGP
rostrata	CAbb CBrP CCCN CDTJ CTrC EAmu EBee ETod LPal MREP SChr
'Sapphire Star'	CBow
schidigera NNS 03-597	WCot
schottii	CAbb CBrP CTrC MAga WCot
§ ***thompsoniana***	CTrC EAmu LPal
- blue-leaved	EAmu
torreyi	CTrC CWit SChr
treculeana	EAmu MAga
'Vittorio Emanuele II'	SMad
whipplei	CAbb CBcs CBrP CCCN CDoC CTsd EBee ELan IGor LRHS MAga NPal SBch SBig WCot WPGP
- NNS 01-412	WCot
- NNS 05-696	WCot
- subsp. ***caespitosa*** new	GAuc WPGP
- subsp. ***intermedia*** NNS 01-413	WCot
- - NNS 05-697	WCot
- subsp. ***parishii*** NNS 01-415	WCot
- - NNS 05-699	WCot
- subsp. ***percursa*** NNS 05-700	WCot
- subsp. ***whipplei*** NNS 05-701	WCot

Yushania (*Poaceae*)

§ ***anceps***	CBcs CDoC CEnt CHEx CPLG EBee ENBC EPfP EPla GBin MBar MGos MMoz MMuc MWht SAPC SArc SBig SEND WFar WMoo WPGP
- 'Pitt White'	CEnt CGHE EBee EPla MWht WJun WPGP
- 'Pitt White Rejuvenated'	EPla ERod WPGP
brevipaniculata	EPla WJun
chungii	CEnt EPla WJun WPGP
* ***equatus*** new	WJun
maculata	CEnt CMCo EPla ERod MMoz MWht SBig WJun
§ ***maling***	EPfP EPla ERod MMoz WJun
Yunnan 5	EPla WPGP

Z

Zaluzianskya (*Scrophulariaceae*)

sp.	NMen
JCA 15665	WAbe
capensis	LPio
'Katherine'	SIng SRot
microsiphon	SPlb
'Orange Eye'	ELon LPio NSla WAbe
ovata	CPBP EDAr EPot LHop LPio LRHS MTho NBur NSla NWCA SAga SIng SPoG WCom
pulvinata	SPlb WAbe
'Semonkong'	GCal LPio LSou

Zamia (*Zamiaceae*)

furfuracea	CBrP
muricata	LPal
skinneri	LPal

Zamioculcas (*Araceae*)

zamiifolia	CCCN

Zantedeschia (*Araceae*)

§ ***aethiopica*** ♀H3	Widely available
- 'Apple Court Babe'	CAby CElw CRow CStu GCal MAvo MNrw SMrm WDyG
- 'Caerwent'	CPen
- 'Childsiana'	SApp
I - 'Childsiana Lisa'	EBrs
- 'Crowborough' ♀H3	Widely available
- 'Gigantea'	CHEx
- 'Glow'	CBct CBgR CMac EBee LAst LRHS LSou MAvo MBel MNrw MRav NCGa NGdn SMrm SPer WClo WCot WGwG
- 'Green Goddess' ♀H3	Widely available
- 'Little Gem'	SMad WFar
- 'Luzon Lovely'	WCru
* - 'Marshmallow'	EAEE EBee ECtt ELan EPfP EShb LRHS NCGa SPet WFar
- 'Mr Martin'	CBct CCCN CHid CMac CStu CTrC EBee ECtt EWll LAst LOck LRHS MNrw NCGa SBch SBig SMad SWvt WCot WPGP
- 'Pershore Fantasia' (v)	CBct EBee MAvo MSKA WCom WCot WFar
- pink-flowered	CHEx
- 'Tiny Tim'	SChr WWEG
- 'Whipped Cream'	MDKP MNrw
- 'White Gnome'	WCot WFar WPGP
- 'White Mischief'	EBee
- 'White Sail'	CBct CPrp EAEE EBee GBuc GCal LRHS MNrw MRav NGdn SWat WFar
albomaculata	CPLG EBrs EPfP LAma LRHS MNrw SGar SPlb
'Anneke'	CCCN EBrs ECho EPfP GGar LRHS SPer WBrE

'Apricot Glow'	CHll
'Black Eyed Beauty'	EBrs LAma
'Black Magic'	CCCN CMac EBrs ECho EPfP SPer
'Black Pearl'	LAma
'Black Star'	see Z. 'Edge of Night'
black-flowered	CSut WCom
'Cameo'	CCCN EBrs ECho LAma
(Captain Series)	LAma
'Captain Chelsea' **new**	
- 'Captain Palermo'PBR **new**	LAma
- 'Captain Samos' **new**	LAma
- 'Captain Tendens'PBR	LAma
- 'Captain Volante'PBR **new**	LRHS
'Carmine Red'	WBrE
'Celeste'	EBrs
'Crystal Blush'	LAma LRHS
§ 'Edge of Night'	CCCN ERCP LRHS
elliottiana ♀H1	CBcs CFir CHEx CTri EBrs EPfP GQui LAma MNrw
- 'Cream'	SWal
'Flame'	EBrs LRHS
'Gabrielle'PBR **new**	LRHS
'Galaxy'	EBrs
'Harvest Moon'	EBrs LAma
'Kiwi Blush'	CAbP CBen CBro CCCN CFir CHEx CSpe EAEE EBee ELan EPfP EWll LPBA LRHS MAvo MCCP NGdn NPal SApp SBch SEND SPad SPer SPet SWat WFar WGwG
'Lime Lady'	CBct ECha
'Lipstick' **new**	LRHS
'Majestic Red'	EBrs
'Mango'	EBrs EWll LAma WCot
'Mozart'	LRHS
'Peach Chiffon'PBR **new**	LRHS
'Picasso'PBR **new**	ERCP LRHS
'Pink Mist'	CBct EBrs ERCP EShb LAma SWal WPnP
'Pink Persuasion'	EBrs LAma
'Red Embers' **new**	LRHS
rehmannii ♀H1	EBrs GQui LAma MNrw NLar SGar SRms
- 'Superba'	LRHS
'Schwarzwalder'PBR	EBrs EGxp ERCP LRHS
'Selina' **new**	LRHS
'Sensation'	EBrs
'Silver Lining'	LAma
'Solfatare'	EBrs ECho EWTr
'Sunshine'	EWll
'Treasure'	EBrs
'White Pixie'	EPfP SAga WViv

Zanthorhiza see *Xanthorhiza*

Zanthoxylum (*Rutaceae*)

acanthopodium GWJ 9287	WCru
ailanthoides	EPfP
- B&SWJ 8535	WCru
- B&SWJ 11115 from Japan	WCru
- B&SWJ 11394 from Japan	WCru
- f. ***inermis*** RWJ 10048 **new**	WCru
americanum	CAgr ELan IArd IFFs LEdu
armatum	CAgr
- HWJK 2178	WCru
bungeanum HWJK 2131	WCru
fauriei B&SWJ 11080	WCru
aff. ***fauriei*** B&SWJ 11371 **new**	WCru
I ***giraldii*** **new**	GAuc
laetum WWJ 11678 **new**	WCru
myriacanthum B&SWJ 11844 **new**	WCru
oxyphyllum	WPGP
- HWJK 2199	WCru
piperitum	CAgr EBee GPoy IArd IFFs SEND SPoG WPGP
- B&SWJ 8543	WCru
- purple-leaved	WPGP
schinifolium	CAgr EBee LEdu
- B&SWJ 8593	WCru
- B&SWJ 11080	WCru
- B&SWJ 11391	WCru
simulans	CArn CBcs CPLG EBee GBin LEdu MBlu MBri NLar WPGP

Zauschneria (*Onagraceae*)

§ ***californica***	CHll CSam CTri ECGP ECho EDAr EPfP MBrN NMen SGar SLon SWat WHrl WPnn
§ - subsp. ***cana***	ECha SWat
- - 'Sir Cedric Morris'	EPfP LRHS MAsh
§ - 'Dublin' ♀H3	CBcs EBee ECha ECho ECtt EDAr EPfP EPot GGar LHop LRHS MAsh MHer MWat NWCA SAga SIng SPer SPlb SPoG SRkn SRot SUsu WFar WHlf WHoo WKif WPat WSHC
- 'Ed Carman'	ECtt LSou
§ - subsp. ***garrettii***	ECho NWCA SDys SWat
- 'Glasnevin'	see *Z. californica* 'Dublin'
- subsp. ***latifolia*** 'Sally Walker'	EWes
§ - subsp. ***mexicana***	EPot MHer SRms
- 'Olbrich Silver'	EBee ECha ECtt EShb EWes LRHS MAsh NMen NWCA SUsu WAbe WCom WFar WHil WHoo WPat
- 'Schieffelin's Choice'	WCom
- 'Sierra Salmon'	WPat
- 'Solidarity Pink'	ECha LHop MTho NMen NWCA WAbe WPat
- 'Western Hills' ♀H4	CFir CSpe CTri EBee ECha ECho ECtt EDAr EPfP LHop LRHS LSou MRav NWCA SAga SEND SIng SPhx WAbe WCom WPat
cana villosa	see *Z. californica* subsp. ***mexicana***
I 'Pumilio'	EPot NMen WAbe
§ ***septentrionalis***	WAbe

Zea (*Poaceae*)

mays 'Quadricolor' (v)	SBch

Zebrina see *Tradescantia*

Zelkova ✿ (*Ulmaceae*)

carpinifolia	CDoC CMCN CMen CTho NHol SPlb WDin
'Kiwi Sunset'	EBee LRHS MAsh NWea
schneideriana	CMen EGFP
serrata ♀H4	CBcs CDul CLnd CMCN CMen CTho ECrN ELan EPfP GKir LMaj MBar MBri MMuc NBea NHol NMun NWea SBir SEND SPer STre WDin WFar WHCr
- B&SWJ 8491 from Korea	WCru
- 'Goblin'	MAsh WPat
- 'Green Vase'	LMaj LRHS MBlu
- 'Urban Ruby'	MGos
- 'Variegata' (v)	CMac CPMA MBlu
- 'Yatsubusa'	STre
sinica	CMCN CMen

Zenobia (*Ericaceae*)

pulverulenta	CAbP CBcs CDoC CDul CMac CSBt CTrG EBee ELan EPfP GQui IDee LRHS MAsh MBar MBlu MBri MGos SBod SLon SPer SReu SSpi SSta WAbe WBVN WDin WFar WPat WSHC
- 'Blue Sky'	CAbP CMCN EPfP LRHS MAsh MBlu MBri MGos NLar SPoG SSpi SSta WPGP
- 'Misty Blue'	GGGa
- f. ***nitida***	CMac
- 'Raspberry Ripple'	MBlu MBri NLar SSta
- 'Viridis'	NLar

Zephyranthes ✿ (*Amaryllidaceae*)

atamasca	CStu ERos
candida	CAvo CBro CFFs CPBP CSpe CStu EBee EBrs ECho EPot ERos EShb ITim LAma LRHS SDix WHil
citrina	CBgR CGrW CPLG EBee EBrs ECho EPot ERos LAma WCot
drummondii	CStu ECho WCot
flavissima	CBro CPBP EBrs ECho WCot WHil WPGP
grandiflora ♀H2-3	ECho
'Grandjax'	WCot
'La Buffa Rose'	CStu WCot
lindleyana	WCot
mexicana	ERos
minima	CStu EBee ECho LLHF
minuta	CStu
robusta	see *Habranthus robustus*
rosea	CGrW EBee EBrs EPot

Zieria (*Rutaceae*)

cytisoides	ECou

Zigadenus (*Melanthiaceae*)

elegans	EBee ECGP ECha EDAr ERos GBee GCal LRHS MAvo SMad SUsu WSHC WTin
fremontii	WCot
nuttallii	EBrs ECho ERos MDKP SPhx WCot
venenosus NNS 03-605	WCot
virescens	EBee EBrs

Zingiber (*Zingiberaceae*)

mioga	CMac EBee GPoy IMou LEdu SPlb WDyG WPGP
- B&SWJ 4379	WCru
- 'Dancing Crane' (v)	CMac EBee IFro
officinale	CTsd

Zinnia (*Asteraceae*)

'Red Spider'	CSpe

Zizania (*Poaceae*)

caducifolia	see *Z. latifolia*
§ ***latifolia***	IMou

Zizia (*Apiaceae*)

aptera	CDes EBee SPhx WPGP
aurea	SDix SPhx WSHC WTin

Ziziphus (*Rhamnaceae*)

§ ***jujuba*** (F)	CAgr CBcs
- 'Lang' (F)	CAgr
- 'Li' (F)	CAgr
- var. ***spinosa***	CArn
sativa	see *Z. jujuba*

BIBLIOGRAPHY

This is by no means exhaustive but lists some of the more useful works used in the preparation of the *RHS Plant Finder*. The websites of raisers of new plants (not listed here) are also an invaluable source of information.

GENERAL

Allan, H.H., et al. 2000. *Flora of New Zealand.* Wellington. (5 vols).

Ball Colegrave. 2007. *Plant Catalogue 2008*. West Adderbury, Oxon: Ball Colegrave.

Ball Colegrave. 2007. *Seed Catalogue 2008*. West Adderbury, Oxon: Ball Colegrave.

Bean, W.J. 1988. *Trees and Shrubs Hardy in the British Isles.* (8th ed. edited by Sir George Taylor & D.L. Clarke & Supp. ed. D.L. Clarke). London: John Murray.

Beckett, K. (ed.). 1994. *Alpine Garden Society Encyclopaedia of Alpines.* Pershore, Worcs.: Alpine Garden Society.

Boufford, D.E., et al. (eds). 2003. *Flora of Taiwan Checklist*. A checklist of the vascular plants of Taiwan. Taipei, Taiwan: NTU. http://tai2.ntu.edu.tw

Bramwell, D. & Bramwell, Z.I. 2001. *Wild Flowers of the Canary Islands.* (2nd ed.). Madrid: Editorial Rueda, S.L.

Brickell, C. (ed.). 2003. *The Royal Horticultural Society A-Z Encyclopedia of Garden Plants.* (2nd ed.) London: Dorling Kindersley.

Brickell, C.D. et al (eds.). 2004. *International Code of Nomenclature for Cultivated Plants* (7th ed.). ISHS.

Brummitt, R.K. (comp.). 1992. *Vascular Plant Families and Genera.* Kew: Royal Botanic Gardens. http://data.kew.org

Castroviejo, S. et al. (eds). *Flora Iberica.* 1987-2007. (Vols 1-8,, 10, 14, 15, 21). Madrid: Real Jardín Botánico, C.S.I.C.

Cave, Y. & Paddison, V. 1999. *The Gardener's Encyclopaedia of New Zealand Native Plants.* Auckland: Godwit.

Cooke, I. 1998. *The Plantfinder's Guide to Tender Perennials.* Newton Abbot, Devon: David & Charles.

Cronquist, A., Holmgren, A.H., Holmgren, N.H., Reveal, J.L. & Holmgren, P.H. et al. (eds). *Intermountain Flora: Vascular Plants of the Intermountain West, USA.* (1986-97). (Vols 1, 3-6). New York: New York Botanical Garden.

Davis, P.H., Mill, R.R. & Tan, K. (eds). 1965-88. *Flora of Turkey and the East Aegean Island.* (Vols 1-10). Edinburgh University Press.

Goldblatt, P. & Manning, J. 2000. *Cape Plants. A Conspectus of the Cape Flora of South Africa.* South Africa/USA: National Botanical Institute of South Africa/Missouri Botanical Garden.

Greuter, W., Brummitt, R.K., Farr, E., Kilian, N., Kirk, P.M. & Silva, P.C. (comps). 1993. *NCU-3.* Grierson, A.J.C., Long, D.G. & Noltie, H.J. et al. (eds). 2001. *Flora of Bhutan.* Edinburgh: Royal Botanic Garden.

Güner, A., Özhatay, N., Ekîm, T., Baser, K.H.C. & Hedge, I.C. 2000. *Flora of Turkey and the East Aegean Islands.* Supp. 2. Vol. 11. Edinburgh: Edinburgh University Press.

Hickman, J.C. (ed.). 1993. *The Jepson Manual. Higher Plants of California*. Berkeley & Los Angeles: University of California Press. May 2007. http://ucjeps.berkeley.edu

Hillier, J. & Coombes, A. (eds). 2002. *The Hillier Manual of Trees & Shrubs.* (7th ed.). Newton Abbot, Devon: David & Charles.

Hirose, Y. & Yokoi, M. 1998. *Variegated Plants in Colour.* Iwakuni, Japan: Varie Nine.

Hirose, Y. & Yokoi, M. 2001. *Variegated Plants in Colour.* Vol. 2. Iwakuni, Japan: Varie Nine.

Hoffman, M. (ed.). 2005. *List of Woody Plants. International Standard ENA 2005-2010.* Netherlands: Applied Plant Research.

Huxley, A., Griffiths, M. & Levy, M. (eds). 1992. *The New RHS Dictionary of Gardening.* London: Macmillan.

Iwatsuki, K., et al. 1995. *Flora of Japan*. Vols I-IIIb. Tokyo, Japan: Kodansha Ltd.

Jelitto, L. & Schacht, W. 1990. *Hardy Herbaceous Perennials.* Portland, Oregon: Timber Press. (2 vols).

Krüssmann, G. & Epp, M.E. (trans.). 1986. *Manual of Cultivated Broad-leaved Trees and Shrubs.* London: Batsford (3 vols).

Leslie, A.C. (trans.). *New Cultivars of Herbaceous Perennial Plants 1985-1990.* Hardy Plant Society.

Mabberley, D.J. 1997. *The Plant-Book. A Portable Dictionary of the Vascular Plants.* (2nd ed.). Cambridge: Cambridge University Press.

McNeill, J. et al. (eds). 2006. *International Code of Botanical Nomenclature (Vienna Code).* Ruggell, Liechtenstein: A.R.G. Gantner Verlag. http://ibot.sav.sk. Mar 2007.

Metcalf, L.J. 1987. *The Cultivation of New Zealand Trees and Shrubs.* Auckland: Reed Methuen.

Nelson, E.C. 2000. *A Heritage of Beauty: The Garden Plants of Ireland: An Illustrated Encyclopaedia.* Dublin: Irish Garden Plant Society.

Ohwi, J. 1965. *Flora of Japan.* Washington DC: Smithsonian Institution.

Phillips, R. & Rix, M. 1997. *Conservatory and Indoor Plants.* London: Macmillan. (2 vols).

Platt, K. (comp.). 2002. *The Seed Search.* (5th ed.). Sheffield: Karen Platt.

Press, J.R. & Short, M.J. (eds). 1994. *Flora of Madeira.* London: Natural History Museum/ HMSO.

Rehder, A. 1940. *Manual of Cultivated Trees and Shrubs Hardy in North America.* (2nd ed.). New York: Macmillan.

Rice, G. (ed.), 2006. *Encyclopedia of Perennials.* London: Dorling Kindersley.

Stace, C. 1997. *New Flora of the British Isles.* (2nd ed.). Cambridge: Cambridge University Press.

Stearn, W.T. 1992. *Botanical Latin.* (4th ed.). Newton Abbot, Devon: David & Charles.

Stearn, W.T. 1996. *Stearn's Dictionary of Plant Names for Gardeners.* London: Cassell.

Thomas, G.S. 1990. *Perennial Garden Plants. A Modern Florilegium.* (3rd ed.). London: Dent.

Trehane, P. (comp.). 1989. *Index Hortensis. Vol. 1: Perennials.* Wimborne: Quarterjack

Tutin, T.G., et al. (ed.). 1993. *Flora Europaea. Vol. 1. Psilotaceae to Platanaceae.* (2nd ed.). Cambridge University Press.

Tutin, T.G., et al. 1964. *Flora Europaea.* Cambridge University Press. Vols 1-5. http://rbg-web2.rbge.org.uk

Walter, K.S. & Gillett, H.J. (eds). 1998. *1997 IUCN Red List of Threatened Plants.* Gland, Switzerland and Cambridge, UK: IUCN.

Walters, S.M. & Cullen, J. et al. (eds). 2000. *The European Garden Flora.* Cambridge: Cambridge University Press. (6 vols).

World Checklist of Selected Plant Families

GENERAL PERIODICALS

Dendroflora

New, Rare and Unusual Plants.

The Hardy Plant Society. *The Hardy Plant.*

The Hardy Plant Society. *The Sport.*

Internationale Stauden-Union. *ISU Yearbook.*

Royal Horticultural Society. *Hanburyana.*

Royal Horticultural Society. *The Garden.*

Royal Horticultural Society. *The Plantsman.*

Royal Horticultural Society. *The New Plantsman.*

Royal Horticultural Society. *The Plantsman* (new series).

GENERAL WEBSITES

Annotated Checklist of the Flowering Plants of Nepal. www.efloras.org

Australian Cultivar Registration Authority. Oct 2007. www.anbg.gov.au/acra.

Australian Plant Breeders Rights – Database Search. May 2006. http://pbr.ipaustralia.optus.com.au

Australian Plant Names Index. Australian National Botanic Gardens (comp.). Mar 2006. www.anbg.gov.au/anbg

Bolivia Checklist. www.efloras.org

Botanical Expedition in Myanmar Checklist. Apr 2003. http://persoon.si.edu/myanmar

Brand, H. UConn Plant Database of Trees Shrubs and Vines. www.hort.uconn.edu

Canadian Ornamental Plant Foundation. Dec 2007. www.copf.org

Canadian Plant Breeders' Rights Office: Canadian Food Inspection Agency. Dec 2007. www.inspection.gc.ca

Catálogo de las Plantas Vasculares de las República Argentina. 2007. www.darwin.edu.ar/Publicaciones

Darwin Checklist of Moroccan Vascular Plants www.herbarium.rdg.ac.uk/

DEFRA Plant Varieties and Seeds Gazette. Nov 2007. www.defra.gov.uk

Fischer France. Apr 2002. www.pelfi.fr

Flora Himalaya Checklist www.leca.univ-savoie.fr

Flora Mesoamericana Internet Version (W3FM). Oct 2006. Missouri Botanical Garden. www.mobot.org

Flora of Australia Online. Jul 2007. Australian Biological Resources Study. www.environment.gov.au/biodiversity

Flora of Chile. www.efloras.org

Flora of China Checklist. Jan 2008. http://flora.huh.harvard.edu/china

Flora of North America Website. Jan 2006. Morin, N. R., et al. www.efloras.org

GRIN (Germplasm Resources Information Network) Taxonomy. Dec 2007. www.ars-grin.gov

Hatch, D. Jan 2008. New Ornamentals Society Database. http://members.tripod.com

Index Synonymique de la Flore de France. Oct 1999. www.dijon.inra.fr

International Plant Names Index. Oct 2007. www.ipni.org

International Plant Names Index: Author Query. Oct 2006. www.ipni.org/ipni

IOPI Provisional Global Plant Checklist. Feb 2005. www.bgbm.fu-berlin.de

Manaaki Whenua: Landcare Research in New Zealand Plants Database http://nzflora.landcareresearch.co.nz

Manual de plantas de Costa Rica. Apr 2001. www.mobot.org

Plants Database. Jan 2008. USDA, NRCS. http://plants.usda.gov

Plants of Southern Africa: an Online Checklist. Jan 2007. http://posa.sanbi.org

New Zealand Plant Variety Rights Office www.pvr.govt.nz

SKUD Database for Cultivated and Utilized Plants. http://skud.ngb.se

Synonymized Checklist of the Vascular Flora of the United States, Puerto Rico and the Virgin Isles. BIOTA of North America Program. Jul 1998. www.csdl.tamu.edu

US Patent Full-Text Database. US Patent and Trademark Office, (comp.). Jan 2008. www.uspto.gov/patft

VAST TROPICOS. Jan 2004. http://mobot.mobot.org
World Checklist of Selected Families. 2007. www.kew.org

Genera and other Plant Groupings

Acer

Harris, J.G.S. 2000. *The Gardener's Guide to Growing Maples.* Newton Abbot, Devon: David & Charles.
Van Gelderen, C.J. & Van Gelderen, D.M. 1999. *Maples for Gardens.* A Color Encyclopedia. Portland, Oregon: Timber Press.
Vertrees, J.D. 2001. *Japanese Maples.* Momiji and Kaede. (3rd ed.). Portland, Oregon: Timber Press.

Actaea

Compton, J.A. & Culham, A. 2000. The Name is the Game. *The Garden* (RHS) 125(1):48-52.
Compton, J.A., Culham, A. & Jury, S.L. 1998. Reclassification of *Actaea* to Include *Cimicifuga* and *Souliea* (*Ranunculaceae*). *Taxon* 47:593-634.

Adiantum

Goudey, C.J. 1985. *Maidenhair Ferns in Cultivation.* Melbourne: Lothian.

Agapanthus

Snoeijer, W. 2004. *Agapanthus. A Revision of the Genus.* Portland, Oregon: Timber Press.

Agavaceae

Irish, M. & Irish, G. 2000. *Agaves, Yuccas and Related Plants.* A Gardener's Guide. Portland, Oregon: Timber Press.

Aizoaceae

Burgoyne, P. et al. 1998. *Mesembs of the World. Illustrated Guide to a Remarkable Succulent Group.* South Africa: Briza Publications.

Allium

Davies, D. 1992. *Alliums. The Ornamental Onions.* London: Batsford
Gregory, M., et al. 1998. *Nomenclator Alliorum.* Kew: Royal Botanic Gardens.
Mathew, B. 1996. *A Review of Allium Section Allium.* Kew: Royal Botanic Gardens.

Androsace

Smith, G. & Lowe, D. 1997. *The Genus Androsace.* Pershore, Worcs.: Alpine Garden Society.

***Anemone*, Japanese**

McKendrick, M. 1990. Autumn Flowering Anemones. *The Plantsman* 12(3):140-151.
McKendrick, M. 1998. Japanese Anemones. *The Garden* (RHS) 123(9):628-633.

Anthemis

Leslie, A. 1997. Focus on Plants: *Anthemis tinctoria. The Garden* (RHS) 122(8):552-555.

Apiaceae

Pimenov, M.G. & Leonov, M.V. 1993. *The Genera of the Umbelliferae.* Kew: Royal Botanic Gardens.

Aquilegia

Munz, P.A. 1946. *Aquilegia:* the Cultivated and Wild Columbines. *Gentes Herb.* 7(1):1-150.

Araceae

Govaerts, R. & Frodin, D.G. 2002. *World Checklist and Bibliography of Araceae (and Acoraceae).* Kew: Royal Botanic Gardens

***Arecaceae* (palms)**

Craft, P. & Riffle, R.L. 2003. *Encyclopedia of Cultivated Palms.* Portland, Oregon: Timber Press.
Uhl, N.W. & Dransfield, J. 1987. *Genera Palmarum.* A Classification of Palms Based on the Work of Harold E. Moore Jr. Lawrence, Kansas: Allen Press.

Argyranthemum

Humphries, C.J. 1976. A Revision of the Macaronesian Genus *Argyranthemum. Bull. Brit. Mus. (Nat. Hist.) Bot.* 5(4):145-240.

Araliaceae

Govaerts, R. & Frodin, D.G. 2002. *World Checklist and Bibliography of Araliaceae.* Kew: Royal Botanic Gardens

Arisaema

Gusman, G. & Gusman, L. 2002. *The Genus Arisaema: A Monograph for Botanists and Nature Lovers.* Ruggell, Leichtenstein: A.R. Gantner Verlag Kommanditgesellschaft.
Pradhan, U.C. 1997. *Himalayan Cobra Lilies* (Arisaema). Their Botany and Culture. (2nd ed.). Kalimpong, West Bengal, India: Primulaceae Books.

Arum

Bown, D. 2000. *Plants of the Arum Family.* (2nd ed.). Portland, Oregon: Timber Press.
Boyce, P. 1993. *The Genus Arum.* London: HMSO.

Asclepiadaceae

Eggli, U. (ed.). 2002. *Illustrated Handbook of Succulent Plants: Asclepiadaceae.* Heidelberg, Germany: Springer-Verlag.

Aster

Picton, P. 1999. *The Gardener's Guide to Growing Asters.* Newton Abbot: David & Charles.

Asteraceae

Bremer, K. et al. 1994. *Asteraceae: Cladistics and Classification.* Portland, Oregon: Timber Press.
Cubey, J. & Grant, M. 2004. *Perennial Yellow Daisies: RHS Bulletin No 6.* Wisley, Surrey: RHS. www.rhs.org.uk/plants/documents/yellowdaisies04.pdf

Astilbe

Noblett, H. 2001. *Astilbe.* A Guide to the Identification of Cultivars and Common Species. Cumbria: Henry Noblett.

Aubrieta

1975. *International Registration Authority Checklist.* Weihenstephan, Germany: (Unpublished).

Bamboos

Ohrnberger, D. 1999. *The Bamboos of the World.* Amsterdam: Elsevier.

Begonia

American Begonia Society Astro Branch Begonia Data Base. Jan 2000. http://absastro.tripod.com
American Begonia Society Registered Begonias. 2007. http://www.begonias.org

Ingles, J. 1990. *American Begonia Society Listing of Begonia Cultivars.* Revised Edition Buxton Checklist. American Begonia Society.

Tebbitt, M.C. 2005. *Begonias: Cultivation, Identification and Natural History*. Portland, Oregon: Timber Press.

Thompson, M.L. & Thompson, E.J. 1981. *Begonias.* The Complete Reference Guide. New York: Times Books.

Berberidaceae

Stearn, W.T. & Shaw, J.M.H. 2002. *The Genus Epimedium and Other Herbaceous Berberidaceae including the Genus Podophyllum.* Kew: Royal Botanic Gardens.

Betula

Ashburner, K. & Schilling. T. 1985. *Betula utilis* and its Varieties. *The Plantsman* 7(2):116-125.

Ashburner, K.B. 1980. *Betula* – a Survey. *The Plantsman* 2(1):31-53.

Hunt, D. (ed.). 1993. *Betula: Proceedings of the IDS Betula Symposium 1992.* Richmond, Surrey: International Dendrology Society.

Boraginaceae

Bennett, M. 2003. *Pulmonarias and the Borage Family.* London: Batsford.

Bougainvillea

Gillis, W.T. 1976. Bougainvilleas of Cultivation (*Nyctaginaceae*). *Baileya* 20(1):34-41.

Iredell, J. 1990. *The Bougainvillea Grower's Handbook.* Brookvale, Australia: Simon & Schuster.

Iredell, J. 1994. *Growing Bougainvilleas.* London: Cassell.

MacDaniels, L.H. 1981. A Study of Cultivars in *Bougainvillea* (*Nyctaginaceae*). *Baileya* 21(2):77-100.

Singh, B., Panwar, R.S., Voleti, S.R., Sharma, V.K. & Thakur, S. 1999. *The New International Bougainvillea Check List.* (2nd ed.). New Delhi: Indian Agricultural Research Institute.

Bromeliaceae

Beadle, D.A. 1991. *A Preliminary Listing of all the Known Cultivar and Grex Names for the Bromeliaceae.* Corpus Christi, Texas: Bromeliad Society.

Bromeliad Cultivar Registry Online Databases. Jan 2007. Bromeliad Society International www.bsi.org

Brugmansia

Wreggitt, L. et al. (comp.). Dec 2007. *Register of Brugmansia Cultivars and Checklist of Names in Use.* American Brugmansia and Datura Society. www.abads.org

Buddleja

Stuart, D.D. 2006. *Buddlejas: Royal Horticultural Society Collector Guide.* Portland, Oregon: Timber Press.

Bulbs

Leeds, R. 2000. *The Plantfinder's Guide to Early Bulbs.* Newton Abbot, Devon: David & Charles.

KAVB Online registration pages http://kavb.back2p.soft-orange.com

Buxus

Batdorf, L.R. 1995. *Boxwood Handbook. A Practical Guide to Knowing and Growing Boxwood.* Boyce, VA, USA: The American Boxwood Society.

Cactaceae

Hunt, D. et al. 2006. *New Cactus Lexicon.* (2 vols.) Sherborne, Dorset: DH Books.

Camellia

Trujillo, D. J. (ed.). 2002. *Camellia Nomenclature.* (24th revd ed.). Southern California Camellia Society.

Savige, T.J. (comp.). 1993. *The International Camellia Register.* The International Camellia Society. (2 vols).

Savige, T.J. (comp.). 1997. *The International Camellia Register.* Supp. to vols 1 and 2. The International Camellia Society.

Campanula

Lewis, P. & Lynch, M. 1998. *Campanulas.* A Gardeners Guide. (2nd ed.). London: Batsford.

Lewis, P 2002. *Campanulas in the Garden.* Pershore, Worcs.: Hardy Plant Society.

Campanulaceae

Lammers, T.G. 2007. *World Checklist and Bibliography of Campanulaceae.* Kew Publishing.

Canna

Cooke, I. 2001. *The Gardener's Guide to Growing Cannas.* Newton Abbot, Devon: David & Charles.

Gray, J. & Grant, M. 2003. Canna; RHS Bulletin No 3. Wisley, Surrey: RHS. www.rhs.org.uk/plants/documents/canna03.pdf

Hayward, K. Jan 2007. http://www.hartcanna.com

Carnivorous Plants

Schlauer, J. (comp.). Aug 2006. Carnivorous Plant Database. www.omnisterra.com

Ceanothus

Fross, D. & D. Wilken. 2006. *Ceanothus.* Portland, Oregon: Timber Press.

Cercidiphyllum

Dosmann, M.S. 1999. Katsura: a Review of *Cercidiphyllum* in Cultivation and in the Wild. *The New Plantsman* 6(1):52-62.

Dosmann, M., Andrews, S., Del Tredici, P. & Li, J. 2003. Classification and Nomenclature of Weeping Katsuras. *The Plantsman* 2(1):21-27.

Chaenomeles

Weber, C. 1963. Cultivars in the Genus *Chaenomeles.* *Arnoldia (Jamaica Plain)* 23(3):17-75.

Chrysanthemum

Brummitt, D. 1997. *Chrysanthemum* Once Again. *The Garden* (RHS) 122(9):662-663.

Gosling, S.G. (ed.). 1964. *British National Register of Chrysanthemums.* Whetstone, London: National Chrysanthemum Society.

National Chrysanthemum Society. 2000. *British National Register of Names of Chrysanthemums Amalgamated Edition 1964-1999.* Tamworth, Staffordshire: The National Chrysanthemum Society.

National Chrysanthemum Society UK Cultivar Database. Jan 2008. www.nationalchrysanthemumsociety.org.uk

Cistus

Demoly, J.-P. 2005. The identity of *Cistus* 'Grayswood Pink' and related plants. *The Plantsman* 4(2):76-80.

Page, R.G. Feb 2007. Cistus and Halimium Website. www.cistuspage.org.uk

Citrus

Davies, F.S. & Albrigo, L.G. 1994. *Citrus.* Wallingford, Oxon: Cab International.

Saunt, J. 1990. *Citrus Varieties of the World.* An Illustrated Guide. Norwich: Sinclair

Clematis

Clematis on the Web. Jan 2008. www.clematis.hull.ac.uk

Grey-Wilson, C. 2000. *Clematis: the Genus.* London: Batsford

HelpMeFind Clematis. Nov 2006. www.helpmefind.com/clematis

Johnson, M. 2001. *The Genus Clematis.* Södertälje, Sweden: Magnus Johnsons Plantskola AB & Bengt Sundström.

Matthews, V. (comp.). 2002. *The International Clematis Register and Checklist 2002.* London: RHS.

Supps 1 (2004) & 2 (2006). http://www.rhs.org.uk/learning

Toomey, M. & Leeds, E. 2001. *An Illustrated Encyclopedia of Clematis.* Portland, Oregon: Timber Press.

Conifers

den Ouden, P. & Boom, B.K. 1965. *Manual of Cultivated Conifers.* The Hague: Martinus Nijhof.

Farjon, A. 1998. *World Checklist and Bibliography of Conifers.* Kew: Royal Botanic Gardens.

Knees, S. Feb 2005. Complete List of Conifer Taxa Accepted for Registration. RHS. www.rhs.org.uk/research

Krüssmann, G. & Epp, M.E. (trans.). 1985. *Manual of Cultivated Conifers.* London: Batsford.

Lewis, J. & Leslie, A.C. 1987. *The International Conifer Register. Pt 1. Abies* to *Austrotaxus.* London: RHS.

Lewis, J. & Leslie, A.C. 1989. *The International Conifer Register. Pt 2. Belis* to *Pherosphaera,* excluding the Cypresses. London: RHS.

Lewis, J. & Leslie, A.C. 1992. *The International Conifer Register. Pt 3. The Cypresses.* London: RHS.

Lewis, J. & Leslie, A.C. 1998. *The International Conifer Register. Pt 4. Juniperus.* London: RHS.

Welch, H.J. 1979. *Manual of Dwarf Conifers.* New York: Theophrastus.

Welch, H.J. 1991. *The Conifer Manual.* Vol. 1. Dordrecht, Netherlands: Kluwer Academic Publishers.

Welch, H.J. 1993. *The World Checklist of Conifers.* Bromyard, Herefordshire: Landsman's Bookshops Ltd.

Cornus

Cappiello, P. & Shadow, D. 2005. *Dogwoods.* Portland, Oregon: Timber Press.

Howard, R.A. 1961. Registration Lists of Cultivar Names in *Cornus L. Arnoldia (Jamaica Plain)* 21(2):9-18.

Corydalis

Lidén, M. & Zetterlund, H. 1997. *Corydalis. A Gardener's Guide and a Monograph of the Tuberous Species.* Pershore, Worcs.: Alpine Garden Society Publications Ltd.

Corylus

Crawford, M. 1995. *Hazelnuts: Production and Culture.* Dartington, Devon: Agroforestry Research Trust.

Cotoneaster

Fryer, J. & Hylmö, B. 1998. Seven New Species of *Cotoneaster* in Cultivation. *The New Plantsman* 5(3):132-144.

Fryer, J. & Hylmö, B. 2001. Captivating Cotoneasters. *The New Plantsman* 8(4):227-238.

Fryer, J. 1996. Undervalued Versatility. *Cotoneaster. The Garden* (RHS) 121(11):709-715.

Crassulaceae

Rowley, G. 2003. *Crassula: A Grower's Guide.* Venegono superiore, Italy: Cactus & Co.

Eggli, U. (ed.) 2003. *Illustrated Handbook of Succulent Plants.* Springer.

Crocosmia

Goldblatt, P., Manning, J.C. & Dunlop, G. 2004. *Crocosmia and Chasmanthe.* Portland, Oregon: Timber Press.

Crocus

Jacobsen, N., van Scheepen, J. & Ørgaard, M. 1997. The *Crocus chrysanthus – biflorus* Cultivars. *The New Plantsman* 4(1):6-38.

Mathew, B. 1982. *The Crocus. A Review of the Genus Crocus (Iridaceae).* London: Batsford.

Mathew, B. 2002. *Crocus* Up-date. *The Plantsman* 1(1):44-56.

Cyclamen

Clennett, C. Jan. 2003. Register of Cultivar Names. www.cyclamen.org

Grey-Wilson, C. 2003. *Cyclamen. A Guide for Gardeners, Horticulturists & Botanists.* London: Batsford.

Grey-Wilson, C. 2002 Sprenger's Alpine Cyclamen. *The Plantsman* 1(3):173-177.

Cypripedium

Cribb, P. 1997. *The Genus Cypripedium.* Portland, Oregon: Timber Press.

Dahlia

American Dahlia Society website. 2006. www.dahlia.org

Bates, D. Dahlia Plant Finder 2007. Dec 2007. www.dahliaworld.co.uk

National Dahlia Society. 2005. *Classified Directory and Judging Rules.* (28th ed.) Aldershot, Hants: National Dahlia Society.

RHS & Hedge, R. (comps). 1969. *Tentative Classified List and International Register of Dahlia Names 1969.* (& Supps 1-13). London: RHS. Supps 13-17. 2002-06. http://www.rhs.org.uk/learning
Winchester Growers Ltd English National Dahlia Collection website. 2007. www.national-dahlia-collection.co.uk

Daphne

Brickell, C.D. & Mathew, B. 1976. *Daphne. The Genus in the Wild and in Cultivation.* Woking, Surrey: Alpine Garden Society.

Grey-Wilson, C. (ed.). 2001. *The Smaller Daphnes. The Proceedings of 'Daphne 2000', a Conference held at the Royal Horticultural Society.* Pershore, Worcs.: Alpine Garden Society.

White, R. 2006. *Daphnes: A Practical Guide for Gardeners.* Portland, Oregon: Timber Press.

Delphinium

1949. *A Tentative Check-list of Delphinium Names.* London: RHS.

1970. *A Tentative Check-list of Delphinium Names.* Addendum to the 1949 tentative check-list of *Delphinium* names. London: RHS.

Bassett, D. & Wesley, W. 2004. *Delphinium: RHS Bulletin No 5.* Wisley, Surrey: RHS. www.rhs.org.uk/plants/documents/delph04.pdf

Leslie, A.C. 1996. *The International Delphinium Register Cumulative Supp. 1970-1995.* London: RHS.

Leslie, A.C. 1996-2005. The International Delphinium Register Supp. 1994-99. *The Delphinium Society Year Book 1996-2005.* London: RHS.

Dianthus

Galbally, J. & Galbally, E. 1997. *Carnations and Pinks for Garden and Greenhouse.* Portland, Oregon: Timber Press.

Leslie, A.C. *The International Dianthus Register.* 1983-2002. (2nd ed. & Supps 1-19). London: RHS.
Supps 19-23. 2002-06. http://www.rhs.org.uk/learning

Dierama

Hilliard, O.M. & Burtt, B.L. 1991. *Dierama. The Harebells of Africa.* Johannesburg; London: Acorn Books.

Dionysia

Grey-Wilson, C. 1989. *The Genus Dionysia.* Woking, Surrey: Alpine Garden Society.

Douglasia

Mitchell, B. 1999. Celebrating the Bicentenary of David Douglas: a Review of *Douglasia* in Cultivation. *The New Plantsman* 6(2):101-108.

Dracaena

Bos, J.J., Graven, P., Hetterscheid, W.L.A. & van de Wege, J.J. 1992. Wild and cultivated *Dracaena fragrans. Edinburgh J. Bot.* 49(3):311-331.

Episcia

Dates, J.D. 1993. *The Gesneriad Register 1993.* Check List of Names with Descriptions of Cultivated Plants in the Genera *Episcia* & *Alsobia.* Galesburg, Illinois: American Gloxinia & Gesneriad Society, Inc.

***Erica* (see also Heathers)**

Baker, H.A. & Oliver, E.G.H. 1967. *Heathers in Southern Africa.* Cape Town: Purnell.

Schumann, D., Kirsten, G. & Oliver, E.G.H. 1992. *Ericas of South Africa.* Vlaeberg, South Africa: Fernwood Press.

Erodium

Clifton, R. 1994. *Geranium Family Species Checklist. Pt 1 Erodium.* (4th ed.). The Geraniaceae Group.

Leslie, A.C. 1980. The Hybrid of *Erodium corsicum* with *Erodium reichardii. The Plantsman* 2:117-126.

Toomey, N., Cubey, J. & Culham, A. 2002. *Erodium × variabile. The Plantsman* 1(3): 166-172

Victor, D.X. (comp.). 2000. *Erodium: Register of Cultivar Names.* The Geraniaceae Group.

Erythronium

Mathew, B. 1992. A Taxonomic and Horticultural Review of *Erythronium* L. (*Liliaceae*). *J. Linn. Soc., Bot.* 109:453-471.

Mathew, B. 1998. The Genus *Erythronium. Bull. Alpine Gard. Soc. Gr. Brit.* 66(3):308-321.

***Eupatorium* sensu lato**

Hind, D.J.N. 2006. Splitting *Eupatorium. The Plantsman* (n.s.) 5(2):185-189.

Euonymus

Brown, N. 1996. Notes on Cultivated Species of *Euonymus. The New Plantsman* 3(4):238-243.

Lancaster, C.R. 1981. An Account of *Euonymus* in Cultivation and its Availability in Commerce. *The Plantsman* 3(3):133-166.

Lancaster, C.R. 1982. *Euonymus* in Cultivation – Addendum. *The Plantsman* 4:61-64, 253-254.

Euphorbia

Govaerts, R., Frodin, D.G. & Radcliffe-Smith, A. 2000. *World Checklist and Bibliography of Euphorbiaceae.* Kew: Royal Botanic Gardens.

Turner, R. 1995. *Euphorbias. A Gardeners Guide.* London: Batsford.

Witton, D. 2000. *Euphorbias.* Pershore, Worcs.: Hardy Plant Society.

Fagales

World Checklist and Bibliography Series: About the *Fagales.* Jan 2002. www.rbgkew.org.uk

Fagus

Dönig, G. 1994. *Die Park-und Gartenformen der Rotbuche Fagus sylvatica L.* Erlangen, Germany: Verlag Gartenbild Heinz Hansmann.

Wyman, D. 1964. Registration List of Cultivar Names of *Fagus* L. *J. Arnold Arbor.* 24(1):1-8.

Fascicularia

Nelson, E.C. & Zizka, G. 1997. *Fascicularia* (*Bromeliaceae*): Which Species are Cultivated and Naturalized in Northwestern Europe. *The New Plantsman* 4(4):232-239.

Nelson, E.C., Zizka, G., Horres, R. & Weising, K. 1999. Revision of the Genus *Fascicularia* Mez (*Bromeliaceae*). *Botanical Journal of the Linnean Society* 129(4):315-332.

Ferns

Checklist of World Ferns. March 2003. http://homepages.caverock.net.nz

Johns, R.J. 1996. *Index Filicum.* Supplementum Sextum pro annis 1976-1990. Kew:Royal Botanic Gardens.

Johns, R.J. 1997. *Index Filicum.* Supplementum Septimum pro annis 1991-1995. Kew:Royal Botanic Gardens.

Jones, D.L. 1987. *Encyclopaedia of Ferns.* Melbourne, Australia: Lothian.

Kaye, R. 1968. *Hardy Ferns.* London: Faber & Faber

Rickard, M.H. 2000. *The Plantfinder's Guide to Garden Ferns.* Newton Abbot, Devon: David & Charles.

Rush, R. 1984. *A Guide to Hardy Ferns.* London: British Pteridological Society.

Forsythia

INRA Forsythia website. Dec 2000. www.angers.inra.fr

Fritillaria

Clark, T. & Grey-Wilson, C. 2003. Crown Imperials. *The Plantsman* 2(1):33-47.

Mathew, B., et al. 2000. *Fritillaria* Issue. *Bot. Mag.* 17(3):145-185.

Pratt, K. & Jefferson-Brown, M. 1997. *The Gardener's Guide to Growing Fritillaries.* Newton Abbot: David & Charles.

Turrill, W.B. & Sealy, J.R. 1980. *Studies in the Genus Fritillaria (Liliaceae).* Hooker's Icones Plantarum Vol. 39 (1 & 2). Kew: Royal Botanic Gardens.

Fruit

Brogdale Horticultural Trust National Fruit Collection. Jul 2007. http://www.brogdale.org.uk/nfc_home.php

Bowling, B.L. 2000. *The Berry Grower's Companion.* Portland, Oregon: Timber Press.

Hogg, R. 1884. *The Fruit Manual.* (5th ed.). London: Journal of Horticulture Office.

Fuchsia

American Fuchsia Society Registration Database. Jan 2008. www.americanfuchsiasociety.org

Bartlett, G. 1996. *Fuchsias – A Colour Guide.* Marlborough, Wilts: Crowood Press.

Boullemier, Leo.B. (comp.). 1991. *The Checklist of Species, Hybrids and Cultivars of the Genus Fuchsia.* London, New York, Sydney: Blandford Press.

Boullemier, Leo.B. (comp.). 1995. *Addendum No 1 to the 1991 Checklist of Species, Hybrids and Cultivars of the Genus Fuchsia.* Dyfed, Wales: The British Fuchsia Society.

Goulding, E. 1995. *Fuchsias: The Complete Guide.* London: Batsford.

Johns, E.A. 1997. *Fuchsias of the 19th and Early 20th Century.* An Historical Checklist of Fuchsia Species & Cultivars, pre-1939. Kidderminster, Worcs.: British Fuchsia Society

Jones, L. & Miller, D.M. 2005. *Hardy Fuchsias: RHS Bulletin No 12.* Wisley, Surrey: RHS. www.rhs.org.uk/plants/documents/fuchsia05.pdf

Stevens, R. Dec 2007. Find That Fuchsia. www.findthatfuchsia.info

Van Veen, G. Nov 2007. Gelderse Fuchsia Info-site. www.geldersefuchsia.info

Galanthus

Bishop, M., Davis, A. & Grimshaw, J. 2001. *Snowdrops. A monograph of cultivated Galanthus.* Maidenhead: Griffin Press.

Davis, A.P., Mathew, B. (ed.) & King, C. (ill.). 1999. *The Genus Galanthus. A Botanical Magazine Monograph.* Oregon: Timber Press.

Gentiana

Bartlett, M. 1975. *Gentians.* Dorset: Blandford Press.

Halda, J.J. 1996. *The Genus Gentiana.* Dobré, Czech Republic: Sen.

Ho T.N. & Liu S. 2001. *Worldwide Monograph of Gentiana.* Beijing: Science Press.

Geranium

Armitage, J. 2005. *Hardy Geraniums – Stage 1: RHS Bulletin No 10.* Wisley, Surrey: RHS. www.rhs.org.uk/plants/documents/geranium05.pdf

Armitage, J. 2006. *Hardy Geraniums – Stage 2: RHS Bulletin No 14.* Wisley, Surrey: RHS. www.rhs.org.uk/plants/documents/geranium06.pdf

Armitage, J. 2007. *Hardy Geraniums – Stage 3: RHS Bulletin No 18.* Wisley, Surrey: RHS.
http://www.rhs.org.uk

Bath, T. & Jones, J. 1994. *The Gardener's Guide to Growing Hardy Geraniums.* Newton Abbot, Devon: David & Charles.

Bendtsen, B.H. 2005. *Gardening with Hardy Geraniums.* Portland, Oregon: Timber Press.

Clifton, R.T.F. 1995. *Geranium Family Species Check List Pt 2.* Geranium. (4th ed. issue 2). Dover: The Geraniaceae Group.

Jones, J., et al. 2001. *Hardy Geraniums for the Garden.* (3rd ed.). Pershore, Worcs.: Hardy Plant Society.

Victor, D.X. 2004. *Register of Geranium Cultivar Names.* (2nd ed.). The Geraniaceae Group.

Yeo, P.F. 2002. *Hardy Geraniums.* (3rd ed.). Kent: Croom Helm.

Gesneriaceae

American Gloxinia and Gesneriad Society. Listing of registered gesneriads. 2005. www.aggs.org

Dates, J.D. 1986-1990. *The Gesneriad Register 1986-1987 & 1990.* Galesburg, Illinois: American Gloxinia & Gesneriad Society, Inc.

Gladiolus

British Gladiolus Society List of Cultivars Classified for Show Purposes 1994. Mayfield, Derbyshire: British Gladiolus Society.

1997-1998. British Gladiolus Society List of European, New Zealand & North American

Cultivars Classified for Exhibition Purposes 1997 & 1998. Mayfield, Derbyshire: British Gladiolus Society.

Goldblatt, P. & Manning, J. 1998. *Gladiolus in Southern Africa.* Vlaeberg, South Africa: Fernwood Press.

Goldblatt, P. 1996. *Gladiolus in Tropical Africa.* Systematics Biology and Evolution. Oregon: Timber Press.

Lewis, G.J., Obermeyer, A.A. & Barnard, T.T. 1972. A Revision of the South African Species of *Gladiolus. J. S. African Bot.* (Supp. Vol. 10)

Gleditsia

Santamour, F.S. & McArdle, A.J. 1983. Checklist of Cultivars of Honeylocust (*Gleditsia triacanthos* L.). *J. Arboric.* 9:271-276.

Grevillea

Olde, P. & Marriott, N. 1995. *The Grevillea Book.* (3). Kenthurst, NSW: Kangaroo Press.

Haemanthus

Snijman, D. 1984. A Revision of the Genus *Haemanthus. J. S. African Bot.* (Supp. Vol. 12).

Hamamelis

Lane, C. 2005. *Witch Hazels.* Portland, Oregon: Timber Press.

Heathers

Nelson, E.C. Aug 2007. International Cultivar Registration Authority for Heathers. www.heathersociety.org.uk

Hebe

Chalk, D. 1988. *Hebes and Parahebes.* Bromley, Kent: Christopher Helm (Publishers) Ltd.

Hutchins, G. 1997. *Hebes: Here and There.* A Monograph on the Genus *Hebe.* Caversham, Berks: Hutchins & Davies.

Metcalf, L.J. 2001. *International Register of Hebe Cultivars.* Canterbury, New Zealand: Royal New Zealand Institute of Horticulture (Inc.).

Metcalf, L.J. 2006. *Hebes: A Guide to Species, Hybrids and Allied Genera.* Portland, Oregon: Timber Press.

Hedera

Jury, S. et al. 2006. *Hedera algeriensis*, a Fine Species of Ivy. *Sibbaldia* 4: 93-108.

McAllister, H. 1988. Canary and Algerian Ivies. *The Plantsman* 10(1):27-29.

McAllister, H.A. & Rutherford, A. 1990. *Hedera helix and H. hibernica* in the British Isles. *Watsonia* 18:7-15.

Rose, P.Q. 1996. *The Gardener's Guide to Growing Ivies.* Newton Abbot, Devon: David & Charles.

Rutherford, A., McAllister, H. & Mill, R.R. 1993. New Ivies from the Mediterranean Area and Macaronesia. *The Plantsman* 15(2):115-128.

Heliconia

Berry, F. & Kress, W.J. 1991. *Heliconia.* An Identification Guide. Washington: Smithsonian Institution Press.

Helleborus

Burrell, C.C. & Tyler, J.K. 2006. *Hellebores: A Comprehensive Guide.* Portland, Oregon: Timber Press.

Mathew, B. 1989. *Hellebores.* Woking: Alpine Garden Society.

Rice, G. & Strangman, E. 1993. *The Gardener's Guide to Growing Hellebores.* Newton Abbot, Devon: David & Charles.

Hemerocallis

Baxter, G.J. (comp.). Jun 2007. American Daylily Society Registry of Daylily Cultivars. www.daylilydatabase.org

Kitchingman, R.M. 1985. Some Species and Cultivars of *Hemerocallis. The Plantsman* 7(2):68-89.

Herbs

Page, M. & Stearn, W. *Culinary Herbs: A Wisley Handbook.* London: RHS.

Phillips, R. & Foy, N. 1990. *Herbs.* London: Pan Books Ltd.

Heuchera* and × *Heucherella

Heims, D. & Ware, G. 2005. *Heucheras and Heucherellas: Coral Bells and Foamy Bells.* Portland, Oregon: Timber Press.

Hibiscus

Noble, C. Apr 2007. Australian Hibiscus Society Database Register. www.australianhibiscus.com/

Hosta

Hammelman, T. 2002. Giboshi.com Hosta Database. www.giboshi.com

Hosta Library. Aug 2006. www.hostalibrary.org

Grenfell, D. & Shadrack, M. 2004. *The Color Encyclopedia of Hostas.* Portland, Oregon: Timber Press.

Schmid, W.G. 1991. *The Genus Hosta.* London: Batsford.

Hyacinthaceae

Dashwood, M. & Mathew, B. 2006. *Hyacinthaceae – little blue bulbs: RHS Bulletin No 11.* Wisley, Surrey: RHS. www.rhs.org.uk/plants/documents/hyacinthaceae05.pdf

Mathew, B. 2005. *Hardy Hyacinthaceae* Pt 1: *Muscari. The Plantsman* 4(1):40-53.

Mathew, B. 2005. *Hardy Hyacinthaceae* Pt 2: *Scilla, Chionodoxa* and × *Chinoscilla. The Plantsman* 4(2):110-121.

Hydrangea

Dirr, M.A. 2004. *Hydrangeas for American Gardens.* Portland, Oregon: Timber Press.

Haworth-Booth, M. 1975. *The Hydrangeas.* London: Garden Book Club.

Van Gelderen, C.J. & Van Gelderen, D.M. 2004. *Encyclopedia of Hydrangeas.* Portland, Oregon: Timber Press.

Hypericum

Lancaster, R. & Robson, N. 1997. Focus on Plants: Bowls of Beauty. *The Garden* (RHS) 122(8):566-571.

Ilex

Bailes, C. 2006. *Hollies for Gardeners.* Portland, Oregon: Timber Press.

Dudley, T.R. & Eisenbeiss, G.K. 1973 & 1992. *International Checklist of Cultivated Ilex.* Pt 1 *Ilex opaca* (1973), Pt 2 *Ilex crenata* (1992). Washington DC: United States Dept of Agriculture.

Galle, F.C. 1997. *Hollies: the Genus Ilex.* Portland, Oregon: Timber Press.

Impatiens

Morgan, R.J. 2007. *Impatiens: The Vibrant World of Busy Lizzies, Balsams and Touch-me-nots.* Portland, Oregon: Timber Press.

Iris

Austin, C. 2005. *Irises: A Gardener's Encyclopedia.* Oregon:Timber Press.

Hoog, M.H. 1980. Bulbous Irises . *The Plantsman* 2(3):141-64.

Keppel, K. (ed.) 2001. *Iris Check List of Registered Cultivar Names 1990-1999.* Hannibal, New York: the American Iris Society.

Mathew, B. 1981. *The Iris.* London: Batsford.

Mathew, B. 1993. The Spuria Irises. *The Plantsman* 15(1):14-25.

Service, N. 1990. *Iris unguicularis. The Plantsman* 12(1):1-9.

Stebbings, G. 1997. *The Gardener's Guide to Growing Iris.* Newton Abbot: David & Charles.

The Species Group of the British Iris Society, (ed.). 1997. *A Guide to Species Irises.* Their Identification and Cultivation. Cambridge: Cambridge University Press.

Jovibarba* see under *Sempervivum

Kalmia

Jaynes, R.A. 1997. *Kalmia. Mountain Laurel and Related Species.* Portland, Oregon: Timber Press.

Kniphofia

Grant-Downton, R. 1997. Notes on *Kniphofia thomsonii* in Cultivation and in the Wild. *The New Plantsman* 4(3):148-156.

Taylor, J. 1985. *Kniphofia* – a Survey. *The Plantsman* 7(3):129-160.

Kohleria

Dates, J.D. (ed.) & Batcheller, F.N. (comp.). 1985. *The Gesneriad Register 1985. Check List of Names with Descriptions of Cultivated Plants in the Genus Kohleria.* Lincoln Acres, California: American Gloxinia and Gesneriad Society, Inc.

Lachenalia

Duncan, G.D. 1988. *The Lachenalia Hand Book.* Kirstenbosch, South Africa: National Botanic Gardens.

Lantana

Howard, R.A. 1969. A Check List of Names Used in the Genus *Lantana. Arnoldia.* 29(11):73-109.

Lathyrus

Norton, S. 1996. *Lathyrus. Cousins of Sweet Pea.* Surrey: NCCPG.

Lavandula

Upson, T. & Andrews, S. 2004. *The Genus Lavandula.* Kew: Royal Botanic Garden.

Legumes

ILDIS. International Legume Database and Information Service. Nov 2005. Version 10.01. www.ildis.org/LegumeWeb

Leptospermum

Check List of *Leptospermum* Cultivars. 1963. *J. Roy. New Zealand Inst. Hort.* 5(5):224-30.

Dawson, M. 1997. A History of *Leptospermum scoparium* in Cultivation – Discoveries from the Wild. *The New Plantsman* 4(1):51-59.

Dawson, M. 1997. A History of *Leptospermum scoparium* in Cultivation – Garden Selections. *The New Plantsman* 4(2):67-78.

Lewisia

Davidson, B.L.R. 2000. *Lewisias.* Portland, Oregon: Timber Press.

Elliott, R. 1978. *Lewisias.* Woking: Alpine Garden Society.

Mathew, B. 1989. *The Genus Lewisia.* Bromley, Kent: Christopher Helm.

***Liliaceae* sensu lato**

Mathew, B. 1989. Splitting the *Liliaceae. The Plantsman* 11(2):89-105.

Lilium

Leslie, A.C. *The International Lily Register 1982-2002.* (3rd ed. & supps 1-20). London: RHS.

Supps 20-23. 2002-06. www.rhs.org.uk/learning

Online Lily Register. May 2007. www.lilyregister.com

Lonicera

Blahník, Z. 2006. *Lonicera* Cultivar Names: The First World List. *Acta Pruhoniciana* 81:59-64.

Magnolia

Callaway, D.J. Sep 2001. Magnolia Cultivar Checklist. www.magnoliasociety.org

Frodin, D.G. & Govaerts, R. 1996. *World Checklist and Bibliography of Magnoliaceae.* Kew: Royal Botanic Garden.

Maianthemum

Cubey, J.J. 2005 *The Incorporation of Smilacina within Maianthemum. The Plantsman* N.S.4(4).

Malus

Crawford, M. 1994. *Directory of Apple Cultivars.* Devon: Agroforestry Research Trust.

Fiala, J.L. 1994. *Flowering Crabapples.* The genus *Malus.* Portland, Oregon: Timber Press.

Rouèche, A. Oct 2007. Les Crets Fruits et Pomologie. www.pomologie.com

Smith, M.W.G. 1971. *National Apple Register of the United Kingdom.* London: MAFF

Spiers, V. 1996. *Burcombes, Queenies and Colloggetts.* St Dominic, Cornwall: West Brendon.

Meconopsis

Grey-Wilson, C. 1992. A Survey of the Genus *Meconopsis* in Cultivation. *The Plantsman* 14(1): 1-33.

Grey-Wilson, C. 2002. The True Identity of *Meconopsis napaulensis*. *Bot. Mag.* 23(2):176-209.

Meconopsis Group website www.meconopsis.org

Stevens, E. & Brickell, C. 2001. Problems with the Big Perennial Poppies. *The New Plantsman* 8(1):48-61.

Stevens, E. 2001. Further Observations on the Big Perennial Blue Poppies. *The New Plantsman* 8(2):105-111.

Miscanthus

Jones, L. 2004. Miscanthus: RHS Bulletin No 7. Wisley, Surrey: RHS. www.rhs.org.uk/plant/documents/miscanthus04.pdf

Moraea

Goldblatt, P. 1986. *The Moraeas of Southern Africa.* Kirstenbosch, South Africa: National Botanic Gardens.

Musa

INIBAP *Musa* Germplasm Information System. Dec 2006. http//195.220.148.3:8013/mgis_2/homepage.htm

Musalogue 2: Diversity in the Genus *Musa*. 2001. http://bananas.bioversityinternational.org

Narcissus

Blanchard, J.W. 1990. *Narcissus – A Guide to Wild Daffodils.* Woking, Surrey: Alpine Garden Society.

Kington, S. (comp.). 1998. *The International Daffodil Register and Classified List 1998* (3rd ed. & Supps 1-5, 1998-2002). London: RHS. www.rhs.org.uk/research

Supps 6-9. 2002-06. http://www.rhs.org.uk/learning

Nematanthus

Arnold, P. 1978. *The Gesneriad Register 1978.* Check List of *Nematanthus.* American Gloxinia and Gesneriad Society, Inc.

Nerium

Pagen, F.J.J. 1987. *Oleanders. Nerium L. and the Oleander Cultivars.* Wageningen, The Netherlands: Agricultural University Wageningen.

Nymphaea

Liechti, V. & J. Purcell. George Salford Torrey Herbarium Registration and Checklist of *Nymphaeaceae*. http://collections2.eeb.uconn.edu

Orchidaceae

Shaw, J.M.H. Dec 2007. The International Orchid Register. www.rhs.org.uk/plants

Origanum

Paton, A. 1994. Three Membranous-bracted Species of *Origanum. Kew Mag.* 11(3):109-117.

White, S. 1998. *Origanum. The Herb Marjoram and its Relatives*. Surrey: NCCPG.

Paeonia

HelpMeFind Peonies. Jan 2008. www.helpmefind.com/peony/index.html

Jakubowski, R. American Peony Society Peony Checklist. www.americanpeonysociety.org

Osti, G.L. 1999. *The Book of Tree Peonies.* Turin: Umberto Allemandi.

Wang, L., et al. 1998. *Chinese Tree Peony.* Beijing: China Forestry Publishing House.

Papaver

Grey-Wilson, C. 1998. Oriental Glories. *The Garden* (RHS) 123(5):320-325.

Grey-Wilson, C. 2000. *Poppies. The Poppy Family in the Wild and in Cultivation*. London: Batsford.

Passiflora

King, L.A. Jan 2008. Passiflora online passion flower cultivar register. www.passionflow.co.uk

Pelargonium

Abbott, P.G. 1994. *A Guide to Scented Geraniaceae.* Angmering, West Sussex: Hill Publicity Services.

Anon. 1978. *A Checklist and Register of Pelargonium Cultivar Names.* Pt 1 A-B. Australian Pelargonium Society.

Anon. 1985. *A Checklist and Register of Pelargonium Cultivar Names*. Pt 2: C-F. Australian Pelargonium Society.

Bagust, H. 1988. *Miniature and Dwarf Geraniums.* London: Christopher Helm.

Clifford, D. 1958. *Pelargoniums.* London: Blandford Press.

Clifton, R. 1999. *Geranium Family Species Checklist, Pt 4: Pelargonium*. The Geraniaceae Group.

Complete Copy of the Spalding Pelargonium Checklist. (Unpublished). USA.

Key, H. 2000. *1001 Pelargoniums.* London: Batsford.

Miller, D. 1996. *Pelargonium.* A Gardener's Guide to the Species and Cultivars and Hybrids. London: Batsford.

Pelargonium Palette: The Geranium and Pelargonium Society of Sydney Incorporated. Varieties – Alphabetical List. July 2000. www.elj.com/geranium

Van der Walt, J.J.A., et al. 1977. *Pelargoniums of South Africa.* (1-3). Kirstenbosch, South Africa: National Botanic Gardens.

Penstemon

Lindgren, D.T. & Davenport, B. 1992. List and description of named cultivars in the genus *Penstemon* (1992). University of Nebraska.

Nold, R. 1999. *Penstemons.* Portland, Oregon: Timber Press.

Way, D. & James, P. 1998. *The Gardener's Guide to Growing Penstemons.* Newton Abbott, Devon: David & Charles.

Way, D. 2006. *Penstemons*. Pershore, Worcs.: Hardy Plant Society.

Phlomis

Mann Taylor, J. 1998. *Phlomis: The Neglected Genus.* Wisley: NCCPG.

Phlox

Harmer, J. & Elliott, J. 2001. *Phlox.* Pershore, Worcs.: Hardy Plant Society.

Stebbings, G. 1999. Simply Charming. *The Garden* (RHS) 124(7):518-521.

Wherry, E.T. 1955. *The Genus Phlox.* Philadelphia, Pennsylvania: Morris Arboretum.

Phormium
Heenan, P.B. 1991. *Checklist of Phormium Cultivars.* Royal New Zealand Institute of Horticulture.
McBride-Whitehead, V. 1998. Phormiums of the Future. *The Garden* (RHS) 123(1):42-45.
Pieris
Bond, J. 1982. *Pieris* – a Survey. *The Plantsman* 4(2):65-75.
Wagenknecht, B.L. 1961. Registration Lists of Cultivar Names in the Genus *Pieris* D. Don. *Arnoldia (Jamaica Plain)* 21(8):47-50.
Pittosporum
Miller, D.M. 2006. RHS Plant Assessments: *Pittosporum tenuifolium* hybrids & cultivars. www.rhs.org.uk/plants/documents/pittosporum06HI.pdf.
Plectranthus
Addink, Wouter. Dec 2007. Coleus Finder. http://coleusfinder.org
Miller, D. & Morgan, N. 2000. Focus on Plants: A New Leaf. *The Garden* (RHS) 125(11):842-845.
Shaw, J.M.H. 1999. Notes on the Identity of Swedish Ivy and Other Cultivated *Plectranthus. The New Plantsman* 6(2):71-74.
Van Jaarsveld, E.J. 2006. *South African Plectranthus.* Vlaeberg, South Africa: Fernwood Press.
Pleione
Cribb, P. & Butterfield, I. 1999. *The Genus Pleione.* (2nd ed.). Kew: Royal Botanic Gardens.
Shaw, J.M.H. (comp.). Oct 2002. Provisional List of *Pleione* Cultivars. RHS. www.rhs.org.uk/plants/registerpages/Pleione_cv.PDF
***Poaceae* (grasses)**
Clayton, W.D., Harman, K.T. & Williamson, H. Mar 2006. World Grass Species Synonymy. www.kew.org/data
Clayton, W.D. & Renvoize, S.A. 1986. *Genera Graminum.* Grasses of the World. London: HMSO.
Darke, R. 2007. *Encyclopedia of Grasses for Livable Landscapes.* Portland, Oregon: Timber Press.
Grounds, R. 1998. *The Plantfinder's Guide to Ornamental Grasses.* Newton Abott, Devon: David & Charles.
Wood, T. 2002. *Garden Grasses, Rushes and Sedges.* (3rd ed.). Abingdon, Oxon: John Wood.
Polemonium
Nichol-Brown, D. 2000. *Polemonium.* Wisley: NCCPG.
Potentilla
Davidson, C.G., Enns, R.J. & Gobin, S. 1994. *A Checklist of Potentilla fruticosa: the Shrubby Potentillas.* Morden, Manitoba: Agriculture & Agri-Food Canada Research Centre. Data also on Plant Finder Reference Library professional version CD-ROM 1999/2000.
Miller, D.M. 2002. *Shrubby Potentilla: RHS Bulletin No 1.* Wisley, Surrey: RHS. www.rhs.org.uk/plants/documents/potentilla_report.pdf
Primula
Richards, J. 2002 (2nd ed.). *Primula.* London: Batsford.
Primula allionii
Archdale, B. & Richards, D. 1997. *Primula allionii Forms and Hybrids.* National Auricula & Primula Society, Midland & West Section.
Primula auricula misapplied
Baker, G. *Double Auriculas.* National Auricula & Primula Society, Midland & West Section.
Baker, G. & Ward, P. 1995. *Auriculas.* London: Batsford.
Hawkes, A. 1995. Striped Auriculas. National Auricula & Primula Society, Midland & West Section.
Nicholle, G. 1996. *Border Auriculas.* National Auricula & Primula Society, Midland & West Section.
Robinson, M.A. 2000. *Auriculas for Everyone.* How to Grow and Show Perfect Plants. Lewes, Sussex: Guild of Master Craftsmen Publications.
Telford, D. 1993. *Alpine Auriculas.* National Auricula & Primula Society, Midland & West Section.
Ward, P. 1991. *Show Auriculas.* National Auricula & Primula Society, Midland & West Section.
Proteaceae
International *Proteaceae* Register. July 2002. (7th ed.). http://www.nda.agric.za/docs/Protea2002/proteaceae_register.htm
Rebelo, T. 1995. *Proteas.* A Field Guide to the Proteas of Southern Africa. Vlaeberg: Fernwood Press/National Botanical Institute.
Prunus
Crawford, M. 1996. *Plums.* Dartington, Devon: Agroforestry Research Trust.
Crawford, M. 1997. *Cherries: Production and Culture.* Dartington, Devon: Agroforestry Research Trust.
Jacobsen, A.L. 1992. *Purpleleaf Plums.* Portland, Oregon: Timber Press.
Jefferson, R.M. & Wain, K.K. 1984. *The Nomenclature of Cultivated Flowering Cherries (Prunus).* The Sato-Zakura Group. Washington DC: USDA.
Kuitert, W. 1999. *Japanese Flowering Cherries.* Portland, Oregon: Timber Press.
Pulmonaria
Bennett, M. 2003. *Pulmonarias and the borage family.* London: B.T. Batsford.
Hewitt, J. 1994. *Pulmonarias.* Pershore, Worcs.: Hardy Plant Society.
Hewitt, J. 1999. Well Spotted. *The Garden* (RHS) 124(2):98-103.
Pyracantha
Egolf, D.R. & Andrick, A.O. 1995. *A Checklist of Pyracantha Cultivars.* Washington DC: Agricultural Research Service.
Pyrus
Crawford, M. 1996. *Directory of Pear Cultivars.* Totnes, Devon: Agroforestry Research Institute.
Smith, M.W.G. 1976. *Catalogue of the British Pear.* Faversham, Kent: MAFF.

Quercus

Miller, H.A. & Lamb, S.H. 1985. *Oaks of North America.* Happy Camp, California: Naturegraph Publishers.

Mitchell, A. 1994. The Lucombe Oaks. *The Plantsman* 15(4):216-224.

Rhododendron

Argent, G., Fairweather, C. & Walter, K. 1996. *Accepted Names in Rhododendron section Vireya.* Edinburgh: Royal Botanic Garden.

Argent, G., Bond, J., Chamberlain, D., Cox, P. & Hardy, A. 1997. *The Rhododendron Handbook 1998.* Rhododendron Species in Cultivation. London: RHS.

Chamberlain, D.F. & Rae, S.J. 1990. A Revision of *Rhododendron* IV. Subgenus *Tsutsusi. Edinburgh J. Bot.* 47(2).

Chamberlain, D.F. 1982. A Revision of *Rhododendron* II. Subgenus *Hymenanthes. Notes Roy. Bot. Gard. Edinburgh* 39(2).

Chamberlain, D., Hyam, R., Argent, G., Fairweather, G. & Walter, K.S. 1996. *The Genus Rhododendron.* Edinburgh:Royal Botanic Garden.

Cullen, J. 1980. A Revision of *Rhododendron* I. Subgenus *Rhododendron* sections *Rhododendron* and *Pogonanthum. Notes Roy. Bot. Gard. Edinburgh* 39(1).

Davidian, H.H. 1982-1992 *The Rhododendron Species* (Vols 1-4). London: Batsford.

Galle, F.C. 1985. *Azaleas.* Portland, Oregon: Timber Press.

Leslie, A. C. (comp.). 1980. *The Rhododendron Handbook 1980.* London: RHS.

Leslie, A.C. (comp.) 2004. *The International Rhododendron Register and Checklist* (2nd ed.). London: RHS. 1st Supp. 2006. http://www.rhs.org.uk/learning

Tamura, T. (ed.). 1989. *Azaleas in Kurume.* Kurume, Japan: International Azalea Festival '89.

Ribes

Crawford, M. 1997. *Currants and Gooseberries: Production and Culture.* Dartington, Devon: Agroforestry Research Trust.

Rosa

Beales, P., Cairns, T., et al. 1998. *Botanica's Rose: The Encyclopedia of Roses.* Hoo, Kent: Grange Books.

Cairns, T. (ed.). 2000. *Modern Roses XI. The World Encyclopedia of Roses.* London: Academic Press.

Dickerson, B.C. 1999. *The Old Rose Advisor.* Portland, Oregon: Timber Press.

Haw, S.G. 1996. Notes on Some Chinese and Himalayan Rose Species of Section *Pimpinellifoliae. The New Plantsman* 3(3):143-146.

HelpMeFind Roses. Nov 2007. www.helpmefind.com

McCann, S. 1985. *Miniature Roses.* Newton Abbot, Devon: David & Charles.

Quest-Ritson, C. 2003. *Climbing Roses of the World.* Portland, Oregon: Timber Press.

Quest-Ritson, C. & Quest-Ritson, B. 2003. *The Royal Horticultural Society Encyclopedia of Roses: The Definitive A-Z Guide.* London: Dorling Kindersley.

Thomas, G.S. 1995. *The Graham Stuart Thomas Rose Book.* London: John Murray.

Verrier, S. 1996. *Rosa Gallica.* Balmain, Australia: Florilegium.

Roscoea

Cowley, J. 2007. *The Genus Roscoea.* Kew Publishing.

Rosularia

Eggli, U. 1988. A Monographic Study of the Genus *Rosularia. Bradleya* (Supp.) 6:1-118.

Rubiaceae

Govaerts, R. et al. 2005. *World Checklist & Bibliography of Rubiaceae.* http://apps.kew.org

Saintpaulia

Goodship, G. 1987. *Saintpaulia Variety List* (Supp.). Slough, Bucks: Saintpaulia & Houseplant Society.

Moore, H.E. 1957. *African Violets, Gloxinias and Their Relatives.* A Guide to the Cultivated Gesneriads. New York: Macmillan.

Salix

Newsholme, C. 1992. *Willows.* The Genus *Salix.* London: Batsford.

Stott, K.G. 1971 *Willows for Amenity, Windbreaks and Other Uses.* Checklist of the Long Ashton Collection of Willows, with Notes on their Suitability for Various Purposes. Long Ashton Research Station: University of Bristol.

Salvia

Clebsch, B. 2003. *A Book of Salvias.* (2nd ed.). Portland, Oregon: Timber Press.

Compton, J. 1994. Mexican Salvias in Cultivation. *The Plantsman* 15(4):193-215.

Middleton, R. *Robin's Salvias.* www.robinssalvias.com

Saxifraga

Bland, B. 2000. *Silver Saxifrages.* Pershore, Worcs.: Alpine Garden Society.

Dashwood, M. & Bland, B. 2005. Silver Saxifrages: RHS Bulletin No 9. Wisley, Surrey: RHS. www.rhs.org.uk/plants/documents/saxifraga05.pdf

McGregor, M. Jan 2006. Saxbase. Saxifrage Society. www.saxifraga.org

McGregor, M. 1995. *Saxifrages: The Complete Cultivars & Hybrids: International Register of Saxifrages.* (2nd ed.). Driffield, E. Yorks: Saxifrage Society.

Webb, D.A. & Gornall, R.J. 1989. *Saxifrages of Europe.* Bromley, Kent: Christopher Helm.

Sedum

Evans, R.L. 1983. *Handbook of Cultivated Sedums.* Motcombe, Dorset: Ivory Head Press.

Lord, T. 2006. *Sedum* up for assessment. *The Plantsman* 5(4):244-252.

Stephenson, R. 1994. *Sedum.* The Cultivated Stonecrops. Portland, Oregon: Timber Press.

Sempervivum
Diehm, H. Jan 2006. www.semperhorst.de
Miklánek, M. 2002. *The List of Cultivars: Sempervivum and Jovibarba v. 7.01*. Pieštany, Slovakia: M. Miklánek (private distribution).
Miklánek, M. 2000. *List of Cultivars: Sempervivum and Jovibarba* v. 15.1. http://miklanek.tripod.com
Sinningia
Dates, J.D. 1988. *The Gesneriad Register 1988. Check List of Names with Descriptions of Cultivated Plants in the Genus Sinningia.* Galesburg, Illinois: American Gloxinia and Gesneriad Society, Inc.
Solenostemon
Pedley, W.K. & Pedley, R. 1974. *Coleus – A Guide to Cultivation and Identification.* Edinburgh: Bartholemew.
Sorbus
McAllister, H. 2005. *The Genus Sorbus: Mountain Ash and Other Rowans.* Kew: Royal Botanical Gardens.
Snyers d'Attenhoven, C. 1999. *Sorbus* Lombarts hybrids *Belgische Dendrologie*: 76-81. Belgium.
Wright, D. 1981. *Sorbus* – a Gardener's Evaluation. *The Plantsman* 3(2):65-98.
Spiraea
Miller, D.M. 2003. *Spiraea japonica with coloured leaves: RHS Bulletin No 4.* Wisley, Surrey: Royal Horticultural Society. www.rhs.org.uk/plants/documents/spiraea03.pdf
Streptocarpus
Arnold, P. 1979. *The Gesneriad Register 1979: Check List of Streptocarpus.* Binghamton, New York: American Gloxinia & Gesneriad.
Dibleys Nurseries Online Catalogue. Oct 2005. www.dibleys.com.
Succulents
Eggli, U. (ed.) 2002. *Illustrated Handbook of Succulent Plants.* Heidelberg, Germany: Springer-Verlag.
Eggli, U. & Taylor, N. 1994. *List of Names of Succulent Plants other than Cacti Published 1950-92.* Kew: Royal Botanic Gardens.
Grantham, K. & Klaassen, P. 1999. *The Plantfinder's Guide to Cacti and Other Succulents.* Newton Abbot, Devon: David & Charles.
Jacobsen, H. 1973. *Lexicon of Succulent Plants.* London: Blandford.
Syringa
Vrugtman, F. 2000. *International Register of Cultivar Names in the Genus Syringa L. (Oleaceae).* (Contribution No 91). Hamilton, Canada: Royal Botanic Gardens.
Tiliaceae
Wild, H. 1984. *Flora of Southern Africa 21 (1: Tiliaceae).* Pretoria: Botanical Research Institute, Dept of Agriculture.
Tillandsia
Kiff, L.F. 1991. *A Distributional Checklist of the Genus Tillandsia.* Encino, California: Botanical Diversions.
Trillium
Case, F.W.J. & Case, R.B. 1997. *Trilliums.* Portland, Oregon: Timber Press.
Jacobs, D.L. & Jacobs, R.L. 1997. *American Treasures.* Trilliums in Woodland Garden. Decatur, Georgia: Eco-Gardens.
Tulipa
KAVB Online registration pages. http://kavb.back2p.soft-orange.com
Ulmus
Green, P.S. 1964. Registratration of Cultivar Names in *Ulmus. Arnoldia (Jamaica Plain)* 24:41-80.
Vaccinium
Trehane, J. 2004. *Blueberries, Cranberries and Other Vacciniums.* Portland, Oregon: Timber Press.
Vegetables
Official Journal of the European Communities. Dec 2007. Common catalogue of varieties of agricultural plant species: 26th complete ed. http://europa.eu.int
Official Journal of the European Communities. Oct 2007. Common catalogue of varieties of vegetable species: consolidated version. http://ec.europa.eu/food
Viburnum
Dirr, M.A. 2007. *Viburnums: Flowering Shrubs for Every Season.* Portland, Oregon: Timber Press.
Viola
Coombes, R.E. 2003. *Violets.* (2nd ed.). London: Batsford.
Fuller, R. 1990. *Pansies, Violas & Violettas.* The Complete Guide. Marlborough: The Crowood Press.
Perfect, E.J. 1996. *Armand Millet and his Violets.* High Wycombe: Park Farm Press.
Robinson, P.M. & Snocken, J. 2003. Checklist of the Cultivated Forms of the Genus *Viola* including the Register of Cultivars. American Violet Society. http://americanvioletsociety.org
Zambra, G.L. 1950. *Violets for Garden and Market.* (2nd ed.). London: Collingridge.
Vitis
Pearkes, G. 1989. *Vine Growing in Britain.* London: Dent.
Robinson, J. 1989. *Vines, Grapes and Wines.* London: Mitchell Beazley.
Watsonia
Goldblatt, P. 1989. *The Genus Watsonia.* A Systematic Monograph. South Africa: National Botanic Gardens.
Weigela
Howard, R.A. 1965. A Checklist of Cultivar Names in *Weigela. Arnoldia (Jamaica Plain)* 25:49-69.
Wisteria
Valder, P. 1995. *Wisterias.* A Comprehensive Guide. Balmain, Australia: Florilegium.
Yucca
Smith, C. 2004. *Yuccas: Giants among the Lilies.* NCCPG.

Zauschneria

Raven, P.H. 1977. Generic and Sectional Delimitation in *Onagraceae,* Tribe *Epilobieae. Ann. Missouri Bot. Gard.* 63(2):326-340.

Robinson, A. 2000. Focus on Plants: Piping Hot (*Zauschneria* Cultivars). *The Garden* (RHS) 125(9):698-699.

International Plant Finders

New Zealand

Gaddum, Meg (comp.) *New Zealand Plant Finder* (2008). 46,000 plants and where to buy them. Available online only at www.plantfinder.co.nz

United Kingdom

Pawsey, Angela (ed.) (26th ed.) 2008-2009, *Find That Rose!* Pub. May 2008. Lists approximately 3,475 varieties available in the UK together with basic type, colour and fragrance, including all forms of standard roses. New varieties are highlighted and cross-referenced, where applicable, to alternative selling names. Gives full details of around 50 growers/suppliers, many offering mail order. Includes useful information on how to find a rose with a particular Christian name, or to celebrate a special event, on charity roses and where to see roses in bloom.

For further information send sae to 303 Mile End Road, Colchester, Essex CO4 5EA. To order a copy send payment of £3.60 made out to *Find That Rose!* to above address.

Visit the website on www.findthatrose.net

Nurseries

The following nurseries between them stock an unrivalled choice of plants. Before making a visit, please remember to check with the nursery that the plant you seek is currently available.

Nursery Codes and Symbols

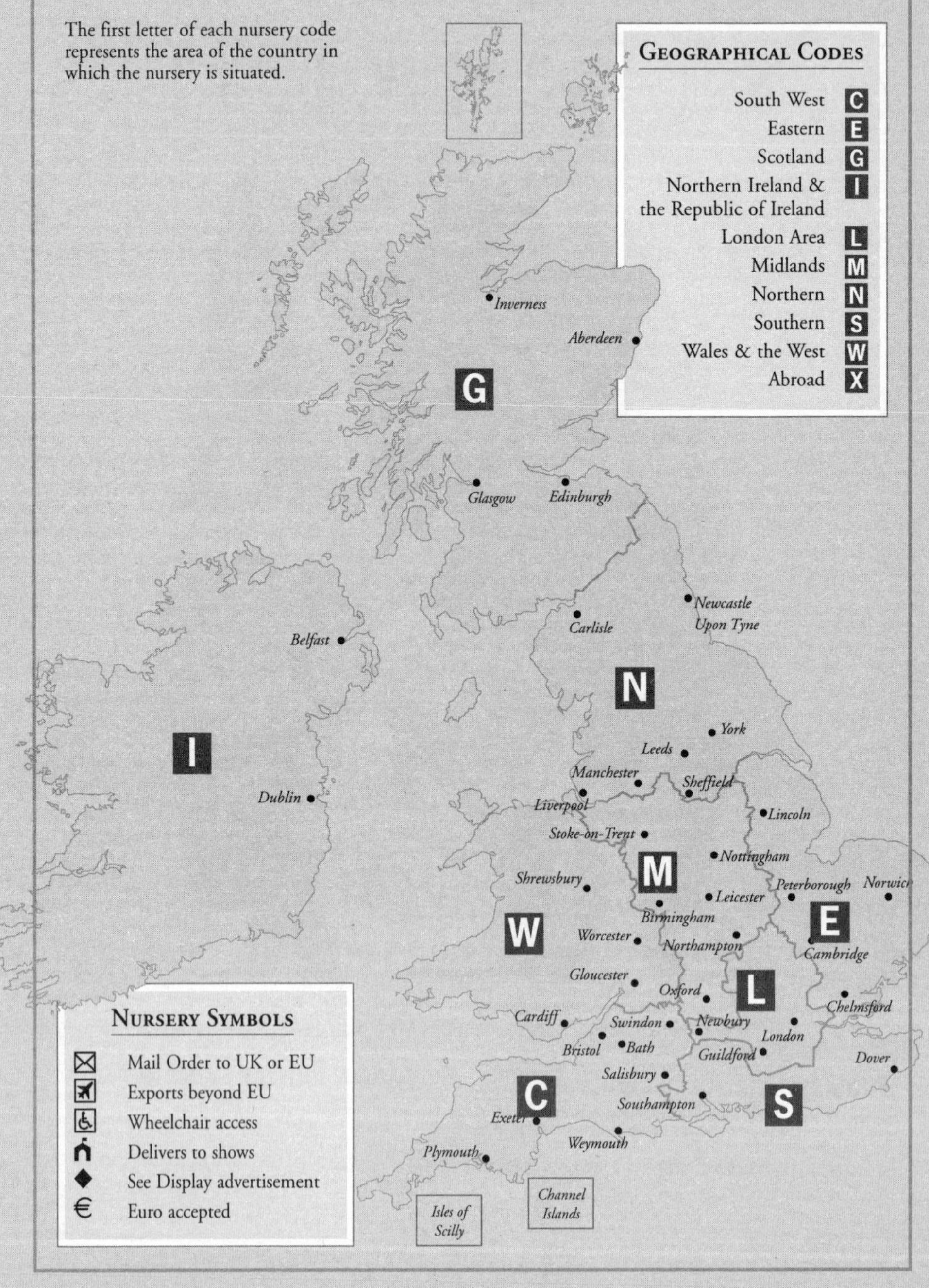

Using the Three Nursery Listings

Your main reference from the Plant Directory is the Nursery Details by Code listing, which includes all relevant information for each nursery in order of nursery code. The Nursery Index by Name is an alphabetical list for those who know a nursery's name but not its code and wish to check its details in the main list. The Specialist Nurseries index is to aid those searching for a particular plant group.

1 Nursery Details by Code

Once you have found your plant in the Plant Directory, turn to this list to find out the name, address, opening times and other details of the nurseries whose codes accompany the plant.

KEY
- ⊠ Mail order to UK or EU
- Exports beyond EU
- Wheelchair access
- Delivers to shows
- € Euro accepted
- ◆ See Display advertisement

A geographical code is followed by three letters reflecting the nursery's name

WHil **Hillview Hardy Plants** ⊠ € ◆ — *Refer to the box at the base of each right-hand page for a key to the symbols*

(off B4176), Worfield, Nr Bridgnorth, Shropshire, WV15 5NT
Ⓣ (01746) 716454
Ⓕ (01746) 716454
Ⓔ hillview@themutual.net
Ⓦ www.hillviewhardyplants.com
Contact: Ingrid, John & Sarah Millington
Opening Times: 0900-1700 Mon-Sat Mar-mid Oct. At other times, please phone first.
Min Mail Order UK: £15.00 + p&p
Min Mail Order EU: £15.00 + p&p
Cat. Cost: 5 × 2nd class.
Credit Cards: All major credit/debit cards
Specialities: Choice herbaceous perennials incl. *Acanthus* & *Acanthaceae*, *Albuca*, *Aquilegia*, *Auricula*, *Primula*, *Canna*, *Crocosmia*, *Eucomis*, *Ixia*, South African bulbs. Nat. Collection of *Acanthus*.
Notes: Also sells wholesale.
Map Ref: W, B4 **OS Grid Ref:** SO772969

A brief summary of the plants available

Other information about the nursery

The map letter is followed by the map square in which the nursery is located

The Ordnance Survey national grid reference for use with OS maps

2 Nursery Index by Name

If you seek a particular nursery, look it up in this alphabetical index. Note its code and turn to the Nursery Details by Code list for full information.

Highfield Hollies	SHHo
Hill Garth Nursery	SHGN
Hill House Nursery & Gardens	CHll
Hillview Hardy Plants	WHil
Himalayan Garden Co., The	NHim
Hoecroft Plants	EHoe
Holden Clough Nursery	NHol
Home Plants	SHom

3 Specialist Nurseries

A list of 32 categories under which nurseries have classified themselves if they exclusively, or predominantly, supply this range of plants.

Drought Tolerant

CBot, CKno, EAlp, ECha, EGln, EGoo, EHoe, ETod, LLWP, LOck, LPal, MBPg, MHrb, NFir, NHoy, SAll, SDow, SIde, SIoW, SJoh, SPhx, SUsu, WHil, WJek, WPnn

How to Use the Nursery Listings

The details given for each nursery have been compiled from information supplied to us in answer to a questionnaire. In some cases, because of constraints of space, the entries have been slightly abbreviated.

Nurseries are not charged for their entries and inclusion in no way implies a value judgement.

Nursery Details by Code (*page 820*)

Each nursery is allocated a code, for example GPoy. The first letter of each code indicates the main area of the country in which the nursery is situated. In this example, G=Scotland. The remaining three letters reflect the nursery's name, in this case Poyntzfield Herb Nursery.

In this main listing the nurseries are given in alphabetical order of codes for quick reference from the Plant Directory. All of the nurseries' details, such as address, opening times, mail order service etc., will be found here.

Opening Times

Although opening times have been published as submitted and where applicable, **it is always advisable, especially if travelling a long distance, to check with the nursery first**. The initials NGS indicate that the nursery is open under the National Gardens Scheme.

Mail Order ⊠

Many nurseries provide a mail order service. **This is, however, often restricted to certain times of the year or to particular genera**. Please check the **Notes** section of each nursery's entry for any restrictions or special conditions.

In some cases, the mail order service extends to all members of the European Union. Where this is offered, the minimum charge to the EU will be noted in the Nursery entry.

Where '**No minimum charge**' (Nmc) is shown, please note that to send even one plant may involve the nursery in substantial postage and packing costs. Some nurseries may not be prepared to send tender or bulky plants.

Where a nursery offers a **mail order only** service, this will be noted under **Opening Times** in the nursery entry.

Export ✈

Export refers to mail order beyond the European Union. Nurseries that are prepared to consider exporting are indicated. However, there is usually a substantial minimum charge and, in addition, all the costs of Phytosanitary Certificates and Customs have to be met by the purchaser.

Catalogue Cost

Some nurseries offer their catalogue free, or for a few stamps, but a large (at least A5) stamped addressed envelope is always appreciated as well. Overseas customers should use an equivalent number of International Reply Coupons (IRCs) in place of stamps.

Increasingly, nurseries are finding it more cost effective to produce catalogues on the Internet rather than printing them. Many nurseries also offer an online mail order facility.

Wheelchair Access ♿

Nurseries are asked to indicate if their premises are suitable for wheelchair users. Where only partial access is indicated, this is noted in the Notes field and the nursery is not marked with the symbol.

The assessment of ease-of-access is entirely the responsibility of the individual nursery.

Specialities

Nurseries list here the plants or genera that they supply and any National Collections of plants they may hold. Please note that some nurseries may charge an entry fee to visit a National Collection. Always enquire before visiting.

Nurseries will also note here if they only have small quantities of individual plants available for sale or if they will propagate to order.

Notes

In this section, you will find notes on any restrictions to mail order or export; on limited wheelchair access; or the nursery site address, if this differs from the office address; together with any other non-horticultural information.

Delivery to Shows

Many nurseries will deliver pre-ordered plants to flower shows for collection by customers. These are indicated by a marquee symbol. Contact the nursery for details of shows they attend.

Payment in Euros €

A number of UK nurseries have indicated that they will accept payment in Euros. You should, however, check with the nursery concerned before making such a payment, as some will only accept cash and some only cheques, whilst others will expect the purchaser to pay bank charges.

Maps

If you wish to visit any of the nurseries you can find its approximate location on the relevant map (following p.937), unless the nursery has requested this is not shown. Nurseries are also encouraged to provide their Ordnance Survey national grid reference for use with OS publications such as the Land Ranger series.

Nursery Index by Name

For convenience, an alphabetical index of nurseries is included on p.928. This gives the names of all nurseries listed in the book in alphabetical order of nursery name together with their code.

Specialist Nurseries (*page 935*)

This list of nurseries is intended to help those with an interest in finding specialist categories of plant. Nurseries have been asked to classify themselves under one or more headings where this represents the type of plant they *predominantly* or *exclusively* have in stock. For example, if you wish to find a nursery specialising in ornamental grasses, look up 'Grasses' in the listing where you will find a list of nursery codes. Then turn to the Nursery Details by Code, for details of the nurseries.

Please note that not all nurseries shown here will have plants listed in the Plant Directory. This may be their choice or because the *RHS Plant Finder* does not list seeds or annuals and only terrestrial orchids and hardy cacti. For space reasons, it is rare to find a nursery's full catalogue listed in the Plant Directory.

In all cases, please ensure you ring to confirm the range available before embarking on a journey to the nursery.
The specialist plant groups listed in this edition are:

Acid-loving
Alpines/rock
Aquatics/marginals
Bamboos
British wild flowers
Bulbous plants
Cacti & succulents
Carnivorous
Chalk-loving
Climbers
Coastal
Conifers
Conservatory
Drought-tolerant
Ferns
Fruit
Grasses
Hedging
Herbs
Marginal/bog plants
Orchids
Organic
Ornamental trees
Peat-free
Period plants
Propagate to order
Roses
Seeds
Specimen-sized plants
Topiary
Tropical plants

Perennials and shrubs have been omitted as these are considered to be too general and serviced by a great proportion of the nurseries.

Deleted Nurseries

Every year some nurseries ask to be removed from the book. This may be a temporary measure because they are moving, or it may be permanent due to closure, sale, retirement, or a change in the way in they trade. Occasionally, nurseries are unable to meet the closing date and will re-enter the book in the following edition. Some nurseries simply do not reply and, as we have no current information on them, they are deleted.

Please, never use an old edition

NURSERY DETAILS BY CODE

Please note that all these nurseries are listed in alphabetical order by their code. All nurseries are listed in alphabetical order by their name in the **Nursery Index by Name** on page 928.

SOUTH WEST

CAbb **ABBOTSBURY SUB-TROPICAL GARDENS** ⊠ ♿
Abbotsbury, Nr Weymouth, Dorset, DT3 4LA
Ⓣ (01305) 871344
Ⓕ (01305) 871344
Ⓔ info@abbotsburygardens.co.uk
Ⓦ www.abbotsburyplantsales.co.uk
Contact: David Sutton
Opening Times: 1000-1800 daily mid Mar-1st Nov. 1000-1500 Nov-mid Mar.
Min Mail Order UK: £10.00 + p&p
Cat. Cost: £2.00 + A4 sae + 42p stamp
Credit Cards: Access Visa MasterCard Switch
Specialities: Less common & tender shrubs incl. palms, tree ferns, bamboos & plants from Australia, New Zealand & S. Africa.

CAbP **ABBEY PLANTS** ⊠ ♿
Chaffeymoor, Bourton, Gillingham, Dorset, SP8 5BY
Ⓣ (01747) 840841
Contact: K Potts
Opening Times: 1000-1300 & 1400-1700 Wed-Sat Mar-Nov. Dec-Feb by appt.
Min Mail Order UK: Nmc
Cat. Cost: 2 × 2nd class.
Credit Cards: None
Specialities: Flowering trees & shrubs. Shrub roses incl. many unusual varieties. Limited stock.
Map Ref: C, B4 **OS Grid Ref:** ST762304

CAbx **ABRAXAS GARDENS** ⊠
7 Little Keyford Lane, Frome, Somerset, BA11 5BB
Ⓣ (01373) 472879
Contact: Duncan Skene
Opening Times: Mainly mail order. For Open Days see plant list.
Min Mail Order UK: £20.00
Cat. Cost: Free.
Credit Cards: None
Specialities: *Crocosmia*, *Iris sibirica*, *Hemerocallis* (spiders, spider variants & unusual forms). Many recent introductions available only in small numbers.
Notes: New list annually in Jan. Plants despatched in Apr/May only. Partial wheelchair access.
Map Ref: C, B5 **OS Grid Ref:** ST775465

CAby **THE ABBEY NURSERY** ⌂ ♿
Forde Abbey, Chard, Somerset, TA20 4LU
Ⓣ (01460) 220088
Ⓕ (01460) 220088
Ⓔ TheAbbeyNursery@btconnect.com
Contact: Peter Sims
Opening Times: 1000-1700 7 days, 1st Mar-31st Oct. Please phone first to check opening times in Mar.
Cat. Cost: None issued.
Credit Cards: All major credit/debit cards
Specialities: Hardy herbaceous perennials.
Map Ref: C, C4 **OS Grid Ref:** ST359052

CAgr **AGROFORESTRY RESEARCH TRUST** ⊠
46 Hunters Moon, Dartington, Totnes, Devon, TQ9 6JT
Ⓣ (01803) 840776
Ⓕ (01803) 840776
Ⓔ mail@agroforestry.co.uk
Ⓦ www.agroforestry.co.uk
Contact: Martin Crawford
Opening Times: Not open. Mail order only.
Min Mail Order UK: Nmc
Min Mail Order EU: Nmc
Cat. Cost: 4 × 1st class.
Credit Cards: All major credit/debit cards
Specialities: Top & soft fruit, nut trees including *Castanea*, *Corylus*, *Juglans*, *Pinus*. Also seeds. Some plants in small quantities only.

CAlb **ALBION PLANTS** ⊠ €
Roborough, Winkleigh, Devon,
EX19 8TD
Ⓣ (01805) 603502
Ⓕ 08000 112024
Ⓔ huggons@albion-plants.co.uk
Ⓦ www.albion-plants.co.uk
Contact: Neil & Brenda Huggons
Opening Times: Mail order only. Open by appt. for wholesale quantites only.
Min Mail Order UK: Nmc
Cat. Cost: Available by email on request.
Credit Cards: All major credit/debit cards
Specialities: *Vinca*, *Cornus*, *Viburnum*, *Salix*, *Ceanothus*. Specimen-sized shrubs & container-grown trees.
Notes: Also sells wholesale.
Map Ref: C, B3 **OS Grid Ref:** SS584173

CAni **ANITA ALLEN** ⊠
Shapcott Barton Estate,
East Knowstone, South Molton, Devon,
EX36 4EE
Ⓣ (01398) 341664
Ⓕ (01398) 341664
Contact: Anita Allen
Opening Times: By appt. only. Garden open under NGS.
Min Mail Order UK: Nmc.
Cat. Cost: 5 × 1st class & state which catalogue, Shasta daisies or *Buddleja*.
Credit Cards: None
Specialities: Nat. Collections of *Leucanthemum* × *superbum* & *Buddleja davidii* & hybrids, 70+ cvs. 80+ accurately named Shasta daisies, a few in very short supply. Also many hardy perennials.
Map Ref: C, B3 **OS Grid Ref:** SS846235

CArn **ARNE HERBS** ⊠ ✈ € ♿
Limeburn Nurseries, Limeburn Hill, Chew Magna, Bristol, BS40 8QW
Ⓣ (01275) 333399
Ⓔ anthony@arneherbs.co.uk
Ⓦ www.arneherbs.co.uk
Contact: A Lyman-Dixon & Jenny Thomas
Opening Times: 1000-1600 most weekdays, Sat mid-Mar-end Jun. Other times by telephone appt. only.
Min Mail Order UK: Nmc
Min Mail Order EU: Nmc
Cat. Cost: £3.75 UK, 10 × IRC, or A4 sae for free non-descriptive plantlist. Also online.
Credit Cards: None
Specialities: Herbs, some very rare. North American, Mediterranean & UK wild flowers. Also plants for reseach, conservation projects & historical recreations.
Notes: Will deliver to Bristol Farmers' Markets. Also sells wholesale.
Map Ref: C, A5 **OS Grid Ref:** ST563638

CAvo **AVON BULBS** ⊠ ♠
Burnt House Farm, Mid-Lambrook, South Petherton, Somerset, TA13 5HE
Ⓣ (01460) 242177
Ⓕ (01460) 249025
Ⓔ info@avonbulbs.co.uk
Ⓦ www.avonbulbs.co.uk
Contact: C Ireland-Jones
Opening Times: Mail order only. Open Thu, Fri, Sat, mid-Sep-end Oct & mid Feb-end Mar for collection of pre-booked orders.
Min Mail Order UK: £10.00 + p&p
Min Mail Order EU: £20.00 + p&p
Cat. Cost: 4 × 2nd class.
Credit Cards: Visa Access Switch MasterCard
Specialities: Some special snowdrops are only available in small quantities.

CBar **BARTERS PLANT CENTRE & NURSERY** ♿
Chapmanslade, Westbury, Wiltshire,
BA13 4AL
Ⓣ (01373) 832694
Ⓕ (01373) 832677
Ⓔ sales@barters.co.uk
Ⓦ www.barters.co.uk
Contact: Giles Hall
Opening Times: 0900-1700 Mon-Thu, 0900-1730 Fri & Sat, summer. 0900-1630 Mon-thu, 0900-1700 Fri & Sat, winter. 1030-1630 Sun.
Cat. Cost: A4 Sae
Credit Cards: All major credit/debit cards
Specialities: Wide range of shrubs. Ground cover, patio plants, container trees, ferns, half-hardy perennials, grasses, herbaceous & climbers. Bamboos, hedging, fruit trees, old fashioned roses & bare-root stock.
Notes: Also sells wholesale.
Map Ref: C, B5

CBcs **BURNCOOSE NURSERIES** ⊠ ✈ ♠ ♿
Gwennap, Redruth, Cornwall,
TR16 6BJ
Ⓣ (01209) 860316
Ⓕ (01209) 860011
Ⓔ burncoose@eclipse.co.uk
Ⓦ www.burncoose.co.uk
Contact: C H Williams

KEY
⊠ Mail order to UK or EU ♠ Delivers to shows
✈ Exports beyond EU € Euro accepted
♿ Accessible by wheelchair ◆ See Display advertisement

C

Opening Times: 0830-1700 Mon-Sat & 1100-1700 Sun.
Min Mail Order UK: Nmc
Min Mail Order EU: Individual quotations for EU sales.
Cat. Cost: Free
Credit Cards: Visa Access Switch
Specialities: Extensive range of over 3500 ornamental trees & shrubs and herbaceous. Rare & unusual *Magnolia*, *Rhododendron*. Conservatory plants. 30 acre garden.
Notes: Also sells wholesale.
Map Ref: C, D1 **OS Grid Ref:** SW742395

CBct **Barracott Plants** ⊠ € ♿
Old Orchard, Calstock Road, Gunnislake, Cornwall, PL18 9AA
Ⓣ (01822) 832234
Ⓔ GEOFF@geoff63.freeserve.co.uk
Ⓦ www.barracottplants.co.uk
Contact: Geoff & Thelma Turner
Opening Times: 0900-1700 Thu & Fri, Mar-end Sep. Other times by appt.
Min Mail Order UK: Nmc
Cat. Cost: 2 × 1st class.
Credit Cards: None
Specialities: Herbaceous plants: shade-loving, foliage & form. *Acanthus*, *Aspidistra*, *Astrantia*, *Bergenia*, *Convallaria*, *Disporum*, *Liriope*, *Maianthemum*, *Polygonatum*, *Roscoea*, *Trillium*, *Tricyrtis* & *Uvularia*.
Notes: Also sells wholesale.
Map Ref: C, C3 **OS Grid Ref:** SX436702

CBdn **Bowden Hostas** ⊠ ✈ ♿
Sticklepath, Okehampton, Devon, EX20 2NL
Ⓣ (01837) 840989
Ⓔ info@bowdenhostas.com
Ⓦ www.bowdenhostas.com
Contact: Tim Penrose
Opening Times: By appt. only.
Min Mail Order UK: Nmc
Min Mail Order EU: Nmc
Cat. Cost: Free.
Credit Cards: Visa Access EuroCard Switch
Specialities: *Hosta* only. Nat. Collection of modern hybrid *Hosta*.
Notes: Also sells wholesale.
Map Ref: C, C3 **OS Grid Ref:** SX640940

CBen **Bennetts Water Gardens** ⊠ ♿
B3157 Chickerell Link Road, Chickerell, Weymouth, Dorset, DT3 4AF
Ⓣ (01305) 785150
Ⓔ enquiries@waterlily.co.uk
Ⓦ www.waterlily.co.uk
Contact: James Bennett
Opening Times: 1000-1700 Apr-Sep. Closed Mon & Sat.
Min Mail Order UK: Nmc
Cat. Cost: Sae for price list
Credit Cards: Visa Access MasterCard Switch
Specialities: Aquatic plants. Bog Plants. Nat. Collection of *Nymphaea*.
Notes: Mail order Mar-Sep only.
Map Ref: C, C5 **OS Grid Ref:** SY651797

CBgR **Beggar's Roost Plants** ⊠ € ♿
Lilstock, Bridgwater, Somerset, TA5 1SU
Ⓣ (01278) 741519
Ⓕ (01278) 741519
Ⓔ ro@beggarsroostplants.co.uk
Ⓦ www.beggarsroostplants.co.uk
Contact: Rosemary FitzGerald
Opening Times: Any time by appt.
Min Mail Order UK: Nmc
Min Mail Order EU: Nmc
Credit Cards: None
Specialities: Garden-worthy bulbs & herbaceous, emphasising species. Classic perennials, unusual small shrubs, winter interest plants. Small quantities only.
Notes: Mail order for specialities: *Crocosmia*, *Hemerocallis*, *Iris*, *Galanthus*. Ask for list.
Map Ref: C, B4 **OS Grid Ref:** ST168450

CBod **Bodmin Plant and Herb Nursery** ♿
Laveddon Mill, Laninval Hill, Bodmin, Cornwall, PL30 5JU
Ⓣ (01208) 72837
Ⓕ (01208) 76491
Ⓔ bodminnursery@aol.com
Ⓦ www.bodminnursery.co.uk
Contact: Mark Lawlor
Opening Times: 0900-1700 Mon-Sat Nov-Mar, 0900-1800 Mon-Sat Apr-Oct. 1000-1600 Sun.
Credit Cards: All major credit/debit cards
Specialities: Herbs, herbaceous & grasses, hardy geraniums & coastal plants. Interesting shrubs, fruit & ornamental trees.
Map Ref: C, C2 **OS Grid Ref:** SX053659

CBot **The Botanic Nursery** ⊠ ⌂ €
Atworth, Nr Melksham, Wiltshire, SN12 8NU
Ⓣ mobile 07850 328756
Ⓕ (01225) 700953
Ⓦ www.thebotanicnursery.co.uk
Contact: T. Baker
Opening Times: 1000-1700 Tue-Sat, Mar-Nov. Please avoid lunch time if possible.
Min Mail Order UK: £11.00 for 24hr carriage service.

Cat. Cost: £1.00 in stamps.
Credit Cards: MasterCard Visa
Specialities: Nursery propagates from large range of lime-tolerant plants in varying quantities all peat free. Nat. Collection of *Digitalis*.
Notes: If travelling, please phone first to confirm specific plant availability. Partially accessible for wheelchairs.

CBow **Bowley Plants** ⊠ ◆
Church Farm, North End, Ashton Keynes, Nr Swindon, Wiltshire, SN6 6QR
Ⓣ (01285) 640352
Ⓜ 07855 524929
Ⓔ bowleyplants@btinternet.com
Ⓦ www.bowleyplants.co.uk
Contact: Piers Bowley
Opening Times: Some Sat, Mar-Oct, please phone first. Other times by appt.
Min Mail Order UK: Nmc
Cat. Cost: 2 × 1st class.
Credit Cards: None
Specialities: Variegated plants & coloured foliage. Alpines, perennials, shrubs, ferns, grasses & herbs. Some varieties in small numbers.
Notes: Also sells wholesale.
Map Ref: C, A6 **OS Grid Ref:** SU043945

CBrd **Broadleas Gardens Ltd**
Broadleas, Devizes, Wiltshire, SN10 5JQ
Ⓣ (01380) 722035
Ⓕ (01380) 722970
Ⓔ broadleasgardens@btinternet.com
Contact: Lady Anne Cowdray
Opening Times: 1400-1800 Wed, Thu & Sun Apr-Oct.
Cat. Cost: 1 × 1st class.
Credit Cards: None
Specialities: General range.

CBre **Bregover Plants** ⊠
Hillbrooke, Middlewood, North Hill, Nr Launceston, Cornwall, PL15 7NN
Ⓣ (01566) 782661
Contact: Jennifer Bousfield
Opening Times: 1100-1700 Wed, Mar-mid Oct and by appt.
Min Mail Order UK: Nmc
Min Mail Order EU: Nmc
Cat. Cost: 3 × 1st class.
Credit Cards: None
Specialities: Unusual hardy perennials grown in small garden nursery. Available in small quantities only.
Notes: Mail order Oct-Mar only.
Map Ref: C, C2 **OS Grid Ref:** SX273752

CBro **Broadleigh Gardens** ⊠ € ♿
Bishops Hull, Taunton, Somerset, TA4 1AE
Ⓣ (01823) 286231
Ⓕ (01823) 323646
Ⓔ info@broadleighbulbs.co.uk
Ⓦ www.broadleighbulbs.co.uk
Contact: Lady Skelmersdale
Opening Times: 0900-1600 Mon-Fri for viewing only. Orders collected if notice given.
Min Mail Order UK: Nmc
Min Mail Order EU: Nmc
Cat. Cost: 2 × 1st class.
Credit Cards: Switch MasterCard Maestro Visa
Specialities: Jan catalogue: bulbs in growth (*Galanthus*, *Cyclamen* etc.) & herbaceous woodland plants (trilliums, hellebores etc). Extensive list of *Agapanthus*. June catalogue: dwarf & unusual bulbs, *Iris* (DB & PC). Nat. Collection of Alec Grey hybrid daffodils.
Notes: Euro payment accepted as cash only.
Map Ref: C, B4 **OS Grid Ref:** ST195251

CBrP **Brooklands Plants** ⊠
25 Treves Road, Dorchester, Dorset, DT1 2HE
Ⓣ (01305) 265846
Ⓔ cycads@btinternet.com
Contact: Ian Watt
Opening Times: By appt. only for collection of plants.
Min Mail Order UK: £25.00 + p&p
Min Mail Order EU: £25.00 + p&p
Cat. Cost: 2 × 2nd class.
Credit Cards: None
Specialities: Cycad nursery specialising in the more cold-tolerant species of *Encephalartos*, *Dioon*, *Macrozamia* & *Cycas*. Also specialist in cold-tolerant palms as well as *Aloe*, *Agave* and *Dasylirion*. Some species available in small quantities only.
Map Ref: C, C5 **OS Grid Ref:** SY682897

CBty **Bentley Plants** ⊠ € ♿
1 Bentley Wood Cottages, West Tytherley, Salisbury, Wiltshire, SP5 1QB
Ⓣ (01794) 340775
Ⓕ (01794) 340775
Ⓔ john@bentleyplants.fsnet.co.uk
Ⓦ www.bentleyplants.co.uk
Contact: John Wilson
Opening Times: By appt. only.

KEY
⊠ Mail order to UK or EU — Delivers to shows
✈ Exports beyond EU — € Euro accepted
♿ Accessible by wheelchair — ◆ See Display advertisement

C

Min Mail Order UK: Nmc
Credit Cards: All major credit/debit cards
Specialities: Grows 90 varieties of ferns, a large range of shrubs, incl. more than 20 varieties of *Pittosporum*, bamboos & Japanese maples.
Map Ref: C, B6 **OS Grid Ref:** SU258306

CBur BURNHAM NURSERIES ⊠ ✈ ⌂ € ♿
Forches Cross, Newton Abbot, Devon, TQ12 6PZ
Ⓣ (01626) 352233
Ⓕ (01626) 362167
Ⓔ mail@orchids.uk.com
Ⓦ www.orchids.uk.com
Contact: Any member of staff
Opening Times: 1000-1600 Mon-Sun.
Min Mail Order UK: Nmc
Min Mail Order EU: £100.00 + p&p
Cat. Cost: A4 sae + 55p stamp.
Credit Cards: Visa American Express MasterCard Maestro
Specialities: All types of orchid except British native types.
Notes: Please ask for details on export beyond EU.
Map Ref: C, C4 **OS Grid Ref:** SX841732

CCAT CIDER APPLE TREES ⊠ €
Kerian, Corkscrew Lane, Woolston, Nr North Cadbury, Somerset, BA22 7BP
Ⓣ (01963) 441101
Ⓦ www.ciderappletrees.co.uk
Contact: Mr J Dennis
Opening Times: By appt. only.
Min Mail Order UK: £9.50
Min Mail Order EU: £9.50
Cat. Cost: Free.
Credit Cards: None
Specialities: *Malus* (speciality standard trees).
Notes: Also sells wholesale.
Map Ref: C, B5

CCCN CROSS COMMON NURSERY ⊠ ◆
The Lizard, Helston, Cornwall, TR12 7PD
Ⓣ (01326) 290722 or 290668
Ⓔ info@crosscommonnursery.co.uk
Ⓦ www.crosscommonnursery.co.uk
Contact: Kevin Bosustow
Opening Times: 1000-1700 7 days, Apr, May & Jun. Reduced hours Jul-Sep, please phone for opening times.
Min Mail Order UK: Nmc
Cat. Cost: Online only.
Credit Cards: All major credit/debit cards
Specialities: Tropical/sub-tropical, coastal plants & conservatory plants. Wide range of grapevines and citrus trees. Some plants available in small quantities only.
Map Ref: C, D1 **OS Grid Ref:** SW704116

CCha CHAPEL FARM HOUSE NURSERY € ♿
Halwill Junction, Beaworthy, Devon, EX21 5UF
Ⓣ (01409) 221594
Ⓕ (01409) 221594
Contact: Robin or Toshie Hull
Opening Times: 1000-1600 Tue-Sat, 1000-1600 Sun & B/hol Mons.
Cat. Cost: None issued.
Credit Cards: None
Specialities: Plants from Japan. Also herbaceous. Japanese garden design service offered.
Map Ref: C, C3

CChe CHERRY TREE NURSERY ⌂ ♿
(Sheltered Work Opportunities), off New Road Roundabout, Northbourne, Bournemouth, Dorset, BH10 7DA
Ⓣ (01202) 593537 (01202) 590840
Ⓕ (01202) 590626
Contact: Stephen Jailler
Opening Times: 0830-1530 Mon-Fri, 0900-1500 Sat, Apr-Sep & 0900-1200 Sat, Oct-Mar.
Cat. Cost: A4 sae + 66p stamps.
Credit Cards: Debit cards only accepted.
Specialities: Hardy shrubs, perennials, climbers, grasses.
Notes: Also sells wholesale.
Map Ref: C, C6

CCVN CULM VIEW NURSERY ⊠ ✈ ⌂
Waterloo Farm, Clayhidon, Devon, EX15 3TN
Ⓣ (01823) 680698
Ⓕ 0870 7058866
Ⓔ plants@culmviewnursery.co.uk
Ⓦ www.culmviewnursery.co.uk
Contact: Brian & Alison Jacobs
Opening Times: By appt. only for collection.
Min Mail Order UK: Nmc
Min Mail Order EU: Nmc
Credit Cards: None
Specialities: Hebaceous perennials grown in peat-free compost.
Notes: Mail order seed only.

CCVT CHEW VALLEY TREES ⊠
Winford Road, Chew Magna, Bristol, BS40 8HJ
Ⓣ (01275) 333752
Ⓕ (01275) 333746

Ⓔ info@chewvalleytrees.co.uk
Ⓦ www.chewvalleytrees.co.uk
Contact: J Scarth
Opening Times: 0800-1700 Mon-Fri all year. 0900-1600 Sat, Sep-Jun. Closed Sun & B/hols.
Min Mail Order UK: Nmc
Cat. Cost: Free.
Credit Cards: All major credit/debit cards
Specialities: Native British & ornamental trees, shrubs, apple trees & hedging.
Notes: Partial wheelchair access. Also sells wholesale.
Map Ref: C, A5 **OS Grid Ref:** ST558635

CDes **Desirable Plants** ⊠ ⛫
(Office) Pentamar, Crosspark, Totnes, Devon, TQ9 5BQ
Ⓣ (01803) 864489 evenings
Ⓔ sutton.totnes@lineone.net
Ⓦ www.desirableplants.com
Contact: Dr J J & Mrs S A Sutton
Opening Times: Not open. Mail order only.
Min Mail Order UK: £15.00
Cat. Cost: 5 × 1st class.
Credit Cards: None
Specialities: Eclectic range of choice & interesting herbaceous plants by mail order.
Notes: Nursery not at this address.

CDob **Samuel Dobie & Son** ⊠
Long Road, Paignton, Devon, TQ4 7SX
Ⓣ 0844 701 7623
Ⓕ 0844 701 7624
Ⓦ www.dobies.co.uk
Contact: Customer Services
Opening Times: Not open. Mail order only. Phone line open 0830-1700 Mon-Fri (office). Also answerphone.
Min Mail Order UK: Nmc
Cat. Cost: Free.
Credit Cards: Visa MasterCard Switch Delta
Specialities: Wide selection of popular flower & vegetable seeds. Also includes young plants, summer-flowering bulbs & garden sundries.
Notes: Mail order to UK & Rep. of Ireland only.

CDoC **Duchy of Cornwall** ⊠ ◆
Cott Road, Lostwithiel, Cornwall, PL22 0HW
Ⓣ (01208) 872668
Ⓕ (01208) 872835
Ⓔ sales@duchyofcornwallnursery.co.uk
Ⓦ www.duchyofcornwallnursery.co.uk
Contact: Jim Stephens
Opening Times: 0900-1700 Mon-Sat, 1000-1700 Sun & B/hols.
Min Mail Order UK: £14.00
Cat. Cost: None issued.
Credit Cards: All major credit/debit cards
Specialities: *Camellia*, *Fuchsia*, conifers & *Magnolia*. Also a huge range of garden plants incl. trees, shrubs, roses, perennials, fruit & conservatory plants.
Notes: Nursery partially accessible to wheelchair users.
Map Ref: C, C2 **OS Grid Ref:** SX112614

CDTJ **Desert to Jungle** ⊠ ⛫ ♿
Henlade Garden Nursery, Lower Henlade, Taunton, Somerset, TA3 5NB
Ⓣ (01823) 443701
Ⓕ (01458) 250521
Ⓔ plants@deserttojungle.com
Ⓦ www.deserttojungle.com
Contact: Rob Gudge, Dave Root
Opening Times: 1000-1700 Mon-Sun, 1st Mar-31st Oct. Thu, Fri & Sat only Nov-Feb, or phone first.
Min Mail Order UK: Nmc
Cat. Cost: 1 × 1st class sae.
Credit Cards: All major credit/debit cards
Specialities: Exotic-looking plants giving a desert or jungle effect in the garden. Incl. *Canna*, aroids, succulents, tree ferns & bamboos.
Notes: Nursery shares drive with Mount Somerset Hotel. Also sells wholesale.
Map Ref: C, B4 **OS Grid Ref:** ST273232

CDul **Dulford Nurseries** ⊠ ♿
Cullompton, Devon, EX15 2DG
Ⓣ (01884) 266361
Ⓕ (01884) 266663
Ⓔ dulford.nurseries@virgin.net
Ⓦ www.dulford-nurseries.co.uk
Contact: Paul & Mary Ann Rawlings
Opening Times: 0730-1630 Mon-Fri.
Min Mail Order UK: Nmc
Min Mail Order EU: Nmc
Cat. Cost: Free.
Credit Cards: All major credit/debit cards
Specialities: Native, ornamental & unusual trees & shrubs incl. oaks, maples, beech, birch, chestnut, ash, lime, *Sorbus* & pines.
Notes: Also sells wholesale.
Map Ref: C, C4 **OS Grid Ref:** SY062062

KEY
⊠ Mail order to UK or EU ⛫ Delivers to shows
✈ Exports beyond EU € Euro accepted
♿ Accessible by wheelchair ◆ See Display advertisement

C

CEls **Elsworth Herbs** ⊠ ♿
Farthingwood, Broadway, Sidmouth, Devon, EX10 8HS
Ⓣ (01395) 578689
Ⓔ john.twibell@btinternet.com
Contact: Drs J D & J M Twibell
Opening Times: By appt. only.
Min Mail Order UK: £10.00
Cat. Cost: 3 × 1st class.
Credit Cards: None
Specialities: Nat. Collections of *Artemisia* (incl. *Seriphidium*) & *Nerium oleander*. Wide range of *Artemisia* & *Seriphidium, Nerium oleander*. Stock available in small quantities only. Orders may require propagation from Collection material, for which we are the primary reference source.
Map Ref: E, C4 **OS Grid Ref:** SY119881

CElw **Elworthy Cottage Plants** ♿
Elworthy Cottage, Elworthy, Nr Lydeard St Lawrence, Taunton, Somerset, TA4 3PX
Ⓣ (01984) 656427
Ⓔ mike@elworthy-cottage.co.uk
Ⓦ www.elworthy-cottage.co.uk
Contact: Mrs J M Spiller
Opening Times: 1000-1600 Thu & Fri, late Mar-end Aug. Also by appt. Feb-Nov.
Cat. Cost: 3 × 2nd class.
Credit Cards: None
Specialities: *Clematis* & unusual herbaceous plants esp. hardy *Geranium*, *Geum*, grasses, *Campanula*, *Crocosmia*, *Pulmonaria*, *Astrantia*, *Viola* & *Galanthus*. Some varieties only available in small quantities.
Notes: Nursery on B3188, 5 miles north of Wiveliscombe, in centre of Elworthy village.
Map Ref: C, B4 **OS Grid Ref:** ST084349

CEnd **Endsleigh Gardens** ⊠ ♿ ◆
Milton Abbot, Tavistock, Devon, PL19 0PG
Ⓣ (01822) 870235
Ⓕ (01822) 870513
Ⓔ Treemail@endsleigh-gardens.com
Ⓦ www.endsleigh-gardens.com
Contact: Michael Taylor
Opening Times: 0800-1700 Mon-Sat. 1000-1700 Sun.
Min Mail Order UK: Nmc
Cat. Cost: 2 × 1st class.
Credit Cards: Visa Access Switch MasterCard
Specialities: Choice & unusual trees & shrubs incl. *Acer* & *Cornus* cvs. Old apples & cherries. Wisteria. Grafting service.
Map Ref: C, C3

CEnt **Entwood Farm Plants**
Harcombe, Lyme Regis, Dorset, DT7 3RN
Ⓣ (01297) 444034
Contact: Jenny & Ivan Harding
Opening Times: 1000-1700 Wed & Fri, Easter-end Sep. Other times, please phone first.
Cat. Cost: 3 × 1st class.
Credit Cards: None
Specialities: Perennials & bamboos. Selection of shrubs, grasses, herbs & bulbs. Stock propagated & grown at nursery, some in small quantities.
Map Ref: C, C4 **OS Grid Ref:** SY335953

CFee **Feebers Hardy Plants** ⊠ ♿ ◆
1 Feeber Cottage, Westwood, Broadclyst, Nr Exeter, Devon, EX5 3DQ
Ⓣ (01404) 822118
Ⓔ Feebers@onetel.com
Contact: Mrs E Squires
Opening Times: Open at any reasonable time by prior telephone arrangement.
Min Mail Order UK: Nmc
Min Mail Order EU: Nmc
Cat. Cost: Sae + 36p stamp.
Credit Cards: None
Specialities: Plants for wet clay soils, alpines & hardy perennials incl. those raised by Amos Perry. Small quantities of plants held unless grown from seed.
Notes: Mail order limited. Nursery accessible for wheelchairs in dry weather only.
Map Ref: C, C4

CFFs **Floral Fireworks** ⊠
Burnt House Farm, Mid Lambrook, South Petherton, Somerset, TA13 5HE
Ⓣ (01460) 249060
Ⓕ (01460) 249025
Ⓔ info@floralfireworks.co.uk
Ⓦ www.floralfireworks.co.uk
Contact: Carol Atkins
Opening Times: Not open. Mail order only. Orders can be collected by prior arrangement.
Min Mail Order UK: £10.00 + p&p
Min Mail Order EU: £20.00 + p&p
Cat. Cost: 4 × 2nd class.
Credit Cards: All major credit/debit cards
Specialities: Bulbs.

CFir **Fir Tree Farm Nursery** ⊠ € ♿
Tresahor, Constantine, Falmouth, Cornwall, TR11 5PL
Ⓣ (01326) 340593
Ⓔ plants@cornwallgardens.com

Ⓦ www.cornwallgardens.com
Contact: Glynn Wrapson & Sorcha Hitchcox
Opening Times: 1000-1700 Tue-Sat & 1100-1600 Sun, closed Mon, Feb-Oct. By appt. Nov-Jan.
Min Mail Order UK: £25.00 + p&p
Min Mail Order EU: £40.00 + p&p
Cat. Cost: 6 × 1st class.
Credit Cards: Visa Access Delta Switch
Specialities: Over 4000 varieties of cottage garden & rare perennials with many specialities. Also 80 varieties of *Clematis*. Some rare varieties available in small quantities only.
Map Ref: C, D1

CFwr **THE FLOWER BOWER** ⊠
Woodlands, Shurton, Stogursey,
Nr Bridgwater, Somerset,
TA5 1QE
Ⓣ (01278) 732134
Ⓔ theflowerbower@yahoo.co.uk
Contact: Sheila Tucker
Opening Times: By appt. only.
Min Mail Order UK: Nmc
Min Mail Order EU: Nmc
Cat. Cost: 2 × 1st class.
Credit Cards: None
Specialities: Unusual perennials, hardy geraniums, *Asclepiad*, *Clivia*, *Epiphyllum* & ferns. Nat. Collection of *Clivia*, Chinese & Japanese taxa.
Notes: Mail order Mar-Oct.
Map Ref: C, B4 **OS Grid Ref:** ST203442

CGHE **GARDEN HOUSE ENTERPRISES** ♿
The Garden House, Buckland Monachorum,
Yelverton, Devon, PL20 7LQ
Ⓕ (01822) 855358
Ⓦ www.thegardenhouse.org.uk
Contact: Ms Selman
Opening Times: 1030-1700 7 days 1st Mar-31st Oct.
Cat. Cost: 4 × 1st class.
Credit Cards: All major credit/debit cards
Specialities: Fortescue & Buckland plants. South African plants.
Map Ref: C, C3 **OS Grid Ref:** SX496683

CGro **C W GROVES & SON LTD** ⊠ ♿
West Bay Road, Bridport, Dorset,
DT6 4BA
Ⓣ (01308) 422654
Ⓕ (01308) 420888
Ⓔ violets@grovesnurseries.co.uk
Ⓦ www.grovesnurseries.co.uk
Contact: Clive Groves
Opening Times: 0830-1700 Mon-Sat, 1030-1630 Sun.
Min Mail Order UK: Nmc
Min Mail Order EU: £15.00 + p&p
Cat. Cost: 2 × 1st class.
Credit Cards: Visa Switch MasterCard
Specialities: Nursery & garden centre specialising in Parma & hardy *Viola*. Nat. Collection of *Viola odorata* cvs & Parma Violets.
Notes: Mainly violets by mail order. Main display at nursery in Feb, Mar & Apr.
Map Ref: C, C5 **OS Grid Ref:** SY466918

CGrW **THE GREAT WESTERN GLADIOLUS NURSERY** ⊠ €
17 Valley View, Clutton, Bristol,
BS39 5SN
Ⓣ (01761) 452036
Ⓕ (01761) 452036
Ⓔ clutton.glads@btinternet.com
Ⓦ www.greatwesterngladiolus.co.uk
Contact: G F & J C Hazell
Opening Times: Mail order only. Open by appt. only.
Min Mail Order UK: Nmc
Min Mail Order EU: Nmc
Cat. Cost: 4 × 1st class (2 catalogues).
Credit Cards: None
Specialities: *Gladiolus* species & hybrids, corms & seeds. Other South African bulbous plants.
Notes: Also sells wholesale.

CHar **WEST HARPTREE NURSERY** ⊠ ⛟ €
Bristol Road, West Harptree,
Bath, Somerset, BS40 6HG
Ⓣ (01761) 221370
Ⓕ (01761) 221989
Ⓔ bryn@harptreenursery.co.uk
Ⓦ www.harptreenursery.co.uk
Contact: Bryn & Helene Bowles
Opening Times: From 1000 Mon-Sun 7 days.
Min Mail Order UK: Nmc
Min Mail Order EU: Nmc
Cat. Cost: Large sae for free names list.
Credit Cards: MasterCard Visa Maestro Paypal
Specialities: Unusual herbaceous perennials & shrubs. Bulbs & grasses. Many AGM plants.
Notes: Also sells wholesale.
Map Ref: C, B5

KEY
⊠ Mail order to UK or EU ⛟ Delivers to shows
✈ Exports beyond EU € Euro accepted
♿ Accessible by wheelchair ◆ See Display advertisement

C

CHby **The Herbary** ⊠ ✈ €
161 Chapel Street, Horningsham,
Warminster, Wiltshire,
BA12 7LU
Ⓣ (01985) 844442
Ⓔ info@beansandherbs.co.uk
Ⓦ www.beansandherbs.co.uk
Contact: Pippa Rosen
Opening Times: May-Sep strictly by appt. only.
Min Mail Order UK: Nmc
Min Mail Order EU: Nmc
Cat. Cost: 4 × 1st class or online.
Credit Cards: None
Specialities: Culinary, medicinal & aromatic herbs organically grown in small quantities.
Notes: Mail order all year for organic vegetable seed & large variety of organic bean & herb seed.
Map Ref: C, B5 **OS Grid Ref:** ST812414

CHew **Hewitt-Cooper Carnivorous Plants** ⊠ ⌂ €
The Homestead, Glastonbury Road,
West Pennard, Somerset, BA6 8NN
Ⓣ (01458) 832844
Ⓕ (01458) 832712
Ⓔ sales@hccarnivorousplants.co.uk
Ⓦ www.hccarnivorousplants.co.uk
Contact: Nigel Hewitt-Cooper
Opening Times: By appt.
Min Mail Order UK: £10.00 + p&p
Min Mail Order EU: £30.00
Cat. Cost: 1 × 1st class/1× IRC.
Credit Cards: All major credit/debit cards
Specialities: Carnivorous plants.
Notes: Mail order May-Nov.

CHEx **Hardy Exotics** ⊠ ♿
Gilly Lane, Whitecross, Penzance, Cornwall,
TR20 8BZ
Ⓣ (01736) 740660
Ⓕ (01736) 741101
Ⓔ contact@hardyexotics.co.uk
Ⓦ www.hardyexotics.co.uk
Contact: C Shilton/J Smith
Opening Times: 1000-1700 7 days Apr-Oct, 1000-1700 Mon-Sat Nov-Feb. Please phone first in winter months if travelling a long way.
Min Mail Order UK: £40 + carriage.
Cat. Cost: 4 × 1st class (no cheques).
Credit Cards: All major credit/debit cards
Specialities: Largest selection in the UK of trees, shrubs & herbaceous plants for tropical & desert effects. Hardy & half-hardy plants for gardens, patios & conservatories.
Map Ref: C, D1 **OS Grid Ref:** SW524345

CHid **Hidden Valley Nursery** ⌂ €
Umberleigh, Devon,
EX37 9BU
Ⓣ (01769) 560567
Ⓜ 07899 788789
Ⓔ plalindley@itsosbroadband.co.uk
Contact: Linda & Peter Lindley
Opening Times: Daylight hours, but please phone first.
Cat. Cost: None issued.
Credit Cards: None
Specialities: Hardy perennials esp. shade lovers & Chatham Islands forget-me-nots (*Myosotidium hortensia.*)
Map Ref: C, B3 **OS Grid Ref:** SS567205

CHII **Hill House Nursery & Gardens** ⊠ € ♿
Landscove, Nr Ashburton, Devon,
TQ13 7LY
Ⓣ (01803) 762273
Ⓕ (01803) 158218
Ⓔ sacha@garden.506.fsnet.co.uk
Ⓦ www.hillhousenursery.co.uk
Contact: Raymond, Sacha & Matthew Hubbard
Opening Times: 1100-1700 7 days, all year. Open all B/hols incl. Easter Sun. Closed 24th Dec-7th Jan. Tearoom open 1st Mar-30th Sep.
Min Mail Order UK: £25
Cat. Cost: None issued.
Credit Cards: Delta MasterCard Switch Visa
Specialities: 3000+ varieties of plants, most propagated on premises, many rare or unusual. The garden, open to the public, was laid out by Edward Hyams. Pioneers of glasshouse pest control by beneficial insects.
Map Ref: C, C3 **OS Grid Ref:** SX774664

CHrt **Hortus Nursery** ⊠ ♿
Shrubbery Bungalow, School Lane, Rousdon,
Lyme Regis, Dorset, DT7 3XW
Ⓣ (01297) 444019
Ⓜ 07747 043997
Ⓕ (01297) 444019
Ⓔ plants@hortusnursery.com
Ⓦ www.hortusnursery.com
Contact: Marie-Elaine Houghton
Opening Times: 1000-1700 Wed-Sat, Mar-Oct. Other times by appt. Garden open as nursery.
Min Mail Order UK: £15.00 + p&p
Cat. Cost: 3 × 1st class.
Credit Cards: None
Specialities: Ornamental grasses & perennials, particularly plants suitable for coastal gardens. Garden design & planting service.
Map Ref: C, C4 **OS Grid Ref:** SY296914

CHVG **Hidden Valley Gardens** ♿
Treesmill, Nr Par, Cornwall,
PL24 2TU
Ⓣ (01208) 873225
Ⓔ hiddenvalleygardens@yahoo.co.uk
Ⓦ www.hiddenvalleygardens.co.uk
Contact: Mrs P Howard
Opening Times: 1000-1800 7 days, 20th Mar-end Oct. Please phone for directions. Garden open as nursery.
Cat. Cost: None issued.
Credit Cards: None
Specialities: Cottage garden plants, *Crocosmia*, *Iris sibirica* & many unusual perennials which can be seen growing in the garden. Some stock available in small quantities. Display garden.
Map Ref: C, D2 **OS Grid Ref:** SX094567

CIri **The Iris Garden** ⊠ €
Yard House, Pilsdon,
Bridport, Dorset,
DT6 5PA
Ⓣ (01308) 868797
Ⓔ theirisgarden@aol.com
Ⓦ www.theirisgarden.co.uk
Contact: Clive Russell
Opening Times: Show garden open by appt. Please email or phone for details.
Min Mail Order UK: £15.00 + p&p
Min Mail Order EU: £25.00 + p&p
Cat. Cost: 6 × 1st class.
Credit Cards: All major credit/debit cards
Specialities: Modern bearded & beardless *Iris* from breeders in UK, USA, France, Italy & Australia. Nat. Collection of Space Age *Iris*.
Notes: Orders for bearded iris & sibiricas must be received by end Jun & by end Aug for spurias.
Map Ref: C, C5 **OS Grid Ref:** SY421988

CJas **Jasmine Cottage Gardens** ♿
26 Channel Road, Walton St Mary,
Clevedon, Somerset,
BS21 7BY
Ⓣ (01275) 871850
Ⓔ margaret@bologrew.demon.co.uk
Ⓦ www.bologrew.pwp.blueyonder.co.uk
Contact: Mr & Mrs M Redgrave
Opening Times: May to Sep, daily by appt. Garden open at the same times.
Cat. Cost: None issued.
Credit Cards: None
Specialities: *Rhodochiton*, *Lophospermum*, *Maurandya*, *Dicentra macrocapnos*, *Salvia*, *Isotoma*, half-hardy geraniums.
Map Ref: C, A4 **OS Grid Ref:** ST405725

CKel **Kelways Ltd** ⊠ 🚚 € ♿
Langport, Somerset, TA10 9EZ
Ⓣ (01458) 250521
Ⓕ (01458) 253351
Ⓔ sales@kelways.co.uk
Ⓦ www.kelways.co.uk
Contact: David Root
Opening Times: 0900-1700 Mon-Fri, 1000-1700 Sat, 1000-1600 Sun.
Min Mail Order UK: £4.00 + p&p
Min Mail Order EU: £8.00 + p&p
Cat. Cost: Free.
Credit Cards: All major credit/debit cards
Specialities: *Paeonia*, *Iris*, *Hemerocallis* & herbaceous perennials. Nat. Collection of *Paeonia lactiflora*. Wide range of trees, shrubs & herbaceous.
Notes: Mail order for *Paeonia* & *Iris* only. Also sells wholesale.
Map Ref: C, B5 **OS Grid Ref:** ST434273

CKen **Kenwith Nursery (Gordon Haddow)** ⊠ ✈ € ♿ ◆
Blinsham, Nr Torrington,
Beaford, Winkleigh, Devon,
EX19 8NT
Ⓣ (01805) 603274
Ⓕ (01805) 603663
Ⓔ conifers@kenwith63.freeserve.co.uk
Ⓦ www.kenwithnursery.co.uk
Contact: Gordon Haddow
Opening Times: 1000-1630 Tue-Sat all year. Closed all B/hols.
Min Mail Order UK: £15.00 + p&p
Min Mail Order EU: £50.00 + p&p
Cat. Cost: 3 × 1st class.
Credit Cards: Visa MasterCard
Specialities: All conifer genera. Grafting a speciality. Many new introductions to UK. Nat. Collection of Dwarf Conifers.
Map Ref: C, B3 **OS Grid Ref:** SS518160

CKno **Knoll Gardens** ⊠ 🚚 ♿
Hampreston, Stapehill, Nr Wimborne, Dorset,
BH21 7ND
Ⓣ (01202) 873931
Ⓕ (01202) 870842
Ⓔ enquiries@knollgardens.co.uk
Ⓦ www.knollgardens.co.uk
Contact: N R Lucas
Opening Times: 1000-1700 (or dusk if earlier) Tue-Sun, May-Nov. 1000-1600 Wed-Sat, Feb-Apr & Dec. Open B/hol Mons.

KEY
⊠ Mail order to UK or EU — 🚚 Delivers to shows
✈ Exports beyond EU — € Euro accepted
♿ Accessible by wheelchair — ◆ See Display advertisement

C

Closed 17th Dec 2008-31st Jan 2009 incl.
Min Mail Order UK: Nmc
Min Mail Order EU: Nmc
Cat. Cost: 9 × 2nd class or order online.
Credit Cards: Visa MasterCard
Specialities: Grasses (main specialism). Select perennials. Nat. Collections of *Pennisetum*, *Phygelius* & deciduous *Ceanothus*.
Notes: Also sells wholesale.
Map Ref: C, C6

CLak **Lakka Bulbs** ⊠
(Office) 127 Mill Street, Torrington, North Devon, EX38 8AW
Ⓣ (01805) 625071
Ⓔ lakkabulbs@tesco.net
Contact: Jonathan Hutchinson
Opening Times: Not open. Mail order only.
Min Mail Order UK: Nmc
Min Mail Order EU: Nmc
Cat. Cost: None issued.
Specialities: Nat. Collections of *Urginea*, *Veltheimia* & *Scadoxus*. Other South African bulbs of families *Amaryllidaceae* & *Hyacinthaceae*. All available in small quantities only.

CLAP **Long Acre Plants** ⊠ ♿
South Marsh, Charlton Musgrove, Nr Wincanton, Somerset, BA9 8EX
Ⓣ (01963) 32802
Ⓕ (01963) 32802
Ⓔ info@longacreplants.co.uk
Ⓦ www.plantsforshade.co.uk
Contact: Nigel & Michelle Rowland
Opening Times: 1000-1300 & 1400-1700 Thu-Fri, Feb-Jun, Sep & Oct.
Min Mail Order UK: £25.00 + p&p
Cat. Cost: 3 × 1st class.
Credit Cards: Switch MasterCard Visa Maestro
Specialities: Ferns, woodland bulbs & perennials. Nat. Collection of *Asarum*.
Map Ref: C, B5

CLnd **Landford Trees** €
Landford Lodge, Landford, Salisbury, Wiltshire, SP5 2EH
Ⓣ (01794) 390808
Ⓕ (01794) 390037
Ⓔ trees@landfordtrees.co.uk
Ⓦ www.landfordtrees.co.uk
Contact: C D Pilkington
Opening Times: 0800-1700 Mon-Fri.
Cat. Cost: Free.
Credit Cards: None
Specialities: Deciduous ornamental trees.
Notes: Mail order maximum size 120cms. Also sells wholesale.
Map Ref: C, B6 **OS Grid Ref:** SU247201

CLng **Longcombe Nursery and Garden Centre** ⊠ ♿ ◆
Longcombe, Totnes, Devon, TQ9 6PL
Ⓣ (01803) 863098
Ⓕ (01803) 552558
Ⓔ info@simplyclematis.co.uk
Ⓦ www.simplyclematis.co.uk
Contact: Linda Clarke
Opening Times: 0900-1700 Mon-Sat, 1000-1600 Sun.
Min Mail Order UK: Nmc
Cat. Cost: Online only.
Credit Cards: All major credit/debit cards
Specialities: *Clematis*.
Notes: Also sells wholesale.
Map Ref: C, C3 **OS Grid Ref:** SX834601

CLoc **C S Lockyer (Fuchsias)** ⊠ ✈ € ◆
Lansbury, 70 Henfield Road, Coalpit Heath, Bristol BS36 2UZ
Ⓣ (01454) 772219
Ⓕ (01454) 772219
Ⓔ sales@lockyerfuchsias.co.uk
Ⓦ www.lockyerfuchsias.co.uk
Contact: C S Lockyer
Opening Times: 1000-1300, 1430-1700 most days, please ring.
Min Mail Order UK: 6 plants + p&p
Min Mail Order EU: £12.00 + p&p
Cat. Cost: 4 × 1st class.
Credit Cards: None
Specialities: *Fuchsia*.
Notes: Many open days & coach parties. Limited wheelchair access. Also sells wholesale.
Map Ref: C, A5

CMac **Mac Pennys Nurseries** ⊠
154 Burley Road, Bransgore, Christchurch, Dorset, BH23 8DB
Ⓣ (01425) 672348
Ⓕ (01425) 673917
Ⓔ office@macpennys.co.uk
Ⓦ www.macpennys.co.uk
Contact: T & V Lowndes
Opening Times: 0900-1700 Mon-Sat, 1100-1700 Sun. Closed Xmas & New Year.
Min Mail Order UK: Nmc
Cat. Cost: A4 sae with 4 × 1st class.
Credit Cards: All major credit/debit cards
Specialities: General. Plants available in small quantities only.
Notes: Mail order available Sep-Mar, UK only. Nursery partially accessible for wheelchairs.
Map Ref: C, C6

CMCN **Mallet Court Nursery** ⊠ ✈ ♞ € ♿
Curry Mallet, Taunton, Somerset, TA3 6SY
Ⓣ (01823) 481493
Ⓕ (01823) 481493
Ⓔ malletcourtnursery@btinternet.com
Ⓦ www.malletcourt.co.uk
Contact: J G S & P M E Harris F.L.S.
Opening Times: 0930-1700 Mon-Fri summer, 0930-1600 winter. Sat & Sun by appt.
Min Mail Order UK: Nmc
Min Mail Order EU: Nmc
Cat. Cost: £1.50
Credit Cards: All major credit/debit cards
Specialities: Maples, oaks, *Magnolia*, hollies & other rare and unusual plants including those from China & South Korea.
Notes: Mail order Oct-Mar only. Also sells wholesale.
Map Ref: C, B4

CMCo **Meadow Cottage Plants** €
Pitt Hill, Ivybridge, Devon, PL21 0JJ
Ⓣ (01752) 894532
Ⓔ phil@pitthill.fsworld.co.uk
Contact: Mrs L P Hunt
Opening Times: By appt. only.
Cat. Cost: None issued.
Credit Cards: None
Specialities: Large ornamental grasses and bamboos. Some varieties available in small numbers only. All plants grown in peat-free compost. Large specimens available.
Notes: Also sells wholesale.
Map Ref: C, D3

CMdw **Meadows Nursery** ⊠
5 Rectory Cottages, Mells, Frome, Somerset, BA11 3PN
Ⓣ (01373) 812268
Ⓔ plants@meadowsnurserymells.co.uk
Contact: Sue Lees & Eddie Wheatley
Opening Times: 1000-1800 Wed-Sun 1st Feb-31st Oct & B/hols.
Min Mail Order UK: Nmc
Cat. Cost: 3 × 1st class.
Credit Cards: None
Specialities: Hardy perennials, shrubs & some conservatory plants.
Map Ref: C, B5 **OS Grid Ref:** ST729492

CMea **The Mead Nursery** ♿
Brokerswood, Nr Westbury, Wiltshire, BA13 4EG
Ⓣ (01373) 859990
Ⓦ www.themeadnursery.co.uk
Contact: Steve & Emma Lewis-Dale
Opening Times: 0900-1700 Wed-Sat & B/hols, 1200-1700 Sun, 1st Feb-10th Oct. Closed Easter Sun.
Cat. Cost: 5 × 1st class.
Credit Cards: All major credit/debit cards
Specialities: Perennials, alpines, pot-grown bulbs and grasses.
Map Ref: C, B5 **OS Grid Ref:** ST833517

CMen **Mendip Bonsai Studio** ⊠ ♞ ♿
Byways, Back Lane, Downside, Shepton Mallet, Somerset, BA4 4JR
Ⓣ (01749) 344274
Ⓕ (01749) 344274
Ⓔ jr.trott@ukonline.co.uk
Ⓦ www.mendipbonsai.co.uk
Contact: John Trott
Opening Times: Private nursery. Visits by appt. only.
Cat. Cost: Large sae for plant & workshop lists
Credit Cards: All major credit/debit cards
Specialities: Bonsai, Potensai, accent plants & garden stock. Acers, conifers, incl. many *Pinus thunbergii* species. Many plants available in small numbers only. Young trees for garden or bonsai culture.
Notes: Education classes, lectures, demonstrations & club talks on bonsai. Stockist of most bonsai sundries. Mail orders will be normally despatched late Sep/early Oct.
Map Ref: C, B5

CMHG **Marwood Hill Gardens** ♿
Marwood, Barnstaple, Devon, EX31 4EB
Ⓣ (01271) 342528
Ⓕ (01271) 342528
Ⓔ info@marwoodhillgarden.co.uk
Ⓦ www.marwoodhillgarden.co.uk
Contact: Malcolm Pharoah
Opening Times: 1100-1630, 7 days.
Cat. Cost: 3 × 1st class.
Credit Cards: Visa Delta MasterCard Switch Solo
Specialities: Large range of unusual trees & shrubs. *Eucalyptus*, alpines, *Camellia*, *Astilbe*, bog plants & perennials. Nat. Collections of *Astilbe*, *Tulbaghia* & *Iris ensata*.
Map Ref: C, B3 **OS Grid Ref:** SS545375

CMil **Mill Cottage Plants** ⊠ ♿
The Mill, Henley Lane, Wookey, Somerset, BA5 1AP
Ⓣ (01749) 676966

KEY
⊠ Mail order to UK or EU ♞ Delivers to shows
✈ Exports beyond EU € Euro accepted
♿ Accessible by wheelchair ◆ See Display advertisement

C

Ⓔ millcottageplants@tiscali.co.uk
Ⓦ www.millcottageplants.co.uk
Contact: Sally Gregson
Opening Times: 1000-1800 Wed Mar-Sep or by appt. Phone for directions.
Min Mail Order UK: Nmc.
Min Mail Order EU: £25.00 + p&p
Cat. Cost: 4 × 1st class.
Credit Cards: All major credit/debit cards
Specialities: Rare *Hydrangea serrata* cvs, *H. aspera* cvs. Shade-loving perennials, *Tricyrtis*, *Epimedium*, ferns & grasses.
Map Ref: C, B5

CMMP **M & M Plants** ♿
Lloret, Chittlehamholt, Umberleigh, Devon, EX37 9PD
Ⓣ (01769) 540448
Ⓕ (01769) 540448
Ⓔ mmplants@mail.com
Contact: Mr M Thorne
Opening Times: 0930-1700 Tue-Sat, Apr-Oct & 1000-1600 Tue-Fri, Nov-Mar. Sat by appt. in Aug.
Cat. Cost: 3 × 1st class.
Credit Cards: None
Specialities: Perennials. We also carry a good range of alpines, shrubs, trees & roses.
Map Ref: C, B3

CMoH **Monita House Garden** ⊠
Eggesford, Chulmleigh, Devon, EX18 7JZ
Ⓣ (01769) 580081
Ⓜ 07748 563032
Ⓔ monitahouse@tiscali.co.uk
Contact: David Mitchell
Opening Times: 1000-1700, Sun & B/hols, 1st Apr-30th Oct. Please ring first.
Min Mail Order UK: Nmc
Cat. Cost: 4 × 1st class.
Credit Cards: None
Specialities: Small nursery specialising in herbaceous perennials, many available in small quantities only.
Map Ref: C, B3 **OS Grid Ref:** SS681119

CNat **Natural Selection** ⊠ €
4 Cowage Farm Cottage, Foxly, Chippenham, Wiltshire, SN16 0JH
Ⓣ (01666) 824631
Ⓔ paulmewton@yahoo.com
Contact: Paul Mewton
Opening Times: Please phone first.
Min Mail Order UK: £9.00 + p&p
Cat. Cost: 2 × 2nd class.
Credit Cards: None
Specialities: Unusual British natives & others. Also seed. Only available in small quantities.
Map Ref: C, A5 **OS Grid Ref:** ST903860

CNMi **Newport Mills Nursery** ⊠
Wrantage, Taunton, Somerset, TA3 6DJ
Ⓣ (01823) 490231
Ⓜ 07940 872800
Ⓕ (01823) 490231
Contact: John Barrington
Opening Times: By appt. only.
Min Mail Order UK: Nmc
Min Mail Order EU: Nmc
Cat. Cost: Free.
Credit Cards: None
Specialities: *Delphinium*. English scented varieties of perpetual flowering carnations. Some varieties only available in small quantities & propagated to order.
Notes: Mail order Apr-Sep for young delphiniums in 7cm pots. Dormant plants can be sent out in autumn/winter if requested.

COld **The Old Mill Herbary**
Helland Bridge, Bodmin, Cornwall, PL30 4QR
Ⓣ (01208) 841206
Ⓔ oldmillherbary@aol.com
Ⓦ www.oldmillherbary.co.uk
Contact: Mrs B Whurr
Opening Times: 1000-1700 Thu-Tue 1st Apr-30th Sep. Closed Wed.
Cat. Cost: 6 × 1st class.
Credit Cards: None
Specialities: Culinary, medicinal & aromatic herbs.
Notes: Limited sales of medicinal herbs. Historical site in Area of Outstanding Natural Beauty. SSSI, SAC & AONB.
Map Ref: C, C2 **OS Grid Ref:** SX065717

COIW **The Old Withy Garden Nursery** ⊠
Grange Fruit Farm, Gweek, Helston, Cornwall, TR12 6BE
Ⓣ (01326) 221171
Ⓔ sales@theoldwithygardennursery.co.uk
Ⓦ www.theoldwithygardennursery.co.uk
Contact: Sheila Chandler or Nick Chandler
Opening Times: 1000-1700 7 days, Feb-end Oct. 1000-1600 Mon-Fri, Jan & Nov.
Min Mail Order UK: £15.00
Cat. Cost: 4 × 1st class.
Credit Cards: Maestro MasterCard Visa Delta
Specialities: Cottage garden plants, perennials, some biennials & grasses. Some varieties in small quantities only.
Notes: Partially accessible for wheelchairs (gravel paths). Also sells wholesale.
Map Ref: C, D1 **OS Grid Ref:** SW688255

C

CPar **PARKS PERENNIALS** ⌂
242 Wallisdown Road, Wallisdown, Bournemouth, Dorset, BH10 4HZ
Ⓣ (01202) 524464
Ⓔ parks.perennials@ntlworld.com
Contact: S. Parks
Opening Times: Apr-Oct most days, please phone first.
Cat. Cost: None issued.
Credit Cards: None
Specialities: Hardy herbaceous perennials.
Map Ref: C, C6

CPBP **PARHAM BUNGALOW PLANTS** ⊠ ⌂ €
Parham Lane, Market Lavington, Devizes, Wiltshire, SN10 4QA
Ⓣ (01380) 812605
Ⓔ jjs@pbplants.freeserve.co.uk
Contact: Mrs D E Sample
Opening Times: Please ring first.
Min Mail Order UK: Nmc
Min Mail Order EU: Nmc
Cat. Cost: Sae.
Credit Cards: None
Specialities: Alpines.
Map Ref: C, B6

CPen **PENNARD PLANTS** ⊠ ✈ ⌂ €
3 The Gardens, East Pennard, Shepton Mallet, Somerset, BA4 6TU
Ⓣ (01749) 860039
Ⓕ 07043 017270
Ⓔ sales@pennardplants.com
Ⓦ www.pennardplants.com
Contact: Chris Smith
Opening Times: 1000-1500 Wed, 1st Mar-31st Oct.
Min Mail Order UK: Nmc
Min Mail Order EU: Nmc
Cat. Cost: 3 × 1st class.
Credit Cards: All major credit/debit cards
Specialities: Ornamental grasses, *Agapanthus*, *Dierama*, *Eucomis* & *Gladioli* species. South African bulbous plants.
Notes: Nursery at The Walled Garden at East Pennard.
Map Ref: C, B5

CPhi **ALAN PHIPPS CACTI** ⊠ €
62 Samuel White Road, Hanham, Bristol, BS15 3LX
Ⓣ (0117) 9607591
Ⓦ www.cactus-mall.com/alan-phipps/index.html
Contact: A Phipps
Opening Times: 10.00-1700 but prior phone call essential to ensure a greeting.
Min Mail Order UK: £5.00 + p&p
Min Mail Order EU: £20.00 + p&p
Cat. Cost: Sae or 2 × IRC (EC only).
Credit Cards: None
Specialities: *Mammillaria*, *Astrophytum* & *Ariocarpus*. Species & varieties will change with times. Ample quantities exist in spring. Limited range of *Agave*.
Notes: Euro accepted as cash only.
Map Ref: C, A5 **OS Grid Ref:** ST644717

CPHo **THE PALM HOUSE** ⊠
8 North Street, Ottery St Mary, Devon, EX11 1DR
Ⓣ (01404) 815450
Ⓜ 07815 673397
Ⓔ george@thepalmhouse.co.uk
Ⓦ www.thepalmhouse.co.uk
Contact: George Gregory
Opening Times: Mail order only. Open by appt. only.
Min Mail Order UK: £15.00
Min Mail Order EU: £10.00
Cat. Cost: 2 × 1st class.
Credit Cards: All major credit/debit cards
Specialities: Palms.
Notes: Also sells wholesale.
Map Ref: C, C4 **OS Grid Ref:** SY098955

CPHT **CLASSIC GARDENER (FORMERLY POUND HILL TOPIARY)** ♿
Pound Barn, West Kington, Nr Chippenham, Wiltshire, SN14 7JQ
Ⓣ (01249) 783880
Ⓕ (01249) 783031
Ⓔ info@classicgardener.co.uk
Ⓦ www.classicgardener.co.uk
Contact: Philip Stockitt
Opening Times: 1000-1700 Sat by prior appt. only.
Cat. Cost: Free
Credit Cards: MasterCard Visa
Specialities: Topiary.
Map Ref: C, A5

CPLG **EXCLUSIVE PLANTS (INCORPORATING PINE LODGE GARDENS & NURSERY)** ⊠ ♿
Pine Lodge Gardens, Holmbush, St Austell, Cornwall, PL25 3RQ
Ⓣ (01726) 77960
Ⓜ 07775 811385
Ⓕ (01726) 77960
Ⓔ pbonavia@lycos.co.uk

KEY
⊠ Mail order to UK or EU ⌂ Delivers to shows
✈ Exports beyond EU € Euro accepted
♿ Accessible by wheelchair ◆ See Display advertisement

C

Ⓦ www.exclusiveplants.co.uk
Contact: Paul Bonavia & Barry Thornley
Opening Times: 1000-1700 7 days all year, except 24th/25th/26th Dec.
Min Mail Order UK: Nmc
Cat. Cost: 6 × 2nd class.
Credit Cards: All major credit/debit cards
Specialities: Rare & unusual shrubs & herbaceous, some from seed collected on plant expeditions each year. Nat. Collection of *Grevillea*.
Map Ref: C, D2 **OS Grid Ref:** SX045527

CPMA **P M A PLANT SPECIALITIES** ⊠ ✈ €
Junker's Nursery Ltd., Lower Mead, West Hatch, Taunton, Somerset, TA3 5RN
Ⓣ (01823) 480774
Ⓔ karan@junker.co.uk
Ⓦ www.junker.co.uk
Contact: Karan or Nick Junker
Opening Times: Strictly by appt. only.
Min Mail Order UK: Nmc
Min Mail Order EU: Nmc
Cat. Cost: 6 × 2nd class.
Credit Cards: None
Specialities: Choice & unusual shrubs incl. grafted *Acer palmatum*, *Cornus*, *Magnolia* & a wide range of *Daphne*. Small quantities of some hard to propagate plants, esp. daphnes. Reserve orders accepted. Planted areas showing how the plants look growing in "real world" conditions. We propagate and grow all our own plants.
Notes: Partial wheelchair access. Also sells wholesale.
Map Ref: C, B4 **OS Grid Ref:** ST280203

CPne **PINE COTTAGE PLANTS** ⊠ ✈ ⌂ €
Pine Cottage, Fourways, Eggesford, Chulmleigh, Devon, EX18 7QZ
Ⓣ (01769) 580076
Ⓔ pcplants@supanet.com
Ⓦ www.pcplants.co.uk
Contact: Dick Fulcher
Opening Times: Special open weeks for *Agapanthus*, 1000-1500 daily excl. Sun 15th-22nd Jul, 29th Jul-30th Aug 2008. Other times by appt. only.
Min Mail Order UK: £20.00 + p&p
Min Mail Order EU: £50.00 + p&p
Cat. Cost: 4 × 1st class.
Credit Cards: Maestro MasterCard Visa
Specialities: Nat. Collection of *Agapanthus*. 150+ cvs available.
Notes: Mail order *Agapanthus* from Sep-Jun. Also sells wholesale.
Map Ref: C, B3 **OS Grid Ref:** SS683099

CPom **POMEROY PLANTS**
Tower House, Pomeroy Lane, Wingfield, Trowbridge, Wiltshire, BA14 9LJ
Ⓣ (01225) 769551
Ⓜ 07895 096564
Ⓔ drsimonyoung@yahoo.co.uk
Contact: Simon Young
Opening Times: Mar-Nov. Please phone first.
Cat. Cost: 2 × 1st class.
Credit Cards: None
Specialities: Hardy, mainly species, herbaceous perennials. Many unusual and often small numbers. Specialities *Allium*, *Salvia* & shade-lovers, esp. *Epimedium*.
Map Ref: C, B5 **OS Grid Ref:** ST817569

CPou **POUNSLEY PLANTS** ⊠ ⌂ € ♿
Pounsley Combe, Spriddlestone, Brixton, Plymouth, Devon, PL9 0DW
Ⓣ (01752) 402873
Ⓕ (01752) 402873
Ⓔ pou599@aol.com
Ⓦ www.pounsleyplants.com
Contact: Mrs Jane Hollow
Opening Times: Normally 1000-1700 Mon-Sat but please phone first.
Min Mail Order UK: £10.00 + p&p
Min Mail Order EU: £20.00 + p&p
Cat. Cost: 2 × 1st class.
Credit Cards: None
Specialities: Unusual herbaceous perennials & cottage plants. Selection of *Clematis* & old roses. Large selection of South African monocots.
Notes: Mail order Nov-Feb only. Also sells wholesale.
Map Ref: C, D3 **OS Grid Ref:** SX521538

CPrp **PROPERPLANTS.COM** ⊠ ✈ ⌂
Penknight, Edgcumbe Road, Lostwithiel, Cornwall, PL22 0JD
Ⓣ (01208) 872291
Ⓕ (01208) 872291
Ⓔ info@Properplants.com
Ⓦ www.ProperPlants.com
Contact: Sarah Wilks
Opening Times: 1000-1800 or dusk if earlier, Tue & B/hols mid-Mar to end-Sep & by appt.
Min Mail Order UK: Nmc
Min Mail Order EU: Nmc
Cat. Cost: 4 × 1st class.
Credit Cards: All major credit/debit cards
Specialities: Wide range of unusual & easy herbaceous perennials, esp. of South African origin. Ferns & grasses. Less common herbs.
Notes: Partially accessible for wheelchair users.
Map Ref: C, C2 **OS Grid Ref:** SX093596

CPSs **Plants for the Senses** ⊠
Corner Cottage, North Street,
Dolton, Winkleigh, Devon,
EX19 8QQ
Ⓣ (01805) 804467
Ⓔ michaelross@freenetname.co.uk
Contact: Michael Ross
Opening Times: Not open. Mail order only.
Min Mail Order UK: Nmc
Cat. Cost: 1 × 1st class.
Credit Cards: None
Specialities: Some emphasis on scented plants. Some stock in small quantities only.
Notes: Nursery moving early 2008. Ltd stock until summer 2008.

CQua **Quality Daffodils** ⊠ ✈ € ◆
14 Roscarrack Close, Falmouth, Cornwall,
TR11 4PJ
Ⓣ (01326) 317959
Ⓕ (01326) 317959
Ⓔ rascamp@daffodils.uk.com
Ⓦ www.qualitydaffodils.com
Contact: R A Scamp
Opening Times: Not open. Mail order only.
Min Mail Order UK: Nmc
Min Mail Order EU: Nmc
Cat. Cost: 3 × 1st class.
Credit Cards: All major credit/debit cards
Specialities: *Narcissus* hybrids & species. Some stocks are less than 100 bulbs.
Notes: Also sells wholesale.
Map Ref: C, D1

CRea **Really Wild Flowers** ⊠
H V Horticulture Ltd, Spring Mead,
Bedchester, Shaftesbury, Dorset, SP7 0JU
Ⓣ (01747) 811778
Ⓕ 0845 009 1778
Ⓔ info@reallywildflowers.co.uk
Ⓦ www.reallywildflowers.co.uk
Contact: Grahame Dixie
Opening Times: Not open. Mail order only.
Min Mail Order UK: £40.00 + p&p
Cat. Cost: 3 × 1st class.
Credit Cards: All major credit/debit cards
Specialities: Native wild flowers for grasslands, woodlands & wetlands. Seeds, orchids & bulbs. Hedge plants & trees. Advisory & soil analysis services.
Notes: Also sells wholesale. Credit card payment accepted for online orders only.

CRHN **Roseland House Nursery** ⊠ ⛫
Chacewater, Truro, Cornwall, TR4 8QB
Ⓣ (01872) 560451
Ⓔ clematis@roselandhouse.co.uk
Ⓦ www.roselandhouse.co.uk
Contact: C R Pridham
Opening Times: 1300-1800 Tue & Wed, Apr-Sep. Other times by appt.
Min Mail Order UK: Nmc
Cat. Cost: Online only.
Credit Cards: All major credit/debit cards
Specialities: Climbing & conservatory plants. Nat. Collections of *Clematis viticella* & *Lapageria rosea*.
Notes: Garden open to the public. Credit cards accepted from mail order customers only.
Map Ref: C, D1 **OS Grid Ref:** SW752445

CRow **Rowden Gardens** ⊠ ✈ ♿
Brentor, Nr Tavistock, Devon,
PL19 0NG
Ⓣ (01822) 810275
Ⓕ (01822) 810275
Ⓔ rowdengardens@btopenworld.com
Ⓦ www.rowdengardens.com
Contact: John R L Carter
Opening Times: By appt only.
Min Mail Order UK: Nmc
Min Mail Order EU: Nmc
Cat. Cost: 6 × 1st class.
Credit Cards: None
Specialities: Aquatics, damp loving & associated plants incl. rare & unusual varieties. Nat. Collections of *Caltha* & Water *Iris*. Some stock available in small quantities only.
Notes: Also sells wholesale.
Map Ref: C, C3

CRWN **The Really Wild Nursery** ⊠ ✈ €
19 Hoopers Way, Torrington, Devon,
EX38 7NS
Ⓣ (01805) 624739
Ⓕ (01805) 624739
Ⓔ thereallywildnursery@yahoo.co.uk
Ⓦ www.thereallywildnursery.co.uk
Contact: Kathryn Moore
Opening Times: Not open. Mail order only.
Min Mail Order UK: £10.00 + p&p
Min Mail Order EU: £20.00 + p&p
Cat. Cost: 3 × 1st class.
Credit Cards: Paypal
Specialities: Wildflowers, bulbs & seeds.
Notes: Also sells wholesale. Mail order all year round, grown to order (plants in pots or plugs). Credit card payment accepted via Paypal online only.

KEY
⊠ Mail order to UK or EU ⛫ Delivers to shows
✈ Exports beyond EU € Euro accepted
♿ Accessible by wheelchair ◆ See Display advertisement

C

CSam **Sampford Shrubs** ✉ € ♿
Sampford Peverell, Tiverton, Devon,
EX16 7EN
Ⓣ (01884) 821164
Ⓔ via website
Ⓦ www.samshrub.co.uk
Contact: M Hughes-Jones & S Proud
Opening Times: 0900-1700 Mon-Sat, 1000-1600 Sun, Feb-Jun. 0900-1700 Tue-Sat, Jul-Oct.
Cat. Cost: A5 sae 35p stamps.
Credit Cards: All major credit/debit cards
Specialities: Large displays of *Pulmonaria* & *Crocosmia*. Nat. Collection of *Helenium*. Plants suitable for naturalistic schemes.
Notes: Mail order only via website & for selected list through dedicated e-commerce website. Despatched Mar.
Map Ref: C, B4 **OS Grid Ref:** ST043153

CSBt **St Bridget Nurseries Ltd** ✉ ♿
Old Rydon Lane,
Exeter, Devon,
EX2 7JY
Ⓣ (01392) 873672
Ⓕ (01392) 876710
Ⓔ info@stbridgetnurseries.co.uk
Ⓦ www.stbridgetnurseries.co.uk
Contact: Garden Centre Plant Advice
Opening Times: 0800-1700 Mon-Sat, 1030-1630 Sun, 0900-1700 Bank Hols. Closed Xmas Day, Boxing Day, New Year's Day & Easter Sunday.
Min Mail Order UK: Nmc
Cat. Cost: Free.
Credit Cards: All major credit/debit cards
Specialities: Large general nursery, with two garden centres.
Notes: Mail order available between Nov & Mar.
Map Ref: C, C4 **OS Grid Ref:** SX955905

CSdC **Sherwood Cottage** €
Newton St Cyres, Exeter, Devon,
EX5 5BT
Ⓣ (01392) 851589
Ⓔ vaughan.gallavan@connectfree.co.uk
Contact: Vaughan Gallavan
Opening Times: 1400-1700 Sun with Sherwood Gardens or by appt.
Cat. Cost: 2 × 1st class.
Credit Cards: None
Specialities: Magnolias, trees & shrubs. Nat. Coll. of Knap Hill azaleas. Ghent & species deciduous azaleas. Sherwood Garden new Nat. Collection of *Magnolia*. Stock available in small quantities only.
Map Ref: C, C3 **OS Grid Ref:** SX863967

CSev **Lower Severalls Nursery** ✉ ♿
Crewkerne, Somerset, TA18 7NX
Ⓣ (01460) 73234
Ⓔ mary@lowerseveralls.co.uk
Ⓦ www.lowerseveralls.co.uk
Contact: Mary R Pring
Opening Times: 1000-1700 Tue, Wed, Fri, Sat, Mar-end Sep. Closed Aug.
Min Mail Order UK: £20.00
Cat. Cost: 4 × 1st class.
Credit Cards: None
Specialities: Herbs, herbaceous.
Notes: Mail order perennials only.
Map Ref: C, B5 **OS Grid Ref:** ST457111

CSil **Silver Dale Nurseries** €
Shute Lane, Combe Martin, Devon, EX34 0HT
Ⓣ (01271) 882539
Ⓔ silverdale.nurseries@virgin.net
Contact: Roger Gilbert
Opening Times: 1000-1700 7 days. Closed Nov-Jan.
Cat. Cost: 4 × 1st class.
Credit Cards: Visa MasterCard EuroCard
Specialities: Nat. Collection of *Fuchsia*. Hardy fuchsias (cultivars and species).
Map Ref: C, B3

CSim **Simpson's Seeds Ltd** ✉ ♿
The Walled Garden Nursery, Horningsham, Warminster, Wiltshire, BA12 7NT
Ⓣ (01985) 845004
Ⓕ (01985) 845052
Ⓔ sales@simpsonsseeds.co.uk
Ⓦ www.simpsonsseeds.co.uk
Contact: Matthew Simpson
Opening Times: 1000-1700 Wed-Sun, Apr-May. 1000-1700 Tue-Fri & 1000-1230 Sat, rest of the year.
Min Mail Order UK: Nmc
Min Mail Order EU: Nmc
Credit Cards: Visa MasterCard Switch Maestro
Specialities: Large range of hardy perennials, limited quantities of each. Large range of seeds & vegetable plants. Specialities tomato & pepper.
Notes: Mail order catalogue currently only for seed & veg plants.
Map Ref: C, B5

CSli **Slipps Garden Centre** ♿
Butts Hill, Frome, Somerset, BA11 1HR
Ⓣ (01373) 467013
Ⓕ (01373) 467013
Contact: James Hall
Opening Times: 0900-1730 Mon-Sat, 1000-1630 Sun.

Cat. Cost: None issued.
Credit Cards: Visa Access MasterCard Delta Switch
Specialities: *Achillea*.
Notes: Also sells wholesale.
Map Ref: C, B5

CSNP **Second Nature Plant Nursery**
Croft House, Aller, Somerset,
TA10 0RA
Ⓣ (01458) 259190
Ⓔ allernursery@aol.com
Contact: Sarah Adamson
Opening Times: 0900-1700 Tue-Sat (closed Mon), 1000-1600 Sun. Closed Nov-Jan.
Credit Cards: All major credit/debit cards
Specialities: Hardy perennials.
Map Ref: C, B4

CSpe **Special Plants** ⊠ €
Hill Farm Barn, Greenways Lane, Cold Ashton, Chippenham, Wiltshire, SN14 8LA
Ⓣ (01225) 891686
Ⓔ derry@specialplants.net
Ⓦ www.specialplants.net
Contact: Derry Watkins
Opening Times: 1000-1700 7 days Mar-Oct. Other times please ring first to check.
Min Mail Order UK: £10.00 + p&p
Min Mail Order EU: £20.00 + p&p
Cat. Cost: 5 × 1st class (A5 sae only for seed list).
Credit Cards: All major credit/debit cards
Specialities: Tender perennials, *Pelargonium*, *Salvia*, *Streptocarpus*, hardy geraniums, *Anemone*, *Erysimum*, *Papaver*, *Viola* & grasses. Many varieties prop. in small numbers only. New introductions of S. African plants.
Notes: Mail order Sep-Mar only.
Map Ref: C, A5 **OS Grid Ref:** ST749726

CSPN **Sherston Parva Nursery** ⊠ ✈ ⌂ € ♿
Malmesbury Road, Sherston, Wiltshire,
SN16 0NX
Ⓣ (01666) 840348
Ⓜ 07887 814843
Ⓕ (01666) 840059
Ⓔ sherstonparva@aol.com
Ⓦ www.sherstonparva.com
Contact: Martin Rea
Opening Times: 1000-1700 7 days 1st Feb-31th Dec. Closed Jan.
Min Mail Order UK: Nmc
Min Mail Order EU: Nmc
Cat. Cost: Free.
Credit Cards: MasterCard Delta Visa Switch
Specialities: *Clematis*, wall shrubs & climbers.
Map Ref: C, A5

CSpr **Springfield Plants**
Springfield, Woolsery, Bideford, Devon,
EX39 5PZ
Ⓣ (01237) 431162
Ⓔ asta.munro@tiscali.co.uk
Contact: Asta Munro
Opening Times: All year by appt.
Cat. Cost: List only, free by email.
Credit Cards: None
Specialities: Hardy perennials for wide variety of situations & plants with interesting foliage. Small quantities only.
Map Ref: C, B2 **OS Grid Ref:** SS347206

CSsd **Sunnyside Plants** ⊠
Sunnyside, Leigh Road, Bradford-on-Avon, Wiltshire, BA15 2RQ
Ⓣ (01225) 862096
Ⓔ Filoman@fsmail.net
Contact: James Tracey
Opening Times: By prior arrangement only.
Min Mail Order UK: £6.00
Credit Cards: None
Specialities: Dry & lime-tolerant hardy plants. Smaller quantities of choice plants for damp or humus-rich conditions. Some plants available in small quantities only.
Notes: Mail order pre-arranged by phone.
Map Ref: C, A5 **OS Grid Ref:** ST832621

CSto **Stone Lane Gardens** ⊠
Stone Farm, Chagford, Devon,
TQ13 8JU
Ⓣ (01647) 231311
Ⓔ orders@mythicgarden.eclipse.co.uk
Ⓦ www.stonelanegardens.com
Contact: Paul Bartlett
Opening Times: 0900-1700 Mon-Fri. Collection at w/ends possible. Please phone first if travelling a long distance.
Min Mail Order UK: Nmc
Cat. Cost: £1.75 or 6 × 1st class for colour catalogue with photos.
Credit Cards: None
Specialities: Comprehensive selection of wild origin *Betula* & *Alnus*, both bare-root & in pots. Choice selection of specially grafted cvs. Nat. Collection of Birch & Alder.
Notes: Arboretum open all year with summer sculpture exhibition (charges apply). Planting service available in West Country, details on request. Also sells wholesale.
Map Ref: C, C3 **OS Grid Ref:** SX708908

KEY
⊠ Mail order to UK or EU ⌂ Delivers to shows
✈ Exports beyond EU € Euro accepted
♿ Accessible by wheelchair ◆ See Display advertisement

C

CStu **Stuckey's Alpines**
38 Phillipps Avenue, Exmouth, Devon, EX8 3HZ
Ⓣ (01395) 273636
Ⓔ stuckeysalpines@aol.com
Contact: Roger & Brenda Stuckey
Opening Times: As NGS dates or by appt.
Cat. Cost: None issued.
Credit Cards: None
Specialities: Alpines in general. Hardy & half-hardy bulbs. Extensive choice of plants, many available only in small quantities.
Map Ref: C, C4

CSut **Suttons Seeds** ⊠
Woodview Road, Paignton, Devon, TQ4 7NG
Ⓣ 0844 922 2899
Ⓕ 0844 922 2265
Ⓦ www.suttons.co.uk
Contact: Customer Services
Opening Times: (Office) 0830-1700 Mon-Fri. Also answerphone.
Min Mail Order UK: Nmc
Min Mail Order EU: £5.00
Cat. Cost: Free.
Credit Cards: Visa MasterCard Switch Delta
Specialities: Over 1,000 varieties of flower & vegetable seed, bulbs, plants & sundries.

CSWC **South West Carnivorous Plants** ⊠ ✈ ⌂
Blackwater Nursery, Blackwater Road, Culmstock, Cullompton, Devon, EX15 3HP
Ⓣ (01823) 681669
Ⓕ 0870 705 3083
Ⓔ flytraps@littleshopofhorrors.co.uk
Ⓦ www.littleshopofhorrors.co.uk
Contact: Jenny Pearce & Alistair Pearce
Opening Times: By appt.
Min Mail Order UK: Nmc
Min Mail Order EU: Nmc
Cat. Cost: 2 × 2nd class.
Credit Cards: All major credit/debit cards
Specialities: *Cephalotus*, *Nepenthes*, *Dionea*, *Drosera*, *Darlingtonia*, *Sarracenia*, *Pinguicula* & *Utricularia*. Specialists in hardy carnivorous plants & *Dionea muscipula* cvs.
Map Ref: C, B4

CSWP **Sonia Wright Plants** ⊠ ♿
Buckerfields Nursery, Ogbourne St George, Marlborough, Wiltshire, SN8 1SG
Ⓣ (01672) 841065
Ⓕ (01672) 541047
Contact: Sonia Wright & Alison Gee
Opening Times: 1000-1800 Tue-Sat.
Min Mail Order UK: £15.00 primulas only
Min Mail Order EU: £15.00 primulas only
Cat. Cost: 4 × 1st class.
Credit Cards: All major credit/debit cards
Specialities: Barnhaven polyanthus & primroses. Grasses, *Iris*, *Euphorbia*, *Penstemon*, old roses.
Notes: Mail order primroses only despatched autumn. Credit cards not accepted over the phone.
Map Ref: C, A6

CTgr **Tregrehan Garden** ♿
Tregrehan Garden Cottages & Nursery, Par, Cornwall, PL24 2SJ
Ⓣ (01726) 812438
Ⓕ (01726) 814389
Ⓔ info@tregrehan.org
Ⓦ www.tregrehan.org
Contact: Tom Hudson
Opening Times: 1030-1700 Wed-Sun, mid-Mar-end May. 1400-1700 Wed only, Jun-Aug.
Credit Cards: None
Specialities: *Camellia*, *Rhododendron*, *Nothofagus*, *Myosotidium*, tender trees & shrubs.
Notes: Also sells wholesale.
Map Ref: C, D2 **OS Grid Ref:** SX0553

CTho **Thornhayes Nursery** ⊠ €
St Andrews Wood, Dulford, Cullompton, Devon, EX15 2DF
Ⓣ (01884) 266746
Ⓕ (01884) 266739
Ⓔ trees@thornhayes-nursery.co.uk
Ⓦ www.thornhayes-nursery.co.uk
Contact: K D Croucher
Opening Times: 0800-1600 Mon-Fri. 0930-1400 Sat (Sep-Apr).
Min Mail Order UK: £100
Min Mail Order EU: Nmc
Credit Cards: None
Specialities: A broad range of forms of ornamental, amenity & fruit trees incl. West Country apple varieties.
Notes: Also sells wholesale.
Map Ref: C, C4

CTrC **Trevena Cross Nurseries** ⊠ € ♿
Breage, Helston, Cornwall, TR13 9PS
Ⓣ (01736) 763880
Ⓕ (01736) 762828
Ⓔ sales@trevenacross.co.uk
Ⓦ www.trevenacross.co.uk
Contact: Graham Jeffery, John Eddy
Opening Times: 0900-1700 Mon-Sat, 1030-1630 Sun.
Min Mail Order UK: Nmc
Cat. Cost: Online only.
Credit Cards: Access Visa Switch
Specialities: South African, Australian & New

Zealand plants, incl. *Aloe*, *Protea*, tree ferns, palms, *Restio*, hardy succulents & wide range of other exotics.
Map Ref: C, D1 **OS Grid Ref:** SW614284

CTrG **TREGOTHNAN NURSERY** ⊠ ✈ € ♿
The Woodyard, Tregothnan, Truro, Cornwall, TR2 4AN
Ⓣ (01872) 520000
Ⓕ (01872) 520583
Ⓔ info@tregothnan.co.uk
Ⓦ www.tregothnan.com
Contact: Lucy Simpson
Opening Times: By appt. for collection only.
Min Mail Order UK: £15.00
Min Mail Order EU: £50.00
Cat. Cost: Online only.
Credit Cards: MasterCard Visa Delta EuroCard
Specialities: Unusual & rare plants from own stock. Extra large specimens available for instant effect. Known wild origin plants. *Camellia*, incl. large collection of *C. sasanqua*.
Notes: English tea production & marketing. Also sells wholesale.
Map Ref: C, D2 **OS Grid Ref:** SW859421

CTrh **TREHANE CAMELLIA NURSERY** ⊠ ⌂ € ♿
J Trehane & Sons Ltd, Stapehill Road, Hampreston, Wimborne, Dorset, BH21 7ND
Ⓣ (01202) 873490
Ⓕ (01202) 873490
Ⓔ camellias@trehanenursery.co.uk
Ⓦ www.trehanenursery.co.uk
Contact: Lorraine or Jeanette
Opening Times: 0900-1630 Mon-Fri all year (excl. Xmas & New Year). 1000-1600 Sat-Sun in spring & by special appt.
Min Mail Order UK: Nmc
Cat. Cost: £1.50 cat./book.
Credit Cards: All major credit/debit cards
Specialities: Extensive range of *Camellia* species, cultivars & hybrids. Many new introductions. Evergreen azaleas, *Pieris*, *Magnolia* & blueberries.
Notes: Also sells wholesale.
Map Ref: C, C6

CTri **TRISCOMBE NURSERIES** ⊠ ♿ ◆
West Bagborough, Nr Taunton, Somerset, TA4 3HG
Ⓣ (01984) 618267
Ⓔ triscombe.nurseries2000@virgin.net
Ⓦ www.triscombenurseries.co.uk
Contact: S Parkman
Opening Times: 0900-1300 & 1400-1730 Mon-Sat. 1400-1730 Sun & B/hols.
Min Mail Order UK: Nmc
Cat. Cost: 2 × 1st class.
Credit Cards: None
Specialities: Trees, shrubs, roses, fruit, *Clematis*, herbaceous & rock plants.
Map Ref: C, B4

CTsd **TRESEDERS** ⊠ ♿
Wallcottage Nursery, Lockengate, St. Austell, Cornwall, PL26 8RU
Ⓣ (01208) 832234
Ⓔ Treseders@btconnect.com
Contact: James Treseder
Opening Times: 1000-1700 Mon-Sat, 1000-1600 Sun.
Min Mail Order UK: Nmc
Cat. Cost: 60p
Credit Cards: All major credit/debit cards
Specialities: A wide range of choice & unusual plants grown in peat-free compost, incl. 200+ *Fuchsia* varieties.
Notes: Also sells wholesale.
Map Ref: C, C2 **OS Grid Ref:** SX034620

CTuc **EDWIN TUCKER & SONS** ⊠ ♿
Brewery Meadow, Stonepark, Ashburton, Newton Abbot, Devon, TQ13 7DG
Ⓣ (01364) 652233
Ⓕ (01364) 654211
Ⓔ seeds@edwintucker.com
Ⓦ www.edwintucker.com
Contact: Geoff Penton
Opening Times: 0800-1700 Mon-Fri, 0800-1600 Sat.
Min Mail Order UK: Nmc
Min Mail Order EU: Nmc
Cat. Cost: Free.
Credit Cards: Visa MasterCard Switch
Specialities: Nearly 120 varieties of seed potatoes, incl. 50 organic varieties. Wide range of vegetables, flowers, green manures & sprouting seeds in packets. None treated. Nearly 200 varieties of organically produced seeds.

CWan **WANBOROUGH HERB NURSERY** ⌂ ♿
Callas Hill, Wanborough, Swindon, Wiltshire, SN4 0AG
Ⓣ (01793) 790327 (answering machine)
Ⓔ wanboroughnursery@btinternet.com
Contact: Peter Biggs
Opening Times: 1000-1700 Tue-Fri,

KEY
⊠ Mail order to UK or EU ⌂ Delivers to shows
✈ Exports beyond EU € Euro accepted
♿ Accessible by wheelchair ◆ See Display advertisement

C

w/ends 1000-1600, Mar-Oct. Other times by appt.
Cat. Cost: £1.00
Credit Cards: None
Specialities: Herbs, herbaceous, esp. culinary. Available in small quantities only.
Map Ref: C, A6 **OS Grid Ref:** SU217828

CWat **THE WATER GARDEN** ⊠ ♿
Hinton Parva, Swindon, Wiltshire, SN4 0DH
Ⓣ (01793) 790558
Ⓕ (01793) 791298
Ⓔ mike@thewatergarden.co.uk
Ⓦ www.thewatergarden.co.uk
Contact: Mike & Anne Newman
Opening Times: 1000-1700 Wed-Sun.
Min Mail Order UK: £10.00 + p&p
Cat. Cost: 4 × 1st class.
Credit Cards: Visa Access Switch
Specialities: Water lilies, marginal & moisture plants, oxygenators & alpines.
Notes: Also sells wholesale.
Map Ref: C, A6

CWCL **WESTCOUNTRY NURSERIES** ⊠ ⌂ ♿
Donkey Meadow, Woolsery, Devon, EX39 5QH
Ⓣ (01237) 431111
Ⓕ (01237) 431111
Ⓔ info@westcountry-nurseries.co.uk
Ⓦ www.westcountry-nurseries.co.uk
Contact: Sarah Conibear
Opening Times: 1000-1600 Mar-Sep.
Min Mail Order UK: £10.00
Min Mail Order EU: £10.00
Cat. Cost: 2 × 1st class + A5 sae for full colour cat.
Credit Cards: All major credit/debit cards
Specialities: *Lupinus, Lewisia, Hellebore, Clematis, Cyclamen*, acers, lavender, select perennials, grasses, ferns & climbers. Nat. Collection of Lupins.
Map Ref: C, B2 **OS Grid Ref:** SS351219

CWGN **WALLED GARDEN NURSERY** ⊠ ♿
Brinkworth House, Brinkworth, Nr Malmesbury, Wiltshire, SN15 5DF
Ⓣ (01666) 826637
Ⓔ f.wescott@btinternet.com
Ⓦ www.clematis-nursery.co.uk
Contact: Fraser Wescott
Opening Times: 1000-1700, 7 days Mar-Oct. 1000-dusk, Mon-Fri Nov & Feb. Closed Dec & Jan.
Min Mail Order UK: £12.95
Cat. Cost: 3 × 1st class.
Credit Cards: All major credit/debit cards
Specialities: *Clematis* & climbers, with a selection of unusual perennials & shrubs.
Map Ref: C, A6 **OS Grid Ref:** SU002849

CWib **WIBBLE FARM NURSERIES** ⊠ ♿
Wibble Farm, West Quantoxhead, Nr Taunton, Somerset, TA4 4DD
Ⓣ (01984) 632303
Ⓕ (01984) 633168
Ⓔ sales@wibblefarmnurseries.co.uk
Ⓦ www.wibblefarmnurseries.co.uk
Contact: Mrs M L Francis
Opening Times: 0800-1700 Mon-Fri, 1000-1600 Sat. All year excl. B/hols.
Min Mail Order UK: Nmc
Min Mail Order EU: Nmc
Cat. Cost: 3 × 1st class.
Credit Cards: All major credit/debit cards
Specialities: Growers of a wide range of hardy plants, many rare & unusual. Display gardens.
Notes: Also sells wholesale.
Map Ref: C, B4

CWil **FERNWOOD NURSERY** ⊠ ☒ ⌂ € ♿
Peters Marland, Torrington, Devon, EX38 8QG
Ⓣ (01805) 601446
Ⓔ hw@fernwood-nursery.co.uk
Ⓦ www.fernwood-nursery.co.uk
Contact: Howard Wills & Sally Wills
Opening Times: Any time by appt. Please phone first.
Min Mail Order UK: Nmc
Min Mail Order EU: Nmc
Cat. Cost: Sae for list.
Credit Cards: None
Specialities: Nat. Collection of *Sempervivum, Jovibarba, Rosularia* & *Phormium*.
Notes: Mail order for *Sempervivum, Jovibarba* & *Rosularia* only. 5 miles from RHS Rosemoor.
Map Ref: C, C3 **OS Grid Ref:** SS479133

CWit **WITHLEIGH NURSERIES** ◆
Withleigh, Tiverton, Devon EX16 8JG
Ⓣ (01884) 253351
Ⓔ Withleigh@aol.com
Ⓦ www.withleighnurseries.co.uk
Contact: Terry Watling
Opening Times: 0900-1730 Mon-Sat, Mar-Jun, Tue-Sat, Jul-Feb. 1000-1600 Sun, Apr-Jun.
Cat. Cost: None issued.
Credit Cards: All major credit/debit cards
Specialities: Shrubs & herbaceous.

CWiW **WINDRUSH WILLOW** ⊠ €
Higher Barn, Sidmouth Road, Aylesbeare, Exeter, Devon, EX5 2JJ
Ⓣ (01395) 233669
Ⓕ (01395) 233669
Ⓔ windrushw@aol.com
Ⓦ www.windrushwillow.com
Contact: Richard Kerwood
Opening Times: Mail order only. Open by appt.
Min Mail Order UK: Nmc
Min Mail Order EU: Nmc
Cat. Cost: 2 × 1st class.
Credit Cards: None
Specialities: *Salix*. Unrooted cuttings available Dec-Mar.
Notes: Also sells wholesale.

CWon **THE WONDER TREE** ⊠
35 Beaconsfield Road, Knowle, Bristol, BS4 2JE
Ⓣ 0117 908 9057
Ⓜ 07989 333507
Ⓔ Kevin@wondertree.org.uk
Ⓦ www.wondertree.org.uk
Contact: Kevin Lindegaard
Opening Times: Not open. Mail order only.
Min Mail Order UK: £8.00
Cat. Cost: 2 × 1st class.
Credit Cards: None
Specialities: *Salix*.
Notes: Also sells wholesale.

CWri **NIGEL WRIGHT RHODODENDRONS** ♿
The Old Glebe, Eggesford, Chulmleigh, Devon, EX18 7QU
Ⓣ (01769) 580632
Ⓔ wrightrhodos@aol.com
Contact: Nigel Wright
Opening Times: By appt. only. 7 days.
Cat. Cost: 2 × 1st class.
Credit Cards: None
Specialities: *Rhododendron* & deciduous azaleas. 200 varieties field grown, root-balled, some potted. For collection only. Specialist grower. Free advice & planting plans.
Notes: Also sells wholesale.
Map Ref: C, B3 **OS Grid Ref:** SS684106

CWSG **WEST SOMERSET GARDEN CENTRE** ⊠ ♿
Mart Road, Minehead, Somerset, TA24 5BJ
Ⓣ (01643) 703812
Ⓕ (01643) 706476
Ⓔ wsgc@btconnect.com
Ⓦ www.westsomersetgardencentre.co.uk
Contact: Ms J K Shoulders
Opening Times: 0800-1700 Mon-Sat, 1000-1600 Sun.
Min Mail Order UK: Nmc
Cat. Cost: None issued.
Credit Cards: Access Visa Switch Solo
Specialities: Wide general range. *Ceanothus*.
Map Ref: C, B4

CWVF **WHITE VEIL FUCHSIAS** ⊠ ♿
Verwood Road, Three Legged Cross, Wimborne, Dorset, BH21 6RP
Ⓣ (01202) 813998
Contact: A. C. Holloway
Opening Times: 0900-1300 & 1400-1700 Mon-Sat, 1000-1300 & 1400-1600 Sun, Jan-Aug. Closed Sat & Sun, Sep-Dec.
Min Mail Order UK: 8 plants of your choice.
Cat. Cost: 4 × 1st class.
Credit Cards: None
Specialities: Fuchsias. Small plants grown from Jan-Apr. Available in small quantities only.
Map Ref: C, C6

EASTERN

EABi **ALISON BILVERSTONE** ⊠
22 Kings Street, Swaffham, Norfolk, PE37 7BU
Ⓣ (01760) 725026
Ⓔ a.bilverstone@tiscali.co.uk
Contact: Alison Bilverstone
Opening Times: Not open. Mail order only.
Min Mail Order UK: Nmc
Cat. Cost: A4 sae.
Credit Cards: None
Specialities: *Achemene*, *Kohleria* & *Smithiantha* rhizomes, available Dec to mid-Apr. Stocked in small quantities.

EAEE **AEE** ⊠
38 Church Close, Roydon, Diss, Norfolk, IP22 5RQ
Ⓣ (01379) 651230
Ⓕ (01379) 651230
Ⓔ aeeloverofplants@fsmail.net
Contact: Anne Etheridge
Opening Times: Plant stall 1000-1500 Wed-Fri & Sun, Mar-Sep at Roydon White Hart Garden, Roydon, Norfolk (A1066).
Min Mail Order UK: Nmc.
Min Mail Order EU: Nmc.

KEY
⊠ Mail order to UK or EU | Delivers to shows
Exports beyond EU | € Euro accepted
♿ Accessible by wheelchair | ◆ See Display advertisement

E

Cat. Cost: 3 × 1st class.
Specialities: Perennials & grasses plus a few enticing alpines & shrubs. Alpines & shrubs available in small quantities only.
Notes: Garden maintenance, spring & autumn pruning. Talks available, contact nursery for details. Plants may be reserved with a £5.00 deposit. Wheelchair access at plant stall site.

EAlp **The Alpine and Grass Nursery** ⊠
Northgate, Pinchbeck, Spalding, Lincolnshire, PE11 3TB
Ⓣ (01775) 640935
Ⓔ info@alpinesandgrasses.co.uk
Ⓦ www.alpinesandgrasses.co.uk
Contact: Hayley Merrison
Opening Times: Please telephone.
Min Mail Order UK: 15 plants.
Cat. Cost: Online only.
Credit Cards: Paypal
Specialities: Alpines, rockery plants & ornamental grasses.
Notes: Also sells wholesale.
Map Ref: E, B1 **OS Grid Ref:** TF211262

EAmu **Amulree Exotics** ⊠ ♿
The Turnpike, Norwich Road (B1113), Fundenhall, Norwich, Norfolk, NR16 1EL
Ⓣ (01508) 488101
Ⓔ SDG@exotica.fsbusiness.co.uk
Ⓦ www.turn-it-tropical.co.uk
Contact: S Gridley
Opening Times: 0930-1730 7 days spring-autumn, 1000-1630 7 days autumn-spring.
Min Mail Order UK: Nmc
Cat. Cost: 2 × 1st class.
Credit Cards: Visa MasterCard Electron Solo Switch
Specialities: Hardy & half-hardy plants for home, garden & conservatory. Palms, bamboos, bananas, tree ferns, cannas, gingers & much more.
Notes: Also sells wholesale.
Map Ref: E, B3 **OS Grid Ref:** DX123740

EAro **Aromafolia** ⊠
Barbers Farm, Leys Lane, Old Buckenham, Norfolk, NR17 1NT
Ⓣ (01953) 887713
Ⓔ enquiries@aromafolia.co.uk
Ⓦ www.aromafolia.co.uk
Contact: John Holden
Opening Times: 1000-1700 Fri, Sat, Sun & B/hols, Mar-Sep. Other times by appt.
Min Mail Order UK: £15.00
Min Mail Order EU: £50.00
Cat. Cost: 3 × 1st class.
Credit Cards: None
Specialities: Wide range of plants with aromatic foliage, incl. *Salvia*, *Monarda*, *Agastache*, *Nepeta*. All plants grown in peat-free compost. Some varieties only available in small quantities.
Map Ref: E, C3 **OS Grid Ref:** TM042913

EBak **B & H M Baker** ♿
Bourne Brook Nurseries, Greenstead Green, Halstead, Essex, CO9 1RJ
Ⓣ (01787) 476369
Contact: B, HM and C Baker
Opening Times: 0800-1630 Mon-Fri, 0900-1200 & 1400-1630 Sat & Sun, Mar-30th Jun.
Cat. Cost: 2 × 1st class + 33p.
Credit Cards: All major credit/debit cards
Specialities: *Fuchsia* & conservatory plants.
Notes: Also sells wholesale.
Map Ref: E, C2

EBar **Barcham Trees** ⊠ €
Eye Hill Drove, Ely, Cambridgeshire, CB7 5XF
Ⓣ (01353) 720748
Ⓕ (01353) 723060
Ⓔ sales@barchamtrees.co.uk
Ⓦ www.barcham.co.uk
Contact: Keith Sacre
Opening Times: 0900-1700 Mon-Fri. Visits to the nursery by appt. only.
Min Mail Order UK: Nmc
Cat. Cost: Free.
Credit Cards: All major credit/debit cards
Specialities: Containerised trees.
Notes: Also sells wholesale.
Map Ref: E, C2

EBee **Beeches Nursery** ⊠ ♿
Village Centre, Ashdon, Saffron Walden, Essex, CB10 2HB
Ⓣ (01799) 584362
Ⓕ (01799) 584421
Ⓔ sales@beechesnursery.co.uk
Ⓦ www.beechesnursery.co.uk
Contact: Alan Bidwell/Kevin Marsh
Opening Times: 0830-1700 Mon-Sat, 1000-1700 Sun & B/hols.
Min Mail Order UK: £12.00
Min Mail Order EU: £20.00
Cat. Cost: 6 × 2nd class for herbaceous list.
Credit Cards: Visa Access MasterCard EuroCard Switch
Specialities: Herbaceous specialists & extensive range of other garden plants.
Notes: Plants dispatched Oct-Feb only.

Orders accepted throughout the year. No trees by mail order.
Map Ref: E, C2 **OS Grid Ref:** TL586420

EBla **Blacksmiths Cottage Nursery** ⊠ ⌂ € ♿
Langmere Road, Langmere, Dickleburgh, Nr Diss, Norfolk, IP21 4QA
Ⓣ (01379) 741136/740982
Ⓔ Blackcottnursery@aol.com
Ⓦ www.blackcottnursery.co.uk
Contact: Ben or Jill Potterton
Opening Times: 1000-1700 Thu-Sun & B/hol Mon, Mar-Oct.
Min Mail Order UK: Nmc
Min Mail Order EU: Nmc
Cat. Cost: Online only.
Credit Cards: All major credit/debit cards
Specialities: Over 2000 species grown. Large selection of shade plants esp. *Anemone nemorosa* & *Poygonatum*, also large collection of *Geranium*, *Astrantia* & *Sanguisorba*.
Notes: Coffee Shop & toilets. Barn Garden only open Aug-Sep. Also sells wholesale.
Map Ref: E, C3 **OS Grid Ref:** TM192821

EBls **Peter Beales Roses** ⊠ ✈ ♿
London Road, Attleborough, Norfolk, NR17 1AY
Ⓣ (01953) 454707
Ⓕ (01953) 456845
Ⓔ info@peterbealesroses.co.uk
Ⓦ www.peterbealesroses.co.uk
Contact: Customer Advisers
Opening Times: 0900-1700 Mon-Sat, 1000-1600 Sun & B/hols.
Min Mail Order UK: Nmc
Min Mail Order EU: Nmc
Cat. Cost: Free to UK. Outside UK £5.00.
Credit Cards: All major credit/debit cards
Specialities: Old fashioned roses & classic roses. Nat. Collection of Species Roses. Some stock available in small quantities only. Other plants on site.
Notes: Does not accept American Express. Shop & bistro.
Map Ref: E, C3 **OS Grid Ref:** TM026929

EBrs **Bressingham Gardens (incorp. Van Tubergen UK)** ⊠ ♿
Bressingham, Diss, Norfolk, IP22 2AG
Ⓣ (01379) 688282
Ⓕ (01379) 687227
Ⓔ info@bressinghamgardens.com
Ⓦ www.bressinghamgardens.com
Contact: Fiona-Louise Tilden
Opening Times: Mail order 0900-1700 Mon-Fri. Gardens open daily 1030-1730 1st Apr-31st Oct.
Min Mail Order UK: Nmc
Min Mail Order EU: £100
Cat. Cost: None issued.
Credit Cards: Maestro Visa Access MasterCard
Specialities: Bulbs, grafted conifers, grasses & perennials. Nat. Collection of *Miscanthus*.
Notes: Also sells wholesale.
Map Ref: E, C3 **OS Grid Ref:** TM071807

EBtc **Botanica** ⊠
Chantry Farm, Campsea Ashe, Wickham Market, Suffolk, IP13 0PZ
Ⓣ (01728) 747113
Ⓕ (01728) 747725
Ⓔ tlc-botanica@btconnect.com
Ⓦ www.botanica.org.uk
Contact: Jon Rose
Opening Times: 1000-1700 6 days summer, 1000-1600 7 days winter.
Min Mail Order UK: Nmc
Min Mail Order EU: £20.00 + p&p
Cat. Cost: 6 × 1st class.
Credit Cards: None
Specialities: Range of rare & unusual hardy plants.
Notes: Also sells wholesale.
Map Ref: E, C3

EBur **Jenny Burgess** ♿
Alpine Nursery, Sisland, Norwich, Norfolk, NR14 6EF
Ⓣ (01508) 520724
Contact: Jenny Burgess
Opening Times: Any time by appt.
Cat. Cost: None issued.
Credit Cards: None
Specialities: Alpines, *Sisyrinchium* & *Campanula*. Nat. Collection of *Sisyrinchium*.
Map Ref: E, B3

EBWF **British Wild Flower Plants** ⊠ ♿
Burlingham Gardens, 31 Main Road, North Burlingham, Norfolk, NR13 4TA
Ⓣ (01603) 716615
Ⓕ (01603) 716615
Ⓔ office@wildflowers.co.uk
Ⓦ www.wildflowers.co.uk
Contact: Helen Tweed
Opening Times: 1000-1600 Mon-Fri. Weekends by appt.
Min Mail Order UK: Nmc

KEY
⊠ Mail order to UK or EU ⌂ Delivers to shows
✈ Exports beyond EU € Euro accepted
♿ Accessible by wheelchair ◆ See Display advertisement

E

Min Mail Order EU: Nmc
Cat. Cost: £2.00 + p&p
Credit Cards: All major credit/debit cards
Specialities: Native wild flowers. 400 species. Quantities vary from 1 to 50,000.
Notes: Also sells wholesale.
Map Ref: E, B3 **OS Grid Ref:** TG371101

ECGP **Cambridge Garden Plants** ♿
The Lodge, Clayhithe Road, Horningsea, Cambridgeshire, CB25 9JD
Ⓣ (01223) 861370
Contact: Mrs Nancy Buchdahl
Opening Times: 1100-1730 Thu-Sun mid Mar-31st Oct. Other times by appt.
Cat. Cost: 4 × 1st class.
Credit Cards: None
Specialities: Hardy perennials incl. wide range of *Geranium*, *Allium*, *Euphorbia*, *Penstemon*, *Digitalis*. Some shrubs, roses & *Clematis*.
Map Ref: E, C2 **OS Grid Ref:** TL497637

ECha **The Beth Chatto Gardens Ltd** ⊠ ♿
Elmstead Market, Colchester, Essex, CO7 7DB
Ⓣ (01206) 822007
Ⓕ (01206) 825933
Ⓔ info@bethchatto.fsnet.co.uk
Ⓦ www.bethchatto.co.uk
Contact: Beth Chatto
Opening Times: 0900-1700 Mon-Sat 1st Mar-31st Oct. 0900-1600 Mon-Fri 1st Nov-1st Mar. Closed Sun.
Min Mail Order UK: £20.00
Min Mail Order EU: Ask for details
Cat. Cost: Free plant list.
Credit Cards: Visa Switch MasterCard
Specialities: Predominantly herbaceous. Many unusual for special situations.
Map Ref: E, D3 **OS Grid Ref:** TM069238

ECho **Choice Landscapes** ⊠ ☒ ⌂ € ♿
Priory Farm, 101 Salts Road, West Walton, Wisbech, Cambridgeshire, PE14 7EF
Ⓣ (01945) 585051
Ⓕ (01945) 580053
Ⓔ info@choicelandscapes.org
Ⓦ www.choicelandscapes.org
Contact: Michael Agg & Jillian Agg
Opening Times: 1000-1700 Tue-Sat 12th Feb-31st Oct 2008. Not open on show dates, please phone. Other times by appt.
Min Mail Order UK: £10.00
Min Mail Order EU: £10.00 + p&p
Cat. Cost: 6 × 1st class or 6 IRC
Credit Cards: Maestro Visa MasterCard Solo
Specialities: Dwarf conifers, alpines, acers, rhododendrons, bulbs, pines & lilies.
Map Ref: E, B1

ECnt **Cants of Colchester** ⊠ ☒
Nayland Road, Mile End, Colchester, Essex, CO4 5EB
Ⓣ (01206) 844008
Ⓕ (01206) 855371
Ⓔ finder@cantsroses.co.uk
Ⓦ www.cantsroses.co.uk
Contact: Angela Pawsey
Opening Times: 0900-1300, 1400-1630 Mon-Fri. Sat varied, please phone first. Sun closed.
Min Mail Order UK: Nmc
Min Mail Order EU: Nmc
Cat. Cost: Free
Credit Cards: Visa MasterCard Delta Solo Switch
Specialities: Roses. Unstaffed rose field can be viewed dawn-dusk every day from end Jun-end Sep.
Notes: Bare-root mail order end Oct-end Mar, containers Apr-Aug. Partial wheelchair access.
Map Ref: E, C3

ECou **County Park Nursery**
Essex Gardens, Hornchurch, Essex, RM11 3BU
Ⓣ (01708) 445205
Ⓦ www.countyparknursery.co.uk
Contact: G Hutchins
Opening Times: 1000-1700 Mon-Sat excl. Wed, 1000-1700 Sun Mar-Oct. Nov-Feb by appt. only.
Cat. Cost: 3 × 1st class
Credit Cards: None
Specialities: Alpines & rare and unusual plants from New Zealand, Tasmania & the Falklands. Nat. Collection of *Coprosma*. Many plants in small quantities only.
Map Ref: E, D2

ECrc **The Crocosmia Gardens** ⊠
9 North Street, Caistor, Lincolnshire, LN7 6QU
Ⓣ (01472) 859269
Ⓔ crocosmia@tiscali.co.uk
Ⓦ www.simplesite.com/crocosmia
Contact: Mark Fox
Opening Times: 0800-1900 Mon-Sat.
Min Mail Order UK: Nmc
Min Mail Order EU: Nmc
Credit Cards: None
Specialities: Nat. Collection of *Crocosmia*.

ECre **Creake Plant Centre** ♿
Nursery View, Leicester Road, South Creake, Fakenham, Norfolk, NR21 9PW
Ⓣ (01328) 823018
Contact: Mr T Harrison

Opening Times: 1000-1300 & 1400-1730 7 days excl. Xmas.
Cat. Cost: None issued
Credit Cards: All major credit/debit cards
Specialities: Unusual shrubs, herbaceous, conservatory plants, old roses.
Map Ref: E, B1 **OS Grid Ref:** TF864353

ECrN **Crown Nursery** ⊠ ♿
High Street, Ufford, Woodbridge, Suffolk, IP13 6EL
Ⓣ (01394) 460755
Ⓕ (01394) 460142
Ⓔ enquiries@crown-nursery.co.uk
Ⓦ www.crown-nursery.co.uk
Contact: Jill Proctor
Opening Times: 0900-1700 (1600 in winter) Mon-Sat.
Min Mail Order UK: Nmc
Cat. Cost: 2 × 1st class.
Credit Cards: All major credit/debit cards
Specialities: Mature & semi-mature native, ornamental & fruit trees. Heritage fruit varieties.
Notes: Mail order for small/young stock only. Also sells wholesale.
Map Ref: E, C3 **OS Grid Ref:** TM292528

ECtt **Cottage Nurseries** ⊠ ♿
Thoresthorpe, Alford, Lincolnshire, LN13 0HX
Ⓣ (01507) 466968
Ⓕ (01507) 463409
Ⓔ bill@cottagenurseries.net
Ⓦ www.cottagenurseries.net
Contact: W H Denbigh
Opening Times: 0900-1700 7 days 1st Mar-31st Oct, 1000-1600 w/ends only Nov-Feb.
Min Mail Order UK: Nmc
Cat. Cost: 3 × 1st class.
Credit Cards: Visa MasterCard Maestro
Specialities: Hardy perennials. Wide general range.
Map Ref: E, A2 **OS Grid Ref:** TF423716

EDAr **D'Arcy & Everest** ⊠ ♠ € ♿
(Office) PO Box 78, St Ives, Huntingdon, Cambridgeshire PE27 4UQ
Ⓣ (01480) 497672
Ⓜ 07715 374440/1
Ⓕ (01480) 466042
Ⓔ angela@darcyeverest.co.uk
Ⓦ www.darcyeverest.co.uk
Contact: Angela Whiting, Richard Oliver
Opening Times: Wed-Fri, Mar-Sep, except show dates. Coach parties welcome by appt.
Min Mail Order UK: £10.00 + p&p
Min Mail Order EU: £10.00 + p&p
Cat. Cost: 6 × 1st class.
Credit Cards: None
Specialities: Alpines, sempervivums & selected perennials.
Notes: Nursery is at Pidley Sheep Lane (B1040), Somersham, Huntingdon, Cambs.
Map Ref: E, C2 **OS Grid Ref:** TL533276

EDif **Different Plants** ♿
The Mellis Stud, Gate Farm, Cranley Green, Eye, Suffolk, IP23 7NX
Ⓣ (01379) 870291
Contact: Fleur Waters
Opening Times: Sat-Thu by appt. only, closed Fri. Plant stall Eye market Fri 0900-1200.
Cat. Cost: 4 × 1st class.
Credit Cards: None
Specialities: *Mimulus aurantiacus* & hybrids, half-hardy bulbous/cormous perennials incl. *Dietes*, *Aristea*, *Cypella*, *Tigridia* & *Anomatheca laxa*. Bulbs may be available in small quantities only.
Map Ref: E, C3

EECP **Essex Carnivorous Plants** ⊠ ♠
12 Strangman Avenue, Thundersley, Essex, SS7 1RB
Ⓣ (01702) 551467
Ⓔ Markecp@aol.com
Ⓦ www.essexcarnivorousplants.com
Contact: Mark Haslett
Opening Times: By appt. only.
Min Mail Order UK: Nmc
Min Mail Order EU: Nmc
Cat. Cost: 2 × 1st class or online.
Credit Cards: None
Specialities: Good range of carnivorous plants. *Sarracenia*, *Drosera*. Nat. Collection of *Dionaea* forms & cvs. Some stock available in small quantities only. Nat. Collection of *Sarracenia* (hybrids & ssp.).
Notes: Also sells wholesale.
Map Ref: E, D2 **OS Grid Ref:** TQ797875

EFer **The Fern Nursery** ⊠ ♠ ♿
Grimsby Road, Binbrook, Lincolnshire, LN8 6DH
Ⓣ (01472) 398092
Ⓔ richard@timm984.fsnet.co.uk
Ⓦ www.fernnursery.co.uk
Contact: R N Timm
Opening Times: 0900-1700 Fri, Sat & Sun Apr-Oct or by appt.

KEY
⊠ Mail order to UK or EU ♠ Delivers to shows
✈ Exports beyond EU € Euro accepted
♿ Accessible by wheelchair ◆ See Display advertisement

Min Mail Order UK: Nmc
Min Mail Order EU: Nmc
Cat. Cost: 2 × 1st class.
Credit Cards: None
Specialities: Ferns. Display garden.
Notes: Only plants listed in the mail order part of the catalogue will be sent mail order. Also sells wholesale.
Map Ref: E, A1 **OS Grid Ref:** TF212942

EFEx FLORA EXOTICA ⊠ ✈ €
Pasadena, South-Green, Fingringhoe, Colchester, Essex, CO5 7DR
Ⓣ (01206) 729414
Contact: J Beddoes
Opening Times: Not open. Mail order only.
Min Mail Order UK: Nmc
Min Mail Order EU: Nmc
Cat. Cost: 4 × 1st class.
Credit Cards: None
Specialities: Exotica flora incl. orchids.

EFtx FERNATIX ⊠ ⌂ ♿
Stoke Ash, Suffolk, IP23 7EN
Ⓣ (01379) 678197
Ⓕ (01379) 678197
Ⓔ mail@fernatix.co.uk
Ⓦ www.fernatix.co.uk
Contact: Steven Fletcher & Kerry Robinson
Opening Times: By appt. only.
Min Mail Order UK: £15.00
Cat. Cost: 6 × 1st or 9 × 2nd class for cat., or sae for plant list.
Credit Cards: None
Specialities: Ferns, hardy & greenhouse species & cultivars. Some available in small quantities only.

EGFP GRANGE FARM PLANTS ⊠ ♿
Grange Farm, 38 Fishergate Road, Sutton St James, Spalding, Lincolnshire, PE12 0EZ
Ⓣ (01945) 440240
Ⓜ 07742 138760
Ⓕ (01945) 440355
Ⓔ ellis.family@tinyonline.co.uk
Contact: M C Ellis
Opening Times: Mail order only. Open by appt. only.
Min Mail Order UK: Nmc
Min Mail Order EU: Nmc
Cat. Cost: 1 × 1st class.
Credit Cards: None
Specialities: Rare trees & shrubs, esp. *Juglans*, *Fraxinus*. Some species available in small quantities only.
Map Ref: E, B2 **OS Grid Ref:** TF382186

EGHG GOLTHO HOUSE GARDENS & NURSERY ♿
Lincoln Road, Goltho, Market Rasen, Lincolnshire, LN8 5NF
Ⓣ (01673) 857768
Ⓔ s.hollingworth@homecall.co.uk
Ⓦ www.golthogardens.com
Contact: Debbie Hollingworth
Opening Times: 1000-1600 Sun & Wed only.
Credit Cards: None
Specialities: Hardy herbaceous perennials.
Map Ref: E, A1 **OS Grid Ref:** TF116783

EGln GLENHIRST CACTUS NURSERY ⊠ €
Station Road, Swineshead, Nr Boston, Lincolnshire, PE20 3NX
Ⓣ (01205) 820314
Ⓕ (01205) 820614
Ⓔ info@cacti4u.co.uk
Ⓦ www.cacti4u.co.uk
Contact: N C & S A Bell
Opening Times: Visitors welcome, but by telephone appt. only.
Min Mail Order UK: £5.00
Min Mail Order EU: €15.00
Cat. Cost: 2 × 1st class.
Credit Cards: Maestro Visa MasterCard Switch
Specialities: Extensive range of cacti & succulent plants, incl. orchid cacti.
Notes: Will accept payment in euros online only.
Map Ref: E, B1 **OS Grid Ref:** TF245408

EGol GOLDBROOK PLANTS ⊠ ✈
Hoxne, Eye, Suffolk, IP21 5AN
Ⓣ (01379) 668770
Ⓕ (01379) 668770
Contact: Sandra Bond
Opening Times: 1000-1700 or dusk if earlier, Thu-Sun Apr-Sep, Sat & Sun Oct-Mar or by appt. Closed during Jan & Hampton Court Flower Show.
Min Mail Order UK: £15.00 + p&p
Min Mail Order EU: £100.00 + p&p
Cat. Cost: 4 × 1st class.
Credit Cards: None
Specialities: Very large range of *Hosta* (1100+), *Hemerocallis*.
Notes: Also sells wholesale.
Map Ref: E, C3

EGoo ELISABETH GOODWIN NURSERIES ⊠ ⌂ ♿
Elm Tree Farm, 1 Beeches Road, West Row, Bury St Edmunds, Suffolk, IP28 8NP
Ⓣ (01638) 713050
Ⓕ 0870 7053256

Ⓔ mail@e-g-n.co.uk
Ⓦ www.e-g-n.co.uk
Contact: Elisabeth Goodwin
Opening Times: By appt.
Min Mail Order UK: Nmc
Cat. Cost: Online only.
Credit Cards: None
Specialities: Drought tolerant plants for both sun & shade esp. *Helianthemum*, *Sedum*, *Teucrium*, *Vinca*, grasses, *Aquilegia*, *Achillea*, *Agastache* & *Onosma*. Some plants grown in ltd. quantities.
Notes: Also sells wholesale.
Map Ref: E, C2

EGxp **Gardening Express** ⊠ ◆
Mashbury Road, Chignal St James, Chelmsford, Essex, CM1 4UA
Ⓣ 08000 336161
Ⓔ orders@gardeningexpress.co.uk
Ⓦ www.GardeningExpress.co.uk
Contact: Chris Bonnett
Opening Times: Not open. Mail order only.
Min Mail Order UK: Nmc
Cat. Cost: Online only.
Credit Cards: All major credit/debit cards
Specialities: 4-acre site growing wide range of perenials and shrubs.
Notes: Also sells wholesale.

EHoe **Hoecroft Plants** ⊠ € ♿
Severals Grange, Holt Road, Wood Norton, Dereham, Norfolk, NR20 5BL
Ⓣ (01362) 684206
Ⓔ hoecroft@hotmail.co.uk
Ⓦ www.hoecroft.co.uk
Contact: Jane Lister
Opening Times: 1000-1600 Thu-Sun 22nd Mar-31st Oct or by appt.
Min Mail Order UK: Nmc
Min Mail Order EU: Nmc
Cat. Cost: 5 × 2nd class/£1coin.
Credit Cards: None
Specialities: 270 varieties of variegated and 350 varieties of coloured-leaved plants in all species. 250 grasses. Free entry to display gardens.
Notes: Nursery 2 miles north of Guist on B1110.

EHon **Honeysome Aquatic Nursery** ⊠
The Row, Sutton, Nr Ely, Cambridgeshire, CB6 2PB
Ⓣ (01353) 778889
Ⓕ (01353) 777291
Ⓔ honeysomeaquaticnursery@hotmail.co.uk
Contact: Mrs L S Bond
Opening Times: At all times by appt. only.
Min Mail Order UK: Nmc
Cat. Cost: 2 × 1st class.
Credit Cards: None
Specialities: Hardy aquatic, bog & marginal.
Notes: Also sells wholesale.

EHrv **Harveys Garden Plants** ⊠ ✈ ♠ € ♿
Great Green, Thurston, Bury St Edmunds, Suffolk, IP31 3SJ
Ⓣ (01359) 233363
Ⓕ (01359) 233363 & answerphone
Ⓔ admin@harveysgardenplants.co.uk
Ⓦ www.harveysgardenplants.co.uk
Contact: Roger Harvey
Opening Times: 0930-1630 Tue-Sat.
Min Mail Order UK: 6 plants + p&p
Min Mail Order EU: Please enquire.
Cat. Cost: 8 × 2nd class.
Credit Cards: All major credit/debit cards
Specialities: *Helleborus*, *Anemone*, *Epimedium*, *Euphorbia*, *Eryngium*, *Galanthus*, *Astrantia*, *Pulmonaria* & other herbaceous perennials. Woodland plants.
Map Ref: E, C2 **OS Grid Ref:** 660939

EHul **Hull Farm** ⊠ ♿
Spring Valley Lane, Ardleigh, Colchester, Essex, CO7 7SA
Ⓣ (01206) 230045
Ⓕ (01206) 230820
Contact: J Fryer & Sons
Opening Times: 1000-1600 Mon-Sat, excl. Xmas.
Min Mail Order UK: £50.00 + p&p
Cat. Cost: 5 × 2nd class.
Credit Cards: MasterCard Visa
Specialities: Conifers, grasses.
Notes: Also sells wholesale.
Map Ref: E, C3 **OS Grid Ref:** GR043274

EIri **Irisesonline** ⊠
Slade Cottage, Petts Lane, Little Walden, Essex, CB10 1XH
Ⓣ (01799) 526294
Ⓕ (01799) 526294
Ⓔ sales@irisesonline.co.uk
Ⓦ www.irisonline.co.uk
Contact: Clare Kneen
Opening Times: By appt. only.
Min Mail Order UK: Nmc.
Cat. Cost: 3 × 1st class or online.
Credit Cards: None

KEY
⊠ Mail order to UK or EU ♠ Delivers to shows
✈ Exports beyond EU € Euro accepted
♿ Accessible by wheelchair ◆ See Display advertisement

Specialities: *Iris.* Small family-run nursery. Some varieties available in small quantities only.
Map Ref: E, C2 **OS Grid Ref:** TL546416

E

EJRN **John Ray Nursery** € ♿
36 Station Road, Braintree, Essex, CM7 3QJ
Ⓜ 07826 162406
Ⓕ (01376) 322858
Ⓔ johnraynursery@talktalk.net
Contact: Brian James
Opening Times: 0900-1730 Sat, 1030-1630 Sun & B/Hol.
Cat. Cost: None issued.
Credit Cards: None
Specialities: *Pittosporum.*
Notes: Also sells wholesale.

EJWh **Jill White** ⊠ ♿
78 Hurst Green, Brightlingsea, Essex, CO7 0NJ
Ⓣ (01206) 303547
Contact: Jill White
Opening Times: By appt. only.
Min Mail Order UK: Nmc
Min Mail Order EU: Nmc
Cat. Cost: Sae.
Credit Cards: None
Specialities: *Cyclamen* species esp. *Cyclamen parviflorum. Cyclamen elegans.* Also seed.
Notes: Also sells wholesale.
Map Ref: E, D3 **OS Grid Ref:** TM088171

EKen **Kenwick Farmhouse Nurseries** ⊠ ♿ ◆
Kenwick Road, Louth, Lincolnshire, LN11 8NW
Ⓣ (01507) 606469
Ⓕ (01507) 606469
Ⓔ info@kenwicknursery.co.uk
Ⓦ www.kenwicknursery.co.uk
Contact: Janet Elmhirst
Opening Times: 0930-1700 (dusk in winter)Tue-Sat, closed Mon except B/hol. 1000-1600 Sun. Closed Jan.
Min Mail Order UK: £12.00
Credit Cards: None
Specialities: Hardy plants, grown in small quantities.
Notes: Mail order only if stock is available.
Map Ref: E, A2 **OS Grid Ref:** TF342853

EKMF **Kathleen Muncaster Fuchsias** ♿
18 Field Lane, Morton, Gainsborough, Lincolnshire, DN21 3BY
Ⓣ (01427) 612329
Ⓔ jim@kathleenmuncasterfuchsias.co.uk
Ⓦ www.kathleenmuncasterfuchsias.co.uk
Contact: Kathleen Muncaster
Opening Times: 1000-dusk Thu-Tue. After mid-Jun please phone to check.
Cat. Cost: 2 × 1st class.
Credit Cards: None
Specialities: *Fuchsia.* Nat. Collection of Hardy *Fuchsia* (full status).
Map Ref: E, A1

ELan **Langthorns Plantery** ⊠ ♿
High Cross Lane West, Little Canfield, Dunmow, Essex, CM6 1TD
Ⓣ (01371) 872611
Ⓕ 0871 661 4093
Ⓔ info@langthorns.com
Ⓦ www.langthorns.com
Contact: E Cannon
Opening Times: 1000-1700 or dusk (if earlier) 7 days excl. Xmas fortnight.
Min Mail Order UK: £15.00
Cat. Cost: £1.50
Credit Cards: Visa Access Switch MasterCard Delta
Specialities: Wide general range with many unusual plants.
Notes: Mail order anything under 5ft tall.
Map Ref: E, D2 **OS Grid Ref:** TL592204

ELar **Larkspur Nursery** ⊠
Fourways, Dog Drove South, Holbeach Drove, Spalding, Lincolnshire, PE12 0SD
Ⓣ (01406) 330830
Ⓔ info@larkspur-nursery.co.uk
Ⓦ www.larkspur-nursery.co.uk
Contact: Ashley Ramsbottom
Opening Times: Mail order only. Open by prior arrangement only.
Min Mail Order UK: Nmc
Min Mail Order EU: Nmc
Cat. Cost: 2 × 1st class.
Credit Cards: None
Specialities: Delphiniums. Some varieties in small quantities. Order early to avoid disappointment.
Notes: Plants despatched from June in 7 or 8cm pots. See website for details.

ELau **Laurel Farm Herbs** ⊠ ♿
Main Road, Kelsale, Saxmundham, Suffolk, IP13 2RG
Ⓣ (01728) 668223
Ⓔ laurelfarmherbs@aol.com
Ⓦ www.laurelfarmherbs.co.uk
Contact: Chris Seagon
Opening Times: Please phone or check website for opening hours as times can vary.

Min Mail Order UK: 6 plants + p&p
Min Mail Order EU: 12 plants
Cat. Cost: Online only.
Credit Cards: Visa MasterCard Switch Delta
Specialities: Herbs esp. rosemary, thyme, mint & sage.
Notes: Mail orders accepted by email, phone or post.
Map Ref: E, C3

ELon **LONG HOUSE PLANTS** ♿
The Long House, Church Road, Noak Hill, Romford, Essex, RM4 1LD
Ⓣ (01708) 371719
Ⓕ (01708) 346649
Ⓔ tim@longhouse-plants.co.uk
Contact: Tim Carter
Opening Times: 1000-1700 Fri, Sat & B/hols, 1000-1600 Sun, Mar-Oct or by appt.
Cat. Cost: None issued.
Credit Cards: All major credit/debit cards
Specialities: Interesting range of choice shrubs, grasses & herbaceous perennials. Many unusual varieties.
Map Ref: E, D2 **OS Grid Ref:** TQ554194

EMac **FIRECREST (TREES & SHRUBS NURSERY)** ⊠ € ♿
Hall Road, Little Bealings, Woodbridge, Suffolk, IP13 6LU
Ⓣ (01473) 625937
Ⓕ (01473) 625937
Ⓔ mac@firecrest.org.uk
Ⓦ www.firecrest.org.uk
Contact: Mac McGregor
Opening Times: 0830-1630 Mon-Fri, 1230 Sat.
Min Mail Order UK: Nmc
Cat. Cost: 2 × 1st class (bare root only).
Credit Cards: None
Specialities: Trees & shrubs.
Notes: Also sells wholesale.

EMal **MARSHALL'S MALMAISONS** ⊠ ✈ €
Hullwood Barn, Shelley, Ipswich, Suffolk, IP7 5RE
Ⓣ (01473) 822400
Ⓔ jim@malmaisons.plus.com
Contact: J M Marshall/Sarah Cook
Opening Times: By appt. only.
Min Mail Order UK: £24.00 incl. p&p
Min Mail Order EU: £35.00 incl. p&p
Cat. Cost: 1st class sae.
Credit Cards: None
Specialities: Nat. Collections of Malmaison Carnations & Cedric Morris Irises. *Iris* stock only available in small quantities.
Notes: Also sells wholesale.
Map Ref: E, C3 **OS Grid Ref:** TM006394

EMar **LESLEY MARSHALL** ⊠ ♿
Islington Lodge Cottage, Tilney All Saints, King's Lynn, Norfolk, PE34 4SF
Ⓣ (01553) 765103
Ⓔ daylilies@tiscali.co.uk
Ⓦ www.dazzlingdaylilies.co.uk
Contact: Lesley Marshall
Opening Times: 0930-1800 Mon, Wed, Fri-Sun May-Sep.
Min Mail Order UK: Nmc
Cat. Cost: 3 × 1st class.
Credit Cards: None
Specialities: *Hemerocallis* only, new & old varieties.
Notes: Nursery on A47 east of Tilney All Saints.
Map Ref: E, B1

EMFW **MICKFIELD WATERGARDEN CENTRE LTD** ⊠ ♿
Debenham Road, Mickfield, Stowmarket, Suffolk, IP14 5LP
Ⓣ (01449) 711336
Ⓕ (01449) 711018
Ⓔ info@mickfield.co.uk
Ⓦ www.mickfield.co.uk
Contact: Phil Desmond
Opening Times: 0900-1700 7 days.
Min Mail Order UK: Nmc
Cat. Cost: Free.
Credit Cards: All major credit/debit cards
Specialities: Hardy aquatics, *Nymphaea* & moisture lovers.
Notes: Also sells wholesale.
Map Ref: E, C3 **OS Grid Ref:** TM141616

EMic **MICKFIELD HOSTAS** ⊠ ⛺ € ♿
The Poplars, Mickfield, Stowmarket, Suffolk, IP14 5LH
Ⓣ (01449) 711576
Ⓕ (01449) 711576
Ⓔ mickfieldhostas@btconnect.com
Ⓦ www.mickfieldhostas.co.uk
Contact: Mr & Mrs R L C Milton
Opening Times: For specified dates see catalogue or website.
Min Mail Order UK: Nmc
Min Mail Order EU: Nmc
Cat. Cost: 4 × 1st class.
Credit Cards: Visa MasterCard
Specialities: *Hosta*, over 1000 varieties (some subject to availability) mostly from USA. New

KEY
⊠ Mail order to UK or EU ⛺ Delivers to shows
✈ Exports beyond EU € Euro accepted
♿ Accessible by wheelchair ◆ See Display advertisement

varieties become available during the season. Waiting list option for rarities.
Map Ref: E, C3

E

EMil **MILL RACE GARDEN CENTRE** ⊠ ♿
New Road, Aldham, Colchester, Essex, CO6 3QT
Ⓣ (01206) 242521
Ⓕ (01206) 242073
Ⓔ admin@millracegardencentre.co.uk
Ⓦ www.millracegardencentre.co.uk
Contact: Annette Bayliss
Opening Times: 0900-1730 7 days.
Min Mail Order UK: £15.00
Credit Cards: All major credit/debit cards
Specialities: Around 4000 varieties of plants always in stock.
Notes: Trees not sent by mail order.
Map Ref: E, C2 **OS Grid Ref:** TL918268

EMui **KEN MUIR LTD** ⊠
Honeypot Farm, Rectory Road, Weeley Heath, Essex, CO16 9BJ
Ⓣ 0870 7479111
Ⓕ (01255) 831534
Ⓔ info@kenmuir.co.uk
Ⓦ www.kenmuir.co.uk
Contact: Ming Yang, Claire Higgins
Opening Times: 1000-1600.
Min Mail Order UK: Nmc
Cat. Cost: Free.
Credit Cards: Visa Access Switch
Specialities: Fruit.
Notes: Also sells wholesale.
Map Ref: E, D3

ENBC **NORFOLK BAMBOO COMPANY** ⊠
Vine Cottage, The Drift, Ingoldisthorpe, King's Lynn, Norfolk, PE31 6NW
Ⓣ (01485) 543935
Ⓕ (01485) 543314
Ⓔ Lewdyer@hotmail.com
Ⓦ www.norfolkbamboo.co.uk
Contact: Lewis Dyer
Opening Times: 1000-1700 Fri, Apr-Sep, or by appt.
Min Mail Order UK: £10.00 + p&p
Cat. Cost: 1 × 1st class sae for price list.
Credit Cards: None
Specialities: Bamboos.
Map Ref: E, B2 **OS Grid Ref:** TF683333

ENor **NORFOLK LAVENDER** ⊠ ♿
Caley Mill, Heacham, King's Lynn, Norfolk, PE31 7JE
Ⓣ (01485) 570384
Ⓕ (01485) 571176
Ⓔ admin@norfolk-lavender.co.uk
Ⓦ www.norfolk-lavender.co.uk
Contact: Henry Head
Opening Times: 0930-1700 7 days, Apr-Oct. 0930-1600 7 days, Nov-Mar.
Min Mail Order UK: Nmc
Cat. Cost: Free.
Credit Cards: All major credit/debit cards
Specialities: Nat. Collection of *Lavandula*.
Map Ref: E, B2 **OS Grid Ref:** TF685368

EOHP **OLD HALL PLANTS** ⊠
1 The Old Hall, Barsham, Beccles, Suffolk, NR34 8HB
Ⓣ (01502) 717475
Ⓔ info@oldhallplants.co.uk
Ⓦ www.oldhallplants.co.uk
Contact: Janet Elliott
Opening Times: By appt. only. Please phone first.
Min Mail Order UK: Nmc
Min Mail Order EU: Nmc
Cat. Cost: 4 × 1st class.
Credit Cards: Paypal
Specialities: A variety of rare herbs, house plants, *Plectranthus* & *Streptocarpus*. Some plants available in small quantities.
Notes: Partial wheelchair access.
Map Ref: E, C3 **OS Grid Ref:** TM395904

EOrn **ORNAMENTAL CONIFERS** ◆
22 Chapel Road, Terrington St Clement, King's Lynn, Norfolk, PE34 4ND
Ⓣ (01553) 828874
Ⓕ (01553) 828874
Ⓦ www.japanesegardenplants.co.uk
Contact: Peter Rotchell
Opening Times: 0930-1700 Thu-Mon, closed Tue & Wed. Closed 20th Dec-2nd Feb.
Credit Cards: None
Specialities: Conifers.
Map Ref: E, B1

EPau **PAUGERS PLANTS** ♿
Bury Road, Depden, Bury St Edmunds, Suffolk, IP29 4BU
Ⓣ (01284) 850527
Contact: Geraldine Arnold
Opening Times: 0900-1730 Wed-Sat, 1000-1700 Sun & B/hols, 1st Mar-30th Nov.
Cat. Cost: None issued
Credit Cards: None
Specialities: Hardy shrubs & perennials in large or small quantities.
Notes: Also sells wholesale.
Map Ref: E, C2 **OS Grid Ref:** TL783568

EPfP **THE PLACE FOR PLANTS** ♔ € ♿
East Bergholt Place, East Bergholt, Suffolk, CO7 6UP
Ⓣ (01206) 299224
Ⓕ (01206) 299229
Ⓔ sales@placeforplants.co.uk
Contact: Rupert & Sara Eley
Opening Times: 1000-1700 (or dusk if earlier) 7 days. Closed Easter Sun. Garden open Mar-Oct.
Cat. Cost: 2 × 1st class.
Credit Cards: All major credit/debit cards
Specialities: Wide range of specialist & popular plants. Nat. Collection of Deciduous *Euonymus*. 15 acre mature garden with free access to RHS members during season.
Map Ref: E, C3

EPGN **PARK GREEN NURSERIES** ⊠ ✈ ♔
Wetheringsett, Stowmarket, Suffolk, IP14 5QH
Ⓣ (01728) 860139
Ⓕ (01728) 861277
Ⓔ nurseries@parkgreen.co.uk
Ⓦ www.parkgreen.co.uk
Contact: Richard & Mary Ford
Opening Times: 1000-1600 Mon-Sat, 1 Mar-30 Sep.
Min Mail Order UK: £3.00
Min Mail Order EU: £5.00
Cat. Cost: 4 × 1st class.
Credit Cards: Visa MasterCard Delta Switch
Specialities: *Hosta*, ornamental grasses & herbaceous.
Notes: Mail order *Hosta* only.
Map Ref: E, C3 **OS Grid Ref:** TM136644

EPla **P W PLANTS** ⊠ ♔ ♿
Sunnyside, Heath Road, Kenninghall, Norfolk, NR16 2DS
Ⓣ (01953) 888212
Ⓔ pw@hardybamboo.com
Ⓦ www.hardybamboo.com
Contact: Paul Whittaker
Opening Times: Every Fri & last Sat in every month, plus all Sats Apr-Sep.
Min Mail Order UK: Nmc
Cat. Cost: 5 × 1st class or online.
Credit Cards: All major credit/debit cards
Specialities: Bamboos, grasses, choice shrubs & perennials.
Notes: Does not deliver to Chelsea Show.
Map Ref: E, C3 **OS Grid Ref:** TM036846

EPln **THE PLANT LOVERS** ⊠ ♔
Candlesby House, Candlesby, Spilsby, Lincolnshire, PE23 5RU
Ⓣ (01754) 890256
Ⓕ (01754) 890594
Contact: Tim Wilson
Opening Times: Daily but please phone first.
Min Mail Order UK: Nmc
Cat. Cost: None issued.
Credit Cards: None
Specialities: A wide range of cacti and other succulents also *Sempervivum* (houseleeks).
Notes: Also sells wholesale.
Map Ref: E, B1

EPot **POTTERTONS NURSERY** ⊠ ✈ ♔ € ♿
Moortown Road, Nettleton, Caistor, Lincolnshire, LN7 6HX
Ⓣ (01472) 851714
Ⓕ (01472) 852580
Ⓔ sales@pottertons.co.uk
Ⓦ www.pottertons.co.uk
Contact: Robert Potterton
Opening Times: 0900-1600 7 days.
Min Mail Order UK: Nmc
Min Mail Order EU: Nmc
Cat. Cost: £2.00 in stamps
Credit Cards: Maestro MasterCard Visa
Specialities: Alpines, dwarf bulbs & woodland plants. Hardy orchids & *Pleione*.
Notes: External talks to garden clubs & societies & nursery tours by arrangement.
Map Ref: E, A1 **OS Grid Ref:** TA091001

EPPr **THE PLANTSMAN'S PREFERENCE** ⊠ ♔ ♿
(Office) Lynwood, Hopton Road, Garboldisham, Diss, Norfolk, IP22 2QN
Ⓣ (01953) 681439 (office)
Ⓜ (07799) 855559 (nursery)
Ⓔ tim@plantpref.co.uk
Ⓦ www.plantpref.co.uk
Contact: Jenny & Tim Fuller
Opening Times: 0930-1700 Fri, Sat & Sun Mar-Oct. Other times by appt.
Min Mail Order UK: £15.00
Min Mail Order EU: £30.00
Cat. Cost: 5 × 1st class/IRCs or online.
Credit Cards: All major credit/debit cards
Specialities: Hardy geraniums (450), grasses & sedges (600+). Unusual & interesting perennials incl. shade/woodland. Nat. Collection of *Molinia*.
Notes: Nursery is at Hall Farm, Church Road, South Lopham, Diss.
Map Ref: E, C3 **OS Grid Ref:** TM041819

KEY
⊠ Mail order to UK or EU ♔ Delivers to shows
✈ Exports beyond EU € Euro accepted
♿ Accessible by wheelchair ◆ See Display advertisement

E

EPts **POTASH NURSERY** ⊠ ♿
Cow Green, Bacton, Stowmarket, Suffolk, IP14 4HJ
Ⓣ (01449) 781671
Ⓔ enquiries@potashnursery.co.uk
Ⓦ www.potashnursery.co.uk
Contact: M W Clare
Opening Times: Pre-ordered plants can be collected by appt. only.
Min Mail Order UK: £12.00
Cat. Cost: 4 × 1st class.
Credit Cards: Visa Delta MasterCard
Specialities: *Fuchsia*.
Map Ref: E, C3 **OS Grid Ref:** TM0565NE

EPyc **PENNYCROSS PLANTS** ⊠
Earith Road, Colne, Huntingdon, Cambridgeshire, PE28 3NL
Ⓣ (01487) 841520
Ⓔ plants4u@tiscali.co.uk
Contact: Janet M Buist
Opening Times: 1000-1600 Mon-Fri, 1st Mar-31st Oct by appt.
Min Mail Order UK: Nmc
Cat. Cost: 1 × 2nd class for *Salvia* list only.
Credit Cards: None
Specialities: Hardy perennials. Salvias. Some plants available in ltd. quantities only.
Notes: Mail order for young *Salvia* plants only.
Map Ref: E, C2 **OS Grid Ref:** TL378759

EQua **QUAYMOUNT NURSERY** ⊠ ♿
The Row, Wereham, Kings Lynn, Norfolk, PE33 9AY
Ⓣ (01366) 500691
Ⓕ (01366) 500611
Ⓔ info@quaymountplants.co.uk
Ⓦ www.quaymountplants.co.uk
Contact: Paul Markwell
Opening Times: 0900-1700 (or dusk if earlier) Mon-Fri, 1000-1600 Sat & Sun. Closed Sun Dec & Jan.
Min Mail Order UK: Nmc
Cat. Cost: 2 ×1st class.
Credit Cards: All major credit/debit cards
Specialities: Wide range of specialist & popular plants. *Hydrangea*.
Notes: Specimen plants collection only. Also sells wholesale.
Map Ref: E, B2 **OS Grid Ref:** TF679006

ERas **RASELL'S NURSERIES** ♿
Little Bytham, Grantham, Lincolnshire, NG33 4QY
Ⓣ (01780) 410345
Ⓕ (01780) 410475
Ⓔ rasells.nurseries@virgin.net
Contact: Tim Rasell
Opening Times: 0900-1700 Mon-Sat, 1000-1600 Sun. Please check for winter opening times.
Cat. Cost: None issued.
Credit Cards: All major credit/debit cards
Notes: Also sells wholesale.
Map Ref: E, B1 **OS Grid Ref:** TF016178

ERCP **ROSE COTTAGE PLANTS** ⊠
Bay Tree Farm, Epping Green, Essex, CM16 6PU
Ⓣ (01992) 573775
Ⓕ (01992) 561198
Ⓔ anne@rosecottageplants.co.uk
Ⓦ www.rosecottageplants.co.uk
Contact: Anne & Jack Barnard
Opening Times: By appt. & for special events (see website for details).
Min Mail Order UK: Nmc
Min Mail Order EU: £20.00
Cat. Cost: Online or A5 sae for bulb list.
Credit Cards: All major credit/debit cards
Specialities: Bulbs.
Notes: Mail order, bulbs only. Separate mail order catalogue available online.
Map Ref: E, B1 **OS Grid Ref:** TL435053

ERea **READS NURSERY** ⊠ ♿
Hales Hall, Loddon, Norfolk, NR14 6QW
Ⓣ (01508) 548395
Ⓕ (01508) 548040
Ⓔ plants@readsnursery.co.uk
Ⓦ www.readsnursery.co.uk
Contact: Stephen Read
Opening Times: 1000-1700, or dusk if earlier, Wed-Sat.
Min Mail Order UK: Nmc
Min Mail Order EU: £25.00
Cat. Cost: Free.
Credit Cards: All major credit/debit cards
Specialities: Fruit trees, conservatory plants. Nat. Collections. of *Citrus*, figs, *Vitis*.
Notes: Mostly accessible by wheelchair (some gravel paths).
Map Ref: E, C3 **OS Grid Ref:** TM369960

ERhR **RHODES & ROCKLIFFE** ⊠ €
2 Nursery Road, Nazeing, Essex, EN9 2JE
Ⓣ (01992) 451598 (office hours)
Ⓕ (01992) 440673
Ⓔ RRBegonias@aol.com
Contact: David Rhodes or John Rockliffe
Opening Times: By appt.
Min Mail Order UK: £3.00 + p&p

Min Mail Order EU: £5.00 + p&p
Cat. Cost: 2 × 1st class.
Credit Cards: None
Specialities: *Begonia* species & hybrids. Nat. Collection of *Begonia*. Plants propagated to order.
Notes: Mail order Apr-Sep only.
Map Ref: E, D2

ERod THE RODINGS PLANTERY ⊠ ✈ ⌂ €
Anchor Lane, Abbess Roding, Essex, CM5 0JW
Ⓣ (01279) 876421
Ⓔ janeandandy@therodingsplantery.co.uk
Ⓦ www.therodingsplantery.co.uk
Contact: Jane & Andy Mogridge
Opening Times: By appt. only. Occasional open days, please phone for details.
Min Mail Order UK: Nmc
Min Mail Order EU: £500.00 + p&p
Cat. Cost: 3 × 1st class.
Credit Cards: None
Specialities: Bamboos. Rare & unusual trees.
Map Ref: E, D2

ERom THE ROMANTIC GARDEN ⊠ ✈ € ♿ ◆
Swannington, Norwich, Norfolk, NR9 5NW
Ⓣ (01603) 261488
Ⓕ (01603) 864231
Ⓔ enquiries@romantic-garden-nursery.co.uk
Ⓦ www.romantic-garden-nursery.co.uk
Contact: John Powles/John Carrick
Opening Times: 1000-1700 Wed, Fri & Sat all year, plus B/hol Mons.
Min Mail Order UK: £5.00 + p&p
Min Mail Order EU: £30.00 + p&p
Cat. Cost: 4 × 1st class.
Credit Cards: All major credit/debit cards
Specialities: Conservatory. *Buxus* topiary, ornamental standards, large specimens. Hedging. Topiary
Notes: Also sells wholesale.
Map Ref: E, B3

ERos ROSEHOLME NURSERY ⊠ ✈ ♿
Roseholme Farm, Howsham, Market Rasen, Lincolnshire, LN7 6JZ
Ⓣ (01652) 678661
Ⓕ (01472) 852450
Ⓔ Pbcenterpr@aol.com
Contact: P B Clayton
Opening Times: Mail order only. By appt. for collection of orders.
Min Mail Order UK: Nmc
Min Mail Order EU: Nmc
Cat. Cost: 2 × 2nd class.
Credit Cards: None
Specialities: Underground lines – bulbs, corms, rhizomes & tubers (esp. *Crocus*, *Iris*).
Notes: Also sells wholesale.
Map Ref: E, A1 **OS Grid Ref:** TA042048

ESCh SHEILA CHAPMAN CLEMATIS ⊠ ⌂ ♿
Within Shalesmere Nursery, Epping Lane, Stapleford Tawney, Romford, Essex, RM4 1ST
Ⓣ (01708) 688090
Ⓕ (01708) 688090
Ⓔ sheilachapman@hotmail.co.uk
Ⓦ www.sheilachapman.com
Contact: Sheila Chapman
Opening Times: 1000-1600 (dusk in winter).
Min Mail Order UK: Nmc
Cat. Cost: 5 × 2nd class.
Credit Cards: All major credit/debit cards
Specialities: Over 700 varieties of *Clematis*.
Map Ref: E, D2 **OS Grid Ref:** TQ488982

ESgI SEAGATE IRISES ⊠ ✈ € ♿
A17 Long Sutton By-Pass, Long Sutton, Lincolnshire, PE12 9RX
Ⓣ (01406) 365138
Ⓕ (01406) 365447
Ⓔ Sales@irises.co.uk
Ⓦ www.irises.co.uk
Contact: Julian Browse or Wendy Browse
Opening Times: 1000-1700 daily Apr-Sep. Please phone for appt. Oct-Mar.
Min Mail Order UK: Nmc
Min Mail Order EU: Nmc. Carriage at cost.
Cat. Cost: £3.50 or €8.00.
Credit Cards: Maestro Visa MasterCard
Specialities: Different types of *Iris*, bearded, beardless & species hybrids with about 1000 varieties in all, both historic & modern. Nat. Collection of Historic Tall Bearded Irises (pre-1964). Some only available in small quantities. Many container-grown, available to callers.
Map Ref: E, B1 **OS Grid Ref:** TF437218

EShb SHRUBLAND PARK NURSERIES ⊠ ⌂ €
Coddenham, Ipswich, Suffolk, IP6 9QJ
Ⓣ (01473) 833187
Ⓜ 07890 527744
Ⓕ (01473) 832838
Ⓔ gill@shrublandparknurseries.co.uk
Ⓦ www.shrublandparknurseries.co.uk
Contact: Gill & Catherine Stitt
Opening Times: 1000-1700 Wed-Sun, Easter-30th Sep. Oct-Feb, please ring first. Times may vary in 2008.
Min Mail Order UK: £15.00

KEY
⊠ Mail order to UK or EU ⌂ Delivers to shows
✈ Exports beyond EU € Euro accepted
♿ Accessible by wheelchair ◆ See Display advertisement

E

Min Mail Order EU: £30.00
Cat. Cost: 5 × 1st class or free by email.
Credit Cards: All major credit/debit cards Nochex Paypal
Specialities: Hardy perennials, grasses, ferns. Tender plants, climbers, ferns, conservatory plants, houseplants & succulents. Display beds in glasshouse & walled garden.
Notes: For directions phone or see website. Nearest postcode for SatNav IP6 0PG. Partial wheelchair access.
Map Ref: E, C3 **OS Grid Ref:** TM128524

EStC **ST CLARE NURSERY** ⊠
Chapel Drove, Holbeach Drove, Lincolnshire, PE12 0PT
Ⓣ (01406) 330233
Ⓕ (01406) 330233
Ⓔ stclarenursery@aol.com
Ⓦ www.stclarenursery.co.uk
Contact: Carlos Zeferino
Opening Times: Not open. Mail order only.
Min Mail Order UK: Nmc
Cat. Cost: £1.00
Credit Cards: All major credit/debit cards
Specialities: Small family-run nursery providing good quality plants.

ESty **STYLE ROSES** ⊠ €
10 Meridian Walk, Holbeach, Spalding, Lincolnshire, PE12 7NR
Ⓣ (01406) 424089
Ⓜ 07932 044093 or 07780 860415
Ⓕ (01406) 424089
Ⓔ styleroses@aol.com
Ⓦ www.styleroses.co.uk
Contact: Chris Styles, Margaret Styles
Opening Times: Vary, please phone.
Min Mail Order UK: Nmc
Min Mail Order EU: Nmc
Cat. Cost: Free.
Credit Cards: All major credit/debit cards
Specialities: Standard & bush roses.
Notes: Export subject to countries' plant health requirements, carriage & export certificates where required charged at cost. Also sells wholesale.
Map Ref: E, B1

ESul **BRIAN & PEARL SULMAN** ⊠
54 Kingsway, Mildenhall, Bury St Edmunds, Suffolk, IP28 7HR
Ⓣ (01638) 712297
Ⓕ (01638) 712297
Ⓔ enquiries@sulmanspelargoniums.co.uk
Ⓦ www.sulmanspelargoniums.co.uk
Contact: Pearl Sulman
Opening Times: Mail order only. Not open except for Open Days 3rd/4th May & 31st May/1st Jun 2008. Phone for information about 2009 dates.
Min Mail Order UK: £23.00
Cat. Cost: 4 × 1st class.
Credit Cards: Visa MasterCard
Specialities: *Pelargonium*. Some varieties only available in small quantities.
Map Ref: E, C2 **OS Grid Ref:** TL715747

ESwi **SWINES MEADOW GARDEN CENTRE** € ◆
47 Towngate East, Market Deeping, Peterborough, PE6 8LQ
Ⓜ 01778 343340
Ⓔ info@swinesmeadowgardencentre.co.uk
Ⓦ www.swinesmeadowgardencentre.co.uk
Contact: Colin Ward
Specialities: Hardy exotics, tree ferns, bamboos & phormiums. Wollemi pine stockist. Many specialities available in small quantities only.
Map Ref: E, B1 **OS Grid Ref:** TF150113

ETho **THORNCROFT CLEMATIS NURSERY** ⊠
The Lings, Reymerston, Norwich, Norfolk, NR9 4QG
Ⓣ (01953) 850407
Ⓕ (01953) 851788
Ⓔ sales@thorncroft.co.uk
Ⓦ www.thorncroft.co.uk
Contact: Ruth P Gooch
Opening Times: 1000-1600 Tue-Sat all year, closed Sun & Mon. Open B/hol Mon.
Min Mail Order UK: Nmc
Min Mail Order EU: Nmc
Cat. Cost: 6 × 2nd class.
Credit Cards: All major credit/debit cards
Specialities: *Clematis*.
Notes: Does not export to USA, Canada or Australia.
Map Ref: E, B3 **OS Grid Ref:** TG039062

ETMg **THOMPSON & MORGAN YOUNG PLANTS LTD** ⊠
Poplar Lane, Ipswich, Suffolk, IP8 3BU
Ⓣ 0844 573 2020
Ⓕ (01787) 882252
Ⓔ ypenq@thompson-morgan.com
Ⓦ www.thompson-morgan.com/plants
Contact: Customer Care
Opening Times: Mail order only. Not open except for Open Weekend 26th/27th Aug 2008.
Min Mail Order UK: Nmc
Cat. Cost: Free
Credit Cards: Visa MasterCard
Notes: Also sells wholesale.

ETod **TODD'S BOTANICS** ⊠ ⛟ ♿
West Street, Coggeshall, Colchester, Essex, CO6 1NT
Ⓣ (01376) 561212
Ⓜ 07970 643711
Ⓕ (01376) 561212
Ⓔ info@toddsbotanics.co.uk
Ⓦ www.toddsbotanics.co.uk
Contact: Emma Macdonald
Opening Times: 0900-1700 Tue-Sun.
Min Mail Order UK: £20.00
Cat. Cost: 2 × 1st class.
Credit Cards: All major credit/debit cards
Specialities: Hardy exotics, herbaceous. Bamboos, olives, palms, ferns, grasses, *Canna* & *Hedychium*.
Notes: Also sells wholesale.
Map Ref: E, D2 **OS Grid Ref:** TL843224

EWal **J WALKERS BULBS** ⊠
Washway House Farm, Holbeach, Spalding, Lincs, PE12 7PP
Ⓣ (01406) 426216
Ⓕ (01406) 421259
Ⓔ walkers@taylors-bulbs.com
Ⓦ www.bulbs.co.uk
Contact: Johnny Walkers
Opening Times: Not open. Mail order only.
Min Mail Order UK: Nmc
Min Mail Order EU: Nmc
Cat. Cost: Free.
Credit Cards: All major credit/debit cards
Specialities: Daffodils, *Fritillaria* & lilies.
Notes: Does not accept American Express. Also sells wholesale.

EWes **WEST ACRE GARDENS** ⛟ ♿
West Acre, King's Lynn, Norfolk, PE32 1UJ
Ⓣ (01760) 755562
Contact: J J Tuite
Opening Times: 1000-1700 7 days 1st Feb-30th Nov. Other times by appt.
Cat. Cost: None issued.
Credit Cards: Visa MasterCard Delta Switch
Specialities: Very wide selection of herbaceous & other garden plants incl. *Rhodohypoxis* & *Primula auricula*.
Map Ref: E, B1 **OS Grid Ref:** TF792182

EWld **WOODLANDS**
Peppin Lane, Fotherby, Louth, Lincolnshire, LN11 0UW
Ⓣ (01507) 603586
⊠ 07866 161864
Ⓔ annbobarmstrong@uwclub.net
Contact: Ann Armstrong
Opening Times: Flexible, but please phone or email to avoid disappointment.
Cat. Cost: None issued.
Credit Cards: None
Specialities: Small but interesting range of unusual plants, esp. woodland and *Salvia*, all grown on the nursery in limited quantity.
Notes: Mature garden, art gallery & refreshments.
Map Ref: E, A2 **OS Grid Ref:** TF322918

EWll **THE WALLED GARDEN** ♿ ◆
Park Road, Benhall, Saxmundham, Suffolk, IP17 1JB
Ⓣ (01728) 602510
Ⓕ (01728) 602510
Ⓔ jim@thewalledgarden.co.uk
Ⓦ www.thewalledgarden.co.uk
Contact: Jim Mountain
Opening Times: 0930-1700 Tue-Sun Mar-Oct, Tue-Sat Nov-Feb.
Cat. Cost: 2 × 1st class.
Credit Cards: All major credit/debit cards
Specialities: Tender & hardy perennials, over 1000 varieties, & wall shrubs.
Map Ref: E, C3 **OS Grid Ref:** TM371613

EWTr **WALNUT TREE GARDEN NURSERY** ⊠ €
Flymoor Lane, Rocklands, Attleborough, Norfolk, NR17 1BP
Ⓣ (01953) 488163
Ⓔ info@wtgn.co.uk
Ⓦ www.wtgn.co.uk
Contact: Jim Paine & Clare Billington
Opening Times: 0900-1800 Tue-Sun Feb-Nov & B/hols.
Min Mail Order UK: Nmc
Min Mail Order EU: £20.00
Cat. Cost: 4 × 1st class.
Credit Cards: All major credit/debit cards
Map Ref: E, B1 **OS Grid Ref:** TL978973

SCOTLAND

GAbr **ABRIACHAN NURSERIES** ⊠ ⛟ ♿
Loch Ness Side, Inverness, Inverness-shire, IV3 8LA
Ⓣ (01463) 861232
Ⓕ (01463) 861232
Ⓔ info@lochnessgarden.com
Ⓦ www.lochnessgarden.com
Contact: Mr & Mrs D Davidson
Opening Times: 0900-1900 daily (dusk if earlier) Feb-Nov.
Min Mail Order UK: Nmc

KEY
⊠ Mail order to UK or EU ⛟ Delivers to shows
✈ Exports beyond EU € Euro accepted
♿ Accessible by wheelchair ◆ See Display advertisement

G

Min Mail Order EU: Nmc
Cat. Cost: 4 × 1st class.
Credit Cards: None
Specialities: Herbaceous, *Primula*, *Helianthemum*, hardy geraniums, *Sempervivum* & *Primula auricula*.
Notes: Wheelchair access to nursery only.
Map Ref: G, B2 **OS Grid Ref:** NH571347

GAgs **Angus Plants** ⊠ ♿
3 Balfour Cottages, Menmuir, By Brechin, Angus, DD9 7RN
Ⓣ (01356) 660280
Ⓔ alison@angusplants.co.uk
Ⓦ www.angusplants.co.uk
Contact: Alison S. Goldie & Mark A. Hutson
Opening Times: By appt. only. Please phone first. Light refreshments provided.
Min Mail Order UK: Nmc
Cat. Cost: 4 × 1st class
Credit Cards: None
Specialities: Predominantly *Primula auricula*, although other *Primula* species are offered. A few available in small quantities only.
Notes: Mail order available all year.
Map Ref: G, B3 **OS Grid Ref:** NO528643

GAsh **Ashbrook Nursery** ♿
Forfar Road, Arbroath, Angus, DD11 3RB
Ⓣ (01241) 873408
Ⓕ (01241) 873408
Ⓔ annewebster@hotmail.co.uk
Ⓦ www.ashbrooknursery.co.uk
Contact: Anne Webster
Opening Times: 1000-1730 daily in Summer, 1000-1630 Nov-Feb incl.
Credit Cards: All major credit/debit cards
Specialities: Wide range of alpine & herbaceous perennials, bedding & patio plants.
Notes: Nursery located opposite RM Condor Marine Base. Also sells wholesale.
Map Ref: G, C3 **OS Grid Ref:** NO618428

GAuc **Auchgourish Gardens** ⊠ € ♿
Street of Kincardine, by Boat of Garten, Inverness-shire, PH24 3BY
Ⓣ (01479) 831464
Ⓜ 07746 122775
Ⓕ (01479) 831672
Ⓔ auchgourishgardens@falsyde.sol.co.uk
Ⓦ www.thebotanicalnursery.com
Contact: Iain Brodie of Falsyde
Opening Times: 1000-1700 Mon-Fri, closed Sat, 1100-1700 Sun, 1st Apr-31st Oct.
Min Mail Order UK: £25.00
Min Mail Order EU: £30.00 + p&p at cost
Cat. Cost: Online only.
Credit Cards: All major credit/debit cards
Specialities: Botanical species. *Betulaceae*, *Rosaceae*, *Ericaceae*, *Iridaceae*, *Liliaceae* & *Primulaceae*. Nursery is at Auchgourish Gardens, Boat of Garten. Anchgourish Gardens are open Apr-Oct.
Notes: Mail order despatch Sep-Apr incl. subject to weather. No despatch May-Aug but plants can be uplifted any time by prior arrangement. Credit cards accepted online only.
Map Ref: G, B2

GBar **Barwinnock Herbs** ⊠ €
Barrhill, Girvan, Ayrshire, KA26 0RB
Ⓣ (01465) 821338
Ⓔ herbs@barwinnock.com
Ⓦ www.barwinnock.com
Contact: Dave & Mon Holtom
Opening Times: 1000-1700 12th Apr-end Sep. Closed Wed.
Min Mail Order UK: Nmc
Min Mail Order EU: Nmc
Cat. Cost: UK free, EU 2 × IRC.
Credit Cards: All major credit/debit cards
Specialities: Culinary, medicinal, fragrant-leaved plants & wildflowers organically grown.

GBBs **Border Belles** ⊠ ⌂ ♿
Old Branxton Cottages, Innerwick, Nr Dunbar, East Lothian, EH42 1QT
Ⓣ (01368) 840325
Ⓕ (01368) 840325
Ⓔ mail@borderbelles.com
Ⓦ www.borderbelles.com
Contact: Gillian Moynihan
Opening Times: 1000-1700 Mar-Sep.
Min Mail Order UK: Nmc
Min Mail Order EU: On request
Cat. Cost: 3 × 1st class.
Credit Cards: None
Specialities: Hardy perennials & woodland plants.
Notes: Mail order Oct-Mar only. Also sells wholesale.
Map Ref: G, C3

GBee **Beeches Cottage Nursery**
High Boreland, Lesmahagow, South Lanarkshire, ML11 9PY
Ⓣ (01555) 893369
Ⓜ 07930 343131
Contact: Margaret Harrison
Opening Times: 1000-1630 Wed-Sat, Mar-Oct. Other times by appt.
Cat. Cost: None issued.
Credit Cards: None
Specialities: Traditional & unusual hardy & half-hardy cottage garden perennials. Some

plants available in small quantities only.
Map Ref: G, C2 **OS Grid Ref:** NS837403

GBin **BINNY PLANTS** ⊠ € ♿
West Lodge, Binny Estate, Ecclesmachen Road, Nr Broxbourn, West Lothian, EH52 6NL
Ⓣ (01506) 858931
Ⓕ (01506) 858155
Ⓔ binnyplants@aol.com
Ⓦ www.binnyplants.co.uk
Contact: Billy Carruthers
Opening Times: 1000-1700 7 days. Closed mid-Dec to mid-Jan.
Min Mail Order UK: £25.00
Min Mail Order EU: £25.00
Cat. Cost: £2.50 refundable on ordering.
Credit Cards: Visa MasterCard Switch EuroCard
Specialities: Perennials incl. *Astilbe*, *Geranium*, *Hosta*, *Paeonia* & *Iris*. Plus large selection of grasses & ferns.
Notes: Mail order Sep-Apr only. Also sells wholesale.
Map Ref: G, C3

GBuc **BUCKLAND PLANTS** ⊠ € ♿
Whinnieliggate, Kirkcudbright, Kirkcudbrightshire, DG6 4XP
Ⓣ (01557) 331323
Ⓕ (01557) 331323
Ⓦ www.bucklandplants.co.uk
Contact: Rob or Dina Asbridge
Opening Times: 1000-1700 Thu-Sun 1st Mar-1st Nov & B/hols.
Min Mail Order UK: £20.00 + p&p
Min Mail Order EU: £50.00 + p&p
Cat. Cost: 3 × 1st class.
Credit Cards: All major credit/debit cards
Specialities: A very wide range of scarce herbaceous & woodland plants incl. *Anemone*, *Cardamine*, *Crocosmia*, *Erythronium*, *Helleborus*, *Lilium*, *Meconopsis*, *Primula*, *Tricyrtis* & *Trillium*.
Map Ref: G, D2 **OS Grid Ref:** NX719524

GBut **BUTTERWORTHS' ORGANIC NURSERY** ⊠
Garden Cottage, Auchinleck Estate, Cumnock, Ayrshire, KA18 2LR
Ⓣ (01290) 551088
Ⓜ 07732 254300
Ⓔ butties@webage.co.uk
Ⓦ www.butterworthsorganicnursery.co.uk
Contact: John Butterworth
Opening Times: By appt. only.
Min Mail Order UK: £27.00
Cat. Cost: 3 × 1st class.
Credit Cards: None
Specialities: Fruit trees incl. Scottish apple varieties. Much of stock is available in small quantities only. All stock is certified organic.

GCai **CAIRNSMORE NURSERY** ⊠ ⛺ ♿
Chapmanton Road, Castle Douglas, Kirkcudbrightshire, DG7 2NU
Ⓣ (01556) 504819
Ⓜ 07980 176458
Ⓔ cairnsmorenursery@hotmail.com
Ⓦ www.cairnsmorenursery.co.uk
Contact: Valerie Smith
Opening Times: 1000-1700, Thu-Sat, Apr-Sep.
Min Mail Order UK: Nmc
Cat. Cost: 4 × 1st class.
Credit Cards: All major credit/debit cards
Specialities: *Primula auricula*, show cultivars. *Heuchera* & *Tiarella*.
Map Ref: G, D2 **OS Grid Ref:** NX756637

GCal **CALLY GARDENS** ⊠ ♿
Gatehouse of Fleet, Castle Douglas, Kirkcudbrightshire, DG7 2DJ
Ⓣ (01557) 815029 recorded information only.
Ⓔ cally.gardens@virgin.net
Ⓦ www.callygardens.co.uk
Contact: Michael Wickenden
Opening Times: 1000-1730 Sat-Sun, 1400-1730 Tue-Fri. Easter Sat-last Sun in Sept.
Min Mail Order UK: £15.00 + p&p
Cat. Cost: 3 × 1st class.
Credit Cards: None
Specialities: Unusual perennials. *Agapanthus*, *Crocosmia*, *Eryngium*, hardy *Geranium* & grasses. Some rare shrubs, climbers & conservatory plants. 3500 varieties growing in an C18th walled garden.
Notes: Also sells wholesale.

GCoc **JAMES COCKER & SONS** ⊠ ♿
Whitemyres, Lang Stracht, Aberdeen, Aberdeenshire, AB15 6XH
Ⓣ (01224) 313261
Ⓕ (01224) 312531
Ⓔ sales@roses.uk.com
Ⓦ www.roses.uk.com
Contact: Alec Cocker
Opening Times: 0900-1730 7 days.
Min Mail Order UK: Nmc
Min Mail Order EU: £5.65 + p&p

KEY
⊠ Mail order to UK or EU ⛺ Delivers to shows
✈ Exports beyond EU € Euro accepted
♿ Accessible by wheelchair ◆ See Display advertisement

Cat. Cost: Free
Credit Cards: Visa MasterCard Delta Maestro
Specialities: Roses.
Notes: Also sells wholesale.
Map Ref: G, B3

G

GCra **Craigieburn Garden** ♿
Craigieburn House, by Moffat, Dumfriesshire, DG10 9LF
Ⓣ (01683) 221250
Ⓕ (01683) 221250
Ⓔ ajmw1@aol.com
Ⓦ www.craigieburngarden.com
Contact: Janet & Andrew Wheatcroft
Opening Times: 1030-1800 Tue-Sun, Easter-31st Oct. Plus all English & Scottish B/hols. Other times by appt.
Credit Cards: None
Specialities: *Meconopsis* plants for damp gardens, herbaceous perennials.
Map Ref: G, D3

GEdr **Edrom Nurseries** ⊠ ♿
Coldingham, Eyemouth, Berwickshire, TD14 5TZ
Ⓣ (01890) 771386
Ⓕ (01890) 71387
Ⓔ info@edromnurseries.co.uk
Ⓦ www.edromnurseries.co.uk
Contact: Mr Terry Hunt
Opening Times: 0900-1700 Mon-Sun, 1 Mar-30 Sep. Other times by appt.
Min Mail Order UK: Nmc
Min Mail Order EU: £20.00
Cat. Cost: 3 × 2nd class. More plants listed online than in printed catalogue.
Credit Cards: All major credit/debit cards
Specialities: *Trillium*, *Arisaema*, *Primula*, *Gentiana*, *Meconopsis*, *Anemone* & other alpines. *Fritillaria*, hardy orchids.
Map Ref: G, C3 **OS Grid Ref:** NT873663

GFai **Fairholm Plants** ⊠
Fairholm, Larkhall, Lanarkshire, ML9 2UQ
Ⓣ (01698) 881671
Ⓕ (01698) 888135
Ⓔ fairholm.plants@stevenson-hamilton.co.uk
Contact: Mrs J M Hamilton
Opening Times: Apr-Oct by appt.
Min Mail Order UK: Nmc
Cat. Cost: 1 × 2nd class for descriptive list.
Credit Cards: None
Specialities: *Abutilon* & unusual half-hardy perennials esp. South African. Nat. Collection of *Abutilon* cvs.
Notes: Mail order for young/small plants.
Map Ref: G, C2 **OS Grid Ref:** NS754515

GFor **Fordmouth Croft Ornamental Grass Nursery** ⊠ ♿
Fordmouth Croft, Meikle Wartle, Inverurie, Aberdeenshire, AB51 5BE
Ⓣ (01467) 671519
Ⓔ Ann-Marie@fmcornamentalgrasses.co.uk
Ⓦ www.fmcornamentalgrasses.co.uk
Contact: Robert & Ann-Marie Grant
Opening Times: Mail order only. Open strictly by appt. only.
Min Mail Order UK: Nmc
Cat. Cost: 2 × 1st class.
Credit Cards: None
Specialities: Grasses, sedges, rushes. Small orders available.
Notes: Also sells wholesale.
Map Ref: G, B3 **OS Grid Ref:** NJ718302

GGal **Galloway Plants** ⊠ ♿
Claymoddie, Whithorn, Newton Stewart, Dumfries & Galloway, DG8 8LX
Ⓣ (01988) 500422
Ⓕ (01988) 500422
Ⓔ NICM567@aol.com
Ⓦ www.gallowayplants.co.uk
Contact: Robin & Mary Nicholson
Opening Times: 1400-1700 Fri, Sat & Sun, 8th Mar-28th Sep 2008, other times by prior appt.
Min Mail Order UK: £50.00 + p&p
Min Mail Order EU: £50.00 + p&p
Cat. Cost: 2 × 1st class.
Credit Cards: None
Specialities: Southern hemisphere *Hydrangea*. Available in small quantities only.
Notes: Also sells wholesale.
Map Ref: G, D2 **OS Grid Ref:** NX450377

GGar **Garden Cottage Nursery** ⊠ ♿
Tournaig, Poolewe, Achnasheen, Ross-shire, IV22 2LH
Ⓣ (01445) 781777
Ⓔ ben@gcnursery.co.uk
Ⓦ www.gcnursery.co.uk
Contact: Ben Rushbrooke
Opening Times: 1000-1800 Mon-Sat mid Mar-mid Oct or by appt.
Min Mail Order UK: Nmc
Cat. Cost: Free.
Credit Cards: Visa Switch MasterCard
Specialities: A wide range of plants esp. those from the southern hemisphere & plants for bog & coastal gardens.
Map Ref: G, A2 **OS Grid Ref:** NG878835

GGGa **Glendoick Gardens Ltd** ⊠
Glencarse, Perth, Perthshire, PH2 7NS
Ⓣ (01738) 860205
Ⓕ (01738) 860630

Ⓔ orders@glendoick.com
Ⓦ www.glendoick.com
Contact: P A, E P & K N E Cox
Opening Times: 1000-1600 Mon-Fri only, mid-Apr-mid-Jun, otherwise by appt. 1400-1700 1st & 3rd Sun in May. Garden centre open 7 days.
Min Mail Order UK: £40.00 + p&p
Min Mail Order EU: £100.00 + p&p
Cat. Cost: £2.00 or £1.50 stamps.
Credit Cards: Visa MasterCard Delta Switch JCB
Specialities: Rhododendrons, azaleas and ericaceous, *Primula* & *Meconopsis*. Plants from wild seed. Many catalogue plants available at garden centre. 3 Nat. Collections.
Notes: Wheelchair access to Garden Centre. Also sells wholesale.
Map Ref: G, C3 **OS Grid Ref:**

GJos JO'S GARDEN ENTERPRISE ♿
Easter Balmungle Farm, Eathie Road, by Rosemarkie, Ross-shire, IV10 8SL
Ⓣ (01381) 621006
Ⓔ anne.chance@ukonline.co.uk
Contact: Joanna Chance
Opening Times: 1000 to dusk, 7 days.
Cat. Cost: None
Credit Cards: None
Specialities: Alpines & herbaceous perennials. Selection of native wild flowers.
Map Ref: G, B2 **OS Grid Ref:** NH600742

GKev KEVOCK GARDEN PLANTS ⊠ ✈ ⌂ €
16 Kevock Road, Lasswade, Midlothian, EH18 1HT
Ⓣ 0131 454 0660
Ⓜ 07811 321585
Ⓕ 0131 454 0660
Ⓔ info@kevockgarden.co.uk
Ⓦ www.kevockgarden.co.uk
Contact: Stella Rankin
Opening Times: Not open. Mail order & plant stalls only.
Min Mail Order UK: £20.00
Min Mail Order EU: £20.00
Cat. Cost: 4 × 1st class.
Credit Cards: Visa MasterCard Switch
Specialities: Chinese & Himalayan plants. *Androsace*, *Daphne*, *Paeonia*, *Primula*, *Meconopsis*, *Iris*, woodland plants.
Notes: Also sells wholesale.

GKir KIRKDALE NURSERY ⊠ € ♿
Daviot, Nr Inverurie, Aberdeenshire, AB51 0JL
Ⓣ (01467) 671264
Ⓕ (01467) 671282
Ⓔ kirkdalenursery@btconnect.com
Ⓦ www.kirkdalenursery.co.uk
Contact: Geoff or Alistair
Opening Times: 1000-1700 7 days (summer), 1000-1600 7 days (winter).
Min Mail Order UK: £30.00 + p&p
Min Mail Order EU: £50.00 + p&p
Cat. Cost: None issued
Credit Cards: Visa Access Switch
Specialities: Trees, herbaceous, conifers. Some plants available in small quantities only.
Notes: Mail order strictly mid-Oct to mid-Mar, carriage at cost.
Map Ref: G, B3

GLin LINN BOTANIC GARDENS €
Cove, Helensburgh, Dunbartonshire, G84 0NR
Ⓣ (01436) 842084
Ⓔ jamie@linnbotanicgardens.org.uk
Ⓦ www.linnbotanicgardens.org.uk
Contact: Jamie Taggart
Opening Times: 1100-1700, 7 days.
Cat. Cost: 4 × 1st class or by email.
Credit Cards: None
Specialities: Small plant sales area offering diverse range of plants. Botanic Gardens open (charges apply).
Notes: Wheelchair access to plant sales area but not gardens.
Map Ref: G, C2 **OS Grid Ref:** NS223827

GLld LOCHLANDS (HRB LTD) ⊠ ♿
Dundee Road, Forfar, Angus, DD8 1XF
Ⓣ (01307) 463621
Ⓕ (01307) 469665
Ⓔ lochlands@btinternet.com
Ⓦ lochlands.co.uk
Contact: John van Delft
Opening Times: 0830-1730 Mon-Sat, 1030-1630 Sun.
Min Mail Order UK: £25.00
Cat. Cost: Free.
Credit Cards: All major credit/debit cards
Specialities: Camellias.
Notes: Also sells wholesale.
Map Ref: G, C3 **OS Grid Ref:** NO444478

GMac ELIZABETH MACGREGOR ⊠ ♿
Ellenbank, Tongland Road, Kirkcudbright, Dumfries & Galloway, DG6 4UU
Ⓣ (01557) 330620
Ⓕ (01557) 330620
Ⓔ elizabeth.violas@btinternet.com
Contact: Elizabeth MacGregor

KEY
⊠ Mail order to UK or EU ⌂ Delivers to shows
✈ Exports beyond EU € Euro accepted
♿ Accessible by wheelchair ◆ See Display advertisement

Opening Times: 1000-1700 Mon, Fri & Sat May-Sep, or please phone.
Min Mail Order UK: 6 plants £16.80 + p&p
Min Mail Order EU: £50.00 + p&p
Cat. Cost: 4 × 1st class or 5 × 2nd class
Credit Cards: All major credit/debit cards
Specialities: Violets, violas & violettas, old and new varieties. *Campanula*, *Geranium*, *Eryngium*, *Penstemon*, *Aster*, *Primula*, *Iris* & other unusual herbaceous.
Map Ref: G, D2 **OS Grid Ref:** NX692525

G

GMaP **Macplants** ⌂
Berrybank Nursery, 5 Boggs Holdings, Pencaitland, East Lothian, EH34 5BA
Ⓣ (01875) 341179
Ⓕ (01875) 340842
Ⓔ sales@macplants.co.uk
Ⓦ www.macplants.co.uk
Contact: Gavin McNaughton
Opening Times: 1030-1700, 7 days, Mar-end Sep.
Cat. Cost: 4 × 2nd class.
Credit Cards: MasterCard Switch Visa
Specialities: Herbaceous perennials, alpines, hardy ferns, violas & grasses.
Notes: Nursery partially accessible to wheelchairs. Also sells wholesale.
Map Ref: G, C3 **OS Grid Ref:** NT447703

GPoy **Poyntzfield Herb Nursery** ⊠ ✈ ♿
Nr Balblair, Black Isle, Dingwall, Ross-shire, IV7 8LX
Ⓣ (01381) 610352
Ⓕ (01381) 610352
Ⓔ info@poyntzfieldherbs.co.uk
Ⓦ www.poyntzfieldherbs.co.uk
Contact: Duncan Ross
Opening Times: 1300-1700 Mon-Sat 1st Mar-30th Sep, 1300-1700 Sun May-Aug.
Min Mail Order UK: £10.00 + p&p
Min Mail Order EU: £10.00 + p&p
Credit Cards: All major credit/debit cards
Specialities: Over 400 popular, unusual & rare herbs esp. medicinal. Also seeds.
Notes: Phone between 1200-1300 & 1800-1900 Mon-Sat only.
Map Ref: G, B2 **OS Grid Ref:** NH711642

GPri **Privick Mill Nursery** ⊠ ♿
Privick Mill Road, Annbank, Ayr, KA6 5JA
Ⓣ (01292) 521003
Ⓔ jackie.jess@tiscali.co.uk
Ⓦ www.trootnfroot.co.uk
Contact: Jackie Jess
Opening Times: By appt. only for collection of plants.
Min Mail Order UK: Nmc
Cat. Cost: Free.
Credit Cards: None
Specialities: Soft fruit bushes. Blueberries. Black raspberries. *Rubus* hybrids. Available in small quantities only. All plants organically grown but not certified by Soil Assoc.
Map Ref: G, D2 **OS Grid Ref:** NS405224

GPWP **Plants With Purpose** ⊠ ⌂
Middlebank Cottage, Smith's Brae, Bankfoot, Perthshire, PH1 4AH
Ⓣ (01738) 787278
Ⓜ 07871 451579
Ⓔ mail@plantswithpurpose.co.uk
Ⓦ www.plantswithpurpose.co.uk
Contact: Margaret Lear
Opening Times: By appt. only.
Min Mail Order UK: £12.00
Min Mail Order EU: £12.00
Cat. Cost: Online or on application.
Credit Cards: All major credit/debit cards
Specialities: Herbs, esp. *Mentha* & *Artemisia*.
Notes: Credit cards online only. Partial wheelchair access.
Map Ref: G, C3 **OS Grid Ref:** NO067356

GQue **Quercus Garden Plants** ♿
Rankeilour Gardens, Rankeilour Estate, Springfield, Fife, KY15 5RE
Ⓣ (01337) 810444
Ⓕ (01337) 810444
Ⓔ colin@quercus.uk.net
Contact: Colin McBeath
Opening Times: 1000-1700 Thu-Sun, end Mar-mid Oct. By appt. only, Nov-Mar.
Cat. Cost: 4 × 1st class.
Credit Cards: All major credit/debit cards
Specialities: Easy & unusual plants for contemporary Scottish gardens.
Notes: Delivery service available on large orders at nursery's discretion. Also sells wholesale.
Map Ref: G, C3 **OS Grid Ref:** NO330118

GQui **Quinish Garden Nursery** ⊠
Dervaig, Isle of Mull, Argyll, PA75 6QL
Ⓣ (01688) 400344
Ⓕ (01688) 400344
Ⓔ quinishplants@aol.com
Ⓦ www.Q-gardens.org
Contact: Nicholas Reed
Opening Times: By appt. only.
Min Mail Order UK: Nmc
Min Mail Order EU: Nmc
Cat. Cost: 2 × 1st class.
Credit Cards: None
Specialities: Choice garden shrubs & conservatory plants.
Map Ref: G, C1

GSec **The Secret Garden** ⊠
10 Pilmuir Road West, Forres, Moray, IV36 2HL
Ⓣ (01309) 674634
Ⓔ fixandig@aol.com
Contact: Mrs L. Dingwall
Opening Times: Mail order only. Open by appt. only.
Min Mail Order UK: Nmc
Min Mail Order EU: Nmc.
Cat. Cost: 84p
Credit Cards: None
Specialities: *Hosta.*

GTwe **J Tweedie Fruit Trees** ⊠
Maryfield Road Nursery, Nr Terregles, Dumfriesshire, DG2 9TH
Ⓣ (01387) 720880
Contact: John Tweedie
Opening Times: Please ring for times. Collections by appt.
Min Mail Order UK: Nmc
Cat. Cost: Sae
Credit Cards: None
Specialities: Fruit trees & bushes. A wide range of old & new varieties.
Map Ref: G, D2

N. Ireland & Republic

IArd **Ardcarne Garden Centre** € ♿
Ardcarne, Boyle, Co. Roscommon, Ireland
Ⓣ 00 353 (0)7196 67091
Ⓕ 00 353 (0)7196 67341
Ⓔ ardcarne@indigo.ie
Ⓦ www.ardcarnegc.com
Contact: James Wickham, Mary Frances Dwyer, Kirsty Ainge
Opening Times: 0900-1800 Mon-Sat, 1300-1800 Sun & B/hols.
Credit Cards: Access Visa American Express
Specialities: Coastal plants, native & unusual trees, specimen plants & semi-mature trees. Wide general range.
Map Ref: I, B1

IBal **Bali-hai Mail Order Nursery** ⊠ ✈ €
42 Largy Road, Carnlough, Ballymena, Co. Antrim, N. Ireland, BT44 0EZ
Ⓣ 028 2888 5289
Ⓕ 028 2888 5976
Ⓔ ianwscroggy@btopenworld.com
Ⓦ www.mailorderplants4me.com
Contact: Mrs M E Scroggy
Opening Times: Mon-Sat by appt. only.
Min Mail Order UK: Nmc
Min Mail Order EU: Nmc
Cat. Cost: £3.00 cheque, made payable to Mrs M.E. Scroggy.
Credit Cards: All major credit/debit cards
Specialities: *Hosta, Phormium, Rhodohypoxis* & other perennials. Tree ferns.
Notes: Exports beyond EU restricted to bare root perennials, no grasses. Also sells wholesale.
Map Ref: I, A3 **OS Grid Ref:** D287184

IBlr **Ballyrogan Nurseries** ⊠ € ♿
The Grange, Ballyrogan, Newtownards, Co. Down, N. Ireland, BT23 4SD
Ⓣ (028) 9181 0451 (evenings)
Ⓔ gary.dunlop@btinternet.com
Contact: Gary Dunlop
Opening Times: Only open by appt.
Min Mail Order UK: £10.00 + p&p
Min Mail Order EU: £20.00 + p&p
Cat. Cost: 2 × 1st class.
Credit Cards: None
Specialities: Choice herbaceous. *Agapanthus, Celmisia, Crocosmia, Rodgersia, Iris, Dierama, Erythronium, Roscoea* & *Phormium.*
Notes: Also sells wholesale.
Map Ref: I, B3

ICro **Crocknafeola Nursery** €
Killybegs, Co. Donegal, Ireland
Ⓣ 00 353 (0)74 97 51018
Ⓕ 00 353 (0)74 97 51095
Ⓔ crocknafeola@hotmail.com
Contact: Fionn McKenna
Opening Times: 0900-1800 Mon, Tue, Thu-Sat, closed Wed. 1200-1800 Sun.
Cat. Cost: None issued
Credit Cards: None
Specialities: Bedding plants, herbaceous perennials, rhododendrons, plants for containers, roses, plus shrubs & hedging for coastal areas.
Notes: Also sells wholesale.
Map Ref: I, D2

IDee **Deelish Garden Centre** ⊠ €
Skibbereen, Co. Cork, Ireland
Ⓣ 00 353 (0)28 21374
Ⓕ 00 353 (0)28 21374
Ⓔ deel@eircom.net
Ⓦ www.deelish.ie
Contact: Bill & Rain Chase
Opening Times: 1000-1800 Mon-Sat, 1400-1800 Sun.

KEY
⊠ Mail order to UK or EU — Delivers to shows
✈ Exports beyond EU — € Euro accepted
♿ Accessible by wheelchair — ◆ See Display advertisement

Min Mail Order EU: €50 (Ireland only).
Cat. Cost: Sae
Credit Cards: Visa Access
Specialities: Unusual plants for the mild coastal climate of Ireland. Conservatory plants. Sole Irish agents for Chase Organic Seeds.
Notes: No mail order outside Ireland.
Map Ref: I, D1

IDic **DICKSON NURSERIES LTD** ⊠ ✈
Milecross Road, Newtownards, Co. Down, N. Ireland, BT23 4SS
Ⓣ (028) 9181 2206
Ⓕ (028) 9181 3366
Ⓔ mail@dickson-roses.co.uk
Ⓦ www.dickson-roses.co.uk
Contact: Colin Dickson
Opening Times: 0800-1230 & 1300-1700 Mon-Thu. 0800-1230 Fri. Closes at 1600 Mon-Thu Dec-Jan.
Min Mail Order UK: Nmc
Min Mail Order EU: £25.00 + p&p
Cat. Cost: Free
Credit Cards: None
Specialities: Roses esp. modern Dickson varieties. Most varieties are available in small quantities only.
Notes: Also sells wholesale.
Map Ref: I, B3

IFFs **FUTURE FORESTS** ⊠ € ♿
Kealkil, Bantry, Co. Cork, Ireland
Ⓣ 00 353 (0)27 66176
Ⓕ 00 353 (0)27 66939
Ⓔ futureforests@eircom.net
Ⓦ www.futureforests.net
Contact: Nick Lain
Opening Times: 1000-1800 Mon-Sat (incl. B/hols), 1430-1800 Sun.
Min Mail Order UK: Nmc
Min Mail Order EU: Nmc
Cat. Cost: Free.
Credit Cards: Laser Visa MasterCard
Specialities: Trees, shrubs, hedging, climbers, roses. Fruit trees. Ferns, grasses & perennials.
Map Ref: I, D1 **OS Grid Ref:** W 083587

IFoB **FIELD OF BLOOMS** ⊠ € ♿
Ballymackey, Lisnamoe, Nenagh, Co. Tipperary, Ireland
Ⓣ 00 353 (0)67 29974
Ⓜ 08764 06044
Ⓔ guy2002@eircom.ie
Ⓦ www.fieldofblooms.ie
Contact: Guy de Schrijver
Opening Times: Strictly by appt.
Min Mail Order UK: Nmc
Min Mail Order EU: Nmc
Cat. Cost: Free.
Credit Cards: None
Specialities: Hellebores, herbaceous, hardy perennials, ornamental grasses & woodland plants.
Map Ref: I, C2

IFro **FROGSWELL NURSERY** €
Cloonconlon, Straide, Foxford, Co. Mayo, Ireland
Ⓣ 00 353 (0)94 903 1420
Ⓕ 00 353 (0)94 903 1420
Ⓔ frogswell@gmail.com
Ⓦ www.frogswell.net
Contact: Celia Graebner
Opening Times: Feb-Oct by appt. Please phone first. Also Garden Open Days & workshops; see website for details.
Cat. Cost: Online list for 2008.
Credit Cards: None
Specialities: A small nursery specialising in shade & woodland plants incl. hybrid hellebores & hardy geraniums, plus unusual perennials for the Irish climate, all raised on site, some in small quantities. Garden visits by arrangement.
Notes: See website for location details.
Map Ref: I, B1 **OS Grid Ref:** M2497

IGor **GORTKELLY CASTLE NURSERY** ⊠ €
Upperchurch, Thurles, Co. Tipperary, Ireland
Ⓣ 00 353 (0)504 54441
Contact: Clare Beumer
Opening Times: Mail order only. Not open to the public.
Min Mail Order UK: £50.00
Min Mail Order EU: €50
Cat. Cost: 5 × 1st class (UK), 5 × 48c (Rep. of Ireland).
Credit Cards: None
Specialities: Choice perennials.
Map Ref: I, C2

IHer **HERITAGE BULBS** ⊠ € ◆
Tullynally Castle, Castlepollard, Co. Westmeath, Ireland
Ⓣ 00 353 (0)44 96 62744
Ⓕ 00 353 (0)44 96 62746
Ⓔ info@heritagebulbs.com
Ⓦ www.heritagebulbs.com
Contact: Octavia Tulloch
Opening Times: Not open. Mail order only. Tullynally Castle Gardens open afternoons in Jun, Jul & Aug.
Min Mail Order UK: Nmc
Min Mail Order EU: Nmc
Cat. Cost: Free
Credit Cards: MasterCard Visa

Specialities: Rare & historic bulbs (www.heritagebulbs.com) & native bulbs for naturalising (www.wildaboutbulbs.com).
Notes: Also sells wholesale.
Map Ref: I, B2

IKil **Kilmurry Nursery** ⊠ € ♿ ◆
Gorey, Co. Wexford, Ireland
Ⓣ 00 353 (0)53 948 0223
Ⓜ 00 353 (0)86 8180623
Ⓕ 00 353 (0)53 948 0223
Ⓔ info@kilmurrynursery.com
Ⓦ www.kilmurrynursery.com
Contact: Paul & Orla Woods
Opening Times: 0900-1700 Mon-Fri, Mar-Sep. Wintertime by appt.
Min Mail Order UK: Nmc
Min Mail Order EU: Nmc
Cat. Cost: 3 × 1st class.
Credit Cards: None
Specialities: Herbaceous perennials and grasses.
Notes: Also sells wholesale.
Map Ref: I, C3 **OS Grid Ref:** 3C

ILad **Ladybird Garden Nursery** ⊠
32 Ballykeigle Road, off Moss Road, Nr Ballygowan, County Down, BT23 5SD
Ⓣ (028) 9752 8025
Ⓔ millarjoyce@hotmail.com
Ⓦ www.ladybirdgarden.co.uk
Contact: Joyce Millar
Opening Times: Afternoons, Apr-Sep (not Wed or Sun). Other times (incl. evenings) by appt. Garden open to groups by appt. Please phone first if travelling a distance.
Min Mail Order UK: Nmc
Cat. Cost: 2 × 1st class or free by email.
Credit Cards: None
Specialities: Over 200 varieties of herbaceous perennials & grasses, beneficial for wildlife ranges. Some in small quantities only.
Notes: Partial wheelchair access. Also sells wholesale.
Map Ref: I, B3 **OS Grid Ref:** J453633

ILis **Lisdoonan Herbs** ⊠ € ♿
98 Belfast Road, Saintfield, Co. Down, N. Ireland, BT24 7HF
Ⓣ (028) 9081 3624
Ⓔ b.pilcher@lisdoonanherbs.co.uk
Ⓦ www.lisdoonanherbs.co.uk
Contact: Barbara Pilcher
Opening Times: Wed & Fri am. For other times, please phone to check.
Min Mail Order UK: Nmc
Min Mail Order EU: Nmc
Cat. Cost: 2 × 1st class.
Credit Cards: None
Specialities: Aromatics, herbs, kitchen garden plants, period plants, some native species. Freshly cut herbs & salads. Some stock available in limited quantities only. All peat-free.
Map Ref: I, B3 **OS Grid Ref:** J390624

IMGH **M G H Nurseries** € ♿
50 Tullyhenan Road, Banbridge, Co. Down, N. Ireland, BT32 4EY
Ⓣ (028) 4062 2795
Contact: Miss M G Heslip
Opening Times: By appt. only.
Cat. Cost: 3 × 1st class.
Credit Cards: None
Specialities: Grafted conifers, holly, maples, box, ornamental trees & flowering shrubs.
Notes: Also sells wholesale.
Map Ref: I, B3

IMon **Montana Garden Nursery** €
Lislevane, Bandon, Co. Cork, Ireland
Ⓣ 00 353 (0)23 57859
Ⓔ montana-gn@iol.ie
Contact: Sandra O'Hagan
Opening Times: 1000-1700 Tue-Sat, 1100-1600 Sun. Closed Mon except B/hols.
Credit Cards: All major credit/debit cards
Specialities: Coastal nursery specialising in salt-tolerant plants. Also unusual shrubs & perennials.
Map Ref: I, D2

IMou **Mount Venus Nursery** ⊠ ♿
The Walled Garden, Mutton Lane, Dublin, 16 Ireland
Ⓣ 00 353 (0)1 493 3813
Ⓜ 08632 18789
Ⓔ schurmann@ireland.com
Ⓦ www.mountvenusnursery.com
Contact: Oliver & Liat Schurmann
Opening Times: 1000-1800 Mon-Sat, Feb-Nov.
Min Mail Order UK: €20
Min Mail Order EU: €35
Credit Cards: All major credit/debit cards
Specialities: Specialist perennials. Grasses & Bamboos. Unusual woodland plants.
Notes: Also sells wholesale.
Map Ref: I, C3

KEY
⊠ Mail order to UK or EU — Delivers to shows
Exports beyond EU — € Euro accepted
♿ Accessible by wheelchair — ◆ See Display advertisement

IPen **Peninsula Primulas** ⊠ ⌂ €
72 Ballyeasborough Road, Kircubbin, Co. Down, N. Ireland, BT22 1AD
Ⓣ (028) 4277 2193
Ⓔ Peninsula.Primulas@btinternet.com
Contact: Philip Bankhead
Opening Times: Mail order only. Not open.
Min Mail Order UK: Nmc
Min Mail Order EU: Nmc
Cat. Cost: Free
Credit Cards: None
Specialities: Extensive selection of *Primula* species, plus auriculas.
Map Ref: I, B3

IPot **The Potting Shed** ⊠ ⌂ €
Bolinaspick, Camolin, Enniscorthy, Co. Wexford, Ireland
Ⓣ 00 353 (0)5393 83629
Ⓕ 00 353 (0)5393 83629
Ⓔ sricher@iol.ie
Ⓦ www.camolinpottingshed.com
Contact: Susan Carrick
Opening Times: 1300-1800, Thu-Sun (incl.), Mar-Sep 2008. Other times by appt.
Min Mail Order UK: Nmc
Min Mail Order EU: Nmc
Cat. Cost: 3 × 1st class.
Credit Cards: MasterCard Visa
Specialities: Herbaceous & ornamental grasses.
Map Ref: I, C3

IPPN **Perennial Plants Nursery** ⊠ ⌂ €
Nr Ballymaloe, Barnabrow, Midleton, Co. Cork, Ireland
Ⓣ 00 353 (0)21 465 2122
Ⓕ 00 353 (0)21 465 2122
Ⓔ perennialplants@eircom.net
Contact: Sandy McCarthy
Opening Times: Please ring for times.
Min Mail Order UK: Nmc
Min Mail Order EU: Nmc
Cat. Cost: None issued.
Credit Cards: None
Specialities: Many unusual herbaceous, ornamental grasses, tender perennials. Some available in small quantities only.
Notes: Will accept payment in Sterling.
Map Ref: I, D2 **OS Grid Ref:** W9568

IRhd **Ringhaddy Daffodils** ⊠ €
Ringhaddy Road, Killinchy, Newtownards, Co. Down, N. Ireland, BT23 6TU
Ⓣ (028) 9754 1007
Ⓕ (028) 9754 2276
Ⓔ ringdaff@nireland.com
Contact: Nial Watson
Opening Times: Mail order only. Not open.
Min Mail Order UK: £20.00 + p&p
Min Mail Order EU: £50.00 + p&p
Cat. Cost: £2.50 redeemable on order.
Credit Cards: None
Specialities: New daffodil varieties for exhibitors and hybridisers. Small stock of some varieties.

ISea **Seaforde Gardens** ⊠ € ♿
Seaforde, Co. Down, N. Ireland, BT30 8PG
Ⓣ (028) 4481 1225
Ⓕ (028) 4481 1370
Ⓔ plants@seafordegardens.com
Ⓦ www.seafordegardens.com
Contact: P Forde
Opening Times: 1000-1700 Mon-Fri all year. 1000-1700 Sat & 1300-1800 Sun, Easter-end Sep.
Min Mail Order UK: Nmc
Min Mail Order EU: Nmc
Cat. Cost: Free.
Credit Cards: None
Specialities: Over 600 varieties of self-propagated trees & shrubs. Nat. Collection of *Eucryphia*.
Notes: Also sells wholesale.
Map Ref: I, B3

ISsi **Seaside Nursery** ⊠ € ♿
Claddaghduff, Co. Galway, Ireland
Ⓣ 00 353 (0)95 44687
Ⓕ 00 353 (0)95 44761
Ⓔ seaside@anu.ie
Ⓦ www.anu.ie/seaside/
Contact: Tom Dyck
Opening Times: 1000-1300 & 1400-1800 Mon-Sat, 1400-1800 Sun. Closed Sun 1 Nov-31 Mar.
Min Mail Order UK: Nmc
Min Mail Order EU: Nmc
Cat. Cost: €3.50
Credit Cards: Visa MasterCard
Specialities: Plants & hedging suitable for seaside locations. Rare plants originating from Australia & New Zealand esp. *Phormium*, *Astelia*.
Notes: Also sells wholesale.
Map Ref: I, B1

ITim **Timpany Nurseries & Gardens** ⊠ ⌂ ♿
77 Magheratimpany Road, Ballynahinch, Co. Down, N. Ireland, BT24 8PA
Ⓣ (028) 9756 2812
Ⓕ (028) 9756 2812
Ⓔ s.tindall@btconnect.com
Ⓦ www.timpanynurseries.com

Contact: Susan Tindall
Opening Times: 1000-1730 Tue-Sat, Sun by appt.
Min Mail Order UK: Nmc
Min Mail Order EU: £30.00 + p&p
Cat. Cost: £2.00
Credit Cards: Visa MasterCard
Specialities: *Celmisia, Androsace, Primula, Saxifraga, Dianthus, Meconopsis, Cassiope, Rhodohypoxis, Cyclamen* & *Primula auricula*.
Notes: Also sells wholesale.
Map Ref: I, B3

IVic **Victoria's Garden**
Golden Mile, Upper Kells, Caherciveen, Co Kerry, Ireland
Ⓣ 00 353 (0)879 111465
Ⓔ kellshouse@eircom.net
Contact: Victoria Vogel
Opening Times: 1100-1500 Wed-Sun, 1st Apr-31st Oct. Closed Mon & Tue except B/hols. Other times by appt.
Specialities: *Rhododendron*, coastal plants, shrubs, herbaceous & some bulbs. Southern hemisphere plants. Please phone first to ensure plants are in stock.
Notes: Sells at some plants fairs.
Map Ref: I, D1

London Area

LAma **Jacques Amand International** ⊠ ✈ € ♿
The Nurseries, 145 Clamp Hill, Stanmore, Middlesex, HA7 3JS
Ⓣ (020) 8420 7110
Ⓕ (020) 8954 6784
Ⓔ bulbs@jacquesamand.co.uk
Ⓦ www.jacquesamand.com
Contact: John Amand & Stuart Chapman
Opening Times: 0900-1700 Mon-Fri, 1000-1400 Sat.
Min Mail Order UK: Nmc
Min Mail Order EU: Nmc
Cat. Cost: 1 × 1st class.
Credit Cards: All major credit/debit cards
Specialities: Rare and unusual species bulbs esp. *Arisaema, Trillium, Fritillaria*, tulips.
Notes: Also sells wholesale.
Map Ref: L, B3

LAst **Asterby & Chalkcroft Nursery** ♿
The Ridgeway, Blunham, Bedfordshire, MK44 3PH
Ⓣ (01767) 640148
Ⓔ sales@asterbyplants.co.uk
Ⓦ www.asterbyplants.co.uk
Contact: Simon & Eva Aldridge
Opening Times: 1000-1700 7 days. Closed Xmas & Jan.
Cat. Cost: 2 × 1st class.
Credit Cards: Visa MasterCard Switch
Specialities: Hardy shrubs, herbaceous & trees.
Map Ref: L, A3 **OS Grid Ref:** TL151497

LAyl **Aylett Nurseries Ltd** ♿ ◆
North Orbital Road, St Albans, Hertfordshire, AL2 1DH
Ⓣ (01727) 822255
Ⓕ (01727) 823024
Ⓔ info@aylettnurseries.co.uk
Ⓦ www.aylettnurseries.co.uk
Contact: Roger S Aylett
Opening Times: 0830-1730 Mon-Fri, 0830-1700 Sat, 1030-1630 Sun.
Cat. Cost: Free.
Credit Cards: All major credit/debit cards
Specialities: *Dahlia*. 2-acre trial ground adjacent to garden centre.
Notes: Also sells wholesale.

LBee **Beechcroft Nursery** ♿
127 Reigate Road, Ewell, Surrey, KT17 3DE
Ⓣ (020) 8393 4265
Ⓕ (020) 8393 4265
Contact: C Kimber
Opening Times: 1000-1600 Mon-Sat, 1000-1400 Sun and B/hols. Closed Xmas-New Year week.
Cat. Cost: None issued.
Credit Cards: All major credit/debit cards
Specialities: Conifers & alpines.
Notes: Also sells wholesale.
Map Ref: L, C3

LBMP **Blooming Marvellous Plants** (Delivers to shows)
Korketts Farm, Aylesbury Road, Shipton, Winslow, Buckinghamshire, MK18 3JL
Ⓜ 07963 747305
Ⓔ alex@bmplants.co.uk
Ⓦ www.bmplants.co.uk
Contact: Alexia Ballance
Opening Times: 0900-1700 Mon-Sat & 1000-1600 Sun, 1st Mar-30th Sep. 1000-1600 Sat & by appt. Oct-Dec. By appt. only in Jan & Feb.
Credit Cards: All major credit/debit cards
Specialities: A mixture of unusual and familiar perennials, shrubs, grasses, ferns &

KEY
⊠ Mail order to UK or EU — (Delivers to shows symbol) Delivers to shows
✈ Exports beyond EU — € Euro accepted
♿ Accessible by wheelchair — ◆ See Display advertisement

bedding plants, most in more generous sizes than usually found in nurseries.
Notes: Located on the A413 just outside Winslow (in the Aylesbury direction). Partial wheelchair access.
Map Ref: L, A2 **OS Grid Ref:** SP777271

LBuc **Buckingham Nurseries** ⊠ € ♿ ◆
14 Tingewick Road, Buckingham,
MK18 4AE
Ⓣ (01280) 822133
Ⓕ (01280) 815491
Ⓔ enquiries@buckingham-nurseries.co.uk
Ⓦ www.buckingham-nurseries.co.uk
Contact: R J & P L Brown
Opening Times: 0830-1730 (1800 in summer) Mon-Sat, 1030-1630 Sun.
Min Mail Order UK: Nmc
Min Mail Order EU: Nmc
Cat. Cost: Free.
Credit Cards: Visa MasterCard Switch
Specialities: Bare rooted and container grown hedging. Trees, shrubs, herbaceous perennials, alpines, grasses & ferns.
Map Ref: L, A2 **OS Grid Ref:** SP675333

LBur **Burton Grange Nursery** ⊠
Rags Lane, Cheshunt, Hertfordshire,
EN7 6TE
Ⓣ 0844 800 9464
Ⓕ 0844 800 9465
Ⓔ info@burtongrangenursery.com
Ⓦ www.burtongrangenursery.com
Contact: Shelley Antscherl
Opening Times: Not open. Mail order only.
Min Mail Order UK: 5 cuttings + p&p
Min Mail Order EU: 5 cuttings + p&p
Cat. Cost: Online only.
Credit Cards: All major credit/debit cards
Specialities: Tropical *Hibiscus*. Rooted cuttings & mature plants. Many unusual varieties. Some stocked in small quantities only.
Notes: Also sells wholesale.
Map Ref: L, B4

LCla **Clay Lane Nursery** ⊠ ⌂
3 Clay Lane, South Nutfield, Nr Redhill,
Surrey, RH1 4EG
Ⓣ (01737) 823307
Ⓔ claylane.nursery@btinternet.com
Ⓦ www.claylane-fuchsias.co.uk
Contact: K W Belton
Opening Times: 1000-1700 Tue-Sun 1st Feb-30th Jun. Other times by appt. Please phone before travelling.
Min Mail Order UK: £7.00
Cat. Cost: 4 × 2nd class.
Credit Cards: None
Specialities: *Fuchsia*. Many varieties in small quantities only.
Notes: Mail order by telephone pre-arangement only.
Map Ref: L, C4

LCtg **Cottage Garden Nursery** ◆
Barnet Road, Arkley,
Barnet, Hertfordshire,
EN5 3JX
Ⓣ (020) 8441 8829
Ⓕ (020) 8531 3178
Ⓔ nurseryinfo@cottagegardennursery-barnet.co.uk
Ⓦ www.cottagegardennursery-barnet.co.uk
Contact: David and Wendy Spicer
Opening Times: 0930-1700 Tue-Sat Mar-Oct, 0930-1600 Tue-Sat Nov-Feb, 1000-1600 Sun & B/hol Mon all year.
Cat. Cost: None issued.
Credit Cards: All major credit/debit cards
Specialities: General range of hardy shrubs, trees & perennials. Architectural & exotics, *Fuchsia*, seasonal bedding, patio plants.
Map Ref: L, B3 **OS Grid Ref:** TQ226958

LDai **Daisy Roots** ⊠ ⌂
(office) 8 Gosselin Road, Bengeo,
Hertford, Hertfordshire,
SG14 3LG
Ⓣ (01992) 582401
Ⓕ (01992) 582401
Ⓔ anne@daisyroots.com
Ⓦ www.daisyroots.com
Contact: Anne Godfrey
Opening Times: 1000-1600 Fri & Sat Mar-Oct, or by appt.
Min Mail Order UK: Nmc
Cat. Cost: 4 × 1st class.
Credit Cards: All major credit/debit cards
Specialities: Ever-increasing range of choice & unusual perennials, particularly *Agastache*, *Anthemis*, *Centaurea*, *Digitalis*, *Erysimum*, *Salvia* & *Sedum*.
Notes: Also sells wholesale. Nursery is at Jenningsbury, London Road, Hertford Heath.
Map Ref: L, B4

LDea **Derek Lloyd Dean** ⊠ ☒ ⌂
8 Lynwood Close, South Harrow, Middlesex,
HA2 9PR
Ⓣ (020) 8864 0899
Ⓔ lloyddeancbtinternet.com
Ⓦ www.dereklloyddean.com
Contact: Derek Lloyd Dean
Opening Times: Not open. Mail order only.
Min Mail Order UK: £2.50 + p&p

Min Mail Order EU: £2.50 + p&p
Cat. Cost: 2 × 1st class.
Credit Cards: None
Specialities: Regal, angel, ivy & scented leaf *Pelargonium*. Nat. Collection of Angel *Pelargonium*.

LEdu **EDULIS** ⊠ ⌂ € ♿
(office) 1 Flowers Piece, Ashampstead, Berkshire, RG8 8SG
Ⓣ (01635) 578113
Ⓕ (01635) 578113
Ⓔ edulis.nursery@virgin.net
Ⓦ www.edulis.co.uk
Contact: Paul Barney
Opening Times: By appt. only.
Min Mail Order UK: £10.00 + p&p
Min Mail Order EU: £50.00 + p&p
Cat. Cost: 6 × 1st class.
Credit Cards: None
Specialities: Unusual edibles, architectural plants, permaculture plants.
Notes: Also sells wholesale. Nursery is at Bere Court Farm, Tidmarsh Lane, Pangbourne, RG8 8HT.
Map Ref: L, B2 **OS Grid Ref:** SU615747

LFCN **FARNHAM COMMON NURSERIES LTD** ♿
Crown Lane, Farnham Royal, Nr Slough, Bucks, SL2 3SF
Ⓣ (01753) 643108
Ⓕ (01753) 646818
Ⓔ sales@fcn.co.uk
Ⓦ www.fcn.co.uk
Contact: Elizabeth Apedaile
Opening Times: 0800-1700 Mon-Fri, 0900-1700 Sat, 1000-1600 Sun (w/end retail only).
Cat. Cost: No retail cat. issued.
Credit Cards: All major credit/debit cards
Specialities: Good selection of ornamental trees, shrubs & herbaceous perennials, esp. *Pittosporum*, *Phormium*, *Iris* & *Heuchera*.
Notes: Also sells wholesale.
Map Ref: L, B3 **OS Grid Ref:** SU955832

LFol **FOLIAGE SCENTED & HERB PLANTS** ♿
Walton Poor, Crocknorth Road, Ranmore Common, Dorking, Surrey, RH5 6SX
Ⓣ (01483) 282273
Ⓕ (01483) 282273
Contact: Mrs Prudence Calvert
Opening Times: Open during Apr-Sep, please phone for appt. if possible.
Cat. Cost: 3 × 2nd class.
Credit Cards: None
Specialities: Herbs, aromatic & scented plants.
Map Ref: L, C3 **OS Grid Ref:** TQ141278

LFur **FURZE PARK NURSERY** ⊠ ⌂
Furze Park Farm, Bycell Road, Maids Moreton, Buckingham, Buckinghamshire, MK18 5AA
Ⓣ (01280) 821999
Ⓔ lucyhyde@btinternet.com
Contact: Lucy Hyde
Opening Times: 1000-1700 Thu & Fri. Other days by appt. Closed 1st Nov-3rd Apr.
Min Mail Order UK: Nmc
Cat. Cost: 2 × 1st class.
Credit Cards: None
Specialities: Friendly & helpful nursery specialising in new & unusual hardy perennials, many woodlanders incl. Himalayan & Japanese *Arisaema*.
Map Ref:

LGod **GODLY'S ROSES** ⊠ ♿
Redbourn, St Albans, Hertfordshire, AL3 7PS
Ⓣ (01582) 792255
Ⓕ (01582) 794267
Contact: Colin Godly
Opening Times: 0900-1700 summer, 7 days. 0900-dusk winter, 7 days. Closed Xmas to New Year's Day.
Min Mail Order UK: Nmc
Cat. Cost: Free
Credit Cards: Visa American Express Switch MasterCard
Specialities: Roses.
Notes: Standard roses not sent mail order. Also sells wholesale.
Map Ref: L, B3 **OS Grid Ref:** TL096137

LHel **HERTS HELLEBORES** ⊠ €
Sandersted, Giffords Lane, Haultwick, Hertfordshire, SG11 1JE
Ⓣ (01920) 438458
Ⓔ lorna@herts-hellebore.co.uk
Ⓦ www.herts-hellebores.co.uk
Contact: Lorna Jones
Opening Times: Not open. Mail order only. Special w/end sale, phone for date & details.
Min Mail Order UK: £18
Min Mail Order EU: £18
Cat. Cost: Free.
Credit Cards: All major credit/debit cards
Specialities: *Hellebore* hybrids. Specialising in developments of double & anemone centred hybrids. Seed-raised plants offered by colour. Some available in small quantities only.

KEY
⊠ Mail order to UK or EU ⌂ Delivers to shows
✈ Exports beyond EU € Euro accepted
♿ Accessible by wheelchair ◆ See Display advertisement

L

L

LHop **Hopleys Plants Ltd** ⊠ ♦
High Street, Much Hadham, Hertfordshire, SG10 6BU
Ⓣ (01279) 842509
Ⓕ (01279) 843784
Ⓔ plants@hopleys.co.uk
Ⓦ www.hopleys.co.uk
Contact: Aubrey Barker
Opening Times: 0900-1700 Mon & Wed-Sat, 1400-1700 Sun. Closed Nov-Feb except by appt.
Min Mail Order UK: Nmc
Cat. Cost: 5 × 1st class.
Credit Cards: Visa Access Switch
Specialities: Wide range of hardy & half-hardy shrubs & perennials.
Map Ref: L, A4 **OS Grid Ref:** TL428196

LHyd **Hydon Nurseries** ⊠ € ♦
Clock Barn Lane, Hydon Heath, Godalming, Surrey, GU8 4AZ
Ⓣ (01483) 860252
Ⓕ (01483) 419937
Contact: A F George, Rodney Longhurst & Mrs A M George
Opening Times: 0930-1245 & 1400-1700 Mon-Sat, Feb-mid Jun & Oct-mid Nov, except Sat Oct-mid Mar 0930-1245 only. Other months 0930-1600 Mon-Fri, 0930-1245 Sat. Sun by appt.
Min Mail Order UK: Nmc
Min Mail Order EU: £25.00 + p&p
Cat. Cost: £2.00 or 7 × 1st class or 10 × 2nd class.
Credit Cards: None
Specialities: Large and dwarf *Rhododendron*, *yakushimanum* hybrids, azaleas (deciduous & evergreen), *Camellia* & other trees & shrubs. Specimen *Rhododendron*. Conservatory: scented tender rhododendrons & camellias.
Notes: Also sells wholesale.

LIMB **I.M.B. Plants** ⊠
2 Ashdown Close, Giffard Park, Milton Keynes, Buckinghamshire, MK14 5PX
Ⓣ (01908) 618911
Ⓔ imbrazier@btinternet.com
Contact: Ian Brazier
Opening Times: Not open. Mail order only.
Min Mail Order UK: Nmc
Credit Cards: None
Specialities: *Helianthemum*. All plants propagated in small quantities. Will propagate to order.

LLHF **Little Heath Farm (UK) (formerly Two Jays Alpines)**
Little Heath Lane, Potten End, Berkhamsted, Hertfordshire, HP4 2RY
Ⓣ (01442) 864951
Ⓕ (01442) 864951
Ⓔ john.spokes@talk21.com
Ⓦ www.littleheathfarmnursery.co.uk
Contact: John Spokes
Opening Times: 1000-1700 or dusk if earlier, 7 days.
Cat. Cost: Online only.
Credit Cards: Visa MasterCard
Specialities: Large range of alpines, herbaceous, shrubs, many available in small quantities only.
Map Ref: L, B3

LLWG **Lilies Water Gardens** ⊠
Broad Lane, Newdigate, Surrey, RH5 5AT
Ⓣ (01306) 631064
Ⓕ (01306) 631693
Ⓔ mail@lilieswatergardens.co.uk
Ⓦ www.lilieswatergardens.co.uk
Contact: Simon Harman
Opening Times: 0900-1700 Tues-Sat, Mar-Aug. By appt. only Sep-Feb.
Min Mail Order UK: Nmc, but flat rate £10.00 delivery charge.
Cat. Cost: Online only.
Credit Cards: All major credit/debit cards
Specialities: Waterlilies, moist herbaceous. Astilbes, primulas, marginal plants. Tropical & semi-tropical frost-tender marginal & bog-garden plants. Dry-loving plants, attractive to bees & butterflies. Ferns, alpines.
Map Ref: L, C3

LLWP **L W Plants** ⊠
23 Wroxham Way, Harpenden, Hertfordshire, AL5 4PP
Ⓣ (01582) 768467
Ⓔ lwplants@waitrose.com
Ⓦ www.thymus.co.uk
Contact: Mrs Margaret Easter
Opening Times: 1000-1700 most days, but please phone first.
Min Mail Order UK: Nmc
Cat. Cost: A5 sae + 5 × 2nd class (loose).
Credit Cards: None
Specialities: Plants from a plantsman's garden, esp. *Geranium*, grasses, *Penstemon* & *Thymus*. Nat. Collections of *Thymus* (Scientific), *Hyssopus* & *Satureja*.
Notes: Mail order *Thymus* only.
Map Ref: L, B3 **OS Grid Ref:** TL141153

LMaj **Majestic Trees**
Chequers Meadow, Chequers Hill, Flamstead, St Albans, Hertfordshire, AL3 8ET
Ⓣ (01582) 843881
Ⓕ (01582) 843882
Ⓔ info@majesticgroup.co.uk

Ⓦ www.majestictrees.co.uk
Contact: Sarah Shynn
Opening Times: 0830-1700 Mon-Fri. 1000-1600 (1700 Mar-Oct) Sat. Closed Sun, B/hols & Xmas/New Year.
Cat. Cost: 6 × 1st class.
Credit Cards: MasterCard Visa Switch Maestro
Specialities: Semi-mature & mature containerised trees grown in airpot from 50ltr to 5000 ltr.
Notes: Also sells wholesale.
Map Ref: L, B3 **OS Grid Ref:** TL08140815

LMil **Millais Nurseries** ⊠ ♿
Crosswater Lane, Churt,
Farnham, Surrey,
GU10 2JN
Ⓣ (01252) 792698
Ⓕ (01252) 792526
Ⓔ sales@rhododendrons.co.uk
Ⓦ www.rhododendrons.co.uk
Contact: David Millais
Opening Times: 1000-1300 & 1400-1700 Mon-Fri. Sat spring & autumn. Daily in May.
Min Mail Order UK: £30.00 + p&p
Min Mail Order EU: £100.00 + p&p
Cat. Cost: 4 × 1st class.
Credit Cards: All major credit/debit cards
Specialities: Rhododendrons, azaleas, magnolias & acers.
Notes: Mail order Sep-May only. Also sells wholesale.
Map Ref: L, C3 **OS Grid Ref:** SU856397

LMor **Morehavens** ⊠ ♿
Sandpit Hill, Buckland Common,
Tring, Hertfordshire,
HP23 6NG
Ⓣ (01494) 758642
Ⓦ www.camomilelawns.co.uk
Contact: B Farmer
Opening Times: Mail order only. Open only for collection.
Min Mail Order UK: £19.00
Min Mail Order EU: £19.00 + p&p
Cat. Cost: Free.
Credit Cards: None
Specialities: Camomile 'Treneague' and dwarf variety.
Notes: Also sells wholesale.

LOck **Ockley Court Nursery** ♿
Coles Lane, Ockley, Surrey, RH5 5LS
Ⓣ (01306) 713571
Ⓜ 07786 998743
Ⓕ (01306) 713755
Ⓔ ma_gibbison@hotmail.com
Contact: Martin Gibbison
Opening Times: 8000-1730 Spring-Autumn, 1000-1600 Winter.
Cat. Cost: £1.00 for stocklist.
Credit Cards: All major credit/debit cards
Specialities: *Clematis* & new herbaceous.
Notes: Does not accept American Express. Also sells wholesale.

LPal **The Palm Centre** ⊠ ✈ € ♿
Ham Central Nursery, opposite Riverside Drive, Ham Street, Ham, Richmond, Surrey, TW10 7HA
Ⓣ (020) 8255 6191
Ⓕ (020) 8255 6192
Ⓔ mail@palmcentre.co.uk
Ⓦ thepalmcentre.co.uk
Contact: Martin Gibbons
Opening Times: 0900-1700 (dusk in winter) 7 days. Admin & Order Dept. 0900-1700 Mon-Fri.
Min Mail Order UK: £10.00 + p&p
Min Mail Order EU: £10.00 + p&p
Cat. Cost: Free.
Credit Cards: Visa MasterCard Switch
Specialities: Palms & cycads, exotic & sub-tropical, hardy, half-hardy & tropical. Seedlings to mature trees. Also bamboos, tree ferns & many other exotics.
Notes: Also sells wholesale.

LPBA **Paul Bromfield – Aquatics** ⊠ ✈ € ♿
Maydencroft Lane, Gosmore, Hitchin, Hertfordshire, SG4 7QD
Ⓣ (01462) 457399
Ⓔ info@bromfieldaquatics.co.uk
Ⓦ www.bromfieldaquatics.co.uk
Contact: Debbie Edwards
Opening Times: Mail order only. Order online at website. Office open 1000-1700 Mon-Sat, Feb-Oct. Visitors please ring for appt.
Min Mail Order UK: £25.00 incl.
Min Mail Order EU: £100.00 incl.
Cat. Cost: Online only.
Credit Cards: Visa MasterCard Delta JCB Switch
Specialities: Water lilies, marginals & bog.
Notes: Also sells wholesale.

LPen **Penstemons by Colour** ⊠
Peterley Manor, Peterley, Prestwood, Great Missenden, Buckinghamshire, HP16 0HH
Ⓣ (01494) 866420

KEY
⊠ Mail order to UK or EU — Delivers to shows
✈ Exports beyond EU — € Euro accepted
♿ Accessible by wheelchair — ◆ See Display advertisement

Ⓕ (01494) 866420
Ⓔ debra.hughes1@virgin.net
Contact: Debra Hughes
Opening Times: Any time by appt.
Min Mail Order UK: Nmc
Cat. Cost: Free
Credit Cards: None
Specialities: *Penstemon.*
Map Ref: L, B3 **OS Grid Ref:** SU880994

LPio **Pioneer Nursery** ⊠ € ♿
Baldock Lane, Willian, Letchworth, Hertfordshire, SG6 2AE
Ⓣ (01462) 675858
Ⓔ milly@pioneerplants.com
Ⓦ www.pioneerplants.com
Contact: Nick Downing or John Hoyland
Opening Times: 0900-1700 Wed-Sat, Mar-Oct. 1000-1600 Thu-Sat, Nov, Dec & Feb.
Min Mail Order UK: £15.00 + p&p
Min Mail Order EU: €30
Cat. Cost: Online only.
Credit Cards: MasterCard Visa
Specialities: *Salvia*, tender perennials. Wide range of hard-to-find perennials & bulbs. Species *Pelargonium.*
Notes: Mail order via internet only. Also sells wholesale.
Map Ref: L, A3 **OS Grid Ref:** TL224307

LPJP **PJ's Palms and Exotics** ⊠ €
41 Salcombe Road, Ashford, Middlesex, TW15 3BS
Ⓣ (01784) 250181
Contact: Peter Jenkins
Opening Times: Mail order only 1st Mar-30th Nov. Visits by arrangement.
Min Mail Order UK: Nmc
Min Mail Order EU: Nmc
Cat. Cost: 2 × 1st class.
Credit Cards: None
Specialities: Palms, bananas & other exotic foliage plants, hardy & half-hardy. *Trachycarpus wagnerianus* seeds available. Plants available in small quantities.
Notes: Also sells wholesale.
Map Ref: L, B3

LPla **The Plant Specialist**
7 Whitefield Lane, Great Missenden, Buckinghamshire, HP16 0BH
Ⓣ (01494) 866650
Ⓕ (01494) 866650
Ⓔ enquire@theplantspecialist.co.uk
Ⓦ www.theplantspecialist.co.uk
Also sells wholesale
Contact: Sean Walter
Opening Times: 1000-1700 Wed-Sat, 1000-1600 Sun, Apr-Oct.
Cat. Cost: £1.00
Credit Cards: All major credit/debit cards
Specialities: Herbaceous perennials, grasses, half-hardy perennials, bulbs.
Notes: Also sells wholesale.

LRHS **Wisley Plant Centre (RHS)** ♿ ◆
RHS Garden, Wisley, Woking, Surrey, GU23 6QB
Ⓣ (01483) 211113
Ⓕ (01483) 212372
Ⓔ wisleyplantcentre@rhs.org.uk
Ⓦ www.rhs.org.uk/wisleyplantcentre
Opening Times: 0930-1700 Mon-Sat, Oct-Feb. 0930-1800 Mon-Sat, Mar-Sep. 1030-1630 Sun all year, browsing from 1000.
Cat. Cost: Online only.
Credit Cards: All major credit/debit cards
Specialities: Over 10,000 plants, many rare or unusual, reflecting the range of the RHS flagship garden at Wisley. Plants subject to seasonal availability. For plants not in stock, we operate a reservation service.
Notes: Programme of free special events throughout the year. Please ring or check website for details.
Map Ref: L, C3

LSee **Seeds by Size** ⊠ ☒ €
45 Crouchfield, Boxmoor, Hemel Hempstead, Hertfordshire, HP1 1PA
Ⓣ (01442) 251458
Ⓔ john-robert-size@seeds-by-size.co.uk
Ⓦ www.seeds-by-size.co.uk
Contact: John Robert Size
Opening Times: Not open. Mail order only.
Min Mail Order UK: Nmc
Min Mail Order EU: Nmc
Cat. Cost: Online only.
Credit Cards: Paypal
Specialities: Seeds. 19,000 varieties of flower, vegetable & herb seeds, including sweet peas, pansies, petunias, *Impatiens*, marigolds, ornamental grasses, cabbages, tomatoes, cauliflowers, herbs & onions. Oriental vegetables, hot peppers & sweet peppers.
Notes: Euros accepted only as cash payments. Also sells wholesale.

LShp **Squire's Garden Centre, Shepperton** ♿
Halliford Road, Upper Halliford, Shepperton, Middlesex, TW17 8RU
Ⓣ (01932) 784121
Ⓕ (01932) 780569
Ⓔ shepp.plants@squiresgardencentres.co.uk
Ⓦ www.squiresgardencentres.co.uk

Contact: Plant Area Manager
Opening Times: 0900-1800 Mon-Sat, 1030-1630 Sun.
Cat. Cost: None issued.
Credit Cards: All major credit/debit cards
Specialities: Roses.
Notes: Other garden centres in Middlesex & Surrey.
Map Ref: L, C3

LSou **SOUTHON PLANTS** ⊠ ♿
Mutton Hill, Dormansland, Lingfield, Surrey, RH7 6NP
Ⓣ (01342) 870150
Ⓔ info@southonplants.com
Ⓦ www.southonplants.com
Contact: Mr Southon
Opening Times: 0900-1730 Mar-Oct. For Nov, Dec & Jan please phone first.
Min Mail Order UK: Nmc
Cat. Cost: Online only.
Credit Cards: All major credit/debit cards
Specialities: New & unusual hardy & tender perennials, incl. many *Agapanthus*, *Coreopsis*, *Euphorbia*, *Heuchera* and variegated plants.
Notes: Mail order. Please phone/email for details.
Map Ref: L, C4

LSqH **SQUIRE'S GARDEN CENTRE, WEST HORSLEY** ♿
Epsom Road, West Horsley, Leatherhead, Surrey, KT24 6AR
Ⓣ (01483) 282911
Ⓕ (01483) 281380
Ⓔ hors.plants.squiresgardencentres.co.uk
Ⓦ www.squiresgardencentres.co.uk
Contact: Plant Area Manager
Opening Times: 0900-1800 Mon-Sat, 1030-1630 Sun.
Cat. Cost: None issued.
Credit Cards: All major credit/debit cards
Specialities: Herbaceous.
Notes: Other garden centres in Middlesex & Surrey.
Map Ref: L, C3

LSqu **SQUIRE'S GARDEN CENTRE, TWICKENHAM**
Sixth Cross Road, Twickenham, Middlesex, TW2 5PA
Ⓣ (020) 8977 9241
Ⓕ (020) 8943 4024
Ⓔ twic.plants@squiresgardencentres.co.uk
Ⓦ www.squiresgardencentres.co.uk
Contact: Plant Area Manager
Opening Times: 0900-1800 Mon-Sat, 1030-1630 Sun.
Cat. Cost: None issued.
Credit Cards: All major credit/debit cards
Specialities: *Clematis*.
Notes: Other garden centres in Middlesex & Surrey.
Map Ref: L, B3

LSRN **SPRING REACH NURSERY** ⊠ ⌂ ♿
Long Reach, Ockham, Guildford, Surrey, GU23 6PG
Ⓣ (01483) 284769
Ⓜ 07884 432666
Ⓕ (01483) 284769
Ⓔ info@springreachnursery.co.uk
Ⓦ www.giftaplant.com
Contact: Nick & Lissa Hourhan
Opening Times: 7 days. 1000-1700 Mon-Sat, 1030-1630 Sun. Open B/hols.
Min Mail Order UK: Nmc
Cat. Cost: 3 × 1st class.
Credit Cards: All major credit/debit cards
Specialities: Shrubs, evergreen climbers, *Clematis*, perennials, roses, grasses, ferns, bamboos, trees, plants for chalk & clay, deer & rabbit proof plants, hedging, specimen plants, acid-loving plants, soft fruit & top fruit.
Notes: Also sells wholesale.
Map Ref: L, C3

LStr **HENRY STREET NURSERY** ⊠ ♿
Swallowfield Road, Arborfield, Reading, Berkshire, RG2 9JY
Ⓣ (0118) 9761223
Ⓕ (0118) 9761417
Ⓔ info@henrystreet.co.uk
Ⓦ www.henrystreet.co.uk
Contact: Mr M C Goold
Opening Times: 0900-1730 Mon-Sat, 1030-1630 Sun.
Min Mail Order UK: Nmc
Min Mail Order EU: Nmc
Cat. Cost: Free
Credit Cards: Visa Access Switch
Specialities: Roses.
Notes: Also sells wholesale.
Map Ref: L, C3

LYaf **YAFFLES** ⊠ ♿
Harvest Hill, Bourne End, Buckinghamshire, SL8 5JJ
Ⓣ (01628) 525455
Contact: I Butterfield

KEY
⊠ Mail order to UK or EU ⌂ Delivers to shows
✈ Exports beyond EU € Euro accepted
♿ Accessible by wheelchair ◆ See Display advertisement

Opening Times: 0900-1300 & 1400-1700. Please phone beforehand in case we are attending shows.
Min Mail Order UK: Nmc
Min Mail Order EU: £30.00 + p&p
Cat. Cost: 2 × 2nd class.
Credit Cards: None
Specialities: Nat. Collection of *Pleione*. *Dahlia* for collection. Scientific Award 1999.
Notes: Only *Pleione* by mail order.
Map Ref: L, B3

L

Midlands

MACG **Ashdale Cottage Garden Plants** ♿
204 Lambley Lane, Gedling, Nottinghamshire, NG4 4PB
Ⓣ (0115) 966 6060
Ⓕ (0115) 966 6060
Contact: Stephen Mills
Opening Times: 0900-1700 Wed-Sun, Mar-Oct. Closed Nov-Feb.
Cat. Cost: None issued.
Credit Cards: All major credit/debit cards
Specialities: Wide range of rare and unusual herbaceous perennials.
Map Ref: M, B3

MAga **Agave Nursery** ⊠ ✈ €
15 Sleetmoor Lane, Somercotes, Derbyshire, DE55 1RB
Ⓜ 01773 605843 or 07814 787555 or 07791 627358
Ⓔ jon@agavenursery.wanadoo.co.uk
Ⓦ www.agave-nursery.co.uk
Contact: Jon & Sue Dudek
Opening Times: Mail order only. Open by appt. only.
Min Mail Order UK: Nmc
Min Mail Order EU: Nmc
Cat. Cost: Free
Credit Cards: None
Specialities: *Agave*, *Furcraea*, *Manfreda* & *Yucca*.
Map Ref: M, B2

MAJR **A J Robinson** ⊠
Sycamore Farm, Foston, Derbyshire, DE65 5PW
Ⓣ (01283) 815635
Ⓕ (01283) 815635
Contact: A J Robinson
Opening Times: By appt. for collection of plants only.
Min Mail Order UK: £13.00
Cat. Cost: 2 × 1st class for list.
Credit Cards: None
Specialities: Extensive collection of tender perennials. Salvias. Nat. Collection of *Argyranthemum*.
Notes: Mail order argyranthemums only.
Map Ref: M, B2

MArl **Arley Hall Nursery** ♿
Arley Hall Nursery, Northwich, Cheshire, CW9 6NA
Ⓣ (01565) 777479/777231
Ⓕ (01565) 777465
Ⓦ www.arleyhallandgardens.com
Contact: Jane Foster
Opening Times: 1100-1730 Tue-Sun Easter-end Sep. Also B/hol Mons.
Cat. Cost: 4 × 1st class.
Credit Cards: All major credit/debit cards
Specialities: Wide range of herbaceous incl. many unusual varieties, some in small quantities. Wide range of unusual pelargoniums.
Notes: Nursery is beside car park at Arley Hall Gardens.
Map Ref: M, A1 **OS Grid Ref:** SJ673808

MAsh **Ashwood Nurseries Ltd** ⊠ ⌂ ♿
Ashwood Lower Lane, Ashwood, Kingswinford, West Midlands, DY6 0AE
Ⓣ (01384) 401996
Ⓕ (01384) 401108
Ⓔ info@ashwoodnurseries.com
Ⓦ www.ashwoodnurseries.com
Contact: Mark Warburton & Philip Baulk
Opening Times: 0900-1700 Mon-Sat & 0930-1700 Sun excl. Xmas & Boxing Day.
Min Mail Order UK: £15.00
Cat. Cost: 6 × 1st class.
Credit Cards: Visa Access MasterCard
Specialities: Large range of hardy plants, shrubs & dwarf conifers. Also specialise in *Cyclamen*. Hellebores, *Hepatica*, *Hydrangea* & *Salvia*. Nat. Collections of *Lewisia*
Map Ref: M, C2 **OS Grid Ref:** SO865879

MAvo **Avondale Nursery** ⌂ ♿
(Office) 3 Avondale Road, Earlsdon, Coventry, Warwickshire, CV5 6DZ
Ⓣ (024) 766 73662
Ⓜ 07979 093096
Ⓕ (024) 766 73662
Ⓔ enquiries@avondalenursery.co.uk
Ⓦ www.avondalenursery.co.uk
Contact: Brian Ellis
Opening Times: 1000-1230, 1400-1700 Mon-Sat, 1030-1230, 1400-1630 Sun, Mar-Sep. Other times by appt.
Cat. Cost: 4 × 1st class.
Credit Cards: All major credit/debit cards
Specialities: Rare & unusual perennials esp.

Aster, *Eryngium*, *Leucanthemum*, *Geum*, *Crocosmia* & grasses. Display garden now open.
Notes: Nursery is at Russell's Nursery, Mill Hill, Baginton, Nr Coventry, CV8 3AG.
Map Ref: M, C2 **OS Grid Ref:** SP339751

MBar **Barncroft Nurseries** ♿
Dunwood Lane, Longsdon, Nr Leek, Stoke-on-Trent, Staffordshire, ST9 9QW
Ⓣ (01538) 384310
Ⓕ (01538) 384310
Ⓦ www.barncroftnurseries.com
Contact: S Warner
Opening Times: 1030-1730 or dusk if earlier Fri-Sun all year. Closed Xmas to New Year.
Cat. Cost: Online only.
Credit Cards: None
Specialities: Extensive range of over 2000 heathers, conifers, shrubs, trees, climbers, dwarf grasses & rhododendrons. Display garden containing 400 heather cvs.
Map Ref: M, B1 **OS Grid Ref:** SJ948552

MBec **Beechcroft Nurseries & Garden Centre** ♿ ◆
Madeley Road, Madeley Heath, Belbroughton, Stourbridge, West Midlands, DY9 9XA
Ⓣ (01562) 710358
Ⓕ (01562) 710507
Ⓔ mail@beechcroft.com
Ⓦ www.beechcroft.com
Contact: Paul Billingham
Opening Times: 0900-1730 Mon-Sat, 1100-1700 Sun. Close half-hour earlier in winter.
Credit Cards: All major credit/debit cards
Specialities: Shrubs, conifers, rhododendrons, azaleas, heathers, alpine & rockery plants, climbers & *Clematis*, outdoor ferns, wild flowers & trees. Large range of herbaceous perennials & roses.
Notes: Set in beautiful countryside just minutes from the centre of Birmingham & M5 Jct. 4. Does not accept American Express.
Map Ref: M, C2 **OS Grid Ref:** SO951772

MBel **Bluebell Cottage Gardens and Lodge Lane Nursery** ⊠ ♿
Lodge Lane, Dutton, Nr Warrington, Cheshire, WA4 4HP
Ⓣ (01928) 713718
Ⓕ (01928) 713718
Ⓔ info@lodgelane.co.uk
Ⓦ www.lodgelane.co.uk
Contact: Sue Beesley
Opening Times: 1000-1700 Wed-Sun & B/hols, mid Mar-mid Sep. By appt. outside these dates.
Min Mail Order UK: £10.00
Cat. Cost: By email or online.
Credit Cards: All major credit/debit cards
Specialities: Unusual perennials & shrubs incl. *Achillea*, *Allium*, *Astrantia*, *Campanula*, *Digitalis*, *Penstemon*, *Euphorbia*, *Geranium*, *Heuchera*, *Inula*, *Kniphofia*, *Nepeta*, *Papaver*, *Penstemon*, *Salvia* & ornamental grasses.
Notes: Plants delivered to Tatton Show.
Map Ref: M, A1 **OS Grid Ref:** SJ586779

MBlu **Bluebell Arboretum & Nursery** ⊠ ⌂ € ♿
Annwell Lane, Smisby, Nr Ashby de la Zouch, Derbyshire, LE65 2TA
Ⓣ (01530) 413700
Ⓕ (01530) 417600
Ⓔ sales@bluebellnursery.co.uk
Ⓦ www.bluebellnursery.com
Contact: Robert & Suzette Vernon
Opening Times: 0900-1700 Mon-Sat & 1030-1630 Sun Mar-Oct, 0900-1600 Mon-Sat (not Sun) Nov-Feb. Closed 24th Dec-1st Jan incl. & Easter Sun.
Min Mail Order UK: £9.50
Min Mail Order EU: Nmc
Cat. Cost: £1.50 + 3 × 1st class.
Credit Cards: Visa Access Switch MasterCard
Specialities: Uncommon trees & shrubs. Woody climbers. Display garden & arboretum.
Map Ref: M, B1 **OS Grid Ref:** SK344187

MBNS **Barnsdale Gardens** ⊠ ⌂ ♿ ◆
Exton Avenue, Exton, Oakham, Rutland, LE15 8AH
Ⓣ (01572) 813200
Ⓕ (01572) 813346
Ⓔ info@barnsdaleplants.co.uk
Ⓦ www.barnsdaleplants.co.uk
Contact: Nick or Sue Hamilton
Opening Times: 0900-1700 Mar-May & Sep-Oct, 0900-1900 Jun-Aug, 1000-1600 Nov-Feb, 7 days. Closed 23rd & 25th Dec.
Min Mail Order UK: Nmc
Min Mail Order EU: Nmc
Cat. Cost: A5 + 5 × 1st class.
Credit Cards: All major credit/debit cards
Specialities: Wide range of choice & unusual garden plants. Over 160 varieties of *Penstemon*, over 250 varieties of *Hemerocallis*.
Map Ref: M, B3 **OS Grid Ref:** SK912108

KEY
⊠ Mail order to UK or EU ⌂ Delivers to shows
✈ Exports beyond EU € Euro accepted
♿ Accessible by wheelchair ◆ See Display advertisement

M

MBPg **BARNFIELD PELARGONIUMS** ⊠
Barnfield, Off Wilnecote Lane, Belgrave, Tamworth, Staffordshire, B77 2LF
Ⓣ (01827) 250123
Ⓕ (01827) 250123
Ⓔ brianandjenniewhite@hotmail.com
Contact: Jennie & Brian White
Opening Times: Open by appt. only.
Min Mail Order UK: £6.00
Min Mail Order EU: £10.00
Cat. Cost: 4 × 2nd class.
Credit Cards: None
Specialities: Over 200 varieties of scented leaf pelargoniums.

MBri **BRIDGEMERE NURSERIES** € ♿ ◆
Bridgemere, Nr Nantwich, Cheshire, CW5 7QB
Ⓣ (01270) 521100
Ⓕ (01270) 520215
Ⓔ info@bridgemere.co.uk
Ⓦ www.bridgemere.co.uk
Contact: Keith Atkey, Roger Pierce
Opening Times: 0900-1900 7 days, summer. 0900-1800 winter. Closed 25th & 26th Dec.
Cat. Cost: None issued.
Credit Cards: Visa Access MasterCard Switch
Specialities: Huge range outdoor & indoor plants, many rare & unusual. Specimen shrubs.
Map Ref: M, B1 **OS Grid Ref:** SJ727435

MBrN **BRIDGE NURSERY** € ♿
Tomlow Road, Napton-on-the-Hill, Nr Rugby, Warwickshire, CV47 8HX
Ⓣ (01926) 812737
Ⓔ pemartino@tiscali.co.uk
Ⓦ www.Bridge-Nursery.co.uk
Contact: Christine Dakin & Philip Martino
Opening Times: 1000-1600 Mon-Sun 1st Feb-mid Dec. Other times by appt.
Cat. Cost: 4 × 1st class.
Credit Cards: All major credit/debit cards
Specialities: Ornamental grasses, sedges & bamboos. Also range of shrubs & perennials. Display garden.
Notes: Also sells wholesale.
Map Ref: M, C2 **OS Grid Ref:** SP463625

MCCP **COLLECTORS CORNER PLANTS** ⊠ ⌂
33 Rugby Road, Clifton-upon-Dunsmore, Rugby, Warwickshire, CV23 0DE
Ⓣ (01788) 571881
Contact: Pat Neesam
Opening Times: By appt. only.
Min Mail Order UK: £20.00
Cat. Cost: 6 × 1st class.
Credit Cards: None
Specialities: General range of choice herbaceous perennials, grasses, shrubs, palms, ferns & bamboos.
Map Ref: M, C3

MCoo **COOL TEMPERATE** ⊠ ✈
(office) 45 Stamford Street, Awsworth, Nottinghamshire, NG16 2QL
Ⓣ (0115) 916 2673
Ⓕ (0115) 916 2673
Ⓔ phil.corbett@cooltemperate.co.uk
Ⓦ www.cooltemperate.co.uk
Contact: Phil Corbett
Opening Times: 0900-1700, 7 days. Please ring/write first.
Min Mail Order UK: Nmc
Min Mail Order EU: Nmc
Cat. Cost: 3 × 1st class.
Credit Cards: None
Specialities: Tree fruit, soft fruit, nitrogen-fixers, hedging, own-root fruit trees. Many species available in small quantities only.
Notes: Also sells wholesale. Nursery at Trinity Farm, Awsworth Lane, Cossall, Notts.
Map Ref: M, B2 **OS Grid Ref:** SK482435

MCot **COTON MANOR GARDEN**
Guilsborough, Northampton, Northamptonshire, NN6 8RQ
Ⓣ (01604) 740219
Ⓕ (01604) 740838
Ⓔ nursery@cotonmanor.co.uk
Ⓦ www.cotonmanor.co.uk
Contact: Caroline Tait
Opening Times: 1200-1730 Tue-Sat, 1st April (or Easter if earlier) to 30th Sep. Also Sun Apr, May & B/hol w/ends. Other times in working hours by appt.
Cat. Cost: None issued.
Credit Cards: MasterCard Visa
Specialities: Wide-range of herbaceous perennials (3000+ varieties), some available in small quantities only. Also tender perennials & selected shrubs.
Notes: Garden open. Tea rooms. Garden School. Partial wheelchair access.
Map Ref: M, C3 **OS Grid Ref:** SP675715

MCri **CRIN GARDENS** ⊠ €
79 Partons Road, Kings Heath, Birmingham, B14 6TD
Ⓣ (0121) 443 3815
Ⓕ (0121) 443 3815
Ⓔ cringardens@tiscali.co.uk
Contact: M Milinkovic
Opening Times: Not open. Mail order only.
Min Mail Order UK: Nmc
Min Mail Order EU: Nmc

Cat. Cost: 2 × 1st class.
Credit Cards: None
Specialities: Lilies. Limited stock available on first come, first served basis.

MDKP **D K Plants** (Delivers to shows)
(Office) 19 Harbourne Road, Cheadle, Stoke on Trent, Staffordshire, ST10 1JU
Ⓣ (01538) 754460 (office)
Ⓜ 07779 545015 (nursery)
Ⓔ davidknoxc@aol.com
Contact: Dave Knox
Opening Times: 0900-2000 (or dusk if earlier) Mon-Tue & Thu-Fri. Other times by appt.
Cat. Cost: 4 × 1st class A4 sae plus 44p 1st or 37p 2nd class.
Credit Cards: None
Specialities: Unusual hardy alpines & perennials. All grown on the nursery.
Notes: Nursery is at new roundabout across from Queen's Arms pub, Freehay Crossroads, Freehay, Cheadle, ST10 1TR.
Map Ref: M, B1

MDun **Dunge Valley Gardens** € ♿
Windgather Rocks, Kettleshulme, High Peak, Cheshire, SK23 7RF
Ⓣ (01663) 733787
Ⓕ (01663) 733787
Ⓔ david@dungevalley.co.uk
Ⓦ www.dungevalley.co.uk
Contact: David Ketley
Opening Times: 1030-1700 Thu-Sun Mar-Jun. 1030-1700 Sat & Sun Jul & Aug. Open B/hols. Otherwise by appt.
Cat. Cost: Online only.
Credit Cards: All major credit/debit cards
Specialities: *Rhododendron* species & hybrids. Azaleas, acers, *Meconopsis*, shrubs & perennials, some rare & wild collected.
Notes: Also sells wholesale.
Map Ref: M, A2 **OS Grid Ref:** SJ989777

MFie **Field House Nursery** ⊠ € ♿
Leake Road, Gotham, Nottinghamshire, NG11 0JN
Ⓣ (01159) 372537
Ⓕ (01159) 831486
Ⓔ val.woolley@btinternet.com
Contact: Valerie A Woolley
Opening Times: 0900-1600 Fri-Wed or by appt.
Min Mail Order UK: 4 plants.
Min Mail Order EU: £30.00
Cat. Cost: 4 × 1st class or 4 × IRC.
Credit Cards: Visa MasterCard Electron Maestro Solo
Specialities: *Primula auricula* & seed. Nat. Collection of *Primula auricula* (Shows & Alpines).
Notes: Mail order for auriculas, small *Primula*, & seeds.

MGan **Gandy's (Roses) Ltd** ⊠
North Kilworth, Nr Lutterworth, Leicestershire, LE17 6HZ
Ⓣ (01858) 880398
Ⓕ (01858) 880433
Ⓔ sales@gandys-roses.co.uk
Ⓦ www.gandys-roses.co.uk
Contact: Miss R D Gandy
Opening Times: 0930-1630 Mon-Sat.
Min Mail Order UK: Nmc
Min Mail Order EU: £25.00 + p&p
Cat. Cost: Free
Credit Cards: All major credit/debit cards
Specialities: Wide range of rose varieties, hardy nursery stock & fruit.
Notes: Also sells wholesale.

MGos **Goscote Nurseries Ltd** ♿ ◆
Syston Road, Cossington, Leicestershire, LE7 4UZ
Ⓣ (01509) 812121
Ⓕ (01509) 814231
Ⓔ sales@goscote.co.uk
Ⓦ www.goscote.co.uk
Contact: James Toone, Brian Phipps
Opening Times: 7 days, year round, apart from between Xmas & New Year.
Cat. Cost: Online only.
Credit Cards: Visa Access MasterCard Delta Switch
Specialities: Japanese maples, rhododendrons & azaleas, *Magnolia*, *Camellia*, *Pieris* & other *Ericaceae*. Ornamental trees & shrubs, conifers, fruit, heathers, alpines, roses, *Clematis* & unusual climbers. Show Garden to visit.
Notes: Design & landscaping service available. Also sells wholesale.
Map Ref: M, B3 **OS Grid Ref:** SK602130

MHav **Haven Nurseries Ltd.** ⊠ ♿
Crab Lane, Bobbington, Nr Stourbridge, West Midlands, DY7 5DZ
Ⓣ (01384) 221543
Ⓕ (01384) 221320
Ⓔ info@havennurseries.co.uk
Ⓦ www.havennurseries.co.uk

KEY
⊠ Mail order to UK or EU — Delivers to shows
Exports beyond EU — € Euro accepted
♿ Accessible by wheelchair — ◆ See Display advertisement

M

Contact: Lynda Brettell
Opening Times: 0900-1730 Mon-Sat, 1000-1700 Sun, Mar-Oct. 0900-1630 Mon-Sat, 1030-1600 Sun, Nov-Feb.
Min Mail Order UK: Nmc
Cat. Cost: 4 × 1st class.
Credit Cards: All major credit/debit cards
Specialities: *Fuchsia*, *Geranium*, roses. Wide range of shrubs, conifers, home-grown bedding & many unusual cottage garden plants.
Notes: Also sells wholesale. Does not accept American Express. Mail order bare-root roses only.
Map Ref: M, C2

MHer **The Herb Nursery** ♿
Thistleton, Oakham, Rutland, LE15 7RE
Ⓣ (01572) 767658
Ⓔ herbnursery@southwitham.net
Ⓦ www.herbnursery.co.uk
Contact: Peter Bench
Opening Times: 0900-1800 (or dusk) 7 days excl. Xmas-New Year.
Cat. Cost: A5 sae.
Credit Cards: None
Specialities: Herbs, wild flowers, cottage garden plants, scented-leaf pelargoniums. Esp. *Thymus*, *Mentha*, *Lavandula*.
Map Ref: M, B3

MHom **Homestead Plants** ⊠
The Homestead, Normanton, Bottesford, Nottingham, NG13 0EP
Ⓣ (01949) 842745
Ⓕ (01949) 842745
Contact: Mrs S Palmer
Opening Times: By appt.
Min Mail Order UK: Nmc
Cat. Cost: 4 × 2nd class.
Credit Cards: None
Specialities: Unusual hardy & half-hardy perennials, esp. *Paeonia* species. *Hosta*, *Jovibarba*, *Salvia*, *Sempervivum* & *Heliotrope*. Drought-tolerant asters. Most available only in small quantities. Nat. Collection of *Heliotropium* cultivars.
Map Ref: M, B3 **OS Grid Ref:** SK812407

MHrb **The Herb Garden** ⊠ ♿
Kingston House Estate, Race Farm Lane, Kingston Bagpuize, Oxfordshire, OX13 5AU
Ⓣ (01865) 823101
Ⓕ (01865) 820159
Ⓔ vcjw37@yahoo.com
Ⓦ www.KingstonHerbGarden.co.uk
Contact: Val Williams
Opening Times: Phone for appt. or check website for details.
Min Mail Order UK: £20
Cat. Cost: 2 × 1st class.
Credit Cards: None
Specialities: Small nursery specialising in the more unusual lavenders, herbs, dye plants, olive & citrus fruit trees according to season, displayed in a walled garden setting.
Map Ref: M, D2

MJac **Jackson's Nurseries**
Clifton Campville, Nr Tamworth, Staffordshire, B79 0AP
Ⓣ (01827) 373307
Contact: N Jackson
Opening Times: 0900-1800 Mon Wed-Sat, 1000-1700 Sun.
Cat. Cost: 2 × 1st class.
Credit Cards: None
Specialities: *Fuchsia*.
Notes: Also sells wholesale.
Map Ref: M, B1

MJon **C & K Jones** ⊠ ✈ € ♿
Golden Fields Nurseries, Barrow Lane, Tarvin, Cheshire, CH3 8JF
Ⓣ (01829) 740663
Ⓕ (01829) 741877
Ⓔ ck.jones@btconnect.com
Ⓦ www.jonestherose.co.uk
Contact: Keith Jones
Opening Times: Office hours 0930-1600 Fri-Mon. 1st w/end in each month only & the Fri & Mon either side. Closed Jan & Feb.
Min Mail Order UK: 1 plant + p&p
Min Mail Order EU: Nmc.
Cat. Cost: £1.00
Credit Cards: MasterCard Visa Maestro Electron Solo
Specialities: Roses.
Notes: Also sells wholesale.
Map Ref: M, B1

MKay **Kayes Garden Nursery** ♿
1700 Melton Road, Rearsby, Leicestershire, LE7 4YR
Ⓣ (01664) 424578
Ⓔ hazelkaye.kgn@nascr.net
Contact: Hazel Kaye
Opening Times: 1000-1700 Tue-Sat & B/hols 1000-1200 Sun Mar-Oct. By appt. Nov, Dec & Feb. Closed Jan.
Cat. Cost: 2 × 1st class.
Credit Cards: None
Specialities: Herbaceous, climbers & aquatic plants. Grasses. Nat. Collection of *Tradescantia* Andersoniana Group.
Map Ref: M, B3 **OS Grid Ref:** SK648140

MLBr **LEATHERBRITCHES KITCHEN GARDEN & NURSERY** ♿
(Office) 6 Sycamore Cottages,
Parwich, Ashbourne, Derbyshire,
DE6 1QL
Ⓣ (01335) 390571 answerphone
Ⓜ 07713 743295
Ⓔ leatherbritchesnursery@yahoo.com
Contact: Bill Whitfield
Opening Times: 1000-1700, 7 days (times vary in winter & poor weather).
Credit Cards: None
Specialities: Herbaceous, shrubs, alpines, bedding.
Notes: Nursery is situated opposite the Bentley Brook Inn, Bakewell Rd (A5056), Fenny Bentley, Ashbourne, DE6 1LF.
Map Ref: M, A2 **OS Grid Ref:** SK185503

MLea **LEA RHODODENDRON GARDENS LTD** ⊠ ✈ ♿
Lea, Matlock, Derbyshire, DE4 5GH
Ⓣ (01629) 534380/534260
Ⓕ (01629) 534260
Ⓦ www.leagarden.co.uk
Contact: Peter Tye
Opening Times: 1000-1730 7 days 20 Mar-30 Jun. Out of season by appt.
Min Mail Order UK: £15.00 + p&p
Min Mail Order EU: £15.00 + p&p
Cat. Cost: 30p + sae.
Credit Cards: All major credit/debit cards
Specialities: Rhododendrons & azaleas.
Map Ref: M, B1 **OS Grid Ref:** SK324571

MLHP **LONGSTONE HARDY PLANT NURSERY** ♿
(office) Stancil House, Barn Furlong,
Great Longstone, Nr Bakewell, Derbyshire,
DE45 1TR
Ⓣ (01629) 640136
Ⓜ 07762 083674
Ⓔ lucyinlongstone@hotmail.com
Ⓦ www.longstonehardyplants.co.uk
Contact: Lucy Wright
Opening Times: 1300-1700 Tue-Sat & B/hols, 1st Apr-30th Sep. 1300-1700 Sat, Mar-Oct. Other times by appt.
Cat. Cost: 2 × 1st class.
Credit Cards: None
Specialities: Specialist peat-free nursery displaying all our own hardy perennials, ornamental grasses, herbs & shrubs, incl. many unusual varieties. Some stock available in small quantities only. Can propagate to order.
Notes: Nursery at Station Road 150 yds on right after turning onto it at the village green.
Map Ref: M, A2 **OS Grid Ref:** SK198717

MLod **LODGE FARM PLANTS & WILDFLOWERS** ⊠ ⌂ € ♿
Case Lane, Fiveways, Hatton, Warwickshire,
CV35 7JD
Ⓣ (01926) 484649
Ⓜ 07977 631368
Ⓕ (01926) 484649
Ⓔ lodgefarmplants@btinternet.com
Ⓦ www.lodgefarmplants.com
Contact: Janet Cook & Nick Cook
Opening Times: Open 7 days all year, except Xmas Day & Boxing Day.
Min Mail Order UK: Nmc
Cat. Cost: Online only.
Credit Cards: None
Specialities: Wildflowers. Vegetable plants, soft fruit, topiary. Native trees & hedging. Wildflower seeds. Fruit trees, espalier, fan, stepovers & cordons.
Notes: Also sells wholesale.
Map Ref: M, C2 **OS Grid Ref:** SP223700

MLul **LULWORTH PLANTS** ⌂ ♿
28 Gladstone Street, Wigston Magna,
Leicestershire, LE18 1AE
Ⓜ 07814 042889
Contact: Chris Huscroft
Opening Times: By appt. only.
Cat. Cost: Sae
Credit Cards: None
Specialities: *Arisaema*, plus small selection of shade-loving plants, small quantities only.
Map Ref: M, B3

MMHG **MORTON HALL GARDENS** ⊠ ⌂ ♿
Morton Hall, Ranby, Retford,
Nottinghamshire, DN22 8HW
Ⓣ (01777) 702530
Ⓔ gill@mortonhall.fsbusiness.co.uk
Ⓦ www.morton-nurseries.co.uk
Contact: Gill McMaster
Opening Times: By appt.only
Min Mail Order UK: £5.00 + p&p
Cat. Cost: 3 × 1st class.
Credit Cards: None
Specialities: Shrubs & perennials.
Map Ref: M, A3

MMoz **MOZART HOUSE NURSERY GARDEN** ⌂
84 Central Avenue, Wigston, Leicestershire,
LE18 2AA
Ⓣ (0116) 288 9548
Contact: Des Martin

KEY
⊠ Mail order to UK or EU ⌂ Delivers to shows
✈ Exports beyond EU € Euro accepted
♿ Accessible by wheelchair ◆ See Display advertisement

M

Opening Times: By appt. only.
Cat. Cost: 5 × 1st class.
Credit Cards: None
Specialities: Bamboos, ornamental grasses, rushes & sedges, ferns. Some stock available in small quantities.
Map Ref: M, C3

MMuc **Mucklestone Nurseries** ⊠ ♿ ◆
Rock Lane, Mucklestone, Nr Market Drayton, Shropshire, TF9 4DN
Ⓜ 07985 425829
Ⓔ info@botanyplants.com
Ⓦ www.botanyplants.com
Contact: Brian Watkins
Opening Times: 0900-1700 Fri-Sun, all year. Other times by appt.
Min Mail Order UK: Nmc
Cat. Cost: Online only.
Credit Cards: None
Specialities: Trees, shrubs, grasses & perennials for acid & damp soils of the north & west UK.
Map Ref: M, B2 **OS Grid Ref:** SJ728373

MNew **Newington Nurseries** € ♿
Newington, Wallingford, Oxfordshire, OX10 7AW
Ⓣ (01865) 400533
Ⓔ plants@newington-nurseries.co.uk
Ⓦ www.newington-nurseries.co.uk
Contact: Mrs A T Hendry
Opening Times: 1000-1700 Tues-Sun Mar-Oct, 1000-1600 Tues-Sun Nov-Feb.
Credit Cards: Access MasterCard Visa Switch
Specialities: Unusual cottage garden plants, alpines, hardy exotics, conservatory plants & herbs. Nat. Collection of *Alocasia* (*Araceae*).
Notes: Also sells wholesale.
Map Ref: M, D3

MNFA **The Nursery Further Afield** ⊠ ♿
Evenley Road, Mixbury, Nr Brackley, Northamptonshire, NN13 5YR
Ⓣ (01280) 848808
Ⓔ sinclair@nurseryfurtherafield.co.uk
Ⓦ www.nurseryfurtherafield.co.uk
Contact: Gerald & Mary Sinclair
Opening Times: 1000-1700 Wed-Sat, late Mar-end Sep. Other times by appt.
Min Mail Order UK: £15.00
Cat. Cost: 2 × 1st class.
Credit Cards: None
Specialities: Worthwhile hardy perennials, many unusual. Large selection of *Geranium* & *Hemerocallis*. Nat. Collection of *Hemerocallis*.
Notes: Mail order for *Hemerocallis* only.
Map Ref: M, C3 **OS Grid Ref:** SP608344

MNHC **The National Herb Centre** ⊠ ♿
Banbury Road, Warmington, Nr Banbury, Oxfordshire, OX17 1DF
Ⓣ (01295) 690999
Ⓕ (01295) 690034
Ⓦ www.herbcentre.co.uk
Contact: Plant Centre Staff
Opening Times: 0900-1730 Mon-Sat, 1030-1700 Sun.
Min Mail Order UK: Nmc
Credit Cards: All major credit/debit cards
Specialities: Herbs, culinary & medicinal. Extensive selection of rosemary, thyme & lavender, in particular.
Notes: Carriage charge of £25 up to 10kg, higher for heavier parcels. Next day delivery. UK mainland only. Signature required.
Map Ref: M, C2 **OS Grid Ref:** SP413471

MNrw **Norwell Nurseries** ⊠ ♿ ◆
Woodhouse Road, Norwell, Newark, Nottinghamshire, NG23 6JX
Ⓣ (01636) 636337
Ⓔ wardha@aol.com
Ⓦ www.norwellnurseries.co.uk
Contact: Dr Andrew Ward
Opening Times: 1000-1700 Mon, Wed-Fri & Sun (Wed-Mon May & Jun). By appt. Aug & 20th Oct-1st Mar.
Min Mail Order UK: £15.00 + p&p
Min Mail Order EU: £40.00
Cat. Cost: 3 × 1st class.
Credit Cards: None
Specialities: A large collection of unusual & choice herbaceous perennials & alpines esp., hardy geraniums, *Geum*, cottage garden plants, *Hemerocallis*, grasses, chrysanthemums & woodland plants. Gardens open.
Notes: Also sells wholesale.
Map Ref: M, B3 **OS Grid Ref:** SK767616

MOne **One House Nursery** ⊠ ♿
Buxton New Road, Macclesfield, Cheshire, SK11 0AD
Ⓣ (01625) 427087
Ⓔ louisebaylis@supanet.com
Ⓦ www.onehousenursery.co.uk
Contact: Miss J L Baylis
Opening Times: Limited opening. See website or phone for appt.
Min Mail Order UK: Nmc
Credit Cards: None
Specialities: Alpines & perennials. Good range of *Sempervivum* & *Erodium*.
Notes: Mail order for *Sempervivum* & *Erodium* only.
Map Ref: M, A2 **OS Grid Ref:** SJ943741

MPet **Peter Grayson (Sweet Pea Seedsman)** ⊠ ✈
34 Glenthorne Close, Brampton, Chesterfield, Derbyshire, S40 3AR
Ⓣ (01246) 278503
Ⓕ (01246) 278503
Contact: Peter Grayson
Opening Times: Not open. Mail order only.
Min Mail Order UK: Nmc
Min Mail Order EU: Nmc
Cat. Cost: C5 sae, 1 × 2nd class.
Credit Cards: None
Specialities: *Lathyrus* species & cvs. Large collection of old-fashioned sweet peas & over 100 Spencer sweet peas incl. own cultivars and collection of old-fashioned cottage garden annuals & perennials.
Notes: Also sells wholesale. Mail order for seeds only.

MPhe **Phedar Nursery** ⊠ ✈ €
Bunkers Hill, Romiley, Stockport, Cheshire, SK6 3DS
Ⓣ (0161) 430 3772
Ⓕ (0161) 430 3772
Ⓔ mclewin@phedar.com
Ⓦ www.phedar.com
Contact: Will McLewin
Opening Times: Frequent esp. in spring but very irregular. Please phone to arrange appt.
Min Mail Order UK: Nmc
Min Mail Order EU: Nmc
Cat. Cost: 2 × A5 envelopes or address labels + 4 × 1st class.
Credit Cards: None
Specialities: *Helleborus, Paeonia*. Limited stock of some rare items.
Notes: Non-EU exports subject to destination & on an ad hoc basis only. Please contact nursery for details. Also sells wholesale.
Map Ref: M, A2 **OS Grid Ref:** SJ936897

MPkF **Packhorse Farm Nursery** ♠ ♿
Sandyford House, Lant Lane, Tansley, Matlock, Derbyshire, DE4 5FW
Ⓣ (01629) 57206
Ⓜ 07974 095752
Ⓕ (01629) 57206
Contact: Hilton W Haynes
Opening Times: 1000-1700 Tues & Wed, 1st Mar-31st Oct.. Any other time by appt. only.
Cat. Cost: 2 × 1st class for plant list.
Credit Cards: None
Specialities: *Acer*, rare stock is limited in supply. Other more unusual hardy shrubs, trees & conifers.
Map Ref: M, B2 **OS Grid Ref:** SK322617

MPnt **Plantagogo.com** ⊠ ♠ ♿
Jubilee Cottage Nursery, Snape Lane, Englesea Brook, Crewe, Cheshire, CW2 5QN
Ⓣ (01270) 820335
Ⓕ (01270) 820335
Ⓔ foxy@plantagogo.freeserve.co.uk
Ⓦ www.plantagogo.com
Contact: Vicky & Richard Fox
Opening Times: By appt. only.
Min Mail Order UK: £7.50 single payment.
Min Mail Order EU: Price on application
Cat. Cost: 4 × 1st class.
Credit Cards: All major credit/debit cards
Specialities: *Heuchera*, perennials.
Map Ref: M, B1 **OS Grid Ref:** SJ750516

MPoH **Poppy Heads Ltd** ⊠
Alcombe, 7 Bosden Fold Road, Hazel Grove, Stockport, Cheshire, SK7 4LQ
Ⓣ (0161) 456 9009
Ⓔ kevinpratt@supanet.com
Ⓦ www.poppyheadltd.co.uk
Contact: Kevin & Suzanne Pratt
Opening Times: Not open. Mail order only.
Min Mail Order UK: £5.00
Cat. Cost: 30p or 1 × 1st class.
Credit Cards: None
Specialities: Large collection of cottage poppies. *Fritillaria, Polygonatum, Allium*. Large collection of *Eucomis* specialist bulbs.

MRav **Ravensthorpe Nursery** ⊠ ♿
6 East Haddon Road, Ravensthorpe, Northamptonshire, NN6 8ES
Ⓣ (01604) 770548
Ⓕ (01604) 770548
Ⓔ ravensthorpenursery@hotmail.com
Contact: Jean & Richard Wiseman
Opening Times: 1000-1800 (dusk if earlier) Tue-Sun. Also B/hol Mons.
Min Mail Order UK: Nmc
Min Mail Order EU: Nmc
Cat. Cost: None issued.
Credit Cards: Visa MasterCard
Specialities: Over 3000 different trees, shrubs & perennials with many unusual varieties.
Notes: Search & delivery service for large orders, winter months only.
Map Ref: M, C3 **OS Grid Ref:** SP665699

KEY
⊠ Mail order to UK or EU ♠ Delivers to shows
✈ Exports beyond EU € Euro accepted
♿ Accessible by wheelchair ◆ See Display advertisement

M

MREP **Rare and Exotic Plants (formerly Plants for All Reasons)** ⊠ ♿
Woodshoot Nurseries, King's Bromley, Burton-upon-Trent, Staffordshire, DE13 7HN
Ⓣ (01543) 472233
Ⓕ (01543) 472115
Ⓔ sales@rareandexoticplants.com
Ⓦ www.rareandexoticplants.com
Contact: Richard Flint
Opening Times: 0900-1700, 7 days.
Min Mail Order UK: £20.00 + p&p
Cat. Cost: 1 × 1st class.
Credit Cards: All major credit/debit cards
Specialities: *Acacia*, *Agave*, bamboos, *Citrus*, *Cordyline*, *Dicksonia*, *Nerium*, *Phormium*, *Pittosporum*, palms, olives, *Yucca* & topiary.
Notes: Also sells wholesale.
Map Ref: M, B2 **OS Grid Ref:** SK127164

MSCN **Stonyford Cottage Nursery** ⊠ ♿ ♿
Stonyford Lane, Cuddington, Northwich, Cheshire, CW8 2TF
Ⓣ (01606) 888970
Ⓔ stonyfordplants@yahoo.co.uk
Ⓦ www.gardenchoice.co.uk
Contact: F A Overland
Opening Times: 1000-1730 Tue-Sun & B/hol Mons 1st Mar-31st Oct.
Min Mail Order UK: Nmc
Min Mail Order EU: Nmc
Cat. Cost: Not available this year
Credit Cards: All major credit/debit cards
Specialities: Wide range of herbaceous perennials, *Iris*, *Salvia*, hardy *Geranium*, moisture-loving & bog plants.
Notes: Also sells wholesale.
Map Ref: M, A1 **OS Grid Ref:** SJ580710

MSKA **Sweet Knowle Aquatics** ⊠ ♿
Wimpstone-Ilmington Road, Stratford-upon-Avon, Warwickshire, CV37 8NR
Ⓣ (01789) 450036
Ⓕ (01789) 450036
Ⓔ sweetknowleaquatics@hotmail.com
Ⓦ www.sweetknowleaquatics.co.uk
Contact: Zoe Harding
Opening Times: 0930-1700 Sun-Fri, closed Sat. Open B/hols.
Min Mail Order UK: Nmc
Cat. Cost: By email only.
Credit Cards: All major credit/debit cards
Specialities: Aquatics. Hardy & tropical water lilies, marginals & oxygenators. 2-acre display garden open to the public (no charge).
Map Ref: M, C2 **OS Grid Ref:** SP207480

MSmi **John Smith & Son** ⊠ ♿
Fuchsia Centre, Thornton Nurseries, Thornton, Leicestershire, LE67 1AN
Ⓣ (01530) 230331
Ⓕ (01530) 230331
Ⓔ david@fuchsiaplants.co.uk
Ⓦ www.fuchsiaplants.co.uk
Contact: David Smith
Opening Times: 0800-1730 Mon-Fri, 1000-1600 Sat & Sun all year round.
Min Mail Order UK: Nmc
Cat. Cost: Sae.
Credit Cards: None
Specialities: Hardy, Half-hardy & large American fuchsias.
Notes: Also sells wholesale.
Map Ref: M, B2

MSnd **Sound Garden Rhododendrons (formerly Penton Mill)** ⊠ ♿
(office) 184 Crow Lane East, Newton-le-Willows, Merseyside, WA12 9UA
Ⓣ (01925) 229100 or (0161) 430 4150
Ⓜ 07931 340836
Ⓔ info@soundgardendesign.com
Ⓦ www.soundgardendesign.com
Contact: Tim Atkinson & Jez Clark
Opening Times: By appt. only.
Min Mail Order UK: £50.00 + p&p
Min Mail Order EU: £100.00
Cat. Cost: 2 × 1st class
Credit Cards: None
Specialities: Species & rare rhododendrons.
Notes: Nursery at Middledale Farm, Dale Road, Marple, Cheshire SK6 6NL.
Map Ref: N, B1 **OS Grid Ref:** SJ948901

MSpe **SpecialPerennials.com** ⊠ ♿ ♿
(office) Yew Tree House, Hall Lane, Hankelow, Crewe, Cheshire, CW3 0JB
Ⓣ (01270) 811443
Ⓜ 07716 990695
Ⓔ plants@specialperennials.com
Ⓦ www.specialperennials.com
Contact: Janet & Martin Blow
Opening Times: By appt. only, or when garden is open (see website for details).
Min Mail Order UK: Nmc
Cat. Cost: 3 × 1st class or online.
Credit Cards: None
Specialities: Herbaceous perennials. Large range of *Helenium*, *Hemerocallis*, *Centaurea*, *Geum*, *Salvia* & *Kniphofia*. Some plants available in small quantities only. Scarce plants & those only propagated to order listed on website.

Notes: Plants may be collected from nursery. See website for plant fairs attended. Border design service available.
Map Ref: M, B1 **OS Grid Ref:** SJ699452

MSSP **S & S Perennials** ⊠
24 Main Street, Normanton Le Heath, Leicestershire, LE67 2TB
Ⓣ (01530) 262250
Contact: Shirley Pierce
Opening Times: Afternoons only, otherwise please phone.
Min Mail Order UK: Nmc
Cat. Cost: 2 × 1st class.
Credit Cards: None
Specialities: *Erythronium*, *Fritillaria*, dwarf *Narcissus* & *Anemone*. Stock available in small quantities only.
Map Ref: M, B1

MSwo **Swallows Nursery** ⊠ ♿
Mixbury, Brackley, Northamptonshire, NN13 5RR
Ⓣ (01280) 847721
Ⓕ (01280) 848611
Ⓔ enq@swallowsnursery.co.uk
Ⓦ www.swallowsnursery.co.uk
Contact: Chris Swallow
Opening Times: 0900-1300 & 1400-1700 (earlier in winter) Mon-Fri, 0900-1300 Sat.
Min Mail Order UK: £15.00
Cat. Cost: 3 × 1st class (plus phone number).
Credit Cards: Visa MasterCard Switch
Specialities: Growing a wide range, particularly shrubs, trees, roses and heathers.
Notes: Trees not for mail order unless part of larger order. Nursery transport used where possible, esp. for trees. Also sells wholesale.
Map Ref: M, C3 **OS Grid Ref:** SP607336

MTho **A & A Thorp**
Bungalow No 5, Main Street, Theddingworth, Leicestershire, LE17 6QZ
Ⓣ (01858) 880496
Contact: Anita & Andrew Thorp
Opening Times: 1000-1700.
Cat. Cost: 4 × 1st class.
Credit Cards: None
Specialities: Unusual plants or those in short supply.
Map Ref: M, C3

MTis **Tissington Nursery** ♿
(office) 7 Bensley Close, Chellaston, Derbyshire, DE73 6TL
Ⓣ (01335) 390650
Ⓜ 07929 720284
Ⓔ info@tissington-nursery.co.uk
Ⓦ www.tissington-nursery.co.uk
Contact: Mairi Longdon
Opening Times: 1000-1700 daily, 3rd Mar-end Oct.
Cat. Cost: 4 × 1st class.
Credit Cards: All major credit/debit cards
Specialities: Choice & unusual perennials esp. *Achillea*, *Geranium*, *Geum*, *Helenium*, *Heuchera*, *Pulmonaria*, grasses & ferns.
Notes: Nursery is at The Old Kitchen Gardens, Tissington, Ashbourne, Derbyshire, DE6 1RA
Map Ref: M, B1 **OS Grid Ref:** SK176521

M

MWar **Ward Fuchsias** ⊠
5 Pollen Close, Sale, Cheshire, M33 3LS
Ⓣ (0161) 282 7434
Ⓔ kms.ward@ntlworld.com
Ⓦ www.wardfuchsias.co.uk
Contact: K Ward
Opening Times: 0930-1700 Tue-Sun Feb-Jun incl. B/hols.
Min Mail Order UK: Nmc
Cat. Cost: Free.
Credit Cards: None
Specialities: *Fuchsia*. Available in small quantities.
Map Ref: M, A2

MWat **Waterperry Gardens Ltd** ⊠ ♿
Waterperry, Nr Wheatley, Oxfordshire, OX33 1JZ
Ⓣ (01844) 339226/254
Ⓕ (01844) 339883
Ⓔ management@waterperrygardens.co.uk
Ⓦ www.waterperrygardens.co.uk
Contact: Mr R Jacobs
Opening Times: 1000-1730 summer. 1000-1700 winter.
Min Mail Order UK: £30.00
Cat. Cost: Online only.
Credit Cards: All major credit/debit cards
Specialities: General, large range of herbaceous esp. *Aster*, also Nat. Collection of *Saxifraga* (subsect. *Kabschia* & *Engleria*).
Map Ref: M, D3 **OS Grid Ref:** SP630064

MWBu **Wilford Bulb Co. Ltd** ⊠ €
Lennox House, Station Road, East Leake, Leicestershire, LE12 6LQ
Ⓣ (01509) 852905
Ⓕ (01509) 852905

KEY
⊠ Mail order to UK or EU — Delivers to shows
Exports beyond EU — € Euro accepted
♿ Accessible by wheelchair — ◆ See Display advertisement

Contact: Tony Cross
Opening Times: Not open. Mail order only.
Min Mail Order UK: £10.00 + p&p
Min Mail Order EU: £10.00 + p&p
Cat. Cost: 3 × 1st class.
Credit Cards: None
Specialities: *Lilium* & bulbous plants, available in small quantities only.
Notes: Also sells wholesale.

MWea **Wear's Nursery** ♿
(office) 84 Wantage Road, Wallingford, Oxfordshire, OX10 0LY
Ⓜ 07790 425284
Ⓕ (01491) 837803
Ⓦ www.wearsnursery.co.uk
Contact: David Wear
Opening Times: 1000-1700 Mon-Sat, Feb-Oct. 1000-1600 Sun (closed Sun in Aug). 1000-1600 Mon-Sat, Nov-Jan, please telephone first as may be closed on some days in winter.
Cat. Cost: Plant list online only.
Credit Cards: None
Specialities: Unusual herbaceous varieties & shrubs. Large selection of *Geranium*. Some plants only available in small numbers.
Notes: Nursery sited at High Road, Brightwell-cum-Sotwell, Wallingford.
Map Ref: M, D3 **OS Grid Ref:** SU590910

MWhi **Whitehill Farm Nursery** ✉ € ♿
Whitehill Farm, Burford, Oxfordshire, OX18 4DT
Ⓣ (01993) 823218
Ⓕ (01993) 822894
Ⓔ a.youngson@virgin.net
Ⓦ www.whitehillfarmnursery.co.uk
Contact: P J M Youngson
Opening Times: 0900-1800 (or dusk if earlier) 7 days, Feb-Nov.
Min Mail Order UK: £5.00 + p&p
Min Mail Order EU: £5.00 + p&p
Cat. Cost: 4 × 1st class.
Credit Cards: All major credit/debit cards
Specialities: Grasses & bamboos, less common shrubs & perennials. Some available in small quantities only.
Notes: £1.00 of catalogue cost refunded on 1st order.

MWht **Whitelea Nursery** ✉ ♿
Whitelea Lane, Tansley, Matlock, Derbyshire, DE4 5FL
Ⓣ (01629) 55010
Ⓔ sales@uk-bamboos.co.uk
Ⓦ www.uk-bamboos.co.uk
Contact: David Wilson
Opening Times: By appt.
Min Mail Order UK: Nmc
Cat. Cost: Online only. Price list available 2 × 1st class.
Credit Cards: None
Specialities: Bamboos, ivies. Substantial quantities of 45 cvs & species of bamboo, remainder stocked in small numbers only.
Notes: Also sells wholesale.
Map Ref: M, B1 **OS Grid Ref:** SK325603

MWte **White House Plants** ✉
(office) The White House, Nicker Hill, Keyworth, Nottinghamshire, NG12 5EA
Ⓣ (0115) 937 2049
Ⓜ 07804 865607
Ⓔ gillyhill@aol.com
Ⓦ www.whitehouseplants.com
Contact: Gillian Hill
Opening Times: Not open. Mail order only.
Min Mail Order UK: £10.00 + p&p
Cat. Cost: Online only.
Credit Cards: Paypal
Specialities: *Agapanthus*, *Aster*, *Euphorbia*, *Geranium*, *Iris*, *Kniphofia*, *Miscanthus*, *Papaver orientale*, *Penstemon* & *Phlox*.

MYeo **Yeomans' Exotics** ✉ ⌂ € ♿
2 Carrington Lane, Calverton, Nottingham, NG14 6HQ
Ⓣ 0115 965 4350
Ⓦ www.yeomansexotics.co.uk
Contact: Chris Yeomans
Opening Times: By appt. only Feb-Dec.
Min Mail Order UK: Nmc
Min Mail Order EU: Nmc
Cat. Cost: 1 × 1st class.
Credit Cards: None
Specialities: Carnivorous plants.
Notes: Mail order seeds only. Also sells wholesale.

Northern

NBea **Beamish Clematis Nursery** € ♿
Burntwood Cottage, Stoney Lane, Beamish, Co. Durham, DH9 0SJ
Ⓣ (0191) 370 0202
Ⓕ (0191) 370 0202
Ⓦ www.beamishclematisnursery.co.uk
Contact: Colin Brown or Jan Wilson
Opening Times: 0900-1700 Wed-Mon, closed Tue. Closed Easter Sun & Xmas week.

Cat. Cost: Online only.
Credit Cards: All major credit/debit cards
Specialities: *Clematis*, climbers, shrubs & ornamental trees.
Map Ref: N, B2 **OS Grid Ref:** NZ231535

NBhm **Beetham Nurseries** ♿
Pool Darkin Lane, Beetham,
Nr Milnthorpe, Cumbria,
LA7 7AP
Ⓣ (01539) 563630
Ⓕ (01539) 564487
Contact: S & L Abbit
Opening Times: 0900-1730 summer, 0900-1730 winter.
Cat. Cost: None issued.
Credit Cards: All major credit/debit cards
Specialities: Comprehensive range of trees, shrubs & herbaceous plants. Many unusual varieties.
Map Ref: N, C1

NBid **Bide-A-Wee Cottage Gardens** ⊠ ♿
Stanton, Netherwitton, Morpeth,
Northumberland, NE65 8PR
Ⓣ (01670) 772238
Ⓕ (01670) 772238
Ⓔ bideaweecg@aol.com
Ⓦ www.bideawee.co.uk
Contact: Mark Robson
Opening Times: 1330-1700 Sat & Wed, 19th Apr-30th Aug 2008.
Min Mail Order UK: £20.00
Cat. Cost: 3 × 1st class.
Credit Cards: All major credit/debit cards
Specialities: Unusual herbaceous perennials, *Primula*, ferns, grasses. Nat. Collection of *Centaurea*.
Map Ref: N, B2 **OS Grid Ref:** NZ132900

NBir **Birkheads Secret Gardens & Nursery** ⊠ ♿
Nr Hedley Hall Woods,
Sunniside, Gateshead,
NE16 5EL
Ⓣ (01207) 232262
Ⓜ 07778 447920
Ⓕ (01207) 232262
Ⓔ birkheads.nursery@virgin.net
Ⓦ www.birkheadsnursery.co.uk
Contact: Mrs Christine Liddle
Opening Times: 1000-1700 daily (except Mon) Mar-Oct. Groups by appt.
Min Mail Order UK: £10
Cat. Cost: None issued.
Credit Cards: All major credit/debit cards
Specialities: Hardy herbaceous perennials, grasses, bulbs & herbs. *Allium*, *Digitalis*, *Euphorbia*, *Galanthus* & *Geranium*. Max. 30 of any plant propagated each year.
Notes: Mail order Nov-Feb only. Orders taken all year for winter deliveries.
Map Ref: N, B2 **OS Grid Ref:** NZ220569

NBlu **Blundell's Nurseries** ♿
68 Southport New Road, Tarleton, Preston,
Lancashire, PR4 6HY
Ⓣ (01772) 815442
Ⓕ (01772) 613917
Ⓔ jerplusjeff@aol.com
Contact: Any member of staff
Opening Times: 0900-1700 daily. Closed Dec-Jan.
Cat. Cost: None issued.
Credit Cards: All major credit/debit cards
Specialities: Trees, shrubs, incl. topiary & large specimens, conifers. Perennials, alpines, ferns, heathers, herbs, hanging basket/bedding/conservatory plants, hedging, roses.
Notes: Also sells wholesale.
Map Ref: N, D1

NBPC **The Barn Plant Centre & Gift Shop** ♿
The Square, Scorton, Preston, Lancashire,
PR3 1AU
Ⓣ (01524) 793533
Ⓕ (01524) 793533
Ⓔ sales@plantsandgifts.co.uk
Ⓦ www.plantsandgifts.co.uk
Contact: Neil Anderton
Opening Times: 0900-1700 Mon-Sat, 1000-1800 Sun.
Cat. Cost: 2 × 1st class.
Credit Cards: All major credit/debit cards
Specialities: 800 varieties of perennials.
Map Ref: N, C1 **OS Grid Ref:** GR501487

NBre **Breezy Knees Nurseries** ♿
Common Lane, Warthill, York,
YO19 5XS
Ⓣ (01904) 488800
Ⓦ www.breezyknees.co.uk
Contact: Any member of staff
Opening Times: 1000-1700 7 days (open 1100 Sun), 1st Apr-15th Sep.
Credit Cards: All major credit/debit cards
Specialities: Very wide range of perennials. All can be viewed in 10-acre display gardens (open 24th May-15th Sep).
Map Ref: N, C3 **OS Grid Ref:** SE675565

KEY
⊠ Mail order to UK or EU — Delivers to shows
Exports beyond EU — € Euro accepted
♿ Accessible by wheelchair — ◆ See Display advertisement

N

NBro **Brownthwaite Hardy Plants** ⊠ ♿
Fell Yeat, Casterton, Kirkby Lonsdale, Lancashire, LA6 2JW
Ⓣ (01524) 271340 (after 1800).
Ⓦ www.browthwaitesplantscumbria.co.uk
Contact: Chris Benson
Opening Times: 1000-1700, 1st Apr-30th Sep.
Min Mail Order UK: Nmc
Cat. Cost: 3 × 1st class sae for general list. 3 × 1st class for *Hydrangea* catalogue. Sae for auricula list.
Credit Cards: None
Specialities: Herbaceous perennials incl. *Geranium, Hosta, Iris ensata* & *I. sibirica*, also *Tiarella, Heucherella* & *Primula auricula*. Mail order for *Hydrangea*. Nat. Collection of *Ligularia*.
Notes: Follow brown signs from A65 between Kirkby Lonsdale & Cowan Bridge.
Map Ref: N, C1 **OS Grid Ref:** SD632794

NBur **Burton Agnes Hall Nursery** ♿ ◆
Burton Agnes Hall Preservation Trust Ltd, Estate Office, Burton Agnes, Driffield, East Yorkshire, YO25 0ND
Ⓣ (01262) 490324
Ⓕ (01262) 490513
Ⓔ burton.agnes@farmline.com
Ⓦ www.burtonagnes.com
Contact: Mrs S Cunliffe-Lister
Opening Times: 1100-1700 Feb-Dec.
Cat. Cost: 4 × 1st class.
Credit Cards: None
Specialities: Large range perennials & alpines. Many unusual varieties esp. *Penstemon, Osteospermum, Digitalis, Anemone, Geranium*. Nat. Collection of *Campanula*.
Map Ref: N, C3 **OS Grid Ref:** TA103631

NCGa **Cath's Garden Plants** ⊠ ⌂ ♿
The Walled Garden, Heaves Hotel, Levens, Nr Kendal, Cumbria, LA8 8EF
Ⓣ (01539) 561126
Ⓕ (01539) 561126
Ⓔ cath@cathsgardenplants.co.uk
Ⓦ www.cathsgardenplants.co.uk
Contact: Bob Sanderson
Opening Times: 1030-1630 Mon-Fri all year, except Xmas & New Year weeks. 1030-1700 Sat & Sun, Mar-Oct.
Min Mail Order UK: £15.00 + p&p
Min Mail Order EU: £25.00
Cat. Cost: 6 × 1st class.
Credit Cards: All major credit/debit cards
Specialities: Wide variety of perennials, incl. uncommon varieties & selections of grasses, ferns, shrubs & climbing plants.
Notes: On A590 not in Levens village.
Map Ref: N, C1 **OS Grid Ref:** SD497867

NChi **Chipchase Castle Nursery** ⊠ ⌂ ♿
Chipchase Castle, Wark, Hexham, Northumberland, NE48 3NT
Ⓣ (01434) 230083
Ⓔ info@chipchaseplants.co.uk
Ⓦ www.chipchaseplants.co.uk
Contact: Joyce Hunt & Alison Jones
Opening Times: 1000-1700 Thu-Sun & B/hol Mons Easter (or 1st Apr)-mid Oct.
Min Mail Order UK: Nmc
Min Mail Order EU: Nmc
Cat. Cost: A5 sae for list
Credit Cards: All major credit/debit cards
Specialities: Unusual herbaceous esp. *Eryngium, Geranium, Penstemon* & *Viola*. Some plants only available in small quantities.
Notes: Suitable for accompanied wheelchair users.
Map Ref: N, B2 **OS Grid Ref:** NY880758

NChl **Chiltern Seeds** ⊠ ✈ € ◆
Bortree Stile, Ulverston, Cumbria, LA12 7PB
Ⓣ (01229) 581137 (24 hrs)
Ⓕ (01229) 584549
Ⓔ info@chilternseeds.co.uk
Ⓦ www.chilternseeds.co.uk
Opening Times: Mail order only. Normal office hours, Mon-Fri.
Min Mail Order UK: Nmc
Min Mail Order EU: Nmc
Cat. Cost: 3 × 2nd class.
Credit Cards: All major credit/debit cards
Specialities: Over 4,500 items of all kinds – wild flowers, trees, shrubs, cacti, annuals, houseplants, vegetables & herbs.

NChu **Churchtown Carnivores** ⊠ ⌂ € ♿
8 Sandheys Drive, Churchtown, Southport, Merseyside, PR9 9PQ
Ⓣ (01704) 228175
Ⓔ churchtowncarnivores@yahoo.co.uk
Ⓦ www.churchtowncarnivores.co.uk
Contact: Alan Leyland
Opening Times: By appt. only.
Min Mail Order UK: Nmc
Min Mail Order EU: Nmc
Cat. Cost: 2 × 1st class or online.
Credit Cards: None
Specialities: Carnivorous plants. *Sarracenia, Dionaea muscipula* & forms, *Darlingtonia, Drosera*.
Map Ref: N, D1 **OS Grid Ref:** SD355183

NCli

Clifton Plants ⊠ ♦

Kirkley Mill Farm Yard, Kirkley Mill, Berwick Hill, Ponteland, Newcastle-upon-Tyne, NE20 0BQ
Ⓣ (01661) 820033
Ⓕ (01661) 820034
Ⓔ graeme@cliftonplants.com
Ⓦ www.cliftonplants.com
Contact: Graeme Ord
Opening Times: 1000-1600, 7 days all year round.
Min Mail Order UK: £9.00
Cat. Cost: 3 × 1st class.
Credit Cards: All major credit/debit cards
Specialities: *Fuchsia*. 700 varieties: bush, trailing, hardy & species.
Notes: Also sells wholesale.
Map Ref: N, B2 **OS Grid Ref:** NZ091745

NCob

Cobble Hey Gardens

Off Hobbs Lane, Claughton-on-Brock, Garstang, Nr Preston, Lancashire, PR3 0QN
Ⓣ (01995) 602643
Ⓕ (01995) 602643
Ⓔ cobblehey@aol.com
Ⓦ www.cobblehey.co.uk
Contact: Edwina Miller
Opening Times: 1030-1630 Thu-Mon 1st Feb-24th Dec 2008. Please email or phone before visiting to check stock availability.
Credit Cards: None
Specialities: Wide range of unusual plants grown on hill farm at over 600ft. Specialises in *Phlox paniculata* & geraniums.
Map Ref: N, C1

NCot

Cottage Garden Plants ⊠ €

1 Sycamore Close, Whitehaven, Cumbria, CA28 6LE
Ⓣ (01946) 695831
Ⓔ expressplants@aol.com
Ⓦ www.cottagegardenplants.com
Contact: Mrs J Purkiss
Opening Times: Open by appt. only for collecting orders & viewing garden. Consult local press & radio for charity openings.
Min Mail Order UK: Nmc
Min Mail Order EU: Nmc
Cat. Cost: 4 × 1st class sae.
Credit Cards: Paypal
Specialities: Hardy perennials incl. *Crocosmia*, *Geranium*, *Primula*, *Schizostylis* & bog plants. Small quantities only. Nat. Collection of *Geranium phaeum* Group.
Notes: Also sells wholesale.
Map Ref: N, C1

NCro

Croston Cactus ⊠ €

43 Southport Road, Eccleston, Chorley, Lancashire, PR7 6ET
Ⓣ (01257) 452555
Ⓔ sales@croston-cactus.co.uk
Ⓦ www.croston-cactus.co.uk
Contact: John Henshaw
Opening Times: 0930-1700 by appt. only.
Min Mail Order UK: £5.00 + p&p
Min Mail Order EU: £10.00 + p&p
Cat. Cost: 2 × 1st class or 2 × IRCs.
Credit Cards: None
Specialities: Mexican cacti, *Echeveria* hybrids & some bromeliads & *Tillandsia*. Some items held in small quantities only. See catalogue.
Map Ref: N, D1 **OS Grid Ref:** SD522186

NDlv

Dalesview Nursery ⊠

24 Braithwaite Edge Road, Keighley, West Yorkshire, BD22 6RA
Ⓣ (01535) 606531
Ⓔ nursery@dalesviewnursery.co.uk
Ⓦ www.dalesviewnursery.co.uk
Contact: David Ellis & Eileen Morgan
Opening Times: 1000-1700 Thu-Sun, Mar-Sep. Oct-Feb by appt., please telephone.
Min Mail Order UK: Nmc
Min Mail Order EU: Nmc
Cat. Cost: Plant list online.
Credit Cards: None
Specialities: Dwarf *Hebe*, *Saxifraga*, *Primula*, *Rhododendron*, *Fuchsia* & conifers.
Notes: Also sells wholesale.
Map Ref: N, C2

NEgg

Eggleston Hall Gardens €

Eggleston, Barnard Castle, Co. Durham, DL12 0AG
Ⓣ (01833) 650115
Ⓕ (01833) 650971
Ⓔ mbhock@btinternet.com
Ⓦ www.egglestonhallgardens.co.uk
Contact: Malcolm Hockham
Opening Times: 1000-1700 7 days. Closed Xmas Day, Boxing Day & New Year's Day only.
Cat. Cost: Online only.
Credit Cards: All major credit/debit cards
Notes: Collection from nusery only. Possible mail order in the next 18 months.

KEY
⊠ Mail order to UK or EU — Delivers to shows
Exports beyond EU — € Euro accepted
Accessible by wheelchair — ♦ See Display advertisement

N

NEqu **Equatorial Plant Co.** ⊠ ✈ ♿ €
7 Gray Lane, Barnard Castle, Co. Durham, DL12 8PD
Ⓣ (01833) 690519
Ⓕ (01833) 690519
Ⓔ equatorialplants@teesdaleonline.co.uk
Ⓦ www.equatorialplants.com
Contact: Dr Richard Warren
Opening Times: By appt. only.
Min Mail Order UK: Nmc
Min Mail Order EU: Nmc
Cat. Cost: Free.
Credit Cards: Visa Access
Specialities: Laboratory-raised orchids only.
Notes: Also sells wholesale.

N

NExo **Exotic Unusual.co.uk** ⊠ ✈
8 Hoskers Nook, Westhoughton, Bolton, Lancashire, BL5 2RS
Ⓣ (01942) 790027
Ⓔ info@exoticunusual.co.uk
Ⓦ www.exoticunusual.co.uk
Contact: Lou Davies
Opening Times: Not Open. Mail order only.
Min Mail Order UK: £10.00
Min Mail Order EU: £15.00
Cat. Cost: Online only.
Credit Cards: All major credit/debit cards
Specialities: Rare, exotic & unusual plants, particularly *Agave*, chillies & passionflowers. Some plants in small quantities only.

NFir **Fir Trees Pelargonium Nursery** ⊠ ♿ ♿
Stokesley, Middlesbrough, Cleveland, TS9 5LD
Ⓣ (01642) 713066
Ⓕ (01642) 713066
Ⓔ mark@firtreespelargoniums.co.uk
Ⓦ www.firtreespelargoniums.co.uk
Contact: Helen Bainbridge
Opening Times: 1000-1600 7 days 1st Apr-31st Aug, 1000-1600 Mon-Fri 1st Sep-31st Mar.
Min Mail Order UK: £3.50 + p&p
Cat. Cost: 4 × 1st class or £1.00 coin.
Credit Cards: MasterCard Visa Switch
Specialities: All types of *Pelargonium* – fancy leaf, regal, decorative regal, oriental regal, angel, miniature, zonal, ivy leaf, stellar, scented, dwarf, unique, golden stellar & species. Also dieramas.
Map Ref: N, C2

NGBl **Garden Blooms** ⊠ ♿
(office) The Ridings, Netherfield Drive, Guiseley, West Yorkshire, LS20 9DF
Ⓣ 0845 904937
Ⓕ 0870 0528148
Ⓔ info@gardenblooms.co.uk
Ⓦ www.gardenblooms.co.uk
Contact: Liz Webster
Opening Times: 1200-1600 Sat, Sun & B/hols end Mar-end Aug, but please check before travelling. Up-to-date details on website.
Min Mail Order UK: £5.00
Cat. Cost: A5 sae or online.
Credit Cards: All major credit/debit cards
Specialities: Hardy perennials & ornamental grasses. Available in small quantities only.
Notes: Credit cards accepted online only. Nursery at Carlton Lane, East Carlton, Yeadon, LS19 7BE.
Map Ref: N, D2 **OS Grid Ref:** SE213430

NGby **Gilbey's Plants** € ♿
The Walled Garden, Cemetery Road, Thirsk, North Yorkshire, YO7 4DA
Ⓣ (01765) 689927 or (01845) 525285
Ⓕ (01765) 688272
Ⓔ gilbeyplants@aol.com
Contact: Giles N Gilbey
Opening Times: 1000-1700 Mon-Sat (closed Sun) 1st Mar-1st Oct. Winter by appt. only.
Cat. Cost: 4 × 1st class.
Credit Cards: All major credit/debit cards
Specialities: Unusual hardy perennials & ferns.
Notes: Mail order Oct-Mar only. Also sells wholesale.
Map Ref: N, C2

NGdn **Garden House Nursery** ♿
The Square, Dalston, Carlisle, Cumbria, CA5 7LL
Ⓣ (01228) 710297
Ⓔ stephickso@hotmail.com
Ⓦ www.gardenhousenursery.co.uk
Contact: Stephen Hickson
Opening Times: 0900-1700 7 days Mar-Oct.
Cat. Cost: Plant list online only.
Credit Cards: None
Specialities: *Geranium*, *Hosta*, *Hemerocallis*, *Iris*, grasses & bamboos.
Notes: Also sells wholesale.
Map Ref: N, B1 **OS Grid Ref:** NY369503

NGHP **Green Garden Herbs** ⊠ ♿ ♿
13 West Bank, Carlton, North Yorkshire, DN14 9PZ
Ⓣ (01405) 860708
Ⓔ info@greengardenherbs.co.uk
Ⓦ www.greengardenherbs.co.uk
Contact: Sarah Clark
Opening Times: 1000-1600 Wed-Mon, Mar-Sep. Other times by appt.
Min Mail Order UK: £15.00
Min Mail Order EU: £15.00
Cat. Cost: Free with sae or online.

Credit Cards: All major credit/debit cards
Specialities: Herbs, aromatic, culinary, medicinal & ornamental, incl. *Salvia*, *Echinacea*, *Monarda*, *Thymus* & wide selection of *Lavandula*. Plants & seed available.
Notes: Also sells wholesale. Coaches welcome. Talks given.
Map Ref: N, D3 **OS Grid Ref:** SE626242

NHaw **THE HAWTHORNES NURSERY** ⊠ ♿
Marsh Road, Hesketh Bank, Nr Preston, Lancashire, PR4 6XT
Ⓣ (01772) 812379
Ⓔ richardhaw@talktalk.net
Ⓦ www.hawthornes-nursery.co.uk
Contact: Irene & Richard Hodson
Opening Times: 0900-1800 7 days 1st Mar-30th Jun, Thu-Sun July-Oct. Gardens open for NGS.
Min Mail Order UK: £10.00
Cat. Cost: None issued.
Credit Cards: None
Specialities: *Clematis*, honeysuckle, choice selection of shrub & climbing roses, extensive range of perennials, mostly on display in the garden. Nat. Collection of *Clematis viticella*.
Map Ref: N, D1

NHer **HERTERTON HOUSE GARDEN NURSERY**
Hartington, Cambo, Morpeth, Northumberland, NE61 4BN
Ⓣ (01670) 774278
Contact: Mrs M Lawley & Mr Frank Lawley
Opening Times: 1330-1730 Mon, Wed, Fri-Sun 1st Apr-end Sep. (Earlier or later in the year weather permitting.)
Cat. Cost: None issued.
Credit Cards: None
Specialities: Country garden flowers.
Map Ref: N, B2 **OS Grid Ref:** NZ022880

NHim **THE HIMALAYAN GARDEN CO.** ⊠ ⌂
The Hutts, Grewelthorpe, Ripon, Yorkshire, HG4 3DA
Ⓣ (01765) 658009
Ⓕ (01765) 658912
Ⓔ info@himalayangarden.com
Ⓦ www.himalayangarden.com
Contact: Peter Roberts
Opening Times: 1000-1600, Tues-Sun & B/hol Mon, mid Apr-mid Jun. During the rest of the year by appt. only.
Min Mail Order UK: £20.00
Min Mail Order EU: £50.00
Cat. Cost: Free.
Credit Cards: All major credit/debit cards
Specialities: Rare and unusual species & hybrid rhododendrons, azaleas, magnolias & *Cornus*, as well as other Himalayan plants.
Notes: Limited wheelchair access. Also sells wholesale.
Map Ref: N, C2 **OS Grid Ref:** SE218769

NHol **HOLDEN CLOUGH NURSERY** ⊠ ✈ ⌂ ♿ ◆
Holden, Bolton-by-Bowland, Clitheroe, Lancashire, BB7 4PF
Ⓣ (01200) 447615
Ⓕ (01200) 447197
Ⓔ enquiries@holdencloughnursery.co.uk
Ⓦ www.holdencloughnursery.co.uk
Contact: P J Foley
Opening Times: 0900-1630 Mon-Fri Mar-Oct & B/hol Mons, 0900-1630 Sat all year. Closed 25th Dec-1st Jan 2009 & Good Fri. Other times by appt. only.
Min Mail Order UK: Nmc
Min Mail Order EU: Nmc
Cat. Cost: 5 × 1st class.
Credit Cards: MasterCard Visa Delta
Specialities: Large general list incl. *Crocosmia*, *Primula*, *Saxifraga*, *Sempervivum*, *Jovibarba*, *Astilbe*, grasses, *Hosta*, heathers & conifers.
Notes: Seasonal mail order on some items. Also sells wholesale.
Map Ref: N, C2 **OS Grid Ref:** SD773496

NHor **HORN'S GARDEN CENTRE** ♿
Dixon Estate, Shotton Colliery, Co. Durham, DH6 2PX
Ⓣ (0191) 526 2987
Ⓕ (0191) 526 2889
Contact: G Horn & Theresa Horn
Opening Times: 0900-1730 Mon-Sat 1000-1600 Sun, all year excl. Easter Mon.
Cat. Cost: 3 × 1st class.
Credit Cards: All major credit/debit cards
Specialities: *Fuchsia*, *Solenostemon*. Wide range of trees, shrubs & perennials.
Map Ref: N, B2

NHoy **HOYLAND PLANT CENTRE** ⊠ ✈ ⌂ € ♿
54 Greenside Lane, Hoyland, Barnsley, Yorkshire, S74 9PZ
Ⓣ (01226) 744466
Ⓜ 07717 182169
Ⓕ (01226) 744466
Ⓔ hickman@hoyland13.freeserve.co.uk
Ⓦ www.somethingforthegarden.co.uk

KEY
⊠ Mail order to UK or EU ⌂ Delivers to shows
✈ Exports beyond EU € Euro accepted
♿ Accessible by wheelchair ◆ See Display advertisement

N

Contact: Steven Hickman
Opening Times: All year round by appt. only.
Min Mail Order UK: Nmc
Min Mail Order EU: Nmc
Cat. Cost: 4 × 1st class.
Credit Cards: None
Specialities: *Agapanthus* (400+ cvs) & *Tulbaghia* (80+ cvs). Some available in small quantities only.
Notes: Also sells wholesale.
Map Ref: N, D2 **OS Grid Ref:** SE372010

NLan **Landlife Wildflowers Ltd** ⊠ ♿
National Wildflower Centre,
Court Hey Park, Liverpool,
L16 3NA
Ⓣ (0151) 737 1819
Ⓕ (0151) 737 1820
Ⓔ gill@landlife.org.uk
Ⓦ www.wildflower.org.uk
Contact: Gillian Watson
Opening Times: 1000-1700, 7 days, 1st Mar-31st Aug.
Min Mail Order UK: £30.00 (plants), no min. for seeds.
Cat. Cost: Free.
Credit Cards: Visa Delta Access Switch Solo
Specialities: Wild herbaceous plants & seeds.
Notes: Cafe & shop. Visitor centre, admission charge. Also sells wholesale.
Map Ref: N, D1

NLAp **Laneside Alpines** ⊠ ♠ € ♿
74 Croston Road, Garstang, Preston,
Lancashire, PR3 1HR
Ⓣ (01995) 605537
Ⓜ 0794 6659661
Ⓔ jcrhutch@aol.com
Ⓦ www.lanesidealpines.com
Contact: Jeff Hutchings
Opening Times: Please contact nursery. Orders can be taken at Shows. Shows list on website.
Min Mail Order UK: £25.00
Min Mail Order EU: £25.00
Cat. Cost: Sae.
Credit Cards: None
Specialities: Large selection of hardy terrestrial orchids plus composts & cultivation notes. Wide rane of alpines.
Notes: Mail order for orchids only during the winter. Also tufa & Seramis from the nursery.
Map Ref: N, D1

NLar **Larch Cottage Nurseries** ⊠ € ♿ ◆
Melkinthorpe, Penrith, Cumbria, CA10 2DR
Ⓣ (01931) 712404
Ⓕ (01931) 712727
Ⓔ plants@larchcottage.co.uk
Ⓦ www.larchcottage.co.uk
Contact: Joanne McCullock & Peter Stott
Opening Times: Daily from 1000-1730, all year round.
Min Mail Order UK: £7.00
Min Mail Order EU: Nmc
Cat. Cost: £3.50
Credit Cards: All major credit/debit cards
Specialities: Unusual & old-fashioned perennials. Rare & dwarf conifers. Unusual shrubs & trees.
Notes: Terraced restaurant & art gallery.
Map Ref: N, C1 **OS Grid Ref:** NY315602

NLLv **Leeds Lavender** ⊠
at Greenscapes Nursery, Brandon Crescent,
Shadwell, Leeds, LS17 9JH
Ⓣ (0113) 2892922
Ⓦ www.leedslavender.co.uk
Contact: Ruth Dorrington
Opening Times: 1000-1700, Mon-Sun, Feb-Nov. 1200-1600 Mon-Sun, Nov/Dec/Jan.
Min Mail Order UK: Nmc
Cat. Cost: 2 × 1st class.
Credit Cards: None
Specialities: *Lavandula*. Limited numbers of particular varieties available at certain times, esp. at end of summer.
Notes: Plugs only by mail order. Wheelchair access difficult in some areas.
Map Ref: N, D2

NMen **Mendle Nursery** ⊠ ♠ ♿
Holme, Scunthorpe, Lincolnshire, DN16 3RF
Ⓣ (01724) 850864
Ⓔ annearnshaw@lineone.net
Ⓦ www.mendlenursery.com
Contact: Mrs A Earnshaw
Opening Times: 1000-1600 Tue-Sun.
Min Mail Order UK: Nmc
Min Mail Order EU: Nmc
Cat. Cost: 3 × 1st class.
Credit Cards: All major credit/debit cards
Specialities: Many unusual alpines esp. *Saxifraga* & *Sempervivum*.
Map Ref: N, D3 **OS Grid Ref:** SE925070

NMil **Millthorpe Nursery**
(office) 74 Meadowhead, Sheffield, Yorkshire,
S8 7UE
Ⓣ 0114 258 4007
Ⓜ 07899 963939
Ⓦ www.millthorpenursery.co.uk
Contact: John & Anne Dawson
Opening Times: 0900-1630 Tue-Sat, 1000-1630 Sun. Closed Mon, except B/hols. Open by appt. only in Jan.
Credit Cards: None

Specialities: Good range of shrubs, herbaceous, ferns, grasses & edibles.
Notes: Nursery at Millthorpe Lane, Millthorpe, near Holmesfield, Derbyshire S18 7SA.
Map Ref: N, D2 **OS Grid Ref:** SK321767

NMin **Miniature Bulbs & Choice Bulbs** ⊠ ♠ €
The Warren Estate, 9 Greengate Drive, Knaresborough, North Yorkshire, HG5 9EN
Ⓣ (01423) 542819
Ⓕ (01423) 542819
Ⓦ www.miniaturebulbs.co.uk
Contact: Ivor Fox
Opening Times: Not open. Mail order only.
Min Mail Order UK: £10.00
Min Mail Order EU: £15.00
Cat. Cost: 2 × 1st class.
Credit Cards: All major credit/debit cards
Specialities: Rare & unusual miniature bulbs, incl. *Narcissus, Tulipa, Iris, Crocus, Fritillaria* & others. Spring bulb list sent out in April. Some stock in small quantities.
Notes: Credit cards accepted online only.

NMir **Mires Beck Nursery** ⊠ ♿
Low Mill Lane, North Cave, Brough, East Riding, Yorkshire, HU15 2NR
Ⓣ (01430) 421543
Ⓔ admin@miresbeck.co.uk
Ⓦ www.miresbeck.co.uk
Contact: Judy Burrow & Martin Rowland
Opening Times: 1000-1600 Mon-Sat 1st Mar-30th Sep. 1000-1500 Mon-Fri 1st Oct-30th Nov & by appt.
Min Mail Order UK: Nmc
Min Mail Order EU: Nmc
Cat. Cost: 3 × 1st class.
Credit Cards: None
Specialities: Wildflower plants of Yorkshire provenance.
Notes: Mail order for wildflower plants, plugs & seeds only. Also sells wholesale.
Map Ref: N, D3 **OS Grid Ref:** SE889316

NMoo **Moor Monkton Nurseries** ⊠ ♿
Moor Monkton, York Road,
Nr York, Yorkshire,
YO26 8JJ
Ⓣ (01904) 738770
Ⓕ (01904) 738770
Ⓔ sales@bamboo-uk.co.uk
Ⓦ www.bamboo-uk.co.uk
Contact: Peter Owen
Opening Times: 0900-1700.
Min Mail Order UK: Nmc
Cat. Cost: 5 × 2nd class or email for details.
Credit Cards: All major credit/debit cards
Specialities: Bamboos, palms, ferns, unusual trees, shrubs & perennials.
Notes: Mail order for bamboos only. Also sells wholesale.
Map Ref: N, C2 **OS Grid Ref:**

NMRc **Millrace Nursery** ♿
84 Selby Road, Garforth, Leeds, LS25 1LP
Ⓣ (0113) 286 9233
Ⓕ (0113) 286 9908
Ⓔ carol@millrace-plants.co.uk
Ⓦ www.millrace-plants.co.uk
Contact: C Carthy
Opening Times: 1000-1700 Tue, Thu-Sat, Mar-Sep.
Cat. Cost: 4 × 1st class.
Credit Cards: None
Specialities: Unusual perennials, especially drought-resistant, incl. hardy geraniums, alliums, campanulas, penstemnons, potentillas & veronicas. Some plants in small quantities only.
Map Ref: N, D2

NMun **Muncaster Castle** ⊠ ♿
Ravenglass, Cumbria, CA18 1RQ
Ⓣ (01229) 717614
Ⓕ (01229) 717010
Ⓔ info@muncasterplantcentre.co.uk
Ⓦ www.muncasterplantcentre.co.uk
Contact: Jason Haine
Opening Times: 1030-1700, 7 days, 10th Feb-5th Nov. Other times by appt.
Min Mail Order UK: Nmc
Cat. Cost: 2 × 1st class.
Credit Cards: All major credit/debit cards
Specialities: Hardy plants. *Rhododendron, Camellia, Magnolia*. Some rarer varieties may be in limited supply.
Notes: Mail order mainly Oct-Apr.
Map Ref: N, C1 **OS Grid Ref:** SD103964

NMyG **Mary Green** ⊠ ♠ ♿
The Walled Garden, Hornby, Lancaster, Lancashire, LA2 8LD
Ⓣ (01524) 221989
Ⓜ 07778 910348
Ⓕ (01524) 221989
Ⓔ Marygreenplants@aol.com
Contact: Mary Green
Opening Times: By appt. only.
Min Mail Order UK: £10.00

KEY
⊠ Mail order to UK or EU ♠ Delivers to shows
✈ Exports beyond EU € Euro accepted
♿ Accessible by wheelchair ◆ See Display advertisement

Cat. Cost: 4 × 1st class.
Credit Cards: None
Specialities: Hostas, astilbes, ferns & other shade-loving perennials.
Map Ref: N, C1 **OS Grid Ref:** SD588688

NNor **Norcroft Nurseries** ⊠ ♿
Roadends, Intack, Southwaite, Carlisle, Cumbria, CA4 0LH
Ⓣ (016974) 73933
Ⓕ (016974) 73969
Ⓔ stellaandkeithbell@sbell44.fsnet.co.uk
Contact: Keith Bell
Opening Times: Every afternoon excl. Mon (open B/hol), Mar-Oct, or ring for appt.
Min Mail Order UK: Nmc
Cat. Cost: 2 × 2nd class
Credit Cards: None
Specialities: Hardy herbaceous, hostas, *Lilium*, *Hemerocallis*, *Penstemon*.
Map Ref: N, B1 **OS Grid Ref:** NY474433

NOaD **Oak Dene Nurseries** ⊠ ⌂
10 Back Lane West, Royston, Barnsley, South Yorkshire, S71 4SB
Ⓣ (01226) 722253
Contact: J Foster or G Foster
Opening Times: 0900-1800 1st Apr-30th Sep, 1000-1600 1st Oct-31st Mar. (Closed 1230-1330.)
Min Mail Order UK: Phone for details.
Min Mail Order EU: Phone for details.
Cat. Cost: None issued.
Credit Cards: None
Specialities: Cacti, succulents (*Lithops*) & South African bulbs.
Notes: Also sells wholesale.
Map Ref: N, D2

NOak **Oak Tree Nursery** ⊠ ⌂ ♿
Mill Lane, Barlow, Selby, North Yorkshire, YO8 8EY
Ⓣ (01757) 618409
Ⓔ gill.plowes@tesco.net
Ⓦ www.oaktreenursery.com
Contact: Gill Plowes
Opening Times: By appt. only.
Min Mail Order UK: £10.00 + p&p
Cat. Cost: 4 × 1st class.
Credit Cards: None
Specialities: Ornamental grasses & grass-like plants.

NOrc **Orchard House Nursery**
Orchard House, Wormald Green, Nr Harrogate, North Yorkshire, HG3 3NQ
Ⓣ (01765) 677541
Ⓕ (01765) 677541
Contact: Mr B M Corner
Opening Times: 0800-1630 Mon-Fri. Closed B/hols.
Cat. Cost: Retail catalogue may be consulted at nursery.
Credit Cards: None
Specialities: Herbaceous perennials, ferns, grasses, water plants & unusual cottage garden plants.
Notes: Also sells wholesale.
Map Ref: N, C2

NPal **The Palm Farm** ⊠ € ♿
Thornton Hall Gardens, Station Road, Thornton Curtis, Nr Ulceby, Humberside, DN39 6XF
Ⓣ (01469) 531232
Ⓕ (01469) 531232 (please phone first)
Ⓔ bill@thepalmfarm.co.uk
Ⓦ www.thepalmfarm.co.uk
Contact: W W Spink
Opening Times: 1400-1700 7 days. Please phone first in winter.
Min Mail Order UK: £11.00 + p&p
Min Mail Order EU: £25.00 + p&p
Cat. Cost: 1 × 2nd class.
Credit Cards: None
Specialities: Hardy & half-hardy palms, unusual trees, shrubs & conservatory plants. Some plants available only in small quantities.
Notes: Euro payment accepted only if purchaser pays bank commission. Mail order only if small enough to go by post (min. charge £12.50 p&p) or large enough to go by Palletline (min. charge £39.00 p&p). Also sells wholesale.
Map Ref: N, D3 **OS Grid Ref:** TA100183

NPCo **Plantsman's Corner** ◆
Sunniside, Barningham, Richmond, Yorkshire, DL11 7DW
Ⓜ 07707 694310
Ⓔ plantsmanscorner@btinternet.com
Ⓦ www.plantsmanscorner.co.uk
Contact: Malcolm Hockham
Opening Times: Not yet fully open. Visits by appt. only. Plant orders can be collected by prior arrangement or from Eggleston Hall Gardens (see nursery NEgg for opening hours). Please contact nursery for details.
Credit Cards: All major credit/debit cards
Specialities: *Cornus*, *Ilex*, & Japanese maples. Variable stock levels.

NPer **Perry's Plants** € ♿
The River Garden, Sleights, Whitby, North Yorkshire, YO21 1RR
Ⓣ (01947) 810329
Ⓔ sharon.perry@virgin.net

Ⓦ www.perrysplants.co.uk
Contact: Pat & Richard Perry
Opening Times: 1000-1700 mid-March to Oct.
Cat. Cost: Large (A4) sae.
Credit Cards: None
Specialities: *Lavatera*, *Malva*, *Erysimum*, *Euphorbia*, *Anthemis*, *Osteospermum* & *Hebe*. Uncommon hardy & container plants & aquatic plants.
Map Ref: N, C3 **OS Grid Ref:** NZ869082

NPol POLEMONIUM PLANTERY ⊠ ♠ ♿
28 Sunnyside Terrace, Trimdon Grange, Trimdon Station, Co. Durham, TS29 6HF
Ⓣ (01429) 881529
Ⓔ dandd@polemonium.co.uk
Ⓦ www.polemonium.co.uk
Contact: David or Dianne Nichol-Brown
Opening Times: By appt. only.
Min Mail Order UK: £10.00
Cat. Cost: Sae for list.
Credit Cards: None
Specialities: Nat. Collection of *Polemonium* & related genera, plus some rare North American plants. The Collection holds scientific status.
Notes: Also sells wholesale.
Map Ref: N, B2 **OS Grid Ref:** NZ369353

NPri PRIMROSE COTTAGE NURSERY ♿ ◆
Ringway Road, Moss Nook, Wythenshawe, Manchester, M22 5WF
Ⓣ (0161) 437 1557
Ⓔ info@primrosecottagenursery.co.uk
Ⓦ www.primrosecottagenursery.co.uk
Contact: Caroline Dumville
Opening Times: 0900-1730 Mon-Sat, 0930-1730 Sun (summer). 0900-1700 Mon-Sat, 0930-1700 Sun (winter).
Cat. Cost: 1 × 70p stamp.
Credit Cards: All major credit/debit cards
Specialities: Hardy herbaceous perennials, alpines, herbs, roses, patio & hanging basket plants. Shrubs.
Notes: Coffee shop open daily.
Map Ref: N, D2

NPro PROUDPLANTS ♠ ♿
East of Eden Nurseries, Ainstable, Carlisle, Cumbria, CA4 9QN
Ⓣ (01768) 896604
Ⓕ (01768) 896604
Ⓔ rogereastofeden@hotmail.com
Contact: Roger Proud
Opening Times: 0900-1800 7 days Mar-Nov. Please phone first if possible. Other times by appt.
Cat. Cost: None issued
Credit Cards: None
Specialities: Interesting & unusual shrubs, perennials & alpines, esp. dwarf & ground cover plants.
Map Ref: N, B1 **OS Grid Ref:** HA1336186

NRar RARER PLANTS ♿
Ashfield House, Austfield Lane, Monk Fryston, Leeds, LS25 5EH
Ⓣ (01977) 682263
Contact: Anne Watson
Opening Times: Feb, Mar. By appt. only.
Cat. Cost: Sae.
Credit Cards: None
Specialities: *Helleborus*.
Map Ref: N, D2

NRib RIBBLESDALE NURSERIES ♿
Newsham Hall Lane, Woodplumpton, Preston, Lancashire, PR4 0AS
Ⓣ (01772) 863081
Ⓕ (01772) 861884
Ⓔ angela@psadunnett.freeserve.co.uk
Ⓦ www.ribblesdalenurseries.co.uk
Contact: Mr & Mrs Dunnett
Opening Times: 0900-1800 Mon-Sat Apr-Sep, 0900-1700 Mon-Sat Oct-Mar. 1030-1630 Sun.
Credit Cards: Visa MasterCard Delta Switch
Specialities: Trees, shrubs & perennials. Conifers, hedging, alpines, fruit, climbers, herbs, aquatics, ferns & wildflowers.
Map Ref: N, D1 **OS Grid Ref:** SD515351

NRob W ROBINSON & SONS LTD ⊠ ✈ € ♿
Sunny Bank, Forton, Nr Preston, Lancashire, PR3 0BN
Ⓣ (01524) 791210
Ⓕ (01524) 791933
Ⓔ info@mammothonion.co.uk
Ⓦ www.mammothonion.co.uk
Contact: Miss Robinson
Opening Times: 0900-1700 7 days Mar-Jun, 0800-1700 Mon-Fri Jul-Feb.
Min Mail Order UK: Nmc
Min Mail Order EU: Nmc
Cat. Cost: Free.
Credit Cards: Visa Access American Express Switch
Specialities: Mammoth vegetable seed. Onions, leeks, tomatoes & beans. Range of vegetable plants in the spring.
Notes: Also sells wholesale.

KEY
⊠ Mail order to UK or EU ♠ Delivers to shows
✈ Exports beyond EU € Euro accepted
♿ Accessible by wheelchair ◆ See Display advertisement

NRya **Ryal Nursery**
East Farm Cottage, Ryal, Northumberland, NE20 0SA
Ⓣ (01661) 886562
Ⓕ (01661) 886918
Ⓔ alpines@ryal.freeserve.co.uk
Contact: R F Hadden
Opening Times: 1000-1600 Sun Mar-Jul & other times by appt.
Cat. Cost: Sae.
Credit Cards: None
Specialities: Alpine & woodland plants. Mainly available in small quantities only. Nat. Collection of *Primula marginata*.
Notes: Also sells wholesale.
Map Ref: N, B2 **OS Grid Ref:** NZ015744

N

NSco **Scott's Wildflowers** ⊠
Swallow Hill Barn, 31 Common Side, Distington, Workington, Cumbria, CA14 4PU
Ⓣ (01946) 830486
Ⓔ scotts.wildflowers@virgin.net
Ⓦ www.scottswildflowers.co.uk
Contact: Ted Scott
Opening Times: 1000-1600 Mar-Oct, 1130-1500 Nov-Feb, 7 days.
Min Mail Order UK: £10.40 + £4.50 p&p
Cat. Cost: 3 × 1st class.
Credit Cards: None
Specialities: Native British wildflowers, including aquatics.
Notes: Also sells wholesale.
Map Ref: N, C1

NScw **Scawsby Hall Nurseries** ⊠
Barnsley Road, Scawsby, Doncaster, South Yorkshire, DN5 7UB
Ⓣ (01302) 783434
Ⓔ mail@the-plant-directory.com
Ⓦ www.the-plant-directory.com
Contact: David Lawson
Opening Times: 0930-1700 Mon-Sat 1100-1700 Sun.
Min Mail Order UK: Nmc
Cat. Cost: None issued
Credit Cards: Maestro Visa MasterCard Solo
Specialities: A wide range of herbaceous perennials, hardy trees, shrubs & indoor plants. Some indoor & aquatic plants in small quantities only.
Map Ref: N, D3 **OS Grid Ref:** SE542049

NShi **Shirley Tasker** ⊠
6 Sandheys Drive, Churchtown, Southport, Merseyside, PR9 9PQ
Ⓣ (01704) 213048
Ⓜ 07951 834066
Ⓔ shirley@shirleysplants.fsnet.co.uk
Ⓦ www.stbegonias.com
Contact: Shirley & Terry Tasker
Opening Times: By appt. only.
Min Mail Order UK: Nmc
Cat. Cost: 2 × 1st class.
Credit Cards: None
Specialities: Nat. Collection of *Begonia* species & hybrids.
Map Ref: N, D1 **OS Grid Ref:** SD355183

NSla **Slack Top Nurseries** ⊠ €
Hebden Bridge, West Yorkshire, HX7 7HA
Ⓣ (01422) 845348
Ⓔ enquiries@slacktopnurseries.co.uk
Ⓦ www.slacktopnurseries.co.uk
Contact: M R or R Mitchell
Opening Times: 1000-1700 Fri-Sun 1st Mar-30th Sep & B/hol Mons 1st Mar-30th Sep.
Min Mail Order UK: £30.00
Cat. Cost: Sae.
Credit Cards: None
Specialities: Alpine & rockery plants. *Celmisia semi-cordata*, *Saxifraga*, *Hepatica* & *Paeonia*. *Anemone nemorosa* cvs.
Notes: Suitable for wheelchairs but 2 steps at entrance.
Map Ref: N, D2 **OS Grid Ref:** SD977286

NSti **Stillingfleet Lodge Nurseries**
Stillingfleet, North Yorkshire, YO19 6HP
Ⓣ (01904) 728506
Ⓕ (01904) 728506
Ⓔ vanessa.cook@stillingfleetlodgenurseries.co.uk
Ⓦ www.stillingfleetlodgenurseries.co.uk
Contact: Vanessa Cook
Opening Times: 1300-1700 Wed & Fri 16th Apr-30th Sep. 1300-1700, 1st & 3rd Sat in each month.
Cat. Cost: None issued.
Credit Cards: None
Specialities: Foliage & unusual perennials. Hardy geraniums, *Pulmonaria*, variegated plants & grasses, interesting climbers.
Map Ref: N, C2

NSum **Summerdale Garden Nursery**
Summerdale House, Cow Brow, Lupton, Carnforth, Lancashire, LA6 1PE
Ⓣ (01539) 567210
Ⓔ summerdalenursery@btinternet.com
Ⓦ www.summerdalegardenplants.co.uk
Contact: Abi Attwood
Opening Times: 0930-1630 Thu, Fri & Sat, 1st Feb-31st Oct. Other times by appt. only.
Cat. Cost: 4 × 1st class.
Credit Cards: All major credit/debit cards

Specialities: Wide variety of pernnials, large collection of *Primula*. Many moist and shade-loving plants incl. *Meconopsis* & hellebores.
Map Ref: N, C1 **OS Grid Ref:** SD545819

NTay **Taylors Clematis Nursery** ⊠ ♦
Sutton Road, Sutton, Nr Askern, Doncaster, South Yorkshire, DN6 9JZ
Ⓣ (01302) 700716
Ⓕ (01302) 708415
Ⓔ info@taylorsclematis.co.uk
Ⓦ www.taylorsclematis.co.uk
Contact: Chris & Suzy Cocks
Opening Times: Open by appt. only. Please ring for details.
Min Mail Order UK: Nmc
Min Mail Order EU: Nmc
Cat. Cost: 6 × 1st class.
Credit Cards: All major credit/debit cards
Specialities: *Clematis* (over 300 varieties).

NVic **The Vicarage Garden** ⊠
Carrington, Manchester, M31 4AG
Ⓣ (0161) 775 2750
Ⓔ info@vicaragebotanicalgardens.co.uk
Ⓦ www.vicaragebotanicalgardens.co.uk
Contact: Paul Haine
Opening Times: 0900-1700 Mon-Sat, closed Thu. 1000-1630 Sun all year.
Min Mail Order UK: Nmc
Cat. Cost: 2 × 2nd class for list.
Credit Cards: All major credit/debit cards
Specialities: Herbaceous, alpines, grasses, ferns.
Notes: Free admission to 7-acre gardens with coffee shop & mini zoo.
Map Ref: N, D2 **OS Grid Ref:** SJ729926

NWCA **White Cottage Alpines** ⊠ ♦
Sunnyside Nurseries, Hornsea Road, Sigglesthorne, East Yorkshire, HU11 5QL
Ⓣ (01964) 542692
Ⓕ (01964) 542692
Ⓔ plants@whitecottagealpines.co.uk
Ⓦ www.whitecottagealpines.co.uk
Contact: Sally E Cummins
Opening Times: 1000-1700 (or dusk) Thu-Sun & B/hol Mon 1 Mar-30 Sep. If travelling far, please phone first. In winter by appt. only.
Min Mail Order UK: Nmc.
Min Mail Order EU: £15.00 + p&p by card only.
Cat. Cost: 4 × 1st class.
Credit Cards: Visa MasterCard Switch
Specialities: Alpines & rock plants. 500+ species incl. American, dwarf *Salix* & *Helichrysum*, also increasing range of *Penstemon*.
Notes: Euro payments by card only.
Map Ref: N, C3

NWea **Weasdale Nurseries Ltd.** ⊠
Newbiggin-on-Lune, Kirkby Stephen, Cumbria, CA17 4LX
Ⓣ (01539) 623246
Ⓕ (01539) 623277
Ⓔ sales@weasdale.com
Ⓦ www.weasdale.com
Contact: Andrew Forsyth
Opening Times: 0830-1730 Mon-Fri. Closed w/ends, B/hols, Xmas through to the New Year.
Min Mail Order UK: Nmc
Min Mail Order EU: Nmc
Cat. Cost: £2.00 or 7 × 1st class. £2.00 by debit card, £2.50 by credit card.
Credit Cards: All major credit/debit cards
Specialities: Hardy forest trees, hedging, broadleaved & conifers. Specimen trees & shrubs grown at 850 feet (260 metre) elevation.
Notes: Mail order a speciality. Mail order Nov-Apr only. Also sells wholesale to VAT registered customers.
Map Ref: N, C1 **OS Grid Ref:** NY690039

NWit **D S Witton** ⊠
26 Casson Drive, Harthill, Sheffield, Yorkshire, S26 7WA
Ⓣ (01909) 771366
Ⓕ (01909) 771366
Ⓔ donshardyeuphorbias@btopenworld.com
Ⓦ www.euphorbias.co.uk
Contact: Don Witton
Opening Times: By appt. only. Open Day, 1300-1600, Sun 4 May 2008.
Min Mail Order UK: Nmc
Cat. Cost: 1 × 1st class + sae.
Credit Cards: None
Specialities: Nat. Collection of Hardy *Euphorbia*. Over 130 varieties.
Notes: Mail order plants, Oct-Feb. Mail order seed Oct-June.
Map Ref: N, D2 **OS Grid Ref:** SK494812

NWsh **Westshores Nurseries** ⊠
82 West Street, Winterton, Lincolnshire, DN15 9QF
Ⓣ (01724) 733940
Ⓔ westshnur@aol.com
Ⓦ www.westshores.co.uk

KEY
⊠ Mail order to UK or EU — Delivers to shows
Exports beyond EU — € Euro accepted
Accessible by wheelchair — ♦ See Display advertisement

N

Contact: Gail & John Summerfield
Opening Times: 0930-1800 (or dusk) w/ends & B/hols, 1st Mar-31st Oct. Other times by appt.
Min Mail Order UK: £15.00
Credit Cards: All major credit/debit cards
Specialities: Ornamental grasses & herbaceous perennials.
Map Ref: N, D3 **OS Grid Ref:** SE927187

NWyk **WYKEHAM MATURE PLANTS** ⊠ €
The Walled Garden, Wykeham Abbey, Scarborough, N. Yorkshire, YO13 9QS
Ⓣ (01723) 862406
Ⓕ (01723) 865643
Ⓔ a.smith@wykeham.co.uk
Ⓦ www.wykehammatureplants.co.uk
Contact: Martin Howe
Opening Times: 0930-1630 Mon-Sat, 10.30-1500 Sun, Mar-May. Closed throughout Xmas.
Min Mail Order UK: Nmc
Cat. Cost: None issued.
Credit Cards: All major credit/debit cards
Specialities: Trees, shrubs, hedging as mature plants for instant effect.
Notes: Large stock only. Delivery by pallet or large hauliage wagon, heavy stock. Also sells wholesale. Does not accept American Express.
Map Ref: N, C3

N

SOUTHERN

SAga **BLUEBELL COTTAGE NURSERY (FORMERLY AGAR'S)** € ♿
Agars Lane, Hordle, Lymington, Hampshire, SO41 0FL
Ⓜ 07947 702767
Contact: Debbie Ursell
Opening Times: 0930-1500 Mon-Wed & Fri (closed Thu), 1000-1700 Sat & Sun, Mar-Sep. Oct-Feb open most days but please phone first.
Specialities: *Penstemon* & *Salvia*. Also wide range of hardy plants incl. hardy & tender shrubs, climbers & herbaceous.
Map Ref: S, D2 **OS Grid Ref:** SZ275960

SAll **ALLWOODS** ⊠ ♿
London Road, Hassocks, West Sussex, BN6 9NB
Ⓣ (01273) 844229
Ⓕ (01273) 846022
Ⓔ info@allwoods.net
Ⓦ www.allwoods.net
Contact: David & Emma James
Opening Times: Office: 0900-1630 Mon-Fri, answer machine all other times. Nursery: 1st Mar-30th Jun, 7 days.
Min Mail Order UK: Nmc
Min Mail Order EU: Nmc
Cat. Cost: 2 × 1st class.
Credit Cards: Access Visa MasterCard Switch Maestro
Specialities: *Dianthus* incl. hardy border carnations, pinks, perpetual & *D. allwoodii*, some available as seed. Certain lavender varieties. Penstemons.
Notes: Exports seed only.
Map Ref: S, D4 **OS Grid Ref:** TQ303170

SAPC **ARCHITECTURAL PLANTS (CHICHESTER) LTD** ⊠ € ♿ ◆
Lidsey Road Nursery, Westergate, Nr Chichester, West Sussex, PO20 6SU
Ⓣ (01243) 545008
Ⓕ (01243) 545009
Ⓔ chichester@architecturalplants.com
Ⓦ www.architecturalplants.com
Contact: Christine Shaw
Opening Times: 1000-1600 Sun-Fri all year. Closed Sat & B/hol Mons. Open Good Fri.
Min Mail Order UK: Nmc
Min Mail Order EU: £150.00
Cat. Cost: Free.
Credit Cards: All major credit/debit cards
Specialities: Architectural plants & hardy exotics esp. rare evergreen broadleaved trees & seaside exotics, spiky plants, yuccas/agaves.
Notes: Also sells wholesale. Second nursery near Horsham, Code SArc.
Map Ref: S, D3 **OS Grid Ref:** SU937040

SApp **APPLE COURT** ⊠ € ♿
Hordle Lane, Hordle, Lymington, Hampshire, S041 0HU
Ⓣ (01590) 642130
Ⓕ (01590) 644220
Ⓔ applecourt@btinternet.com
Ⓦ www.applecourt.com
Contact: Angela & Charles Meads
Opening Times: 1000-1700 Fri, Sat, Sun & B/hol 1st Mar-31st Oct. Closed Nov-Feb.
Min Mail Order UK: Nmc
Min Mail Order EU: Nmc
Cat. Cost: 4 × 1st class.
Credit Cards: All major credit/debit cards
Specialities: *Hemerocallis*, *Hosta*, grasses & ferns.
Map Ref: S, D2 **OS Grid Ref:** SZ270941

SArc **ARCHITECTURAL PLANTS** ⊠ € ♿ ◆
Cooks Farm, Nuthurst, Horsham, West Sussex, RH13 6LH
Ⓣ (01403) 891772
Ⓕ (01403) 891056

Ⓔ enquiries@architecturalplants.com
Ⓦ www.architecturalplants.com
Contact: Sarah Chandler
Opening Times: 0900-1700 Mon-Sat, closed Sun.
Min Mail Order UK: Nmc
Min Mail Order EU: £150.00
Cat. Cost: Free
Credit Cards: All major credit/debit cards
Specialities: Architectural plants & hardy exotics & rare broadleaved trees, bamboos, spiky plants, ferns & climbers.
Notes: Also sells wholesale Second nursery near Chichester, code SAPC.
Map Ref: S, C3 **OS Grid Ref:** TQ192262

SBch **Birchfield Nursery** ⊠ ♿
Kidders Lane, Henfield, West Sussex, BN5 9AB
Ⓣ (01273) 494058
Ⓕ (01273) 493696
Ⓔ sales@birchfieldnursery.com
Ⓦ www.birchfieldnursery.com
Contact: Clive Parker or Ron Jenkins
Opening Times: 0830-1700 Mon-Fri, 0930-1630 Sat 7 Sun, all year except Xmas/New Year period. For winter hours please phone first.
Min Mail Order UK: Nmc
Cat. Cost: Online only.
Credit Cards: All major credit/debit cards
Specialities: Wide general range incl. many unusual varieties, plus fruit, young veg. plants & seasonal bedding. Some plants available in small quantities only. Please phone before visiting to ensure plant availability.
Notes: Also sells wholesale.
Map Ref: S, D3 **OS Grid Ref:** TQ213178

SBch **Birchwood Plants**
(office) 10 Westering, Romsey, Hampshire, SO51 7LY
Ⓣ (01794) 502192 or 02380 814345
Ⓔ lesleybaker@lycos.co.uk
Ⓦ www.birchwoodplants.co.uk
Contact: Lesley Baker
Opening Times: By appt. at nursery, only for collection of plants. Plants available at Mottisfont Abbey (NT) but ring first to check availability.
Cat. Cost: Online only.
Credit Cards: None
Specialities: Wide range of plants, mainly herbaceous, many unusual. Good selection of salvias, hardy geraniums, scented plants & herbs, also good range for bees & butterflies & drought-tolerant plants. Some stock available in small quantities only.
Notes: Nursery at Gardener's Lane, nr Romsey, SO51 6AD, open for collection only. Mottisfont accessible for wheelchairs.
Map Ref: S, D3 **OS Grid Ref:** SU333190

SBHP **Bleak Hill Plants** ♿
Braemoor, Bleak Hill, Harbridge, Ringwood, Hampshire, BH24 3PX
Ⓣ (01425) 652983
Ⓔ tracey_netherway@btopenworld.com
Contact: Tracy Netherway
Opening Times: 0900-1800, Mon, Tue, Fri, Sat & 1000-1600 Sun, Mar-Oct. Closed Wed & Thu.
Cat. Cost: 2 × 1st class.
Credit Cards: None
Specialities: Hardy & half-hardy herbaceous perennials. Stock available in small quantities.
Map Ref: S, D1 **OS Grid Ref:** SU132111

SBig **Big Plant Nursery** ⊠ ♿ ◆
Hole Street, Ashington, West Sussex, RH20 3DE
Ⓣ (01903) 891466
Ⓕ (01903) 892829
Ⓔ info@bigplantnursery.co.uk
Ⓦ www.bigplantnursery.co.uk
Contact: Bruce Jordan
Opening Times: 0900-1700 Mon-Sat, 1000-1600 Sun & B/hols.
Min Mail Order UK: Please phone for further info.
Cat. Cost: A5 sae with 2 × 1st class.
Credit Cards: All major credit/debit cards
Specialities: Bamboos, hardy exotics & palms, *Ginkgo*, *Betula*.
Notes: Also sells wholesale.
Map Ref: S, D3 **OS Grid Ref:** TQ132153

SBir **Birchfleet Nurseries** ◆
Nyewood, Petersfield, Hampshire, GU31 5JQ
Ⓣ (01730) 821636
Ⓕ (01730) 821636
Ⓔ gammoak@aol.com
Ⓦ www.birchfleetnurseries.co.uk
Contact: John & Daphne Gammon
Opening Times: By appt. only. Please phone.
Cat. Cost: 2 × 1st class.
Credit Cards: None
Specialities: Oaks. Beech. *Carpinus*. Nat. Collection of *Liquidambar*.
Notes: Also sells wholesale. Nursery accessible for wheelchairs in dry weather.
Map Ref: S, C3

KEY
⊠ Mail order to UK or EU — Delivers to shows
Exports beyond EU — € Euro accepted
♿ Accessible by wheelchair — ◆ See Display advertisement

S

S

SBmr **BLACKMOOR NURSERIES** ⊠ ♿
Blackmoor Estate, Blackmoor, Liss, Hampshire, GU33 6BS
Ⓣ (01420) 473576
Ⓕ (01420) 487813
Ⓔ jonmunday@blackmoor.co.uk
Ⓦ www.blackmoor.co.uk
Contact: Jon Munday
Opening Times: 0730-1600.
Min Mail Order UK: Nmc
Min Mail Order EU: Nmc
Cat. Cost: None issued.
Credit Cards: All major credit/debit cards
Specialities: Fruit trees, soft fruit & ornamental trees.
Notes: Also sells wholesale.
Map Ref: S, C3 **OS Grid Ref:** SU779336

SBod **BODIAM NURSERY** ♿
Bodiam, Robertsbridge, East Sussex, TN32 5RA
Ⓣ (01580) 830811
Ⓔ contact@bodiamnursery.com
Ⓦ www.bodiamnursery.co.uk
Contact: Anne-Marie Sapsted
Opening Times: 1000-1700 7 days. Closed Jan.
Cat. Cost: None issued.
Credit Cards: All major credit/debit cards
Specialities: Herbaceous perennials, grasses, conifers, *Camellia* & climbers. Acers. Shrubs & trees.

SBrm **BRAMBLY HEDGE** ⊠
Mill Lane, Sway, Hampshire, SO41 8LN
Ⓣ (01590) 683570
Contact: Kim Williams
Opening Times: By appt. only.
Min Mail Order UK: Nmc
Cat. Cost: Sae for descriptive list.
Credit Cards: None
Specialities: Nat. Collection of *Streptocarpus*. Available in small quantities only.
Notes: Mail order Mar-Aug, small quantities only available.

SBst **BEAST PLANTS**
24 Arundel Road, Boyatt Wood, Eastleigh, Hampshire, SO50 4PQ
Ⓣ 02380 485307
Ⓜ 07887 997263
Ⓔ beastplants@tiscali.co.uk
Contact: Toni & Steve Newell
Opening Times: By appt. only.
Cat. Cost: Free.
Credit Cards: None
Specialities: Exotic, sub-tropical & unusual plants.

SCac **CACTI & SUCCULENTS** ⊠
Hammerfield, Crockham Hill, Edenbridge, Kent, TN8 6RR
Ⓣ (01732) 866295
Contact: Geoff Southon
Opening Times: Flexible. Please phone first.
Min Mail Order UK: Nmc.
Cat. Cost: None issued.
Credit Cards: None
Specialities: *Echeveria* & related genera & hybrids. *Agave*, haworthias, aloes, gasterias, crassulas & aeoniums. (Large range of plants available in small quantities.)

SCam **CAMELLIA GROVE NURSERY** ⊠ ✈ ⌂ € ♿
Market Garden, Lower Beeding, West Sussex, RH13 6PP
Ⓣ (01403) 891412
Ⓔ sales@camellia-grove.com
Ⓦ www.camellia-grove.com
Contact: Chris Loder
Opening Times: 1000-1600 Mon-Sat, please phone first so we can give you our undivided attention.
Min Mail Order UK: Nmc
Min Mail Order EU: Nmc
Cat. Cost: 2 × 1st class.
Credit Cards: Switch MasterCard Visa
Specialities: Camellias & azaleas.
Notes: Also sells wholesale.
Map Ref: S, C3

SChF **CHARLESHURST FARM NURSERY** ⊠ ⌂ €
Loxwood Road, Plaistow, Billingshurst, West Sussex, RH14 0NY
Ⓣ (01403) 752273
Ⓜ 07736 522788
Ⓔ Charleshurstfarm@aol.com
Ⓦ www.charleshurstplants.co.uk
Contact: Clive Mellor
Opening Times: Normally 0800-1700 Fri, Sat, Sun, Feb-Oct, but please ring first before travelling.
Min Mail Order UK: Nmc
Min Mail Order EU: Nmc
Cat. Cost: 2 × 1st class.
Credit Cards: None
Specialities: Shrubs including some more unusual species. Good range of daphnes & Japanese maples.
Map Ref: S, C3 **OS Grid Ref:** TQ015308

SChr **JOHN CHURCHER** ⊠ ✈
47 Grove Avenue, Portchester, Fareham, Hampshire, PO16 9EZ
Ⓣ (023) 9232 6740
Ⓕ (023) 9232 6740

Ⓔ churchers.47@tiscali.co.uk
Contact: John Churcher
Opening Times: By appt. only. Please phone or email.
Min Mail Order UK: Nmc
Min Mail Order EU: Nmc
Cat. Cost: None issued.
Credit Cards: None
Specialities: Hardy exotics for the Mediterranean-style garden, incl. palms, tree ferns, *Musa*, hedychiums, cycads, *Agave*, *Aloe*, *Opuntia* & echiums. Stock available in small quantities only.
Map Ref: S, D2 **OS Grid Ref:** SU614047

SCko **Cookoo Box Nursery** ⊠ ✈ ⌂
Longfield, 63 Charlesford Avenue, Kingswood, Maidstone, Kent, ME17 3PH
Ⓜ 07749 828168
Ⓔ info@cookooboxchillies.com
Ⓦ www.cookooboxchillies.com
Contact: P Drew-Cook
Opening Times: By appt. only.
Min Mail Order UK: Nmc
Min Mail Order EU: Nmc
Cat. Cost: 2 × 1st class.
Credit Cards: None
Specialities: *Capsicum*
Notes: Also sells wholesale.

SCmr **Cromar Nursery** ⊠ ♿
39 Livesey Street, North Pole, Wateringbury, Maidstone, Kent, ME18 5BQ
Ⓣ (01622) 812380
Ⓔ CromarNursery@aol.com
Ⓦ www.cromarnursery.co.uk
Contact: Debra & Martin Cronk
Opening Times: 0930-1700 daily except Wed.
Min Mail Order UK: Nmc
Min Mail Order EU: Nmc
Cat. Cost: 2 × 1st class.
Credit Cards: All major credit/debit cards
Specialities: Ornamental & fruit trees.
Map Ref: S, C4 **OS Grid Ref:** TQ697547

SCnR **Colin Roberts** ⊠
Tragumna, Morgay Wood Lane, Three Oaks, Guestling, East Sussex, TN35 4NF
Ⓜ 07933 060905
Contact: Colin Roberts
Opening Times: Not open. Mail order only.
Min Mail Order UK: £20.00
Cat. Cost: 2 × 1st class.
Credit Cards: None
Specialities: Dwarf bulbs & woodland plants incl. many rare & unusual, in small numbers.

SCog **Coghurst Camellias** ⊠ ⌂ € ♿
Ivy House Lane, Near Three Oaks, Hastings, East Sussex, TN35 4NP
Ⓣ (01424) 756228
Ⓔ rotherview@btinternet.com
Ⓦ www.rotherview.com
Contact: R Bates & W Bates
Opening Times: 0930-1600 7 days.
Min Mail Order UK: Nmc
Min Mail Order EU: Nmc
Cat. Cost: 6 × 1st class.
Credit Cards: All major credit/debit cards
Specialities: *Camellia.*
Notes: Also sells wholesale. Nursery is on the same site as Rotherview Nursery.
Map Ref: S, D5

SCoo **Cooling's Nurseries Ltd** ♿
Rushmore Hill, Knockholt, Sevenoaks, Kent, TN14 7NN
Ⓣ (01959) 532269
Ⓕ (01959) 534092
Ⓔ Plantfinder@coolings.co.uk
Ⓦ www.coolings.co.uk
Contact: Mark Reeve or Dan Short
Opening Times: 0900-1700 Mon-Sat & 1000-1630 Sun.
Cat. Cost: None issued
Credit Cards: All major credit/debit cards
Specialities: Large range of perennials, conifers & bedding plants. Many unusual shrubs & trees. Third generation family business. Display garden.
Notes: Does not accept American Express. Coffee shop.
Map Ref: S, C4 **OS Grid Ref:** TK477610

SCrf **Crofters Nurseries** € ♿
Church Hill, Charing Heath, Near Ashford, Kent, TN27 0BU
Ⓣ (01233) 712798
Ⓕ (01233) 712798
Ⓔ crofters@sky.com
Contact: John & Sue Webb
Opening Times: 1000-1700. Closed Sun-Tue. Please check first.
Cat. Cost: 3 × 1st class.
Credit Cards: None
Specialities: Fruit, ornamental trees & conifers. Old apple varieties. Small number of *Prunus serrula* with grafted ornamental heads.
Map Ref: S, C5 **OS Grid Ref:** TQ923493

KEY
⊠ Mail order to UK or EU ⌂ Delivers to shows
✈ Exports beyond EU € Euro accepted
♿ Accessible by wheelchair ◆ See Display advertisement

SDay **A LA CARTE DAYLILIES** ⊠ €
Little Hermitage, St Catherine's Down, Nr Ventnor, Isle of Wight, PO38 2PD
Ⓣ (01983) 730512
Ⓔ andy@alacartedaylilies.co.uk
Ⓦ www.alacartedaylilies.co.uk
Contact: Jan & Andy Wyers
Opening Times: Mail order only. Open by appt. only. Difficult to find, on an unmade private road.
Min Mail Order UK: Nmc
Min Mail Order EU: Nmc
Cat. Cost: 3 × 1st class.
Credit Cards: None
Specialities: *Hemerocallis*. Nat. Collections of Miniature & Small Flowered *Hemerocallis* & Large Flowered *Hemerocallis* (post-1960 award-winning cultivars).
Notes: Also sells wholesale.
Map Ref: S, D2 **OS Grid Ref:** SZ499787

S

SDea **DEACON'S NURSERY** ⊠ ⊠ € ◆
Moor View, Godshill, Isle of Wight, PO38 3HW
Ⓣ (01983) 840750 (24 hrs) or (01983) 522243
Ⓕ (01983) 523575
Ⓔ info@deaconsnurseryfruits.co.uk
Ⓦ www.deaconsnurseryfruits.co.uk
Contact: G D & B H W Deacon
Opening Times: 0800-1600 Mon-Fri May-Sep, 0800-1700 Mon-Fri 0800-1200 Sat Oct-Apr.
Min Mail Order UK: Nmc
Min Mail Order EU: Nmc
Cat. Cost: Free.
Credit Cards: All major credit/debit cards
Specialities: Over 300 varieties of apple, old & new, pears, plums, gages, damsons, cherries. Modern soft fruit, grapes, hops, nuts & family trees.
Notes: Also sells wholesale.
Map Ref: S, D2

SDix **GREAT DIXTER NURSERIES** ⊠ ♿
Northiam, Rye, East Sussex, TN31 6PH
Ⓣ (01797) 253107
Ⓕ (01797) 252879
Ⓔ nursery@greatdixter.co.uk
Ⓦ www.greatdixter.co.uk
Contact: K Leighton
Opening Times: 0900-1700 Mon-Fri, 0900-1230 Sat all year. Also 1400-1700 Sat, Sun & B/hols Apr-Oct.
Min Mail Order UK: Nmc
Min Mail Order EU: Nmc
Cat. Cost: 5 × 1st class.
Credit Cards: All major credit/debit cards
Specialities: *Clematis*, shrubs and plants. Gardens open.
Notes: Plants dispatched Sep-Mar only.

SDnm **DENMANS GARDEN, (JOHN BROOKES LTD)** ♿
Denmans Lane, Fontwell, West Sussex, BN18 0SU
Ⓣ (01243) 542808
Ⓕ (01243) 544064
Ⓔ denmans@denmans-garden.co.uk
Ⓦ www.denmans-garden.co.uk
Contact: Mrs Claudia Murphy
Opening Times: 0900-1700 (dusk in winter) 7 days all year, except 25th & 26th Dec & 1st Jan.
Cat. Cost: None issued
Credit Cards: Visa MasterCard
Specialities: Rare and unusual plants.
Map Ref: S, D3 **OS Grid Ref:** SU944070

SDow **DOWNDERRY NURSERY** ⊠ ⊠ € ♿
Pillar Box Lane, Hadlow, Nr Tonbridge, Kent, TN11 9SW
Ⓣ (01732) 810081
Ⓕ (01732) 811398
Ⓔ info@downderry-nursery.co.uk
Ⓦ www.downderry-nursery.co.uk
Contact: Dr S J Charlesworth
Opening Times: 1000-1700 Tue-Sun 1st May-31st Oct & B/hols. Other times by appt.
Min Mail Order UK: Nmc
Min Mail Order EU: Nmc
Cat. Cost: 3 × 1st class.
Credit Cards: Delta MasterCard Maestro Visa
Specialities: Nat. Collections of *Lavandula* and *Rosmarinus*.
Map Ref: S, C4 **OS Grid Ref:** TQ625521

SDys **DYSONS NURSERIES** ♿
Great Comp Garden, Platt, Sevenoaks, Kent, TN15 8QS
Ⓣ (01732) 886154
Ⓔ info@dysons-salvias.co.uk
Ⓦ www.dysons-salvias.co.uk
Contact: William T Dyson
Opening Times: 1100-1700 7 days 1st Apr-31st Oct. Other times by appt.
Cat. Cost: Online only.
Credit Cards: None
Specialities: Salvias, esp. New World species and cultivars.
Map Ref: S, C4

SECG **THE ENGLISH COTTAGE GARDEN NURSERY** ⊠ ⌂ €
Eggarton Cottages, Eggarton Lane, Godmersham, Kent, CT4 7DY
Ⓣ (01227) 730242
Ⓕ (01227) 730242
Ⓔ enquiries@englishplants.co.uk
Ⓦ www.englishplants.co.uk

Contact: Teresa Sinclair
Opening Times: 7 days, please phone first.
Min Mail Order UK: Nmc
Cat. Cost: Free.
Credit Cards: MasterCard Visa Solo Electron Switch
Specialities: Small nursery offering variety of traditional cottage garden plants, wildflowers & herbs. Some wildflowers available in small quantities only. Native hedging. Meadow seed. Wildflower seed & plugs.
Notes: Plants can be ordered & paid for online. Regular updates on plant availability on website. Also sells wholesale.
Map Ref: S, C5

SEND **EAST NORTHDOWN FARM** ⊠ € ♿ ◆
Margate, Kent, CT9 3TS
Ⓣ (01843) 862060
Ⓕ (01843) 860206
Ⓔ friend.northdown@btinternet.com
Ⓦ www.botanyplants.com
Contact: Louise & William Friend
Opening Times: 0900-1700 Mon-Sat, 1000-1700 Sun all year. Closed Xmas week & Easter Sun.
Min Mail Order UK: Nmc
Cat. Cost: Online only.
Credit Cards: Visa Switch MasterCard
Specialities: Chalk & coast-loving plants.
Map Ref: S, B6

SEWo **ENGLISH WOODLANDS** ⊠
Burrow Nursery, Cross in Hand, Heathfield, East Sussex, TN21 0UG
Ⓣ (01435) 862992
Ⓕ (01435) 867742
Ⓔ michael@ewburrownursery.co.uk
Ⓦ www.ewburrownursery.co.uk
Contact: Michael Hardcastle
Opening Times: 8000-1700 Mon-Sat. Closed Sun.
Min Mail Order UK: £25.00
Cat. Cost: 4 × 1st class.
Credit Cards: All major credit/debit cards
Specialities: Trees, large & small.
Notes: Also sells wholesale.
Map Ref: S, C4 **OS Grid Ref:** TQ557122

SFam **FAMILY TREES** ⊠ ♿
Sandy Lane, Shedfield, Hampshire, SO32 2HQ
Ⓣ (01329) 834812
Contact: Philip House
Opening Times: 0930-1230 Tue, Wed, Fri & Sat mid-Oct-end Apr (closed 15th Dec-15th Jan).
Min Mail Order UK: £8.00
Cat. Cost: Free
Credit Cards: None
Specialities: Fruit & ornamental trees. Trained fruit tree specialists: standards, espaliers, cordons. Other trees, old-fashioned & climbing roses, evergreens. Trees, except evergreens, sold bare-rooted.

SFgr **FIRGROVE PLANTS** ⊠
24 Wykeham Field, Wickham, Fareham, Hampshire, PO17 5AB
Ⓣ (01329) 835206 after 1900 hours.
Ⓔ jenny@firgroveplants.demon.co.uk
Ⓦ www.firgroveplants.demon.co.uk
Contact: Jenny MacKinnon
Opening Times: Not open. Mail order only.
Min Mail Order UK: £7.00
Cat. Cost: Sae.
Credit Cards: None
Specialities: Wide range of houseleeks & smaller range of other alpines in small quantities.
Notes: Houseleeks by mail order Apr-mid Oct.

SGar **GARDEN PLANTS** ⊠ ⌂
Windy Ridge, Victory Road, St Margarets-at-Cliffe, Dover, Kent, CT15 6HF
Ⓣ (01304) 853225
Ⓔ GardenPlants@GardenPlants-nursery.co.uk
Ⓦ www.GardenPlants-nursery.co.uk
Contact: Teresa Ryder & David Ryder
Opening Times: 1000-1730 summer, 1000-1700 winter. Closed Tues.
Min Mail Order UK: Nmc
Cat. Cost: 2 × 1st class + A5 sae.
Credit Cards: None
Specialities: Unusual perennials, *Penstemon* & *Salvia*.
Notes: Plantsman's garden open to view. Map essential for first visit. Also sells wholesale.
Map Ref: S, C6 **OS Grid Ref:** TR358464

SGol **GOLDEN HILL NURSERIES** ⊠ € ♿
Lordsfield, Goudhurst Road, Marden, Kent, TN12 9LT
Ⓣ (01622) 833218
Ⓕ (01622) 832528
Ⓔ enquiries@goldenhillplants.com
Ⓦ www.goldenhillplants.com
Contact: Roger Butler
Opening Times: 0900-1700 Mon-Sat, 1st

KEY
⊠ Mail order to UK or EU ⌂ Delivers to shows
✈ Exports beyond EU € Euro accepted
♿ Accessible by wheelchair ◆ See Display advertisement

S

Mar-31st Oct. 0900-1600 Mon-Sat, 1st Nov-29th Feb. Closed Sun from 1st Jan, reopen 3rd Sun in Feb from 1100-1600.
Min Mail Order UK: Nmc
Cat. Cost: Online only.
Credit Cards: All major credit/debit cards
Specialities: Specimen plants, shrubs, grasses, bamboos, Japanese maples, conifers & trees. 80% of stock produced at nursery.
Notes: Also sells wholesale.

SGSe **Garden Secrets** ♿
Green Pastures, Pitmore Lane, Sway, Hampshire, SO41 8LL
Ⓜ 07779 084245
Ⓦ www.gardensecretsnursery.co.uk
Contact: Tim Woodford
Opening Times: 0900-1700 Sat & Sun, Mar-Jan. Other times by appt. only. Please phone first.
Credit Cards: None
Specialities: Perennials, grasses and ferns.
Map Ref: S, D2 **OS Grid Ref:** SZ295971

SHaC **Hart Canna** ⊠ € ♿
27 Guildford Road West, Farnborough, Hampshire, GU14 6PS
Ⓣ (01252) 514421
Ⓕ (01252) 378821
Ⓔ plants@hartcanna.com
Ⓦ www.hartcanna.com
Contact: Keith Hayward
Opening Times: Visitors by arrangement.
Min Mail Order UK: Nmc
Min Mail Order EU: Nmc
Cat. Cost: Free.
Credit Cards: All major credit/debit cards
Specialities: *Canna*. Nat. Collection of *Canna*.
Notes: Also sells wholesale.
Map Ref: S, C3

SHar **Hardy's Cottage Garden Plants** ⊠ ♿
Priory Lane Nursery, Freefolk Priors, Whitchurch, Hampshire, RG28 7NJ
Ⓣ (01256) 896533
Ⓕ (01256) 896572
Ⓔ info@hardys-plants.co.uk
Ⓦ www.hardys-plants.co.uk
Contact: Rosy Hardy
Opening Times: 1000-1700 7 days, 1st Mar-31st Oct. 1000-1500 Mon-Fri, 1st Nov-28th Feb.
Min Mail Order UK: Nmc
Cat. Cost: 10 × 1st class.
Credit Cards: Visa Access Electron Switch Solo
Specialities: Wide range of herbaceous perennials incl. *Heuchera*, *Penstemon*, *Salvia*, *Verbascum* & *Viola*.
Notes: A charge of £2.00 is made for delivery of pre-ordered plants to shows. Offers trade discount.
Map Ref: S, C2

SHDw **Highdown Nursery** ⊠ €
New Hall Lane, Small Dole, Nr Henfield, West Sussex, BN5 9YH
Ⓣ (01273) 492976
Ⓕ (01273) 492976
Ⓔ highdown.herbs@btopenworld.com
Contact: A G & J H Shearing
Opening Times: 0900-1700 7 days.
Min Mail Order UK: £10.00 + p&p
Min Mail Order EU: £10.00 + p&p
Cat. Cost: 3 × 1st class.
Credit Cards: None
Specialities: Herbs. Grasses.
Notes: Also sells wholesale. Partial wheelchair access.
Map Ref: S, D3

SHea **Heaselands Garden Nursery** €
The Old Lodge, Isaacs Lane, Haywards Heath, West Sussex, RH16 4SA
Ⓣ (01444) 458084
Ⓕ (01444) 458084
Ⓔ headgardener@heaselands.wanadoo.co.uk
Ⓦ www.heaselandsnursery.co.uk
Contact: Stephen Harding
Opening Times: 0800-1700, Mon-Fri, but please phone first. W/ends by appt. only.
Cat. Cost: Online only. Monthly availability lists.
Credit Cards: None
Specialities: *Rhododendron* hybrids and deciduous azaleas, home-produced from cuttings. Some varieties in small quantities. Nat. Collection of Mollis Azaleas & Knaphill/Exbury Azaleas.
Notes: Also sells wholesale.
Map Ref: S, C4 **OS Grid Ref:** TQ314230

SHeS **The Heather Society (Plant Ordering Service)** ⊠ €
78 Woodland Way, West Wickham, Kent, BR4 9LR
Ⓣ 020 8777 5161
Ⓜ 07905 825818
Ⓔ allisonfitzearle@yahoo.co.uk
Ⓦ www.heathersociety.org.uk
Contact: Allison Fitz-Earle
Opening Times: Not open. Mail order only.
Min Mail Order UK: Nmc
Min Mail Order EU: Nmc

Cat. Cost: Free.
Credit Cards: None
Specialities: Heathers.
Notes: Mail order plants available year round.

SHGN **Hill Garth Nursery** ♿
Woodgreen Road, Godshill, Fordingbridge, Hampshire, SP6 2LP
Ⓣ (01425) 657619
Ⓕ (01425) 657619
Contact: Mrs S J Giddins
Opening Times: 0930-1700 Thu & Sun, Mar-end Oct.
Cat. Cost: None issued.
Credit Cards: None
Specialities: Small nursery offering a range of rare, unusual & traditional hardy perennials, shrubs & trees. Some stock may be limited.
Map Ref: S, D1

SHHo **Highfield Hollies** ⊠ ◆
Highfield Farm, Hatch Lane,
Liss, Hampshire,
GU33 7NH
Ⓣ (01730) 892372
Ⓕ (01730) 894853
Ⓔ louise@highfieldhollies.com
Ⓦ www.highfieldhollies.com
Contact: Mrs Louise Bendall Duck
Opening Times: By appt.
Min Mail Order UK: £60.00
Cat. Cost: £3.50 for illustrated cat.
Credit Cards: None
Specialities: 150+ species & cultivars *Ilex* incl. specimen trees, hedging & topiary. Some in short supply.
Map Ref: S, C3 **OS Grid Ref:** SU787276

SHlg **The Healing Garden** ♿
35 Hayling Rise, High Salvington, Worthing, Sussex, BN13 3AL
Ⓣ (01903) 263183
Contact: Ivan & Janice Mitchell
Opening Times: Apr-Oct by appt.
Cat. Cost: 1 × 1st class for list.
Credit Cards: None
Specialities: Small specialist nursery growing medicinal herbs. Medicinal herb garden with 700 different plants. Stock available in small quantities only.
Map Ref: S, D3 **OS Grid Ref:** TQ125059

SHmp **Hampshire Carnivorous Plants** ⊠ ✈ 🚐 €
Ya-Mayla, Allington Lane, West End, Southampton, Hampshire, SO30 3HQ
Ⓣ (023) 8047 3314
Ⓜ 07703 258296
Ⓕ (023) 80473314
Ⓔ matthew@msoper.freeserve.co.uk
Ⓦ www.hantsflytrap.com
Contact: Matthew Soper
Opening Times: Mail order only. Open by appt. only.
Min Mail Order UK: Nmc
Min Mail Order EU: £50.00 + p&p
Cat. Cost: 2 × 2nd class.
Credit Cards: Visa MasterCard
Specialities: Carnivorous plants esp. *Nepenthes*, *Heliamphora*, *Sarracenia* *Pinguicula* & *Utricularia*.
Notes: Also sells wholesale.

SHom **Home Plants**
52 Dorman Ave North, Aylesham, Canterbury, Kent, CT3 3BW
Ⓣ (01304) 841746
Ⓔ homeplants@tiscali.co.uk
Contact: Stuart & Sue Roycroft
Opening Times: By appt. only, please phone first.
Cat. Cost: Sae for list.
Credit Cards: None
Specialities: *Phygelius* & unusual South African hardy plants. Limited stock, please phone first. Map Ref:

SHyH **Hydrangea Haven** ⊠ ✈ 🚐 € ♿
Market Garden, Lower Beeding, West Sussex, RH13 6PP
Ⓣ (01403) 891412
Ⓔ sales@hydrangea-haven.com
Ⓦ www.hydrangea-haven.com
Contact: Chris Loder
Opening Times: 1000-1600 Mon-Sat, please phone first, so we can give you our undivided attention.
Min Mail Order UK: Nmc
Min Mail Order EU: £100.00 + p&p
Cat. Cost: 2 × 1st class.
Credit Cards: Switch MasterCard Visa
Specialities: *Hydrangea*.
Notes: Also sells wholesale.
Map Ref: S, C3

SIde **Iden Croft Herbs** ⊠ ♿ ◆
Frittenden Road, Staplehurst, Kent, TN12 0DH
Ⓣ (01580) 891432
Ⓕ (01580) 892416
Ⓔ idencroftherbs@yahoo.co.uk

KEY
⊠ Mail order to UK or EU 🚐 Delivers to shows
✈ Exports beyond EU € Euro accepted
♿ Accessible by wheelchair ◆ See Display advertisement

S

Ⓦ www.herbs-uk.com
Contact: Tracey Pearman
Opening Times: 0900-1700 Mon-Sat & 1100-1700 Sun & B/hols, Mar-Sep. 0900-1600 Oct-Feb, closed w/ends.
Min Mail Order UK: £10.00
Min Mail Order EU: £25.00
Cat. Cost: 4 × 1st class.
Credit Cards: All major credit/debit cards
Specialities: Herbs, aromatic & wildflower plants & plants for bees & butterflies. Nat. Collections of *Mentha*, *Nepeta* & *Origanum*.
Notes: Wheelchairs available at nursery.
Map Ref: S, C5

SIng **W E Th. Ingwersen Ltd** ⊠ ♠
Birch Farm Nursery, Gravetye,
East Grinstead, West Sussex,
RH19 4LE
Ⓣ (01342) 810236
Ⓔ info@ingwersen.co.uk
Ⓦ www.ingwersen.co.uk
Contact: M P & M R Ingwersen
Opening Times: 0900-1600 daily excl. Sun & B/hols, Mar-Sep. 0900-1600 Mon-Fri Oct-Feb.
Min Mail Order UK: Nmc
Cat. Cost: 2 × 1st class.
Credit Cards: None
Specialities: Very wide range of hardy plants, mostly alpines. Also seed. See website or catalogue for mail order instructions.
Notes: Wheelchair-accessible with assistance.
Map Ref: S, C4

SIoW **Isle of Wight Lavender** ⊠ ♠ € ♿
Staplehurst Grange, Newport, Isle of Wight, PO30 2NQ
Ⓣ (01983) 825272
Ⓕ (01983) 825272
Ⓔ sales@lavender.co.uk
Ⓦ www.lavender.co.uk
Contact: Paul Abbott
Opening Times: 1000-1800 daily, except closed Wed Oct-Mar. Closed Xmas week.
Min Mail Order UK: Nmc
Cat. Cost: 1st class sae.
Credit Cards: All major credit/debit cards
Specialities: Lavender.
Map Ref: S, D2

SIri **Iris of Sissinghurst** ⊠ ♠ € ◆
Roughlands Farm, Goudhurst Road, Marden, Kent, TN12 9NH
Ⓣ (01622) 831511
Ⓔ orders@irisofsissinghurst.com
Ⓦ www.irisofsissinghurst.com
Contact: Sue Marshall
Opening Times: Contact nursery or see website for opening times.
Min Mail Order UK: Nmc
Min Mail Order EU: Nmc
Cat. Cost: 2 × 1st class.
Credit Cards: None
Specialities: *Iris*, short, intermediate & tall bearded, *ensata*, *sibirica* & many species.
Map Ref: S, C4 **OS Grid Ref:** TQ735437

SJoh **Vic Johnstone and Claire Wilson** €
43 Winchester Street, Whitchurch, Hampshire, RG28 7AJ
Ⓣ (01256) 893144
Contact: Vic Johnstone, Claire Wilson
Opening Times: By appt. Please telephone first.
Cat. Cost: 2 × 1st class.
Credit Cards: None
Specialities: Nat. Collection of *Verbascum*. Stock available in small quantities.
Map Ref: S, C2 **OS Grid Ref:** SU463478

SKee **Keepers Nursery** ⊠
Gallants Court, Gallants Lane, East Farleigh, Maidstone, Kent, ME15 0LE
Ⓣ (01622) 726465
Ⓕ 0870 705 2145
Ⓔ info@keepers-nursery.co.uk
Ⓦ www.keepers-nursery.co.uk
Contact: Hamid Habibi
Opening Times: Only on a limited number of Open Days & for collection of trees & plants by arrangement.
Min Mail Order UK: Nmc
Cat. Cost: Online only.
Credit Cards: Visa MasterCard Switch Maestro
Specialities: A very large range of fruit trees incl. old & rare varieties as well as modern varieties. Soft fruit plants & nut trees.
Map Ref: S, C4

SKen **Kent Street Nurseries** ⊠ € ♿
Kent Street (A21), Sedlescombe, Battle, East Sussex, TN33 0SF
Ⓣ (01424) 751134
Ⓔ peter@1066-countryplants.co.uk
Ⓦ www.1066-countryplants.co.uk
Contact: P Stapley
Opening Times: 0900-1700 Mon-Sat, 1030-1600 Sun.
Min Mail Order UK: £12.00
Cat. Cost: 2 × 1st class.
Credit Cards: All major credit/debit cards
Specialities: *Pelargonium*, bedding & perennials.

Notes: Mail order *Pelargonium* list only. Credit cards not accepted for mail order. Nursery partially accessible for wheelchair users.

SLan **LANGLEY BOXWOOD NURSERY LTD** ⊠ ✈ € ♿ ◆
Langley Lane, Rake, Nr Liss, Hampshire, GU33 7JN
Ⓣ (01730) 894467
Ⓕ (01730) 894703
Ⓔ sales@boxwood.co.uk
Ⓦ www.boxwood.co.uk
Contact: Russell Coates
Opening Times: 0800-1630 Mon-Fri, 1000-1600 Sat. Please phone for directions.
Min Mail Order UK: Nmc
Min Mail Order EU: Nmc
Cat. Cost: 4 × 1st class.
Credit Cards: All major credit/debit cards
Specialities: *Buxus* species, cultivars & hedging. Good range of topiary, *Taxus*, and 'character-pruned' specimens. Nat. Collection of *Buxus*. Evergreen topiary & hedging.
Notes: Also sells wholesale. Topiary courses run throughout the summer months. Topiary hire available.
Map Ref: S, C3 **OS Grid Ref:** SU812290

SLau **THE LAURELS NURSERY** ⊠ €
Benenden, Cranbrook, Kent, TN17 4JU
Ⓣ (01580) 240463
Ⓕ (01580) 240463
Ⓦ www.thelaurelsnursery.co.uk
Contact: Peter or Sylvia Kellett
Opening Times: 0800-1600 Mon-Fri, 0900-1200 Sat, Sun by appt. only.
Min Mail Order UK: £20.00
Cat. Cost: Free.
Credit Cards: None
Specialities: Open ground & container ornamental trees, shrubs & climbers incl. birch, beech & *Wisteria*.
Notes: Mail order of small *Wisteria* only. Also sells wholesale.
Map Ref: S, C5 **OS Grid Ref:** TQ815313

SLay **LAYHAM GARDEN CENTRE & NURSERY** ⊠ ♿
Lower Road, Staple, Nr Canterbury, Kent, CT3 1LH
Ⓣ (01304) 813267
Ⓕ (01304) 814007
Ⓔ layham@gcstaple.fsnet.co.uk
Ⓦ www.layhamgardencentre.co.uk
Contact: Ellen Wessel
Opening Times: 0900-1700 7 days.
Min Mail Order UK: Nmc
Min Mail Order EU: £25.00 + p&p
Cat. Cost: Free.
Credit Cards: Visa Switch MasterCard
Specialities: Roses, herbaceous, shrubs, trees & hedging plants.
Notes: Also sells wholesale.
Map Ref: S, C6 **OS Grid Ref:** TR276567

SLBF **LITTLE BROOK FUCHSIAS** ♿
Ash Green Lane West, Ash Green, Nr Aldershot, Hampshire, GU12 6HL
Ⓣ (01252) 329731
Ⓔ carol.gubler@business.ntl.com
Ⓦ www.littlebrookfuchsias.co.uk
Contact: Carol Gubler
Opening Times: 0900-1700 Wed-Sun 1st Jan-29th Jun.
Cat. Cost: 50p + sae.
Credit Cards: None
Specialities: Fuchsias, old & new.
Map Ref: S, C3

SLdr **LODER PLANTS** ⊠ ✈ ⛺ € ♿
Market Garden, Lower Beeding, West Sussex, RH13 6PP
Ⓣ (01403) 891412
Ⓔ sales@rhododendrons.com
Ⓦ www.rhododendrons.com
Contact: Chris Loder
Opening Times: 1000-1600 Mon-Sat, please ring first so we can give you our undivided attention.
Min Mail Order UK: Nmc
Min Mail Order EU: £100.00 + p&p
Cat. Cost: 2 × 1st class.
Credit Cards: Switch MasterCard Visa
Specialities: Rhododendrons & azaleas in all sizes. *Camellia* & *Hydrangea*.
Notes: Also sells wholesale.
Map Ref: S, C3

SLim **LIME CROSS NURSERY** ⊠ ♿ ◆
Herstmonceux, Hailsham, East Sussex, BN27 4RS
Ⓣ (01323) 833229
Ⓕ (01323) 833944
Ⓔ LimeCross@aol.com
Ⓦ www.Limecross.co.uk
Contact: Jonathan Tate, Anita Green
Opening Times: 0830-1700 Mon-Sat & 1000-1600 Sun.
Min Mail Order UK: Nmc
Min Mail Order EU: £50.00

KEY
⊠ Mail order to UK or EU ⛺ Delivers to shows
✈ Exports beyond EU € Euro accepted
♿ Accessible by wheelchair ◆ See Display advertisement

S

Cat. Cost: 3 × 1st class.
Credit Cards: All major credit/debit cards
Specialities: Conifers, trees & shrubs, climbers.
Notes: Also sells wholesale.
Map Ref: S, D4 **OS Grid Ref:** TQ642125

SLon **Longstock Park Nursery** ⊠ € ♿
Longstock, Stockbridge, Hampshire, SO20 6EH
Ⓣ (01264) 810894
Ⓕ (01264) 810924
Ⓔ longstocknursery@leckfordestate.co.uk
Ⓦ www.longstocknursery.co.uk
Contact: Peter Moore
Opening Times: 0830-1630 Mon-Sat all year excl. Xmas & New Year, & 1100-1700 Sun Mar-Oct, 1000-1600 Sun, Nov-Feb.
Min Mail Order UK: Nmc
Cat. Cost: 2 × 1st class or email for lists of *Buddleja*, *Penstemon*, roses & fruit
Credit Cards: All major credit/debit cards
Specialities: A wide range, over 2000 varieties, of trees, shrubs, perennials, climbers, aquatics & ferns. Nat. Collections of *Buddleja* & *Clematis viticella*.
Notes: Mail order for *Buddleja* only.
Map Ref: S, C2 **OS Grid Ref:** SO365389

SLPl **Landscape Plants** ⊠ ✈ ♿
Cattamount, Grafty Green, Maidstone, Kent, ME17 2AP
Ⓣ (01622) 850245
Ⓕ (01622) 858063
Ⓔ landscapeplants@aol.com
Contact: Tom La Dell
Opening Times: 0800-1600 Mon-Fri, by appt. only.
Min Mail Order UK: £100.00 + p&p
Min Mail Order EU: £200.00 + p&p
Cat. Cost: 2 × 1st class.
Credit Cards: None
Specialities: Garden & landscape shrubs & perennials.
Notes: Also sells wholesale.
Map Ref: S, C5 **OS Grid Ref:** TQ772468

SMac **MacGregors Plants for Shade** ⊠
Carters Clay Road, Lockerley, Romsey, Hampshire, SO51 0GL
Ⓣ (01794) 340256
Ⓔ For email use contact form on website.
Ⓦ www.macgregors-shadeplants.co.uk
Contact: Irene & Stuart Bowron
Opening Times: Generally by appt. only. Please phone before travelling to check plant availability.
Min Mail Order UK: Nmc
Cat. Cost: Online only.
Credit Cards: MasterCard Visa
Specialities: Less usual plants for all types of shade. Available in small numbers for immediate delivery or collection.
Notes: Mail order available Oct-Jan & restricted to small numbers of young, dormant plants. Larger mature specimens available all year by negotiation. Also sells wholesale. See website for details of nursery & garden open days.
Map Ref: S, C2 **OS Grid Ref:** SU308239

SMad **Madrona Nursery** ⊠ ⌂ € ♿
Pluckley Road, Bethersden, Kent, TN26 3DD
Ⓣ (01233) 820100
Ⓕ (01233) 820091
Ⓔ madrona@fsmail.net
Ⓦ www.madrona.co.uk
Contact: Liam MacKenzie
Opening Times: 1000-1700 Sat-Tue 15th Mar-28th Oct. Closed 2nd-15th Aug.
Min Mail Order UK: Nmc
Cat. Cost: Free
Credit Cards: All major credit/debit cards
Specialities: Unusual shrubs, conifers & perennials. Eryngiums, *Pseudopanax*.
Map Ref: S, C5 **OS Grid Ref:** TQ918419

SMDP **Marcus Dancer Plants** ⊠ ⌂ ♿
Kilcreggan, Alderholt Road, Sandleheath, Fordingbridge, Hampshire, SP6 1PT
Ⓣ (01425) 652747
Ⓔ marcus.dancer@btopenworld.com
Ⓦ clematisplants.co.uk
Contact: Marcus Dancer
Opening Times: By appointment only.
Cat. Cost: 2 × 1st class.
Credit Cards: None
Specialities: Wide range of *Clematis*, smaller range of *Daphne*. Some varieties available in small quantities only.
Notes: Mail order plants in 9cm pots when available. Contact nursery for details.
Map Ref: S, D1

SMeo **Meon Valley Plants** ⌂ ♿
Broadhanger Farm, Froxfield, Nr Petersfield, Hampshire, GU32 1DW
Ⓜ 07818 088019
Ⓔ info@meonvalleyplants.co.uk
Ⓦ www.meonvalleyplants.co.uk
Contact: Camilla Moreton
Opening Times: 1000-1700 Fri only, 14th Mar-17th Oct 2008 or by appt.
Cat. Cost: 2 × 1st class for list.
Credit Cards: None

Specialities: Unusual bulbs, perennials & grasses. Many plants produced in small quantities but can be propagated to order.
Map Ref: S, C2 **OS Grid Ref:** SU713259

SMHT **MOUNT HARRY TREES** € ♿ ◆
Offham, Lewes, East Sussex, BN7 3QW
Ⓣ (01273) 474456
Ⓔ mountharry@btopenworld.com
Contact: A Renton
Opening Times: By appt., 7 days.
Cat. Cost: 1 × 1st class.
Credit Cards: None
Specialities: Deciduous trees, specialising in heavy-standard to semi-mature sizes, also crab apples.
Map Ref: S, D4 **OS Grid Ref:** TQ313913

SMrm **MERRIMENTS GARDENS** ♿
Hawkhurst Road, Hurst Green, East Sussex, TN19 7RA
Ⓣ (01580) 860666
Ⓕ (01580) 860324
Ⓔ info@merriments.co.uk
Ⓦ www.merriments.co.uk
Contact: Taryn Cook
Opening Times: 0930-1730 Mon-Sat, 1030-1730 Sun (or dusk in winter).
Cat. Cost: Online only.
Credit Cards: Visa Access American Express
Specialities: Extensive range of unusual perennials, tender perennials, grasses & annuals. Also large selection of roses & seasonal shrubs. 4-acre show garden.
Map Ref: S, C4

SMrs **MRS MITCHELL'S KITCHEN & GARDEN** ⌂ € ♿
2 Warren Farm Cottages, The Warren, West Tytherley, Salisbury, Wiltshire, SP5 1LU
Ⓣ (01980) 863101
Ⓔ julianm05@aol.com
Ⓦ www.mrsmitchellskitchenandgarden.co.uk
Contact: Louise Mitchell
Opening Times: 1000-1700 Thu, Fri & some Sat, Apr-Oct. Check web or phone to confirm weekly opening times.
Cat. Cost: Online only.
Credit Cards: None
Specialities: Family-run nursery stocking less usual cottage garden plants, esp. hardy geraniums, oriental poppies, *Phlox*, *Echinacea*, heleniums, *Rudbeckia* & Michaelmas daisies. Some items in small quantities. Grown in peat-free in compost.
Notes: Despite postal designation, nursery is in Hampshire. Accessible, but difficult, for wheelchairs because of deep gravel. See website for list of shows attended.
Map Ref: S, C2 **OS Grid Ref:** SU261333

SOkt **OAKTREE NURSERIES** ⌂ ♿
Malt House Farm Bungalow, Queen Street, Sandhurst, Kent, TN18 5HR
Ⓣ (01580) 850859
Ⓕ (01580) 850859
Ⓔ oaktree.nurseries@btinternet.com
Ⓦ www.oaktree-nurseries.co.uk
Contact: Stephen Roff
Opening Times: 0900-1700 Mon-Sat, 1000-1700 Sun.
Credit Cards: All major credit/debit cards
Specialities: Hardy geraniums & Japanese maples, around 50 varieties of each. Expanding plant range.
Map Ref: S, C5

SPad **PADDOCK PLANTS** ☒ ⌂
The Paddock, Upper Toothill Road, Rownhams, Southampton, Hampshire, SO16 8AL
Ⓣ (023) 8073 9912
Ⓔ rob@paddockplants.co.uk
Ⓦ www.paddockplants.co.uk
Contact: Robert Courtney
Opening Times: By appt. only. Please telephone in advance.
Min Mail Order UK: Nmc
Cat. Cost: Free.
Credit Cards: None
Specialities: Family-run nursery offering interesting range of perennials, grasses, ferns & shrubs, incl. some more unusual varieties. Some varieties grown in small quantities.
Notes: Online descriptive catalogue & ordering. Local delivery by our own transport.

SPav **PAVILION PLANTS** ☒
18 Pavilion Road, Worthing, West Sussex, BN14 7EF
Ⓣ (01903) 821338
Ⓔ rewrew18@hotmail.com
Contact: Andrew Muggeridge
Opening Times: Mail order only. Please phone for details.
Min Mail Order UK: Nmc
Cat. Cost: 4 × 1st class.
Credit Cards: None
Specialities: Perennials and bulbs. *Digitalis*.
Notes: Also sells wholesale.
Map Ref: S, D3

KEY
☒ Mail order to UK or EU ⌂ Delivers to shows
✈ Exports beyond EU € Euro accepted
♿ Accessible by wheelchair ◆ See Display advertisement

S

SPer **PERRYHILL NURSERIES LTD** ⊠ ♿
Edenbridge Road, Hartfield, East Sussex, TN7 4JP
Ⓣ (01892) 770377
Ⓕ (01892) 770929
Ⓔ sales@perryhillnurseries.co.uk
Ⓦ www.perryhillnurseries.co.uk
Contact: P J Chapman
Opening Times: 0900-1700 7 days 1st Mar-31st Oct. 0900-1630 1st Nov-28th Feb.
Min Mail Order UK: Nmc
Cat. Cost: Online only.
Credit Cards: Maestro Visa Access MasterCard
Specialities: Wide range of trees, shrubs, conifers, *Rhododendron* etc. Over 1300 herbaceous varieties, over 500 rose varieties. Unusual & rare plants may be available in small quantities.
Notes: Mail order despatch depends on size & weight of plants.
Map Ref: S, C4 **OS Grid Ref:** TQ480375

S

SPet **PETTET'S NURSERY** ⊠ ⌂ € ♿
Poison Cross, Eastry, Sandwich, Kent, CT13 0EA
Ⓣ (01304) 613869
Ⓕ (01304) 613869
Ⓔ terry@pettetsnursery.fsnet.co.uk
Ⓦ www.pettetsnursery.co.uk
Contact: T & E H P Pettet
Opening Times: 0900-1700 daily Mar-Jul. 1000-1600 Aug-Oct weekdays only.
Min Mail Order UK: £10.00
Min Mail Order EU: £20.00
Credit Cards: None
Specialities: Climbers, herbaceous perennials, alpines, pelargoniums, fuchsias.
Notes: Mail order Oct-Mar only. Also sells wholesale.
Map Ref: S, C6

SPhx **PHOENIX PERENNIAL PLANTS** ⌂ ♿
Paice Lane, Medstead, Alton, Hampshire, GU34 5PR
Ⓣ (01420) 560695
Ⓕ (01420) 563640
Ⓔ GreenFarmPlants.Marina.Christopher@Care4free.net
Contact: Marina Christopher
Opening Times: 1000-1800 Thu, Fri & Sat, 20th Mar-25th Oct 2008. Early openings 2009: 1000-1600 Fri & Sat 6th/7th Feb, 20th/21st Feb, 6th/7th Mar. 1000-1800 Thurs, Fri & Sat 19th Mar-24th Oct 2009. Other times by appt. only.
Cat. Cost: 4 × 1st class.
Credit Cards: All major credit/debit cards
Specialities: Perennials, many uncommon. *Achillea*, *Eryngium*, hardy chrysanthemums, *Monarda*, *Phlox*, *Sanguisorba*, *Thalictrum*, *Verbascum*, centaureas, bulbs, grasses & late-flowering perennials.
Notes: Co-located with Select Seeds SSss.
Map Ref: S, C2 **OS Grid Ref:** SU657362

SPin **JOHN AND LYNSEY'S PLANTS** ♿
2 Hillside Cottages, Trampers Lane, North Boarhunt, Fareham, Hampshire, PO17 6DA
Ⓣ (01329) 832786
Contact: Mrs Lynsey Pink
Opening Times: By appt. only. Open under NGS 1400-1800 Sun 14th Sep 2008.
Cat. Cost: None issued.
Credit Cards: None
Specialities: Mainly *Salvia* with a wide range of other unusual perennials. Stock available in small quantities only, we will be happy to propagate to order. Nat. Collection of *Salvia* species.
Map Ref: S, D2 **OS Grid Ref:** SU603109

SPlb **PLANTBASE** ⊠ € ♿
Sleepers Stile Road, Cousley Wood, Wadhurst, East Sussex, TN5 6QX
Ⓜ 07967 601064
Ⓔ graham@plantbase.freeserve.co.uk
Ⓦ www.plantbase.co.uk
Contact: Graham Blunt
Opening Times: 1000-1700, 7 days all year (appt. advisable).
Min Mail Order UK: Nmc
Min Mail Order EU: Nmc
Cat. Cost: Online only.
Credit Cards: All major credit/debit cards
Specialities: Wide range of alpines, perennials, shrubs, climbers, waterside plants, herbs, Australasian shrubs & South African plants.
Map Ref: S, C5

SPoG **THE POTTED GARDEN NURSERY** ♿
Ashford Road, Bearsted, Maidstone, Kent, ME14 4NH
Ⓣ (01622) 737801
Ⓔ pottedgarden@btconnect.com
Ⓦ www.thepottedgarden.co.uk
Contact: Any staff member
Opening Times: 0900-1730 (dusk in winter) 7 days. Xmas period opening times on website or answerphone. (Closed Xmas Day & Boxing Day.)
Credit Cards: All major credit/debit cards
Notes: Mail order not available.
Map Ref: S, C5

SPol **Pollie's Perennials and Daylily Nursery** ⊠ ♿
Lodore, Mount Pleasant Lane,
Sway, Lymington, Hampshire,
SO41 8LS
Ⓣ (01590) 682577
Ⓕ (01590) 682577
Ⓔ terry@maasz.fsnet.co.uk
Ⓦ www.polliesdaylilies.co.uk
Contact: Pollie Maasz
Opening Times: 0930-1730 w/ends & Tue-Fri 1400-1730 during the daylily season, mid-May to mid-Aug. Other times by appt. only.
Min Mail Order UK: Nmc
Min Mail Order EU: £10.00
Cat. Cost: 2 × 1st class.
Credit Cards: None
Specialities: *Hemerocallis*, also less commonly available hardy perennials. Stock available in small quantities only. Nat. Collection of Spider & Unusual Form *Hemerocallis*. 1400+ different cvs can be viewed, late Jun-mid Sep.
Notes: Mail order, daylilies only.
Map Ref: S, D2

SPop **Pops Plants** ⊠ ✈ ⛫ €
Pops Cottage, Barford Lane,
Downton, Salisbury, Wiltshire,
SP5 3PZ
Ⓣ (01725) 511421
Ⓔ mail@popsplants
Ⓦ www.popsplants.com
Contact: G Dawson or L Roberts
Opening Times: By appt. only.
Min Mail Order UK: 5 plants.
Min Mail Order EU: 5 plants.
Cat. Cost: £2.00
Credit Cards: None
Specialities: *Primula auricula*. Some varieties in ltd. numbers. Nat. Collection of Show, Alpine & Double Auriculas.
Notes: Credit cards accepted online only. Min. mail order outside EC, 30 plants.

SPPs **POGS Penstemons** ⊠ €
78 Woodland Way, West Wickham, Kent,
BR4 9LR
Ⓣ 020 8777 5161
Ⓔ Alipog2004@yahoo.co.uk
Ⓦ www.pogspenstemons.co.uk
Contact: Allison Fitz-Earle
Opening Times: Not open. Mail order only.
Min Mail Order UK: Nmc
Min Mail Order EU: Nmc
Cat. Cost: Free.
Credit Cards: None
Specialities: *Penstemon*.

SPur **Pure Plants**
Blackboys Nursery, Blackboys, Uckfield,
East Sussex, TN22 5LS
Ⓣ (01825) 890858
Ⓕ (01825) 890878
Ⓔ info@pureplants.com
Ⓦ www.pureplants.com
Contact: Brian Fidler
Opening Times: 0900-1700 Tue-Sat. Closed Sun & Mon except B/hol Mon 0900-1700.
Cat. Cost: 2 × 1st class.
Credit Cards: All major credit/debit cards
Specialities: Trees, shrubs, herbaceous, grasses & ferns. Many unusual varieties offered.
Map Ref: S, C4 **OS Grid Ref:** TQ515206

SReu **G Reuthe Ltd** ⊠
Crown Point Nursery, Sevenoaks Road,
Ightham, Nr Sevenoaks, Kent, TN15 0HB
Ⓣ (01732) 810694
Ⓕ (01732) 862166
Ⓔ reuthe@hotmail.co.uk
Contact: C & P Tomlin
Opening Times: 0900-1600 Thu-Sat. 1000-1600 Sun & B/hols Apr & May only, occasionally in Jun, please check. Closed Jan, Jul & Aug.
Min Mail Order UK: £30.00 + p&p
Min Mail Order EU: £500.00
Cat. Cost: £2.50
Credit Cards: Visa Access
Specialities: Rhododendrons & azaleas, trees, shrubs & climbers.
Notes: Mail order certain plants only to EU.

SRGP **Rosie's Garden Plants** ⊠ ✈ ⛫
Fieldview Cottage, Pratling Street, Aylesford,
Kent, ME20 7DG
Ⓣ (01622) 715777
Ⓜ 07740 696277
Ⓕ (01622) 715777
Ⓔ jcaviolet@aol.com
Ⓦ www.rosiesgardenplants.biz
Contact: J C Aviolet
Opening Times: Check website or telephone for opening times.
Min Mail Order UK: Nmc
Min Mail Order EU: Nmc
Cat. Cost: Free by post, email or online.
Credit Cards: Visa MasterCard Switch
Specialities: Hardy *Geranium*, *Buddleja* & *Aster*. 'Named' herbaceous & shrubs. Roses.
Map Ref: S, C5

KEY
⊠ Mail order to UK or EU ⛫ Delivers to shows
✈ Exports beyond EU € Euro accepted
♿ Accessible by wheelchair ◆ See Display advertisement

SRiv **River Garden Nurseries** ⊠ ♠ €
Troutbeck, Otford, Sevenoaks, Kent,
TN14 5PH
Ⓣ (01959) 525588
Ⓕ (01959) 525810
Ⓔ box@river-garden.co.uk
Ⓦ www.river-garden.co.uk
Contact: Jenny Alban Davies
Opening Times: By appt. only.
Min Mail Order UK: £10.00 + p&p
Min Mail Order EU: £50.00 + p&p
Cat. Cost: 2 × 1st class.
Credit Cards: All major credit/debit cards
Specialities: *Buxus* species, cultivars & *Buxus* hedging. *Buxus* topiary.
Notes: Also sells wholesale.
Map Ref: S, C4 **OS Grid Ref:** TQ523593

S

SRkn **Rapkyns Nursery** ⊠ ♠ ♿
(Office) Brinkwells, School Lane,
Hadlow Down, East Sussex,
TN22 4HY
Ⓣ (01825) 830065
Ⓜ 07771 916933
Ⓕ (01825) 830065
Ⓔ rapkyns@homecall.co.uk
Contact: Steven & Fiona Moore
Opening Times: 1000-1700 Tue, Thu & Fri, Mar-Oct incl.
Min Mail Order UK: Nmc
Cat. Cost: 2 × 1st class.
Credit Cards: None
Specialities: Unusual shrubs, perennials & climbers. Asters, Campanulas, *Ceanothus*, geraniums, lavenders, *Clematis*, penstemons & grasses. New collections of *Phormium*, *Phygelius*, *Crocosmia*, *Anemone*, *Heuchera*, *Heucherella*, *Echinacea*, *Phlox* & *Salvias*.
Notes: Mail order Sep-Apr incl. Also sells wholesale. Nursery at Scotsford Farm, Street End Lane, Broad Oak. Heathfield, TN21 8UB.
Map Ref: S, C4 **OS Grid Ref:** TQ604248

SRms **Rumsey Gardens** ⊠ ♿ ◆
117 Drift Road, Clanfield,
Waterlooville, Hampshire,
PO8 0PD
Ⓣ (023) 9259 3367
Ⓔ info@rumsey-gardens.co.uk
Ⓦ www.rumsey-gardens.co.uk
Contact: Mrs M A Giles
Opening Times: 0900-1700 Mon-Sat & 1000-1600 Sun & B/hols. Closed Sun Nov-Feb.
Min Mail Order UK: £15.00
Cat. Cost: Online only.
Credit Cards: Visa MasterCard Switch
Specialities: Wide general range. Herbaceous, alpines, heathers & ferns. Nat. & International Collection of *Cotoneaster*.
Map Ref: S, D2

SRos **Rosewood Daylilies** ⊠
70 Deansway Avenue, Sturry, Nr Canterbury, Kent, CT2 0NN
Ⓣ (01227) 711071
Ⓕ (01227) 711071
Ⓔ Rosewoodgdns@aol.com
Contact: Chris Searle
Opening Times: By appt. only. Please phone.
Min Mail Order UK: Nmc
Cat. Cost: 2 × 1st class.
Credit Cards: None
Specialities: *Hemerocallis*, mainly newer American varieties. *Agapanthus*.
Map Ref: S, C5

SRot **Rotherview Nursery** ⊠ ♠ € ♿
Ivy House Lane, Three Oaks, Hastings,
East Sussex, TN35 4NP
Ⓣ (01424) 756228
Ⓔ rotherview@btinternet.com
Ⓦ www.rotherview.com
Contact: Ray & Wendy Bates
Opening Times: 1000-1700 Mar-Oct, 1000-1530 Nov-Feb, 7 days.
Min Mail Order UK: Nmc
Min Mail Order EU: Nmc
Cat. Cost: 6 × 1st class.
Credit Cards: All major credit/debit cards
Specialities: Alpines.
Notes: Also sells wholesale. Nursery is on same site as Coghurst Camellias.
Map Ref: S, D5

SSea **Seale Nurseries** ♿ ◆
Seale Lane, Seale, Farnham, Surrey, GU10 1LD
Ⓣ (01252) 782410
Contact: David & Catherine May
Opening Times: 1000-1600 Tue-Sat incl. Other times by appt. Closed 25th Dec-mid Jan.
Cat. Cost: None issued.
Credit Cards: Visa Switch Access Delta
Specialities: Roses & *Pelargonium*. Some varieties in short supply, please phone first.
Map Ref: S, C3 **OS Grid Ref:** SU887477

SSpi **Spinners Garden** € ♿
School Lane, Boldre, Lymington, Hampshire,
SO41 5QE
Ⓣ (01590) 673347
Contact: Peter Chappell
Opening Times: 1000-1700 Tue-Sat, Feb-Oct. By appt. only Nov, Dec & Jan.

Cat. Cost: Sae for plant list.
Credit Cards: None
Specialities: Less common trees & shrubs esp. *Acer*, *Magnolia*, species & lace-cap *Hydrangea*. Bog & woodland plants, esp. trilliums.
Map Ref: S, D2 **OS Grid Ref:** SZ323981

SSPN **Spring Park Nursery** ⊠ €
78 Woodland Way, West Wickham, Kent, BR4 9LR
Ⓣ 020 8777 5161
Ⓔ julianfitzearle@aol.com
Ⓦ www.springparknursery.co.uk
Contact: Julian Fitz-Earle
Opening Times: Not open. Mail order only.
Min Mail Order UK: Nmc
Min Mail Order EU: Nmc
Cat. Cost: Free.
Credit Cards: None
Specialities: Heathers.
Notes: Also sells wholesale.

SSss **Select Seeds** ⊠ ♞ ♿
Paice Lane, Medstead, Nr Alton, Hampshire, GU34 5PR
Ⓣ (01420) 560695
Ⓕ (01420) 563640
Ⓔ GreenFarmPlants.Marina.Christopher@Care4free.net
Contact: Marina Christopher
Opening Times: Not open. Mail order only.
Min Mail Order UK: £10.00
Cat. Cost: 3 × 1st class.
Credit Cards: All major credit/debit cards
Specialities: Seeds. *Aconitum*, *Eryngium*, *Thalictrum*, *Sanguisorba* & *Angelica*.
Notes: Co-located with Phoenix Perennial Plants SPhx.
Map Ref: S, C2 **OS Grid Ref:** SU657362

SSta **Starborough Nursery** ⊠ ♿
Starborough Road, Marsh Green, Edenbridge, Kent, TN8 5RB
Ⓣ (01732) 865614
Ⓕ (01732) 862166
Ⓔ starborough@hotmail.co.uk
Contact: C & P Tomlin
Opening Times: 0900-1600 Mon-Sat (closed Wed & Sun). Closed Jan, Jul & Aug.
Min Mail Order UK: £30.00 + p&p
Min Mail Order EU: £500.00
Cat. Cost: £2.50
Credit Cards: Visa Access
Specialities: Rare and unusual shrubs esp. *Daphne*, *Acer*, rhododendrons & azaleas, *Magnolia* & *Hamamelis*.
Notes: Certain plants only to EU.

SSth **Southease Plants** ♿
Corner Cottage, Southease, Nr Lewes, East Sussex, BN7 3HX
Ⓣ (01273) 513681
Ⓜ 07791 856206
Ⓕ (01273) 513681
Contact: Adrian Orchard
Opening Times: 1100-1700 Wed-Sat, 1400-1700 Sun & by appt.
Cat. Cost: None issued.
Credit Cards: None
Specialities: A small nursery concentrating on *Helleborus* hybrids, grown on the nursery from seed collected from selected plants or obtained from specialist growers. Small quantities only.
Map Ref: S, D4 **OS Grid Ref:** TQ422052

SSvw **Southview Nurseries** ⊠ ♞ ♿
Chequers Lane, Eversley Cross, Hook, Hampshire, RG27 0NT
Ⓣ (0118) 9732206
Ⓕ (0118) 9736160
Ⓔ Mark@Trenear.freeserve.co.uk
Ⓦ www.southviewnurseries.co.uk
Contact: Mark & Elaine Trenear
Opening Times: By appt. only, Mon-Fri, Apr-Jun.
Min Mail Order UK: Nmc
Cat. Cost: Free
Credit Cards: None
Specialities: Unusual hardy plants, specialising in old-fashioned pinks & period plants. Nat. Collection of Old Pinks. Pinks collection open in June. Please ring for details.
Notes: Orders by prior arrangement only. Talks given to garden societies.
Map Ref: S, C3 **OS Grid Ref:** SU795612

SSwd **Springwood Nursery** ⊠
5 Southview Drive, Uckfield, East Sussex, TN22 1TA
Ⓜ 07760 152587
Ⓔ springwood.nurserysx@tiscali.co.uk
Ⓦ SpringwoodNurserySussex.co.uk
Contact: Kevin Clift
Opening Times: Mail order only. Open by appt. only.
Min Mail Order UK: Nmc
Credit Cards: None
Specialities: *Hedychium*. Some plants available in small quantities.
Notes: Also sells wholesale.

KEY
⊠ Mail order to UK or EU ♞ Delivers to shows
✈ Exports beyond EU € Euro accepted
♿ Accessible by wheelchair ◆ See Display advertisement

S

STes **Test Valley Nursery** ⊠ ⌂
Stockbridge Road, Timsbury, Romsey, Hampshire, SO51 0NG
Ⓣ (01794) 368881
Ⓔ julia@testvalleynursery.co.uk
Ⓦ www.testvalleynursery.co.uk
Contact: Julia Benn
Opening Times: 1000-1700 Tue-Sun Mar-Oct. Nov-Feb, please phone first.
Min Mail Order UK: Nmc.
Cat. Cost: 3 × 1st class.
Credit Cards: All major credit/debit cards
Specialities: Large range of herbaceous perennials, incl. unusual & new varieties. Some varieties available in small quantities only. Phone first to avoid disappointment.
Notes: Mail order Oct-Mar only.
Map Ref: S, C2

S

STil **Tile Barn Nursery** ⊠ ⌂ €
Standen Street, Iden Green, Benenden, Kent, TN17 4LB
Ⓣ (01580) 240221
Ⓕ (01580) 240221
Ⓔ tilebarn.nursery@virgin.net
Ⓦ www.tilebarn-cyclamen.co.uk
Contact: Peter Moore
Opening Times: 0900-1700 Wed-Sat.
Min Mail Order UK: £10.00 + p&p
Min Mail Order EU: £25.00 + p&p
Cat. Cost: Sae
Credit Cards: None
Specialities: *Cyclamen* species.
Notes: Also sells wholesale.
Map Ref: S, C5 **OS Grid Ref:** TQ805301

STre **Peter Trenear** ⊠ ♿
Chantreyland, Chequers Lane, Eversley Cross, Hampshire, RG27 0NX
Ⓣ (0118) 9732300
Ⓔ petertrenear@fsmail.net
Ⓦ www.babytrees.co.uk
Contact: Peter Trenear
Opening Times: 0900-1630 Mon-Sat.
Min Mail Order UK: £7.00 + p&p
Cat. Cost: 1 × 1st class.
Credit Cards: Paypal
Specialities: Trees, shrubs, conifers, bonsai & succulents.
Map Ref: S, C3 **OS Grid Ref:** SU795612

STrG **Terrace Gardener** ⊠ €
8 Foxbush, Hildenbrook, Kent, TN11 9HT
Ⓣ (01732) 832762
Ⓔ johan@terracegardener.com
Ⓦ www.terracegardener.co.uk
Contact: Johan Hall
Opening Times: Not open. Mail order only, incl. online & by phone. Telephone orders 0800-1700 Mon-Fri.
Min Mail Order UK: Nmc
Cat. Cost: Free
Credit Cards: All major credit/debit cards
Specialities: Mediterranean trees & plants. Container gardening. Architectural & hardy exotics.

SUsu **Usual & Unusual Plants** ⌂ €
Onslow House, Magham Down, Hailsham, East Sussex, BN27 1PL
Ⓣ (01323) 840967
Ⓔ jennie@uuplants.co.uk
Ⓦ www.uuplants.co.uk
Contact: Jennie Maillard
Opening Times: 0930-1730 Wed-Sat, 17th Mar-16th Oct. Other times strictly by appt. only.
Cat. Cost: £1.50 + sae or online.
Credit Cards: None
Specialities: Small quantities of a wide variety of unusual garden-worthy perennials esp. *Erysimum*, *Euphorbia*, *Geum*, hardy *Geranium*, *Salvia* & grasses.
Map Ref: S, D4 **OS Grid Ref:** TQ607113

SVic **Victoriana Nursery Gardens** ⊠ ♿
Challock, Ashford, Kent, TN25 4DG
Ⓣ (01233) 740529
Ⓕ (01233) 740030
Ⓔ For email, use contact form on website.
Ⓦ www.victoriananursery.co.uk
Contact: Stephen Shirley
Opening Times: 0930-1630 (or dusk) Mon-Fri, 1030-1630 Sat. (1030-1630 Sun in summer months.)
Min Mail Order UK: Nmc
Cat. Cost: Free or online.
Credit Cards: All major credit/debit cards
Specialities: *Fuchsia*, 600+ varieties. Also heritage & unusual vegetable plants, seeds, fruit trees & bushes.
Notes: Also sells wholesale.
Map Ref: S, C5 **OS Grid Ref:** TR018501

SVil **The Village Nurseries** ⌂ € ♿
Sinnocks, West Chiltington, Pulborough, West Sussex, RH20 2JX
Ⓣ (01798) 813040
Ⓕ (01798) 817240
Ⓔ villagenurseries@btconnect.com
Ⓦ www.village-nurseries.co.uk
Contact: Peter Manfield
Opening Times: 0900-1800 or dusk, 7 days.
Cat. Cost: None issued
Credit Cards: All major credit/debit cards

Specialities: Extensive selection of hardy perennials, plus wide range of seasonal patio & bedding plants. Many plants grown in biodegradable pots.
Map Ref: S, D3 **OS Grid Ref:** TQ095182

SWal **Wallace Plants** ⌂
Lewes Road Nursery, Lewes Road, Laughton, East Sussex, BN8 6BN
Ⓣ (01323) 811729
Ⓕ (01323) 811729
Ⓔ info.wp@virgin.net
Ⓦ www.wallace-plants.co.uk
Contact: Simon Wallace
Opening Times: 1000-1800 7 days, incl. B/hols, Mar-Sep, 1000-1600 Oct-Feb.
Cat. Cost: 2 × 1st class for availability list.
Credit Cards: None
Specialities: Ornamental grasses, hebes, herbaceous/perennials, shrubs, salvias, penstemons, herbs & choice rare & unusual plants.
Map Ref: S, D4 **OS Grid Ref:** TQ513126

SWat **Water Meadow Nursery** ⊠ ✈ ⌂ ♿
Cheriton, Nr Alresford, Hampshire, SO24 0QB
Ⓣ (01962) 771895
Ⓕ (01962) 771895
Ⓔ plantaholic@onetel.com
Ⓦ www.plantaholic.co.uk
Contact: Mrs Sandy Worth
Opening Times: 1000-1700 Wed-Sat, Mar-Jul. 1000-1700 or dusk Fri & Sat, Aug-Oct.
Min Mail Order UK: £10.00 + p&p
Min Mail Order EU: £50.00 + p&p
Cat. Cost: 6 × 1st class or £2.00 cheque.
Credit Cards: All major credit/debit cards
Specialities: Water lilies, extensive water garden plants, unusual herbaceous perennials, aromatic herbs & wildflowers. New Super Poppy Range. Nat. Collection of *Papaver orientale* group & *Papaver* Super Poppy Series.
Notes: Mail order by 24 or 48 hour courier service only. Also sells wholesale.
Map Ref: S, C2

SWCr **Wych Cross Nurseries** ♿
Wych Cross, Forest Row, East Sussex, RH18 5JW
Ⓣ (01342) 822705
Ⓕ (01342) 828246
Ⓔ roses@wychcross.co.uk
Ⓦ www.wychcross.co.uk
Contact: J Paisley
Opening Times: 0900-1730 Mon-Sat.
Cat. Cost: Free
Credit Cards: All major credit/debit cards
Specialities: Roses.
Map Ref: S, C4 **OS Grid Ref:** TQ420320

SWvt **Wolverton Plants Ltd** € ♿ ◆
Wolverton Common, Tadley, Hampshire, RG26 5RU
Ⓣ (01635) 298453
Ⓕ (01635) 299075
Ⓔ Julian@wolvertonplants.co.uk
Ⓦ www.wolvertonplants.co.uk
Contact: Julian Jones
Opening Times: 0900-1800 (or dusk Nov-Feb), 7 days. Closed Xmas/New Year.
Cat. Cost: Online only.
Credit Cards: All major credit/debit cards
Specialities: Wide range of herbaceous perennials & shrubs grown on a commercial scale for the public.
Notes: Also sells wholesale. Horticultural club visits welcome by prior arrangement.
Map Ref: S, C2 **OS Grid Ref:** SU555589

Wales and the West

WAba **Abacus Nurseries** ⊠ €
Drummau Road, Skewen, Neath, West Glamorgan, SA10 6NW
Ⓣ (01792) 817994
Ⓔ plants@abacus-nurseries.co.uk
Ⓦ www.abacus-nurseries.co.uk
Contact: David Hill
Opening Times: Not open to the public. Collection by arrangement.
Min Mail Order UK: Nmc
Min Mail Order EU: Nmc
Cat. Cost: 2 × 2nd class.
Credit Cards: None
Specialities: *Dahlia.*
Notes: Euros accepted as cash only. Also sells wholesale.

WAbb **Abbey Dore Court Garden** € ♿
Abbey Dore Court, Abbey Dore, Herefordshire, HR2 0AD
Ⓣ (01981) 240419
Ⓕ (01981) 240419
Ⓦ www.abbeydorecourt.co.uk
Contact: Mrs C Ward
Opening Times: Garden & nursery can be open any day. A prior phone call is essential.
Cat. Cost: None issued
Credit Cards: None

KEY
⊠ Mail order to UK or EU ⌂ Delivers to shows
✈ Exports beyond EU € Euro accepted
♿ Accessible by wheelchair ◆ See Display advertisement

Specialities: Mainly hardy perennials, many unusual, which may be seen growing in the garden. *Astrantia, Crocosmia, Helleborus, Paeonia, Pulmonaria* & *Sedum*.
Map Ref: W, C4 **OS Grid Ref:** SO388308

WAbe **ABERCONWY NURSERY**
Graig, Glan Conwy, Colwyn Bay, Conwy, LL28 5TL
Ⓣ (01492) 580875
Contact: Dr & Mrs K G Lever
Opening Times: 1000-1700 Tue-Sun mid-Feb-mid-Oct.
Cat. Cost: 2 × 2nd class.
Credit Cards: Visa MasterCard
Specialities: Alpines, including specialist varieties, esp. autumn gentians, *Saxifraga* & dwarf ericaceous plants. Shrubs & woodland plants incl. smaller ferns.
Map Ref: W, A3 **OS Grid Ref:** SH799744

W

WAct **ACTON BEAUCHAMP ROSES** ⊠
Acton Beauchamp, Worcestershire, WR6 5AE
Ⓣ (01531) 640433
Ⓕ (01531) 640802
Ⓔ enquiries@acton-beauchamp-roses.co.uk
Ⓦ www.acton-beauchamp-roses.co.uk
Contact: Lindsay Bousfield
Opening Times: 1100-1600 Wed-Sat, Oct-Dec. Closed 21st Dec-23rd Feb. 1100-1700 last w/end (Fri-Mon) of each calendar month, Feb-Jun. Other times by appt. only.
Min Mail Order UK: Nmc
Min Mail Order EU: Nmc
Cat. Cost: 3 × 1st class.
Credit Cards: Maestro Solo Visa MasterCard
Specialities: Species roses, Old roses, modern shrub, English, climbers, ramblers & ground-cover roses.
Map Ref: W, C4 **OS Grid Ref:** SO683492

WAln **L A ALLEN** ⊠
Windy Ridge, Cerrigwibber, Llandrindod Wells, Powys, LD1 5NY
Ⓔ lesallen2006@yahoo.co.uk
Contact: L A Allen
Opening Times: By prior appt.
Min Mail Order UK: Nmc
Min Mail Order EU: Nmc
Cat. Cost: 4 × 1st class.
Credit Cards: None
Specialities: Nat. Collection of *Primula auricula*. Type: alpine auricula, show edged, show self, doubles, stripes. Surplus plants from the Collection, so available in small quantities. Occasionally only 1 or 2 available of some cvs.
Notes: Also sells wholesale.

WAlt **ALTERNATIVE PLANTS** ⊠
The Brackens, Yorkley Wood, Nr Lydney, Gloucestershire, GL15 4TU
Ⓣ (01594) 562457
Ⓔ alternativeplants@tiscali.co.uk
Ⓦ alternativeplants.co.uk
Contact: Mrs Rosemary Castle
Opening Times: Mail order only.
Min Mail Order UK: £10.00
Min Mail Order EU: £20.00
Cat. Cost: 3 × 1st class.
Credit Cards: None
Specialities: Unusual native plants. Small stocks, spring/autumn supply.

WAul **AULDEN FARM** ⊠
Aulden, Leominster, Herefordshire, HR6 0JT
Ⓣ (01568) 720129
Ⓔ pf@auldenfarm.co.uk
Ⓦ www.auldenfarm.co.uk
Contact: Alun & Jill Whitehead
Opening Times: 1000-1700 Tue & Thu Apr-Aug. Thu only in Mar & Sep. Other times by appt. Please phone.
Min Mail Order UK: Nmc
Min Mail Order EU: £20.00
Cat. Cost: 2 × 1st class.
Credit Cards: Paypal.
Specialities: Hardy herbaceous perennials, with a special interest in *Hemerocallis* & *Iris*.
Notes: Mail order principally for *Hemerocallis* & *Iris*, other plants available in small quantities.
Map Ref: W, C4 **OS Grid Ref:** SO462548

WBor **BORDERVALE PLANTS**
Nantyderi, Sandy Lane, Ystradowen, Cowbridge, Vale of Glamorgan, CF71 7SX
Ⓣ (01446) 774036
Ⓦ www.bordervale.co.uk
Contact: Claire E Jenkins
Opening Times: 1000-1700 Fri-Sun & B/hols Mar-early Oct. Other times by appt.
Cat. Cost: 2 × 1st class large sae or online.
Credit Cards: None
Specialities: Unusual herbaceous perennials, trees & shrubs, as well as cottage garden plants, many displayed in the 2-acre garden.
Notes: Garden open May-Sep when nursery open. Also open for NGS. See website for details.
Map Ref: W, D3 **OS Grid Ref:** ST022776

WBou **BOUTS COTTAGE NURSERIES** ⊠ €
Bouts Lane, Inkberrow, Worcestershire, WR7 4HP
Ⓣ (01386) 792923
Ⓦ www.boutsviolas.co.uk
Contact: M & S Roberts
Opening Times: Strictly by appt. only.
Min Mail Order UK: Nmc

Min Mail Order EU: Nmc
Cat. Cost: 1st class sae.
Credit Cards: None
Specialities: *Viola.*

WBrE **BRON EIFION NURSERY** ⊠ €
Bron Eifion, Criccieth, Caernarfonshire, LL52 0SA
Ⓣ (01766) 522890
Ⓔ gardencottage@talktalk.net
Contact: Suzanne Evans
Opening Times: 1000-dusk 7 days 1st Mar-31st Oct. 1st Nov-29th Feb by appt. only.
Min Mail Order UK: £30.00 + p&p
Min Mail Order EU: £50.00 + p&p
Cat. Cost: None issued.
Credit Cards: None
Specialities: *Kalmia*, *Daphne*, *Embothrium*, plants for coastal regions & wide and interesting range of hardy plants.
Map Ref: W, B2

WBrk **BROCKAMIN PLANTS** ♠ ♿
Brockamin, Old Hills, Callow End, Worcestershire, WR2 4TQ
Ⓣ (01905) 830370
Ⓔ dickstonebrockamin@tinyworld.co.uk
Contact: Margaret Stone
Opening Times: By appt. only.
Cat. Cost: Free.
Credit Cards: None
Specialities: Hardy perennials, esp. hardy geraniums and some asters. Stock available in small quantities only.
Map Ref: W, C5 **OS Grid Ref:** SO830488

WBuc **BUCKNELL NURSERIES** ⊠
Bucknell, Shropshire, SY7 0EL
Ⓣ (01547) 530606
Ⓕ (01547) 530699
Contact: A N Coull
Opening Times: 0800-1700 Mon-Fri & 1000-1300 Sat.
Min Mail Order UK: Nmc
Cat. Cost: Free
Credit Cards: None
Specialities: Bare-rooted hedging conifers & forest trees.
Notes: Also sells wholesale.
Map Ref: W, C4 **OS Grid Ref:** SO356736

WBVN **BANWY VALLEY NURSERY** ⊠ ♿
Foel, Llangadfan, Nr Welshpool, Powys, SY21 0PT
Ⓣ (01938) 820281
Ⓔ syd@banwnursery.co.uk
Ⓦ www.banwnursery.co.uk
Contact: Syd Luck
Opening Times: 1000-1700 Tue-Sat.
Min Mail Order UK: Nmc
Cat. Cost: 2 × 1st class or email.
Credit Cards: All major credit/debit cards
Specialities: Perennials, shrubs, incl. climbers, ornamental & fruit trees. Ever expanding range of magnolias & rhododendrons. All grown on the nursery.
Notes: Large specimens not available by mail order.
Map Ref: W, B3 **OS Grid Ref:** SH993107

WCAu **CLAIRE AUSTIN HARDY PLANTS** ⊠ ✈ € ♿
Edgebolton, Shawbury, Shrewsbury, Shropshire, SY4 4EL
Ⓣ (01939) 251173
Ⓕ (01939) 251311
Ⓔ enquiries@claireaustin-hardyplants.co.uk
Ⓦ www.claireaustin-hardyplants.co.uk
Contact: Claire Austin
Opening Times: 0900-1700 Mon-Sat, 1000-1600 Sun. Closed Xmas to New Year.
Min Mail Order UK: Nmc
Min Mail Order EU: £50.00 + p&p
Cat. Cost: UK £3.50, Europe €7.00.
Credit Cards: MasterCard Visa Switch
Specialities: *Paeonia*, *Iris*, *Hemerocallis* & hardy plants. Nat. Collections of Bearded *Iris* & Hybrid Herbaceous *Paeonia.*
Map Ref: W, B4

WCCa **CLAINES CANNA COLLECTION** ⊠ €
197 Northwick Road, Claines, Worcester, Worcestershire, WR3 7EJ
Ⓣ (01905) 456459
Ⓜ 07798 8150
Ⓕ (01905) 458713
Ⓔ mdalebo@clainescanna.co.uk
Ⓦ www.clainescanna.co.uk
Contact: Malcolm Dalebo
Opening Times: W/ends only by appt.
Min Mail Order UK: Nmc
Min Mail Order EU: Nmc
Cat. Cost: Free or online.
Credit Cards: Paypal
Specialities: *Canna.*
Notes: Also sells wholesale.

WCFE **CHARLES F ELLIS** ⊠ €
Oak Piece Nurseries, Stanton, Nr Broadway, Worcestershire, WR12 7NQ
Ⓣ (01386) 584077

KEY
⊠ Mail order to UK or EU ♠ Delivers to shows
✈ Exports beyond EU € Euro accepted
♿ Accessible by wheelchair ◆ See Display advertisement

Ⓕ (01386) 584491
Ⓔ ellisplants@cooptel.net
Ⓦ www.ellisplants.co.uk
Contact: Charles Ellis
Opening Times: 1000-1600 7 days 1st Apr-30th Sep. Other times by appt.
Min Mail Order UK: Nmc
Cat. Cost: None issued.
Credit Cards: None
Specialities: Wide range of more unusual shrubs, conifers & climbers.
Map Ref: W, C5

WCHb **The Cottage Herbery**
Mill House, Boraston, Nr Tenbury Wells, Worcestershire, WR15 8LZ
Ⓣ (01584) 781575
Ⓕ (01584) 781483
Ⓦ www.thecottageherbery.co.uk
Contact: K & R Hurst
Opening Times: By appt. only. Order collection service available.
Cat. Cost: 6 × 1st class.
Credit Cards: None
Specialities: Over 600 varieties of herbs. Aromatic & scented foliage plants, esp. *Monarda*, *Rosmarinus*, *Campanula*, alliums & seeds. Soil Assoc. licence no. G6475.
Notes: Group visits & courses, lectures & talks. Sae for list or see website.

WChG **Chennels Gate Gardens & Nursery** ♿
Eardisley, Herefordshire, HR3 6LT
Ⓣ (01544) 327288
Contact: Mark Dawson
Opening Times: 1000-1700 7 days Mar-Oct.
Cat. Cost: None issued.
Credit Cards: None
Specialities: Interesting & unusual cottage garden plants, grasses & shrubs.

WClo **Close Nursery (Duchy of Cornwall)** ♿
Shipton-Moyne Road, Tetbury, Gloucestershire, GL8 8PJ
Ⓣ (01666) 504349
Ⓕ (01666) 504349
Ⓔ OSpencer@duchyofcornwall.gov.uk
Contact: Olly Spencer
Opening Times: 0900-1700 Mon-Sat, 1000-1700 Sun & B/hols.
Cat. Cost: None issued.
Credit Cards: All major credit/debit cards
Specialities: Herbaceous.
Map Ref: W, D5 **OS Grid Ref:** ST884918

WCom **Brown's Barn Ltd. (formerly Compton Lane Nurseries)** ✉ ♿
Little Compton, Moreton-in-Marsh, Gloucestershire, GL56 0SJ
Ⓣ (01608) 674578
Ⓕ (01608) 674578
Ⓔ brownsbarn@tiscali.co.uk
Contact: Chris Brown
Opening Times: 1000-1700 Wed-Sun, 1st Mar-31st Sep. Other times by appt. only.
Min Mail Order UK: £25.00 + p&p
Min Mail Order EU: £25.00 + p&p
Cat. Cost: 5 × 1st class, sae for separate mail order list.
Credit Cards: None
Specialities: Mainly alpines/herbaceous & a few unusual shrubs. *Saxifraga*, *Primula* & *Cyclamen*.
Notes: Evening visits for horticultural groups by prior arrangement.
Map Ref: W, C5

WCon **The Connoisseur's Plant Corner** € ♿
(office) Bwlchauduon, Ffarmers, Llanwrda, Carmarthenshire, SA19 8JJ
Ⓣ (01558) 650187
Ⓕ (01558) 650187
Ⓔ plantcorner@aol.com
Ⓦ www.norwoodgardens.co.uk
Contact: Brenda Timms
Opening Times: 1000-1800 (closed Tues) 19th Mar-26th Oct.
Specialities: A choice selection of traditional & unusual perennials which can be seen growing in the gardens. Available in small quantities only this year.
Notes: Nursery at Norwood Gardens, Llanllwni, Pencader, SA39 9DU. Tea room open as nursery. Partial wheelchair access to gardens. For special events see website.
Map Ref: W, C3 **OS Grid Ref:** SN492400

WCor **Corseside Nursery** ✉
Angle, Pembrokeshire, SA71 5AA
Ⓣ (01646) 641505
Ⓔ corsesidenursery@btinternet.com
Ⓦ www.pembrokeshiregrowers.co.uk
Contact: Sandra Williams
Opening Times: 1000-1600, 7 days. Open all year.
Min Mail Order UK: Nmc
Cat. Cost: Online only.
Credit Cards: None
Specialities: Coastal hardy shrubs, perennials and succulents. *Lanpranthus* & *Aeonium*. All stock seed-raised or from cuttings/division.

Notes: Gardens open 3 times a year or by appt. Specialist advice by appt. Also sells wholesale.
Map Ref: W, D1

WCot **Cotswold Garden Flowers** ⊠ ♠ €
Sands Lane, Badsey, Evesham, Worcestershire, WR11 7EZ
Ⓣ (01386) 833849 nursery or (01386) 422829 mail order
Ⓜ 07812 833849
Ⓕ nursery (01386) 49844
Ⓔ info@cgf.net
Ⓦ www.cgf.net
Contact: Bob Brown/Vicky Parkhouse
Opening Times: 0900-1730 Mon-Fri all year. 1000-1730 Sat & Sun Mar-Sep. Sat & Sun Oct-Feb by appt.
Min Mail Order UK: Nmc
Min Mail Order EU: Nmc
Cat. Cost: £1.50 or 6 × 1st class.
Credit Cards: MasterCard Access Visa Switch
Specialities: A very wide range of easy & unusual perennials.
Notes: Also sells wholesale. Ltd wheelchair access.
Map Ref: W, C5 **OS Grid Ref:** SP077426

WCre **Crescent Plants** ⊠ € ♿
Stoney Cross, Marden, Hereford, HR1 3EW
Ⓣ (01432) 880262
Ⓕ (01432) 880262
Ⓔ june@auriculas.co.uk
Ⓦ www.auriculas.co.uk
Contact: June Poole
Opening Times: Open by appt. Please phone.
Min Mail Order UK: Nmc
Min Mail Order EU: Nmc
Cat. Cost: Free
Credit Cards: All major credit/debit cards
Specialities: Named varieties of *Primula auricula* incl. show, alpine, double, striped & border types.
Notes: Payment by Paypal via website. Orders dispatched post free.
Map Ref: W, C4 **OS Grid Ref:** SO525477

WCru **Crûg Farm Plants** ⊠ ♿
Griffith's Crossing, Caernarfon, Gwynedd, LL55 1TU
Ⓣ (01248) 670232
Ⓔ info@crug-farm.co.uk
Ⓦ www.crug-farm.co.uk
Contact: B and S Wynn-Jones
Opening Times: 1000-1700 Thu-Sun 2nd Sat Mar to last Sun Jun, plus B/hols, then Thu-Sat until last Sat in Sep.
Min Mail Order UK: Nmc
Cat. Cost: 5 × 2nd class or online.
Credit Cards: All major credit/debit cards
Specialities: Shade plants, climbers, species *Hydrangea*, *Araliaceae*, rare trees & shrubs, *Convallariaceae*, herbaceous & bulbous. Most self-collected new introductions from the Far East & the Americas. Nat. Collections of *Coriaria*, *Paris* & *Polygonatum*.
Notes: Delivery by overnight carrier.
Map Ref: W, A2 **OS Grid Ref:** SH509652

WDib **Dibley's Nurseries** ⊠ ♠ € ♿ ◆
Llanelidan, Ruthin, Denbighshire, LL15 2LG
Ⓣ (01978) 790677
Ⓕ (01978) 790668
Ⓔ sales@dibleys.com
Ⓦ www.dibleys.com
Contact: R Dibley
Opening Times: 1000-1700 7 days Mar-Oct.
Min Mail Order UK: Nmc
Min Mail Order EU: Nmc
Cat. Cost: Free
Credit Cards: Visa Access Switch Electron Solo
Specialities: *Streptocarpus*, *Columnea*, *Solenostemon* & other gesneriads & *Begonia*. Nat. Collection of *Streptocarpus*.
Notes: Also sells wholesale.
Map Ref: W, A3

WDin **Dingle Nurseries** ♠ ♿ ◆
Welshpool, Powys, SY21 9JD
Ⓣ (01938) 555145
Ⓕ (01938) 555778
Ⓔ info@dinglenurseryandgarden.co.uk
Ⓦ www.dinglenurseryandgarden.co.uk
Contact: Jill Rock
Opening Times: 0900-1700, 7 days.
Cat. Cost: Free plant list.
Credit Cards: MasterCard Switch EuroCard Delta Visa
Specialities: Largest range of trees & shrubs in Wales. Wide seasonal selection of garden plants incl. roses, herbaceous perennials, conifers & bare-rooted forestry, hedging & fruit. All sizes incl. many mature specimens.
Notes: Also sells wholesale.
Map Ref: W, B4 **OS Grid Ref:** SJ196082

KEY
⊠ Mail order to UK or EU ♠ Delivers to shows
✈ Exports beyond EU € Euro accepted
♿ Accessible by wheelchair ◆ See Display advertisement

W

WDol **Dolau-hirion Fruit Tree Nursery** ⊠
Capel Isaac, Llandeilo, Carmarthernshire, SA19 7TG
Ⓣ (01558) 668744
Ⓔ applewise@tiscali.co.uk
Ⓦ http://users.tinyonline.co.uk/applewise
Contact: Paul Davis
Opening Times: 0900-1800 Mon-Sat by prior arrangement.
Min Mail Order UK: £15.00
Cat. Cost: Free.
Credit Cards: None
Specialities: Small fruit tree nursery in the picturesque Towy Valley selling apple, pear, plum & cherry trees, especially Welsh varieties, incl. Welsh perry & cider trees. Grafting service available.
Map Ref: W, C3

WDyG **Dyffryn Gwyddno Nursery**
Dyffryn Farm, Lampeter Velfrey, Narberth, Pembrokeshire, SA67 8UN
Ⓣ (01834) 861684
Ⓔ sally.polson@virgin.net
Ⓦ www.pembrokeshireplants.co.uk
Contact: Mrs S L Polson
Opening Times: By appt. only.
Credit Cards: None
Specialities: Eclectic, yet wide-ranging, from tender salvias & grasses to bog. Bamboos. Peat-free & principled. Plants available in small quantities only. Bamboo collection open by appt. in aid of NGS.
Notes: Also sells wholesale.
Map Ref: W, D2 **OS Grid Ref:** SR138148

WEas **Eastgrove Cottage Garden Nursery**
Sankyns Green, Nr Shrawley, Little Witley, Worcestershire, WR6 6LQ
Ⓣ (01299) 896389
Ⓦ www.eastgrove.co.uk
Contact: Malcolm & Carol Skinner
Opening Times: 1400-1700 Thu, Fri & Sat 24th Apr-19th Jul, plus May B/hol Sun & Mon. Also Sun 15th Jun & 29 Jun. Closed throughout Aug. 1400-1700 Thu only 11th Sep-9th Oct.
Cat. Cost: Online only.
Credit Cards: None
Specialities: Unique cottage garden & arboretum. Many varieties of *Viola*, *Iris*, *Dianthus* & *Aquilegia*, plus a wide range of old favourites & many unusual plants. Small quantities only.
Notes: RHS Partnership garden. See website for directions. 2 acres of arboretum plus grass labyrinth.
Map Ref: W, C5 **OS Grid Ref:** SO795644

WEve **Evergreen Conifer Centre** ⊠ ◆
Tenbury Road, Rock, Nr Kidderminster, Worcestershire, DY14 9RB
Ⓣ (01299) 266581
Ⓕ (01299) 266755
Ⓔ brian@evergreen-conifers.co.uk
Ⓦ www.evergreen-conifers.co.uk
Contact: Brian Warrington
Opening Times: 0900-1630 Tue-Sat (closed Sun & Mon).
Min Mail Order UK: Nmc
Cat. Cost: 4 × 1st class.
Credit Cards: All major credit/debit cards
Specialities: Acers. Dwarf, ornamental, rare & specimen conifers. Hedging conifers. Ornamental trees & heathers.
Notes: Mail order for conifers only. Also sells wholesale
Map Ref: W, C4 **OS Grid Ref:** SO731737

WFar **Farmyard Nurseries** ⊠ ◆
Dol Llan Road, Llandysul, Carmarthenshire, SA44 4RL
Ⓣ (01559) 363389
Ⓕ (01559) 362200
Ⓔ richard@farmyardnurseries.co.uk
Ⓦ www.farmyardnurseries.co.uk
Contact: Richard Bramley
Opening Times: 1000-1700 7 days excl. Xmas, Boxing & New Year's Day.
Min Mail Order UK: Nmc
Min Mail Order EU: Nmc
Cat. Cost: 4 × 1st class.
Credit Cards: Visa Switch MasterCard
Specialities: Excellent general range esp. *Helleborus*, *Hosta*, *Tricyrtis* & *Schizostylis*, plus shrubs, trees, climbers, alpines & esp. herbaceous. Nat. Collection of *Tricyrtis*.
Notes: Also sells wholesale.
Map Ref: W, C2 **OS Grid Ref:** SN421406

WFib **Fibrex Nurseries Ltd** ⊠
Honeybourne Road, Pebworth, Stratford-on-Avon, Warwickshire, CV37 8XP
Ⓣ (01789) 720788
Ⓕ (01789) 721162
Ⓔ sales@fibrex.co.uk
Ⓦ www.fibrex.co.uk
Contact: U Key-Davis & R L Godard-Key
Opening Times: 0900-1700 Mon-Fri 1st Mar-31st Aug. 0900-1600 Mon-Fri 1st Sep-29th Feb. 1030-1600 Sat & Sun 23rd Feb-27th Jul. Closed last 2 weeks Dec & 1st week Jan. Closed Easter Sun & Aug B/hol Mon.
Min Mail Order UK: £10.00 + p&p
Min Mail Order EU: £20.00 + p&p
Cat. Cost: 2 × 1st class.

Credit Cards: Switch MasterCard Visa
Specialities: *Hedera*, ferns, *Pelargonium* & *Helleborus*. Nat. Collections of *Pelargonium* & *Hedera*. Plant collections subject to time of year, please check by phone.
Notes: Also sells wholesale.
Map Ref: W, C5 **OS Grid Ref:** SP133458

WFoF **Flowers of the Field**
Field Farm, Weobley, Herefordshire, HR4 8QJ
Ⓣ (01544) 318262
Ⓕ (01544) 318262
Ⓔ info@flowersofthefield.co.uk
Ⓦ www.flowersofthefield.co.uk
Contact: Kathy Davies
Opening Times: 0900-1900 7 days.
Cat. Cost: 2 × 1st class.
Credit Cards: None
Specialities: Traditional & unusual perennials, grasses, shrubs, trees & herbs. Oriental lilies & freesias for cutting.
Notes: Also sells wholesale. Nursery partially accessible for wheelchairs.
Map Ref: W, C4

WFut **Futureprimitive Plants** ⊠
11 The Leys, Evesham, Worcestershire, WR11 3AP
Ⓜ 07792 376401
Ⓔ sales@futureprimitiveplants.co.uk
Ⓦ www.futureprimitiveplants.co.uk
Contact: Tiggy Fiander
Opening Times: Not open. Mail order only.
Min Mail Order UK: Nmc
Min Mail Order EU: Nmc
Cat. Cost: 3 × 1st class.
Credit Cards: All major credit/debit cards
Specialities: Rare *Aspidistra* & orchids. Herbaceous perennials.

WFuv **Fuchsiavale Nurseries** ⊠ ♔ ♿
Worcester Road, Torton, Kidderminster, Worcestershire, DY11 7SB
Ⓣ (01299) 251162
Ⓕ (01299) 251256
Ⓔ helen@fuchsiavale.co.uk
Ⓦ www.fuchsiavale.co.uk
Contact: Helen Andre
Opening Times: 0900-1700 Mon-Sat, Apr-Jul. 1000-1600 Mon-Sat, Jan-Mar & Aug-Dec. 1000-1600 Sun & B/hols all year.
Min Mail Order UK: £9.00 (6 plants @ £1.50 incl. p&p)
Cat. Cost: Free.
Credit Cards: All major credit/debit cards
Specialities: *Fuchsia*. A good range of shrubs, perennials & trees also available.
Map Ref: W, C5 **OS Grid Ref:** SO843723

WGob **The Gobbett Nursery** ⊠
Farlow, Kidderminster, Worcestershire, DY14 8TD
Ⓣ (01746) 718647
Ⓕ (01746) 718647
Ⓔ christine.link@lineone.net
Ⓦ www.thegobbettnursery.co.uk
Contact: C H Link
Opening Times: 1030-1700, Mon-Sat.
Min Mail Order UK: £10.00
Min Mail Order EU: £50.00
Cat. Cost: 3 × 1st class.
Credit Cards: None
Specialities: *Syringa*, *Magnolia*, *Camellia* & *Cornus*. Some varieties available in small quantities only.
Map Ref: W, B4 **OS Grid Ref:** SO648811

WGor **Gordon's Nursery** ⊠ ♔ ♿
1 Cefnpennar Cottages, Cefnpennar, Mountain Ash, Mid-Glamorgan, CF45 4EE
Ⓣ (01443) 474593
Ⓕ (01443) 475835
Ⓔ sales@gordonsnursery.co.uk
Ⓦ www.gordonsnursery.co.uk
Contact: D A Gordon
Opening Times: 1000-1800 7 days Mar-Jun. 1000-1700 7 days Jul-Oct. 1100-1600 weekends only Nov & Feb. Closed Dec-Jan.
Min Mail Order UK: Nmc
Cat. Cost: 3 × 1st class.
Credit Cards: All major credit/debit cards
Specialities: Shrubs, perennials, alpines & dwarf conifers. Some plants available in small quantities only.
Notes: Mail order only available in some cases, please check for conditions in catalogue.
Map Ref: W, D3 **OS Grid Ref:** SO037012

WGrn **Green's Leaves (formerly Leba Orchard)** ⊠ ♔ ♿
36 Ford House Road, Newent, Gloucestershire, GL18 1LQ
Ⓣ (01531) 820154
Ⓜ 07890 413036
Contact: Paul Green
Opening Times: By appt. only, w/ends preferred.
Min Mail Order UK: £10.00 + p&p
Cat. Cost: 4 × 2nd class.
Credit Cards: None
Specialities: Ornamental grasses, sedges &

W

KEY
⊠ Mail order to UK or EU ♔ Delivers to shows
✈ Exports beyond EU € Euro accepted
♿ Accessible by wheelchair ◆ See Display advertisement

phormiums. Increasing range of rare & choice shrubs, also some perennials.
Notes: Also sells wholesale. Nursery moved to larger site in 2008.
Map Ref: W, C4 **OS Grid Ref:** SO732273

WGwG **Gwynfor Growers** ⊠ ♿
Gwynfor, Pontgarreg, Llangranog, Llandysul, Ceredigion, SA44 6AU
Ⓣ (01239) 654151
Ⓔ info@gwynfor.co.uk
Ⓦ www.gwynfor.co.uk
Contact: Steve & Angie Hipkin
Opening Times: 1000 to 2000 or sunset if earlier, Wed, Thu & Sun, all year round.
Min Mail Order UK: Nmc
Cat. Cost: Free by email or write for current list.
Credit Cards: None
Specialities: Plants to intrigue & delight the gardener, incl. heritage Welsh apple varieties, scented shrubs & ground cover. Some plants available in small quantities only.
Notes: Plants also available at Aberystwyth & Lampeter Farmers' Markets.
Map Ref: W, C2 **OS Grid Ref:** SN331536

WHal **Hall Farm Nursery** ⊠ €
Vicarage Lane, Kinnerley, Nr Oswestry, Shropshire, SY10 8DH
Ⓣ (01691) 682135
Ⓕ (01691) 682135
Ⓔ hallfarmnursery@ukonline.co.uk
Ⓦ www.hallfarmnursery.co.uk
Contact: Christine & Nick Ffoulkes-Jones
Opening Times: 1000-1700 Tue-Sat 1st Mar-31st Oct 2008.
Min Mail Order UK: £20.00
Cat. Cost: 5 × 1st class.
Credit Cards: Visa MasterCard Electron Maestro
Specialities: Unusual herbaceous plants, grasses, bog plants & pool marginals, late-flowering perennials, foliage plants.
Notes: Nursery partially accessible for wheelchairs.
Map Ref: W, B4 **OS Grid Ref:** SJ333209

WHar **Harley Nursery** ♿
Harley, Shropshire, SY5 6LN
Ⓣ (01952) 510241
Ⓕ (01952) 510570
Ⓔ njmurphy@hotmail.co.uk
Contact: Duncan Murphy, Moira Murphy & Nicholas Murphy
Opening Times: 0900-1730 Mon-Sat, 1000-1600 Sun & B/hols. Winter hours 0900-1700 Sun & B/hols.
Cat. Cost: 2 × 1st class.
Credit Cards: All major credit/debit cards
Specialities: Wide range of ornamental & fruit trees. Own grown shrubs, climbers, wide range of hedging plants. Conservation & wildlife plants & native trees a speciality.
Map Ref: W, B4

WHCG **Hunts Court Garden & Nursery** ♿
North Nibley, Dursley, Gloucestershire, GL11 6DZ
Ⓣ (01453) 547440
Ⓕ (01453) 549944
Ⓔ huntscourt@tiscali.co.uk
Contact: T K & M M Marshall
Opening Times: 0900-1230 & 1345-1700 Tue-Sat excl. Aug, nursery & garden. Also by appt. See NGS for Sun openings.
Cat. Cost: 5 × 2nd class.
Credit Cards: None
Specialities: Old roses species & climbers. Hardy *Geranium*, *Penstemon* & unusual shrubs.

WHCr **Hergest Croft Gardens**
Kington, Herefordshire, HR5 3EG
Ⓣ (01544) 230160
Ⓕ (01544) 232031
Ⓔ gardens@hergest.co.uk
Ⓦ www.hergest.co.uk
Contact: Stephen Lloyd
Opening Times: 1200-1730, 7 days, Apr-Oct.
Cat. Cost: None issued
Credit Cards: All major credit/debit cards
Specialities: *Acer*, *Betula* & unusual woody plants.
Notes: Limited wheelchair access.

WHer **The Herb Garden & Historical Plant Nursery** ⊠
Ty Capel Pensarn, Pentre Berw, Anglesey, Gwynedd, LL60 6LG
Ⓣ (01248) 422208 or (01545) 580893
Ⓜ 07751 583958
Ⓕ (01248) 422208
Ⓦ www.HistoricalPlants.co.uk
Contact: Corinne & David Tremaine-Stevenson
Opening Times: By appt. only.
Min Mail Order UK: £15.00 + p&p
Min Mail Order EU: £50.00 + p&p sterling only.
Cat. Cost: List £2.50
Credit Cards: None
Specialities: Rarer herbs, rare natives & wild flowers; rare & unusual & historical perennials & old roses.
Map Ref: W, A2

WHil **HILLVIEW HARDY PLANTS** ⊠ ✈ ♠ € ♿ ◆
(off B4176), Worfield, Nr Bridgnorth, Shropshire, WV15 5NT
Ⓣ (01746) 716454
Ⓕ (01746) 716454
Ⓔ hillview@themutual.net
Ⓦ www.hillviewhardyplants.com
Contact: Ingrid, John & Sarah Millington
Opening Times: 0900-1700 Mon-Sat Mar-mid Oct. At other times, please phone first.
Min Mail Order UK: £15.00 + p&p
Min Mail Order EU: £15.00 + p&p
Cat. Cost: 5 × 2nd class.
Credit Cards: All major credit/debit cards
Specialities: Choice herbaceous perennials incl. *Acanthus* & *Acanthaceae*, *Albuca*, *Aquilegia*, *Auricula*, *Primula*, *Canna*, *Crocosmia*, *Eucomis*, *Ixia*, South African bulbs. Nat. Collection of *Acanthus*.
Notes: Also sells wholesale.
Map Ref: W, B4 **OS Grid Ref:** SO772969

WHlf **HAYLOFT PLANTS** ⊠
Manor Farm, Pensham, Pershore, Worcestershire, WR10 3HB
Ⓣ (01386) 554440 or (01386) 562999
Ⓕ (01386) 553833
Ⓔ info@hayloftplants.co.uk
Ⓦ www.hayloftplants.co.uk
Contact: Yvonne Walker
Opening Times: Not open. Mail order only.
Min Mail Order UK: Nmc
Min Mail Order EU: Nmc
Cat. Cost: Free.
Credit Cards: All major credit/debit cards

WHoo **HOO HOUSE NURSERY** € ♿ ◆
Hoo House, Gloucester Road, Tewkesbury, Gloucestershire, GL20 7DA
Ⓣ (01684) 293389
Ⓕ (01684) 293389
Ⓔ nursery@hoohouse.co.uk
Ⓦ www.hoohouse.co.uk
Contact: Robin & Julie Ritchie
Opening Times: 1000-1700 Mon-Sat, 1100-1700 Sun.
Cat. Cost: 3 × 1st class.
Credit Cards: None
Specialities: Wide range of herbaceous & alpines – many unusual, incl. *Aster*, *Papaver*, *Geranium* & *Penstemon*. Nat. Collections of *Platycodon* & *Gentiana asclepiadea* cvs.
Notes: Also sells wholesale.
Map Ref: W, C5 **OS Grid Ref:** SO893293

WHrl **HARRELLS HARDY PLANTS** ⊠
(Office) 15 Coxlea Close, Evesham, Worcestershire, WR11 4JS
Ⓣ (01386) 443077
Ⓔ mail@harrellshardyplants.co.uk
Ⓦ www.harrellshardyplants.co.uk
Contact: Liz Nicklin & Kate Phillips
Opening Times: 1000-1200 Sun Mar-Nov. Other times by appt. Please phone.
Min Mail Order UK: Nmc
Cat. Cost: 4 × 2nd class.
Credit Cards: None
Specialities: Display gardens showcase wide range of hardy perennials, esp. *Hemerocallis* & grasses.
Notes: Nursery located off Rudge Rd, Evesham. Please phone for directions or see catalogue. Partial wheelchair access. Mail order Nov-Mar only.
Map Ref: W, C5 **OS Grid Ref:** SP033443

WIvy **IVYCROFT PLANTS** ⊠ € ♿
Upper Ivington, Leominster, Herefordshire, HR6 0JN
Ⓣ (01568) 720344
Ⓔ rogerandsue@ivycroft.freeserve.co.uk
Ⓦ www.ivycroft.freeserve.co.uk
Contact: Roger Norman
Opening Times: 0900-1600 Thu Apr-Sep & 5th, 12th & 26th Feb 2009. Other times by appt., please phone.
Min Mail Order UK: Nmc
Min Mail Order EU: Nmc
Cat. Cost: 2 × 1st class.
Credit Cards: None
Specialities: *Cyclamen*, *Galanthus*, *Salix*, alpines, herbaceous & ferns.
Notes: Mail order Feb/Mar & Jul/Aug, *Galanthus* & *Salix* in winter only.
Map Ref: W, C4 **OS Grid Ref:** SO464562

WJas **PAUL JASPER TREES** ⊠
The Lighthouse, Bridge Street, Leominster, Herefordshire, HR6 8DX
Ⓕ (01568) 616499 for orders.
Ⓔ enquiries@jaspertrees.co.uk
Ⓦ www.jaspertrees.co.uk
Contact: Paul Jasper
Opening Times: Not open. Mail order only.
Min Mail Order UK: £40.00 + p&p
Cat. Cost: Online only.
Credit Cards: None
Specialities: Full range of fruit & ornamental trees. Over 100 modern and traditional apple varieties + 220 others all direct from the

KEY
⊠ Mail order to UK or EU ♠ Delivers to shows
✈ Exports beyond EU € Euro accepted
♿ Accessible by wheelchair ◆ See Display advertisement

grower. Many unusual varieties of *Malus domestica* & *Prunus*.
Notes: Also sells wholesale. Regular catalogue updates & notes on website.
Map Ref: W, C4 **OS Grid Ref:** 495595

WJek **Jekka's Herb Farm** ⊠ 🏠 ♿
Rose Cottage, Shellards Lane, Alveston, Bristol, BS35 3SY
Ⓣ (01454) 418878
Ⓔ info@jekkasherbfarm.com
Ⓦ www.jekkasherbfarm.com
Contact: Jekka McVicar
Opening Times: 4 times a year. Please check website for dates.
Min Mail Order UK: £15 plants
Min Mail Order EU: Seeds only to the EU.
Cat. Cost: 4 × 1st class.
Credit Cards: Visa MasterCard Delta Maestro
Specialities: Culinary, medicinal, aromatic, decorative herbs. Soil Association licensed herb farm.
Map Ref: W, D4

W

WJun **Jungle Giants** ⊠ ✈ € ♿
Ferney, Onibury, Craven Arms, Shropshire, SY7 9BJ
Ⓣ (01584) 856200
Ⓕ (01584) 856663
Ⓔ bamboo@junglegiants.co.uk
Ⓦ www.junglegiants.co.uk
Contact: Michael Brisbane
Opening Times: 7 days. By appt. only please.
Min Mail Order UK: £25.00 + p&p
Min Mail Order EU: £100.00 + p&p
Cat. Cost: 2 × 1st class.
Credit Cards: Access MasterCard Visa
Specialities: Bamboos.
Notes: Also sells wholesale.
Map Ref: W, C4 **OS Grid Ref:** SO430779

WKif **Kiftsgate Court Gardens** ♿
Kiftsgate Court, Chipping Camden, Gloucestershire, GL55 6LN
Ⓣ (01386) 438777
Ⓕ (01386) 438777
Ⓔ anne@kiftsgate.co.uk
Ⓦ www.kiftsgate.co.uk
Contact: Mrs J Chambers
Opening Times: 1200-1800 Sat-Wed, May, Jun & Jul. 1400-1800 Sun, Mon & Wed, Apr, Aug, Sep.
Cat. Cost: None issued
Credit Cards: All major credit/debit cards
Specialities: Small range of unusual plants.
Notes: Does not accept American Express.
Map Ref: W, C5 **OS Grid Ref:** SP170430

WLav **The Lavender Garden** ⊠ 🏠 €
Ashcroft Nurseries, Nr Ozleworth, Kingscote, Tetbury, Gloucestershire, GL8 8YF
Ⓣ (01453) 860356 or 549286
Ⓜ 07837 582943
Ⓔ Andrew007Bullock@aol.com
Ⓦ www.TheLavenderG.co.uk
Contact: Andrew Bullock
Opening Times: 1100-1700 Sat & Sun. Weekdays variable, please phone. 1st Nov-1st Mar by appt. only.
Min Mail Order UK: £30.00 + p&p
Min Mail Order EU: £30.00 + p&p
Cat. Cost: 2 × 1st class.
Credit Cards: None
Specialities: *Lavandula*, *Buddleja*, plants to attract butterflies. Herbs, wildflowers. Nat. Collection of *Buddleja*.
Notes: Also sells wholesale.
Map Ref: W, D5 **OS Grid Ref:** ST798948

WMAq **Merebrook Water Plants** ⊠
Kingfisher Barn, Merebrook Farm, Hanley Swan, Worcestershire, WR8 0DX
Ⓣ (01684) 310950
Ⓜ 07876 777066
Ⓔ enquiries@pondplants.co.uk
Ⓦ www.pondplants.co.uk
Contact: Roger Kings & Biddi Kings
Opening Times: Not open. Mail order only.
Min Mail Order UK: Nmc
Min Mail Order EU: £25.00
Cat. Cost: Online only.
Credit Cards: All major credit/debit cards
Specialities: *Nymphaea*, Louisiana irises & other aquatic plants. International Waterlily & Water Gardening Soc. accredited collection.

WMnd **Mynd Hardy Plants** ♿
Delbury Hall Estate, Diddlebury, Craven Arms, Shropshire, SY7 9DH
Ⓣ (01584) 841222
Ⓔ myndhardyplants@aol.com
Ⓦ www.myndplants.co.uk
Contact: Mark Zenick
Opening Times: 1300-1700 Wed-Fri, 1000-1700 Sat, 1st Apr-Sep. Other times phone for appt.
Cat. Cost: 4 × 2nd class.
Credit Cards: All major credit/debit cards
Specialities: Herbaceous plants, specialising in American bred, British grown, *Hemerocallis*. Home to New Hope Garden's *Hemerocallis* plants.
Notes: Also sells wholesale.
Map Ref: W, B4 **OS Grid Ref:** SO510852

WMoo **Moorland Cottage Plants** ⊠ ♿
Rhyd-y-Groes, Brynberian,
Crymych, Pembrokeshire,
SA41 3TT
Ⓣ (01239) 891363
Ⓔ jenny@moorlandcottageplants.co.uk
Ⓦ www.moorlandcottageplants.co.uk
Contact: Jennifer Matthews
Opening Times: 1030-1730 daily excl. Wed 1st Mar-30th Sep.
Min Mail Order UK: See cat. for details.
Cat. Cost: 4 × 1st class.
Credit Cards: None
Specialities: Traditional & unusual hardy perennials. Many garden-worthy rarities. Cottage garden plants; ferns & many shade plants; moisture lovers; ornamental grasses & bamboos; colourful ground cover.
Notes: Display garden open for NGS from mid-May.
Map Ref: W, C2 **OS Grid Ref:** SN091343

WMou **Mount Pleasant Trees** €
Rockhampton, Berkeley, Gloucestershire,
GL13 9DU
Ⓣ (01454) 260348
Ⓔ info@mountpleasanttrees.com
Ⓦ www.mountpleasanttrees.com
Contact: Tom Locke & Elizabeth Murphy
Opening Times: By appt. only.
Cat. Cost: 3 × 2nd class.
Credit Cards: None
Specialities: Wide range of trees for forestry, hedging, woodlands & gardens esp. *Populus*, *Platanus* & *Salix*.
Notes: Also sells wholesale.
Map Ref: W, D4 **OS Grid Ref:** ST654929

WNHG **New Hope Gardens** ⊠ ♿
Batch Farm, Cockshutford,
Craven Arms, Shropshire,
SY7 9DY
Ⓣ (01746) 712898 (office) or (01584) 841222 (nursery)
Ⓔ Newhopegardensmz@aol.com
Ⓦ www.newhopegardens.com
Contact: Mark Zenick
Opening Times: 1300-1700 Wed-Fri, 1000-1700 Sat, Apr-Sep. Other times phone nursery for appt.
Min Mail Order UK: Nmc
Cat. Cost: Online only. Plant list on request.
Credit Cards: All major credit/debit cards
Specialities: American bred, British grown, *Hemerocallis*. Ships bare-rooted plants.
Map Ref: W, B4 **OS Grid Ref:** SO510852

WOld **Old Court Nurseries** ⊠ € ♿
Colwall, Nr Malvern, Worcestershire,
WR13 6QE
Ⓣ (01684) 540416
Ⓔ paulpicton@btinternet.com
Ⓦ www.autumnasters.co.uk
Contact: Paul & Meriel Picton
Opening Times: 1330-1700 Fri-Sun, May-Oct. 1100-1700 7 days, 1st week Sep-2nd week Oct.
Min Mail Order UK: Nmc
Min Mail Order EU: Nmc
Cat. Cost: 1 × 1st class.
Credit Cards: None
Specialities: Nat. Collection of Michaelmas Daisies. Herbaceous perennials.
Notes: Mail order for *Aster* only.
Map Ref: W, C4 **OS Grid Ref:** SO759430

WOut **Out of the Common Way** ⊠ ⌂ €
(Office) Penhyddgan, Boduan, Pwllheli,
Gwynedd, LL53 8YH
Ⓣ (01758) 721577 (Office) or (01407) 720431 (Nursery)
Ⓔ jo.davidson@virgin.net
Contact: Joanna Davidson (nursery) Margaret Mason (office & mail order)
Opening Times: By arrangement.
Min Mail Order UK: Nmc
Min Mail Order EU: Nmc
Cat. Cost: A5 sae letter rate postage.
Credit Cards: None
Specialities: Labiates, esp. *Nepeta* & *Salvia*. *Aster*, *Geranium* & *Crocosmia*. Native plants. Some plants propagated in small quantities only. Will propagate salvias to order.
Notes: Nursery is at Pandy Treban, Bryngwran, Anglesey. Partially accessible for wheelchairs.
Map Ref: W, A2 **OS Grid Ref:** SH370778

WPat **Chris Pattison** ⊠ € ♿
Brookend, Pendock, Gloucestershire,
GL19 3PL
Ⓣ (01531) 650480
Ⓕ (01531) 650480
Ⓔ cp@chris-pattison.co.uk
Ⓦ www.chris-pattison.co.uk
Contact: Chris Pattison
Opening Times: 0900-1700 Mon-Fri. W/ends by appt. only.
Min Mail Order UK: £10.00 +p&p
Cat. Cost: 3 × 1st class.

KEY
⊠ Mail order to UK or EU ⌂ Delivers to shows
✈ Exports beyond EU € Euro accepted
♿ Accessible by wheelchair ◆ See Display advertisement

Credit Cards: None
Specialities: Choice rare shrubs & alpines. Grafted stock esp. Japanese maples & liquidambars. Wide range of *Viburnum* & dwarf/miniature trees & shrubs.
Notes: Mail order Nov-Feb only. Also sells wholesale.
Map Ref: W, C5 **OS Grid Ref:** SO781327

WPBF **P & B FUCHSIAS** ⊠ € ♿
Penclawdd Road, Penclawdd, Swansea, West Glamorgan, SA4 3RB
Ⓣ (01792) 851669
Ⓔ sales@gower-fuchsias.co.uk
Ⓦ www.gower-fuchsias.co.uk
Contact: Paul Fisher
Opening Times: 0900-1800 7 days 1 Mar-30 Sep.
Min Mail Order UK: £11.00 (6 plants) incl. p&p
Cat. Cost: 3 × 1st class.
Credit Cards: None
Specialities: Fuchsias. Hybrid & species.
Notes: Cuttings only available Mar-May. Very ltd. quantities of each.
Map Ref: W, D3

W

WPen **PENPERGWM PLANTS** ♿
Penpergwm Lodge, Abergavenny, Monmonthshire, NP7 9AS
Ⓣ (01873) 840422/840208
Ⓔ boyle@penpergwm.co.uk
Ⓦ www.penplants.com
Contact: Mrs J Kerr/Mrs S Boyle
Opening Times: 1400-1800 Thu-Sun, 20th Mar-28th Sep 2008
Cat. Cost: 2 × 1st class.
Credit Cards: None
Specialities: Hardy perennials.
Map Ref: W, D4 **OS Grid Ref:** SO335104

WPer **PERHILL NURSERIES** ⊠ € ♿
Worcester Road, Great Witley, Worcestershire, WR6 6JT
Ⓣ (01299) 896329
Ⓕ (01299) 896990
Ⓔ PerhillP@aol.com
Ⓦ www.perhillplants.co.uk
Contact: Duncan Straw
Opening Times: 0900-1700 Mon-Sat, 1000-1600 Sun, 1st Feb-31st Jul. 0900-1700 Mon-Fri, 1st Aug-31st Jan.
Min Mail Order UK: Nmc
Min Mail Order EU: £10.00
Cat. Cost: 6 × 2nd class.
Credit Cards: All major credit/debit cards
Specialities: 2500+ varieties of rare, unusual alpines & herbaceous perennials incl. *Penstemon*, *Campanula*, *Salvia*, *Thymus*, herbs, *Veronica*.
Notes: Also sells wholesale.
Map Ref: W, C4 **OS Grid Ref:** SO763656

WPGP **PAN-GLOBAL PLANTS** ♿
The Walled Garden, Frampton Court, Frampton-on-Severn, Gloucestershire, GL2 7EX
Ⓣ (01452) 741641
Ⓜ 07801 275138
Ⓕ (01453) 768858
Ⓔ info@panglobalplants.com
Ⓦ www.panglobalplants.com
Contact: Nick Macer
Opening Times: 1100-1700 Wed-Sun 1st Feb-31st Oct. Also B/hols. Closed 2nd Sun in Sep. Winter months by appt., please phone first.
Cat. Cost: 6 × 1st class.
Credit Cards: Maestro MasterCard Visa Solo Delta
Specialities: A plantsman's nursery offering a very wide selection of rare & desirable trees, ornamental trees, shrubs, herbaceous, bamboos, exotics, climbers, ferns etc. Specialities incl. *Magnolia*, *Hydrangea*, bamboos & *Agavaceae*.
Map Ref: W, D5 **OS Grid Ref:** SO750080

WPnn **THE PERENNIAL NURSERY** ⊠
Rhosygilwen, Llanrhian Road, St Davids, Pembrokeshire, SA62 6DB
Ⓣ (01437) 721954
Ⓦ www.droughttolerantplants.co.uk
Contact: Mrs Philipa Symons
Opening Times: 1030-1700 Mar-Oct. Nov-Feb by appt.
Min Mail Order UK: Nmc
Min Mail Order EU: Nmc
Cat. Cost: Online only.
Credit Cards: None
Specialities: *Rosmarinus*, *Lampranthus*, wind & drought-tolerant plants.
Notes: Also sells wholesale.
Map Ref: W, C1 **OS Grid Ref:** SM775292

WPnP **PENLAN PERENNIALS** ⊠ € ♿
Penlan Farm, Penrhiw-pâl, Llandysul, Ceredigion, SA44 5QH
Ⓣ (01239) 851244
Ⓜ 07857 675312
Ⓕ (01239) 851244
Ⓔ rcain@penlanperennials.co.uk
Ⓦ www.penlanperennials.co.uk
Contact: Richard Cain
Opening Times: 0930-1730 Fri-Sun & B/hols 1st Mar-30th Jun only. Jul-Feb by appt.

Min Mail Order UK: Nmc
Min Mail Order EU: Nmc
Cat. Cost: Online, or sae for CD-ROM.
Credit Cards: All major credit/debit cards
Specialities: Aquatic, marginal & bog plants. Shade-loving & woodland perennials, ferns, grasses & hardy geraniums, all grown peat-free.
Notes: Mail order all year, next day delivery. Secure online web ordering.
Map Ref: W, C2 **OS Grid Ref:** SN344457

WPrP **Prime Perennials** ⊠ ♠
Llety Moel, Rhos-y-Garth, Llanilar,
Nr Aberystwyth, Ceredigion, SY23 4SG
Ⓣ (01974) 241505
Ⓜ 07891 333656
Ⓔ liz@prime-perennials.co.uk
Ⓦ www.prime-perennials.co.uk
Contact: Elizabeth Powney
Opening Times: Open by appt. only.
Min Mail Order UK: Nmc
Min Mail Order EU: £12.00
Cat. Cost: 4 × 1st class.
Credit Cards: None
Specialities: Specialist growers of rare, unusual & obscure perennials, ferns, bulbs & grasses. Some plants in small quanitites. Peat free. Grown 650ft above sea level. Nat. Collection of *Tulbaghia*.
Notes: Mail order all year.
Map Ref: W, C3

WPtf **Pantyfod Garden Nursery** ⊠
Llandewi Brefi, Tregaron, Ceredigion,
SY25 6PE
Ⓣ (01570) 493564
Ⓔ sales@pantyfodgarden.co.uk
Ⓦ www.pantyfodgarden.co.uk
Contact: Susan Rowe
Opening Times: Mail order only. Not open, except by prior arrangement.
Min Mail Order UK: Nmc
Min Mail Order EU: Nmc
Cat. Cost: Online only.
Credit Cards: Paypal
Specialities: Hardy geraniums, unusual hardy perennials, black plants, woodland plants, plants for moist soil, all grown largely peat-free. Many plants available in small quantities. Nursery at 950ft with spectacular views.
Map Ref: W, C3 **OS Grid Ref:** SN654540

WRai **Rails End Nursery** ⊠ ♿
Back Lane, Ashton under Hill, Evesham,
Worcestershire, WR11 7RG
Ⓣ (01386) 881884
Ⓕ (01386) 881407
Ⓔ salski@quinweb.net
Ⓦ www.ashtonunderhill.org.uk/business/railsend
Contact: Sally Skinner
Opening Times: 1000-1700 6 days, Mar-end Oct. Nov-Feb by appt. only. Closed Mon except for b/hols.
Min Mail Order UK: Nmc
Cat. Cost: Free or online.
Credit Cards: All major credit/debit cards
Specialities: Family-run nursery, specialising in hardy herbaceous perennials, with an extending range of the unusual. All stock in small quantities.
Notes: Partially accessible for wheelchair users.
Map Ref: W, C5 **OS Grid Ref:** SO999375

WRHF **Red House Farm** ♿
Flying Horse Lane, Bradley Green,
Nr Redditch, Worcestershire, B96 6QT
Ⓣ (01527) 821269
Ⓕ (01527) 821674
Ⓔ contact@redhousefarmgardenandnursery.co.uk
Ⓦ www.redhousefarmgardenandnursery.co.uk
Contact: Mrs Maureen Weaver
Opening Times: 0900-1700 Mon-Sat all year. 1000-1700 Sun & B/hols.
Cat. Cost: 2 × 1st class.
Credit Cards: None
Map Ref: W, C5 **OS Grid Ref:** SO986623

WRic **World of Ferns (Rickards Ferns Ltd)** ⊠ ✈ € ◆
Carreg y Fedwen, Lôn Rallt, Pentir, Bangor,
Gwynedd, LL57 4RP
Ⓣ (01248) 600385
Ⓕ (01248) 600385
Ⓔ info@world-of-ferns.co.uk
Ⓦ www.world-of-ferns.co.uk
Contact: Ben Kettle
Opening Times: Open by appt. only.
Min Mail Order UK: £30.00 + p&p
Min Mail Order EU: £50.00 + p&p
Cat. Cost: 5 × 1st class or 6 × 2nd class or online.
Credit Cards: All major credit/debit cards
Specialities: Ferns, incl. tree ferns.

WRou **Roualeyn Nurseries** ⊠ ♠ ♿
Trefriw, Conwy, LL27 0SX
Ⓣ (01492) 640548
Ⓕ (01492) 640548
Ⓔ roualeynnursery@btinternet.com
Contact: Doug Jones

KEY
⊠ Mail order to UK or EU ♠ Delivers to shows
✈ Exports beyond EU € Euro accepted
♿ Accessible by wheelchair ◆ See Display advertisement

Opening Times: 1000-1700 weekdays 1st Mar-31st Aug, 1000-1600 Sat, Sun & B/hols.
Min Mail Order UK: £18.00
Cat. Cost: 2 × 1st class.
Credit Cards: None
Specialities: Fuchsias, incl. species.
Notes: Orders may be collected from any of the flower shows listed in current catalogue.
Map Ref: W, A3 **OS Grid Ref:** SH632778

WSFF **Saith Ffynnon Farm** ⊠ € ♿
Whitford, Holywell, Flintshire, CH8 9EQ
Ⓣ (01352) 711198
Ⓕ (01352) 716777
Ⓔ jan@7wells.org
Ⓦ www.7wells.co.uk
Contact: Jan Miller
Opening Times: By appt. only.
Min Mail Order UK: Nmc
Min Mail Order EU: Nmc
Cat. Cost: 2 × 1st class or online.
Credit Cards: All major credit/debit cards
Specialities: Plants and seeds to attract butterflies and moths. Natural dye plants. Nat. Collection of *Eupatorium* (Provisional). Stock available in small quantities unless ordered well in advance.
Notes: Also sells wholesale. Credit cards accepted via website only. Percentage of profits go to Butterfly Conservation.
Map Ref: W, A3 **OS Grid Ref:** SJ154775

WSHC **Stone House Cottage Nurseries** ♿
Stone, Nr Kidderminster, Worcestershire, DY10 4BG
Ⓣ (01562) 69902
Ⓔ louisa@shcn.co.uk
Ⓦ www.shcn.co.uk
Contact: L N Arbuthnott
Opening Times: 1000-1700 Wed-Sat. By appt. only mid Sep-mid Mar.
Cat. Cost: Sae
Credit Cards: None
Specialities: Small general range esp. wall shrubs, climbers & unusual plants.
Map Ref: W, C5 **OS Grid Ref:** SO863750

WShi **Shipton Bulbs** ⊠ €
Y Felin, Henllan Amgoed, Whitland, Carmarthenshire, SA34 0SL
Ⓣ (01994) 240125
Ⓕ (01994) 241180
Ⓔ bluebell@zoo.co.uk
Ⓦ www.bluebellbulbs.co.uk
Contact: John Shipton & Alison Foot
Opening Times: By appt. only.
Min Mail Order UK: Nmc
Min Mail Order EU: Nmc
Cat. Cost: Sae.
Credit Cards: All major credit/debit cards
Specialities: Native British bulbs, & bulbs & plants for naturalising.
Map Ref: W, D2 **OS Grid Ref:** SN188207

WSpi **Spinneywell Nursery** ⊠ ◆
Waterlane, Oakridge, Bisley, Gloucestershire, GL6 7PH
Ⓣ (01452) 770151 or 770092
Ⓕ (01452) 770151
Ⓔ wendy.spinneywell@virgin.net
Ⓦ www.spinneywellplants.co.uk
Contact: Wendy Asher
Opening Times: 1000-1600 Mon-Sat, spring, summer, autumn. 1000-1500 Mon-Fri, winter. Alternate Sats 1400-1700, Oct-Mar.
Min Mail Order UK: £10.00 + p&p
Min Mail Order EU: £30.00 + p&p
Cat. Cost: Online only.
Credit Cards: All major credit/debit cards
Specialities: *Buxus*, *Taxus* & unusual herbaceous & shrubs. Hellebores, euphorbias, *Ceanothus*, hardy geraniums.
Notes: Also sells wholesale. Plant sourcing service available.
Map Ref: W, D5 **OS Grid Ref:** SO921044

WSSs **Shropshire Sarracenias** ⊠ ☒ € ♿
5 Field Close, Malinslee, Telford, Shropshire, TF4 2EH
Ⓣ (01952) 501598
Ⓔ mike@carnivorousplants.uk.com
Ⓦ www.carnivorousplants.uk.com
Contact: Mike King
Opening Times: By appt. only.
Min Mail Order UK: Nmc
Min Mail Order EU: Nmc
Cat. Cost: 2 × 1st class.
Credit Cards: Paypal
Specialities: *Sarracenia. Dionaea muscipula* & forms. Some stock available in small quantities only. Nat. Collections of *Sarracenia* & *Dionaea.*
Map Ref: W, B4 **OS Grid Ref:** SJ689085

WSuV **Sunnybank Vine Nursery (National Vine Collection)** ⊠ ☒
King Street, Ewyas Harold, Rowlestone, Herefordshire, HR2 OEE
Ⓣ (01981) 240256
Ⓔ vinenursery@hotmail.com
Ⓦ vinenursery.netfirms.com
Contact: B R Edwards
Opening Times: Not open. Mail order only.

Min Mail Order UK: £8.00 incl. p&p
Min Mail Order EU: £13.00 incl. p&p
Cat. Cost: Free.
Credit Cards: None
Specialities: Vines. Nat. Collection of *Vitis vinifera* (hardy, incl. dessert & wine).
Notes: EU sales by arrangement.
Map Ref: W, C4

WTan **Tan-y-Llyn Nurseries** ⊠
Meifod, Powys, SY22 6YB
T. (01938) 500370
Ⓔ info@tanyllyn.the-nursery.co.uk
Ⓦ www.tanyllyn.the-nursery.co.uk
Contact: Callum Johnston
Opening Times: 1000-1700 Tue-Fri Mar-Jun and at other times by appt.
Min Mail Order UK: Nmc
Cat. Cost: 2 × 1st class.
Credit Cards: None
Specialities: Herbs, alpines, perennials.
Map Ref: W, B3 **OS Grid Ref:** SJ167125

WThu **Thuya Alpine Nursery** ⊠
Glebelands, Hartpury, Gloucestershire, GL19 3BW
Ⓣ (01452) 700548
Contact: S W Bond
Opening Times: 1000-dusk Sat & Bank hol. 1100-dusk Sun, Weekdays appt. advised.
Min Mail Order UK: £4.00 + p&p
Min Mail Order EU: £10.00 + p&p
Cat. Cost: 4 × 2nd class.
Credit Cards: None
Specialities: Wide and changing range including rarities, available in smallish numbers.
Notes: Partially accessible for wheelchair users. Will deliver plants to AGS shows.
Map Ref: W, C5

WTin **Tinpenny Plants** ♿
Tinpenny Farm, Fiddington, Tewkesbury, Gloucestershire, GL20 7BJ
Ⓣ (01684) 292668
Ⓔ elaine@lime.ws
Ⓦ www.tinpenny.plus.com
Contact: Elaine Horton
Opening Times: 0900-1300 Tue-Thu or by appt. all year round.
Cat. Cost: None issued.
Credit Cards: None
Specialities: Wide range of hardy garden-worthy plants esp. *Helleborus*, *Iris* & *Sempervivum*. Small nursery will propagate to order rare plants from own stock. Small quantities only of some plants.
Map Ref: W, C5 **OS Grid Ref:** SO919318

WTou **Touchwood Plants** ⊠ ✈ ⛺
4 Clyne Valley Cottages, Killay, Swansea, West Glamorgan, SA2 7DU
Ⓣ (01792) 522443
Ⓔ Carrie.Thomas@ntlworld.com
Ⓦ www.touchwoodplants.co.uk
Contact: Carrie Thomas
Opening Times: Most reasonable days/times. Please phone first.
Min Mail Order UK: Nmc
Cat. Cost: 2 × 1st class.
Credit Cards: Paypal
Specialities: Seeds & plants. Nat. Collection of *Aquilegia vulgaris* cvs & hybrids. Plant stocks held in small quantities. Main stock is seed. Garden & *Aquilegia* Collection open.
Notes: Plants sent bare-rooted at relevant times of the year. Exports seeds only beyond UK.
Map Ref: W, D3 **OS Grid Ref:** SS600924

WViv **Viv Marsh Postal Plants** ⊠
Walford Heath, Shrewsbury, Shropshire, SY4 2HT
Ⓣ (01939) 291475
Ⓔ mail@postalplants.co.uk
Ⓦ www.postalplants.co.uk
Contact: Mr Viv Marsh
Opening Times: Selected w/ends in spring & autumn. Please phone for details. Other times by appt. only.
Min Mail Order UK: £30.00 plant value
Min Mail Order EU: £30.00 plant value
Cat. Cost: 5 × 1st class or online.
Credit Cards: Visa MasterCard Switch Electron Maestro
Specialities: Specialists in *Alstroemeria*, *Iris* & *Lathyrus*.
Notes: Wheelchair access with assistance. No disabled toilet.
Map Ref: W, B4 **OS Grid Ref:** SJ446198

WWEG **World's End Garden Nursery** ♿ ◆
Moseley Road, Hallow, Worcester, Worcestershire, WR2 6NJ
Ⓣ (01905) 640977
Ⓕ (01905) 641373
Ⓔ garden@robinpearce.co.uk
Ⓦ www.worldsendgarden.co.uk
Contact: Kristina & Robin Pearce
Opening Times: 1030-1700 Tue-Sat, Mar-Oct. Other times by appt.
Cat. Cost: 4 × 1st class or online.

KEY
⊠ Mail order to UK or EU ⛺ Delivers to shows
✈ Exports beyond EU € Euro accepted
♿ Accessible by wheelchair ◆ See Display advertisement

Credit Cards: All major credit/debit cards
Specialities: Wide range of herbaceous perennials, ferns & ornamental grasses. Especially *Hosta*, *Geum*, *Leucantheum*, *Helenium* & ferns.
Notes: Also sells wholesale.
Map Ref: W, C5 **OS Grid Ref:** SO815597

WWFP **Whitehall Farmhouse Plants** ⊠ ♠
Sevenhampton, Cheltenham, Gloucestershire, GL54 5TL
Ⓣ (01242) 820772
Ⓜ 07711 021034
Ⓕ (01242) 821226
Ⓔ info@wfplants.co.uk
Ⓦ www.wfplants.co.uk
Contact: Victoria Logue
Opening Times: By appt. only.
Min Mail Order UK: Nmc
Cat. Cost: 2 × 1st class.
Credit Cards: None
Specialities: A small nursery producing a range of interesting & easy hardy perennials for the garden. Some plants held in small quantities only.
Map Ref: W, C5 **OS Grid Ref:** SP018229

W

WWHy **Welsh Holly** ⊠ € ♿
Llyn-y-gors, Tenby Road, St Clears, Carmarthenshire, SA33 4JP
Ⓣ (01994) 231789
Ⓕ (01994) 231789
Ⓔ info@welsh-holly.co.uk
Ⓦ www.welsh-holly.co.uk
Contact: Philip Lanc
Opening Times: By appt. only.
Min Mail Order UK: Nmc
Min Mail Order EU: Nmc
Cat. Cost: 2 × 1st class.
Credit Cards: None
Specialities: Hollies. Limited stock of less common plants.
Notes: Also sells wholesale.

WWlt **Wollerton Old Hall Garden** ♿
Wollerton, Market Drayton, Shropshire, TF9 3NA
Ⓣ (01630) 685760
Ⓕ (01630) 685583
Ⓔ info@wollertonoldhallgarden.com
Ⓦ www.wollertonoldhallgarden.com
Contact: Mr John Jenkins
Opening Times: 1200-1700 Fri, Sun & B/hols Easter-end Sep.
Cat. Cost: None issued
Credit Cards: All major credit/debit cards
Specialities: Perennials, hardy & half-hardy.
Map Ref: W, B4 **OS Grid Ref:** SJ624296

WWst **Westonbirt Plants** ⊠ ✈ €
9 Westonbirt Close, Worcester, WR5 3RX
Ⓣ (01905) 350429 (answerphone)
Ⓔ office@westonbirtplants.co.uk
Ⓦ www.westonbirtplants.co.uk
Contact: Garry Dickerson
Opening Times: Not open. Mail order only.
Min Mail Order UK: Nmc
Min Mail Order EU: Nmc
Cat. Cost: 3 × 1st class.
Credit Cards: None
Specialities: Bulbs & woodland plants incl. *Anemonella*, *Arisaema*, *Colchicum*, *Corydalis*, *Erythronium*, *Fritillaria*, *Iris* (Juno & Oncocyclus), *Lilium*, *Paeonia*, *Roscoea*, *Trillium* & hardy orchids (*Calanthe*, *Cypripedium* & *Epipactis*). Many rare plants in ltd. numbers.

Abroad

XBlo **Table Bay View Nursery** ⊠ ✈ €
(Office) 60 Molteno Road, Oranjezicht, Cape Town 8001, South Africa
Ⓣ 00 27 21 683 5108
Ⓕ 00 27 21 683 5108
Ⓔ info@tablebayviewnursery.co.za
Contact: Terence Bloch
Opening Times: Mail order only. No personal callers.
Min Mail Order UK: £15.00 + p&p
Min Mail Order EU: £15.00
Cat. Cost: £3.40 (postal order)
Credit Cards: None
Specialities: Tropical & sub-tropical ornamental & fruiting plants.
Notes: Due to high local bank charges, can no longer accept foreign bank cheques, only undated postal orders.

XBTW **B & T World Seeds** ⊠ ✈ €
Paguignan, 34210 Aigues-Vives, France
Ⓣ 00 33 (0) 4689 12963
Ⓕ 00 33 (0) 4689 13039
Ⓔ le@b-and-t-world-seeds.com
Ⓦ www.b-and-t-world-seeds.com
Contact: Lesley Sleigh
Opening Times: Not open. Mail order only.
Min Mail Order UK: £14.00 inc. carriage
Min Mail Order EU: £14.00 inc. carriage
Cat. Cost: £10 Europe, £14 elsewhere.
Credit Cards: Visa MasterCard
Specialities: Master list contains over 30,000 items. 700 sub-lists available.
Notes: Also sells wholesale. Exports seed only. Catalogue/botanical reference system available on CD Rom. SeedyRom (TM) catalogue £20 worldwide.

XFro **Frosch Exclusive Perennials** ⊠ ✈ €
Zielgelstadelweg 5, D-83623 Dietramszell-Lochen, Germany
Ⓣ 00 49 (0)172 8422050
Ⓕ 00 49 (0)8027 9049975
Ⓔ info@cypripedium.de
Ⓦ www.cypripedium.de
Contact: Michael Weinert
Opening Times: Not open. Mail order only. Orders taken between 0700-2200 hours.
Min Mail Order UK: £350.00 + p&p
Min Mail Order EU: £350.00 + p&p
Cat. Cost: Online only.
Credit Cards: None
Specialities: *Cypripedium* hybrids. Hardy orchids.
Notes: Also sells wholesale.

XPde **Pépinière de l'Île** ⊠ €
Keranroux, 22870, Ile de Brehat, France
Ⓣ 00 33 (0)2 96 200384
Ⓜ 0686 128609
Ⓕ 00 33 (0)2 96 200384
Ⓔ contact@pepiniere-brehat.com
Ⓦ www.pepiniere-brehat.com
Contact: Laurence Blasco & Charles Blasco
Opening Times: 1400-1800 spring & summer. Other times by appt. incl. Aug.
Min Mail Order UK: Nmc
Min Mail Order EU: Nmc
Cat. Cost: €6.00.
Credit Cards: None
Specialities: *Agapanthus* & *Echium*. Plants from South Africa.

Nursery Index by Name

Nurseries that are included in the *RHS Plant Finder* for the first time this year (or have been reintroduced) are marked in **bold type**. Full details of the nurseries will be found in **Nursery Details by Code** on page 820. For a key to the geographical codes, see the start of **Nurseries**.

Bodiam Nursery	SBod
Bodmin Plant and Herb Nursery	CBod
Border Belles	GBBs
Bordervale Plants	WBor
Botanic Nursery, The	**CBot**
Botanica	**EBtc**
Bouts Cottage Nurseries	WBou
Bowden Hostas	CBdn
Bowley Plants	CBow
Brambly Hedge	SBrm
Breezy Knees Nurseries	NBre
Bregover Plants	CBre
Bressingham Gardens (incorp. Van Tubergen UK)	EBrs
Brian & Pearl Sulman	ESul
Bridge Nursery	MBrN
Bridgemere Nurseries	MBri
British Wild Flower Plants	EBWF
Broadleas Gardens Ltd	CBrd
Broadleigh Gardens	CBro
Brockamin Plants	WBrk
Bron Eifion Nursery	WBrE
Brooklands Plants	CBrP
Brown's Barn (formerly Compton Lane Nurseries)	**WCom**
Brownthwaite Hardy Plants	NBro
Buckingham Nurseries	LBuc
Buckland Plants	GBuc
Bucknell Nurseries	WBuc
Burncoose Nurseries	CBcs
Burnham Nurseries	CBur
Burton Agnes Hall Nursery	NBur
Burton Grange Nursery	**LBur**
Butterworths' Organic Nursery	**GBut**
C & K Jones	MJon
C S Lockyer (Fuchsias)	CLoc
C W Groves & Son Ltd	CGro
Cacti & Succulents	SCac
Cairnsmore Nursery	GCai
Cally Gardens	GCal
Cambridge Garden Plants	ECGP
Camellia Grove Nursery	SCam
Cants of Colchester	ECnt
Cath's Garden Plants	NCGa
Chapel Farm House Nursery	CCha
Charles F Ellis	WCFE
Charleshurst Farm Nursery	SChF
Chennels Gate Gardens & Nursery	WChG
Cherry Tree Nursery	CChe
Chew Valley Trees	CCVT
Chiltern Seeds	NChl
Chipchase Castle Nursery	NChi
Choice Landscapes	ECho
Chris Pattison	WPat
Churchtown Carnivores	**NChu**
Cider Apple Trees	CCAT
Claines Canna Collection	WCCa
Claire Austin Hardy Plants	WCAu
Classic Gardener (formerly Pound Hill Topiary)	**CPHT**
Clay Lane Nursery	LCla
Clifton Plants	**NCli**
Close Nursery (Duchy of Cornwall)	WClo
Cobble Hey Gardens	NCob
Coghurst Camellias	SCog
Colin Roberts	SCnR
Collectors Corner Plants	MCCP
Connoisseur's Plant Corner, The	**WCon**
Cookoo Box Nursery	**SCko**
Cool Temperate	MCoo
Cooling's Nurseries Ltd	SCoo
Corseside Nursery	WCor
Coton Manor Garden	MCot
Cotswold Garden Flowers	WCot
Cottage Garden Nursery	LCtg
Cottage Garden Plants	NCot
Cottage Herbery, The	WCHb
Cottage Nurseries	ECtt
County Park Nursery	ECou
Craigieburn Garden	GCra
Creake Plant Centre	ECre
Crescent Plants	WCre
Crin Gardens	MCri
Crocknafeola Nursery	ICro
Crocosmia Gardens, The	**ECrc**
Crofters Nurseries	SCrf
Cromar Nursery	SCmr
Cross Common Nursery	CCCN
Croston Cactus	NCro
Crown Nursery	ECrN
Crûg Farm Plants	WCru
Culm View Nursery	CCVN
D K Plants	MDKP
D S Witton	NWit
Daisy Roots	LDai
Dalesview Nursery	NDlv
D'Arcy & Everest	EDAr
Deacon's Nursery	SDea
Deelish Garden Centre	IDee
Denmans Garden, (John Brookes Ltd)	SDnm
Derek Lloyd Dean	LDea
Desert to Jungle	CDTJ
Desirable Plants	CDes
Dibley's Nurseries	WDib
Dickson Nurseries Ltd	IDic
Different Plants	EDif
Dingle Nurseries	WDin
Dolau-hirion Fruit Tree Nursery	**WDol**
Downderry Nursery	SDow
Duchy of Cornwall	CDoC
Dulford Nurseries	CDul
Dunge Valley Gardens	MDun
Dyffryn Gwyddno Nursery	WDyG
Dysons Nurseries	SDys
East Northdown Farm	SEND
Eastgrove Cottage Garden Nursery	WEas

Hydon Nurseries	LHyd
Hydrangea Haven	SHyH
I.M.B. Plants	LIMB
Iden Croft Herbs	SIde
Iris Garden, The	CIri
Iris of Sissinghurst	SIri
Irisesonline	**EIri**
Isle of Wight Lavender	SIoW
Ivycroft Plants	WIvy
J Tweedie Fruit Trees	GTwe
J Walkers Bulbs	**EWal**
Jackson's Nurseries	MJac
Jacques Amand International	LAma
James Cocker & Sons	GCoc
Jasmine Cottage Gardens	CJas
Jekka's Herb Farm	WJek
Jenny Burgess	EBur
Jill White	EJWh
John and Lynsey's Plants	SPin
John Churcher	SChr
John Ray Nursery	EJRN
John Smith & Son	MSmi
Jo's Garden Enterprise	GJos
Jungle Giants	**WJun**
Kathleen Muncaster Fuchsias	EKMF
Kayes Garden Nursery	MKay
Keepers Nursery	SKee
Kelways Ltd	CKel
Ken Muir Ltd	EMui
Kent Street Nurseries	**SKen**
Kenwick Farmhouse Nurseries	**EKen**
Kenwith Nursery (Gordon Haddow)	CKen
Kevock Garden Plants	GKev
Kiftsgate Court Gardens	WKif
Kilmurry Nursery	**IKil**
Kirkdale Nursery	GKir
Knoll Gardens	CKno
L A Allen	WAln
L W Plants	LLWP
Ladybird Garden Nursery	ILad
Lakka Bulbs	**CLak**
Landford Trees	CLnd
Landlife Wildflowers Ltd	NLan
Landscape Plants	SLPl
Laneside Alpines	NLAp
Langley Boxwood Nursery Ltd	SLan
Langthorns Plantery	ELan
Larch Cottage Nurseries	NLar
Larkspur Nursery	ELar
Laurel Farm Herbs	ELau
Laurels Nursery, The	SLau
Lavender Garden, The	WLav
Layham Garden Centre & Nursery	SLay
Lea Rhododendron Gardens Ltd	MLea
Leatherbritches Kitchen Garden & Nursery	MLBr
Leeds Lavender	NLLv
Lesley Marshall	EMar
Lilies Water Gardens	LLWG
Lime Cross Nursery	SLim
Linn Botanic Gardens	**GLin**
Lisdoonan Herbs	ILis
Little Brook Fuchsias	SLBF
Little Heath Farm (UK) (formerly Two Jays Alpines)	LLHF
Lochlands (HRB Ltd)	GLld
Loder Plants	SLdr
Lodge Farm Plants & Wildflowers	MLod
Long Acre Plants	CLAP
Long House Plants	ELon
Longcombe Nursery and Garden Centre	**CLng**
Longstock Park Nursery	SLon
Longstone Hardy Plant Nursery	MLHP
Lower Severalls Nursery	CSev
Lulworth Plants	MLul
M & M Plants	CMMP
M G H Nurseries	IMGH
Mac Pennys Nurseries	CMac
MacGregors Plants for Shade	SMac
Macplants	GMaP
Madrona Nursery	SMad
Majestic Trees	LMaj
Mallet Court Nursery	CMCN
Marcus Dancer Plants	SMDP
Marshall's Malmaisons	EMal
Marwood Hill Gardens	CMHG
Mary Green	NMyG
Mead Nursery, The	CMea
Meadow Cottage Plants	CMCo
Meadows Nursery	CMdw
Mendip Bonsai Studio	CMen
Mendle Nursery	NMen
Meon Valley Plants	SMeo
Merebrook Water Plants	WMAq
Merriments Gardens	SMrm
Mickfield Hostas	EMic
Mickfield Watergarden Centre Ltd	EMFW
Mill Cottage Plants	CMil
Mill Race Garden Centre	EMil
Millais Nurseries	LMil
Millrace Nursery	**NMRc**
Millthorpe Nursery	**NMil**
Miniature Bulbs & Choice Bulbs	NMin
Mires Beck Nursery	NMir
Monita House Garden	CMoH
Montana Garden Nursery	**IMon**
Moor Monkton Nurseries	NMoo
Moorland Cottage Plants	WMoo
Morehavens	LMor
Morton Hall Gardens	MMHG
Mount Harry Trees	SMHT
Mount Pleasant Trees	WMou
Mount Venus Nursery	**IMou**
Mozart House Nursery Garden	MMoz
Mrs Mitchell's Kitchen & Garden	SMrs
Mucklestone Nurseries	MMuc

Rotherview Nursery	SRot
Roualeyn Nurseries	WRou
Rowden Gardens	CRow
Rumsey Gardens	SRms
Ryal Nursery	NRya
S & S Perennials	MSSP
St Bridget Nurseries Ltd	CSBt
St Clare Nursery	EStC
Saith Ffynnon Farm	WSFF
Sampford Shrubs	CSam
Samuel Dobie & Son	CDob
Scawsby Hall Nurseries	NScw
Scott's Wildflowers	NSco
Seaforde Gardens	ISea
Seagate Irises	ESgI
Seale Nurseries	SSea
Seaside Nursery	ISsi
Second Nature Plant Nursery	CSNP
Secret Garden, The	GSec
Seeds by Size	LSee
Select Seeds	SSss
Sheila Chapman Clematis	ESCh
Sherston Parva Nursery	CSPN
Sherwood Cottage	CSdC
Shipton Bulbs	WShi
Shirley Tasker	NShi
Shropshire Sarracenias	WSSs
Shrubland Park Nurseries	EShb
Silver Dale Nurseries	CSil
Simpson's Seeds Ltd	CSim
Slack Top Nurseries	NSla
Slipps Garden Centre	CSli
Sonia Wright Plants	CSWP
Sound Garden Rhododendrons (formerly Penton Mill)	**MSnd**
South West Carnivorous Plants	CSWC
Southease Plants	SSth
Southon Plants	LSou
Southview Nurseries	SSvw
Special Plants	CSpe
SpecialPerennials.com	**MSpe**
Spinners Garden	SSpi
Spinneywell Nursery	WSpi
Spring Park Nursery	**SSPN**
Spring Reach Nursery	LSRN
Springfield Plants	**CSpr**
Springwood Nursery	SSwd
Squire's Garden Centre, Shepperton	**LShp**
Squire's Garden Centre, Twickenham	**LSqu**
Squire's Garden Centre, West Horsley	**LSqH**
Starborough Nursery	SSta
Stillingfleet Lodge Nurseries	NSti
Stone House Cottage Nurseries	WSHC
Stone Lane Gardens	CSto
Stonyford Cottage Nursery	MSCN
Stuckey's Alpines	CStu
Style Roses	ESty
Summerdale Garden Nursery	NSum
Sunnybank Vine Nursery (National Vine Collection)	WSuV
Sunnyside Plants	CSsd
Suttons Seeds	CSut
Swallows Nursery	MSwo
Sweet Knowle Aquatics	MSKA
Swines Meadow Garden Centre	ESwi
Table Bay View Nursery	XBlo
Tan-y-Llyn Nurseries	WTan
Taylors Clematis Nursery	NTay
Terrace Gardener	STrG
Test Valley Nursery	STes
Thompson & Morgan Young Plants Ltd	**ETMg**
Thorncroft Clematis Nursery	ETho
Thornhayes Nursery	CTho
Thuya Alpine Nursery	WThu
Tile Barn Nursery	STil
Timpany Nurseries & Gardens	ITim
Tinpenny Plants	WTin
Tissington Nursery	MTis
Todd's Botanics	ETod
Touchwood Plants	WTou
Tregothnan Nursery	CTrG
Tregrehan Garden	CTgr
Trehane Camellia Nursery	CTrh
Treseders	CTsd
Trevena Cross Nurseries	CTrC
Triscombe Nurseries	CTri
Usual & Unusual Plants	SUsu
Vic Johnstone and Claire Wilson	SJoh
Vicarage Garden, The	NVic
Victoria's Garden	**IVic**
Victoriana Nursery Gardens	SVic
Village Nurseries, The	SVil
Viv Marsh Postal Plants	WViv
W E Th. Ingwersen Ltd	SIng
W Robinson & Sons Ltd	NRob
Wallace Plants	SWal
Walled Garden, The	EWll
Walled Garden Nursery	CWGN
Walnut Tree Garden Nursery	EWTr
Wanborough Herb Nursery	CWan
Ward Fuchsias	MWar
Water Garden, The	CWat
Water Meadow Nursery	SWat
Waterperry Gardens Ltd	MWat
Wear's Nursery	MWea
Weasdale Nurseries Ltd.	NWea
Welsh Holly	WWHy
West Acre Gardens	EWes
West Harptree Nursery	CHar
West Somerset Garden Centre	CWSG
Westcountry Nurseries	CWCL
Westonbirt Plants	WWst
Westshores Nurseries	NWsh
White Cottage Alpines	NWCA
White House Plants	MWte

SPECIALIST NURSERIES

Nurseries have classified themselves under the following headings where they *exclusively* or *predominantly* supply this range of plants. Plant groups are set out in alphabetical order. Refer to **Nursery Details by Code** on page 820 for details of the nurseries whose codes are listed under the plant group which interests you. See page 817 for a fuller explanation.

ACID-LOVING PLANTS

CBcs, CMen, CPne, CTrh, CWCL, CWri, GAuc, GGar, GGGa, GLld, IBlr, IPen, ITim, LHyd, LMil, MBar, MCri, MGos, MLea, MSnd, MWBu, MYeo, NHim, NLar, NMun, SCam, SCog, SHea, SLdr, SReu, WAbe, WRic, WThu

ALPINE/ROCK PLANTS

CEls, CStu, CWat, CWil, CWon, EAlp, EBur, ECho, EDAr, EPot, GAgs, GEdr, GKev, IBal, IPen, ITim, MACG, MOne, NBro, NHoy, NLAp, NMen, NMin, NPol, NRya, NSla, NWCA, SCog, SIng, SPop, SRot, WAbe, WCom, WCre, WGor, WHoo, WThu, WWst

AQUATIC PLANTS

CBen, CRow, CWat, EBWF, EHon, EMFW, LLWG, LPBA, MSKA, NSco, SWat, WMAq, WPnP, WRic, XBlo

BAMBOOS

CAgr, CEnt, ENBC, EPla, ESwi, ETod, GBin, GLin, IMou, LEdu, LPal, MBrN, MMoz, MMuc, MWhi, MWht, NGdn, NPal, SArc, SBig, WDyG, WJun, WPGP

BRITISH WILD FLOWERS

COld, CRea, EBWF, GBar, GPoy, GPWP, MHer, NBir, NExo, NLan, NMir, NSco, SECG, SIde, SWat, WCHb, WLav, WSFF, WShi

BULBOUS PLANTS

CAvo, CBro, CFFs, CGrW, CQua, CRea, CStu, CWCL, ECho, ECrc, EMui, EPot, ERCP, ERos, EWal, IHer, LAma, MCri, MPoH, MSSP, MWBu, NHoy, NMin, SPhx, WPrP, WShi, WWst

CACTI & SUCCULENTS

CFwr, CPhi, CTrC, EAmu, EGln, EPln, EShb, LSou, MAga, NCro, NExo, SBst, SCac, SChr, WCor

CARNIVOROUS PLANTS

CHew, CSWC, EECP, EFEx, MYeo, NChu, SHmp, WSSs

CHALK-LOVING PLANTS

CBot, CCVN, CSev, CSpe, EGoo, LSRN, MWBu, SAll, SHar, SJoh, SMrs, SSss, SUsu

CLIMBERS

CLng, CRHN, CSPN, CTri, CWGN, ELan, ESCh, ETho, LOck, LSRN, MBlu, MGos, NBea, NExo, NSti, NTay, SDea, SLau, SMDP, WCru, WFib, WSHC

COASTAL PLANTS

CBod, CCCN, CHrt, CPne, CTrC, EBWF, GGar, IBal, ISsi, SChr, SDea, WCor, WPnn

CONIFERS

CKen, CLnd, CMen, CTho, ECho, EOrn, MACG, MBar, MBlu, MPkF, NLar, SLim, WEve, WGor, WMou, WThu

CONSERVATORY PLANTS

CBcs, CBrP, CCCN, CEls, CFwr, CPne, CRHN, CSpe, EABi, EBak, EBls, EGln, EOHP, ERea, EShb, ESul, LBur, LHyd, MBPg, MNew, NFir, SHaC, SMDP, WSFF, XBlo

DROUGHT TOLERANT

CBot, CKno, EAlp, ECha, EGln, EGoo, EHoe, ETod, LLWP, LOck, LPal, MBPg, MHrb, NFir, NHoy, SAll, SDow, SIde, SIoW, SJoh, SPhx, SUsu, WHil, WJek, WPnn

FERNS

CBty, CLAP, CRWN, EFer, EFtx, GBin, GLin, IBal, IMou, LLWG, LPBA, MMoz, NMyG, SApp, SHmp, WAbe, WFib, WMoo, WPnP, WRic, WSpi

FRUIT

CAgr, CBar, CCAT, CTho, CTri, EBtc, ECrN, EMui, ERea, GBut, GPri, GTwe, IFFs, LBuc, LEdu, MCoo, SBmr, SCko, SCmr, SCrf, SDea, SFam, SKee, SLay, SVic, WDol, WHar, WJas, XBlo

GRASSES

CBod, CKno, CWCL, EAlp, EHoe, ELan, EPla, EPPr, EPyc, GBin, GCal, GFor, IFoB, IMou, LEdu, LLWP, LSRN, MBel, MBrN, MMoz, MNrw, MWhi, NBro, NGdn, NOak, NSti, NWsh, SApp, SHDw, SPhx, SSss, SUsu, SWal, WGrn, WHal, WMoo, WPGP, WPrP

Hedging

CBar, CCVT, CLnd, CTrC, CTrG, CTri, EBtc, ECrN, EMac, ERom, ISsi, LBuc, MBar, MCoo, MHrb, NSco, NWyk, SDow, SECG, SHHo, SLan, SRiv, SVic, WBuc, WEve, WHar, WLav, WMou, WSpi, WWHy

Herbs

CArn, CBod, CHby, COld, CSev, CWan, ELau, EOHP, GBar, GPoy, GPWP, ILis, LFol, LLWP, LMor, MHer, MHrb, NBir, NGHP, NLan, NLLv, SDow, SECG, SHDw, SHlg, SIde, SWat, WCHb, WJek, WLav

Marginal/Bog Plants

CBen, CCVN, CLAP, CMHG, COld, CRow, CWat, EHoe, EHon, EMFW, GKev, IPen, LLWG, LPBA, MMuc, MSKA, MYeo, NBir, NCot, NHim, SHaC, WHal, WMoo, WPnP, WShi

Orchids

CBur, CLAP, EFEx, LYaf, MNew, NEqu, NLAp, WFut, WWst, XFro

Organic

CAbx, CBgR, CHby, COld, CPne, CTrG, CTuc, GAuc, GBar, GBut, GPoy, GPri, GPWP, ILis, LEdu, LLWP, MBel, MLod, MYeo, NHoy, NOak, NPol, SECG, SHlg, SJoh, SPol, WCHb, WGwG, WJek, WPnP, WShi

Ornamental Trees

CBcs, CBot, CBty, CCVT, CDul, CEnd, CLnd, CMCN, CMen, CPMA, CSto, CTho, CTri, CWon, EBtc, ECrN, EGFP, ELan, EMac, EMui, ERom, GAuc, IMGH, LBuc, LMaj, MBlu, MGos, MMuc, MPkF, NBea, NLar, NPal, NWyk, SBig, SBir, SBmr, SCrf, SLan, SLau, SLay, SLim, SMHT, WBuc, WCru, WEve, WHar, WJas, WMou, WPGP, WWHy

Palms

CPHo, EAmu, ESwi, ETod, LPal, LPJP, MREP, NPal, SArc, SBig, SBst, SChr

Peat free

CAbx, CBgR, CBot, CBre, CCVN, CElw, CHby, CLAP, CMdw, CMea, CPHo, CPom, CRHN, CRWN, CSam, CSev, CSNP, CSsd, CTho, CTsd, EAro, EBla, EBtc, EBWF, ECrN, EGoo, ELau, EMal, EPts, ERea, GBut, GPoy, IBlr, ILis, LEdu, LLWP, MBel, MBNS, MCri, MLHP, MLod, MMoz, MPhe, MWhi, NLan, NMir, NPol, NSco, NWCA, SAll, SBch, SECG, SMDP, SMrs, STes, WCHb, WCor, WDyG, WGwG, WHoo, WJek, WPnP, WPrP, WShi, WSpi

Period Plants

CArn, CKel, CSev, EBls, EKMF, EMal, ESgI, GBut, IHer, ILis, SAll, WFuv

Propagate to Order

CAbx, CArn, CCAT, CCCN, CEls, CElw, CFir, CKel, CLAP, CMdw, CMen, CPne, CSev, CTsd, CWon, CWVF, EAlp, EBla, EBls, EBtc, EBWF, ECho, ECrN, EECP, EGFP, EOHP, EPyc, ERea, ERhR, EShb, ESul, GBuc, GBut, GFor, GKev, IFro, IGor, ILis, IMou, IPPN, LEdu, LIMB, LLWP, LMil, LOck, MLHP, MLod, MMoz, MSpe, MYeo, NChi, NCli, NCot, NHoy, NLan, NLLv, NPol, NRya, NSco, NShi, NWCA, SAga, SBch, SCam, SChr, SDea, SECG, SHDw, SHlg, SHyH, SJoh, SLau, SLdr, SMDP, SPin, SPol, SPop, STes, SUsu, SWat, WCHb, WCom, WCru, WDol, WDyG, WHil, WJek, WLav, WPat, WPBF, WPnP, WPrP, WSpi, WSSs, WTin, WWHy, XBlo

Roses

CBar, CPou, EBls, ECnt, ESty, GCoc, IDic, LFol, LGod, LShp, LStr, MGan, MHav, SFam, SLay, SRGP, SSea, SWCr, WAct

Seed

CCVN, CDob, CHby, CKno, CRea, CSpe, CSut, CTuc, ETMg, GAuc, GPoy, LSee, MFie, MPet, MPoH, NChl, NGHP, NLan, NPol, SCko, SSss, WCHb, WJek, WSFF, WTou, XBTW

Specimen Sized Plants

CArn, CBar, CBdn, CBen, CBty, CCCN, CCVT, CKel, CPHo, CPHT, CPMA, CPne, CTho, CTrG, CWon, CWVF, EAmu, EBla, EBtc, EBWF, ECrN, EECP, EFer, EGol, EHrv, EKMF, EQua, ERea, EShb, ESwi, ETod, GAuc, GLld, IMGH, IMou, LBuc, LEdu, LHyd, LLWG, LMaj, LMil, LOck, LSRN, MBrN, MGos, MLea, MLod, MNew, MPhe, MREP, MSnd, MWht, MYeo, NCro, NHim, NHoy, NPal, NPol, SArc, SCam, SFam, SGol, SHDw, SHHo, SHmp, SHyH, SLan, SLdr, SRiv, SWat, WCru, WEve, WJek, WPat, WRic, WSpi

Topiary

CPHT, ERom, MREP, NWyk, SHHo, SLan, SRiv, WSpi

Tropical Plants

CCCN, EAmu, EShb, ESwi, ISsi, LBur, MNew, MREP, SArc, SBst, SHaC, WCru, WFut, WRic

INDEX MAP

The maps on the following pages show the approximate location of the nurseries whose details are listed in this directory.

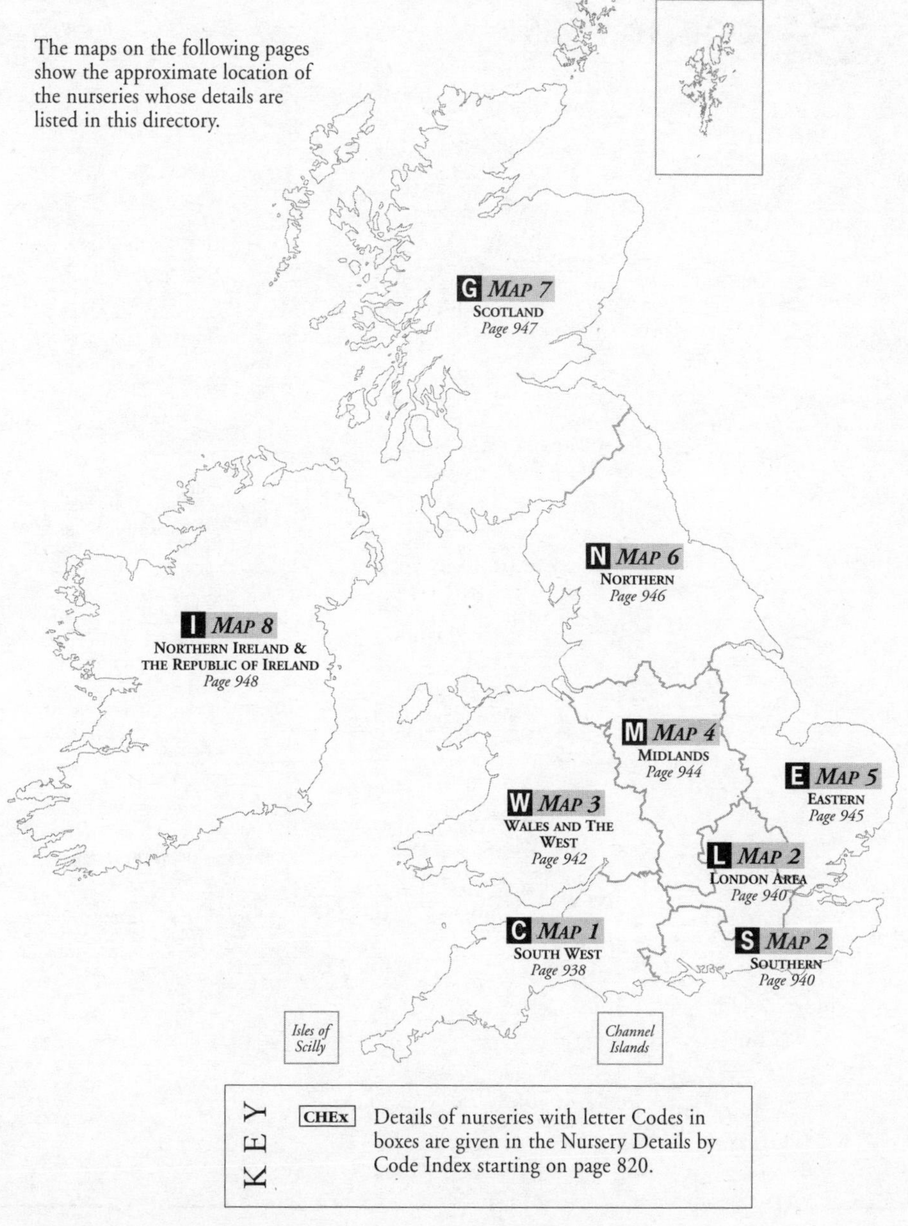

KEY

CHEx Details of nurseries with letter Codes in boxes are given in the Nursery Details by Code Index starting on page 820.

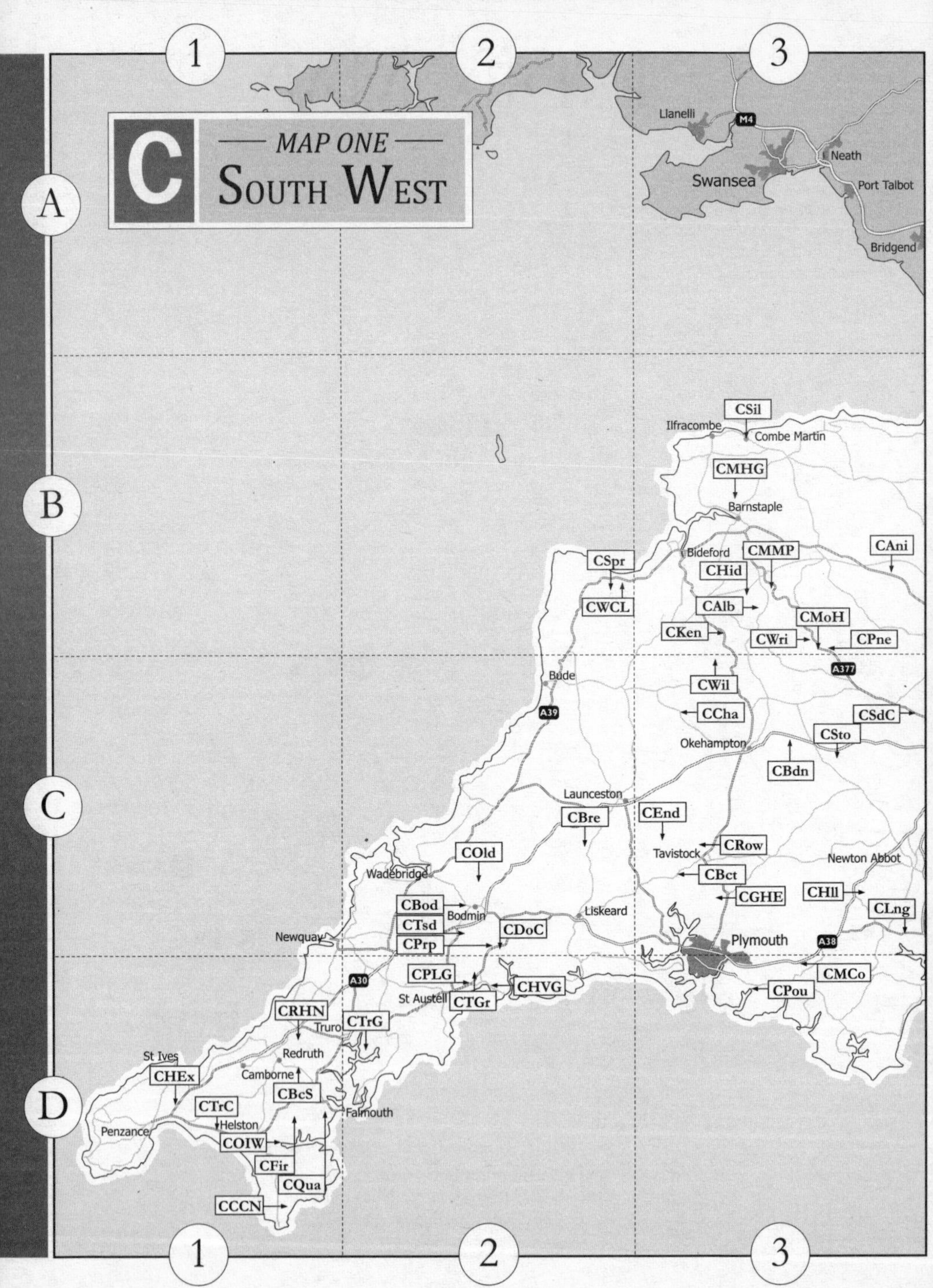
1
2
3
A
B
C
D
C
MAP ONE
South West
Llanelli
M4
Neath
Swansea
Port Talbot
Bridgend
CSil
Ilfracombe
Combe Martin
CMHG
Barnstaple
Bideford
CMMP
CAni
CSpr
CHid
CWCL
CAlb
CMoH
CKen
CWri
CPne
A377
Bude
CWil
A39
CCha
CSdC
CSto
Okehampton
CBdn
Launceston
CEnd
CBre
CRow
Tavistock
Newton Abbot
COld
Wadebridge
CBct
CBod
CGHE
CHll
CTsd
Bodmin
Liskeard
CLng
CDoC
Newquay
CPrp
Plymouth
A38
A30
CPLG
CMCo
CHVG
CPou
St Austell
CTGr
CRHN
Truro
CTrG
St Ives
Redruth
CHEx
Camborne
CBcS
CTrC
Falmouth
Helston
Penzance
COIW
CFir
CQua
CCCN
1
2
3

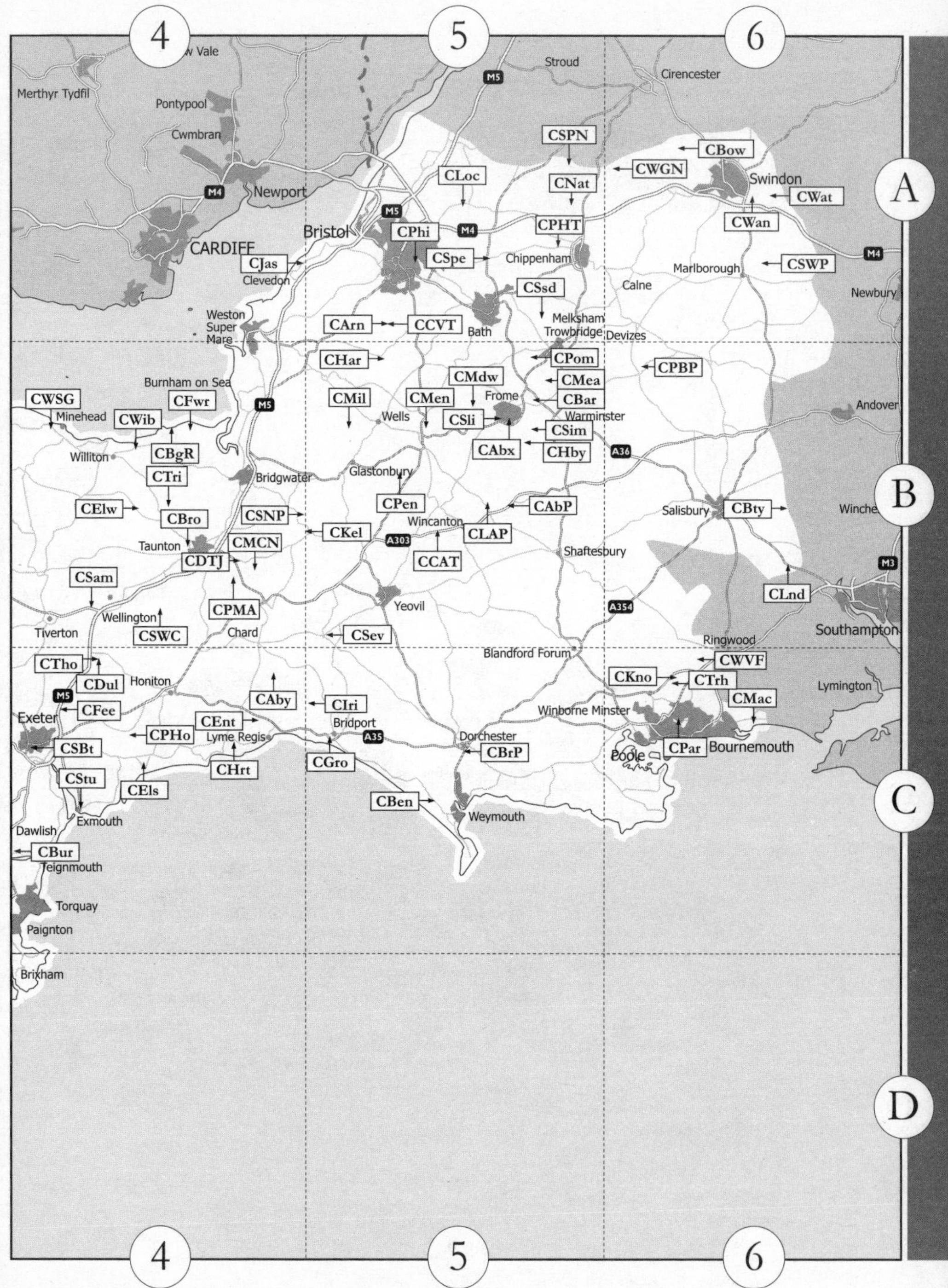
4
5
6
A
B
C
D
Merthyr Tydfil
Pontypool
Cwmbran
Newport
M4
CARDIFF
Bristol
M5
Stroud
Cirencester
Swindon
CSPN
CBow
CWGN
CLoc
CNat
CWat
CPHT
CWan
CPhi
M4
CJas
CSpe
Chippenham
Clevedon
Marlborough
CSWP
Calne
CSsd
Newbury
Weston
Super
Mare
CArn
CCVT
Bath
Melksham
Trowbridge
Devizes
CPom
CHar
CPBP
CMdw
CMea
Burnham on Sea
CWSG
CFwr
CMil
CMen
Frome
CBar
Minehead
CWib
Wells
CSli
Warminster
Andover
CSim
CBgR
CAbx
CHby
A36
Williton
CTri
Bridgwater
Glastonbury
CElw
CPen
CAbP
CSNP
Salisbury
CBty
CBro
CKel
Wincanton
CLAP
Taunton
CMCN
A303
CDTJ
CCAT
Shaftesbury
M3
CSam
CLnd
CPMA
Yeovil
A354
Wellington
Tiverton
CSWC
Chard
CSev
Southampton
Ringwood
Blandford Forum
CWVF
CTho
CKno
CTrh
CDul
Honiton
Lymington
CMac
M5
CAby
CIri
Exeter
CFee
CEnt
Bridport
Winborne Minster
CPHo
Lyme Regis
A35
Dorchester
CSBt
CBrP
Poole
CPar
Bournemouth
CHrt
CGro
CStu
CEls
CBen
Exmouth
Weymouth
Dawlish
CBur
Teignmouth
Torquay
Paignton
Brixham

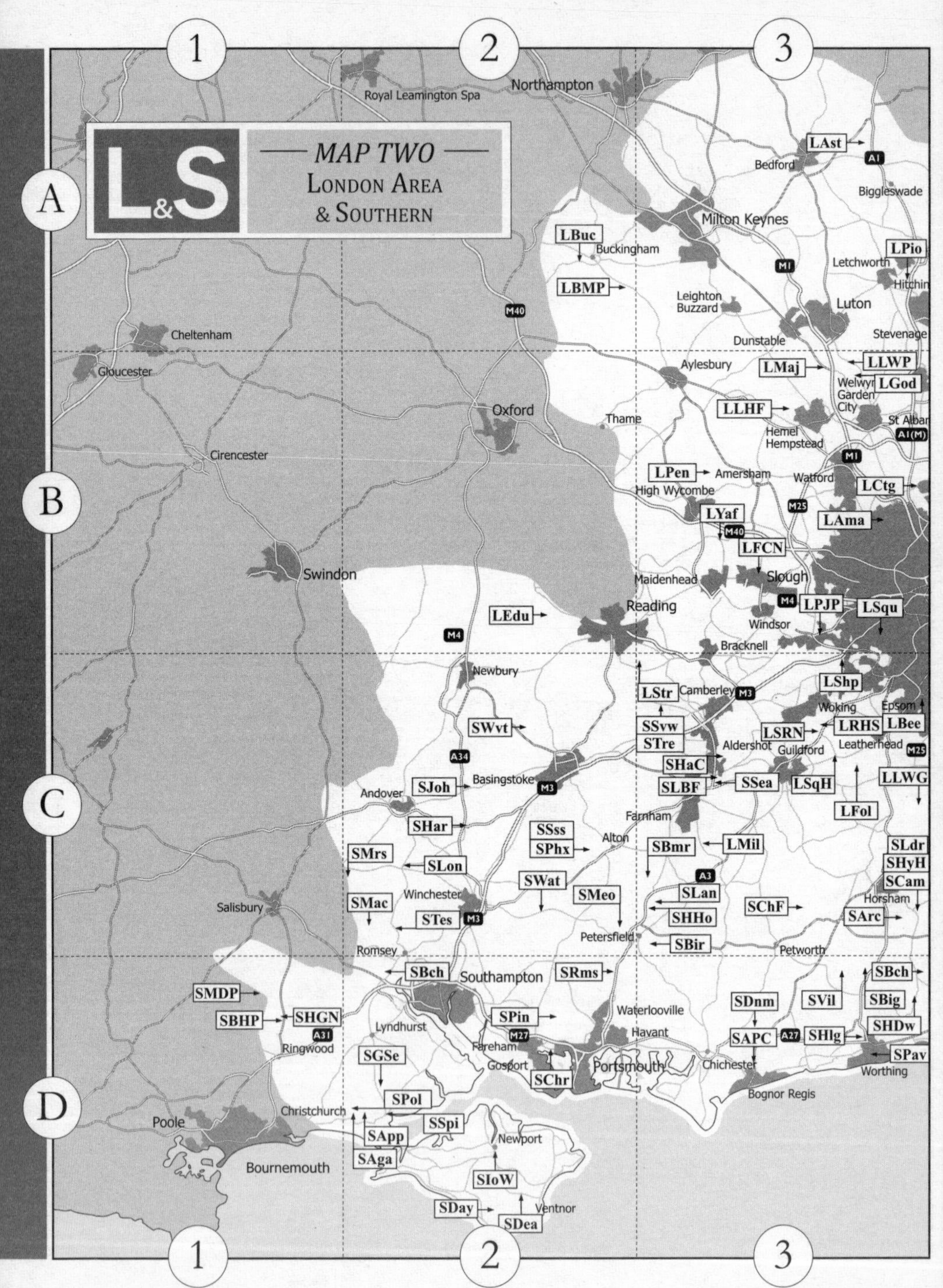
L&S
MAP TWO
LONDON AREA
& SOUTHERN
1
2
3
A
B
C
D
Northampton
Royal Leamington Spa
LAst
Bedford
Biggleswade
Milton Keynes
LBuc
Buckingham
LPio
Letchworth
Hitchin
LBMP
Leighton Buzzard
Luton
Stevenage
Cheltenham
Gloucester
Dunstable
Aylesbury
LLWP
LMaj
Welwyn Garden City
LGod
Oxford
Thame
LLHF
Hemel Hempstead
St Albans
Cirencester
LPen
Amersham
High Wycombe
Watford
LCtg
LYaf
LAma
LFCN
Swindon
Maidenhead
Slough
Reading
LPJP
LSqu
LEdu
Windsor
Bracknell
Newbury
LStr
Camberley
LShp
Woking
Epsom
SWvt
SSvw
STre
LSRN
LRHS
LBee
Aldershot
Guildford
Leatherhead
SHaC
SJoh
Basingstoke
Andover
SLBF
SSea
LSqH
LLWG
LFol
SHar
Farnham
SSss
SPhx
Alton
SBmr
LMil
SMrs
SLon
SLdr
SHyH
SCam
SWat
Winchester
SMac
SMeo
SLan
Horsham
SChF
SArc
Salisbury
STes
SHHo
Petersfield
SBir
Romsey
Petworth
SBch
Southampton
SRms
SBch
SMDP
SDnm
SVil
SBig
SPin
Waterlooville
SBHP
SHGN
Lyndhurst
Havant
SAPC
SHlg
SHDw
Ringwood
Fareham
SGSe
Gosport
Portsmouth
Chichester
SPav
Worthing
SChr
Bognor Regis
SPol
Christchurch
SSpi
Poole
SApp
Newport
Bournemouth
SAga
SIoW
SDay
Ventnor
SDea
M1
M40
M4
M25
M3
A34
A3
A31
M27
A27
A1
A1(M)

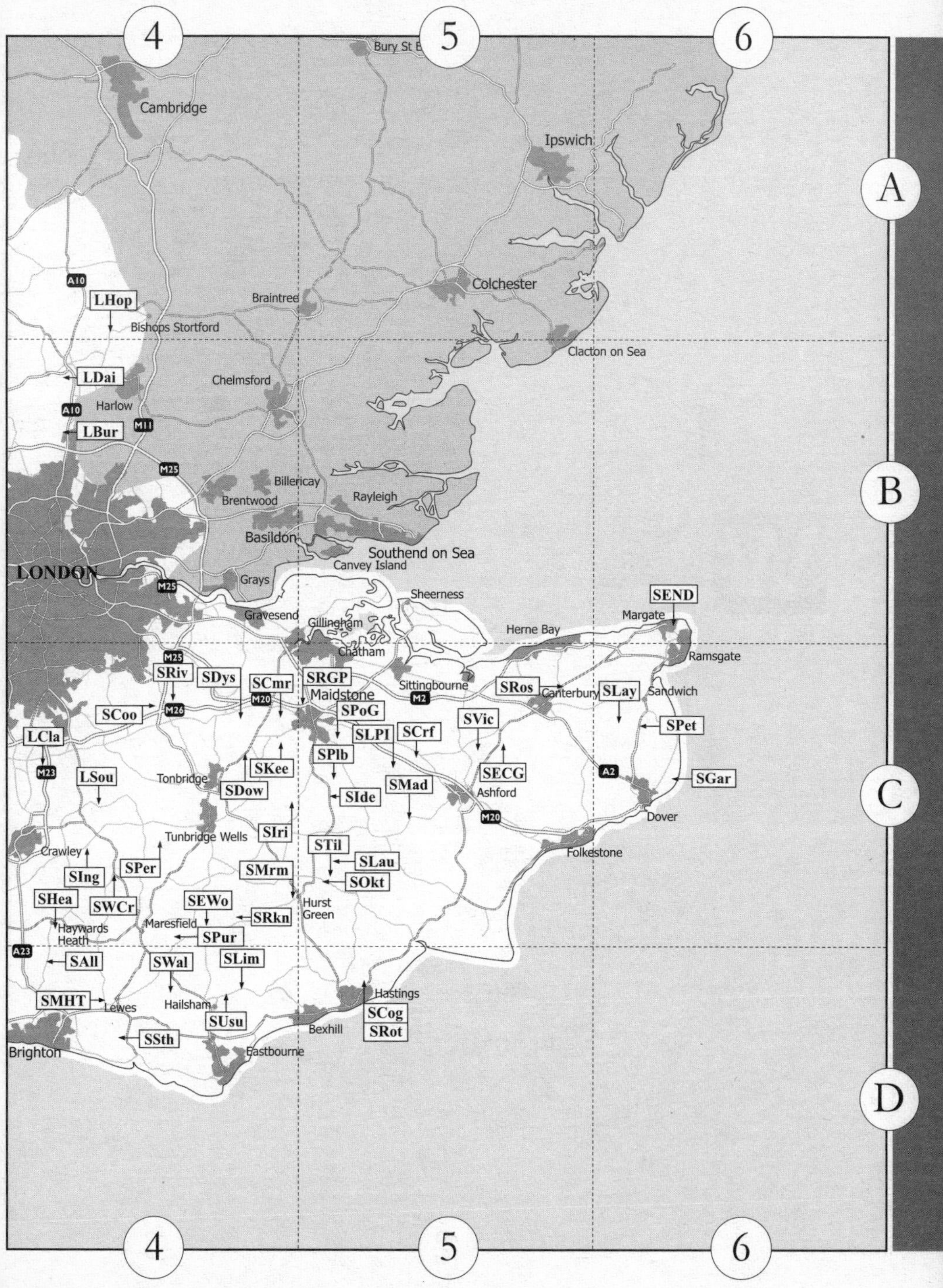
4
5
6
A
B
C
D
Bury St E
Cambridge
Ipswich
Colchester
Braintree
LHop
Bishops Stortford
Clacton on Sea
LDai
Chelmsford
Harlow
LBur
Billericay
Brentwood
Rayleigh
Basildon
Southend on Sea
Canvey Island
LONDON
Grays
Sheerness
SEND
Margate
Gravesend
Gillingham
Herne Bay
Chatham
Ramsgate
SRiv
SDys
SCmr
SRGP
Maidstone
Sittingbourne
SRos
Canterbury
SLay
Sandwich
SCoo
SPoG
SVic
SPet
LCla
SLPI
SCrf
SPlb
LSou
Tonbridge
SKee
SECG
SGar
SDow
SMad
SIde
Ashford
Dover
SIri
Tunbridge Wells
STil
Folkestone
Crawley
SLau
SPer
SMrm
SIng
SOkt
SHea
SWCr
SEWo
Hurst Green
SRkn
Haywards Heath
Maresfield
SPur
SAll
SWal
SLim
SMHT
Lewes
Hailsham
Hastings
SUsu
SCog
Bexhill
SRot
SSth
Brighton
Eastbourne
A10
M11
M25
M26
M20
M2
M23
A23
A2

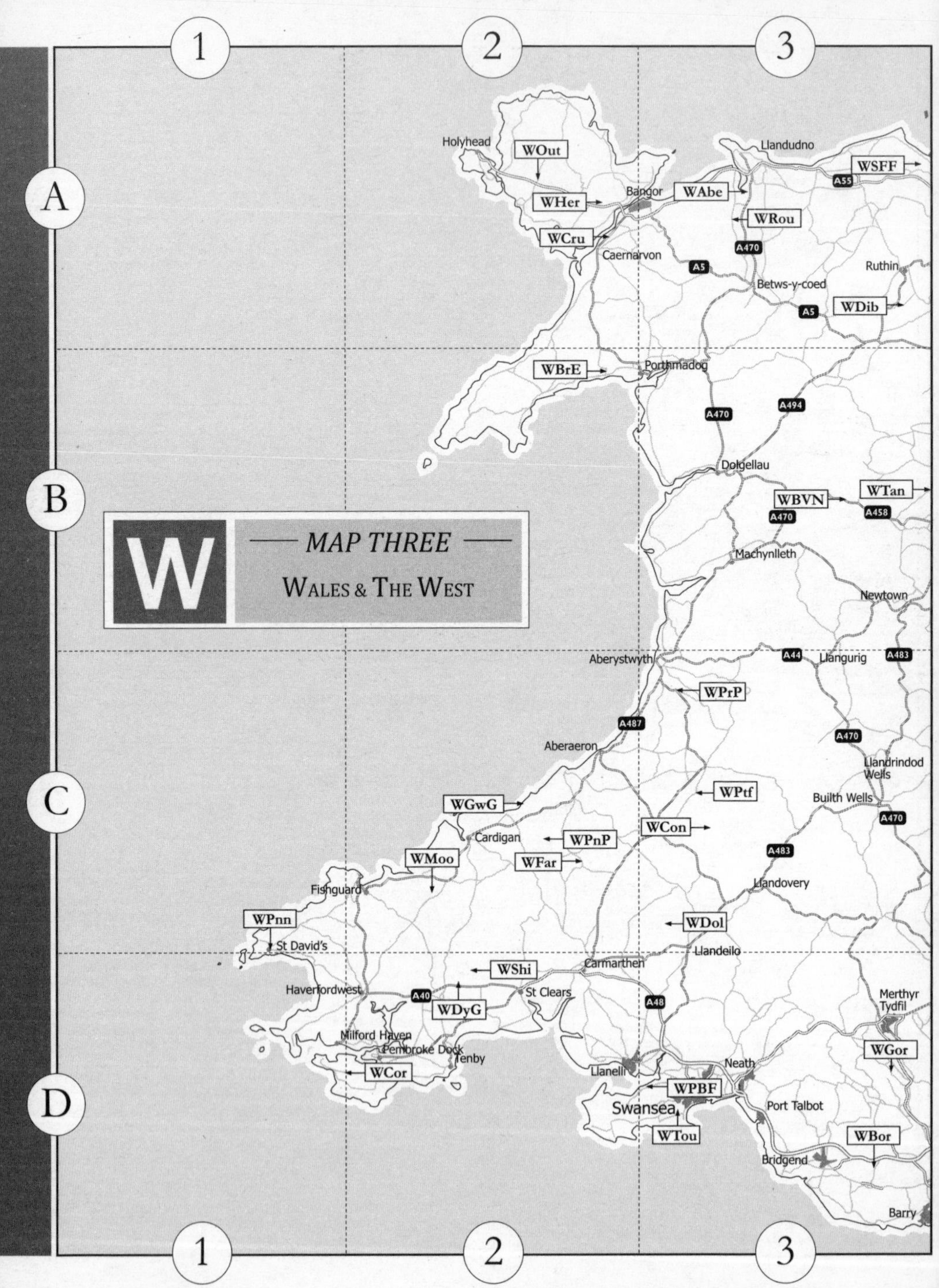
MAP THREE
Wales & The West
W
1
2
3
A
B
C
D
Holyhead
WOut
Llandudno
WSFF
A55
Bangor
WAbe
WHer
WRou
WCru
A470
Caernarvon
A5
Ruthin
Betws-y-coed
WDib
WBrE
Porthmadog
A470
A494
Dolgellau
WBVN
WTan
A470
A458
Machynlleth
Newtown
Aberystwyth
A44
Llangurig
A483
WPrP
A487
A470
Aberaeron
Llandrindod Wells
WPtf
WGwG
Builth Wells
WCon
A470
Cardigan
WPnP
A483
WMoo
WFar
Fishguard
Llandovery
WPnn
WDol
St David's
Llandeilo
WShi
Carmarthen
Haverfordwest
St Clears
A40
WDyG
A48
Merthyr Tydfil
Milford Haven
Pembroke Dock
Tenby
WGor
Llanelli
Neath
WCor
WPBF
Swansea
Port Talbot
WTou
WBor
Bridgend
Barry

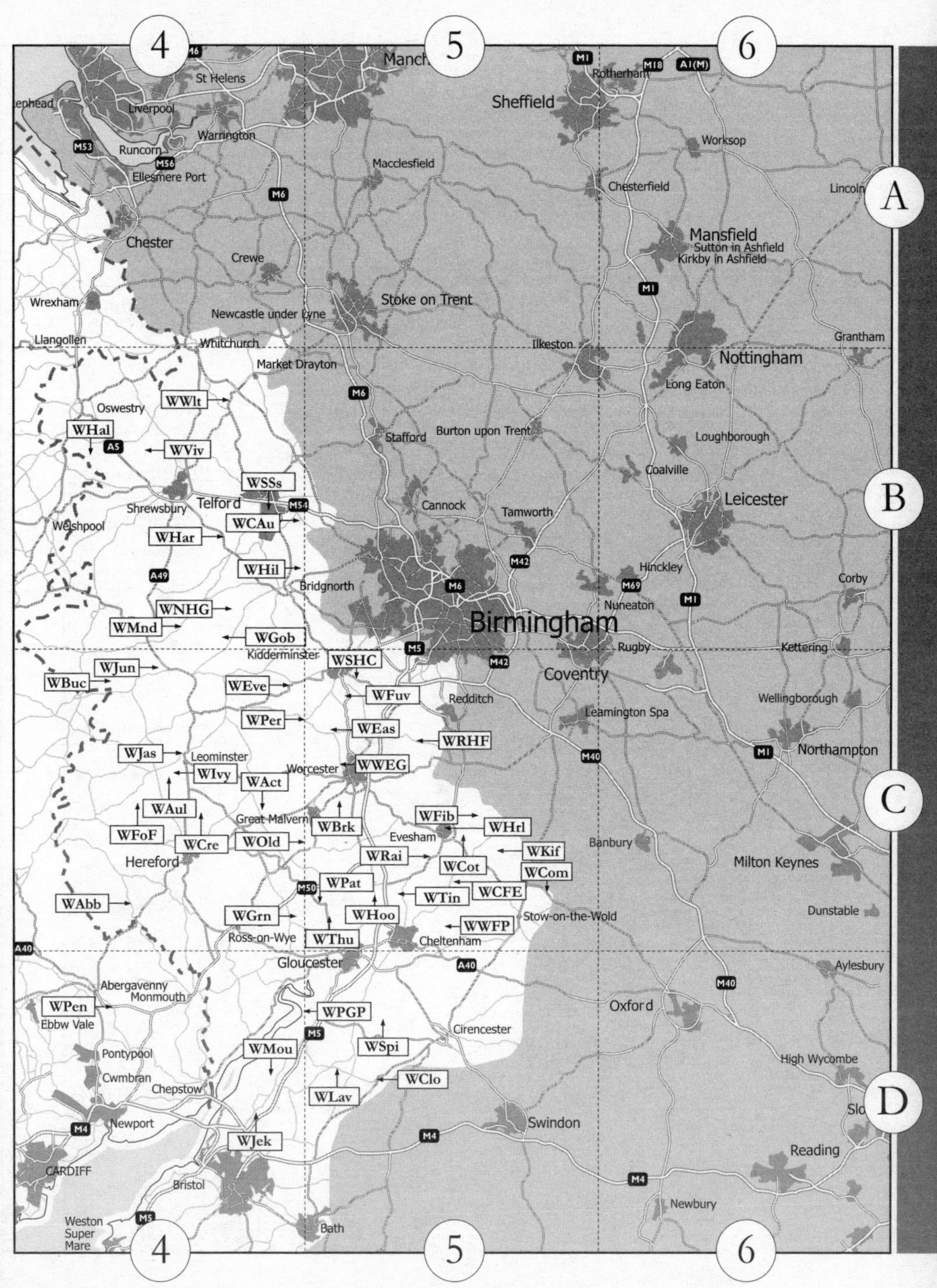
4
5
6
A
B
C
D
WWlt
WHal
WViv
WSSs
WCAu
WHar
WHil
WNHG
WMnd
WGob
WSHC
WJun
WBuc
WEve
WFuv
WPer
WEas
WRHF
WJas
WWEG
WIvy
WAct
WAul
WFib
WHrl
WFoF
WBrk
WCre
WOld
WKif
WRai
WCot
WCom
WPat
WCFE
WTin
WAbb
WHoo
WGrn
WWFP
WThu
WPen
WPGP
WMou
WSpi
WClo
WLav
WJek
Manchester
St Helens
Liverpool
Warrington
Runcorn
Ellesmere Port
Chester
Crewe
Wrexham
Newcastle under Lyne
Stoke on Trent
Llangollen
Whitchurch
Market Drayton
Oswestry
Shrewsbury
Telford
Welshpool
Bridgnorth
Kidderminster
Leominster
Worcester
Great Malvern
Hereford
Ross-on-Wye
Gloucester
Abergavenny
Monmouth
Ebbw Vale
Pontypool
Cwmbran
Chepstow
Newport
CARDIFF
Bristol
Weston Super Mare
Bath
Macclesfield
Stafford
Cannock
Burton upon Trent
Tamworth
Birmingham
Redditch
Evesham
Cheltenham
Stow-on-the-Wold
Cirencester
Swindon
Sheffield
Rotherham
Worksop
Chesterfield
Mansfield
Sutton in Ashfield
Kirkby in Ashfield
Ilkeston
Nottingham
Long Eaton
Loughborough
Coalville
Leicester
Hinckley
Nuneaton
Rugby
Coventry
Leamington Spa
Banbury
Oxford
Newbury
Reading
Lincoln
Grantham
Corby
Kettering
Wellingborough
Northampton
Milton Keynes
Dunstable
Aylesbury
High Wycombe
M6
M1
M18
A1(M)
M53
M56
A5
M54
A49
M42
M69
M5
M50
A40
M40
M4

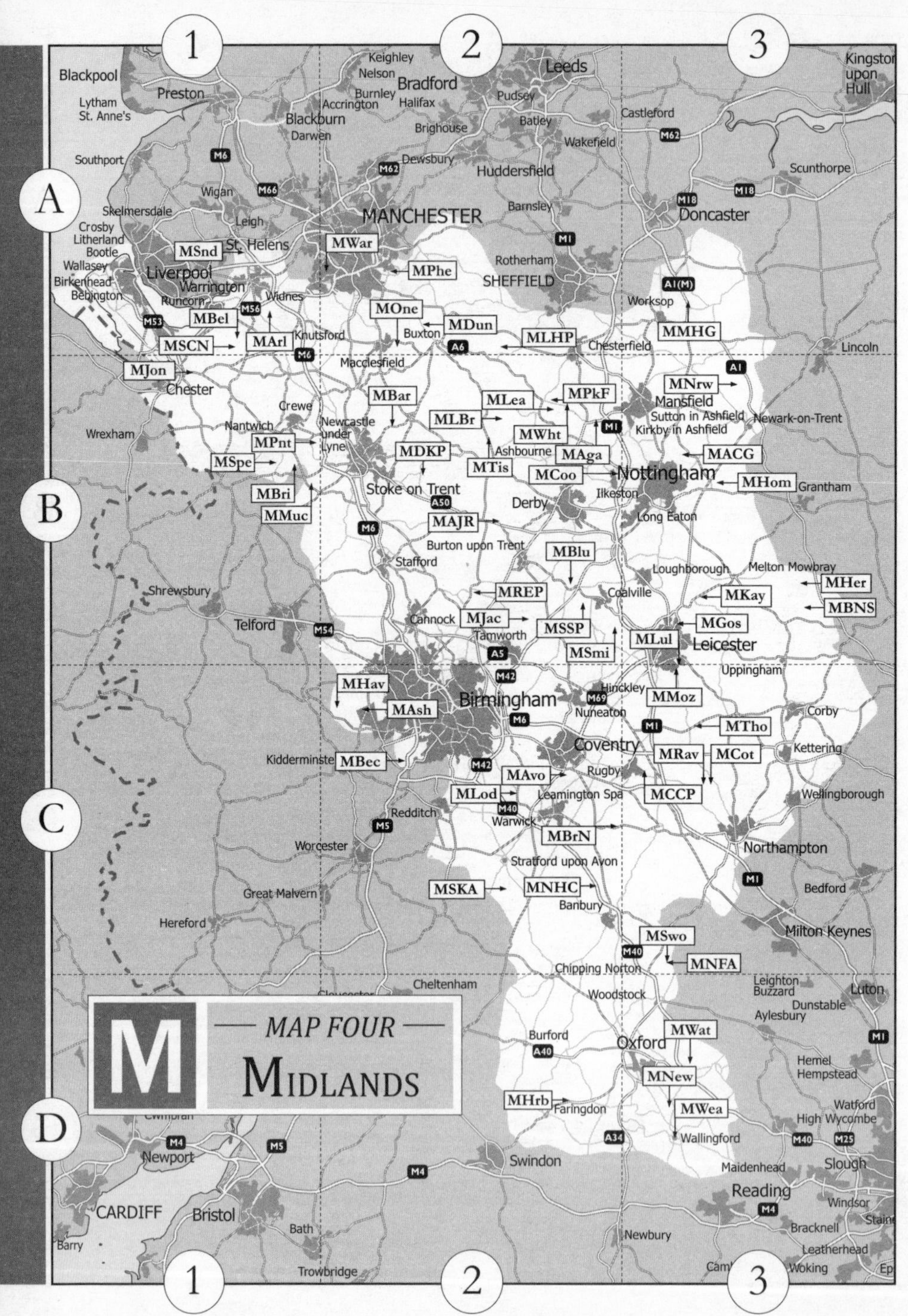
1
2
3
A
B
C
D
Blackpool
Preston
Lytham St. Anne's
Keighley
Nelson
Burnley
Bradford
Leeds
Kingston upon Hull
Accrington
Halifax
Pudsey
Blackburn
Darwen
Brighouse
Batley
Castleford
M62
Wakefield
M6
Southport
Dewsbury
M62
Huddersfield
Scunthorpe
Wigan
M66
M18
M18
Barnsley
Doncaster
Skelmersdale
MANCHESTER
Crosby
Leigh
Litherland
Bootle
MSnd
St. Helens
MWar
M1
Wallasey
Liverpool
MPhe
Rotherham
Birkenhead
Warrington
SHEFFIELD
A1(M)
Bebington
Runcorn
Widnes
Worksop
MOne
M53
M56
MBel
MDun
MMHG
Buxton
MArl
Knutsford
MLHP
MSCN
A6
Chesterfield
Lincoln
M6
Macclesfield
A1
MJon
Chester
MNrw
MBar
MPkF
MLea
Mansfield
Crewe
Sutton in Ashfield
Newark-on-Trent
MLBr
M1
Wrexham
Nantwich
Newcastle under Lyne
Kirkby in Ashfield
MWht
MPnt
MDKP
MAga
MACG
Ashbourne
MSpe
MTis
MCoo
Nottingham
MHom
Grantham
Stoke on Trent
MBri
Derby
Ilkeston
A50
MMuc
MAJR
Long Eaton
M6
Burton upon Trent
MBlu
Stafford
Loughborough
Melton Mowbray
MHer
Shrewsbury
MREP
Coalville
MKay
MBNS
Telford
Cannock
MJac
MGos
M54
MSSP
Tamworth
MLul
Leicester
MSmi
A5
Uppingham
M42
MHav
Hinckley
MMoz
Birmingham
M69
MAsh
Nuneaton
Corby
M6
M1
MTho
Coventry
Kettering
Kidderminster
MBec
MRav
MCot
M42
MAvo
Rugby
MLod
Leamington Spa
MCCP
Wellingborough
M40
Redditch
Warwick
M5
MBrN
Worcester
Northampton
Stratford upon Avon
MSKA
MNHC
Great Malvern
M1
Bedford
Banbury
Hereford
Milton Keynes
MSwo
M40
MNFA
Chipping Norton
Cheltenham
Leighton Buzzard
Woodstock
Luton
Dunstable
Aylesbury
M
MAP FOUR
MIDLANDS
MWat
Burford
Oxford
M1
A40
Hemel Hempstead
MNew
MHrb
Faringdon
Watford
MWea
High Wycombe
A34
Wallingford
M40
M25
M4
M5
Newport
Swindon
M4
Maidenhead
Slough
Reading
CARDIFF
Bristol
Windsor
M4
Bracknell
Bath
Newbury
Barry
Leatherhead
Trowbridge
Woking

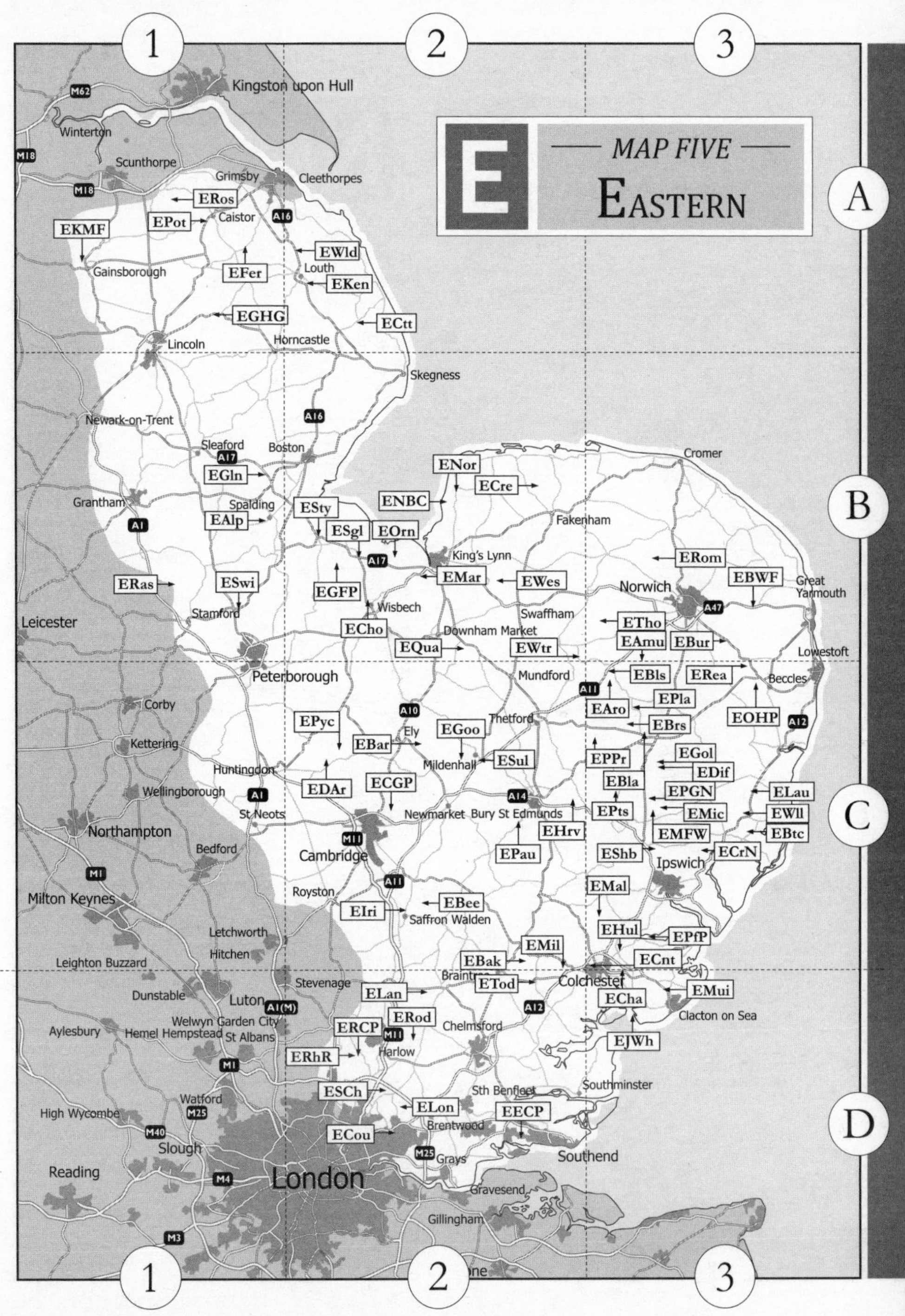
MAP FIVE
Eastern
E
A
B
C
D
1
2
3
Kingston upon Hull
Winterton
Scunthorpe
Grimsby
Cleethorpes
ERos
EPot
Caistor
EKMF
EWld
Louth
Gainsborough
EFer
EKen
EGHG
ECtt
Lincoln
Horncastle
Skegness
Newark-on-Trent
Sleaford
Boston
EGln
Grantham
Spalding
EAlp
ESty
ESgl
EOrn
ENor
ECre
ENBC
Cromer
Fakenham
King's Lynn
EMar
EWes
ERom
EBWF
Norwich
Great Yarmouth
ERas
ESwi
EGFP
Wisbech
Stamford
Swaffham
ETho
Leicester
ECho
Downham Market
EQua
EWtr
EAmu
EBur
Lowestoft
Peterborough
Mundford
EBls
ERea
Beccles
Corby
EPyc
Thetford
EAro
EPla
EOHP
Kettering
EBar
Ely
EGoo
EBrs
Mildenhall
ESul
EPPr
EGol
EDif
Huntingdon
EDAr
ECGP
EBla
EPGN
ELau
Wellingborough
St Neots
Newmarket
Bury St Edmunds
EPts
EMic
EWll
Northampton
EHrv
EMFW
EBtc
Bedford
Cambridge
EPau
EShb
Ipswich
ECrN
Milton Keynes
Royston
EMal
EIri
EBee
Saffron Walden
Letchworth
EHul
EPfP
Hitchen
EMil
Leighton Buzzard
EBak
ECnt
Braintree
ETod
Colchester
Stevenage
Dunstable
ELan
ECha
EMui
Luton
Welwyn Garden City
ERod
Clacton on Sea
Aylesbury
Hemel Hempstead
St Albans
ERCP
Chelmsford
EJWh
Harlow
ERhR
ESCh
Sth Benfleet
Southminster
Watford
ELon
High Wycombe
EECP
Brentwood
ECou
Slough
Grays
Southend
Reading
London
Gravesend
Gillingham
M62
M18
A16
A17
A1
A47
A10
A12
A11
A14
M11
M1
A1(M)
M25
M40
M4
M3

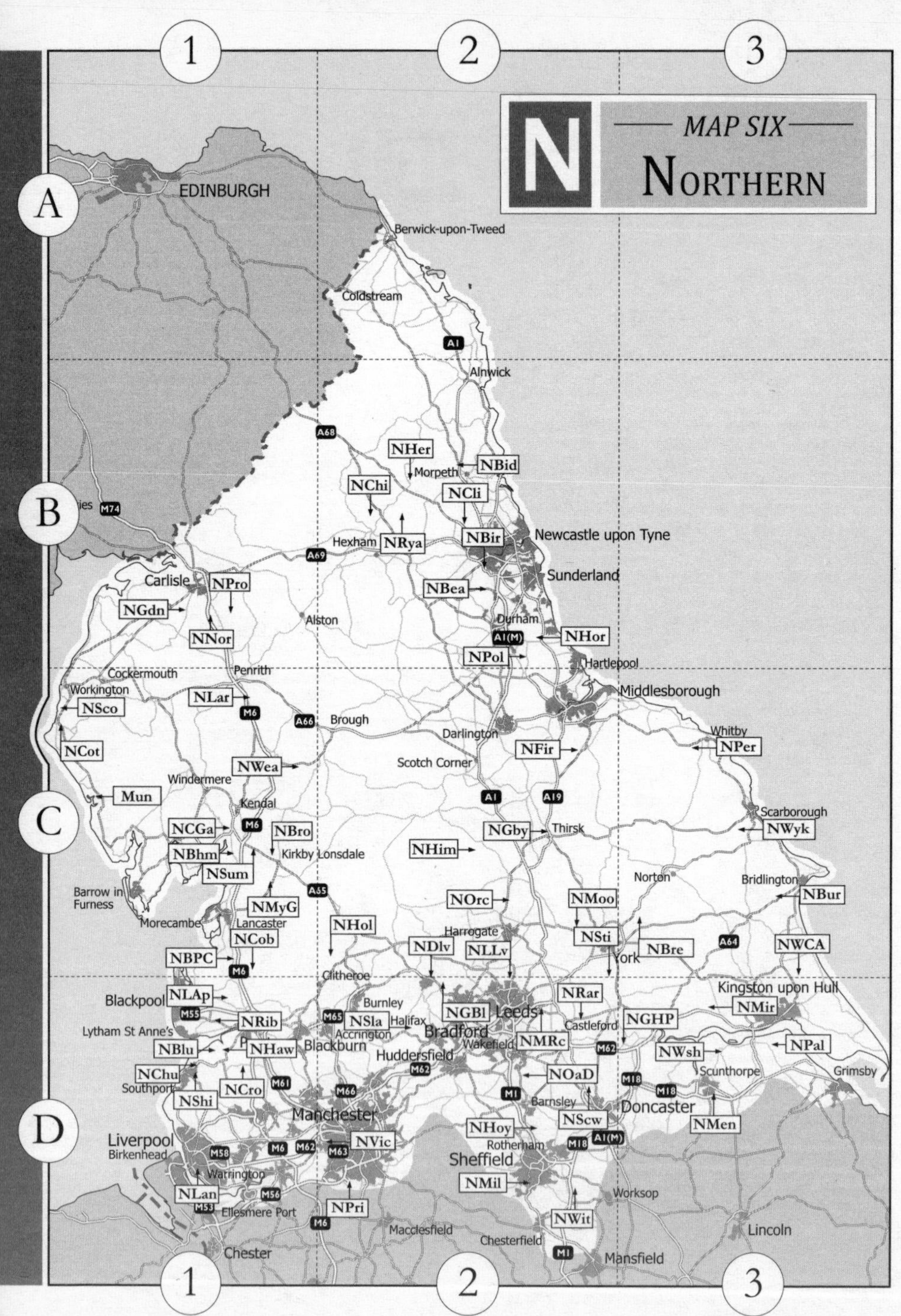
N
MAP SIX
NORTHERN
1
2
3
A
B
C
D
EDINBURGH
Berwick-upon-Tweed
Coldstream
A1
Alnwick
A68
NHer
Morpeth
NBid
NChi
NCli
M74
Newcastle upon Tyne
Hexham
NRya
NBir
A69
Sunderland
Carlisle
NPro
NBea
NGdn
Alston
Durham
NNor
A1(M)
NHor
NPol
Hartlepool
Cockermouth
Penrith
Middlesborough
Workington
NLar
NSco
M6
A66
Brough
Whitby
Darlington
NFir
NPer
NCot
NWea
Scotch Corner
Windermere
Mun
A1
A19
Scarborough
Kendal
NCGa
M6
NBro
NGby
Thirsk
NWyk
NBhm
Kirkby Lonsdale
NHim
NSum
Norton
Bridlington
Barrow in Furness
A65
NOrc
NMoo
NBur
NMyG
Morecambe
Lancaster
NHol
Harrogate
NCob
NSti
A64
NWCA
NBPC
NDlv
NLLv
York
NBre
M6
Clitheroe
Kingston upon Hull
NRar
Blackpool
NLAp
M55
Burnley
NGBl
Leeds
NMir
M65
NSla
Halifax
Castleford
NGHP
NRib
Lytham St Anne's
Accrington
Bradford
NBlu
NHaw
Blackburn
Wakefield
NMRc
M62
NWsh
NPal
Huddersfield
M62
NOaD
Scunthorpe
Grimsby
NChu
M61
M18
Southport
NCro
M66
M1
M18
NShi
Barnsley
Doncaster
Manchester
NScw
NMen
NHoy
Liverpool
Birkenhead
M58
M6
M62
NVic
Rotherham
M18
A1(M)
M63
Sheffield
Warrington
NMil
Worksop
NLan
M56
M53
Ellesmere Port
NPri
NWit
M6
Macclesfield
Lincoln
Chesterfield
Chester
M1
Mansfield

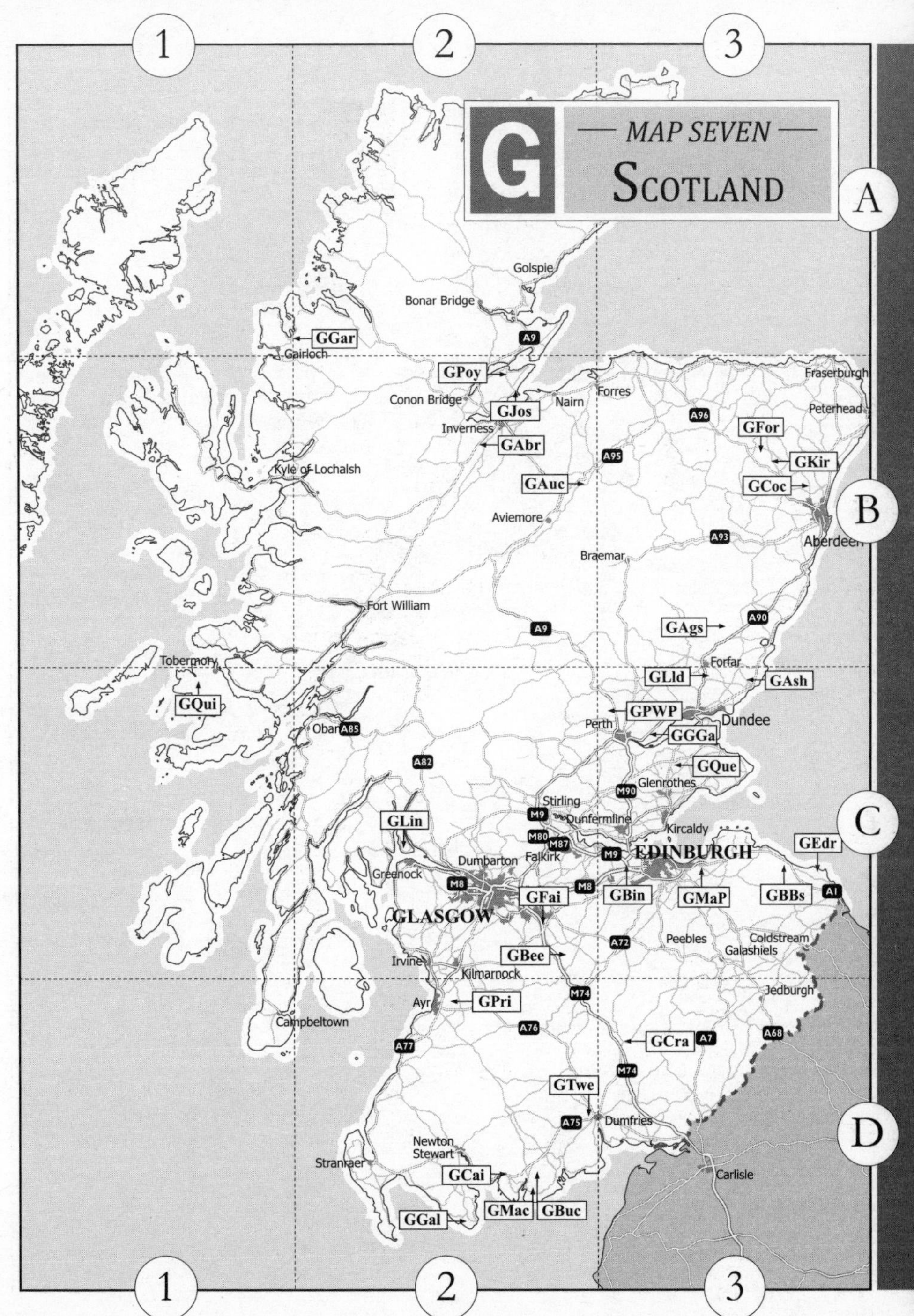
G
— MAP SEVEN —
Scotland
1
2
3
A
B
C
D
Golspie
Bonar Bridge
A9
GGar
Gairloch
GPoy
Conon Bridge
GJos
Nairn
Forres
Inverness
GAbr
Fraserburgh
Peterhead
A96
GFor
GKir
A95
GAuc
GCoc
Kyle of Lochalsh
Aviemore
A93
Aberdeen
Braemar
Fort William
A9
GAgs
A90
Tobermory
Forfar
GLld
GAsh
GQui
GPWP
Dundee
Perth
GGGa
Oban
A85
A82
GQue
Glenrothes
M90
Stirling
M9
Dunfermline
GLin
Kircaldy
M80
M87
GEdr
Dumbarton
Falkirk
M9
EDINBURGH
Greenock
M8
M8
GFai
GBin
GMaP
GBBs
A1
GLASGOW
A72
Peebles
Coldstream
Galashiels
GBee
Irvine
Kilmarnock
Jedburgh
M74
Ayr
GPri
Campbeltown
A76
GCra
A7
A68
A77
M74
GTwe
A75
Dumfries
Newton Stewart
Stranraer
GCai
Carlisle
GMac
GBuc
GGal

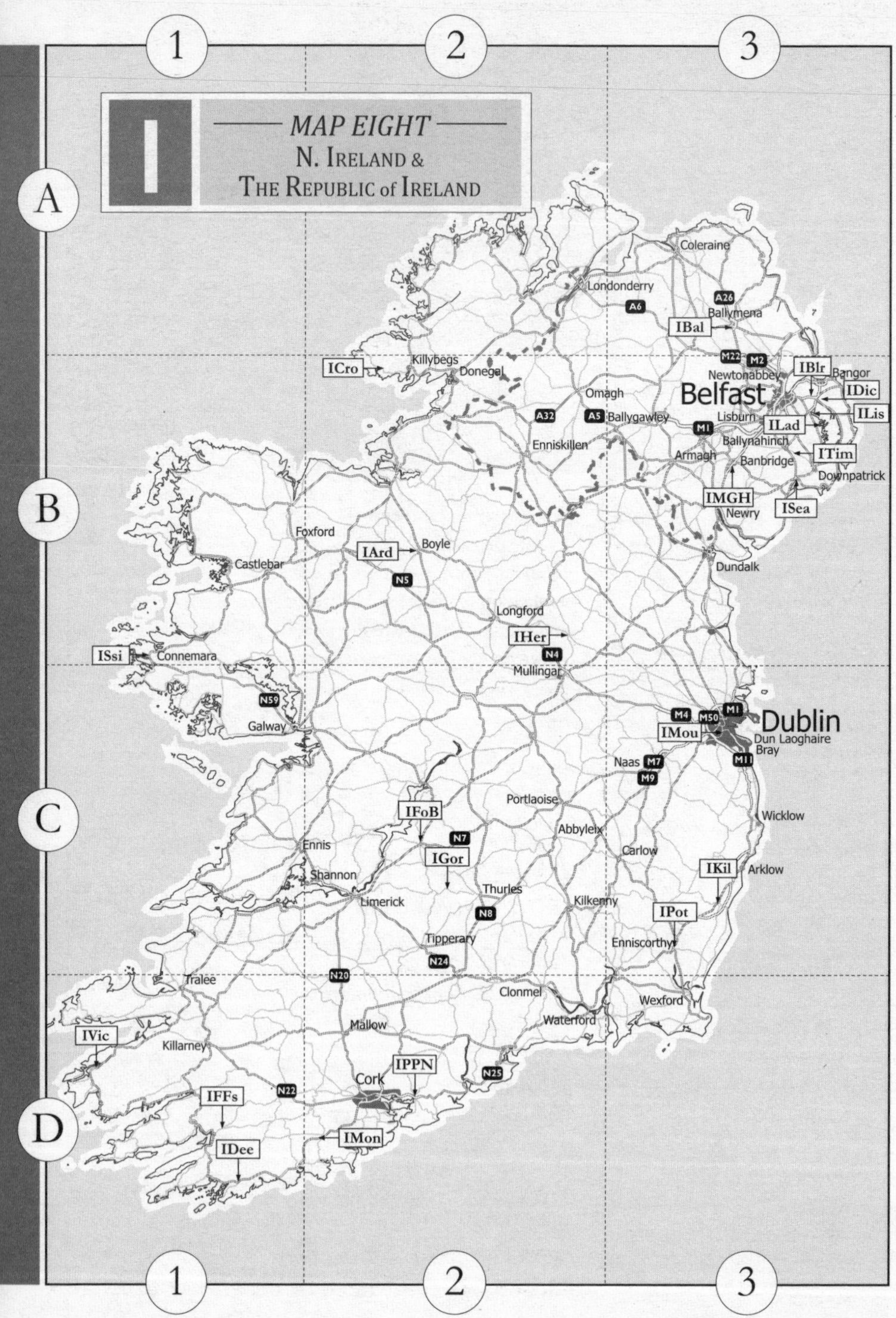
1
2
3
A
B
C
D
I
MAP EIGHT
N. IRELAND &
THE REPUBLIC of IRELAND
Coleraine
Londonderry
A26
A6
Ballymena
IBal
M22
M2
ICro
Killybegs
Donegal
Newtonabbey
IBlr
Bangor
IDic
Belfast
Omagh
ILis
A32
A5
Ballygawley
M1
Lisburn
ILad
Enniskillen
Ballynahinch
Armagh
ITim
Banbridge
Downpatrick
IMGH
Newry
ISea
Foxford
IArd
Boyle
Castlebar
N5
Dundalk
Longford
IHer
N4
ISsi
Connemara
Mullingar
N59
M4
M50
M1
Dublin
Galway
IMou
Dun Laoghaire
Bray
Naas
M7
M11
M9
Portlaoise
IFoB
Wicklow
N7
Abbyleix
Ennis
IGor
Carlow
IKil
Arklow
Shannon
Thurles
Limerick
Kilkenny
N8
IPot
Tipperary
Enniscorthy
N24
Tralee
N20
Clonmel
Wexford
Waterford
Mallow
IVic
Killarney
IPPN
N25
Cork
N22
IFFs
IMon
IDee

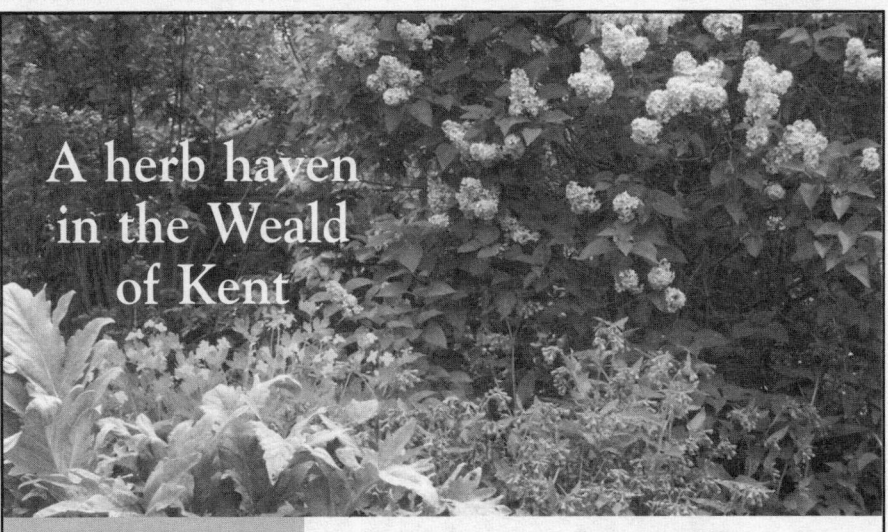

Wide range of Crocosmia, Auricula.
Canna, South African and other
unusual or hard-to-find plants.
Holders of the National
Collection of Acanthus
Hillview Hardy
Plants
For a copy of our full catalogue,
please send 5 x 2nd class stamps
to:
Hillview Hardy Plants (WHil)
Worfield, Nr Bridgnorth,
Shropshire WV15 5NT
Phone/Fax 01746 716454
Email: hillview@themutual.net
www.hillviewhardyplants.com

Triscombe Nurseries
Offer old fashioned quality
value and service
Wide range of plants
our speciality
TREES * SHRUBS * CONIFERS
ROSES * FRUIT * CLEMATIS
HERBACEOUS & ROCK PLANTS
Open 7 days a week, Mon-Sat 9-1, 2-5.30;
Sundays and Bank Holidays 2-5.30
Tel (01984) 618267
www.triscombenurseries.co.uk
Email: triscombe.nurseries2000@virgin.net
West Bagborough
Taunton, Somerset
TA4 3HG
Turning off A358
at Triscombe
between
West Bagborough
and
Crowcombe

The Dingle
Nurseries
& Garden
We have one of the largest ranges of trees and shrubs in the country, including native trees, hedging, conifers, roses, perennials and fruit. Semi mature and standard trees are also available, as well as specimen shrubs and many rarities all at competitive prices.
Open 7 days a week 9am to 5pm.
DINGLE NURSERIES & GARDEN
Welshpool, Powys, Wales SY21 9JD
T: 01938 555145
E: info@dinglenurseryandgarden.co.uk

LONGFRAMLINGTON GARDENS

- ~ 12 ACRE GARDENS & ARBORETUM
- ~ NURSERY & PLANT CENTRE
- ~ GARDEN DESIGN & LANDSCAPE
- ~ ENROUTE COFFEE STOP

OPEN: 8.30 – 5.00 every day all year (PLUS EVENINGS & GROUPS BY APPOINTMENT)

PLEASE CONTACT US FOR FURTHER INFORMATION AT:

Longframlington, Morpeth, Northumberland NE65 8BE
TEL/FAX: 01665 570382
www.longframlingtongardens.co.uk
EMAIL: info@longframlingtongardens.co.uk

30 MILES NORTH OF NEWCASTLE-UPON-TYNE, FOLLOW THE SIGNS OFF THE A697 AT LONGFRAMLINGTON VILLAGE

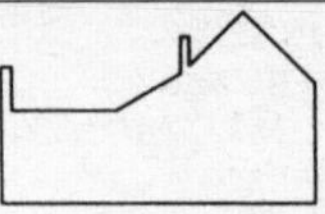

White Cottage Alpines

East Yorkshire's own specialist growers of alpines, rockery plants and low growing perennials.
Excellent mail order service, debit/credit cards welcome.
See nursery details at **NWCA** for opening times.
Find us on the B1244 Beverley-Hornsea Rd. at Sunnyside Nurseries, Sigglesthorne, HU11 5QL
www.whitecottagealpines.co.uk

Perennial specialist.
Good range of interesting shrubs, climbers and seasonal plants.
Garden open - free entry

The Walled Garden

Park Road, Benhall, Saxmundham, Suffolk, IP17 1JB 01728 602510
Signed off the A12 nr. A1094 Aldeburgh turn.
Open Tues - Sun and Bank Holidays
9.30 - 5.00pm. Ring for winter hours

Kenwick Farmhouse Nursery

Set in picturesque site on the edge of the Lincolnshire Wolds
Wide choice of unusual perennials, vegetable, bedding/basket plants
Open Tues-Sun & Bank Holiday Mondays
Light refreshments served in our Tea Room
Tel/Fax: 01507 606469
Mobile: 07930 217369
www.kenwicknursery.co.uk
email: info@kenwicknursery.co.uk

WORLDS END GARDEN NURSERY

(Kristina and Robin Pearce)
Growing a very wide range of Herbaceous Perennials, Ornamental Grasses and Hardy Ferns, including many unusual plants.
Open 10.30am to 5.00pm Tuesday to Saturday March/October. Other times by appointment.
Moseley Road, Hallow, Worcester WR2 6NJ
Tel: 01905 640977
Email: garden@robinpearce.co.uk
Web: www.worldsendgarden.co.uk
National Garden Gift Vouchers Sold & Exchanged

Welcome to the

World of Ferns

Europe's leading supplier of ferns.
Wonderful variety of indoor, conservatory, garden & tree-ferns from around the world - many exclusive to us
RHS medal winners.
Delivery throughout the UK and Europe
Ferneries created, conservatory planting, Wardian cases.
Call 01248 600385 for a brochure
www.world-of-ferns.co.uk
Email: info@world-of-ferns.co.uk
World of Ferns is a trading name of Rickards Ferns Ltd

TAYLORS CLEMATIS

Sutton, Askern, Doncaster, South Yorkshire DN6 9JZ
Over 350 varieties for sale all year round.

- All our plants are mature 2 year old specimens grown in 2 litre pots on 3ft canes
- Next day delivery anywhere in the UK any time of year
- EU deliveries (26 countries covered) 2-4 day service. Please ring for pricing or check website.

Open by Appointment Only
Send 4 x 1st class stamps for colour catalogue
Email: info@taylorsclematis.co.uk
Web: www.taylorsclematis.co.uk
For enquiries and to order plants.
Tel: (01302) 700716

RHS Medallists for Roses

Seale Nurseries celebrating 60 years - 1948-2008

Seale Lane, Seale, Farnham, Surrey GU10 1LD
Open 10.00-4.00 Tues-Sat
We are 20 mins from RHS Wisley off the A31

Seale Super Roses

Beautiful scented varieties for arches, walls, obelisks, borders and pots.
Grown by our innovative container growing method so **plant anytime and get rapid results!**
Also an exceptional collection of pelargoniums
01252 782410

Langley Boxwood Nursery Ltd

- Topiary in all shapes and sizes, in Box, Yew and other evergreen species.
- Box, Yew and other hedging.
- Topiary Courses.

Tel: 01730 894467 Fax: 01730 894703
E-mail: Sales@boxwood.co.uk
www.boxwood.co.uk

Chiltern Seeds

The World's Best Seed Catalogue?

Send for our world famous catalogue

"Grow Something New from Seed"

(50p in stamps appreciated) and enjoy a cheerful read! (We send it to over 100 countries in the world - we must be getting something right!) Select from more than 4,500 items (of which 97% always in stock), all described in interesting detail. Thousands of popular and unusual seeds, including vegetables and herbs - taste something new from seed this year.

Tel: 01229 581137 (24 hours) Fax: 01229 584549
email: PF@chilternseeds.co.uk • www.chilternseeds.co.uk
CHILTERN SEEDS, Dept. PF, Bortree Stile, Ulverston, Cumbria, LA12 7PB

NEW, UNUSUAL and VARIEGATED PLANTS by MAIL ORDER

www.bowleyplants.co.uk

Nursery code - C.Bow

Tel: 07855 524929

ENDSLEIGH GARDEN NURSERY

A Pretty Country Nursery growing a wide range of stock.
Our specialities are new and unusual grafted plants including Maples, Cornus, Old Apples and Cherries.

* YOUR OLD FAVOURITES GRAFTED TO ORDER *

Mail order, 2 x 1st class stamps for list
Open: 8-5 Mon-Sat, 10-5 Sun

TEL: 01822 870235 FAX: 01822 870513
Email: info@endsleigh-gardens.com
www.endsleigh-gardens.com
MILTON ABBOT, TAVISTOCK, DEVON PL19 0PG

A miscellany of plants - reflective of our interests and of plants that will grow (even thrive) in wet clay; our ¾ acre garden is open to visitors.

FEEBERS HARDY PLANTS

(PROP: MRS E. SQUIRES)

1 FEEBERS COTTAGE, WESTWOOD BROADCLYST, DEVON EX5 3DQ
Telephone: 01404 822118

Anytime by prior appointment.
Limited mail order.

From B3181 Dog Village, Broadclyst, take Whimple Road for 1.25m; take left turn (signed Westwood) continue further 1.25m; Nursery on right entering Westwood.

C.S. LOCKYER

(Fuchsias)

Established over 50 years - 45 years Chelsea Exhibitor
Colour mail order catalogue 4 x 1st class stamps
All Fuchsia lovers welcome inc. Clubs & Parties
Please ring to avoid disappointment
Many Talks and Demonstrations,
Video or DVD £14.99 p&p £1.50
Fuchsias The Easy Way
Fuchsias Advanced Techniques
See Cloc Nursery code

C.S. Lockyer (Fuchsias) "Lansbury"
70 Henfield Road, Coalpit Heath,
Bristol BS36 2UZ - Tel/Fax: 01454 772219
Web Site: www.lockyerfuchsias.co.uk
Email: sales@lockyerfuchsias.co.uk

EVERGREEN CONIFER CENTRE

Extensive collection of miniature, dwarf, slow growing and unusual conifers. Mature conifers and hedging conifers.

CLOSED ON SUNDAY & MONDAY

For further details including mail order

Tel: 01299 266581

Email: brian@evergreen-conifers.co.uk
Web Site: evergreen-conifers.co.uk
Tenbury Road, Rock, Kidderminster, Worcs DY14 9RB

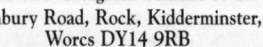

INDEX OF ADVERTISERS

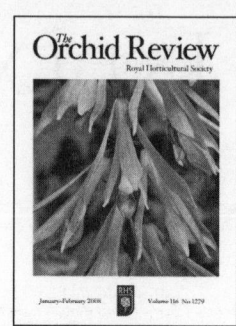

RHS Show Awards 2007

RHS Plant Finder nurseries that were awarded RHS medals at the three major RHS Shows in 2007

Chelsea Gold

Avon Bulbs
Bowden Hostas
Brian & Pearl Sulman
Burncoose Nurseries
Burnham Nurseries
Dibley's Nurseries
Farmyard Nurseries
Fernatix
Hampshire Carnivorous Plants
Hardy's Cottage Garden Plants
Harveys Garden Plants
J Walkers Bulbs
Jacques Amand International
Jekka's Herb Farm
Ken Muir Ltd
Knoll Gardens
Mendip Bonsai Studio
Peter Beales Roses
Romantic Garden, The
Roualeyn Nurseries
South West Carnivorous Plants
Thorncroft Clematis Nursery

Chelsea Silver-Gilt

Broadleigh Gardens
Claire Austin Hardy Plants
Culm View Nursery
D'Arcy & Everest
Downderry Nursery
Hewitt-Cooper Carnivorous Plants
Kelways Ltd
Potash Nursery
Rhodes & Rockliffe
Squire's Garden Centre
Wilford Bulb Co. Ltd

Chelsea Silver-Gilt Knightian

W Robinson & Sons Ltd

Chelsea Silver-Gilt Lindley

Thompson & Morgan Young Plants Ltd

Chelsea Silver

Barnsdale Gardens
C S Lockyer (Fuchsias)
Green Garden Herbs
Isle of Wight Lavender
Oak Tree Nursery
Rotherview Nursery
Sheila Chapman Clematis
Westcountry Nurseries

Chelsea Bronze

Botanic Nursery, The

Hampton Court Gold

Avon Bulbs
Brian & Pearl Sulman
C S Lockyer (Fuchsias)
Dibley's Nurseries
Downderry Nursery
Farmyard Nurseries
Fernatix
Fernwood Nursery
Fir Trees Pelargonium Nursery
Goldbrook Plants
Hampshire Carnivorous Plants
Hardy's Cottage Garden Plants
Hoyland Plant Centre
Jekka's Herb Farm (& **Tudor Rose Award**)
Long Acre Plants
Mendip Bonsai Studio
P W Plants
Park Green Nurseries
Roualeyn Nurseries

Hampton Court Silver Gilt

Botanic Nursery, The
Burncoose Nurseries
Burnham Nurseries

Culm View Nursery
D'Arcy & Everest
Derek Lloyd Dean
Desert to Jungle
Dibley's Nurseries
Fibrex Nurseries Ltd
Harveys Garden Plants
Hewitt-Cooper Carnivorous Plants
Hopleys Plants Ltd
Jacques Amand International
Kelways Ltd
Oak Tree Nursery
Pine Cottage Plants
Plant Lovers, The
Potash Nursery
Sheila Chapman Clematis
South West Carnivorous Plants (& **Most Creative Floral Marquee Exhibit**)

Hampton Court Silver

Big Plant Nursery
Blacksmiths Cottage Nursery
Isle of Wight Lavender
Mallet Court Nursery
Palm Centre, The
Rotherview Nursery
Squire's Garden Centre
Wilford Bulb Co. Ltd

Hampton Court Silver Hogg

Ken Muir Ltd

Hampton Court Silver Knightian

Cookoo Box Nursery
Highdown Nursery

Hampton Court Bronze

W E Th. Ingwersen Ltd

Hampton Court Festival of Roses Silver-Gilt

Peter Beales Roses

Hampton Court Festival of Roses Silver

Seale Nurseries
Style Roses

Tatton Gold

Cath's Garden Plants
Dibley's Nurseries
Edrom Nurseries
Elizabeth MacGregor
Fernatix
Fernwood Nursery
Fir Trees Pelargonium Nursery
Hall Farm Nursery
Hampshire Carnivorous Plants
Mary Green
Mendip Bonsai Studio
Packhorse Farm Nursery
Potash Nursery
Roualeyn Nurseries
South West Carnivorous Plants

Tatton Silver-Gilt

Blacksmiths Cottage Nursery
Brian & Pearl Sulman
Broadleigh Gardens
Cairnsmore Nursery
Croston Cactus
D'Arcy & Everest
Fibrex Nurseries Ltd
Green Garden Herbs
Hardy's Cottage Garden Plants
Holden Clough Nursery
Hoyland Plant Centre
Isle of Wight Lavender
Oak Tree Nursery
Poppy Heads Ltd
Shirley Tasker

Tatton Silver-Gilt Knightian

Cookoo Box Nursery
W Robinson & Sons Ltd

Tatton Silver

Big Plant Nursery
Bluebell Arboretum & Nursery
Border Belles
Botanic Nursery, The
Brownthwaite Hardy Plants
Culm View Nursery
Mickfield Hostas
Pennard Plants
Taylors Clematis Nursery
Wilford Bulb Co. Ltd

Tatton Bronze

Sheila Chapman Clematis
White Cottage Alpines

The Hardy Plant Society

Explores, encourages and conserves all that is best in gardens

The Hardy Plant Society encourages interest in growing hardy perennial plants and provides members with information about familiar and less well known perennial plants that flourish in our gardens, how to grow them and where they may obtained. This friendly society offers a range of activities locally and nationally, giving members plenty of opportunity to meet other keen gardeners to share ideas and information in a convivial atmosphere. The activities and work of the Society inform and encourage the novice gardener, stimulate and enlighten the more knowledgeable, and entertain and enthuse all gardeners bonded by a love for, and an interest in, hardy perennial plants.

Local Groups

There are over 40 local groups across the UK and national members are invited to join the group nearest to them. Each group offers a wide range of gardening activities including informative lectures, garden visits and plant plus educational and social events throughout the year. Most groups produce their own newsletters. Full details of how to join a local group are sent out to new members.

Specialist Groups and Gardening by Post

Specialist Groups produce their own newsletters and organise meetings and events for fellow enthusiasts. The Correspondents Group ensures that members who are unable to attend meetings can exchange gardening ideas and information.

Seed Distribution

Every member can join in the annual Seed Distribution Scheme by obtaining or donating hardy perennial seed. The Seed List offers over 2,500 tempting varieties of rare, unusual and familiar seeds and is sent to every member in December.

Please see overleaf for an application form

Shows and Events

Exhibits at major shows throughout the country let visitors see hardy plants in bloom and leaf in their natural season and more information about the work of the Society is available. Events hosted by local group members are also organised, from plant study days to residential weekends to garden visits. The Society also organises overseas garden tours.

Conservation

The Hardy Plant Society is concerned about the conservation of garden plants and is working towards ensuring that older, rarer and lesser-known perennial plants are conserved and made available to gardeners generally.

Publications and the Slide Library

The Society's journal, *The Hardy Plant*, is published twice a year and regular newsletters provide information on all the Society's events, activities, interests and group contacts. The Society also publishes a series of booklets on special plant families which include Hardy Geraniums, Pulmonarias, Hostas, Grasses, Iris, Epemendiums, Success with Seeds, Euphorbias, Phlox, Campanulas for the garden and Umbellifers. Other publications for members include a B&B list and a gardens to visit list. The Slide Library has a wide range of hardy plant slides available on loan.

Information about the Society is available from:

The Administrator
Mrs Pam Adams
The Hardy Plant Society
Little Orchard
Great Comberton
Pershore
Worcestershire WR10 3DP

Tel: 01386 710317
Fax: 01386 710117
E-mail: admin@hardy-plant.org.uk
Website: www.hardy-plant.org.uk

Membership Application for 2008

The Annual Subscriptions are:
Single **£13.00** per year (one member)
Joint **£15.00** per year (two members at the same address)

• Subscriptions are renewable annually on **1 January.**
• Subscriptions of members joining after 1 October are valid until the end of the following year.
• Overseas members are requested to pay in pounds sterling by International Money Order or by credit card. An optional charge of £10.00 is made for airmail postage outside Western Europe of all literature, if preferred.

Please fill in the details in BLOCK CAPITALS, tear off this form and send it with your payment to the Administrator or telephone the Administrator with details of your credit card.

Please tick the type of membership required

☐ Single £13.00 per year (one member)
☐ Joint £15.00 per year (two members at one address)
☐ Airmail postage £10.00 per year (optional for members outside Western Europe)

NAME/S ....

ADDRESS ....

....

.... POST CODE ....

TELEPHONE NUMBER ....

E-mail ....

I enclose a cheque/postal order* payable to **THE HARDY PLANT SOCIETY** (in pounds sterling ONLY) for £.........

OR

Please debit my Visa/Master Card* by the sum of £ ....
(* delete as required)

CARD NUMBER ☐☐☐☐ ☐☐☐☐ ☐☐☐☐ ☐☐☐☐

EXPIRY DATE ☐☐☐☐

Name as embossed on card ....

Signature ....

Please print your name and address clearly, tear out the page and send it to The Administrator at the address overleaf

The Hardy Plant Society is a Registered Charity, number 208080

THE NATIONAL PLANT COLLECTIONS®

National Council for the Conservation of Plants & Gardens

Patron: HRH The Prince of Wales

The Lost Garden of Britain

We have a long history of gardening, plant collecting and breeding in the British Isles so our gardens contain an amazing diversity of plants. Due to the imperatives of marketing and fashion, the desire for 'new' varieties and the practicalities of bulk cultivation, many plants unique to British gardens have been lost. This diversity is important as a genetic resource for the future and as a cultural link to the past.

What is The National Council for the Conservation of Plants & Gardens?

The NCCPG's mission is to conserve, document and make available this resource for the benefit of horticulture, education and science. The main conservation vehicle is the National Plant Collection® scheme where individuals or organisations undertake to preserve a group of related plants in trust for the future. Our 40 local groups across Britain support the administration of the scheme, the collection holders and propagate rare plants; working to promote the conservation of cultivated plants.

Who are the National Plant Collection® Holders?

Collection holders come from every sector of horticulture, amateur and professional. Almost half of the existing 660 National Collections are in private ownership and include allotments, back gardens and large estates. 121 collections are found in nurseries, which range from large commercial concerns to the small specialist grower. 57 local authorities are involved in the scheme, including Sir Harold Hillier Gardens & Arboretum (Hampshire County Council) and Leeds City Council. Universities, agricultural colleges, schools, arboreta and botanic gardens all add to the diversity, and there are also a number of collections on properties belonging to English Heritage, The National Trust and The National Trust for Scotland.

Please see overleaf for Membership Application Form

What do Collection Holders do?

Collection holders subscribe to the scheme's ideals and stringent regulations. As well as protecting the living plants in their chosen group, they also work on areas including education, scientific research and nomenclature, with the common aim of conserving cultivated plants.

How can you Help the Plant Heritage?

You can play your part in supporting plant conservation by becoming a member of NCCPG. Regular journals will keep you informed of how your support is helping to save our plant biodiversity. Through your local group you can play a more active role in plant conservation working with collection holders, attending talks, plant sales, local horticultural shows and nursery visits.

How to Join:

Please contact
Membership
NCCPG National Office
Home Farm, Loseley Park
Guildford
Surrey
GU3 1HS

Tel: (01483) 447540
Fax: (01483) 458933
E-mail: membership@nccpg.org.uk
Website: www.nccpg.com

'The NCCPG seeks to conserve, document, promote and make available Britain and Ireland's rich biodiversity of garden plants for the benefit of everyone through horticulture, education and science'

National Council for the Conservation of Plants & Gardens

Membership Application Form

Please complete and detach this form enclosing your payment and send to: Membership, NCCPG, Home Farm, Loseley Park, Guildford, Surrey GU3 1HS.

How to Join

By post: complete form and send to theabove address
On line: www.nccpg.com

Annual Subscription Rates

(please tick relevant boxes)

- ☐ Individual UK **£20**
- ☐ Joint UK **£34** (two people at same address)
- ☐ Student (up to age 25 in full time education) **£5**
- ☐ Gardening clubs and non-commercial groups **£30**
- ☐ Corporate **£55**
- ☐ Friend ______________ **(min £100)**
  Friends make annual donations in support of our work (in addition to the membership fee)
- ☐ Please send me information on legacies
- ☐ Please send me information on becoming a Collection Holder
- ☐ I would like to make an additional donation of ________ towards the conservation work of NCCPG

Please complete in CAPITALS

Title ______ First Name ______________

Last Name ______________

Date of Birth ______________

Address ______________

____

______________ Postcode ______________

Daytime Telephone ______________

Email ______________

giftaid it **Gift Aid Declaration: Are you a UK taxpayer? If you are, we can claim 28% from the government on your subscription at no extra cost to you.**

☐ I would like the National Council for the Conservation of Plants & Gardens to reclaim the tax on any membership subscription or donation that I make/have made since 6th April 2000 and all subscriptions and donations I make in the future, until I notify you otherwise. I have paid an amount of UK income tax or capital gains tax equal to any tax reclaimed. (Remember that if you receive a company pension, income tax may well be paid at source.)

Instruction to your Bank or Building Society to pay by Direct Debit

DIRECT Debit

Please fill in the form and send to:
Membership, NCCPG, Home Farm, Loseley Park, Guildford, Surrey GU3 1HS.

Originators Identification Numbe

9 7 4 2 1 2

Name and full postal address of your Bank or Building Socie

To: The Manager ______________

Bank/Building Society

Address ______________

____

____

Postcode

Name(s) of Account Holder

Branch Sort Code

Bank/Building Society account number

Reference No. (NCCPG use only)

Instruction to your Bank or Building Society
Please pay the NCCPG Direct Debits from the account detailed in the instructior subject to the safeguards assured by the Direct Debit Guarantee. I understanc that this instruction may remain with the NCCPG and if so, details will be passec electronically to my Bank/Building Society.

Signature(s)

Date / /

Banks and Building Societies may not accept Direct Debit Instructions for some types of account.

Payment by Credit or Debit card (Excluding American Express/Diners)

Card No:

Issue No *(Switch only)* **Security code**

Start Date / **Expiry Date** /

Bank Name ______________

Name on Card ______________

Signature **Date**

Payment by cheque: Please make sterling cheques payable to **NCCPG.**

Data Protection Act: Records for each member are kept at NCCPG National Office and by local Group Membership Secretaries. Under no circumstances are membership records used for purposes other than those connected to the legitimate activities of The National Council for the Conservation of Plants & Gardens. Registered charity number: 1004009.

National Council for the Conservation of Plants and Gardens
Home Farm, Loseley Park, Guildford, Surrey GU3 1HS. **T** 01483 447540 **F** 01483 458933 **E** membership@nccpg.org.uk **W** www.nccpg.com

Company Registration No. 2222953. Registered charity No.1004009